SECTION I:
PERIODICAL LITERATURE AND ESSAYS

Sample Entry

HUMAN EXPERIMENTATION/ SPECIAL POPULATIONS/ FOREIGN NATIONALS [1]

Hyder, Adnan A.; Dawson, Liza.[2] Defining standard of care in the developing world: the intersection of international research ethics and health systems analysis.[3] *Developing World Bioethics* [4] 2005 May 5[5]; 5(2)[6]: 142-152[7]. NRCBL: 18.5.9; 9.2; 9.8 [8]. SC: an [9].

Abstract: In recent years there has been intense debate regarding the level of medical care provided to 'standard care' control groups in clinical trials in developing countries, particularly when the research sponsors come from wealthier countries. The debate revolves around the issue of how to define a standard of medical care in a country in which many people are not receiving the best methods of medical care available in other settings. In this paper, we argue that additional dimensions of the standard of care have been hitherto neglected, namely, the structure and efficiency of the national health system. The health system affects locally available medical care in two important ways: first, the system may be structured to provide different levels of care at different sites with referral mechanisms to direct patients to the appropriate level of care. Second, inefficiencies in this system may influence what care is available in a particular locale. As a result of these two factors locally available care cannot be equated with a national 'standard'. A reasonable approach is to define the national standard of care as the level of care that ought to be delivered under conditions of appropriate and efficient referral in a national system. This standard is the minimum level of care that ought to be provided to a control group. There may be additional moral arguments for higher levels of care in some circumstances. This health system analysis may be helpful to researchers and ethics committees in designing and reviewing research involving standard care control groups in developing country research.[14]

1. Subject heading: **HUMAN EXPERIMENTATION/ SPECIAL POPULATIONS/ FOREIGN NATIONALS**
2. Author(s): **Hyder, Adnan A.; Dawson, Liza.**
3. Title of article: Defining standard of care in the developing world: the intersection of international research ethics and health systems analysis.
4. Title of journal: *Developing World Bioethics*
5. Date of publication: 2005 May
6. Volume and issue number (if available): 5(2)
7. Pagination: 142-152
8. NRCBL (all classification numbers): 18.5.9; 9.2; 9.8
9. SC (Subject Captions): an [analytical] (optional)
10. Identifiers: (optional)
11. Note: additional information (optional)
12. Conference: (optional)
13. Comments: information about related publications (optional)
14. Abstract: In recent years there has been intense debate regarding the level of medical care provided to . . . (optional)

BIBLIOGRAPHY
OF
BIOETHICS

BIBLIOGRAPHY
OF
BIOETHICS

Volume 32

Editors

LeRoy Walters
Tamar Joy Kahn
Doris Mueller Goldstein

Associate Editors
Frances Amitay Abramson
Richard M. Anderson
Laura Jane Bishop
Martina Darragh
Jeanne Ryan Furcron
Harriet Hutson Gray
Lucinda Fitch Huttlinger
Patricia C. Martin
Hannelore S. Ninomiya
Anita Lonnes Nolen
Leslie B. Pendley
Susan Cartier Poland

Managing Editor
Mara R. Snyder

Editorial Production
Roxie France-Nuriddin

KENNEDY INSTITUTE OF ETHICS
GEORGETOWN UNIVERSITY
Box 571212
WASHINGTON, DC 20057-1212

Publication of the annual *Bibliography of Bioethics* is a project of the Kennedy Institute of Ethics, Georgetown University. This book benefits from acquisition, classification, and database development activities funded by Contract HHSN276200553501C with the National Library of Medicine, and by Grant 5 P41 HG01115 from the National Human Genome Research Institute. It also reflects the contributions of The Anderson Partnership; Max M. and Marjorie B. Kampelman; and the National Endowment for the Humanities.

ISSN 0363-0161
ISBN 1-883913-13-6

This volume of the *Bibliography of Bioethics*
is dedicated to the memory of
our dear colleague and friend

Kathleen Andrew Reynolds
(1946-2005)

who was Administrative Officer and
Managing Editor, *Bibliography of Bioethics*
Library and Information Services
Kennedy Institute of Ethics.

Contents

Staff.. xiii

Editorial Advisory Board. xv

Introduction.. 3

    The Field of Bioethics

    The Scope of the *Bibliography*

    Arrangement of the *Bibliography*

    The *Bibliography of Bioethics*: History and Current Availability on the
        World Wide Web

    Acknowledgments

    Distribution of the *Bibliography of Bioethics* and Related Publications

    International Bioethics Exchange Project

Section I: Periodical Literature and Essays — Subject Entries

    Abortion. 13

        Legal Aspects
        Moral and Religious Aspects
        Social Aspects

    Advance Directives.. 22

    AIDS. 28

        Confidentiality
        Human Experimentation
        Legal Aspects

    Animal Experimentation.. 37

    Artificial Insemination and Surrogate Mothers. 41

    Assisted Suicide. 45

    Behavior Control.. 50

    Behavioral Genetics. 51

    Behavioral Research.. 52

    Bioethics and Medical Ethics.. 53

        Commissions
        Education
        History
        Legal Aspects
        Philosophical Perspectives
        Religious Perspectives

Biomedical Research. 79

Research Ethics and Scientific Misconduct
Social Control of Science and Technology

Blood Donation and Transfusion. 94

Capital Punishment. 95

Care for Specific Groups. 96

Aged
Fetuses
Indigents
Mentally Disabled
Minorities
Minors
Substance Abusers
Women

Cloning. 117

Legal Aspects

Codes of Ethics. 123

Confidentiality. 126

Contraception. 133

Cryobanking of Sperm, Ova, and Embryos. 137

Cultural Pluralism. 139

Death and Dying. 139

Attitudes to Death
Determination of Death
Terminal Care
 Terminal Care for Minors

Drug Industry. 148

Electroconvulsive Therapy. 156

Enhancement. 157

Ethicists and Ethics Committees. 158

Eugenics. 163

Euthanasia and Allowing to Die. 165

Legal Aspects
Minors
Philosophical Aspects
Religious Aspects

Force Feeding of Prisoners. 197

Gene Therapy. 197

Genetic Counseling. 200

Genetic Research. 206

Genetic Screening. 208

Genetics. 217

Legal Aspects

Genetics and Human Ancestry. 231

Genome Mapping. 232

Health Care. 233

Health Care Economics
    Managed Care Programs
Health Care Quality

Health, Concept of. 248

Human Experimentation. 251

Ethics Committees and Policy Guidelines
    Legal Aspects
Informed Consent
Regulation
Special Populations
    Aged and Terminally Ill
    Embryos and Fetuses
    Foreign Nationals
    Mentally Disabled
    Military Personnel
    Minors
    Prisoners
    Women

In Vitro Fertilization. 314

Informed Consent. 317

Incompetents
Minors

International Human Rights. 331

International Migration of Health Care Professionals. 332

Involuntary Commitment. 332

Journalism and Publishing. 335

Malpractice and Professional Misconduct. 338

Medical Education. 340

Mental Health, Concept of. 344

Mental Health Therapies. 345

Nursing Ethics and Philosophy. 353

Occupational Health.. 357

Organ and Tissue Transplantation. 358

Allocation
Donation and Procurement
Economic Aspects
Legal Aspects
Xenotransplantation

Patents. 374

Philosophy of Medicine. 377

Population Policy. 380

Professional Ethics.. 381

Professional Patient Relationship. 383

Professional Professional Relationship. 392

Psychopharmacology. 395

Psychotherapy. 397

Public Health. 398

Quality and Value of Life. 400

Recombinant DNA Research. 409

Reproductive Technologies. 410

Resource Allocation.. 415

Right to Health Care. 420

Sex Determination. 423

Sexuality.. 425

Sociology of Medicine. 426

Sterilization. 428

Telemedicine and Informatics. 430

Torture, Genocide, and War Crimes. 430

Treatment Refusal. 432

Truth Disclosure.. 436

War and Terrorism. 439

Section II: Periodical Literature and Essays — Author Index.. 443

Section III: Monographs — Subject Entries.. 733

    Monographs: Contents

Section IV: Monographs — Title Index. 783

Staff

Editorial Advisory Board

Jane K. Setlow, Ph.D.
Biologist
Brookhaven National Laboratory

Mark Siegler, M.D.
Lindy Bergman Distinguished
    Service Professor of Medicine
Department of Medicine
Director, The MacLean Center for Clinical
    Medical Ethics
University of Chicago

M. Therese Southgate, M.D.
Senior Contributing Editor
JAMA

Laurence R. Tancredi, M.D., J.D.
Clinical Professor of Psychiatry
New York University School of
    Medicine; and
Clinical Professor of Health Care
    Sciences
School of Medicine
University of California at San Diego

Robert M. Veatch, Ph.D.
Senior Research Scholar, Kennedy
    Institute of Ethics; and
Professor of Medical Ethics
Georgetown University

INTRODUCTION

INTRODUCTION

The Field of Bioethics

Bioethics can be defined as the systematic study of value questions that arise in health care delivery and in biomedicine. Specific bioethical issues that have recently received national and international attention include euthanasia, assisted suicide, new reproductive technologies, cloning, human experimentation, genetic engineering, abortion, informed consent, acquired immunodeficiency syndrome (AIDS), organ donation and transplantation, and managed care and other concerns in the allocation of health care resources.

As this list of topics suggests, the field of bioethics includes several dimensions. The first is the ethics of the professional patient relationship. Traditionally, the accent has been on the duties of health professionals–duties that, since the time of Hippocrates, have frequently been delineated in codes of professional ethics. In more recent times the rights of patients have also received considerable attention. Research ethics, the study of value problems in biomedical and behavioral research, constitutes a second dimension of bioethics. During the 20th century, as both the volume and visible achievements of such research have increased, new questions have arisen concerning the investigator-subject relationship and the potential social impact of biomedical and behavioral research and technology. In recent years a third dimension of bioethics has emerged–the quest to develop reasonable public policy guidelines for both the delivery of health care and the allocation of health care resources, as well as for the conduct of research.

No single academic discipline is adequate to discuss these various dimensions of bioethics. For this reason bioethics has been, since its inception in the late 1960s, a cross-disciplinary field. The primary participants in the interdisciplinary discussion have been physicians and other health professionals, biologists, psychologists, sociologists, lawyers, historians, and philosophical and religious ethicists.

During the past thirty-two years there has been a rapid growth of academic, professional, and public interest in the field of bioethics. One evidence of this interest is the establishment of numerous research institutes and teaching programs in bioethics, both in the United States and abroad. Professional societies, federal and state legislatures, and the courts have also turned increasing attention to problems in the field. In addition, there has been a veritable explosion of literature on bioethical issues.

The literature of bioethics appears in widely scattered sources and is reported in diverse indexes which employ a bewildering variety of subject headings. This annual *Bibliography* is the product of a unique information retrieval system designed to identify the central issues of bioethics, to develop a subject classification scheme appropriate to the field, and to provide comprehensive, cross-disciplinary coverage of current English-language materials on bioethical topics.

Volume 32 of the *Bibliography* contains one year's worth of the literature garnered by this comprehensive information system. Specifically, it includes all of the citations that were acquired by the National Reference Center for Bioethics Literature (NRCBL) in 2005 and selected for indexing for the bioethics subset of the U.S. National Library of Medicine's PubMed/MEDLINE journal database and the NLM Catalog, its book database.

The Table of Contents for this volume includes a list of subject headings under which the citations are arranged. Most citations are listed once, under their primary subject heading. Classification numbers at the end of each citation represent additional topics covered by the publication. These classification numbers are drawn from the NRCBL's Classification Scheme, which is reproduced on the inside front cover.

BIBLIOGRAPHY OF BIOETHICS

The Scope of the *Bibliography*

This thirty-second volume of the *Bibliography of Bioethics* includes materials which discuss the ethical aspects of the following major topics and subtopics:

BIOETHICS, MEDICAL ETHICS, AND
PROFESSIONAL ETHICS
    Codes of Ethics
    Commissions
    Ethicists and Ethics Committees
    Nursing Ethics and Philosophy
    Philosophy of Medicine
    Professional Misconduct
    Quality and Value of Life
    Religious Perspectives
DEATH AND DYING
    Advance Directives
    Assisted Suicide
    Attitudes to Death
    Capital Punishment
    Determination of Death
    Euthanasia and Allowing to Die
    Terminal Care
GENETICS
    Behavioral Genetics
    Eugenics
    Gene Therapy
    Genetic Counseling
    Genetic Research
    Genetic Screening
    Genetics and Human Ancestry
    Genome Mapping
    Patents
    Recombinant DNA Research
HEALTH CARE AND PUBLIC HEALTH
    AIDS
    Care for Specific Groups
    Drug Industry
    Health, Concept of
        Mental Health, Concept of
    Health Care
        Health Care Economics
        Health Care Quality
        Right to Health Care
    Occupational Health
    Organ and Tissue Donation and Transplantation
    Public Health

    Resource Allocation
    Telemedicine and Informatics
MENTAL HEALTH THERAPIES
    Behavior Control
    Electroconvulsive Therapy
    Involuntary Commitment
    Psychopharmacology
    Psychotherapy
PROFESSIONAL PATIENT RELATIONSHIP
    Confidentiality
    Informed Consent
    Sexuality
    Treatment Refusal
    Truth Disclosure
REPRODUCTION AND REPRODUCTIVE
TECHNOLOGIES
    Abortion
    Artificial Insemination and Surrogate Mothers
    Cloning
    Contraception
    Cryobanking of Sperm, Ova, and Embryos
    In Vitro Fertilization
    Population Policy
    Reproductive Technologies
    Sex Determination
RESEARCH
    Animal Experimentation
    Behavioral Research
    Biomedical Research
    Enhancement
    Human Experimentation
    Research Ethics and Scientific Misconduct
SOCIOLOGY OF MEDICINE
    Cultural Pluralism
    Journalism and Publishing
    Medical Education
    Professional-Professional Relationship
WAR AND HUMAN RIGHTS ABUSES
    International Human Rights
    Torture, Genocide, and War Crimes
    War and Terrorism

This volume of the *Bibliography* cites 8,350 documents (primarily in English) that discuss ethical and related public policy aspects of the topics and subtopics listed above. Documents cited in this volume include journal and newspaper articles, laws, court decisions, monographs, and chapters in books. Most of the documents listed were published since 2003. In the *Periodical*

Literature and Essays section, for example, 3,751 of the 7,573 entries were published in 2005; 1,389 in 2004; and 605 in 2003; therefore, 76 per cent of the literature cited in Section I was published since 2003.

A cross-disciplinary monitoring system has been devised in an effort to secure documents falling within the subject-matter scope outlined above. Among the reference tools and databases the staff searches for pertinent citations are the following:

AGRICOLA

All England Law Reports (subject index)

America: History & Life

ATLA Religion Database

Choice

Cumulative Index to Nursing and Allied Health Literature (CINAHL)

Current Contents: Clinical Medicine

Current Contents: Social and Behavioral Sciences

Digital Dissertations and Theses (UMI Proquest)

Dominion Law Reports (subject index)

ERIC

GPO Access

Historical Abstracts

Index to Canadian Legal Periodical Literature

Index to Foreign Legal Periodicals

Library Journal

MEDLINE

Mental and Physical Disability Law Reporter

Month in Review (GAO reports and other publications)

New Titles in Bioethics

PAIS International

Philosopher's Index

POPLINE

PsycInfo

Social Sciences Index

Sociological Abstracts

Specialty Law Digest: Health Care

Tarlton Law Library Legal Bibliography Series

WorldCat

In addition, the *Bibliography* staff directly monitors 200 journals and newspapers for articles falling within the scope of bioethics. Those preceded by an asterisk (*) have given permission for abstracts to be included in this volume. It is important to note that the journal articles cited in this volume are actually drawn from many more journals than those listed below.

Academic Medicine

*Accountability in Research

Agriculture and Human Values

AIDS and Public Policy Journal

America

*American Journal of Bioethics

*American Journal of Law and Medicine

American Journal of Nursing

American Journal of Psychiatry

*American Journal of Public Health

Annals of Health Law

*Annals of Internal Medicine

APA Newsletter on Philosophy and Medicine

*Archives of Internal Medicine

ATLA: Alternatives to Laboratory Animals

*Bioethics

Bioethics Forum

BMC Medical Ethics [electronic resource]

*BMJ (British Medical Journal)

British Journal of Nursing

Bulletin of Medical Ethics

Business and Professional Ethics Journal

Business Ethics Quarterly

*Cambridge Quarterly of Healthcare Ethics

Canadian Medical Association Journal

CCAR Journal

Cerebrum

*Christian Bioethics

Christian Century

Christian Medical Society Journal

Community Genetics

Conservative Judaism

Criminal Justice Ethics

Decisions; Journal of the Federation Internationale des Associations Medicales Catholiques

DePaul Journal of Health Care Law

Developing World Bioethics

Dolentium Hominum

Environmental Ethics

Environmental Values

Ethical Human Psychology and Psychiatry

Ethical Perspectives

Ethical Theory and Moral Practice

*Ethics

*Ethics and Behavior

Ethics and Intellectual Disability

Ethics and Medicine

Ethics and Medics

*Eubios Journal of Asian and International Bioethics

European Journal of Health Law

BIBLIOGRAPHY OF BIOETHICS

First Things: A Monthly Journal of Religion and Public Life

Formosan Journal of Medical Humanities

Free Inquiry

Genetic Testing

Genetics in Medicine

GeneWatch

Georgetown Journal of Legal Ethics

*Hastings Center Report

Health Affairs

Health and Human Rights

*Health Care Analysis

Health Care Ethics USA [online]

Health Care Financing Review

Health Law in Canada

Health Law Journal

Health Law Review

Health Matrix (Cleveland)

Health Policy [ISSN 0168-8510]

Health Progress

*HEC Forum

Human Genome News

Human Life Review

Human Reproduction

Human Reproduction and Genetic Ethics

Human Research Report

Humane Health Care [electronic resource]

Hypatia

IDHL: International Digest of Health Legislation [online]

Indian Journal of Medical Ethics [electronic resource]

International Journal of Applied Philosophy

*International Journal of Bioethics (Journal International de Bioéthique)

International Journal of Health Services

International Journal of Law and Psychiatry

International Journal of Technology Assessment in Health Care

IRB: Ethics and Human Research

Issues in Ethics

Issues in Law and Medicine

Issues in Science and Technology

*JAMA

Jewish Medical Ethics and Halacha

JONA's Healthcare Law, Ethics, and Regulation

Journal of Advanced Nursing

Journal of Applied Animal Welfare Science

Journal of Applied Philosophy

*Journal of Bioethical Inquiry

Journal of Biolaw and Business

*Journal of Clinical Ethics

Journal of Contemporary Health Law and Policy

Journal of Ethics

Journal of General Internal Medicine

Journal of Genetic Counseling

Journal of Halacha and Contemporary Society

Journal of Health Care Law and Policy

*Journal of Health Politics, Policy and Law

Journal of Information Ethics

Journal of Intellectual Disability Research

Journal of Law and Health

Journal of Law and Religion

*Journal of Law, Medicine and Ethics

Journal of Legal Medicine

*Journal of Medical Ethics

Journal of Medical Genetics

*Journal of Medical Humanities

*Journal of Medicine and Philosophy

Journal of Moral Education

Journal of Nursing Administration

Journal of Nursing Law

Journal of Palliative Care

Journal of Philosophy, Science and Law

Journal of Professional Nursing

Journal of Psychiatry and Law

Journal of Public Health Policy

Journal of Religion and Health

Journal of Religious Ethics

Journal of Social Philosophy

Journal of the American Academy of Psychiatry and the Law

Journal of the American College of Dentists

Journal of the American Geriatrics Society

Journal of the American Medical Women's Association

Journal of the Society of Christian Ethics

Judaism

*Kennedy Institute of Ethics Journal

*Lancet

Law and the Human Genome Review (Revista de Derecho y Genoma Humano)

Legal Medical Quarterly

Linacre Quarterly

Literature and Medicine

Medical Ethics & Bioethics (Medicinska Etika & Bioetika)

Medical Humanities

Medical Humanities Review

Medical Law International

Medical Law Review

Medical Trial Technique Quarterly

Medicine and Law

Medicine, Conflict and Survival

Medicine, Health Care and Philosophy

Mental Retardation [ISSN 0047-6765]

*Milbank Quarterly

Minnesota Medicine

Monash Bioethics Review
*National Catholic Bioethics Quarterly
*Nature
Nature Biotechnology
Nature Medicine
NCEHR Communiqué (National Council on Ethics in Human
    Research)
New Atlantis
*New England Journal of Medicine
New Genetics and Society
New Scientist
New York Times
Newsweek
Notizie de Politeia
Notre Dame Journal of Law, Ethics and Public Policy
*Nursing Ethics
Omega: Journal of Death and Dying
Online Journal of Issues in Nursing
Origins
Perspectives in Biology and Medicine
Perspectives on the Professions: Ethical & Policy Issues
Pharos
*Philosophy and Public Affairs
Philosophy and Public Policy Quarterly
Politics and the Life Sciences
Professional Ethics Report
Protecting Human Subjects

Psychiatric Services
Public Affairs Quarterly
Res Publica
Responsive Community
Review of Metaphysics
Romanian Journal of Bioethics (Revista Romana de Bioetica)
*Science
Science and Engineering Ethics
Science as Culture
Science, Technology, and Human Values
Sh'ma
Social Justice Research
Social Philosophy and Policy
*Social Science and Medicine
Social Theory and Practice
Society and Animals
Studies in Christian Ethics
*Theoretical Medicine and Bioethics
Tradition
UNOS Update
Update (Loma Linda University Ethics Center)
U.S. News and World Report
Virtual Mentor: Ethics Journal of the American Medical
    Association [electronic resource]
Washington Post
Women's Health Issues
Yale Journal of Health Policy, Law, and Ethics

All documents cited by the *Bibliography* are in the collection of the NRCBL.

Arrangement of the *Bibliography*

This volume of the *Bibliography of Bioethics* is divided into five parts:
1. Introduction
2. Section I: Periodical Literature and Essays — Subject Entries
3. Section II: Periodical Literature and Essays — Author Index
4. Section III: Monographs — Subject Entries
5. Section IV: Monographs — Title Index.

Sections 2 and 4 constitute the core of the *Bibliography*.

Section 1: Periodical Literature and Essays — Subject Entries

This Section, one of the two main parts of the *Bibliography*, contains usually one entry for each of the documents selected by the bioethics information retrieval system during the preceding year. In Volume 32 of the *Bibliography*, entries for 7,573 documents have been included in the Section. The format of these documents is as follows:

Journal articles	6,081
Essays in books	877
Newspaper articles	474
Pamphlets and similar materials	107
Legal documents	34

BIBLIOGRAPHY OF BIOETHICS

Section I is organized under 73 major subject headings, of which 13 are further divided by subheadings. Each subheading is separated from the major subject term by a slash.

Readers of the *Bibliography* should first scan the alphabetic list of subject headings in the Table of Contents to determine where citations of interest to them are likely to be found.

Section I includes cross references of two types. *See* cross references lead the reader from terms that are not used as subject headings to terms that are used. *See also* cross references suggest additional subject headings where the reader may find citations of related interest.

Citations appear alphabetically by author, with anonymous citations at the top of the section, sorted alphabetically by title. Entries with both corporate and personal authors are sorted by the corporate author. As explained below, the citations are accompanied by NRCBL Classification Scheme numbers as well as, in some cases, Subject Captions denoting approach or content. Subject Caption definitions can be found on page footers. Abstracts are included in this volume. In addition, we have instituted several optional fields in Section I that provide additional information: identifiers (such as persons, places, organizations, acronym equivalents), conference information, comments regarding related publications, and general notes.

Fourteen data elements may appear in an entry for a journal article. A sample subject heading and entry for a journal article follow:

HUMAN EXPERIMENTATION/ SPECIAL POPULATIONS/ FOREIGN NATIONALS [1]

Hyder, Adnan A.; Dawson, Liza.[2] Defining standard of care in the developing world: the intersection of international research ethics and health systems analysis.[3] *Developing World Bioethics* [4] 2005 May 5[5]; 5(2)[6]: 142-152[7]. NRCBL: 18.5.9; 9.2; 9.8 [8]. SC: an [9].

Abstract: In recent years there has been intense debate regarding the level of medical care provided to 'standard care' control groups in clinical trials in developing countries, particularly when the research sponsors come from wealthier countries. The debate revolves around the issue of how to define a standard of medical care in a country in. . . .

1. Subject heading: **HUMAN EXPERIMENTATION/ SPECIAL POPULATIONS/ FOREIGN NATIONALS**
2. Author(s): **Hyder, Adnan A.; Dawson, Liza.**
3. Title of article: Defining standard of care in the developing world: the intersection of international research ethics and health systems analysis.
4. Title of journal: *Developing World Bioethics*
5. Date of publication: 2005 May
6. Volume and issue number (if available): 5(2)
7. Pagination: 142-152
8. NRCBL (all classification numbers): 18.5.9; 9.2; 9.8
9. SC (Subject Captions): an [analytical] (optional)
10. Identifiers: (optional)
11. Note: additional information (optional)
12. Conference: (optional)
13. Comments: information about related publications (optional)
14. Abstract: In recent years there has been intense debate regarding the level of medical care provided to . . . . (optional)

The sample entry presented above displays the format and elements which appear in a journal article, the most prevalent publication type. The title field may be augmented by terms in square brackets which indicate additional aspects of the document, such as: letter, editorial, and news. The complete NRCBL Classification Scheme can be found on the inside front cover, and the Subject Captions equivalents are on alternating footers in Section I. The inside back cover displays the Subject Heading Key for Section II, leading the reader from the primary, i.e. first, NRCBL number to the corresponding Subject Heading(s) in Section I. Most citations appear only once in this volume.

Section II: Periodical Literature and Essays — Author Index

Citations in the Author Index are followed by the primary NRCBL Classification Number (Subject). Citations that have no personal or corporate author are listed at the end of the Author Index for Periodical Literature and Essays under ANONYMOUS. The two-page SUBJECT HEADING KEY FOR SECTION II appears on the inside back cover; it provides subject heading equivalents in Section I for the subject numbers appearing at the end of each citation in Section II.

Section III: Monographs — Subject Entries

These records have been derived from the annual publication of the NRCBL's *New Titles in Bioethics*, and cite monographs added to the collection in 2005 that cover bioethics and related areas of ethics and applied ethics. The NRCBL Classification Scheme (reproduced in full on the inside front cover) provides the arrangement for these citations. The Monographs section includes 777 records for books, reports, audiovisuals, special issues of journals, and new periodical subscriptions. Only subject headings actually occurring in Volume 32 are included on this list.

The monograph citations are arranged according to the primary subject category of the volume, and then, under subject category, by author, editor, producer, or title. Each citation in the Section usually appears only once. Classification numbers at the end of each citation represent additional bioethics topics covered by the publication. Monograph entries also include acquisition information, especially important for the so-called "gray literature." Monographs in foreign languages are included in the *Bibliography*.

Section IV: Monographs — Title Index

This Section provides a title index to all the entries in the Monographs Section. The title is followed by the subject section and author within which the complete citation can be found.

The *Bibliography of Bioethics*: History and Current Availability on the World Wide Web

Through December 2000, the entries in all of the annual volumes of the *Bibliography of Bioethics* were available online in BIOETHICSLINE®, a database produced for the National Library of Medicine (NLM) by the Bioethics Information Retrieval Project at the Kennedy Institute of Ethics, Georgetown University. As of 2001, NLM incorporated its subject-oriented databases into two large databases, PubMed/MEDLINE for journal articles and related documents, and LOCATOR*plus*/NLM Catalog for books and related documents.

Bibliographic records in the BIOETHICSLINE® database were retrospectively converted to PubMed or LOCATOR*plus* records based on publication type. The Bioethics Information Retrieval Project now selects and indexes bioethics-related journal articles, newspaper articles, court decisions, and laws directly for PubMed/MEDLINE and books, book chapters, audiovisual materials, and unpublished documents for LOCATOR*plus* (also distributed as the NLM Catalog). This effort is funded by a contract with NLM, with additional support from the National Human Genome Research Institute.

Citations from the *Bibliography of Bioethics* are available on the World Wide Web via the National Library of Medicine's PubMed/MEDLINE and LOCATOR*plus* databases, where they are indexed with NLM's Medical Subject Headings (MeSH) indexing vocabulary, and via the ETHX on the Web and Genetics and Ethics databases, maintained by NRCBL. Access to the NLM and NRCBL databases, along with searching information, is available through the Web gateway of the Kennedy Institute of Ethics at http://bioethics.georgetown.edu. In addition, a comprehensive NRCBL publication provides advice for database searchers: *Bioethics Searchers Guides: Using Databases of the National Library of Medicine and National Reference Center for Bioethics Literature*. (See "Distribution" paragraph below for ordering information.)

BIBLIOGRAPHY OF BIOETHICS
Acknowledgments

It is a pleasure to acknowledge the assistance of several people and organizations who played significant roles in the production of this thirty-second volume of the *Bibliography of Bioethics*. Although this publication is not a direct product of federal funding, it depends upon critical support from the National Library of Medicine and the National Human Genome Research Institute, both at the National Institutes of Health. We wish to thank, in particular, our NLM Project Officer, Sara Tybaert, and her Alternate Project Officers, Martha Cohn and Susan Von Braunsberg; our NLM Contracting Officer, Alex Navas; and Joy Boyer, Program Director, The Ethical, Legal, and Social Implications Program, National Human Genome Research Institute, for their interest and support. Other support is provided by the National Endowment for the Humanities, the Anderson Partnership, Max M. and Marjory B. Kampelman, and many publishers and individuals who contributed copies of books and journal articles to NRCBL.

Patricia Milmoe McCarrick, former reference librarian at NRCBL, continues as a library volunteer. Several Georgetown University students carried out document acquisition and data entry tasks: Ah-Hyun Cho, Rebecca Kruser, Vilija MicKute, Nana Hasegawa, Kevin C. Kwiatkowski, Tessa Munekiyo, Ayah Nuriddin, Allison M. Oelschlaeger, Christa Pugh, and Katarvia Taylor.

Distribution of the *Bibliography of Bioethics* and Related Publications

Inquiries about purchasing Volumes 10-32 of the *Bibliography* or the current edition of *Bioethics Searchers Guides* should be directed to Library Publications, Kennedy Institute of Ethics, Georgetown University, Box 571212, Washington, DC 20057-1212, telephone 202-687-3885 or 888-BIO-ETHX (outside the Washington, DC metropolitan area); fax 202-687-6770, e-mail: bioethics@georgetown.edu.

International Bioethics Exchange Project (IBEP)

IBEP, a project of the Kennedy Institute of Ethics, promotes research and education in bioethics in the developing world by donating multiple volumes of the *Bibliography* to libraries abroad in order to encourage the development of bioethics reference resources in those countries. In turn, IBEP is eager to collect documents about bioethics from the exchange participants. Any books, policy statements, periodicals and other materials about bioethical issues in the participant countries that are donated to IBEP are added to the NRCBL collection and considered for inclusion in the *Bibliography*. This project relies upon the support of donors to underwrite the transport of the volumes to the developing country library.

To date libraries in the following countries have become participants in the project: Argentina, Brazil, Burkina Faso, Cameroon, Croatia, Eritrea, Grenada, Jamaica, Lithuania, Mexico, Papua New Guinea, Peoples Republic of China, Philippines, Poland, Republic of Belarus, Republic of Korea, Republic of Slovenia, Republic of the Congo, Republic of Trinidad and Tobago, Romania, Rwanda, St. Lucia, Sierre Leone, Sri Lanka, Thailand, Turkey, Uzbekistan, Venezuela, Yemen, and Zambia.

Contributions in support of an IBEP library or donations of bioethics books, reprints, audiovisual materials, and other documents should be sent to Lucinda Fitch Huttlinger, Acquisitions Librarian, Kennedy Institute of Ethics, Georgetown University, Box 571212, Washington, DC 20057-1212; Telephone: +202-687-6433; Toll-free telephone: 1-888-BIO-ETHX (U.S. and Canada); FAX +202-687-6770; e-mail: bioethics@georgetown.edu. All donations are reviewed for inclusion in the NRCBL collection as well as for this *Bibliography*.

The staff welcomes suggestions for the improvement of future volumes of the *Bibliography of Bioethics*. Please send all comments to:

> Editors, *Bibliography of Bioethics*
> Kennedy Institute of Ethics, Box 571212
> Georgetown University
> Washington, DC 20057-1212

June 21, 2006

SECTION I:
PERIODICAL LITERATURE
AND ESSAYS

SUBJECT ENTRIES

SECTION I: PERIODICAL LITERATURE AND ESSAYS
SUBJECT ENTRIES

ABORTION

Abortion drugs must become WHO essential medicines [editorial]. *Lancet* 2005 May 28-June 3; 365(9474): 1826. NRCBL: 12.1; 9.7; 21.1; 5.3. Identifiers: World Health Organization.

Arthur, Joyce. Fetal pain: a red herring in the abortion debate. *Free Inquiry* 2005 August-September; 25(5): 44-47. NRCBL: 12.1; 4.4.

Ba-Thike, Katherine. Abortion: a public health problem in Myanmar. *Reproductive Health Matters* 1997 May; (9); 7 p. [Online]. Available: http://www.hsph.harvard.edu/Organizations/healthnet/SAsia/suchana/9999/rh141.html [7 October 2005]. NRCBL: 12.1; 9.5.5; 11.4; 9.1. SC: cs.

Brind, Joel. The abortion-breast cancer connection. *National Catholic Bioethics Quarterly* 2005 Summer; 5(2): 303- 329. NRCBL: 12.1; 9.5.5; 7.1; 1.3.7; 1.3.9.

Dyer, Frederick N. Horatio Robinson Storer, M.D. and the physicians' crusade against abortion. *In:* Koterski, Joseph W., ed. Life and Learning IX: Proceedings of the Ninth University Faculty for Life Conference. Washington, DC: University Faculty for Life; 2000: 267-294. NRCBL: 12.1; 7.1; 2.2.

Gangoli, Geetanjali. Abortion: a fundamental right [letter]. *Issues in Medical Ethics* 2000 October-December; 8(4): 104. NRCBL: 12.1; 12.4.1. Comments: comment on S.G. Kabra, "Abortion in India," Issues in Medical Ethics 2000 July-September; 8(3): 70.

Grady, Denise. Study finds 29-week fetuses probably feel no pain and need no abortion anesthesia. *New York Times* 2005 August 24; p. A10. NRCBL: 12.1; 9.5.3. SC: po; em.

Harris, John; Holm, Søren. Abortion. *In:* LaFollette, Hugh, ed. The Oxford Handbook of Practical Ethics. New York: Oxford University Press; 2003: 112-135. NRCBL: 12.1; 4.4. SC: an.

Hobin, Terrence J. Abortion as liberty and right. *Human Life Review* 2005 Winter; 31(1): 67-78. NRCBL: 12.1; 12.4.1.

Kabra, S.G. Abortion in India: not a right but a state-sponsored programme [letter]. *Issues in Medical Ethics* 2000 July-September; 8(3): 70. NRCBL: 12.1; 12.5.1; 13.3.

Kabra, S.G. Unsafe abortions and experimental excesses. *Issues in Medical Ethics* 2003 July-September; 11(3): 79-80. NRCBL: 12.1; 18.5.3.

Maifeld, Michelle; Hahn, Sandra; Titler, Marita G.; Mullen, Meredithe. Decision making regarding multifetal reduction. *JOGNN: Journal of Obstetric, Gynecologic and Neonatal Nursing* 2003 May-June; 32(3): 357-369. NRCBL: 12.1; 14.1; 14.4. SC: em.

Marcin, Raymond B. "Posterity" in the preamble and a positivist pro-life position. *American Journal of Jurisprudence* 1993; 38: 273-295. NRCBL: 12.1; 1.1. SC: le.

Mathai, Saramma T. Making abortion safer. *Journal of Family Welfare* 1997 June; 43(2); 9 p. [Online]. Available: http://www.hsph.harvard.edu/Organizations/healthnet/SAsia/suchana/0617/mathai.html [7 October 2005]. NRCBL: 12.1; 9.5.5; 21.1; 1.3.5. SC: le. Identifiers: India.

Orr, Wendy. Abortion reform — imperative or outrageous? [editorial]. *South African Medical Journal* 1995 March; 85(3): 139-140. NRCBL: 12.1; 12.5.1; 21.1.

Paulsen, Michael Stokes. Looking for a model answer: may Congress prohibit sex- selective abortions? *Constitutional Commentary* 2000; 17(2): 165-169. NRCBL: 12.1; 14.3. SC: le.

Prothro, Gwendolyn. RU 486 examined: impact of a new technology on an old controversy. *University of Michigan Journal of Law Reform* 1997 Summer; 30(4): 715-741. NRCBL: 12.1; 9.7; 14.1; 11.1. SC: le.

Rasch, Vibeke; Muhammad, Hamed; Urassa, Ernest; Bergström, Staffan. The problem of illegally induced abortion: results from a hospital-based study conducted at district level in Dar es Salaam. *Tropical Medicine and International Health* 2000 July; 5(7): 495-502. NRCBL: 12.1; 9.5.5; 9.5.8. SC: em. Identifiers: Tanzania.

NRCBL: National Reference Center for Bioethics Literature Classification Scheme   See inside front cover for terms.

Ring-Cassidy, Elizabeth. Multifetal pregnancy reduction (MFPR): the psychology of desperation and the ethics of justification. *In:* Koterski, Joseph W., ed. Life and Learning IX: Proceedings of the Ninth University Faculty for Life Conference. Washington, DC: University Faculty for Life; 2000: 331-346. NRCBL: 12.1; 14.1; 12.5.2.

Schwarz, Eleanor Bimla; Luetkemeyer, Anne; Foster, Diana Greene; Weitz, Tracy A.; Lindes, Deborah; Stewart, Felicia H. Willing and able? Provision of medication for abortion by future internists. *Women's Health Issues* 2005 January-February; 15(1): 39-44. NRCBL: 12.1; 9.7; 7.2. SC: em. Identifiers: RU 486.

Abstract: INTRODUCTION AND BACKGROUND: The development of medications such as mifepristone (RU486) has created the opportunity to introduce medication abortion as a component of office practice. METHODS: Two hundred twelve residents training in internal medicine, family practice, and gynecology at 11 residency programs completed anonymous surveys assessing willingness to provide medication for abortion and perceived barriers to future provision of mifepristone. RESULTS: Residents training in internal medicine knew less about mifepristone and preabortion screening than other primary care trainees. Forty-two percent of internists, 84% of family practitioners, and 83% of gynecologists were willing to prescribe mifepristone (p .001). Many internists were concerned about lacking adequate "backup" access to vacuum aspiration services (84% of internists, 74% of family practitioners, 35% of gynecologists; p .001). In multivariable analysis, the training-related factors most predictive of whether an internist was willing to provide medication for abortion were feeling that mifepristone is very safe, abortion services are needed by the patients served, knowing to check an ultrasound before inducing abortion, and having no concern of how to manage bleeding or of lacking adequate backup should vacuum aspiration be needed. CONCLUSIONS AND DISCUSSION: Many (42%) future internists are willing to provide mifepristone, but most lack adequate knowledge of mifepristone and preabortion screening. As access to abortion services is limited in many U.S. counties, internists who are willing to provide mifepristone should be offered the necessary training to do so safely.

Stotland, Nada L. Induced abortion in the United States. *In:* Stotland, Nada L.; Stewart, Donna E., eds. Psychological Aspects of Women's Health Care: The Interface Between Psychiatry and Obstetrics and Gynecology. Washington, DC: American Psychiatric Press; 2001: 219-239. NRCBL: 12.1.

Williams, Melanie. An ethics ensemble: abortion, Thomson, Finnis and the case of the violin-player. *Ratio Juris* 2004 September; 17(3): 381-397. NRCBL: 12.1; 1.1; 4.4; 12.4.2. SC: le.

ABORTION/ LEGAL ASPECTS

The next abortion decision [editorial]. *New York Times* 2005 November 30; p. A34. NRCBL: 12.4.1.

Adler, Nancy E.; Ozer, Emily J.; Tschann, Jeanne. Abortion among adolescents. *American Psychologist* 2003 March; 58(3): 211-217. NRCBL: 12.4.2; 8.3.2; 9.5.7; 12.5.2. SC: le.

Araujo, Robert John. The legal order and the common good: abortion rights as contradiction of constitutional purposes. *In:* Koterski, Joseph W., ed. Life and Learning XI: Proceedings of the Eleventh University Faculty for Life Conference. Washington, DC: University Faculty for Life; 2002: 65-84. NRCBL: 12.4.1; 1.1. SC: le.

Australia. Parliament. Law and Bills Digest Group; Cica, Natasha. Abortion law in Australia: Research Paper 1: 1998-1999. Australia: Parliamentary Library 1998-1999; 42 p. [Online] Available: http://www.aph.gov.au/library/pubs/rp/1998-99/99rp01.htm [13 September 2005]. NRCBL: 12.4.1. SC: le.

Baker, Hunter. Storming the gates of a massive cultural investment: reconsidering Roe in light of its flawed foundation and undesirable consequences. *Regent University Law Review* 2002; 14: 35-65. NRCBL: 12.4.1; 4.4; 12.4.2; 12.5.1; 15.2. SC: le.

Barnes, Andrea. Update on abortion law. *In her:* Barnes, Andrea, ed. The Handbook of Women, Psychology, and the Law. San Francisco: Jossey-Bass; 2005: 147-177. NRCBL: 12.4.1. SC: le.

Bazzelle, Roslyn Y. Mazurek v. Armstrong: should states be allowed to restrict the performance of abortions to licensed physicians only? *Thurgood Marshall Law Review* 1998 Fall; 24(1): 149-182. NRCBL: 12.4.3; 9.8. SC: le. Note: 117 S.Ct. 1865 (1997).

Bourne, Richard W. Abortion in 1938 and today: plus ca change, plus c'est la meme chose. *Southern California Review of Law and Women's Studies* 2003 Spring; 12(2): 225-275. NRCBL: 12.4.1; 12.5.1; 12.4.3. SC: le.

Browne, Alister; Sullivan, Bill. Abortion in Canada. *CQ: Cambridge Quarterly of Healthcare Ethics* 2005 Summer; 14(3): 287-291. NRCBL: 12.4.1; 12.4.2; 9.4; 9.2. SC: le.

Brunner, S. Dresden. Cultural feminism: it sounds good, but will it work? Application to a husband's interest in his wife's abortion decision. *University of Dayton Law Review* 1996 Fall; 22(1): 101-123. NRCBL: 12.4.2; 10. SC: le.

Câncio, Fernanda. When abortion is a crime: the reality that rhetoric ignores. *Conscience* 2004-2005 Winter; 25(3): 28-31. NRCBL: 12.4.2. SC: le. Identifiers: Portugal; Spain.

Catholic Medical Association. Task Force on Issues of Conscience. Report of the task force on issues of conscience. *Linacre Quarterly* 2005 May; 72(2): 133-173. NRCBL: 12.4.3; 7.1; 7.2; 1.2; 8.1; 12.3; 4.1.3. SC: cs; le. Identifiers: Health Care Providers Rights of Conscience Act.

Ching, Bruce. Inverting the viability test for abortion law. *Women's Rights Law Reporter* 2000 Fall-Winter; 22(1): 37-45. NRCBL: 12.4.1. SC: le.

Connolly, Ceci. Access to abortion pared at state level. *Washington Post* 2005 August 29; p. A1, A4. NRCBL: 12.4.1. SC: po.

Czerwinski, Alicia. Sex, politics, and religion: the clash between Poland and the European Union over abortion. *Denver Journal of International Law and Policy* 2004 Fall; 32(4): 653-674. NRCBL: 12.4.1; 21.1; 10; 12.5.2. SC: le.

de Crespigny, Lachlan; Frcog, Franzcog; Cogu, Ddu. Australian abortion laws: do they pose a 'health hazard'? *O and G magazine* 2005 Autumn; 7(1): 52-54. NRCBL: 12.4.1; 12.4.2; 12.5.1; 9.4. SC: le.

Dickinson, Jan E. Late pregnancy termination within a legislated medical environment. *Australian and New Zealand Journal of Obstetrics and Gynaecology* 2004 August; 44(4): 337-341. NRCBL: 12.4.1. SC: em; le. Identifiers: Australia.

Dyer, Clare. Doctors who performed late abortion will not be prosecuted [news]. *BMJ: British Medical Journal* 2005 March 26; 330(7493): 688. NRCBL: 12.4.3. SC: le.

Dyer, Clare. Woman fights for parents' right to know abortion advice to under 16s [news]. *BMJ: British Medical Journal* 2005 November 19; 331(7526): 1161. NRCBL: 12.4.2; 11.2; 8.3.2. SC: le.

Ehrlich, J. Shoshanna. Journey through the courts: minors, abortion and the quest for reproductive fairness. *Yale Journal of Law and Feminism* 1998; 10(1): 1-27. NRCBL: 12.4.2; 8.3.2. SC: le.

Flanagan, Pádraig P. Banning partial-birth abortions: a few inches away from testing post-viability jurisprudence. *Seton Hall Legislative Journal* 1998; 23(1): 141-177. NRCBL: 12.4.1; 12.1. SC: le.

Fletcher, Ruth. "Pro-life" absolutes, feminist challenges: the fundamentalist narrative of Irish abortion law 1986-1992. *Osgoode Hall Law Journal* 1998 Spring; 36(1): 1-62. NRCBL: 12.4.2; 12.5.1; 2.2; 9.5.5. SC: le.

Flood, Patrick J. Mandatory viability testing and post-viability abortion restriction: the best way forward in the immediate future? *In:* Koterski, Joseph W., ed. Life and Learning XI: Proceedings of the Eleventh University Faculty for Life Conference. Washington, DC: University Faculty for Life; 2002: 111-130. NRCBL: 12.4.4; 9.5.8. SC: le.

Forde, Catherine. Must we really make the case for abortion rights all over again? *Conscience* 2005 Spring; 26(1): 22-23. NRCBL: 12.4.2. SC: le. Identifiers: Europe; United States.

Forero, Juan. Push to loosen abortion laws in Latin America. *New York Times* 2005 December 3; p. A1, A6. NRCBL: 12.4.1. SC: po.

Furedi, Ann. The case for second trimester abortion. *Conscience* 2004-2005 Winter; 25(3): 26-27. NRCBL: 12.4.2. SC: le. Identifiers: United Kingdom (Great Britain).

Goodnough, Abby. Florida halts fight to bar girl's abortion: after resisting, Governor Bush says state will abide by ruling. *New York Times* 2005 May 4; p. A19. NRCBL: 12.4.1; 9.5.7. SC: po; le.

Gordon, Alex. The Partial-Birth Abortion Ban Act of 2003. *Harvard Journal on Legislation* 2004 Summer; 41(2) 501-515. NRCBL: 12.4.2. SC: le.

Green, Jason. Refusal clauses and the Weldon amendment: inherently unconstitutional and a dangerous precedent. *Journal of Legal Medicine* 2005 September; 26(3): 401-415. NRCBL: 12.4.3; 8.1; 9.7; 11.1. SC: le.

Greenhouse, Linda. Case reopens abortion issue for justices. *New York Times* 2005 November 29; p. A19. NRCBL: 12.4.1. SC: po.

Greenhouse, Linda. Court to tackle abortion again after 5 years; parent notification case; in considering technical issues, justices rejoin a fractious debate. *New York Times* 2005 May 24; p. A1, A17. NRCBL: 12.4.1; 8.3.2. SC: le; po.

Greenwood, Jason S. Congressional control of federal court jurisdiction: the case study of abortion. *South Carolina Law Review* 2003 Summer; 54(4): 1069-1112. NRCBL: 12.4.1; 1.3.5. SC: le.

Guenther, Hilary. The development of the undue burden standard in Stenberg v. Carhart: will proposed RU-486 legislation survive? *Indiana Law Review* 2002; 35(3): 1021-1044. NRCBL: 12.4.2; 9.7. SC: le.

Hayhurst, Matthew B. Parental notification of abortion and minors' rights under the Montana constitution. *Montana Law Review* 1997 Summer; 58(2): 565-598. NRCBL: 12.4.2; 8.4; 8.3.2. SC: le.

Heffernan, Liz. Stenberg v Carhart: a divided US Supreme Court debates partial birth abortion. *Modern Law Review* 2001 July; 64(4): 618-627. NRCBL: 12.4.1; 12.1; 12.4.2. SC: le. Identifiers: 530 US_, 120 S.Ct. 2597 , 147L ED 743 (2000) [Date of Decision: 28 June 2000].

Hewson, Barbara. The law of abortion in Northern Ireland. *Public Law* 2004 Summer: 234-245. NRCBL: 12.4.1; 12.4.2; 12.4.3. SC: le.

Hurwitz, Andrew D. Jon O. Newman and the abortion decisions: a remarkable first year. *New York Law School Law Review* 2002-2003; 46(1 and 2): 231-247. NRCBL: 12.4.2; 12.4.1; 4.4. SC: le.

Isaac, K. Abortion legislation in Eritrea: an overview of law and practice. *Medicine and Law: World Association for Medical Law* 2005 March; 24(1): 137-161. NRCBL: 12.4.1; 12.5.1; 21.1. SC: le.

NRCBL: National Reference Center for Bioethics Literature Classification Scheme   See inside front cover for terms.

15

Abstract: This article discusses legal issues related to the abortion provisions of the Transitional Penal Code of Eritrea. As is the case in many African countries, the current abortion law of Eritrea mainly was adopted from continental Europe four decades ago, reflecting the reality of the time. Despite the advancement in science and technology, which significantly determines the very definition and concept of abortion and contraception, the abortion law remains the same, save for minor amendments taken place in 1991. Due to the background of the abortion law and the shortcomings occurred during the amendment process, the law manifests legal gaps and limitations resulting in discrepancies between law and practice. The article, therefore, identifies and analyses the gaps of the abortion law in light of principles of criminal law, existing medical technology related to abortion, and experience of other countries.

Janoff, Abby F. Rights of the pregnant child vs. rights of the unborn under the Convention on the Rights of the Child. *Boston University International Law Journal* 2004 Spring; 22(1): 163-188. NRCBL: 12.4.2; 9.5.7; 9.5.8; 4.4; 21.1. SC: le.

Johnson, Timothy R.B.; Harris, Lisa H.; Dalton, Vanessa K.; Howell, Joel D. Language matters: legislation, medical practice, and the classification of abortion procedures. *Obstetrics and Gynecology* 2005 January; 105(1): 201-204. NRCBL: 12.4.1; 12.1. SC: le.

Kelly, Linda. Reproductive liberty under the threat of care: deputizing private agents and deconstructing state action. *Michigan Journal of Gender and Law* 1998-1999; 5(1): 81-111. NRCBL: 12.4.2; 10. SC: le.

Kolenc, Antony Barone. Easing abortion's pain: the new fight to help the unborn. *America* 2005 September 26; 193(8): 18-21. NRCBL: 12.4.4; 12.3.

Krisberg, Kim. Law takes effect — refusal clause seen as threat to reproductive health, gag on information. *Nation's Health* 2005 February; 35(1): 1, 10. NRCBL: 12.4.1. SC: le.

Lee, Ellie. Debating late abortion: time to tell the truth [opinion]. *Journal of Family Planning and Reproductive Health Care* 2005 January; 31(1): 7, 9. NRCBL: 12.4.1; 12.5.1.

Lesser, Harry. The case of back-street abortion. *In:* Häyry, Matti; Takala, Tuija; Herissone-Kelly, Peter, eds. Bioethics and Social Reality. New York: Rodopi, 2005: 7-15. NRCBL: 12.4.1; 12.3. SC: an; le.

Leuck, Jared C. Roe v. Wade and its Supreme Court progeny. *Journal of Contemporary Legal Issues* 2004; 14(1): 209-227. NRCBL: 12.4.1; 12.4.2; 9.5.5; 12.4.3. SC: le.

Lewis, Karen J.; Shimabukuro, Jon O. Abortion law development: a brief overview. Congressional Research Service 2001 January 2; 20 p. [Online]. Available: http://www.law.maryland.edu/marshall/crsreports/crsdocuments/95-724_A.pdf [31 August 2005]. NRCBL: 12.4.4. SC: le; rv.

Liptak, Adam. On moral grounds, some judges are opting out of abortion cases. *New York Times* 2005 September 4; p. A21. NRCBL: 12.4.1; 8.3.2. SC: po; le.

Little, Margaret Olivia. Abortion, intimacy, and the duty to gestate. *Ethical Theory and Moral Practice* 1999; 2: 295-312. NRCBL: 12.4.2; 1.1.

Lovering, Robert P. Does a normal foetus really have a future of value? A reply to Marquis. *Bioethics* 2005 April; 19(2): 131-145. NRCBL: 12.4.2; 4.4. SC: le; an.

Abstract: The traditional approach to the abortion debate revolves around numerous issues, such as whether the foetus is a person, whether the foetus has rights, and more. Don Marquis suggests that this traditional approach leads to a standoff and that the abortion debate 'requires a different strategy.' Hence his 'future of value' strategy, which is summarized as follows: (1) A normal foetus has a future of value. (2) Depriving a normal foetus of a future of value imposes a misfortune on it. (3) Imposing a misfortune on a normal foetus is prima facie wrong. (4) Therefore, depriving a normal foetus of a future of value is prima facie wrong. (5) Killing a normal foetus deprives it of a future value. (6) Therefore, killing a normal foetus is prima facie wrong. In this paper, I argue that Marquis's strategy is not different since it involves the concept of person—a concept deeply rooted in the traditional approach. Specifically, I argue that futures are valuable insofar as they are not only dominated by goods of consciousness, but are experienced by psychologically continuous persons. Moreover, I argue that his strategy is not sound since premise (1) is false. Specifically, I argue that a normal foetus, at least during the first trimester, is not a person. Thus, during that stage of development it is not capable of experiencing its future as a psychologically continuous person and, hence, it does not have a future of value.

Lowe, LaShunda R. An inside look at partial birth abortion. *Thurgood Marshall Law Review* 1998-1999; 24: 327-357. NRCBL: 12.4.2; 9.5.5. SC: le.

Majors, M. Jason. Constitutional law — clarity or confusion? The constitutionality of a Nebraska statute prohibiting partial-birth abortion procedures. Stenberg v. Carhart, 120 S.Ct. 2597 (2000). *Wyoming Law Review* 2001; 1(1): 231-261. NRCBL: 12.4.3. SC: le.

Mariner, Joanne. Latin America's abortion battles. *Conscience* 2005 Autumn; 26(3): 10-14. NRCBL: 12.4.2; 12.3; 12.5.2; 11.1; 21.1.

Martin, Jennifer. Coercive abortions and criminalizing the birth of children: some thoughts on the impact on women of State v. Oakley. *Western New England Law Review* 2004; 26(1): 67-80. NRCBL: 12.4.2. SC: le.

Means, Cyril C., Jr. The phoenix of abortional freedom: is a penumbral or Ninth-Amendment right about to arise from the nineteenth-century legislative ashes of a fourteenth-century common-law liberty? *New York Law Forum* 1971; 17(2): 335-410. NRCBL: 12.4.1; 12.4.2; 4.4. SC: le.

Meehan, Mary. Tiptoeing around Roe. *Human Life Review* 2005 Fall; 31(4): 44-64. NRCBL: 12.4.4. SC: le.

Meyer, David D. Lochner redeemed: family privacy after Troxel and Carhart. *UCLA Law Review* 2001 June; 48(5): 1125-1190. NRCBL: 12.4.2; 1.1. SC: le. Identifiers: Lockner v. New York, 25 S.Ct. 539 (1905); Troxel v. Granville, 120 S.Ct. 2054 (2000); Stenberg v. Carhart, 120 S.Ct.2597 (2000).

Morelli, Mariano G. La peligrosa pendiente que convierte los delitos en derechos / The dangerous slope that changes crimes into rights: juridical protection of the embryo 30 years after Roe v. Wade. *Vida y Etica* 2003 December; 4(2): 67-96. NRCBL: 12.4.2; 9.5.5; 1.2.

Murphy, Dean E. Court rules U.S. need not pay for abortion of doomed fetus. *New York Times* 2005 August 19; p. A16. NRCBL: 12.4.1; 9.3.1. SC: po; le.

Murthy, Laxmi. 'Foeticide' is problematic terminology [letter]. *Issues in Medical Ethics* 2002 January-March; 10(1): 138. NRCBL: 12.4.2; 10. Comments: comment on Rao Mohan, "Female Foeticide: where do we go?" Issues in Medical Ethics 2001 October-December; 9(4): 123-124.

NARAL Pro-Choice America Foundation. Mandatory parental consent and notice laws burden the freedom to choose. Washington, DC: NARAL Pro-Choice America 2003 January 20; 9 p. [Online]. Available: http://www.naral.org/facts/loader.cfm?url=commonspot/security/getfile.cfm&PageID=2058 [27 May 2005]. NRCBL: 12.4.2; 8.3.2; 9.5.7; 9.5.5. SC: le.

NARAL Pro-Choice America Foundation. Refusal Clauses: Dangerous for Women's Health. Washington, DC: The Foundation 2005 January 1; 9 p. [Online]. Available: http://www.naral.org/facts/loader.cfm?url=/commonspot/security/getfile.cfm&PageID=16140 [24 May 2005]. NRCBL: 12.4.3; 12.3; 8.1. SC: an; le.

NARAL Pro-Choice America Foundation. State Refusal Clauses for Abortion. Washington, DC: The Foundation 2004 January 1; 12 p. [Online]. Available: http://www.naral.org/facts/loader.cfm?url=/commonspot/security/getfile.cfm&PageID=7839 [26 May 2005]. NRCBL: 12.4.3; 12.3; 8.1. SC: le; rv. Identifiers: United States.

Ngwena, Charles. An appraisal of abortion laws in Southern Africa from a reproductive health rights perspective. *Journal of Law, Medicine and Ethics* 2004 Winter; 32(4): 708- 717. NRCBL: 12.4.1; 12.5.1; 21.1. SC: le.

Oliver, Leah. Abortion laws in the states. *NCSL Legisbrief* 2004 October; 12(38): 1-2. NRCBL: 12.4.1. SC: le.

Paulsen, Michael Stokes. Abrogating stare decisis by statute: may Congress remove the precedential effect of Roe and Casey? *Yale Law Journal* 2001; 109(7): 1535-1602. NRCBL: 12.4.1; 1.3.8. SC: le.

Paxson, Heather. Abortion/anti-abortion conflict. *In:* Restivo, Sal, ed. Science, Technology, and Society: An En-

cyclopedia. New York: Oxford University Press; 2005: 1-2. NRCBL: 12.4.1; 12.4.4.

Pear, Robert. New attention for 2002 law on survivors of abortions. *New York Times* 2005 April 23; p. A10. NRCBL: 12.4.2; 9.5.7; 9.2. SC: le; po.

Pence, Gregory E. Classic cases about the beginning of life. *In his:* Classic Cases in Medical Ethics: Accounts of Cases That Have Shaped Medical Ethics, with Philosophical, Legal, and Historical Backgrounds. Fourth edition. Boston, MA: McGraw- Hill; 2004: 121-243. NRCBL: 12.4.1; 14.1; 18.5.4; 20.5.2. SC: le.

Perry, Ronen; Adar, Yehuda. Wrongful abortion: a wrong in search of a remedy. *Yale Journal of Health Policy, Law, and Ethics* 2005 Summer; 5(2): 507-586. NRCBL: 12.4.2; 12.5.3; 8.5; 1.3.5. SC: le.

Pojman, Louis P.; Beckwith, Francis J. The major Supreme Court decisions. *In their:* Pojman, Louis P.; Beckwith, Francis J., eds. The Abortion Controversy: A Reader. Boston: Jones and Bartlett; 1994: 13-83. NRCBL: 12.4.1; 9.5.5; 12.4.2; 12.4.3. SC: le.

Pojman, Louis P.; Beckwith, Francis J.; Horan, Dennis J.; Balch, Thomas J.; MacKinnon, Catharine; Ginsburg, Ruth Bader. Evaluations of Roe v. Wade. *In:* Pojman, Louis P.; Beckwith, Francis J., eds. The Abortion Controversy: A Reader. Boston: Jones and Bartlett; 1994: 85-128. NRCBL: 12.4.2; 9.5.5. SC: le.

Rankin, Mark J. Contemporary Australian abortion law: the description of a crime and the negation of a woman's right to abortion. *Monash University Law Review* 2001; 27(2): 229-252. NRCBL: 12.4.1; 12.4.2; 12.4.3; 1.3.5. SC: le.

Rao, Mohan. Female foeticide: where do we go? *Issues in Medical Ethics* 2001 October-December; 9(4): 123-124. NRCBL: 12.4.2; 10.

Reagan, Leslie J. Crossing the border for abortions: California activists, Mexican clinics, and the creation of a feminist health agency in the 1960s. *Feminist Studies* 2000 Summer; 26(2): 323-348. NRCBL: 12.4.1; 12.5.2; 21.1.

Reardon, David C.; Strahan, Thomas W.; Thorp, John M., Jr.; Shuping, Martha W. Deaths associated with abortion compared to childbirth — a review of new and old data and the medical and legal implications. *Journal of Contemporary Health Law and Policy* 2004 Spring; 20(2): 279-327. NRCBL: 12.4.3; 20.1; 9.5.5. SC: em; rv.

Reilly, Elizabeth A. The rhetoric of disrespect: uncovering the faulty premises infecting reproductive rights. *American University Journal of Gender, Social Policy, and the Law* 1996 Fall; 5(1): 147-205. NRCBL: 12.4.2; 10. SC: le.

NRCBL: National Reference Center for Bioethics Literature Classification Scheme   See inside front cover for terms.

17

Ruse, Cathy Cleaver. Partial-birth abortion on trial. *Human Life Review* 2005 Spring; 31(2): 87-104. NRCBL: 12.4.1; 12.4.2. SC: le.

Sarkin, Jeremy. Patriarchy and discrimination in apartheid South Africa's abortion law. *Buffalo Human Rights Law Review* 1998; 4: 141-184. NRCBL: 12.4.1; 9.5.4; 12.4.2; 10. SC: le.

Schecter, Alissa. Choosing balance: congressional powers and the Partial-Birth Abortion Ban Act of 2003. *Fordham Law Review* 2005 March; 73(4): 1987-2026. NRCBL: 12.4.1; 12.1; 1.3.5. SC: le.

Schlafly, Andrew L. Brief of amicus curiae Eagle Forum Education and Legal Defense Fund in support of petitioner. *Issues in Law and Medicine* 2005 Fall; 21(2): 147-158. NRCBL: 12.4.2. SC: le.

Scuder, Amanda C. The inapplicability of parental involvement laws to the distribution of mifepristone (RU-486) to minors. *American University Journal of Gender, Social Policy, and the Law* 2002; 10(3): 711-741. NRCBL: 12.4.2; 8.3.2; 8.4. SC: le.

Semensohn, Jaime. Roe vs. Casey. *Ivy Journal of Ethics* 2003; 3(1): 6-9. NRCBL: 12.4.2; 8.4. SC: an.

Shultz, Marjorie M. Abortion and maternal-fetal conflict: broadening our concerns. *Southern California Review of Law and Women's Studies* 1992; 1: 79-98. NRCBL: 12.4.2; 9.5.5; 9.5.8; 4.4. SC: le.

Skov, Suzanne E. Stenberg v. Carhart: the abortion debate goes technical. *Journal of Contemporary Legal Issues* 2004; 14(1): 235-241. NRCBL: 12.4.3; 12.4.2; 12.4.1; 12.1. SC: le.

Smolin, David M. Fourteenth Amendment unenumerated rights jurisprudence: an essay in response to Stenberg v. Carhart. *Harvard Journal of Law and Public Policy* 2001; 24(3): 815-839. NRCBL: 12.4.2; 4.4. SC: le. Note: 120 S. Ct. 2597 (2000).

Stone, A.J., III. Consti-tortion: tort law as an end-run around abortion rights after Planned Parenthood v. Casey [112 S.Ct 2791 (1992)]. *American University Journal of Gender, Social Policy and the Law* 2000; 8(2): 471-515. NRCBL: 12.4.2; 11.4; 8.5. SC: le.

Storrow, Richard F.; Martinez, Sandra. "Special weight" for best-interests minors in the new era of parental autonomy. *Wisconsin Law Review* 2003; (5): 789-841. NRCBL: 12.4.2; 8.3.2; 9.5.7. SC: le.

Strahan, Thomas W. The natural law philosophy of Lon L. Fuller in contrast to Roe v. Wade and its progeny. *In:* Koterski, Joseph W., ed. Life and Learning XI: Proceedings of the Eleventh University Faculty for Life Conference. Washington, DC: University Faculty for Life; 2002: 85-97. NRCBL: 12.4.4; 1.1; 1.2. SC: le. Identifiers: Planned Parenthood v. Casey; Stenberg v. Carhart.

Telman, D.A. Jeremy. Abortion and women's legal personhood in Germany: a contribution to the feminist theory of the state. *New York University Review of Law and Social Change* 1998; 24(1): 91-148. NRCBL: 12.4.2; 12.5.1; 2.2; 9.5.5. SC: le.

Toner, Robin; Liptak, Adam. In new court, Roe may stand, so foes look to limit its scope. *New York Times* 2005 July 10; p. A1, A16. NRCBL: 12.4.1. SC: po.

Torzilli, Paolo. Reconciling the sanctity of human life, the Declaration of Independence and the Constitution. *Catholic Lawyer* 2000-2001; 40(2): 197-226. NRCBL: 12.4.1; 12.4.2; 4.4; 1.3.5. SC: le.

Van Detta, Jeffrey A. Constitutionalizing Roe, Casey and Carhart: a legislative due-process anti-discrimination principle that gives constitutional content to the "undue burden" standard of review applied to abortion control legislation. *Southern California Review of Law and Women's Studies* 2001 Spring; 10(2): 211-292. NRCBL: 12.4.1; 12.4.2. SC: le.

Weinstein, Brent. The state's constitutional power to regulate abortion. *Journal of Contemporary Legal Issues* 2004; 14(1): 229-234. NRCBL: 12.4.3; 12.4.1; 1.3.5; 12.1. SC: le.

Wicks, Elizabeth; Wyldes, Michael; Kilby, Mark. Late termination of pregnancy for fetal abnormality: medical and legal perspectives. *Medical Law Review* 2004 Autumn; 12(3): 285-305. NRCBL: 12.4.3; 8.5; 15.2. SC: le.

Wilgoren, Jodi. Clinics' bid to withhold abortion files is criticized. *New York Times* 2005 March 4; p. A15. NRCBL: 12.4.1. SC: le; po.

Wilgoren, Jodi. Kansas prosecutor demands files on late-term abortion patients. *New York Times* 2005 February 25; p. A1, A19. NRCBL: 12.4.1. SC: le; po.

Wivel, Ashley. Abortion policy and politics on the Lane Committee of Enquiry, 1971-1974. *Social History of Medicine* 1998 April; 11(1): 109-135. NRCBL: 12.4.1; 1.3.5. SC: le. Identifiers: United Kingdom (Great Britain).

Zenkich, Sabina. X marks the spot while Casey strikes out: two controversial abortion decisions. *Golden Gate University Law Review* 1993 Summer; 23(3): 1001- 1040. NRCBL: 12.4.1; 12.4.2; 12.4.3; 12.5.1. SC: le. Identifiers: Attorney General v. X; Planned Parenthood of Southeastern Pennsylvania v. Casey; Ireland; United States.

ABORTION/ MORAL AND RELIGIOUS ASPECTS

Abortion: facing facts [opinion]. *Christian Century* 2005 February 22; 122(4): 5. NRCBL: 12.3.

Adams, Karen E. Moral diversity among physicians and conscientious refusal of care in the provision of abortion services. *JAMWA: Journal of the American Medical*

Women's Association 2003 Fall; 58(4): 223-226. NRCBL: 12.3; 8.1.

Albar, Mohammed A. Induced abortion from an Islamic perspective: is it criminal or just elective? *Journal of Family and Community Medicine* 2001 December; 8(3): 25-35. NRCBL: 12.3; 12.1. Note: Abstract in English and Arabic.

Bandewar, Sunita. Exploring the ethics of induced abortion. *Indian Journal of Medical Ethics* 2005 January-March; 2(1): 18- 21. NRCBL: 12.3; 10; 4.4; 14.3.

Binion, Gayle. Feminist theory confronts US Supreme Court rhetoric: the case of abortion rights. *International Journal of Law, Policy and Family* 1997; 11(1): 63-85. NRCBL: 12.3; 10. SC: le.

Blackburn, William Ross. Abortion and the voice of scripture. *Human Life Review* 2005 Spring; 31(2): 67-85. NRCBL: 12.3. Comments: comment on Richard Hays, "Abortion", The Moral Vision of the New Testament, 1996.

Coleman, Stephen. Abortion and the foetus as non-person. *In his:* The Ethics of Artificial Uteruses: Implications for Reproduction and Abortion. Burlington, VT: Ashgate Pub.; 2004: 117- 149. NRCBL: 12.3; 4.4. SC: an.

Coleman, Stephen. Abortion, ectogenesis and the foetus as person. *In his:* The Ethics of Artificial Uteruses: Implications for Reproduction and Abortion. Burlington, VT: Ashgate Pub.; 2004: 57- 83. NRCBL: 12.3; 4.4; 1.1. SC: an.

Coleman, Stephen. The status of the embryo and foetus. *In his:* The Ethics of Artificial Uteruses: Implications for Reproduction and Abortion. Burlington, VT: Ashgate Pub.; 2004: 85- 115. NRCBL: 12.3; 4.4. SC: an.

Diamond, Eugene F. Post-rape medications. *In:* McMahon, Kevin T., ed. Moral Issues in Catholic Health Care. Wynnewood, PA: Saint Charles Borromeo Seminary; 2004: 36-56. NRCBL: 12.3; 9.5.5; 10.

Dickens, Bernard M. Interactions of law and ethics affecting reproductive choice. *Medicine and Law: World Association for Medical Law* 2005 September; 24(3): 549-559. NRCBL: 12.3; 9.5.5; 8.3.4; 11.3. SC: cs.
Abstract: Controversies affecting reproductive choice can often be resolved within interactions of legal and ethical decision-making. This paper addresses three topics, following the methodology presented in Reproductive Health and Human Rights: Integrating Medicine, Ethics, and Law, by R.J. Cook, B.M. Dickens and M.F. Fathalla (Oxford University Press, 2003). The book's 15 case studies each addresses medical, ethical, legal and human rights aspects, and structural approaches at clinical, healthcare system and societal levels. STERILIZATION: Individual self-determination supports legal and ethical rights of intellectually competent persons to sterilization. Sterilization of intellectually compromised persons was historically abused, causing reactions of excessively protective prohibition. ABORTION: Most developed countries have liberalized abortion legislation, thereby reducing abortion-related mortality and morbidity, but many developing countries retain repressive colonial laws. Over 95% of the estimated 20 million unsafe abortions annually occur in developing countries. COURT-ORDERED CAESAREAN DELIVERIES: A concern in developed countries is the willingness of some courts to order Caesarean procedures over competent women's objections.

Elon, Menachem; Auerbach, Bernard; Chazin, Daniel D.; Sykes, Melvin J. Abortion. *In their:* Jewish Law (Mishpat Ivri): Cases and Materials. New York: M. Bender; 1999: 609-624. NRCBL: 12.3; 1.2; 12.4.1. SC: le.

English, Jane; Gensler, Henry J.; Marquis, Don; McInerney, Peter K.; Paske, Gerald H. Beyond the personhood argument. *In:* Pojman, Louis P.; Beckwith, Francis J., eds. The Abortion Controversy: A Reader. Boston: Jones and Bartlett; 1994: 293-369. NRCBL: 12.3; 4.4; 1.1.

Farrell, Susan A. Reframing social justice, feminism and abortion. *Conscience* 2005 Spring; 26(1): 42-44. NRCBL: 12.3; 1.1; 1.2; 10; 14.1.

Fry, Sara T.; Veatch, Robert M. Abortion, contraception, and sterilization. *In their:* Case Studies in Nursing Ethics. Third edition. Sudbury, MA: Jones and Bartlett Publishers; 2006: 227-245. NRCBL: 12.3; 11.1; 11.3.

Gill, Robin. Response to: The human embryo in the Christian tradition. *Journal of Medical Ethics* 2005 December; 31(12): 713-714. NRCBL: 12.3; 1.2; 4.4.

Hall, Timothy. Abortion, the right to life, and dependence. *Social Theory and Practice* 2005 July; 31(3): 405-429. NRCBL: 12.3. SC: an.

Hall, Timothy. Life extension and creation: a reply to Silverstein and Boonin. *Journal of Social Philosophy* 2004 Winter; 35(4): 485-492. NRCBL: 12.3; 1.4.1; 1.1; 9.1. SC: an. Identifiers: Harry S. Silverstein; David Boonin; responsibility objection.

Hershenov, David B.; Koch, Rose J. How a hylomorphic metaphysics constrains the abortion debate. *National Catholic Bioethics Quarterly* 2005 Winter; 5(4): 751- 764. NRCBL: 12.3; 1.1; 4.4; 14.1.

Himma, K.E. A dualist analysis of abortion: personhood and the concept of self qua experiential subject. *Journal of Medical Ethics* 2005 January; 31(1): 48-55. NRCBL: 12.3; 4.4; 1.1. SC: an.
Abstract: There is no issue more central to the abortion debate than the controversial issue of whether the fetus is a moral person. Abortion-rights opponents almost universally claim that abortion is murder and should be legally prohibited because the fetus is a moral person at the moment of conception. Abortion-rights proponents almost universally deny the crucial assumption that the fetus is a person; on their view, whatever moral disvalue abortion involves does not rise to the level of murder and hence does not rise to the level of something that should be legally prohibited. In this essay, I argue that, under dualist assumptions about the nature of mind, the fetus is not a person until brain activity has begun.(i) First, I argue it is a necessary condition for a thing to be a moral person that it is (or has) a self. Second, I argue it is a necessary condition for a fetus to be

NRCBL: National Reference Center for Bioethics Literature Classification Scheme   See inside front cover for terms.

19

(or have) a self, under dualist assumptions, that there has been some electrical activity in the brain. I conclude that a dualist can take the position that abortion ought to be legally permitted at least until the beginning of brain activity in the fetus. I make no attempt to determine what conditions are sufficient for moral personhood; for this reason, the relevant claim about personhood is purely negative.

Hunt, John. Abortion and the Nuremberg prosecutors: a deeper analysis. *In:* Koterski, Joseph W., ed. Life and Learning VII: Proceedings of the Seventh University Faculty for Life Conference. Washington, DC: University Faculty for Life; 1998: 198-209. NRCBL: 12.3; 2.2.

Johnson, Andrew. How not to argue for abortion rights: fighting for choice is not enough. *Free Inquiry* 2005 February-March; 25(2): 38-41. NRCBL: 12.3.

Jonsen, Albert R. Abortion. *In his:* Bioethics Beyond the Headlines: Who Lives? Who Dies? Who Decides? Lanham, MD: Rowman and Littlefield; 2005: 77-84. NRCBL: 12.3.

Kissling, Frances. Is there life after Roe? How to think about the fetus. *Conscience* 2004-2005 Winter; 25(3): 10-18. NRCBL: 12.3; 12.4.2; 4.4.

Korcz, Keith Allen. Two moral strategies regarding abortion. *Journal of Social Philosophy* 2002 Winter; 33(4): 581-605. NRCBL: 12.3; 12.4.2. SC: an. Identifiers: Judith Jarvis Thomson; Donald Marquis.

Lee, Patrick; George, Robert P. The wrong of abortion. *In:* Cohen, Andrew I.; Wellman, Christopher Heath, eds. Contemporary Debates in Applied Ethics. Malden, MA: Blackwell Pub., 2005: 13-26. NRCBL: 12.3; 4.4. SC: an.

Liebman, Monte Harris. Democracy and abortion. *Linacre Quarterly* 2005 November; 72(4): 331-337. NRCBL: 12.3; 12.4.2.

Little, Margaret Olivia. The moral permissibility of abortion. *In:* Cohen, Andrew I.; Wellman, Christopher Heath, eds. Contemporary Debates in Applied Ethics. Malden, MA: Blackwell Pub., 2005: 27-39. NRCBL: 12.3; 4.4. SC: an.

Lugosi, Charles I. Respecting human life in 21st century America: a moral perspective to extend civil rights to the unborn from creation to natural death. *St. Louis University Law Journal* 2004 Winter; 48(2): 425-474. NRCBL: 12.3; 4.4; 14.5. SC: le.

Marquis, D. Savulescu's objections to the future of value argument. *Journal of Medical Ethics* 2005 February; 31(2): 119-122. NRCBL: 12.3; 1.1. SC: an.

May, Simon Cabulea. Principled compromise and the abortion controversy. *Philosophy and Public Affairs* 2005 Fall; 33(4): 317-348. NRCBL: 12.3; 1.3.5; 1.1; 9.3.1. SC: an.

Mullaney, Patrick J. John Paul II and America's laws on life. *Human Life Review* 2005 Summer; 31(3): 78-86. NRCBL: 12.3. SC: le. Identifiers: United States.

O'Brien, Dennis. No to abortion: posture, not policy. *America* 2005 May 30; 192(19): 7-9. NRCBL: 12.3; 12.4.1. SC: le.

Oderberg, David S. Abortion. *In his:* Applied Ethics: A Non-Consequentialist Approach. Malden, MA: Blackwell Publishers; 2000: 1-47. NRCBL: 12.3; 1.1. SC: an.

Peach, Lucinda. Religious lawmakers on moral identity and abortion law. *In her:* Legislating Morality: Pluralism and Religious Identity in Lawmaking. New York: Oxford University Press; 2002: 63-94. NRCBL: 12.3; 12.4.1; 1.3.5; 1.2. SC: le.

Perry, Michael J. Religion, politics, and abortion. *University of Detroit Mercy Law Review* 2001 Fall; 79(1): 1-37. NRCBL: 12.3; 12.4.1. SC: le.

Pojman, Louis P.; Beckwith, Francis J.; Markowitz, Sally; Whitbeck, Caroline; Wolf-Devine, Celia; Warren, Mary Anne. Feminist arguments on abortion. *In:* Pojman, Louis P.; Beckwith, Francis J., eds. The Abortion Controversy: A Reader. Boston: Jones and Bartlett; 1994: 371-444. NRCBL: 12.3; 10. SC: an.

Pojman, Louis P.; Beckwith, Francis J.; Nathanson, Bernard; Davis, Susan E. Abortion and militancy. *In:* Pojman, Louis P.; Beckwith, Francis J., eds. The Abortion Controversy: A Reader. Boston: Jones and Bartlett; 1994: 445-461. NRCBL: 12.3; 12.5.1.

Pojman, Louis P.; Beckwith, Francis J.; Noonan, John T.; Tooley, Michael; Devine, Philip; Schwarz, Stephen; Gillespie, Norman C.; Summer, L.W. Personhood arguments on abortion. *In:* Pojman, Louis P.; Beckwith, Francis J., eds. The Abortion Controversy: A Reader. Boston: Jones and Bartlett; 1994: 177-292. NRCBL: 12.3; 4.4; 1.1. SC: an.

Pojman, Louis P.; Beckwith, Francis J.; Thompson, Judith Jarvis; Tribe, Laurence. Arguments from a woman's right to her body. *In:* Pojman, Louis P.; Beckwith, Francis J., eds. The Abortion Controversy: A Reader. Boston: Jones and Bartlett; 1994: 129-175. NRCBL: 12.3; 12.4.2; 1.1. SC: an.

Silverstein, Harry S. Creation and abortion: a reply to Hall. *Journal of Social Philosophy* 2004 Winter; 35(4): 493-505. NRCBL: 12.3. SC: an. Identifiers: Timothy Hall; responsibility objection.

Sterba, James P. Abortion and euthanasia. *In his:* Sterba, James P., ed. Morality in Practice. 7th edition. Belmont, CA: Wasworth/Thompson Learning; 2004: 121-189. NRCBL: 12.3; 20.5.1; 20.7; 1.1. SC: an.

ABORTION/ SOCIAL ASPECTS

Bandewar, Sunita. Cultural barriers, 'competence' and informed consent in population-based surveys. *Issues in Medical Ethics* 2003 April-June; 11(2): 49-51. NRCBL: 12.5.2; 8.3.1; 1.3.9. SC: em.

Baumgardner, Jennifer. Giving women room to exhale: listening to women who have had abortions. *Conscience* 2005 Autumn; 26(3): 28-30. NRCBL: 12.5.1.

Belden, Nancy; Wade, Alexis. Caveat lector: the true results of polling are in the small print. *Conscience* 2004 Spring; 25(1): 34-35. NRCBL: 12.5.2; 12.4.1. SC: em.

Cassidy, Keith. The road to Roe: cultural change and the growth of acceptance of abortion prior to 1973. *In:* Koterski, Joseph W., ed. Life and Learning VII: Proceedings of the Seventh University Faculty for Life Conference. Washington, DC: University Faculty for Life; 1998: 231-245. NRCBL: 12.5.2; 2.2.

Dommergues, Marc; Cahen, Françoise; Garel, Micheline; Mahieu-Caputo, Dominique; Dumez, Yves. Feticide during second- and third-trimester termination of pregnancy: opinions of health care professionals. *Fetal Diagnosis and Therapy* 2003 March-April; 18(2): 91-97. NRCBL: 12.5.2; 7.1. SC: em.

Donohoe, Martin. Increase in obstacles to abortion: the American perspective in 2004. *Journal of the American Medical Women's Association* 2005; 60(1): 16-25. NRCBL: 12.5.1; 9.3.1; 12.4.2. Identifiers: United States.

French, Howard W. As girls "vanish", Chinese city battles tide of abortions. *New York Times* 2005 February 17; p. A3. NRCBL: 12.5.1; 13.3; 12.5.2; 10. SC: po.

Fried, Marlene Gerber. The economics of abortion access in the US: restrictions on government funding for abortion is the post-Roe battleground. *Conscience* 2005-2006 Winter; 26(4): 10-15. NRCBL: 12.5.1.

Funk, Nanette. Abortion counselling and the 1995 German abortion law. *Connecticut Journal of International Law* 1996 Fall; 12(1): 33-65. NRCBL: 12.5.3; 12.4.2. SC: le.

Hammarstedt, Meta; Jacobsson, Lars; Wulff, Marianne; Lalos, Ann. Views of midwives and gynecologists on legal abortion — a population-based study. *Acta Obstetricia et Gynecologica Scandinavica* 2005 January; 84(1): 58-64. NRCBL: 12.5.2. SC: em. Identifiers: Sweden.

Hamoda, Haitham; Critchley, Hilary O.D.; Paterson, Kate; Guthrie, Kate; Rodger, Mary; Penney, Gillian C. The acceptability of home medical abortion to women in UK settings. *BJOG: An International Journal of Obstetrics and Gynaecology* 2005 June; 112(6): 781-785. NRCBL: 12.5.2. SC: em. Identifiers: United Kingdom (Great Britain).

Hunt, John. Out of respect for life: Nazi abortion policy in the eastern occupied territories. *In:* Koterski, Joseph W., ed. Life and Learning IX: Proceedings of the Ninth University Faculty for Life Conference. Washington, DC: University Faculty for Life; 2000: 295-304. NRCBL: 12.5.1; 13.3; 15.5; 21.4; 2.2.

Jackson, Emily. Abortion, autonomy and prenatal diagnosis. *Social and Legal Studies* 2000 December; 9(4): 467-494. NRCBL: 12.5.1; 15.2; 1.1; 12.4.1; 14.3.

Joffe, C.E.; Weitz, T.A.; Stacey, C.L. Uneasy allies: pro-choice physicians, feminist health activists and the struggle for abortion rights. *Sociology of Health and Illness* 2004 September; 26(6): 775-796. NRCBL: 12.5.1; 12.4.3; 2.2. SC: le; an.

Kero, A.; Högberg, U.; Jacobsson, L.; Lalos, A. Legal abortion: a painful necessity. *Social Science and Medicine* 2001 December; 53(11): 1481-1490. NRCBL: 12.5.2. SC: em. Identifiers: Sweden.

Kero, A.; Lalos, Ann. Reactions and reflections in men, 4 and 12 months post-abortion. *Journal of Psychosomatic and Obstetric Gynaecology* 2004 June; 25(2): 135-143. NRCBL: 12.5.2; 10. SC: em. Identifiers: Sweden.

Learman, Lee A.; Drey, Eleanor A.; Gates, Elena A.; Kang, Mi-Suk; Washington, A. Eugene; Kuppermann, Miriam; Nelson, Anita; Powers, Thomas; Schwartz, Martin; Smith, Wendy; Burgoine, Gary. Abortion attitudes of pregnant women in prenatal care. *American Journal of Obstetrics and Gynecology* 2005 June; 192(6): 1939-1947. NRCBL: 12.5.2; 21.7. SC: em.

Lee, Ellie. Tensions in the regulation of abortion in Britain. *Journal of Law and Society* 2003 December; 30(4): 532-553. NRCBL: 12.5.3; 9.5.5. SC: le.

Leland, John. Under din of abortion debate, an experience shared quietly. *New York Times* 2005 September 18; p. A1, A28. NRCBL: 12.5.1; 12.5.3; 12.4.2. SC: po.

Mavroforou, Anna; Koumantakis, Evgenios; Michalodimitrakis, Emmanuel. Adolescence and abortion in Greece: women's profile and perceptions. *Journal of Pediatric and Adolescent Gynecology* 2004 October; 17(5): 321-326. NRCBL: 12.5.2; 11.2; 9.5.7. SC: em.

McIntosh, Tania. "An abortionist city": maternal mortality, abortion, and birth control in Sheffield, 1920-1940. *Medical History* 2000 January; 44(1): 75-96. NRCBL: 12.5.2; 12.1. SC: em. Identifiers: United Kingdom (Great Britain).

Mullally, Siobhán. Debating reproductive rights in Ireland. *Human Rights Quarterly* 2005; 27: 78-104. NRCBL: 12.5.1; 21.1; 10.

Okonofua, Friday E.; Shittu, S.O.; Oronsaye, F.; Ogunsakin, D.; Ogbomwan, S.; Zayyan, M. Attitudes and practices of private medical providers towards family

NRCBL: National Reference Center for Bioethics Literature Classification Scheme   See inside front cover for terms.

21

planning and abortion services in Nigeria. *Acta Obstetricia Gynecologica Scandinavica* 2005 March; 84(3): 270-280. NRCBL: 12.5.2; 7.1; 9.5.5. SC: em.

Patterson, Laura. Communication and termination: whose choice? *Journal of Family Planning and Reproductive Health Care* 2005 January; 31(1): 75-76. NRCBL: 12.5.3; 8.1; 21.7. SC: cs.

Pojman, Louis P.; Beckwith, Francis J. Breaking through the stereotypes. *In their:* Pojman, Louis P.; Beckwith, Francis J., eds. The Abortion Controversy: A Reader. Boston: Jones and Bartlett; 1994: 1-11. NRCBL: 12.5.2.

Rademakers, J.; Koster, E.; Jansen-van Hees, A.C.V.; Willems, F. Medical abortion as an alternative to vacuum aspiration: first experiences with the 'abortion pill' in The Netherlands. *European Journal of Contraception and Reproductive Health Care* 2001 December; 6(4): 185-191. NRCBL: 12.5.2; 9.7. SC: em.

Reardon, David C. Abortion decisions and the duty to screen: clinical, ethical, and legal implications of predictive risk factors of post-abortion maladjustment. *Journal of Contemporary Health Law and Policy* 2003 Winter; 20(1): 33-114. NRCBL: 12.5.3; 8.3.1; 9.5.5; 9.8. SC: le.

Richards, Amy. What is abortion? *Conscience* 2005-2006 Winter; 26(4): 35-37. NRCBL: 12.5.2.

Rørbye, Christina; Nørgaard, Mogens; Nilas, Lisbeth. Medical versus surgical abortion: comparing satisfaction and potential confounders in a partly randomized study. *Human Reproduction* 2005 March; 20(3): 834-838. NRCBL: 12.5.2; 9.5.5. SC: em.

Schoen, Johanna. I knew that it was a serious crime: negotiating abortion before Roe v. Wade. *In her:* Choice and Coercion: Birth Control, Sterilization and Abortion in Public Health and Welfare. Chapel Hill: University of North Carolina Press; 2005: 139-196. NRCBL: 12.5.1; 12.4.1; 2.2. SC: le.

Shoham-Vardi, I.; Weiner, N.; Weitzman, D.; Levcovich, A. Termination of pregnancy: attitudes and behavior of women in a traditional society. *Prenatal Diagnosis* 2004 November; 24(11): 869-875. NRCBL: 12.5.2; 12.3; 15.2. SC: em. Identifiers: Bedouin Arabs; Islam; Israel.

Thomas, James; Williams, A. Susan. Women and abortion in 1930s Britain: a survey and its data. *Social History of Medicine* 1998 August; 11(2): 283-309. NRCBL: 12.5.2; 9.5.5; 2.2. SC: em. Identifiers: United Kingdom (Great Britain).

Thorp, John M., Jr.; Hartmann, Katherine E.; Shadigan, Elizabeth. Long-term physical and psychological health consequences of induced abortion: a review of the evidence. *Linacre Quarterly* 2005 February; 72(1): 44-69. NRCBL: 12.5.2; 9.5.5. SC: em.

ADVANCE DIRECTIVES
See also DEATH AND DYING; TREATMENT REFUSAL

'Code' called contrary to pt.'s advance directives. *Nursing Law's Regan Report* 2005 January; 45(8): 1. NRCBL: 20.5.4; 20.5.1. SC: le; cs. Identifiers: Furlong v. Catholic Healthcare West.

Living wills. *Bulletin of Medical Ethics* 2003 November; (193): 2. NRCBL: 20.5.4; 8.3.1; 8.3.4. SC: le. Identifiers: United Kingdom (Great Britain).

Allen, Rose; Ventura, Nestor. Advance directives use in acute care hospitals. *JONA's Healthcare Law, Ethics, and Regulation* 2005 July- September; 7(3): 86-91. NRCBL: 20.5.4; 7.1. SC: em.

Alters, Sandra. Advance directives. *In her:* Death and Dying. Who Decides? Detroit: Thomson Gale; 2005: 79-99. NRCBL: 20.5.4. SC: le.

American Hospital Association [AHA]. Put It in Writing: Questions and Answers on Advance Directives. Chicago, Illinois: American Hospital Association 1994 October; 9 p. NRCBL: 20.5.4.

Amering, Michaela; Stastny, Peter; Hopper, Kim. Psychiatric advance directives: qualitative study of informed deliberations by mental health service users. *British Journal of Psychiatry* 2005 March; 186: 247-252. NRCBL: 20.5.4; 17.1. SC: em. Identifiers: United States.

Biegler, Paul; Stewart, Cameron; Savulescu, Julian; Skene, Loane. Determining the validity of advance directives. *Medical Journal of Australia* 2000 June 5; 172(11): 545-548. NRCBL: 20.5.4; 7.1; 8.1. SC: le.

Bosek, Marcia Sue DeWolf; Fitzpatrick, Joyce. A nursing perspective on advance directives. *Medsurg Nursing* 1992 September; 1(1): 33-38. NRCBL: 20.5.4; 7.1; 8.1; 4.1.3.

Bostrom, Barry A. Pettis v. Smith and Braddock in the Louisiana Court of Appeal. *Issues in Law and Medicine* 2005 Spring; 20(3): 271-273. NRCBL: 20.5.4. SC: le.

Brown, Margaret. The law and practice associated with advance directives in Canada and Australia: similarities, differences and debates. *International Journal of the Sociology of Law* 2002 December; 30(4): 59-76. NRCBL: 20.5.4; 1.3.5. SC: le.

Brown, Margaret; Grbich, Carol; Maddocks, Ian; Parker, Deborah; Connellan, Penny Roe; Willis, Eileen. Documenting end of life decisions in residential aged care facilities in South Australia. *Australian and New Zealand Journal of Public Health* 2005 February; 29(1): 85-90. NRCBL: 20.5.4; 20.5.1; 9.5.2. SC: em.

Bryan, Debra M. It's my body and I'll die if I want to: a plan for keeping personal autonomy from spinning out of control. *Journal of Medicine and Law* 2003 Fall-2004 Spring; 8(1-2): 45-67. NRCBL: 20.5.4; 1.1. SC: le.

Burkett, Teresa Meinders; Weyrauch, Samantha. An Oklahoma perspective: end of life decision-making and termination of treatment. *Tulsa Law Journal* 2000 Spring-Summer; 35(3-4): 565-581. NRCBL: 20.5.4; 20.5.1. SC: le.

Burt, John G. Compliance with advance directives: a legal view. *Critical Care Nursing Quarterly* 1999 November; 22(3): 72-74. NRCBL: 20.5.4; 20.5.1. SC: le.

Carpenter, Alan F.; Neher, Jon O. In defense of living wills [letter and reply]. *Hastings Center Report* 2004 July-August; 34(4): 5-6. NRCBL: 20.5.4.

Carpenter, Betsy; Fagerlin Angela; Schnieder, Carl E. In defense of living wills [letter and reply]. *Hastings Center Report* 2004 July-August; 34(4): 6. NRCBL: 20.5.4.

Cartwright, Colleen M.; Parker, Malcolm H. Advance care planning and end of life decision making. *Australian Family Physician* 2004 October; 33(10): 815-817, 819. NRCBL: 20.5.4; 8.1. SC: le. Identifiers: Australia.

Chaudhari, Bimal P.; Grodin, Michael A. What about proxies? [letter]. *Health Affairs* 2005 November-December; 24(6): 1686-1687. NRCBL: 20.5.4.

Dake, Amanda Christine. The application of "out-of-hospital" do not resuscitate order legislation to commercial airline travel. *Journal of Air Law and Commerce* 1997 November-December; 63(2): 443-473. NRCBL: 20.5.4; 20.5.1. SC: le.

DeGrazia, David. Advance directives, dementia, and the someone else problem. *In his:* Human Identity and Bioethics. New York: Cambridge University Press; 2005: 159-202. NRCBL: 20.5.4; 4.4; 9.5.2; 17.1; 1.1. SC: an.

Doukas, David John. "Family" in advance care planning: the family covenant in the wake of Terri Schiavo. *Journal of Law, Medicine and Ethics* 2005 Summer; 33(2): 372-374. NRCBL: 20.5.4; 20.3.3; 8.3.3. SC: le.

Enck, Robert E. Advance directives: burden or benefit? [editorial]. *American Journal of Hospice and Palliative Care* 2003 September-October; 20(5): 329-330. NRCBL: 20.5.4.

Fins, Joseph J.; Maltby, Barbara S.; Friedmann, Erika; Greene, Michele G.; Norris, Kaye; Adelman, Ronald; Byock, Ira. Contracts, covenants and advance care planning: an empirical study of the moral obligations of patient and proxy. *Journal of Pain and Symptom Management* 2005 January; 29(1): 55-68. NRCBL: 20.5.4; 8.3.3. SC: em.

Foti, Mary Ellen; Bartels, Stephen J.; Merriman, Melanie P.; Fletcher, Kenneth E.; Van Citters, Aricca D. Medical advance care planning for persons with serious mental illness. *Psychiatric Services* 2005 May; 56(5): 576-584. NRCBL: 20.5.4; 17.1. SC: em.

Gaughan, Mary C. Legal review: the Patient Self-Determination Act — "Miranda" rights in health care. *Topics in Health Record Management* 1991 August; 12(1): 83-88. NRCBL: 20.5.4. SC: le.

Gerald, Lynn B.; Sanderson, Bonnie; Fish, Larry; Li, Yufeng; Bittner, Vera; Brooks, Michael; Bailey, William C. Advance directives in cardiac and pulmonary rehabilitation patients. *Journal of Cardiopulmonary Rehabilitation* 2000 November- December; 20(6): 340-345. NRCBL: 20.5.4; 9.5.1. SC: em.

Germany. Bundestag. Study Commission on Ethics and Law in Modern Medicine. Interim Report on Living Wills: Short Version. Berlin, Germany: Secretariat of the Study Commission on the Law and Ethics of Modern Medicine, German Bundestag 2004 December; 12 p. [Online]. Available: http://www.bundestag.de/parlament/kommissionen/archiv15/ethik_med/berichte_stellg/04_12_16_kurzfassung_zwischenbericht_patienten verfuegungen_engl.pdf [29 November 2005]. NRCBL: 20.5.4.

Gilbert, Michele; Counsell, Colleen M.; Guin, Peggy; O'Neill, Rebecca; Briggs, Sandra. Determining the relationship between end-of-life decisions expressed in advance directives and resuscitation efforts during cardiopulmonary resuscitation. *Outcomes Management for Nursing Practice* 2001 April-June; 5(2): 87-92. NRCBL: 20.5.4; 20.5.1. SC: em.

Goldblatt, David. A messy necessary end: health care proxies need our support. *Neurology* 2001 January 23; 56(2): 148-152. NRCBL: 20.5.4; 20.5.1; 17.1; 8.1. SC: em.

Goodman, Martin D.; Tarnoff, Michael; Slotman, Gus J. Effect of advance directives on the management of elderly critically ill patients. *Critical Care Medicine* 1998 April; 26(4): 701-704. NRCBL: 20.5.4; 9.5.2; 7.1; 20.5.1; 9.4.

Goodnough, Abby. Schiavo autopsy says brain, withered, was untreatable; Florida woman's collapse in 1990 is still a mystery. *New York Times* 2005 June 16; p. A1, A24. NRCBL: 20.5.4. SC: po.

Goodwin, ZellaJane; Kiehl, Ermalynn M.; Peterson, Janice Z. King's theory as foundation for an advance directive decision-making model. *Nursing Science Quarterly* 2002 July; 15(3): 237-241. NRCBL: 20.5.4; 4.1.3; 8.1.

Griffith, Richard. Living wills, duty of care and the right to treatment. *British Journal of Community Nursing* 2004

NRCBL: National Reference Center for Bioethics Literature Classification Scheme　　　　See inside front cover for terms.

23

November; 9(11): 488-491. NRCBL: 20.5.4; 20.5.1; 9.2. SC: cs; le.

Hackleman, Tricia Jonas. Violation of an individual's right to die: the need for a wrongful living cause of action. *University of Cincinnati Law Review* 1996 Summer; 64(4): 1355-1381. NRCBL: 20.5.4; 8.5; 8.3.4. SC: le.

Hattori, Toshiko. End-of-life care and advance directives in Japan. *Journal International de Bioethique / International Journal of Bioethics* 2005 March-June; 16(1-2): 135-142, 198. NRCBL: 20.5.4; 20.4.1; 20.3.2; 1.3.5. Note: Abstract in English and French.

Hawkins, Nikki Ayers; Ditto, Peter H.; Danks, Joseph H.; Smucker, William D. Micromanaging death: process preferences, values, and goals in end-of-life medical decision making. *Gerontologist* 2005 February; 45(1): 107-117. NRCBL: 20.5.4; 8.1. SC: em.

Heffner, John E.; Fahy, Bonnie; Hilling, Lana; Barbieri, Celia. Attitudes regarding advance directives among patients in pulmonary rehabilitation. *American Journal of Respiratory and Critical Care Medicine* 1996 December; 154(6 Part 1): 1735-1740. NRCBL: 20.5.4; 9.5.1; 8.3.1; 20.5.1. SC: em.

Hickey, Daniel P. The disutility of advance directives: we know the problems, but are there solutions? *Journal of Health Law* 2003 Summer; 36(3): 455-473. NRCBL: 20.5.4; 8.1.

Hoffmeister, Thaddeus A. The growing importance of advance medical directives. *Military Law Review* 2003 Fall; 177: 110-132. NRCBL: 20.5.4; 1.3.5. SC: le.

Horttor, Bretton J. A survey of living will and advanced health care directives. *North Dakota Law Review* 1998; 74(2): 233-293. NRCBL: 20.5.4. SC: le.

Howe, Edmund G. Commentary on "psychiatric advance directives: an alternative to coercive treatment": lessons from advance directives for PADs. *Psychiatry* 2000 Summer; 63(2): 173-177. NRCBL: 20.5.4; 17.1. Identifiers: psychiatric advance directives.

Hunt, William E. The right to die in Montana: the Montana Uniform Rights of the Terminally Ill Act. *Montana Law Review* 1993 Summer; 54(2): 339-356. NRCBL: 20.5.4. SC: le.

Karel, Michele J.; Powell, Jean; Cantor, Michael D. Using a values discussion guide to facilitate communication in advance care planning. *Patient Education and Counseling* 2004 October; 55(1): 22-31. NRCBL: 20.5.4; 8.1. SC: em.

Kelly, David F. Forgoing treatment, pillar three: advance directives. *In his:* Contemporary Catholic Health Care Ethics. Washington, DC: Georgetown University Press; 2004: 170-182. NRCBL: 20.5.4; 1.2. SC: le.

Kolodner, Deborah E. Advance medical directives after Cruzan [opinion]. *Medsurg Nursing* 1992 September; 1(1): 56-59. NRCBL: 20.5.4; 20.5.1; 7.1. SC: le.

Lahn, Michael; Friedman, Benjamin; Bijur, Polly; Haughey, Marianne; Gallagher, E.J. Advance directives in skilled nursing facility residents transferred to emergency departments. *Academic Emergency Medicine* 2001 December; 8(12): 1158-1162. NRCBL: 20.5.4; 9.5.2; 20.5.1; 7.1. SC: em.

Landman, Willem A.; Henley, Lesley D. Legalising advance directives in South Africa [editorial]. *South African Medical Journal* 2000 August; 90(8): 785-787. NRCBL: 20.5.4; 1.3.5. SC: le.

Langerman, Alex; Angelos, Peter; Johnston, Chad. Opinions and use of advance directives by physicians at a tertiary care hospital. *Quality Management in Health Care* 2000 Spring; 8(3): 14-18. NRCBL: 20.5.4; 7.1; 8.1. SC: em.

Levine, Carol. She died the same way she lived: planning well in advance. *New York Times* 2005 December 6; p. F5. NRCBL: 20.5.4. SC: po.

Lewis, Rodney S.; Wilson, Roger D.; Biegler, Paul; Stewart, Cameron; Savulescu, Julian; Skene, Loane. Determining the validity of advance directives [letter and reply]. *Medical Journal of Australia* 2000 September 18; 173(6): 335-336. NRCBL: 20.5.4; 8.3.3.

Lieberson, Alan D. Commentary: advance medical directives — 1998: a medical view. *Quinnipiac Probate Law Journal* 1998; 12(3): 305-338. NRCBL: 20.5.4; 20.5.1. SC: le.

Liu, A. Legal recognition of advance refusal needed. *Hong Kong Medical Journal* 2005 April; 11(2): 133-134. NRCBL: 20.5.4. SC: le. Identifiers: Hong Kong.

Martyn, Susan R.; Reagan, James E.; Minogue, Brendan; Dippel, Debra L.; Schimer, Maria R.; Taraszewski, Robert. Redrafting Ohio's advance directive laws. *Akron Law Review* 1992 Fall; 26(2): 229-292. NRCBL: 20.5.4; 20.5.1. SC: le.

McAuley, William J.; Travis, Shirley S. Advance care planning among residents in long-term care. *American Journal of Hospice and Palliative Care* 2003 September-October; 20(5): 353-359. NRCBL: 20.5.4. SC: em.

Meyers, Judy L.; Moore, Crystal; McGrory, Alice; Sparr, Jennifer; Ahern, Melissa. Physician orders for life-sustaining treatment form: honoring end-of-life directives for nursing home residents. *Journal of Gerontological Nursing* 2004 September; 30(9): 37-46. NRCBL: 20.5.4; 20.4.1; 9.5.2. SC: em.

Miller, Gary D.; Key, Charles M. Health Care Decisions Act — problems with consents, surrogacy, and end-of-life choices addressed by the new Tennessee Health Care Deci-

---

sions Act. *Tennessee Medicine* 2004 October; 97(10): 448-451. NRCBL: 20.5.4; 8.3.3; 20.5.1. SC: le.

Minnesota Medical Association [MMA]; University of Minnesota Extension Service. The Minnesota Health Care Directive: A Suggested Form, Suggestions for Completing. Minneapolis, MN: The Association [MMA], 1998 August; various pagings. NRCBL: 20.5.4.
  Abstract: Part I: Instructions/Cover, Part IA: Minnesota Health Care Directive, Part IB: Suggestions for Completing a Minnesota Health Care Directive, Part II: Health Care Instructions Worksheet. Also includes Minnesota Medical Association Emergency Resuscitation Guidelines.

Morrison, R. Sean; Chichin, Eileen; Carter, John; Burack, Orah; Lantz, Melinda; Meier, Diane E. The effect of a social work intervention to enhance advance care planning documentation in the nursing home. *Journal of the American Geriatrics Society* 2005 February; 53(2): 290-294. NRCBL: 20.5.4; 1.3.10; 9.5.2. SC: em.

National Physician Orders for Life-Sustaining Treatment [POLST]. Paradigm Task Force. The National POLST Paradigm Initiative. Portland, Oregon: Center for Ethics in Health Care; 6 p. [Online]. Available: http://www.ohsu.edu/ethics/polst/docs/POLST_nppi.pdf [25 January 2006]. NRCBL: 20.5.4.

Navarro-Michel, Monica. Advance directives: the Spanish perspective. *Medical Law Review* 2005 Summer; 13(2): 137-169. NRCBL: 20.5.4; 21.6. SC: an; le.

Nelson, Lawrence J. The Wendland case: on families and fantasies. *Medical Ethics Newsletter [Lahey Clinic]* 2003 Spring; 10(2): 8, 12. NRCBL: 20.5.4; 8.3.3. SC: le.

Nys, Herman. Emerging legislation in Europe on the legal status of advance directives and medical decision-making with respect to an incompetent patient ('living wills'). *European Journal of Health Law* 1997; (4): 61-70. NRCBL: 20.5.4; 8.3.3. SC: le.

O'Connell, Maria J.; Stein, Catherine H. Psychiatric advance directives: perspectives of community stakeholders. *Administration and Policy in Mental Health* 2005 January; 32(3): 241-265. NRCBL: 20.5.4; 17.1. SC: em.

Orr, Robert D. Clinical ethics consultation. *Update [Loma Linda University Center for Christian Bioethics]* 1999 December; 15(4); 4 p. NRCBL: 20.5.4.

Papageorgiou, Alexia; King, Michael; Janmohamed, Anis; Davidson, Oliver; Dawson, John. Advance directives for patients compulsorily admitted to hospital with serious mental illness. Randomised controlled trial. *British Journal of Psychiatry* 2002 December; 181(6): 513-519. NRCBL: 20.5.4; 17.7. SC: em.

Partridge, Robert A.; Virk, Alam; Sayah, Assaad; Antosia, Robert. Field experience with prehospital advance directives. *Annals of Emergency Medicine* 1998 November; 32(5); 6 p. [Online]. Available: http://home.

mdconsult.com/das/article/body/50990752-3/jorg= journal&source=MI7sp=10 [3 October 2005]. NRCBL: 20.5.4; 20.5.1. SC: em.

Petersen, Andrea. Negotiating the terms of your death: medical advances give patients more control over how and when they die. *Wall Street Journal* 2005 May 10; p. D1, D3. NRCBL: 20.5.4. SC: po.

Pollack, Simeon. A new approach to advance directives. *Critical Care Medicine* 2000 September; 28(9): 3146-3148. NRCBL: 20.5.4; 9.3.1; 9.5.2.

Prendergast, Thomas J. Advance care planning: pitfalls, progress, promise. *Critical Care Medicine* 2001 February; 29(2, Supplement): N34-N39. NRCBL: 20.5.4; 8.1; 9.4.

Rein, Andrea J.; Harshman, Dana L.; Frick, Trisha; Phillips, Jean M.; Lewis, Shirley; Nolan, Marie T. Advance directive decision making among medical inpatients. *Journal of Professional Nursing* 1996 January-February; 12(1): 39-46. NRCBL: 20.5.4. SC: em; le. Identifiers: Patient Self-Determination Act.

Rempusheski, Veronica F.; Hurley, Ann C. Advance directives and dementia. *Journal of Gerontological Nursing* 2000 October; 26(10): 27-34. NRCBL: 20.5.4; 17.1; 4.1.3.

Rurup, Mette L.; Onwuteaka-Philipsen, Bregje D.; van der Heide, Agnes; van der Wal, Gerrit; van der Maas, Paul J. Physicians' experiences with demented patients with advance euthanasia directives in the Netherlands. *Journal of the American Geriatrics Society* 2005 July; 53(7): 1138-1144. NRCBL: 20.5.4; 9.5.2; 17.1; 20.5.1. SC: em.

Rutsohn, Phil; Ibrahim, Nabil. An analysis of provider attitudes toward end-of-life decision-making. *American Journal of Hospice and Palliative Care* 2003 September-October; 20(5): 371-378. NRCBL: 20.5.4; 20.3.2. SC: em. Note: Erratum in: American Journal of Hospice and Palliative Care 2004 January-February; 21(1): 9.

Ryan, Catherine J.; Santucci, Mary Ann; Gattuso, Michele C.; Czurylo, Kathy; O'Brien, Jim; Stark, Barbara. Perceptions about advance directives by nurses in a community hospital. *Clinical Nurse Specialist* 2001 November; 15(6): 246-252. NRCBL: 20.5.4; 4.1.3. SC: em.

Sahm, S.; Will, R.; Hommel, G. Attitudes towards and barriers to writing advance directives amongst cancer patients, healthy controls, and medical staff. *Journal of Medical Ethics* 2005 August; 31(8): 437-440. NRCBL: 20.5.4. SC: em. Identifiers: Germany.
  Abstract: OBJECTIVES: After years of public discussion too little is still known about willingness to accept the idea of writing an advance directive among various groups of people in EU countries. We investigated knowledge about and willingness to accept such a directive in cancer patients, healthy controls, physicians, and nursing staff in Germany. METHODS: Cancer patients, healthy controls, nursing staff, and physicians (n = 100 in

NRCBL: National Reference Center for Bioethics Literature Classification Scheme   See inside front cover for terms.

25

each group) were surveyed by means of a structured questionnaire. RESULTS: Only 18% and 19% of the patients and healthy controls respectively, and 10% of the medical staff had written an advance directive. However, 50-81% of those surveyed indicated that they wished to write one. This intention was associated with deteriorating health (p 0.001). Only 29% of the healthy controls and 43% of the patients knew about the possibility of appointing a health care proxy. A majority in all groups believed that advance directives may influence the course of treatment (79-85%), yet half of those surveyed in all groups fear that patients could be pressurised into writing an advance directive, and 38-65% thought that relatives could abuse such documents. CONCLUSIONS: Only a minority of the participants had written an advance directive and knew about the possibility of authorizing a health care proxy. Deteriorating health was associated with increasing willingness to make a directive. Despite a majority belief that advance directives may influence treatment at the end of life, other factors limit their employment, such as fear of abuse.

Sahm, S.; Will, R.; Hommel, G. Would they follow what has been laid down? Cancer patients' and healthy controls' views on adherence to advance directives compared to medical staff. *Medicine, Health Care and Philosophy: A European Journal* 2005; 8(3): 297-305. NRCBL: 20.5.4. SC: em.

Abstract: Advance directives are propagated as instruments to maintain patients' autonomy in case they can no longer decide for themselves. It has been [sic] never been examined whether patients' and healthy persons themselves are inclined to adhere to these documents. Patients' and healthy persons' views on whether instructions laid down in advance directives should be followed because that is (or is not) "the right thing to do", not because one is legally obliged to do so, were studied and compared with that of medical staff. METHOD: Vignette study presenting five cases. Cancer patients, healthy persons, nursing staff and physicians (n = 100 in each group) were interviewed. An adherence score was calculated (maximum value 5). The adherence score is found to be low in all groups, yet lowest in patients (1.55; standard deviation 1.13) and healthy controls (1.60; 1.37). The scores are significantly different between nursing staff on the one hand and patients and healthy controls on the other (p 0.005 and p 0.05, respectively), and between doctors and patients (p 0.05). Interviewees who want these documents to be followed tend to live alone and to have already written an advance directive. CONCLUSIONS: Cancer patients and healthy persons widely disregard instructions laid down in advance directives and consider them less binding than physicians and nursing staff do. Only a minority tends to adhere more to advance directives. To improve decision-making at the end of life when patients are no longer able to decide for themselves alternative concepts, such as advanced care planning, should be considered.

Salmond, Susan W.; David, Estrella. Attitudes toward advance directives and advance directive completion rates. *Orthopaedic Nursing* 2005 March-April; 24(2): 117-129. NRCBL: 20.5.4. SC: em.

Schears, Raquel M.; Marco, Catherine A.; Iserson, Kenneth V. "Do not attempt resuscitation" (DNAR) in the out-of-hospital setting. *Annals of Emergency Medicine* 2004 July; 44(1): 68-70. NRCBL: 20.5.4; 20.5.1. SC: rv. Identifiers: American College of Emergency Physicians [ACEP] Ethics Committee.

Schneider, Carl E. Liability for life. *Hastings Center Report* 2004 July-August; 34(4): 10-11. NRCBL: 20.5.4; 8.3.4. SC: le. Identifiers: Marshall Klavan; right to refuse medical treatment.

Schultz-Grant, Lois D.; Young-Cureton, Virginia; Kataoka-Yahiro, Merle. Advance directives and do not resuscitate orders: nurses' knowledge and the level of practice in school settings. *Journal of School Nursing* 1998 April; 14(2): 4, 6-10, 12-13. NRCBL: 20.5.4; 20.5.2; 20.3.2. SC: em.

Schwartz, John. New openness in deciding when and how to die. *New York Times* 2005 March 21; p. A1, A14. NRCBL: 20.5.4. SC: po.

Schwartz, John; Estrin, James. Many seeking one final say on end of life. *New York Times* 2005 June 17; p. A1, A22. NRCBL: 20.5.4. SC: po.

Shapiro, Jane D.; Bowles, Kathleen. Nurses' and consumers' understanding of and comfort with the Patient Self-determination Act. *Journal of Nursing Administration* 2002 October; 32(10): 503- 508. NRCBL: 20.5.4; 4.1.3.

Sinsky, Christine. Unreimbursed services in primary care [letter]. *Archives of Internal Medicine* 2005 March 28; 165(6): 702-703. NRCBL: 20.5.4; 9.3.1.

Skeen, Andrew. Living wills and advance directives in South African law. *Medicine and Law: World Association for Medical Law* 2004; 23(4): 937-943. NRCBL: 20.5.4; 20.5.1. SC: le.

Abstract: The legal status of living wills and advance directives in South African Law will be considered. Presently there is no reported judgment of a court in South Africa which has directly ruled on the validity of an advance directive or living will. In a case decided in 1992 the issue as to whether to discontinue life supporting treatment was decided with reference to the legal persuasions of society and whether, in light of these, it would be reasonable to discontinue artificial feeding of the patient. The judge indicated that just as a living person has an interest in the disposal of his body so did he think that the patient's wishes as expressed when he was in good health should be given effect. In South African law every person is legally entitled to refuse medical treatment even if the consequences may be to hasten death. The South African Law Convention has extensively investigated the issue in its report entitled Report on Euthanasia and the Artificial Preservation of Life in 1998. Certain problems were identified and a draft bill was suggested.

Sperling, Daniel. Do pregnant women have (living) will? *Journal of Health Care Law and Policy* 2005; 8(2): 331-342. NRCBL: 20.5.4; 8.3.4; 9.5.8. SC: le.

Stewart, Kevin; Bowker, Lesley. Advance directives and living wills. *Postgraduate Medical Journal* 1998 March; 74(869): 151-156. NRCBL: 20.5.4. SC: cs; le.

Taylor, James Stacey. Autonomy and informed consent on the Navajo Reservation. *Journal of Social Philosophy* 2004 Winter; 35(4): 506-516. NRCBL: 20.5.4; 8.3.1; 1.1;

21.7. Identifiers: Patient Self-Determination Act (PSDA); Ruth Macklin.

Texas Partnership for End-of-Life Care [TxPEC]. Directive to Physicians and Family or Surrogates (Living Will). Austin, TX: Texas Department of State Health Services undated; 4 p. [Online]. Available: http://www.txpec.org/docs/DirtoPhysFamilySurrogates.doc [25 May 2005]. NRCBL: 20.5.4.

Texas Partnership for End-Of-Life Care [TxPEC]. Medical Power of Attorney. Austin, TX: Texas Partnership for End-Of-Life Care undated; 6 p. [Online]. Available: http://www.txpec.org/docs/MedicalPowerofAttorney.doc [25 May 2005]. NRCBL: 20.5.4.

Travis, Sara; Mason, Jill; Mallett, Jane; Laverty, Diane. Guidelines in respect of advance directives: the position in England. *International Journal of Palliative Nursing* 2001 October; 7(10): 493-500. NRCBL: 20.5.4. SC: le. Identifiers: United Kingdom (Great Britain).

Tulsky, James A. Beyond advance directives: importance of communication skills at the end of life. *JAMA: The Journal of the American Medical Association* 2005 July 20; 294(3): 359-365. NRCBL: 20.5.4.
Abstract: Patients and their families struggle with myriad choices concerning medical treatments that frequently precede death. Advance directives have been proposed as a tool to facilitate end- of-life decision making, yet frequently fail to achieve this goal. In the context of the case of a man with metastatic cancer for whom an advance directive was unable to prevent a traumatic death, I review the challenges in creating and implementing advance directives, discuss factors that can affect clear decision making; including trust, uncertainty, emotion, hope, and the presence of multiple medical providers; and offer practical suggestions for physicians. Advance care planning remains a useful tool for approaching conversations with patients about the end of life. However, such planning should occur within a framework that emphasizes responding to patient and family emotions and focuses more on goals for care and less on specific treatments.

University of California San Francisco [UCSF] Mount Zion Hospital; University of California San Francisco Mount Zion Cancer Center. Planning for your future: a gift of love. An approach to life and death with dignity: a guide to help you make decisions on advance directives and organize your life. San Francisco, CA: University of California, 1996; 31 p. NRCBL: 20.5.4.

Upadya, Anupama; Muralidharan, Visvanathan; Thorevska, Natalya; Amoateng-Adjepong, Yaw; Manthous, Constantine A. Patient, physician, and family member understanding of living wills. *American Journal of Respiratory and Critical Care Medicine* 2002 December 1; 166(11): 1430-1435. NRCBL: 20.5.4; 20.3.1. SC: em.

Wallace, Susannah Kish; Martin, Charles G.; Shaw, Andrew D.; Price, Kristen J. Influence of an advance directive on the initiation of life support technology in critically ill cancer patients. *Critical Care Medicine* 2001

December; 29(12): 2294-2298. NRCBL: 20.5.4; 20.5.1; 9.5.1. SC: em.

Wareham, Pauline; McCallin, Antoinette; Diesfeld, Kate. Advance directives: the New Zealand context. *Nursing Ethics* 2005 July; 12(4): 349-359. NRCBL: 20.5.4. SC: le.
Abstract: Advance directives convey consumers' wishes about accepting or refusing future treatment if they become incompetent. They are designed to communicate a competent consumer's perspective regarding the preferred treatment, should the consumer later become incompetent. There are associated ethical issues for health practitioners and this article considers the features that are relevant to nurses. In New Zealand, consumers have a legal right to use an advance directive that is not limited to life-prolonging care and includes general health procedures. Concerns may arise regarding a consumer's competence and the document's validity. Nurses need to understand their legal and professional obligations to comply with an advance directive. What role does a nurse play and what questions arise for a nurse when advance directives are discussed with consumers? This article considers the cultural dimensions, legal boundaries, consumers' and providers' perspectives, and the medical and nursing positions in New Zealand.

White, Bruce David; Singer, Peter A.; Siegler, Mark. Continuing problems with patient self-determination. *American College of Medical Quality* 1993 Winter; 8(4): 187-193. NRCBL: 20.5.4; 20.7; 7.1; 20.5.1.

Yang, Anthony D.; Bentrem, David J.; Pappas, Sam G.; Amundsen, Elizabeth; Ward, James E.; Ujiki, Michael B.; Angelos, Peter. Advance directive use among patients undergoing high-risk operations. *American Journal of Surgery* 2004 July; 188(1): 98-101. NRCBL: 20.5.4. SC: em.

Yates, Ferdinand D., Jr. Clinical ethics case consultation [case study]. *Ethics and Medicine* 2005 Fall; 21(3): 163-165. NRCBL: 20.5.4; 20.5.1. SC: cs.

Young, Amanda J.; Ofori-Boateng, Terri; Rodriguez, Keri L.; Plowman, Judith L. Meaning and agency in discussing end-of-life care: a study of elderly veterans' values and interpretations. *Qualitative Health Research* 2003 October; 13(8): 1039-1062. NRCBL: 20.5.4; 8.1; 18.5.7. SC: em.

Zientek, David M. The Texas Advance Directives Act of 1999: an exercise in futility? *HEC (Healthcare Ethics Committee) Forum* 2005 December; 17(4): 245-259. NRCBL: 20.5.4; 20.5.1; 1.1; 9.6; 7.1; 8.3.3. SC: le.

ADVISORY COMMITTEES ON BIOETHICS
See BIOETHICS AND MEDICAL ETHICS/ COMMISSIONS

AGED *See* CARE FOR SPECIFIC GROUPS/ AGED; HUMAN EXPERIMENTATION/ SPECIAL POPULATIONS/ AGED AND TERMINALLY ILL

NRCBL: National Reference Center for Bioethics Literature Classification Scheme   See inside front cover for terms.

27

AIDS

The case for confidentiality. *Southern Africa HIV/AIDS Action* 2002 April-June; (52): 6. NRCBL: 9.5.6; 8.4.

Abraham, Joy. Unethical practices. *Issues in Medical Ethics* 2002 October-December; 10(4): 85-86. NRCBL: 9.5.6; 7.2.

Agarwal, Dinesh. Public health, human rights and HIV. *Issues in Medical Ethics* 2002 October-December; 10(4): 87. NRCBL: 9.5.6; 21.1.

Arie, Sophie. Crusading for change [news]. *BMJ: British Medical Journal* 2005 April 23; 330(7497): 926. NRCBL: 9.5.6; 11.1; 1.2. Identifiers: Catholic church; condoms; HIV/AIDS.

Asia Pacific Network of People Living with HIV/AIDS [APN+]. AIDS discrimination in Asia. Auckland, New Zealand: Asia Pacific Network of People Living with HIV/AIDS 2004; 56 p. [Online]. Available: http://www. gnpplus.net/regions/files/AIDS-asia.pdf [24 May 2005]. NRCBL: 9.5.6; 8.1; 16.3.

Balasubramaniam, K. Improving access to essential drugs for people living with HIV/AIDS. *Issues in Medical Ethics* 2000 January-March; 8(1): 26-27. NRCBL: 9.5.6; 9.7; 9.3.1; 21.1.

Bale, Harvey E., Jr. Industry, innovation and social values. *Science and Engineering Ethics* 2005 January; 11(1): 31-40. NRCBL: 9.5.6; 9.7; 7.1; 5.3; 21.1. Conference: 5th International Conference on Bioethics: The Ethics of Intellectual Property Rights and Patents; Warsaw, Poland; 23-24 April 2004; Minister of Science and the Minister of Health, Poland.

Bennett, Jo Anne. Nurses' attitudes about acquired immunodeficiency syndrome care: what research tells us. *Journal of Professional Nursing* 1995 November-December; 11(6): 339-350. NRCBL: 9.5.6; 8.1; 4.1.3. SC: em.

Bozzette, Samuel A. Routine screening for HIV infection — timely and cost- effective [editorial]. *New England Journal of Medicine* 2005 February 10; 352(6): 620- 621. NRCBL: 9.5.6; 9.1; 5.2; 9.7.

Broyles, Lauren M.; Colbert, Alison M.; Erlen, Judith A. Medication practice and feminist thought: a theoretical and ethical response to adherence in HIV/AIDS. *Bioethics* 2005 August; 19(4): 362-378. NRCBL: 9.5.6; 9.7; 8.3.4; 1.1; 10.

Abstract: Accurate self-administration of antiretroviral medication therapy for HIV/AIDS is a significant clinical and ethical concern because of its implications for individual morbidity and mortality, the health of the public, and escalating healthcare costs. However, the traditional construction of patient medication adherence is oversimplified, myopic, and ethically problematic. Adherence relies on existing social power structures and western normative assumptions about the proper roles of patients and providers, and principally focuses on patient variables, obscuring the powerful socioeconomic and institutional influences on behaviour. Some professionals advocate for alternate approaches to adherence, but many of the available alternatives remain conceptually underdeveloped. Using HIV/AIDS as an exemplar, this paper presents medication practice as a theoretical reconstruction and explicates its conceptual and ethical evolution. We first propose that one of these alternatives, medication practice, broadens the understanding of individuals' medication-taking behaviour, speaks to the inherent power inequities in the patient-provider interaction, and addresses the ethical shortcomings in the traditional construal. We then integrate medication practice with feminist thought, further validating individuals' situated knowledge, choices, and multiple roles; more fully recognizing the individual as a multidiminsional, autonomous human being; and reducing notions of obedience and deference to authority. Blame is thus extricated from the healthcare relationship, reshaping the traditionally adversarial components of the interaction, and eliminating the view of adherence as a patient problem in need of patient-centred interventions.

Byrd, Conswella M.; Baulch, Michael N. Crossing the rubicon on HIV confidentiality: medical information security in the 90's and beyond. *Progress in Cardiovascular Nursing* 1995 Spring; 10(2): 41-44. NRCBL: 9.5.6; 8.4.

Castro, Arachu; Farmer, Paul. Understanding and addressing AIDS-related stigma: from anthropological theory to clinical practice in Haiti. *American Journal of Public Health* 2005 January; 95(1): 53-59. NRCBL: 9.5.6; 9.5.4; 21.1.

Abstract: For the past several years, diverse and often confused concepts of stigma have been invoked in discussions on AIDS. Many have argued compellingly that AIDS-related stigma acts as a barrier to voluntary counseling and testing. Less compelling are observations regarding the source of stigma or its role in decreasing interest in HIV care. We reviewed these claims as well as literature from anthropology, sociology, and public health. Preliminary data from research in rural Haiti suggest that the introduction of quality HIV care can lead to a rapid reduction in stigma, with resulting increased uptake of testing. Rather than stigma, logistic and economic barriers determine who will access such services. Implications for scale-up of integrated AIDS prevention and care are explored.

Center for Reproductive Rights. Pregnant Women Living with HIV/AIDS: Protecting Human Rights in Programs to Prevent Mother-to-Child Transmission of HIV. Briefing Paper. New York: Center for Reproductive Rights 2005 August; 16 p. [Online]. Available: http://www.crlp. org/pdf/pub_bp_HIV.pdf [27 September 2005]. NRCBL: 9.5.6; 9.5.5; 8.3.1; 9.5.7.

Daniels, Norman. Fair process in patient selection for antiretroviral treatment in WHO's goal of 3 by 5. *Lancet* 2005 July 9-15; 366(9480): 169-171. NRCBL: 9.5.6; 9.7; 9.4; 21.1. Identifiers: World Health Organization.

Daniels, Norman. How to Achieve Fair Distribution of ARTs in 3 by 5: Fair Process and Legitmacy in Patient Selection. Geneva, Switzerland: World Health Organization 2004 January 26-27; 41 p. [Online]. Available: http://www.who.int/ethics/en/background-daniels.pdf [8 March 2005]. NRCBL: 9.5.6; 9.2; 9.4. Identifiers: antiretroviral therapy. Conference: Consultation on Equitable Access to Treatment and Care for HIV/AIDS;

Geneva, Switzerland; 26-27 January 2004; World Health Organization.

de Souza, Eustace J. The patient with AIDS — a response. *Indian Journal of Medical Ethics* 1994 May-July; 1(4): 5. NRCBL: 9.5.6. Comments: comment on S.K. Pandya, Indian Journal of Medical Ethics 1994 February-April; 1(3): 1-3.

Desvarieux, Moïse; Landman, Roland; Liautaud, Bernard; Girard, Pierre-Marie. Antiretroviral therapy in resource-poor countries: illusions and realities. *American Journal of Public Health* 2005 July; 95(7): 1117-1122. NRCBL: 9.5.6; 9.7; 21.1; 9.1.

Abstract: The prospects for antiretroviral therapy in resource-poor settings have changed recently and considerably with the availability of generic drugs, the drastic price reduction of brand-name drugs, and the simplification of treatment. However, such cost reductions, although allowing the implementation of large-scale donor programs, have yet to render treatment accessible and possible in the general population. Successfully providing HIV treatment in high-prevalence/high-caseload countries may require that we redefine the problem as a public health mass therapy program rather than a multiplication of clinical situations. The public health goal cannot simply be the reduction of morbidity and mortality for those treated but must be the reduction in morbidity and mortality for the many, that is, at a population level.

Dhai, Amaboo; Noble, Ray. Ethical issues in HIV. *Best Practice and Research: Clinical Obstetrics and Gynaecology* 2005 April; 19(2): 255-267. NRCBL: 9.5.6; 10; 21.1.

Diedrich, Lisa. AIDS and its treatments: two doctors' narratives of healing, desire, and belonging. *Journal of Medical Humanities* 2005 Winter; 26(4): 237-257. NRCBL: 9.5.6; 8.1; 1.1; 4.4.

Abstract: In this essay, I analyze two memoirs—Rafael Campo's The Poetry of Healing: A Doctor's Education in Empathy, Identity, and Desire and Abraham Verghese's My Own Country: A Doctor's Story of a Town and Its People in the Age of AIDS—which describe the effects of treating HIV/AIDS on each doctor's identity, on his desire for community and belonging, and on his identification and/or disidentification with the medical profession in the United States. My readings of Campo and Verghese revolve around three key terms provided by Campo's subtitle: identity, empathy, and desire. I shift the order of these terms in Campo's subtitle because I want to read identity, empathy, and desire in Campo and Verghese through and along with the theoretical "pragmatics" of Gilles Deleuze and Felix Guattari.

Ding, Lin; Landon, Bruce E.; Wilson, Ira B.; Wong, Mitchell D.; Shapiro, Martin F.; Cleary, Paul D. Predictors and consequences of negative physician attitudes toward HIV-infected injection drug users. *Archives of Internal Medicine* 2005 March 28; 165(6): 618-623. NRCBL: 9.5.6; 9.5.9. SC: em.

Abstract: BACKGROUND: We evaluated physicians' training, experience, and practice characteristics and examined associations between their attitudes toward human immunodeficiency virus (HIV)-infected persons who are injection drug users (IDUs) and quality of care. METHODS: Cross-sectional surveys were conducted among a probability sample of noninstitutionalized HIV-infected individuals in the United States and their main HIV care physicians. Physician and practice characteristics, training, HIV knowledge, experience, attitudes toward HIV-infected IDUs, stress levels, and satisfaction with practice were assessed. The main quality-of-care measures were patient exposure to highly active antiretroviral therapy, reported problems, satisfaction with care, unmet needs, and perceived access to care. RESULTS: Nationally, 23.2% of HIV-infected patients had physicians with negative attitudes toward IDUs. Seeing more IDUs, having higher HIV treatment knowledge scores, and treating fewer patients per week were independently associated with more positive attitudes toward IDUs. Injection drug users who were cared for by physicians with negative attitudes had a significantly lower adjusted rate of exposure to highly active antiretroviral therapy by December 1996 (13.5%) than non-IDUs who were cared for by such physicians (36.1%) or IDUs who were cared for by physicians with positive attitudes (32.3%). Physician attitudes were not associated with other problems with care, satisfaction with care, unmet needs, or perceived access to care. CONCLUSIONS: Negative attitudes may lead to less than optimal care for IDUs and other marginalized populations. Providing education or experience-based exercises or ensuring that clinicians have adequate time to deal with complex problems might result in better attitudes and higher quality of care.

Edge, J.M.; van Rensburg, E. Janse; Mostert, E. Ethico-legal aspects of the protocol for needlestick injuries. *South African Medical Journal* 2000 December; 90(12): 1182-1184. NRCBL: 9.5.6; 16.3; 8.1.

Francis, Omar. The legal and ethical issues related to the control of HIV [opinion]. *West Indian Medical Journal* 2001 September; 50(3): 183-185. NRCBL: 9.5.6; 21.1; 9.1.

Fraser, John. Ethics of HIV testing in general practice without informed consent: a case series. *Journal of Medical Ethics* 2005 December; 31(12): 698-699. NRCBL: 9.5.6; 8.3.1. SC: cs.

Frith, Lucy. HIV testing and informed consent. *Journal of Medical Ethics* 2005 December; 31(12): 699-700. NRCBL: 9.5.6; 8.3.1. SC: cs.

Fry, Sara T.; Veatch, Robert M. HIV/AIDS care. *In their:* Case Studies in Nursing Ethics. Third edition. Sudbury, MA: Jones and Bartlett Publishers; 2006: 299-329. NRCBL: 9.5.6.

Galvão, Jane. Brazil and access to HIV/AIDS drugs: a question of human rights and public health. *American Journal of Public Health* 2005 July; 95(7): 1110-1116. NRCBL: 9.5.6; 9.7; 9.2; 9.3.1; 9.4; 21.1; 9.1.

Abstract: I explore the relationship between public health and human rights by examining the Brazilian government's policy of free and universal access to anti-retroviral medicines for people with HIV/AIDS. The Brazilian government's management of the HIV/AIDS epidemic arose from initiatives in both civil society and the governmental sector following the democratization of the country. The dismantling of authoritarian rule in Brazil was accompanied by a strong orientation toward human rights, which formed the sociopolitical framework of Brazil's response to the HIV/AIDS epidemic. Even if the Brazilian experience cannot be easily transferred to other countries, the model of the Brazilian government's response may nonetheless

NRCBL: National Reference Center for Bioethics Literature Classification Scheme   See inside front cover for terms.

29

serve as inspiration for finding appropriate and lifesaving solutions in other national contexts.

Gostin, Lawrence O. The global reach of HIV/AIDS: science, politics, economics, and research. *Emory International Law Review* 2003 Spring; 17(1): 1-54. NRCBL: 9.5.6; 7.1; 9.3.1; 18.5.9; 21.1.

Grant, Robert M.; Buchbinder, Susan; Cates, Willard, Jr.; Clarke, Edith; Coates, Thomas; Cohen, Myron S.; Delaney, Martin; Flores, Guiselly; Goicochea, Pedro; Gonsalves, Gregg; Harrington, Mark; Lama, Javier R.; MacQueen, Kathleen M.; Moore, John P.; Peterson, Leigh; Sanchez, Jorge; Thompson, Melanie; Wainberg, Mark A. Promote HIV chemoprophylaxis research, don't prevent it. *Science* 2005 September 30; 309(5744): 2170-2171. NRCBL: 9.5.6; 18.5.9.

Grusky, Oscar; Roberts, Kathleen Johnston; Swanson, Aimee Noelle; Joniak, Elizabeth; Leich, Jennifer; McEvoy, Gwen; Murphy, Keith; Schilt, Kristen; Wilson, Valerie. Anonymous versus confidential HIV testing: client and provider decision making under uncertainty. *AIDS Patient Care and STDs* 2005 March; 19(3): 157-166. NRCBL: 9.5.6; 8.4. SC: em.

Guenter, Dale; Kaczorowski, Janusz; Carroll, June; Sellors, John. Prenatal HIV tests: routine testing or informed choice? *Canadian Family Physician* 2003 October; 49: 1334-1340. NRCBL: 9.5.6; 9.5.5; 9.5.8; 9.1. SC: em. Identifiers: Canada. Note: Abstract in English and French.

Gupta, Amit Sen. Intellectual capital as property. *Indian Journal of Medical Ethics* 2004 October-December; 1(4): 115-116. NRCBL: 9.5.6; 9.7. Comments: comment on Omar Swartz, "Access to AIDS medicine: ethical considerations," Indian Journal of Medical Ethics 2004 July-September; 1(3): 75-76.

Halpern, Scott D. HIV testing without consent in critically ill patients. *JAMA: The Journal of the American Medical Association* 2005 August 10; 294(6): 734-737. NRCBL: 9.5.6; 8.3.1.

Harris, Gardiner. FDA to weight at-home testing for AIDS virus. *New York Times* 2005 October 13; p. A1, A16. NRCBL: 9.5.6; 8.1. SC: po.

Herring, Lynn W. The increasing role of constituencies of a federal public health agency: a case study on acquired immunodeficiency syndrome (AIDS). *International Journal of Public Administration* 1987; 10(3): 235-253. NRCBL: 9.5.6.

Hoffman, Jascha. New York City foster home accused of unethical AIDS drug trials [news]. *Nature Medicine* 2005 January; 11(1): 5. NRCBL: 9.5.6; 18.5.2.

Hoffman, Sarah Z. HIV/AIDS in Cuba: a model for care or an ethical dilemma? *African Health Sciences* 2004 December; 4(3): 208-209. NRCBL: 9.5.6; 9.1.

Indian Council of Medical Research [ICMR]. AIDS: Indian Council of Medical Research (ICMR) Guidelines. *Medical Ethics: Journal of Forum for Medical Ethics Society* 1995 April-June; 3(2): 35. NRCBL: 9.5.6.

Jeena, P.M.; McNally, L.M.; Stobie, M.; Coovadia, H.M.; Adhikari, M.A.; Petros, A.J. Challenges in the provision of ICU services to HIV infected children in resource poor settings: a South African case study. *Journal of Medical Ethics* 2005 April; 31(4): 226-230. NRCBL: 9.5.6; 9.5.7; 19.4. SC: cs.
Abstract: The HIV/AIDS epidemic has placed increasing demands on limited paediatric intensive care services in developing countries. The decision to admit HIV infected children with Pneumocystis carinii pneumonia (PCP) into the paediatric intensive care unit (PICU) has to be made on the best available evidence of outcome and the ethical principles guiding appropriate use of scarce resources. The difficulty in confirming the diagnosis of HIV infection and PCP in infancy, issues around HIV counselling, and the variance in the outcome of HIV infected children with PCP admitted to the PICU in African studies compound this process. Pragmatic decision making will require evaluation of at least three ethical questions: are there clinical and moral reasons for admitting HIV positive children with PCP to the PICU, should more resources be committed to caring for HIV children who require the PICU, and how can we morally choose candidates for the PICU? Those working in the PICU in HIV endemic regions need to make difficult personal decisions on effective triage of admissions of HIV infected children with PCP based on individual case presentation, availability of resources, and applicable ethical principles.

Jesani, Amar; Kalantri, S.P.; Thomas, George; Srinivasan, Sandhya. Government-funded anti-retroviral therapy for HIV/AIDS: new ethical challenges [editorial]. *Indian Journal of Medical Ethics* 2004 July-September; 1(3): 70-71. NRCBL: 9.5.6; 9.7.

Jones, James W.; Richman, Bruce W.; McCullough, Laurence B. HIV-infected surgeon: professional responsibility and self interest. *Journal of Vascular Surgery* 2003 April; 37(4): 914-915. NRCBL: 9.5.6; 4.1.2; 1.3.1; 8.2. SC: cs.

Kim, Jim Yong; Gilks, Charlie. Scaling up treatment — why we can't wait [editorial]. *New England Journal of Medicine* 2005 December 1; 353(22): 2392-2394. NRCBL: 9.5.6; 9.7; 21.1.

Kimsma, Gerrit K.; van Leeuwen, Evert. The human body as field of conflict between discourses. *Theoretical Medicine and Bioethics* 2005; 26(6): 559-574. NRCBL: 9.5.6; 4.2; 7.1.
Abstract: The approach to AIDS as a disease and a threat for social discrimination is used as an example to illustrate a conceptual thesis. This thesis is a claim that concerns what we call a medical issue or not, what is medicalised or needs to be demedicalised. In the friction between medicalisation and demedicalisation as discursive strategies the latter approach can only be effected through the employment of discourses or discursive strategies other than medicine, such as those of the law and of economics. These discourses each realise different values, promote a different subject, and have a different concept of man. The concept of discourse is briefly outlined against

---

concepts such as the linear growth concept of science and the growth model of science as changes in paradigm. The issue of testing for AIDS shows a conflict between the medical and the legal discourse and illustrates the title of our contribution: the human body as field of conflict between discourses.

Lawless, Sonia; Kippax, Susan; Crawford, June. Dirty, diseased and undeserving: the positioning of HIV positive women. *Social Science and Medicine* 1996 November; 43(9): 1371-1377. NRCBL: 9.5.6; 9.5.5; 9.5.9; 8.1; 10. SC: em.

London, Leslie; Benjamin, Paul; Bass, David H. HIV testing and the Employment Equity Act — putting an end to the confusion [opinion]. *South African Medical Journal* 2002 March; 92(3): 199-201. NRCBL: 9.5.6; 9.1; 8.4; 16.3.

Macklin, Ruth. Ethics and Equity in Access to HIV Treatment — 3 by 5 Initiative. Geneva, Switzerland: World Health Organization 2004 January 26-27; 18 p. [Online]. Available: http://www.who.int/ethics/en/background-macklin.pdf [8 March 2005]. NRCBL: 9.5.6; 9.2; 9.4. Conference: Consultation on Equitable Access to Treatment and Care for HIV/AIDS; Geneva, Switzerland; 26-27 January 2004 World Health Organization.

Manavi, Kaveh; Welsby, Philip D. HIV testing: should no longer be accorded any special status [editorial]. *BMJ: British Medical Journal* 2005 March 5; 330(7490): 492-493. NRCBL: 9.5.6; 9.1.

Mathiharan, K. Some legal and ethical implications for the medical profession. *Issues in Medical Ethics* 2002 October-December; 10(4): 79-82. NRCBL: 9.5.6; 8.4; 8.3.1.

Muthuswamy, Vasantha. Ethical issues in HIV/AIDS research. *Indian Journal of Medical Research* 2005 April; 121(4): 601-610. NRCBL: 9.5.6; 18.5.1; 21.1.

Muula, Adamson S. What should HIV/AIDS be called in Malawi? *Nursing Ethics* 2005 March; 12(2): 187-192. NRCBL: 9.5.6; 8.2.
Abstract: HIV/AIDS is the leading cause of morbidity and mortality in the southern African country of Malawi. At the largest referral health facility in Blantyre, the Queen Elizabeth Central Hospital, the majority of patients hospitalized in medical wards and up to a third of those in the maternity unit are infected with HIV. Many patients in the surgical wards also have HIV/AIDS. Health professionals in Blantyre, however, often choose not to write down the diagnosis of HIV or AIDS; rather, they prefer to use 'SGOT', 'ELISA' and 'spot test' to represent the HIV test, while 'immunosuppression', '\CD4 disease' and 'ARC' are preferred instead of 'AIDS'. It is possible that health professionals' belief that mentioning HIV and/or AIDS will harm patients is encouraging them to use these euphemisms. The use of less than exact terms to label HIV and AIDS may not be without cost. For instance, future attempts to conduct retrospective case study research may be hampered by this practice, which is not in accordance with the international classification of diseases. It is suggested that, although stigmatization and discrimination could be important driving factors in the use of cryptic language, it may be more worthy to fight discrimination and stigmatization head-on, rather than create avenues where these reactions may be perpetuated.

Muula, Adamson S.; Mfutso-Bengo, Joseph M. When is public decision disclosure of HIV seropositivity acceptable? *Nursing Ethics* 2005 May; 12(3): 288-295. NRCBL: 9.5.6; 8.4. Identifiers: Malawi.
Abstract: HIV/AIDS is a major public health problem in Africa. Stigmatization, discrimination and lack of appropriate health care are among the commonest challenges that HIV infected persons and their families face. It has been suggested that among the tools available in the fight against stigmatization and discrimination is public disclosure of a person's HIV seropositive status. While public disclosure of HIV status has a place in the fight against HIV and AIDS, especially by resulting in behavioural change among people who know of an HIV infected person, we argue that such disclosure also has potential attendant harms. The posthumous disclosure of HIV status is particularly problematic. Public disclosure should be accompanied by appropriate individual counselling and preparation of the community to deal with the situation, and should have regard for cultural sensitivity after consideration of the risks and benefits to individuals, families and the community. Health practitioners should keep in mind that their main duty is to the best interest of the patient, the family and the community, in that order.

O'Leary, Ian P. AIDS: the attitudes and experience of final year European dental students. *Journal of the Irish Dental Association* 2005 Spring; 51(1): 19-22. NRCBL: 9.5.6; 8.1; 7.2; 21.1. SC: em.

Ojikutu, Bisola O.; Stone, Valerie E. Women, inequality, and the burden of HIV [opinion]. *New England Journal of Medicine* 2005 February 17; 352(7): 649-652. NRCBL: 9.5.6; 9.5.5; 21.1; 9.5.10; 9.5.4.

Onotai, L.O.; Nwaorgu, O.G.B.; Okoye, B.C.C. Ethical issues in HIV/AIDS infections. *Nigerian Journal of Medicine* 2004 July-September; 13(3): 282-285. NRCBL: 9.5.6; 8.4; 8.3.1.

Pandya, Sunil K. Patients testing positive for HIV — ethical dilemmas in India. *Issues in Medical Ethics* 1997 April-June; 5(2): 49-55. NRCBL: 9.5.6; 8.4; 18.5.9.

Pandya, Sunil K. The patient with AIDS. *Medical Ethics: Journal of Forum for Medical Ethics Society* 1994 February-April; 1(3): 1-3. NRCBL: 9.5.6.

Parikh, Ketan. The right to refuse treatment. *Issues in Medical Ethics* 2003 July-September; 11(3): 75-76. NRCBL: 9.5.6; 8.1.

Parsa, Michael; Walsh, Matthew J. Ethics seminars: HIV testing, consent, and physician responsibilities. *Academic Emergency Medicine* 2001 December; 8(12): 1197-1199. NRCBL: 9.5.6; 8.3.1; 7.1; 1.1. SC: cs.

Phadke, Anant. Doctors do not have the right to refuse treatment to HIV-positive patients. *Issues in Medical Ethics* 2003 July-September; 11(3): 77-78. NRCBL: 9.5.6; 8.1.

Preston, Deborah Bray; Forti, Esther M.; Kassab, Cathy; Koch, Patricia Barthalow. Personal and social determinants of rural nurses' willingness to care for persons

NRCBL: National Reference Center for Bioethics Literature Classification Scheme   See inside front cover for terms.

31

with AIDS. *Research in Nursing and Health* 2000 February; 23(1): 67-78. NRCBL: 9.5.6; 8.1; 4.1.3. SC: em.

Pujari, Sanjay. Antiretrovirals in India [opinion]. *Issues in Medical Ethics* 1998 January; 6(1): 24-25. NRCBL: 9.5.6; 18.5.9.

Rosen, Sydney; Sanne, Ian; Collier, Alizanne; Simon, Jonathon L. Hard choices: rationing antiretroviral therapy for HIV/AIDS in Africa. *Lancet* 2005 January 22-28; 365(9456): 354-356. NRCBL: 9.5.6; 9.7; 9.4; 21.1.

Rosengarten, Marsha. The measure of HIV as a matter of bioethics. *In:* Shildrick, Margrit; Mykitiuk, Roxanne, eds. Ethics of the Body: Postconventional Challenges. Cambridge, MA: MIT Press; 2005: 71-90. NRCBL: 9.5.6; 1.1; 2.1.

Sahay, Seema; Mehendale, Sanjay. Addressing ethical concerns in the Indian HIV vaccine trials. *Indian Journal of Medical Ethics* 2004 October-December; 1(4): 109-112. NRCBL: 9.5.6; 18.5.9; 18.2. Comments: comment on Joe Thomas, "Unmet ethical concerns of the proposed preventive HIV vaccine trials in India," Indian Journal of Medical Ethics 2004 July-September; 1(3): 87-88.

Schuster, Mark A.; Collins, Rebecca; Cunningham, William E.; Morton, Sally C.; Zierler, Sally; Wong, Myra; Tu, Wenli; Kanouse, David E. Perceived discrimination in clinical care in a nationally representative sample of HIV-infected adults receiving health care. *JGIM: Journal of General Internal Medicine* 2005 September; 20(9): 807-813. NRCBL: 9.5.6; 8.1. SC: em.

Selemogo, Mpho. An unequal activism for an unequal epidemic? *Developing World Bioethics* 2005 May; 5(2): 153-168. NRCBL: 9.5.6; 9.7.
Abstract: This paper observes that a substantially large moral duty of dealing with the AIDS situation in Africa has been placed on the drug companies and argues that this approach is inequitable. Using the poverty-AIDS relationship and the human rights framework it argues for a more balanced AIDS activism, which puts equal pressure on all potential stakeholders in the war against AIDS. It argues that this redistribution of the HIV/AIDS moral burden is perhaps the only hope for curbing the African AIDS epidemic that continues to ravage communities on that continent

Selemogo, Mpho. The future of AIDS and the ethics of seclusion in the face of an impending danger. *Indian Journal of Medical Ethics* 2005 January-March; 2(1): 14- 15. NRCBL: 9.5.6.

Shapiro, K.; Benatar, S.R. HIV prevention research and global inequality: steps towards improved standards of care. *Journal of Medical Ethics* 2005 January; 31(1): 39-47. NRCBL: 9.5.6; 9.8; 18.5.9. SC: cs; rv.
Abstract: Intensification of poverty and degradation of health infrastructure over recent decades in countries most affected by HIV/AIDS present formidable challenges to clinical research. This paper addresses the overall standard of health care (SOC) that should be provided to research participants in developing countries, rather than the narrow definition of SOC that has
characterised the international debate on standards of health care. It argues that contributing to sustainable improvements in health by progressively ratcheting the standard of care upwards for research participants and their communities is an ethical obligation of those in resource-rich countries who sponsor and implement research in poorer ones.

Sheon, Amy R.; Wagner, Lois; McElrath, M. Juliana; Keefer, Michael C.; Zimmerman, Eric; Israel, Heidi; Berger, David; Fast, Patricia. Preventing discrimination against volunteers in prophylactic HIV vaccine trials: lessons from a phase II trial. *Journal of Acquired Immune Deficiency Syndromes and Human Retrovirology* 1998 December 15; 19(5): 519-526. NRCBL: 9.5.6; 9.7; 18.3. SC: em.

Širinskiene, Agne; Juškevicius, Jonas; Naberkovas, Andrius. Confidentiality and duty to warn the third parties in HIV/AIDS context. *Medical Ethics and Bioethics / Medicinska Etika & Bioetika* 2005 Spring-Summer; 12(1): 2-7. NRCBL: 9.5.6; 8.4; 8.1; 20.1. Note: Abstract in English and Slovakian.

Slack, Catherine; Kruger, Mariana. The South African Medical Research Council's Guidelines on Ethics for Medical Research — implications for HIV-preventive vaccine trials with children. *South African Medical Journal* 2005 April; 95(4): 269-271. NRCBL: 9.5.6; 18.5.2; 9.7; 6.

Smith, Mable H. Legal obligations to human immunodeficiency virus-seropositive patients and health care providers. *Journal of Professional Nursing* 1995 May-June; 11(3): 183-191. NRCBL: 9.5.6; 8.1; 16.3.

Sokol, Daniel K. Commentary on ethics of HIV testing in general practice without informed consent: a case series [commentary]. *Journal of Medical Ethics* 2005 December; 31(12): 701-702. NRCBL: 9.5.6; 8.3.1. SC: cs.

Srinivasan, Sandhya. Physician, do no harm [opinion]. *Issues in Medical Ethics* 1998 January; 6(1): 22-23. NRCBL: 9.5.6; 18.5.9.

Stebbing, Justin; Bower, Mark. Lessons for HIV from Tuskegee. *Journal of HIV Therapy* 2004 September; 9(3): 50-52. NRCBL: 9.5.6; 2.2; 18.5.1; 18.3.

Swartz, Omar. Access to AIDS medicine: ethical considerations. *Indian Journal of Medical Ethics* 2004 July-September; 1(3): 75-76. NRCBL: 9.5.6; 9.7.

Thomas, Joe. Essential AIDS medications in India. *Issues in Medical Ethics* 2000 April-June; 8(2): 62. NRCBL: 9.5.6; 9.7; 21.1.

Thomas, Joe. Unmet ethical concerns of the proposed preventive HIV vaccine trials in India. *Indian Journal of Medical Ethics* 2004 July-September; 1(3): 87-88. NRCBL: 9.5.6; 18.5.9.

United Nations. Office of the High Commissioner for Human Rights [OHCHR]; Joint United Nations Programme on HIV/AIDS [UNAIDS]. HIV/AIDS and

Human Rights International Guidelines. Revised Guideline 6: Access to Prevention, Treatment, Care and Support. New York: United Nations, Revised reprint 2003 March; 25 p. [Online]. Available: http://www.unaids.org/html/pub/Publications/IRC-pub02/JC905-Guide line6_en_pdf.pdf [4 August 2005]. NRCBL: 9.5.6; 6; 21.1; 9.2. Conference: Third International Consultation on HIV/AIDS and Human Rights; Geneva, Switzerland; 25-26 July 2002.

Veljkovic, Veljko; Prljic, Jelena; Veljkovic, Tatjana. Safety and ethical consideration of AIDS vaccine. *International Reviews of Immunology* 2004 September-December; 23(5-6): 465-486. NRCBL: 9.5.6; 9.7; 9.8; 18.6.

Wills, David J. A survey of nurses attitudes to AIDS related issues. *New Zealand Nursing Forum* 1990 November-December; 18(4): 7-9. NRCBL: 9.5.6; 8.1; 4.1.3.

World Health Organization [WHO]; Joint United Nations Programme on HIV/AIDS [UNAIDS]. Consultation on Ethics and Equitable Access to Treatment and Care for HIV/AIDS. Summary of Issues and Discussion. Geneva, Switzerland: World Health Organization 2004; 29 p. [Online]. Available: http://www.who.int/ethics/en/equity_art_meeting_report_e.pdf [4 March 2004]. NRCBL: 9.5.6; 9.2; 9.4; 9.7; 21.1. Conference: Global Consultation on Ethics and Equitable Access to Treatment and Care for HIV/AIDS; Geneva, Switzerland; 26-27 January 2004; World Health Organization; Joint United Nations Programme on HIV/AIDS.

World Health Organization [WHO]. Joint United Nations Programme on HIV/AIDS [UNAIDS]. Consultation on ethics and equitable access to treatment and care for HIV/AIDS. Geneva, Switzerland: World Health Organization 2004; 29 p. [Online]. Available: http://www.who.int/hiv/pub/advocacy/en/ethicsmeetingreport_e.pdf [27 May 2005]. NRCBL: 9.5.6; 9.7; 21.1; 9.2. Conference: Global consultation on ethics and equitable access to treatment and care for HIV/AIDS; Geneva, Switzerland; 26-27 January 2004; World Health Organizatio; Joint United Nations Programme on HIV/AIDS [UNAIDS].

Wynia, Matthew K. Science, faith and AIDS: the battle over harm reduction. *American Journal of Bioethics* 2005 March-April; 5(2): 3-4. NRCBL: 9.5.6; 1.2; 9.1.

Zion, Deborah. Community without communitarianism: HIV/AIDS research, prevention and treatment in Australia and the developing world. *Monash Bioethics Review* 2005 April; 24(2): 20-31. NRCBL: 9.5.6; 10; 9.7; 18.5.1.

Zion, Deborah. Does autonomy require freedom? The importance of options in international HIV/AIDS research. *Health Care Analysis: An International Journal of Health Care Philosophy and Policy* 2005 September; 13(3): 189-202. NRCBL: 9.5.6; 1.1; 18.3; 18.5.9.
Abstract: This paper analyses the way in which being in possession of an adequate range of options is an essential component of autonomy. I discuss the way in which the conceptualisation of options in terms of basic rights might assist this argument,

and apply these ideas to HIV/AIDS clinical research in the developing world. Finally, I suggest that mechanisms should be put in place through which vulnerable research participants can express their views about the relationship between the research in which they are involved, and needs of a worthwhile life.

AIDS/ CONFIDENTIALITY

The case for confidentiality. *Southern Africa HIV/AIDS Action* 2002 April-June; (52): 6. NRCBL: 9.5.6; 8.4.

Byrd, Conswella M.; Baulch, Michael N. Crossing the rubicon on HIV confidentiality: medical information security in the 90's and beyond. *Progress in Cardiovascular Nursing* 1995 Spring; 10(2): 41-44. NRCBL: 9.5.6; 8.4.

Chenneville, Tiffany. HIV, confidentiality, and duty to protect: a decision-making model. *Professional Psychology: Research and Practice* 2000 December; 31(6): 661-670. NRCBL: 9.5.6; 8.4; 17.1; 4.3. SC: le.

Chipeur, Gerald D. Blood testing without consent: the right to privacy versus the right to know (Part 2). *Medicine and Law: World Association for Medical Law* 1994; 13(1-2): 55-67. NRCBL: 9.5.6; 8.3.1; 8.4. SC: le; an.

Dancaster, J.T.; Dancaster, L.A. Confidentiality concerning HIV/AIDS status — the implications of the Appeal Court decision. *South African Medical Journal* 1995 March; 85(3): 141-144. NRCBL: 9.5.6; 8.4. SC: le.

Grimes, Richard M.; Helfgott, Andrew W.; Watson, Julie R.; Eriksen, Nancy L. For children's sake. New law mandates HIV testing of pregnant patients. *Texas Medicine* 1996 January; 92(1): 36-40. NRCBL: 9.5.6; 9.5.5; 8.3.1; 8.4. SC: le.

Grusky, Oscar; Roberts, Kathleen Johnston; Swanson, Aimee Noelle; Joniak, Elizabeth; Leich, Jennifer; McEvoy, Gwen; Murphy, Keith; Schilt, Kristen; Wilson, Valerie. Anonymous versus confidential HIV testing: client and provider decision making under uncertainty. *AIDS Patient Care and STDs* 2005 March; 19(3): 157-166. NRCBL: 9.5.6; 8.4. SC: em.

Jansen, L.A. HIV exceptionalism, CD4+ cell testing, and conscientious subversion. *Journal of Medical Ethics* 2005 June; 31(6): 322-326. NRCBL: 9.5.6; 8.3.1; 8.4. SC: le.
Abstract: In recent years, many states in the United States have passed legislation requiring laboratories to report the names of patients with low CD4 cell counts to their state Departments of Health. This name reporting is an integral part of the growing number of "HIV Reporting and Partner Notification Laws" which have emerged in response to recently revised guidelines suggested by the National Centers for Disease Control (CDC). Name reporting for patients with low CD4 cell counts allows for a more accurate tracking of the natural history of HIV disease. However, given that this test is now considered to be an "indicator" of HIV, should it be subject to the same strict consent required for HIV testing? While the CDC has recommended that each state develop its own consent requirements for CD4 cell testing, most states have continued to rely on the presumed consent standards for CD4 cell testing that were in place before the passage of name reporting statutes. This allows

NRCBL: National Reference Center for Bioethics Literature Classification Scheme   See inside front cover for terms.

33

physicians who treat patients who refuse HIV testing to order a CD4 cell blood analysis to gather information that is indicative of their patient's HIV status. This paper examines the ethical and legal issues associated with the practice of "conscientious subversion" as it arises when clinicians use CD4 cell counts as a surrogate for HIV testing.

Lagitch, Kellie E. Mandatory HIV testing: an Orwellian proposition. *St. John's Law Review* 1998 Winter; 72(1): 103-139. NRCBL: 9.5.6; 8.3.4; 8.4; 9.5.7. SC: le.

London, Leslie; Benjamin, Paul; Bass, David H. HIV testing and the Employment Equity Act — putting an end to the confusion [opinion]. *South African Medical Journal* 2002 March; 92(3): 199-201. NRCBL: 9.5.6; 9.1; 8.4; 16.3.

Mathiharan, K. Some legal and ethical implications for the medical profession. *Issues in Medical Ethics* 2002 October-December; 10(4): 79-82. NRCBL: 9.5.6; 8.4; 8.3.1.

McPhee, John; Stewart, Cameron. Recent developments in law. *Journal of Bioethical Inquiry* 2005; 2(3): 122-129. NRCBL: 9.5.6; 8.4; 8.5; 20.5.1; 8.3.3; 12.4.4. SC: le.

Mills, John W. HIV confidentiality law has serious flaws [editorial]. *Pennsylvania Medicine* 2000 May; 103(5): 6. NRCBL: 9.5.6; 8.4; 8.1. SC: le.

Moayery, Sheedeh. National HIV reporting: what's in a name? *Virginia Journal of Social Policy and the Law* 2001 Winter; 8(2): 439-473. NRCBL: 9.5.6; 8.4; 1.3.12; 1.3.5. SC: le.

Muula, Adamson S.; Mfutso-Bengo, Joseph M. When is public decision disclosure of HIV seropositivity acceptable? *Nursing Ethics* 2005 May; 12(3): 288-295. NRCBL: 9.5.6; 8.4. Identifiers: Malawi.
Abstract: HIV/AIDS is a major public health problem in Africa. Stigmatization, discrimination and lack of appropriate health care are among the commonest challenges that HIV infected persons and their families face. It has been suggested that among the tools available in the fight against stigmatization and discrimination is public disclosure of a person's HIV seropositive status. While public disclosure of HIV status has a place in the fight against HIV and AIDS, especially by resulting in behavioural change among people who know of an HIV infected person, we argue that such disclosure also has potential attendant harms. The posthumous disclosure of HIV status is particularly problematic. Public disclosure should be accompanied by appropriate individual counselling and preparation of the community to deal with the situation, and should have regard for cultural sensitivity after consideration of the risks and benefits to individuals, families and the community. Health practitioners should keep in mind that their main duty is to the best interest of the patient, the family and the community, in that order.

Onotai, L.O.; Nwaorgu, O.G.B.; Okoye, B.C.C. Ethical issues in HIV/AIDS infections. *Nigerian Journal of Medicine* 2004 July-September; 13(3): 282-285. NRCBL: 9.5.6; 8.4; 8.3.1.

Pandya, Sunil K. Patients testing positive for HIV — ethical dilemmas in India. *Issues in Medical Ethics* 1997 April-June; 5(2): 49-55. NRCBL: 9.5.6; 8.4; 18.5.9.

Rediger, Bryon B. Living in a world with HIV: balancing privacy, privilege and the right to know between patients and health care professionals. *Hamline Journal of Public Law and Policy* 2000; 21(2): 443-487. NRCBL: 9.5.6; 8.4. SC: le.

Riestra, Sergio Gallego; Jarreta, Begoña Martinez; Fonseca, Rafael Hinojal; Caro, Javier Sanchez. Medicolegal problems arising from AIDS and health care personnel with special reference to Spanish law. *Medicine and Law: World Association for Medical Law* 1994; 13(3-4): 241-249. NRCBL: 9.5.6; 8.1; 8.4. SC: le.

Širinskiene, Agne; Juškevicius, Jonas; Naberkovas, Andrius. Confidentiality and duty to warn the third parties in HIV/AIDS context. *Medical Ethics and Bioethics / Medicinska Etika & Bioetika* 2005 Spring-Summer; 12(1): 2-7. NRCBL: 9.5.6; 8.4; 8.1; 20.1. Note: Abstract in English and Slovakian.

Thomas, Joe. HIV and confidentiality in India. *Issues in Medical Ethics* 1998 July-September; 6(3): 87. NRCBL: 9.5.6; 8.4. SC: le.

AIDS/ HUMAN EXPERIMENTATION

Berman, Jennifer. Using the doctrine of informed consent to improve HIV vaccine access in the post-TRIPS era. *Wisconsin International Law Journal* 2004 Spring; 22(2): 273-321. NRCBL: 9.5.6; 18.3; 18.5.1; 21.1; 9.2; 9.7; 18.2. SC: le. Identifiers: Trade-Related Aspects of Intellectual Property Rights.

Gostin, Lawrence O. The global reach of HIV/AIDS: science, politics, economics, and research. *Emory International Law Review* 2003 Spring; 17(1): 1-54. NRCBL: 9.5.6; 7.1; 9.3.1; 18.5.9; 21.1.

Grant, Robert M.; Buchbinder, Susan; Cates, Willard, Jr.; Clarke, Edith; Coates, Thomas; Cohen, Myron S.; Delaney, Martin; Flores, Guiselly; Goicochea, Pedro; Gonsalves, Gregg; Harrington, Mark; Lama, Javier R.; MacQueen, Kathleen M.; Moore, John P.; Peterson, Leigh; Sanchez, Jorge; Thompson, Melanie; Wainberg, Mark A. Promote HIV chemoprophylaxis research, don't prevent it. *Science* 2005 September 30; 309(5744): 2170-2171. NRCBL: 9.5.6; 18.5.9.

Hoffman, Jascha. New York City foster home accused of unethical AIDS drug trials [news]. *Nature Medicine* 2005 January; 11(1): 5. NRCBL: 9.5.6; 18.5.2.

Muthuswamy, Vasantha. Ethical issues in HIV/AIDS research. *Indian Journal of Medical Research* 2005 April; 121(4): 601-610. NRCBL: 9.5.6; 18.5.1; 21.1.

Pandya, Sunil K. Patients testing positive for HIV — ethical dilemmas in India. *Issues in Medical Ethics* 1997 April-June; 5(2): 49-55. NRCBL: 9.5.6; 8.4; 18.5.9.

Pujari, Sanjay. Antiretrovirals in India [opinion]. *Issues in Medical Ethics* 1998 January; 6(1): 24-25. NRCBL: 9.5.6; 18.5.9.

Sahay, Seema; Mehendale, Sanjay. Addressing ethical concerns in the Indian HIV vaccine trials. *Indian Journal of Medical Ethics* 2004 October-December; 1(4): 109-112. NRCBL: 9.5.6; 18.5.9; 18.2. Comments: comment on Joe Thomas, "Unmet ethical concerns of the proposed preventive HIV vaccine trials in India," Indian Journal of Medical Ethics 2004 July-September; 1(3): 87-88.

Shapiro, K.; Benatar, S.R. HIV prevention research and global inequality: steps towards improved standards of care. *Journal of Medical Ethics* 2005 January; 31(1): 39-47. NRCBL: 9.5.6; 9.8; 18.5.9. SC: cs; rv.
Abstract: Intensification of poverty and degradation of health infrastructure over recent decades in countries most affected by HIV/AIDS present formidable challenges to clinical research. This paper addresses the overall standard of health care (SOC) that should be provided to research participants in developing countries, rather than the narrow definition of SOC that has characterised the international debate on standards of health care. It argues that contributing to sustainable improvements in health by progressively ratcheting the standard of care upwards for research participants and their communities is an ethical obligation of those in resource-rich countries who sponsor and implement research in poorer ones.

Sheon, Amy R.; Wagner, Lois; McElrath, M. Juliana; Keefer, Michael C.; Zimmerman, Eric; Israel, Heidi; Berger, David; Fast, Patricia. Preventing discrimination against volunteers in prophylactic HIV vaccine trials: lessons from a phase II trial. *Journal of Acquired Immune Deficiency Syndromes and Human Retrovirology* 1998 December 15; 19(5): 519-526. NRCBL: 9.5.6; 9.7; 18.3. SC: em.

Slack, Catherine; Kruger, Mariana. The South African Medical Research Council's Guidelines on Ethics for Medical Research — implications for HIV-preventive vaccine trials with children. *South African Medical Journal* 2005 April; 95(4): 269-271. NRCBL: 9.5.6; 18.5.2; 9.7; 6.

Srinivasan, Sandhya. Physician, do no harm [opinion]. *Issues in Medical Ethics* 1998 January; 6(1): 22-23. NRCBL: 9.5.6; 18.5.9.

Stebbing, Justin; Bower, Mark. Lessons for HIV from Tuskegee. *Journal of HIV Therapy* 2004 September; 9(3): 50-52. NRCBL: 9.5.6; 2.2; 18.5.1; 18.3.

Thomas, Joe. Unmet ethical concerns of the proposed preventive HIV vaccine trials in India. *Indian Journal of Medical Ethics* 2004 July-September; 1(3): 87-88. NRCBL: 9.5.6; 18.5.9.

Veljkovic, Veljko; Prljic, Jelena; Veljkovic, Tatjana. Safety and ethical consideration of AIDS vaccine. *International Reviews of Immunology* 2004 September-December; 23(5-6): 465-486. NRCBL: 9.5.6; 9.7; 9.8; 18.6.

Zion, Deborah. Community without communitarianism: HIV/AIDS research, prevention and treatment in Australia and the developing world. *Monash Bioethics Review* 2005 April; 24(2): 20-31. NRCBL: 9.5.6; 10; 9.7; 18.5.1.

Zion, Deborah. Does autonomy require freedom? The importance of options in international HIV/AIDS research. *Health Care Analysis: An International Journal of Health Care Philosophy and Policy* 2005 September; 13(3): 189-202. NRCBL: 9.5.6; 1.1; 18.3; 18.5.9.
Abstract: This paper analyses the way in which being in possession of an adequate range of options is an essential component of autonomy. I discuss the way in which the conceptualisation of options in terms of basic rights might assist this argument, and apply these ideas to HIV/AIDS clinical research in the developing world. Finally, I suggest that mechanisms should be put in place through which vulnerable research participants can express their views about the relationship between the research in which they are involved, and needs of a worthwhile life.

AIDS/ LEGAL ASPECTS

Does mother know best? *Hospital Law Newsletter* 1999 May; 16(7): 1-4. NRCBL: 9.5.6; 8.3.2; 8.3.4. SC: le. Identifiers: Maine; In re Nikolas E.

Alesch, Jill. The Americans with Disabilities Act: an end to discrimination against HIV/AIDS patients or simply another loophole to bypass? *Drake Law Review* 2004; 52(3): 523-551. NRCBL: 9.5.6; 9.3.1; 9.2; 9.4. SC: le.

Barnes, Mark. Legal and ethical issues in revising human immunodeficiency virus postexposure protocols. *American Journal of Medicine* 1997 May 19; 102(5B): 111-112. NRCBL: 9.5.6; 16.3. SC: le.

Berman, Jennifer. Using the doctrine of informed consent to improve HIV vaccine access in the post-TRIPS era. *Wisconsin International Law Journal* 2004 Spring; 22(2): 273-321. NRCBL: 9.5.6; 18.3; 18.5.1; 21.1; 9.2; 9.7; 18.2. SC: le. Identifiers: Trade-Related Aspects of Intellectual Property Rights.

Casper, Edward. Doe v. Mutual of Omaha: do insurance policy caps on AIDS treatments violate the Americans with Disabilities Act? *Notre Dame Law Review* 2000 May; 75(4): 1539-1569. NRCBL: 9.5.6; 9.3.1. SC: le. Note: 179 F. 2d 557 (7th Cir. 1999).

Chenneville, Tiffany. HIV, confidentiality, and duty to protect: a decision-making model. *Professional Psychology: Research and Practice* 2000 December; 31(6): 661-670. NRCBL: 9.5.6; 8.4; 17.1; 4.3. SC: le.

Chipeur, Gerald D. Blood testing without consent: the right to privacy versus the right to know (Part 2). *Medicine and Law: World Association for Medical Law* 1994; 13(1-2): 55-67. NRCBL: 9.5.6; 8.3.1; 8.4. SC: le; an.

NRCBL: National Reference Center for Bioethics Literature Classification Scheme   See inside front cover for terms.

35

Dancaster, J.T.; Dancaster, L.A. Confidentiality concerning HIV/AIDS status — the implications of the Appeal Court decision. *South African Medical Journal* 1995 March; 85(3): 141-144. NRCBL: 9.5.6; 8.4. SC: le.

Ehman, Amy Jo. Saskatchewan MDs oppose new mandatory testing law [news]. *CMAJ/JAMC: Canadian Medical Association Journal* 2005 December 6; 173(12): 1437-1438. NRCBL: 9.5.6; 9.1. SC: le. Identifiers: Canada; Mandatory Testing and Exposure (Bodily Substances) Act.

Ferreira, Lissett. Access to affordable HIV/AIDS drugs: the human rights obligations of multinational pharmaceutical corporations. *Fordham Law Review* 2002 December; 71(3): 1133-1179. NRCBL: 9.5.6; 9.7; 5.3; 9.2; 21.1. SC: le.

Garfield, Christopher. Enabling responsibility: adolescent autonomy and the teen HIV crisis in the United States. *Journal of Medicine and Law* 2003 Fall-2004 Spring; 8(1-2): 87-100. NRCBL: 9.5.6; 9.5.7; 8.3.2. SC: le.

Graham, Peter E.; Harel-Raviv, Mili. The law and ethics in relation to dentists treating HIV-positive patients: report on a recent U.S. Supreme Court case. *Journal of the Canadian Dental Association* 1999 January; 65(1): 27-30. NRCBL: 9.5.6; 4.1.1; 7.1; 8.1. SC: le. Identifiers: Bragdon v. Abbott.

Grimes, Richard M.; Helfgott, Andrew W.; Watson, Julie R.; Eriksen, Nancy L. For children's sake. New law mandates HIV testing of pregnant patients. *Texas Medicine* 1996 January; 92(1): 36-40. NRCBL: 9.5.6; 9.5.5; 8.3.1; 8.4. SC: le.

Grover, Anand; Dhaliwal, Mandeep; Dadwal, Sandeep. HIV bills, Maharashtra; Karnataka. *Issues in Medical Ethics* 2000 April-June; 8(2): 60-61. NRCBL: 9.5.6. SC: le.

Halem, Samantha Catherine. At what cost?: An argument against mandatory AZT treatment of HIV-positive pregnant women. *Harvard Civil Rights-Civil Liberties Law Review* 1997 Summer; 32(2): 492-528. NRCBL: 9.5.6; 9.5.5; 8.3.4. SC: le. Identifiers: Azidothymidine.

Havlir, Diane V.; Hammer, Scott M. Patents versus patients? Antiretroviral therapy in India [opinion]. *New England Journal of Medicine* 2005 August 25; 353(8): 749-751. NRCBL: 9.5.6; 9.7; 21.1. SC: le.

Häyry, Heta. AIDS, discimination and legal restrictions. *In her:* Individual Liberty and Medical Control. Brookfield, VT: Ashgate Pub., 1998: 82-91. NRCBL: 9.5.6. SC: an; le.

Hellsten, Sirkku K. Bioethics in Tanzania: legal and ethical concerns in medical care and research in relation to the HIV/AIDS epidemic. *CQ: Cambridge Quarterly of Healthcare Ethics* 2005 Summer; 14(3): 256-267. NRCBL: 9.5.6; 9.4. SC: le.

Hodge, James G., Jr.; Parini, Michael J. Perinatal HIV transmission: a children's human rights perspective. *Children's Legal Rights Journal* 1998 Spring; 18(2): 6-19. NRCBL: 9.5.6; 9.5.8; 9.5.5; 21.1; 9.1. SC: le.

Jansen, L.A. HIV exceptionalism, CD4+ cell testing, and conscientious subversion. *Journal of Medical Ethics* 2005 June; 31(6): 322-326. NRCBL: 9.5.6; 8.3.1; 8.4. SC: le.
Abstract: In recent years, many states in the United States have passed legislation requiring laboratories to report the names of patients with low CD4 cell counts to their state Departments of Health. This name reporting is an integral part of the growing number of "HIV Reporting and Partner Notification Laws" which have emerged in response to recently revised guidelines suggested by the National Centers for Disease Control (CDC). Name reporting for patients with low CD4 cell counts allows for a more accurate tracking of the natural history of HIV disease. However, given that this test is now considered to be an "indicator" of HIV, should it be subject to the same strict consent required for HIV testing? While the CDC has recommended that each state develop its own consent requirements for CD4 cell testing, most states have continued to rely on the presumed consent standards for CD4 cell testing that were in place before the passage of name reporting statutes. This allows physicians who treat patients who refuse HIV testing to order a CD4 cell blood analysis to gather information that is indicative of their patient's HIV status. This paper examines the ethical and legal issues associated with the practice of "conscientious subversion" as it arises when clinicians use CD4 cell counts as a surrogate for HIV testing.

Lagitch, Kellie E. Mandatory HIV testing: an Orwellian proposition. *St. John's Law Review* 1998 Winter; 72(1): 103-139. NRCBL: 9.5.6; 8.3.4; 8.4; 9.5.7. SC: le.

McGovern, Theresa M. Mandatory HIV testing and treating of child-bearing women: an unnatural, illegal, and unsound approach. *Columbia Human Rights Law Review* 1997 Spring; 28(3): 469-499. NRCBL: 9.5.6; 9.5.5; 9.5.8; 8.3.4; 9.5.7. SC: le.

McPhee, John; Stewart, Cameron. Recent developments in law. *Journal of Bioethical Inquiry* 2005; 2(3): 122-129. NRCBL: 9.5.6; 8.4; 8.5; 20.5.1; 8.3.3; 12.4.4. SC: le.

Mills, John W. HIV confidentiality law has serious flaws [editorial]. *Pennsylvania Medicine* 2000 May; 103(5): 6. NRCBL: 9.5.6; 8.4; 8.1. SC: le.

Moayery, Sheedeh. National HIV reporting: what's in a name? *Virginia Journal of Social Policy and the Law* 2001 Winter; 8(2): 439-473. NRCBL: 9.5.6; 8.4; 1.3.12; 1.3.5. SC: le.

Rediger, Bryon B. Living in a world with HIV: balancing privacy, privilege and the right to know between patients and health care professionals. *Hamline Journal of Public Law and Policy* 2000; 21(2): 443-487. NRCBL: 9.5.6; 8.4. SC: le.

Riestra, Sergio Gallego; Jarreta, Begoña Martinez; Fonseca, Rafael Hinojal; Caro, Javier Sanchez. Medicolegal problems arising from AIDS and health care personnel with special reference to Spanish law. *Medicine and Law: World Association for Medical Law* 1994; 13(3-4): 241-249. NRCBL: 9.5.6; 8.1; 8.4. SC: le.

Satchwill, Allison A. Asymptomatic HIV and the Americans with Disabilities Act: Runnebaum v. Nationsbank of Maryland, N.A. *University Of Cincinnati Law Review* 1998 Summer; 66(4): 1387-1410. NRCBL: 9.5.6. SC: le. Note: 123 F3d 156 (4th Cir. 1997) (en banc).

Spectar, J.M. Patent necessity: intellectual property dilemmas in the biotech domain and treatment equity for developing countries. *Houston Journal of International Law* 2002; 24(2): 227-278. NRCBL: 9.5.6; 9.7; 21.1; 9.3.1. SC: le.

Spindelman, Marc S. Some initial thoughts on sexuality and gay men with AIDS in relation to physician-assisted suicide. *Georgetown Journal of Gender and the Law* 2000 Fall; 2(1): 91-105. NRCBL: 9.5.6; 10; 20.7; 20.5.1. SC: le.

Thomas, Joe. HIV and confidentiality in India. *Issues in Medical Ethics* 1998 July-September; 6(3): 87. NRCBL: 9.5.6; 8.4. SC: le.

Turner, Dwayne C. Safer laws?: problematic civil/criminal liability and curbing New York's HIV/AIDS epidemic. *Quinnipac Health Law Journal* 2003; 6(2): 173-192. NRCBL: 9.5.6; 9.1. SC: le.

United States. Congress. United States Leadership Against HIV/AIDS, Tuberculosis, and Malaria Act of 2003. [approved: 2003 May 27]. United States: Public Law 108-025 [HR 1298], 117 Stat. 2003 May 27: 711-750 [Online]. Available: http://frwebgate.access.gpo.gov/cgi-bin/getdoc/cgi?dbname=108_cong_public_laws&docid=f:publ025.108.pdf [22 February 2006]. NRCBL: 9.5.6; 21.1; 1.3.5; 9.5.1; 9.7. SC: le. Identifiers: 108th Congress.

ALLOCATION *See* ORGAN AND TISSUE TRANSPLANTATION/ ALLOCATION

ALLOWING TO DIE *See* EUTHANASIA AND ALLOWING TO DIE

ANIMAL EXPERIMENTATION

A less toxic solution: industry should get behind a European partnership that will explore alternatives to animal testing [editorial]. *Nature* 2005 November 10; 438(7065): 129-130. NRCBL: 22.2.

Still not deterred: universities should back researchers determined to stand up for animal research in the face of terrorism. *Nature* 2005 September 1; 437(7055): 1-2. NRCBL: 22.2. Identifiers: Declaration on Animals in Medical Research.

The ethics of research involving animals. *ATLA: Alternatives to Laboratory Animals* 2005 August; 33(4): 324-325. NRCBL: 22.2.

Abbott, Alison. More than a cosmetic change [news]. *Nature* 2005 November 10; 438(7065): 144-146. NRCBL: 22.2. Identifiers: Europe.

Alleva, Enrico; Scattoni, Maria Luisa. Introductory keynote. The state of the art in animal experimentation. *Annali dell Istituto Superiore di Sanita* 2004; 40(2): 151-155. NRCBL: 22.2; 22.1; 21.1.

American College of Toxicology. Animals in Research Committee. American College of Toxicology: policy statement on the use of animals in toxicology. *International Journal of Toxicology* 2004 March-April; 23(2): n.p. NRCBL: 22.2; 6.

Anchustegui, A.T. Biocentric ethics and animal prosperity. *International Journal of Applied Philosophy* 2005 Spring; 19(1): 105-119. NRCBL: 22.1; 1.1. SC: an. Identifiers: Peter Singer; Tom Regan.

Archibald, Kathy. Test people, not animals [letter]. *New Scientist* 2005 September 24-30; 187(2518): 24. NRCBL: 22.2.

Baumans, V. Use of animals in experimental research: an ethical dilemma? *Gene Therapy* 2004 October; 11(Supplement 1): S64-S66. NRCBL: 22.2.

Bernstein, Mark. Marginal cases and moral relevance. *Journal of Social Philosophy* 2002 Winter; 33(4): 523-539. NRCBL: 22.2; 1.1. SC: an.

Bernstein, Mark H. Animal experimentation. *In his:* Without a Tear: Our Tragic Relationship with Animals. Urbana: University of Illinois Press; 2004: 129-149. NRCBL: 22.2.

Bhogal, Nirmala; Hudson, Michelle; Balls, Michael; Combes, Robert D. The use of non-human primates in biological and medical research: evidence submitted by FRAME to the Academy of Medical Sciences/Medical Research Council/Royal Society/Wellcome Trust Working Group. *ATLA: Alternatives to Laboratory Animals* 2005 October; 33(5): 519-527. NRCBL: 22.2; 15.7. Identifiers: Fund for the Replacement of Animals in Medical Experiments.

Borrego, Anne Marie. Politics, culture, and the lab: public attitudes toward animals and human embryonic stem cells have fostered different research agendas in Britain and the United States. *Chronicle of Higher Education* 2005 March 11; 51(27): A43-A45. NRCBL: 22.1; 18.5.4; 15.1; 1.3.9.

Brainard, Jeffrey. Report knocks agriculture department's protection of research animals. *Chronicle of Higher Education* 2005 November 11; 52(12): 27. NRCBL: 22.2; 22.1.

NRCBL: National Reference Center for Bioethics Literature Classification Scheme   See inside front cover for terms.

Brettingham, Madeleine. Committee calls for more guidance on animal experiments [news]. *BMJ: British Medical Journal* 2005 May 28; 330(7502): 1226. NRCBL: 22.2.

Carter, Alan. Animals, pain and morality. *Journal of Applied Philosophy* 2005; 22(1): 17-22. NRCBL: 22.1; 4.4. SC: an.

Abstract: While it is widely agreed that the infliction upon innocents of needless pain is immoral, many have argued that, even though nonhuman animals act as if they feel pain, there is no reason to think that they actually suffer painful experiences. And if our actions only appear to cause nonhuman animals pain, then such actions are not immoral. On the basis of the claim that certain behavioural responses to organismic harm are maladaptive, whereas the ability to feel pain is itself adaptive, this article argues that the experience of pain should be viewed as the proximate cause of such occasionally maladaptive behaviour. But as nonhuman animals also display such maladaptive traits, we have reason to conclude that they feel pain. Hence, we have reason to hold that it is indeed possible to inflict needless pain on nonhuman animals, which would be immoral.

Combes, Robert. "Europe goes alternative" — what's all the fuss about? [editorial]. *ATLA: Alternatives to Laboratory Animals* 2005 December; 33(6): 549-552. NRCBL: 22.2; 21.1.

Cyranoski, David. Japanese call for more bite in animal rules [news]. *Nature* 2005 March 3; 434(7029): 6. NRCBL: 22.2. SC: le. Identifiers: Japan.

Dunckley, Catherine; Foley, Mary; Hall, Geoff. Research with animals. *In:* Dawson, John; Peart, Nicola, eds. The Law of Research: A Guide. Dunedin, NZ: University of Otago Press; 2003: 155-174. NRCBL: 22.2. SC: le.

European Commission; Matthiessen, Line; Lucaroni, Beatrice; Sachez, Elena. The Process of Addressing the Ethical Dimension of Animal Experimentation and Implementing the Principle of the Three Rs under the "Quality of Life" Programme. Brussells, Belgium: European Commission, 2002 July; 2 p. [Online]. Available: http://europa.eu.int/comm/research/biosociety/pdf/animal_experim.pdf [22 January 2004]. NRCBL: 22.2.

Festing, Simon; Patel, Tarah. The Ethics of Research Involving Animals: a review of the Nuffield Council on Bioethics Report from a research perspective. *ATLA: Alternatives to Laboratory Animals* 2005 December; 33(6): 654-658. NRCBL: 22.2.

Fox, Fiona. Come out and fight. *New Scientist* 2005 September 24-30; 187(2518): 22. NRCBL: 22.2.

Francione, Gary. One right for all [opinion]. *New Scientist* 2005 October 8-14; 188(2520): 24. NRCBL: 22.1.

Francione, Gary L. You hypocrites! *New Scientist* 2005 June 4-10; 186(2502): 51-52. NRCBL: 22.1. Identifiers: moral status of animals.

Franklin, Julian H. Appendix 2: Biomedical testing and use of animals. *In her:* Animal Rights and Moral Philoso-phy. New York: Columbia University Press; 2005: 125-128. NRCBL: 22.2.

Frey, R.G. Animals. *In:* LaFollette, Hugh, ed. The Oxford Handbook of Practical Ethics. New York: Oxford University Press; 2003: 161-187. NRCBL: 22.2; 22.1; 1.1. SC: an.

Frey, R.G. Animals and their medical use. *In:* Cohen, Andrew I.; Wellman, Christopher Heath, eds. Contemporary Debates in Applied Ethics. Malden, MA: Blackwell Pub., 2005: 91-103. NRCBL: 22.2; 22.1; 1.1. SC: an.

Frey, R.G. Autonomy, diminished life, and the threshold for use. *In:* Taylor, James Stacey, ed. Personal Autonomy: New Essays on Personal Autonomy and Its Role in Contemporary Moral Philosophy. New York: Cambridge University Press; 2005: 330-346. NRCBL: 22.1; 22.2; 1.1. SC: an.

Frey, R.G. On the ethics of using animals for human benefit. *In:* Sherlock, Richard; Morrey, John D., eds. Ethical Issues in Biotechnology. Lanham: Rowman and Littlefield; 2002: 287-297. NRCBL: 22.2.

Frey, R.G.; Thomas, D. Pain, vivisection, and the value of life. *Journal of Medical Ethics* 2005 April; 31(4): 202-204. NRCBL: 22.2.

Gagneux, Pascal; Moore, James J.; Varki, Ajit. The ethics of research on great apes. *Nature* 2005 September 1; 437(7055): 27-29. NRCBL: 22.2. SC: rv.

Giles, Jim. UK panel urges animal researchers to go public [news]. *Nature* 2005 May 26; 435(7041): 392. NRCBL: 22.2. Identifiers: United Kingdom (Great Britain).

Gökçora, Ismail Haluk. Ethics and animal use in biomedical research. *Advances in Experimental Medicine and Biology* 2004; 553: 359-371. NRCBL: 22.2; 22.1. SC: an.

Goldberg, Alan M. Animals and alternatives: societal expectations and scientific need. *ATLA: Alternatives to Laboratory Animals* 2004 December; 32(6): 545-551. NRCBL: 22.2; 22.1; 21.1.

Greene, Mark; Schill, Kathryn; Takahashi, Shoji; Bateman- House, Alison; Beauchamp, Tom; Bok, Hilary; Cheney, Dorothy; Coyle, Joseph; Deacon, Terrence; Dennett, Daniel; Donovan, Peter; Flanagan, Owen; Goldman, Steven; Greely, Henry; Martin, Lee; Miller, Earl; Mueller, Dawn; Siegel, Andrew; Solter, Davor; Gearhart, John; McKhann, Guy; Faden, Ruth. Moral issues of human-nonhuman primate neural grafting. *Science* 2005 July 15; 309(5733): 385-386. NRCBL: 22.2; 19.1; 18.6; 5.3; 1.1. SC: an.

Grindon, Christina; Bhogal, Nirmala. The Fourth EC Report on the statistics of laboratory animal use: trends, recommendations and future prospects. *ATLA: Alternatives to Laboratory Animals* 2005 August; 33(4): 417-426. NRCBL: 22.2; 21.1; 15.1.

Gruber, Franz P.; Dewhurst, David G. Alternatives to animal experimentation in biomedical education. *ALTEX: Alternativen zu Tierexperimenten* 2004; 21 (Supplement 1): 33-48. NRCBL: 22.2; 22.1; 7.2.

Hagelin, J. Use of live nonhuman primates in research in Asia. *Journal of Postgraduate Medicine* 2004 October-December; 50(4): 253-256. NRCBL: 22.2; 21.1. SC: em.

Hendricksen, Coenraad F.M. The ethics of Research Involving Animals: a review of the Nuffield Council on Bioethics Report from a three Rs perspective. *ATLA: Alternatives to Laboratory Animals* 2005 December; 33(6): 659-662. NRCBL: 22.2.

Hill, William Allen. PI and vet: potential conflict of interest? PI can't act as AV. *Lab Animal* 2004 October; 33(9): 22-23. NRCBL: 22.2; 1.3.9; 9.6. SC: cs. Identifiers: principal investigator; attending veterinarian.

Hogan, Walter; Bucciarelli, Elizabeth Retzel. Ethical treatment of animals. *Choice* 2005 December; 43(4): 595-600, 602-609. NRCBL: 22.1; 1.2; 1.3.11; 22.2; 22.3. SC: rv.

Hudson, Michelle; Bhogal, Nirmala; Balls, Michael. The use of non-human primates in regulatory toxicology: comments submitted by FRAME to the home office. *ATLA: Alternatives to Laboratory Animals* 2005 October; 33(5): 529-538. NRCBL: 22.2. Identifiers: Fund for the Replacement of Animals in Medical Experiments.

Ingham, Kim M.; Schmitt, Gina. Novel IACUC outreach effort to facilitate animal protocol submission and review. *Contemporary Topics in Laboratory Animal Science* 2005 March; 44(2): 72-74. NRCBL: 22.2. Identifiers: Institutional Animal Care and Use Committees.

Jansen, Brigitte E.S.; Paslack, Rainer. Social risks and social perception of animal cloning. *Revista de Derecho y Genoma Humano / Law and the Human Genome Review* 2003 July-December; (19): 231-236. NRCBL: 22.2; 14.5; 15.7. Note: abstract in Spanish.

Jonsen, Albert R. Animal ethics. *In his:* Bioethics Beyond the Headlines: Who Lives? Who Dies? Who Decides? Lanham, MD: Rowman and Littlefield; 2005: 160-166. NRCBL: 22.2.

Jurgus, Maryann; Welsh, Thomas J. PI and vet: potential conflict of interest? Definite potential for conflict of interest. *Lab Animal* 2004 October; 33(9): 22. NRCBL: 22.2; 1.3.9; 9.6. Identifiers: principal investigator.

Kemdal, Anna Blom; Montgomery, Henry. Explaining own and others' behavior in a controversial issue: animal experimentation. *Journal of Social Psychology* 2001 December; 141(6): 693-713. NRCBL: 22.2. SC: em.

Kondro, Wayne. Animal rules keep grad students out of the lab [news]. *Science* 2005 December 2; 310(5753): 1405. NRCBL: 22.2.

Markie, Peter J. Respect for people and animals. *Journal of Value Inquiry* 2004; 38(1): 33-47. NRCBL: 22.1; 22.2; 1.1.

Marris, Emma; Simonite, Tom. Animal-rights militancy exported to US and Europe [news]. *Nature* 2005 December 8; 438(7069): 717. NRCBL: 22.2; 21.1.

McArdle, John. Legal protection for rats, mice, and birds: long overdue and the right thing to do [opinion]. *Comparative Medicine* 2001 June; 51(3): 203-204. NRCBL: 22.2; 22.1. SC: le.

McTighe, Maggie; Hanley, Greg. IACUC replacement parts: what are the requirements? Inappropriate actions. *Lab Animal* 2004 November; 33(10): 17. NRCBL: 22.2; 9.6. SC: cs. Identifiers: Institutional Animal Care and Use Committees.

Michael, Steve. Animal personhood — a threat to research? *Physiologist* 2004 December; 47(6): 447, 449-450. NRCBL: 22.1; 22.2; 4.4.

National Health and Medical Research Council [NHMRC] (Australia). Policy on the care and use of non-human primates for scientific purposes — to be read in conjunction with The Australian Code of Practice for the Care and Use of Animals for Scientific Purposes. Canberra, ACT: The Council 2003; 22 p. [Online]. Available: http://www7.health.gov.au/nhmrc/research/awc/nonhum2.pdf [31 March 2005]. NRCBL: 22.2. Note: Prepared by the Animal Welfare Committee of the NHMRC. Endorsed June 6, 2003.

National Health and Medical Research Council [NHMRC] (Australia); Royal Australasian College of Surgeons. NHMRC guidelines on the use of animals for training surgeons and demonstrating new surgical equipment and techniques. Canberra, ACT: The Council 1997 September; 4 p. [Online]. Available: http://www7.health.gov.au/nhmrc/research/awc/surgeon.pdf [31 March 2005]. NRCBL: 22.2; 6.

Orlans, F. Barbara. Case studies of ethical dilemmas. *Laboratory Animal Science* 1987 January; 37: 59-64. NRCBL: 22.2.

Orlans, F. Barbara. Scientists' attitudes toward animal care and use committees. *Laboratory Animal Science* 1987 January; 37: 162-166. NRCBL: 22.2.

Panzini, Gianluca; Lorenzini, Rodolfo Nello. Animal experimentation in Italy. Legislation and the authorisation of research protocols. *Annali dell Istituto Superiore di Sanita* 2004; 40(2): 205-210. NRCBL: 22.2; 22.1.

Pereira, Shiranee; Tettamanti, Massimo. Ahimsa and alternatives — the concept of the 4th R. The CPCSEA in

NRCBL: National Reference Center for Bioethics Literature Classification Scheme   See inside front cover for terms.

39

India. *ALTEX: Alternativen zu Tierexperimenten* 2005; 22(1): 3-6. NRCBL: 22.1; 22.2; 1.2. SC: le. Identifiers: Committee for the Purpose of Control and Supervision of Experiments on Animals.

Ravelingien, An. Use of pigs for xenotransplantation: the speciesism by proxy syndrome. *Xenotransplantation* 2005 May; 12(3): 235-239. NRCBL: 22.2; 22.1; 19.5.

Regan, Tom. Empty cages: animal rights and vivisection. *In:* Cohen, Andrew I.; Wellman, Christopher Heath, eds. Contemporary Debates in Applied Ethics. Malden, MA: Blackwell Pub., 2005: 77-90. NRCBL: 22.2; 1.1. SC: an.

Rohlf, Vanessa; Bennett, Pauleen. Perpetration-induced traumatic stress in persons who euthanize nonhuman animals in surgeries, animal shelters, and laboratories. *Society and Animals: Journal of Human-Animal Studies* 2005; 13(3): 201-219. NRCBL: 22.1; 22.2. SC: em.

Rollin, B.E.; Universities Federation for Animal Welfare [UFAW]; Fund for the Replacement of Animals in Medical Experiments [FRAME]; Seriously Ill for Medical Research [SIMR]; Research Defence Society [RDS]. Defending the use of animals to research human disease [letters]. *Molecular Medicine Today* 1995 October; 1(7): 308-309. NRCBL: 22.1; 22.2. Comments: comment on Kathryn Senior "Defending the use of animals to research human disease," Molecular Medicine Today 1995 August; 1(5): 220-225.

Rollin, Bernard E. Reasonable partiality and animal ethics. *Ethical Theory and Moral Practice* 2005 April; 8(1-2): 105-121. NRCBL: 22.1; 1.1; 22.2.

Rowan, Andrew N. The use of animals in experimentation: an examination of the 'technical' arguments used to criticize the practice. *In:* Garner, Robert, ed. Animal Rights: The Changing Debate. New York: New York University Press; 1996: 104-122. NRCBL: 22.1.

Rowan, Andrew N.; Loew, Franklin M. Animal research: a review of developments, 1950-2000. *In:* Salem, Deborah J.; Rowan, Andrew N., eds. The State of the Animals 2001. Washington, DC: Humane Society Press; 2001: 111-120. NRCBL: 22.2.

Rusche, Brigitte. The 3Rs and animal welfare — conflict or the way forward? *ALTEX: Alternativen zu Tierexperimenten* 2003; 20(Supplement 1): 63-76. NRCBL: 22.2; 21.1.

Russell, W.M.S. A comment from a humane experimental technique perspective on the Nuffield Council on Bioethics Report on The Ethics of Research Involving Animals. *ATLA: Alternatives to Laboratory Animals* 2005 December; 33(6): 650-653. NRCBL: 22.2.

Schuppli, Catherine A.; Fraser, David. The interpretation and application of the three Rs by animal ethics committee members. *ATLA: Alternatives to Laboratory Animals* 2005 October; 33(5): 487-500. NRCBL: 22.2. SC: em.

Schuppli, Catherine A.; McDonald, Michael. Contrasting modes of governance for the protection of humans and animals in Canada: lessons for reform. *Health Law Review* 2005; 13(2-3): 97-106. NRCBL: 22.2; 18.2. SC: le.

Senior, Kathryn. Defending the use of animals to research human disease [opinion]. *Molecular Medicine Today* 1995 August; 1(5): 220-225. NRCBL: 22.1; 22.2.

Siebert, Charles. What does an aging chimp do when his working days are done? A journey into the realm - and the issue - of primate retirement sanctuaries. *New York Times Magazine* 2005 July 24; p. 28-35, 61-63. NRCBL: 22.2. SC: po.

Simonite, Tom; Giles, Jim. UK animal labs still under siege [news]. *Nature* 2005 December 8; 438(7069): 716. NRCBL: 22.2. Identifiers: United Kingdom (Great Britain).

Slaughter, Bill. Animal use in biomedicine: an annotated bibliography of Buddhist and related perspectives. *Journal of Buddhist Ethics [electronic]* 2002; 9: 149-158. Available: http://jbe.gold.ac.uk/9/current9.html [16 May 2003]. NRCBL: 22.2; 1.2.

Small, Bruce H.; Fisher, Mark W. Measuring biotechnology employees' ethical attitudes towards a controversial transgenic cattle project: the Ethical Valence Matrix. *Journal of Agricultural and Environmental Ethics* 2005; 18(5): 495-508. NRCBL: 22.3; 15.1; 1.1; 5.3. SC: em.

Stephens, Martin L.; Goldberg, Alan M.; Rowan, Andrew N. The first forty years of the alternatives approach: refining, reducing, and replacing the use of laboratory animals. *In:* Salem, Deborah J.; Rowan, Andrew N., eds. The State of the Animals 2001. Washington, DC: Humane Society Press; 2001: 121-135. NRCBL: 22.2; 2.2.

Taussig, Karen-Sue. Bovine abominations: genetic culture and politics in the Netherlands. *Cultural Anthropology* 2004 August; 19(3): 305-336. NRCBL: 22.2; 15.7; 15.1; 15.5.

Thomas, D. Laboratory animals and the art of empathy. *Journal of Medical Ethics* 2005 April; 31(4): 197-202. NRCBL: 22.2.
Abstract: Consistency is the hallmark of a coherent ethical philosophy. When considering the morality of particular behaviour, one should look to identify comparable situations and test one's approach to the former against one's approach to the latter. The obvious comparator for animal experiments is non-consensual experiments on people. In both cases, suffering and perhaps death is knowingly caused to the victim, the intended beneficiary is someone else, and the victim does not consent. Animals suffer just as people do. As we condemn non-consensual experiments on people, we should, if we are to be consistent, condemn non-consensual experiments on animals. The alleged differences between the two practices often put forward do not stand up to scrutiny. The best guide to ethical behaviour

is empathy—putting oneself in the potential victim's shoes. Again to be consistent, we should empathise with all who may be adversely affected by our behaviour. By this yardstick, too, animal experiments fail the ethical test.

Thomas, David. The Ethics of Research Involving Animals: a review of the Nuffield Council on Bioethics Report from an antivivisectionist perspective. *ATLA: Alternatives to Laboratory Animals* 2005 December; 33(6): 663-667. NRCBL: 22.2.

United States. Department of Agriculture. Office of Inspector General, Western Region. Audit report: APHIS animal care program inspection and enforcement activities. Washington, DC: United States Department of Agriculture. Office of Inspector General Western Region 2005 September; 60 p. [Online]. Available: http://www.usda.gov/oig/webdocs/33002-03-SF.pdf [10 November 2005]. NRCBL: 22.2. SC: le. Identifiers: Animal and Plant Health Inspection Service.

VandeBerg, John L.; Zola, Stuart M. A unique biomedical resource at risk. *Nature* 2005 September 1; 437(7055): 30-32. NRCBL: 22.2.

Wade, Nicholas. Ethicists offer advice for testing human brain cells in primates. *New York Times* 2005 July 15; p. A12. NRCBL: 22.2; 18.5.4. SC: po.

Wade, Nicholas. Stem cell test tried on mice saves embryo; technique could shift debate on humans. *New York Times* 2005 October 17; p. A1, A16. NRCBL: 22.2; 19.1; 18.5.4. SC: po.

Weaver, Lara A.; Andrutis, Karl. IACUC replacement parts: what are the requirements? Bad choices. *Lab Animal* 2004 November; 33(10): 17-18. NRCBL: 22.2; 9.6. SC: cs. Identifiers: Institutional Animal Care and Use Committees.

Weed, James L.; Raber, James M. Balancing animal research with animal well-being: establishment of goals and harmonization of approaches. *ILAR Journal* 2005; 46(2): 118-128. NRCBL: 22.2; 22.1.

Weiss, Rick. Lab animal violations decried: activists urge NIH to sanction university for repeat offense. *Washington Post* 2005 December 2; p. A21. NRCBL: 22.2. SC: po.

White, Paul S. The experimental animal in Victorian Britain. *In:* Daston, Lorraine; Mitman, Gregg, eds. Thinking with Animals: New Perspectives on Anthropomorphism. New York: Columbia University Press; 2005: 59-81. NRCBL: 22.2.

Zupp, Jacqueline. Concern at animal research should not be dismissed [letter]. *Nature* 2005 October 20; 437(7062): 1089. NRCBL: 22.2.

ARTIFICIAL INSEMINATION AND SURROGATE MOTHERS
See also REPRODUCTIVE TECHNOLOGIES

Anonymity vanishes for sperm donors [editorial]. *New Scientist* 2005 November 5-11; 188(2524): 3. NRCBL: 14.2; 8.4.

Making babies: will a new UK law stop people donating eggs and sperm? [editorial]. *New Scientist* 2005 March 12-18; 185(2490): 3. NRCBL: 14.2; 14.4; 8.4. SC: le. Identifiers: United Kingdom (Great Britain).

Adams, Karen E. Gestational surrogacy for a human immunodeficiency virus seropositive sperm donor: what are the ethics? *JAMWA: Journal of the American Medical Women's Association* 2003 Summer; 58(3): 138-140. NRCBL: 14.2; 9.5.6; 8.3.1.

Appleton, Tim. Emotional aspects of surrogacy: a case for effective counselling and support. *In:* Cook, Rachel; Sclater, Shelley Day; Kaganas, Felicity, eds. Surrogate Motherhood: International Perspectives. Portland, OR: Hart; 2003: 199-207. NRCBL: 14.2; 17.1. SC: em.

Archer, Colette. Scrambled eggs: defining parenthood and inheritance rights of children born of reproductive technology. *Loyola Journal of Public Interest Law* 2002 Spring; 3(2): 152-173. NRCBL: 14.2; 14.1. SC: le.

Belling, Catherine. Imaginary fathers: a sentimental perspective on the question of identifying sperm donors. *Journal of Clinical Ethics* 2005 Winter; 16(4): 321-328. NRCBL: 14.2; 14.6; 7.1.

Belling, Catherine. The purchase of fruitfulness: assisted conception and reproductive disability in a seventeenth-century comedy. *Journal of Medical Humanities* 2005 Fall; 26(2-3): 79-96. NRCBL: 14.2; 9.5.5; 7.1; 10; 9.5.7. Identifiers: Thomas Middleton; "A Chaste Maid in Cheapside".
Abstract: The relationships between socioeconomic and biogenetic reproduction are always socially constructed but not always acknowledged. These relationships are examined as they apply to an instance of infertility and assisted reproduction presented in a seventeenth-century English play, Thomas Middleton's 1613 comedy, A Chaste Maid in Cheapside. Middleton's satirization of the effects of secrecy on the category of reproductive disability is analyzed and its applicability to our own time considered. The discussion is in four parts, focusing on: the attribution of disabled status to one member of the couple, the wife; the use of this attribution to protect the husband's reputation for sexual and reproductive health; the concealment of the nature of assisted reproduction; and the interests of the child conceived with such assistance.

Blyth, Eric; Potter, Claire. Paying for it? Surrogacy, market forces and assisted conception. *In:* Cook, Rachel; Sclater, Shelley Day; Kaganas, Felicity, eds. Surrogate Motherhood: International Perspectives. Portland, OR: Hart; 2003: 227-242. NRCBL: 14.2; 9.3.1.

Brewaeys, A.; de Bruyn, J.K.; Louwe, L.A.; Helmerhorst, F.M. Anonymous or identity-registered sperm donors? A study of Dutch recipients' choices. *Human Reproduction* 2005 March; 20(3): 820-824. NRCBL: 14.2; 8.4. SC: em.

NRCBL: National Reference Center for Bioethics Literature Classification Scheme   See inside front cover for terms.

41

Brinsden, Peter R. Clinical aspects of IVF surrogacy in Britain. *In:* Cook, Rachel; Sclater, Shelley Day; Kaganas, Felicity, eds. Surrogate Motherhood: International Perspectives. Portland, OR: Hart; 2003: 99-112. NRCBL: 14.2.

Carmeli, Yoram S.; Birenbaum-Carmeli, Daphna; Madgar, Igael; Weissenberg, Ruth. Donor insemination in Israel: recipients' choice of donor. *Journal of Reproductive Medicine* 2001 August; 46(8): 757-762. NRCBL: 14.2; 19.5. SC: em.

Cateforis, Elizabeth Seale. Surrogate motherhood: an argument for regulation and a blueprint for legislation in Kansas. *Kansas Journal of Law and Public Policy* 1995; 4(2): 101-114. NRCBL: 14.2. SC: le.

Chester, Ronald. Freezing the heir apparent: a dialogue on postmortem conception, parental responsibility, and inheritance. *Houston Law Review* 1996 Winter; 33(4): 967-1025. NRCBL: 14.2; 19.5; 8.3.3; 14.6. SC: le.

Cohen, Sharon R. The invisible man. Artificial insemination by donor and the legislation on donor anonymity: a review. *Journal of Family Planning and Reproductive Health Care* 2004 October; 30(4): 270-273. NRCBL: 14.2; 8.4; 19.5. SC: le; rv.

Cook, Rachel. Safety in the multitude of counsellors: do we need counselling in surrogacy? *In:* Cook, Rachel; Sclater, Shelley Day; Kaganas, Felicity, eds. Surrogate Motherhood: International Perspectives. Portland, OR: Hart; 2003: 179-197. NRCBL: 14.2; 17.1.

Corinaldi, Michael. Towards the practice of surrogacy in Israel. *Medicine and Law: World Association for Medical Law* 1995; 14(5-6): 425-427. NRCBL: 14.2. SC: le.

Daniels, K.; Blyth, E.; Crawshaw, M.; Curson, R. Short communication: previous semen donors and their views regarding the sharing of information with offspring. *Human Reproduction* 2005 June; 20(6): 1670-1675. NRCBL: 14.2; 15.1; 8.4. SC: em.

Daniels, Ken. The policy and practice of surrogacy in New Zealand. *In:* Cook, Rachel; Sclater, Shelley Day; Kaganas, Felicity, eds. Surrogate Motherhood: International Perspectives. Portland, OR: Hart; 2003: 55-73. NRCBL: 14.2.

Davin, Jim; Kaczor, Christopher. Would artificial wombs produce more harm than good? [letter and reply]. *National Catholic Bioethics Quarterly* 2005 Winter; 5(4): 657- 658. NRCBL: 14.2; 12.5.1; 12.3.

de Souza, Eustace J. Surrogacy and human reproductive biology. *Issues in Medical Ethics* 1997 October-December; 5(4): 117-118. NRCBL: 14.2.

Dempsey, Deborah. Donor, father or parent? Conceiving paternity in the Australian Family Court. *International Journal of Law, Policy and the Family* 2004 April; 18(1): 76-102. NRCBL: 14.2; 10; 8.4. SC: le.

Denmark. Council of Ethics. Scandinavian recommendations: sperm donation [policy statement]. *Bulletin of Medical Ethics* 2003 September; (191): 8-9. NRCBL: 14.2; 19.5; 14.6; 8.4. Identifiers: Denmark.

Dodd, Gena. Surrogacy and the law in Britain: users' perspectives. *In:* Cook, Rachel; Sclater, Shelley Day; Kaganas, Felicity, eds. Surrogate Motherhood: International Perspectives. Portland, OR: Hart; 2003: 113-120. NRCBL: 14.2. SC: le.

Edelmann, Robert J. Psychological assessment in 'surrogate' motherhood relationships. *In:* Cook, Rachel; Sclater, Shelley Day; Kaganas, Felicity, eds. Surrogate Motherhood: International Perspectives. Portland, OR: Hart; 2003: 143-159. NRCBL: 14.2; 17.1.

Elon, Menachem; Auerbach, Bernard; Chazin, Daniel D.; Sykes, Melvin J. Artificial insemination. *In their:* Jewish Law (Mishpat Ivri): Cases and Materials. New York: M. Bender; 1999: 625-635. NRCBL: 14.2; 1.2. SC: le.

Elon, Menachem; Auerbach, Bernard; Chazin, Daniel D.; Sykes, Melvin J. Surrogate motherhood, in vitro fertilization, and genetic engineering. *In their:* Jewish Law (Mishpat Ivri): Cases and Materials. New York: M. Bender; 1999: 742-746. NRCBL: 14.2; 14.4; 15.1; 1.2. SC: le.

European Society for Human Reproduction and Embryology [ESHRE]. Task Force on Ethics and Law; Shenfield, F.; Pennings, G.; Cohen, J.; Devroey, P.; de Wert, G.; Tarlatzis, B. ESHRE task force on ethics and law 10: surrogacy. *Human Reproduction* 2005 October; 20(10): 2705-2707. NRCBL: 14.2; 4.4; 8.3.1.

Galbraith, Mhairi; McLachlan, Hugh V.; Swales, J. Kim. Commercial agencies and surrogate motherhood: a transaction cost approach. *Health Care Analysis: An International Journal of Health Care Philosophy and Policy* 2005 March; 13(1): 11-31. NRCBL: 14.2; 9.3.1. SC: le.
Abstract: In this paper we investigate the legal arrangements involved in UK surrogate motherhood from a transaction-cost perspective. We outline the specific forms the transaction costs take and critically comment on the way in which the UK institutional and organisational arrangements at present adversely influence transaction costs. We then focus specifically on the potential role of surrogacy agencies and look at UK and US evidence on commercial and voluntary agencies. Policy implications follow.

Garrison, Marsha. Law making for baby making: an interpretive approach to the determination of legal parentage. *Harvard Law Review* 2000 February; 113(4): 835-923. NRCBL: 14.2; 14.4; 4.4. SC: le.

Ginsberg, Karen M. FDA approved? A critique of the artificial insemination industry in the United States. *University of Michigan Journal of Law Reform* 1997 Summer; 30(4): 823-851. NRCBL: 14.2; 5.3; 15.3; 19.5. SC: le. Identifiers: Food and Drug Administration.

Goold, Imogen. Surrogacy: is there a case for legal prohibition? *Journal of Law and Medicine* 2004 November; 12(2): 205-216. NRCBL: 14.2. SC: le; an.

Gordon-Ceresky, Daryl L. Artificial insemination: its effect on paternity and inheritance rights. *Connecticut Probate Law Journal* 1995; 9(2): 245-271. NRCBL: 14.2. SC: le.

Gory, Simona. Constructing the heterosexually inactive lesbian: assisted insemination in Queensland. *Australian Feminist Law Journal* 2002 June; 16: 75-94. NRCBL: 14.2; 10. SC: le.

Hampton, Tracy. Anonymity of gamete donations debated [news]. *JAMA: The Journal of the American Medical Association* 2005 December 7; 294(21): 2681-2683. NRCBL: 14.2; 8.4; 14.4; 14.6.

Harrington, Lindsay S. Life-term inmates' right to procreate via artificial insemination: why so much fuss over the contents of a plastic cup? *McGeorge Law Review* 2002; 33(3): 521-535. NRCBL: 14.2; 14.1; 1.3.5. SC: le.

Illinois. Laws. An act concerning family law [effective: 29 July 1999]. Illinois General Assembly, Public Act 093-1095; 3 p. [Online]. Available: http://www.ilga.gov/legislation/publicacts/93/093-1095.htm [8 September 2005]. NRCBL: 14.2; 14.1; 1.3.5. SC: le. Identifiers: Illinois Parentage Act of 1984.

Johnson, Martin H. Surrogacy and the Human Fertilisation and Embryology Act. *In:* Cook, Rachel; Sclater, Shelley Day; Kaganas, Felicity, eds. Surrogate Motherhood: International Perspectives. Portland, OR: Hart; 2003: 93-97. NRCBL: 14.2. SC: le.

Jonas, Monique. Choosing between claims: allocating parental responsibility in surrogacy disputes. *In:* Häyry, Matti; Takala, Tuija; Herissone-Kelly, Peter, eds. Bioethics and Social Reality. New York: Rodopi, 2005: 39-51. NRCBL: 14.2; 14.1. SC: an.

Karkal, Malini. Surrogacy from a feminist perspective. *Issues in Medical Ethics* 1997 October-December; 5(4): 115-116. NRCBL: 14.2; 10.

Kerian, Christine L. Surrogacy: a last resort alternative for infertile women or a commodification of women's bodies and children? *Wisconsin Women's Law Journal* 1997 Spring; 12(1): 113-166. NRCBL: 14.2; 4.4. SC: le.

Lacey, Linda J. "O wind, remind him that I have no child": infertility and feminist jurisprudence. *Michigan Journal of Gender and Law* 1998-1999; 5(1): 163-203. NRCBL: 14.2; 4.4; 10. SC: le.

Lane, Melissa. Ethical issues in surrogacy arrangements. *In:* Cook, Rachel; Sclater, Shelley Day; Kaganas, Felicity, eds. Surrogate Motherhood: International Perspectives. Portland, OR: Hart; 2003: 121-139. NRCBL: 14.2.

Li, L.J.; Lu, G.X. How medical ethical principles are applied in treatment with artificial insemination by donors (AID) in Hunan, China: effective practice at the Reproductive and Genetic Hospital of CITIC-Xiangya. *Journal of Medical Ethics* 2005 June; 31(6): 333-337. NRCBL: 14.2.
   Abstract: This paper investigates the efficiency of application of medical ethics principles in the practice of artificial insemination by donors (AID) in China, in a culture characterised by traditional ethical values and disapproval of AID. The paper presents the ethical approach to AID treatment as established by the Reproduction and Genetics Hospital of CITIC-Xiangya (CITIC Hunan-Yale Approach) in the central southern area of China against the social ethical background of China and describes its general features. The CITIC-Xiangya Approach facilitates the implementation of ethical relations between clinicians and patients participating in AID treatment procedures in Hunan-Yale.

Lycett, E.; Daniels, K.; Curson, R.; Golombok, S. School-aged children of donor insemination: a study of parents' disclosure patterns. *Human Reproduction* 2005 March; 20(3): 810-819. NRCBL: 14.2; 8.4. SC: em.

Lycett, Emma; Daniels, Ken; Curson, Ruth; Golombok, Susan. Offspring created as a result of donor insemination: a study of family relationships, child adjustment, and disclosure. *Fertility and Sterility* 2004 July; 82(1): 172-179. NRCBL: 14.2; 19.5; 8.2. SC: em. Identifiers: United Kingdom (Great Britain).

Mamo, Laura. Biomedicalizing kinship: sperm banks and the creation of affinity-ties. *Science as Culture* 2005 September; 14(3): 237-264. NRCBL: 14.2; 14.6; 8.1; 19.5. SC: em.

Massachusetts. Supreme Judicial Court. *Culliton v. Beth Israel Deaconess Medical Center* [Date of Decision: 2001 October 12]. *West's North Eastern Reporter*, 2d Series, 2001; 756: 1133-1141. NRCBL: 14.2; 8.4; 9.1. SC: le.
   Abstract: Court Decision: 756 *North Eastern Reporter*, 2d Series 1133; 2001 Oct 12 (date of decision). The Supreme Judicial Court of Massachusetts ordered the defendant hospital to designate the plaintiffs as parents on the birth certificates of their genetic children, delivered at the defendant hospital by a gestational carrier. Steven and Marla Culliton entered into a gestational surrogacy agreement with Melissa Carroll to have embryos which were created by in vitro fertilization with the plaintiffs' own sperm and ova, implanted in the carrier. Before the children's births the plaintiffs requested a declaration of paternity and maternity and an order directing the hospital to enter the plaintiffs' names in the children's birth certificates. The Family Court dismissed the complaint, citing lack of authority to issue any prebirth order of parentage. On appeal, the Supreme Judicial Court held the Family Court has the authority to consider the complaint because the plaintiffs are the only genetic sources of the children, and neither party contests the complaint. Because the children were born while the case was on appeal, the Supreme Judicial Court entered judgment for the plaintiffs and ordered they be listed as the mother and father of the children on their birth records. The Supreme Judicial Court also held that the defendant hospital was still required to supply the state Department of Health with confidential information regarding the identity of the woman who delivered the children and "her prenatal health, labor and delivery, and postpartum care and condition" under the hospital's duties and

NRCBL: National Reference Center for Bioethics Literature Classification Scheme   See inside front cover for terms.

43

responsibilities to report vital records information for research and public health purposes. [KIE/INW]

McLachlan, Hugh V. Surrogate motherhood: beyond the Warnock and Brazier reports. *Human Reproduction and Genetic Ethics: An International Journal* 2005; 11(1): 12-23. NRCBL: 14.2.

McLachlan, Hugh V.; Swales, J.K. Exploitation and commercial surrogate motherhood. *Human Reproduction and Genetic Ethics: An International Journal* 2001; 7(1): 8-14. NRCBL: 14.2; 1.3.2.

Meltzer, Bari; Rothman, Barbara Katz. Bioengineering. *In:* Restivo, Sal, ed. Science, Technology, and Society: An Encyclopedia. New York: Oxford University Press; 2005: 23-28. NRCBL: 14.2; 14.4; 15.2; 14.5.

Morgan, Derek. Enigma variations: surrogacy, rights and procreative tourism. *In:* Cook, Rachel; Sclater, Shelley Day; Kaganas, Felicity, eds. Surrogate Motherhood: International Perspectives. Portland, OR: Hart; 2003: 75-92. NRCBL: 14.2; 21.1. SC: le.

Motluk, Alison. Tracing dad online [news]. *New Scientist* 2005 November 5-11; 188(2524): 6-7. NRCBL: 14.2; 8.4.

New York (State). Civil Court. Kings County. *Itskov v. New York Fertility Institute* [Date of Decision: 29 July 2004]. *West's New York Supplement*, 2d Series, 2004; 782: 584-589. NRCBL: 14.2; 14.4. SC: le.

Abstract: Court Decision: 782 *New York Supplement*, 2d Series 584; 2004 Jul 29 (date of decision). The Civil Court of the City of New York held that a contract between a genetic mother and a physician concerning a gestational surrogacy is not an unenforceable "surrogate parenting contract" and is therefore not void. Ilona Itskov consulted with the New York Fertility Institute about transferring her embryos to another woman as a gestational surrogate. The defendant physician allegedly agreed to perform the embryo transfer. Once he had removed twelve ova from Itskov and preserved eight embryos created by in vitro fertilization, the physician refused to perform any further procedures, including implanting the embryos into a surrogate. Surrogate parenting contracts, where a woman is artificially inseminated by donor or gives up a child resulting from artificial insemination by donor, are considered contrary to state public policy and are thus void and unenforceable. [KIE/INW]

Ngwafor, Ephraim N. Childlessness in Cameroon: artificially assisted fertility or the customary law solution. *Medicine and Law: World Association for Medical Law* 1994; 13(3-4): 297-306. NRCBL: 14.2; 14.6; 8.5.

Papadimos, Thomas J.; Papadimos, Alexa T. The student and the ovum: the lack of autonomy and informed consent in trading genes for tuition. *Reproductive Biology and Endocrinology [electronic]* 2004 July 12; 2(1): 56; 6 p. Available: http://www.rbej.com/content/2/1/56 [21 March 2005]. NRCBL: 14.2; 14.4; 1.1; 19.5; 9.3.1. SC: an.

Pennsylvania. Court of Common Pleas. Erie County. *J.F. v. D.B.* [Date of Decision: 2 April 2004]. *Pennsylvania District and County Reports*, 4th Series, 2004; 66: 1-33. NRCBL: 14.2; 15.1. SC: le.

Abstract: Court Decision: 66 *Pennsylvania District and County Reports*, 4th Series 1; 2004 Apr 2 (date of decision). The Court of Common Pleas of Erie County held that a gestational surrogacy contract that failed to identify the legal mother of the children and allowed parties to bargain away the children's custody and support rights was void and against public policy. Plaintiff J.F. arranged to have his sperm fertilize a donor egg and to have the resulting fertilized egg implanted in defendant D.B., a gestational surrogate. After D.B. gave birth to slightly premature triplets, J.F. and his paramour showed sporadic interest and involvement in the babies. Alarmed, D.B. took the triplets home and cared for them. J.F. sought sole custody of the triplets. The court granted temporary custody to D.B., but allowed J.F. and his paramour visitation rights. The court declared D.B. the legal mother of the children, even though she was not genetically related to the triplets, because she carried, bore, and took care of the children as a natural parent would. D.B.'s actions were more in line with the behavior of a natural parent than J.F.'s sporadic interest and haphazard visitation. D.B, as the legal mother, thereby has standing to pursue custody, and J.F., as the full biological father, has a legal duty to provide child support. [KIE/INW]

Purdy, Laura. Like a motherless child: fetal eggs and families. *Journal of Clinical Ethics* 2005 Winter; 16(4): 329-334. NRCBL: 14.2; 14.4; 19.5; 14.1.

Ragone, Helena. The gift of life: surrogate motherhood, gamete donation and constructions of altruism. *In:* Cook, Rachel; Sclater, Shelley Day; Kaganas, Felicity, eds. Surrogate Motherhood: International Perspectives. Portland, OR: Hart; 2003: 209-226. NRCBL: 14.2; 1.1.

Rao, Radhika. Surrogacy law in the United States: the outcome of ambivalence. *In:* Cook, Rachel; Sclater, Shelley Day; Kaganas, Felicity, eds. Surrogate Motherhood: International Perspectives. Portland, OR: Hart; 2003: 23-34. NRCBL: 14.2. SC: le.

Robertson, John A. Assisted reproduction in Germany and the United States: an essay in comparative law and bioethics. Bepress Legal Repository, Paper 226 2004: 1-47 [Online] Available: http://law.bepress.com/cgi/viewcontent/cgi?article=1552&content=expresso [31 August 2005]. NRCBL: 14.2; 14.4; 18.5.4; 14.6; 15.2; 19.5; 21.1. SC: le.

Rosner, Fred. Assisted reproduction: a Jewish perspective. *Mount Sinai Journal of Medicine* 2001 May; 68(3): 219-223. NRCBL: 14.2; 2.1; 14.4.

Scheib, J.E.; Riordan, M.; Rubin, S. Adolescents with open-identity sperm donors: reports from 12-17 year olds. *Human Reproduction* 2005 January; 20(1): 239-252. NRCBL: 14.2; 8.4; 15.1. SC: em.

Schenker, Joseph. Legitimising surrogacy in Israel: religious perspectives. *In:* Cook, Rachel; Sclater, Shelley Day; Kaganas, Felicity, eds. Surrogate Motherhood: International Perspectives. Portland, OR: Hart; 2003: 243-260. NRCBL: 14.2; 1.2.

Schreiber, Hans-Ludwig. The legal situation regarding assisted reproduction in Germany. *Reproductive*

BioMedicine Online [electronic] 2003 January-February; 6(1): 8-12. Available: http://www.rbmonline.com/article/729 [1 September 2005]. NRCBL: 14.2; 15.2; 14.4. SC: le.

Schuz, Rhona. Surrogacy in Israel: an analysis of the law in practice. *In:* Cook, Rachel; Sclater, Shelley Day; Kaganas, Felicity, eds. Surrogate Motherhood: International Perspectives. Portland, OR: Hart; 2003: 35-53. NRCBL: 14.2. SC: le.

Schwartz, Lita Linzer. Surrogacy arrangements in the USA: what relationships do they spawn? *In:* Cook, Rachel; Sclater, Shelley Day; Kaganas, Felicity, eds. Surrogate Motherhood: International Perspectives. Portland, OR: Hart; 2003: 161-178. NRCBL: 14.2; 8.1.

Sera, Jean M. Surrogacy and prostitution: a comparative analysis. *American University Journal of Gender and the Law* 1997 Spring; 5(2): 315-342. NRCBL: 14.2; 9.5.5; 4.4. SC: an.

Shanley, Mary Lyndon. Collaboration and commodification in assisted procreation: reflections on an open market and anonymous donation in human sperm and eggs. *Law and Society Review* 2002; 36(2): 257-283. NRCBL: 14.2; 14.6; 4.4. SC: le.

Srinivasan, Sandhya. Surrogacy comes out of the closet. *Sunday Times of India* 1997 July 6; 3 p. [Online]. Available: http://www.hsph.harvard.edu/Organizations/healthnet/SAsia/suchana/0400/h012.html [3 October 2005]. NRCBL: 14.2. SC: cs. Identifiers: India.

Strathern, Marilyn. Still giving nature a helping hand? Surrogacy: a debate about technology and society. *In:* Cook, Rachel; Sclater, Shelley Day; Kaganas, Felicity, eds. Surrogate Motherhood: International Perspectives. Portland, OR: Hart; 2003: 281-296. NRCBL: 14.2; 5.1. SC: le.

Teman, Elly. 'Knowing' the surrogate body in Israel. *In:* Cook, Rachel; Sclater, Shelley Day; Kaganas, Felicity, eds. Surrogate Motherhood: International Perspectives. Portland, OR: Hart; 2003: 261-279. NRCBL: 14.2; 4.4.

Teman, Elly. The medicalization of "nature" in the "artificial body": surrogate motherhood in Israel. *Medical Anthropology Quarterly* 2003 March; 17(1): 78-98. NRCBL: 14.2; 10.

United States. District Court. Eastern District of Virginia. *United States v. Jacobson* [Date of Decision: 9 January 1992]. *Federal Supplement* 1992; 785: 563-569. NRCBL: 14.2; 8.4; 1.3.5. SC: le.
   Abstract: Court Decision: 785 *Federal Supplement*, 563; 1992 Jan 9 (date of decision). The United States District Court for the Eastern District of Virginia granted in part the Government's motion to protect the true identities of parents and children involved in a criminal fraud case against a doctor accused of using his own sperm in the artificial insemination of his patients. Dr. Cecil B. Jacobson represented that the female patients would be inseminated with sperm from an anonymous donor. The Government alleged that the doctor used his own sperm to inseminate the patients. The District Court decided that significant

psychological harm may result to the children if the parents' true identities were disclosed in an open court. In order to safeguard the children's well-being, "information regarding their paternity should be revealed to them in a careful manner and directed by their parents." Rather than close the courtroom, the District Court balanced a First Amendment and common law interest in openness and narrowly tailored measures to protect parent and child privacy. The court permitted the parent witnesses to use pseudonyms, excluded sketch artists from the courtroom, sealed judicial documents containing identifying information regarding the parents or children, and redacted all identifying information from copies of the sealed documents in the public file. [KIE/INW]

van Niekerk, Anton. Commercial surrogacy and the commodification of children: an ethical perspective. *Medicine and Law: World Association for Medical Law* 1995; 14(3-4): 163-170. NRCBL: 14.2; 4.4.

Vanfraussen, Katrien; Ponjaert-Kristoffersen, I.; Brewaeys, A. What does it mean for youngsters to grow up in a lesbian family created by means of donor insemination? *Journal of Reproductive and Infant Psychology* 2002 November; 20(4): 237-252. NRCBL: 14.2; 9.5.7; 10. SC: em. Identifiers: Belgium.

Vonk, Machteld. One, two or three parents? Lesbian co-mothers and a known donor with 'family life' under Dutch law. *International Journal of Law, Policy and the Family* 2004 April; 18(1): 103-117. NRCBL: 14.2; 10; 8.4. SC: le.

Wertheimer, Alan. Exploitation and commercial surrogacy. *Denver University Law Review* 1997; 74(4): 1215-1229. NRCBL: 14.2; 10; 9.3.1. SC: le.

Willmott, Lindy. Surrogacy: ill-conceived rights. *Journal of Law and Medicine* 2002 November; 10(2): 198-220. NRCBL: 14.2; 21.1; 1.3.5. SC: le. Identifiers: Australia.

Wilson, Sarah. Identity, genealogy, and the social family: the case of donor insemination. *International Journal of Law, Policy, and the Family* 1997; 11(2): 270-297. NRCBL: 14.2; 8.4. SC: le.

Woodward, Bryan J.; Norton, W.J.; Neuberg, R.W. Case report: grandmother, mother and another — an intergenerational surrogacy using anonymous donated embryos. *Reproductive BioMedicine Online [electronic]* 2004 September; 9(3): 260-263. Available: http://www.rbmonline.com/index.html [14 July 2005]. NRCBL: 14.2; 14.4. SC: cs; le.

ARTIFICIAL NUTRITION AND HYDRATION
See EUTHANASIA AND ALLOWING TO DIE

ASSISTED REPRODUCTIVE TECHNOLOGIES *See* REPRODUCTIVE TECHNOLOGIES

ASSISTED SUICIDE
See also EUTHANASIA AND ALLOWING TO DIE

NRCBL: National Reference Center for Bioethics Literature Classification Scheme   See inside front cover for terms.

45

Assisted dying elsewhere in Europe [news]. *Bulletin of Medical Ethics* 2003 October; (192): 5-6. NRCBL: 20.7; 20.5.1; 8.1; 7.1; 21.1; 20.5.4. SC: em; le.

Euthanasia and assisted dying [news]. *Bulletin of Medical Ethics* 2003 October; (192): 3-4. NRCBL: 20.7; 20.5.1; 8.1; 21.1. SC: le.

French mother helps son to die [news]. *Bulletin of Medical Ethics* 2003 October; (192): 4-5. NRCBL: 20.7; 20.5.1; 8.1; 1.3.5. SC: le.

The right to die [editorial]. *New York Times* 2005 October 5; p. A26. NRCBL: 20.7; 20.5.1. SC: po.

A troubling but necessary debate [editorial]. *Lancet* 2005 October 15-21; 366(9494): 1332. NRCBL: 20.7; 20.5.1; 8.1; 9.7; 1.3.5. SC: le.

Adams, Maurice; Nys, Herman. Comparative reflections on the Belgian Euthanasia Act 2002. *Medical Law Review* 2003 Autumn; 11(3): 353-376. NRCBL: 20.7; 20.5.1; 20.5.4. SC: le.

Alexander, Marc. The problems with physician-assisted suicide. *Origins* 2005 April 7; 34(42): 676-680. NRCBL: 20.7; 4.4; 1.2; 20.4.1; 20.5.1. SC: le.

Allen, Anne. Right to die, freedom of choice, and assisted death: implications for nurses. *Journal of Post Anesthesia Nursing* 1991 April; 6(2): 150-151. NRCBL: 20.7; 20.5.1; 20.5.4.

Anderson, Ron J. Holistic healers and physician-assisted suicide. *Alternative Therapies in Health and Medicine* 1996 November; 2(6): 77-83. NRCBL: 20.7; 20.5.1; 4.1.1; 8.1.

Azevedo, David. Should you help patients die? *Medical Economics* 1997 January 13; 74(1): 137-140, 143-144, 147-149. NRCBL: 20.7; 20.5.1; 7.1. SC: le.

Becker-Schwarze, Kathrin. Legal restrictions of physician-assisted suicide. *European Journal of Health Law* 2005 March; 12(1): 11-24. NRCBL: 20.7; 20.5.1. SC: le.

Berger, Jeffrey T.; Rosner, Fred; Bennett, Allen J. Current events and bioethical concerns in physician-assisted death. *Mount Sinai Journal of Medicine* 1998 September; 65(4): 257-264. NRCBL: 20.7; 20.5.1; 4.4; 20.4.1.

Biggs, Hazel M. The Assisted Dying for the Terminally Ill Bill 2004: will English law soon allow patients the choice to die? *European Journal of Health Law* 2005 March; 12(1): 43-56. NRCBL: 20.7; 20.5.1. SC: le.

Bilsen, Johan; Bauwens, Marc; Bernheim, Jan; Stichele, Robert Vander; Deliens, Luc. Physician-assisted death: attitudes and practices of community pharmacists in East Flanders, Belgium. *Palliative Medicine* 2005 February; 19(2): 151-157. NRCBL: 20.7; 20.5.1; 8.1; 4.1.1; 9.7. SC: em.

Boyle, Brian. The Oregon Death with Dignity Act: a successful model or a legal anomaly vulnerable to attack? *Houston Law Review* 2004 Spring; 40(5): 1387-1421. NRCBL: 20.7; 20.5.1; 8.1. SC: le.

Bristow, Lonnie. Physician's role as healer: American Medical Association's opposition to physician-assisted suicide. *St. John's Journal of Legal Commentary* 1997 Summer; 12(3): 653-658. NRCBL: 20.7; 20.5.1; 8.1. SC: le.

Byk, Christian. Euthanasia and the right to life—the Pretty case. *In:* Council of Europe Publishing, ed. Euthanasia. Volume I. Ethical and Human Aspects. Strasbourg: Council of Europe; Croton- on-Hudson, NY: Manhattan Publishing Co.; 2003: 109-127. NRCBL: 20.7; 20.5.1. SC: le.

Cahana, Michael Z. "Who shall live . . .": a report from the CCAR Task Force on Assisted Suicide. *CCAR Journal: A Reform Jewish Quarterly* 2005 Winter; 52(1): 42-58. NRCBL: 20.7; 20.5.1; 1.2.

Campbell, Deborah A. Physician-assisted suicide: experience and controversy [editorial]. *Medical Journal of Australia* 2001 April 2; 174(7): 325-326. NRCBL: 20.7; 20.5.1.

Cantor, Norman L. On Kamisar, killing, and the future of physician-assisted death. *Michigan Law Review* 2004 August; 102(8): 1793-1842. NRCBL: 20.7; 20.5.1; 8.1.

Carolan, Bruce. US Supreme Court confronts 'right to die'. *Medico-Legal Journal* 1998; 66(2): 65-69. NRCBL: 20.7; 20.5.1. SC: le.

Clark, Annette E. Autonomy and death. *Tulane Law Review* 1996 November; 71(1): 45-137. NRCBL: 20.7; 20.5.1; 1.1; 1.3.5. SC: le.

Cohen-Almagor, Raphael; Hartman, Monica G. The Oregon Death with Dignity Act: review and proposals for improvement. *Journal of Legislation* 2001; 27(2): 269-298. NRCBL: 20.7; 20.5.1. SC: le.

Connelly, Robert. Assisted suicide is consistent with the ideals of holistic healing. *Alternative Therapies in Health and Medicine* 1996 November; 2(6): 77-82. NRCBL: 20.7; 20.5.1; 4.1.1; 8.1.

Dallner, James E.; Manning, D. Scott. Death with dignity in Montana. *Montana Law Review* 2004 Winter; 65(1): 309-341. NRCBL: 20.7; 20.5.1; 8.1. SC: le.

Daniels, Peter G. An Illinois Physician-Assisted Suicide Act: a merciful end to a terminally ill criminal tradition. *Loyola University of Chicago Law Journal* 1997 Summer; 28(4): 763-837. NRCBL: 20.7; 20.5.1; 8.1; 1.3.5. SC: le.

de Cruz, Peter. The terminally ill adult seeking assisted suicide abroad: the extent of the duty owed by a local authority. *Medical Law Review* 2005 Summer; 13(2):

257-267. NRCBL: 20.7; 20.5.1; 21.1. SC: le. Identifiers: Re Z (an adult: capacity); Local Authority v. Z and another.

Doolan, Eddie; Brown, Joe. Lessons in death. *Nursing Standard* 2004 September 15-21; 19(1): 22-23. NRCBL: 20.7; 20.5.1; 8.1; 4.1.3; 21.1. Identifiers: Switzerland.

Dyck, Arthur J. The moral bases of homicide law: the case against assisted suicide. *In his:* Rethinking Rights and Responsiblities: The Moral Bonds of Community. Revised edition. Washington, DC: Georgetown University Press; 2005: 241-279. NRCBL: 20.7; 20.5.1. SC: an; le.

Dyer, Clare. GP is disciplined for willingness to help friend commit suicide [news]. *BMJ: British Medical Journal* 2005 October 1; 331(7519): 717. NRCBL: 20.7; 7.1; 9.8; 8.1; 20.5.1. SC: le. Identifiers: Michael Irwin; general practitioner.

Dyer, Clare. Lords back bill to legalise assisted suicide [news]. *BMJ: British Medical Journal* 2005 November 19; 331(7526): 1160. NRCBL: 20.7; 20.5.1. SC: le.

Eby, Maureen. Whose life is it anyway — the dying patient's or the nurse's? [editorial]. *Nursing Ethics* 2005 March; 12(2): 121-122. NRCBL: 20.7; 20.5.1; 7.1. SC: le. Identifiers: Assisted Dying for the Terminally Ill Bill; United Kingdom (Great Britain).

Edgerton, Tracy J. Fundamental rights and physician-assisted suicide: protecting personal autonomy. *Journal of Gender, Race and Justice* 1997-1998; 1: 283-294. NRCBL: 20.7; 20.5.1; 8.1. SC: le.

Ersek, Mary. Assisted suicide: unraveling a complex issue. *Nursing* 2005 April; 35(4): 48-52. NRCBL: 20.7; 20.5.1; 4.1.3; 1.1.

Farberman, Rhea K. Terminal illness and hastened death requests: the important role of the mental health professional. *Professional Psychology: Research and Practice* 1997 December; 28(6): 544-547. NRCBL: 20.7; 20.4.1; 17.1; 4.3; 20.5.1.

Ganzini, Linda; Back, Anthony. From the USA: understanding requests for physician-assisted death. *Palliative Medicine* 2003 March; 17(2): 113-114. NRCBL: 20.7; 20.5.1; 8.1.

Garchar, Kimberly. The loyal patient at the end of life: a Roycean argument for assisted suicide. *CQ: Cambridge Quarterly of Healthcare Ethics* 2005 Spring; 14(2): 147-155. NRCBL: 20.7; 20.5.1; 8.1; 1.1; 4.4.

Gevers, Sjef. Terminal sedation: a legal approach. *European Journal of Health Law* 2003 December; 10(4): 359-367. NRCBL: 20.7; 20.5.1; 20.4.1. SC: le.

Goodwin, Peter A.; Schmidt, Terri A.; Zechnich, Andrew D. Death with dignity [letter and reply]. *Academic Emergency Medicine* 1997 September; 4(9): 926-928. NRCBL: 20.7; 20.5.1; 8.1.

Gostin, Lawrence O. The constitutional right to die: ethical considerations. *St. John's Journal of Legal Commentary* 1997 Summer; 12(3): 599-609. NRCBL: 20.7; 20.5.1; 8.1. SC: le.

Green, Kelly. Physician-assisted suicide and euthanasia: safeguarding against the "slippery slope" — The Netherlands versus the United States. *Indiana International and Comparative Law Review* 2003; 13(2): 639-681. NRCBL: 20.7; 20.5.1. SC: le.

Greenhouse, Linda. Justices accept case weighing assisted suicide. *New York Times* 2005 February 23; p. A1, A14. NRCBL: 20.7; 20.5.1. SC: po.

Greenhouse, Linda. Justices explores U.S. authority over states on assisted suicide. *New York Times* 2005 October 6; p. A1, A32. NRCBL: 20.7; 20.5.1. SC: po.

Guillod, Olivier; Schmidt, Aline. Assisted suicide under Swiss law. *European Journal of Health Law* 2005 March; 12(1): 25-38. NRCBL: 20.7; 20.5.1. SC: le.

Halloran, Liz. Of life and death: the Supreme Court opens its new term with arguments in a case whose implications could not be more profound. *U.S. News and World Report* 2005 October 10; 139(13): 31-33. NRCBL: 20.7; 20.5.1; 8.1. SC: le; po. Identifiers: Gonzales v. Oregon.

Hamilton, N. Gregory; Hamilton, Catherine A. Competing paradigms of response to assisted suicide requests in Oregon. *American Journal of Psychiatry* 2005 June; 162(6): 1060-1065. NRCBL: 20.7; 20.5.1; 4.3; 17.1.

Hampton, W.A. Legalising assistance with dying in South Africa [letter]. *South African Medical Journal* 2000 July; 90(7): 656-657. NRCBL: 20.7; 20.5.1; 8.1; 1.1.

Harris, Curtis E.; Orr, Robert D. The end of care [letter and reply]. *First Things* 2004 December; (148): 6-8. NRCBL: 20.7; 8.1; 20.5.1; 4.4; 20.5.4.

Heath, K.V.; Wood, E.; Bally, G.; Cornelisse, P.G.A.; Hogg, Robert S. Experience in treating persons with HIV/AIDS and the legalization of assisted suicide: the views of Canadian physicians. *AIDS Care* 1999 October; 11(5): 501-510. NRCBL: 20.7; 9.5.6; 7.1; 20.5.1. SC: em.

Hilliard, Bryan. Evaluating the dissent in State of Oregon v. Ashcroft: implications for the patient-physician relationship and the democratic process. *Journal of Law, Medicine and Ethics* 2005 Spring; 33(1): 142- 153. NRCBL: 20.7; 20.5.1; 8.1; 9.5.9. SC: le.

Hittinger, Russell. Private uses of lethal force: the case of assisted suicide. *Loyola Law Review* 1997 Summer; 43(2): 151-179. NRCBL: 20.7; 20.5.1; 1.1. SC: le.

Hull, Richard T. The case for physician-assisted suicide. *Free Inquiry* 2003 Spring; 23(2): 35-36. NRCBL: 20.7; 20.5.1; 8.1.

NRCBL: National Reference Center for Bioethics Literature Classification Scheme   See inside front cover for terms.

47

Jeffrey, David I. Time to legalise assisted dying? Response from the Association for Palliative Medicine [letter]. *BMJ: British Medical Journal* 2005 October 8; 331(7520): 841. NRCBL: 20.7; 20.5.1. SC: le.

Kansas. Laws. Prevention of Assisted Suicide Act [effective 1 July 1998]. Kansas Statutes Annotated, Sections 60-4401 through 60-4407; 7 p. [Online]. Available: http://www.kslegislature.org/legsrv-statutes/ getStatute.do [22 September 2005]. NRCBL: 20.7; 20.5.3; 20.5.1. SC: le.

Keizer, Garret. Life everlasting: the religious right and the right to die. *Harper's Magazine* 2005 February; 310(1857): 53-61. NRCBL: 20.7; 20.5.1; 1.2. SC: po.

Kline, Robert L. Give me liberty and give me death: assisted suicide as a fundamental liberty interest. *Boston University Public Interest Law Journal* 1997 Winter; 6(2): 527- 550. NRCBL: 20.7; 20.5.1; 8.1; 1.1. SC: le.

Larson, Edward J. Prescription for death: a second opinion. *DePaul Law Review* 1995 Winter; 44(2): 461-482. NRCBL: 20.7; 20.5.1. SC: le.

Laurie, Graeme. Physician assisted suicide in Europe: some lessons and trends [editorial]. *European Journal of Health Law* 2005 March; 12(1): 5-9. NRCBL: 20.7; 20.5.1; 21.1. SC: le.

Leidig, Michael. Dignitas is investigated for helping healthy woman to die [news]. *BMJ: British Medical Journal* 2005 November 19; 331(7526): 1160. NRCBL: 20.7; 20.5.1; 21.1.

Licht, Eugene. Paging Dr. Death. *Ivy Journal of Ethics; 3(1): 18-*20. NRCBL: 20.7; 8.1; 20.5.1; 4.4; 9.7; 9.3.1.

Lister, Sam; Charter, David. BMA drops its opposition to doctor-assisted suicide. *Times (London)* 2005 July 1; p. 11. NRCBL: 20.7; 20.5.1; 12.4.1; 12.2. SC: le. Identifiers: British Medical Association.

Little, Traci R. Protecting the right to live: international comparison of physician-assisted suicide systems. *Indiana International and Comparative Law Review* 1997; 7(2): 433-465. NRCBL: 20.7; 20.5.1; 8.1; 21.1. SC: le.

Margalith, Ilana; Musgrave, Catherine F.; Goldschmidt, Lydia. Physician-assisted dying: are education and religious beliefs related to nursing students' attitudes? *Journal of Nursing Education* 2003 February; 42(2): 91-96. NRCBL: 20.7; 4.1.3; 7.2; 1.2; 20.3.2; 20.5.1. SC: em.

McKenzie, David. Church, state, and physician-assisted suicide. *Journal of Church and State* 2004 Autumn; 46(4): 787-809. NRCBL: 20.7; 20.5.1; 8.1. SC: le.

Meehan, Michael J. The constitutionality of physician-assisted suicide: the cases and issues before the US Supreme Court. *Cleveland Clinic Journal of Medicine* 1997 January; 64(1): 13-15. NRCBL: 20.7; 20.5.1; 1.3.5. SC: le.

Meisel, Alan. Thwarting assisted suicide threatens palliative care. *Medical Ethics Newsletter [Lahey Clinic]* 2003 Winter; 10(1): 4, 8. NRCBL: 20.7; 20.5.1; 8.1; 20.4.1.

Melchoir, Jill A. The quiet battle for the heart of liberty — a victory for the cautious: Washington v. Glucksberg, 117 S. Ct. 2258 (1997). *University of Cincinnati Law Review* 1998 Summer; 66(4): 1359- 1386. NRCBL: 20.7; 20.5.1; 8.1. SC: le.

Milani, Adam A. Better off dead than disabled?: should courts recognize a "wrongful living" cause of action when doctors fail to honor patients' advance directives? *Washington and Lee Law Review* 1997; 54(1): 149-228. NRCBL: 20.7; 20.5.1; 8.5. SC: le.

Miller, Colin. A death by any other name: the federal government's inconsistent treatment of drugs used in lethal injections and physician-assisted suicide. *Journal of Law and Health* 2002-2003; 17(2): 217-240. NRCBL: 20.7; 20.5.1; 20.6; 9.7. SC: le.

Miller, Lois L.; Harvath, Theresa A.; Ganzini, Linda; Goy, Elizabeth R.; Delorit, Molly A.; Jackson, Ann. Attitudes and experiences of Oregon hospice nurses and social workers regarding assisted suicide. *Palliative Medicine* 2004 December; 18(8): 685-691. NRCBL: 20.7; 20.3.2; 20.5.1. SC: em.

Miller, Pamela J. Care at the end of life: Oregon's Death with Dignity Act. *Continuum* 1998 September-October; 18(5): 7-13. NRCBL: 20.7; 20.5.1; 8.1; 7.1.

Moodley, Keymanthri. Physician-assisted suicide — an oxymoron? [letter]. *South African Medical Journal* 2000 July; 90(7): 657. NRCBL: 20.7; 20.5.1; 8.1.

Morgan, Rebecca C.; Sutherland, D. Dixon. Last rights? Confronting physician-assisted suicide in law and society: legal liturgies on physician-assisted suicide. *Stetson Law Review* 1996 Winter; 26(2): 481-528. NRCBL: 20.7; 20.5.1; 8.1; 1.1. SC: le.

Myers, Richard S. Physician-assisted suicide and euthanasia: a current legal perspective. *In:* Koterski, Joseph W., ed. Life and Learning XI: Proceedings of the Eleventh University Faculty for Life Conference. Washington, DC: University Faculty for Life; 2002: 3-27. NRCBL: 20.7; 20.5.1; 21.1. SC: le.

Netherlands. Laws. Review procedures for the termination of life on request and assisted suicide and amendment of the Criminal Code and the Burial and Cremation Act (Termination of Life on Request and Assisted Suicide (Review Procedures) Act). *European Journal of Health Law* 2001 June; 8(2): 183-191. NRCBL: 20.7; 20.5.1; 20.5.3. SC: le.

Nys, Herman. Physician assisted suicide in Belgian law. *European Journal of Health Law* 2005 March; 12(1): 39-41. NRCBL: 20.7; 20.5.1. SC: le.

O'Connor, Nancy K. Physician-assisted suicide and 'moral neutrality' [letter]. *American Family Physician* 1998 February 1; 57(3): 427-429, 433. NRCBL: 20.7; 8.1; 20.5.1.

O'Dowd, Adrian. Joffe will amend role for doctors in new bill on assisted dying [news]. *BMJ: British Medical Journal* 2005 October 15; 331(7521): 863. NRCBL: 20.7; 20.5.1. SC: le.

Okie, Susan. Physician-assisted suicide — Oregon and beyond [opinion]. *New England Journal of Medicine* 2005 April 21; 352(16): 1627- 1630. NRCBL: 20.7; 20.5.1; 20.4.1. SC: le.

Oregon Department of Human Services. Office of Disease Prevention and Epidemiology. Fifth Annual Report on Oregon's Death with Dignity Act. Portland, Oregon: Oregon Department of Human Services 2003 March 6; 21 p. [Online]. Available: http://www.oregon.gov/DHS/ph/pas/docs/year5.pdf [5 October 2005]. NRCBL: 20.7; 20.5.1; 8.1; 7.1. SC: em.

Oregon Department of Human Services. Office of Disease Prevention and Epidemiology. Seventh Annual Report on Oregon's Death with Dignity Act. Portland, Oregon: Oregon Department of Human Services, 2005 March 10; 25 p. [Online]. Available: http://www.oregon.gov/DHS/ph/pas/docs/year7.pdf [2005 October 5]. NRCBL: 20.7; 20.5.1; 8.1; 7.1. SC: em.

Orentlicher, David; Callahan, Christoper M. Feeding tubes, slippery slopes, and physician-assisted suicide. *Journal of Legal Medicine* 2004 December; 25(4): 389-409. NRCBL: 20.7; 20.5.1; 8.1. SC: le.

Parker, Frederick R., Jr.; Rubin, Harvey W.; Winslade, William J. Life insurance, living benefits, and physician-assisted death. *Behavioral Sciences and the Law* 2004; 22(5): 615-626. NRCBL: 20.7; 20.5.1; 9.3.1. SC: le.

Pearlman, Robert A.; Hsu, Clarissa; Starks, Helene; Back, Anthony L.; Gordon, Judith R.; Bharucha, Ashok J.; Koenig, Barbara A.; Battin, Margaret P. Motivations for physician-assisted suicide: patient and family voices. *Journal of General Internal Medicine* 2005 March; 20(3): 234- 239. NRCBL: 20.7; 20.5.1; 8.1. SC: em.

Piotrowicz, Michael S.; Leahy, William J. Assisted suicide and terminating life support: the state of the law. *Medsurg Nursing* 1996 October; 5(5): 367-369, 379. NRCBL: 20.7; 20.5.1. SC: le.

Praskwiecz, Beth H. Assisted suicide: right or wrong? *Plastic Surgical Nursing* 2000 Spring; 20(1): 37-40. NRCBL: 20.7; 2.1; 20.5.1.

Pratt, David A. Too many physicians: physician-assisted suicide after Glucksberg/Quill. *Albany Law Journal of Science and Technology* 1999; 9(2): 161-234. NRCBL: 20.7; 20.5.1; 8.1; 1.1; 4.4. SC: le.

Rao, Neomi. A backdoor to policy making: the use of philosophers by the Supreme Court. *University of Chicago Law Review* 1998 Fall; 65(4): 1371-1401. NRCBL: 20.7; 20.5.1; 1.3.8; 1.1. SC: le.

Roscoe, Lori A.; Malphurs, Julie E.; Dragovic, L.J.; Cohen, Donna. Antecedents of euthanasia and suicide among older women. *JAMWA: Journal of the American Medical Women's Association* 2003 Winter; 58(1): 44-48. NRCBL: 20.7; 20.5.1; 9.5.5; 9.5.2. SC: em. Identifiers: Jack Kevorkian.

Rothschild, Alan. Oregon: does physician-assisted suicide work? *Journal of Law and Medicine* 2004 November; 12(2): 217-225. NRCBL: 20.7; 20.5.1; 8.1. SC: le.

Rurup, Mette L.; Onwuteaka-Philipsen, Bregje D.; Jansen-van der Weide, Marijke; van der Wal, Gerrit. When being 'tired of living' plays an important role in a request for euthanasia or physician-assisted suicide: patient characteristics and the physician's decision. *Health Policy* 2005 October; 74(2): 157-166. NRCBL: 20.7; 8.1; 20.5.1; 7.1. SC: em. Identifiers: Netherlands.

Salladay, Susan A. Clinician-assisted suicide: merciful release or unlawful death? *Journal of Christian Nursing* 2004 Fall; 21(4): 14-17. NRCBL: 20.7; 20.5.1; 1.2. SC: cs.

Sanbar, S. Sandy; Selkin, Stuart G. Physician-assisted suicide. *In:* American College of Legal Medicine Textbook Committee, Sanbar, S. Sandy; Firestone, Marvin H.; Buckner, Fillmore; Gibofsky, Allan; LeBlang, Theodore R.; Snyder, Jack W.; Wecht, Cyril H.; Zaremski, Miles J. Legal Medicine. 6th ed. St. Louis: Mosby; 2004: 315-320. NRCBL: 20.7; 20.5.1.

Schroeder, Doris. Suicide, self-sacrifice, and the duty to die. *In:* Häyry, Matti; Takala, Tuija; Herissone-Kelly, Peter, eds. Bioethics and Social Reality. New York: Rodopi, 2005: 17-29. NRCBL: 20.7; 20.5.1. SC: an.

Schwartz, John; Estrin, James. In Vermont, a bid to legalize physician-assisted suicide. *New York Times* 2005 March 30; p. A12. NRCBL: 20.7; 20.5.1. SC: po; le.

Schwartz, Michael Alan. Practical reasons for lifting bans on physician-assisted suicide. *St. John's Journal of Legal Commentary* 1997 Summer; 12(3): 626-633. NRCBL: 20.7; 20.5.1; 8.1. SC: le.

Scoccia, Danny. Slippery-slope objections to legalizing physician assisted suicide and voluntary euthanasia. *Public Affairs Quarterly* 2005 April; 19(2): 143-161. NRCBL: 20.7; 20.5.1; 1.1. SC: le.

Sharma, B.R. The end of life decisions — should physicians aid their patients in dying? *Journal of Clinical Foren-*

NRCBL: National Reference Center for Bioethics Literature Classification Scheme   See inside front cover for terms.

49

sic Medicine 2004 June; 11(3): 133-140. NRCBL: 20.7; 20.5.1; 8.1. SC: le.

Sheldon, Tony. Dutch approve euthanasia for a patient with Alzheimer's disease [news]. *BMJ: British Medical Journal* 2005 May 7; 330(7499): 1041. NRCBL: 20.7; 20.5.1; 17.1; 9.5.2. SC: le.

Singer, Peter. Law reform, or DIY suicide [editorial]. *Free Inquiry* 2005 February-March; 25(2): 19-20. NRCBL: 20.7; 20.5.1; 21.1. SC: le. Identifiers: Do-it-yourself suicide.

Smith, Hazel; Smith, Richard. Time to legalise assisted dying? Doctors cannot simultaneously be patient centred and reject assisted suicide [letter]. *BMJ: British Medical Journal* 2005 October 8; 331(7520): 842- 843. NRCBL: 20.7; 20.5.1. SC: le.

Smith, Stephen W. Evidence for the practical slippery slope in the debate on physician-assisted suicide and euthanasia. *Medical Law Review* 2005 Spring; 13(1): 17-44. NRCBL: 20.7; 20.5.1; 1.1. SC: an; le.

Smith, Stephen W. Fallacies of the logical slippery slope in the debate on physician-assisted suicide and euthanasia. *Medical Law Review* 2005 Summer; 13(2): 224-243. NRCBL: 20.7; 20.5.1; 1.1. SC: an; le.

Smith, Wesley J. Why secular humanism is wrong about assisted suicide. *Free Inquiry* 2003 Spring; 23(2): 31-32. NRCBL: 20.7; 20.5.1; 8.1.

Sneiderman, Barney; Deutscher, Raymond. Dr. Nancy Morrison and her dying patient: a case of medical necessity. *Health Law Journal* 2002; 10: 1-30. NRCBL: 20.7; 20.5.1. SC: le.

Somerville, Margaret. The case against euthanasia and physician-assisted suicide. *Free Inquiry* 2003 Spring; 23(2): 33-34. NRCBL: 20.7; 20.5.1; 8.1.

Tallis, Raymond; Saunders, John. The Assisted Dying for the Terminally Ill Bill, 2004. *Clinical Medicine* 2004 November-December; 4(6): 534-540. NRCBL: 20.7; 20.5.1; 8.1; 4.1.2. SC: le. Identifiers: United Kingdom (Great Britain).

Tur, Richard H.S. Legislative technique and human rights: the sad case of assisted suicide. *Criminal Law Review* 2003 January: 3-12. NRCBL: 20.7; 20.5.1. SC: le.

Volker, Deborah L. Assisted dying and end-of-life symptom management. *Cancer Nursing* 2003 October; 26(5): 392-399. NRCBL: 20.7; 20.5.1; 8.1. SC: em.

Werth, James L., Jr. The relationships among clinical depression, suicide, and other actions that may hasten death. *Behavioral Sciences and the Law* 2004; 22(5): 627-649. NRCBL: 20.7; 20.5.1; 17.1. SC: rv.

Williams, Anne M.H. Time to legalise assisted dying? Do we make decisions by our feelings or the truth? [letter].

BMJ: British Medical Journal 2005 October 8; 331(7520): 842. NRCBL: 20.7; 20.5.1. SC: le.

Wolfson, Adam. Killing off the dying? *Public Interest* 1998 Spring; 131: 50-70. NRCBL: 20.7; 20.5.1.

Wright, Stephen. Speak up for life. *Nursing Standard* 2004 September 15-21; 19(1): 22-23. NRCBL: 20.7; 20.5.1; 8.1.

Yardley, William. For role in suicide, a friend to the end is now facing jail. *New York Times* 2005 March 4; p. A1, B7. NRCBL: 20.7; 20.5.1. SC: po.

Young, Hilary Hughes. Assisted suicide and physician liability. *Review of Litigation* 1992; 11(3): 623-656. NRCBL: 20.7; 20.5.1; 8.1. SC: le.

Ziegler, Stephen J. Physician-assisted suicide and criminal prosecution: are physicians at risk? *Journal of Law, Medicine and Ethics* 2005 Summer; 33(2): 349- 358. NRCBL: 20.7; 20.5.1. SC: em; le.

ATTITUDES TO DEATH *See* DEATH AND DYING/ ATTITUDES TO DEATH

BEHAVIOR CONTROL
See also CARE FOR SPECIFIC GROUPS/ MENTALLY DISABLED; ELECTROCONVULSIVE THERAPY; INVOLUNTARY COMMITMENT; MENTAL HEALTH THERAPIES; PSYCHOPHARMACOLOGY; PSYCHOTHERAPY

Bosek, Marcia Sue DeWolf. The use of restraints: ethical considerations. *Medsurg Nursing* 1993 April; 2(2): 154-156. NRCBL: 17.3; 1.1; 8.3.1.

Broome, Annabel. Psychology in medical settings. *In:* Fairbairn, Susan; Fairbairn, Gavin, eds. Psychology, Ethics and Change. New York: Routledge & Kegan Paul; 1987: 173- 190. NRCBL: 17.3; 8.1.

Colaizzi, Janet. Seclusion and restraint: a historical perspective. *Journal of Psychosocial Nursing and Mental Health Services* 2005 February; 43(2): 31-37. NRCBL: 17.3; 17.7; 2.2.

Collins, Pauline. Restraining children for painful procedures. *Paediatric Nursing* 1999 April; 11(3): 14-16. NRCBL: 17.3; 9.5.7; 4.1.3; 8.3.2.

Craig, Debra. Mechanically restraining the ill and elderly: ethical problems and proposals. *Update [Loma Linda University Center for Christian Bioethics]* 1999 December; 15(4): 12 p. NRCBL: 17.3; 9.5.2.

Curie, Charles G. SAMHSA's commitment to eliminating the use of seclusion and restraint. *Psychiatric Services* 2005 September; 56(9): 1139-1140. NRCBL: 17.3. Identifiers: Substance Abuse and Mental Health Services Administration.

SC (Subject Caption):   an=analytical   cs=case studies   em=empirical   le=legal   po=popular   rv=review

Donat, Dennis C. Encouraging alternatives to seclusion, restraint, and reliance on PRN drugs in a public psychiatric hospital. *Psychiatric Services* 2005 September; 56(9): 1105-1108. NRCBL: 17.3. Identifiers: pro re nata, or as needed.

Glover, Robert W. Reducing the use of seclusion and restraint: a NASMHPD priority. *Psychiatric Services* 2005 September; 56(9): 1141-1142. NRCBL: 17.3. Identifiers: National Association of State Mental Health Program Directors.

Hinshaw, Stephen P. Objective assessment of covert antisocial behavior: predictive validity and ethical considerations. *Ethics and Behavior* 2005; 15(3): 259-269. NRCBL: 17.3; 18.5.2; 18.3; 8.3.2; 18.4. SC: em.

Abstract: Although less observable than the overt actions of fighting and assault, covert antisocial behaviors such as stealing and property destruction comprise an important subclass of externalizing behavior patterns, displaying considerable predictive power toward delinquency in adolescence. I discuss a laboratory paradigm for objective observation of such behaviors in children that has shown impressive concurrent and predictive validity among samples of boys with and without attention deficit hyperactivity disorder. Addressed herein are crucial questions regarding the ethics of tempting children to steal objects and small amounts of money and to deface property as well as the types of informed consent and debriefing procedures utilized in research with this paradigm. Weighing ethical considerations alongside the ability to predict delinquent behavior presents provocative issues for those interested in understanding the development of antisocial behavior.

Hubbard, Julie A. Eliciting and measuring children's anger in the context of their peer interactions: ethical considerations and practical guidelines. *Ethics and Behavior* 2005; 15(3): 247-258. NRCBL: 17.3; 18.5.2; 18.2; 18.4. SC: em.

Abstract: Ecologically valid procedures for eliciting and measuring children's anger are needed to enhance researchers' theories of children's emotional competence and to guide intervention efforts aimed at reactive aggression. The purpose of this article is to describe a laboratory-based game-playing procedure that has been used successfully to elicit and measure children's anger across observational, physiological, and self-report channels. Steps taken to ensure that participants are treated ethically and fairly are discussed. The article highlights recently published data that emphasize the importance of provoking and assessing children's anger across multiple channels using laboratory-based procedures. Finally, it presents preliminary data that suggests that the safeguards taken to protect children were successful in making both children and their parents feel well treated and comfortable.

Kean, Brian. The risk society and attention deficit hyperactivity disorder (ADHD): a critical social research analysis concerning the development and social impact of the ADHD diagnosis. *Ethical Human Psychology and Psychiatry* 2005 Summer; 7(2): 131-142. NRCBL: 17.3; 9.5.7.

Kirkevold, Øyvind; Engedal, Knut. Prevalence of patients subjected to constraint in Norwegian nursing homes. *Scandinavian Journal of Caring Sciences* 2004 September; 18(3): 281-286. NRCBL: 17.3; 9.5.2; 17.1. SC: em.

Owens, Glynn. Radical behaviourism and the ethics of clinical psychology. *In:* Fairbairn, Susan; Fairbairn, Gavin, eds. Psychology, Ethics and Change. New York: Routledge & Kegan Paul; 1987: 91-114. NRCBL: 17.3.

Reigle, Juanita. The ethics of physical restraints in critical care. *AACN Clinical Issues* 1996 November; 7(4): 585-591. NRCBL: 17.3; 9.5.1; 8.1; 4.1.3.

Reinders, Hans S. The ethics of behavior modification. *Ethics and Intellectual Disability Newsletter* 2003 Spring; 7(2): 1-3. NRCBL: 17.3.

Sullivan-Marx, Eileen M.; Strumpf, Neville E. Restraint-free care for acutely ill patients in the hospital. *AACN Clinical Issues* 1996 November; 7(4): 572-578. NRCBL: 17.3; 9.5.2; 4.4.

Trower, Peter. On the ethical basis of 'scientific' behaviour therapy. *In:* Fairbairn, Susan; Fairbairn, Gavin, eds. Psychology, Ethics and Change. New York: Routledge & Kegan Paul; 1987: 74-90. NRCBL: 17.3.

Underwood, Marion K. Observing anger and aggression among preadolescent girls and boys: ethical dilemmas and practical solutions. *Ethics and Behavior* 2005; 15(3): 235-245. NRCBL: 17.3; 18.5.2; 18.3; 18.4. SC: em.

Abstract: To understand how children manage anger and engage in various forms of aggression, it is important to observe children responding to peer provocation. Observing children's anger and aggression poses serious ethical and practical challenges, especially with samples of older children and adolescents. This article describes 2 laboratory methods for observing children's responses to peer provocation: 1 involves participants playing a game with a provoking child actor, and the other involves a pair of close friends responding to an actor posing as a difficult play partner. Both methods are described in detail, ethical safeguards are discussed, and evidence is presented to show that children understand their research rights in these types of investigations.

BEHAVIORAL GENETICS

Alper, Joseph; Beckwith, Jonathan. Genetic fatalism and social policy: the implications of behavior genetics research. *Yale Journal of Biology and Medicine* 1993 November-December; 66(6): 511-524. NRCBL: 15.6.

Coletta, Raymond R. Biotechnology and the creation of ethics. *McGeorge Law Review* 2000; 32(1): 89-110. NRCBL: 15.6; 5.1; 5.3; 15.1. SC: le.

de Melo-Martín, Inmaculada. Firing up the nature/nurture controversy: bioethics and genetic determinism. *Journal of Medical Ethics* 2005 September; 31(9): 526-530. NRCBL: 15.6. SC: an.

Abstract: It is argued here that bioethicists might inadvertently be promoting genetic determinism: the idea that genes alone determine human traits and behaviours. Discussions about genetic testing are used to exemplify how they might be doing so. Quite often bioethicists use clinical cases to support particular moral obligations or rights as if these cases were representative of the kind of information we can acquire about human diseases through genetic testing, when they are not. On other occasions,

NRCBL: National Reference Center for Bioethics Literature Classification Scheme   See inside front cover for terms.

51

the clinical cases are presented in simplistic ways that portray genetic testing as yielding information more accurate than it actually is. It is concluded that, because of the problematic implications that the ideology of genetic determinism might have for individuals' wellbeing and for our public policies, bioethicists should be careful to present these issues in ways that do not promote questionable ideas about the causal role of genes in human diseases and behaviours.

Elger, Bernice S. Attitudes of future lawyers and psychologists to the use of genetic testing for criminal behavior. *CQ: Cambridge Quarterly of Healthcare Ethics* 2005 Summer; 14(3): 329-345. NRCBL: 15.6; 15.3; 1.3.5; 7.1; 15.5. SC: em.

Elger, Bernice S.; Harding, Timothy W. Teaching changes attitudes to genetic testing for aggressive behaviour. *Medical Law International* 2004; 6(4): 277-295. NRCBL: 15.6; 15.2. SC: em. Identifiers: Switzerland.

Harris, Victoria. 22q11 deletion syndrome and forensic research: can we go there? *Journal of the American Academy of Psychiatry and the Law* 2005; 33(1): 106-111. NRCBL: 15.6; 18.5.5; 18.5.6; 18.4.

Jensen, Arthur R. The ethical issues. *In his:* Genetics and Education. New York: Harper & Row, Publishers; 1972: 327-332. NRCBL: 15.6; 15.11.

Shields, Alexandra E.; Lerman, Caryn; Sullivan, Patrick F. Translating emerging research on the genetics of smoking into clinical practice: ethical and social considerations. *Nicotine and Tobacco Research* 2004 August; 6(4): 675-688. NRCBL: 15.6; 9.5.9; 18.4.

Washington, Harriet A. Born for evil? Stereotyping the karyotype: a case history in the genetics of aggressiveness. *In:* Roelcke, Volker; Maio, Giovanni, eds. Twentieth Century Ethics of Human Subjects Research: Historical Perspectives on Values, Practices, and Regulations. Stuttgart: Franz Steiner Verlag; 2004: 319-333. NRCBL: 15.6; 15.11; 18.4; 18.5.1; 2.2.

BEHAVIORAL RESEARCH
See also BIOMEDICAL RESEARCH; HUMAN EXPERIMENTATION

'Stutterers' sue over research study [news]. *Bulletin of Medical Ethics* 2003 September; (191): 3-4. NRCBL: 18.4; 18.5.2; 1.3.9.

Abraham, Leena. Ethical and methodological conflicts in sexuality research. *Issues in Medical Ethics* 2001 January-March; 9(1): 9-11. NRCBL: 18.4; 10; 18.3.

Barai-Jaitly, Tejal. Use the data but take consent [case study]. *Indian Journal of Medical Ethics* 2005 October-December; 2(4): 131. NRCBL: 18.4; 17.1; 8.4; 18.3.

Cain, Harry I.; Harkness, Jennifer L.; Smith, Angela L.; Markowski, Edward Mel. Protecting persons in family therapy research: an overview of ethical and regulatory

standards. *Journal of Marital and Family Therapy* 2003 January; 29(1): 47- 57. NRCBL: 18.4; 18.2; 18.3.

Centre for Enquiry into Health and Allied Themes. Ethics in social sciences and health research: a draft code of conduct. *Issues in Medical Ethics* 2000 April-June; 8(2): 53-57. NRCBL: 18.4; 18.2; 6.

Chaitin, Julia. "I wish he hadn't told me that": methodological and ethical issues in social trauma and conflict research. *Qualitative Health Research* 2003 October; 13(8): 1145-1154. NRCBL: 18.4; 21.2.

Deosthali, Padma. Should case documentations be used for research? [case study]. *Indian Journal of Medical Ethics* 2005 October-December; 2(4): 129. NRCBL: 18.4; 8.4; 18.3; 18.5.3; 17.1. SC: cs.

Finney, Phillip D. When consent information refers to risk and deception: implications for social research. *Journal of Social Behavior and Personality* 1987; 2(1): 37-48. NRCBL: 18.4; 18.3.

Ganatra, Bela; Hirve, Siddhi. A community-based study on induced abortions. *Issues in Medical Ethics* 2001 January-March; 9(1): 7-8. NRCBL: 18.4; 18.5.3; 12.5.2.

Hofman, Nila Ginger. Toward critical research ethics: transforming ethical conduct in qualitative health care research. *Health Care for Women International* 2004 August; 25(7): 647-662. NRCBL: 18.4; 1.3.9; 9.5.9; 18.3; 18.5.9.

Koocher, Gerald P. Behavioral research with children: the fenfluramine challenge. *In:* Kodish, Eric, ed. Ethics and Research with Children: A Case-Based Approach. New York: Oxford University Press; 2005: 179- 193. NRCBL: 18.4; 18.5.2.

Kralik, Debbie; Warren, Jim; Price, Kay; Koch, Tina; Pignone, Gino. The ethics of research using electronic mail discussion groups. *Journal of Advanced Nursing* 2005 December; 52(5): 537-545. NRCBL: 18.4; 1.3.12; 8.4; 18.3.

Madhiwalla, Neha. National meeting on ethical guidelines for social science research. *Issues in Medical Ethics* 2000 October-December; 8(4): 131. NRCBL: 18.4; 18.2.

Mize, Selene. Non-disclosing and deceptive research design. *In:* Dawson, John; Peart, Nicola, eds. The Law of Research: A Guide. Dunedin, NZ: University of Otago Press; 2003: 253-267. NRCBL: 18.4; 18.2; 8.4; 8.2; 18.3.

Penney, Darby; McGee, Glenn. Chemical trust: oxytocin oxymoron? [editorial]. *American Journal of Bioethics* 2005 May-June; 5(3): 1-2. NRCBL: 18.4; 18.3; 17.3.

Pittenger, David J. Preserving the ethical propriety of statistical devices. *Journal of Psychology* 2002 March; 136(2): 117-124. NRCBL: 18.4; 18.3. SC: an.

Ravindran, T.K. Sundari; Ramanathan, Mala; Alex, Shiney C. A community-based study on induced abortions: some unanswered questions [letter]. *Issues in Medical Ethics* 2001 April-June; 9(2): 36-37. NRCBL: 18.4; 18.5.3; 12.5.2.

Sriram, Sujata. Data can be used with safeguards [case study]. *Indian Journal of Medical Ethics* 2005 October-December; 2(4): 130. NRCBL: 18.4; 8.4; 17.1. SC: cs.

te Braake, Trees A.M. The Dutch 2002 Embryos Act and the Convention on Human Rights and Biomedicine: some issues. *European Journal of Health Law* 2004 June; 11(2): 139-151. NRCBL: 18.4; 18.2; 14.3.; 14.5; 18.3. SC: le.

Widom, Cathy Spatz; Czaja, Sally J. Reactions to research participation in vulnerable subgroups. *Accountability in Research* 2005 April-June; 12(2): 115-138. NRCBL: 18.4. SC: em.
Abstract: This paper describes the extent to which vulnerable individuals (defined by economic, social, psychological, physical health, and child maltreatment status) react to research participation. As part of an ongoing longitudinal study, participants (N=896) completed a lengthy and intrusive in-person interview and provided a small amount of blood through finger pricks. At the end of the interview, participants were asked eight questions about their reactions to the research experience. Vulnerable individuals in general agreed more strongly about having an emotional reaction, but were not less willing to continue to participate. In addition, psychologically vulnerable individuals more strongly agreed they would continue to participate, were treated with respect and dignity, and found their participation meaningful. Compared to whites, nonwhites reported stronger agreement about the meaningfulness of the research and the belief that their responses would be kept private. Like others, individuals vulnerable by virtue of their prisoner status or homelessness (past or current) agreed more strongly about having an emotional reaction to the interview, but otherwise did not differ in their reactions. These results suggest that researchers and institutional review boards should not be deterred from conducting research on sensitive topics with potentially vulnerable populations.

Wolpe, Paul Root. Ethics and social policy in research on the neuroscience of human sexuality [opinion]. *Nature Neuroscience* 2004 October; 7(10): 1031-1033. NRCBL: 18.4; 10.

BIOETHICISTS *See* ETHICISTS AND ETHICS COMMITTEES

BIOETHICS AND MEDICAL ETHICS
See also CODES OF ETHICS; NURSING ETHICS AND PHILOSOPHY; PROFESSIONAL ETHICS

Bioethics. *In:* Concise Routledge Encyclopedia of Philosophy. New York: Routledge; 2000: 89. NRCBL: 2.1.

Medical ethics. *In:* Concise Routledge Encyclopedia of Philosophy. New York: Routledge; 2000: 551-552. NRCBL: 2.1.

Medical ethics — as prescribed by Caraka, Susruta, and other ancient Indian physicians. *Medical Ethics: Journal of Forum for Medical Ethics Society* 1995 January-March; 3(1): CI-CIV. NRCBL: 2.1; 2.2. Identifiers: India.

Medical ethics — general principles. *Medical Ethics: Journal of Forum for Medical Ethics Society* 1995 April-June; 3(2): CV-CVIII. NRCBL: 2.1; 2.2. Identifiers: India.

Professional values. London: British Medical Association 2005 November; 12 p. [Online]. Available: http://www.bma.org/ap.nsf/AttachmentsByTitle/PDFprofval/$FILE/professional.pdf [6 March 2006]. NRCBL: 2.1; 7.1. SC: em. Identifiers: Report on BMA cohort study of 1995 graduates.

American College of Physicians [ACP]. Ethics and Human Rights Committee; Snyder, Lois; Leffler, Cathy. Ethics manual. Philadelphia, PA: American College of Physicians 2005; 66 p. NRCBL: 2.1; 6; 7.1.

American College of Physicians [ACP]. Ethics and Human Rights Committee; Snyder, Lois; Leffler, Cathy. Ethics manual. *Annals of Internal Medicine* 2005 April 5; 142(7): 560-582. NRCBL: 2.1.
Abstract: Medicine, law, and social values are not static. Reexamining the ethical tenets of medical practice and their application in new circumstances is a necessary exercise. The fifth edition of the College's Ethics Manual covers emerging issues in medical ethics and revisits old ones. It reflects on many of the ethical tensions faced by internists and their patients and attempts to shed light on how existing principles extend to emerging concerns. In addition, by reiterating ethical principles that have provided guidance in resolving past ethical problems, the Manual may help physicians avert future problems. The Manual is not a substitute for the experience and integrity of individual physicians, but it may serve as a reminder of the shared obligations and duties of the medical profession.

Annas, George J. American bioethics and human rights: the end of all our exploring. *Journal of Law, Medicine and Ethics* 2004 Winter; 32(4): 658- 663. NRCBL: 2.1; 21.1.

Asai, Atsushi; Oe, Sachi. A valuable up-to-date compendium of bioethical knowledge. *Developing World Bioethics* 2005 September; 5(3): 216-219. NRCBL: 2.1; 21.1; 6.
Abstract: In this brief article, we examine the document entitled Universal Draft Declaration on Bioethics and Human Rights, published by UNESCO in June 2005. We examine it in terms of its content and its appropriate role in global bioethics movements in the future. We make clear our view on the Declaration: the Declaration, despite a variety of serious problems, remains a valuable bioethical document and can contribute in substantial ways to the happiness of people throughout the world.

Asch, Adrienne. Big tent bioethics: toward an inclusive and reasonable bioethics. *Hastings Center Report* 2005 November-December; 35(6): 11-12. NRCBL: 2.1; 21.1; 4.5.

Bard, Jennifer. Standing together: how bioethics and public health can join forces to provide equitable health care. *American Journal of Bioethics [Online]* 2005 September-October; 5(5): W20-W22. NRCBL: 2.1; 9.1.

NRCBL: National Reference Center for Bioethics Literature Classification Scheme   See inside front cover for terms.

53

Benatar, David. The trouble with universal declarations. *Developing World Bioethics* 2005 September; 5(3): 220-224. NRCBL: 2.1; 21.1; 6.

Abstract: A number of problems plague universal declarations. To the extent that those drafting and adopting the declaration represent a range of different views, consensus can only be obtained if the declaration makes minimalist claims that all can support, or makes claims that are vague enough that they can be interpreted to everybody's satisfaction. To the extent that a universal declaration avoids these problems, and takes an unequivocal and controversial stand, it does so by privileging the view that is hegemonic (at least among those responsible for the declaration). After discussing these problems I ask whether such declarations could nonetheless do any good.

Berlinger, Nancy. The ethics of facilitating sausage-making. *Hastings Center Report* 2005 September-October; 35(5): inside front cover. NRCBL: 2.1; 1.3.5.

Blizzard, Deborah. Patients' rights. *In:* Restivo, Sal, ed. Science, Technology, and Society: An Encyclopedia. New York: Oxford University Press; 2005: 374-379. NRCBL: 2.1; 9.2; 1.3.12; 8.4.

Borry, Pascal; Schotsmans, Paul; Dierickx, Kris. The birth of the empirical turn in bioethics. *Bioethics* 2005 February; 19(1): 49-71. NRCBL: 2.1; 18.4; 5.1; 7.1. SC: em.

Bowman, Kerry. Bioethics and cultural pluralism. *Humane Health Care International* 1997 Summer; 13(2): 31-34. NRCBL: 2.1; 21.7.

Buchstein, Fred. Bioethics. *In:* Ness, Bryan D., ed. Encyclopedia of Genetics. Revised edition. Volume I. Pasadena, Calif.: Salem Press; 2004: 73-77. NRCBL: 2.1.

Caplan, Arthur L. Reports of bioethics' demise are premature [letter]. *Lancet* 2005 February 19-25; 365(9460): 654-655. NRCBL: 2.1; 2.3.

Caplan, Arthur L. "Who lost China?" A foreshadowing of today's ideological disputes in bioethics. *Hastings Center Report* 2005 May-June; 35(3): 12-13. NRCBL: 2.1; 21.1.

Capron, Alexander Morgan; Biller-Andorno, Nikola. Ethics and health at the World Health Organization. *Issues in Medical Ethics* 2003 April-June; 11(2): 47-48. NRCBL: 2.1; 21.1.

Carlisle, John R. Ethics and bioethics. *In:* American College of Legal Medicine Textbook Committee, Sanbar, S. Sandy; Firestone, Marvin H.; Buckner, Fillmore; Gibofsky, Allan; LeBlang, Theodore R.; Snyder, Jack W.; Wecht, Cyril H.; Zaremski, Miles J. Legal Medicine. 6th ed. St. Louis: Mosby; 2004: 221-229. NRCBL: 2.1.

Chambers, Tod. The art of bioethics. *Hastings Center Report* 2005 March-April; 35(2): 3. NRCBL: 2.1; 7.1.

Charo, R. Alta. Realbioethik. *Hastings Center Report* 2005 July-August; 35(4): 13-14. NRCBL: 2.1.

Check, Erika. US progressives fight for a voice in bioethics [news]. *Nature* 2005 October 13; 437(7061): 932-933. NRCBL: 2.1; 1.3.5; 9.6. Identifiers: Center for American Progress.

Chinoy, R.F. Medical ethics: relationships between doctors. *Issues in Medical Ethics* 1997 October-December; 5(4): 105-109. NRCBL: 2.1; 7.3.

Cohn, Felicia G. Growing pains: the debate begins [comment]. *American Journal of Bioethics* 2005 September-October; 5(5): 52-53. NRCBL: 2.1; 1.3.1; 6; 9.6. Comments: comment on Robert Baker, "A draft model aggregated code of ethics for bioethicists," American Journal of Bioethics 2005 September-October; 5(5): 33-41.

Collins, Suzanne Edgett. Rethinking the Patient Self Determination Act: implementation without effectiveness. *Journal of Nursing Law* 1999 November; 6(3): 29-46. NRCBL: 2.1; 9.5.2.

Correa, Francisco Javier León. La bioetica: de la etica clinica a una bioetica social / Bioethics: from clinical ethics to social bioethics. *Vida y Etica* 2003 December; 4(2): 109-115. NRCBL: 2.1; 2.2; 9.6.

Cowley, C. The dangers of medical ethics. *Journal of Medical Ethics* 2005 December; 31(12): 739-742. NRCBL: 2.1; 2.3; 7.2.

Abstract: The dominant conception of medical ethics being taught in British and American medical schools is at best pointless and at worst dangerous, or so it will be argued. Although it is laudable that medical schools have now given medical ethics a secure place in the curriculum, they go wrong in treating it like a scientific body of knowledge. Ethics is a unique subject matter precisely because of its widespread familiarity in all areas of life, and any teaching has to start from this shared ethical understanding and from the familiar ethical concepts of ordinary language. Otherwise there is a real risk that spurious technocratic jargon will be deployed by teacher and student alike in the futile search for intellectual respectability, culminating in a misplaced sense of having "done" the ethics module. There are no better examples of such jargon than "consequentialism", "deontology", and the "Four Principles". At best, they cannot do the work they were designed to do and, at worst, they can lead student and practitioner into ignoring their own healthy ethical intuitions and vocabulary.

Coyne, James C.; Tsai, Alexander C. Industry-funded bioethics articles [letters]. *Lancet* 2005 September 24-30; 366(9491): 1077-1078. NRCBL: 2.1; 9.7; 1.3.2; 1.3.9; 1.3.7.

Crombie, H. David. Technology and bioethics: two interviews and a forum. *Connecticut Medicine* 2004 October; 68(9): 595-597. NRCBL: 2.1. Identifiers: Arthur Caplan; Francis Fukuyama.

DeBaets, Amy Michelle. UNESCO bioethics declaration. *Ethics and Medicine* 2005 Fall; 21(3): 190-191. NRCBL: 2.1; 21.1. Identifiers: United Nations Educational, Scientific and Cultural Organization.

Dekkers, Wim; Gordijn, Bert. The proper role of bioethics [editorial]. *Medicine, Health Care and Philosophy: A European Journal* 2005; 8(3): 271-272. NRCBL: 2.1.

Döring, Ole. Searching for advances in biomedical ethics in China: recent trends. *China Analysis* 2003 October; (27); 14 p. [Online]. Available: http://www.chinapolitik.de/studien/china_analysis/no_27.pdf [31 August 2005]. NRCBL: 2.1; 2.3; 2.4; 1.3.5. Identifiers: Revision of the article "China's struggle for practical regulations in medical ethics," Nature Review Genetics 2003; 4: 233-239.

Elliott, Carl. Should journals publish industry-funded bioethics articles? [opinion]. *Lancet* 2005 July 30-August 5; 366(9483): 422-424. NRCBL: 2.1; 1.3.7; 1.3.2; 9.6; 9.7; 5.3.

Elliott, Carl. The soul of a new machine: bioethicists in the bureaucracy. *CQ: Cambridge Quarterly of Healthcare Ethics* 2005 Fall; 14(4): 379-384. NRCBL: 2.1; 2.2; 9.6; 1.3.2; 1.3.1; 2.4; 1.3.9; 5.1; 18.5.4. SC: an.

Fins, Joseph J. Baseball and bioethics. *CQ: Cambridge Quarterly of Healthcare Ethics* 2005 Fall; 14(4): 434-443. NRCBL: 2.1; 7.3.

Fortun, Mike. For an ethics of promising, or: a few kind words about James Watson. *New Genetics and Society* 2005 August; 24(2): 157-173. NRCBL: 2.1; 15.10; 1.3.9.

Fryer-Edwards, Kelly; Calogero, Carla. The challenge of the other. *American Journal of Bioethics* 2005 November-December; 5(6): 65-66. NRCBL: 2.1. Comments: comment on Lawrence J. Nelson and Michael J. Meyer, "Confronting deep moral disagreement: the President's Council on Bioethics, moral status, and human embryos," American Journal of Bioethics 2005 November-December; 5(6): 33-42.

Fulford, K.W.M. Facts/values: ten principles of values-based medicine. *In:* Radden, Jennifer, ed. The Philosophy of Psychiatry: A Companion. New York: Oxford University Press; 2004: 205-234. NRCBL: 2.1; 17.1; 17.4.

Garrard, Eve; Wilkinson, Stephen. Mind the gap: the use of empirical evidence in bioethics. *In:* Häyry, Matti; Takala, Tuija; Herissone-Kelly, Peter, eds. Bioethics and Social Reality. New York: Rodopi, 2005: 77-91. NRCBL: 2.1. SC: em; an.

Glasa, Jozef. Perspectives of bioethics in the Central and East European context. *Medical Ethics and Bioethics / Medicinska Etika & Bioetika* 2003 Autumn-Winter; 10(3-4): 16. NRCBL: 2.1; 21.1.

Goldenberg, Maya J. Evidence-based ethics? On evidence-based practice and the "empirical turn" from normative bioethics. *BMC Medical Ethics [electronic]* 2005; 6(11); 9 p. Available: http://www.biomedcentral.com/bmcmedethics/ [21 December 2005]. NRCBL: 2.1; 9.8.

Abstract: BACKGROUND: The increase in empirical methods of research in bioethics over the last two decades is typically perceived as a welcomed broadening of the discipline, with increased integration of social and life scientists into the field and ethics consultants into the clinical setting, however it also represents a loss of confidence in the typical normative and analytic methods of bioethics. DISCUSSION: The recent incipiency of "Evidence-Based Ethics" attests to this phenomenon and should be rejected as a solution to the current ambivalence toward the normative resolution of moral problems in a pluralistic society. While "evidence-based" is typically read in medicine and other life and social sciences as the empirically-adequate standard of reasonable practice and a means for increasing certainty, I propose that the evidence-based movement in fact gains consensus by displacing normative discourse with aggregate or statistically-derived empirical evidence as the "bottom line". Therefore, along with wavering on the fact/value distinction, evidence-based ethics threatens bioethics' normative mandate. The appeal of the evidence-based approach is that it offers a means of negotiating the demands of moral pluralism. Rather than appealing to explicit values that are likely not shared by all, "the evidence" is proposed to adjudicate between competing claims. Quantified measures are notably more "neutral" and democratic than liberal markers like "species normal functioning". Yet the positivist notion that claims stand or fall in light of the evidence is untenable; furthermore, the legacy of positivism entails the quieting of empirically non-verifiable (or at least non-falsifiable) considerations like moral claims and judgments. As a result, evidence-based ethics proposes to operate with the implicit normativity that accompanies the production and presentation of all biomedical and scientific facts unchecked. SUMMARY: The "empirical turn" in bioethics signals a need for reconsideration of the methods used for moral evaluation and resolution, however the options should not include obscuring normative content by seemingly neutral technical measure.

Gutman, Virginia. Ethical reasoning and mental health services with deaf clients. *Journal of Deaf Studies and Deaf Education* 2005 Spring; 10(2): 171-183. NRCBL: 2.1; 17.1; 9.5.1. SC: cs.

Halpern, Scott D. Towards evidence based bioethics. *BMJ: British Medical Journal* 2005 October 15; 331(7521): 901-903. NRCBL: 2.1; 9.8; 18.4.

Harling, Christopher C.; Bloche, M. Gregg; Marks, Jonathan H. When doctors go to war [letter and reply]. *New England Journal of Medicine* 2005 April 7; 352(14): 1497-1499. NRCBL: 2.1; 1.3.5; 16.3.

Harrington, Jennifer. Letter to the editor [letter]. *American Journal of Bioethics [Online]* 2005 March-April; 5(2): W2. NRCBL: 2.1. Comments: comment on Ruth Levy Guyer and Jonathan Moreno, "Slouching Toward Policy: Lazy Bioethics and the Perils of Science Fiction," American Journal of Bioethics [Online] 2004 Fall; 4(4): W14-W17.

Harris, John. Putting empirical studies in their place. *In:* Holm, Søren; Jonas, Monique F., eds. Engaging the World: The Use of Empirical Research in Bioethics and the Regulation of Biotechnology. Washington, DC: IOS Press; 2004: 18-27. NRCBL: 2.1. SC: em.

NRCBL: National Reference Center for Bioethics Literature Classification Scheme   See inside front cover for terms.

Häyry, Matti. A defense of shallow listening. *Bioethics* 2005 October; 19(5-6): 565-567. NRCBL: 2.1.

Häyry, Matti; Takala, Tuija. Human dignity, bioethics, and human rights. *Developing World Bioethics* 2005 September; 5(3): 225-233. NRCBL: 2.1; 21.1; 6.
Abstract: The authors analyse and assess the Universal Draft Declaration on Bioethics and Human Rights published by UNESCO. They argue that the Draft has two main weaknesses. It unnecessarily confines the scope of bioethics to life sciences and their practical applications. And it fails to spell out the intended role of human dignity in international ethical regulation.

Holm, Søren. Bioethics down under — medical ethics engages with political philosophy [editorial]. *Journal of Medical Ethics* 2005 January; 31(1): 1. NRCBL: 2.1. Identifiers: Australia; New Zealand.

Holm, Søren. What empirical bioethics can learn from empirical business ethics. *In:* Häyry, Matti; Takala, Tuija; Herissone-Kelly, Peter, eds. Bioethics and Social Reality. New York: Rodopi, 2005: 107-111. NRCBL: 2.1; 1.3.2. SC: em.

Holm, Søren; Irving, Louise. Empirical research in bioethics: report for the European Commission. *In:* Holm, Søren; Jonas, Monique F., eds. Engaging the World: The Use of Empirical Research in Bioethics and the Regulation of Biotechnology. Washington, DC: IOS Press; 2004: 131-155. NRCBL: 2.1. SC: an; em.

Husted, Gladys L.; Husted, James H. The bioethical standards: the analysis of dilemmas through the analysis of persons. *Advanced Practice Nursing Quarterly* 1995 Fall; 1(2): 69-76. NRCBL: 2.1; 8.1. SC: cs.

Irving, Louise; Hallowell, Nina. Can there be moral experts? *In:* Holm, Søren; Jonas, Monique F., eds. Engaging the World: The Use of Empirical Research in Bioethics and the Regulation of Biotechnology. Washington, DC: IOS Press; 2004: 28-37. NRCBL: 2.1; 9.6.

Jameton, Andrew. Sustainable bioethics: extending care to an aging planet. *Bulletin of Science, Technology and Society* 1999 August; 19(4): 314-322. NRCBL: 2.1; 16.1.

Jing-Bao, Nie. Cultural values embodying universal norms: a critique of a popular assumption about cultures and human rights. *Developing World Bioethics* 2005 September; 5(3): 251-257. NRCBL: 2.1; 21.1; 21.7.
Abstract: In Western and non-Western societies, it is a widely held belief that the concept of human rights is, by and large, a Western cultural norm, often at odds with non-Western cultures and, therefore, not applicable in non-Western societies. The Universal Draft Declaration on Bioethics and Human Rights reflects this deep-rooted and popular assumption. By using Chinese culture(s) as an illustration, this article points out the problems of this widespread misconception and stereotypical view of cultures and human rights. It highlights the often ignored positive elements in Chinese cultures that promote and embody universal human values such as human dignity and human rights. It concludes, accordingly, with concrete suggestions on how to modify the Declaration.

Jonsen, Albert R. Cultural bioethics. *In his:* Bioethics Beyond the Headlines: Who Lives? Who Dies? Who Decides? Lanham, MD: Rowman and Littlefield; 2005: 154-159. NRCBL: 2.1; 21.7.

Kelly, Susan E. Bioethics and rural health: theorizing place, space, subjects. *Social Science and Medicine* 2003 June; 56(11): 2277-2288. NRCBL: 2.1.

Klugman, Craig M. As advisors, nondirectional consultation is best [comment]. *American Journal of Bioethics* 2005 September-October; 5(5): 56-57. NRCBL: 2.1; 6; 9.6. Comments: comment on Robert Baker, "A draft model aggregated code of ethics for bioethicists," American Journal of Bioethics 2005 September-October; 5(5): 33-41.

Kolker, Emily S.; Timmermans, Stefan. Medical values and ethics. *In:* Restivo, Sal, ed. Science, Technology, and Society: An Encyclopedia. New York: Oxford University Press; 2005: 318-323. NRCBL: 2.1; 14.4.

Komesaroff, Paul A.; Cohen, Alex. The growth of ethics in medicine over the past 50 years. *Medical Journal of Australia* 2001 January 1; 174(1): 41-44. NRCBL: 2.1; 8.1; 18.1.

Kopelman, Loretta M. The incompatibility of the United Nation's goals and conventionalist ethical relativism. *Developing World Bioethics* 2005 September; 5(3): 234-243. NRCBL: 2.1; 21.1; 6; 21.7. SC: an.
Abstract: The Universal Draft Declaration on Bioethics and Human Rights seeks to provide moral direction to nations and their citizens on a series of bioethical concerns. In articulating principles, it ranks respect for human rights, human dignity and fundamental freedoms ahead of respect for cultural diversity and pluralism. This ranking is controversial because it entails the rejection of the popular theory, conventionalist ethical relativism. If consistently defended, this theory also undercuts other United Nations activities that assume member states and people around the world can reach trans-cultural judgments having moral authority about health, pollution, aggression, rights, slavery, and so on. To illustrate problems with conventionalist ethical relativism and the importance of rejecting it for reasons of health, human rights, human dignity and fundamental freedoms, the widespread practice of female genital circumcision or cutting is discussed. These surgeries are virtually a test case for conventionalist ethical relativism since they are widely supported within these cultures as religious and health practices and widely condemned outside them, including by the United Nations.

Krosnick, Arthur; Costante, Patricia A.; Hirsch, Paul J.; Gutmann, Amy. Biomedical ethics in a democratic society. A conversation with Amy Gutmann, PhD [interview]. *New Jersey Medicine* 2003 October; 100(10): 14-20. NRCBL: 2.1.

Landman, Willem; Schüklenk, Udo. UNESCO 'declares' universals on bioethics and human rights — many unexpected universal truths unearthed by UN body. *Developing World Bioethics* 2005 September; 5(3): iii-vi. NRCBL: 2.1; 21.1; 6. Identifiers: United Nations Educational, Scientific and Cultural Organization.

Lantos, John D. Commentary on "A draft model aggregated code for bioethicists" [comment]. *American Journal of Bioethics* 2005 September-October; 5(5): 45-46. NRCBL: 2.1; 9.6; 6. Comments: comment on Robert Baker, "A draft model aggregated code of ethics for bioethicists," American Journal of Bioethics 2005 September-October; 5(5): 33-41.

Lanzerath, Dirk. Bioethics in Germany: debates and infrastructure. *Annali dell'Istituto Superiore di Sanita* 2004; 40(3): 287-296. NRCBL: 2.1; 2.4. Identifiers: German Reference Centre for Ethics in the Life Sciences [DRZE].

Lebacqz, Karen. We sure are older but are we wiser? *In:* Childress, James F.; Meslin, Eric M.; Shapiro, Harold T., eds. Belmont Revisited: Ethical Principles for Research with Human Subjects. Washington, DC: Georgetown University Press; 2005: 99-110. NRCBL: 2.1; 2.2; 2.4; 10. SC: an.

Loewy, Erich H.; Loewy, Roberta Springer. Use and abuse of bioethics: integrity and professional standing. *Health Care Analysis: An International Journal of Health Care Philosophy and Policy* 2005 March; 13(1): 73-86. NRCBL: 2.1; 1.3.1.
Abstract: This paper sets out to examine the integrity and professional standing of "Bioethics." It argues that professions have certain responsibilities that start with setting criteria for and credentialing those that have met the criteria and goes on to ultimately have social responsibilities to the community. As it now stands we claim that Bioethics—while it certainly has achieved some progress in the way medicine has developed—has failed to become a profession and has to a large extent failed in its social responsibility. We feel that Bioethics has to define itself, set criteria for membership in the profession, police itself and—above all—meet its social responsibility to become a profession meriting that name.

Loff, Bebe; Hofman, Karen; Muthuswamy, Vasantha. The Global Forum for Bioethics in Research: report of a meeting. *Issues in Medical Ethics* 2001 April-June; 9(2): 63-64. NRCBL: 2.1; 21.1. Conference: Second Global Forum on Bioethics in Research; October 2000; Bangkok, Thailand; sponsored by the World Health Organization.

London, Leslie; Baldwin-Ragaven, Laurel; Bloche, M. Gregg; Marks, Jonathan H. When doctors go to war [letter and reply]. *New England Journal of Medicine* 2005 April 7; 352(14): 1497-1499. NRCBL: 2.1; 1.3.5.

López, José. How sociology can save bioethics . . . maybe. *Sociology of Health and Illness* 2004 November; 26(7): 875-896. NRCBL: 2.1; 7.1. SC: an.

Loughlin, Michael. Camouflage is still no defence — another plea for a straight answer to the question 'what is bioethics?'. *Journal of Evaluation in Clinical Practice* 2004 February; 10(1): 75-83. NRCBL: 2.1.

Lovat, Terence J. The implications of bioethics for teachers and teacher researchers. *British Educational Research Journal* 1994; 20(2): 187-196. NRCBL: 2.1; 1.3.3.

Lustig, B. Andrew. Challenging "common-sense" assumptions in bioethics. *Journal of Medicine and Philosophy* 2005 August; 30(4): 325-329. NRCBL: 2.1.

Macklin, Ruth. Yet another guideline? The UNESCO draft declaration. *Developing World Bioethics* 2005 September; 5(3): 244-250. NRCBL: 2.1; 21.1; 6. Identifiers: United Nations Educational, Scientific and Cultural Organization.

McCullough, Laurence B. The critical turn in clinical ethics and its continuous enhancement. *Journal of Medicine and Philosophy* 2005 February; 30(1): 1-8. NRCBL: 2.1.
Abstract: Taking the critical turn is one of the main tools of the humanities and inculcates an intellectual discipline that prevents ossification of thinking about issues and of organizational policies in clinical ethics. The articles in this "Clinical Ethics" number of the Journal take the critical turn with respect to cherished ways of thinking in Western clinical ethics, life extension, the clinical determination of death, physicians' duty to treat even at personal risk, clinical ethics at the interface of research ethics, and the pertinence of the Hippocratic Oath to clinical ethics. These articles challenge clinical ethicists to inculcate the intellectual discipline of the critical turn into everyday practice and continuous quality enhancement of clinical ethics.

McCullough, Laurence B.; Coverdale, John H.; Chervenak, Frank A. Argument-based medical ethics: a formal tool for critically appraising the normative medical ethics literature. *American Journal of Obstetrics and Gynecology* 2004 October; 191(4): 1097-1102. NRCBL: 2.1. SC: an.

McGregor, Joan. Culture clashes in bioethics. *In her:* War and Border Crossings: Ethics When Cultures Clash. Lanham, MD: Rowman & Littlefield; 2005: 225-237. NRCBL: 2.1; 21.7.

Meyer, Charles R. Slippery concepts for a slippery slope [review of Life, Liberty, and the Defense of Dignity: The Challenge for Bioethics, by Leon R. Kass]. *Minnesota Medicine* 2004 June; 87(6): 46. NRCBL: 2.1.

Montello, Martha. Novel perspectives on bioethics. *Chronicle of Higher Education* 2005 May 13; 51(36): B6-B8. NRCBL: 2.1; 1.3.9; 7.1; 5.1.

Moreno, Jonathan D. In the wake of Katrina: has "bioethics" failed? *American Journal of Bioethics [Online]* 2005 September- October; 5(3): W18-W19. NRCBL: 2.1; 2.2; 9.1.

Nagral, Sanjay. Wanted: ethical 'role models'! *Medical Ethics: Journal of Forum for Medical Ethics Society* 1994 November-December; 2(2): 8-9. NRCBL: 2.1.

Nelson, John C.; Bloche, M. Gregg; Marks, Jonathan H. When doctors go to war [letter and reply]. *New England Journal of Medicine* 2005 April 7; 352(14): 1497-1499. NRCBL: 2.1; 1.3.5; 21.2; 21.4.

Newson, Ainsley J.; Ashcroft, Richard E. Whither authenticity? [comment]. *American Journal of Bioethics*

NRCBL: National Reference Center for Bioethics Literature Classification Scheme   See inside front cover for terms.

57

2005 May-June; 5(3): 53-55. NRCBL: 2.1; 4.4. Comments: comment on Ilina Singh, "Will the 'real boy' please behave: dosing dilemmas for parents of boys with ADHD," American Journal of Bioethics 2005 May-June; 5(3): 34-47.

Ogundiran, Temidayo O. Enhancing the African bioethics initiative. *BMC Medical Education [electronic]* 2004 October 15; 4(1); 6 p. [Online]. Available: http://www.biomedcentral.com/1472-6920/4/21 [14 July 2005]. NRCBL: 2.1; 2.3; 2.2.

Pandya, Sunil K. Bioethics in Asia. *Issues in Medical Ethics* 1999 January-March; 7(1): 27-28. NRCBL: 2.1; 21.1. Conference: Fourth International Tsukuba Bioethics Roundtable; 31 October- 2 November 1998; University of Tsukuba, Japan.

Parmar, H.R. Doctor-doctor ethics [letter]. *Issues in Medical Ethics* 1998 January; 6(1): 2. NRCBL: 2.1; 7.3. Comments: comment on R.F. Chinoy, "Medical Ethics: Relationships between Doctors," Issues in Medical Ethics 1997 October-December; 5(4): 105-109.

Pasetti, Carlo. The teaching of bioethics to the health care team: the neurologist's role. *Medicine and Law: World Association for Medical Law* 1995; 14(1-2): 87-91. NRCBL: 2.1; 20.3.4; 7.2.

Pike, Jeff H.; McLean, Deirdre. Ethical concerns in isolating patients with methicillin-resistant staphylococcus aureus on the rehabilitation ward: a case report. *Archives of Physical Medicine and Rehabilitation* 2002 July; 83(7): 1028-1030. NRCBL: 2.1; 9.8; 9.5.1. SC: cs.

Rajput, Vijay; Golden, William E.; Doherty, Robert B. Position paper: ethics manual [letter and reply]. *Annals of Internal Medicine* 2005 October 18; 143(8): 618. NRCBL: 2.1.

Rawlinson, Mary C.; Donchin, Anne. The quest for universality: reflections on the universal draft declaration on bioethics and human rights. *Developing World Bioethics* 2005 September; 5(3): 258-266. NRCBL: 2.1; 21.1; 6.
Abstract: This essay focuses on two underlying presumptions that impinge on the effort of UNESCO to engender universal agreement on a set of bioethical norms: the conception of universality that pervades much of the document, and its disregard of structural inequalities that significantly impact health. Drawing on other UN system documents and recent feminist bioethics scholarship, we argue that the formulation of universal principles should not rely solely on shared ethical values, as the draft document affirms, but also on differences in ethical values that obtain across cultures. UNESCO's earlier work on gender mainstreaming illustrates the necessity of thinking from multiple perspectives in generating universal norms. The declaration asserts the 'fundamental equality of all human beings in dignity and rights'(1) and insists that 'the highest attainable standard of health is one of the fundamental rights of every human being without distinction of race, religion, political belief, economic or social condition'(2) yet it does not explicitly recognize disparities of power and wealth that deny equal dignity and rights to many. Without attention to structural (as opposed to merely accidental) inequities, UNESCO's invocation of rights is so abstract as to be incompatible with its avowed intention.

Regenberg, Alan C.; Mathews, Debra J.H. Resisting the tide of professionalization: valuing diversity in bioethics [comment]. *American Journal of Bioethics* 2005 September-October; 5(5): 44-45. NRCBL: 2.1; 1.3.1; 6. Comments: comment on Robert Baker, "A draft model aggregated code of ethics for bioethicists," American Journal of Bioethics 2005 September-October; 5(5): 33-41.

Ricoeur, Paul. The just and medical ethics. *In:* Thomasma, David C.; Weisstub, David N.; Herve, Christian eds. Personhood and Health Care. Boston: Kluwer Academic Pub.; 2001: 115-120. NRCBL: 2.1; 1.3.8.

Royal College of Physicians of London (United Kingdom). Doctors in society: medical professionalism in a changing world; report of a working party of the Royal College of Physicians of London. London: Royal College of Physicians of London 2005 December; 65 p. [Online]. Available: http://www.rcplondon.ac.uk/pubs/books/docinsoc/docinsoc.pdf [6 March 2006]. NRCBL: 2.1.

Schroeder, Doris. Human rights and their role in global bioethics. *CQ: Cambridge Quarterly of Healthcare Ethics* 2005 Spring; 14(2): 221-223. NRCBL: 2.1; 21.1.

Selgelid, Michael J. Universal norms and conflicting values. *Developing World Bioethics* 2005 September; 5(3): 267-273. NRCBL: 2.1; 21.1; 6.
Abstract: While UNESCO's Universal Draft Declaration on Bioethics and Human Rights highlights appropriate ethical values, its principles are stated in absolute terms and conflict with one another. The Draft Declaration fails to sufficiently address the possibility of conflict between principles, and it provides no real guidance on how to strike a balance between them in cases where conflict occurs. The document's inadequate treatment of conflicting values is revealed by examination of cases where principles aimed at the promotion of autonomy and liberty conflict with those aimed at benefit maximization and harm minimization. I argue that liberty (and autonomy) may be less important in the context of health care than in other contexts, and I conclude by suggesting specific ways in which some of UNESCO's principles should be revised in order to better address the reality of conflicting values.

Smith, Katharine V. Ethical issues related to health care: the older adult's perspective. *Journal of Gerontological Nursing* 2005 February; 31(2): 32-39. NRCBL: 2.1; 9.5.2. SC: em.

Solomon, Mildred Z. Realizing bioethics' goals in practice: ten ways "is" can help "ought". *Hastings Center Report* 2005 July-August; 35(4): 40-47. NRCBL: 2.1. SC: an; em.
Abstract: A familiar criticism of bioethics charges it with being more conceptual than practical—having little application to the "real world." In order to answer its critics and keep its feet on the ground, bioethics must utilize the social sciences more effectively. Empirical research can provide the bridge between conceiving a moral vision of a better world, and actually enacting it.

Sponholz, Gerlinde; Baitsch, Helmut. Der Bochumer Arbeitsbogen zur medizinethischen Praxis und die Kluft zwischen Wissen und Handeln. *In:* Baumann, Eva; Brink, Alexander; May, Arnd T.; Schröder, Peter; Schutzeichel, Corinna Iris, eds. Weltanschauliche Offenheit in der Bioethik. Berlin: Duncker & Humblot; 2004: 291-303. NRCBL: 2.1.

Squier, Susan. Coda: the pluripotent discourse of stem cells: liminality, reflexivity, and literature. *In her:* Liminal Lives: Imaging the Human at the Frontiers of Biomedicine. Durham: Duke University Press; 2004: 253-280. NRCBL: 2.1; 7.1.

Sutton, Victoria. A multidisciplinary approach to an ethic of biodefense and bioterrorism. *Journal of Law, Medicine and Ethics* 2005 Summer; 33(2): 310- 322. NRCBL: 2.1; 21.3; 9.1; 18.2; 18.5.8. SC: an.

Tandon, P.N. Bioethics: an emerging discipline [editorial]. *Indian Journal of Medical Research* 2005 January; 121(1): 1-4. NRCBL: 2.1; 2.2.

Torjuul, Kirsti; Nordam, Ann; Sørlie, Venke. Action ethical dilemmas in surgery: an interview study of practicing surgeons. *BMC Medical Ethics [electronic]* 2005; 6(7); 9 p. Available: http://www.biomedcentral.com/bmcmedethics/. NRCBL: 2.1; 7.1; 20.5.1; 8.1. SC: em.
Abstract: BACKGROUND: The aim of this study was to describe the kinds of ethical dilemmas surgeons face during practice. METHODS: Five male and five female surgeons at a University hospital in Norway were interviewed as part of a comprehensive investigation into the narratives of physicians and nurses about ethically difficult situations in surgical units. The transcribed interview texts were subjected to a phenomenological-hermeneutic interpretation. RESULTS: No gender differences were found in the kinds of ethical dilemmas identified among male and female surgeons. The main finding was that surgeons experienced ethical dilemmas in deciding the right treatment in different situations. The dilemmas included starting or withholding treatment, continuing or withdrawing treatment, overtreatment, respecting the patients and meeting patients' expectations. The main focus in the narratives was on ethical dilemmas concerning the patients' well-being, treatment and care. The surgeons narrated about whether they should act according to their own convictions or according to the opinions of principal colleagues or colleagues from other departments. Handling incompetent colleagues was also seen as an ethical dilemma. Prioritization of limited resources and following social laws and regulations represented ethical dilemmas when they contradicted what the surgeons considered was in the patients' best interests. CONCLUSION: The surgeons seemed confident in their professional role although the many ethical dilemmas they experienced in trying to meet the expectations of patients, colleagues and society also made them professionally and personally vulnerable.

Turner, Leigh. Bioethics, social class, and the sociological imagination. *CQ: Cambridge Quarterly of Healthcare Ethics* 2005 Fall; 14(4): 374-378. NRCBL: 2.1; 2.2; 7.1; 9.1; 9.2.

Turner, Leigh. From the local to the global: bioethics and the concept of culture. *Journal of Medicine and Philosophy* 2005 June; 30(3): 305-320. NRCBL: 2.1; 21.7. SC: an.
Abstract: Cultural models of health, illness, and moral reasoning are receiving increasing attention in bioethics scholarship. Drawing upon research tools from medical and cultural anthropology, numerous researchers explore cultural variations in attitudes toward truth telling, informed consent, pain relief, and planning for end-of-life care. However, culture should not simply be equated with ethnicity. Rather, the concept of culture can serve as an heuristic device at various levels of analysis. In addition to considering how participation in particular ethnic groups and religious traditions can shape moral reasoning, bioethicists need to consider processes of socialization into professional cultures, organizational cultures, national civic culture, and transnational culture. From the local world of the community clinic or oncology unit to the transnational workings of human rights agencies, attentiveness to the concept of culture can illuminate how patients, family members, and health care providers interpret illness, healing, and moral obligations.

United Kingdom. Royal College of Physicians of London[RCP]. Working Party. Ethics in practice: background and recommendations for enhanced support. London: Royal College of Physicians 2005 June; 8 p. [Online]. Available: http://www.rcplondon.ac.uk/pubs/books/ethics/ethicsinpractice.pdf [6 March 2006]. NRCBL: 2.1; 7.1.

United Nations Educational, Scientific and Cultural Organization [UNESCO]. Reflections on the UNESCO draft declaration on bioethics and human rights: universal draft declaration on bioethics and human rights. *Developing World Bioethics* 2005 September; 5(3): 197-209. NRCBL: 2.1; 21.1; 6.

United Nations Educational, Scientific and Cultural Organization [UNESCO]. Division of Ethics of Science and Technology. Explanatory memorandum on the elaboration of the preliminary draft declaration on universal norms on bioethics. Paris, France: UNESCO 2005 February 21; 18 p. [Online] Available: http://portal.unesco.org/shs/en/file_download.php/d3b7e79dd46a023o46ff9392ofb6oc35EXplanMemorandum_en.pdf [6 April 2005]. NRCBL: 2.1; 21.1; 2.4.

United Nations Educational, Scientific and Cultural Organization [UNESCO]. Division of Ethics of Science and Technology. International Bioethics Committee. Preliminary Draft Declaration on Universal Norms on Bioethics. Paris, France: UNESCO 2005 February 9; 9 p. [Online]. Available: http://portal.unesco.org/shs/en/file_download.php/10d16a8d802Caebf882673e444395ofdPreliminary_Draft_EN.pdf [6 April 2005]. NRCBL: 2.1; 2.4; 21.1.

University of Toronto Joint Centre for Bioethics. Clinical Ethics Group; Breslin, Jonathan M.; MacRae, Susan K.; Bell, Jennifer; Singer, Peter A. Top 10 health care ethics challenges facing the public: views of Toronto bioethicists. *BMC Medical Ethics [electronic]* 2005 June 26; 6(5); 10 p. Available: http://www.biomedcentral.com/

NRCBL: National Reference Center for Bioethics Literature Classification Scheme   See inside front cover for terms.

59

content/pdf/1472-6939-6-5.pdf [1 February 2006].
NRCBL: 2.1; 9.6; 9.4; 8.1. SC: em.

Abstract: BACKGROUND: There are numerous ethical challenges that can impact patients and families in the health care
setting. This paper reports on the results of a study conducted
with a panel of clinical bioethicists in Toronto, Ontario, Canada, the purpose of which was to identify the top ethical challenges facing patients and their families in health care. A
modified Delphi study was conducted with twelve clinical
bioethicist members of the Clinical Ethics Group of the University of Toronto Joint Centre for Bioethics. The panel was asked
the question, what do you think are the top ten ethical challenges that Canadians may face in health care? The panel was
asked to rank the top ten ethical challenges throughout the
Delphi process and consensus was reached after three rounds.
DISCUSSION: The top challenge ranked by the group was disagreement between patients/families and health care professionals about treatment decisions. The second highest ranked
challenge was waiting lists. The third ranked challenge was access to needed resources for the aged, chronically ill, and mentally ill. SUMMARY: Although many of the challenges listed
by the panel have received significant public attention, there
has been very little attention paid to the top ranked challenge.
We propose several steps that can be taken to help address this
key challenge.

Üstün, Cagatay. Medical ethics at Ege University Faculty
of Medicine [letter]. *Nursing Ethics* 2005 March; 12(2):
198-199. NRCBL: 2.1; 2.3; 7.2. Identifiers: Turkey.

Williams, John R. International medical ethics [opinion].
World Hospitals and Health Services 2005; 41(1): 47-48.
NRCBL: 2.1; 2.3; 21.1.

Williams, John R. UNESCO's proposed declaration on
bioethics and human rights — a bland compromise. *Developing World Bioethics* 2005 September; 5(3): 210-215.
NRCBL: 2.1; 21.1; 6. Identifiers: United Nations Educational, Scientific and Cultural Organization.

Abstract: The latest (June 2005) draft of UNESCO's proposed
Universal Declaration on Bioethics and Human Rights is a major disappointment. The committee of government 'experts'
that produced it made sure that it would not introduce any new
obligations for States, and so the document simply restates existing agreements and lists desirable goals without specifying
how they can be achieved. This article focuses on the shortcomings of the document as it would apply to health care. These
shortcomings are evident in the document's scope, aims and
principles. The conclusion is that if UNESCO still thinks that
such a declaration is needed, it should produce either an ethical
document addressed to individuals and groups, which would be
primarily educational in nature, or a legal document addressed
to States, which should not have the word 'ethics' in its title.

Wolpe, Paul Root; Robinson, Walter M. Bioethics in
space (dialogue). *Medical Ethics Newsletter [Lahey
Clinic]* 2005 Winter; 12(1): 10-11. NRCBL: 2.1.

Wright, Linda; Ross, Kelley; Daar, Abdallah S. The
roles of a bioethicist on an organ transplantation service.
American Journal of Transplantation 2005 April; 5(4 Part
1): 821-826. NRCBL: 2.1; 19.1.

Yesley, Michael. What's in a name? Bioethics — and human rights — at UNESCO. *Hastings Center Report* 2005
March-April; 35(2): 8. NRCBL: 2.1; 21.1; 2.4. Identifiers:

United Nations Educational, Scientific and Cultural Organization.

Zwanziger, Lee L. Biology, ethics, and public policy: deliberations at an unstable intersection [opinion]. *Anatomical Record. Part B, New Anatomist* 2003 December;
275(1): 185-189. NRCBL: 2.1; 3.1; 5.3; 18.5.4.

BIOETHICS AND MEDICAL ETHICS/ COMMISSIONS

Beauchamp, Tom L. Reflections on the appointment of
Edmund Pellegrino to the President's Council on
Bioethics. *American Journal of Bioethics [Online]* 2005
September- October; 5(5): W23-W24. NRCBL: 2.4.

Blackburn, Elizabeth. Thoughts of a former council
member. *Perspectives in Biology and Medicine* 2005
Spring; 48(2): 172-180. NRCBL: 2.4; 14.5.

Blackburn, Elizabeth; Rowley, Janet. Reason as our
guide. *PLoS Biology* 2004 April; 2(4): 0420-0422 [elec-
tronic] Available: http://biology.plosjournals.org [2005
July 5]. NRCBL: 2.4; 1.3.9.

Caplan, Arthur L. Free the National Bioethics Commission. *Issues in Science and Technology* 2003 Summer;
19(4): 85-87. NRCBL: 2.4.

Cohen, Cynthia B. Promises and perils of public deliberation: contrasting two national bioethics commissions on
embryonic stem cell research. *Kennedy Institute of Ethics
Journal* 2005 September; 15(3): 269-288. NRCBL: 2.4;
2.2; 1.1; 5.1; 18.5.4; 7.1; 5.3.

Abstract: National bioethics commissions have struggled to develop ethically warranted methods for conducting their deliberations. The National Bioethics Advisory Commission in its
report on stem cell research adopted an approach to public deliberation indebted to Rawls in that it sought common ground
consistent with shared values and beliefs at the foundation of a
well-ordered democracy. In contrast, although the research
cloning and stem cell reports of the President's Council on
Bioethics reveal that it broached two different methods of public deliberation—balancing goods and following an overarching moral principle—it adopted neither. Thereupon its primer
mover, Leon Kass, influenced particularly by the approach of
Leo Strauss, sought to develop a method of public deliberation
guided by tradition and practical wisdom. When this failed, the
Council fell back on a method that took account of shared fundamental values of a free democracy—a method remarkable
akin to that employed by the National Bioethics Advisory Commission. Respect for diverse reasonable conceptions of the
good in a democratic polity requires national bioethics
commissions to seek and incorporate that which is valuable in
opposing positions.

Derse, Arthur R. The seven-year itch. *American Journal
of Bioethics* 2005 September-October; 5(5): 1- 5. NRCBL:
2.4; 2.3. Identifiers: American Society for Bioethics and
Humanities (ASBH).

France. National Consultative Ethics Committee. Congenital handicaps and prejudice: recommendation no. 68
of the National Consultative Ethics Committee May 29,

2001. *European Journal of Health Law* 2002 June; 9(2): 150-163. NRCBL: 2.4; 4.4; 8.5; 12.4.2. SC: le.

Glasa, Jozef. Activities of the Central Ethics Committee of the Ministry of Health of the Slovak Republic June 2002-May 2005. *Medical Ethics and Bioethics / Medicinska Etika & Bioetika* 2005 Spring-Summer; 12(1): 8-9. NRCBL: 2.4.

Glasa, Jozef. Relationships between the central ("national") ethics committees and local ethics committees in the Slovak Republic. *Medical Ethics and Bioethics / Medicinska Etika & Bioetika* 2004 Autumn-Winter; 11(3-4): 9-10. NRCBL: 2.4; 9.6.

Holden, Constance. Pellegrino to succeed Kass on U.S. panel [news]. *Science* 2005 September 16; 309(5742): 1800. NRCBL: 2.4. Identifiers: President's Council on Bioethics; Edmund D. Pellegrino; Leon R. Kass.

International Association of Catholic Bioethicists. Consensus statement on dignity in illness, disability, and dying; and a response to the UNESCO Universal Draft Declaration on Bioethics and Human Rights. *National Catholic Bioethics Quarterly* 2005 Winter; 5(4): 767- 781. NRCBL: 2.4; 2.1; 1.2; 21.1; 20.5.1; 4.4. Identifiers: United Nations Educational, Scientific and Cultural Organization.

Jafarey, Aamir M. The bioethics group of the Aga Khan University, Karachi. *Issues in Medical Ethics* 2002 January-March; 10(1): 163-164. NRCBL: 2.4.

Kass, Leon R. Reflections on public bioethics: a view from the trenches. *Kennedy Institute of Ethics Journal* 2005 September; 15(3): 221-250. NRCBL: 2.4; 5.1; 5.3; 14.1; 7.1; 14.5; 18.5.4; 4.5; 4.4.
Abstract: For many reasons, and more than its predecessors, the President's Council on Bioethics has been the subject of much public attention and heated controversy. But little of that attention and controversy has been informed by knowledge of the Council's mission, its ways of working, and, most importantly, its actual work. This essay describes the Council's mission, discusses its public ways of working, and reviews the five major works produced during the Council's first term. In all its activities, the Council has sought to develop a richer bioethics, one that recognizes and tries to do justice to the deep issues of our humanity raised by the age of biotechnology. Believing that these issues are properly matters to be discussed and governed by the polity as a whole, the Council also has sought to contribute to a genuinely public or political bioethics, beyond the rule of "experts," scientific and bioethical.

Kelly, Susan E. Public bioethics and publics: consensus, boundaries, and participation in biomedical science policy. *Science, Technology, and Human Values* 2003 Summer; 28(3): 339- 364. NRCBL: 2.4; 5.1; 18.5.4.

Kettner, Matthias. Überlegungen zu einer integrierten Theorie von Ethik- Kommissionen und Ethik-Komitees. *In:* Jahrbuch für Wissenschaft und Ethik. Bd. 7. Berlin: Walter de Gruyter; 2002: 53-71. NRCBL: 2.4; 9.6; 18.2.

Mahowald, Mary B. The President's Council on Bioethics, 2002-2004: an overview. *Perspectives in Biology and Medicine* 2005 Spring; 48(2): 159-171. NRCBL: 2.4; 14.5; 14.1; 18.5.4; 15.1.

Majumder, Mary Anderlik. Respecting difference and moving beyond regulation: tasks for U.S. bioethics commissions in the twenty-first century. *Kennedy Institute of Ethics Journal* 2005 September; 15(3): 289-303. NRCBL: 2.4; 2.2; 1.1; 7.1; 5.1; 5.3; 2.1.
Abstract: This article focuses on two possible missions for a national bioethics commission. The first is handling differences of worldview, political orientation, and discipline. Recent work in political philosophy emphasizes regard for the dignity of difference manifested in "conversation" that seeks understanding rather than agreement. The President's Council on Bioethics gets a mixed review in this area. The second is experimenting with prophetic bioethics. "Prophetic bioethics" is a term coined by Daniel Callahan to describe an alternative to compromise-seeking "regulatory bioethics." It involves a critique of modern medicine. In the contemporary context, the areas of biotechnology and access to health care cry out for prophetic attention. The Council has addressed biotechnology; unfortunately, that experience suggests that the kind of prophecy that it practices poses risks to conversation. With regard to access issues, the article proposes an effort that unites themes of human dignity, solidarity, and limits in support of reform, while highlighting, rather than papering over, differences.

Maloney, Dennis M. Creation of new national committee on bioethics. *Human Research Report* 2002 January; 17(1): 4. NRCBL: 2.4; 18.2.

Matsuura, Koïchiro. Address on the occasion of the opening of the International Congress of Bioethics 2005. Geneva, Switzerland: UNESCO 2005 March 26; 5 p. [Online]. Available: http://unesdoc.unesco.org/images/0013/001390/139o41e.pdf [6 April 2005]. NRCBL: 2.4; 21.1. Identifiers: United Nations Educational, Scientific and Cultural Organization. Conference: International Congress of Bioethics 2005;Tehran, Iran; 26-28 March 2005; UNESCO, Ministry of Science, Research and Technology of Iran and the National Research Center of Genetic Engineering and Biotechnology [NRCGEB].

May, William F. The President's Council on Bioethics: my take on some of its deliberations. *Perspectives in Biology and Medicine* 2005 Spring; 48(2): 229-240. NRCBL: 2.4; 14.5; 5.3; 18.5.7; 4.4; 18.5.1; 15.1.

McDermott, Margaret. Attempting to "correct some of the misimpressions": a review of the President's Council on Bioethics website. *Journal of Law, Medicine and Ethics* 2005 Fall; 33(3): 608-610. NRCBL: 2.4; 1.3.12.

Mpendawatu, Jean-Marie Musivi. Bioethics in UNESCO. *Dolentium Hominum* 2004; 19(2): 48-50. NRCBL: 2.4; 21.1; 15.1. Identifiers: United Nations Educational, Scientific and Cultural Organization.

Nelson, James Lindemann. The baroness's committee and the president's council: ambition and alienation in public bioethics. *Kennedy Institute of Ethics Journal* 2005

NRCBL: National Reference Center for Bioethics Literature Classification Scheme   See inside front cover for terms.

61

September; 15(3): 251-267. NRCBL: 2.4; 2.2; 2.1; 1.1; 5.1; 5.3; 7.1; 14.1; 14.5; 4.4.

Abstract: The President's Council on Bioethics has tried to make a distinctive contribution to the methodology of such public bodies in developing what it has styled a "richer bioethics." The Council's procedure contrasts with more modest methods of public bioethical deliberation employed by the United Kingdom's Warnock Committee. The practices of both bodies are held up against the backdrop of concerns about moral and political alienation, prompted by the limitations of moral reasoning and by moral dissent from state policy under even the most democratic of governments. Although the President's Council's rhetoric is often scrupulously conciliatory, recurring features of its argumentative practice are regrettably divisive. They order these things better in Britain.

Saunders, William L. Washington insider. The Terri Schiavo case. *National Catholic Bioethics Quarterly* 2005 Summer; 5(2): 229- 239. NRCBL: 2.4; 20.5.3; 18.5.4; 14.5; 20.7.

Schüklenk, Udo; Lott, Jason P. Bioethics and (public) policy advice. *In:* Thiele, F.; Ashcroft, R.E., eds. Bioethics in a Small World. Berlin: Springer; 2005: 129-138. NRCBL: 2.4; 2.1; 9.6.

Slovak Republic. Ministry of Health. Central Ethics Committee. Statut: centralnej etickej komisie ministerstva zdravotnictva Slovenskej Republiky / Statute: Central Ethics Committee Ministry of Health of the Slovak Republic. *Medical Ethics and Bioethics / Medicinska Etika & Bioetika* 2004 Spring-Summer; 11(1-2): 7-13. NRCBL: 2.4. Note: Full text in English and Slovakian.

Takala, Tuija. Who should decide and why? The futility of philosophy, sociology and law in institutionalised bioethics, and the unwarrantability of ethics committees. *In:* Holm, Søren; Jonas, Monique F., eds. Engaging the World: The Use of Empirical Research in Bioethics and the Regulation of Biotechnology. Washington, DC: IOS Press; 2004: 69-75. NRCBL: 2.4; 2.1; 9.6.

Thomas, David L. Bioethics and corrections: an experiment in bioethics in the Florida Department of Corrections. *Corrections Today* 2003 October; 4 p. [Online]. Available: http://www.aca.org/publications/ctarchivespdf/october03/thomas.pd f [25 May 2005]. NRCBL: 2.4; 9.2; 1.3.5; 9.5.1.

Wade, Nicholas. Bioethics panel suggests stem cell alternatives. *New York Times* 2005 May 13; p. A21. NRCBL: 2.4; 18.5.4. SC: po.

White, Angela; MacDonald, Chris. Deep disagreement and Rawlsian "public reasons". *American Journal of Bioethics* 2005 November-December; 5(6): 62-63. NRCBL: 2.4; 1.1; 4.4. Identifiers: President's Council on Bioethics. Comments: comment on Lawrence J. Nelson and Michael J. Meyer, "Confronting deep moral disagreement: the President's Council on Bioethics, moral status, and human embryos," American Journal of Bioethics 2005 November-December; 5(6): 33-42.

Williams, John R. The ethics activities of the World Medical Association. *Science and Engineering Ethics* 2005 January; 11(1): 7-12. NRCBL: 2.4; 21.1. Conference: 5th International Conference on Bioethics: The Ethics of Intellectual Property Rights and Patents; Warsaw, Poland; 23-24 April 2004; Minister of Science and the Minister of Health, Poland.

Zaner, Richard M. Reflections on the appointment of Edmund Pellegrino to the President's Council on Bioethics. *American Journal of Bioethics [Online]* 2005 September- October; 5(5): W25-W26. NRCBL: 2.4.

Zaner, Richard M.; Beauchamp, Tom L. Reflections on the appointment of Dr. Edmund Pellegrino to the President's Council on Bioethics. *American Journal of Bioethics [Online]* 2005 November- December; 5(6): W8-W9. NRCBL: 2.4.

Zonana, Howard. AAPL's new ethics guidelines. *AAPL (American Academy of Psychiatry and the Law) Newsletter* 2005 September; 30(3): 5, 9. NRCBL: 2.4.

BIOETHICS AND MEDICAL ETHICS/ EDUCATION
See also MEDICAL EDUCATION

Aveyard, Helen; Edwards, Sarah; West, Sharon. Core topics of health care ethics. The identification of core topics for interprofessional education. *Journal of Interprofessional Care* 2005 January; 19(1): 63-69. NRCBL: 2.3; 7.2. SC: em. Identifiers: United Kingdom (Great Britain).

Booth, Joan M.; Garrett, Jinnie M. Instructors' practices in and attitudes toward teaching ethics in the genetics classroom. *Genetics* 2004 November; 168(3): 1111-1117. NRCBL: 2.3; 15.1.

Caldicott, Catherine V.; Faber-Langendoen, Kathy. Deception, discrimination, and fear of reprisal: lessons in ethics from third-year medical students. *Academic Medicine* 2005 September; 80(9): 866-873. NRCBL: 2.3; 8.2; 9.5.4; 7.2. SC: em.

Davis, Dena S. Tell me a story: using short fiction in teaching law and bioethics. *Journal of Legal Education* 1997 June; 47(2): 240-245. NRCBL: 2.3. SC: le.

DeLisa, Joel A.; Jain, Sudesh Sheela; Kirshblum, Steven. Medical ethics teaching in psychiatry residency training programs: a commentary. *American Journal of Physical Medicine and Rehabilitation* 1998 July-August; 77(4): 4 p. [Online]. Available: http://gateway.ut.ovid.com/gw1/ovidweb.cgi [29 September 2005]. NRCBL: 2.3; 7.2.

Eckles, Rachael E.; Meslin, Eric M.; Gaffney, Margaret; Helft, Paul R. Medical ethics education: where are we? Where should we be going? A review. *Academic Med-*

icine 2005 December; 80(12): 1143-1152. NRCBL: 2.3; 7.2. SC: rv.

Hagger, L.E.; Woods, S. Law and ethics support for health professionals: an alternative model. *Journal of Medical Ethics* 2005 February; 31(2): 111. NRCBL: 2.3. Identifiers: United Kingdom (Great Britain).

Hanson, Stephen. Teaching health care ethics: why we should teach nursing and medical students together. *Nursing Ethics* 2005 March; 12(2): 167-176. NRCBL: 2.3; 7.2.
  Abstract: This article argues that teaching medical and nursing students health care ethics in an interdisciplinary setting is beneficial for them. Doing so produces an education that is theoretically more consistent with the goals of health care ethics, can help to reduce moral stress and burnout, and can improve patient care. Based on a literature review, theoretical arguments and individual observation, this article will show that the benefits of interdisciplinary education, specifically in ethics, outweigh the difficulties many schools may have in developing such courses.

Howarth, G.R. A plea for a bioethics elite? [letter]. *South African Medical Journal* 2002 May; 92(5): 323. NRCBL: 2.3; 7.2.

Hu, Xiangen; Graesser, Arthur C. Human use regulatory affairs advisor (HURAA): learning about research ethics with intelligent learning modules. *Behavior Research Methods, Instruments, and Computers* 2004 May; 36(2): 241-249. NRCBL: 2.3; 18.1. SC: em.

Jaeger, Suzanne M. Teaching health care ethics: the importance of moral sensitivity for moral reasoning. *Nursing Philosophy* 2001 July; 2(2): 131-142. NRCBL: 2.3; 7.2; 4.1.3; 10; 1.3.1.

Johansen, Carol K.; Harris, David E. Teaching the ethics of biology. *American Biology Teacher* 2000 May; 62(5): 352-358. NRCBL: 2.3; 5.1; 3.1. SC: em.

Kim, Scott Y.H. The dilemma of hidden ethical dilemmas. *Academic Psychiatry* 2004 Fall; 28(3): 168-169. NRCBL: 2.3; 7.2; 17.1.

Lantos, John. Ethics class. *Hastings Center Report* 2005 May-June; 35(3): 9. NRCBL: 2.3; 7.2.

Maekawa, Fumi; Macer, Darryl. Bioethics of teaching about reproductive technology and prenatal diagnosis choices in Japan. *Journal International de Bioethique / International Journal of Bioethics* 2005 March-June; 16(1-2): 53-67, 192. NRCBL: 2.3; 14.1; 15.2; 7.1; 1.3.3. Note: Abstract in English and French.

Melton, Pamela Rogers. Reviews in medical ethics: an open access electronic journal comes to bioethics: a review of BMC Biomedical Ethics. *Journal of Law, Medicine and Ethics* 2004 Winter; 32(4): 770- 772. NRCBL: 2.3; 1.3.12.

Mielke, J. Teaching medical ethics. *Central African Journal of Medicine* 2000 March; 46(3): 79-81. NRCBL: 2.3; 1.3.1; 7.2.

Neitzke, Gerald; Fehr, Folkert. Teachers' responsibility: a Socratic dialogue about teaching medical ethics [opinion]. *Medical Teacher* 2003 January; 25(1): 92-93. NRCBL: 2.3; 7.2.

Pegoraro, Renzo. The challenges for clinical ethics education in Europe. *Medical Ethics and Bioethics / Medicinska Etika & Bioetika* 2005; 11(Supplement): 11-13. NRCBL: 2.3; 21.1; 9.6; 7.1. Conference: Ethics Support in Clinical Practice: Status Quo and Perspectives in Europe; Bratislava, Slovak Republic; 18-19 November, 2004.

Ravindran, G.D.; Kalam, T.; Lewin, S.; Pais, P. Teaching medical ethics: a model. *Issues in Medical Ethics* 1998 July-September; 6(3): 83-84. NRCBL: 2.3.

Repenshek, Mark; Belde, David. Honoring experience in moral discourse. *Health Care Ethics USA [electronic]* 2005; 13(1); 3 p. Available: http://www.slu.edu/centers/chce/hceusa/1_2005_2.html [19 September 2005]. NRCBL: 2.3; 1.2.

Resnik, David B. Using electronic discussion boards to teach responsible conduct of research. *Science and Engineering Ethics* 2005 October; 11(4): 617-630. NRCBL: 2.3; 1.3.12; 1.3.9. SC: em.

Robb, Anja; Etchells, Edward; Cusimano, Michael D.; Cohen, Robert; Singer, Peter A.; McKneally, Martin. A randomized trial of teaching bioethics to surgical residents. *American Journal of Surgery* 2005 April; 189(4): 453-457. NRCBL: 2.3; 8.3.1. SC: em. Identifiers: Canada.

Rodríguez del Pozo, Pablo; Fins, Joseph J. The globalization of education in medical ethics and humanities: evolving pedagogy at Weill Cornell Medical College in Qatar. *Academic Medicine* 2005 February; 80(2): 135-140. NRCBL: 2.3; 7.2.

Sanbar, S. Sandy; Annas, George J.; Grodin, Michael A.; Wecht, Cyril H. Legal medicine: historical roots and current status. *In:* Sanbar, S. Sandy; Firestone, Marvin H.; Buckner, Fillmore; Gibofsky, Allan; LeBlang, Theodore R.; Snyder, Jack W.; Wecht, Cyril H.; Zaremski, Miles J. Legal Medicine. 6th ed. St. Louis: Mosby; 2004: 3-23. NRCBL: 2.3. SC: le.

Schans, Bette A. Radiologic technologists and ethical reasoning. *Radiologic Technology* 2004 March-April; 75(4): 263-271. NRCBL: 2.3. SC: em.

Shiraz, B.; Shamim, M. Shahzad; Shamim, M. Shahid; Ahmed, Asif. Medical ethics in surgical wards: knowledge, attitude and practice of surgical team members in Karachi. *Indian Journal of Medical Ethics* 2005 July-September; 2(3): 94-96. NRCBL: 2.3; 4.1.2; 7.2. SC: em. Identifiers: Pakistan.

Supe, Avinash N.; Kumar, Nishant; Ramakanthan, Ravi; D'Souza, Ravi; Ashtekar, Shyam. Medical ethics

NRCBL: National Reference Center for Bioethics Literature Classification Scheme   See inside front cover for terms.

63

and medical education: some thoughts [discussion]. *Issues in Medical Ethics* 1998 July-September; 6(3): 79-82. NRCBL: 2.3.

ten Have, Henk A.M.J.; Borovecki, Ana; Oreškovic, Stjepan. Master programme "Health, human rights and ethics": a curriculum development experience at Andrija Stampar School of Public Health, medical school, University of Zagreb. *Medicine, Health Care and Philosophy: A European Journal* 2005; 8(3): 371-376. NRCBL: 2.3. Identifiers: Croatia.

Wolf, Susan M.; Kahn, Jeffrey P. Bioethics matures: the field faces the future. *Hastings Center Report* 2005 July-August; 35(4): 22-24. NRCBL: 2.3.

Woogara, Jay. International Centre for Nursing Ethics summer school: teaching ethics to healthcare students, 21-23 July 2004, European Institute of Health and Medical sciences, University of Surrey, Guildford, UK. *Nursing Ethics* 2005 January; 12(1): 108-109. NRCBL: 2.3; 21.1.

BIOETHICS AND MEDICAL ETHICS/ HISTORY

Caton, Donald. Medical science and social values. *International Journal of Obstetric Anesthesia* 2004 July; 13(3): 167-173. NRCBL: 2.2; 9.5.5; 9.5.7.

Moreno, Jonathan D. The end of the great bioethics compromise. *Hastings Center Report* 2005 January-February; 35(1): 14-15. NRCBL: 2.2; 2.4.

Pressel, David M. Nuremberg and Tuskegee: lessons for contemporary American medicine. *Journal of the National Medical Association* 2003 December; 95(12): 1216-1225. NRCBL: 2.2; 15.5; 21.4.

Seto, Belinda. History of medical ethics and perspectives on disparities in minority recruitment and involvement in health research. *American Journal of the Medical Sciences* 2001 November; 322(5): 246-250. NRCBL: 2.2; 18.2; 18.5.1; 21.7.

Short, Bradford William. The healing philosopher: John Locke's medical ethics. *Issues in Law and Medicine* 2004 Fall; 20(2): 103-154. NRCBL: 2.2; 4.1.2; 12.3; 20.7; 20.5.1; 8.1.

Smith, Cedric M. Origin and uses of primum non nocere — above all, do no harm! [opinion]. *Journal of Clinical Pharmacology* 2005 April; 45(4): 371-377. NRCBL: 2.2; 4.1.1.

Wiener, Martin J. The health of prisoners and the two faces of Benthamism. *Clio Medica* 1995; 34: 44-58. NRCBL: 2.2; 9.5.4; 9.1.

BIOETHICS AND MEDICAL ETHICS/ LEGAL ASPECTS

Annas, George J. American Bioethics after Nuremberg: Pragmatism, Politics, and Human Rights. Boston, MA: Boston University, University Lecture, 2005; 26 p. NRCBL: 2.1; 21.1; 21.4; 2.2. SC: le. Note: Adapted from the final chapter of his American Bioethics: Crossing Human Rights and Health Law Boundaries. New York: Oxford University Press, 2005.

Appelbaum, Paul S. Legalism, postmodernism, and the vicissitudes of teaching ethics [opinion]. *Academic Psychiatry* 2004 Fall; 28(3): 164-167. NRCBL: 2.1; 2.3; 17.1. SC: le.

Barnes, David W. Imwinkelried's argument for normative ethical testimony. *Journal of Law, Medicine and Ethics* 2005 Summer; 33(2): 234- 241. NRCBL: 2.1; 1.3.8; 1.1. SC: le.

Bryan, Bradley. Biotechnology, bioethics and liberalism: problematizing risk, consent and law. *Health Law Journal* 2003; 11: 119-135. NRCBL: 2.1; 8.3.1; 5.2. SC: le.

Cherry, Mark J. Bioethics in the ruins of Christendom: why John Paul II's diagnosis requires a more radical cure than May and Colvert provide. *In:* Tollefsen, Christopher, ed. John Paul II's Contribution to Catholic Bioethics. Norwell, MA: Springer; 2004: 73-92. NRCBL: 2.1; 1.2. SC: le.

Davis, Dena S. Tell me a story: using short fiction in teaching law and bioethics. *Journal of Legal Education* 1997 June; 47(2): 240-245. NRCBL: 2.3. SC: le.

France. National Consultative Ethics Committee. Congenital handicaps and prejudice: recommendation no. 68 of the National Consultative Ethics Committee May 29, 2001. *European Journal of Health Law* 2002 June; 9(2): 150-163. NRCBL: 2.4; 4.4; 8.5; 12.4.2. SC: le.

Gostin, Lawrence O. The Supreme Court's influence on medicine and health: the Rehnquist Court, 1986-2005. *JAMA: The Journal of the American Medical Association* 2005 October 5; 294(13): 1685-1687. NRCBL: 2.1; 1.3.8; 8.3.4; 9.1; 12.4.4; 20.5.3. SC: le.

Imwinkelried, Edward J. Expert testimony by ethicists: what should be the norm? *Journal of Law, Medicine and Ethics* 2005 Summer; 33(2): 198- 221. NRCBL: 2.1; 1.3.8. SC: le.

Islamic Organization for Medical Sciences [IOMS]; Al-Abd, Osama Muhammad. Islamic law rulings on certain medical questions: the arguments and the supporting evidence. Cairo, Egypt: Islamic Organization for Medical Sciences 2004 April 10; 37 p. [Online]. Available: http://www.islamset.com/ioms/Code2004/Islamic_vision2.html [5 August 2005]. NRCBL: 2.1; 1.2. SC: le. Conference: International Conference on Islamic Code of Medical Ethics; Cairo, Egypt; 11-14 December 2004; Islamic Organization of Medical Sciences, World Health Organization Eastern Mediterranean Regional Office, Islamic Educational, Scientific and Cultural Organization.

Kipnis, Kenneth. Ethics expertise in civil litigation. *Journal of Law, Medicine and Ethics* 2005 Summer; 33(2): 274- 278. NRCBL: 2.1; 1.3.8; 1.1. SC: le.

Kuflik, Arthur. Liberalism, legal moralism and moral disagreement. *Journal of Applied Philosophy* 2005; 22(2): 185-198. NRCBL: 2.1; 1.3.8; 1.3.5; 4.4; 12.3. SC: an; le.

Abstract: According to "legal moralism" it is part of law's proper role to "enforce morality as such". I explore the idea that legal moralism runs afoul of morality itself: there are good moral reasons not to require by law all that there is nevertheless good moral reason to do. I suggest that many such reasons have broad common-sense appeal and could be appreciated even in a society in which everyone completely agreed about what morality requires. But I also critique legal moralism from the special perspective of liberal political justice. Liberalism requires that citizens who disagree with one another on a number of morally significant matters nevertheless coexist and cooperate within a political framework of basic rights protections. When it comes to working out the most basic terms of their political association, citizens are expected to address one another within the limits of what Rawls has called "public reason". Critics of liberalism claim that this is an essentially a-moral (or expedient) attempt to evade substantive moral issues—such as the moral status of the fetus. I argue, on the contrary, that liberalism's emphasis on public reason is itself grounded in very deep—though (suitably) "non-comprehensive"—moral considerations.

Latham, Stephen R. Expert bioethics testimony. *Journal of Law, Medicine and Ethics* 2005 Summer; 33(2): 242- 247. NRCBL: 2.1; 1.3.8. SC: le.

Majumder, Mary Anderlik. The roles of ethicists in managed care litigation. *Journal of Law, Medicine and Ethics* 2005 Summer; 33(2): 264- 273. NRCBL: 2.1; 1.3.8; 9.3.2. SC: le.

Manaouil, Cécile; Graser, Marie; Chatelain, Denis; Jardé, Olivier. The examination of genetic characteristics since the adoption of the French law on bioethics. *Medicine and Law: World Association for Medical Law* 2005 December; 24(4): 783-789. NRCBL: 2.1; 15.1; 8.3.1; 15.2. SC: le.

Abstract: The French bioethics law of July 1994 was due to be revised five years after its enactment. It was not until 6 August 2004, that the revised law was finally adopted. The examination of the genetic characteristics of a person may only be undertaken for medical purposes or for the purposes of scientific research. Consent must therefore be obtained in writing, after fully informing the patient, and may be withdrawn at any time, in either form (orally or in writing). French law nevertheless authorises carrying out such an examination where there is no consent, solely for medical purposes and in the interest of the patient. The issue has arisen of the detection of a serious genetic anomaly during an examination of genetic characteristics. In this respect, certain anomalies may lead to the patient's relatives being tested, in order to suggest suitable treatment. A procedure for informing families has been implemented by the French Biomedicine Agency (details of which will be specified in a decree).

McPhee, John; Stewart, Cameron. Recent developments. *Journal of Bioethical Inquiry* 2004; 1(1): 43-48. NRCBL: 2.1; 20.5.4; 20.5.3; 12.4.4. SC: le.

McPhee, John; Stewart, Cameron. Recent developments in law. *Journal of Bioethical Inquiry* 2005; 2(2): 63-68. NRCBL: 2.1; 14.6; 8.3.5; 17.7; 8.1; 19.4; 8.3.3; 20.1; 20.5.1; 20.5.2. SC: le. Identifiers: AB v. Attorney General; Kevin Presland; Northern Sydney and Central Coast Area Health Service v. CT; Martin v. R; Wyatt v. Portsmouth NHS Trust; Royal Alexandra Hospital for Children v. Joseph; Geoffrey Langham.

Miola, José. Medical law and medical ethics — complementary or corrosive? *Medical Law International* 2004; 6(3): 251-274. NRCBL: 2.1; 8.3.2; 12.3. SC: le.

Nelson, Lawrence J. Is there any indication for ethics evidence? An argument for the admissibility of some expert bioethics testimony. *Journal of Law, Medicine and Ethics* 2005 Summer; 33(2): 248- 263. NRCBL: 2.1; 1.3.8. SC: le.

Paaso, Ilpo. Current challenges to the principles of medical law and their new interpretation. *Medicine and Law: World Association for Medical Law* 1995; 14(7-8): 611-621. NRCBL: 2.1; 9.1; 8.1. SC: le.

Poland, Susan Cartier. Bioethics, biolaw, and western legal heritage. *Kennedy Institute of Ethics Journal* 2005 June; 15(2): 211-218. NRCBL: 2.1; 2.2; 21.1; 1.1. SC: le.

Rich, Ben A. Introduction: bioethics in court. *Journal of Law, Medicine and Ethics* 2005 Summer; 33(2): 194- 197. NRCBL: 2.1. SC: le.

Sanbar, S. Sandy; Annas, George J.; Grodin, Michael A.; Wecht, Cyril H. Legal medicine: historical roots and current status. *In:* Sanbar, S. Sandy; Firestone, Marvin H.; Buckner, Fillmore; Gibofsky, Allan; LeBlang, Theodore R.; Snyder, Jack W.; Wecht, Cyril H.; Zaremski, Miles J. Legal Medicine. 6th ed. St. Louis: Mosby; 2004: 3-23. NRCBL: 2.3. SC: le.

Schneider, Carl E. Reaching disclosure. *Hastings Center Report* 2005 January-February; 35(1): 12-13. NRCBL: 2.1; 5.3. SC: le.

Short, Bradford William. More history "lite" in modern American bioethics. *Issues in Law and Medicine* 2005 Summer; 21(1): 3-34. NRCBL: 2.1; 2.2; 1.1; 20.7; 20.5.1. SC: le.

Siep, Ludwig. Konsens und Dissens in Recht und Ethik. *In:* Jahrbuch für Wissenschaft und Ethik. Bd. 7. Berlin: Walter de Gruyter; 2002: 23-31. NRCBL: 2.1; 21.7. SC: le.

Skene, Loane. Courts as communicators: can doctors learn from judges' decisions? *Journal of Bioethical Inquiry* 2004; 1(1): 49-56. NRCBL: 2.1; 1.3.8; 8.2. SC: le.

Smith, George P., II. Law, medicine and religion: towards a dialogue and a partnership in biomedical technology and

NRCBL: National Reference Center for Bioethics Literature Classification Scheme   See inside front cover for terms.

65

decision making. *Journal of Contemporary Health Law and Policy* 2005 Summer; 21(2): 169-203. NRCBL: 2.1; 1.2; 5.1; 3.2. SC: le.

Smith, George P., II. Of Panjandrums, Pooh Bahs, Parvenus, and Prophets: Law, Religion, and Medical Sciences. Sydney, Australia: Macquarie University, Division of Law, 2005; 92 p. NRCBL: 2.1; 1.2; 7.1; 5.1. SC: le. Note: Derives from a lecture — under the same title — given, originally in honor of Justice Michael D. Kirby, AC, CMG, High Court of Australia, in the Banco Court of the Supreme Court Building, Queen's Square, Sydney, Australia, on July 27, 2005, and in commemoration of the thirtieth anniversary of the founding of the Division of Law at Macquarie University.

Somerville, Margaret. Commentary: social-ethical values issues in the political public square: principles vs. packages. *Journal of Law, Medicine and Ethics* 2004 Winter; 32(4): 731- 740. NRCBL: 2.1; 12.5.1; 18.5.4; 20.5.1. SC: le.

Spielman, Bethany J. Bioethics testimony: untangling the strands and testing their reliability. *Journal of Law, Medicine and Ethics* 2005 Summer; 33(2): 222- 233. NRCBL: 2.1; 1.3.8. SC: le.

BIOETHICS AND MEDICAL ETHICS/ PHILOSOPHICAL PERSPECTIVES

Agich, George J. What kind of doing is clinical ethics? *Theoretical Medicine and Bioethics* 2005; 26(1): 7-24. NRCBL: 2.1; 1.1; 9.6. SC: an.
Abstract: This paper discusses the importance of Richard M. Zaner's work on clinical ethics for answering the question: what kind of doing is ethics consultation? The paper argues first, that four common approaches to clinical ethics — applied ethics, casuistry, principlism, and conflict resolution cannot adequately address the nature of the activity that makes up clinical ethics; second, that understanding the practical character of clinical ethics is critically important for the field; and third, that the practice of clinical ethics is bound up with the normative commitments of medicine as a therapeutic enterprise.

Allmark, Peter. Can the study of ethics enhance nursing practice? *Journal of Advanced Nursing* 2005 September; 51(6): 618-624. NRCBL: 2.1; 4.1.3.

Árnason, Vilhjálmur. Sensible discussion in bioethics: reflections on interdisciplinary research. *CQ: Cambridge Quarterly of Healthcare Ethics* 2005 Summer; 14(3): 322-328. NRCBL: 2.1; 1.1; 1.3.9. Identifiers: metabioethics.

Barnes, David W. Imwinkelried's argument for normative ethical testimony. *Journal of Law, Medicine and Ethics* 2005 Summer; 33(2): 234- 241. NRCBL: 2.1; 1.3.8; 1.1. SC: le.

Barragán, Javier Lozano. Fundamentos filosoficos y teologicos de la bioetica / Philosophical and theological foundations of bioethics. *Vida y Etica* 2003 December; 4(2): 5-43. NRCBL: 2.1; 1.1; 1.2.

Bayertz, Kurt. Dissens in Fragen von Leben und Tod: Konnen wir damit leben? *In:* Baumann, Eva; Brink, Alexander; May, Arnd T.; Schröder, Peter; Schutzeichel, Corinna Iris, eds. Weltanschauliche Offenheit in der Bioethik. Berlin: Duncker & Humblot; 2004: 23-36. NRCBL: 2.1; 1.1; 21.7.

Beauchamp, Tom L. Who deserves autonomy, and whose autonomy deserves respect? *In:* Taylor, James Stacey, ed. Personal Autonomy: New Essays on Personal Autonomy and Its Role in Contemporary Moral Philosophy. New York: Cambridge University Press; 2005: 310-329. NRCBL: 2.1; 1.1. SC: an.

Berry, Roberta M. Three stages in the lifecycle of bioethics: observations on "bioethics as co-PI". *American Journal of Bioethics* 2005 November-December; 5(6): 30-32. NRCBL: 2.1; 18.5.4; 1.1. Identifiers: primary investigator. Comments: comment on S. Matthew Liao, "Rescuing human embryonic stem cell research: the blastocyst transfer method," American Journal of Bioethics 2005 November-December; 5(6): 8-16.

Birnbacher, Dieter. Das Dilemma des bioethischen Pluralismus. *In:* Baumann, Eva; Brink, Alexander; May, Arnd T.; Schröder, Peter; Schutzeichel, Corinna Iris, eds. Weltanschauliche Offenheit in der Bioethik. Berlin: Duncker & Humblot; 2004: 51-64. NRCBL: 2.1; 1.1; 21.7.

Bolletino, Ruth Cohn. The need for a new ethical model in medicine: a challenge for conventional, alternative, and complementary practitioners. *Advances in Mind-Body Medicine* 1998 Winter; 14(1): 11 p. [Online]. Available: http://weblinks3.epnet.com/DeliveryPrintSave.asp?tb=1 &_ua=bo+B_+s hn+1_db+aphjnh+ [23 September 2005]. NRCBL: 2.1; 4.1.1; 1.1.

Boyd, K.M. Medical ethics: principles, persons, and perspectives: from controversy to conversation. *Journal of Medical Ethics* 2005 August; 31(8): 481-486. NRCBL: 2.1; 18.5.4; 1.1. SC: an.
Abstract: Medical ethics, principles, persons, and perspectives is discussed under three headings: History, Theory, and Practice. Under Theory, the author will say something about some different approaches to the study and discussion of ethical issues in medicine—especially those based on principles, persons, or perspectives. Under Practice, the author will discuss how one perspectives based approach, hermeneutics, might help in relation first to everyday ethical issues and then to public controversies. In that context some possible advantages of moving from controversy to conversation will be explored; and that will then be illustrated with reference to a current controversy about the use of human embryos in stem cell therapy research. The paper begins with history, and it begins in the author's home city of Edinburgh.

Breithaupt, Holger; Hadley, Caroline; Caplan, Arthur. Building stairs into slippery slopes. An interview with Arthur Caplan, director of the Center for Bioethics at the University of Pennsylvania (Philadelphia, PA, USA) [interview]. *EMBO Reports* 2005 January; 6(1): 8-12. NRCBL: 2.1; 1.1.

Buckle, Stephen. Peter Singer's argument for utilitarianism. *Theoretical Medicine and Bioethics* 2005; 26(3): 175-194. NRCBL: 2.1; 1.1. SC: an.

Abstract: The paper begins by situating Singer within the British meta-ethical tradition. It sets out the main steps in his argument for utilitarianism as the 'default setting' of ethical thought. It argues that Singer's argument depends on a hierarchy of reasons, such that the ethical viewpoint is understood to be an adaptation—an extension—of a fundamental self-interest. It concludes that the argument fails because it is impossible to get from this starting-point in self-interest to his conception of the ethical point of view. The fundamental problem is its mixing the immiscible: the Humean subordination of reason to interest with the Kantian conception of reason as universal and authoritative

Callahan, Daniel. Bioethics and the culture wars. *CQ: Cambridge Quarterly of Healthcare Ethics* 2005 Fall; 14(4): 424-431. NRCBL: 2.1; 2.2; 7.1; 21.1; 1.1; 1.2. SC: rv.

Charlesworth, Max. Don't blame the 'bio' — blame the 'ethics': varieties of (bio)ethics and the challenge of pluralism. *Journal of Bioethical Inquiry* 2005; 2(1): 10-17. NRCBL: 2.1; 1.1; 2.2. SC: rv.

Abstract: We tend to think that the difficulties in bioethics spring from the novel and alarming issues that arise due to discoveries in the new biosciences and biotechnologies. But many of the crucial difficulties in bioethics arise from the assumption we make about ethics. This paper offers a brief overview of bioethics, and relates ethical 'principlism' to 'ethical fundamentalism.' It then reviews some alternative approaches that have emerged during the second phase of bioethics and argues for a neo-Aristotelian approach. Misconceptions about ethical principles and ethical reasoning not only distort our views of the business of bioethics, but they also prevent us from facing up to the formidable problems posed by ethical pluralism in so-called liberal societies.

Chartier, Gary. The rule of double effect: a valuable contemporary resource. *Update [Loma Linda University Center for Christian Bioethics]* 2000 December; 16(4): 3-7. NRCBL: 2.1; 1.1; 1.2; 8.1.

Childress, James F. Epilogue: looking back to look forward. *In:* Childress, James F.; Meslin, Eric M.; Shapiro, Harold T., eds. Belmont Revisited: Ethical Principles for Research with Human Subjects. Washington, DC: Georgetown University Press; 2005: 244-251. NRCBL: 2.1; 1.1; 18.2; 2.2; 2.4. SC: an.

Churchill, Larry R.; Schenck, David. One cheer for bioethics: engaging the moral experiences of patients and practitioners beyond the big decisions. *CQ: Cambridge Quarterly of Healthcare Ethics* 2005 Fall; 14(4): 389-403. NRCBL: 2.1; 2.2; 20.5.1; 20.1; 1.1; 20.4.1; 8.1; 8.3.1; 9.5.5; 9.5.8. SC: cs.

Coghlan, Peter. The prodigal and his brother: impartiality and the equal consideration of interests. *Theoretical Medi-* cine and Bioethics 2005; 26(3): 195-206. NRCBL: 2.1; 1.1; 9.4; 9.2. SC: an.

Abstract: At the heart of Peter Singer's utilitarianism is the impartial weighing of the interests of those affected by our actions. Singer calls this the Principle of Equal Consideration of Interests. This paper argues that Singer's Principle does not accord with our moral intuitions and the logic of our moral thinking. It discusses the Principle in the context of the parable of the Prodigal Son and his Brother—a parable that raises the issue of impartiality in a particularly challenging way. What the parable shows is, first, that our moral thinking often turns on judgements of fairness that are prior to any impartial weighing of interests; and, second, that impartial fairness itself is sometimes transcended by compassionate love. Both of these points have important implications for bioethics.

Cohen, Cynthia B. Promises and perils of public deliberation: contrasting two national bioethics commissions on embryonic stem cell research. *Kennedy Institute of Ethics Journal* 2005 September; 15(3): 269-288. NRCBL: 2.4; 2.2; 1.1; 5.1; 18.5.4; 7.1; 5.3.

Abstract: National bioethics commissions have struggled to develop ethically warranted methods for conducting their deliberations. The National Bioethics Advisory Commission in its report on stem cell research adopted an approach to public deliberation indebted to Rawls in that it sought common ground consistent with shared values and beliefs at the foundation of a well-ordered democracy. In contrast, although the research cloning and stem cell reports of the President's Council on Bioethics reveal that it broached two different methods of public deliberation—balancing goods and following an overarching moral principle—it adopted neither. Thereupon its primer mover, Leon Kass, influenced particularly by the approach of Leo Strauss, sought to develop a method of public deliberation guided by tradition and practical wisdom. When this failed, the Council fell back on a method that took account of shared fundamental values of a free democracy—a method remarkable akin to that employed by the National Bioethics Advisory Commission. Respect for diverse reasonable conceptions of the good in a democratic polity requires national bioethics commissions to seek and incorporate that which is valuable in opposing positions.

Cowley, Christopher. A new rejection of moral expertise. *Medicine, Health Care and Philosophy: A European Journal* 2005; 8(3): 273-279. NRCBL: 2.1; 1.1; 9.6.

Abstract: There seem to be two clearly-defined camps in the debate over the problem of moral expertise. On the one hand are the "Professionals", who reject the possibility entirely, usually because of the intractable diversity of ethical beliefs. On the other hand are the "Ethicists", who criticise the Professionals for merely stipulating science as the most appropriate paradigm for discussions of expertise. While the subject matter and methodology of good ethical thinking is certainly different from that of good clinical thinking, they argue, this is no reason for rejecting the possibility of a distinctive kind of expertise in ethics, usually based on the idea of good justification. I want to argue that both are incorrect, partly because of the reasons given by one group against the other, but more importantly because both neglect what is most distinctive about ethics: that it is personal in a very specific way, without collapsing into relativism.

Cozby, Dimitri. So finally, what is Christian about Christian bioethics? *Christian Bioethics* 2005 December; 11(3): 255-267. NRCBL: 2.1; 1.2; 1.1.

Abstract: The author criticizes the essays in this issue by Waters, Erickson, Trotter and Verhey for not placing an adequate

NRCBL: National Reference Center for Bioethics Literature Classification Scheme   See inside front cover for terms.

67

Christology at the center of their definitions what is Christian bioethics.

Crawford, Gail W. A practical application for a framework for ethical decision making [opinion]. *Dimensions of Critical Care Nursing* 2005 March-April; 24(2): 80-81. NRCBL: 2.1; 4.1.3; 2.3.

Cutas, Daniela-Ecaterina. Looking for the meaning of dignity in the Bioethics Convention and the Cloning Protocol. *Health Care Analysis: An International Journal of Health Care Philosophy and Policy* 2005 December; 13(4): 303-313. NRCBL: 2.1; 1.1; 4.4; 14.5; 21.1.

Abstract: This paper is focused on the analysis of two documents (the Council of Europe's Bioethics Convention and the Additional Cloning Protocol) inasmuch as they refer to the relationship between human dignity and human genetic engineering. After presenting the stipulations of the abovementioned documents, I will review various proposed meanings of human dignity and will try to identify which of these seem to be at the core of their underlying assumptions. Is the concept of dignity proposed in the two documents coherent? Is it morally legitimate? Is it, as some might assume, of Kantian origin? Does it have any philosophical roots?

Delkeskamp-Hayes, Corinna. Between morality and repentance: recapturing "sin" for bioethics. *Christian Bioethics* 2005 August; 11(2): 93-132. NRCBL: 2.1; 1.2; 1.1.

Abstract: Distinguishing within "sin" the dimensions of anomia, hamartia, and asthenia makes it possible to analyze in greater detail the contrary manners in which traditional and post-traditional Christianities in this issue of Christian Bioethics endeavor to recapture what was lost when secular bioethics reconstructed the specifically spiritual-context-oriented normative commitments of Christianity in one-dimensionally moral terms. Various post-traditional attempts at securing moral orientation and resources for forgiveness, both of which secular bioethics finds increasingly difficult to provide, are critically reviewed. Their engagement of secular moral concepts and concerns, and even their adoption of an academically philosophical posture and language, is presented as responsible for their failure to adequately preserve what in traditional Christianity would count as prohibited vs. permitted, and advisable vs. non-advisable, or what would allow to resolve "tragic conflicts." The deeper reason for this failure lies in post-traditional Christianity's restricting the Christian life (with its central tension between love and the law) to what can be captured by cognitive categories. As the survey of several traditionally Christian accounts of sin in bioethics makes clear, both moral orientation (along with the resolution of "tragic" conflicts) and the sources of forgiveness are available, once that Christian life is framed in terms of persons' spirit-supported practical involvement in ascesis and liturgy, and once bioethical reflections are situated in the experiential context of such involvement.

DeMarco, J.P. Principlism and moral dilemmas: a new principle. *Journal of Medical Ethics* 2005 February; 31(2): 101-105. NRCBL: 2.1; 1.1; 8.3.4; 8.3.2. SC: an.

Engelhardt, H. Tristram, Jr. Sin and bioethics: why a liturgical anthropology is foundational. *Christian Bioethics* 2005 August; 11(2): 221-239. NRCBL: 2.1; 1.2; 1.1.

Abstract: The project of articulating a coherent, canonical, content-full, secular morality-cum-bioethics fails, because it does not acknowledge sin, which is to say, it does not acknowledge the centrality of holiness, which is essential to a non-distorted understanding of human existence and of morality. Secular morality cannot establish a particular moral content, the harmony of the good and the right, or the necessary precedence of morality over prudence, because such is possible only in terms of an ultimate point of reference: God. The necessity of a rightly ordered appreciation of God places centrally the focus on holiness and the avoidance of sin. Because the cardinal relationship of creatures to their Creator is worship, and because the cardinal corporate act of human worship is the Liturgy, morality in general and bioethics in particular can be understood in terms of the conditions necessary, so as worthily to enter into Eucharistic liturgical participation. Morality can be summed up in terms of the requirements of ritual purity. A liturgical anthropology is foundational to an account of the content-full morality and bioethics that should bind humans, since humans are first and foremost creatures obliged to join in rightly ordered worship of their Creator. When humans worship correctly, when they avoid sin and pursue holiness, they participate in restoring created reality.

Engelhardt, H. Tristram, Jr. What is Christian about Christian bioethics? Metaphysical, epistemological, and moral differences. *Christian Bioethics* 2005 December; 11(3): 241-253. NRCBL: 2.1; 1.2; 1.1; 7.1.

Erickson, Stephen A. On the Christian in Christian bioethics. *Christian Bioethics* 2005 December; 11(3): 269-279. NRCBL: 2.1; 1.2; 1.1; 4.4.

Abstract: What is Christian about Christian bioethics? And is an authentically Christian bioethics a practical possibility in the world in which we find ourselves? In my essay I argue that personhood and the personal are so fundamental to the Christian understanding of our humanity that body, soul, and spirit are probably best understood as the components of a triune (as opposed to dual) aspect theory of personhood. To confess to a Christian bioethics is to admit that Christians cannot pretend fully to understand either cures or their meaning. However effective and "knowledge-based" contemporary medical interventions are, a Christian must humbly and honestly confess a lack of complete knowledge on both levels. At the same time, a Christian bioethicist must express a total personal commitment to Christian Faith.

Evans, John H. Max Weber meets the Belmont Report: toward a sociological interpretation of principlism. *In:* Childress, James F.; Meslin, Eric M.; Shapiro, Harold T., eds. Belmont Revisited: Ethical Principles for Research with Human Subjects. Washington, DC: Georgetown University Press; 2005: 228-243. NRCBL: 2.1; 1.1; 5.1. SC: an.

Fjellstrom, Roger. Respect for persons, respect for integrity. *Medicine, Health Care and Philosophy: A European Journal* 2005; 8(2): 231-242. NRCBL: 2.1; 4.4; 1.1. SC: an.

Abstract: Even though respect for integrity is hailed in several authoritative legal and ethical documents, and is typically presented as a complement to respect for autonomy, it is largely neglected in many leading works in ethics. Is such neglect warranted, or does it express a prejudice? This article argues that the latter is the case, and that this is due to misplaced conceptual concerns. It offers some proposals as regards the conceptualization of integrity in social ethics in general and in biomedical ethics in particular. Five main directions of interpretation of "integrity" are discerned and shown to be relevant for different areas of biomedical ethics. The defense of respect for integrity is served by a softening of principlism and by greater attention to context among the initial critics of this principle.

Fletcher, James J. Virtues, moral decisions, and health care. *NursingConnections* 1999 Winter; 12(4): 26-32. NRCBL: 2.1; 1.1; 4.1.2.

Fox, Renée C.; Swazey, Judith P. Examining American bioethics: its problems and prospects. *CQ: Cambridge Quarterly of Healthcare Ethics* 2005 Fall; 14(4): 361-373. NRCBL: 2.1; 2.2; 7.1; 7.3; 1.1; 2.3; 20.5.1. SC: an.

Francis, C.M. Medical ethics in India: ancient and modern (I). *Issues in Medical Ethics* 1996 October-December; 4(4): 115-118. NRCBL: 2.1; 2.2; 1.2; 1.1; 8.3.1. Identifiers: India.

Gillett, Grant. Bioethics and cara sui. *Journal of Bioethical Inquiry* 2005; 2(1): 24-33. NRCBL: 2.1; 1.1; 8.2; 8.1.

Abstract: Cara sui (care of the self) is a guiding thread in Foucault's later writings on ethics. Following Foucault in that inquiry, we are urged beyond our fairly superficial conceptions of consequences, harms, benefits, and the rights of persons, and led to examine ourselves and try to articulate the sense of life that animates ethical reasoning. The result is a nuanced understanding with links to virtue ethics and post-modern approaches to ethics and subjectivity. The approach I have articulated draws on the phenomenology of Levinas and Heidegger, the Virtue ethics of Baier, and the post-structuralist writing of Michel Foucault. The subject is seen as negotiable, embodied, provisional and able to be transformed in a way that denies essentialism about human beings, their moral status, and the idea of the good. The human being emerges as responsible because, properly, responsive to the context of discourse in which morality becomes articulated. When we import this style of thinking into bioethics we find that it reaches beyond issues of policy or right conduct and allows us to use the biomedical sciences and the clinical world to revise and interrogate our understanding of ourselves and the theoretical foundations of health care ethics.

Gräb-Schmidt, Elisabeth. Freedom in responsibility: on the relevance of "sin" as a hermeneutic guiding principle in bioethical decision making. *Christian Bioethics* 2005 August; 11(2): 147-165. NRCBL: 2.1; 1.2; 1.1; 5.1; 5.3; 18.5.4; 14.5.

Abstract: This essay deals with questions of responsibility concerning technology, in particular, gene technology and the special problem of research on embryos. I raise issues concerning the extent of humans' authority to act and the limits of human freedom. In what way is that freedom given, and what kind of responsibility results from it? By discussing various concepts of human freedom in the tradition of European philosophy, as juxtaposed to the Protestant understanding of freedom, this essay discusses the restricting limits, and the obligation to take responsibility. It will turn out that the question concerning freedom cannot be answered without understanding what being human involves. From a Christian perspective, this implies that the foundational relationship between human freedom and sin will be central to an assessment of the human ability to take responsibility. By obliterating the limits of human freedom, sin jeopardizes the very essence of that freedom. The project of taking into account the sinful state of the human condition thus

aims at developing a realistic picture of the authority of humans in action, even in view of the human tasks of promoting science and research.

Hanson, Stephen. Engelhardt and children: the failure of libertarian bioethics in pediatric interactions. *Kennedy Institute of Ethics Journal* 2005 June; 15(2): 179-198. NRCBL: 2.1; 1.1; 9.5.7; 4.4; 8.3.2.

Abstract: In Engelhardt's secular bioethics, moral obligations derive from contracts and agreements between rational persons, and no infants or children and few adolescents meet Engelhardt's requirements for being a rational person. This is a problem, as one cannot have any direct secular moral obligations toward nonpersons such as infants and adolescents. The Engelhardtian concepts of ownership, indenture, and social personhood, which are meant to allow the theory to accommodate children and adolescents adequately, fail to give an Engelhardtian any actual means of determining the right action to take in difficult cases, even on his or her own terms. Thus, the theory is incapable of determining the morally correct action to take in cases involving children and therefore is unhelpful in dealing with moral questions involving children.

Harris-Fain, Darren. Does it make sense to use fiction as a guide to bioethics? [letter]. *Chronicle of Higher Education* 2005 July 8; 51(44): B13. NRCBL: 2.1; 7.1; 1.1.

Häyry, Matti. Can arguments address concerns? *Journal of Medical Ethics* 2005 October; 31(10): 598-600. NRCBL: 2.1; 1.1. SC: an.

Abstract: People have concerns, and ethicists often respond to them with philosophical arguments. But can conceptual constructions properly address fears and anxieties? It is argued in this paper that while it is possible to voice, clarify, create and-to a certain extent- tackle concerns by arguments, more concrete practices, choices, and actions are normally needed to produce proper responses to people's worries. While logical inconsistencies and empirical errors can legitimately be exposed by arguments, the situation is considerably less clear when it comes to moral, cultural, and emotional norms, values, and expectations.

Häyry, Matti. Precaution and solidarity. *CQ: Cambridge Quarterly of Healthcare Ethics* 2005 Spring; 14(2): 199-206. NRCBL: 2.1; 1.1; 21.1.

Häyry, Matti. The tension between self governance and absolute inner worth in Kant's moral philosophy. *Journal of Medical Ethics* 2005 November; 31(11): 645-647. NRCBL: 2.1; 1.1.

Abstract: The concepts of autonomy as the self governance of individuals and dignity as the inner worth of human beings play an important role in contemporary bioethics. Since both notions are crucial to Immanuel Kant's moral theory, it would be tempting to think that Kantian ethics could ease the friction between the two concepts. It is argued in this paper, however, that this line of thought cannot be supported by Kant's original ideas. While he did make a conscious effort to bring autonomy and dignity together, his emphasis on the absolute inner worth of our collective humanity made it impossible for him to embrace fully the personal self determination of individuals, as it is usually understood in today's liberal thinking.

Herissone-Kelly, Peter. Bioethics, rights-based consequentialism, and social reality. *In:* Häyry, Matti; Takala, Tuija; Herissone-Kelly, Peter, eds. Bioethics and

NRCBL: National Reference Center for Bioethics Literature Classification Scheme   See inside front cover for terms.

69

Social Reality. New York: Rodopi, 2005: 161-171. NRCBL: 2.1; 1.1.

Heubel, Friedrich; Biller-Andorno, Nikola. The contribution of Kantian moral theory to contemporary medical ethics: a critical analysis. *Medicine, Health Care and Philosophy: A European Journal* 2005; 8(1): 5-18. NRCBL: 2.1; 1.1.

Abstract: Kantian deontology is one of three classic moral theories, among virtue ethics and consequentialism. Issues in medical ethics are frequently addressed within a Kantian paradigm, at least — although not exclusively—in European medical ethics. At the same time, critical voices have pointed to deficits of Kantian moral philosophy which must be examined and discussed. It is argued that taking concrete situations and complex relationships into account is of paramount importance in medical ethics. Encounters between medical or nursing staff and patients are rarely symmetrical relationships between autonomous and rational agents. Kantian ethics, the criticism reads, builds on the lofty ideal of such a relationship. In addition to the charge of an individualist and rationalist focus on autonomy, Kantian ethics has been accused of excluding those not actually in possession of these properties or of its rigorism. It is said to be focussed on laws and imperatives to an extent that it cannot appreciate the complex nuances of real conflicts. As a more detailed analysis will show, these charges are inadequate in at least some regards. This will be demonstrated by drawing on the Kantian notion of autonomy, the role of maxims and judgment and the conception of duties, as well as the role of emotions. Nevertheless the objections brought forward against Kantian moral theory can help determine, with greater precision, its strengths and shortcomings as an approach to current problems in medical ethics.

Holm, Søren. The phenomenological ethics of K.E. Løgstrup — a resource for health care ethics and philosophy? *Nursing Philosophy* 2001 April; 2(1): 26-33. NRCBL: 2.1; 1.1; 4.1.1.

Honnefelder, Ludger. Bioethik und Menschenbild. *In:* Jahrbuch für Wissenschaft und Ethik. Bd. 7. Berlin: Walter de Gruyter; 2002: 33-52. NRCBL: 2.1; 1.1; 4.4.

Husted, Gladys L.; Husted, James H. Strength of character through the ethics of nursing. *Advanced Practice Nursing Quarterly* 1998 Spring; 3(4): 23-25. NRCBL: 2.1; 8.1; 4.1.3. SC: cs.

Imrényi, Tibor. Sin and bioethics. *Christian Bioethics* 2005 August; 11(2): 133-145. NRCBL: 2.1; 1.2; 12.3; 1.1; 15.4; 14.5.

Abstract: The essay starts out with defining the biblical concept of sin in the Old and the New Testaments. The literal knowledge of divine truth is distinguished from its truthful and spiritual interpretation. A further distinction should be made between the Creator of life (God) and the medium or "intermediary creator" (man) of life. I argue for the "single wholeness" of the human race and for the unity of human responsibility in bioethics. In delineating the teaching of the Church on abortion and family planning, I show that the healing of all human diseases, from traditional interventions to genetic ones, is a Christian duty and is in accordance with Christ's mission on earth as long as one has not been directly or indirectly involved in "reproducing" or "designing" one's descendants or destroying or damaging human life even at its very beginnings.

Ip, Po-Keung. Developing medical ethics in China's reform era. *Developing World Bioethics* 2005 May; 5(2): 176-187. NRCBL: 2.1; 2.2; 2.3; 4.1.2.

Abstract: The paper gives an analytical synopsis of the problem of developing medical ethics in the early half of the 1990s in China, as perceived by Chinese scholars and medical professionals interested in medical ethics. The views captured and analyzed here were expressed in one of the two major journals on medical ethics in China: Chinese Medical Ethics. The economic reform unleashed profound changes in Chinese society, including in the medical field, creating irregularities and improprieties in the profession. Furthermore, the market reform also created new values that were in tension with existing values. In this transitional period, Chinese medical ethicists saw the need to rebuild medical morality for the new era. Using the code of conduct promulgated by the Chinese Ministry of Health in 1989 as a basis, assessment and education aspects of the institutionalization of medical ethics are discussed. In addition to institutional problems of institutionalising ethics, there are philosophical and methodological issues that are not easy to solve. After all, to institutionalize medical ethics is no easy task for a country as old and as big as China. Chinese medical ethicists seem ready to confront these difficulties in their effort to develop medical ethics in Reform China.

Jaeger, Suzanne M. Teaching health care ethics: the importance of moral sensitivity for moral reasoning. *Nursing Philosophy* 2001 July; 2(2): 131-142. NRCBL: 2.3; 7.2; 4.1.3; 10; 1.3.1.

Jamison, John E. Spirituality and medical ethics. *American Journal of Hospice and Palliative Care* 1995 May-June; 12(3): 41-45. NRCBL: 2.1; 1.2; 1.1.

Kaminsky, Carmen. Kann man bio- und medizinethische Probleme lösen? *In:* Baumann, Eva; Brink, Alexander; May, Arnd T.; Schröder, Peter; Schutzeichel, Corinna Iris, eds. Weltanschauliche Offenheit in der Bioethik. Berlin: Duncker & Humblot; 2004: 81-93. NRCBL: 2.1; 1.1; 21.7.

Kappauf, Herbert W.; Bolletino, Ruth Cohn. More on a new medical ethics: do we really need a new ethical model in medicine? [letter and reply]. *Advances in Mind-Body Medicine* 1998 Spring; 14(2); 8 p. [Online]. Available: http://weblinks3.epnet.com/citation.asp?tb=1&_ua= bo+B%5F+shn+1+db+aphjnh+bt+TD [23 September 2005]. NRCBL: 2.1; 4.1.1; 1.1.

Keenan, James F. Developments in bioethics from the perspective of HIV/AIDS. *CQ: Cambridge Quarterly of Healthcare Ethics* 2005 Fall; 14(4): 416-423. NRCBL: 2.1; 2.2; 1.1; 9.1; 9.5.6; 21.1.

Kenny, Nuala; Giacomini, Mita. Wanted: a new ethics field for health policy analysis. *Health Care Analysis: An International Journal of Health Care Philosophy and Policy* 2005 December; 13(4): 247-260. NRCBL: 2.1; 9.1; 1.1. SC: an.

Abstract: Ethics guidance and ethical frameworks are becoming more explicit and prevalent in health policy proposals. However, little attention has been given to evaluating their roles and impacts in the policy arena. Before this can be investigated, fundamental questions must be asked about the nature of ethics in relation to policy, and about the nexus of the fields of applied ethical analysis and health policy analysis. This paper examines the interdisciplinary stretch between bioethics and health policy analysis. In particular, it highlights areas of scholarship where a health policy ethics specialization—as distinctive from bioethics—might develop to address health policy concerns. If policy and ethics both ask the same question, that question is: "What is the good, and how do we achieve (create, protect, cultivate) it?" To answer this question, the new field of "health policy ethics" requires development. First, we should develop a full set of ethical principles and complementary ethical theories germane to public policy per se. Second, we must understand better how explicit attention to ethical concerns affects policy dynamics. Third, we require new policy and ethical analytic approaches that contribute to constructive (not obstructive) policy making. Finally, we need indicators of robust, high quality ethical analysis for the purpose of public policy making.

Kipnis, Kenneth. Ethics expertise in civil litigation. *Journal of Law, Medicine and Ethics* 2005 Summer; 33(2): 274- 278. NRCBL: 2.1; 1.3.8; 1.1. SC: le.

Kottow, Michael H. Vulnerability: what kind of principle is it? *Medicine, Health Care and Philosophy: A European Journal* 2004; 7(3): 281-287. NRCBL: 2.1; 4.4; 9.5.1; 21.1; 1.1. SC: an.

Abstract: The so-called European principles of bioethics are a welcome enrichment of principlist bioethics. Nevertheless, vulnerability, dignity and integrity can perhaps be more accurately understood as anthropological descriptions of the human condition. They may inspire a normative language, but they do not contain it primarily lest a naturalistic fallacy be committed. These anthropological features strongly suggest the need to develop deontic arguments in support of the protection such essential attributes of humanity require. Protection is to be universalized, since all human beings share vulnerability, integrity and dignity, thus fundamenting a mandate requiring justice and respect for fundamental human rights. Being a feature of all humanity, vulnerability is improperly extended to designate destitute individuals and populations. Rather, they are in a state of fallen vulnerability, for they already are harmed in some way, and have become deprived of their range of capabilities. These individuals are destitute and are no longer in command of their fundamental human rights. They have lost the status of unharmed vulnerability; identifying them as susceptible—vulnerated and no longer only vulnerable—stresses the point that bioethics demands specific social action to palliate or remove their distress. When harm does occur—in the form of disease, for example-, individuals are no longer vulnerable—for they have ceased to be intact -, they become susceptible to additional deprivations and sickness; integrity is demeaned and dignity is offended, leading to states of dysfunction that require specific remedial social practices, aimed at treating and removing injuries. The main point this paper addresses is that vulnerability—as well as dignity and integrity—are descriptive characteristics of human beings qua humans, which are not normative in themselves, but fundamental enough to inspire bioethical requirements of protection and respect for human rights in the wake of social justice. A clear distinction must be made in regard to human beings who are injured by poverty, sickness, discriminating deprivations or suffer other destitutions, having ceased to be only vulnerable for they are no longer intact. These individuals and populations require more than protection, their needs must be met by specific care and remedial measures to be identified and instigated by bioethics qua applied ethics.

Ladikas, Miltos; Schroeder, Doris. Too early for global ethics? *CQ: Cambridge Quarterly of Healthcare Ethics*

2005 Fall; 14(4): 404-415. NRCBL: 2.1; 21.1; 7.1; 21.7; 1.1; 1.3.6.

Little, M. Understanding medical ethics. *Central African Journal of Medicine* 2000 March; 46(3): 69-76. NRCBL: 2.1; 1.1.

Louhiala, Pekka. But who can say what's right and wrong? Medicine as a moral enterprise. *In:* Evans, Martyn; Louhiala, Pekka; Puustinen, Raimo, eds. Philosophy for Medicine: Applications in a Clinical Context. San Francisco: Radcliffe Medical Press; 2004: 135-142. NRCBL: 2.1; 9.5.7; 1.1.

Majumder, Mary Anderlik. Respecting difference and moving beyond regulation: tasks for U.S. bioethics commissions in the twenty-first century. *Kennedy Institute of Ethics Journal* 2005 September; 15(3): 289-303. NRCBL: 2.4; 2.2; 1.1; 7.1; 5.1; 5.3; 2.1.

Abstract: This article focuses on two possible missions for a national bioethics commission. The first is handling differences of worldview, political orientation, and discipline. Recent work in political philosophy emphasizes regard for the dignity of difference manifested in "conversation" that seeks understanding rather than agreement. The President's Council on Bioethics gets a mixed review in this area. The second is experimenting with prophetic bioethics. "Prophetic bioethics" is a term coined by Daniel Callahan to describe an alternative to compromise-seeking "regulatory bioethics." It involves a critique of modern medicine. In the contemporary context, the areas of biotechnology and access to health care cry out for prophetic attention. The Council has addressed biotechnology; unfortunately, that experience suggests that the kind of prophecy that it practices poses risks to conversation. With regard to access issues, the article proposes an effort that unites themes of human dignity, solidarity, and limits in support of reform, while highlighting, rather than papering over, differences.

May, Thomas. The concept of autonomy in bioethics: an unwarranted fall from grace. *In:* Taylor, James Stacey, ed. Personal Autonomy: New Essays on Personal Autonomy and Its Role in Contemporary Moral Philosophy. New York: Cambridge University Press; 2005: 299-309. NRCBL: 2.1; 1.1. SC: an.

Montgomery, Kathryn. How not to philosophize with a hammer: a reply to Spike. *In:* Thomasma, David C.; Weisstub, David N., eds. The Variables of Moral Capacity. Boston: Kluwer Academic Publishers; 2004: 121-127. NRCBL: 2.1; 1.1.

Murphy, Timothy F. Does it make sense to use fiction as a guide to bioethics? [letter]. *Chronicle of Higher Education* 2005 July 8; 51(44): B13. NRCBL: 2.1; 7.1; 1.1.

Musschenga, Albert W. Empirical ethics, context-sensitivity, and contextualism. *Journal of Medicine and Philosophy* 2005 October; 30(5): 467- 490. NRCBL: 2.1; 1.1. SC: em.

Abstract: In medical ethics, business ethics, and some branches of political philosophy (multi-culturalism, issues of just allocation, and equitable distribution) the literature increasingly combines insights from ethics and the social sciences. Some authors in medical ethics even speak of a new phase in the history of eth-

NRCBL: National Reference Center for Bioethics Literature Classification Scheme   See inside front cover for terms.

71

ics, hailing "empirical ethics" as a logical next step in the development of practical ethics after the turn to "applied ethics." The name empirical ethics is ill-chosen because of its associations with "descriptive ethics." Unlike descriptive ethics, however, empirical ethics aims to be both descriptive and normative. The first question on which I focus is what kind of empirical research is used by empirical ethics and for which purposes. I argue that the ultimate aim of all empirical ethics is to improve the context- sensitivity of ethics. The second question is whether empirical ethics is essentially connected with specific positions in meta- ethics. I show that in some kinds of meta-ethical theories, which I categorize as broad contextualist theories, there is an intrinsic need for connecting normative ethics with empirical social research. But context-sensitivity is a goal that can be aimed for from any meta-ethical position.

Nelson, James Lindemann. The baroness's committee and the president's council: ambition and alienation in public bioethics. *Kennedy Institute of Ethics Journal* 2005 September; 15(3): 251-267. NRCBL: 2.4; 2.2; 2.1; 1.1; 5.1; 5.3; 7.1; 14.1; 14.5; 4.4.
Abstract: The President's Council on Bioethics has tried to make a distinctive contribution to the methodology of such public bodies in developing what it has styled a "richer bioethics." The Council's procedure contrasts with more modest methods of public bioethical deliberation employed by the United Kingdom's Warnock Committee. The practices of both bodies are held up against the backdrop of concerns about moral and political alienation, prompted by the limitations of moral reasoning and by moral dissent from state policy under even the most democratic of governments. Although the President's Council's rhetoric is often scrupulously conciliatory, recurring features of its argumentative practice are regrettably divisive. They order these things better in Britain.

Noys, Benjamin. Bioethics and death. *In his:* The Culture of Death. New York: Berg; 2005: 77-99. NRCBL: 2.1; 20.1; 1.1.

Nyapadi, T.J. What are ethics (more particularly medical ethics)? *Central African Journal of Medicine* 2000 March; 46(3): 76-79. NRCBL: 2.1; 4.1.2; 1.3.1.

Oakley, Justin; Cocking, Dean. Consequentialism, complacency, and slippery slope arguments. *Theoretical Medicine and Bioethics* 2005; 26(3): 227-239. NRCBL: 2.1; 1.1. SC: an.

Pegoraro, Renzo. Dialogue with David C. Thomasma and Renzo Pegoraro. *Theoretical Medicine and Bioethics* 2005; 26(6): 575-589. NRCBL: 2.1; 21.7; 4.1.2; 5.1; 16.1.

Pence, Gregory E. Moral reasoning and ethical theories in medical ethics. *In his:* Classic Cases in Medical Ethics: Accounts of Cases That Have Shaped Medical Ethics, with Philosophical, Legal, and Historical Backgrounds. Fourth edition. Boston, MA: McGraw- Hill; 2004: 1-25. NRCBL: 2.1; 1.1.

Poland, Susan Cartier. Bioethics, biolaw, and western legal heritage. *Kennedy Institute of Ethics Journal* 2005 June; 15(2): 211-218. NRCBL: 2.1; 2.2; 21.1; 1.1. SC: le.

Powers, Madison. Bioethics as politics: the limits of moral expertise. *Kennedy Institute of Ethics Journal* 2005 September; 15(3): 305-322. NRCBL: 2.1; 1.1; 1.3.1; 2.2; 7.1; 5.1; 5.3.
Abstract: The increasing reliance upon, and perhaps the growing public and professional skepticism about, the special expertise of bioethicists suggests the need to consider the limits of moral expertise. For all the talk about method in bioethics, we, bioethicists, are still rather far off the mark in understanding what we are doing, even when we may be going about what we are doing fairly well. Quite often, what is most fundamentally at stake, but equally often insufficiently acknowledged, are inherently political, essentially contested visions of the most compelling and attractive forms of life for individuals and social organization. The current situation in bioethics parallels similar debates in eighteenth-century jurisprudence, especially Jeremy Bentham's withering critique of the prevalent forms of judicial argument and his own, equally unsuccessful, attempt to develop a decision-making procedure in ethics that would operate on a plane above politics. The risk, both then and now, is that we will fail to appreciate the wide range of reasonable disagreement that will remain past the point of extended reflection and discussion.

Pullman, Daryl. Ethics first aid: reframing the role of "principlism" in clinical ethics education and practice. *Journal of Clinical Ethics* 2005 Fall; 16(3): 223-229. NRCBL: 2.1; 4.1.2; 7.2.

Rand, Cynthia S.; Sevick, Mary Ann. Ethics in adherence promotion and monitoring. *Controlled Clinical Trials* 2000 October; 21(5 Supplement): 241S-247S. NRCBL: 2.1; 1.1; 8.4.

Richardson, Henry S. Specifying, balancing, and interpreting bioethical principles. *In:* Childress, James F.; Meslin, Eric M.; Shapiro, Harold T., eds. Belmont Revisited: Ethical Principles for Research with Human Subjects. Washington, DC: Georgetown University Press; 2005: 205-227. NRCBL: 2.1; 1.1. SC: an.

Rothfield, Philipa. Attending to difference: phenomenology and bioethics. *In:* Shildrick, Margrit; Mykitiuk, Roxanne, eds. Ethics of the Body: Postconventional Challenges. Cambridge, MA: MIT Press; 2005: 29-48. NRCBL: 2.1; 1.1; 8.1.

Schmidt, Kurt W. ". . . As we forgive those who trespass against us . . .": theological reflections on sin and guilt in the hospital environment. *Christian Bioethics* 2005 August; 11(2): 201-219. NRCBL: 2.1; 1.2; 1.1; 20.5.1; 8.5.
Abstract: In general parlance the term sin has lost its existential meaning. Originally a Jewish-Christian term within a purely religious context, referring to a wrongdoing with regard to God, sin has slowly become reduced to guilt in the course of the secularization process. Guilt refers to a wrongdoing, especially with regard to fellow human beings. It also refers to errors of judgement with what can be tragic consequences. These errors can occur whenever human beings are called upon to act, including the hospital environment. A Christian hospital has to address the issue of how to deal not only with guilt-ridden misdemeanors, but also with wrongdoing unto God, which overshadows every instance of guilt-ridden human behavior. Here, as in every parish, the Church Service is the place to acknowledge sin, confess sin, and forgive sin, beyond the boundaries of the parish itself.

Sheehan, Mark. Healthcare and (a kind of) virtue ethics. *In:* Häyry, Matti; Takala, Tuija; Herissone-Kelly, Peter, eds. Bioethics and Social Reality. New York: Rodopi, 2005: 149-160. NRCBL: 2.1; 4.1.2; 1.1.

Shildrick, Margrit. Beyond the body of bioethics: challenging the conventions. *In:* Shildrick, Margrit; Mykitiuk, Roxanne, eds. Ethics of the Body: Postconventional Challenges. Cambridge, MA: MIT Press; 2005: 1-26. NRCBL: 2.1; 1.1.

Shiraz, B.; Shamim, M. Shahzad; Shamim, M. Shahid; Ahmed, Asif. Medical ethics in surgical wards: knowledge, attitude and practice of surgical team members in Karachi. *Indian Journal of Medical Ethics* 2005 July-September; 2(3): 94-96. NRCBL: 2.3; 4.1.2; 7.2. SC: em. Identifiers: Pakistan.

Short, Bradford William. More history "lite" in modern American bioethics. *Issues in Law and Medicine* 2005 Summer; 21(1): 3-34. NRCBL: 2.1; 2.2; 1.1; 20.7; 20.5.1. SC: le.

Short, Bradford William. The healing philosopher: John Locke's medical ethics. *Issues in Law and Medicine* 2004 Fall; 20(2): 103-154. NRCBL: 2.2; 4.1.2; 12.3; 20.7; 20.5.1; 8.1.

Smith, Cedric M. Origin and uses of primum non nocere — above all, do no harm! [opinion]. *Journal of Clinical Pharmacology* 2005 April; 45(4): 371-377. NRCBL: 2.2; 4.1.1.

Solomon, David. Christian bioethics, secular bioethics, and the claim to cultural authority. *Christian Bioethics* 2005 December; 11(3): 349-359. NRCBL: 2.1; 1.2; 1.1; 7.1.
Abstract: Though the papers in this volume for the most part address the question, "What is Christian about Christian Bioethics", this paper addresses instead a closely related question, "How would a Christian approach to bioethics differ from the kind of secular academic bioethics that has emerged as such an important field in the contemporary university?" While it is generally assumed that a secular bioethics rooted in moral philosophy will be more culturally authoritative than an approach to bioethics grounded in the contingent particularities of a religious tradition, I will give reasons for rejecting this assumption. By examining the history of the recent revival of academic bioethics as well as the state of the contemporary moral philosophy on which it is based I will suggest that secular bioethics suffers from many of the same liabilities as a carefully articulated Christian bioethics. At the end of the paper I will turn briefly to examine the question of how, in light of this discussion, a Christian bioethics might best be pursued.

Song, Robert. Christian bioethics and the church's political worship. *Christian Bioethics* 2005 December; 11(3): 333-348. NRCBL: 2.1; 1.2; 1.1; 7.1.
Abstract: Christian bioethics springs from the worship that is the response of the Church to the Gospel of Jesus Christ. Such worship is distinctively political in nature, in that it acknowledges Christ as Lord. Because it is a political worship, it can recognize no other lords and no other prior claims on its allegiance: these include the claims of an allegedly universal ethics and politics determined from outside the Church. However the Church is called not just to be a contrast society, but also to witness to the freeing of the world from salvific pretensions in order that it may embrace its proper temporality. The implications of this for the distinctiveness of Christian bioethics are brought out in three movements: first, the Church's itself learning how it is to conceive bioethics; second, the Church's role in unmasking the idols of secular bioethics; and third, the Church's witnessing to the freeing of medicine from idolatrous aspirations.

Spike, Jeffrey. How not to philosophize with a hammer: reply to Montgomery. *In:* Thomasma, David C.; Weisstub, David N., eds. The Variables of Moral Capacity. Boston: Kluwer Academic Publishers; 2004: 129- 135. NRCBL: 2.1; 1.1; 7.1.

Tai, Michael Cheng-tek. The contextualized Asian principles of medical ethics. *Synthesis Philosophica* 2002 February; 34: 351-360. NRCBL: 2.1; 1.1; 1.2.

Takala, Tuija. Demagogues, firefighters, and window dressers: who are we and what should we be? *CQ: Cambridge Quarterly of Healthcare Ethics* 2005 Fall; 14(4): 385-388. NRCBL: 2.1; 2.2; 9.6; 1.1; 1.3.2; 1.3.1. Identifiers: experts in bioethics.

Tao, J.L.P.W.; Engelhardt, H.T., Jr. Towards a "One Country Two Systems" medical ethics for the regulation of practice promotion: Hong Kong as a case study. *Hong Kong Medical Journal* 2004 December; 10(6): 435-437. NRCBL: 2.1; 4.1.2; 9.1; 9.8.

Tobin, Bernadette. Australian consequentialism: an Australian critique. *Theoretical Medicine and Bioethics* 2005; 26(3): 165-173. NRCBL: 2.1; 1.1; 21.1.

Trotter, Griffin. Bioethics, Christian charity and the view from no place. *Christian Bioethics* 2005 December; 11(3): 317-331. NRCBL: 2.1; 1.2; 1.1; 7.1.

Tsai, D.F.-C. The bioethical principles and Confucius' moral philosophy. *Journal of Medical Ethics* 2005 March; 31(3): 159-163. NRCBL: 2.1; 1.1; 21.7.
Abstract: This paper examines whether the modern bioethical principles of respect for autonomy, beneficence, non-maleficence, and justice proposed by Beauchamp and Childress are existent in, compatible with, or acceptable to the leading Chinese moral philosophy-the ethics of Confucius. The author concludes that the moral values which the four prima facie principles uphold are expressly identifiable in Confucius' teachings. However, Confucius' emphasis on the filial piety, family values, the "love of gradation", altruism of people, and the "role specified relation oriented ethics" will inevitably influence the "specification" and application of these bioethical principles and hence tend to grant "beneficence" a favourable position that diminishes the respect for individual rights and autonomy. In contrast, the centrality of respect for autonomy and its stance of "first among equals" are more and more stressed in Western liberal viewpoints. Nevertheless, if the Confucian "doctrine of Mean" (chung-yung) and a balanced "two dimensional personhood" approach are properly employed, this will require both theorists and clinicians, who are facing medical ethical dilemmas, of searching to attain due mean out of competing moral principles thus preventing "giving beneficence a priority" or "asserting autonomy must triumph".

NRCBL: National Reference Center for Bioethics Literature Classification Scheme   See inside front cover for terms.

73

Twine, Richard. Constructing critical bioethics by deconstructing culture/nature dualism. *Medicine, Health Care and Philosophy: A European Journal* 2005; 8(3): 285-295. NRCBL: 2.1; 1.1.

Abstract: This paper seeks to respond to some of the recent criticisms directed toward bioethics by offering a contribution to a "critical bioethics". Here this concept is principally defined in terms of the three features of interdisciplinarity, self-reflexivity and the avoidance of uncritical complicity. In a partial reclamation of the ideas of V.R. Potter, it is argued that a critical bioethics requires a meaningful challenge to culture/nature dualism, expressed in bioethics as the distinction between medical ethics and ecological ethics. Such a contesting of the "bio" in bioethics arrests its ethical bracketing of environmental and animal ethics. Taken together, the triadic definition of a critical bioethics offered here provides a potential framework with which to fend off critiques of commercial capture or of being "too close to science" commonly directed toward bioethics.

Upton, Hugh. Ethical theories and practical problems. *Nursing Philosophy* 2003 July; 4(2): 170-172. NRCBL: 2.1; 1.1.

Veatch, Robert M. Common morality and human finitude: a foundation for bioethics. *In:* Baumann, Eva; Brink, Alexander; May, Arnd T.; Schröder, Peter; Schutzeichel, Corinna Iris, eds. Weltanschauliche Offenheit in der Bioethik. Berlin: Duncker & Humblot; 2004: 37-50. NRCBL: 2.1; 1.1; 21.7.

Waisel, David B.; Truog, Robert D. An introduction to ethics. *Anesthesiology* 1997 August; 87(2): 411-417. NRCBL: 2.1; 4.1.1; 7.1.

Waters, Brent. Freedom in responsibility: a response. *Christian Bioethics* 2005 August; 11(2): 167-173. NRCBL: 2.1; 1.2; 1.1; 18.5.4; 14.5.

Waters, Brent. What is Christian about Christian bioethics? *Christian Bioethics* 2005 December; 11(3): 281-295. NRCBL: 2.1; 1.2; 1.1; 4.4; 4.5; 7.1.

Abstract: What is Christian about Christian bioethics? The short answer to this question is that the Incarnation should shape the form and content of Christian bioethics. In explicating this answer it is argued that contemporary medicine is unwittingly embracing and implementing the transhumanist dream of transforming humans into posthumans. Contemporary medicine does not admit that there are any limits in principle to the extent to which it should intervene to improve the quality of human life. This largely inarticulate, yet ambitious, agenda is derived first in late modernity's failed, but nonetheless ongoing, attempt to transform necessity into goodness, and second the loss of any viable concept of eternity, thereby stripping temporal existence of any normative significance. In short, medicine has become the vanguard of a profane attempt to save humankind by extracting data from flesh. In response, it is contended that an alternative Christian bioethics must be shaped by the Incarnation, the Word made flesh. This assertion does not entitle Christians to oppose the posthuman trajectory of contemporary medicine on the basis of any natural or biological essentialism. Rather, it is an evangelical witness to the grace of Christ's redemption instead of the work of self-transformation. It is Christ alone who thereby makes the vulnerability and mortality of finitude a gift and blessing. Specifically, it is maintained that the chasm separating necessity and goodness cannot be filled but only bridged through the suffering entailed in Christ's cross, and through Christ's resurrection eternity becomes the standard against which the temporal lives of human creatures are properly formed and measured. Consequently, Christian bioethics should help us become conformed to Christ rather than enabling self- transformation.

White, Angela; MacDonald, Chris. Deep disagreement and Rawlsian "public reasons". *American Journal of Bioethics* 2005 November-December; 5(6): 62-63. NRCBL: 2.4; 1.1; 4.4. Identifiers: President's Council on Bioethics. Comments: comment on Lawrence J. Nelson and Michael J. Meyer, "Confronting deep moral disagreement: the President's Council on Bioethics, moral status, and human embryos," American Journal of Bioethics 2005 November-December; 5(6): 33-42.

Wiggins, Osborne P.; Sadler, John Z. A window into Richard M. Zaner's clinical ethics. *Theoretical Medicine and Bioethics* 2005; 26(1): 1-6. NRCBL: 2.1; 4.1.2; 9.6.

Abstract: This essay introduces a thematic issue focused on the contributions to clinical ethics and the philosophy of medicine by Richard M. Zaner. We consider the apparent divorce of Zaner's philosophical roots from his recent narrative immersions into the blooming, buzzing confusions of clinical-moral lifeworlds. Our considerations of the Zanerian context and origins of the clinical encounter introduce the fundamental questions faced by Zaner and his commentators in this issue, questions about the role of ethics consultants, moral authority, and clinical truths.

Wiggins, Osborne P.; Schwartz, Michael A. Richard Zaner's phenomenology of the clinical encounter. *Theoretical Medicine and Bioethics* 2005; 26(1): 73-87. NRCBL: 2.1; 1.1; 9.6; 8.1. SC: an.

Abstract: The "clinical ethics" propounded by Richard Zaner is unique. Partly because of his phenomenological orientation and partly because of his own daily practice as a clinical ethicist in a large university hospital, Zaner focuses on the particular concrete situations in which patients and their families confront illness and injury and struggle toward workable ways for dealing with them. He locates ethical reality in the "clinical encounter." This encounter encompasses not only patient and physician but also the patient's family and friends and indeed the entire "lifeworld" in which the patient is still striving to live. In order to illuminate the central moral constituents of such human predicaments, Zaner discusses the often-overlooked features of disruption and crisis, the changed self, the patient's dependence and the physician's power, the violation of personal boundaries and their necessary reconfiguring, and the art of listening.

Wueste, Daniel E. A philosophical yet user-friendly framework for ethical decision making in critical care nursing. *Dimensions of Critical Care Nursing* 2005 March-April; 24(2): 70-79. NRCBL: 2.1; 4.1.3; 2.3.

Yeun, Eun-Ja; Kwon, Young-Mi; Kim, Hung-Kyu. A Q-methodological study on nursing students' attitudes toward nursing ethics. *Journal of Korean Academy of Nursing* 2004 December; 34(8): 1434-1442. NRCBL: 2.1; 4.1.3; 1.2; 7.2. SC: em. Identifiers: Korea.

Zaner, Richard M. A work in progress. *Theoretical Medicine and Bioethics* 2005; 26(1): 89-104. NRCBL: 2.1; 1.1; 9.6; 8.1.

SC (Subject Caption):   an=analytical   cs=case studies   em=empirical   le=legal   po=popular   rv=review

Abstract: After expressing gratitude to each contributor, and briefly commenting on each, I probe several main themes of my work, addressing the question of the apparent difference between my earlier "philosophical" and later "clinical" writings. Central to both is the reflexivity of the human agent, and that each exhibits a form of practice regardless of the specific aims embedded in each. I then address the theme of narrative writing as my work has developed over the past several decades at the heart of which are questions of self and integrity.

Zubatov, Alex. Does it make sense to use fiction as a guide to bioethics? [letter]. *Chronicle of Higher Education* 2005 July 8; 51(44): B13. NRCBL: 2.1; 7.1; 1.1.

BIOETHICS AND MEDICAL ETHICS/ RELIGIOUS PERSPECTIVES

Barragán, Javier Lozano. Challenges for Christians in Europe in medicine and health care. *Dolentium Hominum* 2004; 19(2): 24-29. NRCBL: 2.1; 1.2; 21.1; 4.2.

Barragán, Javier Lozano. Fundamentos filosoficos y teologicos de la bioetica / Philosophical and theological foundations of bioethics. *Vida y Etica* 2003 December; 4(2): 5-43. NRCBL: 2.1; 1.1; 1.2.

Brooks, Michael. Not by the book [opinion]. *New Scientist* 2005 November 19-25; 188(2526): 22. NRCBL: 2.1; 1.2; 1.3.5.

Butler, Declan. Conclave kindles hope for bioethical reform [news]. *Nature* 2005 April 21; 434(7036): 944. NRCBL: 2.1; 1.2; 11.1.

Callahan, Daniel. Bioethics and the culture wars. *CQ: Cambridge Quarterly of Healthcare Ethics* 2005 Fall; 14(4): 424-431. NRCBL: 2.1; 2.2; 7.1; 21.1; 1.1; 1.2. SC: rv.

Campbell, Courtney S. Authority and agency: policies and principles in Latter-day Saints bioethics. *In:* Peppin, John F.; Cherry, Mark J., eds. Religious Perspectives in Bioethics. New York: Taylor & Francis; 2004: 109- 130. NRCBL: 2.1; 1.2.

Caplan, Arthur L. Arthur Caplan on the future of bioethics [interview]. *Free Inquiry* 2002-2003 Winter; 23(1): 28-29. NRCBL: 2.1; 5.1; 14.5; 15.1; 1.2.

Chahal, Devinder Singh. Sikh perspectives on bioethics. *In:* Peppin, John F.; Cherry, Mark J., eds. Religious Perspectives in Bioethics. New York: Taylor & Francis; 2004: 211- 220. NRCBL: 2.1; 1.2.

Chan, Jonathan. Daoism and bioethics: Daode Jin's doctrine of naturalness and the principle of non-action. *In:* Peppin, John F.; Cherry, Mark J., eds. Religious Perspectives in Bioethics. New York: Taylor & Francis; 2004: 221- 231. NRCBL: 2.1; 1.2.

Chartier, Gary. The rule of double effect: a valuable contemporary resource. *Update [Loma Linda University Center for Christian Bioethics]* 2000 December; 16(4): 3-7. NRCBL: 2.1; 1.1; 1.2; 8.1.

Cherry, Mark J. Bioethics in the ruins of Christendom: why John Paul II's diagnosis requires a more radical cure than May and Colvert provide. *In:* Tollefsen, Christopher, ed. John Paul II's Contribution to Catholic Bioethics. Norwell, MA: Springer; 2004: 73-92. NRCBL: 2.1; 1.2. SC: le.

Cohen, Cynthia B.; Smith, David H. Bioethics in the Episcopal tradition. *In:* Peppin, John F.; Cherry, Mark J., eds. Religious Perspectives in Bioethics. New York: Taylor & Francis; 2004: 31-51. NRCBL: 2.1; 1.2.

Cohen, Eric. A Jewish-Catholic bioethics? *First Things* 2005 June-July; (154): 7-10. NRCBL: 2.1; 1.2; 18.5.4; 4.4.

Cohen, Philip M. Toward a methodology of Reform Jewish bioethics. *CCAR Journal: A Reform Jewish Quarterly* 2005 Summer; 52(3): 3- 21. NRCBL: 2.1; 1.2.

Collange, Jean-Francois. Bioethics and sin. *Christian Bioethics* 2005 August; 11(2): 175-182. NRCBL: 2.1; 1.2; 4.4; 14.5.

Colvert, Gavin T. Liberty and responsibility: John Paul II, ethics and the law. *In:* Tollefsen, Christopher, ed. John Paul II's Contribution to Catholic Bioethics. Norwell, MA: Springer; 2004: 51-72. NRCBL: 2.1; 1.2.

Cornwell, John. Against holy orders: will the papacy ever come to terms with progress in reproductive science? *New Scientist* 2005 April 23-29; 186(2496): 23. NRCBL: 2.1; 1.2; 14.1; 18.5.4.

Council for International Organizations of Medical Sciences [CIOMS]; World Health Organization [WHO]; Islamic Organization for Medical Sciences [IOMS]. International Ethical Guidelines for Biomedical Research Involving Human Subjects (An Islamic Perspective). Geneva: The Council 2004; 74 p. [Online]. Available: http://www.islamset.com/ioms/Code2004/index.html [5 August 20055]. NRCBL: 2.1; 1.2.

Cozby, Dimitri. Notes on "Bioethics and Sin" by Jean-Francois Collange. *Christian Bioethics* 2005 August; 11(2): 183-188. NRCBL: 2.1; 1.2; 4.4; 14.5.
Abstract: Placing the notion of sin in the context of a meontic account of evil, and emphasizing the effect of sin on the sinner himself, this commentary exposes the insufficiency of restricting oneself to human efforts at atonement, and of thus underemphasizing the role of Christ. Collange's claim that the teaching of "predestination" is rooted in Paul and that the doctrine of merits and indulgences is rooted in Augustine is criticized, and Luther's "forensic" understanding is linked with Augustine, rather than with Paul. Collange's reduction of the concern for holiness to respect and trust is contrasted with holiness's essential context of loving unification with God. The commentary closes by exposing the unsatisfactory scantiness of Collange's treatment of cloning, health-care economy, and of the evils of life.

NRCBL: National Reference Center for Bioethics Literature Classification Scheme   See inside front cover for terms.

75

Cozby, Dimitri. So finally, what is Christian about Christian bioethics? *Christian Bioethics* 2005 December; 11(3): 255-267. NRCBL: 2.1; 1.2; 1.1.

Abstract: The author criticizes the essays in this issue by Waters, Erickson, Trotter and Verhey for not placing an adequate Christology at the center of their definitions what is Christian bioethics.

Crawford, Cromwell. Hindu bioethics. *In:* Peppin, John F.; Cherry, Mark J., eds. Religious Perspectives in Bioethics. New York: Taylor & Francis; 2004: 189- 209. NRCBL: 2.1; 1.2.

Dabrock, Peter. "Suchet der Stadt Bestes" (Jer 29,7)—Transpartikularisierung als Aufgabe einer theologischen Bioethik—entwickelt im Gespräch mit der Differentialethik von Hans-Martin Sass. *In:* Baumann, Eva; Brink, Alexander; May, Arnd T.; Schröder, Peter; Schutzeichel, Corinna Iris, eds. Weltanschauliche Offenheit in der Bioethik. Berlin: Duncker & Humblot; 2004: 115-146. NRCBL: 2.1; 1.2; 21.7.

Delkeskamp-Hayes, Corinna. Between morality and repentance: recapturing "sin" for bioethics. *Christian Bioethics* 2005 August; 11(2): 93-132. NRCBL: 2.1; 1.2; 1.1.

Abstract: Distinguishing within "sin" the dimensions of anomia, hamartia, and asthenia makes it possible to analyze in greater detail the contrary manners in which traditional and post- traditional Christianities in this issue of Christian Bioethics endeavor to recapture what was lost when secular bioethics reconstructed the specifically spiritual-context-oriented normative commitments of Christianity in one-dimensionally moral terms. Various post-traditional attempts at securing moral orientation and resources for forgiveness, both of which secular bioethics finds increasingly difficult to provide, are critically reviewed. Their engagement of secular moral concepts and concerns, and even their adoption of an academically philosophical posture and language, is presented as responsible for their failure to adequately preserve what in traditional Christianity would count as prohibited vs. permitted, and advisable vs. non-advisable, or what would allow to resolve "tragic conflicts." The deeper reason for this failure lies in post-traditional Christianity's restricting the Christian life (with its central tension between love and the law) to what can be captured by cognitive categories. As the survey of several traditionally Christian accounts of sin in bioethics makes clear, both moral orientation (along with the resolution of "tragic" conflicts) and the sources of forgiveness are available, once that Christian life is framed in terms of persons' spirit-supported practical involvement in ascesis and liturgy, and once bioethical reflections are situated in the experiential context of such involvement.

Delkeskamp-Hayes, Corinna; Zierenberg, Matthias. Gospel truth and societal consensus: recent bioethics statements by the Protestant church in Germany (EKD). *In:* Peppin, John F.; Cherry, Mark J., eds. Religious Perspectives in Bioethics. New York: Taylor & Francis; 2004: 53-78. NRCBL: 2.1; 1.2.

Engelhardt, H. Tristram, Jr. Orthodox Christian bioethics: medical morality in the mind of the fathers. *In:* Peppin, John F.; Cherry, Mark J., eds. Religious Perspec-

tives in Bioethics. New York: Taylor & Francis; 2004: 21-30. NRCBL: 2.1; 1.2.

Engelhardt, H. Tristram, Jr. Sin and bioethics: why a liturgical anthropology is foundational. *Christian Bioethics* 2005 August; 11(2): 221-239. NRCBL: 2.1; 1.2; 1.1.

Abstract: The project of articulating a coherent, canonical, content- full, secular morality-cum-bioethics fails, because it does not acknowledge sin, which is to say, it does not acknowledge the centrality of holiness, which is essential to a non-distorted understanding of human existence and of morality. Secular morality cannot establish a particular moral content, the harmony of the good and the right, or the necessary precedence of morality over prudence, because such is possible only in terms of an ultimate point of reference: God. The necessity of a rightly ordered appreciation of God places centrally the focus on holiness and the avoidance of sin. Because the cardinal relationship of creatures to their Creator is worship, and because the cardinal corporate act of human worship is the Liturgy, morality in general and bioethics in particular can be understood in terms of the conditions necessary, so as worthily to enter into Eucharistic liturgical participation. Morality can be summed up in terms of the requirements of ritual purity. A liturgical anthropology is foundational to an account of the content-full morality and bioethics that should bind humans, since humans are first and foremost creatures obliged to join in rightly ordered worship of their Creator. When humans worship correctly, when they avoid sin and pursue holiness, they participate in restoring created reality.

Engelhardt, H. Tristram, Jr. What is Christian about Christian bioethics? Metaphysical, epistemological, and moral differences. *Christian Bioethics* 2005 December; 11(3): 241-253. NRCBL: 2.1; 1.2; 1.1; 7.1.

Erickson, Stephen A. On the Christian in Christian bioethics. *Christian Bioethics* 2005 December; 11(3): 269-279. NRCBL: 2.1; 1.2; 1.1; 4.4.

Abstract: What is Christian about Christian bioethics? And is an authentically Christian bioethics a practical possibility in the world in which we find ourselves? In my essay I argue that personhood and the personal are so fundamental to the Christian understanding of our humanity that body, soul, and spirit are probably best understood as the components of a triune (as opposed to dual) aspect theory of personhood. To confess to a Christian bioethics is to admit that Christians cannot pretend fully to understand either cures or their meaning. However effective and "knowledge-based" contemporary medical interventions are, a Christian must humbly and honestly confess a lack of complete knowledge on both levels. At the same time, a Christian bioethicist must express a total personal commitment to Christian Faith.

Foran, John E. The human act and medical practice. *Linacre Quarterly* 2005 February; 72(1): 27-30. NRCBL: 2.1; 1.2.

Francis, C.M. Medical ethics in India: ancient and modern (I). *Issues in Medical Ethics* 1996 October-December; 4(4): 115-118. NRCBL: 2.1; 2.2; 1.2; 1.1; 8.3.1. Identifiers: India.

Gordon, Harvey L.; Washofsky, Mark. Jewish bioethics. *In:* Peppin, John F.; Cherry, Mark J., eds. Religious Perspectives in Bioethics. New York: Taylor & Francis; 2004: 131- 146. NRCBL: 2.1; 1.2.

Gormally, Luke. Pope John Paul II's teaching on human dignity and its implications for bioethics. *In:* Tollefsen, Christopher, ed. John Paul II's Contribution to Catholic Bioethics. Norwell, MA: Springer; 2004: 7-33. NRCBL: 2.1; 1.2; 4.4.

Gräb-Schmidt, Elisabeth. Freedom in responsibility: on the relevance of "sin" as a hermeneutic guiding principle in bioethical decision making. *Christian Bioethics* 2005 August; 11(2): 147-165. NRCBL: 2.1; 1.2; 1.1; 5.1; 5.3; 18.5.4; 14.5.
Abstract: This essay deals with questions of responsibility concerning technology, in particular, gene technology and the special problem of research on embryos. I raise issues concerning the extent of humans' authority to act and the limits of human freedom. In what way is that freedom given, and what kind of responsibility results from it? By discussing various concepts of human freedom in the tradition of European philosophy, as juxtaposed to the Protestant understanding of freedom, this essay discusses the restricting limits, and the obligation to take responsibility. It will turn out that the question concerning freedom cannot be answered without understanding what being human involves. From a Christian perspective, this implies that the foundational relationship between human freedom and sin will be central to an assessment of the human ability to take responsibility. By obliterating the limits of human freedom, sin jeopardizes the very essence of that freedom. The project of taking into account the sinful state of the human condition thus aims at developing a realistic picture of the authority of humans in action, even in view of the human tasks of promoting science and research.

Griniezakis, Makarios; Symeonides, Nathanael. Bioethics and Christian theology. *Journal of Religion and Health* 2005 Spring; 44(1): 7-11. NRCBL: 2.1; 1.2. SC: an.

Groenhout, Ruth. Reformed perspectives in bioethics. *In:* Peppin, John F.; Cherry, Mark J., eds. Religious Perspectives in Bioethics. New York: Taylor & Francis; 2004: 79-95. NRCBL: 2.1; 1.2.

Hanford, Jack T. A public religion and biomedical ethics. *Pastoral Psychology* 2000 January; 48(3): 191-195. NRCBL: 2.1; 1.2.

Holm, Søren. Religion and bioethics. *Medical Ethics and Bioethics / Medicinska Etika & Bioetika* 2004 Spring-Summer; 11(1-2): 2-4. NRCBL: 2.1; 1.2; 8.1; 21.1.

IMANA Ethics Committee [Islamic Medical Association of North America]; Athar, Shahid; Fadel, Hossam E.; Ahmed, Wahaj D.; Haque, Malika; Nagamia, Hussain F.; Hathout, Hassan; Amine, Abdul R.C.; Khan, Faroque A.; Shanawani, Hasan. Islamic medical ethics: the IMANA perspective. Illinois: Islamic Medical Association of North America 2005 May 15; 12 p. [Online]. Available: http://data.memberclicks.com/site/imana/IMANAEthicsPaperPartl.pdf [20 September 2005]. NRCBL: 2.1; 1.2. Identifiers: Islam.

Imrényi, Tibor. Sin and bioethics. *Christian Bioethics* 2005 August; 11(2): 133-145. NRCBL: 2.1; 1.2; 12.3; 1.1; 15.4; 14.5.
Abstract: The essay starts out with defining the biblical concept of sin in the Old and the New Testaments. The literal knowledge of divine truth is distinguished from its truthful and spiritual interpretation. A further distinction should be made between the Creator of life (God) and the medium or "intermediary creator" (man) of life. I argue for the "single wholeness" of the human race and for the unity of human responsibility in bioethics. In delineating the teaching of the Church on abortion and family planning, I show that the healing of all human diseases, from traditional interventions to genetic ones, is a Christian duty and is in accordance with Christ's mission on earth as long as one has not been directly or indirectly involved in "reproducing" or "designing" one's descendants or destroying or damaging human life even at its very beginnings.

International Association of Catholic Bioethicists. Consensus statement on dignity in illness, disability, and dying; and a response to the UNESCO Universal Draft Declaration on Bioethics and Human Rights. *National Catholic Bioethics Quarterly* 2005 Winter; 5(4): 767-781. NRCBL: 2.4; 2.1; 1.2; 21.1; 20.5.1; 4.4. Identifiers: United Nations Educational, Scientific and Cultural Organization.

Islamic Organization for Medical Sciences [IOMS]; Al-Abd, Osama Muhammad. Islamic law rulings on certain medical questions: the arguments and the supporting evidence. Cairo, Egypt: Islamic Organization for Medical Sciences 2004 April 10; 37 p. [Online]. Available: http://www.islamset.com/ioms/Code2004/Islamic_vision2.html [5 August 2005]. NRCBL: 2.1; 1.2. SC: le. Conference: International Conference on Islamic Code of Medical Ethics; Cairo, Egypt; 11-14 December 2004; Islamic Organization of Medical Sciences, World Health Organization Eastern Mediterranean Regional Office, Islamic Educational, Scientific and Cultural Organization.

Jamison, John E. Spirituality and medical ethics. *American Journal of Hospice and Palliative Care* 1995 May-June; 12(3): 41-45. NRCBL: 2.1; 1.2; 1.1.

Keown, Damien. Buddhism and bioethics. *In:* Peppin, John F.; Cherry, Mark J., eds. Religious Perspectives in Bioethics. New York: Taylor & Francis; 2004: 173-188. NRCBL: 2.1; 1.2.

Lustig, Andrew. John Paul II on the good of life. *In:* Tollefsen, Christopher, ed. John Paul II's Contribution to Catholic Bioethics. Norwell, MA: Springer; 2004: 131-150. NRCBL: 2.1; 1.2.

Lustig, B. Andrew. Introduction: text, tradition, authority, and method in religious bioethics. *In:* Peppin, John F.; Cherry, Mark J., eds. Religious Perspectives in Bioethics. New York: Taylor & Francis; 2004: ix-xiii. NRCBL: 2.1; 1.2.

Maas, Susan. Thoughtful Trekkie: medical practice, faith, philosophy, and a bit of sci-fi inform the thinking of Mayo Clinic hematologist and ethicist C. Christopher Hook. *Minnesota Medicine* 2004 June; 87(6): 18-22. NRCBL: 2.1; 1.2; 5.1.

NRCBL: National Reference Center for Bioethics Literature Classification Scheme   See inside front cover for terms.

77

May, William E. John Paul II's encyclical *Veritatis Splendor* and bioethics. *In:* Tollefsen, Christopher, ed. John Paul II's Contribution to Catholic Bioethics. Norwell, MA: Springer; 2004: 35-50. NRCBL: 2.1; 1.2.

Mitchell, C. Ben. Southern Baptists and bioethics. *In:* Peppin, John F.; Cherry, Mark J., eds. Religious Perspectives in Bioethics. New York: Taylor & Francis; 2004: 97-108. NRCBL: 2.1; 1.2.

Moazam, Farhat; Jafarey, Aamir M. Pakistan and biomedical ethics: report from a Muslim country. *CQ: Cambridge Quarterly of Healthcare Ethics* 2005 Summer; 14(3): 249-255. NRCBL: 2.1; 1.2.

Mulligan, James J. Catholic identity and the rationale for the ethical and religiouss directives. *In:* McMahon, Kevin T., ed. Moral Issues in Catholic Health Care. Wynnewood, PA: Saint Charles Borromeo Seminary; 2004: 19-35. NRCBL: 2.1; 1.2; 4.4; 8.1.

Phaosavasdi, Sukhit; Thamkhantho, Manopchai; Uerpairojkit, Boonchai; Pruksapong, Chumask; Kanjanapitak, Aurchart. Searching for medical ethics in Dharma conversation. *Journal of the Medical Association of Thailand* 2005 March; 88(3): 440-441. NRCBL: 2.1; 1.2.

Repenshek, Mark; Belde, David. Honoring experience in moral discourse. *Health Care Ethics USA [electronic]* 2005; 13(1); 3 p. Available: http://www.slu.edu/centers/chce/hceusa/1_2005_2.html [19 September 2005]. NRCBL: 2.3; 1.2.

Rosner, Fred. An observant Jewish physician working in a secular ethical society: ethical dilemmas. *Israel Medical Association Journal* 2005 January; 7(1): 53-57. NRCBL: 2.1; 1.2.

Sachedina, Abdulaziz. Islamic bioethics. *In:* Peppin, John F.; Cherry, Mark J., eds. Religious Perspectives in Bioethics. New York: Taylor & Francis; 2004: 153- 171. NRCBL: 2.1; 1.2.

Sajoo, Amyn B. Taking ethics seriously: adab to zygotes. *In his:* Muslim Ethics: Emerging Vistas. New York:I.B. Tauris Publishers; 2004: 1-24. NRCBL: 2.1; 1.2.

Scalise, Daniele Maria; Bognolo, Giulio. The new pope and medical ethics — can Benedict XVI strike a balance between Catholic doctrines and health? [editorial]. *BMJ: British Medical Journal* 2005 June 4; 330(7503): 1281-1282. NRCBL: 2.1; 9.5.6; 11.1; 1.2.

Schmidt, Kurt W. ". . . As we forgive those who trespass against us . . .": theological reflections on sin and guilt in the hospital environment. *Christian Bioethics* 2005 August; 11(2): 201-219. NRCBL: 2.1; 1.2; 1.1; 20.5.1; 8.5.
Abstract: In general parlance the term sin has lost its existential meaning. Originally a Jewish-Christian term within a purely religious context, referring to a wrongdoing with regard to God, sin has slowly become reduced to guilt in the course of the secularization process. Guilt refers to a wrongdoing, especially with regard to fellow human beings. It also refers to errors of judgement with what can be tragic consequences. These errors can occur whenever human beings are called upon to act, including the hospital environment. A Christian hospital has to address the issue of how to deal not only with guilt-ridden misdemeanors, but also with wrongdoing unto God, which overshadows every instance of guilt-ridden human behavior. Here, as in every parish, the Church Service is the place to acknowledge sin, confess sin, and forgive sin, beyond the boundaries of the parish itself.

Sievernich, Michael. The significance of the concept of sin for bioethics. *Christian Bioethics* 2005 August; 11(2): 189-199. NRCBL: 2.1; 1.2.
Abstract: After a period during which the theological categories of sin and forgiveness were ignored or trivialized, presently these notions are being rediscovered. What could their impact be on bioethics, either in the narrow sense of medical ethics, or in the more encompassing sense of the ethics of the life sciences? This essay begins with describing the processes of transcending and ethitization, which gave rise to the biblical notion of sin. It portrays the theological foundation of sin in terms of a twofold refusal of proper relations to God and other humans. Through the practise of confession in the face of God (coram deo), sin is placed into a horizon of hope for forgiveness and reconciliation. The heuristic and hermeneutical significance of these categories results from their introducing a "surplus value," which transcends biological and ethical considerations. This additional dimension is illustrated in view of care (cura) for the injured, and in view of individual as well as collective willingness to forgive.

Smith, George P., II. Law, medicine and religion: towards a dialogue and a partnership in biomedical technology and decision making. *Journal of Contemporary Health Law and Policy* 2005 Summer; 21(2): 169-203. NRCBL: 2.1; 1.2; 5.1; 3.2. SC: le.

Smith, George P., II. Of Panjandrums, Pooh Bahs, Parvenus, and Prophets: Law, Religion, and Medical Sciences. Sydney, Australia: Macquarie University, Division of Law, 2005; 92 p. NRCBL: 2.1; 1.2; 7.1; 5.1. SC: le. Note: Derives from a lecture — under the same title — given, originally in honor of Justice Michael D. Kirby, AC, CMG, High Court of Australia, in the Banco Court of the Supreme Court Building, Queen's Square, Sydney, Australia, on July 27, 2005, and in commemoration of the thirtieth anniversary of the founding of the Division of Law at Macquarie University.

Solomon, David. Christian bioethics, secular bioethics, and the claim to cultural authority. *Christian Bioethics* 2005 December; 11(3): 349-359. NRCBL: 2.1; 1.2; 1.1; 7.1.
Abstract: Though the papers in this volume for the most part address the question, "What is Christian about Christian Bioethics", this paper addresses instead a closely related question, "How would a Christian approach to bioethics differ from the kind of secular academic bioethics that has emerged as such an important field in the contemporary university?" While it is generally assumed that a secular bioethics rooted in moral philosophy will be more culturally authoritative than an approach to bioethics grounded in the contingent particularities of a religious tradition, I will give reasons for rejecting this assumption.

By examining the history of the recent revival of academic bioethics as well as the state of the contemporary moral philosophy on which it is based I will suggest that secular bioethics suffers from many of the same liabilities as a carefully articulated Christian bioethics. At the end of the paper I will turn briefly to examine the question of how, in light of this discussion, a Christian bioethics might best be pursued.

Song, Robert. Christian bioethics and the church's political worship. *Christian Bioethics* 2005 December; 11(3): 333-348. NRCBL: 2.1; 1.2; 1.1; 7.1.

Abstract: Christian bioethics springs from the worship that is the response of the Church to the Gospel of Jesus Christ. Such worship is distinctively political in nature, in that it acknowledges Christ as Lord. Because it is a political worship, it can recognize no other lords and no other prior claims on its allegiance: these include the claims of an allegedly universal ethics and politics determined from outside the Church. However the Church is called not just to be a contrast society, but also to witness to the freeing of the world from salvific pretensions in order that it may embrace its proper temporality. The implications of this for the distinctiveness of Christian bioethics are brought out in three movements: first, the Church's itself learning how it is to conceive bioethics; second, the Church's role in unmasking the idols of secular bioethics; and third, the Church's witnessing to the freeing of medicine from idolatrous aspirations.

Tai, Michael Cheng-tek. The contextualized Asian principles of medical ethics. *Synthesis Philosophica* 2002 February; 34: 351-360. NRCBL: 2.1; 1.1; 1.2.

Tollefsen, Christopher; Boyle, Joseph. Roman Catholic bioethics. *In:* Peppin, John F.; Cherry, Mark J., eds. Religious Perspectives in Bioethics. New York: Taylor & Francis; 2004: 1-20. NRCBL: 2.1; 1.2.

Trotter, Griffin. Bioethics, Christian charity and the view from no place. *Christian Bioethics* 2005 December; 11(3): 317-331. NRCBL: 2.1; 1.2; 1.1; 7.1.

Verhey, Allen. What makes Christian bioethics Christian? Bible, story, and communal discernment. *Christian Bioethics* 2005 December; 11(3): 297-315. NRCBL: 2.1; 1.2; 7.1.

Abstract: Scripture is somehow normative for any bioethic that would be Christian. There are problems, however, both with Scripture and with those who read Scripture. Methodological reflection is necessary. Scripture must be read humbly and in Christian community. It must be read not as a timeless code but as the story of God and of our lives. That story moves from creation to a new creation. At the center of the Christian story are the stories of Jesus of Nazareth as healer, preacher of good news to the poor, and sufferer. The story shapes character and conduct and enables communal discernment.

Waters, Brent. Freedom in responsibility: a response. *Christian Bioethics* 2005 August; 11(2): 167-173. NRCBL: 2.1; 1.2; 1.1; 18.5.4; 14.5.

Waters, Brent. What is Christian about Christian bioethics? *Christian Bioethics* 2005 December; 11(3): 281-295. NRCBL: 2.1; 1.2; 1.1; 4.4; 4.5; 7.1.

Abstract: What is Christian about Christian bioethics? The short answer to this question is that the Incarnation should shape the form and content of Christian bioethics. In explicating this answer it is argued that contemporary medicine is un-wittingly embracing and implementing the transhumanist dream of transforming humans into posthumans. Contemporary medicine does not admit that there are any limits in principle to the extent to which it should intervene to improve the quality of human life. This largely inarticulate, yet ambitious, agenda is derived first in late modernity's failed, but nonetheless ongoing, attempt to transform necessity into goodness, and second the loss of any viable concept of eternity, thereby stripping temporal existence of any normative significance. In short, medicine has become the vanguard of a profane attempt to save humankind by extracting data from flesh. In response, it is contended that an alternative Christian bioethics must be shaped by the Incarnation, the Word made flesh. This assertion does not entitle Christians to oppose the posthuman trajectory of contemporary medicine on the basis of any natural or biological essentialism. Rather, it is an evangelical witness to the grace of Christ's redemption instead of the work of self-transformation. It is Christ alone who thereby makes the vulnerability and mortality of finitude a gift and blessing. Specifically, it is maintained that the chasm separating necessity and goodness cannot be filled but only bridged through the suffering entailed in Christ's cross, and through Christ's resurrection eternity becomes the standard against which the temporal lives of human creatures are properly formed and measured. Consequently, Christian bioethics should help us become conformed to Christ rather than enabling self-transformation.

Yavarone, Mark. Is bioethics "pastorally relevant?". *Ethics and Medics* 2003 September; 28(9): 1-2. NRCBL: 2.1; 1.2.

Yeun, Eun-Ja; Kwon, Young-Mi; Kim, Hung-Kyu. A Q-methodological study on nursing students' attitudes toward nursing ethics. *Journal of Korean Academy of Nursing* 2004 December; 34(8): 1434-1442. NRCBL: 2.1; 4.1.3; 1.2; 7.2. SC: em. Identifiers: Korea.

BIOETHICS COMMISSIONS *See* BIOETHICS AND MEDICAL ETHICS/ COMMISSIONS

BIOLOGICAL WARFARE *See* WAR AND TERRORISM

BIOMEDICAL RESEARCH
See also BEHAVIORAL RESEARCH; HUMAN EXPERIMENTATION; JOURNALISM AND PUBLISHING

The perils of public debate [editorial]. *Nature Neuroscience* 2005 May; 8(5): 535. NRCBL: 5.1; 5.3; 20.5.1. Identifiers: Terri Schiavo.

Andrew, Louise. Punishing experts, or protecting the courts? *Journal of Philosophy, Science and Law [electronic]* 2005 May 18; 5; 6 p. Available: http://www.psljournal.com/archives/index.cfm [25 May 2005]. NRCBL: 5.1; 1.3.5. SC: le. Identifiers: Daubert v. Merrell-Dow Pharmaceuticals Inc.

Bhattacharya, Kaushik; Cathrine, A. Neela. Ethical considerations in laparoscopic surgery. *Indian Journal of Medical Ethics* 2004 January-March; 1(1): 22- 23. NRCBL: 5.2.

NRCBL: National Reference Center for Bioethics Literature Classification Scheme   See inside front cover for terms.

79

Binetti, Paola. Biotechnology and the birth of a third culture. *Journal of Biological Regulators and Homeostatic Agents* 2004 July-December; 18(3-4): 255-260. NRCBL: 5.1; 2.1; 5.3; 4.4.

Bonkovsky, F.E. Resistance and biotechnology debates. *In:* Stone, Richard H.; Stivers, Robert L. Resistance and Theological Ethics. Lanham, MD: Rowan and Littlefield Publishers; 2004: 97-116. NRCBL: 5.1; 5.3; 15.3; 1.2.

Bruce, Donald. Making the world better? *New Scientist* 2005 June 11-17; 186(2503): 21. NRCBL: 5.1; 15.1. Identifiers: nanotechnology.

Elliott, Carl. Adventure! Comedy! Tragedy! Robots! How bioethicists learned to stop worrying and embrace their inner cyborgs. *Journal of Bioethical Inquiry* 2005; 2(1): 18-23. NRCBL: 5.1; 15.1; 9.7; 4.4; 7.1.

Ganchoff, Chris. Regenerating movements: embryonic stem cells and the politics of potentiality. *Sociology of Health and Illness* 2004 September; 26(6): 757-774. NRCBL: 5.1; 18.5.4; 15.1. SC: an.

Giacomini, Mita. One of these things is not like the others: the idea of precedence in health technology assessment and coverage decisions. *Milbank Quarterly* 2005; 83(2): 193-223. NRCBL: 5.2. SC: an.
Abstract: Health plans often deliberate covering technologies with challenging purposes, effects, or costs. They must integrate quantitative evidence (e.g., how well a technology works) with qualitative, normative assessments (e.g., whether it works well enough for a worthwhile purpose). Arguments from analogy and precedent help integrate these criteria and establish standards for their policy application. Examples of arguments are described for three technologies (ICSI, genetic tests, and Viagra). Drawing lessons from law, ethics, philosophy, and the social sciences, a framework is developed for case-based evaluation of new technologies. The decision-making cycle includes (1) taking stock of past decisions and formulating precedents, (2) deciding new cases, and (3) assimilating decisions into the case history and evaluation framework. Each stage requires distinctive decision maker roles, information, and methods.

Gordijn, Bert. Nanoethics: from utopian dreams and apocalyptic nightmares towards a more balanced view. *Science and Engineering Ethics* 2005 October; 11(4): 521-533. NRCBL: 5.1; 4.4.

Hails, Rosie. Bioethics for technology? *Current Opinion in Biotechnology* 2004 June; 15(3): 250-253. NRCBL: 5.1; 14.5; 15.1; 1.3.11.

Hanft, Ruth S.; Spernak, Stephanie M. Social, ethical, and legal concerns: experimentation, rationing, and practice standards. *In their:* Technology in American Health Care: Policy Directions for Effective Evaluation and Management. Ann Arbor: The University of Michigan Press; 2004: 350-363, 387-431. NRCBL: 5.2.

Hofmann, Bjørn. Toward a procedure for integrating moral issues in health technology assessment. *International Journal of Technology Assessment in Health Care* 2005 Summer; 21(3): 312-318. NRCBL: 5.2; 1.1; 9.1.

Hogle, Linda F. Medical technologies. *In:* Restivo, Sal, ed. Science, Technology, and Society: An Encyclopedia. New York: Oxford University Press; 2005: 311-318. NRCBL: 5.1.

Jones, D. Gareth. Making human life captive to biomedical technology: Christianity and the demise of human values. *Update [Loma Linda University Center for Christian Bioethics]* 1995 December; 11(4); 18 p. NRCBL: 5.1; 15.1; 14.1; 2.1; 1.2.

Kurzweil, Ray. Human 2.0. *New Scientist* 2005 September 24-30; 187(2518): 32-37. NRCBL: 5.2; 15.1.

Lehoux, Pascale; Denis, Jean-Louis; Tailliez, Stéphanie; Hivon, Myriam. Dissemination of health technology assessments: identifying the visions guiding an evolving policy innovation in Canada. *Journal of Health Politics, Policy and Law* 2005 August; 30(4): 603-641. NRCBL: 5.2; 5.3.
Abstract: Health technology assessment (HTA) has received increasing support over the past twenty years in both North America and Europe. The justification for this field of policy-oriented research is that evidence about the efficacy, safety, and cost-effectiveness of technology should contribute to decision and policy making. However, concerns about the ability of HTA producers to increase the use of their findings by decision makers have been expressed. Although HTA practitioners have recognized that dissemination activities need to be intensified, why and how particular approaches should be adopted is still under debate. Using an institutional theory perspective, this article examines HTA as a means of implementing knowledge-based change within health care systems. It presents the results of a case study on the dissemination strategies of six Canadian HTA agencies. Chief executive officers and executives (n = 11), evaluators (n = 19), and communications staff (n = 10) from these agencies were interviewed. Our results indicate that the target audience of HTA is frequently limited to policy makers, that three conflicting visions of HTA dissemination coexist, that active dissemination strategies have only occasionally been applied, and that little attention has been paid to the management of diverging views about the value of health technology. Our discussion explores the strengths, limitations, and trade-offs associated with the three visions. Further efforts should be deployed within agencies to better articulate a shared vision and to devise dissemination strategies that are consistent with this vision.

Leigh, Greg; Marschark, Marc. Ethics and deafness: a matter of perspective? [editorial]. *Journal of Deaf Studies and Deaf Education* 2005 Spring; 10(2): 109-110. NRCBL: 5.1; 4.4; 4.2.

McKneally, Martin F.; Daar, Abdallah S. Introducing new technologies: protecting subjects of surgical innovation and research. *World Journal of Surgery* 2003; 27: 930-935. NRCBL: 5.1; 18.2; 18.6. Identifiers: Canada.

Moore, Linda Weaver; Rieg, Linda S. The ethics of using cybernetics and cyborg technologies: what every rehabilitation nurse should know. *Rehabilitation Nursing* 2005 March-April; 30(2): 40-43. NRCBL: 5.1; 5.3.

SC (Subject Caption):   an=analytical   cs=case studies   em=empirical   le=legal   po=popular   rv=review

Priest, Susanna Hornig; Eyck, Toby Ten. Transborder information, local resistance, and the spiral of silence: biotechnology and public opinion in the United States. *In:* Braman, Sandra, ed. Biotechnology and Communication: The Meta-Technologies of Information. Mahwah, NJ: Lawrence Erlbaum Associates; 2004: 175-194. NRCBL: 5.1; 1.3.7; 15.1.

Reuter, Lars. The saving power of biotechnology: on public perceptions of a field of technology. *Ethical Perspectives* 2005 March; 12(1): 3-16. NRCBL: 5.1.

Schiffer, David. The limits of scientific research [debate]. *Neurological Sciences* 2005 February; 25(6): 351-354. NRCBL: 5.1.

Selgelid, Michael J. Ethics and infectious disease. *Bioethics* 2005 June; 19(3): 272-289. NRCBL: 5.1; 9.5.4; 9.5.10; 21.1; 9.1; 21.3; 1.1.

Abstract: Bioethics apparently suffers from a misdistribution of research resources analogous to the '10/90' divide in medical research. Though infectious disease should be recognized as a topic of primary importance for bioethics, the general topic of infectious disease has received relatively little attention from the discipline of bioethics in comparison with things like abortion, euthanasia, genetics, cloning, stem cell research, and so on. The fact that the historical and potential future consequences of infectious diseases are almost unrivalled is one reason that the topic of infectious disease warrants more attention from bioethicists. The 'Black Death' eliminated one third of the European population during the 14th Century; the 1989 flu killed between 20 and 100 million people; and, in the 20th Century smallpox killed perhaps three times more people than all the wars of that period. In the contemporary world, epidemics (AIDS, multi-drug resistant turberculosis, and newly emerging infectious diseases such as SARS) continue to have dramatic consequences. A second reason why the topic of infectious disease deserves further attention is that it raises difficult ethical questions of its own. While infected individuals can threaten the health of other individuals and society as a whole, for example, public health care measures such as surveillance, isolation, and quarantine can require the infringement of widely accepted basic human rights and liberties. An important and difficult ethical question asks how to strike a balance between the utilitarian aim of promoting public health, on the one hand, and libertarian aims of protecting privacy and freedom of movement, on the other, in contexts involving diseases that are—to varying degrees—contagious, deadly, or otherwise dangerous. Third, since their burden is most heavily shouldered by the poor (in developing countries), infectious diseases involve issues of justice—which should be a central concern of ethics. I conclude by providing sociological and historical explanations of why the topic of infectious disease has not already received more attention from bioethicists.

Squier, Susan. Giant babies: graphing growth in the early twentieth century. *In her:* Liminal Lives: Imaging the Human at the Frontiers of Biomedicine. Durham: Duke University Press; 2004: 112-145. NRCBL: 5.1; 7.1; 9.5.7; 4.5.

Squier, Susan. Liminal performances of aging: from replacement to regeneration. *In her:* Liminal Lives: Imaging the Human at the Frontiers of Biomedicine. Durham: Duke University Press; 2004: 214-252. NRCBL: 5.1; 9.5.2.

Steinbruner, John; Okutani, Stacy. The protective oversight of biotechnology. *Biosecurity and Bioterrorism* 2004; 2(4): 273-280. NRCBL: 5.1; 5.3; 21.3.

Zimmerli, Walter Ch. Natur als technische Kultur: Veränderung der Ethik durch Gentechnik. *In:* Baumann, Eva; Brink, Alexander; May, Arnd T.; Schröder, Peter; Schutzeichel, Corinna Iris, eds. Weltanschauliche Offenheit in der Bioethik. Berlin: Duncker & Humblot; 2004: 65-80. NRCBL: 5.1; 1.1; 15.1.

BIOMEDICAL RESEARCH/ RESEARCH ETHICS AND SCIENTIFIC MISCONDUCT
See also MALPRACTICE AND PROFESSIONAL MISCONDUCT

Agency under siege: conflicts-of-interest at the US National Institutes of Health justify the agency's ethics crackdown [editorial]. *Nature* 2005 July 21; 436(7049): 304. NRCBL: 1.3.9; 1.3.5.

Bad medicine [editorial]. *Nature Medicine* 2005 March; 11(3): 235. NRCBL: 1.3.9; 5.3.

Breach of trust: events in South Korea have highlighted a deep-seated problem [editorial]. *New Scientist* 2005 December 24-2006 January 6; 188(2531-2532): 3. NRCBL: 1.3.9. Identifiers: Woo Suk Hwang.

Divided loyalties: trust in science is being eroded. How can we restore it? [editorial]. *New Scientist* 2005 February 26-March 4; 185(2488): 3. NRCBL: 1.3.9; 1.3.5; 14.5; 18.6.

Insider trading versus medical professionalism [editorial]. *Lancet* 2005 September 3-9; 366(9488): 781. NRCBL: 1.3.9; 1.3.2; 7.4.

New ethics rules at NIH. *Journal of Investigative Medicine* 2004 May; 52(4): 233. NRCBL: 1.3.9. Identifiers: National Institutes of Health.

NIH announces aweeping ethics reform [press release]. *Bethesda, MD: National Institutes of Health* 2005 February 1; 2 p. [Online]. Available: http://www.nih.gov/news/pr/feb2005/od-01.htm [1 February 20051]. NRCBL: 1.3.9. Identifiers: National Institutes of Health.

No such thing as a non-lethal weapon [editorial]. *New Scientist* 2005 March 5-11; 185(2489): 3. NRCBL: 1.3.9; 21.3; 21.4.

On the shoulders of fraudsters [editorial]. *New Scientist* 2005 March 19-25; 185(2491): 5. NRCBL: 1.3.9.

One bad apple: people will never trust science so long as researchers make up results [editorial]. *New Scientist* 2005 November 5-11; 188(2524): 3. NRCBL: 1.3.9. Identifiers: Luk Van Parijs.

Open sesame [editorial]. *Nature Biotechnology* 2005 June; 23(6): 633. NRCBL: 1.3.9; 15.8; 15.10. Identifiers: Celera

NRCBL: National Reference Center for Bioethics Literature Classification Scheme   See inside front cover for terms.

81

Genomics; Celera Discovery Systems; Human Genome Project; Open Access/Open Source.

Rules of engagement: biologists may soon have little option but to sign up to codes of conduct [editorial]. *Nature* 2005 July 7; 436(7047): 2. NRCBL: 1.3.9; 21.3; 5.3; 1.3.5; 6.

Taking a hard line on conflicts [editorial]. *Nature* 2005 February 10; 433(7026): 557. NRCBL: 1.3.9; 1.3.5; 7.3. Identifiers: National Institutes of Health.

Too strict at NIH [editorial]. *Washington Post* 2005 February 23; p. A18. NRCBL: 1.3.9. SC: po. Identifiers: National Institutes of Health.

Vast abuses cited at National Health Institutes. *New York Times* 2005 April 12; p. A18. NRCBL: 1.3.9. SC: po.

Abbott, Alison. German oncology research shaken by fraud case [news]. *Annals of Oncology* 1998 January; 9(1): 1-2. NRCBL: 1.3.9; 18.2. Identifiers: Friedholm Herrmann; Marion Brach.

Abelson, Reed; Pollack, Andrew. Patient care vs. corporate connections: Cleveland Clinic wants to change but won't cut ties to industry. *New York Times* 2005 January 25; p. C1, C4. NRCBL: 1.3.9; 9.5.1; 9.7. SC: po.

Adams, Douglas; Pimple, Kenneth D. Research misconduct and crime lessons from criminal science on preventing misconduct and promoting integrity. *Accountability in Research* 2005 July-September; 12(3): 225- 240. NRCBL: 1.3.9; 1.3.5.
Abstract: For 200 years, criminologists theorized that delinquent and criminal acts arise from deviant psychological states (such as irrationality or immorality) and/or social conditions that produce these psychological states. This theoretical perspective, which is being duplicated in most efforts to understand and control research misconduct, has not been productive. More recently, criminological perspectives have emerged, emphasizing situational factors that enhance or restrict the opportunity for illegal or imprudent behavior. These so-called "opportunity" theories have been shown to have practical value in reducing crime rates. We explore the promise of these newer theories for the responsible conduct of research (RCR).

Akabayashi, Akira; Slingsby, Brian Taylor; Takimoto, Yoshiyuki. Conflict of interest: a Japanese perspective. *CQ: Cambridge Quarterly of Healthcare Ethics* 2005 Summer; 14(3): 277-280. NRCBL: 1.3.9; 7.3; 1.3.2; 18.3; 8.3.1; 21.1. SC: le.

Alexander, William; Berlin, Joshua; Cyr, Philip; Schofield, Andrew; Platt, Leslie. Realities at the leading edge of research [opinion]. *EMBO Reports* 2004 April; 5(4): 324-329. NRCBL: 1.3.9.

Allison, John R.; Cooper, William W. Data disclosure and data sharing in scientific research. *Accountability in Research* 1992; 2(2): 93-132. NRCBL: 1.3.9; 1.3.7.

Altman, Lawrence; Broad, William J. Global trend: more science, more fraud. *New York Times* 2005 December 20; p. F1, F6. NRCBL: 1.3.9; 14.5. SC: po.

Al-Marzouki, Sanaa; Evans, Stephen; Marshall, Tom; Roberts, Ian. Are these data real? Statistical methods for the detection of data fabrication in clinical trials. *BMJ: British Medical Journal* 2005 July 30; 331(7511): 267-270. NRCBL: 1.3.9. SC: em.
Abstract: OBJECTIVES: To test the application of statistical methods to detect data fabrication in a clinical trial. SETTING: Data from two clinical trials: a trial of a dietary intervention for cardiovascular disease and a trial of a drug intervention for the same problem. OUTCOME MEASURES: Baseline comparisons of means and variances of cardiovascular risk factors; digit preference overall and its pattern by group. RESULTS: In the dietary intervention trial, variances for 16 of the 22 variables available at baseline were significantly different, and 10 significant differences were seen in means for these variables. Some of these P values were extraordinarily small. Distributions of the final recorded digit were significantly different between the intervention and the control group at baseline for 14/22 variables in the dietary trial. In the drug trial, only five variables were available, and no significant differences between the groups for baseline values in means or variances or digit preference were seen. CONCLUSIONS: Several statistical features of the data from the dietary trial are so strongly suggestive of data fabrication that no other explanation is likely.

Armstrong, David. Surgery journal threatens ban for authors' hidden conflicts. *Wall Street Journal* 2005 December 28; p. B1, B2. NRCBL: 1.3.9; 1.3.7. SC: po.

Association of American Medical Colleges [AAMC]. Institutional Oversight of Individual Financial Interests in Human Subjects Resarch: Assessing Policies and Practices. Washington, DC: The Association 2003; 8 p. [Online]. Available: http://www.aamc.org/members/coitf/coisurvey2003.pdf [2 August 2005]. NRCBL: 1.3.9; 18.2; 7.2. Identifiers: survey questions. Note: Survey results available at http://www.aamc.org/members/coitf/coiresults2003.pdf.

Avanzini, G. Discussing "the limits of scientific research" [opinion]. *Neurological Sciences* 2005 February; 25(6): 305-306. NRCBL: 1.3.9; 5.1; 1.2; 15.1.

Barrett, Kirsten A.; Funk, Carolyn L.; Macrina, Francis L. Awareness of publication guidelines and the responsible conduct of research. *Accountability in Research* 2005 July-September; 12(3): 193-206. NRCBL: 1.3.9; 1.3.7. SC: em.
Abstract: We have conducted a longitudinal survey of NIH-funded F32 postdoctoral fellows to determine if mandated instruction in the responsible conduct of research (RCR) has measurable effects on awareness of, attentiveness to, and behavioral judgments about research ethics and authorship and publication. Of 418 F32 fellows participating in the study, 50% were aware of and had referred to guidelines on authorship and publication practices while 50% were either unaware of or had not referred to guidelines. Groups were similar with regard to total number of peer-reviewed publications and total number of first author publications, years of research experience, years since completing their doctoral degree, and receipt of RCR training. The equal distribution of guideline awareness nad use,

and group similarities with regard to career development and achievement provided us with an opportunity to consider whether awareness of and use of guidelines is associated with broader judgments about author roles and responsibilities. The findings suggest that awareness and utilization of guidelines are, at best, only modestly associated with more ethically appropriate judgments and attitudes about author roles and responsibilities among novice F32's.

Batchelor, Paul. Ensuring ethical standards in an international scientific journal: an evolutionary process [editorial]. *Community Dental Health* 2005 March; 22(1): 2-3. NRCBL: 1.3.9; 1.3.7.

Batmanabane, Gitanjali. ICMJE statement on compulsory clinical trial registration: should Indian journals follow suit? [editorial]. *Indian Journal of Medical Ethics* 2005 July-September; 2(3): 74-75. NRCBL: 1.3.9; 1.3.7; 18.6. Identifiers: International Committee of Medical Journal Editors.

Begley, Sharon. Fluoridation, cancer: did researchers ask the right questions? *Wall Street Journal* 2005 July 22; p. B1. NRCBL: 1.3.9; 16.1. SC: po; em.

Bernstein, Alan. New ethical requirements at the NIH: implications for CIHR and Canada. *CMAJ/JAMC: Canadian Medical Association Journal* 2005 August 16; 173(4): 353-354. NRCBL: 1.3.9; 18.2. Identifiers: National Institutes of Health; Canadian Institutes of Health Research.

Bero, Lisa A. Managing financial conflicts of interest in research. *Journal of the American College of Dentists* 2005 Summer; 72(2): 4-9. NRCBL: 1.3.9.

Bero, Lisa A. Tobacco industry manipulation of research. *Public Health Reports* 2005 March-April; 120(2): 200-208. NRCBL: 1.3.9; 1.3.2; 1.3.7; 9.5.9.

Bero, Lisa A.; Glantz, S.; Hong, M.-K. The limits of competing interest disclosures. *Tobacco Control* 2005 April; 14(2): 118-126. NRCBL: 1.3.9; 1.3.7; 9.5.9. SC: em.

Bird, Stephanie J.; Spier, Raymond E. The complexity of competing and conflicting interests [editorial]. *Science and Engineering Ethics* 2005 October; 11(4): 515-517. NRCBL: 1.3.9; 7.3.

Brainard, Jeffrey. Most researchers favor NIH policy that requires less information, survey finds. *Chronicle of Higher Education* 2005 August 12; 51(49): A22. NRCBL: 1.3.9. Identifiers: National Institutes of Health.

Brainard, Jeffrey. NIH consultant finds little evidence of bias against clinical researchers. *Chronicle of Higher Education* 2005 March 18; 51(28): A23. NRCBL: 1.3.9; 18.2. Identifiers: National Institutes of Health.

Brender, Alan. A nation's pride turns to shame. *Chronicle of Higher Education* 2006 January 6; 52(18): A27-A29. NRCBL: 1.3.9; 18.5.4; 14.5. Identifiers: South Korea.

Brooke, James. Korean leaves cloning center in ethics furor; admits lying on source of donated eggs. *New York Times* 2005 November 25; p. A1, A8. NRCBL: 1.3.9; 14.5.

Broome, Marion E.; Pryor, Erica; Habermann, Barbara; Pulley, Leavonne; Kincaid, Harold. The scientific misconduct questionnaire — revised (SMQ-R): validation and psychometric testing. *Accountability in Research* 2005 October-December; 12(4): 263- 280. NRCBL: 1.3.9. SC: em.

Abstract: Purpose: The overall purposes of this article are to report the development of a survey instrument, Scientific Misconduct Questionnaire-Revised (SMQ-R) that elicits the perceptions of research coordinators managing clinical trials about the various aspects of scientific misconduct and to present psychometric analyses for the SMQ-R. Methods: A panel of five researchers and research coordinators reviewed the original SMQ (Rankin and Esteeves, 1997) and suggested an additional 42 items based on the review of the literature and their own experiences in research. The SMQ-Revised (SMQ-R) consists of 68 closed-choice items in six sections and one section with 12 open-ended questions. The SMQ-R was sent to 5302 persons who were members of the Association for Clinical Research Professionals (ACRP) or subscribers to Research Practitioner, published by the Center for Clinical Research Practice (CCRP). Findings: Internal consistency of subscales was assessed with Cronbach's alpha and ranged from .83 to .84. Confirmatory factor analysis was used to test construct validity of the instrument subscales. The factor structure was assessed with the principal factors method, using the squared multiple correlations as initial communality estimates followed by varimax (orthogonal) or biquartimax (oblique) rotations. Analyses revealed five distinct factors among three subscales. Construct validity for the SMQ-R was also assessed by testing hypothesized relationships using the known groups approach. Conclusion: The current effort demonstrated the usefulness of the SMQ-R in obtaining information from a national sample of experienced research coordinators about their perceptions of the prevalence of different types of scientific misconduct and of factors that influence the occurrence of misconduct. The psychometric evaluation of the the SMQ-R suggests good internal consistency for most subscales and suggests adequate construct validity of the instrument as a whole. The analyses also suggest that further refinement of the instrument for future studies is warranted.

Carver, Neil; Ashmore, Russell. Anything to declare? Competing interests in mental health nursing journals [opinion]. *Journal of Psychiatric and Mental Health Nursing* 2004 October; 11(5): 620-622. NRCBL: 1.3.9; 1.3.7.

Catalona, William J.; Hakimian, Rina; Korn, David. Ownership and use of tissue specimens for research [letter and reply]. *JAMA: The Journal of the American Medical Association* 2005 March 16; 293(11): 1325-1326. NRCBL: 1.3.9; 18.3; 19.5.

Caulfield, Timothy. Commentary: an independent voice?: Conflicts of interest and research on ethical, legal and social issues. *Health Law Review* 2005; 13(2-3): 114-116. NRCBL: 1.3.9; 7.3.

Charlton, Bruce G. Conflicts of interest in medical science: peer usage, peer review and 'CoI consultancy' [edi-

NRCBL: National Reference Center for Bioethics Literature Classification Scheme   See inside front cover for terms.

83

torial]. *Medical Hypotheses* 2004; 63(2): 181-186. NRCBL: 1.3.9; 7.3. Identifiers: conflict of interest.

Claxton, Larry D. Scientific authorship. Part 1. A window into scientific fraud? *Mutation Research* 2005 January; 589(1): 17-30. NRCBL: 1.3.9; 1.3.7. SC: rv.

Claxton, Larry D. Scientific authorship. Part 2. History, recurring issues, practices, and guidelines. *Mutation Research* 2005 January; 589(1): 31-45. NRCBL: 1.3.9; 1.3.7. SC: rv.

Crigger, Bette-Jane. The curious saga of Congress, the NIH, and conflict of interest. *Hastings Center Report* 2005 March-April; 35(2): 13-14. NRCBL: 1.3.9; 5.3. Identifiers: National Institutes of Health.

Curfman, Gregory D.; Morrissey, Stephen; Drazen, Jeffrey M. Expression of concern: Bombardier et al., "Comparison of upper gastrointestinal toxicity of rofecoxib and naproxen in patients with rheumatoid arthritis," N Engl J Med 2000; 343: 1520-8 [editorial]. *New England Journal of Medicine* 2005 December 29; 353(26): 2813-2814. NRCBL: 1.3.9; 1.3.7. Identifiers: Vioxx. Comments: comment on C. Bombardier, L. Laine, A. Reicin, et al., "Comparision of upper gastrointestinal toxicity of rofecoxib and naproxen in patients with rheumatoid arthritis," New England Journal of Medicine 2000; 343: 1520-1528.

Dada, M.A.; Dhai, A. South African medical ethics: Biko, Basson, Bezwoda . . . what's next? [letter]. *South African Medical Journal* 2001 January; 91(1): 10. NRCBL: 1.3.9; 18.2; 18.6.

Dalton, Rex. Obesity expert owns up to million-dollar crime [news]. *Nature* 2005 March 24; 434(7032): 424. NRCBL: 1.3.9. Identifiers: Eric Poehlman.

Dalton, Rex; Check, Erika. Universities scramble to assess scope of falsified results [news]. *Nature* 2005 November 3; 438(7064): 7. NRCBL: 1.3.9. Identifiers: Luk Van Parijs.

de Wolf, Virginia A.; Sieber, Joan E.; Steel, Philip M.; Zarate, Alvan O. Part I: what is the requirement for data sharing? *IRB: Ethics and Human Research* 2005 November-December; 27(6): 12-16. NRCBL: 1.3.9; 18.6; 18.1.

Dean, Cornelia. Medical schools found to vary in their drug-testing standards. *New York Times* 2005 May 26; p. A24. NRCBL: 1.3.9; 9.7; 7.2. SC: po.

Dean, Cornelia. Mundane misdeeds skew finding, researchers say. *New York Times* 2005 June 14; p. F6. NRCBL: 1.3.9. SC: po; em.

Dennis, Carina. Diet book attacked for its high-protein advice [news]. *Nature* 2005 December 22-29; 438(7071): 1060-1061. NRCBL: 1.3.9.

DeRenzo, Evan G. Conflict-of-interest policy at the National Institutes of Health: the pendulum swings wildly. *Kennedy Institute of Ethics Journal* 2005 June; 15(2): 199-210. NRCBL: 1.3.9; 1.3.5; 5.3.

Doumbo, Ogobara K. It takes a village: medical research and ethics in Mali. *Science* 2005 February 4; 307(5710): 679-681. NRCBL: 1.3.9; 18.2; 21.1; 18.3.

Ehringhaus, Susan; Korn, David. U.S. Medical School Policies on Individual Financial Conflicts of Interest: Results of an AAMC Survey. Washington, DC: American Association of Medical Colleges [AAMC] 2004 September; 7 p. [Online]. Available: http://www.aamc.org/members/coitf/coiresults2003.pdf [2005 August 2]. NRCBL: 1.3.9; 18.2; 7.2. SC: em. Note: Survey questions available at http://www.aamc.org/members/coitf/coisurvey2003.pdf.

Eisen, Arri; Parker, Kathy P. A model for teaching research ethics. *Science and Engineering Ethics* 2004 October; 10(4): 693-704. NRCBL: 1.3.9; 2.3.

Feder, Ned. NIH must tell whole truth about conflicts of interest [letter]. *Nature* 2005 March 17; 434(7031): 271. NRCBL: 1.3.9; 1.3.5; 7.3. Identifiers: National Institutes of Health.

Feder, Ned. Public disclosure could deter conflicts of interest [letter]. *Nature* 2005 September 29; 437(7059): 620. NRCBL: 1.3.9; 1.3.5; 7.3. Identifiers: National Institutes of Health (NIH).

Field, Kelly. Biosafety committees come under scrutiny. *Chronicle of Higher Education* 2005 April 29; 51(34): A22-A23. NRCBL: 1.3.9; 5.1.

Fielder, John. Following the money at NIH. *IEEE Engineering in Medicine and Biology Magazine* 2004 November-December; 23(6): 64-65, 76. NRCBL: 1.3.9; 9.7; 1.3.2; 9.3.1. Identifiers: National Institutes of Health.

Fontanarosa, Phil B.; Flanagin, Annette; DeAngelis, Catherine D. Reporting conflicts of interest, financial aspects of research, and role of sponsors in funded studies [editorial]. *JAMA: The Journal of the American Medical Association* 2005 July 6; 294(1): 110-111. NRCBL: 1.3.9; 1.3.7.

Giles, Jim. Plans for research watchdog praised, but it may lack teeth [news]. *Nature* 2005 March 17; 434(7031): 263. NRCBL: 1.3.9; 2.4; 9.7; 7.3. Identifiers: United Kingdom (Great Britain).

Giles, Jim. Taking on the cheats. *Nature* 2005 May 19; 435(7040): 258-259. NRCBL: 1.3.9; 1.3.7.

Glaser, Bonnie E.; Bero, Lisa A. Attitudes of academic and clinical researchers toward financial ties in research: a systematic review. *Science and Engineering Ethics* 2005 October; 11(4): 553-573. NRCBL: 1.3.9; 1.3.3; 5.3. SC: rv; em.

SC (Subject Caption):   an=analytical   cs=case studies   em=empirical   le=legal   po=popular   rv=review

Grady, Denise. Study authors didn't report abortion ties. *New York Times* 2005 August 26; p. A15. NRCBL: 1.3.9; 12.1; 1.3.7. SC: po.

Griffin, Leslie. Watch out for whistleblowers. *Journal of Law, Medicine and Ethics* 2005 Spring; 33(1): 160- 162. NRCBL: 1.3.9; 1.3.2; 1.3.5; 1.3.8.

Grimm, David. Is tobacco research turning over a new leaf? [news]. *Science* 2005 January 7; 307(5706): 36-37. NRCBL: 1.3.9; 5.3; 9.5.9.

Hackett, Edward J.; Conz, David; Parker, John. Misconduct, scientific. *In:* Restivo, Sal, ed. Science, Technology, and Society: An Encyclopedia. New York: Oxford University Press; 2005: 338-343. NRCBL: 1.3.9.

Haigh, Carol; Jones, Neil A. An overview of the ethics of cyber-space research and the implication for nurse educators. *Nurse Education Today* 2005 January; 25(1): 3-8. NRCBL: 1.3.9; 1.3.12; 8.4; 18.6.

Hambling, David. Maximum pain is aim of navy study. *New Scientist* 2005 March 5-11; 185(2489): 8. NRCBL: 1.3.9; 21.3; 21.4. Identifiers: U.S. Office of Naval Research; University of Florida, Gainsville.

Hammerschmidt, Dale E.; Franklin, Michael. Secrecy in medical journals. *Minnesota Medicine* 2005 March; 88(3): 34-35. NRCBL: 1.3.9; 1.3.7.

Hampton, Tracy. NIH eases ethics rules on employees: consulting ban to remain [news]. *JAMA: The Journal of the American Medical Association* 2005 October 12; 294(14): 1749-1750. NRCBL: 1.3.9; 1.3.5; 7.3. Identifiers: National Institutes of Health.

Harris, Gardiner. Agency scientists divided over ethics ban on consulting. *New York Times* 2005 February 2; p. A17. NRCBL: 1.3.9.

Harris, Gardiner. Ban on federal scientists' consulting nears. *New York Times* 2005 February 1; p. A15. NRCBL: 1.3.9; 5.3. SC: po.

Harris, Gardiner. Health agency tightens rules governing federal scientists. *New York Times* 2005 August 26; p. A13. NRCBL: 1.3.9. SC: po.

Harvard Medical School; Harvard School of Dental Medicine. Faculty Policies on Integrity in Science. Boston, MA: Harvard Medical School, 2000 October; 22 p. NRCBL: 1.3.9; 6.

Healy, David. Manufacturing consensus [opinion]. *Hastings Center Report* 2004 July-August; 34(4): inside back cover. NRCBL: 1.3.9; 9.7.

Heitman, Elizabeth; Anestidou, Lida; Olsen, Cara; Bulger, Ruth Ellen. Do researchers learn to overlook misbehavior? [opinion]. *Hastings Center Report* 2005 September-October; 35(5): inside back cover. NRCBL: 1.3.9; 2.3.

Heitman, Elizabeth; Bulger, Ruth Ellen. Assessing the educational literature in the responsible conduct of research for core content. *Accountability in Research* 2005 July-September; 12(3): 207- 224. NRCBL: 1.3.9; 7.2; 5.3. SC: em.

Abstract: To determine core content for RCR instruction, content analysis was conducted using key instructional resources for ORI's nine RCR "core instructional areas". Topics discussed in these key RCR resources were identified and their frequency across resources was tabulated. Topics covered most frequently were judged to be core content. Although key educational resources cited a variety of references, specific topics and issues addressed were generally consistent across the materials examined. Nonetheless, key resources varied in organization and depth of coverage for core instructional areas. Recent resources were more systematic and comprehensive than earlier works. This was particularly evident in materials about human participant research, conflicts of interest, and data management and sharing. Key resources presented additional "non-core" issues, such as scientific values, epidemiological issues, and scientists' societal roles, suggesting that ORI's core instructional areas should be reconfigured or expanded. Because educational material available on RCR and professionalism was so comprehensive, we recommend that ORI consider research integrity, not research misconduct, as one core instructional area. We also recommend that compliance with research regulations be restored as a core instructional area to accentuate ethical, financial and legal requirements related to acceptance of federal funding.

Henig, Robin Marantz. Is this a solution? It may mollify some critics, but it's a stem cell shell game. *Washington Post* 2005 November 13; p. B2. NRCBL: 1.3.9; 1.2; 18.5.4; 19.1. SC: po.

Henry, David; Doran, Evan; Kerridge, Ian; Hill, Suzanne; McNeill, Paul M.; Day, Richard. Ties that bind: multiple relationships between clinical researchers and the pharmaceutical industry. *Archives of Internal Medicine* 2005 November 28; 165(21): 2493- 2496. NRCBL: 1.3.9; 1.3.2; 9.3.1; 9.7. SC: em.

Abstract: BACKGROUND: It is believed that pharmaceutical industry sponsorship of clinical research leads to the development of multiple ties between clinicians and the pharmaceutical industry. To quantify this relationship we conducted a survey of medical specialists listed in the Medical Directory of Australia in 2002 and 2003. METHODS: A questionnaire was mailed that elicited information about all aspects of research relationships between clinicians and pharmaceutical companies. The odds of reporting multiple additional ties (financial and professional) with pharmaceutical companies by clinicians who had an active research relationship were compared with those who did not. All clinicians who returned a completed questionnaire about their research activities were included in the study. RESULTS: A questionnaire was mailed to 2120 medical specialists; 823 (39%) responded. Of these, 338 (41%) reported involvement in industry-sponsored research in the previous year. They were more likely than others to have been offered industry-sponsored items or activities valued at more than 500 AU dollars (382 US dollars; odds ratio [OR], 3.5; 95% confidence interval [CI], 2.6-4.7) and support for attending international conferences (OR, 5.4; 95% CI, 3.9-7.4). The strongest associations were seen for acting as a paid consultant to industry (OR, 9.0; 95% CI, 3.9-20.4) and for membership on advisory boards (OR, 6.9; 95% CI, 5.1-9.6). There was a strong relationship between research collaboration and accumulation of industry ties. For 1

NRCBL: National Reference Center for Bioethics Literature Classification Scheme   See inside front cover for terms.

85

additional tie the OR was 2.2 (95% CI, 1.2-3.8) and rose to 6.3 (95% CI, 3.5-11.1) with 3 ties and 41.8 (95% CI, 14.5-143.4) with 6 or more ties. CONCLUSIONS: Medical specialists who have research relationships with the pharmaceutical industry are much more likely to have multiple additional ties than those who do not have research relationships. Institutional review should discourage clinical researchers from developing multiple ties.

Hildebrandt, Martin; Ludwig, W.-D. Clinical research and industrial sponsoring: avenues towards transparency and credibility. *Onkologie* 2003; 26(6): 529-534. NRCBL: 1.3.9; 9.7; 7.3. Note: Abstract in English and German.

Holden, Constance. Korean cloner admits lying about oocyte donations [news]. *Science* 2005 December 2; 310(5753): 1402-1403. NRCBL: 1.3.9; 7.4; 14.5; 15.1; 18.5.4; 19.1; 19.5.

Illingworth, R. Fraud and other misconduct in biomedical research [editorial]. *British Journal of Neurosurgery* 2004 August; 18(4): 325-327. NRCBL: 1.3.9; 1.3.7.

Jacobson, Jennifer. MIT fires biology professor who admitted faking data [news]. *Chronicle of Higher Education* 2005 November 11; 52(12): 13. NRCBL: 1.3.9; 1.3.7. Identifiers: Massachusetts Institute of Technology; Luk Van Parijs.

Jeffers, Brenda Recchia. Continuing education in research ethics for the clinical nurse. *Journal of Continuing Education in Nursing* 2002 November- December; 33(6): 265-269, 284-285. NRCBL: 1.3.9; 4.1.3; 7.2. SC: cs.

Jeffers, Brenda Recchia; Whittemore, Robin. Research environments that promote integrity. *Nursing Research* 2005 January-February; 54(1): 63-70. NRCBL: 1.3.9.

Jones, James W.; McCullough, Laurence B.; Richman, Bruce W. The ethics of odd ideas, good science, and academic freedom. *Journal of Vascular Surgery* 2005 June; 41(6): 1074-1076. NRCBL: 1.3.9; 1.2; 7.3. SC: cs.

Kaiser, Jocelyn. Final NIH rules ease stock limits [news]. *Science* 2005 September 2; 309(5740): 1469. NRCBL: 1.3.9; 1.3.5. Identifiers: National Institutes of Health.

Kaiser, Jocelyn. Forty-four researchers broke NIH consulting rules [news]. *Science* 2005 July 22; 309(5734): 546. NRCBL: 1.3.9. SC: le. Identifiers: National Institutes of Health.

Kaiser, Jocelyn. NIH chief clamps down on consulting and stock ownership [news]. *Science* 2005 February 11; 307(5711): 824-825. NRCBL: 1.3.9; 5.3. Identifiers: National Institutes of Health.

Kaiser, Jocelyn. NIH rules make some pack, others plead [news]. *Science* 2005 March 18; 307(5716): 1703. NRCBL: 1.3.9; 5.3. Identifiers: National Institutes of Health.

Kaiser, Jocelyn. NIH scientists raise fuss about scope of new rules [news]. *Science* 2005 March 4; 307(5714): 1390. NRCBL: 1.3.9; 5.3. Identifiers: National Institutes of Health.

Kansu, E.; Ruacan, S. Research ethics and scientific misconduct in biomedical research. *Acta Neurochirurgica* 2002; 83(supplement): 11-15. NRCBL: 1.3.9.

Karlawish, Jason; Whitehouse, Peter; McShane, Rupert H. Silence science: the problem of not reporting negative trials [editorial]. *Alzheimer Disease and Associated Disorders* 2004 October-December; 18(4): 180-182. NRCBL: 1.3.9; 1.3.7; 9.7; 9.3.1.

Katz, Jay. Experimentation with human beings. *In his:* Experimentation with Human Beings: The Authority of the Investigator, Subject, Professions, and State in the Human Experimentation Process. New York: Russell Sage Foundation; 1972: 283-321. NRCBL: 1.3.9; 18.1; 21.4.

Katz, Jay. The Jewish chronic disease hospital case. *In his:* Experimentation with Human Beings: The Authority of the Investigator, Subject, Professions, and State in the Human Experimentation Process. New York: Russell Sage Foundation; 1972: 9-65. NRCBL: 1.3.9; 18.5.1. SC: cs.

Kintisch, Eli. Researcher faces prison for fraud in NIH grant applications and papers. *Science* 2005 March 25; 307(5717): 1851. NRCBL: 1.3.9; 1.3.7. SC: le. Identifiers: Eric Poehlman; National Institutes of Health.

Klanica, Kaley. Conflicts of interest in medical research: how much conflict should exceed legal boundaries? *Journal of Biolaw and Business* 2005; 8(3): 37-45. NRCBL: 1.3.9; 7.3; 18.6.

Kolata, Gina. Clone scandal: "a tragic turn" for science. *New York Times* 2005 December 16; p. A6. NRCBL: 1.3.9; 14.5. SC: po.

Komesaroff, P.A. Misconduct in medical research: ethics and democracy [editorial]. *Internal Medicine Journal* 2003 April; 33(4): 137-139. NRCBL: 1.3.9.

Kreutzberg, Georg W. The rules of good science [opinion]. *EMBO Reports* 2004 April; 5(4): 330-332. NRCBL: 1.3.9.

Kwok, L.S. The White Bull effect: abusive coauthorship and publication parasitism. *Journal of Medical Ethics* 2005 September; 31(9): 554-556. NRCBL: 1.3.9; 1.3.7.
Abstract: Junior researchers can be abused and bullied by unscrupulous senior collaborators. This article describes the profile of a type of serial abuser, the White Bull, who uses his academic seniority to distort authorship credit and who disguises his parasitism with carefully premeditated deception. Further research into the personality traits of such perpetrators is warranted.

Lavelle, Sylvain. Science, technology and ethics: from critical perspective to dialectical perspective. *Ethical The-*

---

ory and Moral Practice 2005 June; 8(3): 217-238. NRCBL: 1.3.9; 5.1; 1.1.

Lind, Rebecca Ann. Evaluating research misconduct policies at major research universities: a pilot study. *Accountability in Research* 2005 July-September; 12(3): 241- 262. NRCBL: 1.3.9; 1.3.3; 7.2. SC: em.

Abstract: This pilot study evaluates the accessibility and usefulness of the research misconduct (RM) policies at the top-25 universities as ranked by NIH and NSF grant awards. Measuring accessibility demonstrates how readily-available policies are to the people they affect. Evaluating the range of policy content indicates whether policies and procedures on research misconduct are "useful" as opposed to merely "minimal" (Rhoades, 2003). On average, it took five clicks to get from a university's home page to its RM policies. Only nine policies were accessed within three or fewer clicks. Policy information was coded into categories comprising a total of 20 topic areas, which were then grouped into five content domains. The policies reveal a broad range of usefulness. Some provide relevant details on almost every topic area, while others leave most questions unanswered. Three of the 20 topic areas are almost universally covered in the policies analyzed. In contrast, five other topic areas average less than half of the information which could have been included. These policies, from elite U.S. research universities, may serve as role models; as such they should perhaps be held to the highest standards. If the message sent by a policy lacks clarity and precision, it should be revised to include an appropriate level of detail.

Lithuania. Seimas. Law on the Ethics of Biomedical Research. No. VIII-1679. Vilnius: Seimas of the Republic of Lithuania 2000 May 11; 10 p. [Online]. Available: http://www3.lrs.lt/c-bin/eng/preps2?Condition1=148740& Condition2= [11 July 2005]. NRCBL: 1.3.9. SC: le. Note: Effective 1 January 2001.

Lock, Stephen. Fraud in medical research. *Issues in Medical Ethics* 1997 October-December; 5(4): 112-114. NRCBL: 1.3.9.

Loew, Caroline J.; Fontanarosa, Phil B.; DeAngelis, Catherine D. Conflict of interest and independent data analysis in industry-funded studies [letter and reply]. *JAMA: The Journal of the American Medical Association* 2005 November 23-20; 294(20): 2575, 2576-2577. NRCBL: 1.3.9; 1.3.7; 9.7; 5.3.

Lumley, Judith. Conscience, regulation and scientific misconduct. *Res Publica* 1994; 3(1): 1-3. NRCBL: 1.3.9.

Mack, George S. Revolt in Bethesda [news]. *Nature Medicine* 2005 September; 11(9): 914-915. NRCBL: 1.3.9; 9.7.

Maloney, Dennis M. Both accused researchers and whistle-blowers stay anonymous when no misconduct is found. *Human Research Report* 2005 July; 20(7): 8. NRCBL: 1.3.9; 1.1. SC: le. Identifiers: McCutchen v. U.S. Department of Health and Human Services (Part 3).

Maloney, Dennis M. Privacy of researchers versus public's right to know their names. *Human Research Report* 2005 May; 20(5): 8. NRCBL: 1.3.9; 1.1. SC: le. Identifiers: McCutchen v. U.S. Department of Health and Human Services (Part I).

Maloney, Dennis M. Protecting against financial conflict of interest at the NIH. *Human Research Report* 2005 January; 20(1): 3. NRCBL: 1.3.9; 1.3.5.

Maloney, Dennis M. Researcher said his colleague should have revealed possible conflicts of interest. *Human Research Report* 2005 January; 20(1): 8. NRCBL: 1.3.9. SC: le. Identifiers: Cantekin v. University of Pittsburgh (Part 3); Bluestone.

Maloney, Dennis M. Researcher wins the battle but loses the war. *Human Research Report* 2005 April; 20(4): 8. NRCBL: 1.3.9. SC: le. Identifiers: Cantekin v. University of Pittsburgh (Part 6); Bluestone.

Marris, Emma. NIH ethics rules come off probation [news]. *Nature* 2005 September 1; 437(7055): 9. NRCBL: 1.3.9; 1.3.5. Identifiers: National Institutes of Health.

Martinson, Brian C.; Anderson, Melissa S.; de Vries, Raymond. Scientists behaving badly. *Nature* 2005 June 9; 435(7043): 737-738. NRCBL: 1.3.9. SC: em.

Mathews, Anna Wilde; Wonacott, Peter. Playing detective: at medical journal, editor finds truth hard to track down; termite-eaten data plague Dr. Smith's 12-year probe of an Indian researcher; pestering a busy statistician. *Wall Street Journal* 2005 December 27; p. A1, A2. NRCBL: 1.3.9; 1.3.8. SC: po.

McNeil, Donald G., Jr. Review cites ethical lapses by scientists. *New York Times* 2005 July 15; p. A15. NRCBL: 1.3.9. SC: po.

McSorley, Stephen J. It's not just theologians who are morally troubled [letter]. *Nature* 2005 January 27; 433(7024): 355. NRCBL: 1.3.9; 18.5.4.

Meier, Barry. Dispute puts a medical journal under fire. *New York Times* 2005 January 17; p. C1, C5. NRCBL: 1.3.9; 1.3.7. SC: po.

Meland, Eivind. Research ethics — revisited [editorial]. *Scandinavian Journal of Primary Health Care* 2003 September; 21(3): 129-131. NRCBL: 1.3.9; 5.3; 18.6.

Mello, Michelle M.; Clarridge, Brian R.; Studdert, David M. Researchers' views of the acceptability of restrictive provisions in clinical trial agreements with industry sponsors. *Accountability in Research* 2005 July-September; 12(3): 163- 191. NRCBL: 1.3.9; 5.3; 9.7. SC: em.

Abstract: We conducted a mail survey of 884 U.S. medical school faculty active in clinical research to elicit their views about the acceptability of provisions in contracts for industry-sponsored clinical trials that would restrict investigators' academic freedom and control over trials. We compared their responses to results from a similar survey of research administrators at 107 medical schools. There was substantial variation among clinical researchers in their acceptability judgments, with a relatively large proportion of clinical trial investigators

NRCBL: National Reference Center for Bioethics Literature Classification Scheme   See inside front cover for terms.

87

willing to accept provisions tha give industry sponsors considerable control over the dissemination of research results. There were significant differences in the perceptions of clinical trial investigators versus other recently published clinical researchers; investigators with a high versus low percentage of research support from industry; junior versus senior faculty; and investigators at institutions with high versus low National Institute of Health (NIH) funding ranks. There was also a significant divergence of views in a number of areas between clinical trialists and research administrators who negotiate clinical trial contracts on their behalf. Medical school faculty could benefit from additional guidance about what their institution views as acceptable parameters for industry-sponsored clinical trial agreements.

Miller, Franklin G.; Brody, Howard. Professional integrity in industry-sponsored clinical trials [opinion]. *Academic Medicine* 2005 October; 80(10): 899-904. NRCBL: 1.3.9; 18.2; 7.3.

Mojon-Azzi, Stefania M.; Mojon, Daniel S. Scientific misconduct: from salami slicing to data fabrication [editorial]. *Ophthalmologica* 2004 January-February; 218(1): 1-3. NRCBL: 1.3.9; 1.3.7.

Molenberghs, Geert; Imrey, Peter; Drake, Christiana; Fontanarosa, Phil B.; DeAngelis, Catherine D. Conflict of interest and independent data analysis in industry-funded studies [letter and reply]. *JAMA: The Journal of the American Medical Association* 2005 November 23-20; 294(20): 2575-2577. NRCBL: 1.3.9; 1.3.7; 9.7.

Moyer, Anne; Finney, John W. Rating methodological quality: toward improved assessment and investigation. *Accountability in Research* 2005 October-December; 12(4): 299- 313. NRCBL: 1.3.9.

Munhall, Patricia L. Ethical juxtapositions in nursing research. *Topics in Clinical Nursing* 1982 April; 4(1): 66-73. NRCBL: 1.3.9; 4.1.3; 1.1.

Nagl, Sylvia. Biomedicine and moral agency in a complex world. *In:* Shildrick, Margrit; Mykitiuk, Roxanne, eds. Ethics of the Body: Postconventional Challenges. Cambridge, MA: MIT Press; 2005: 155- 174. NRCBL: 1.3.9; 15.1; 1.1.

National Institutes of Health [NIH] (United States). Questions and answers for employees: supplemental standards of ethical conduct and financial disclosure requirements. Bethesda, MD: National Institutes of Health 2005 February 1; 6 p. [Online]. Available: http://www.nih.gov/about/ethics/020105COI_QandA.htm [2 February 2005]. NRCBL: 1.3.9.

National Institutes of Health [NIH] (United States). Summary of NIH-Specific Amendments to Conflict of Interest Ethics Regulations. Bethesda, MD: National Institutes of Health 2005 August 25; 2 p. [Online]. Available: http://www.nih.gov/about/ethics/summary_amendments_08252005.htm [12 September 2005]. NRCBL: 1.3.9; 1.3.5.

Ninth General Assembly of the Pontifical Academy of Life. Concluding communique on the "ethics of biomedical research for a Christian vision" (26 February 2003). *Linacre Quarterly* 2005 February; 72(1): 74-78. NRCBL: 1.3.9; 1.2; 18.1. Conference: Ninth General Assembly of the Pontifical Academy of Life; 26 February 2003.

Normile, Dennis. Tokyo professor asked to redo experiments [news]. *Science* 2005 September 23; 309(5743): 1973. NRCBL: 1.3.9.

Normile, Dennis; Vogel, Gretchen. Korean university will investigate cloning paper [news]. *Science* 2005 December 16; 310(5755): 1748-1749. NRCBL: 1.3.9; 5.3; 14.5; 15.1; 18.5.4; 19.1.

O'Donnell, Máire; Entwistle, Vikki. Consumer involvement in decisions about what health-related research is funded. *Health Policy* 2004 December; 70(3): 281-290. NRCBL: 1.3.9; 9.3.1; 7.1. SC: em. Identifiers: United Kingdom (Great Britain).

Pascal, Chris B. Scientific misconduct and research integrity for the bench scientist. *Proceedings of the Society for Experimental Biology and Medicine* 2000 September; 224(4): 220-230. NRCBL: 1.3.9; 6. SC: le.

Peart, Nicola; Dawson, John; Ferguson, Judy; Foley, Mary; Dunckley, Catherine. Liability for misconduct in research. *In:* Dawson, John; Peart, Nicola, eds. The Law of Research: A Guide. Dunedin, NZ: University of Otago Press; 2003: 323-344. NRCBL: 1.3.9. SC: le.

Pignatelli, B.; Maisonneuve, Hervé; Chapuis, F. Authorship ignorance: views of researchers in French clinical settings. *Journal of Medical Ethics* 2005 October; 31(10): 578-581. NRCBL: 1.3.9; 1.3.7. SC: em.
Abstract: OBJECTIVES: To assess the knowledge and behaviour of researchers regarding criteria for authorship, and the practices of ghost and gift authorship. DESIGN: Semidirective interviews of senior clinical researchers. SETTING: University hospital. PARTICIPANTS: Thirty-nine main investigators of clinical research programmes. MAIN MEASUREMENTS: Awareness and use of International Committee of Medical Journal Editors (ICMJE) criteria for authorship, and perceptions about ghost and gift authorship. RESULTS: A total of 48 protocols submitted by 42 principal investigators between 1994 and 1996 were identified. Thirty-nine investigators were contacted; 37 (one of whom delegated a co- author) were interviewed between May 2002 and March 2003. Two co- authors of two principal investigators were also interviewed. In all, 42 studies were represented. The interviews lasted for 40-90 minutes and were conducted with openness and respect for confidentiality.The choice of names of co-authors did not follow the ICMJE recommendations. Half of the respondents stated they were aware of criteria for authorship and knew of ICMJE, but most of them did not cite any of the ICMJE criteria among those they applied in deciding authorship. Most of them disagreed with the obligation to meet the three criteria justifying co-authorship because they found these too rigid and inapplicable. Gift authorship was a common practice; 59% of the respondents had been a recipient of gift authorship. Twenty-five (64%) were aware of ghost authorship and the majority considered it questionable and blameworthy. CONCLUSIONS: The ICMJE criteria were ig-

nored by clinicians at a university hospital. Ghost and gift authorship were frequent among them. There is a need for French guidelines for authorship to be prepared and implemented.

Pollack, Andrew. Medical researcher moves to sever ties to companies. *New York Times* 2005 January 25; p. C4. NRCBL: 1.3.9. SC: po.

Price, Alan R.; Hallum, Jules V. The Office of Scientific Integrity investigations: the importance of data analysis. *Accountability in Research* 1992; 2(2): 133-137. NRCBL: 1.3.9; 18.6. SC: le.

Pritt, Stacy; Nostrant, J.Fred; Smith, Barbara. PI and vet: potential conflict of interest? PI can't go it alone. *Lab Animal* 2004 October; 33(9): 21-22. NRCBL: 1.3.9; 22.2. SC: cs. Identifiers: principal investigator.

Priya, Ritu. Qualitative research in public health: perspectives and ethics. *Issues in Medical Ethics* 2000 October-December; 8(4): 113-115. NRCBL: 1.3.9; 9.1; 18.4.

Quilligan, Edward J. Conflict of interest [editorial]. *American Journal of Obstetrics and Gynecology* 2004 October; 191(4): 1057-1058. NRCBL: 1.3.9; 1.3.7.

Ready, Tinker. Cornell University scientists face charges of fraud [news]. *Nature Medicine* 2005 August; 11(8): 810. NRCBL: 1.3.9; 18.2.

Redman, Barbara K.; Caplan, Arthur L. Off with their heads: the need to criminalize some forms of scientific misconduct. *Journal of Law, Medicine and Ethics* 2005 Summer; 33(2): 345- 348. NRCBL: 1.3.9; 7.4; 1.3.5. SC: le.
Abstract: Improvement in policy for the management of scientific misconduct has been slow. While assurance of due process at the ORI level is now in place, similar protections at the institutional level and institutional responsibility for further oversight and a workplace where the responsible conduct of research can be practiced have not yet been addressed. In contrast, policy regarding human subject protection has evolved rapidly to reflect firmer norms, with decisive priority given to subject protection over scientific or social needs. Perhaps because scientific misconduct policy has the potential to harm the careers of individual scientists and harms to individual subjects are thought to be indirect, the scientific community has been successful in blocking every move toward testing more rigorous regulation. The mantras that scientists can discipline their own, and the price of competitive science is some level of scientific misconduct are not persuasive. The standards by which science is judged should not be an exception to those governing others who deal with the public's money and have a duty to the public interest.

Reidenberg, Marcus M. Decreasing publication bias [opinion]. *Clinical Pharmacology and Therapeutics* 1998 January; 63(1): 1-3. NRCBL: 1.3.9; 1.3.7.

Resnik, David B. Conflicts of interest at the NIH: no easy solution. *Hastings Center Report* 2005 January-February; 35(1): 18-20. NRCBL: 1.3.9; 5.3. Identifiers: National Institutes of Health.

Rosenthal, Elisabeth. Under a microscope: high-profile cases bring new scrutiny to science's superstars. *New York Times* 2005 December 24; p. A6. NRCBL: 1.3.9. SC: po.

Rubin, Eugene H. The complexities of individual financial conflicts of interest. *Neuropsychopharmacology* 2005 January; 30(1): 1-6. NRCBL: 1.3.9; 1.3.2. SC: cs.

Sang-Hun, Choe; Wade, Nicholas. Korean cloning scientist quits over report he faked research; backers of stem cell work fear larger setback. *New York Times* 2005 December 24; p. A1, A6. NRCBL: 1.3.9; 14.5. SC: po.

Sataloff, Robert T. Correcting the medical literature: ethics and policy [editorial]. *Ear, Nose and Throat Journal* 2005 February; 84(2): 65-66. NRCBL: 1.3.9; 1.3.7.

Saul, Stephanie; Anderson, Jenny. Doctors' links with investors raise concerns. *New York Times* 2005 August 17; p. A1, C6. NRCBL: 1.3.9; 9.7; 9.3.1; 1.3.2. SC: po.

Schachman, Howard K. On scientific freedom and responsibility. *Biophysical Chemistry* 2003; 100(1-3): 615-625. NRCBL: 1.3.9; 5.3; 6; 14.5; 21.1.

Schiermeier, Quirin. German tobacco papers reveal lump sums for health experts [news]. *Nature* 2005 June 16; 435(7044): 866. NRCBL: 1.3.9; 9.5.9; 9.7.

Schneider, Benjamin; Schüklenk, Udo. Module six: special issues. *Developing World Bioethics* 2005 March; 5(1): 92-108. NRCBL: 1.3.9; 2.3.
Abstract: The objective of this module is to cover ground that was not covered in-depth in any of the other modules, including: scientific misconduct, issues concerning the publication and ownership of research results (authorship guidelines - who is eligible to be considered an author, or contributor to a scientific paper etc.), special problems occurring in social science and epidemiological research, and the problems pertaining to conflicts of interest the various players in biomedical research activities could encounter.

Serour, G.I.; Dickens, B.M. Ethics in medical information and advertising. *International Journal of Gynaecology and Obstetrics* 2004 May; 85(2): 195-200. NRCBL: 1.3.9; 1.3.7; 1.3.12; 7.3.

Silver, Ken. Corporate influence on chemical exposure levels. *Science for the People* 1989 January-February; 21(1): 24-25. NRCBL: 1.3.9; 16.3.

Silverman, Jerald. PI and vet: potential conflict of interest? *Lab Animal* 2004 October; 33(9): 21. NRCBL: 1.3.9; 22.2. SC: cs. Identifiers: principal investigator.

Smith, Jane; Godlee, Fiona. Investigating allegations of scientific misconduct: journals can do only so much; institutions need to be willing to investigate [editorial]. *BMJ: British Medical Journal* 2005 July 30; 331(7511): 245-246. NRCBL: 1.3.9; 1.3.7.

Smith, Richard. Investigating the previous studies of a fraudulent author. *BMJ: British Medical Journal* 2005 July 30; 331(7511): 288-291. NRCBL: 1.3.9; 1.3.7.

NRCBL: National Reference Center for Bioethics Literature Classification Scheme   See inside front cover for terms.

89

Sovacool, Benjamin K. Using criminalization and due process to reduce scientific misconduct. *American Journal of Bioethics [Online]* 2005 September- October; 5(5): W1-W7. NRCBL: 1.3.9. Identifiers: Office of Research Integrity (ORI).

Abstract: The issue of how to best minimize scientific misconduct remains a controversial topic among bioethicists, professors, policymakers, and attorneys. This paper suggests that harsher criminal sanctions against misconduct, better protections for whistleblowers, and the creation of due process standards for misconduct investigations are urgently needed. Although the causes of misconduct and estimates of problem remain varied, the literature suggests that scientific misconduct-fraud, fabrication, and plagiarism of scientific research-continues to damage public health and trust in science. Providing stricter criminal statutes against misconduct is necessary to motivate whistleblowers and deter wrongdoers, and the provision of basic due process protections is necessary for ensuring a fair and balanced misconduct investigation.

Squier, Susan. The cultured cell: life and death at strangeways. *In her:* Liminal Lives: Imaging the Human at the Frontiers of Biomedicine. Durham: Duke University Press; 2004: 58-88. NRCBL: 1.3.9; 5.1; 19.1; 20.5.1.

Steinbrook, Robert. Standards of ethics at the National Institutes of Health [opinion]. *New England Journal of Medicine* 2005 March 31; 352(13): 1290- 1292. NRCBL: 1.3.9. SC: le.

Steinbrook, Robert. Wall street and clinical trials [opinion]. *New England Journal of Medicine* 2005 September 15; 353(11): 1091-1093. NRCBL: 1.3.9; 1.3.2; 9.7; 18.6.

Steneck, Nicholas H. The role of professional societies in promoting integrity in research. *American Journal of Health Behavior* 2003 November-December; 27(Supplement 3): S239-S247. NRCBL: 1.3.9; 7.4; 6.

Switzer, David. All medical physicists entering the field should have a specific course on research and practice ethics in their educational background. *Medical Physics* 2003 December; 30(12): 3049-3050. NRCBL: 1.3.9; 7.2.

Tanne, Janice Hopkins. Royalty payments to staff researchers cause new NIH troubles [news]. *BMJ: British Medical Journal* 2005 January 22; 330(7484): 162. NRCBL: 1.3.9; 5.3. Identifiers: National Institutes of Health.

Tereskerz, Patricia M.; Moreno, Jonathan. Ten steps to developing a national agenda to address financial conflicts of interest in industry sponsored clinical research. *Accountability in Research* 2005 April-June; 12(2): 139-155. NRCBL: 1.3.9; 7.3.

Abstract: Financial liaisons between clinical researchers, research institutions, and industrial sponsors have gained momentum in recent years. In the process, it has been argued by many that trust in the research infrastructure is being eroded by the financial conflicts of interest that emerge from these arrangements. Yet, the financial resources of industry are needed to continue technology transfer from the bench to the bedside. Policy makers and government regulators are currently struggling to determine how to best manage financial conflicts of interest that emerge from these liaisons. Various organizations and government entities have proposed different strategies. This paper explores the limitations of existing measures and recommends that a unified national agenda is needed. We propose 10 steps to develop an agenda to address financial conflicts of interest in industry-sponsored clinical research.

Thompson, Dennis F. Conflicts of interest in medicine. *In his:* Restoring Responsibility: Essays on Ethics in Government, Business, and Healthcare. New York: Cambridge University Press; 2005: 290-299. NRCBL: 1.3.9; 7.3.

Tong, Elisa K.; England, Lucinda; Glantz, Stanton A. Changing conclusions on secondhand smoke in a sudden infant death syndrome review funded by the tobacco industry. *Pediatrics* 2005 March; 115(3): e356-e366. NRCBL: 1.3.9; 5.3; 1.3.2; 9.5.9. SC: em.

United States. Department of Health and Human Services [DHHS]. Public Health Service policies on research misconduct; final rule. *Federal Register* 2005 May 17; 70(94): 28370-28400 [Online]. Available:http://a257.g.akamaitech.net/7/257/2422/01jan20051800/edocket.access.gpo.gov/2005/pdf/05-9643.pdf [23 May 2005]. NRCBL: 1.3.9.

United States. Department of Health and Human Services [DHHS]. Supplemental standards of ethical conduct and financial disclosure requirements for employees of the Department of Health and Human Services [interim final rule with request for comments]. *Federal Register* 2005 February 3; 70(22): 5543-5565. NRCBL: 1.3.9; 1.3.5. SC: le.

Abstract: The Department of Health and Human Services, with the concurrence of the Office of Government Ethics (OGE), is amending the HHS regulation that supplements the OGE Standards of Ethical Conduct. This interim final rule specifies additional procedural and substantive requirements that are necessary to address ethical issues at the National Institutes of Health (NIH) and updates nomenclature, definitions, and procedures applicable to other components of the Department. The rule: Revises the definition of a significantly regulated organization for the Food and Drug Administration (FDA); Updates the organization titles of designated separate agencies; Amends the gift exception for native artwork and craft items received from Indian tribes or Alaska Native organizations; Aligns the FDA prohibited holdings limit with the de minimis holdings exemption in OGE regulations; Revises prior approval procedures for outside activities; and, subject to certain exceptions: Prohibits NIH employees from engaging in certain outside activities with supported research institutions, health care providers or insurers, health-related trade or professional associations, and biotechnology, pharmaceutical, medical device, and other companies substantially affected by the programs, policies, or operations of the NIH; Bars NIH employees who file a public or confidential financial disclosure report from holding financial interests in substantially affected organizations; Subjects NIH non-filer employees to a monetary cap on holdings in such organizations; Specifies for NIH employees prior approval procedures for and limitations on the receipt of certain awards from outside sources; and Imposes a one-year disqualification period during which NIH employees are precluded from official actions involving an award donor. In addition, the Department is adding a new supplemental part to expand financial disclosure reporting requirements for certain outside activities and to ensure that prohibited financial interests are identified.

United States. Department of Health and Human Services [DHHS]. Supplemental Standards of Ethical Conduct and Financial Disclosure Requirements for Employees of the Department of Health and Human Services [Final Action]. 5 CFR Parts 5501 and 5502. *Federal Register* 2005 August 31; 70(168): 51559-51574. NRCBL: 1.3.9; 1.3.5.

Van Der Weyden, Martin B. Managing allegations of scientific misconduct and fraud: lessons from the "Hall affair" [editorial]. *Medical Journal of Australia* 2004 February 16; 180(4): 149-151. NRCBL: 1.3.9. Identifiers: Bruce Hall.

van Gorp, Wilfred G.; Tranel, Daniel. Editorial statement: disclosure of funding sources and financial interests by authors. *Journal of Clinical and Experimental Neuropsychology* 2004 May; 26(3): 306. NRCBL: 1.3.9; 1.3.7; 7.3.

Vogel, Gretchen. Landmark paper has an image problem [news]. *Science* 2005 December 9; 310(5754): 1595. NRCBL: 1.3.9; 14.5; 15.1; 18.5.4; 19.1. Identifiers: Korea.

Wade, Nicholas. Clone scientist relied on peers and Korean pride. *New York Times* 2005 December 25; p. A1, A8. NRCBL: 1.3.9; 14.5. SC: po.

Wade, Nicholas. Korean scientist said to admit fabrication in a cloning study. *New York Times* 2005 December 16; p. A1, A6. NRCBL: 1.3.9; 14.5. SC: po.

Wadman, Meredith. NIH workers see red over revised rules for conflicts of interest [news]. *Nature* 2005 March 3; 434(7029): 3-4. NRCBL: 1.3.9; 1.3.5; 7.3. Identifiers: National Institutes of Health.

Wagena, Edwin J. The scandal of unfair behaviour of senior faculty. *Journal of Medical Ethics* 2005 May; 31(5): 308. NRCBL: 1.3.9; 1.3.7.

Wasunna, Angela; Murray, Thomas. Professional responsibilities in medical research. *In:* Restivo, Sal, ed. Science, Technology, and Society: An Encyclopedia. New York: Oxford University Press; 2005: 407-414. NRCBL: 1.3.9.

Weiss, Rick. Many scientists admit to misconduct: degrees of deception vary in poll; researchers say findings could hurt the field. *Washington Post* 2005 June 9; p. A3. NRCBL: 1.3.9. SC: po.

Weiss, Rick. NIH clears most researchers in conflict-of-interest probe. *Washington Post* 2005 February 23; p. A1, A4. NRCBL: 1.3.9; 1.3.5; 7.3. SC: po. Identifiers: National Institutes of Health.

Weiss, Rick. NIH will restrict outside income: tighter rules address concerns about conflicts of interest. *Washington Post* 2005 February 2; p. A1, A7. NRCBL: 1.3.9. Identifiers: National Institutes of Health.

White, Caroline. Suspected research fraud: difficulties of getting at the truth. *BMJ: British Medical Journal* 2005 July 30; 331(7511): 281-288. NRCBL: 1.3.9; 1.3.7.

White, Caroline. UK agency to combat research misconduct [news]. *BMJ: British Medical Journal* 2005 March 19; 330(7492): 616. NRCBL: 1.3.9.

Willcox, Breckinridge L. Fraud in scientific research: the prosecutor's approach. *Accountability in Research* 1992; 2(2): 139-151. NRCBL: 1.3.9. SC: le; cs. Identifiers: Stephen Breuning.

Williams-Jones, Bryn. Knowledge commons or economic engine — what's a university for? [editorial]. *Journal of Medical Ethics* 2005 May; 31(5): 249-250. NRCBL: 1.3.9; 1.3.3.

Wilmshurst, Peter. Fraud in research. *Clinical Medicine* 2002 March-April; 2(2): 159-160. NRCBL: 1.3.9; 18.6.

Wynia, Matthew K. Judging public health research: epistemology, public health and the law. *American Journal of Bioethics* 2005 November-December; 5(6): 4- 7. NRCBL: 1.3.9; 9.1; 1.3.5; 5.1; 16.1. SC: le. Identifiers: Daubert v. Merrell Dow Pharmaceuticals, Inc.

Yidong, Gong. China science foundation takes action against 60 grantees [news]. *Science* 2005 September 16; 309(5742): 1798-1799. NRCBL: 1.3.9.

Zerhouni, Elias. Memorandum (regarding new NIH ethics regulations). Bethesda, MD: National Institutes of Health 2005 February 1; 2 p. [Online]. Available: http://www.nih.gov/about/ethics/020105COImemo.pdf [2 February 2005]. NRCBL: 1.3.9. Identifiers: National Institutes of Health; memorandum to all employees from the Director.

Zimmerman, Rachel; Tomsho, Robert. Medical editor turns activist on drug trials. *Wall Street Journal* 2005 May 26; p. B1, B5. NRCBL: 1.3.9; 9.7; 1.3.7; 1.3.12. SC: po.

Zwillich, Todd. Financial ethics pit NIH scientists against government. *Lancet* 2005 August 13-19; 366(9485): 537-538. NRCBL: 1.3.9; 5.3. Identifiers: National Institutes of Health.

BIOMEDICAL RESEARCH/ SOCIAL CONTROL OF SCIENCE AND TECHNOLOGY

Amdur, Robert J.; Speers, Marjorie A. A practical guideline for identifying research intent with projects that collect private, identifiable health information. *American Journal of Clinical Oncology* 2003 June; 26(3): e7-e12. NRCBL: 5.3; 8.4.

NRCBL: National Reference Center for Bioethics Literature Classification Scheme   See inside front cover for terms.

91

Arbit, Ehud; Stossel, Thomas P. Academic-industrial relationships [letter and reply]. *New England Journal of Medicine* 2005 December 22; 353(25): 2720-2722. NRCBL: 5.3; 1.3.9.

Berenson, Alex. Evidence in Vioxx suits shows intervention by Merck officials. *New York Times* 2005 April 24; p. A1, A32. NRCBL: 5.3; 9.7; 1.3.9. SC: po; le.

Bochatey, Alberto G. La importancia de la sociedad civil ante el proceso de desarrollo de la investigacion cientifica / The importance of civil society to the process of scientific research. *Vida y Etica* 2003 December; 4(2): 97-108. NRCBL: 5.3; 18.6.

Bowman, James. Bioethics at the movies. *New Atlantis* 2005 Spring; 8: 93-100. NRCBL: 20.5.1; 12.1; 5.1; 7.1.

Brand, Richard A.; Buckwalter, Joseph A.; Talman, Charlotte L.; Happe, Daniel G. Industrial support of orthopaedic research in the academic setting. *Clinical Orthopaedics and Related Research* 2003 July; (412): 45-53. NRCBL: 5.3; 1.3.9.

Brody, Howard; Miller, Franklin G.; Stossel, Thomas P. Academic-industrial relationships [letter and reply]. *New England Journal of Medicine* 2005 December 22; 353(25): 2720-2722. NRCBL: 5.3; 1.3.9.

Campbell, Eric G.; Koski, Greg; Zinner, Darren E.; Blumenthal, David. Managing the triple helix in the life sciences. *Issues in Science and Technology* 2005 Winter; 21(2): 48-54. NRCBL: 5.3; 1.3.9; 7.3.

Cha, Ariana Eunjung. A struggling science experiment: states closely watch California's stem cell research initiative. *Washington Post* 2005 February 13; p. A1, A18. NRCBL: 5.3; 18.5.4; 19.1. SC: po.

Chadwick, Ruth; Schüklenk, Udo. Sleeping with the enemy? Where to draw the line on research funding? [editorial]. *Bioethics* 2005 April; 19(2): iii-iv. NRCBL: 5.3; 9.5.9; 9.7; 1.3.9.

Coyne, James. Lessons in conflict of interest: the construction of the martyrdom of David Healy and the dilemma of bioethics. *American Journal of Bioethics [Online]* 2005 January-February; 5(1): W3-W14. NRCBL: 5.3; 1.3.9; 1.3.7; 9.7; 18.1; 2.1.

Derzko, Natalie M. In search of a compromised solution to the problem arising from patenting biomedical research tools. *Santa Clara Computer and High Technology Law Journal* 2004; 20(2): 347-410. NRCBL: 5.3; 15.1. SC: le.

Dorfman, Howard L.; Reig, Linda Pissott. Avoiding legal and ethical pitfalls of industry-sponsored research: the co-existence of research, scholarship, and marketing in the pharmaceutical industry. *Food and Drug Law Journal* 2004; 59(4): 595-615. NRCBL: 5.3; 9.7; 18.2; 1.3.7; 1.3.9. SC: le.

DuVal, Gordon. Institutional conflicts of interest: protecting human subjects, scientific integrity, and institutional accountability. *Journal of Law, Medicine and Ethics* 2004 Winter; 32(4): 613- 625. NRCBL: 5.3; 18.2. SC: le.

Eggertson, Laura. Physicians want transparency as Guidant lawsuits grow [news]. *CMAJ/JAMC: Canadian Medical Association Journal* 2005 October 11; 173(8): 855-856. NRCBL: 5.3; 1.3.2; 8.4. SC: le. Identifiers: United States; Food and Drug Administration.

Eggertson, Laura; Murray, Sally. MPs call for removal of Health Canada's breast-implant panel members [news]. *CMAJ/JAMC: Canadian Medical Association Journal* 2005 November 8; 173(10): 1144. NRCBL: 5.3; 9.5.5; 9.7.

Gaskell, George; Einsiedel, Edna; Hallman, William; Priest, Susanna Hornig; Jackson, Jonathan; Olsthoorn, Johannus. Social values and the governance of science. *Science* 2005 December 23; 310(5756): 1908-1909. NRCBL: 5.3; 5.2.

Górski, Andrzej. The ethics of intellectual property rights in biomedicine and biotechnology: an introduction. *Science and Engineering Ethics* 2005 January; 11(1): 4-6. NRCBL: 5.3; 1.3.9; 15.1; 2.4. SC: le. Conference: 5th International Conference on Bioethics: The Ethics of Intellectual Property Rights and Patents; Warsaw, Poland; 23-24 April 2004; Minister of Science and the Minister of Health, Poland.

Harris, Gardiner. Drugs, politics and the FDA: abortion issue hovers over morning-after pill. *New York Times* 2005 August 28; p. A1, A14. NRCBL: 5.3; 9.7; 12.1. SC: po.

Hurlbut, William B. Patenting humans: clones, chimeras, and biological artifacts. *Science and Engineering Ethics* 2005 January; 11(1): 21-29. NRCBL: 5.3; 14.5; 15.1; 22.1; 4.4. Conference: 5th International Conference on Bioethics: The Ethics of Intellectual Property Rights and Patents; Warsaw, Poland; 23-24 April 2004; Minister of Science and the Minister of Health, Poland.

Jones, James W. Ethics of rapid surgical technological advancement. *Annals of Thoracic Surgery* 2000; 69: 676-677. NRCBL: 5.3; 9.5.1; 18.6.

Kaiser, Jocelyn. NIH wants public access to papers 'as soon as possible' [news]. *Science* 2005 February 11; 307(5711): 825, 827. NRCBL: 5.3; 1.3.7; 1.3.12. Identifiers: National Institutes of Health.

Kaiser, Jocelyn. Scientists, societies blast NIH ethics rules [news]. *Science* 2005 April 8; 308(5719): 175, 177. NRCBL: 5.3; 1.3.9. Identifiers: National Institutes of Health.

Kesselheim, Aaron S.; Avorn, Jerry. University-based science and biotechnology products: defining the boundaries of intellectual property. *JAMA: The Journal of the*

American Medical Association 2005 February 16; 293(7): 850-854. NRCBL: 5.3; 1.3.9; 5.1.

Abstract: The pharmaceutical and biotechnology industries have long relied on patenting as the primary means of allocating ownership and control over new discoveries. Yet, patent protection is a double-edged sword that has major implications for the future of innovation in biomedical science in the United States. Excessive "upstream" patenting of genes and molecular targets could hinder further research by creating a need for expensive and inefficient cross-licensing. However, limiting such basic science patenting could allow private entities to use the results of years of costly publicly funded research to produce and market lucrative products without compensating university- or public sector-based innovators. Academic and other nonprofit research centers would, therefore, be deprived of revenue for pursuing novel therapeutics or other seminal research work that may not be patentable. Recent court cases illustrate the inherent conflicts in allocating ownership and control of basic biomedical discoveries. Several options exist to avoid the complex problems of overlapping basic science patents while still rewarding pivotal discoveries and encouraging further innovation. These include establishing basic science patent pools and mandating arbitration arrangements that would assign credit and royalties for biotechnology innovations that depend on prior research that was performed, financed, or both in the public sector.

Keulartz, Jozef; Schermer, Maartje; Korthals, Michiel; Swierstra, Tsjalling. Ethics in technological culture: a programmatic proposal for a pragmatist approach. *Science, Technology, and Human Values* 2004 Winter; 29(1): 3-29. NRCBL: 5.3; 1.1.

Lipworth, Wendy. Generating a taxonomy of regulatory responses to emerging issues in biomedicine. *Journal of Bioethical Inquiry* 2005; 2(3): 130-141. NRCBL: 5.3; 19.5; 15.1. SC: le.

Abstract: In the biomedical field, calls for the generation of new regulations or for the amendment of existing regulations often follow the emergence of apparently new research practices (such as embryonic stem cell research), clinical practices (such as facial transplantation) and entities (such as Avian Influenza/'Bird Flu'). Calls for regulatory responses also arise as a result of controversies which bring to light longstanding practices, such as the call for increased regulation of human tissue collections that followed the discovery of unauthorised post-mortem organ retention. Whilst it seems obvious that new regulations should only be generated if existing regulations are inadequate (a practice referred to in this paper as 'regulatory syncretism'), this does not always occur in practice. This paper examines the conceptual steps involved in generating regulatory responses to emerging phenomena. Two decision points are identified. First, a stance is taken as to whether the emerging phenomenon raises unique ethical or legal issues (exceptionalism versus non-exceptionalism). Second, the decision is made as to whether new regulation should be generated only for truly unique phenomena (syncretism versus asyncretism). It is argued here that it is important to make a careful assessment of novelty, followed by a reflective and deliberative choice of regulatory syncretism or asyncretism, since each type of regulatory response has advantages which need to be harnessed and disadvantages which need to be managed—something that can only occur if regulators are attentive to the choices they are making.

Meier, Barry. FDA had report of short circuit in heart devices; confidentiality at issue; policies of regulator may keep data on problems away from doctors. *New York Times* 2005 September 12; p. A1, A18. NRCBL: 5.3; 8.4; 1.3.5; 9.7. SC: po.

Mello, Michelle M.; Clarridge, Brian R.; Studdert, David M. Academic medical centers' standards for clinical-trial agreements with industry. *New England Journal of Medicine* 2005 May 26; 352(21): 2202- 2210. NRCBL: 5.3; 18.2; 9.7; 1.3.9; 1.3.7; 18.6. SC: le; em.

Abstract: BACKGROUND: Although industry sponsors provide approximately 70 percent of the funding for clinical drug trials in the United States, little is known about the legal agreements that exist between industry sponsors and academic investigators. We studied institutional standards regarding contractual provisions that restrict investigators' control over trials. METHODS: We used a structured, cross-sectional mail survey of medical-school research administrators responsible for negotiating clinical-trial agreements with industry sponsors. RESULTS: Of 122 institutions approached, 107 participated. There was a high degree of consensus among administrators about the acceptability of several contractual provisions relating to publications. For example, more than 85 percent reported that their office would not approve provisions giving industry sponsors the authority to revise manuscripts or decide whether results should be published. There was considerable disagreement about the acceptability of provisions allowing the sponsor to insert its own statistical analyses in manuscripts (24 percent allowed them, 47 percent disallowed them, and 29 percent were not sure whether they should allow them), draft the manuscript (50 percent allowed it, 40 percent disallowed it, and 11 percent were not sure whether they should allow it), and prohibit investigators from sharing data with third parties after the trial is over (41 percent allowed it, 34 percent disallowed it, and 24 percent were not sure whether they should allow it). Disputes were common after the agreements had been signed and most frequently centered on payment (75 percent of administrators reported at least one such dispute in the previous year), intellectual property (30 percent), and control of or access to data (17 percent). CONCLUSIONS: Standards for certain restrictive provisions in clinical-trial agreements with industry sponsors vary considerably among academic medical centers. Greater sharing of information about legal relationships with industry sponsors is desirable in order to build consensus about appropriate standards.

Mercurio, Bryan C. TRIPS, patents, and access to life-saving drugs in the developing world. *Marquette Intellectual Property Law Review* 2004 Summer; 8(2): 211-253. NRCBL: 5.3; 9.2; 9.7; 21.1. SC: le. Identifiers: Trade-Related Aspects of Intellectual Property Rights.

National Institutes of Health [NIH] (United States). Department of Health and Human Services. Policy on enhancing public access to archived publications resulting from NIH-funded research [policy statement]. *Federal Register* 2005 February 9; 70(26): 6891-6900 [Online]. Available: http://a257.g.akamaitein.net/7/257/2422/01jan20051800/edocket [14 September 2005]. NRCBL: 5.3; 18.2; 1.3.12.

Ng, Mary Ann Chen; Takeda, Chika; Watanabe, Tomoyuki; Macer, Darryl. Attitudes of the public and scientists to biotechnology in Japan at the start of 2000. *Eubios Journal of Asian and International Bioethics* 2000 July; 10(4): 106-113. NRCBL: 5.3. SC: em.

NRCBL: National Reference Center for Bioethics Literature Classification Scheme   See inside front cover for terms.

93

Novak, Kris. US scientific panels Bush-whacked [news]. *Nature Medicine* 2003 February; 9(2): 153. NRCBL: 5.3.

Paterson, I.C.M. The concept of intellectual property and its implications for oncology [opinion]. *Clinical Oncology* 1993; 5(4): 234-236. NRCBL: 5.3. SC: le.

Prainsack, Barbara; Firestine, Ofer. Genetically modified survival: red and green biotechnology in Israel. *Science as Culture* 2005 December; 14(4): 355-372. NRCBL: 5.3; 5.1; 15.1; 2.2.

Redman, Barbara K.; Merz, Jon F. Evaluating the oversight of scientific misconduct. *Accountability in Research* 2005 July-September; 12(3): 157- 162. NRCBL: 5.3; 1.3.9.
Abstract: The office of Research Integrity has proposed a new definition of scientific misconduct that will substantively reduce the federal government's role of oversight of scientific practices. The standard is being changed despite the lack of evidence about the effects of current policies or understanding of why research misconduct occurs, how it can be detected and prevented, and the nature and effectiveness of sanctions. Given this lack of knowledge and the perception that the integrity of science is falling, we believe it would be unwise for the academic and scientific community to adopt this new standard.

Roach, Lynne. Patents and property in the biotechnology sector: some clarifications. *King's College Law Journal* 2002; 13(1): 101-109. NRCBL: 5.3; 15.8. SC: le.

Sadler, Troy D. Moral sensitivity and its contribution to the resolution of socio-scientific issues. *Journal of Moral Education* 2004 September; 33(3): 339-358. NRCBL: 5.3; 15.4; 14.5; 1.1. SC: em.

Splawinski, Jacek. Patents and ethics: is it possible to be balanced? *Science and Engineering Ethics* 2005 January; 11(1): 71-74. NRCBL: 5.3; 9.1; 9.5.5. Identifiers: obstetrical forceps. Conference: 5th International Conference on Bioethics: The Ethics of Intellectual Property Rights and Patents; Warsaw, Poland; 23-24 April 2004; Minister of Science and the Minister of Health, Poland.

Sterckx, Sigrid. Can drug patents be morally justified? *Science and Engineering Ethics* 2005 January; 11(1): 81-92. NRCBL: 5.3; 9.7; 1.1; 21.1. SC: an. Conference: 5th International Conference on Bioethics: The Ethics of Intellectual Property Rights and Patents; Warsaw, Poland; 23-24 April 2004; Minister of Science and the Minister of Health, Poland.

Sterckx, Sigrid. Some ethically problematic aspects of the proposal for a directive on the legal protection of biotechnological inventions [opinion]. *EIPR: European Intellectual Property Review* 1998 April; 20(4): 123-128. NRCBL: 5.3; 5.1; 15.8. SC: le.

Stossel, Thomas P. Regulating academic-industrial research relationships — solving problems or stifling progress? *New England Journal of Medicine* 2005 September 8; 353(10): 1060-1065. NRCBL: 5.3; 5.1; 18.2; 1.3.9; 18.6.

Tanne, Janice Hopkins. US National Institutes of Health issue new ethics guidelines [news]. *BMJ: British Medical Journal* 2005 September 3; 331(7515): 472. NRCBL: 5.3; 9.7; 1.3.9. SC: le.

Tolloczko, Tadeusz. Surgical patents and patients — the ethical dilemmas. *Science and Engineering Ethics* 2005 January; 11(1): 61-69. NRCBL: 5.3; 9.1; 8.1. Identifiers: medical procedure patents; medical process patents. Conference: 5th International Conference on Bioethics: The Ethics of Intellectual Property Rights and Patents; Warsaw, Poland; 23-24 April 2004; Minister of Science and the Minister of Health, Poland.

Trew, Andrew. Regulating life and death: the modification and commodification of nature. *University of Toledo Law Review* 1998 Winter; 29(2): 271-326. NRCBL: 5.3; 8.3.1; 20.5.1; 19.5; 15.1. SC: le.

Walsh, John P.; Cho, Charlene; Cohen, Wesley M. View from the bench: patents and material transfers. *Science* 2005 September 23; 309(5743): 2002-2003. NRCBL: 5.3.

BIOMEDICAL TECHNOLOGIES *See* ENHANCEMENT; ORGAN AND TISSUE TRANSPLANTATION; REPRODUCTIVE TECHNOLOGIES

BLOOD DONATION AND TRANSFUSION
See also ORGAN AND TISSUE TRANSPLANTATION

American Society for Blood and Marrow Transplantation; American Association of Blood Banks; Foundation for the Accreditation of Cellular Therapy; International Bone Marrow Transplant Registry/Autologous Blood and Marrow Transplant Registry; International Society for Cellular Therapy; National Marrow Donor Program. ASBMT Position Statement: joint public policy on legislative and regulatory affairs. *Biology of Blood and Marrow Transplantation* 2004 April; 10(4): 283-284. NRCBL: 19.4.

Apfel, Howard David; Isaacson, Shimon. Halachic and medical perspectives on banking umbilical cord stem cells. *Journal of Halacha and Contemporary Society* 2005 Fall; (50): 5-37. NRCBL: 19.4; 9.5.7; 1.2.

Brooks, Jay P. The rights of blood recipients should supersede any asserted rights of blood donors. *Vox Sanguinis* 2004 November; 87(4): 280-286. NRCBL: 19.4; 10.

Busby, Helen. Blood donation for genetic research: what can we learn from donors' narratives? *In:* Tutton, Richard; Corrigan, Oonagh, eds. Genetic Databases: Socio-ethical Issues in the Collection and Use of DNA. New York: Routledge; 2004: 39-56. NRCBL: 19.4; 15.1; 15.3.

European Commission. European Ethics Group for Science and New Technology. Les aspects ethiques des banques de sang de cordon ombilical: avis no 19 du 16 mars 2004 / Ethical aspects of banks of umbilical cord blood, advice no. 19 of 16 March 2004. *Journal International de Bioethique / International Journal of Bioethics* 2005 March-June; 16(1-2): 169-171. NRCBL: 19.4; 9.5.7.

Fasouliotis, Sozos J.; Schenker, Joseph G. Human umbilical cord blood banking and transplantation: a state of the art. *European Journal of Obstetrics, Gynecology and Reproductive Biology* 2000 May; 90(1): 13-25. NRCBL: 19.4; 9.5.7.

Feldman, Eric A. Blood justice: courts, conflict, and compensation in Japan, France, and the United States. *Law and Society Review* 2000; 34(3): 651-701. NRCBL: 19.4; 9.5.6; 9.8. SC: le.

Gunning, Jennifer. Umbilical cord blood: banking and clinical application. *Revista de Derecho y Genoma Humano / Law and the Human Genome Review* 2004 January-June; (20): 217-226. NRCBL: 19.4; 19.5; 18.6. SC: le. Note: abstract in Spanish.

Hagstad, David. To give blood or not to give: should there be a question? *AJN: American Journal of Nursing* 2005 November; 105(11): 31. NRCBL: 19.4; 19.5; 19.6.

Institute of Medicine (United States) [IOM]. Committee on Establishing a National Cord Blood Stem Cell Bank Program. Ethical and legal issues. *In its: Cord Blood: Establishing a National Hematopoietic Stem Cell Bank Program. Washington, DC: National Academies Press; 2005: 106-119.* NRCBL: 19.4; 9.5.7; 8.3.2. SC: le.

Jones, Richard P.O.; Prasad, V.; Kuruvatti, J.; Tahir, N.; Whitaker, P.; Dawson, A.S.J.; Harrison, M.A.; Williams, R. Remuneration for blood donation and attitudes towards blood donation and receipt in Leeds. *Transfusion Medicine* 2003 June; 13(3): 131-140. NRCBL: 19.4; 9.3.1. SC: em. Identifiers: United Kingdom (Great Britain).

Pennings, G. Demanding pure motives for donation: the moral acceptability of blood donations by haemochromatosis patients. *Journal of Medical Ethics* 2005 February; 31(2): 69-72. NRCBL: 19.4. SC: an.

Saginur, Madelaine; Kharaboyan, Linda; Knoppers, Bartha Maria. Umbilical cord blood stem cells: issues with private and public banks. *Health Law Journal* 2004; 12: 17-34. NRCBL: 19.4; 19.5; 9.8; 4.4. SC: le.

Salbu, Steven R. AIDS and the blood supply: an analysis of law, regulation, and public policy. *Washington University Law Quarterly* 1996 Winter; 74(4): 913-980. NRCBL: 19.4; 9.8; 9.5.6. SC: le.

Witte, Courtney. Cord blood storage: property and liability issues. *Journal of Legal Medicine* 2005 June; 26(2): 275-292. NRCBL: 19.4; 8.3.2; 4.4. SC: le; cs.

CAPITAL PUNISHMENT

Medical collusion in the death penalty: an American atrocity [editorial]. *Lancet* 2005 April 16-22; 365(9468): 1361. NRCBL: 20.6; 7.1.

Appelbaum, Paul S. Comments: a crisis in the ethical and moral behavior of psychiatrists [forum]. *Current Opinion in Psychiatry* 1998 January; 11(1); 2 p. [Online]. Available: http://gateway.ut.ovid.com/gw1/ovidweb.cgi [24 May 2005]. NRCBL: 20.6; 4.1.2. Identifiers: Forum:psychiatrists and the death penalty: some ethical dilemmas.

Bloche, M. Gregg. Comments: a crisis in the ethical and moral behavior of psychiatrists [forum]. *Current Opinion in Psychiatry* 1998 January; 11(1); 3 p. [Online]. Available: http://gateway.ut.ovid.com/gw1/ovidweb.cgi [24 May 2005]. NRCBL: 20.6; 4.1.2. Identifiers: Forum: psychiatrists and the death penalty: some ethical dilemmas.

Bonnie, Richard J. Comments: a crisis in the ethical and moral behavior of psychiatrists [forum]. *Current Opinion in Psychiatry* 1998 January; 11(1); 3 p. [Online]. Available: http://gateway.ut.ovid.com/gw1/ovidweb.cgi [24 May 2005]. NRCBL: 20.6; 4.1.2. Identifiers: Forum: psychiatrists and the death penalty: some ethical dilemmas.

Freedman, Alfred M.; Halpern, Abraham L. A crisis in the ethical and moral behavior of psychiatrists [forum]. *Current Opinion in Psychiatry* 1998 January; 11(1); 3 p. [Online]. Available: http://gateway.ut.ovid.com/gw1/ovidweb.cgi [24 May 2005]. NRCBL: 20.6; 4.1.2. Identifiers: Forum: psychiatrists and the death penalty: some ethical dilemmas.

Freedman, Alfred M.; Halpern, Abraham L. Response: a crisis in the ethical and moral behavior of psychiatrists [forum]. *Current Opinion in Psychiatry* 1998 January; 11(1); 4 p. [Online]. Available: http://gateway.ut.ovid.com/gw1/ovidweb.cgi [24 May 2005]. NRCBL: 20.6; 4.1.2. Identifiers: Forum: psychiatrists and the death penalty: some ethical dilemmas.

Groner, Jonathan. Lethal injection and the medicalization of capital punishment in the United States. *Health and Human Rights: An International Journal* 2002; 6(1): 65-79. NRCBL: 20.6; 2.1; 4.3.

Gunn, John. Comments: a crisis in the ethical and moral behavior of psychiatrists [forum]. *Current Opinion in Psychiatry* 1998 January; 11(1); 2 p. [Online]. Available: http://gateway.ut.ovid.com/gw1/ovidweb.cgi [24 May 2005]. NRCBL: 20.6; 4.1.2. Identifiers: Forum: psychiatrists and the death penalty: some ethical dilemmas.

Gunn, John; Hartmann, Lawrence; Pellegrino, Edmund D.; Bonnie, Richard J.; Bloche, M. Gregg; Appelbaum, Paul S.; Kastrup, Marianne; Okasha, Ahmed; Lopez-Ibor, Juan J. Comments: a crisis in the ethical and moral behavior of psychiatrists [forum]. *Current Opinion in Psychiatry* 1998 January; 11(1); 3 p. [On-

NRCBL: National Reference Center for Bioethics Literature Classification Scheme   See inside front cover for terms.

95

line]. Available: http://gateway.ut.ovid.com/gw1/ovidweb.cgi [24 May 2005]. NRCBL: 20.6; 4.1.2. Identifiers: Forum: psychiatrists and the death penalty: some ethical dilemmas.

Hartmann, Lawrence. Comments: a crisis in the ethical and moral behavior of psychiatrists [forum]. *Current Opinion in Psychiatry* 1998 January; 11(1); 2 p. [Online]. Available: http://gateway.ut.ovid.com/gw1/ovidweb.cgi [24 May 2005]. NRCBL: 20.6; 4.1.2. Identifiers: Forum: psychiatrists and the death penalty: some ethical dilemmas.

Hiremath, Vijay. Law commission report proposes lethal injection for the death penalty. *Issues in Medical Ethics* 2003 July-September; 11(3): 93-94. NRCBL: 20.6. Identifiers: India.

Jesani, Amar. Medicalisation of 'legal' killing: doctors' participation in the death penalty [editorial]. *Indian Journal of Medical Ethics* 2004 October-December; 1(4): 104-105. NRCBL: 20.6; 21.1.

Jones, James W.; McCullough, Laurence B.; Richman, Bruce W. Damned if you do and damned if you don't: medical ethics and a second career. *Journal of Vascular Surgery* 2005 March; 41(3): 556-558. NRCBL: 20.6; 7.1. SC: cs. Identifiers: Ernie Fletcher; Kentucky.

Kastrup, Marianne. Comments: a crisis in the ethical and moral behavior of psychiatrists [forum]. *Current Opinion in Psychiatry* 1998 January; 11(1); 2 p. [Online]. Available: http://gateway.ut.ovid.com/gw1/ovidweb.cgi [24 May 2005]. NRCBL: 20.6; 4.1.2. Identifiers: Forum: psychiatrists and the death penalty: some ethical dilemmas.

Keyes, W. Noel. The choice of participation by physicians in capital punishment. *Whittier Law Review* 2001 Spring; 22(3): 809-840. NRCBL: 20.6. SC: le.

Koniaris, Leonidas G.; Zimmers, Teresa A.; Lubarsky, David A.; Sheldon, Jonathan P. Inadequate anaesthesia in lethal injection for execution. *Lancet* 2005 April 16-22; 365(9468): 1412-1414. NRCBL: 20.6; 9.7; 7.1. SC: em.
Abstract: Anaesthesia during lethal injection is essential to minimise suffering and to maintain public acceptance of the practice. Lethal injection is usually done by sequential administration of thiopental, pancuronium, and potassium chloride. Protocol information from Texas and Virginia showed that executioners had no anaesthesia training, drugs were administered remotely with no monitoring for anaesthesia, data were not recorded and no peer-review was done. Toxicology reports from Arizona, Georgia, North Carolina, and South Carolina showed that post-mortem concentrations of thiopental in the blood were lower than that required for surgery in 43 of 49 executed inmates (88%); 21 (43%) inmates had concentrations consistent with awareness. Methods of lethal injection anaesthesia are flawed and some inmates might experience awareness and suffering during execution.

Levy, Christopher J. Conflict of duty: capital punishment regulations and AMA medical ethics. *Journal of Legal Medicine* 2005 June; 26(2): 261-274. NRCBL: 20.6; 7.3. SC: le. Identifiers: American Medical Association.

Liptak, Adam. On death row, a battle over the fatal cocktail: critics say executions amount to torture. *New York Times* 2004 September 16; p A16. NRCBL: 20.6. SC: po.

Murphy, Timothy F. Physicians, medical ethics, and capital punishment. *Journal of Clinical Ethics* 2005 Summer; 16(2): 160-169. NRCBL: 20.6; 9.5.3; 4.1.1; 6; 1.3.5; 2.2. SC: le.

Okasha, Ahmed. Comments: a crisis in the ethical and moral behavior of psychiatrists [forum]. *Current Opinion in Psychiatry* 1998 January; 11(1); 2 p. [Online]. Available: http://gateway.ut.ovid.com/gw1/ovidweb.cgi [24 May 2005]. NRCBL: 20.6; 4.1.2. Identifiers: Forum: psychiatrists and the death penalty: some ethical dilemmas.

Pellegrino, Edmund D. Comments: a crisis in the ethical and moral behavior of psychiatrists [forum]. *Current Opinion in Psychiatry* 1998 January; 11(1); 4 p. [Online]. Available: http://gateway.ut.ovid.com/gw1/ovidweb.cgi [24 May 2005]. NRCBL: 20.6; 4.1.2. Identifiers: Forum: psychiatrists and the death penalty: some ethical dilemmas.

Royal College of Psychiatrists. Ethics Sub-Committee. Psychiatry and the death penalty: revised statement from the Ethics Sub-Committee. *Psychiatric Bulletin* 2003; 27(10): 396-397. NRCBL: 20.6; 17.1.

Spring, Julia C. Singleton's story: choosing between psychosis and execution. *Hastings Center Report* 2005 May-June; 35(3): 30-33. NRCBL: 20.6; 4.3; 8.3.4; 17.4. SC: le.

CARE FOR SPECIFIC GROUPS
See also HUMAN EXPERIMENTATION/ SPECIAL POPULATIONS

Ethics, molecular biology, and sports medicine [editorial]. *British Journal of Sports Medicine* 2001 June; 35(3): 142-143. NRCBL: 9.5.1; 15.1.

Adams, James G. Opening a dialogue on ethics [opinion]. *Academic Emergency Medicine* 2000 June; 7(6): 689-690. NRCBL: 9.5.1; 1.1; 2.1.

Al-Damegh, Saleh A. Emerging issues in medical imaging. *Indian Journal of Medical Ethics* 2005 October-December; 2(4): 123-125. NRCBL: 9.5.1; 9.3.1; 20.5.1; 8.3.1.

Anderson, L.C.; Gerrard, D.F. Ethical issues concerning New Zealand sports doctors. *Journal of Medical Ethics* 2005 February; 31(2): 88-92. NRCBL: 9.5.1. SC: em.

Appel, Jacob M. In defense of tongue splitting. *Journal of Clinical Ethics* 2005 Fall; 16(3): 236-238. NRCBL: 9.5.1. SC: le.

Bailey, Susan; O'Connell, Bev; Pearce, Julian. The transition from paediatric to adult health care services for young adults with a disability: an ethical perspective. *Australian Health Review* 2003; 26(1): 64-69. NRCBL: 9.5.1; 8.1; 1.1. Identifiers: Australia.

Bal, Arun. Diabetes: ethical, social and economic aspects. *Issues in Medical Ethics* 2000 July-September; 8(3): 77-78. NRCBL: 9.5.1; 9.4.

Baumrucker, Steven J.; Stolick, Matt; Morris, Gerald M.; Sheldon, Joanne. Case study: denying admission of a suicidal patient to a nursing home. *American Journal of Hospice and Palliative Medicine* 2004 September-October; 21(5): 395-397. NRCBL: 9.5.1; 20.7. SC: cs; le.

Becker, Lawrence C. Reciprocity, justice, and disability. *Ethics: An International Journal of Social, Political, and Legal Philosophy* 2005 October; 116(1): 9-39. NRCBL: 9.5.1; 9.5.3; 9.2; 1.1. SC: an.

Bleich, J. David. Choosing between therapies: a painful dilemma. *Tradition* 2004 Fall; 38(3): 96-102. NRCBL: 9.5.1; 1.2.

Boyd, Andrew J. Medical marijuana and personal autonomy. *John Marshall Law Review* 2004 Summer; 37(4): 1253-1288. NRCBL: 9.5.1; 9.7; 9.5.9; 1.3.5; 1.1. SC: le.

Bramstedt, Katrina A.; Morris, Harold H.; Tanner, Adriana. Now we lay them down to sleep: ethical issues with the use of pharmacologic coma for adult status epilepticus. *Epilepsy and Behavior* 2004 October; 5(5): 752-755. NRCBL: 9.5.1; 20.5.1; 9.7.

Brooks, Sharon L. Is it ethical not to . . . ? [editorial]. *Oral Surgery, Oral Medicine, Oral Pathology, Oral Radiology and Endodontics* 2001 May; 91(5): 493. NRCBL: 9.5.1; 16.2; 7.1. Identifiers: dental radiography.

Buetow, S. High need patients receiving targeted entitlements: what responsibilities do they have in primary health care? *Journal of Medical Ethics* 2005 May; 31(5): 304-306. NRCBL: 9.5.1; 9.3.1; 8.1. SC: an.
Abstract: Patient responsibilities in primary health care are controversial and, by comparison, the responsibilities of high need patients are less clear. This paper aims to suggest why high need patients receiving targeted entitlements in primary health care are free to have prima facie special responsibilities; why, given this freedom, these patients morally have special responsibilities; what these responsibilities are, and how publicly funded health systems ought to be able to respond when these remain unmet. It is suggested that the special responsibilities and their place in public policy acquire moral significance as a means to discharge a moral debt, share special knowledge, and produce desirable consequences in regard to personal and collective interests. Special responsibilities magnify ordinary patient responsibilities and require patients not to hesitate regarding attendance for primary health care. Persistent patient disregard of special responsibilities may necessitate limiting the scope of these responsibilities, removing system barriers, or respecifying special rights.

Chisholm, Nick; Gillett, Grant. The patient's journey: living with locked-in syndrome [review]. *BMJ: British Medical Journal* 2005 July 9; 331(7508): 94-97. NRCBL: 9.5.1; 4.4; 8.1.

Clement, Paul D.; Keisler, Peter D.; Kneedler, Edwin S.; Katsas, Gregory G.; Hallward-Driemeier, Douglas; Stern, Mark B.; Levy, Jonathan H. Brief for the petitioners Gonzales v. State of Oregon. *Issues in Law and Medicine* 2005 Summer; 21(1): 59-75. NRCBL: 9.5.1; 9.7; 9.5.9. SC: le.

Das, Rajiv; Gostin, Lawrence O. Regulation of medical marijuana [letter and reply]. *JAMA: The Journal of the American Medical Association* 2005 December 28; 294(24): 3091-3092. NRCBL: 9.5.1; 9.7; 9.5.9.

Davis, Matthew M. Varicella vaccine, cost-effectiveness analyses, and vaccination policy [editorial]. *JAMA: The Journal of the American Medical Association* 2005 August 17; 294(7): 845-846. NRCBL: 9.5.1; 9.5.7; 9.7; 9.3.1.

Dawson, Angus. The determination of the best interests in relation to childhood immunisation. *Bioethics* 2005 February; 19(1): 72-89. NRCBL: 9.5.1; 9.7; 9.5.7. SC: an. Note: A corrected version of this article appears in Bioethics 2005 April; 19(2): 187-205.

Dawson, Angus. Therapeutic vaccines: a solution to the prevention problem? *Vaccine* 2005 March 18; 23(17-18): 2363-2366. NRCBL: 9.5.1; 9.7; 9.1.

Dawson, Angus J. An ethical argument in favour of routine hepatitis B vaccination in very low-incidence countries [opinion]. *Lancet Infectious Diseases* 2005 February; 5(2): 120-125. NRCBL: 9.5.1; 9.7; 21.1; 9.3.1. Identifiers: United Kingdom (Great Britain).

Diekema, Douglas S. The preferential treatment of VIPs in the emergency department. *American Journal of Emergency Medicine* 1996 March; 14(2): 226-229. NRCBL: 9.5.1; 9.2; 9.4; 9.8.

Elkin, Sandy. In that case. *Journal of Bioethical Inquiry* 2005; 2(3): 179. NRCBL: 9.5.1; 9.7; 8.4. SC: cs. Identifiers: erectile dysfunction; direct to consumer advertising of prescription-only drugs.

Ferguson, Lindsay M. A moral emergency and a medical problem: negotiating the control of venereal disease — the Saskatchewan Venereal Disease Protection Act, 1946. *Saskatchewan Law Review* 2004; 67(1): 137-159. NRCBL: 9.5.1; 10; 8.4. SC: le.

Fox, M.; Thomson, Michael. A covenant with the status quo? Male circumcision and the new BMA guidance to doctors. *Journal of Medical Ethics* 2005 August; 31(8): 463-469. NRCBL: 9.5.1; 10; 9.5.7. SC: an. Identifiers: British Medical Association.
Abstract: This article offers a critique of the recently revised BMA guidance on routine neonatal male circumcision and seeks to challenge the assumptions underpinning the guidance

NRCBL: National Reference Center for Bioethics Literature Classification Scheme   See inside front cover for terms.

97

which construe this procedure as a matter of parental choice. Our aim is to problematise continued professional willingness to tolerate the non-therapeutic, non-consensual excision of healthy tissue, arguing that in this context both professional guidance and law are uncharacteristically tolerant of risks inflicted on young children, given the absence of clear medical benefits. By interrogating historical medical explanations for this practice, which continue to surface in contemporary justifications of non-consensual male circumcision, we demonstrate how circumcision has long existed as a procedure in need of a justification. We conclude that it is ethically inappropriate to subject children-male or female-to the acknowledged risks of circumcision and contend that there is no compelling legal authority for the common view that male circumcision is lawful.

Francis, Leslie P.; Battin, Margaret P.; Jacobson, Jay A.; Smith, Charles B.; Botkin, Jeffrey. How infectious diseases got left out — and what this omission might have meant for bioethics. *Bioethics* 2005 August; 19(4): 307-322. NRCBL: 9.5.1; 9.1; 2.1; 8.4; 1.1; 9.5.6; 8.3.1. SC: an.
Abstract: In this article, we first document the virtually complete absence of infectious disease examples and concerns at the time bioethics emerged as a field. We then argue that this oversight was not benign by considering two central issues in the field, informed consent and distributive justice, and showing how they might have been framed differently had infectiousness been at the forefront of concern. The solution to this omission might be to apply standard approaches in liberal bioethics, such as autonomy and the harm principle, to infectious examples. We argue that this is insufficient, however. Taking infectious disease into account requires understanding the patient as victim and as vector. Infectiousness reminds us that as autonomous agents we are both embodied and vulnerable in our relationships with others. We conclude by applying this reunderstanding of agency to the examples of informed consent and distributive justice in health care.

Fricker, P. Commentary: hypoxic air machines. *Journal of Medical Ethics* 2005 February; 31(2): 115. NRCBL: 9.5.1; 9.7.

Fuchs, Michael. Die Einschätzung des Kleinwuchses als Streitfall im Recht und die medizinethische Debatte um Therapie und Enhancement (Verbesserung). *In:* Jahrbuch für Wissenschaft und Ethik. Bd. 7. Berlin: Walter de Gruyter; 2002: 283-293. NRCBL: 9.5.1; 4.5. SC: le.

Getz, Linn; Kirkengen, Anna Luise; Hetlevik, Irene; Romundstad, Solfrid; Sigurdsson, Johann A. Ethical dilemmas arising from implementation of the European guidelines on cardiovascular disease prevention in clinical practice: a descriptive epidemiological study. *Scandinavian Journal of Primary Health Care* 2004 December; 22(4): 202-208. NRCBL: 9.5.1; 9.4; 4.2. SC: em. Identifiers: Norway.

Gilbert, Lyn. In that case. Response [case study]. *Journal of Bioethical Inquiry* 2005; 2(1): 55. NRCBL: 9.5.1; 16.3; 8.1; 9.7; 9.4. SC: cs. Identifiers: occupational health; duty to treat; ribavirin. Comments: comment on Ian Kerridge and Nicole Gilroy, "In that case," Journal of Bioethical Inquiry 2005; 2(1): 51.

Giordano, S. Risk and supervised exercise: the example of anorexia to illustrate a new ethical issue in the traditional debates of medical ethics. *Journal of Medical Ethics* 2005 January; 31(1): 15-20. NRCBL: 9.5.1. SC: an.
Abstract: Sport and physical activity is an area that remains relatively unexplored by contemporary bioethics. It is, however, an area in which important ethical issues arise. This paper explores the case of the participation of people with anorexia nervosa in exercise. Exercise is one of the central features of anorexia. The presence of anorexics in exercise classes is becoming an increasingly sensitive issue for instructors and fitness professionals. The ethics of teaching exercise to anorexics has, however, seldom, if ever, been addressed. Codes of ethics and legislation do not offer guidelines pertinent to the case and it is left unclear whether anorexics should be allowed to participate in exercise classes. It is shown by this paper that there are strong ethical reasons to let anorexics participate in exercise classes. However, the paper also explains why, despite these apparently cogent ethical reasons, there is no moral obligation to allow a person with anorexia to take part in exercise/sports activities.

Glauser, Jonathan. Rationing and the role of the emergency department as society's safety net. *Academic Emergency Medicine* 2001 November; 8(11): 1101-1106. NRCBL: 9.5.1; 9.2; 9.3.1; 9.4.

Gostin, Lawrence O. Medical marijuana, American federalism, and the Supreme Court. *JAMA: The Journal of the American Medical Association* 2005 August 17; 294(7): 842-844. NRCBL: 9.5.1; 9.7; 9.5.9. SC: le. Identifiers: Gonzalez v. Raich.

Haberfield, Les. Responding to "male circumcision: medical or ritual?". *Journal of Law and Medicine* 1997 May; 4(4): 379-385. NRCBL: 9.5.1; 10; 8.3.2; 1.2. SC: le. Identifiers: Australia. Comments: comment on David Richards, "Male Circumcision: Mmedical or Ritual?" Journal of Law and Medicine 1996 May; 3(4): 371-376.

Häyry, Matti. Forget autonomy and give me freedom! *In:* Häyry, Matti; Takala, Tuija; Herissone-Kelly, Peter, eds. Bioethics and Social Reality. New York: Rodopi, 2005: 31-37. NRCBL: 9.5.1; 4.4; 9.7; 9.5.9. SC: an.

Hentoff, Nat. The legacy of Terri Schiavo: the disabled sound the alarm for the nonreligious. *Free Inquiry* 2005 August-September; 25(5): 33-35. NRCBL: 9.5.1; 20.5.1.

Heymann, S. Jody; Sell, Randall L. Mandatory public health programs: to what standards should they be held? *Health and Human Rights: An International Journal* 1999; 4(1): 193-203. NRCBL: 9.5.1; 9.8; 7.1. SC: em. Identifiers: directly observed treatment.

Hickman, Susan E. Honoring resident autonomy in long-term care. Special considerations. *Journal of Psychosocial Nursing and Mental Health Services* 2004 January; 42(1): 12-16. NRCBL: 9.5.1; 1.1.

Holley, Mark T.; Morrissey, Thomas K.; Seabera, David C.; Afessa, Bekele; Wears, Robert L. Ethical dilemmas in a randomized trial of asthma treatment: can Bayesian statistical analysis explain the results? *Academic*

Emergency Medicine 2001 December; 8(12): 1128-1135. NRCBL: 9.5.1; 7.1. SC: em.

Hubbard, Dorothy. An ethical framework for operating room infection control. *Seminars in Perioperative Nursing* 1994 April; 3(2): 88-92. NRCBL: 9.5.1; 2.1; 1.1; 7.1.

John, T. Jacob. Polio eradication and ethical issues. *Indian Journal of Medical Ethics* 2005 October-December; 2(4): 117-118. NRCBL: 9.5.1; 9.7; 21.1.

Jones, James W.; McCullough, Laurence B. Abdominal aortic aneurysm in death row inmate. *Journal of Vascular Surgery* 2002 March; 35(3): 621-622. NRCBL: 9.5.1; 20.6. SC: cs.

Kapp, Marshall B. Decision making for vulnerable populations in the nursing home. *In:* Katz, Paul B.; Mezey, Mathy D.; Kapp, Marshall B., eds. Vulnerable Populations in the Long Term Care Continuum. New York, NY: Springer Pub. Co.; 2004:. NRCBL: 9.5.1; 17.1.

Kerridge, Ian; Gilroy, Nicole. In that case [case study]. *Journal of Bioethical Inquiry* 2005; 2(1): 51. NRCBL: 9.5.1; 9.5.5; 8.1; 9.7; 16.3. SC: cs. Identifiers: Ribavirin; occupational health.

Keshavarz, Reza; Merchant, Roland C.; McGreal, John. Emergency contraception provision: a survey of emergency department practitioners. *Academic Emergency Medicine* 2002 January; 9(1): 69-74. NRCBL: 9.5.1; 7.1; 11.1.

Kipnis, Kenneth; Gerhard, Anita. Some ethical principles for adult critical care. *In:* Thomasma, David C.; Weisstub, David N., eds. The Variables of Moral Capacity. Boston: Kluwer Academic Publishers; 2004: 151- 157. NRCBL: 9.5.1.

Kuczewski, Mark; Fiedler, Irma. Ethical issues in rehabilitation: conceptualizing the next generation of challenges [opinion]. *American Journal of Physical Medicine and Rehabilitation* 2001 November; 80(11): 848-851. NRCBL: 9.5.1; 4.4.

Leclerc, S.; Herrera, C.D. Sport medicine and the ethics of boxing. *British Journal of Sports Medicine* 1999 December; 33(6): 426- 429. NRCBL: 9.5.1; 7.1.

Levy, Michael H.; Reyes, Hernán; Coninx, Rudi. Overwhelming consumption in prisons: human rights and tuberculosis control. *Health and Human Rights: An International Journal* 1999; 4(1): 167-191. NRCBL: 9.5.1; 1.3.5; 21.1; 9.1; 9.7. SC: le.

Matta, Christina. Ambiguous bodies and deviant sexualities: hermaphrodites, homosexuality, and surgery in the United States, 1850-1904. *Perspectives in Biology and Medicine* 2005 Winter; 48(1): 74-83. NRCBL: 9.5.1; 10; 7.1.

May, Thomas. Public communication, risk perception, and the viability of preventive vaccination against communicable diseases. *Bioethics* 2005 August; 19(4): 407-421. NRCBL: 9.5.1; 9.7; 9.4; 5.2; 8.1.

Abstract: Because of the nature of preventive vaccination programs, the viability of these public health interventions is particularly susceptible to public perceptions. This is because vaccination relies on a concept of 'herd immunity', achievement of which requires rational public behavior that can only be obtained through full and accurate communication about risks and benefits. This paper describes how irrational behavior that threatens the effectiveness of vaccination programs—both in crisis and non-crisis situations—can be tied to public perceptions created by media portrayals of health risks. I concentrate on childhood vaccination as an exemplar of 'non-crisis' preventive vaccination, and on the recent flu vaccine shortage as a 'crisis' situation. The paper concludes with an examination of the steps necessary to resolve these threats through better public communication.

McCullagh, Peter. A perspective of disability. *In his:* Conscious in a Vegetative State? A Critique of the PVS Concept. Boston: Kluwer Academic; 2004: 175-192. NRCBL: 9.5.1; 20.5.1.

McCullagh, Peter. Positive management or an exercise in futility? *In his:* Conscious in a Vegetative State? A Critique of the PVS Concept. Boston: Kluwer Academic; 2004: 193-216. NRCBL: 9.5.1; 9.4; 20.5.1.

McGill, Joff; Wood-Harper, Janice. Informing education policy on MMR [letter and reply]. *Nursing Ethics* 2005 September; 12(5): 537-539. NRCBL: 9.5.1; 8.3.2; 9.7. Identifiers: measles, mumps, rubella vaccination.

Medicines Australia. In that case. Response [case study]. *Journal of Bioethical Inquiry* 2005; 2(3): 181-182. NRCBL: 9.5.1; 9.7; 9.8. SC: cs. Identifiers: direct to consumer advertising of prescription-only drugs.

Melville, Craig. Discrimination and health inequalities experienced by disabled people. *Medical Education* 2005 February; 39(2): 124-126. NRCBL: 9.5.1; 9.2; 7.2.

Menzel, Paul T. Determining the value of life: discrimination, advance directives, and the right to die with dignity. *Free Inquiry* 2005 August-September; 25(5): 39-41. NRCBL: 9.5.1; 20.5.4.

Negus, Jennie; Viney, Kerri; Bothamley, Graham. The ethics of legally detaining a patient who has tuberculosis. *Nursing Times* 2004 September 7-13; 100(36): 52-53, 55. NRCBL: 9.5.1; 8.3.4; 4.1.3. SC: cs. Identifiers: United Kingdom (Great Britain).

Norris, Pauline. In that case. Response. *Journal of Bioethical Inquiry* 2005; 2(3): 179-180. NRCBL: 9.5.1; 9.7; 1.3.2; 1.3.12. SC: cs. Identifiers: direct to consumer advertising of prescription-only drugs. Comments: comment on Sandy Elkin, "In that case," Journal of Bioethical Inquiry 2005; 2(3): 179.

NRCBL: National Reference Center for Bioethics Literature Classification Scheme   See inside front cover for terms.

99

Okie, Susan. Glimpses of Guantanamo — medical ethics and the war on terror [opinion]. *New England Journal of Medicine* 2005 December 15; 353(24): 2529-2534. NRCBL: 9.5.1; 1.3.5; 21.2; 21.5.

Oppenheim, Arieh; Sprung, Charles L. Cross-cultural ethical decision-making in critical care. *Critical Care Medicine* 1998 March; 26(3): 423-424. NRCBL: 9.5.1; 21.7; 2.1; 9.1. Comments: comment on M. Ip, T. Gilligan, B. Koenig, et al, "Ethical decision-making in critical care in Hong Kong," Critical Care Medicine 1998 March; 26(3): 447-451.

Paul, Yash. Polio eradication programme: some ethical issues. *Indian Journal of Medical Ethics* 2005 October-December; 2(4): 115-116. NRCBL: 9.5.1; 9.7; 9.5.7; 9.1. Identifiers: World Health Assembly (WHA); World Health Organization (WHO).

Paul, Yash; Dawson, Angus. Some ethical issues arising from polio eradication programmes in India. *Bioethics* 2005 August; 19(4): 393-406. NRCBL: 9.5.1; 9.7; 8.3.1; 8.3.2; 8.5; 9.3.1.
Abstract: The World Health Organisation's programme for the eradication of poliomyelitis as currently practised in India raises many ethical issues. In this paper we concentrate on just two. The first is the balance to be struck between the risks and benefits generated by the eradication programme itself. The issue of risks and benefits arises in relation to the choice between two different vaccine types available for polio programmes: oral polio vaccine (OPV) and inactivated polio vaccine (IPV). OPV is the vaccine currently used in the eradication campaign in India. We argue that given the current risks/benefits profile of this vaccine, there is an urgent need to review the programme and take remedial action to address existing problems (at least in India). The second issue we discuss is the fact that there is little effort to gain the informed consent of the parents of vaccinated children, as they are not currently told about the potential limitations of OPV or the possibility of vaccine-induced harm. We suggest that such a policy might be justifiable, given the importance of polio eradication, but only if there is a system of compensation for vaccine-induced harm as part of the eradication programme itself. There is a real danger that if these issues are not addressed then public trust in the eradication programme and vaccination programmes as a whole will be lost.

Pitetti, Raymond D. Do no harm — but first, do not hurt [opinion]. *CMAJ/JAMC: Canadian Medical Association Journal* 2005 June 21; 172(13): 1699. NRCBL: 9.5.1; 9.7; 4.4.

Redman, Barbara K. The ethics of self-management preparation for chronic illness. *Nursing Ethics* 2005 July; 12(4): 360-369. NRCBL: 9.5.1; 8.1.
Abstract: While nearly all patients with a chronic disease must self- manage their condition to some extent, preparation for these responsibilities is infrequently assured in the USA. The result can be significant harm and the undermining of a patient's ability to take advantage of life opportunities and be productive. Agreeing to care for a patient involves a moral responsibility to see that she or he receives the essential elements of care, including the ability to manage the disease on a daily basis. The research base for the efficacy of self-management and for how patients can be prepared to assume it is sufficiently strong that health care professionals must advocate for its inclusion in the routine evidence-based care of individuals with chronic disease. Because patient education is central to nursing's philosophy and practice, the profession should play a major role in removing structural barriers to self-management preparation and assuring its provision to a high standard of quality.

Restum, Zulficar Gregory. Public health implications of substandard correctional health care. *American Journal of Public Health* 2005 October; 95(10): 1689- 1691. NRCBL: 9.5.1; 1.3.5; 9.8; 9.1.
Abstract: US citizens face a growing threat of contracting communicable diseases owing to the high recidivism rate in state and federal prisons, poor screening and treatment of prisoners, and inferior follow-up health care upon their release. Insufficient education about communicable diseases—for prisoners and citizens alike—and other problems, such as prejudice against prisoners, escalating costs, and an unreliable correctional health care delivery system for inmates, all contribute to a public health problem that requires careful examination and correction for the protection of everyone involved.

Richards, David. Male circumcision: medical or ritual? *Journal of Law and Medicine* 1996 May; 3(4): 371-376. NRCBL: 9.5.1; 10. SC: le. Identifiers: Australia.

Ringel, Eileen W. The morality of cosmetic surgery for aging. *Archives of Dermatology* 1998 April; 134(4): 427-431. NRCBL: 9.5.1; 4.5; 4.1.2.

Rodrigues, Praveen B.E. Dermatology and ethics: some case studies. *Issues in Medical Ethics* 2000 October-December; 8(4): 118. NRCBL: 9.5.1; 2.1.

Saul, Stephanie. Selling dreams and drugs; some diet doctors test the boundaries of accepted practices. *New York Times* 2005 September 22; p. G1, G9. NRCBL: 9.5.1; 9.5.5; 7.1; 7.4. SC: po.

Schneider, Carl E. A government of limited powers. *Hastings Center Report* 2005 July-August; 35(4): 11-12. NRCBL: 9.5.1; 9.7; 9.5.9. SC: le.

Schoub, Barry D. The ethics of immunisation [editorial]. *South African Medical Journal* 2002 January; 92(1): 47. NRCBL: 9.5.1; 9.7.

Selgelid, Michael J. In that case. Response [case study]. *Journal of Bioethical Inquiry* 2005; 2(1): 52. NRCBL: 9.5.1; 16.3; 8.1. SC: cs. Identifiers: Ribavirin; occupational health; duty to treat.

Sellman, Derek. Towards an understanding of nursing as a response to human vulnerability. *Nursing Philosophy* 2005 January; 6(1): 2-10. NRCBL: 9.5.1; 8.1.

Silvers, Anita; Francis, Leslie Pickering. Justice through trust: disability and the "outlier problem" in social contract theory. *Ethics: An International Journal of Social, Political, and Legal Philosophy* 2005 October; 116(1): 40-76. NRCBL: 9.5.1; 9.5.3; 1.1; 1.3.5. SC: an.

Spriggs, M. Hypoxic air machines: performance enhancement through effective training — or cheating? *Journal of*

SC (Subject Caption):   an=analytical   cs=case studies   em=empirical   le=legal   po=popular   rv=review

Medical Ethics 2005 February; 31(2): 112-113. NRCBL: 9.5.1; 9.7. Identifiers: Australia.

Szalavitz, Maia. Give us the drugs. *New Scientist* 2005 January 29-February 4; 185(2484): 19. NRCBL: 9.5.1; 9.7; 9.5.9; 4.4.

Tamburrini, C. Commentary: hypoxic air machines. *Journal of Medical Ethics* 2005 February; 31(2): 114. NRCBL: 9.5.1; 9.7.

Tännsjö, Torbjörn. Commentary: hypoxic air machines. *Journal of Medical Ethics* 2005 February; 31(2): 113. NRCBL: 9.5.1; 9.7.

Taylor, Elizabeth Johnston; Mamier, Iris. Spiritual care nursing: what cancer patients and family caregivers want. *Journal of Advanced Nursing* 2005 February; 49(3): 260-267. NRCBL: 9.5.1; 1.2; 8.1.

von Zielbauer, Paul. As health care in jails goes private, 10 days can be a death sentence. *New York Times* 2005 February 27; p. A1, A32. NRCBL: 9.5.1; 1.3.5; 9.2. SC: po. Identifiers: First of three articles: Harsh Medicine — Dying Behind Bars.

von Zielbauer, Paul. Missed signals in New York jails open way to season of suicides. *New York Times* 2005 February 28; p. A1, B6, B7. NRCBL: 9.5.1; 1.3.5; 20.7. SC: po. Identifiers: Second of three articles: Harsh Medicine — Lost files, Lost Lives.

von Zielbauer, Paul. A spotty record of health care for children in city detention. *New York Times* 2005 March 1; p. A1, B9. NRCBL: 9.5.1; 1.3.5; 9.5.7. SC: po. Identifiers: Last of three articles: Harsh Medicine — Mistreating Tiffany.

Wilson, Clare. Miracle weed: cannabis can be a lifeline, and a fortunate few will soon get it on prescription. *New Scientist* 2005 February 5-11; 185(2485): 38-41. NRCBL: 9.5.1; 9.5.9.

Wilson, Hamish J. In that case. Response [case study]. *Journal of Bioethical Inquiry* 2005; 2(3): 180-181. NRCBL: 9.5.1; 9.7; 8.1; 8.4. SC: cs. Identifiers: erectile dysfunction; direct to consumer advertising of prescription-only drugs.

Wood-Harper, Janice. Informing education policy on MMR: balancing individual freedoms and collective responsibilities for the promotion of public health. *Nursing Ethics* 2005 January; 12(1): 43-58. NRCBL: 9.5.1; 8.3.2; 9.7.

Abstract: The recent decrease in public confidence in the measles, mumps and rubella vaccine has important implications for individuals and public health. This article presents moral arguments relating to conflicts between individual autonomy and collective responsibilities in vaccination decisions with a view to informing and advising health professionals and improving the effectiveness of education policies in avoiding resurgence of endemic measles. Lower population immunity, due to falling uptake, is hastening the need for greater public awareness of the consequences for the population. Vaccination refusals go hand in hand with responsibilities owed to future generations and society in not knowingly contributing to preventable harms. Issues such as parents' rights are considered and balanced against: collective responsibilities for public health; permissibility of 'free- riding'; conflicting duties of health professionals; and possible enforcement of vaccination. It is suggested that the arguments may form a persuasive tool for the practice of health professionals involved in informing and supporting parents' vaccination decisions.

World Health Organization [WHO]. Ethical choices in long-term care: what does justice require? Geneva, Switzerland: World Health Organization 2002; 90 p. [Online]. Available: http://wholibdoc.who.int/publications/2002/9291562285.pdf [7 November 2005]. NRCBL: 9.5.1; 1.1; 21.7. Identifiers: World Health Organization collection on long-term care.

CARE FOR SPECIFIC GROUPS/ AGED

Adelman, Elizabeth. Video surveillance in nursing homes. *Albany Law Journal of Science and Technology* 2002; 12(3): 821-838. NRCBL: 9.5.2; 1.1. SC: le. Conference: Symposium on Living Independently: Impact of Science and Technology on the Elderly.

Aeschleman, Heather K. The White world of nursing homes: the myriad barriers to access facing today's elderly minorities. *Elder Law Journal* 2000; 8(2): 367-391. NRCBL: 9.5.2; 9.5.4. SC: le.

Agich, George J. Implications of aging paradigms for bioethics. *In:* Weisstub, David N.; Thomasma, David C.; Gauthier, Serge; Tomossy, George F., eds. Aging: Culture, Health, and Social Change. Boston: Kluwer Academic Publishers; 2001: 15-28. NRCBL: 9.5.2; 9.4; 4.5.

Arking, Robert. A new age for aging? Ethical questions, scientific insights, and societal outcomes. *Rejuvenation Research* 2004 Spring; 7(1): 53-60. NRCBL: 9.5.2; 4.2; 4.5.

Barker, Ellen; Saulino, Michael F. Life care planning: ethical and legal issues. *In:* American College of Legal Medicine Textbook Committee, Sanbar, S. Sandy; Firestone, Marvin H.; Buckner, Fillmore; Gibofsky, Allan; LeBlang, Theodore R.; Snyder, Jack W.; Wecht, Cyril H.; Zaremski, Miles J. Legal Medicine. 6th ed. St. Louis: Mosby; 2004: 300-307. NRCBL: 9.5.2; 9.3.1. SC: le.

Bergeron, L. Rene; Gray, Betsey. Ethical dilemmas of reporting suspected elder abuse. *Social Work* 2003 January; 48(1): 96-105. NRCBL: 9.5.2; 9.1.

Bogardus, Sidney T., Jr.; Bradley, Elizabeth H.; Williams, Christianna S.; Maciejewski, Paul K.; van Doorn, Carol; Inouye, Sharon K. Goals for the care of frail older adults: do caregivers and clinicians agree? *American Journal of Medicine* 2001 February 1; 110: 97-102. NRCBL: 9.5.2; 8.1; 7.1.

NRCBL: National Reference Center for Bioethics Literature Classification Scheme   See inside front cover for terms.

101

Bramstedt, Katrina A. Age-based health care allocation as a wedge separating the person from the patient and commodifying medicine. *Reviews in Clinical Gerontology* 2001; 11: 185-188. NRCBL: 9.5.2; 9.4.

Bramstedt, Katrina A. Aortic valve replacement in the elderly: frequently indicated yet frequently denied. *Gerontology* 2003; 49: 46-49. NRCBL: 9.5.2; 9.4.

Bramstedt, Katrina A. Left ventricular assist devices and the slippery slope of ageism. *International Journal of Cardiology* 2001; 81: 201-203. NRCBL: 9.5.2; 19.6.

Bramstedt, Katrina A. Scientific breakthroughs: cause or cure of the aging 'problem'. *Gerontology* 2001; 47: 52-54. NRCBL: 9.5.2; 20.5.1.

Brock, Dan W. Discrimination against the elderly within a consequentialist approach to health care resource allocation. *In:* Weisstub, David N.; Thomasma, David C.; Gauthier, Serge; Tomossy, George F., eds. Aging: Culture, Health, and Social Change. Boston: Kluwer Academic Publishers; 2001: 65-82. NRCBL: 9.5.2; 1.1; 9.3.1; 9.4. SC: an.

Chapman, Audrey R. The social and justice implications of extending the human life span. *In:* Post, Stephen G.; Binstock, Robert H., eds. The Fountain of Youth: Cultural, Scientific, and Ethical Perspectives on a Biomedical Goal. New York: Oxford University Press; 2004: 340-361. NRCBL: 9.5.2; 4.5; 1.1.

Chater, Keri. Risk and representation: older people and noncompliance. *Nursing Inquiry* 1999 June; 6(2): 132-138. NRCBL: 9.5.2; 8.3.4; 4.1.3.

Coulson, Brett S.; Fenner, Stephen G.; Almeida, Osvaldo P. Successful treatment of behavioural problems in dementia using a cholinesterase inhibitor: the ethical questions. *Australian and New Zealand Journal of Psychiatry* 2002 April; 36(2): 259-262. NRCBL: 9.5.2; 9.7; 17.4.

Davis, Daniel H.J. Subjective estimates of cognitive impairment in older surgical patients: implications for giving informed consent [letter]. *Journal of the American Geriatrics Society* 2005 October; 53(10): 1842-1843. NRCBL: 9.5.2; 8.3.3. SC: em.

Dodds, S. Gender, ageing, and injustice: social and political contexts of bioethics. *Journal of Medical Ethics* 2005 May; 31(5): 295-298. NRCBL: 9.5.2; 9.5.5; 10. Identifiers: Australia.
Abstract: There has been considerable work in bioethics addressing injustice and gender oppression in the provision of healthcare services, in the interaction between client and healthcare professional, and in allocation of healthcare services within a particular hospital or health service. There remain several sites of continued injustice that can only be addressed adequately from a broader analytical perspective, one that attends to the social and political contexts framing healthcare policy and practice. Feminist bioethicists have a strong track record in providing this kind of analysis. Using current Australian aged care and welfare policy this paper demonstrates some of the ways in which issues of gender, age, and social inequity shape bioethical debate, policy, and practice in the areas of aged care and welfare provision. The author develops an argument that demonstrates the gender injustice underlying health care and welfare policy. This argument recognises the inevitability of human dependency relations, and questions the adequacy of current political theories to address the requirements for full and equal citizenship. The author shows that an adequate analysis of the ethics of aged healthcare depends on sufficient consideration of the social and political context within which healthcare policy is framed and an adequate understanding of human dependency.

Eccles, Jim. Ethical considerations in the care of older people. *Clinical Medicine* 2003 September-October; 3(5): 416-418. NRCBL: 9.5.2; 4.4; 20.5.1; 20.5.4; 8.3.3; 8.3.1.

Elder, Andrew T. Which benchmarks for age discrimination in acute coronary syndromes? *Age and Ageing* 2005 January; 34(1): 4-5. NRCBL: 9.5.2; 9.4. Identifiers: United Kingdom (Great Britain).

Fisher, Alfred L.; Hill, Renée. Ethical and legal issues in antiaging medicine. *Clinics in Geriatric Medicine* 2004 May; 20(2): 361-382. NRCBL: 9.5.2; 4.1.1. SC: le.

Fleming, Jack. Hospital transfers into nursing homes: a potential charter remedy for unwilling transferees. *Journal of Law and Social Policy* 1985; 1: 50-76. NRCBL: 9.5.2; 9.4. SC: le.

Funk, Laura M. Who wants to be involved? Decision-making preferences among residents of long-term care facilities. *Canadian Journal on Aging* 2004 Spring; 23(1): 47-58. NRCBL: 9.5.2; 8.1. SC: em. Identifiers: British Columbia.

Hazzard, William R. The conflict between biogerontology and antiaging medicine - - do geriatricians have a dog in this fight? [editorial]. *Journal of the American Geriatrics Society* 2005 August; 53(8): 1434-1435. NRCBL: 9.5.2; 4.5; 7.1.

Jacelon, Cynthia S. Older adults and autonomy in acute care: increasing patients' independence and control during hospitalization. *Journal of Gerontological Nursing* 2004 November; 30(11): 29-36. NRCBL: 9.5.2; 8.1; 1.1. SC: em.

Jewell, Sarah. Elderly patients' participation in discharge decision making: 1. *British Journal of Nursing* 1996 August 8-September 11; 5(15): 914-916, 929-932. NRCBL: 9.5.2; 8.3.1; 8.1.

Jones, Jeffrey S.; Johnson, Ken; McNinch, Michael. Age as a risk factor for inadequate emergency department analgesia. *American Journal of Emergency Medicine* 1996 March; 14(2): 157-160. NRCBL: 9.5.2; 4.4; 9.7; 9.4.

Juengst, Eric T. Anti-aging research and the limits of medicine. *In:* Post, Stephen G.; Binstock, Robert H., eds. The Fountain of Youth: Cultural, Scientific, and Ethical

---

Perspectives on a Biomedical Goal. New York: Oxford University Press; 2004: 321-339. NRCBL: 9.5.2; 4.5.

Kass, Leon R. Lingering longer: who will care? [opinion]. *Washington Post* 2005 September 25; p. A23. NRCBL: 9.5.2. SC: po.

Kaufman, Sharon R.; Shim, Janet K.; Russ, Ann J. Revisiting the biomedicalization of aging: clinical trends and ethical challenges. *Gerontologist* 2004 December; 44(6): 731-738. NRCBL: 9.5.2; 20.3.1; 20.5.1. SC: an.

Kawakami, Satoru; Arai, Gaku; Ueda, Keiji; Murai, Yoshiro; Yokomichi, Hiroshi; Aoshima, Masao; Takagi, Kentaro. Physician's attitudes towards disclosure of cancer diagnosis to elderly patients: a report from Tokyo, Japan. *Archives of Gerontology and Geriatrics* 2001; 33: 29-36. NRCBL: 9.5.2; 7.1; 8.1; 9.5.1. SC: em.

Kirkevold, Øyvind; Engedal, Knut. Concealment of drugs in food and beverages in nursing homes: cross sectional study. *BMJ: British Medical Journal* 2005 January 1; 330(7481): 20-22. NRCBL: 9.5.2; 8.2; 9.7. SC: em.

Lawhorne, Larry; VandeKieft, Gregg; Fleck, Leonard M. A daughter's duty. *Journal of the American Board of Family Practice* 2005 January-February; 18(1): 57-62. NRCBL: 9.5.2; 8.1; 7.1. SC: cs.

Lesser, Harry. Priorities in the use of research into ageing. *Health Care Analysis: An International Journal of Health Care Philosophy and Policy* 2005 March; 13(1): 53-58. NRCBL: 9.5.2; 4.4; 9.4; 20.5.1; 4.5.

Abstract: This paper considers which applications of research into ageing should be supported. It assumes that both applications which enhance the quality of life for the elderly and applications which extend the life-span are desirable, and then considers which should be prioritised. It is argued that in the present state of our knowledge and under present social and medical conditions there are a number of reasons for favouring the improvement of the quality of life over increasing the life-span, and thinking that this is likely to do more good and for more people.

Macdonald, Alastair J.D.; Roberts, Alice; Carpenter, Iain. De facto imprisonment and covert medication use in general nursing homes for older people in South East England. *Aging Clinical and Experimental Research* 2004 August; 16(4): 326-330. NRCBL: 9.5.2; 8.3.1; 8.3.3; 17.4. SC: em; le.

Mauleon, Annika Larsson; Palo-Bengtsson, Liisa; Ekman, Sirkka- Liisa. Anaesthesia care of older patients as experienced by nurse anaesthetists. *Nursing Ethics* 2005 May; 12(3): 263-272. NRCBL: 9.5.2; 7.1. SC: cs; em.

Abstract: This article analyses problem situations in the context of anaesthesia care. It considers what it means for nurse anaesthetists to be in problematic situations in the anaesthesia care of older patients. Benner's interpretive phenomenological approach proved useful for this purpose. Paradigm cases are used to aid the analysis of individual nurses' experiences. Thirty narrated problematic anaesthesia care situations derived from seven interviews were studied. These show that experienced nurse anaesthetists perceive anaesthesia care as problematic and highly demanding when involving older patients. To be in problematic anaesthesia care situations means becoming morally distressed, which arises from the experience or from being prevented from acting according to one's legal and moral duty of care. An important issue that emerged from this study was the need for an ethical forum to discuss and articulate moral issues, so that moral stress of the kind experienced by these nurse anaesthetists can be dealt with and hopefully reduced.

Maundrell, Richard; Kotalik, Jaro. The ethics of age discrimination and cost-benefit accounting. *Issues in Medical Ethics* 1999 October-December; 7(4): 118-120. NRCBL: 9.5.2; 9.3.1.

Meeks, Suzanne. Age bias in the diagnostic decision-making behavior of clinicians. *Professional Psychology: Research and Practice* 1990 August; 21(4): 279-284. NRCBL: 9.5.2; 17.1. SC: em.

Mueller, Paul S.; Hook, C. Christopher; Fleming, Kevin C. Ethical issues in geriatrics: a guide for clinicians. *Mayo Clinic Proceedings* 2004 April; 79(4): 554-562. NRCBL: 9.5.2; 8.3.1; 8.4; 20.5.4; 20.5.1; 9.4; 8.1. SC: le; em.

National Aged Care Forum. Code of Conduct and Ethical Practice Working Group; Fleming, John; Leaper, John; Hardy, Ian; Moait, Sandra; Heinrich, June; Rimmer, Sheila; Valadian, Bernie; Lyttle, Mary; Ramadge, Joanne. Code of ethics and guide to ethical conduct for residential aged care. Canberra: Commonwealth Department of Health and Aged Care 2001: i-vi, 1-22 [Online] Available: http://www.seniors.gov.au/Internet/wcms/Publishing.nsf/Content/ageing_workforce-codetext.html/$files/code.pdf [5 August 2005]. NRCBL: 9.5.2; 6.

Overall, Christine. Longevity, identity, and moral character: a feminist approach. *In:* Post, Stephen G.; Binstock, Robert H., eds. The Fountain of Youth: Cultural, Scientific, and Ethical Perspectives on a Biomedical Goal. New York: Oxford University Press; 2004: 286-303. NRCBL: 9.5.2; 1.1; 10.

Pauly, Mark V. What if technology never stops improving? Medicare's future under continuous cost increases. *Washington and Lee Law Review* 2003 Fall; 60(4): 1233-1250. NRCBL: 9.5.2; 9.3.1; 9.4.

Perkins, Henry S.; Shepherd, Krysten J.; Cortez, Josie D.; Hazuda, Helen P. Exploring chronically ill seniors' attitudes about discussing death and postmortem medical procedures. *Journal of the American Geriatrics Society* 2005 May; 53(5): 895-900. NRCBL: 9.5.2; 9.5.4; 20.1; 20.3.1. SC: em.

Perry, Daniel. Someone's knocking on the laboratory door [opinion]. *Rejuvenation Research* 2004 Spring; 7(1): 49-52. NRCBL: 9.5.2; 18.5.7; 9.4; 4.5. Identifiers: life extension; rejuvenation research.

NRCBL: National Reference Center for Bioethics Literature Classification Scheme   See inside front cover for terms.

103

Post, Stephen G. Decelerated aging: should I drink from the fountain of youth? *In:* Post, Stephen G.; Binstock, Robert H., eds. The Fountain of Youth: Cultural, Scientific, and Ethical Perspectives on a Biomedical Goal. New York: Oxford University Press; 2004: 72-93. NRCBL: 9.5.2; 1.1.

Post, Stephen G. Dementia care ethics. *In:* Weisstub, David N.; Thomasma, David C.; Gauthier, Serge; Tomossy, George F., eds. Aging: Caring for Our Elders. Boston: Kluwer Academic; 2001: 177-190. NRCBL: 9.5.2; 9.5.3; 20.4.1; 20.5.1; 18.5.6; 8.2.

Powers, Bethel Ann. Everyday ethics in assisted living facilities: a framework for assessing resident-focused issues. *Journal of Gerontological Nursing* 2005 January; 31(1): 31-37. NRCBL: 9.5.2; 4.4; 1.1. SC: cs.

Ramadge, Joanne. Regulating ethics [editorial]. *Collegian* 2001 January; 8(1): 5. NRCBL: 9.5.2; 6.

Rosin, A.J.; van Dijk, Y. Subtle ethical dilemmas in geriatric management and clinical research. *Journal of Medical Ethics* 2005 June; 31(6): 355-359. NRCBL: 9.5.2; 9.5.7.

Abstract: Routine management of geriatric problems often raises ethical problems, particularly regarding autonomy of the old person. The carers or children may be unaware of the sensitivity of role reversal in dealing with the financial affairs; the need for a residential carer may compromise the old person's privacy. Attending a day centre confers much benefit, but one must understand the old person's resistance to change in the proposal of a new daily regimen. Similarly his or her autonomy must be the priority in planning for admittance to an old age home, and not the assumption that the family knows best. A common dilemma is the assessment of an old person's competency in decision making, either about management of his affairs, or regarding consent to treatment, or participation in research. Because cognitive capacity is not always identical with competency, meaningful tools have recently been developed in which the emphasis is on the specific situation to be investigated.

Sanders, Stacy J.; Kittay, Eva Feder. Shouldering the burden of care [case study]. *Hastings Center Report* 2005 September-October; 35(5): 14-15. NRCBL: 9.5.2; 8.1; 7.1. SC: cs.

Sayers, Gwen M.; Nesbitt, Tim. Ageism in the NHS and the Human Rights Act 1998: an ethical and legal enquiry. *European Journal of Health Law* 2002 March; 9(1): 5-18. NRCBL: 9.5.2; 9.4; 9.2. SC: le. Identifiers: National Health Service.

Simmons, Peter; Orrell, Martin. State funded continuing care for the elderly mentally ill: a legal and ethical solution? [editorial]. *International Journal of Geriatric Psychiatry* 2001 October; 16(10): 931-934. NRCBL: 9.5.2; 17.1; 9.3.1.

Spencer, A.; Eggar, R.; Anderson, D. Whose consent is it anyway? [letter]. *British Journal of Psychiatry* 2001 February; 178; 3 p. [Online]. Available: http://bjp.rcpsych.org/cgi/content/full/178/2/177.a [28 October 2005]. NRCBL: 9.5.2; 8.3.1; 8.3.3.

Whitehouse, Peter J.; Juengst, Eric T. Antiaging medicine and mild cognitive impairment: practice and policy issues for geriatrics. *Journal of the American Geriatrics Society* 2005 August; 53(8): 1417-1422. NRCBL: 9.5.2; 4.5; 7.1.

Widdershoven, Guy A.M.; Widdershoven-Heerding, Ineke. Understanding dementia: a hermeneutic perspective. *In:* Fulford, Bill; Morris, Katherine; Sadler, John Z.; Stanghellini, Giovanni, eds. Nature and Narrative: An Introduction to the New Philosophy of Psychiatry. New York: Oxford University Press; 2003: 103-111. NRCBL: 9.5.2; 17.1.

CARE FOR SPECIFIC GROUPS/ FETUSES
See also HUMAN EXPERIMENTATION/ SPECIAL POPULATIONS/ EMBRYOS AND FETUSES

Calhoun, Byron C. The fetus as our patient: the confluence of faith and science in the care of the unborn. *Linacre Quarterly* 2005 August; 72(3): 189-211. NRCBL: 9.5.8; 1.2.

Campion, Bridget. An argument for continuing a pregnancy where the fetus is discovered to be anencephalic. *In:* Koterski, Joseph W., ed. Life and Learning IX: Proceedings of the Ninth University Faculty for Life Conference. Washington, DC: University Faculty for Life; 2000: 319-329. NRCBL: 9.5.8; 12.3; 1.2. SC: an.

Caniano, D.A.; Baylis, F. Ethical considerations in prenatal surgical consultation. *Pediatric Surgery International* 1999 July; 15(5-6): 303-309. NRCBL: 9.5.8; 15.2. SC: cs.

Catholics for a Free Choice. Respecting women's rights and fetal value: reflections on the question of female anesthesia. *Conscience* 2005 Autumn; 26(3): 39-40. NRCBL: 9.5.8; 4.4; 12.1.

Chervenak, Frank A.; McCullough, Laurence B. An ethical critique of boutique fetal imaging: a case for the medicalization of fetal imaging. *American Journal of Obstetrics and Gynecology* 2005 January; 192(1): 31-33. NRCBL: 9.5.8; 9.3.1; 5.3. SC: an.

Coghlan, Andy; Young, Emma. Why fetuses don't feel pain [news]. *New Scientist* 2005 September 3-9; 187(2515): 8-9. NRCBL: 9.5.8; 4.4.

DeGrazia, David. Prenatal identity: genetic interventions, reproductive choices. *In his:* Human Identity and Bioethics. New York: Cambridge University Press; 2005: 244-294. NRCBL: 9.5.8; 12.3; 15.1; 15.4; 1.1.

Derbyshire, Stuart W.G. The fetus does not feel pain [debate]. *Conscience* 2004-2005 Winter; 25(3): 32-35. NRCBL: 9.5.8; 4.4.

Dogan, Hanzade; Sahinoglu, Serap. Fetuses with neural tube defects: ethical approaches and the role of health care professionals in Turkish health care institutions. *Nursing Ethics* 2005 January; 12(1): 59-78. NRCBL: 9.5.8; 7.3; 9.6; 12.1. SC: em.

Abstract: Neural tube defects (NTDs) are very serious malformations for the fetus, causing either low life expectancy or a chance of survival only with costly and difficult surgical interventions. In western countries the average prevalence is 1/1000-2000 and in Turkey it is 4/1000. The aim of the study was to characterize ethical approaches at institutional level to the fetus with an NTD and the mother, and the role of health care professionals in four major centers in Turkey. The authors chose perinatology units of four university hospitals and prepared questionnaires for the responsible professionals concerning their own and their institution's ethical approaches to the fetus with an NTD and the mother. The investigation revealed that there were no institutional ethical frameworks or ethics committees available to professional teams in the units. The roles of the health care professionals and their individual decisions and approaches based on ethical principles are described. The ethical decision-making process concerning fetuses with NTDs, examples of institutional approaches to the topic and institutional frameworks, and the role of nurses and other health care professionals are all discussed, based on a literature review. The authors suggest that institutional ethical frameworks, ethics committees, professionals' ethics education and multidisciplinary teamwork should be established for critical situations such as fetuses with an NTD.

Ford, Norman M. Fetal surgery: the wisdom of Solomon. *Ethics and Medics* 2003 August; 28(8): 3-4. NRCBL: 9.5.8; 9.5.5.

Glover, Vivette. The fetus may feel pain from 20 weeks [debate]. *Conscience* 2004-2005 Winter; 25(3): 35-37. NRCBL: 9.5.8; 4.4.

Greene, Naomi; Platt, Lawrence D. Nonmedical use of ultrasound: greater harm than good? *Journal of Ultrasound in Medicine* 2005 January; 24(1): 123-125. NRCBL: 9.5.8; 15.2; 5.3. SC: cs.

Koren, Gideon; Selby, Peter; Kapur, Bhushan. Is a fetus a non-consenting patient? *Canadian Family Physician* 2004 September; 50: 1219-1221. NRCBL: 9.5.8; 9.5.1; 17.4; 17.5. SC: cs; em.

Lee, Susan J.; Ralston, Henry J. Peter; Drey, Eleanor A.; Partridge, John Colin; Rosen, Mark A. Fetal pain — a systematic multidisciplinary review of the evidence. *JAMA: The Journal of the American Medical Association* 2005 August 24-31; 294(8): 947-954. NRCBL: 9.5.8; 4.4; 12.4.2. SC: em.

Abstract: CONTEXT: Proposed federal legislation would require physicians to inform women seeking abortions at 20 or more weeks after fertilization that the fetus feels pain and to offer anesthesia administered directly to the fetus. This article examines whether a fetus feels pain and if so, whether safe and effective techniques exist for providing direct fetal anesthesia or analgesia in the context of therapeutic procedures or abortion. EVIDENCE ACQUISITION: Systematic search of PubMed for English-language articles focusing on human studies related to fetal pain, anesthesia, and analgesia. Included articles studied fetuses of less than 30 weeks' gestational age or specifically addressed fetal pain perception or nociception. Articles were reviewed for additional references. The search was performed without date limitations and was current as of June 6, 2005. EVIDENCE SYNTHESIS: Pain perception requires conscious recognition or awareness of a noxious stimulus. Neither withdrawal reflexes nor hormonal stress responses to invasive procedures prove the existence of fetal pain, because they can be elicited by nonpainful stimuli and occur without conscious cortical processing. Fetal awareness of noxious stimuli requires functional thalamocortical connections. Thalamocortical fibers begin appearing between 23 to 30 weeks' gestational age, while electroencephalography suggests the capacity for functional pain perception in preterm neonates probably does not exist before 29 or 30 weeks. For fetal surgery, women may receive general anesthesia and/or analgesics intended for placental transfer, and parenteral opioids may be administered to the fetus under direct or sonographic visualization. In these circumstances, administration of anesthesia and analgesia serves purposes unrelated to reduction of fetal pain, including inhibition of fetal movement, prevention of fetal hormonal stress responses, and induction of uterine atony. CONCLUSIONS: Evidence regarding the capacity for fetal pain is limited but indicates that fetal perception of pain is unlikely before the third trimester. Little or no evidence addresses the effectiveness of direct fetal anesthetic or analgesic techniques. Similarly, limited or no data exist on the safety of such techniques for pregnant women in the context of abortion. Anesthetic techniques currently used during fetal surgery are not directly applicable to abortion procedures.

Lenow, Jeffrey L. Fetal interests. *In:* American College of Legal Medicine Textbook Committee, Sanbar, S. Sandy; Firestone, Marvin H.; Buckner, Fillmore; Gibofsky, Allan; LeBlang, Theodore R.; Snyder, Jack W.; Wecht, Cyril H.; Zaremski, Miles J. Legal Medicine. 6th ed. St. Louis: Mosby; 2004: 264-270. NRCBL: 9.5.8; 4.4; 9.5.5. SC: le.

Weinberg, Susan R. A maternal duty to protect fetal health? *Indiana Law Journal* 1983; 58(3): 531-546. NRCBL: 9.5.8; 9.5.5. SC: le.

CARE FOR SPECIFIC GROUPS/ INDIGENTS

Connolly, Erin Lynn. Constitutional issues raised by states' exclusion of fertility drugs from Medicaid coverage in light of mandated coverage of Viagra. *Vanderbuilt Law Review* 2001 March; 54(2): 451-480. NRCBL: 9.5.10; 9.3.1; 14.1; 10. SC: le.

Luna, Florencia. Poverty and inequality: challenges for the IAB: IAB presidential address. *Bioethics* 2005 October; 19(5-6): 451-459. NRCBL: 9.5.10; 2.1; 1.1; 9.3.1; 21.1. Identifiers: International Association of Bioethics.

Abstract: This paper focuses on poverty and inequality in the world today. First, it points out how this topic is a main concern for the IAB. Second, it proposes 'new' theoretical tools in order to analyze global justice and our obligations towards the needy. I present John Rawls's denial that the egalitarian principle can be applied to the global sphere, his proposed weak duty of assistance, and his consideration of endemic poverty as essentially homegrown. In opposition, I focus on Thomas Pogge as representative of a cosmopolitan view who also holds a critical position towards the international systems which allow and cause poverty. I endorse the general normative proposal that defends every human being as an ultimate unit of moral concern, as well as the strategy of moving away from the charity model of bilat-

NRCBL: National Reference Center for Bioethics Literature Classification Scheme   See inside front cover for terms.

105

eral aid to the realm of rights and duties. These ideas should re-design and broaden the normative and practical roles of institutions, and should also help provide a new approach on bioethical issues such as drug patenting or the imbalance in global research and neglected diseases.

O'Connell, James J. Raging against the night: dying homeless and alone. *Journal of Clinical Ethics* 2005 Fall; 16(3): 262-266. NRCBL: 9.5.10; 20.4.1; 4.4; 9.2.

Shi, Leiyu. Vulnerable populations and health insurance. *Medical Care Research and Review* 2000 March; 57(1): 110-134. NRCBL: 9.5.10; 9.3.1; 9.5.4; 9.5.7; 9.2.

Song, John; Ratner, Edward R.; Bartels, Dianne M. Dying while homeless: is it a concern when life itself is such a struggle? *Journal of Clinical Ethics* 2005 Fall; 16(3): 251-261. NRCBL: 9.5.10; 20.4.1; 20.5.1; 4.4; 9.2. SC: em.

Stassen, Glen H. Supporting parents. *Christian Century* 2005 February 22; 122(4): 10-11. NRCBL: 9.5.10; 9.3.1; 12.3.

Young, Janine; Flores, Glenn; Berman, Stephen. Providing life-saving health care to undocumented children: controversies and ethical issues. *Pediatrics* 2004 November; 114(5): 1316-1320. NRCBL: 9.5.10; 9.5.7; 9.3.1; 9.4.

CARE FOR SPECIFIC GROUPS/ MENTALLY DISABLED

See also BEHAVIOR CONTROL; ELECTRO-CONVULSIVE THERAPY; INVOLUNTARY COMMITMENT; MENTAL HEALTH THERA-PIES; PSYCHOPHARMACOLOGY; PSYCHO-THERAPY

Seclusion of psychiatric patients. *Medical Law Review* 2003 Autumn; 11(3): 384-393. NRCBL: 9.5.3. SC: le.

Arends, L.A.P. Legal status of incompetent patients in psychogeriatric settings from a Dutch perspective. *Medicine and Law: World Association for Medical Law* 2004; 23(4): 821-831. NRCBL: 9.5.3; 17.7; 9.5.2. SC: le; em.
Abstract: In 1994 the Compulsory Admissions in Psychiatric Hospitals Act (Bopz) was introduced in the Netherlands. The main purpose of the Bopz is to offer legal protection for patients who are involuntarily admitted to a psychiatric hospital. Although the law was originally designed for psychiatric patients, it also effects the legal position of psycho-geriatric patients in care homes and some rest homes. In 2001 the law was evaluated for the second time. The evaluation study shows that the legislation in psycho-geriatric settings offers only little protection for the residents, mainly because the Bopz-law was originally designed for a psychiatric setting. Therefore the terms, used in the Bopz, are not suitable for nursing homes and rest homes. It is suggested that for psycho- geriatric patients special legislation should be developed, possibly including those with an intellectual handicap.

Bickenbach, Jerome E. The perils of human genetics. *Ethics and Intellectual Disability Newsletter* 1996 Winter; 1(2): 1-3. NRCBL: 9.5.3; 15.10.

Corfield, Lorraine; Granne, Ingrid. Treating non-competent patients: England's new act imposes new obligations but also makes things clearer [editorial]. *BMJ: British Medical Journal* 2005 December 10; 331(7529): 1353-1354. NRCBL: 9.5.3; 4.3. SC: le.

Crombie, H. David. Contrasts and challenges. *Connecticut Medicine* 2004 September; 68(8): 537. NRCBL: 9.5.3.

Gevers, Sjef. Advance directives in psychiatry. *European Journal of Health Law* 2002 March; 9(1): 19-29. NRCBL: 9.5.3; 20.5.4; 8.3.3; 1.1. SC: le.

Green, Carolyn; Schultz, Marina; Corea, Lynda; Dandekar, Ashwin. Perceived barriers to healthcare: a survey of clients of the County Board of Mental Retardation and Developmental Disabilities in Cuyahoga county. *Clinical Pediatrics* 2004 October; 43(8): 721-724. NRCBL: 9.5.3; 9.2; 9.1.

Hamann, Johannes; Cohen, Rudolf; Leucht, Stefan; Busch, Raymonde; Kissling, Werner. Do patients with schizophrenia wish to be involved in decisions about their medical treatment? *American Journal of Psychiatry* 2005 December; 162(12): 2382- 2384. NRCBL: 9.5.3; 8.1. SC: em.

Jones, Melinda. Can international law improve mental health? Some thoughts on the proposed convention on the rights of people with disabilities. *International Journal of Law and Psychiatry* 2005 March- April; 28(2): 183-205. NRCBL: 9.5.3; 21.1; 9.2; 9.5.1; 17.1. SC: le.

Lewis, Oliver. Protecting the rights of people with mental disabilities: the European Convention on Human Rights. *European Journal of Health Law* 2002 December; 9(4): 293-320. NRCBL: 9.5.3; 17.7; 17.8; 8.5. SC: le; an.

Light, Sarah E. Rejecting the logic of confinement: care relationships and the mentally disabled under tort law. *Yale Law Journal* 1999 November; 109(2): 381-416. NRCBL: 9.5.3; 17.7; 4.3; 8.5. SC: le.

Marcus, Amy Dockser. A brother's survey touches a nerve in abortion fight; mothers were asked how they found out their babies had Down syndrome; teaching his sister to read. *Wall Street Journal* 2005 October 3; p. A1, A8. NRCBL: 9.5.3; 12.1; 8.2. SC: po. Identifiers: Brian Skotko.

Meininger, Herman P. Autonomy and professional responsibility in care for persons with intellectual disabilities. *Nursing Philosophy* 2001 October; 2(3): 240-250. NRCBL: 9.5.3; 1.1; 4.1.3.

Meininger, Herman P. Narrative ethics in nursing for persons with intellectual disabilities. *Nursing Philosophy* 2005 April; 6(2): 106-118. NRCBL: 9.5.3; 1.1; 7.1.

Melvin, Louise. Reproductive issues and learning disability: different perspectives of professionals and parents. *Journal of Family Planning and Reproductive Health Care*

2004 October; 30(4): 263-264. NRCBL: 9.5.3; 10; 14.1. SC: cs.

Mitchell, David R. Ethical and legal issues in providing medical treatment for seriously ill handicapped persons. *Australia and New Zealand Journal of Developmental Disabilities* 1985; 10(4): 245-256. NRCBL: 9.5.3; 20.5.1.

Mühlhauser, Ingrid. Understanding breast cancer screening: should the intellectually non-disabled make decisions for the intellectually disabled? [editorial]. *Sozial- und Praventivmedizin* 2004; 49(6): 359-360. NRCBL: 9.5.3; 9.5.5.

Rolph, Sheena. Ethical dilemmas in historical research with people with learning difficulties. *British Journal of Learning Disabilities* 1998 Winter; 26(4): 135-139. NRCBL: 9.5.3; 1.3.1; 7.1.

Saito, Masahiko. Decision-making in social and medical services for patients with dementia in Japan. *In:* Weisstub, David N.; Thomasma, David C.; Gauthier, Serge; Tomossy, George F., eds. Aging: Caring for Our Elders. Boston: Kluwer Academic; 2001: 191-202. NRCBL: 9.5.3; 17.1; 20.5.1; 20.4.1; 8.2.

Scheid, Teresa L. Stigma as a barrier to employment: mental disability and the Americans with Disabilities Act. *International Journal of Law and Psychiatry* 2005 November- December; 28(6): 670-690. NRCBL: 9.5.3; 9.2; 1.3.2; 4.3. SC: em; le.

Skeel, Joy D.; Williams, Kristi S. Helping staff help a "hateful" patient: the case of TJ. *Journal of Clinical Ethics* 2005 Fall; 16(3): 202-205. NRCBL: 9.5.3; 9.6; 8.1. SC: cs.

Van Hoof, Thomas J.; Taggart, W. Blake. Mental retardation and decision making: balancing autonomy and protection. *Connecticut Medicine* 1998 August; 62(8): 455-460. NRCBL: 9.5.3; 1.1; 9.4; 7.1.

Veatch, Robert M. Transplants and mental disability: the meaning of discrimination. *Ethics and Intellectual Disability Newsletter* 2001 Summer; 6(1): 1-5. NRCBL: 9.5.3; 19.6.

Veatch, Robert M. Withholding nutrition on the conscious mentally disabled patient: a review and commentary. *Ethics and Intellectual Disability Newsletter* 2002 Fall; 7(1): 5-7. NRCBL: 9.5.3; 20.5.1. SC: le.

Vitello, Stanley J. On the value of a life with mental retardation: Keene v. Brigham and Women's Hospital, Inc. *Ethics and Intellectual Disability Newsletter* 2002 Fall; 7(1): 1-3. NRCBL: 9.5.3; 4.4; 8.5. SC: le.

CARE FOR SPECIFIC GROUPS/ MINORITIES

Akpunonu, Basil E.; Mutgi, Anand B.; Khuder, Sadik A.; Vaccarino, Viola; Jha, Ashish K.; Epstein, Arnold M.; Orav, E. John. Trends in racial disparities in care [let-ter and reply]. *New England Journal of Medicine* 2005 November 10; 353(19): 2083-2085. NRCBL: 9.5.4; 9.8.

Aspinall, Peter. Language matters: the vocabulary of racism in health care. *Journal of Health Services Research and Policy* 2005 January; 10(1): 57-59. NRCBL: 9.5.4; 8.1.

Ayres, Ian. Three tests for measuring unjustified disparate impacts in organ transplantation: the problem of "included variable" bias. *Perspectives in Biology and Medicine* 2005 Winter; 48(1, Supplement): S68-S87. NRCBL: 9.5.4; 19.1; 9.4; 9.2. Note: Special issue: Disparities and Discrimination in HealthCare and Health Outcomes.

Betancourt, Joseph R. Unequal treatment: the Institute of Medicine report and its public health implications [editorial]. *Public Health Reports* 2003 July-August; 118(3): 287-292. NRCBL: 9.5.4; 9.1.

Bloche, M. Gregg. American medicine and the politics of race. *Perspectives in Biology and Medicine* 2005 Winter; 48(1, Supplement): S54-S67. NRCBL: 9.5.4; 5.3; 21.1; 9.2; 9.3.1; 9.4; 8.1; 9.8; 7.1. Note: Special issue: Disparities and Discrimination in Health Care and Health Outcomes.

Boulware, L. Ebony; Cooper, Lisa A.; Ratner, Lloyd E.; LaVeist, Thomas A.; Powe, Neil R. Race and trust in the health care system. *Public Health Reports* 2003 July-August; 118(3): 358-365. NRCBL: 9.5.4; 9.1. SC: em.

Bowser, René. Race as a proxy for drug response: the dangers and challenges of ethnic drugs. *DePaul Law Review* 2004 Spring; 53(3): 1111-1126. NRCBL: 9.5.4; 9.7; 15.1.

Bowser, René. Racial bias in medical treatment. *Dickinson Law Review* 2001 Spring; 105(3): 365-383. NRCBL: 9.5.4; 9.2. SC: le.

Chan, Evelyn C.Y.; Haynes, Michelle C.; O'Donnell, Frederick T.; Bachino, Carolyn; Vernon, Sally W. Cultural sensitivity and informed decision making about prostate cancer screening. *Journal of Community Health* 2003 December; 28(6): 393-405. NRCBL: 9.5.4; 9.5.1; 8.3.1; 21.7. SC: em.

Chaudhry, Samena. Fighting for justice [news]. *BMJ: British Medical Journal* 2005 January 15; 330(7483): 114. NRCBL: 9.5.4.

Epstein, Richard A. Disparities and discrimination in health care coverage: a critique of the Institute of Medicine study. *Perspectives in Biology and Medicine* 2005 Winter; 48(1, Supplement): S26-S41. NRCBL: 9.5.4; 8.1; 19.1; 9.4; 9.5.2. Note: Special issue: Disparities and Discrimination in Health Care and Health Outcomes.

Freedman, Barry I.; Wagenknecht, Lynne E.; Bowden, Donald W.; Vaccarino, Viola; Jha, Ashish K.; Epstein, Arnold M.; Orav, E. John. Trends in racial disparities in

NRCBL: National Reference Center for Bioethics Literature Classification Scheme   See inside front cover for terms.

107

care [letter and reply]. *New England Journal of Medicine* 2005 November 10; 353(19): 2081-2085. NRCBL: 9.5.4; 9.8.

Halldenius, Lena. Dissecting "discrimination". *CQ: Cambridge Quarterly of Healthcare Ethics* 2005 Fall; 14(4): 455-463. NRCBL: 9.5.4; 9.5.5; 10; 1.1. SC: le.

Harjai, Kishore J.; Nunez, Eduardo; Shah, Mehul; Newman, Jeff. Does racial bias exist in the medical management of heart failure? *Clinical Cardiology* 2002 October; 25(10): 479-483. NRCBL: 9.5.4; 9.2; 9.4.

Ikemoto, Lisa C. The fuzzy logic of race and gender in the mismeasure of Asian American women's health needs. *University of Cincinnati Law Review* 1997 Spring; 65(3): 799-824. NRCBL: 9.5.4; 9.5.5; 9.4.

Jha, Ashish K.; Fisher, Elliott S.; Li, Zhonghe; Orav, E. John; Epstein, Arnold M. Racial trends in the use of major procedures among the elderly. *New England Journal of Medicine* 2005 August 18; 353(7): 683- 691. NRCBL: 9.5.4; 9.5.2; 9.5.1.
Abstract: BACKGROUND: Differences in the use of major procedures according to patients' race are well known. Whether national and local initiatives to reduce these differences have been successful is unknown. METHODS: We examined data for men and women enrolled in Medicare from 1992 through 2001 on annual age-standardized rates of receipt of nine surgical procedures previously shown to have disparities in the rates at which they were performed in black patients and in white patients. We also examined data according to hospital-referral region for three of the nine procedures: coronary-artery bypass grafting (CABG), carotid endarterectomy, and total hip replacement. RESULTS: Nationally, in 1992, the rates of receipt for all the procedures examined were higher among white patients than among black patients. The difference between the rates among whites and blacks increased significantly between 1992 and 2001 for five of the nine procedures, remained unchanged for three procedures, and narrowed significantly for one procedure. We examined rates of CABG, carotid endarterectomy, and total hip replacement in 158 hospital-referral regions (79 hospital-referral regions for black men and white men and 79 for black women and white women) with an adequate number of persons for each procedure. We found that in the early 1990s, whites had higher rates for these procedures than blacks in every hospital-referral region. By 2001, the difference between whites and blacks (both men and women) in the rates of these procedures narrowed significantly in 22 hospital-referral regions, widened significantly in 42, and were not significantly changed in the remaining hospital-referral regions. At the end of the study period, we found no hospital- referral region in which the difference in rates between whites and blacks was eliminated for men or women with regard to any of these three procedures. CONCLUSIONS: For the decade of the 1990s, we found no evidence, either nationally or locally, that efforts to eliminate racial disparities in the use of high-cost surgical procedures were successful.

Keppel, Kenneth G.; Pearcy, Jeffrey N.; Weissman, Joel S.; Vaccarino, Viola; Jha, Ashish K.; Epstein, Arnold M.; Orav, E. John. Trends in racial disparities in care [letter and reply]. *New England Journal of Medicine* 2005 November 10; 353(19): 2082-2085. NRCBL: 9.5.4; 9.8.

King, William D. Examining African Americans' mistrust of the health care system: expanding the research question. Commentary on "Race and trust in the health care system". *Public Health Reports* 2003 July-August; 118(3): 366-367. NRCBL: 9.5.4; 9.1. Comments: comment on L.E. Boulware, L.A. Cooper, L.E. Ratner, T.A. LaVeist, N.R. Powe, "Race and trust in the health care system," Public Health Reports 2003; 118: 358-365.

Kuller, Lewis H.; Vaccarino, Viola; Jha, Ashish K.; Epstein, Arnold M.; Orav, E. John. Trends in racial disparities in care [letter and reply]. *New England Journal of Medicine* 2005 November 10; 353(19): 2081, 2083-2085. NRCBL: 9.5.4; 9.8.

Lebovits, Allen. The ethical implications of racial disparities in pain: are some of us more equal? [editorial]. *Pain Medicine* 2005 January-February; 6(1): 3-4. NRCBL: 9.5.4; 9.4; 4.4.

Lee, Simon J. Craddock. The risks of race in addressing health disparities [opinion]. *Hastings Center Report* 2005 July-August; 35(4): inside back cover. NRCBL: 9.5.4; 15.1; 3.1.

Noah, Barbara A. Racial disparities in the delivery of health care. *San Diego Law Review* 1998 Winter; 35(1): 135-178. NRCBL: 9.5.4; 9.4. SC: le.

Resnicow, Ken; Braithwaite, Ronald L. Cultural sensitivity in public health. *In:* Braithwaite, Ronald L.; Taylor, Sandra E., eds. Health Issues in the Black Community. 2nd ed. San Francisco: Jossey-Bass; 2001: 516-542. NRCBL: 9.5.4.

Satel, Sally; Klick, Jonathan. The Institute of Medicine report: too quick to diagnose bias. *Perspectives in Biology and Medicine* 2005 Winter; 48(1, Supplement): S15-S25. NRCBL: 9.5.4; 8.1; 9.3.1; 7.1. Note: Special issue: Disparities and Discrimination in Health Care and Health Outcomes.

Saul, Stephanie. FDA panel approves heart remedy for blacks. *New York Times* 2005 June 17; p. C4. NRCBL: 9.5.4; 9.7. SC: po.

Saul, Stephanie. Maker of heart drug intended for blacks bases price on patients' wealth. *New York Times* 2005 July 8; p. C3. NRCBL: 9.5.4; 9.7; 9.3.1. SC: po.

Saul, Stephanie. US to review drug intended for one race. *New York Times* 2005 June 13; p. A1, A15. NRCBL: 9.5.4; 9.7. SC: po.

Scott, Andrea K. Gender discrimination in the medical community. *Update [Loma Linda University Center for Christian Bioethics]* 1995 July; 11(2): 12 p. NRCBL: 9.5.4; 10; 7.1; 7.2; 9.5.5; 18.5.3.

Shin, Michael S. Redressing wounds: finding a legal framework to remedy racial disparities in medical care.

California Law Review 2002 December; 90(6): 2047-2100. NRCBL: 9.5.4; 9.2; 9.4. SC: le.

Smith, David Barton. The politics of racial disparities: desegregating the hospitals in Jackson, Mississippi. *Milbank Quarterly* 2005; 83(2): 247-269. NRCBL: 9.5.4.

Abstract: As health care policymakers and providers focus on eliminating the persistent racial disparities in treatment, it is useful to explore how resistance to hospital desegregation was overcome. Jackson, Mississippi, provides an instructive case study of how largely concealed deliberations achieved the necessary concessions in a still rigidly segregated community. The Veterans Administration hospital, the medical school hospital, and the private nonprofit facilities were successively desegregated, owing mainly to the threatened loss of federal dollars. Many of the changes, however, were cosmetic. In contrast to the powerful financial incentives offered to hospitals to desegregate and ensure equal access in the early years of the Medicare program, current trends in federal reimbursement encourage segregation and disparities in treatment.

Sohler, Nancy L.; Bromet, Evelyn J.; Lavelle, Janet; Craig, Thomas J.; Mojtabai, Ramin. Are there racial differences in the way patients with psychotic disorders are treated at their first hospitalization? *Psychological Medicine* 2004 May; 34(4): 705-718. NRCBL: 9.5.4; 9.2; 17.1. SC: em.

Toldson, Ivory Lee; Toldson, Ivory Achebe. Biomedical ethics: an African-centered psychological perspective. *Journal of Black Psychology* 2001 November; 27(4): 401-423. NRCBL: 9.5.4; 2.1; 17.1; 8.1.

Vaccarino, Viola; Rathore, Saif S.; Wenger, Nanette K.; Frederick, Paul D.; Abramson, Jerome L.; Barron, Hal V.; Manhapra, Ajay; Mallik, Susmita; Krumholz, Harlan M. Sex and racial differences in the management of acute myocardial infarction, 1994 through 2002. *New England Journal of Medicine* 2005 August 18; 353(7): 671- 682. NRCBL: 9.5.5; 9.5.4; 9.5.1.

Abstract: BACKGROUND: Although increased attention has been paid to sex and racial differences in the management of myocardial infarction, it is unknown whether these differences have narrowed over time. METHODS: With the use of data from the National Registry of Myocardial Infarction, we examined sex and racial differences in the treatment of patients who were deemed to be "ideal candidates" for particular treatments and in deaths among 598,911 patients hospitalized with myocardial infarction between 1994 and 2002. RESULTS: In the unadjusted analysis, sex and racial differences were observed for rates of reperfusion therapy (for white men, white women, black men, and black women: 86.5, 83.3, 80.4, and 77.8 percent, respectively; P.001), use of aspirin (84.4, 78.7, 83.7, and 78.4 percent, respectively; P.001), use of beta-blockers (66.6, 62.9, 67.8, and 64.5 percent; P.001), and coronary angiography (69.1, 55.9, 64.0, and 55.0 percent; P.001). After multivariable adjustment, racial and sex differences persisted for rates of reperfusion therapy (risk ratio for white women, black men, and black women: 0.97, 0.91, and 0.89, respectively, as compared with white men) and coronary angiography (relative risk, 0.91, 0.82, and 0.76) but were attenuated for the use of aspirin (risk ratio, 0.97, 0.98, and 0.94) and beta-blockers (risk ratio, 0.98, 1.00, and 0.96); all risks were unchanged over time. Adjusted in-hospital mortality was similar among white women (risk ratio, 1.05; 95 percent confidence interval, 1.03 to 1.07) and black men (risk ratio, 0.95; 95 percent confidence interval, 0.89 to 1.00), as compared with white men, but was higher among black women (risk ratio, 1.11; 95 percent confidence interval, 1.06 to 1.16) and was unchanged over time. CONCLUSIONS: Rates of reperfusion therapy, coronary angiography, and in-hospital death after myocardial infarction, but not the use of aspirin and beta-blockers, vary according to race and sex, with no evidence that the differences have narrowed in recent years.

Van Houtven, Courtney Harold; Voils, Corrine I.; Oddone, Eugene Z.; Weinfurt, Kevin P.; Friedman, Joëlle Y.; Schulman, Kevin A.; Bosworth, Hayden B. Perceived discrimination and reported delay of pharmacy prescriptions and medical tests. *JGIM: Journal of General Internal Medicine* 2005 July; 20(7): 578-583. NRCBL: 9.5.4; 9.2; 9.7. SC: em.

Watson, Sidney D. Race, ethnicity and hospital care: the need for racial and ethnic data [opinion]. *Journal of Health and Hospital Law* 1997 June; 30(2): 125-132. NRCBL: 9.5.4; 7.1.

Weisfeld, Alix; Perlman, Robert L. Disparities and discrimination in health care: an introduction. *Perspectives in Biology and Medicine* 2005 Winter; 48(1, Supplement): S1-S9. NRCBL: 9.5.4; 9.3.1; 10. Note: Special issue: Disparities and Discrimination in Health Care and Health Outcomes.

Williams, David R.; Collins, Chiquita. Reparations: a viable strategy to address the enigma of African American health. *American Behavioral Scientist* 2004 March; 47(7): 977-1000. NRCBL: 9.5.4; 9.2; 21.1.

CARE FOR SPECIFIC GROUPS/ MINORS

Infant born to dying mother dies as result of infection. *New York Times* 2005 September 13; p. A18. NRCBL: 9.5.7; 20.1; 20.5.1. SC: po.

Adhikari, M. Caring for babies who survive an abortion attempt — an ethical dilemma [letter]. *South African Medical Journal* 1998 May; 88(5): 578. NRCBL: 9.5.7; 12.1.

Akeson, Nancy; Robertson, John A. Neonatal care for premature infants [letter and reply]. *Hastings Center Report* 2005 January-February; 35(1): 6, 7. NRCBL: 9.5.7; 20.5.2.

Anderson, Lynley; Cunningham, Nikki. In that case. *Journal of Bioethical Inquiry* 2005; 2(2): 109. NRCBL: 9.5.7; 9.5.1; 9.3.1; 9.5.1. SC: cs. Identifiers: haemophilia; health care resources.

Bailey, Donald B., Jr.; Skinner, Debra; Warren, Steven F. Newborn screening for developmental disabilities: reframing presumptive benefit. *American Journal of Public Health* 2005 November; 95(11): 1889- 1893. NRCBL: 9.5.7; 9.1; 15.3; 9.5.3.

Abstract: A fundamental tenet of newborn screening is that screening should lead to a proven benefit for the infant. The standard is usually construed as medical benefit that significantly improves a child's health. Screening for many conditions

NRCBL: National Reference Center for Bioethics Literature Classification Scheme   See inside front cover for terms.

109

that cause developmental disabilities does not currently meet this standard. We argue for expanding concepts of presumptive benefit. Newborn screening provides access to early intervention programs that are shown to positively influence child development and support families. Consumers want information about their children's health and their own reproductive risk, and they have a broader view than policymakers of what constitutes a treatable disorder. Newborn screening provides other societal benefits that, in the absence of data showing harm and with appropriate attention to ethical and legal issues, warrant consideration of an expansion of targets for newborn screening.

Bellieni, Carlo. Pain definitions revised: newborns not only feel pain, they also suffer. *Ethics and Medicine* 2005 Spring; 21(1): 5-9. NRCBL: 9.5.7; 4.4.

Berg, Abbey L.; Herb, Alice; Hurst, Marsha. Cochlear implants in children: ethics, informed consent, and parental decision making. *Journal of Clinical Ethics* 2005 Fall; 16(3): 239-250. NRCBL: 9.5.7; 9.5.1; 8.3.2.

Boyte, W. Richard; Blackston, Joseph W.; Douglas, Sharon; Crook, Errol D. Case studies in ethics from the G.V. "Sonny" Montgomery VA Medical Center and the University of Mississippi Medical Center: caring for adolescent family members of physician colleagues. *American Journal of the Medical Sciences* 2002 January; 323(1): 49-53. NRCBL: 9.5.7; 8.4; 7.3. SC: cs.

Bridge, Caroline. Religion, culture and the body of the child. *In:* Bainham, Andrew; Sclater, Shelley Day; Richards, Martin, eds. Body Lore and Laws. Portland, OR: Hart Pub.; 2002: 265-287. NRCBL: 9.5.7; 8.3.4; 4.4. SC: le.

British Association of Perinatal Medicine [BAPM]. Thames Regional Perinatal Group. Guidelines relating to the birth of extremely immature babies (22-25 weeks gestation). United Kingdom: British Association of Perinatal Medicine 2000 March; 5 p. [Online]. Available: http://www.bapm.org/media/documents/publications/immature.pdf [31 January 2006]. NRCBL: 9.5.7.

Carnahan, Mike. In that case. Response [case study]. *Journal of Bioethical Inquiry* 2005; 2(2): 110-111. NRCBL: 9.5.7; 9.3.1; 9.5.1. SC: cs. Identifiers: haemophilia; health care resources. Comments: comment on Lynley Anderson and Nikki Cunningham, "In that Case," Journal of Bioethical Inquiry 2005; 2(2): 109.

Carter, Brian S.; Merenstein, Gerald B.; Robertson, John A. Neonatal care for premature infants [letter and reply]. *Hastings Center Report* 2005 January-February; 35(1): 4-5, 7. NRCBL: 9.5.7; 20.5.2.

Charchuk, Margo; Simpson, Christy. Hope, disclosure, and control in the neonatal intensive care unit. *Health Communication* 2005; 17(2): 191-203. NRCBL: 9.5.7; 8.1.

Cross, Alan W.; Churchill, Larry R.; Sharp, Michael C.; King, Nancy M.P. Ethical issues in the health care of children with developmental handicaps. *In:* Schopler, Eric; Mesibov, Gary B., eds. Neurobiological Issues in Au-

tism. New York: Plenum Press; 1987: 63-79. NRCBL: 9.5.3; 9.5.7; 2.1. SC: cs.

Cuttler, Leona; Whittaker, June L.; Kodish, Eric D. The overweight adolescent: clinical and ethical issues in intensive treatments for pediatric obesity. *Journal of Pediatrics* 2005 April; 146(4): 559-564. NRCBL: 9.5.7; 4.2. SC: cs.

Denholm, Justin. In that case. Response [case study]. *Journal of Bioethical Inquiry* 2005; 2(2): 112-113. NRCBL: 9.5.7; 9.5.1; 9.3.1. SC: cs. Identifiers: haemophilia; health care resources. Comments: comment on Lynley Anderson and Nikki Cunningham, "In that case," Journal of Bioethical Inquiry 2005; 2(2): 109.

Dickey, Susan B.; Deatrick, Janet. Autonomy and decision making for health promotion in adolescence. *Pediatric Nursing* 2000 September-October; 26(5): 461-467. NRCBL: 9.5.7; 9.1; 8.1. SC: le.

Dudley, Susan Hall. Medical treatment for Asian immigrant children — does mother know best? *Georgetown Law Journal* 2004 August; 92(6): 1287-1307. NRCBL: 9.5.7; 21.7; 8.3.2. SC: le.

Dyer, Clare. Judge over-rules earlier decision on Charlotte Wyatt [news]. *BMJ: British Medical Journal* 2005 October 29; 331(7523): 985. NRCBL: 9.5.7; 20.5.2. SC: le.

Flannery, Michael T. First, do no harm: the use of covert video surveillance to detect Munchausen syndrome by proxy — an unethical means of "preventing" child abuse. *University of Michigan Journal of Law Reform* 1998 Fall; 32(1): 105-194. NRCBL: 9.5.7; 9.1; 8.2. SC: le.

Foreman, David M. Detecting fabricated or induced illness in children: may now necessitate controversial surveillance tools [editorial]. *BMJ: British Medical Journal* 2005 October 29; 331(7523): 978- 979. NRCBL: 9.5.7; 8.4; 8.3.2; 1.3.12; 1.3.5. SC: le.

Furton, Edward J. Catholic refusals of immunization: such actions are often unjustified. *Ethics and Medics* 2005 December; 30(12): 1-2. NRCBL: 9.5.7; 1.2; 8.3.4; 9.7.

Goldworth, Amnon; Robertson, John A. Neonatal care for premature infants [letter and reply]. *Hastings Center Report* 2005 January-February; 35(1): 6. NRCBL: 9.5.7; 20.5.2.

Gopalakrishnan, Somasundari; Pugh, R. Nicholas. Mandatory reporting of all sexually active under-13s: reporting is a public health imperative [letter]. *BMJ: British Medical Journal* 2005 November 5; 331(7524): 1083. NRCBL: 9.5.7; 8.4; 10.

Harrison, Helen; Robertson, John A. Neonatal care for premature infants [letter and reply]. *Hastings Center Report* 2005 January-February; 35(1): 5-6, 7. NRCBL: 9.5.7; 20.5.2.

Haverkamp, Fritz; Rünger, Michaela. Medizinisch-psychosoziale Aspekte der ethischen Diskussion um den kindlichen Kleinwuchs und die Wachstumshormontherapie. *In:* Jahrbuch für Wissenschaft und Ethik. Bd. 7. Berlin: Walter de Gruyter; 2002: 295-310. NRCBL: 9.5.7; 9.7.

Hinds, Heather L. Pediatric obesity: ethical dilemmas in treatment and prevention. *Journal of Law, Medicine and Ethics* 2005 Fall; 33(3): 599-602. NRCBL: 9.5.7. SC: rv.

Holland, Paul; Mlyniec, Wallace J. Whatever happened to the right to treatment?: the modern quest for a historical promise. *Temple Law Review* 1995 Winter; 68(4): 1791-1835. NRCBL: 9.5.7; 1.3.5; 9.2. SC: le.

Hu, W.; Kerridge, I; Kemp, A. Risk, rationality, and regret: responding to the uncertainty of childhood food anaphylaxis. *Medical Humanities* 2005 June; 31(1): 12-16. NRCBL: 9.5.7.

Abstract: Risk and uncertainty are unavoidable in clinical medicine. In the case of childhood food allergy, the dysphoric experience of uncertainty is heightened by the perception of unpredictable danger to young children. Medicine has tended to respond to uncertainty with forms of rational decision making. Rationality cannot, however, resolve uncertainty and provides an insufficient account of risk. This paper compares the medical and parental accounts of two peanut allergic toddlers to highlight the value of emotions in decision making. One emotion in particular, regret, assists in explaining the actions taken to prevent allergic reactions, given the diffuse nature of responsibility for children. In this light, the assumption that doctors make rational judgments while patients have emotion led preferences is a false dichotomy. Reconciling medical and lay accounts requires acknowledgement of the interrelationship between the rational and the emotional, and may lead to more appropriate clinical decision making under conditions of uncertainty.

Karmakar, Santosh J. Dilemmas in the management of neural tube defects. *Issues in Medical Ethics* 2000 April-June; 8(2): 43-44. NRCBL: 9.5.7; 8.3.2; 20.5.2.

Katumba-Lunyenya, J.; Joss, V.; Latham, P.; Abbatuan, C.; Hurley, P.; Isaacs, D.; Pollard, A.J.; Elias-Jones, A.C.; Larcher, V. Pulmonary tuberculosis and extreme prematurity [case study]. *Archives of Disease in Childhood. Fetal and Neonatal Edition* 2005 March; 90(2): F178-F183. NRCBL: 9.5.7; 9.5.6; 9.5.5. SC: cs.

Kerr, Susan M.; McIntosh, Jean B. Disclosure of disability: exploring the perspective of parents. *Midwifery* 1998 December; 14(4): 225-232. NRCBL: 9.5.7; 8.2; 9.5.5; 8.1.

Kerruish, N.J.; Robertson, S.P. Newborn screening: new developments, new dilemmas. *Journal of Medical Ethics* 2005 July; 31(7): 393-398. NRCBL: 9.5.7; 15.3.

Abstract: Scientific and technological advances are lending pressure to expand the scope of newborn screening. Whereas this has great potential for improving child health, it also challenges our current perception of such programmes. Standard newborn screening programmes are clearly justified by the fact that early detection and treatment of affected individuals avoids significant morbidity and mortality. However, proposals to expand the scope and complexity of such testing are not all supported by a similar level of evidence for unequivocal benefit. We argue that screening for genetic susceptibility to complex disorders is inherently different from standard screening and, while of potential value, must be considered separately from conventional testing.

Klein, Jonathan D.; McNulty, Molly; Flatau, Claudia N. Adolescents' access to care: teenagers' self-reported use of services and perceived access to confidential care. *Archives of Pediatric and Adolescent Medicine* 1998 July; 152(7): 676-682. NRCBL: 9.5.7; 9.2; 8.4. SC: em.

Levine, Carol. Acceptance, avoidance, and ambiguity: conflicting social values about childhood disability. *Kennedy Institute of Ethics Journal* 2005 December; 15(4): 371-383. NRCBL: 9.5.7; 9.5.1; 4.4; 5.1; 7.1; 4.2; 1.1. SC: em. Identifiers: Montreal Children's Hospital Study.

Abstract: Advances in medical technology now permit children who need ventilator assistance to live at home rather than in hospitals or institutions. What does this ventilator-dependent life mean to children and their families? The impetus for this essay comes from a study of the moral experience of 12 Canadian families—parents, ventilator-dependent child, and well siblings. These families express great love for their children, take on enormous responsibilities for care, live with uncertainty, and attempt to create "normal" home environments. Nevertheless, they experience social isolation, sometimes even from their extended families and health care providers. Their lives are constrained in many ways. The challenges faced by parents of technology-dependent children raise questions of justice within society and within families.

Loughlin, Kelly. Spectacle and secrecy: press coverage of conjoined twins in 1950s Britain. *Medical History* 2005 April; 49(2): 197-212. NRCBL: 9.5.7; 2.2; 1.3.7; 9.5.1.

McPherson, Jean. In that case. Response [case study]. *Journal of Bioethical Inquiry* 2005; 2(2): 114-115. NRCBL: 9.5.7; 4.4; 9.5.1; 9.3.1. SC: cs. Identifiers: haemophilia; health care resources. Comments: comment on Lynley Anderson and Nikki Cunningham, "In that case," Journal of Bioethical Inquiry 2005; 2(2): 109.

Miah, Andy. Doping and the child: an ethical policy for the vulnerable. *Lancet* 2005 September 10-16; 366(9489): 874-876. NRCBL: 9.5.7; 9.5.1; 9.7; 4.5; 7.3; 2.3.

Miller, Mark; Robertson, John A. Neonatal care for premature infants [letter and reply]. *Hastings Center Report* 2005 January-February; 35(1): 4, 7. NRCBL: 9.5.7; 20.5.2. SC: le.

Mouradian, Wendy E. Who decides? Patients, parents, or gatekeepers: pediatric decisions in the craniofacial setting. *Cleft Palate-Craniofacial Journal* 1995 November; 32(6): 510-514. NRCBL: 9.5.7; 9.4; 8.1; 8.3.3; 4.4. SC: cs.

Newell, Christopher. In that case. Response [case study]. *Journal of Bioethical Inquiry* 2005; 2(2): 113. NRCBL: 9.5.7; 9.4; 9.5.1. SC: cs. Identifiers: haemophilia; health care resources. Comments: comment on Lynley Anderson and Nikki Cunningham, "In that case," Journal of Bioethical Inquiry 2005; 2(2): 109.

NRCBL: National Reference Center for Bioethics Literature Classification Scheme   See inside front cover for terms.

111

Oppenheim, Daniel; Brugières, Laurence; Corradini, Nadège; Vivant, Florence; Hartmann, Olivier. An ethics dilemma: when parents and doctors disagree on the best treatment for the child. *Bulletin du Cancer* 2004 September; 91(9): 735-738. NRCBL: 9.5.7; 8.3.2; 9.6; 20.5.2. SC: cs.

Park, Julie. In that case. Response [case study]. *Journal of Bioethical Inquiry* 2005; 2(2): 111-112. NRCBL: 9.5.7; 9.5.1; 9.3.1. SC: cs. Identifiers: haemophilia; health care resources. Comments: comment on Lynley Anderson and Nikki Cunningham, "In that case," Journal of Bioethical Inquiry 2005; 2(2): 109.

Raabe, Hans-Christian. Mandatory reporting of all sexually active under-13s: confidential sexual health services to young people: part of the solution or part of the problem? [letter]. *BMJ: British Medical Journal* 2005 November 5; 331(7524): 1083. NRCBL: 9.5.7; 8.4; 10.

Rose, Darrell E. The ethics of cochlear implants in young children [letter]. *American Journal of Otology* 1994 November; 15(6): 813-814. NRCBL: 9.5.7; 8.3.2. Comments: comment on Noel L. Cohen, "The ethics of cochlear implants in young children," American Journal of Otology 1994; 15: 1-2.

Runkel, Thomas. Kleinwuchs und medizinethische Beurteilung. Expose eines Forschungsprojekts. *In:* Jahrbuch für Wissenschaft und Ethik. Bd. 7. Berlin: Walter de Gruyter; 2002: 311-318. NRCBL: 9.5.7; 4.5; 9.7.

Sevick, Mary Ann; Nativio, Donna G.; McConnell, Terrance. Genetic testing of children for late onset disease. *CQ: Cambridge Quarterly of Healthcare Ethics* 2005 Winter; 14(1): 47-56. NRCBL: 9.5.7; 15.3; 8.2; 8.3.2.

Shafran, Yigal; Kupietzky, Ari. General anesthesia or conscious sedation with restraint: treating the young child from a Jewish ethical perspective. *Jewish Medical Ethics and Halacha* 2005 August; 5(1): 29-39. NRCBL: 9.5.7; 1.2; 7.3; 9.7.

Silverman, William A.; Robertson, John A. Neonatal care for premature infants [letter and reply]. *Hastings Center Report* 2005 January-February; 35(1): 6, 7. NRCBL: 9.5.7; 20.5.2.

Steinberg, Alan M.; Pynoos, Robert S.; Goenjian, Armen K.; Sossanabadi, Haleh; Sherr, Larissa. Are researchers bound by child abuse reporting laws? *Child Abuse and Neglect* 1999 August; 23(8): 771-777. NRCBL: 9.5.7; 9.1; 1.3.9; 1.3.5. SC: le.

Stenson, B.; McIntosh, N. Some ethical considerations in the neonatal care area. *European Journal of Pediatrics* 1999 December; 158(Supplement 1): S13-S17. NRCBL: 9.5.7; 8.3.2; 20.5.2.

Taylor, Carol. Dilemas en el tratamiento al inicio de la vida / Dilemmas in beginning-of-life treatment. *Vida y Etica* 2003 December; 4(2): 45-52. NRCBL: 9.5.7.

van Straaten, Justine. The minor's limited right to confidential health care and the inverse of confidentiality: a parent's decision not to disclose illness status to a minor child. *Children's Legal Rights Journal* 2000 Spring; 20(1): 46-54. NRCBL: 9.5.7; 8.4; 8.2; 8.3.2; 9.5.6. SC: le.

Webby, Terri. Dealing with ethical challenges in practice. *Nursing New Zealand* 2004 March; 10(2): 26-27. NRCBL: 9.5.7; 8.1; 9.5.9.

Weddle, Melissa; Kokotailo, Patricia. Adolescent substance abuse: confidentiality and consent. *Pediatric Clinics of North America* 2002 April; 49(2): 301-315. NRCBL: 9.5.7; 9.5.9; 8.4; 8.3.1.

Wheeler, R. Children's rights: a surgeon's view. *Archives of Disease in Childhood* 2005 February; 90(2): 174-175. NRCBL: 9.5.7; 4.4; 8.3.2. Identifiers: United Kingdom (Great Britain).

Wilde, Marshall L. Bioethical and legal implications of pediatric gastric bypass. *Willamette Law Review* 2004 Summer; 40(3): 575-625. NRCBL: 9.5.7; 8.3.2. SC: le.

Wocial, Lucia D.; Robertson, John A. Neonatal care for premature infants [letter and reply]. *Hastings Center Report* 2005 January-February; 35(1): 6-7. NRCBL: 9.5.7; 20.5.2.

CARE FOR SPECIFIC GROUPS/ SUBSTANCE ABUSERS

Annas, George J. Jumping frogs, endangered toads, and California's medical- marijuana law. *New England Journal of Medicine* 2005 November 24; 353(21): 2291-2296. NRCBL: 9.5.9; 9.7; 1.3.5; 1.3.8. SC: le.

Berman, Saul J.; Bulka, Reuven; Landes, Daniel; Woolf, Jeffrey R. Rabbis condemn smoking. *Jewish Medical Ethics and Halacha* 2005 August; 5(1): 56-59. NRCBL: 9.5.9; 1.2.

Bühler, Karl-Ernst. Euphoria, ecstasy, inebriation, abuse, dependence, and addiction: a conceptual analysis. *Medicine, Health Care and Philosophy: A European Journal* 2005; 8(1): 79-87. NRCBL: 9.5.9; 17.2; 17.4. SC: an.
Abstract: A conceptual analysis of basic notions of addictiology, i.e., Euphoria, Ecstasy, Inebriation, Abuse, Dependence, and Addiction was presented. Three different forms of dependence were distinguished: purely psychic, psycho-physiological, and purely somatic dependence. Two kinds of addiction were differentiated, i.e. appetitive and deprivative addiction. The conceptual requirements of addiction were discussed. Keeping these in mind some ethical problems of drug therapy and psychotherapy were explained. Criteria for the assessment of therapeutic approaches are suggested: effectiveness, side effects, economic, ethic, and esthetic valuation.

Cerny, T.; Cerny, E.H. Reply to: Hasman A and Holm S. Nicotine conjugate vaccine: is there a right to a smoking future? [letter]. *Journal of Medical Ethics* 2005 September; 31(9): 558. NRCBL: 9.5.9; 9.7.

Diethelm, Pascal A.; Rielle, Jean-Charles; McKee, Martin. The whole truth and nothing but the truth? The research that Philip Morris did not want you to see. *Lancet* 2005 July 2-8; 366(9479): 86-92. NRCBL: 9.5.9; 1.3.9; 1.3.2; 1.3.7; 18.6. Identifiers: Institut fur Industrielle und Biologische Forschung (INBIFO).

Abstract: The tobacco industry maintained, for many years, that it was unaware of research about the toxic effects of smoking. By the 1970s, however, the industry decided that it needed this information but they were unwilling to seek it in a way that was open to public scrutiny. By means of material from internal industry documents it can be revealed that one company, Philip Morris, acquired a research facility, INBIFO, in Germany and created a complex mechanism seeking to ensure that the work done in the facility could not be linked to Philip Morris. In particular it involved the appointment of a Swedish professor as a 'co-ordinator', who would synthesise reports for onward transmission to the USA. Various arrangements were made to conceal this process, not only from the wider public, but also from many within Philip Morris, although it was known to some senior executives. INBIFO appears to have published only a small amount of its research and what was published appears to differ considerably from what was not. In particular, the unpublished reports provided evidence of the greater toxicity of sidestream than mainstream smoke, a finding of particular relevance given the industry's continuing denial of the harmful effects of passive smoking. By contrast, much of its published work comprises papers that convey a message that could be considered useful to the industry, in particular casting doubt on methods used to assess the effects of passive smoking.

Drope, J.; Bialous, S.A.; Glantz, S.A. Tobacco industry efforts to present ventilation as an alternative to smoke-free environments in North America. *Tobacco Control* 2004 March; 13(Supplement 1): i41-i47. NRCBL: 9.5.9; 1.3.2.

Johnson, Sandra. Legal issues in the use of controlled substances in pain management. *Medical Ethics Newsletter [Lahey Clinic]* 2005 Winter; 12(1): 4, 12. NRCBL: 9.5.9; 4.4; 9.5.1. SC: le.

Keane, Helen. Addiction and the bioethics of difference. *In:* Shildrick, Margrit; Mykitiuk, Roxanne, eds. Ethics of the Body: Postconventional Challenges. Cambridge, MA: MIT Press; 2005: 91-112. NRCBL: 9.5.9; 1.1.

Kozlowski, L.T. First, tell the truth: a dialogue on human rights, deception, and the use of smokeless tobacco as a substitute for cigarettes. *Tobacco Control* 2003 March; 12(1): 34-36. NRCBL: 9.5.9; 1.3.2.

Larsson-Kronberg, Marianne; Öjehagen, Agneta; Berglund, Mats. Experiences of coercion during investigation and treatment. *International Journal of Law and Psychiatry* 2005 November-December; 28(6): 613-621. NRCBL: 9.5.9; 17.7. SC: em. Identifiers: Sweden.

Neilsen, K.; Glantz, S.A. A tobacco industry study of airline cabin air quality: dropping inconvenient findings. *Tobacco Control* 2004 March; 13(Supplement 1): i20-i29. NRCBL: 9.5.9; 1.3.2; 5.3.

Okie, Susan. Medical marijuana and the Supreme Court [opinion]. *New England Journal of Medicine* 2005 August 18; 353(7): 648-651. NRCBL: 9.5.9; 9.5.1. SC: le.

Olick, Robert S. Carcinogenic plumes and aerophobia: ethical tensions in the public smoking debate. *Journal of Public Health Management and Practice* 2004 November-December; 10(6): 569-570. NRCBL: 9.5.9; 1.1.

Peterman, J.F.; Desbiens, N.A. Should physicians be allowed to use alcohol while on call? *Journal of Medical Ethics* 2005 January; 31(1): 21-26. NRCBL: 9.5.9; 7.1; 7.4. SC: an.

Abstract: Although physician alcohol use that leads to impairment has been extensively discussed, few statements address the issue of alcohol use of physicians who are on call. In this paper the authors review recent information on physicians' perceptions of alcohol use by themselves and their colleagues while on call. It is argued that conflicts in physicians' perceptions are due to the fact that the larger society has not addressed the question of whether drinking on call is public or private behaviour. The authors argue that when medicine is understood as a practice defined partly in terms of standards of excellence, the present approach of the American Medical Association to prohibit practicing medicine under the influence of alcohol requires a prohibition of drinking alcohol while on call, unless studies determine a clear threshold for drinking alcohol without placing patients at risk.

Rehm, Jürgen; Fischer, Benedikt; Hayden [sic, Haydon], Emma; Room, Robin. Abstinence ideology and somatic treatment for addicts — ethical considerations [editorial]. *Addiction Research and Theory* 2003 October; 11(5): 287-293. NRCBL: 9.5.9; 9.2.

St. Mary, Edward W. Legal and ethical dilemmas in drug management for team physicians and athletic trainers. *Southern Medical Journal* 1998 May; 91(5): 421-424. NRCBL: 9.5.9; 9.5.1. SC: le.

CARE FOR SPECIFIC GROUPS/ WOMEN

Abou Shabana, K.; El-Shiek, M.; El-Nazer, M.; Samir, N. Women's perceptions and practices regarding their rights to reproductive health. *Eastern Mediterranean Health Journal* 2003 May; 9(3): 296-308. NRCBL: 9.5.5; 14.1; 10; 1.2. SC: em. Identifiers: Egypt.

Abushama, Mandy; Ahmed, Badreldeen. Cesarean section on request. *Saudi Medical Journal* 2004 December; 25(12): 1820-1823. NRCBL: 9.5.5; 8.1; 9.5.8.

American College of Obstetricians and Gynecologists [ACOG]. Committee on Ethics. ACOG committee opinion. Surgery and patient choice: the ethics of decision making. Number 289, November 2003. *International Journal of Gynecology and Obstetrics* 2004 February; 84(2): 188-193. NRCBL: 9.5.5; 6; 8.1.

NRCBL: National Reference Center for Bioethics Literature Classification Scheme   See inside front cover for terms.

113

Anderson, Mikeisha T. Criminal penalties for women engaging in substance abuse during pregnancy. *Women's Rights Law Reporter* 2000 Summer; 21(3): 181-188. NRCBL: 9.5.5; 9.5.9. SC: le.

Armstrong, Elizabeth M. Drug and alcohol use during pregnancy: we need to protect, not punish, women [editorial]. *Women's Health Issues* 2005 March-April; 15(2): 45-47. NRCBL: 9.5.5; 9.5.8; 9.5.9; 1.3.5; 14.1.

Arnold, Kendra D. The right to live: a constitutional argument for mandatory preventative health care for female prisoners. *William and Mary Journal of Women and the Law* 2004 Winter; 10(2): 343-366. NRCBL: 9.5.5; 18.5.5; 9.2. SC: le.

Berkowitz, Richard L. Should refusal to undergo a Cesarean delivery be a criminal offense? *Obstetrics and Gynecology* 2004 December; 104(6): 1220-1221. NRCBL: 9.5.5; 8.3.4; 9.5.8. SC: le. Identifiers: Melissa Rowland.

Bornstein, Brian H. Seize this urine test: the implications of Ferguson v. City of Charleston for drug testing during pregnancy. *Journal of Medicine and Law* 2001 Fall; 6(1): 65-79. NRCBL: 9.5.5; 9.5.9; 8.3.4. SC: le.

Brown, Jennifer. A troublesome maternal-fetal conflict: legal, ethical, and social issues surrounding mandatory AZT treatment of HIV positive pregnant women. *Buffalo Public Interest Law Journal* 1999-2000; 18: 67-94. NRCBL: 9.5.5; 9.5.6; 9.5.8; 8.3.4; 4.4; 1.1. SC: le. Identifiers: Zidovudine.

Cameron, Martin J.; Penney, Gillian C. Are national recommendations regarding examination and disposal of products of miscarriage being followed? A need for revised guidelines? *Human Reproduction* 2005 February; 20(2): 531-535. NRCBL: 9.5.5; 4.4. SC: em.

Carmody, Allison R. Legal protection at birth: resolving the maternal-fetal conflict in the context of medical decision-making. *Medical Trial Technique Quarterly* 2001; 48(1): 165-214. NRCBL: 9.5.5; 9.5.8; 4.4; 8.3.4; 4.2. SC: le.

Cataldo, Peter J. The USCCB and rape protocols. *Linacre Quarterly* 2005 August; 72(3): 255-259. NRCBL: 9.5.5; 10; 11.1; 12.3; 9.5.5; 1.2. Identifiers: United States Conference of Catholic Bishops; Ethical and Religious Directive for Catholic Health Care Services.

Chervenak, Frank A.; McCullough, Laurence B. Should all pregnant women have an ultrasound examination? *Croatian Medical Journal* 1998 June; 39(2): 102-106. NRCBL: 9.5.5; 9.2; 9.5.7; 14.1.

Chervenak, Frank A.; McCullough, Laurence B.; Knapp, Robert C.; Caputo, Thomas A.; Barber, Hugh R.K. A clinically comprehensive ethical framework for offering and recommending cancer treatment before and during pregnancy. *Cancer* 2004 January 15; 100(2): 215-222. NRCBL: 9.5.5; 9.5.8; 1.1; 20.5.4.

Coverdale, John H.; McCullough, Laurence B.; Chervenak, Frank A. Assisted and surrogate decision making for pregnant patients who have schizophrenia. *Schizophrenia Bulletin* 2004; 30(3): 659-664. NRCBL: 9.5.5; 8.1; 1.1; 9.5.8; 17.1. SC: cs.

D'Souza, Lalitha. Sexual assault: the role of the examining doctor. *Issues in Medical Ethics* 1998 October-December; 6(4): 113-114. NRCBL: 9.5.5; 21.1. Identifiers: India.

Donohue, Michaela. Maternal-fetal health: ethical issues. *AWHONN's Clinical Issues in Perinatal and Women's Health Nursing* 1993; 4(4): 561-569. NRCBL: 9.5.5; 9.5.8; 9.4.

Dudgeon, Matthew R.; Inhorn, Marcia C. Men's influences on women's reproductive health: medical anthropological perspectives. *Social Science and Medicine* 2004 October; 59(7): 1379-1395. NRCBL: 9.5.5; 10; 14.1.

Epstein, Julia. The pregnant imagination, fetal rights, and women's bodies: a historical inquiry. *Yale Journal of Law and Humanities* 1995 Winter; 7(1): 139-162. NRCBL: 9.5.5; 4.4; 2.2. SC: le.

Fasouliotis, Sozos J.; Schenker, Joseph G. Maternal-fetal conflict. *European Journal of Obstetrics and Gynecology and Reproductive Biology* 2000 March; 89(1): 101-107. NRCBL: 9.5.5; 9.5.8; 8.3.4; 1.1; 4.4. SC: le.

Frith, Lucy. Ethical issues in community midwifery. *In:* Chadwick, Ruth; Levitt, Mairi, eds. Ethical Issues in Community Health Care. New York: Arnold; 1998: 115-124. NRCBL: 9.5.5; 4.1.3.

Gawande, Atul. Naked [opinion]. *New England Journal of Medicine* 2005 August 18; 353(7): 645- 648. NRCBL: 9.5.5; 21.1. Identifiers: customs of physical examination.

Gijsbers van Wijk, Cecile M.T.; van Vliet, Katja P.; Kolk, Annemarie M. Gender perspectives and quality of care: towards appropriate and adequate health care for women. *Social Science and Medicine* 1996 September; 43(5): 707-720. NRCBL: 9.5.5; 9.8; 10; 21.1; 9.4.

Goedken, Jennifer. Pelvic examinations under anesthesia: an important teaching tool. *Journal of Health Care Law and Policy* 2005; 8(2): 232-239. NRCBL: 9.5.5; 8.3.1; 7.2.

Goldberg, Lisa Sara. Introductory engagement within the perinatal nursing relationship. *Nursing Ethics* 2005 July; 12(4): 401-413. NRCBL: 9.5.5; 8.1; 9.5.8; 10. SC: em.
Abstract: In this article, the theme of introductory engagement is developed through the conversational interviews and participatory observations I carried out with perinatal nurses and birthing women in the context of a feminist phenomenological methodology. Positioned against the landscape of hierarchical health care practices embedded with power dynamics and disembodied practices, this research explored the ways in which

perinatal nurses related to birthing women in the context of relational care. The focus of attention in this article is to describe the theme of introductory engagement by way of a storied phenomenological text.

Habiba, M.; Jackson, C.; Akkad, A.; Kenyon, S.; Dixon-Woods, M. Women's accounts of consenting to surgery: is consent a quality problem? *Quality and Safety in Health Care* 2004; 13: 422-427. NRCBL: 9.5.5; 8.3.1; 8.1.

Hallgren, Anita; Kihlgren, Mona; Olsson, Pia. Ways of relating during childbirth: an ethical responsibility and challenge for midwives. *Nursing Ethics* 2005 November; 12(6): 606-621. NRCBL: 9.5.5; 8.1. SC: em. Identifiers: Sweden.

Abstract: The way in which midwives relate to expectant parents during the process of childbirth greatly influences the parents' childbirth experiences for a long time. We believe that examining and describing ways of relating in naturally occurring interactions during childbirth should be considered as an ethical responsibility. This has been highlighted in relation to parents' experiences and in the light of the relational ethics of Logstrup. Four couples' and nine midwives' ways of relating were documented by 27 hours of observation, including 14.5 hours of video-recorded sessions. A qualitative content analysis was conducted. The midwives strongly influenced the different ways of relating and three aspects of professional competence were disclosed. The results can contribute to reflections about current praxis as an ethical demand for midwives.

International Federation of Gynecology and Obstetrics [FIGO]; Society of Obstetricians and Gynaecologists of Canada [SOGC]. International joint policy statement: FIGO professional and ethical responsibilities concerning sexual and reproductive rights / Responsabilites professionnelles et ethiques de la FIGO en ce qui a trait aux droits sexuels et genesiques [policy statement]. *Journal of Obstetrics and Gynaecology Canada* 2004 December; 26(12): 1097-1099, 1105-1107. NRCBL: 9.5.5; 14.1; 10; 21.1; 6. Note: text in English and French.

International Federation of Gynecology and Obstetrics [FIGO]. Committee for Women's Sexual and Reproductive Rights; Shaw, D. History of the FIGO Committee for Women's Sexual and Reproductive Rights. *International Journal of Gynecology and Obstetrics* 2004 August; 86(2): 294-316. NRCBL: 9.5.5; 2.4; 10; 14.1; 21.1.

Johns, Kimberly A. Reproductive rights of women: construction and reality in international and United States law. *Cardozo Women's Law Journal* 1998; 5(1): 1-32. NRCBL: 9.5.5; 10; 21.1; 12.1; 14.1; 13.1; 11.1. SC: le.

Johnson, Louise. The legal implications of abuse of the unborn foetus. *Medicine and Law: World Association for Medical Law* 1994; 13(1-2): 19-27. NRCBL: 9.5.5; 9.5.9. SC: le.

Kimbel, Anne Sullivan. Pregnant drug abusers are treated like criminals or not treated at all: a third option proposed. *Journal of Contemporary Health Law and Policy* 2004 Winter; 21(1): 36-66. NRCBL: 9.5.5; 9.5.9. SC: le.

Klein, Michael C. Quick fix culture: the cesarean-section-on-demand debate [editorial]. *Birth* 2004 September; 31(3): 161-164. NRCBL: 9.5.5.

Kucher, Nils; Tapson, Victor F.; Quiroz, Rene; Mir, Samy S.; Morrison, Ruth B.; McKenzie, David; Goldhaber, Samuel Z. Gender differences in the administration of prophylaxis to prevent deep venous thrombosis. *Thrombosis and Haemostasis* 2005 February; 93(2): 284-288. NRCBL: 9.5.5; 9.5.1; 10. SC: em. Identifiers: DVT FREE Steering Committee.

Lupton, M.L. Is the foetal alcohol syndrome child protected by South African law? *Medicine and Law: World Association for Medical Law* 1994; 13(1-2): 79-94. NRCBL: 9.5.5; 9.5.9; 4.4. SC: le.

McGee, Glenn. Dying for food. *American Journal of Bioethics [Online]* 2005 March-April; 5(2): W1. NRCBL: 9.5.5; 20.5.1. Identifiers: Theresa Schiavo.

Miech, Ralph P. A proposed novel treatment for rape victims. *National Catholic Bioethics Quarterly* 2005 Winter; 5(4): 687- 695. NRCBL: 9.5.5; 9.1; 11.1; 1.2; 12.3; 9.7.

Miller, Monica K. Refusal to undergo a cesarean section: a woman's right or a criminal act? *Health Matrix: Journal of Law-Medicine* 2005 Summer; 15(2): 383-400. NRCBL: 9.5.5; 8.3.4. SC: le.

Minkoff, Howard; Paltrow, Lynn M. Melissa Rowland and the rights of pregnant women [opinion]. *Obstetrics and Gynecology* 2004 December; 104(6): 1234-1236. NRCBL: 9.5.5; 8.3.4; 9.5.8. SC: le.

Morrison, Joanne; MacKenzie, I.Z. Cesarean section on demand. *Seminars in Perinatology* 2003 February; 27(1): 20-33. NRCBL: 9.5.5; 8.3.1; 9.5.7. SC: em.

Nadelson, Carol C. Ethics and women's health. *In:* Stotland, Nada L.; Stewart, Donna E., eds. Psychological Aspects of Women's Health Care: The Interface Between Psychiatry and Obstetrics and Gynecology. Washington, DC: American Psychiatric Press; 2001: 571-584. NRCBL: 9.5.5.

Nekhlyudov, Larissa; Li, Rong; Fletcher, Suzanne W. Information and involvement preferences of women in their 40s before their first screening mammogram. *Archives of Internal Medicine* 2005 June 27; 165(12): 1370-1374. NRCBL: 9.5.5; 8.3.1; 9.1. SC: em.

Abstract: BACKGROUND: Informed decision making regarding screening mammography is recommended for women in their 40s; however, what information women want and how much involvement in decision making they prefer are not known. METHODS: Surveys were mailed to women aged 40 to 44 scheduled for their first screening mammogram. Women were members of a large New England health maintenance organization and received medical care at a multispecialty practice in the greater Boston area. Outcome measures included information needs and decisional control preferences. RESULTS: Ninety-six women responded. Of 93 identifying their ethnicity, 62 (67%) were white, 18 (19%) were black, 10 (11%)

NRCBL: National Reference Center for Bioethics Literature Classification Scheme   See inside front cover for terms.

115

were Asian, 2 (2%) were Hispanic, and 1 (1%) was other. Most (91% [85/93]) wanted their primary care provider to be the source of information regarding screening mammography. Information needs included the next steps to take if the mammogram result was abnormal (89%), how the woman would be contacted (75%), and how quickly (71%). Women also wanted to know about the harms of false-positive (84%) and false-negative (82%) results, benefits of screening in prolonging life (73%), and risk of getting breast cancer (69%). Most women preferred to make the screening decision after considering their medical provider's opinion (38%) or together with their medical provider (46%); fewer than 10% preferred that the decision be made by the woman or her provider alone. CONCLUSIONS: Women cited specific information needs before initiating screening mammography, including screening logistics and potential harms and benefits of screening. They also wanted to participate in the decision-making process. Effective methods should be developed for communicating desired information before screening.

Parker, Judith M.; Gibbs, Martin. Truth, virtue and beauty: midwifery and philosophy. *Nursing Inquiry* 1998 September; 5(3): 146-153. NRCBL: 9.5.5; 1.1; 14.1.

People's Republic of China. Eighth National People's Congress. Standing Committee. Law of the People's Republic of China on maternal and infant health care [effective 1 June 1995]. People's Republic of China: Standing Committee of the Eighth National People's Congress 1994 October 27; 6 p. [Online]. Available: http://isinolaw.com/isinolaw/english/detail.jsp?iscatalog=0&statutes_id=131686&ski [22 September 2005]. NRCBL: 9.5.5; 9.5.7; 21.1; 1.3.5. SC: le.

Perry, Constance K. Personhood and relational persons. *In:* Thomasma, David C.; Weisstud, David N.; Herve, Christian eds. Personhood and Health Care. Boston: Kluwer Academic Pub.; 2001: 333-345. NRCBL: 9.5.5; 4.4; 8.3.4; 9.5.8. SC: an.

Roberts, Laura Weiss; Dunn, Laura B. Ethical considerations in caring for women with substance use disorders. *Obstetrics and Gynecology Clinics of North America* 2003 September; 30(3): 559-582. NRCBL: 9.5.5; 9.5.9; 7.1; 8.1; 14.1.

Ryan, Joseph G. The chapel and the operating room: the struggle of Roman Catholic clergy, physicians, and believers with the dilemmas of obstetric surgery, 1800-1900. *Bulletin of the History of Medicine* 2002 Autumn; 76(3): 461- 494. NRCBL: 9.5.5; 1.2; 9.5.1; 7.1. SC: rv.

Sadasivam, Bharati. The rights framework in reproductive health advocacy — a reappraisal. *Hastings Women's Law Journal* 1997 Fall; 8(2): 313-350. NRCBL: 9.5.5; 21.1; 13.3; 11.1; 12.5.1. SC: le.

Scully, Judith A.M. Maternal mortality, population control, and the war in women's wombs: a bioethical analysis of quinacrine sterilizations. *Wisconsin International Law Journal* 2000-2001; 19(2): 103-151. NRCBL: 9.5.5; 11.3; 9.7; 13.1; 18.5.3. SC: le.

Seamark, Clare; Blake, Sue. Concerning women: questionnaire survey of consultations, embarrassment, and views on confidentiality in general practice among women in their teens, thirties and fifties. *Journal of Family Planning and Reproductive Health Care* 2005 January; 31(1): 31-33. NRCBL: 9.5.5; 8.4; 8.1. SC: em. Identifiers: United Kingdom (Great Britain).

Shaw, Dorothy. Understanding the relevance of sexual and reproductive rights to professional responsibilities / Comprehension de la pertinence des droits sexuels et genesiques en matiere de responsabilites professionnelles. *Journal of Obstetrics and Gynaecology Canada* 2004 December; 26(12): 1095-1096, 1103-1104. NRCBL: 9.5.5; 14.1; 10; 21.1; 6. Note: text in English and French.

Shell-Duncan, Bettina. The medicalization of female "circumcision": harm reduction or promotion of a dangerous practice? *Social Science and Medicine* 2001 April; 52(7): 1013-1028. NRCBL: 9.5.5; 9.5.7; 10; 21.7; 9.1; 4.1.2.

Sinton, Jennifer. Rights discourse and mandatory HIV testing of pregnant women and newborns. *Journal of Law and Policy* 1997; 6(1): 187-245. NRCBL: 9.5.5; 9.5.7; 9.5.6; 8.3.4. SC: le.

Snow, Rachel C. Female genital cutting: distinguishing the rights from the health agenda [editorial]. *Tropical Medicine and International Health* 2001 February; 6(2): 89-91. NRCBL: 9.5.5; 9.5.7; 10; 21.1.

Sullivan, Danny. State-sanctioned intervention on behalf of the fetus. *Journal of Law and Medicine* 2000 August; 8(1): 44-55. NRCBL: 9.5.5; 9.5.8; 8.3.4; 4.4; 1.3.5. SC: le.

Tauer, Carol A. When pregnant patients refuse interventions. *AWHONN's Clinical Issues in Perinatal and Women's Health Nursing* 1993; 4(4): 596-605. NRCBL: 9.5.5; 8.3.4; 8.1; 9.5.8.

Tillett, Jackie. Should elective cesarean birth be an accepted option for women? *Journal of Perinatal and Neonatal Nursing* 2005 January-March; 19(1): 4-6. NRCBL: 9.5.5; 14.1.

Van Court, Rebecca L. Uterine fibroids and women's right to choose: hysterectomies and informed consent. *Journal of Legal Medicine* 2005 December; 26(4): 507-521. NRCBL: 9.5.5; 8.3.1. SC: le.

Van Hollen, Cecilia. Invoking vali: painful technologies of modern birth in south India. *Medical Anthropology Quarterly* 2003 March; 17(1): 49-77. NRCBL: 9.5.5; 10; 7.1; 4.4.

Weaver, Jane. Court-ordered caesarean sections. *In:* Bainham, Andrew; Sclater, Shelley Day; Richards, Martin, eds. Body Lore and Laws. Portland, OR: Hart Pub.; 2002: 229-247. NRCBL: 9.5.5; 9.5.8; 8.3.4. SC: le.

SC (Subject Caption):   an=analytical   cs=case studies   em=empirical   le=legal   po=popular   rv=review

Weyrauch, Samantha. The fetus and the drug addicted mother: whose rights should prevail? *Journal of Medicine and Law* 2001 Spring; 5(2): 95-120. NRCBL: 9.5.5; 9.5.9; 9.5.8; 8.4. SC: le.

Zaner, Richard M. "But how can we choose?". *Journal of Clinical Ethics* 2005 Fall; 16(3): 218-222. NRCBL: 9.5.5; 9.6; 12.1; 8.1. SC: cs.

CARING *See* NURSING ETHICS AND PHILOSOPHY; PHILOSOPHY OF MEDICINE; PROFESSIONAL PATIENT RELATIONSHIP

CIVIL COMMITMENT *See* INVOLUNTARY COMMITMENT

CLINICAL ETHICISTS *See* ETHICISTS AND ETHICS COMMITTEES

CLINICAL ETHICS *See* BIOETHICS AND MEDICAL ETHICS; ETHICISTS AND ETHICS COMMITTEES; NURSING ETHICS AND PHILOSOPHY; PROFESSIONAL ETHICS

CLINICAL ETHICS COMMITTEES *See* ETHICISTS AND ETHICS COMMITTEES

CLINICAL TRIALS *See* BIOMEDICAL RESEARCH; HUMAN EXPERIMENTATION

CLINICAL

See also HUMAN EXPERIMENTATION/ SPECIAL POPULATIONS/ EMBRYOS AND FETUSES; REPRODUCTIVE TECHNOLOGIES

Britain grants "Dolly" scientist cloning license. *New York Times* 2005 February 9; p. A6. NRCBL: 14.5; 5.3. SC: po.

Cloning around [editorial]. *Nature Cell Biology* 2004 December; 6(12): 1145. NRCBL: 14.5; 18.5.4; 15.1; 18.6. Identifiers: California; Proposition 71.

South Korea's cloning crisis [editorial]. *New York Times* 2005 December 4; p. WK11. NRCBL: 14.5; 14.6; 14.6. SC: po.

Aakvaag, Ruth Kleppe. The possibilities of human cloning: the American discussion. *In:* Ostnor, Lars, ed. Bioethics and Cloning: Report from a Workshop Arranged by the Nordic Theological Network for Bioethics in Arhus, September 25-27, 1998. Oslo: Nordic Theological Network for Bioethics; 1998: 24-34. NRCBL: 14.5; 15.4. Identifiers: United States.

Ahuja, Anjana. Could the cure for all diseases be banned? [news]. *Times (London, Features section)* 2004 June 17; p. 8-9. NRCBL: 14.5; 18.5.4; 19.5.

Andersen, Svend. Chance and equality: Habermas on human cloning. *In:* Ostnor, Lars, ed. Bioethics and Cloning: Report from a Workshop Arranged by the Nordic Theolog-

ical Network for Bioethics in Arhus, September 25-27, 1998. Oslo: Nordic Theological Network for Bioethics; 1998: 51-55. NRCBL: 14.5; 1.1.

Anees, Munawar Ahmad. Human clones and God's trust: the Islamic view. *In:* McGee, Glenn; Caplan, Arthur, eds. The Human Cloning Debate. 4th edition. Berkeley, CA: Berkeley Hills Books; 2004: 277- 281. NRCBL: 14.5; 1.2.

Bailey, Ronald. Cloning babies is not inherently immoral. *In:* McGee, Glenn; Caplan, Arthur, eds. The Human Cloning Debate. 4th edition. Berkeley, CA: Berkeley Hills Books; 2004: 211- 219. NRCBL: 14.5.

Bailey, Ronald. Who's afraid of human cloning? *In his:* Liberation Biology: The Scientific and Moral Case for the Biotech Revolution. Amherst, NY: Prometheus Books; 2005: 135- 147. NRCBL: 14.5.

Berkowitz, Peter. The pathos of the Kass report [review of Human Cloning and Human Dignity: An Ethical Inquiry, a report issued by the President's Council on Bioethics]. *Policy Review* 2002 October-November; 115; 7 p. [Online]. Available: http://www.policyreview.org/OCT02/ berkowitz_print.html [14 September 2005]. NRCBL: 14.5; 2.4; 4.4; 5.3; 18.5.4.

Best, Steven; Kellner, Douglas. Biotechnology, democracy, and the politics of cloning. *In:* Braman, Sandra, ed. Biotechnology and Communication: The Meta-Technologies of Information. Mahwah, NJ: Lawrence Erlbaum Associates; 2004: 197-226. NRCBL: 14.5; 21.1.

Bhattacharya, S.K. The cloning bandwagon: a hysterical outburst [comment]. *Issues in Medical Ethics* 1998 July-September; 6(3): 92-96. NRCBL: 14.5; 15.1. Comments: comment on Manu Kothari and Lopa Mehta, Issues in Medical Ethics 1998 January; 6(1): 17-19.

Biller-Andorno, Nikola. It's cloning again! [editorial]. *Journal of Medical Ethics* 2005 February; 31(2): 63. NRCBL: 14.5.

Blackford, Russell. Human cloning and 'posthuman' society. *Monash Bioethics Review* 2005 January; 24(1): 10-26. NRCBL: 14.5; 5.1. SC: an.

Bruce, Donald. Human embryonic cloning. *Human Reproduction and Genetic Ethics: An International Journal* 2001; 7(1): 3-7. NRCBL: 14.5; 18.5.4; 1.2.

Burton, Kelli Whitlock. Cloning in America: The Genetics and Public Policy Center surveys the nation. *GeneWatch* 2005 November-December; 18(6): 13-18. NRCBL: 14.5; 18.6. Identifiers: United States.

Campanella, James J. Cloning: ethical issues. *In:* Ness, Bryan D., ed. Encyclopedia of Genetics. Revised edition. Volume I. Pasadena, Calif.: Salem Press; 2004: 170-174. NRCBL: 14.5.

NRCBL: National Reference Center for Bioethics Literature Classification Scheme   See inside front cover for terms.

117

CLONING

SECTION I

Campbell, Courtney. Buddhism and cloning. *In:* McGee, Glenn; Caplan, Arthur, eds. The Human Cloning Debate. 4th edition. Berkeley, CA: Berkeley Hills Books; 2004: 283- 287. NRCBL: 14.5; 1.2.

Caplan, Arthur L. Attack of the anti-cloners: what the government should do. *Free Inquiry* 2002-2003 Winter; 23(1): 30-31. NRCBL: 14.5; 18.5.4; 15.1; 5.3.

Check, Erika. Where now for stem-cell cloners? [news]. *Nature* 2005 December 22-29; 438(7071): 1058-1059. NRCBL: 14.5; 18.5.4; 15.1; 19.1; 21.1. Identifiers: Korea.

Danforth, William H.; Neaves, William B. Using words carefully [letter]. *Science* 2005 September 16; 309(5742): 1815-1816. NRCBL: 14.5; 18.5.4.

de Souza, Eustace J. The ethics of cloning [comment]. *Issues in Medical Ethics* 1998 July-September; 6(3): 90-91. NRCBL: 14.5; 15.1. Comments: comment on Manu Kothari and Lopa Mehta, Issues in Medical Ethics 1998 January; 6(1): 17-19.

Deane-Drummond, Celia E. The ethics of cloning. *In her:* Ethics of Nature. Malden, MA: Blackwell Pub.; 2004: 111-135. NRCBL: 14.5; 1.2; 15.1; 18.5.4.

Decker, Kevin. Habermas on human rights and cloning: a pragmatist response. *Essays in Philosophy* 2002 June; 3(2): 33 p. [Online]. Available: http://www.humboldt.edu/~essays/decker.html [14 September 2005]. NRCBL: 14.5; 15.1; 4.4; 1.1. SC: an.

Dell'Oro, Roberto. Contextualizando la discusion sobre clonacion: premisas ideologicas y asuntos olvidados / Contextualizing the discussion on cloning: ideological premises and forgotten topics. *Vida y Etica* 2003 December; 4(2): 53-65. NRCBL: 14.5.

Dowty, Rachel. Clones and cloning. *In:* Restivo, Sal, ed. Science, Technology, and Society: An Encyclopedia. New York: Oxford University Press; 2005: 54-55. NRCBL: 14.5.

Dyens, Ollivier. Cloning: burning bright in the forest of the night. *Free Inquiry* 2002-2003 Winter; 23(1): 38-39. NRCBL: 14.5.

Easton, David. All in our genes? *Human Reproduction and Genetic Ethics: An International Journal* 2001; 7(1): 2. NRCBL: 14.5; 15.2; 15.4; 14.3.

Fangerau, H. Can artificial parthenogenesis sidestep ethical pitfalls in human therapeutic cloning? An historical perspective. *Journal of Medical Ethics* 2005 December; 31(12): 733-735. NRCBL: 14.5; 18.5.4; 14.1. SC: an.
Abstract: The aim of regenerative medicine is to reconstruct tissue that has been lost or pathologically altered. Therapeutic cloning seems to offer a method of achieving this aim; however, the ethical debate surrounding human therapeutic cloning is highly controversial. Artificial parthenogenesis-obtaining embryos from unfertilised eggs-seems to offer a way to sidestep these ethical pitfalls. Jacques Loeb (1859-1924), the founding father of artificial parthenogenesis, faced negative public opinion when he published his research in 1899. His research, the public's response to his findings, and his ethical foundations serve as an historical argument both for the communication of science and compromise in biological research.

Fiester, Autumn. Creating Fido's twin: can pet cloning be ethically justified? *Hastings Center Report* 2005 July-August; 35(4): 34-39. NRCBL: 14.5; 22.1.
Abstract: Taken at face value, pet cloning may seem at best a frivolous practice, costly both to the cloned pet's health and its owner's pocket. At worst, its critics say, it is misguided and unhealthy—a way of exploiting grief to the detriment of the animal, its owner, and perhaps even animal welfare in general. But if the great pains we are willing to take to clone Fido raise the status of companion animals in the public eye, then the practice might be defensible.

Fiester, Autumn. Ethical issues in animal cloning. *Perspectives in Biology and Medicine* 2005 Summer; 48(3): 328- 343. NRCBL: 14.5; 22.3; 22.1.

Fiester, Autumn. Reflections on Dolly: what can animal cloning tell us about the human cloning debate? *In:* McGee, Glenn; Caplan, Arthur, eds. The Human Cloning Debate. 4th edition. Berkeley, CA: Berkeley Hills Books; 2004: 107- 125. NRCBL: 14.5. SC: an.

Franklin, Sarah. What we know and what we don't about cloning and society. *New Genetics and Society* 1999; 18(1): 111-120. NRCBL: 14.5; 22.3; 5.1.

Frazzetto, Giovanni. Embryos, cells and God. *EMBO Reports* 2004 June; 5(6): 553-555. NRCBL: 14.5; 18.5.4; 15.1; 1.2.

Frith, Michael. Asian nations approach cloning consensus [news]. *Nature Medicine* 2003 March; 9(3): 248. NRCBL: 14.5; 21.1; 18.6; 18.2.

Gorman, Ulf. A theological approach to human cloning. *In:* Ostnor, Lars, ed. Bioethics and Cloning: Report from a Workshop Arranged by the Nordic Theological Network for Bioethics in Arhus, September 25-27, 1998. Oslo: Nordic Theological Network for Bioethics; 1998: 78-82. NRCBL: 14.5; 1.2.

Great Britain. Parliament. House of Commons. Committee on Science and Technology. Cloning of animals from adult cells (fifth report). *London: The Stationery Office* 1997 March 18; 23 p. NRCBL: 14.5.

Guenin, Louis M. Stem cells, cloning, and regulation. *Mayo Clinic Proceedings* 2005 February; 80(2): 241-250. NRCBL: 14.5; 14.1; 18.5.4; 18.6. SC: an.

The Guild of Catholic Doctors; Jarmulowicz, Michael. The Guild of Catholic Doctors: comments to the chief medical officer's expert group on cloning. *Catholic Medical Quarterly* 2000 August; 50(3); 5 p. [Online]. Available: http://www.catholicdoctors.org.uk/submissions/cloning_expert_committee.htm [4 November 2005]. NRCBL: 14.5; 1.2; 18.2; 18.6.

SC (Subject Caption): an=analytical cs=case studies em=empirical le=legal po=popular rv=review
118

Harris, John. The poverty of objections to human reproductive cloning. *In:* Cohen, Andrew I.; Wellman, Christopher Heath, eds. Contemporary Debates in Applied Ethics. Malden, MA: Blackwell Pub., 2005: 145-158. NRCBL: 14.5; 1.1. SC: an.

Häyry, Matti; Takala, Tuija. Cloning, naturalness and personhood. *In:* Thomasma, David C.; Weisstud, David N.; Herve, Christian eds. Personhood and Health Care. Boston: Kluwer Academic Pub., 2001: 281-298. NRCBL: 14.5; 1.1; 4.4. SC: an.

Hellsten, Iina. Dolly: scientific breakthrough or Frankenstein's monster? Journalistic and scientific metaphors of cloning. *Metaphor and Symbol* 2000; 15(4): 213-221. NRCBL: 14.5; 22.3; 5.1; 1.3.7.

Herissone-Kelly, Peter. The cloning debate in the United Kingdom: the academy meets the public. *CQ: Cambridge Quarterly of Healthcare Ethics* 2005 Summer; 14(3): 268-276. NRCBL: 14.5; 4.4; 1.2; 7.1; 15.1.

Holliman, Richard. Media coverage of cloning: a study of media content, production and reception. *Public Understanding of Science* 2004 April; 13(2): 107-130. NRCBL: 14.5; 1.3.7; 7.1. SC: em.

Isasi, Rosario M.; Annas, George J. Arbitrage, bioethics, and cloning: the ABCs of gestating a United Nations Cloning Convention. *Case Western Reserve Journal of International Law* 2003 Fall; 35(3): 397-414. NRCBL: 14.5; 5.3; 21.1.

Kolata, Gina. Beating hurdles, scientists clone a dog for a first; feat for South Koreans; success with afghan pup is called "dry run" for debate on humans. *New York Times* 2005 August 4; p. A1, A10. NRCBL: 14.5; 22.3; 22.2. SC: po.

Kolata, Gina. Koreans report ease in cloning for stem cells; work on human embryos; researchers say goal is better medicine, not reproduction. *New York Times* 2005 May 20; p. A1, A22. NRCBL: 14.5; 18.5.4. SC: po.

Kvist, Hans-Olof. Cloning of human beings? Theological perspectives. *In:* Ostnor, Lars, ed. Bioethics and Cloning: Report from a Workshop Arranged by the Nordic Theological Network for Bioethics in Arhus, September 25-27, 1998. Oslo: Nordic Theological Network for Bioethics; 1998: 83-88. NRCBL: 14.5; 1.2.

Larijani, Bagher; Zahedi, F. Islamic perspective on human cloning and stem cell research. *Transplantation Proceedings* 2004 December; 36(10): 3188-3189. NRCBL: 14.5; 18.5.4; 15.1; 1.2.

Leather, Suzi. Human cloning — what should we really be frightened of? [editorial]. *Clinical Medicine* 2004 July-August; 4(4): 299-301. NRCBL: 14.5; 18.5.4.

Lenzen, Wolfgang. Therapeutic versus genuine cloning: what are the real moral issues? *Ethical Perspectives* 2003; 10(3-4): 176-184. NRCBL: 14.5; 1.1. SC: an.

Levy, Neil; Lotz, Mianna. Reproductive cloning and a (kind of) genetic fallacy. *Bioethics* 2005 June; 19(3): 232-250. NRCBL: 14.5; 15.1. SC: an.
Abstract: Many people now believe that human reproductive cloning—once sufficiently safe and effective—should be permitted on the grounds that it will allow the otherwise infertile to have children that are biologically closely related to them. However, though it is widely believed that the possession of a close genetic link to our children is morally significant and valuable, we argue that such a view is erroneous. Moreover, the claim that the genetic link is valuable is pernicious; it tends to give rise to highly undesirable consequences, and therefore should be combated rather than pandered to. The emphasis on the genetic is unwarranted and unfortunate; rather than giving us moral reason to support reproductive cloning in the case of infertility, the fact that cloning requests are likely to be motivated by the genetic argument gives us reason to oppose its availability.

Malby, Steven. Human dignity and human reproductive cloning. *Health and Human Rights: An International Journal* 2002; 6(1): 103-135. NRCBL: 14.5; 5.3; 21.1; 4.4; 1.1.

Maloney, Dennis M. Ethical requirements would apply to stem cell research. *Human Research Report* 2002 January; 17(1): 9. NRCBL: 14.5; 18.5.4; 18.6; 5.3.

Marks, Stephen P. Human rights assumptions of restrictive and permissive approaches to human reproductive cloning. *Health and Human Rights: An International Journal* 2002; 6(1): 81-100. NRCBL: 14.5; 5.3; 21.1; 1.1.

Mayor, Susan. UN committee approves declaration on human cloning [news]. *BMJ: British Medical Journal* 2005 March 5; 330(7490): 496. NRCBL: 14.5; 21.1. Identifiers: United Nations.

McLachlan, Hugh V. Unique persons and the replicable gene-sets of their reproducible bodies: a defence of human cloning. *Human Reproduction and Genetic Ethics: An International Journal* 2005; 11(2): 43-48. NRCBL: 14.5.

Meslin, Eric. Of clones, stem cells, and children: issues and challenges in human research ethics. *In:* Actes du Colloque International AMADE-UNESCO sur Bioethique et Droits de L'enfant (Monaco, 28-30 Avril 2000)/Proceedings of the International Symposium AMADE-UNESCO on Bioethics and the Rights of the Child (Monaco, 28-30 April 2000). Paris: UNESCO, Division des Sciences Humaines, de la Philosophie et de L'ethique des Sciences et des Technologies; 2001: 87-104. NRCBL: 14.5; 18.5.4; 18.5.2.

Milani-Comparetti, Marco. Bioethical considerations on cloning and twinning. *Acta Geneticae Medicae et Gemellologicae (Roma)* 1997; 46(3): 135-137. NRCBL: 14.5.

NRCBL: National Reference Center for Bioethics Literature Classification Scheme   See inside front cover for terms.

119

Mitchell, C. Ben. The wisdom of Costa Rica [editorial]. *Ethics and Medicine* 2005 Spring; 21(1): 3-4. NRCBL: 14.5; 18.5.4; 5.3; 21.1.

Morscher, Edgar. Why is it morally wrong to clone a human being? How to evaluate arguments of biopolitics, biomorality, and bioethics. *In:* Thiele, F.; Ashcroft, R.E., eds. Bioethics in a Small World. Berlin: Springer; 2005: 121-128. NRCBL: 14.5. SC: an.

Mosteller, Timothy. Aristotle and headless clones. *Theoretical Medicine and Bioethics* 2005; 26(4): 339-350. NRCBL: 14.5; 19.5; 3.1; 4.4.

Abstract: Cloned organisms can be genetically altered so that they do not exhibit higher brain functioning. This form of therapeutic cloning allows for genetically identical organs and tissues to be harvested from the clone for the use of the organism that is cloned. "Spare parts" cloning promises many opportunities for future medical advances. What is the ontological and ethical status of spare parts, headless clones? This paper attempts to answer this question from the perspective of Aristotle's view of the soul. Aristotle's metaphysics as applied to his view of biological essences generates an ethic that can contribute to moral reasoning regarding the use of headless spare parts clones. The task of this paper is to show the implications that Aristotle's view of the soul, if it is true, would have on the ethics of headless, spare parts cloning.

Neresini, Federico. And man descended from the sheep: the public debate on cloning in the Italian press. *Public Understanding of Science* 2000; 9: 359-382. NRCBL: 14.5; 22.3; 5.1; 1.3.7.

Nerlich, Brigitte; Clarke, David D.; Dingwall, Robert. Fictions, fantasies, and fears: the literary foundations of the cloning debate. *Journal of Literary Semantics* 2001; 30: 37-52. NRCBL: 14.5; 7.1; 15.1.

Normile, Dennis; Vogel, Gretchen; Holden, Constance. Cloning researcher says work is flawed but claims results stand [news]. *Science* 2005 December 23; 310(5756): 1886-1887. NRCBL: 14.5; 18.5.4; 15.1; 1.3.9.

Novak, Kris. New Stanford institute sparks cloning quarrel [news]. *Nature Medicine* 2003 February; 9(2): 156-157. NRCBL: 14.5; 2.4.

Nurmi, Suvielise. Discussion concerning cloning in *Die Zeit*: an introduction. *In:* Ostnor, Lars, ed. Bioethics and Cloning: Report from a Workshop Arranged by the Nordic Theological Network for Bioethics in Arhus, September 25-27, 1998. Oslo: Nordic Theological Network for Bioethics; 1998: 56-64. NRCBL: 14.5; 1.1.

Pavelic, Krešimir. Arguments for human therapeutic cloning. *Bosnian Journal of Basic Medical Sciences* 2004 February 4(1): 15-18. NRCBL: 14.5; 18.5.4; 15.1; 19.1; 22.2. SC: an.

Quammen, David. Clone your troubles away: dreaming of the frontiers of animal husbandry. *Harper's Magazine* 2005 February; 310(1857): 33-43. NRCBL: 14.5; 22.3; 22.1. SC: po.

Reich, Eugenie Samuel. Cloning crisis goes from bad to worse [news]. *New Scientist* 2005 December 24-2006 January 6; 188(2531-2532): 4. NRCBL: 14.5; 1.3.9; 18.5.4; 15.1. Identifiers: Korea; Woo Suk Hwang.

Reuter, Lars. Pandora's box? Theological perspectives on cloning. *In:* Ostnor, Lars, ed. Bioethics and Cloning: Report from a Workshop Arranged by the Nordic Theological Network for Bioethics in Arhus, September 25-27, 1998. Oslo: Nordic Theological Network for Bioethics; 1998: 73-77. NRCBL: 14.5; 1.2.

Revel, Michel. Ethical issues of human embryo cloning technologies for stem cell research. *In:* Blazer, Shraga; Zimmer, Etan Z., eds. The Embryo: Scientific Discovery and Medical Ethics. New York: Karger; 2005: 107-119. NRCBL: 14.5; 18.5.4.

Rifkin, Jeremy. Why I oppose human cloning. *In:* Cohen, Andrew I.; Wellman, Christopher Heath, eds. Contemporary Debates in Applied Ethics. Malden, MA: Blackwell Pub., 2005: 141-144. NRCBL: 14.5; 18.5.4.

Rocklinsberg, Helena. Theocentrism or a re-dressed anthropocentrism? A response to Professor Schroten's lecture. *In:* Ostnor, Lars, ed. Bioethics and Cloning: Report from a Workshop Arranged by the Nordic Theological Network for Bioethics in Arhus, September 25-27, 1998. Oslo: Nordic Theological Network for Bioethics; 1998: 45-50. NRCBL: 14.5; 1.2.

Rollin, Bernard E. Keeping up with the cloneses — issues in human cloning. *Journal of Ethics* 1999; 3(1): 51-71. NRCBL: 14.5.

Schmidt, Ulla. Cloning of human beings? Theological perspectives. *In:* Ostnor, Lars, ed. Bioethics and Cloning: Report from a Workshop Arranged by the Nordic Theological Network for Bioethics in Arhus, September 25-27, 1998. Oslo: Nordic Theological Network for Bioethics; 1998: 65-72. NRCBL: 14.5; 1.2.

Schroten, Egbert. A theological-ethics perspective on cloning. *In:* Ostnor, Lars, ed. Bioethics and Cloning: Report from a Workshop Arranged by the Nordic Theological Network for Bioethics in Arhus, September 25-27, 1998. Oslo: Nordic Theological Network for Bioethics; 1998: 35-44. NRCBL: 14.5; 1.2.

Seng, Kang Phee. Cloning humans? Some moral considerations. *In:* Qiu, Ren-Zong, ed. Bioethics: Asian Perspectives: A Quest for Moral Diversity. Boston: Kluwer Academic Publishers; 2004: 115- 127. NRCBL: 14.5.

Shalev, Carmel. Human cloning and human rights: a commentary. *Health and Human Rights: An International Journal* 2002; 6(1): 137-151. NRCBL: 14.5; 5.3; 21.1; 4.4; 1.1.

Sharma, B.R. Cloning controversies: an overview of the science, ethics and politics. *Medicine, Science, and the*

Law 2005 January; 45(1): 17-26. NRCBL: 14.5; 18.5.4; 18.6; 21.1.

Shermer, Michael. Only God can do that? Cloning and genetic engineering test the moral limits of science. *Skeptic* 1999; 7(2): 58-63. NRCBL: 14.5; 15.4; 2.1; 5.1.

Shuster, Evelyne. My clone, myself, my daughter, my sister: echoes of *Le Petit Prince. In:* Actes du Colloque International AMADE-UNESCO sur Bioethique et Droits de L'enfant (Monaco, 28-30 Avril 2000)/Proceedings of the International Symposium AMADE-UNESCO on Bioethics and the Rights of the Child (Monaco, 28-30 April 2000). Paris: UNESCO, Division des Sciences Humaines, de la Philosophie et de L'ethique des Sciences et des Technologies; 2001: 37-46. NRCBL: 14.5.

Steinberg, Jesse R. Response to Fritz Allhoff, "Telomeres and the Ethics of Human Cloning" (AJOB 4:2). *American Journal of Bioethics [Online]* 2005 January-February; 5(1): W27-W28. NRCBL: 14.5; 1.1. Comments: comment on American Journal of Bioethics [Online] 2004 March-April; 4(2): W29-W31.

Sterba, James P. Genetic engineering. *In his:* Sterba, James P., ed.: Morality in Practice. 7th edition. Belmont, CA: Wasworth/Thompson Learning; 2004: 191-212. NRCBL: 14.5; 1.1. SC: an.

Strong, C. Reproductive cloning combined with genetic modification. *Journal of Medical Ethics* 2005 November; 31(11): 654-658. NRCBL: 14.5; 15.1; 10; 9.2. SC: an.
Abstract: Although there is widespread opposition to reproductive cloning, some have argued that its use by infertile couples to have genetically related children would be ethically justifiable. Others have suggested that lesbian or gay couples might wish to use cloning to have genetically related children. Most of the main objections to human reproductive cloning are based on the child's lack of unique nuclear DNA. In the future, it may be possible safely to create children using cloning combined with genetic modifications, so that they have unique nuclear DNA. The genetic modifications could be aimed at giving such children genetic characteristics of both members of the couple concerned. Thus, cloning combined with genetic modification could be appealing to infertile, lesbian, or gay couples who seek genetically related children who have genetic characteristics of both members. In such scenarios, the various objections to human reproductive cloning that are based on the lack of genetic uniqueness would no longer be applicable. The author argues that it would be ethically justifiable for such couples to create children in this manner, assuming these techniques could be used safely.

Takala, Tuija. The many wrongs of human reproductive cloning. *In:* Häyry, Matti; Takala, Tuija; Herissone-Kelly, Peter, eds. Bioethics and Social Reality. New York: Rodopi, 2005: 53-66. NRCBL: 14.5; 14.1; 1.1. SC: an.

Testa, Giuseppe; Harris, John. Ethics and synthetic gametes. *Bioethics* 2005 April; 19(2): 146-166. NRCBL: 14.5; 18.5.4; 15.1; 14.1.
Abstract: The recent in vitro derivation of gamete-like cells from mouse embryonic stem (mES) cells is a major breakthrough and lays down several challenges, both for the further scientific investigation and for the bioethical and biolegal discourse. We refer here to these cells as gamete-like (sperm-like or oocyte-like, respectively), because at present there is still no evidence that these cells behave fully like bona fide sperm or oocytes, lacking the fundamental proof, i.e. combination with a normally derived gamete of the opposite sex to yield a normal individual. However, the results published so far do show that these cells share some defining features of gametes. We discuss these results in the light of the bioethical and legal questions that are likely to arise would the same process become possible with human embryonic stem (hES) cells.

Triggle, David J. Everybody must get cloned: ideological objections do not hold up. *Free Inquiry* 2002-2003 Winter; 23(1): 32-33. NRCBL: 14.5.

Trounson, Alan O. Cloning: potential benefits for human medicine [editorial]. *Medical Journal of Australia* 1997 December 1-15; 167(11-12): 568-569. NRCBL: 14.5; 18.5.4; 19.5; 21.1.

Trujillo, Alfonso López. Clonacion: perdida de la paternidad y negacion de la familia / Cloning: loss of paternity and negation of the family. *Vida y Etica* 2003 December; 4(2): 119-139. NRCBL: 14.5; 1.2; 4.4.

United Nations General Assembly. United Nations declaration on human cloning. *National Catholic Bioethics Quarterly* 2005 Summer; 5(2): 357- 358. NRCBL: 14.5; 18.2; 21.1.

United Nations High Commissioner for Human Rights [UNHCHR]. Expert Group on Human Rights and Biotechnology. Expert group on human rights and biotechnology convened by the UN high commissioner for human rights: conclusions on human reproductive cloning. *Health and Human Rights: An International Journal* 2002; 6(1): 153-159. NRCBL: 14.5; 5.3; 21.1; 4.4.

Van Dijck, José. Cloning humans, cloning literature: genetics and the imagination deficit. *New Genetics and Society* 1999; 18(1): 9-22. NRCBL: 14.5; 7.1; 5.1.

Vandervert, Larry R. The inheritance of the core self in human clones. *Free Inquiry* 2005 December-2006 January; 26(1): 37-39. NRCBL: 14.5.

Wade, Nicholas. Korean researchers to help others clone cells for study. *New York Times* 2005 October 19; p. A14. NRCBL: 14.5; 18.5.4; 1.3.9. SC: po.

Weasel, Lisa H.; Jensen, Eric. Language and values in the human cloning debate: a web-based survey of scientists and Christian fundamentalist pastors. *New Genetics and Society* 2005 April; 24(1): 1-14. NRCBL: 14.5; 7.1; 1.2. SC: em. Identifiers: United States.

Wexler, Barbara. Cloning. *In her:* Genetics and Genetic Engineering. Detroit, MI: Gale Group; 2004: 101-114. NRCBL: 14.5; 18.5.4.

NRCBL: National Reference Center for Bioethics Literature Classification Scheme   See inside front cover for terms.

121

CLONING/ LEGAL ASPECTS

Declaracion de las Naciones Unidas sobre la Clonacion Humana / United Nations Declaration on Human Cloning. *Revista de Derecho y Genoma Humano / Law and the Human Genome Review* 2005 January-June; (22): 231-234. NRCBL: 14.5; 18.6; 21.1. SC: le.

The United Nations Declaration on Human Cloning [editorial]. *Revista de Derecho y Genoma Humano / Law and the Human Genome Review* 2005 January-June; (22): 15-18. NRCBL: 14.5; 18.6; 21.1. SC: le.

Bahadur, Gulam; Nielsen, H. Ingolf. The human embryo, embryonic stem cells, cloning, legal and political precepts [opinion]. *Reproductive BioMedicine Online [electronic]* 2001; 2(2): 81-83. Available: http://www.rbmonline.com/index.html [1 September 2005]. NRCBL: 14.5; 18.5.4; 14.4. SC: le. Identifiers: Human Fertilisation and Embryology (Research Purposes) Regulations 2000 Bill.

Bellinger, Michael. The constitutional right to therapeutic cloning. *Journal of Medicine and Law* 2002 Fall; 7(1): 37-53. NRCBL: 14.5; 9.2. SC: le.

Berger, K. Protecting the unborn clone: can law and science evolve together? *Medicine and Law: World Association for Medical Law* 2005 September; 24(3): 561-574. NRCBL: 14.5; 4.4. SC: le.

Abstract: The courts have treated the unborn child as neither person nor property. Human cloning will challenge this legal principle. Human cloning provides options for future scientific development and treatment of disease and infertility. However, cloning gives rise to issues not yet considered, in law, let alone resolved. These issues are not present in the context of normal human birth. At present, the common law restricts its scope to normal human birth. Does the donor "own" their unborn clone? Who makes decisions on behalf of the unborn clone? The gap between science and law is too large in human cloning research. Law lags behind in adapting to new technologies. This paper will address legal issues in relation to the unborn clone. Cloning will challenge the law in its current state. Decision-making and control of the unborn child are vital issues, to be determined before human cloning can be permitted to take place. The individuals who might have an interest in the unborn clone include the donor, the scientist, who either developed the finished clone or stored the clone prior to implantation, and the surrogate mother. Claims or conflicts might arise in many areas of medicine and law. Does the scientist have an intellectual property right? Can the surrogate mother terminate the pregnancy at will? If the unborn clone is not aborted, what measures are required to protect the fetus? Can the surrogate mother be liable for neglect? Who decides about disclosure of information and knowledge or choice regarding fetal diagnosis and treatment? Who has custody of the unborn clone? In this paper, the concepts of trusts are explored to develop a means of resolving conflicts among the individuals who might claim an interest in the unborn clone. The trust doctrine is flexible and may be useful in resolving claims or conflicts.

Billingsley, Barbara; Caulfield, Timothy. The regulation of science and the Charter of Rights: would a ban on non-reproductive human cloning unjustifiably violate freedom of expression? *Queen's Law Journal* 2004 Spring; 29(2): 647-679. NRCBL: 14.5; 5.3; 1.1; 4.4. SC: le. Identifiers: Canada.

Campbell, Angela. Ethos and economics: examining the rationale underlying stem cell and cloning research policies in the United States, Germany, and Japan. *American Journal of Law and Medicine* 2005; 31(1): 47-86. NRCBL: 14.5; 18.5.4; 18.2; 18.6; 21.1. SC: le.

Campbell, Angela. A place for criminal law in the regulation of reproductive technologies. *Health Law Journal* 2002; 10: 77-101. NRCBL: 14.5; 1.3.5; 14.4; 18.5.4. SC: le.

Carmen, Ira H. Should human cloning be criminalized? *Journal of Law and Politics* 1997 Fall; 13(4): 745-758. NRCBL: 14.5; 18.6; 5.3. SC: le.

Duddington, John. The legal aspects of human cloning. *Catholic Medical Quarterly* 2000 August; 50(3); 10 p. [Online]. Available: http://www.catholicdoctors.org.uk/CMQ/Aug_2000/cloning_legal_aspects.htm [4 November 2005]. NRCBL: 14.5; 1.2; 14.1; 1.3.5. SC: le.

Ford, Norman M. Cloning and embryo research in Australia: legalization of destructive embryo research. *Ethics and Medics* 2003 March; 28(3): 2-4. NRCBL: 14.5; 18.5.4. SC: le.

Goldberg, Steven. Cloning matters: how Lawrence v. Texas protects therapeutic research. *Yale Journal of Health Policy, Law, and Ethics* 2004 Summer; 4(2): 305-317. NRCBL: 14.5; 18.5.4; 19.5. SC: le.

Graumann, Sigrid; Poltermann, Andreas. No end in sight to cloning debate. *Revista de Derecho y Genoma Humano / Law and the Human Genome Review* 2005 January-June; (22): 209-227. NRCBL: 14.5; 18.5.4; 19.5; 15.1; 18.6. SC: le. Note: Abstract in English and Spanish.

Harvey, Olivia. Regulating stem-cell research and human cloning in an Australian context: an exercise in protecting the status of the human subject. *New Genetics and Society* 2005 August; 24(2): 125-135. NRCBL: 14.5; 18.5.4; 4.4. SC: le.

Heagle, Khristan A. Should there be another ewe? A critical analysis of the European Union cloning legislation. *Dickinson Journal of International Law* 1998 Fall; 17(1): 135-158. NRCBL: 14.5; 18.6; 21.1. SC: le.

Keough, William J. All in the family: a child welfare perspective on human reproductive cloning. *Health Law Journal* 2003; 11: 71-87. NRCBL: 14.5; 4.4. SC: le.

Kintisch, Eli. Anticloning forces launch second-term offensive [news]. *Science* 2005 March 18; 307(5716): 1702-1703. NRCBL: 14.5; 5.3. SC: le. Identifiers: Leon Kass.

Lin, Laura. International stem cell use and regulation in research. *Journal of Biolaw and Business* 2005; 8(1): 47-48. NRCBL: 14.5; 18.5.4; 18.6. SC: le.

McGee, Glenn; Wilmut, Ian. A model for regulating cloning. *In:* McGee, Glenn; Caplan, Arthur, eds. The Human Cloning Debate. 4th edition. Berkeley, CA: Berkeley Hills Books; 2004: 221- 232. NRCBL: 14.5. SC: le.

Merrill, Matthew M. The sheep heard 'round the world: legislation vs. self- regulation of human cloning. *Kansas Journal of Law and Public Policy* 1997-1998; 7(3): 169-188. NRCBL: 14.5; 15.7. SC: le.

Moore, Debra L. Don't rush to judgment on "Dolly": human cloning and its individual procreative liberty implications. *UMKC Law Review* 1997 Winter; 66(2): 425-449. NRCBL: 14.5. SC: le.

Morgan, Derek. Science, medicine and ethical change. *In:* Bainham, Andrew; Sclater, Shelley Day; Richards, Martin, eds. Body Lore and Laws. Portland, OR: Hart Pub.; 2002: 329-342. NRCBL: 14.5; 18.5.4; 2.1. SC: le.

New York (State). Senate; Marchi, John. Cloning of a human being. New York: New York SB 2877, 1997 February 26; 4 p. NRCBL: 14.5; 5.3. SC: le.

Pattinson, Shaun D. Some problems challenging the UK's Human Fertilisation and Embryology Authority. *Medicine and Law: World Association for Medical Law* 2005 June; 24(2): 391-401. NRCBL: 14.5; 22.2; 18.6; 14.4. SC: le.

Abstract: The UK's Human Fertilisation and Embryology Authority (hereafter the HFEA) is a regulatory body facing growing pressures and difficulties. Like any regulatory body, it faces the challenge of regulating with sufficient expertise, legitimacy, and contemporaneity. This challenge is, however, exacerbated by the fact that it seeks to regulate some of the most controversial and rapidly changing technologies of our time. Its decisions and jurisdictional assumptions face increasing challenge. In addition to the multitude of cases brought against it, the HFEA's actions recently led a House of Commons Select Committee to pointedly declare that "democracy is not served by unelected quangos (quasi- autonomous non-governmental organizations) taking decisions on behalf of Parliament". While endorsing the general need to review the legislation under which the HFEA operates (the Human Fertilisation and Embryology Act 1990), this paper will argue that the HFEA was correct in interpreting its jurisdiction to encompass the technique used to produce Dolly the sheep. This paper thereby defends the key feature of the approach of the House of Lords in the recent case of R (Bruno Quintavalle on behalf of the ProLife Alliance) v Secretary of State for Health [2003] UKHL 13.

Post, May Mon. Human cloning: new hope, new implications, new challenges. *Temple International and Comparative Law Journal* 2001 Spring; 15(1): 171-193. NRCBL: 14.5; 18.6; 21.1. SC: le.

Rose, Andre P. Reproductive misconception: why cloning is not just another assisted reproductive technology. *Duke Law Journal* 1999 March; 48(5): 1133-1156. NRCBL: 14.5; 14.1. SC: le.

Thomson, Judith. Legal and ethical problems of human cloning. *Journal of Law and Medicine* 2000 August; 8(1): 31-43. NRCBL: 14.5; 4.4; 14.1. SC: le.

Tully, Paul. Dollywood is not just a theme park in Tennessee anymore: unwarranted prohibitory human cloning legislation and policy guidelines for a regulatory approach to cloning. *John Marshall Law Review* 1998 Summer; 31(4): 1385-1422. NRCBL: 14.5; 18.6; 18.2. SC: le.

Yang, Che-Ming; Chung, Chun-Chih; Lu, Meei-Shiow; Lin, Chiou-Fen; Chen, Jiun-Shyan. Ethical attitudes on human cloning among professionals in Taiwan and the policy implications for regulation. *Issues in Law and Medicine* 2005 Summer; 21(1): 35-44. NRCBL: 14.5. SC: em; le.

CODES OF ETHICS

Code of ethics for emergency physicians [policy statement]. *Annals of Emergency Medicine* 2004 May; 43(5): 686-694. NRCBL: 6; 4.1.2.

Aleksandrova, Silviya. Comparative analysis of the code of professional ethics in Bulgaria and the Hippocratic Oath, Declaration of Geneva and International Code of Medical Ethics. *Medicine and Law: World Association for Medical Law* 2005 September; 24(3): 495-503. NRCBL: 6; 21.1. SC: an; le.

Abstract: In this paper I aim at making a comparative analysis of The Code of Professional Ethics in Bulgaria (CPEB), The Hippocratic Oath, The Declaration of Geneva, and The World Medical Association International Code of Medical Ethics. Two problems of special interest are explored: whether the leading principles of fundamental ethical codes are presented in CPEB and whether the code itself is relevant to the current medical professional and social situation in the country. The conclusion reached after a step-by-step analysis is that CPEB attempts to cover a wide range of principles and problems in medical practice and corresponds with the fundamental ethical codes. Although the code is criticized in some points, it could be very useful, provided that it is well publicized in the profession.

American Association of Neuromuscular and Electrodiagnostic Medicine [AANEM]; Mackin, Glenn A.; Horowitz, Steven H.; Leonard, James A., Jr.; Musick, David W. Guidelines for ethical behavior relating to clinical practice issues in electrodiagnostic medicine [policy statement]. *Muscle and Nerve* 2005 March; 31(3): 400-405. NRCBL: 6; 4.1.1.

American College of Emergency Physicians. Ethics Committee. Financial conflicts of interest in biomedical research [policy statement]. *Annals of Emergency Medicine* 2002; 40(5): 546-547. NRCBL: 6; 1.3.9; 2.1; 7.3.

American Health Information Management Association [AHIMA]. American Health Information Management Association. Position statement. Issue: disclosure of health information. *Journal of AHIMA* 1993 December; 64(12): 101-102. NRCBL: 6; 8.4; 1.3.12; 9.1.

NRCBL: National Reference Center for Bioethics Literature Classification Scheme   See inside front cover for terms.

American Health Information Management Association [AHIMA]. American Health Information Management Association. Position statement. Issue: disclosure of health information relating to alcohol and drug abuse. *Journal of AHIMA* 1993 December; 64(12): 99. NRCBL: 6; 8.4; 1.3.12; 9.5.9.

American Health Information Management Association [AHIMA]. American Health Information Management Association. Position statement. Issue: redisclosure of health information. *Journal of AHIMA* 1993 December; 64(12): 103. NRCBL: 6; 8.4; 1.3.12.

American Indian Law Center. Model tribal research code: with materials for tribal regulation for research and checklist for Indian health boards. *Albuquerque, New Mexico: American Indian Law Center* 1999 September; 28 p. NRCBL: 6; 18.5.9; 18.2; 9.5.4. SC: le.

American Occupational Therapy Association [AOTA]; Arnold, Melba; Nashiro, Nancy; Hill, Diane; Slater, Deborah Y.; Morris, John; Withers, Linda; Kyler, Penny. Occupational therapy code of ethics (2000). *American Journal of Occupational Therapy* 2000 November-December; 54(6): 614-616. NRCBL: 6; 9.8.

American Psychological Association. Ethical principles of psychologists and code of conduct. *American Psychologist* 2002 December; 57(12): 1060-1073. NRCBL: 6; 17.1.

Baker, Robert. A draft model aggregated code of ethics for bioethicists. *American Journal of Bioethics* 2005 September-October; 5(5): 33-41. NRCBL: 6; 2.1.
Abstract: Bioethicists function in an environment in which their peers— healthcare executives, lawyers, nurses, physicians—assert the integrity of their fields through codes of professional ethics. Is it time for bioethics to assert its integrity by developing a code of ethics? Answering in the affirmative, this paper lays out a case by reviewing the historical nature and function of professional codes of ethics. Arguing that professional codes are aggregative enterprises growing in response to a field's historical experiences, it asserts that bioethics now needs to assert its integrity and independence and has already developed a body of formal statements that could be aggregated to create a comprehensive code of ethics for bioethics. A Draft Model Aggregated Code of Ethics for Bioethicists is offered in the hope that analysis and criticism of this draft code will promote further discussion of the nature and content of a code of ethics for bioethicists.

Baker, Robert. Response to commentators on "A draft model aggregated code of ethics for bioethicists" [letter]. *American Journal of Bioethics [Online]* 2005 September-October; 5(5): W12-W13. NRCBL: 6; 2.1.

Beauchamp, Tom L. What can a model professional code for bioethics hope to achieve? [comment]. *American Journal of Bioethics* 2005 September-October; 5(5): 42-43. NRCBL: 6; 2.1. Comments: comment on Robert Baker, "A draft model aggregated code of ethics for bioethicists," American Journal of Bioethics 2005 September-October; 5(5): 33-41.

California Dental Association [CDA]. CDA code of ethics. *Journal of the California Dental Association* 2005 January; 33(1): 65-71. NRCBL: 6; 4.1.1.

Campbell, Angela; Glass, Kathleen Cranley. The legal status of clinical and ethics policies, codes, and guidelines in medical practice and research. *McGill Law Journal* 2001 February; 46(2): 473-489. NRCBL: 6; 4.1.1; 2.1; 7.1. SC: le.

Canadian Medical Association [CMA]. CMA code of ethics. *CMAJ/JAMC: Canadian Medical Association Journal* 2005 April 12; 172(8): 1053-1055. NRCBL: 6.

Catholic Medical Association. Task Force on Ethical and Religious Directives. Report of the task force on ethical and religious directives. *Linacre Quarterly* 2005 May; 72(2): 174-188. NRCBL: 6; 1.2; 9.1. SC: le.

Davis, Michael. Comments on Baker's "Draft model aggregated code of ethics for bioethicists" [comment]. *American Journal of Bioethics* 2005 September-October; 5(5): 57-59. NRCBL: 6; 1.3.1; 2.1. Comments: comment on Robert Baker, "A draft model aggregated code of ethics for bioethicists," American Journal of Bioethics 2005 September-October; 5(5): 33-41.

Divan, Vivek. The Indian Medical Council Regulations 2002: non-application of mind and spirit. *Issues in Medical Ethics* 2002 October-December; 10(4): 83-84. NRCBL: 6; 2.4; 8.3.1; 8.4. Identifiers: India.

Edgar, Andrew. How effective are codes of nursing ethics? *In:* Tadd, Win, ed. Ethical and Professional Issues in Nursing: Perspectives from Europe. New York: Palgrave Macmillan; 2004: 155- 174. NRCBL: 6; 4.1.3.

Glenn, Linda MacDonald. Lessons from other codes: is it the journey or the destination? [comment]. *American Journal of Bioethics* 2005 September-October; 5(5): 59-60. NRCBL: 6; 2.1. Comments: comment on Robert Baker, "A draft model aggregated code of ethics for bioethicists," American Journal of Bioethics 2005 September-October; 5(5): 33-41.

Great Britain. Department of Health. Families and Post Mortems: A Code of Practice. London: Department of Health 2003 April 25; 44 p. NRCBL: 6; 20.1; 8.3.3; 19.5.

Jotterand, Fabrice. The Hippocratic oath and contemporary medicine: dialectic between past ideals and present reality? *Journal of Medicine and Philosophy* 2005 February; 30(1): 107- 128. NRCBL: 6; 4.1.2; 2.1.
Abstract: The Hippocratic Oath, the Hippocratic tradition, and Hippocratic ethics are widely invoked in the popular medical culture as conveying a direction to medical practice and the medical profession. This study critically addresses these invocations of Hippocratic guideposts, noting that reliance on the Hippocratic ethos and the Oath requires establishing (1) what the Oath meant to its author, its original community of reception, and generally for ancient medicine (2) what relationships contemporary invocations of the Oath and the tradition have to the original meaning of the Oath and its original reception (3)

what continuity exists and under what circumstances over the last two-and-a-half millenniums of medical-moral reflections (4) what continuity there is in the meaning of professionalism from the time of Hippocrates to the 21st century, and (5) what social factors in particular have transformed the medical profession in particular countries. This article argues that the resources for a better understanding of medical professionalism lie not in the Hippocratic Oath, tradition, or ethos in and of themselves. Rather, it must be found in a philosophy of medicine that explores the values internal to medicine, thus providing a medical-moral philosophy so as to be able to resist the deformation of medical professionalism by bioethics, biopolitics, and governmental regulation. The Oath, as well as Stephen H. Miles' recent monograph, The Hippocratic Oath and the Ethics of Medicine, are employed as heuristics, so as to throw into better light the extent to which the Hippocratic Oath, tradition, and ethics can provide guidance and direction, as well as to show the necessity of taking seriously the need for a substantive philosophy of medicine.

Kikuchi, June F. 2002 CNA Code of Ethics: some recommendations. *Canadian Journal of Nursing Leadership* 2004 July; 17(3): 28-38. NRCBL: 6; 1.1; 4.2; 8.1. Identifiers: Canadian Nurses Association.

Kipnis, Kenneth. The elements of code development [comment]. *American Journal of Bioethics* 2005 September-October; 5(5): 48-50. NRCBL: 6; 2.1; 1.3.1. Comments: comment on Robert Baker, "A draft model aggregated code of ethics for bioethicists," American Journal of Bioethics 2005 September-October; 5(5): 33-41.

Latham, Stephen R. The (low) life of ethics codes [comment]. *American Journal of Bioethics* 2005 September-October; 5(5): 46-48. NRCBL: 6; 2.1; 1.3.1. Comments: comment on Robert Baker, "A draft model aggregated code of ethics for bioethicists," American Journal of Bioethics 2005 September-October; 5(5): 33-41.

Martin, Linda; Baker, Bud; Fairall, Deborah; Florell, Kenn; Foster, Alice; Gilbert, Karen; O'Donoghue, John. A code of ethics for the medical dosimetrist — the American Association of Medical Dosimetrists experience. *Medical Dosimetry* 1997 Winter; 22(4): 339-340. NRCBL: 6; 4.1.2.

Martin, Linda; Baker, Bud; Fairall, Deborah; Florell, Kenn; Foster, Alice; Gilbert, Karen; O'Donoghue, John. A code of ethics for the medical dosimetrist — the American Association of Medical Dosimetrists experience. *Medical Dosimetry* 1998 Summer; 23(2): 131-132. NRCBL: 6; 4.1.2.

Medical Council of India. The Indian Medical Council (professional conduct, etiquette and ethics) regulations, 2002. *Issues in Medical Ethics* 2002 July-September; 10(3): 66-70. NRCBL: 6; 2.1.

Meyers, Christopher. Codifying but not professionalizing bioethics [comment]. *American Journal of Bioethics* 2005 September-October; 5(5): 68-69. NRCBL: 6; 2.1; 1.3.1. Comments: comment on Robert Baker, "A draft model aggregated code of ethics for

bioethicists," American Journal of Bioethics 2005 September-October; 5(5): 33-41.

Miller, Franklin G. The case for a code of ethics for bioethicists: some reasons for skepticism [comment]. *American Journal of Bioethics* 2005 September-October; 5(5): 50-52. NRCBL: 6; 2.1; 1.3.1. Comments: comment on Robert Baker, "A draft model aggregated code of ethics for bioethicists," American Journal of Bioethics 2005 September-October; 5(5): 33-41.

Miller, Jessica P. A code of ethics for bioethicists: prospects and problems [comment]. *American Journal of Bioethics* 2005 September-October; 5(5): 66-68. NRCBL: 6; 2.1; 1.3.1. Comments: comment on Robert Baker, "A draft model aggregated code of ethics for bioethicists," American Journal of Bioethics 2005 September-October; 5(5): 33-41.

Morin, Karine. Code of ethics for bioethicists: medicine's lessons worth heeding [comment]. *American Journal of Bioethics* 2005 September-October; 5(5): 60-62. NRCBL: 6; 2.1; 1.3.1. Comments: comment on Robert Baker, "A draft model aggregated code of ethics for bioethicists," American Journal of Bioethics 2005 September-October; 5(5): 33-41.

Murphy, Timothy E. Bioethics: past, present, and future [letter]. *Hastings Center Report* 2005 November-December; 35(6): 7. NRCBL: 6; 2.1.

Nishimura, Takahiro. The present state and problems of "The Code of Medical Ethics" in Japan. *Journal International de Bioethique / International Journal of Bioethics* 2005 March-June; 16(1-2): 41-50, 191. NRCBL: 6; 7.4. Identifiers: Japan Medical Association (JMA). Note: Abstract in English and French.

Orr, Robert D. The Hippocratic Oath: is it still relevant? *Update [Loma Linda University Center for Christian Bioethics]* 1998 March; 14(1); 5 p. NRCBL: 6. SC: em.

Perlman, David. Bioethics in industry settings: one situation where a code for bioethicists would help [comment]. *American Journal of Bioethics* 2005 September-October; 5(5): 62-64. NRCBL: 6; 2.1; 1.3.1. Comments: comment on Robert Baker, "A draft model aggregated code of ethics for bioethicists," American Journal of Bioethics 2005 September-October; 5(5): 33-41.

Peter, Elizabeth. Commentary: who will define the values? [opinion]. *Canadian Journal of Nursing Leadership* 2004 July; 17(3): 39-40. NRCBL: 6; 8.1. Identifiers: Canada.

Rappert, Brian. Responsibility in the life sciences: assessing the role of professional codes. *Biosecurity and Bioterrorism: Biodefense Strategy, Practice, and Science* 2004; 2(3): 164-174. NRCBL: 6; 21.3.

NRCBL: National Reference Center for Bioethics Literature Classification Scheme   See inside front cover for terms.

Schüklenk, Udo; Gallagher, Jim. Status, careers and influence in bioethics [comment]. *American Journal of Bioethics* 2005 September-October; 5(5): 64-66. NRCBL: 6; 2.1; 1.3.1. Comments: comment on Robert Baker, "A draft model aggregated code of ethics for bioethicists," American Journal of Bioethics 2005 September-October; 5(5): 33-41.

Sibbald, Bonnie. COPE guidelines on good publication practice: an author's view [editorial]. *Health and Social Care in the Community* 2000 November; 8(6): 355-361. NRCBL: 6; 1.3.7. Identifiers: Committee on Publication Ethics.

Slovak Association of Research Based Pharmaceutical Companies in Slovakia [SAFS]; Association of Producers of Generic Drugs [GENAS]; Association of Distributors of Drugs [ADL]. Ethical code of the pharmaceutical industry in Slovakia. *Medical Ethics and Bioethics / Medicinska Etika & Bioetika* 2004 Autumn-Winter; 11(3-4): 11-22. NRCBL: 6; 9.7; 1.3.2; 7.3. Note: Full text in English and Slovakian.

Spike, Jeffrey. A hearty critique of Baker's proposed code for bioethicists [comment]. *American Journal of Bioethics* 2005 September-October; 5(5): 54-55. NRCBL: 6; 2.1; 9.6. Comments: comment on Robert Baker, "A draft model aggregated code of ethics for bioethicists," American Journal of Bioethics 2005 September-October; 5(5): 33-41.

Thomas, James C. Skills for the ethical practice of public health. *Journal of Public Health Management and Practice* 2005 May-June; 11(3): 260-261. NRCBL: 6; 9.1.

Verpeet, Ellen; Dierckx de Casterle, Bernadette; Van der Arend, Arie; Gastmans, Chris A.E. Nurses' views on ethical codes: a focus group study. *Journal of Advanced Nursing* 2005 July; 51(2): 188-195. NRCBL: 6; 7.1. SC: em. Identifiers: Belgium.

Winslow, Gerald R. Christian theology and the Hippocratic Oath. *Update [Loma Linda University Center for Christian Bioethics]* 1998 March; 14(1): 6 p. NRCBL: 6; 1.2.

COMMISSIONS ON BIOETHICS *See* BIOETHICS AND MEDICAL ETHICS/ COMMISSIONS

CONFIDENTIALITY
See also AIDS/ CONFIDENTIALITY

Abadee, Alister. The medical duty of confidentiality and prospective duty of disclosure: can they co-exist? *Journal of Law and Medicine* 1995 August; 3(1): 75-91. NRCBL: 8.4; 8.2; 9.5.6; 17.2. SC: le.

American College of Occupational and Environmental Medicine [ACOEM]. ACOEM position on the confidentiality of medical information in the workplace. *Journal of*

Occupational and Environmental Medicine 1995 May; 37(5): 594-596. NRCBL: 8.4; 6. SC: le.

American Hospital Association [AHA]; National Association of Police Organizations [NAPO]. Guidelines for releasing patient information to law enforcement. Chicago,IL: American Hospital Association 2005 July; 8p. [Online]. Available: http://www.aha.org/aha/key_issues/ hipaa/content/guidelines.pdf [6 March 2006]. NRCBL: 8.4; 1.3.5; 6.

Annas, George J. Family privacy and death — Antigone, war, and medical research. *New England Journal of Medicine* 2005 February 3; 352(5): 501- 505. NRCBL: 8.4; 15.1; 1.13.12.

Armstrong, David; Kline-Rogers, Eva; Jani, Sandeep M.; Goldman, Edward B.; Fang, Jianming; Mukherjee, Debabrata; Nallamothu, Brahmajee K.; Eagle, Kim A. Potential impact of the HIPAA privacy rule on data collection in a registry of patients with acute coronary syndrome. *Archives of Internal Medicine* 2005 May 23; 165(10): 1125-1129. NRCBL: 8.4; 18.2; 18.3. SC: em. Identifiers: Health Insurance Portability and Accountability Act.
Abstract: BACKGROUND: Implementation of the Health Insurance Portability and Accountability Act (HIPAA) Privacy Rule has the potential to affect data collection in outcomes research. METHODS: To examine the extent to which data collection may be affected by the HIPAA Privacy Rule, we used a quasi-experimental pretest-posttest study design to assess participation rates with informed consent in 2 cohorts of patients eligible for the University of Michigan Acute Coronary Syndrome registry. The pre-HIPAA period included telephone interviews conducted at 6 months that sought verbal informed consent from patients. In the post-HIPAA period, informed consent forms were mailed to ask for permission to call to conduct a telephone interview. The primary outcome measure was the percentage of patients who provided consent. Incremental costs associated with the post-HIPAA period were also assessed. RESULTS: The pre-HIPAA period included 1221 consecutive patients with acute coronary syndrome, and the post-HIPAA period included 967 patients. Consent for follow-up declined from 96.4% in the pre-HIPAA period to 34.0% in the post-HIPAA period (P01). In general, patients who returned written consent forms during the post-HIPAA period were older, were more likely to be married, and had lower mortality rates at 6 months. Incremental costs for complying with the HIPAA Privacy Rule were $8704.50 for the first year and $4558.50 annually thereafter. CONCLUSIONS: The HIPAA Privacy Rule significantly decreases the number of patients available for outcomes research and introduces selection bias in data collection for patient registries.

Artnak, Kathryn E.; Benson, Margaret. Evaluating HIPAA compliance: a guide for researchers, privacy boards, and IRBs. *Nursing Outlook* 2005 March-April; 53(2): 79-87. NRCBL: 8.4; 18.2; 1.3.12. Identifiers: Health Insurance Portability and Accountability Act of 1996; institutional review boards.

Aspen Health and Compliance Center; Aspen Reference Group; Aspen Communications and Data Group. Patient record documentation and confidentiality. *Phar-*

macy Practice Management Quarterly 1999 April; 19(1): 57-62. NRCBL: 8.4; 9.7; 8.1.

Baird, Keith A.; Rupert, Patricia A. Clinical management of confidentiality: a survey of psychologists in seven states. *Professional Psychology: Research and Practice* 1987 August; 18(4): 347-352. NRCBL: 8.4; 17.2.

Bastable, Ruth; Sheather, Julian. Mandatory reporting to the police of all sexually active under-13s [editorial]. *BMJ: British Medical Journal* 2005 October 22; 331(7522): 918- 919. NRCBL: 8.4; 11.2; 9.5.7. SC: le.

Beardwood, John P.; Kerr, J. Alexis. Coming soon to a health sector near you: an advance look at the new Ontario Personal Health Information Protection Act (PHIPA): Part II. *Healthcare Quarterly* 2005; 8(1): 76-83. NRCBL: 8.4. SC: le. Identifiers: Canada.

Beck, Philip. The confidentiality of psychiatric records and the patient's right to privacy. *Canadian Journal of Psychiatry-Revue Canadiene de Psychiatrie* 2001 April; 46(3, Insert): 6. NRCBL: 8.4; 1.1; 17.1.

Berg, Jessica. Grave secrets: legal and ethical analysis of postmortem confidentiality. *Connecticut Law Review* 2001 Fall; 34(1): 81-122. NRCBL: 8.4; 8.1; 17.2. SC: le.

Brandt, Mary. Confidentiality today: where do you stand? *Journal of AHIMA* 1993 December; 64(12): 59-63. NRCBL: 8.4; 1.3.12. SC: le.

Brannigan, Vincent M. Protecting the privacy of patient information in clinical networks: regulatory effectiveness analysis. *Annals of the New York Academy of Sciences* 1992 December 17; 670: 190-201. NRCBL: 8.4; 1.3.12. SC: le.

Brownrigg, Alissa. Mother still knows best: cancer-related gene mutations, familial privacy, and a physician's duty to warn. *Fordham Urban Law Journal* 1999 January; 26(2): 247-279. NRCBL: 8.4; 15.3. SC: le. Identifiers: BRCA mutation.

Calvo, Cheye. Insurance information privacy. *Legisbrief* 2001 March; 9(13): 1-2. NRCBL: 8.4; 9.3.1. SC: le. Note: National Conference of State Legislatures.

Carlisle, John R. Mandatory reporting of gunshot wounds to police . . . not as simple as it seems. *Health Law in Canada* 2004 September; 25(1): 1-10. NRCBL: 8.4; 8.1. SC: le.

Carter, Meredith. Integrated electronic health records and patient privacy: possible benefits but real dangers. *Medical Journal of Australia* 2000 January 3; 172(1): 28-30. NRCBL: 8.4; 1.3.12; 1.1; 9.1.

Claerhout, B.; DeMoor, G.J.E. Privacy protection for clinical and genomic data. The use of privacy-enhancing techniques in medicine. *International Journal of Medical Informatics* 2005 March; 74(2-4): 257-265. NRCBL: 8.4; 1.3.12; 15.1.

Clark, Peter. Confidentiality and the physician-patient relationship — ethical reflections from a surgical waiting room. *Medical Science Monitor* 2002 November; 8(11): SR31-SR34. NRCBL: 8.4; 8.1.

Clayton, Ellen Wright. What should the law say about disclosure of genetic information to relatives? *Journal of Health Care Law and Policy* 1998; 1(2): 373-390. NRCBL: 8.4; 15.1. SC: le.

Clayton, Paul D. Confidentiality and medical information. *Annals of Emergency Medicine* 2001 September; 38(3): 312-316. NRCBL: 8.4; 1.3.12; 8.3.1.

Coleman, Phyllis. Privilege and confidentiality in 12-step self-help programs: believing the promises could be hazardous to an addict's freedom. *Journal of Legal Medicine* 2005 December; 26(4): 435-474. NRCBL: 8.4; 9.5.9; 17.2; 8.3.1. SC: le.

Cross, Michael. UK patients can refuse to let their data be shared across networks [news]. *BMJ: British Medical Journal* 2005 May 28; 330(7502): 1226. NRCBL: 8.4; 1.3.12.

Davey, Monica. Planned Parenthood sues over records request in Indiana. *New York Times* 2005 March 17; p. A27. NRCBL: 8.4; 1.3.11. SC: po.

Davis, Kevin B. Privacy rights in personal information: HIPAA and the privacy gap between fundamental privacy rights and medical information. *John Marshall Journal of Computer and Information Law* 2001 Summer; 19(4): 535-555. NRCBL: 8.4. SC: le. Identifiers: Health Insurance Portability and Accountability Act of 1996.

Dawson, Ellen M. Confidentiality and computerized medical records. *NursingConnections* 1997 Spring; 10(1): 48-53. NRCBL: 8.4; 1.3.12; 5.3.

Dimond, Bridgit. Access to medical reports. *British Journal of Nursing* 2005 September 8-21; 14(16): 860- 861. NRCBL: 8.4; 1.3.12. SC: le. Identifiers: Access to Medical Reports Act 1988.

Dimond, Bridgit. Access to records by persons other than the patient. *British Journal of Nursing* 2005 August 11-September 7; 14(15): 829-830. NRCBL: 8.4; 1.3.12. SC: le.

Dimond, Bridgit. Data protection rights and preserving confidentiality. *British Journal of Nursing* 2005 September 22-October 12; 14(17): 936-937. NRCBL: 8.4; 1.3.12. SC: le.

Dimond, Bridgit. The law regarding health records of the deceased in the UK. *British Journal of Nursing* 2005 April 14-27; 14(7): 391-392. NRCBL: 8.4; 1.3.12; 20.1. SC: le. Identifiers: United Kingdom (Great Britain).

NRCBL: National Reference Center for Bioethics Literature Classification Scheme   See inside front cover for terms.

Dimond, Bridgit. Lawful disclosure of confidential information. *British Journal of Nursing* 2005 October 13-26; 14(18): 984- 985. NRCBL: 8.4. SC: le.

Dossey, Larry. Privacy. *Alternative Therapies in Health and Medicine* 2003 May-June; 9(3): 12-16, 112-121. NRCBL: 8.4; 1.1.

Drociuk, Daniel; Gibson, J.; Hodge, J., Jr. Health information privacy and syndromic surveillance systems. *MMWR: Morbidity and Mortality Weekly Report* 2004 September 24; 53(Supplement): 221-225. NRCBL: 8.4; 21.3. SC: em. Identifiers: Health Insurance Probability and Accountability Act.

Elger, Bernice S.; Harding, Timothy W. Avoidable breaches of confidentiality: a study among students of medicine and of law. *Medical Education* 2005 March; 39(3): 333-337. NRCBL: 8.4; 7.2. SC: em; le. Identifiers: Switzerland.

Erard, Robert E. Release of test data under the 2002 Ethics Code and the HIPAA Privacy Rule: a raw deal or just a half-baked idea? *Journal of Personality Assessment* 2004 February; 82(1): 23- 30. NRCBL: 8.4; 8.3.1; 17.1. Identifiers: Health Insurance Portability and Accountability Act.

Erickson, Jeanette Ives; Millar, Sally. Caring for patients while respecting their privacy: renewing our commitment. *Online Journal of Issues in Nursing [electronic]* 2005; 10(2); E1, 13 p. Available: http://www.nursingworld.org/ojin/ [15 June 2005]. NRCBL: 8.4; 8.1. SC: le. Identifiers: Health Insurance Portability and Accountability Act (HIPAA).

Fernández-Valdivia, A.; Ocón, P.; Osuna, E.; Luna, A. Placing medical information in the hands of the judiciary: medicolegal problems. *Medicine and Law: World Association for Medical Law* 1994; 13(3-4): 277-283. NRCBL: 8.4; 1.3.12. SC: le.

Ford, Carol; English, Abigail; Sigman, Garry. Confidential health care for adolescents: position paper of the Society for Adolescent Medicine. *Journal of Adolescent Health* 2004 August; 35(2): 160-167. NRCBL: 8.4; 9.5.7; 8.3.2.

Frampton, A. Reporting of gunshot wounds by doctors in emergency departments: a duty or a right? Some legal and ethical issues surrounding breaking patient confidentiality. *Emergency Medicine Journal* 2005 February; 22(2): 84-86. NRCBL: 8.4. Identifiers: United Kingdom (Great Britain).

Gellerman, David M.; Suddath, Robert. Violent fantasy, dangerousness, and the duty to warn and protect. *Journal of the American Academy of Psychiatry and the Law* 2005; 33(4): 484-495. NRCBL: 8.4; 1.3.8; 17.2. SC: le.

Gillam, Lynn; Little, J. Miles. Confidentiality. *Medical Journal of Australia* 2001 March 19; 174(6): 296-297. NRCBL: 8.4; 9.5.7; 8.1.

Ginsberg, Brian. Tarasoff at thirty: victim's knowledge shrinks the psychotherapist's duty to warn and protect. *Journal of Contemporary Health Law and Policy* 2004 Winter; 21(1): 1-35. NRCBL: 8.4; 17.2; 4.3. SC: le.

Gordon, Susan M. Privacy standards for health information: the misnomer of administrative simplification. *Delaware Law Review* 2002; 5(1): 23-56. NRCBL: 8.4. SC: le.

Gore, D.M. Ethical, professional, and legal obligations in clinical practice: a series of discussion topics for postgraduate medical education. Topic 4: confidentiality. *Postgraduate Medical Journal* 2001 July; 77(909): 443-444. NRCBL: 8.4.

Graber, Mark A.; Gjerde, Craig; Bergus, George; Ely, John. The use of unofficial "problem patient" files and interinstitutional information transfer in emergency medicine in Iowa. *American Journal of Emergency Medicine* 1995 September; 13(5): 509-511. NRCBL: 8.4; 9.5.9; 1.3.12. SC: em.

Graham-Rowe, Duncan. Privacy and prejudice: whose ID is it anyway? *New Scientist* 2005 September 17-23; 187(2517): 20-23. NRCBL: 8.4; 1.3.12.

Griener, Glenn. Electronic health records as a threat to privacy. *Health Law Review* 2005; 14(1): 14-17. NRCBL: 8.4; 1.3.12; 7.1; 9.1.

Gustafson, Kathryn E.; McNamara, J. Regis. Confidentiality with minor clients: issues and guidelines for therapists. *Professional Psychology: Research and Practice* 1987 October; 18(5): 503-508. NRCBL: 8.4.

Hagger, Lynn; Woods, Simon; Barrow, Paul. Autonomy and audit — striking the balance. *Medical Law International* 2004; 6(2): 105-116. NRCBL: 8.4; 9.6; 8.3.1. SC: le.

Hassol, Andrea; Walker, James M.; Kidder, David; Rokita, Kim; Young, David; Pierdon, Steven; Deitz, Deborah; Kuck, Sarah; Ortiz, Eduardo. Patient experiences and attitudes about access to a patient electronic health care record and linked web messaging. *Journal of the American Medical Informatics Association* 2004 November-December; 11(6): 505-513. NRCBL: 8.4; 1.3.12. SC: em.

Herdy, Wayne. Must the doctor tell? *Journal of Law and Medicine* 1996 February; 3(3): 270-282. NRCBL: 8.4; 8.1; 1.3.12. SC: le.

Higgins, Joan. Two sides of the fence. *Health Service Journal* 2004 October 7; 114(5926): 20-21. NRCBL: 8.4; 18.3. Identifiers: Patient Information Advisory Group; United Kingdom (Great Britain).

Hinshelwood, R.D. A psychoanalytic perspective on confidentiality: the divided mind in treatment. *In:* Koggel, Christine M.; Furlong, Allannah; Levin, Charles, eds. Confidential Relationships: Psychoanalytical, Ethical, and Legal Contexts. New York: Rodopi; 2003: 31-51. NRCBL: 8.4; 17.2.

Hodge, James G., Jr.; Gostin, Kieran G. Challenging themes in American health information privacy and the public's health: historical and modern assessments. *Journal of Law, Medicine and Ethics* 2004 Winter; 32(4): 670-679. NRCBL: 8.4; 8.3.1; 1.1. SC: le.

Inions, Noela J. Substitute decision-makers in privacy legislation that affects health information in Alberta. *Health Law Review* 2005; 14(1): 26-41. NRCBL: 8.4; 8.3.3; 8.3.2. SC: le.

Jenkins, G.; Merz, J.F.; Sankar, P. A qualitative study of women's views on medical confidentiality. *Journal of Medical Ethics* 2005 September; 31(9): 499-504. NRCBL: 8.4; 9.5.5. SC: em.

Abstract: CONTEXT: The need to reinvigorate medical confidentiality protections is recognised as an important objective in building patient trust necessary for successful health outcomes. Little is known about patient understanding and expectations from medical confidentiality. OBJECTIVE: To identify and describe patient views of medical confidentiality and to assess provisionally the range of these views. DESIGN: Qualitative study using indepth, open ended face-to-face interviews. SETTING: Southeastern Pennsylvania and southern New Jersey, USA. PARTICIPANTS: A total of 85 women interviewed at two clinical sites and three community/research centres. MAIN OUTCOME MEASURES: Subjects' understanding of medical confidentiality, beliefs about the handling of confidential information and concerns influencing disclosure of information to doctors. RESULTS: The subjects defined medical confidentiality as the expectation that something done or said would be kept "private" but differed on what information was confidential and the basis and methods for protecting information. Some considered all medical information as confidential and thought confidentiality protections functioned to limit its circulation to medical uses and reimbursement needs. Others defined only sensitive or potentially stigmatising information as confidential. Many of these also defined medical confidentiality as a strict limit prohibiting information release, although some noted that specific permission or urgent need could override this limit. CONCLUSIONS: Patients share a basic understanding of confidentiality as protection of information, but some might have expectations that are likely not met by current practice nor anticipated by doctors. Doctors should recognise that patients might have their own medical confidentiality models. They should address divergences from current practice and provide support to those who face emotional or practical obstacles to self-revelation.

Johnson, Martin. Notes on the tension between privacy and surveillance in nursing. *Online Journal of Issues in Nursing [electronic]* 2005; 10(2); E3, 13 p. Available: http://www.nursingworld.org/ojin/ [15 June 2005]. NRCBL: 8.4; 8.1.

Jurevic, Amy M. When technology and health care collide: issues with electronic medical records and electronic mail. *UMKC Law Review* 1998 Summer; 66(4): 809-836. NRCBL: 8.4; 1.3.12. SC: le.

Kane, Kanoelani M. Driving into the sunset: a proposal for mandatory reporting to the DMV by physicians treating unsafe elderly drivers. *University of Hawaii Law Review* 2002 Winter; 25(1): 59-83. NRCBL: 8.4; 9.5.2; 8.1; 1.3.5; 17.1. SC: le.

Kass, Nancy E.; Hull, Sara Chandros; Natowicz, Marvin R.; Faden, Ruth R.; Plantinga, Laura; Gostin, Lawrence O.; Slutsman, Julia. Medical privacy and the disclosure of personal medical information: the beliefs and experiences of those with genetic and other clinical conditions. *American Journal of Medical Genetics* 2004 July 30; 128A(3): 261-270. NRCBL: 8.4; 15.1; 9.3.1. SC: em.

Katner, David R. Confidentiality and juvenile mental health records in dependency proceedings. *William and Mary Bill of Rights Journal* 2004 February; 12(2): 511-576. NRCBL: 8.4; 9.5.7; 9.5.3. SC: le.

Klinck, Elsabé. Health databases: basic legal and ethical principles. *South African Medical Journal* 2001 August; 91(8): 642. NRCBL: 8.4; 1.3.12. SC: le.

Koggel, Christine M. Confidentiality in the liberal tradition: a relational critique. *In:* Koggel, Christine M.; Furlong, Allannah; Levin, Charles, eds. Confidential Relationships: Psychoanalytical, Ethical, and Legal Contexts. New York: Rodopi; 2003: 113-131. NRCBL: 8.4; 17.2.

Kosseim, Patricia. The landscape of rules governing access to personal information for health research: a view from afar. *Health Law Journal* 2003; 11: 199-215. NRCBL: 8.4; 1.3.12. SC: le.

Krulwich, Andrew S.; McDonald, Bruce L. Evolving constitutional privacy doctrines affecting healthcare enterprises. *Food and Drug Law Journal* 2000; 55(4): 491-516. NRCBL: 8.4; 1.3.12. SC: le.

Kryworuk, Peter W.; Nickle, Susan E. Mandatory physician reporting of drivers with medical conditions: legal considerations. *Canadian Journal of Cardiology* 2004 November; 20(13): 1324-1328. NRCBL: 8.4; 1.3.5. SC: le; em. Identifiers: Canada.

Liang, Angela. The argument against a physician's duty to warn for genetic diseases: the conflicts created by Safer v. Estate of Pack. *Journal of Health Care Law and Policy* 1998; 1(2): 437-453. NRCBL: 8.4; 15.1. SC: le.

Lo, Bernard; Dornbrand, Laurie; Dubler, Nancy N. HIPAA and patient care: the role for professional judgment. *JAMA: The Journal of the American Medical Association* 2005 April 13; 293(14): 1766-1771. NRCBL: 8.4. SC: le.

Abstract: Federal health privacy regulations, commonly known as the Health Insurance Portability and Accountability Act (HIPAA) regulations, came into effect in April 2003. Many cli-

NRCBL: National Reference Center for Bioethics Literature Classification Scheme   See inside front cover for terms.

129

nicians and institutions have relied on consultants and risk managers to tell them how to implement these regulations. Much of the controversy and confusion over the HIPAA regulations concern so-called incidental disclosures. Some interpretations of the privacy regulations would limit essential communication and compromise good patient care. This article analyzes misconceptions regarding what the regulations say about incidental disclosures and discusses the reasons for such misunderstandings. Many misconceptions arise from gaps in the regulations. These gaps are appropriately filled by professional judgment informed by ethical guidelines. The communication should be necessary and effective for good patient care, and the risks of a breach of confidentiality should be proportional to the likely benefit for the patient's care. The alternative for communication should be impractical. We offer specific recommendations to help physicians think through what incidental disclosures in patient care are ethically permissible and what safeguards ought to be taken. Physicians should work with risk managers and practice administrators to develop policies that promote good communication in patient care, while taking appropriate steps to protect patient privacy.

Loughlin, Kevin R. Illness and secrecy on the Supreme Court [letter]. *New England Journal of Medicine* 2005 March 31; 352(13): 1387- 1388. NRCBL: 8.4; 8.2.

Loughrey, Joan. Public bodies and private medical records: the Health and Social Care (Community Health and Standards) Act 2003. *Medical Law International* 2004; 6(4): 317-337. NRCBL: 8.4; 1.3.12. SC: le. Identifiers: United Kingdom (Great Britain).

Louw, André. Doctors advised not to disclose illnesses on sick certificates without patients' signed consent [letter]. *South African Medical Journal* 2002 November; 92(11): 840. NRCBL: 8.4; 16.3.

Lynch, Patrick M. Protection of confidentiality and privacy in family studies. *Progress in Clinical and Biological Research* 1983; 115: 181- 198. NRCBL: 8.4; 15.1. SC: le.

Maccoon, Kathryn. To what extent should a colleague be unnecessarily exposed to risks for the sake of protecting patient privacy: an ethical dilemma. *Health Law in Canada* 2005 November; 26(2): 13-16. NRCBL: 8.4; 8.1; 7.3. SC: le.

Magnusson, Roger S. The changing legal and conceptual shape of health care privacy. *Journal of Law, Medicine and Ethics* 2004 Winter; 32(4): 680- 691. NRCBL: 8.4; 1.3.12; 15.1; 21.1. SC: le.

Malcolm, Helen A. Does privacy matter? Former patients discuss their perceptions of privacy in shared hospital rooms. *Nursing Ethics* 2005 March; 12(2): 156-166. NRCBL: 8.4; 8.1. SC: em.

Abstract: As a relative concept, privacy is difficult to define in universal terms. In the New Zealand setting recent legislation aims to protect patients' privacy but anecdotal evidence suggests that these policies are not well understood by some providers and recipients of health care. This qualitative study set out to identify some of the issues by exploring former patients' perceptions of privacy in shared hospital rooms. The findings suggest a conditional acceptance of a loss of privacy in an environment dictated by architectural structure and by fiscal and time constraints. Participants indicated an awareness that personal information could be overheard and that their preference for a choice of setting for serious discussions was desirable. Some enjoyed the support offered in shared rooms, while, for others, overhearing another person's health issues caused unnecessary distress. The participants suggested that knowing they could be overheard constrained information disclosure. This withholding of information has implications for health professionals' ability to diagnose and treat patients appropriately.

Martin, J.; Guillod, O. The doctor's duty to maintain confidentiality ("medical secret") in Switzerland: what attitude should the practitioner adopt when authorities or outside people ask for information about a patient? *European Journal of Health Law* 2001 June; 8(2): 163-172. NRCBL: 8.4. SC: le.

McSherry, Bernadette. Ethical issues in HealthConnect's shared electronic health record system. *Journal of Law and Medicine* 2004 August; 12(1): 60-68. NRCBL: 8.4; 1.3.12. SC: an. Identifiers: Australia.

Miya, Pamela A.; Megel, Mary E. Confidentiality and electronic medical records. *Medsurg Nursing* 1997 August; 6(4): 222-224, 212. NRCBL: 8.4; 1.3.12.

Mize, Selene; Dawson, John; Peart, Nicola. Privacy and access to information. *In:* Dawson, John; Peart, Nicola, eds. The Law of Research: A Guide. Dunedin, NZ: University of Otago Press; 2003: 81-104. NRCBL: 8.4; 1.3.9. SC: le.

Mosher, Paul W. Psychotherapist-patient privilege: the history and significance of the United States Supreme Court's decision in the case of Jaffee v. Redmond. *In:* Koggel, Christine M.; Furlong, Allannah; Levin, Charles, eds. Confidential Relationships: Psychoanalytical, Ethical, and Legal Contexts. New York: Rodopi; 2003: 177-206. NRCBL: 8.4; 17.2. SC: le.

Moskop, John C.; Marco, Catherine A.; Larkin, Gregory Luke; Geiderman, Joel M.; Derse, Arthur R. From Hippocrates to HIPAA: privacy and confidentiality in emergency medicine — Part I: conceptual, moral, and legal foundations. *Annals of Emergency Medicine* 2005 January; 45(1): 53-59. NRCBL: 8.4; 9.5.1; 9.5.7. SC: le. Identifiers: Health Insurance Portability and Accountability Act of 1996.

Moskop, John C.; Marco, Catherine A.; Larkin, Gregory Luke; Geiderman, Joel M.; Derse, Arthur R. From Hippocrates to HIPAA: privacy and confidentiality in emergency medicine — Part II: challenges in the emergency department. *Annals of Emergency Medicine* 2005 January; 45(1): 60-67. NRCBL: 8.4; 9.5.1; 9.5.7; 1.3.12. Identifiers: Health Insurance Portability and Accountability Act of 1996.

Mulligan, Ea; Paterson, Moira. Patients rarely detect breaches of confidence. *Australian Health Review* 2003;

26(3): 73-78. NRCBL: 8.4. SC: le; em. Identifiers: Australia.

Neufeld, Renata. The realities of implementing health information legislation: the Manitoba experience, 1997-2004. *Health Law Review* 2005; 14(1): 47-50. NRCBL: 8.4. SC: le.

Nowell, David; Spruill, Jean. If it's not absolutely confidential, will information be disclosed? *Professional Psychology: Research and Practice* 1993 August; 24(3): 367-369. NRCBL: 8.4; 17.1; 6.

Okifuji, Akiko. Opinion #1. Confidentiality: a delicate balance [case study]. *Pain Medicine* 2002 June; 3(2): 169. NRCBL: 8.4. SC: cs.

Paasche-Orlow, Michael K.; Jacob, Dan M.; Powell, Joshua N. Notices of privacy practices: a survey of the Health Insurance Portability and Accountability Act of 1996 documents presented to patients at US hospitals. *Medical Care* 2005 June; 43(6): 558-564. NRCBL: 8.4; 21.7; 1.3.12. SC: em.

Paterson, Moira. HealthConnect and privacy: a policy conundrum. *Journal of Law and Medicine* 2004 August; 12(1): 80-90. NRCBL: 8.4; 8.2; 1.3.12. Identifiers: Australia.

Pérez-Cárceles, M.D.; Pereñiguez, J.E.; Osuan, E.; Luna, A. Balancing confidentiality and the information provided to families of patients in primary care. *Journal of Medical Ethics* 2005 September; 31(9): 531-535. NRCBL: 8.4. SC: em; rv.
Abstract: BACKGROUND: Medical confidentiality underpins the doctor- patient relationship and ensures privacy so that intimate information can be exchanged to improve, preserve, and protect the health of the patient. The right to information applies to the patient alone, and, only if expressly desired, can it be extended to family members. However, it must be remembered that one of the primary tenets of family medicine is precisely that patient care occurs ideally within the context of the family. There may be, then, certain occasions when difficulties will arise as to the extent of the information provided to family members. OBJECTIVES: This study aimed to describe family doctors' attitudes to confidentiality and providing patient information to relatives as well as their justifications for sharing information. METHOD: A descriptive postal questionnaire was self-administered by family doctors. RESULTS: Of 227 doctors, 95.1% provided information to a patient's family and over a third (35%) disclosed information to others without prior patient consent. CONCLUSIONS: The findings reveal that family doctors should pay more attention to their patients' rights to information, privacy, and confidentiality, and reflect very carefully on the fine balance between this and the occasional need for the support and collaboration of family members in delivery of care. Emphasis should be placed on ethics and legal problems during undergraduate education and in-service training of doctors.

Reisman, Anna B. Indiscretions. *Hastings Center Report* 2005 September-October; 35(5): 8-9. NRCBL: 8.4. Identifiers: medical records and privacy.

Renke, Wayne. The constitutionality of mandatory reporting of gunshot wounds legislation. *Health Law Review* 2005; 14(1): 3-8. NRCBL: 8.4; 9.1. SC: le.

Ries, Nola M.; Moysa, Geoff. Legal protections of electronic health records: issues of consent and security. *Health Law Review* 2005; 14(1): 18-25. NRCBL: 8.4; 1.3.12; 8.3.1; 9.1. SC: le.

Rose, Mat. A practitioner's response to the Final Report of the Select Special Health Information Act Review Committee. *Health Law Review* 2005; 14(1): 12-13. NRCBL: 8.4; 9.1; 1.3.5. SC: le.

Rothstein, Mark A. Research privacy under HIPAA and the common rule. *Journal of Law, Medicine and Ethics* 2005 Spring; 33(1): 154- 159. NRCBL: 8.4; 18.1. SC: le. Identifiers: Health Insurance Portability and Accountability Act.

Ruschioni, Sherry L. Confidentiality of mental health records in federal courts: the path blazed by Sabree v. United Brotherhood of Carpenters and Joinders of America, Local No. 33. *New England Law Review* 2004 Summer; 38(4): 923-937. NRCBL: 8.4; 17.1. SC: le.

Ryan, Christopher James; Furlong, Mark; Leggatt, Margaret. Comment on reconciling the patient's right to confidentiality and the family's need to know [letter and reply]. *Australian and New Zealand Journal of Psychiatry* 1997 June; 31(3): 429-431. NRCBL: 8.4; 8.3.3; 17.1.

Saltzman, Carl; Beach, Thomas E.; Whitman, Andrew K. Managing obligations: right of privacy and release of clinical records. *Journal of Healthcare Risk Management* 2003 Summer; 23(3): 27-32. NRCBL: 8.4; 1.3.12. SC: le.

Savulescu, Julian; Skene, Loane. Who has the right to access medical information from a deceased person? Ethical and legal perspectives. *Journal of Law and Medicine* 2000 August; 8(1): 81-88. NRCBL: 8.4; 1.1; 1.3.12. SC: le. Identifiers: Australia.

Schatz, Gerald S. Health records privacy and confidentiality: pending questions. *Journal of Contemporary Health Law and Policy* 2002 Fall; 18(3): 685-691. NRCBL: 8.4; 1.3.12. SC: le.

Schouten, Ronald. The psychotherapist-patient privilege. *Harvard Review of Psychiatry* 1998 May-June; 6(1): 44-48. NRCBL: 8.4; 17.2. SC: le.

Sharpe, Virginia A. Privacy and security for electronic health records [opinion]. *Hastings Center Report* 2005 November-December; 35(6): inside back cover. NRCBL: 8.4; 1.3.12. SC: le.

Silver, Stephen Aaron. Beyond Jaffee v. Redmond: should the federal courts recognize a right to physician-patient confidentiality? *Ohio State Law Journal* 1998; 58(5): 1809-1866. NRCBL: 8.4; 17.2. SC: le. Note: 116 S. Ct. 1923 (1996).

NRCBL: National Reference Center for Bioethics Literature Classification Scheme   See inside front cover for terms.

131

Simpson, Christopher S.; Hoffmaster, Barry; Mitchell, L. Brent; Klein, George J. Mandatory physician reporting of drivers with cardiac disease: ethical and practical considerations. *Canadian Journal of Cardiology* 2004 November; 20(13): 1329-1334. NRCBL: 8.4; 1.3.5. Identifiers: Canada.

Slabbert, Melodie Nöthling. Parental access to minors' health records in the South African health care context: concerns and recommendations. *Medicine and Law: World Association for Medical Law* 2005 December; 24(4): 743-759. NRCBL: 8.4; 8.3.2. SC: le.

Abstract: Privacy and confidentiality have long been recognised as essential elements of the doctor-patient relationship. Patients should feel free to disclose the most intimate and private medical facts about themselves to their physicians in order to facilitate optimal patient care. Medical records, whether hand-written or electronic, also play an important role in other contexts, such as medical research, health care management and financial audit. In South Africa there is little consistency in approaches to patient confidentiality. There are also no national standards or policies on patient confidentiality, apart from specific ethical rules, some ad hoc statutory provisions and general constitutional provisions not directly related to the intricacies of the doctor-patient relationship. A closer look at the relevant statutory provisions reveal the existence of conflicting standards, most notably in respect of parental access to a minors' health records. The purpose of this paper is to examine the discrepancies and contradictory provisions relating to the access to and disclosure of health information, in particular parental access to health records of minors. In the final instance, some recommendations will be suggested.

Slutsman, Julia; Kass, Nancy; McGready, John; Wynia, Matthew. Health information, the HIPAA privacy rule, and health care: what do physicians think? *Health Affairs* 2005 May-June; 24(3): 832-842. NRCBL: 8.4. SC: em. Identifiers: Health Insurance Portability and Accountability Act.

Steward, Melissa. Electronic medical records: privacy, confidentiality, liability. *Journal of Legal Medicine* 2005 December; 26(4): 491-506. NRCBL: 8.4; 1.3.12; 8.5. SC: le.

Tatelbaum, Mark F. Practice resource: checklist of federal and state privacy issues. *Journal of Health Law* 2002 Spring; 35(2): 283-290. NRCBL: 8.4. SC: le.

Tilton, Susan Hanley. Right to privacy and confidentiality of medical records. *Occupational Medicine* 1996 January-March; 11(1): 17-29. NRCBL: 8.4. SC: le. Identifiers: Uniform Health-Care Information Act; Americans with Disabilities Act; Occupational Safety and Health Act; workers compensation.

Tovino, Stacey A. Currents in contemporary ethics: the confidentiality and privacy implications of functional magnetic resonance imaging. *Journal of Law, Medicine and Ethics* 2005 Winter; 33(4): 844- 850. NRCBL: 8.4; 17.1.

Tovino, Stacey A. The use and disclosure of protected health information for research under the HIPAA privacy rule: unrealized patient autonomy and burdensome government regulation. *South Dakota Law Review* 2004; 49(3): 447-502. NRCBL: 8.4; 1.3.12; 1.1; 18.5.1; 18.3. SC: le. Identifiers: Health Insurance Portability and Accountability Act of 1996.

Turkoski, Beatrice B. When patients won't share the prognosis with family. *Home Healthcare Nurse* 2004 August; 22(8): 566-568. NRCBL: 8.4; 8.2; 20.3.1. SC: cs.

Valerio, Carlos J. The legal situation concerning notification of sexual partners of HIV/AIDS patients in Costa Rica: problems in contact tracing. *Medicine and Law: World Association for Medical Law* 2004; 23(4): 925-936. NRCBL: 8.4; 9.5.6; 8.2. SC: le.

Abstract: Among solutions to the problems of HIV/AIDS, a public health preventive measure has been proposed to notify the sexual partners of patients, this being a justifiable exception to professional secrecy. Every such measure must conform to a legal framework in order to facilitate the task of the health care worker, to respect the patient's right to privacy and to protect life as a juridical value. The General Law governing HIV/AIDS and its Costa Rican regulations propose a procedure to notify sexual partners. This study analyses how the procedure is developing in Costa Rica as well as its legal justificaitons.

Walfish, Steven; Sharp, Sean P. Readability level of HIPAA notices of privacy practices used by physical rehabilitation centers. *Journal of Clinical Ethics* 2005 Summer; 16(2): 156-159. NRCBL: 8.4; 8.3.1. SC: em. Identifiers: Health Insurance Portability and Accountability Act.

Weisbaum, Karen M.; Slaughter, Pamela M.; Collins, Paulette K. A voluntary privacy standard for health services and policy research: legal, ethical and social policy issues in the Canadian context. *Health Law Review* 2005; 14(1): 42-46. NRCBL: 8.4; 18.3; 18.2; 18.6. SC: le.

Wientjes, Linda. An ethical dilemma: who should know and who should tell. *Pediatric Nursing* 1998 May-June; 24(3): 249-250. NRCBL: 8.4; 4.1.3; 8.1.

Will, Janet C. A dilemma within the family: commentary on who should know and who should tell [opinion]. *Pediatric Nursing* 1998 May-June; 24(3): 251-253. NRCBL: 8.4; 4.1.3. SC: cs.

Willison, Donald J. Trends in collection, use and disclosure of personal information in contemporary health research: challenges for research governance. *Health Law Review* 2005; 13(2-3): 107-113. NRCBL: 8.4; 1.3.12; 18.2.

Wills, Nathan J. A tripartite threat to medical records privacy: technology, HIPAA's privacy rule and the USA Patriot Act. *Journal of Law and Health* 2002-2003; 17(2): 271-296. NRCBL: 8.4; 1.3.12. SC: le. Identifiers: United States; Health Insurance Portability and Accountability Act of 1996.

SC (Subject Caption):   an=analytical   cs=case studies   em=empirical   le=legal   po=popular   rv=review

Woogara, Jay. Patients' privacy of the person and human rights. *Nursing Ethics* 2005 May; 12(3): 273-287. NRCBL: 8.4; 1.1; 21.1. SC: em.

Abstract: The UK Government published various circulars to indicate the importance of respecting the privacy and dignity of NHS patients following the implementation of the Human Rights Act, 1998. This research used an ethnographic method to determine the extent to which health professionals had in fact upheld the philosophy of these documents. Fieldwork using nonparticipant observation, and unstructured and semistructured interviews with patients and staff, took place over six months in three acute care wards in a large district NHS trust hospital. Applying the principles of phenomenology and grounded theory, the data were analysed and the contents organized into 11 key categories, leading to the formulation of a privacy model. The level of intrusion into patients' privacy by health professionals was measured against the benchmarking of the 'dignity and privacy' factors contained in the Department of Health's The essence of care document and Article 8(2) of the Human Rights Act. The findings established that patients had little privacy in the wards, and that the terms 'privacy of the person' and 'dignity' are interrelated.

Woogara, Jay. Patients' rights to privacy and dignity in the NHS. *Nursing Standard* 2005 January 12-18; 19(18): 33-37. NRCBL: 8.4. SC: em. Identifiers: United Kingdom (Great Britain); National Health Service.

Yeo, Michael; Brook, Andrew. The moral framework of confidentiality and the electronic panopticon. *In:* Koggel, Christine M.; Furlong, Allannah; Levin, Charles, eds. Confidential Relationships: Psychoanalytical, Ethical, and Legal Contexts. New York: Rodopi; 2003: 85-112. NRCBL: 8.4; 17.2.

Young, Chari J. Telemedicine: patient privacy rights of electronic medical records. *UMKC Law Review* 1998 Summer; 66(4): 921-937. NRCBL: 8.4; 1.3.12. SC: le.

Zonana, Howard. Physicians should not be agents of the police [opinion]. *Psychiatric Services* 2005 August; 56(8): 1021. NRCBL: 8.4; 17.1; 4.3; 17.7; 1.3.5.

CONTRACEPTION

See also POPULATION POLICY; STERILIZATION

Emergency contraception moves behind the counter [editorial]. *CMAJ/JAMC: Canadian Medical Association Journal* 2005 March 29; 172(7): 845. NRCBL: 11.1; 9.5.5; 9.7. Identifiers: Canada.

Emergency contraception: prudes and prejudice [editorial]. *Lancet* 2005 July 2-8; 366(9479): 2. NRCBL: 11.1; 9.7; 1.2; 9.2.

Appelbaum, Judith C.; Davis, Virginia S. Insurance coverage of contraceptives: narrowing the gender gap in health care coverage. *In:* Barnes, Andrea, ed. The Handbook of Women, Psychology, and the Law. San Francisco: Jossey-Bass; 2005: 178-191. NRCBL: 11.1; 9.3.1. SC: le.

Arons, Jessica R. Misconceived laws: the irrationality of parental involvement requirements for contraception. *William and Mary Law Review* 2000 March; 41(3): 1093-1131. NRCBL: 11.2; 8.3.2. SC: le.

Backmeyer, E. Renee. Lack of insurance coverage for prescription contraception by an otherwise comprehensive plan as a violation of Title VII as amended by the Pregnancy Discrimination Act — stretching the statute too far. *Indiana Law Review* 2004; 37(2): 437-466. NRCBL: 11.1; 9.3.1; 9.7; 9.5.5. SC: le.

Birenbaum, Anna. Shielding the masses: how litigation changed the face of birth control. *Southern California Review of Law and Women's Studies* 2001 Spring; 10(2): 411-449. NRCBL: 11.1; 9.7. SC: le. Identifiers: Norplant; Dalkon Shield.

Bornstein, Stephanie. The undue burden: parental notification requirements for publicly funded contraception. *Berkeley Women's Law Journal* 2000; 15: 40-75. NRCBL: 11.2; 8.3.2; 1.3.5; 10. SC: le.

Brindis, Claire D.; English, Abigail. Measuring public costs associated with loss of confidentiality for adolescents seeking confidential reproductive health care:how high the costs? How heavy the burden? [editorial]. *Archives of Pediatrics and Adolescent Medicine* 2004 December; 158(12): 1182-1184. NRCBL: 11.2; 8.3.2; 8.4; 9.3.1. SC: le. Identifiers: Texas.

Burstein, Paul D.; Greene, Michael F.; Drazen, Jeffrey M.; Wood, Alastair J.J. A sad day for science at the FDA [letter and reply]. *New England Journal of Medicine* 2005 December 15; 353(24): 2619-2621. NRCBL: 11.1; 9.7. Identifiers: Food and Drug Administration.

Calis, Karim Anton; Pucino, Frank, Jr.; Restrepo, Maria L.; Cantor, Julie; Baum, Ken. Pharmacists and emergency contraception [letter and reply]. *New England Journal of Medicine* 2005 March 3; 352(9): 942-944. NRCBL: 11.1; 9.7.

Cooper, Michael; Santora, Marc. Bill allows sales of pill over counter: broader distribution of after-sex pill. *New York Times* 2005 June 23; p. B1, B8. NRCBL: 11.1; 9.7; 12.1. SC: po. Identifiers: New York.

Couzin, Jennifer. Plan B: a collision of science and politics [news]. *Science* 2005 October 7; 310(5745): 38-39. NRCBL: 11.1; 1.3.5. Identifiers: emergency contraception; Food and Drug Administration.

Davey, Monica; Belluck, Pam. Pharmacies balk on after-sex pill and widen fight; right of refusal cited; many states take up the issue, citing religious and moral concerns. *New York Times* 2005 April 19; p. A1, A16. NRCBL: 11.1; 12.1; 9.7; 4.1.1. SC: po.

Dixon, Heather S. Pelvic exam prerequisite to hormonal contraceptives: unjustified infringement on constitutional

NRCBL: National Reference Center for Bioethics Literature Classification Scheme   See inside front cover for terms.

133

rights, governmental coercion, and bad public policy. *Harvard Women's Law Journal* 2004 Spring; 27: 177-233. NRCBL: 11.1; 8.3.4; 9.5.5. SC: le.

Eggertson, Laura; Sibbald, Barbara. Privacy issues raised over Plan B: women asked for names, addresses, sexual history [news]. *CMAJ/JAMC: Canadian Medical Association Journal* 2005 December 6; 173(12): 1435-1436. NRCBL: 11.1; 8.4; 9.7. Identifiers: Canada.

Eisenberg, Marla E.; Swain, Carolyne; Bearinger, Linda H.; Sieving, Renee E.; Resnick, Michael D. Parental notification laws for minors' access to contraception: what do parents say? *Archives of Pediatrics and Adolescent Medicine* 2005 February; 159(2): 120-125. NRCBL: 11.2; 8.3.2. SC: em; le.

Fenton, Elizabeth; Lomasky, Loren. Dispensing with liberty: conscientious refusal and the "morning-after pill". *Journal of Medicine and Philosophy* 2005 December; 30(6): 579- 592. NRCBL: 11.1; 9.7; 1.1; 4.1.1. SC: an.
Abstract: Citing grounds of conscience, pharmacists are increasingly refusing to fill prescriptions for emergency contraception, or the "morning-after pill." Whether correctly or not, these pharmacists believe that emergency contraception either constitutes the destruction of post-conception human life, or poses a significant risk of such destruction. We argue that the liberty of conscientious refusal grounds a strong moral claim, one that cannot be defeated solely by consideration of the interests of those seeking medication. We examine, and find lacking, five arguments for requiring pharmacists to fill prescriptions. However, we argue that in their professional context, pharmacists benefit from liberty restrictions on those seeking medication. What would otherwise amount to very strong claims can be defeated if they rest on some prior restriction of the liberty of others. We conclude that the issue of what policy should require pharmacists to do must be settled by way of a theory of second best. Asking "What is second best?" rather than "What is best?" offers a way to navigate the liberty restrictions that may be fixed obstacles to optimality.

Fernández, José V.; Greene, Michael F.; Drazen, Jeffrey M.; Wood, Alastair J.J. A sad day for science at the FDA [letter and reply]. *New England Journal of Medicine* 2005 December 15; 353(24): 2619-2621. NRCBL: 11.1; 9.7. Identifiers: Food and Drug Administration.

Field, Heather M. Increasing access to emergency contraceptive pills through state law enabled dependent pharmacist prescribers. *UCLA Women's Law Journal* 2000 Fall-Winter; 11(1): 141-253. NRCBL: 11.1; 9.7; 9.5.5; 9.2. SC: le.

Franzini, Luisa; Marks, Elena; Cromwell, Polly F.; Risser, Jan; McGill, Laurie; Markham, Christine; Selwyn, Beatrice; Shapiro, Carrie. Projected economic costs due to health consequences of teenagers' loss of confidentiality in obtaining reproductive health care services in Texas. *Archives of Pediatrics and Adolescent Medicine* 2004 December; 158(12): 1140-1146. NRCBL: 11.2; 8.4; 9.3.1; 9.5.7. SC: le.

Grant, Ellen C. A sad day for science at the FDA [letter and reply]. *New England Journal of Medicine* 2005 December 15; 353(24): 2619-2621. NRCBL: 11.1; 9.7. Identifiers: Food and Drug Administration.

Hamel, Ron. Rape and emergency contraception: a reply to Rev. Kevin McMahon. *Ethics and Medics* 2003 June; 28(6): 1-2. NRCBL: 11.1; 9.5.5; 9.7; 10; 12.1; 1.2.

Hamel, Ron; Panicola, Michael R. Low risks and moral certitude: response to Msgr. Mulligan. *Ethics and Medics* 2003 December; 28(12): 2-4. NRCBL: 11.1; 9.5.5; 9.7; 10; 12.1; 1.2.

Jones, Rachel K.; Boonstra, Heather. Confidential reproductive health services for minors: the potential impact of mandated parental involvement for contraception. *Perspectives on Sexual and Reproductive Health* 2004 September-October; 36(5): 182-191. NRCBL: 11.2; 8.3.2; 9.5.7; 8.4. SC: le.

Jones, Rachel K.; Purcell, Alison; Singh, Susheela; Finer, Lawrence B. Adolescents' reports of parental knowledge of adolescents' use of sexual health services and their reactions to mandated parental notification for prescription contraception. *JAMA: The Journal of the American Medical Association* 2005 January 19; 293(3): 340-348. NRCBL: 11.2; 8.4; 8.3.2. SC: em.
Abstract: CONTEXT: Legislation has been proposed that would mandate parental notification for adolescents younger than 18 years (minors) obtaining prescription contraception from federally funded family planning clinics. OBJECTIVE: To determine the extent to which parents are currently aware that their teenage daughters are accessing reproductive health services and how minors would react in the face of mandated parental involvement laws for prescription birth control. DESIGN, SETTING, AND PARTICIPANTS: A total of 1526 female adolescents younger than 18 years seeking reproductive health services at a national sample of 79 family planning clinics were surveyed between May 2003 and February 2004. MAIN OUTCOME MEASURES: Proportions of minor females who reported that a parent or guardian was aware that they were at the family planning clinic and, under conditions of mandated parental involvement, proportions of minors who would access prescription contraceptives at family planning clinics or engage in unsafe sex. RESULTS: Sixty percent of minors reported that a parent or guardian knew they were accessing sexual health services at the clinic. Fifty-nine percent of all adolescents would use the clinic for prescription contraception even if parental notification were mandated. This response was less common (29.5%) among adolescents whose parents were unaware of their clinic visits and more common (79%) among those whose parents were aware. Many adolescents gave more than 1 response to mandated parental involvement. Forty-six percent would use an over-the- counter method, and 18% would go to a private physician. Seven percent said that they would stop having sex as one response, but only 1% indicated this would be their only reaction. One in 5 adolescents would use no contraception or rely on withdrawal as one response to mandated notification. CONCLUSIONS: Most minor adolescent females seeking family planning services report that their parents are aware of their use of services. Most would continue to use clinic services if parental notification were mandated. However, mandated parental notification laws would likely increase risky or unsafe sexual behavior and, in turn, the

incidence of adolescent pregnancy and sexually transmitted diseases.

Korland, Lee. Sex discrimination or a hard pill for employers to swallow: examining the denial of contraceptive benefits in the wake of Erickson v. Bartell Drug Co. *Case Western Reserve Law Review* 2002; 53(2): 531-567. NRCBL: 11.1; 9.2; 9.5.5; 9.3.1; 10. SC: le.

Lidge, Ernest F., III. An employer's exclusion of coverage for contraceptive drugs is not per se sex discrimination. *Temple Law Review* 2003 Fall; 76(3): 533-577. NRCBL: 11.1; 9.2; 10; 16.3; 9.5.5; 9.3.1. SC: le.

Limoges, Roger J. Prescriptions denied: pharmacy refusal clauses have become the latest battleground in the provision of safe and legal medical services. *Conscience* 2005 Autumn; 26(3): 36-38. NRCBL: 11.1; 1.2; 8.1; 9.7.

Loomis, C. Keanin. A battle over birth "control": legal and legislative employer prescription contraception benefit mandates. *William and Mary Bill of Rights Journal* 2002 December; 11(1): 463-494. NRCBL: 11.1; 9.3.1; 9.7; 9.2; 9.5.5. SC: le.

Mallia, Pierre; Williams, Anne. The use of emergency hormonal contraception in cases of rape—revisiting the Catholic position. *Human Reproduction and Genetic Ethics: An International Journal* 2005; 11(2): 35-42. NRCBL: 11.1; 1.2; 9.5.5; 1.1.

Manasse, Henri R., Jr.; Cantor, Julie; Baum, Ken. Pharmacists and emergency contraception [letter and reply]. *New England Journal of Medicine* 2005 March 3; 352(9): 943-944. NRCBL: 11.1; 9.7.

Marston, Cicely; Meltzer, Howard; Majeed, Azeem. Impact on contraceptive practice of making emergency hormonal contraception available over the counter in Great Britain: repeated cross sectional surveys. *BMJ: British Medical Journal* 2005 July 30; 331(7511): 271-273. NRCBL: 11.1; 9.7. SC: em.
Abstract: OBJECTIVE: To examine the impact on contraceptive practice of making emergency hormonal contraception available over the counter. DESIGN: Analysis of data on contraceptive practice for women aged 16-49 years in the period 2000-2 from the Omnibus Survey, a multipurpose survey in which around 7600 adults living in private households are interviewed each year. SETTING: Private households in Great Britain. MAIN OUTCOME MEASURES: Use of different types of contraception and rates of unprotected sex. RESULTS: After emergency hormonal contraception was made available over the counter, levels of use of different types of contraception by women aged 16-49 remained similar. No significant change occurred in the proportion of women using emergency hormonal contraception (8.4% in 2000, 7.9% in 2001, 7.2% in 2002) or having unprotected sex. A change did, however, occur in where women obtained emergency hormonal contraception; a smaller proportion of women obtained emergency hormonal contraception from physicians and a greater proportion bought it over the counter. No significant change occurred in the proportion of women using more reliable methods of contraception, such as the oral contraceptive pill, or in the proportion of women using emergency hormonal contraception more than once during a

year. CONCLUSIONS: Making emergency hormonal contraception available over the counter does not seem to have led to an increase in its use, to an increase in unprotected sex, or to a decrease in the use of more reliable methods of contraception.

McMahon, Kevin T. Why fear ovulation testing? A response to Ron Hamel. *Ethics and Medics* 2003 June; 28(6): 3-4. NRCBL: 11.1; 9.5.5; 9.7; 10; 12.1; 1.2.

McNulty, Patrick J.; Stanwood, Francis M.; Gallas, Sherrie M.; Zavodny, Madeline. Parental consent for minors to receive contraceptives [letter and reply]. *American Journal of Public Health* 2005 February; 95(2): 191-192. NRCBL: 11.2; 8.3.2; 9.5.7. SC: em; le. Identifiers: Illinois.

Mulligan, James J. Peace of conscience for rape victims: ovulation testing and emergency contraception. *Ethics and Medics* 2003 December; 28(12): 1-2. NRCBL: 11.1; 9.5.5; 9.7; 10; 12.1; 1.2.

Nunn, Amy; Miller, Kate; Alpert, Hilary; Ellertson, Charlotte. Contraceptive emergency: Catholic hospitals overwhelmingly refuse to provide EC. *Conscience* 2003 Summer; 24(2): 38-41. NRCBL: 11.1; 1.2; 9.1; 9.7. SC: em; le. Identifiers: emergency contraception.

Polis, Chelsea; Schaffer, Kate; Harrison, Teresa. Accessibility of emergency contraception in California's Catholic hospitals. *Women's Health Issues* 2005 July-August; 15(4): 174-178. NRCBL: 11.1; 9.7; 9.1; 1.2; 9.2.
Abstract: BACKGROUND: Access to emergency contraception (EC) is an important option for women wanting to prevent an unintended pregnancy. In California, emergency rooms (ERs) are required to provide survivors of sexual assault with information about and access to EC. This study assessed the likelihood that a woman calling a Catholic hospital in California to inquire about EC could access the medication. METHODS: During September 2003, we contacted an ER staff member in each of California's Catholic hospitals (n = 45) using a mystery caller approach. Following a written script, trained female researchers asked ER staff whether they dispense EC at their facility and under what circumstances. If respondents initially stated that their facility would not dispense EC, the caller asked whether EC was available to women who had been raped. If staff confirmed that their facility would not provide EC under any circumstances including rape, callers requested a referral to another facility that would provide the medication. RESULTS: Sixty-six percent of staff contacted stated that their hospital would not provide EC under any circumstances, including rape. Of those that would not dispense EC, fewer than half of respondents (48%) provided a referral. Of the 14 referrals given, only about one third (n = 5) led to a facility that provides EC. CONCLUSIONS: Our findings suggest that access to EC in California's Catholic hospitals is minimal, even for victims of sexual assault. As many as two-thirds of these hospitals may be violating state legislation requiring hospitals to provide EC to sexual assault survivors upon request.

Priaulx, Nicolette. Joy to the world! A (healthy) child is born! Reconceptualizing 'harm' in wrongful conception. *Social and Legal Studies* 2004; 13(1): 5-26. NRCBL: 11.4; 15.2; 14.1; 1.1. SC: le. Identifiers: McFarlane v. Tayside Health Board; Rees v. Darlington Memorial Hospital.

NRCBL: National Reference Center for Bioethics Literature Classification Scheme   See inside front cover for terms.

135

Priaulx, Nicolette M. Conceptualising harm in the case of the 'unwanted' child. *European Journal of Health Law* 2002 December; 9(4): 337-359. NRCBL: 11.4; 4.4. SC: le.

Ratcliff, Kathryn Strother. Contraception and abortion. *In her:* Women and Health: Power, Technology, Inequality, and Conflict in a Gendered World. Boston, MA: Allyn and Bacon; 2002: 191-209. NRCBL: 11.1; 12.1; 15.5; 9.5.5.

Ratcliff, Kathryn Strother. Technology-assisted contraception. *In her:* Women and Health: Power, Technology, Inequality, and Conflict in a Gendered World. Boston, MA: Allyn and Bacon; 2002: 228-244. NRCBL: 11.1; 9.5.5; 9.5.4; 1.3.7.

Rosenberg, Kenneth D.; DeMunter, Jodi K.; Liu, Jihong. Emergency contraception in emergency departments in Oregon, 2003. *American Journal of Public Health* 2005 August; 95(8): 1453- 1457. NRCBL: 11.1; 9.7. SC: em.
Abstract: OBJECTIVES: We sought to learn about access to emergency contraception (EC) in Oregon emergency departments, both for women who are rape patients and for women who have had consensual unprotected sexual intercourse ("nonrape patients"). METHODS: We interviewed emergency department staff in 54 of Oregon's 57 licensed emergency departments in February-March 2003 (response rate = 94.7%). RESULTS: Only 61.1% of Oregon emergency departments routinely offered EC to rape patients. Catholic hospitals were as likely as non-Catholic hospitals to routinely offer EC to rape patients. The hospitals most likely to routinely offer EC to rape patients had a written protocol for the care of rape patients that included offering EC (P = .02) and access to staff with specialized sexual assault training (P=.002). For nonrape patients, 46.3% of emergency departments discouraged the prescribing of EC. Catholic hospitals were significantly less likely than non-Catholic hospitals to provide access to EC for nonrape patients (P=.05). CONCLUSIONS: Oregon emergency departments do not routinely offer EC to women who have been raped or to women who have had consensual unprotected sexual intercourse.

Shuchman, Miriam. Stalled US plan for Plan B [news]. *CMAJ/JAMC: Canadian Medical Association Journal* 2005 December 6; 173(12): 1437. NRCBL: 11.1; 9.7; 5.3; 1.3.5. Identifiers: emergency contraception.

Sibbald, Barbara. Nonprescription status for emergency contraception [news]. *CMAJ/JAMC: Canadian Medical Association Journal* 2005 March 29; 172(7): 861-862. NRCBL: 11.1; 9.5.5; 9.7. Identifiers: Canada.

Soon, Judith A.; Levine, Marc; Osmond, Brenda L.; Ensom, Mary H.H.; Fielding, David W. Effects of making emergency contraception available without a physician's prescription: a population-based study. *CMAJ/JAMC: Canadian Medical Association Journal* 2005 March 29; 172(7): 878-883. NRCBL: 11.1; 9.5.5; 9.7. SC: em.

Tanne, Janice Hopkins. American Medical Association fights pharmacists who won't dispense contraceptives [news]. *BMJ: British Medical Journal* 2005 July 2; 331(7507): 11. NRCBL: 11.1; 9.7; 8.1; 1.2.

Tanne, Janice Hopkins. Emergency contraception is under attack by US pharmacists [news]. *BMJ: British Medical Journal* 2005 April 30; 330(7498): 983. NRCBL: 11.1; 9.7; 8.1.

Tanne, Janice Hopkins. FDA ducks decision on emergency contraceptive [news]. *BMJ: British Medical Journal* 2005 September 17; 331(7517): 596. NRCBL: 11.1; 9.7; 12.1; 21.1. Identifiers: Food and Drug Administration.

Tanne, Janice Hopkins. FDA official resigns over emergency contraception decision [news]. *BMJ: British Medical Journal* 2005 September 10; 331(7516): 532. NRCBL: 11.1; 9.7; 5.3; 11.2; 1.3.5. Identifiers: Susan Wood; Food and Drug Administration.

United States. Government Accountability Office [GAO]. Food and Drug Administration: Decision Process to Deny Initial Application for Over-the-Counter Marketing of the Emergency Contraceptive Drug Plan B Was Unusual. Washington, DC: GAO, 2005 November; 57 p. NRCBL: 11.1; 9.7; 9.5.5; 1.3.5.

Uttley, Lois. An inconceivable argument: does a law ensuring equal access to prescription drugs mean that the Catholic hierarchy will become morally complicit in "immoral acts"? *Conscience* 2005 Summer; 26(2): 39-40. NRCBL: 11.1; 1.2; 9.3.1; 9.7. SC: le.

Waxman, Judy; Laser, Rachel; Cantor, Julie; Baum, Ken. Pharmacists and emergency contraception [letter and reply]. *New England Journal of Medicine* 2005 March 3; 352(9): 942-944. NRCBL: 11.1; 9.7.

Williams, Anne. A response to: the use of emergency hormonal contraception in cases of rape — revisiting the Catholic position. *Human Reproduction and Genetic Ethics: An International Journal* 2005; 11(2): 40-42. NRCBL: 11.1; 1.2; 9.5.5; 1.1.

Wood, Alastair J.J.; Drazen, Jeffrey M.; Greene, Michael F. A sad day for science at the FDA [opinion]. *New England Journal of Medicine* 2005 September 22; 353(12): 1197-1199. NRCBL: 11.1; 9.7; 5.3; 11.2; 21.1. Identifiers: Food and Drug Administration.

Wood, Susan F. Women's health and the FDA [opinion]. *New England Journal of Medicine* 2005 October 20; 353(16): 1650-1651. NRCBL: 11.1; 9.7; 18.5.3; 9.5.5. Identifiers: Food and Drug Administration.

Zwillich, Todd. US pharmacies vow to withhold emergency contraception. *Lancet* 2005 May 14-20; 365(9472): 1677-1678. NRCBL: 11.1; 9.5.5; 9.2; 9.7.

COST OF HEALTH CARE *See* HEALTH CARE ECONOMICS

CRYOBANKING OF SPERM, OVA, OR EMBRYOS

In vitro embryos and DNA profiling: far from clear legal reform / Los embriones in vitro y los perfiles de ADN: reformas legales con tonos en gris [editorial]. *Revista de Derecho y Genoma Humano / Law and the Human Genome Review* 2003 July-December; (19): 15-27. NRCBL: 14.6; 18.5.4; 19.5; 15.1; 1.3.5. SC: le. Note: Article in English and Spanish; English p. 15-20; Spanish p. 21-27.

No use of stored embryos without consent [news]. *Bulletin of Medical Ethics* 2003 September; (191): 5-6. NRCBL: 14.6; 8.3.1; 14.4. SC: le. Identifiers: United Kingdom (Great Britain).

Alghrani, Amel. Deciding the fate of frozen embryos: Natalie Evans v. Amicus Healthcare Ltd and Others. *Medical Law Review* 2005 Summer; 13(2): 244-256. NRCBL: 14.6; 9.5.5; 4.4; 8.3.4. SC: le.

Althaus, Catherine. Can one "rescue" a human embryo? — the moral object of the acting woman. *National Catholic Bioethics Quarterly* 2005 Spring; 5(1): 113- 141. NRCBL: 14.6; 14.4; 10; 1.2.

Bahadur, G. Ethics of testicular stem cell medicine [opinion]. *Human Reproduction* 2004 December; 19(12): 2702-2710. NRCBL: 14.6; 19.5; 8.3.2; 18.5.7; 4.4. SC: le.

Batzer, Frances R.; Hurwitz, Joshua M.; Caplan, Arthur. Postmortem parenthood and the need for a protocol with posthumous sperm procurement. *Fertility and Sterility* 2003 June; 79(6): 1263-1269. NRCBL: 14.6; 20.1.

Baylis, Françoise; Beagan, Brenda; Johnston, Josephine; Ram, Natalie. Cryopreserved human embryos in Canada and their availability for research. *JOGC: Journal of Obstetrics and Gynaecology Canada* 2003 December; 25(12): 1026-1031. NRCBL: 14.6; 18.5.4. SC: em. Note: Abstract in English and French.

Belluck, Pam. From stem cell opponents, an embryo crusade. *New York Times* 2005 June 2; p. A1, A22. NRCBL: 14.6; 14.1; 1.2. SC: po.

Coleman, Carl H. Procreative liberty and contemporaneous choice: an inalienable rights approach to frozen embryo disputes. *Minnesota Law Review* 1999 November; 84(1): 55-127. NRCBL: 14.6; 14.4; 4.4; 14.1; 1.1. SC: le.

Corvalán, Andrea. Fatherhood after death: a legal and ethical analysis of posthumous reproduction. *Albany Law Journal of Science and Technology* 1997; 7(2): 335-365. NRCBL: 14.6; 14.2; 14.1; 14.4. SC: le.

Crockin, Susan L. Legal issues related to parenthood after cancer. *Journal of the National Cancer Institute Monographs* 2005; (34): 111-113. NRCBL: 14.6; 20.1; 8.3.1; 14.1; 4.1.2; 9.5.1. SC: le.

Daniels, Ken R.; Lewis, Gillian M.; Curson, Ruth. Information sharing in semen donation: the views of donors. *Social Science and Medicine* 1997 March; 44(5): 673-680. NRCBL: 14.6; 19.5; 8.4; 14.2; 14.4; 1.3.12. SC: em.

de Lacey, Sheryl. Parent identity and 'virtual' children: why patients discard rather than donate unused embryos. *Human Reproduction* 2005 June; 20(6): 1661-1669. NRCBL: 14.6; 4.4; 8.2. SC: em.

de Wachter, Maurice A.M. Ethical aspects of cryobiology: responsible applications in biomedicine and in clinical practice. *Cryobiology* 2004 April; 48(2): 205-213. NRCBL: 14.6. SC: rv.

Dostal, J.; Utrata, R.; Loyka, S.; Brezinova, J.; Svobodova, M.; Shenfield, F. Post-mortem sperm retrieval in new European Union countries: case report. *Human Reproduction* 2005 August; 20(8): 2359-2361. NRCBL: 14.6; 19.5; 8.3.1; 21.1. SC: le; cs.

Elliott, Michael K. Tales of parenthood from the crypt: the predicament of the posthumously conceived child. *Real Property, Probate and Trust Journal* 2004 Spring; 39(1): 47-69. NRCBL: 14.6; 14.1; 4.4; 14.2; 14.4. SC: le.

Gottenger, E.E.; Nagler, Harris M. The quagmire of postmortem sperm acquisition. *Journal of Andrology* 1999 July-August; 20(4): 458-462. NRCBL: 14.6; 14.4; 14.1.

Harmon, Amy. Hello, I'm your sister. Our father is donor 150. *New York Times* 2005 November 20; p. A1, A34. NRCBL: 14.6; 19.5; 8.4. SC: po.

Haslett, Tracy. J.B. v. M.B.: the enforcement of disposition contracts and the competing interests of the right to procreate and the right not to procreate where donors of genetic material dispute the disposition of unused preembryos. *Temple Environmental Law and Technology Journal* 2002 Spring; 20(2): 195-217. NRCBL: 14.6; 14.1; 4.4; 14.4. SC: le.

Hervey, Tamara K. Buy baby: the European Union and regulation of human reproduction. *Oxford Journal of Legal Studies* 1998 Summer; 18(2): 207-233. NRCBL: 14.6; 19.5; 8.3.3; 21.1; 5.3. SC: le.

Hoffman, Sharona; Morriss, Andrew P. Birth after death: perpetuities and the new reproductive technologies. *Georgia Law Review* 2004 Winter; 38(2): 575-631. NRCBL: 14.6; 14.5; 14.1. SC: le.

Hurwitz, Joshua M.; Batzer, Frances R. Posthumous sperm procurement: demand and concerns [editorial]. *Obstetrical and Gynecological Survey* 2004 December; 59(12): 806-808. NRCBL: 14.6; 14.2; 20.1; 8.3.3; 19.5.

Kerekes, Robert J. My child . . . but not my heir: technology, the law, and post-mortem conception. *Real Property, Probate and Trust Journal* 1996 Summer; 31(2): 213-249. NRCBL: 14.6; 14.1; 14.2; 14.4. SC: le.

NRCBL: National Reference Center for Bioethics Literature Classification Scheme   See inside front cover for terms.

137

Kindregan, Charles P., Jr.; McBrien, Maureen. Embryo donation: unresolved legal issues in the transfer of surplus cryopreserved embryos. *Villanova Law Review* 2004; 49(1): 169-206. NRCBL: 14.6; 4.4; 19.5; 14.1. SC: le.

King, Milandria. Cold shoulder treatment: the disposition of frozen embryos post-divorce. *Thurgood Marshall Law Review* 1999 Fall-2000 Spring; 25(1-2): 99-137. NRCBL: 14.6; 4.4. SC: le.

Kol, Shahar; Itskovitz-Eldor, Joseph. Society's contribution to assisted reproductive technology abuse [letter]. *Human Reproduction* 2005 August; 20(8): 2362. NRCBL: 14.6; 19.5; 8.3.1. SC: le; cs.

Land, Spencer; Ross, Lawrence S. Posthumous reproduction: current and future status. *Urologic Clinics of North America* 2002 November; 29(4): 863-871. NRCBL: 14.6; 14.4; 19.5. SC: le.

Lin, Olivia. Rehabilitating bioethics: recontextualizing in vitro fertilization outside contractual autonomy. *Duke Law Journal* 2004 November; 54(2): 485-511. NRCBL: 14.6; 14.4; 2.1. SC: le.

Manning, Paula J. Baby needs a new set of rules: using adoption doctrine to regulate embryo donation. *Georgetown Journal of Gender and the Law* 2004 Spring; 5(2): 677-721. NRCBL: 14.6; 8.4; 15.1. SC: le.

New Jersey. Superior Court. Appellate Division. *J.B. v. M.B.* [Date of Decision: 1 June 2000]. *Atlantic Reporter*, 2d Series, 2000; 751: 613-620. NRCBL: 14.6; 14.4. SC: le.
   Abstract: Court Decision: 751 *Atlantic Reporter*, 2d Series 613; 2000 Jun 1 (date of decision). The Superior Court of New Jersey held that a contract made between a now divorced couple and their in vitro fertilization (IVF) provider is not enforceable because it constitutes a contract to procreate, and thus it is contrary to state public policy and is unenforceable. After giving birth to a healthy child via IVF, which resulted in extra embryos being cryopreserved, J.B. and M.B. divorced. An agreement with their IVF provider specified that control over the frozen embryos was to be relinquished to the provider if the couple divorced, unless specified by a court order. M.B., the former husband, alleged that he and J.B. had agreed to donate the unused embryos to infertile couples. J.B., the former wife, wished to have the embryos destroyed. The court found that enforcing the alleged contract to donate the embryos would impair the former wife's constitutional right to not procreate. Furthermore, M.B.'s right to procreate would not be impaired if the contract were not enforced because M.B. was not infertile and was capable of having children with another person. The Superior Court affirmed the trial court's judgment in favor of the former wife and ordered the destruction of the frozen embryos. [KIE/INW]

New Jersey. Supreme Court. *J.B. v. M.B.* [Date of Decision: 2001 August 14]. *West's Atlantic Reporter*, 2d Series, 2001; 783: 707-720. NRCBL: 14.6; 14.4. SC: le.
   Abstract: Court Decision: 783 *Atlantic Reporter*, 2d Series 707; 2001 Aug 14 (date of decision). The New Jersey Supreme Court held that a couple's agreement, regarding the fate of their frozen preembryos, and made at the beginning of IVF treatment, is enforceable and subject to either party's right to change his or her mind. Furthermore, the court held that a former wife's desire to destroy preembryos created with her former husband prevails

over his desire to donate or use the preembryos. After suffering fertility problems, plaintiff J.B. and defendant M.B. underwent in vitro fertilization (IVF) procedures during their marriage. The procedures resulted in twelve preembryos, four of which were implanted in J.B., and eight of which were cryopreserved. Shortly after giving birth to their only child, the couple divorced. M.B. sought to donate the preembryos to other couples; J.B. sought to have the preembryos destroyed. The New Jersey Supreme Court held that, ordinarily, the party wishing to avoid procreation should prevail. Because the defendant is capable of fathering additional children, the court affirmed J.B.'s right to prevent procreation and ordered the preembryos destroyed. [KIE/INW]

Nolan, Laurence C. Posthumous conception: a private or public matter? *Brigham Young University Journal of Public Law* 1997; 11(1): 1-32. NRCBL: 14.6; 14.1; 14.2; 14.4; 1.1. SC: le.

Pachman, Tracey S. Disputes over frozen preembryos and the "right not to be a parent". *Columbia Journal of Gender and Law* 2003; 12(1): 128-153. NRCBL: 14.6; 10. SC: le.

Patrizio, Pasquale; Butts, Samantha; Caplan, Arthur. Ovarian tissue preservation and future fertility: emerging technologies and ethical considerations. *Journal of the National Cancer Institute Monographs* 2005; (34): 107-110. NRCBL: 14.6; 9.5.1.

Redman, Paul C., II; Redman, Lauren Fielder. Seeking a better solution for the disposition of frozen embryos: is embryo adoption the answer? *Tulsa Law Journal* 2000 Spring-Summer; 35(3-4): 583-598. NRCBL: 14.6. SC: le.

Regalado, Antonio. Stem-cell rift shows difficulty obtaining eggs. *Wall Street Journal* 2005 November 14; p. B1, B3. NRCBL: 14.6; 14.5; 18.5.4. SC: po.

Robertson, John A. Cancer and fertility: ethical and legal challenges. *Journal of the National Cancer Institute Monograph* 2005; (34): 104-106. NRCBL: 14.6; 9.5.1.

Scully-Hill, Anne. Consent, frozen embryos, procreative choice and the ideal family. *Cambridge Law Journal* 2004 March; 63(1): 47-49. NRCBL: 14.6; 14.4; 8.3.1; 4.4; 8.3.5; 14.1. SC: le. Identifiers: Human Fertilisation and Embryology Act [HFEA]; Evans v. Amicus Healthcare Ltd. and Johnston; Hadley v. Midland Fertility Services and Hadley.

VanCannon, Kayla. Fathering a child from the grave: what are the inheritance rights of children born through new technology after the death of a parent? *Drake Law Review* 2004 Winter; 52(2): 331-362. NRCBL: 14.6; 14.2; 14.4; 14.1; 4.4. SC: le.

Waldman, Ellen. The parent trap: uncovering the myth of "coerced parenthood" in frozen embryo disputes. *American University Law Review* 2004 June; 53(5): 1021-1062. NRCBL: 14.6; 14.2. SC: le.

CULTURAL PLURALISM

Laying the foundations for a transcultural biotechnology law / Las bases para un derecho de la biotecnologia transcultural [editorial]. *Revista de Derecho y Genoma Humano / Law and the Human Genome Review* 2004 January-June; (20): 15-22. NRCBL: 21.7; 4.4; 14.5. SC: le. Note: Article in English and Spanish; English p. 15-18; Spanish p. 19-22.

Berlinger, N.; Wu, A.W. Subtracting insult from injury: addressing cultural expectations in the disclosure of medical error. *Journal of Medical Ethics* 2005 February; 31(2): 106-108. NRCBL: 21.7; 9.8; 7.1; 8.5. SC: le.

Bowman, Kerry. What are the limits of bioethics in a culturally pluralistic society? *Journal of Law, Medicine and Ethics* 2004 Winter; 32(4): 664-669. NRCBL: 21.7; 2.1.

Congress, Elaine P. Cultural and ethical issues in working with culturally diverse patients and their families: the use of the culturagram to promote cultural competent practice in health care settings. *Social Work in Health Care* 2004; 39(3-4): 249-262. NRCBL: 21.7; 8.1; 1.3.10.

Döring, Ole. Was bedeutet "ethische Verständigung zwischen Kulturen"? Ein philosophischer Problemzugang am Beispiel der Auseinandersetzung mit der Forschung an menschlichen Embryonen in China. *In:* Baumann, Eva; Brink, Alexander; May, Arnd T.; Schröder, Peter; Schutzeichel, Corinna Iris, eds. Weltanschauliche Offenheit in der Bioethik. Berlin: Duncker & Humblot; 2004: 179-211. NRCBL: 21.7; 1.1; 2.1; 18.5.4.

Gordon, Elysa. Multiculturalism in medical decisionmaking: the notion of informed waiver. *Fordham Urban Law Journal* 1995-1996; 23(4): 1321-1362. NRCBL: 21.7; 8.3.1; 1.1; 2.1. SC: le.

Halliday, Samantha. A comparative approach to the regulation of human embryonic stem cell research in Europe. *Medical Law Review* 2004 Spring; 12(1): 40-69. NRCBL: 21.7; 18.5.4; 15.1; 19.5; 5.3; 18.6. SC: le.

Hunt, Linda M.; de Voogd, Katherine B. Clinical myths of the cultural "other": implications for Latino patient care. *Academic Medicine* 2005 October; 80(10): 918-924. NRCBL: 21.7; 15.3; 9.5.4; 7.2. SC: em.

Ip, Mary; Gilligan, Timothy; Koenig, Barbara; Raffin, Thomas A. Ethical decision-making in critical care in Hong Kong. *Critical Care Medicine* 1998 March; 26(3): 447-451. NRCBL: 21.7; 9.1; 2.1; 20.5.1; 9.4.

Irvine, Rob; McPhee, John; Kerridge, Ian H. The challenge of cultural and ethical pluralism to medical practice. *Medical Journal of Australia* 2002 February 18; 176(4): 174-175. NRCBL: 21.7; 7.1; 9.1; 9.8; 8.1.

Kalekin-Fishman, Devorah. The impact of globalization on the determination and management of ethical choices in the health arena. *Social Science and Medicine* 1996 September; 43(5): 809-822. NRCBL: 21.7; 21.1; 9.1; 2.1.

Malina, Debra. Compliance, caricature, and culturally aware care [opinion]. *New England Journal of Medicine* 2005 September 29; 353(13): 1317-1318. NRCBL: 21.7; 8.1; 9.5.4; 7.1.

Park, Elyse R.; Betancourt, Joseph R.; Kim, Minah K.; Maina, Angela W.; Blumenthal, David; Weissman, Joel S. Mixed messages: residents' experiences learning cross-cultural care. *Academic Medicine* 2005 September; 80(9): 874-880. NRCBL: 21.7; 8.1; 7.2. SC: em.

Roetz, Heiner. Muss der kulturelle Pluralismus einen substantiellen ethischen Konsens verhindern? Zur Bioethik im Zeitalter der Globalisierung. *In:* Baumann, Eva; Brink, Alexander; May, Arnd T.; Schröder, Peter; Schutzeichel, Corinna Iris, eds. Weltanschauliche Offenheit in der Bioethik. Berlin: Duncker & Humblot; 2004: 213-231. NRCBL: 21.7; 2.1.

Sakamoto, Hyakudai. Globalization of bioethics as an intercultural social tuning technology. *Journal International de Bioethique / International Journal of Bioethics* 2005 March-June; 16(1-2): 17-27, 189-190. NRCBL: 21.7; 2.1; 21.1; 16.1. Note: Abstract in English and French.

DEATH AND DYING/ ATTITUDES TO DEATH
See also ADVANCE DIRECTIVES; ASSISTED SUICIDE; EUTHANASIA AND ALLOWING TO DIE

Burdette, Amy M.; Hill, Terrence D.; Moulton, Benjamin E. Religion and attitudes toward physician-assisted suicide and terminal palliative care. *Journal for the Scientific Study of Religion* 2005 March; 44(1): 79-93. NRCBL: 20.3.1; 20.5.1; 20.7; 1.2. SC: em.

Coyle, Nessa; Sculco, Lois. Expressed desire for hastened death in seven patients living with advanced cancer: a phenomenologic inquiry. *Oncology Nursing Forum* 2004 July 13; 31(4): 699-709. NRCBL: 20.3.1; 20.5.1; 7.2. SC: em.

Davies, Dawn E.; Kreicbergs, Ulrika; Valdimarsdóttir, Unnur; Steineck, Gunnar. Talking about death with dying children [letter and reply]. *New England Journal of Medicine* 2005 January 6; 352(1): 91-92. NRCBL: 20.3.3; 20.4.2.

DeRenzo, Evan G.; Schwartz, Jack; Selinger, Stephen. Talking about dying: ethical obligations and Maryland state law. *Maryland Medicine* 2004 Summer; 5(3): 39-41. NRCBL: 20.3.1; 20.4.1; 8.2; 8.1. SC: le.

Flynn, Tom. Life: medicine, morals, and markets. Right . . . or commodity? *Free Inquiry* 2005 August-September; 25(5): 31-32. NRCBL: 20.3.1; 20.5.1.

NRCBL: National Reference Center for Bioethics Literature Classification Scheme   See inside front cover for terms.

139

Garel, M.; Seguret, S.; Kaminski, M.; Cuttini, M. Ethical decision-making for extremely preterm deliveries: results of a qualitative survey among obstetricians and midwives. *Journal of Maternal-Fetal and Neonatal Medicine* 2004 June; 15(6): 394-399. NRCBL: 20.3.2; 20.5.2; 20.4.2. SC: em. Identifiers: Europe.

Girbes, Armand R.J. Dying at the end of your life [editorial]. *Intensive Care Medicine* 2004 December; 30(12): 2143-2144. NRCBL: 20.3.2; 20.5.1. SC: em.

Haddad, Amy. End-of-life decisions: the family's role. *RN* 2004 January; 67(1): 25-26, 28. NRCBL: 20.3.3; 20.4.

Hsin-Chen Hsin, Dena; Macer, Darryl. Contrasting expectations of biotechnology for medical care in Taiwan between seniors and medical students. *Revista de Derecho y Genoma Humano / Law and the Human Genome Review* 2004 January-June; (20): 195-216. NRCBL: 20.3.1. SC: em.

Iserson, Kenneth V. Teaching without harming the living: performing minimally invasive procedures on the newly dead. *Journal of Health Care Law and Policy* 2005; 8(2): 216-231. NRCBL: 20.3.1; 7.2; 8.3.3; 20.2.1.

Kaldjian, Lauris C.; Wu, Barry J.; Kirkpatrick, James N.; Thomas-Geevarghese, Asha; Vaughan-Sarrazin, Mary. Medical house officers' attitudes toward vigorous analgesia, terminal sedation, and physician-assisted suicide. *American Journal of Hospice and Palliative Medicine* 2004 September-October; 21(5): 381-387. NRCBL: 20.3.2; 7.2; 20.5.1; 20.7; 1.2. SC: em.

Kegley, J. A new framework for facilitating decisions on death and dying. *Medicine and Law: World Association for Medical Law* 2005 June; 24(2): 403-410. NRCBL: 20.3.1; 4.4; 20.4.1; 1.1.
Abstract: The troubling public, moral and legal issues surrounding questions of death and dying need a new focus on the virtues of compassion and respectfulness, on a better understanding of a person as someone who has deep emotional, spiritual, and social aspects and needs, and whose body is more than "physical machine," but is "lived body" which gives persons the capacity to act in the world and to feel and suffer deeply. Western medicine needs to re- humanize death; physicians need to see themselves as "assisting" persons in dealing with health, life and death in the context of being able to assert their values and beliefs and to realize their goals. Western medicine's concepts of 'benefit' and 'harm,' are too narrow, as is their fight to 'preserve life' at all costs. Finally, the present approach to death and dying, except for the Hospice movement, neglects the patient's emotional, psychological, social, and existential suffering.

Klinkenberg, Marianne; Willems, Dick L.; Onwuteaka-Philipsen, Bregje D.; Deeg, Dorly J.H.; van der Wal, Gerrit. Preferences in end-of-life care of older persons: after-death interviews with proxy respondents. *Social Science and Medicine* 2004 December; 59(12): 2467-2477. NRCBL: 20.3.1; 20.4.1; 20.5.4. SC: em. Identifiers: Netherlands.

Lyon, Maureen E.; McCabe, Mary Ann; Patel, Kantilal M.; D'Angelo, Lawrence J. What do adolescents want? An exploratory study regarding end-of-life decision-making. *Journal of Adolescent Health* 2004 December; 35(6): 529.e1- 529.e6 [Online]. Available: http://jahonline.org/issues [22 July 2005]. NRCBL: 20.3.1; 20.4.2; 8.1. SC: em.

Müller-Busch, H.C.; Oduncu, F.S.; Woskanjan, S.; Klaschik, E. Attitudes on euthanasia, physician-assisted suicide and terminal sedation — a survey of the members of the German Association for Palliative Medicine. *Medicine, Health Care and Philosophy: A European Journal* 2004; 7(3): 333-339. NRCBL: 20.3.2; 20.5.1; 20.7; 20.4.1. SC: em. Identifiers: Germany.
Abstract: BACKGROUND: Due to recent legislation on euthanasia and its current practice in the Netherlands and Belgium, issues of end-of- life medicine have become very vital in many European countries. In 2002, the Ethics Working Group of the German Association for Palliative Medicine (DGP) has conducted a survey among its physician members in order to evaluate their attitudes towards different end-of-life medical practices, such as euthanasia (EUT), physician-assisted suicide (PAS), and terminal sedation (TS). METHODS: An anonymous questionnaire was sent to the 411 DGP physicians, consisting of 14 multiple choice questions on positions that might be adopted in different hypothetical scenarios on situations of "intolerable suffering" in end-of-life care. For the sake of clarification, several definitions and legal judgements of different terms used in the German debate on premature termination of life were included. For statistical analysis t-tests and Pearson-correlations were used. RESULTS: The response rate was 61% (n = 251). The proportions of the respondents who were opposed to legalizing different forms of premature termination of life were: 90% opposed to EUT, 75% to PAS, 94% to PAS for psychiatric patients. Terminal sedation was accepted by 94% of the members. The main decisional bases drawn on for the answers were personal ethical values, professional experience with palliative care, knowledge of alternative approaches, knowledge of ethical guidelines and of the national legal frame. CONCLUSIONS: In sharp contrast to similar surveys conducted in other countries, only a minority of 9.6% of the DGP physicians supported the legalization of EUT. The misuse of medical knowledge for inhumane killing in the Nazi period did not play a relevant role for the respondents' negative attitude towards EUT. Palliative care needs to be stronger established and promoted within the German health care system in order to improve the quality of end-of-life situations which subsequently is expected to lead to decreasing requests for EUT by terminally ill patients.

Muraskas, Jonathan. A small life in detail [opinion]. *Journal of Perinatology* 2005 January; 25(1): 72-73. NRCBL: 20.3.1; 20.5.2.

Rose, Julia Hannum; O'Toole, Elizabeth E.; Dawson, Neal V.; Lawrence, Renee; Gurley, Diana; Thomas, Charles; Hamel, Mary Beth; Cohen, Harvey J. Perspectives, preferences, care practices, and outcomes among older and middle-aged patients with late-stage cancer. *Journal of Clinical Oncology* 2004 December 15; 22(24): 4907-4917. NRCBL: 20.3.1; 4.4; 9.5.2; 20.5.1. SC: em.

Rubinow, Alan. The physician and the dying patient: a question of control? [opinion]. *Israel Medical Association*

Journal 2005 January; 7(1): 3-4. NRCBL: 20.3.1; 20.3.2; 20.5.1.

Somerville, Margaret A. Towards taming the tiger: reflections on prothanasia: personal fulfillment and readiness to die [comment]. *Humane Health Care International* 1997 Summer; 13(2): 38-40. NRCBL: 20.3.1; 20.5.1.

Tanvetyanon, Tawee; Kreicbergs, Ulrika; Valdimarsdóttir, Unnur; Steineck, Gunnar. Talking about death with dying children [letter and reply]. *New England Journal of Medicine* 2005 January 6; 352(1): 91-92. NRCBL: 20.3.3; 20.4.2.

van der Heide, Agnes; Vrakking, Astrid; van Delden, Hans; Looman, Caspar; van der Maas, Paul. Medical and nonmedical determinants of decision making about potentially life-prolonging interventions. *Medical Decision Making* 2004 September-October; 24(5): 518-524. NRCBL: 20.3.2; 9.5.2. SC: em.

Vanitzian, Donie; Kopkin, Andrew H. 'In the name of the people' — a Faustian paradox: the betrayal by physicians, lawyers, judges, academics and ethicists of the sovereign people's ultimate civil liberty. *University of West Los Angeles Law Review* 1997; 28: 81-247. NRCBL: 20.3.1; 1.1; 20.5.1; 21.1; 21.4. SC: le.

Wenger, Neil S.; Carmel, Sara. Physicians' religiosity and end-of-life care attitudes and behaviors. *Mount Sinai Journal of Medicine* 2004 October; 71(5): 335-343. NRCBL: 20.3.2; 1.2; 20.4.1; 20.5.1. SC: em. Identifiers: Israel; Judaism.

Wiener, Richard L.; Eton, David; Gibbons, Vincent P.; Goldner, Jesse A.; Johnson, Sandra H. Research report: a preliminary analysis of medical futility decisionmaking: law and professional attitudes. *Behavioral Sciences and the Law* 1998 Autumn; 16(4): 497-508. NRCBL: 20.3.2. SC: em.

Willems, D.L.; Hak, A.; Visser, F.; Van der Wal, G. Thoughts of patients with advanced heart failure on dying. *Palliative Medicine* 2004 September; 18(6): 564-572. NRCBL: 20.3.1; 20.5.1; 9.5.1. SC: em. Identifiers: Netherlands.

Yap, H.Y.; Joynt, G.M.; Gomersall, C.D. Ethical attitudes of intensive care physicians in Hong Kong: questionnaire survey. *Hong Kong Medical Journal* 2004 August; 10(4): 244-250. NRCBL: 20.3.2; 8.3.4; 20.5.1. SC: em.

DEATH AND DYING/ DETERMINATION OF DEATH

Afonso, R.C.; Buttros, D.A.B.; Sakabe, D.; Paranhos, G.C.; Garcia, L.M.C.; Resende, M.B.; Ferraz-Neto, Ben-Hur. Future doctors and brain death: what is the prognosis? *Transplantation Proceedings* 2004 May; 36(4): 816-817. NRCBL: 20.2.1; 19.5. SC: em. Identifiers: Brazil.

Akrami, S.M.; Osati, Z.; Zahedi, F.; Raza, M. Brain death: recent ethical and religious considerations in Iran. *Transplantation Proceedings* 2004 December; 36(10): 2883-2887. NRCBL: 20.2.1; 19.5; 1.2. SC: le. Identifiers: Islam.

Appel, Jacob M. Defining death: when physicians and families differ. *Journal of Medical Ethics* 2005 November; 31(11): 641-642. NRCBL: 20.2.1. SC: le.

Cecchi, Rossana; Del Vecchio, Simona. Diagnosis of brain death in anencephalic infants: medicolegal and ethical aspects. *Medicine and Law: World Association for Medical Law* 1995; 14(1-2): 3-8. NRCBL: 20.2.1; 20.5.2; 4.4. SC: le.

Chiong, Winston. Brain death without definitions. *Hastings Center Report* 2005 November-December; 35(6): 20-30. NRCBL: 20.2.1; 1.1.

DeGrazia, David. Identity, what we are, and the definition of death. *In his:* Human Identity and Bioethics. New York: Cambridge University Press; 2005: 115-158. NRCBL: 20.2.1; 1.1; 4.4. SC: an.

Eberl, Jason T. A Thomistic understanding of human death. *Bioethics* 2005 February; 19(1): 29-48. NRCBL: 20.2.1; 1.2.

Edwards, Steven. Human death. *Nursing Philosophy* 2005 April; 6(2): 148-149. NRCBL: 20.2.1.

Edwards, Steven D.; Forbes, Kevin. Nursing practice and the definition of human death. *Nursing Inquiry* 2003 December; 10(4): 229-235. NRCBL: 20.2.1; 20.3.2; 8.1; 4.1.3.

Evans, H.M. Reply to: Defining death: when physicians and families differ. *Journal of Medical Ethics* 2005 November; 31(11): 642-644. NRCBL: 20.2.1. SC: le. Comments: comment on Jacob M. Appel, "Defining death: when physicians and families differ," Journal of Medical Ethics 2005 November; 31(11): 641-642.

Gillett, Grant. Brain death, vegetative state and the RUB: how does one arrive at the decision that a person's life is no longer worth living? *Issues in Medical Ethics* 1999 April-June; 7(2): 54-55. NRCBL: 20.2.1; 1.1. Identifiers: Risk of Unacceptable Badness.

John Paul II, Pope. Imperative of "signs of clinical death" for organ transplants: message to the Pontifical Academy of Sciences. *Issues in Law and Medicine* 2005 Spring; 20(3): 261-263. NRCBL: 20.2.1; 19.5; 1.2.

Jonsen, Albert R. Defining death. *In his:* Bioethics Beyond the Headlines: Who Lives? Who Dies? Who Decides? Lanham, MD: Rowman and Littlefield; 2005: 26-34. NRCBL: 20.2.1.

NRCBL: National Reference Center for Bioethics Literature Classification Scheme   See inside front cover for terms.

141

Kunin, Joshua. Brain death: revisiting the rabbinic opinions in light of current medical knowledge. *Tradition* 2004 Winter; 38(4): 48-62. NRCBL: 20.2.1; 1.2; 19.5.

Kuramochi, Takeshi. Reconsidering the dead donor rule. *Journal International de Bioethique / International Journal of Bioethics* 2005 March-June; 16(1-2): 117-122, 196-197. NRCBL: 20.2.1; 19.5. SC: le. Note: Abstract in English and French.

Lane, Alan; Westbrook, Andrew; Grady, Deirdre; O'Connor, Rory; Counihan, Timothy J.; Marsh, Brian; Laffey, John G. Maternal brain death: medical, ethical and legal issues. *Intensive Care Medicine* 2004 July; 30(7): 1484-1486. NRCBL: 20.2.1; 20.5.1; 9.5.5; 9.5.8; 20.5.2. SC: cs.

Lizza, John P. Potentiality, irreversibility, and death. *Journal of Medicine and Philosophy* 2005 February; 30(1): 45-64. NRCBL: 20.2.1; 1.1; 19.5.

Abstract: There has been growing concern about whether individuals who satisfy neurological criteria for death or who become non-heart- beating organ donors are really dead. This concern has focused on the issue of the potential for recovery that these individuals may still have and whether their conditions are irreversible. In this article I examine the concepts of potentiality and irreversibility that have been invoked in the discussions of the definition of death and non-heart-beating organ donation. I initially focus on the recent challenge by D. Alan Shewmon to accepting any neurological criterion of death. I argue that Shewmon relies on a problematic and unrealistic concept of potentiality, and that a better, more realistic concept of potentiality is consistent with accepting a neurological criterion for death. I then turn to an analysis of how the concept of irreversibility has been used in discussion of non-heart-beating organ donation. Similarly, I argue that some participants in this discussion have invoked a problematic and unrealistic concept of irreversibility. I then propose an alternative, more realistic account of irreversibility that explains how "irreversibility" should be understood in the definition and criteria of death.

Machado, Calixto. Consciousness as a definition of death: its appeal and complexity. *Clinical Electroencephalography* 1999 October; 30(4): 156-164. NRCBL: 20.2.1; 4.4.

Nevins, Daniel S. Dead or alive? Halakhah and brain death. *Conservative Judaism* 2005 Winter; 57(2): 3-29. NRCBL: 20.2.1; 1.2.

Pandya, Sunil K. Brain death and our transplant law. *Issues in Medical Ethics* 2001 April-June; 9(2): 51-52. NRCBL: 20.2.1. SC: le. Identifiers: India.

Reichman, Edward. Don't pull the plug on brain death just yet. *Tradition* 2004 Winter; 38(4): 63-69. NRCBL: 20.2.1; 1.2. SC: an.

Sato, Hajime; Akabayashi, Akira; Kai, Ichiro. Public appraisal of government efforts and participation intent in medico-ethical policymaking in Japan: a large scale national survey concerning brain death and organ transplant. *BMC Medical Ethics [electronic]* 2005; 6; E1, 12 p. Available: http://www.biomedcentral.com/1472-6939/6/1 [18 February 2005]. NRCBL: 20.2.1; 19.5. SC: le; em.

Abstract: BACKGROUND: Public satisfaction with policy process influences the legitimacy and acceptance of policies, and conditions the future political process, especially when contending ethical value judgments are involved. On the other hand, public involvement is required if effective policy is to be developed and accepted. METHODS: Using the data from a large-scale national opinion survey, this study evaluates public appraisal of past government efforts to legalize organ transplant from brain-dead bodies in Japan, and examines the public's intent to participate in future policy. RESULTS: A relatively large percentage of people became aware of the issue when government actions were initiated, and many increasingly formed their own opinions on the policy in question. However, a significant number (43.3%) remained unaware of any legislative efforts, and only 26.3% of those who were aware provided positive appraisals of the policymaking process. Furthermore, a majority of respondents (61.8%) indicated unwillingness to participate in future policy discussions of bioethical issues. Multivariate analysis revealed the following factors are associated with positive appraisals of policy development: greater age; earlier opinion formation; and familiarity with donor cards. Factors associated with likelihood of future participation in policy discussion include younger age, earlier attention to the issue, and knowledge of past government efforts. Those unwilling to participate cited as their reasons that experts are more knowledgeable and that the issues are too complex. CONCLUSIONS: Results of an opinion survey in Japan were presented, and a set of factors statistically associated with them were discussed. Further efforts to improve policy making process on bioethical issues are desirable.

Veatch, Robert M. The death of whole-brain death: the plague of the disaggregators, somaticists, and mentalists. *Journal of Medicine and Philosophy* 2005 August; 30(4): 353-378. NRCBL: 20.2.1. SC: an.

Abstract: In its October 2001 issue, this journal published a series of articles questioning the Whole-Brain-based definition of death. Much of the concern focused on whether somatic integration-a commonly understood basis for the whole-brain death view-can survive the brain's death. The present article accepts that there are insurmountable problems with whole-brain death views, but challenges the assumption that loss of somatic integration is the proper basis for pronouncing death. It examines three major themes. First, it accepts the claim of the "disaggregators" that some behaviors traditionally associated with death can be unbundled, but argues that other behaviors (including organ procurement) must continue to be associated. Second, it rejects the claims of the "somaticists," that the integration of the body is critical, arguing instead for equating death with the irreversible loss of "embodied consciousness," that is, the loss of integration of bodily and mental function. Third, it defends higher-brain views against the charge that they are necessarily "mentalist," that is, that they equate death with losing some mental function such as consciousness or personhood. It argues, instead, for the integration of bodily and mental function as the critical feature of human life and that its irreversible loss constitutes death.

DEATH AND DYING/ TERMINAL CARE

Abma, Tineke A. Struggling with the fragility of life: a relational-narrative approach to ethics in palliative nursing. *Nursing Ethics* 2005 July; 12(4): 337-348. NRCBL: 20.4.1; 8.1.

Abstract: In nursing ethics the role of narratives and dialogue has become more prominent in recent years. The purpose of this article is to illuminate a relational-narrative approach to ethics in the context of palliative nursing. The case study presented concerns a difficult relationship between oncology nurses and a husband whose wife was hospitalized with cancer. The husband's narrative is an expression of depression, social isolation and the loss of hope. He found no meaning in the process of dying and death. The oncology nurses were not able to recognize his emotional and existential problems. A narrative perspective inspired by relational ethics indicates that participants may develop a relational narrative that seeks good for all involved in a situation. In palliative nursing this entails open communication about the fragility of life and approaching death. In relational narratives, answers to these ethical dilemmas are co-authored, contingent and contextual.

Agarwal, Rajeev. Palliative care — Hinduism. *Dolentium Hominum* 2005; 20(1): 91-93. NRCBL: 20.4.1; 1.2; 20.3.1; 20.5.1. Conference: Proceedings of the XIX International Conference organized by the Pontifical Council for Health Pastoral Care;New Synod Hall, Vatican City; 11-13 November 2004.

Aksoy, Sahin. End-of-life decision making in Turkey. *In:* Blank, Robert H.; Merrick, Janna C., eds. End-of-Life Decision Making: A Cross-National Study. Cambridge, MA: MIT Press; 2005: 183-195. NRCBL: 20.4.1.

American College of Surgeons. Statement on principles guiding care at the end of life. *Journal of the American College of Surgeons* 2005 January; 200(1): 114. NRCBL: 20.4.1; 6.

Aranibar, Fernando Antezana. Legal aspects of forms of palliative care for pain. *Dolentium Hominum* 2005; 20(1): 51-53. NRCBL: 20.4.1; 4.4. SC: le. Conference: Proceedings of the XIX International Conference organized by the Pontifical Council for Health Pastoral Care;New Synod Hall, Vatican City; 11-13 November 2004.

Ashby, Michael A.; Mendelson, Danuta. Gardner; re BWV: Victorian Supreme Court makes landmark Australian ruling on tube feeding. *Medical Journal of Australia* 2004 October 18; 181(8): 442-445. NRCBL: 20.4.1; 20.5.1; 8.3.3.

Barretto, Zulica. Ethical issues in palliative care. *Issues in Medical Ethics* 2003 October-December; 11(4): 118-119. NRCBL: 20.4.1; 20.5.1.

Basta, Lofty L. Ethical issues in the management of geriatric cardiac patients. When referred to hospice care the treating cardiologist believed that his patient would die in a few days. *American Journal of Geriatric Cardiology* 2005 March-April; 14(2): 95-97. NRCBL: 20.4.1; 9.5.1. SC: cs.

Blackall, George F.; Green, Michael J.; Simms, Steve. Application of systems principles to resolving ethical dilemmas in medicine. *Journal of Clinical Ethics* 2005 Spring; 16(1): 20-27. NRCBL: 20.4.1; 20.7; 20.3.3; 20.3.2; 8.1. SC: cs.

Blasszauer, Bela; Palfi, Ilona. Moral dilemmas of nursing in end-of-life care in Hungary: a personal perspective. *Nursing Ethics* 2005 January; 12(1): 92-105. NRCBL: 20.4.1; 4.1.3; 7.1; 8.1. SC: em.
Abstract: The authors' aim is to bring to the attention of readers the inadequacies of care for people in Hungary who are terminally ill. They believe that both objective and subjective factors cause these inadequacies. Most of these factors arise from moral dilemmas that could be eased or even solved if ethics education had a much more prominent place in the nursing curriculum. Even if nurses would not become automatically better persons morally, a much wider knowledge of medical/nursing ethics could significantly improve nursing care both before and at the end of life. Although the article is also critical of the nursing care provided, it is not its purpose to make any generalizations. The study utilized selected passages from essays written by 76 practicing nurses on their personal experience of ethical dilemmas in their work environment, and a questionnaire administered to 250 students (registered nurses and health care students) studying for a college degree. This article is written by two authors who have formed an unusual alliance: a registered nurse with 29 years' experience of bedside nursing, but who is currently a teacher of nursing ethics at a local health college, and a lawyer turned bioethicist.

Blondeau, Danielle; Roy, Louis; Dumont, Serge; Godin, Gaston; Martineau, Isabelle. Physicians' and pharmacists' attitudes toward the use of sedation at the end of life: influence of prognosis and type of suffering. *Journal of Palliative Care* 2005 Winter; 21(4): 238-245. NRCBL: 20.4.1; 9.7; 4.4. SC: em; cs.

Brender, Erin. Palliative sedation. *JAMA: The Journal of the American Medical Association* 2005 October 12; 294(14): 1850. NRCBL: 20.4.1; 9.7; 20.5.4. SC: po.

Brierley, Joe. "Right to die" — changing "right" to "duty" may focus debate [letter]. *BMJ: British Medical Journal* 2005 June 11; 330(7504): 1388. NRCBL: 20.4.1.

Briggs, Linda; Colvin, Elaine. The nurse's role in end-of-life decision-making for patients and families. *Geriatric Nursing* 2002 November; 23(6): 302-310. NRCBL: 20.4.1; 20.5.4; 4.1.3; 8.1.

Buzzee, Sarah E.M. The Pain Relief Promotion Act: Congress's misguided intervention into end-of-life care. *University of Cincinnati Law Review* 2001 Autumn; 70(1): 217-249. NRCBL: 20.4.1; 20.7; 20.5.1. SC: le.

Cantor, Norman L. Glucksberg, the putative right to adequate pain relief, and death with dignity. *Journal of Health Law* 2001 Summer; 34(3): 301-333. NRCBL: 20.4.1; 20.5.1; 20.7. SC: le. Identifiers: Washington v. Glucksberg, 117 S. Ct. 2258 (1997).

Casarett, David J.; Crowley, Roxane L.; Hirschman, Karen B. How should clinicians describe hospice to patients and families? *Journal of the American Geriatrics Society* 2004 November; 52(11): 1923-1928. NRCBL: 20.4.1; 8.1; 8.3.1.

Casarett, David; Crowley, Roxane; Stevenson, Carolyn; Xie, Sharon; Teno, Joan. Making difficult decisions

NRCBL: National Reference Center for Bioethics Literature Classification Scheme   See inside front cover for terms.

143

about hospice enrollment: what do patients and families want to know? *Journal of the American Geriatrics Society* 2005 February; 53(2): 249-254. NRCBL: 20.4.1; 8.3.1. SC: em.

Chiu, Tai-Yuan. End-of-life decision making in Taiwan. *In:* Blank, Robert H.; Merrick, Janna C., eds. End-of-Life Decision Making: A Cross-National Study. Cambridge, MA: MIT Press; 2005: 169-181. NRCBL: 20.4.1; 20.5.1.

Colombo, Sylviane. Not just euthanasia: recognizing a legal positive right to palliative care. *Medicine and Law: World Association for Medical Law* 2005 March; 24(1): 203-210. NRCBL: 20.4.1; 9.2. SC: le.

Abstract: As jurists, doctors, and ethicists are increasingly engaged in the debate as to whether and how to legalize euthanasia as a matter of public policy, less debate takes place on what it is submitted ought naturally to come before, i.e. the affirmation of a legal right to palliative care. In Israel, the draft law The Terminally Ill Patient (2001) includes a palliative care provision. It is submitted that such provision, laudable as it is, appears within a euthanasia-oriented framework and is given too limited a scope. Hence the suggestion that palliative care be given an autonomous role, and be recognized as a positive legal right.

Curtis, J.R.; Engelberg, R.A.; Nielsen, E.L.; Au, D.H.; Patrick, D.L. Patient-physician communication about end-of-life care for patients with severe COPD. *European Respiratory Journal* 2004 August; 24(2): 200-205. NRCBL: 20.4.1; 8.1. SC: em. Identifiers: Washington; chronic obstructive pulmonary disease.

Cutter, William. Terminal sedation: a Jewish perspective. *Update [Loma Linda University Center for Christian Bioethics]* 2002 September; 18(2): 4-6. NRCBL: 20.4.1; 9.7; 20.5.1; 1.2.

Deshpande, Ohm; Reid, M. Carrington; Rao, Arun S. Attitudes of Asian-Indian Hindus toward end-of-life care. *Journal of the American Geriatrics Society* 2005 January; 53(1): 131-135. NRCBL: 20.4.1; 1.2; 9.5.2; 9.5.4; 20.5.1.

Dobson, Roger. Age discrimination denies elderly people a "dignified death" [news]. *BMJ: British Medical Journal* 2005 June 4; 330(7503): 1288. NRCBL: 20.4.1; 9.5.2; 9.5.4.

Evans, Lesley A.M. "Right to die" — sensitivity and humility are needed when dealing with dying people [letter]. *BMJ: British Medical Journal* 2005 June 11; 330(7504): 1388. NRCBL: 20.4.1; 20.5.1.

Fleming, David A. Making difficult choices at the end of life: a personal challenge for all participants. *Missouri Medicine* 2005 March-April; 102(2): 147-152. NRCBL: 20.4.1; 20.5.1; 20.5.4; 20.3.1; 8.1; 1.2.

Fohr, Susan Anderson. The double effect of pain medication: separating myth from reality. *Journal of Palliative Medicine* 1998 Winter; 1(4): 315-328. NRCBL: 20.4.1; 9.7; 20.5.1; 1.1; 4.4.

Ford, Paul J.; Fraser, Thomas G.; Davis, Mellar P.; Kodish, Eric. Anti-infective therapy at end of life: ethical decision-making in hospice-eligible patients. *Bioethics* 2005 August; 19(4): 379-392. NRCBL: 20.4.1; 9.7; 9.4.

Abstract: Clear guidelines addressing the ethically appropriate use of anti-infectives in the setting of hospice care do not exist. There is lack of understanding about key treatment decisions related to infection treatment for patients who are eligible for hospice care. Ethical concerns about anti-infective use at the end of life include: (1) delaying transition to hospice, (2) prolonging a dying process, (3) prescribing regimens incongruent with a short life expectancy and goals of care, (4) increasing the reservoir of potential resistant pathogens, (5) placing unreasonable costs on a capitated hospice system. Although anti- infectives are thought to be relatively safe, they can place a burden on patients and be inconsistent to particular care plans. The current complex, and at times fragmented, medical care often fails to address these issues in decision-making. In many ways, the ethics governing the end of life decisions related to dialysis, hydration/nutrition, and hypercalcemia parallel those of anti-infectives. In this article we articulate important elements in ethical decision-making in the application of anti-infectives for patients who are eligible for hospice care, and we point to the need for prospective studies to help refine particular guidelines in these cases.

Gillett, Grant. Euthanasia from the perspective of hospice care. *Medicine and Law: World Association for Medical Law* 1994; 13(3-4): 263-268. NRCBL: 20.4.1; 20.5.1.

Glare, Paul A.; Tobin, Bernadette. End-of-life issues: case 2. *Medical Journal of Australia* 2002 January 21; 176(2): 80-81. NRCBL: 20.4.1; 20.5.1; 7.1.

Green, Jennifer. Death with dignity: Rastafarianism. *Nursing Times* 1992 February 26; 88(9): 56-57. NRCBL: 20.4.1; 20.3.1; 1.2.

Green, Jennifer. Death with dignity: the Mormon Church. *Nursing Times* 1992 February 5; 88(6): 44-45. NRCBL: 20.4.1; 20.3.1; 1.2.

Green, Jennifer. Death with dignity: Zoroastrianism. *Nursing Times* 1992 February 12; 88(7): 44-45. NRCBL: 20.4.1; 20.3.1; 1.2.

Guevin, Benedict M. Ordinary, extraordinary, and artificial means of care. *National Catholic Bioethics Quarterly* 2005 Autumn; 5(3): 471- 479. NRCBL: 20.4.1; 20.5.1; 8.3.4; 4.1.1; 1.2; 4.4. SC: cs.

Hack, Thomas F.; Chochinov, Harvey Max; Hassard, Thomas; Kristjanson, Linda J.; McClement, Susan; Harlos, Mike. Defining dignity in terminally ill cancer patients: a factor-analytic approach. *Psycho-Oncology* 2004 October; 13(10): 700-708. NRCBL: 20.4.1; 4.4; 17.1. SC: em. Identifiers: Canada.

Hardwig, John. Families and futility: forestalling demands for futile treatment. *Journal of Clinical Ethics* 2005 Winter; 16(4): 335-344. NRCBL: 20.4.1; 20.5.1; 20.3.3; 20.3.2.

Herranz, Jesús Conde. Palliative care: origins, precedents and the history of a Christian approach. *Dolentium Hominum* 2005; 20(1): 54-63. NRCBL: 20.4.1; 2.2; 1.2. Conference: Proceedings of the XIX International Conference organized by the Pontifical Council for Health Pastoral Care; New Synod Hall, Vatican City; 11-13 November 2004.

Heyland, Daren K.; Tranmer, Joan; O'Callaghan, C.J.; Gafni, Amiram. The seriously ill hospitalized patient: preferred role in end-of-life decision making? *Journal of Critical Care* 2003 March; 18(1): 3-10. NRCBL: 20.4.1; 20.5.1; 8.1. SC: em. Identifiers: Canada.

Hoffman, Jan. Doctors' delicate balance in keeping hope alive. *New York Times* 2005 December 24; p. A1, A14. NRCBL: 20.4.1; 4.4. SC: po. Identifiers: Series — Being a patient: the ethics of hope.

Hoffmann, Diane E.; Tarzian, Anita J. Dying in America — an examination of policies that deter adequate end-of-life care in nursing homes. *Journal of Law, Medicine and Ethics* 2005 Summer; 33(2): 294- 309. NRCBL: 20.4.1; 9.5.2; 20.3.1; 9.3.1.

Hofmann, B.; Håheim, L.L.; Søreide, J.A. Ethics of palliative surgery in patients with cancer. *British Journal of Surgery* 2005 July; 92(7): 802-809. NRCBL: 20.4.1; 9.5.1.

Howe, Edmund G. Shame, slap jack, and familes [sic; families] that should lie. *Journal of Clinical Ethics* 2005 Winter; 16(4): 279-291. NRCBL: 20.4.1; 20.3.3; 8.2; 8.1.

Howland, John. Questions about palliative sedation: an act of mercy or of mercy killing? *Ethics and Medics* 2005 August; 30(8): 1-2. NRCBL: 20.4.1; 9.7.

Hughes, Jonathan. Palliative care and the QALY problem. *Health Care Analysis: An International Journal of Health Care Philosophy and Policy* 2005 December; 13(4): 289-301. NRCBL: 20.4.1; 4.4; 9.4. SC: an. Identifiers: quality adjusted life year.

Abstract: Practitioners of palliative care often argue for more resources to be provided by the state in order to lessen its reliance on charitable funding and to enable the services currently provided to some of those with terminal illnesses to be provided to all who would benefit from it. However, this is hard to justify on grounds of cost-effectiveness, since it is in the nature of palliative care that the benefits it brings to its patients are of short duration. In particular, palliative care fares badly under a policy of QALY-maximisation, since procedures which prevent premature death (provided the life is of reasonable quality) or improve quality of life for those with longer life expectancy will produce more QALYs. This paper examines various responses to this problem and argues that in order to justify increased resources for palliative care its advocates must reject the 'atomistic' view of the value of life implicit in the QALY approach in favour of a 'holistic' or 'narrative' account. This, however, has implications which advocates of palliative care may be reluctant to embrace.

Hughes, Nic; Clark, David. "A thoughtful and experienced physician": William Munk and the care of the dying in late Victorian England. *Journal of Palliative Medicine* 2004 October; 7(5): 703-710. NRCBL: 20.4.1; 20.5.1; 2.2.

Johnson, Ian S. Assisted dying for the terminally ill [letter]. *Lancet* 2005 October 22-28; 366(9495): 1433-1434. NRCBL: 20.4.1; 9.7; 4.4. SC: em.

Laughlin, Catherine. U.S. Supreme Court hears oral arguments in Ashcroft v. Raich background. *Journal of Law, Medicine and Ethics* 2005 Summer; 33(2): 396- 399. NRCBL: 20.4.1; 9.5.9. SC: le; an.

Levy, Michael H.; Cohen, Seth D. Sedation for the relief of refractory symptoms in the imminently dying: a fine intentional line. *Seminars in Oncology* 2005 April; 32(2): 237-246. NRCBL: 20.4.1; 20.5.1; 20.7; 4.4. SC: rv.

Lindemann, Hilde. On the mend: Alzheimer's and family caregiving. *Journal of Clinical Ethics* 2005 Winter; 16(4): 314-320. NRCBL: 20.4.1; 20.3.3; 4.4; 1.1.

Lo, Bernard; Rubenfeld, Gordon. Palliative sedation in dying patients: "we turn to it when everything else hasn't worked". *JAMA: The Journal of the American Medical Association* 2005 October 12; 294(14): 1810-1816. NRCBL: 20.4.1; 9.7.

Abstract: Despite skilled palliative care, some dying patients experience distressing symptoms that cannot be adequately relieved. A patient with metastatic breast cancer, receiving high doses of opioids administered to relieve pain, developed myoclonus. After other approaches proved ineffective, palliative sedation was an option of last resort. The doctrine of double effect, the traditional justification for palliative sedation, permits physicians to provide high doses of opioids and sedatives to relieve suffering, provided that the intention is not to cause the patient's death and that certain other conditions are met. Such high doses are permissible even if the risk of hastening death is foreseen. Because intention plays a key role in this doctrine, clinicians must understand and document which actions are consistent with an intention to relieve symptoms rather than to hasten death. The patient or family should agree with plans for palliative sedation. The attending physician needs to explain to them, as well as to the medical and nursing staff, the details of care and the justification for palliative sedation. Because cases involving palliative sedation are emotionally stressful, the patient, family, and health care workers can all benefit from talking about the complex medical, ethical, and emotional issues they raise.

Luce, John M.; Rubenfeld, Gordon D. Can health care costs be reduced by limiting intensive care at the end of life? *American Journal of Respiratory and Critical Care Medicine* 2002 March 15; 165(6): 750-754. NRCBL: 20.4.1; 9.3.1; 9.4; 20.5.1.

Lynch, Maureen. Palliative sedation. *Clinical Journal of Oncology Nursing* 2003 November-December; 7(6): 653-657, 667. NRCBL: 20.4.1; 4.4. SC: em.

NRCBL: National Reference Center for Bioethics Literature Classification Scheme   See inside front cover for terms.

145

Lynn, Joanne. End-of-life options [letter]. *Health Affairs* 2005 September-October; 24(5): 1377-1378. NRCBL: 20.4.1.

Macer, Darryl. End-of-life care in Japan. *In:* Blank, Robert H.; Merrick, Janna C., eds. End-of-Life Decision Making: A Cross-National Study. Cambridge, MA: MIT Press; 2005: 109-129. NRCBL: 20.4.1; 2.1; 19.5; 20.5.1.

Maddocks, Ian. 'Good palliative care' orders. *Palliative Medicine* 1993; 7(1): 35-37. NRCBL: 20.4.1; 20.5.1.

Mino, Jean-Christophe; Lert, France. Beyond the biomedical model: palliative care and its holistic model. *HEC (Healthcare Ethics Committee) Forum* 2005 September; 17(3): 227-236. NRCBL: 20.4.1; 4.1.1; 4.4.

Molmenti, Ernesto P.; Dunn, Geoffrey P. Transplantation and palliative care: the convergence of two seemingly opposite realities. *Surgical Clinics of North America* 2005 April; 85(2): 373-382. NRCBL: 20.4.1; 19.1; 8.1.

O'Brien, Tony. What is palliative care? *In:* Council of Europe Publishing, ed. Euthanasia. Volume I. Ethical and Human Aspects. Strasbourg: Council of Europe; Croton-on-Hudson, NY: Manhattan Publishing Co.; 2003: 73-82. NRCBL: 20.4.1.

Orr, Robert D. Just put me to sleep . . . please! Ethical issues in palliative and "terminal" sedation. *Update [Loma Linda University Center for Christian Bioethics]* 2002 September; 18(2): 1-4, 8. NRCBL: 20.4.1; 9.7; 20.5.1; 1.1.

Pandya, Sunil K. End-of-life decision making in India. *In:* Blank, Robert H.; Merrick, Janna C., eds. End-of-Life Decision Making: A Cross-National Study. Cambridge, MA: MIT Press; 2005: 79-96. NRCBL: 20.4.1; 1.2; 9.3.1; 20.5.1.

Payne, S.A.; Langley-Evans, A.; Hillier, R. Perceptions of a 'good' death: a comparative study of the views of hospice staff and patients. *Palliative Medicine* 1996 October; 10(4): 307-312. NRCBL: 20.4.1; 20.3.1; 20.3.2. SC: em. Identifiers: United Kingdom (Great Britain).

Pekmezaris, Renée; Breuer, Lorraine; Zaballero, Arturo; Wolf-Klein, Gisele; Jadoon, Erum; D'Olimpio, James T.; Guzik, Howard; Foley, Cornelius J.; Weiner, Joseph; Chan, Susanna. Predictors of site of death of end-of-life patients: the importance of specificity in advance directives. *Journal of Palliative Medicine* 2004 February; 7(1): 9-17. NRCBL: 20.4.1; 20.5.4; 20.5.1. SC: em.

Piattelli, Abramo Alberto. Inter-religious dialogue: palliative care in the other great religions: Judaism. *Dolentium Hominum* 2005; 20(1): 87-88. NRCBL: 20.4.1; 1.2. Conference: Proceedings of the XIX International Conference organized by the Pontifical Council for Health Pastoral Care; New Synod Hall, Vatican City; 11-13 November 2004.

Portenoy, Russell; Lupu, Dale. Misconceptions about hospice [letter]. *Health Affairs* 2005 November-December; 24(6): 1686. NRCBL: 20.4.1.

Powell, Tia. Voice: cognitive impairment and medical decision making. *Journal of Clinical Ethics* 2005 Winter; 16(4): 303-313. NRCBL: 20.4.1; 8.1; 8.3.3; 20.5.1. SC: le.

Puchalski, Christina M.; Dorff, Elliot; Hendi, Yahya. Spirituality, religion, and healing in palliative care. *Clinics in Geriatric Medicine* 2004 November; 20(4): 689-714, vi-vii. NRCBL: 20.4.1; 20.3.1; 1.2.

Putnam, Andrew T. Pain management and palliative care. *In:* McMahon, Kevin T., ed. Moral Issues in Catholic Health Care. Wynnewood, PA: Saint Charles Borromeo Seminary; 2004: 139- 152. NRCBL: 20.4.1; 1.2; 9.7.

Rady, Mohamed Y.; Johnson, Daniel J. Admission to intensive care unit at the end-of-life: is it an informed decision? *Palliative Medicine* 2004 December; 18(8): 705-711. NRCBL: 20.4.1; 8.1. SC: em.

Ratner, Edward; Bartels, Dianne; Song, John. A perspective on homelessness, ethics, and medical care. *Minnesota Medicine* 2004 June; 87(6): 50-52. NRCBL: 20.4.1; 20.5.1; 9.5.10.

Rosenthal, Elisabeth. A most personal test for the Church's rules; what is a natural death? *New York Times* 2005 March 27; p. WK5. NRCBL: 20.4.1; 20.3.1; 1.2. SC: po. Identifiers: John Paul II.

Rubenfeld, Gordon D.; Curtis, J. Randall. Beyond ethical dilemmas: improving the quality of end-of-life care in the intensive care unit. *Critical Care* 2003 February; 7(1): 11-13. NRCBL: 20.4.1; 20.5.1.

Rubenfeld, Gordon D.; Curtis, J. Randall. End-of-life care in the intensive care unit: a research agenda. *Critical Care Medicine* 2001 October; 29(10): 2001-2006. NRCBL: 20.4.1; 18.5.1.

Rutkow, Lainie. Dying to live: the effect of the Patient Self-Determination Act on hospice care. *New York University Journal of Legislation and Public Policy* 2004; 7(2): 393-435. NRCBL: 20.4.1; 20.5.4; 20.5.1; 20.7; 1.1. SC: le.

Salacz, Michael E.; Weissman, David E. Controlled sedation for refractory suffering: Part I. *Journal of Palliative Medicine* 2005 February; 8(1): 136-137. NRCBL: 20.4.1; 4.4.

Sandman, Lars. What's the use of human dignity within palliative care? *Nursing Philosophy* 2002 July; 3(2): 177-181. NRCBL: 20.4.1; 4.4.

Schachter, Leora; Emanuel, Ezekiel J.; Emanuel, Linda J. Talking about death, dying, and bereavement with terminally ill patients and their caregivers [letter and reply]. *Archives of Internal Medicine* 2005 June 27; 165(12): 1437. NRCBL: 20.4.1; 8.1.

Sheldon, Tony. Dutch doctors are given guidance on sedation [news]. *BMJ: British Medical Journal* 2005 December 17; 331(7530): 1422. NRCBL: 20.4.1; 20.5.1.

Sherman, Frederick T. Nutrition in advanced dementia — tube-feeding or hand-feeding until death? [editorial]. *Geriatrics* 2003 November; 58(11): 10, 12. NRCBL: 20.4.1; 17.1; 9.5.2.

Shrank, William H.; Kutner, Jean S.; Richardson, Terri; Mularski, Richard A.; Fischer, Stacy; Kagawa-Singer, Marjorie. Focus group findings about the influence of culture on communication preferences in end-of-life care. *JGIM: Journal of General Internal Medicine* 2005 August; 20(8): 703-709. NRCBL: 20.4.1; 1.2; 8.1; 9.5.4. SC: em.

Simha, S.N. Issues faced by a hospice. *Indian Journal of Medical Ethics* 2005 July-September; 2(3): 85. NRCBL: 20.4.1; 8.2. Identifiers: India.

Stollmeyer, Alice. The politics of care: dementia and accounting versus caring for mortification. *Journal of Clinical Ethics* 2005 Summer; 16(2): 116-126. NRCBL: 20.4.1; 8.3.4; 9.5.3; 9.5.2; 20.5.1; 1.1. SC: cs; le. Identifiers: Netherlands.

Street, Annette F.; Love, Anthony. Dimensions of privacy in palliative care: views of health professionals. *Social Science and Medicine* 2005 April; 60(8): 1795-1804. NRCBL: 20.4.1; 8.4. SC: cs; em. Identifiers: Australia.

Sulmasy, Daniel P. Terri Schiavo and the Roman Catholic tradition of forgoing extraordinary means of care. *Journal of Law, Medicine and Ethics* 2005 Summer; 33(2): 359-362. NRCBL: 20.4.1; 1.2; 20.5.1; 20.5.4.

Tanaka, Masahiro. Buddhism and palliative care in Japan. *Dolentium Hominum* 2005; 20(1): 94-96. NRCBL: 20.4.1; 1.2. Conference: Proceedings of the XIX International Conference organized by the Pontifical Council for Health Pastoral Care; New Synod Hall, Vatican City; 11-13 November 2004.

Tardy, B.; Venet, C.; Zeni, F.; Berthet, O.; Viallon, A.; Lemaire, F.; Bertrand, J.C. Death of terminally ill patients on a stretcher in the emergency department: a French specialty? *Intensive Care Medicine* 2002 November; 28(11): 1625-1628. NRCBL: 20.4.1; 20.5.1. SC: em.

Tarzian, Anita J.; Neal, Maggie T.; O'Neil, J. Anne. Attitudes, experiences, and beliefs affecting end-of-life decision-making among homeless individuals. *Journal of Palliative Medicine* 2005 February; 8(1): 36-48. NRCBL: 20.4.1; 9.5.10; 8.1. SC: em.

Taylor, Robert M. Is terminal sedation really euthanasia? *Medical Ethics Newsletter [Lahey Clinic]* 2003 Winter; 10(1): 3, 8. NRCBL: 20.4.1; 20.5.1; 4.4.

Towers, Anna; MacDonald, Neil; Wallace, Ellen. Ethical issues in palliative care: views of patients, families, and nonphysician staff. *Canadian Family Physician* 2003 December; 49: 1626-1631. NRCBL: 20.4.1; 8.1. SC: em.

Tucker, Kathryn L. The chicken and the egg: the pursuit of choice for a human hastened-death as a catalyst for improved end-of-life care; improved end-of-life care as a precondition for legalization of assisted dying. *New York University Annual Survey of American Law* 2004; 60(2): 355-378. NRCBL: 20.4.1; 20.7; 20.5.1; 8.1; 4.4; 9.2. SC: le.

United States. Congress. Senate. Pain Relief Promotion Act of 1999. S. 1272 [introduced 23 June 1999]. United States Senate, 106th Congress; 4 p. [Online]. Available: http://thomas.loc.gov/cgi-bin/query/C?c106:./temp/~106FcIhSs [22 September 2005]. NRCBL: 20.4.1; 9.7; 4.4. SC: le.

Voogt, Elsbeth; van der Heide, Agnes; Rietjens, Judith A.C.; van Leeuwen, Anna F.; Visser, Adriaan P.; van der Rijt, Carin C.D.; van der Maas, Paul J. Attitudes of patients with incurable cancer toward medical treatment in the last phase of life. *Journal of Clinical Oncology* 2005 March 20; 23(9): 2012-2019. NRCBL: 20.4.1; 20.3.1; 4.4. SC: em. Identifiers: Netherlands.

Wagner, Lynn. Providing comfort to dying residents. *Provider* 1999 May; 25(5): 52-54, 57-58, 63-65. NRCBL: 20.4.1; 20.5.1.

Walter, James J. Terminal sedation: a Catholic perspective. *Update [Loma Linda University Center for Christian Bioethics]* 2002 September; 18(2): 6-8. NRCBL: 20.4.1; 9.7; 20.5.1; 1.2.

Wang, Xin Shelley; Di, Li Jun; Reyes-Gibby, Cielito C.; Guo, Hong; Liu, Shu Jun; Cleeland, Charles S. End-of-life care in urban areas of China: a survey of 60 oncology clinicians. *Journal of Pain and Symptom Management* 2004 February; 27(2): 125-132. NRCBL: 20.4.1; 20.3.2; 8.1. SC: em.

Wasunna, Angela. End-of-life decision making in Kenya. *In:* Blank, Robert H.; Merrick, Janna C., eds. End-of-Life Decision Making: A Cross-National Study. Cambridge, MA: MIT Press; 2005: 131-146. NRCBL: 20.4.1.

Welch, Lisa C.; Teno, Joan M.; Mor, Vincent. End-of-life care in black and white: race matters for medical care of dying patients and their families. *Journal of the American Geriatrics Society* 2005 July; 53(7): 1145-1153. NRCBL: 20.4.1; 8.1; 9.5.4; 20.5.1. SC: em.

Welie, Jos V.M. When medical treatment is no longer in order: toward a new interpretation of the ordinary-extraordinary distinction. *National Catholic Bioethics Quarterly* 2005 Autumn; 5(3): 517-536. NRCBL: 20.4.1; 20.5.1; 8.1; 8.3.1; 8.3.4; 4.1.1; 1.2.

White, Ben; Willmott, Lindy. The edge of palliative care: certainty, but at what price? *Flinders Journal of Law Re-*

NRCBL: National Reference Center for Bioethics Literature Classification Scheme   See inside front cover for terms.

147

form 2004 July; 7(2): 225-242. NRCBL: 20.4.1; 4.4; 1.3.5; 8.3.1. SC: le. Identifiers: Australia.

Winston, Carole A.; Leshner, Paula; Kramer, Jennifer; Allen, Gillian. Overcoming barriers to access and utilization of hospice and palliative care services in African-American communities. *Omega: Journal of Death and Dying* 2004-2005; 50(2): 151-163. NRCBL: 20.4.1; 9.5.4; 9.2; 21.7.

Yarborough, Mark. Deciding for others at the end of life: storytelling and moral agency. *Journal of Clinical Ethics* 2005 Summer; 16(2): 127-143. NRCBL: 20.4.1; 20.5.1; 20.3.3; 4.4; 8.3.3; 18.3; 1.1.

Yiting, Li; Döring, Ole; Fang, Liu; Baoqi, Su. End-of-life care in China: a view from Beijing. *In:* Blank, Robert H.; Merrick, Janna C., eds. End-of-Life Decision Making: A Cross-National Study. Cambridge, MA: MIT Press; 2005: 33-59. NRCBL: 20.4.1; 1.2; 20.3.1; 20.5.1.

DEATH AND DYING/ TERMINAL CARE FOR MINORS

Murphy, Dermot M.; Pritchard, Jon; Verhagen, Eduard; Sauer, Pieter J.J. Euthanasia in severely ill newborns [letter and reply]. *New England Journal of Medicine* 2005 June 2; 352(22): 2353- 2355. NRCBL: 20.4.2; 20.5.2.

Segre, Marco. Ethics and the management of terminally ill children [editorial]. *Revista do Hospital das Clinicas* 2004 January; 59(1): 1-2. NRCBL: 20.4.2; 20.5.2.

Spike, Jeffrey. The sound of chains: a tragedy. *Journal of Clinical Ethics* 2005 Fall; 16(3): 212-217. NRCBL: 20.4.2; 9.6; 20.5.2. SC: cs.

Stark, Judith; Thape, Janice. Decision making in neonatal intensive care: a collaboration of parents, physicians, and nurses. *AWHONN's Clinical Issues in Perinatal and Women's Health Nursing* 1993; 4(4): 589-595. NRCBL: 20.4.2; 9.4; 8.1; 7.3.

Torreão, Lara de Araújo; Pereira, Crésio Romeu; Troster, Eduardo. Ethical aspects in the management of the terminally ill patient in the pediatric intensive care unit. *Revista do Hospital das Clinicas* 2004 January; 59(1): 3-9. NRCBL: 20.4.2; 20.5.2. SC: rv.

DELIVERY OF HEALTH CARE *See* CARE FOR SPECIFIC GROUPS

DETERMINATION OF DEATH *See* DEATH AND DYING/ DETERMINATION OF DEATH

DISCLOSURE *See* CONFIDENTIALITY; INFORMED CONSENT; HUMAN EXPERIMENTATION/ INFORMED CONSENT; TRUTH DISCLOSURE

DISTRIBUTIVE JUSTICE *See* RESOURCE ALLOCATION

DIVERSITY *See* CULTURAL PLURALISM

DNA FINGERPRINTING *See* GENETICS/ LEGAL ASPECTS

DONATION *See* BLOOD DONATION AND TRANSFUSION; ORGAN AND TISSUE TRANSPLANTATION/ DONATION AND PROCUREMENT

DRUG INDUSTRY

Clinical practice guidelines and conflict of interest [editorial]. *CMAJ/JAMC: Canadian Medical Association Journal* 2005 November 22; 173(11): 1297. NRCBL: 9.7; 1.3.9; 1.3.7.

Disputes between parents, immunisation and the welfare of the child. *Medical Law Review* 2003 Autumn; 11(3): 377-380. NRCBL: 9.7; 8.3.2; 8.3.4. SC: le.

Doctors with ties to device makers [editorial]. *New York Times* 2005 September 24; p. A14. NRCBL: 9.7; 1.3.2; 9.3.1. SC: po.

Flu vaccine shortage creates ethical issues, safety challenges. *Healthcare Benchmarks and Quality Improvement* 2004 December; 11(12): 133-136. NRCBL: 9.7; 9.4; 9.5.1.

Moralists at the pharmacy [editorial]. *New York Times* 2005 April 3; p. WK12. NRCBL: 9.7; 11.1; 12.1; 4.1.1. SC: po.

No place for conflict of interest [editorial]. *Lancet* 2005 May 14-20; 365(9472): 1664. NRCBL: 9.7; 5.3; 5.2.

Patenting the poor. *Lancet Oncology* 2005 April; 6(4): 191. NRCBL: 9.7; 9.3.1; 5.3; 9.5.10. Identifiers: India.

Prozac papers. *New Scientist* 2005 January 8-14; 185(2481): 4. NRCBL: 9.7; 17.4; 18.5.6. SC: le.

The sounds of silence [editorial]. *Nature Medicine* 2004 July; 10(7): 653. NRCBL: 9.7; 1.3.9; 1.3.7; 1.3.12; 18.6. SC: le.

An unhealthy practice [editorial]. *Nature* 2005 October 20; 437(7062): 1065-1066. NRCBL: 9.7; 9.3.1; 1.3.9.

Alpert, Joseph S. Doctors and the drug industry: how can we handle potential conflicts of interest? [editorial]. *American Journal of Medicine* 2005 February; 118(2): 99-100. NRCBL: 9.7; 7.3; 1.3.2.

American Academy of Pain Medicine; American Pain Society; American Society of Addiction Medicine. Public policy statement on the rights and responsibilities of health care professionals in the use of opioids for the treatment of pain: a consensus document from the American Academy of Pain Medicine, the American Pain Society, and the American Society of Addiction Medicine. *Pain Medicine* 2004 September; 5(3): 301-302. NRCBL: 9.7; 4.4.

Anand, Geeta. Lucrative niches:how drugs for rare diseases became lifeline for companies;federal law gives monopoly for seven years, fueling surge in biotech profits;a teen's $360,000 treatment. *Wall Street Journal* 2005 November 15; p. A1, A18. NRCBL: 9.7; 9.5.1. SC: po. Identifiers: The most expensive drugs: first in a series.

Anand, Geeta. Support system: through charities, drug makers help people — and themselves; by donating money firms keep patients insured and medicine prices high; Mrs. Gushwa's $2000 pills. *Wall Street Journal* 2005 December 1; p. A1, A10. NRCBL: 9.7; 9.3.1; 9.5.10. SC: po. Identifiers: The most expensive drugs: third in a series.

Anand, Geeta. Uncertain miracle: a biotech drug extends a life, but at what price? For Ms. Lees, treatment bill now totals $7 million; her bones keep crumbling; guilt of another $1400 day. *Wall Street Journal* 2005 November 16; p. A1, A15. NRCBL: 9.7; 9.3.1. SC: po. Identifiers: The most expensive drugs: second in a series.

Anand, Geeta. Why Genzyme can charge so much for Cerezyme. *Wall Street Journal* 2005 November 16; p. A15. NRCBL: 9.7. SC: po.

Armstrong, David. Delicate operation: how a famed hospital invests in device it uses and promotes; Cleveland Clinic set up fund that has stock in maker of heart-surgery system; Dr. Cosgrove's multiple roles. *Wall Street Journal* 2005 December 12; p. A1, A16. NRCBL: 9.7; 7.4. SC: po.

Bal, Arun. Can the medical profession and the pharmaceutical industry work ethically for better health care? *Indian Journal of Medical Ethics* 2004 January-March; 1(1): 17. NRCBL: 9.7; 1.3.2; 9.3.1.

Barton, John H.; Emanuel, Ezekiel J. The patents-based pharmaceutical development process: rationale, problems, and potential reforms. *JAMA: The Journal of the American Medical Association* 2005 October 26; 294(16): 2075-2082. NRCBL: 9.7; 5.3.
> Abstract: The pharmaceutical industry is facing substantial criticism from many directions, including financial barriers to access to drugs in both developed and developing countries, high profits, spending on advertising and marketing, and other issues. Underlying these criticisms are fundamental questions about the value of the current patent-based drug development system. Six major problems with the patent system are (1) recovery of research costs by patent monopoly reduces access to drugs; (2) market demand rather than health needs determines research priorities; (3) resources between research and marketing are misallocated; (4) the market for drugs has inherent market failures; (5) overall investment in drug research and development is too low, compared with profits; and (6) the existing system discriminates against US patients. Potential solutions fall into 3 categories: change in drug pricing through either price controls or tiered pricing; change in drug industry structure through a "buy-out" pricing system or with the public sector acting as exclusive research funder; and change in development incentives through a disease burden incentive system, orphan drug approaches, or requiring new drugs to demonstrate improvement over existing products prior to US Food and Drug Administration approval. We recommend 4 complementary reforms: (1) having no requirement to test new drug products against existing products prior to approval but requiring rigorous comparative postapproval testing; (2) international tiered pricing and systematic safeguards to prevent flow-back; (3) increased government-funded research and buy-out for select conditions; and (4) targeted experiments using other approaches for health conditions in which there has been little progress and innovation over the last few decades.

Bates, Benjamin R.; Poirot, Kristan; Harris, Tina M.; Condit, Celeste M.; Achter, Paul J. Evaluating direct-to-consumer marketing of race-based pharmacogenomics: a focus group study of public understandings of applied genomic medication. *Journal of Health Communication* 2004 November-December; 9(6): 541-559. NRCBL: 9.7; 1.3.2; 9.3.1; 9.5.4; 15.1. SC: em.

Berenson, Alex. Cancer drugs offer hope, but a huge expense. *New York Times* 2005 July 12; p. A1, C3. NRCBL: 9.7; 9.3.1; 9.5.1. SC: po.

Berenson, Alex. Despite vow drug makers still withhold data. *New York Times* 2005 May 31; p. A1, C3. NRCBL: 9.7; 18.2. SC: po.

Berezuk, Gregory P.; McCarty, Garland E. Investigational drugs and vaccines fielded in support of Operation Desert Storm. *Military Medicine* 1992 August; 157(8): 404-406. NRCBL: 9.7; 21.2; 21.3.

Bolton, Roger G. The ethics of the drug discovery and development process. *In:* Salek, Sam; Edgar, Andrew, eds. Pharmaceutical Ethics. New York: Wiley; 2002: 45-60. NRCBL: 9.7; 1.3.9.

Bootman, J. Lyle; Grizzle, Amy J. The economics of drug-related morbidity and mortality: ethical considerations. *In:* Salek, Sam; Edgar, Andrew, eds. Pharmaceutical Ethics. New York: Wiley; 2002: 111-122. NRCBL: 9.7; 9.3.1.

Breckenridge, Alasdair. For the good of the patient: risks and benefits of medicines. *Pharmacoepidemiology and Drug Safety* 2003 March; 12(2): 145-150. NRCBL: 9.7; 8.2; 9.1.

Carter, Ivan E. Canadian Psychiatric Association guidelines in relating to the pharmaceutical industry. *Canadian Journal of Psychiatry* 1987 August; 32(6): 476-480. NRCBL: 9.7.

Chimonas, Susan; Rothman, David J. New federal guidelines for physician-pharmaceutical industry relations: the politics of policy formation. *Health Affairs* 2005 July-August; 24(4): 949-960. NRCBL: 9.7; 1.3.2; 9.3.1.

Chin, Marshall H. The patient's role in choice of medications: direct-to-consumer advertising and patient decision

NRCBL: National Reference Center for Bioethics Literature Classification Scheme   See inside front cover for terms.

149

aids. *Yale Journal of Health Policy, Law, and Ethics* 2005 Summer; 5(2): 771-784. NRCBL: 9.7; 1.3.2; 8.1.

Conk, George W. Reactions and overreactions: smallpox vaccination, complications, and compensation. *Fordham Environmental Law Journal* 2003 Summer; 14(3): 439-498. NRCBL: 9.7; 21.3. SC: le.

Cook, David; Owens, Gary; Jacobs, Michael. Human growth hormone treatment in adults: balancing economics and ethics. *American Journal of Managed Care* 2004 October; 10(13, Supplement): S417-S419. NRCBL: 9.7; 9.4. SC: em.

Coombes, Rebecca. Drug industry's new code criticised for lacking teeth [news]. *BMJ: British Medical Journal* 2005 November 26; 331(7527): 1225. NRCBL: 9.7; 1.3.2.

Cooper, Richelle J.; Schriger, David L. The availability of references and the sponsorship of original research cited in pharmaceutical advertisements. *CMAJ/JAMC: Canadian Medical Association Journal* 2005 February 15; 172(4): 487-491. NRCBL: 9.7; 1.3.2; 1.3.7. SC: em.

Dabade, Gopal. Unhealthy drug donations. *Indian Journal of Medical Ethics* 2004 January-March; 1(1): 18. NRCBL: 9.7; 1.3.2; 9.3.1.

Dawson, Angus. The determination of 'best interests' in relation to childhood vaccinations. *Bioethics* 2005 April; 19(2): 188-205. NRCBL: 9.7; 9.5.1; 9.5.7. Note: Corrected version of the article originally published in Bioethics 2005 February; 19(1): 72-89.

Abstract: There are many different ethical arguments that might be advanced for and against childhood vaccinations. In this paper I will explore one particular argument that focuses on the idea that childhood vaccinations are justifiable because they are held to be in the best interests of a particular child. Two issues arise from this idea. The first issue is how best interests are to be determined in the case of childhood vaccinations. The second issue is what follows from this to justify potential interventions within the family in relation to such vaccinations. I argue that best interests must be characterised objectively in such situations and that this means that, in at least some cases, parental decision-making about vaccinating their children may be overridden.

De George, Richard T. Intellectual property and pharmaceutical drugs: an ethical analysis. *Business Ethics Quarterly* 2005 October; 15(4): 549-575. NRCBL: 9.7; 5.3. SC: an.

Dees, Richard H. Slippery slopes, wonder drugs, and cosmetic neurology: the neuroethics of enhancement [editorial]. *Neurology* 2004 September 28; 63(6): 951-952. NRCBL: 9.7; 4.5; 4.1.2; 17.1.

Dessing, R.P. Ethical rationalism applied to pharmaceuticals. *In:* Salek, Sam; Edgar, Andrew, eds. Pharmaceutical Ethics. New York: Wiley; 2002: 27-43. NRCBL: 9.7.

Dickersin, Kay; Goodman, Steven. The long and creative arm of the drug industry [letter]. *Lancet* 2005 February 19-25; 365(9460): 656. NRCBL: 9.7; 1.3.2; 7.1.

Diller, Lawrence. Fallout from the pharma scandals: the loss of doctors' credibility? *Hastings Center Report* 2005 May-June; 35(3): 28-29. NRCBL: 9.7; 9.5.7; 17.4; 18.5.2; 20.7.

Dwyer, Peter. Pharmacists and pharmaceutical manufacturers: some ethical considerations. *Medicine and Law: World Association for Medical Law* 2005 June; 24(2): 437-454. NRCBL: 9.7; 8.1; 4.1.1.

Eaton, Lynn. Drug company chiefs accept the need for more openness [news]. *BMJ: British Medical Journal* 2005 January 22; 330(7484): 163. NRCBL: 9.7; 18.2.

Eggertson, Laura. One-third of panel on breast implants declares conflict [news]. *CMAJ/JAMC: Canadian Medical Association Journal* 2005 August 2; 173(3): 241. NRCBL: 9.7; 1.3.2; 5.3; 9.5.5. Identifiers: Health Canada; Mentor Corporation; Inamed Corporation.

Faunce, Thomas Alured. The UNESCO bioethics declaration 'social responsibility' principle and cost-effectiveness price evaluations for essential medicines. *Monash Bioethics Review* 2005 July; 24(3): 10-19. NRCBL: 9.7; 6; 21.1. Identifiers: Australia; United Nations Scientific, Education and Cultural Organisation.

Faunce, T.S.; Tomossy, G.F. The UK House of Commons report on the influence of the pharmaceutical industry: lessons for equitable access to medicines in Australia. *Monash Bioethics Review* 2005 April; 24(2): 38-42. NRCBL: 9.7; 9.3.1; 21.1. Identifiers: United Kingdom (Great Britain).

Ferner, R.E. The influence of big pharma [editorial]. *BMJ: British Medical Journal* 2005 April 16; 330(7496): 855-856. NRCBL: 9.7; 9.3.1; 7.2; 18.1; 1.3.2; 2.4.

Gebhardt, D.O.E. The use of generic or patent medicines in the Netherlands [letter]. *Journal of Medical Ethics* 2005 July; 31(7): 409. NRCBL: 9.7; 1.3.2.

Geier, David; Geier, Mark. The true story of pertussis vaccination: a sordid legacy? *Journal of the History of Medicine and Allied Sciences* 2002 July; 57(3): 249-284. NRCBL: 9.7; 9.5.7; 9.1; 21.1.

Gemperli, Marcel P.; Stewart, Felicia H.; Phillips, Kathryn A.; Sakowski, Julie; Van Bebber, Stephanie; Bergthold, Linda. A qualitative study of insurers' coverage for mifepristone-induced abortion. *Managed Care Interface* 2005 March; 18(3): 26-30, 32. NRCBL: 9.7; 12.1; 9.3.1.

Gericke, C.A.; Riesberg, A.; Busse, R. Ethical issues in funding orphan drug research and development. *Journal of Medical Ethics* 2005 March; 31(3): 164-168. NRCBL: 9.7; 9.3.1; 1.3.2. SC: an.

Abstract: This essay outlines the moral dilemma of funding orphan drug research and development. To date, ethical aspects of priority setting for research funding have not been an issue of discussion in the bioethics debate. Conflicting moral obligations of beneficence and distributive justice appear to demand very different levels of funding for orphan drug research. The two types of orphan disease, rare diseases and tropical diseases, however, present very different ethical challenges to questions about allocation of research funds. The dilemma is analysed considering utilitarian and rights based theories of justice and moral obligations of non-abandonment and a professional obligation to advance medical science. The limitations of standard economic evaluation tools and other priority setting tools used to inform health policy decision makers on research funding decisions are outlined.

Gibson, Liza. Adverse reaction reports may be vulnerable to manipulation [news]. *BMJ: British Medical Journal* 2005 June 4; 330(7503): 1287. NRCBL: 9.7; 1.3.2.

Giles, Jim. Industry money skews drug overviews [news]. *Nature* 2005 September 22; 437(7058): 458-459. NRCBL: 9.7; 1.3.9.

Good, Chris. Ethical problems of drug categorization for reimbursement. *In:* Salek, Sam; Edgar, Andrew, eds. Pharmaceutical Ethics. New York: Wiley; 2002: 179-190. NRCBL: 9.7; 9.3.1.

Gosfield, Alice G. The hidden costs of free lunches: fraud and abuse in physician-pharmaceutical arrangements. *Journal of Medical Practice Management* 2005 March-April; 20(5): 253-258. NRCBL: 9.7; 1.3.2; 9.3.1.

Greenberger, Marcia D.; Vogelstein, Rachel. Pharmacist refusals: a threat to women's health. *Science* 2005 June 10; 308(5728): 1557-1558. NRCBL: 9.7; 8.1; 11.1; 4.1.1; 9.5.5.

Groopman, Jerome. The pediatric gap: why have most medications never been properly tested on kids? *New Yorker* 2005 January 10; p. 32-37. NRCBL: 9.7; 18.5.2; 9.5.7.

Guha, Amitava. A comparison of codes of pharmaceutical marketing practices. *Indian Journal of Medical Ethics* 2004 January-March; 1(1): 19- 21. NRCBL: 9.7; 6; 21.1; 1.3.2. Identifiers: International Federation of Pharmaceutical Manufacturers and Associations (IFPMA); World Health Organization (WHO); Health Action International (HAI).

Hamilton, David P. How Genentech, Novartis stifled a promising drug; biotech firm tried to pursue peanut allergy injection, but contract got in way; Zach avoids a "kiss of death". *Wall Street Journal* 2005 April 15; p. A1, A10. NRCBL: 9.7. SC: po.

Harris, Gardiner. Drug makers are still giving gifts to doctors, F.D.A. officials tell senators. *New York Times* 2005 March 4; p. A15. NRCBL: 9.7; 9.3.1; 8.1. SC: po.

Harrison, Ivor. Ethical promotion and advertising of medicines: where do we draw the line? *In:* Salek, Sam; Edgar, Andrew, eds. Pharmaceutical Ethics. New York: Wiley; 2002: 161-177. NRCBL: 9.7; 1.3.2.

Hensley, Scott; Martinez, Barbara. To sell their drugs, companies increasingly rely on doctors; for $750 and up, physicians tell peers about products; talks called educational; Dr. Pitts's busy speaking tour. *Wall Street Journal* 2005 July 15; p. A1, A2. NRCBL: 9.7; 1.3.2; 7.1; 9.3.1. SC: po.

Hollon, Matthew F. Direct-to-consumer advertising: a haphazard approach to health promotion [editorial]. *JAMA: The Journal of the American Medical Association* 2005 April 27; 293(16): 2030-2033. NRCBL: 9.7; 9.1; 9.3.1.

Howland, John S. A family physician grapples with vaccine ethics. *Linacre Quarterly* 2005 August; 72(3): 260-266. NRCBL: 9.7; 1.2.

Hughes, James. Beyond "real boys" and back to parental obligations [comment]. *American Journal of Bioethics* 2005 May-June; 5(3): 61-62. NRCBL: 9.7; 17.4; 9.5.7. Comments: comment on Ilina Singh, "Will the 'real boy' please behave: dosing dilemmas for parents of boys with ADHD," American Journal of Bioethics 2005 May-June; 5(3): 34-47.

Jefford, Michael; Savulescu, Julian; Thomson, Jacqui; Schofield, Penelope; Mileshkin, Linda; Agalianos, Emilia; Zalcberg, John. Medical paternalism and expensive unsubsidised drugs. *BMJ: British Medical Journal* 2005 November 5; 331(7524): 1075- 1077. NRCBL: 9.7; 9.3.1; 8.1. SC: em.

Jenny-Avital, Elizabeth R.; Blumenthal, David. Doctors and drug companies [letter and reply]. *New England Journal of Medicine* 2005 February 17; 352(7): 733- 734. NRCBL: 9.7; 1.3.2; 9.3.1.

Jordens, Christopher; Anderson, Lynley. Should we be concerned about direct-to-consumer advertising of prescription drugs? [editorial]. *Journal of Bioethical Inquiry* 2005; 2(2): 61-62. NRCBL: 9.7; 1.3.2.

Joseph, Sarah. Pharmaceutical corporations and access to drugs: the "fourth wave" of corporate human rights scrutiny. *Human Rights Quarterly* 2003 May; 25(2): 425-452. NRCBL: 9.7; 9.5.6; 21.1; 5.3; 1.3.5.

Kalso, Eija. Opioids for persistent non-cancer pain [editorial]. *BMJ: British Medical Journal* 2005 January 22; 330(7484): 156- 157. NRCBL: 9.7; 4.4.

Kamtekar, Rachna. Why life-saving drugs should be public goods. *Indian Journal of Medical Ethics* 2004 July-September; 1(3): 77-78. NRCBL: 9.7; 1.1.

Kassirer, Jerome P. Physicians' financial ties with the pharmaceutical industry: a critical element of a formidable marketing network. *In:* Moore, Don A.; Cain, Daylian M.; Loewenstein, George; Bazerman, Max H., eds. Conflicts

NRCBL: National Reference Center for Bioethics Literature Classification Scheme   See inside front cover for terms.

151

of Interest: Challenges and Solutions in Business, Law, Medicine, and Public Policy. New York: Cambridge University Press; 2005: 133-141. NRCBL: 9.7; 1.3.2; 1.3.9; 7.3; 9.3.1. SC: an.

Kaufman, K.R. Modafinil in sports: ethical considerations. *British Journal of Sports Medicine* 2005 April; 39(4): 241-244. NRCBL: 9.7; 9.5.9; 9.5.1; 4.5. SC: cs. Identifiers: Kelli White.

Kayser, Bengt; Mauron, Alexandre; Miah, Andy. Legalisation of performance-enhancing drugs [opinion]. *Lancet* 2005 December; 366(Medicine and Sport): S21. NRCBL: 9.7; 4.5. SC: le.

Kiel, Helen. Pharmacist misconduct: the pitfalls of practice. *Journal of Law and Medicine* 2005 February; 12(3): 348-353. NRCBL: 9.7; 7.4. SC: le. Identifiers: Australia.

Kravitz, Richard L.; Epstein, Ronald M.; Feldman, Mitchell D.; Franz, Carol E.; Azari, Rahman; Wilkes, Michael S.; Hinton, Ladson; Franks, Peter. Influence of patients' requests for direct-to-consumer advertised antidepressants: a randomized controlled trial. *JAMA: The Journal of the American Medical Association* 2005 April 27; 293(16): 1995-2002. NRCBL: 9.7; 9.1; 9.3.1. SC: em.

Abstract: CONTEXT: Direct-to-consumer (DTC) advertising of prescription drugs in the United States is both ubiquitous and controversial. Critics charge that it leads to overprescribing, while proponents counter that it helps avert underuse of effective treatments, especially for conditions that are poorly recognized or stigmatized. OBJECTIVE: To ascertain the effects of patients' DTC- related requests on physicians' initial treatment decisions in patients with depressive symptoms. DESIGN: Randomized trial using standardized patients (SPs). Six SP roles were created by crossing 2 conditions (major depression or adjustment disorder with depressed mood) with 3 request types (brand-specific, general, or none). SETTING: Offices of primary care physicians in Sacramento, Calif; San Francisco, Calif; and Rochester, NY, between May 2003 and May 2004. PARTICIPANTS: One hundred fifty-two family physicians and general internists recruited from solo and group practices and health maintenance organizations; cooperation rates ranged from 53% to 61%. INTERVENTIONS: The Sps were randomly assigned to make 298 unannounced visits, with assignments constrained so physicians saw 1 SP with major depression and 1 with adjustment disorder. The Sps made a brand-specific drug request, a general drug request, or no request (control condition) in approximately one third of visits. MAIN OUTCOME MEASURES: Data on prescribing, mental health referral, and primary care follow-up obtained from SP written reports, visit audiorecordings, chart review, and analysis of written prescriptions and drug samples. The effects of request type on prescribing were evaluated using contingency tables and confirmed in generalized linear mixed models that accounted for clustering and adjusted for site, physician, and visit characteristics. RESULTS: Standardized patient role fidelity was excellent, and the suspicion rate that physicians had seen an SP was 13%. In major depression, rates of antidepressant prescribing were 53%, 76%, and 31% for Sps making brand-specific, general, and no requests, respectively (P001). In adjustment disorder, antidepressant prescribing rates were 55%, 39%, and 10%, respectively (P001). The results were confirmed in multivariate models. Minimally acceptable initial care (any combination of an antidepressant, mental health referral, or follow-up within 2 weeks) was offered to 98% of Sps in the major depression role making a general request, 90% of those making a brand-specific request, and 56% of those making no request (P001). CONCLUSIONS: Patients' requests have a profound effect on physician prescribing in major depression and adjustment disorder. Direct-to-consumer advertising may have competing effects on quality, potentially both averting underuse and promoting overuse.

Krisberg, Kim. Court decision on medical marijuana use worries patient advocates. *Nation's Health* 2005 August; 35(6): 1, 14. NRCBL: 9.7; 9.5.9. SC: le.

Krugman, Paul. Drugs, devices and doctors [opinion]. *New York Times* 2005 December 16; p. A41. NRCBL: 9.7; 1.3.9; 1.3.2. SC: po.

Kuehn, Bridget M. Pharmaceutical industry funding for residencies sparks controversy. *JAMA: The Journal of the American Medical Association* 2005 April 6; 293(13): 1572, 1579-1580. NRCBL: 9.7; 7.2; 5.3.

Kutlesa, Nicole J. Creating a sustainable immunization system in Canada — the case for a vaccine-related injury compensation scheme. *Health Law Journal* 2004; 12: 201-242. NRCBL: 9.7; 8.3.2; 8.5. SC: le.

Lambert, Laura A.; Blumenthal, David. Doctors and drug companies [letter and reply]. *New England Journal of Medicine* 2005 February 17; 352(7): 733- 734. NRCBL: 9.7; 1.3.2; 9.3.1.

Lau, Yvonne. Is banning direct to consumer advertising of prescription medicine justified paternalism? *Journal of Bioethical Inquiry* 2005; 2(2): 69-74. NRCBL: 9.7; 1.3.2. SC: le.

Abstract: New Zealand is one of two OECD countries in the world where direct-to-consumer advertising of prescription medicine (DTCA-PM) is permitted. Increase in such activity in recent years has resulted in a disproportionate increase in dispensary volume of heavily advertised medicines. Concern for the potential harm to healthcare consumers and the public healthcare system has prompted the medical profession to call for a ban on DTCA-PM as the best way of protecting the public interest. Such blanket prohibition however also interferes with the public's right of access to information. This paper will examine if banning DTCA-PM would constitute a justified form of paternalism in the context of today's New Zealand.

Leisinger, Klaus M. The corporate social responsibility of the pharmaceutical industry: idealism without illusion and realism without resignation. *Business Ethics Quarterly* 2005 October; 15(4): 577-594. NRCBL: 9.7; 1.3.2. SC: an.

Lenhardt, Erin. Why so glum? Toward a fair balance of competitive interests in direct-to-consumer advertising and the well-being of the mentally ill consumers it targets. *Health Matrix: Journal of Law-Medicine* 2005 Winter; 15(1): 165-204. NRCBL: 9.7; 1.3.2; 17.4. SC: le.

Lenzer, Jeanne. American Medical Association rejects proposal to ban consumer adverts for prescription medicines [news]. *BMJ: British Medical Journal* 2005 July 2; 331(7507): 7. NRCBL: 9.7; 1.3.2.

Lenzer, Jeanne. Doctors refuse space to group fighting drug company influence [news]. *BMJ: British Medical Journal* 2005 September 24; 331(7518): 653. NRCBL: 9.7; 1.3.2; 9.3.1; 7.1.

Levy, Stuart B.; Star, Larry; Kupferberg, Eric D.; Roselin, Joel. The misuse of antibiotics [forum]. *Medical Ethics Newsletter [Lahey Clinic]* 2004 Winter; 11(1): 5-8. NRCBL: 9.7; 1.3.2.

Lexchin, Joel R. Implications of pharmaceutical industry funding on clinical research [opinion]. *Annals of Pharmacotherapy* 2005 January; 39(1): 194-197. NRCBL: 9.7; 1.3.2; 9.3.1; 1.3.7; 18.6.

Lexchin, Joel; Cassels, Alan. Does the C in CME stand for "continuing" or "commercial"? [letter]. *CMAJ/JAMC: Canadian Medical Association Journal* 2005 January 18; 172(2): 160-162. NRCBL: 9.7; 7.2; 9.3.1; 1.3.9.

Lipman, Arthur G. Pain and the pharmacist: opinion #3: communication is key. *Pain Medicine* 2003 June; 4(2): 190-194. NRCBL: 9.7; 4.4; 9.5.9. SC: cs.

Lyles, Alan. Must an interest be a conflict? [editorial]. *Clinical Therapeutics* 2005 March; 27(3): 344-345. NRCBL: 9.7; 7.3; 1.3.9.

Malavige, G.N. Doctors, drug companies and medical ethics: a Sri Lankan perspective. *Indian Journal of Medical Ethics* 2004 January-March; 1(1): 26. NRCBL: 9.7; 7.3.

Malone, Kevin M.; Hinman, Alan R. Vaccination mandates: the public health imperative and individual rights. *In:* Goodman, Richard A.; Rothstein, Mark A.; Hoffman, Richard E.; Lopez, Wilfredo; Matthews, Gene W., eds. Law in Public Health Practice. New York: Oxford University Press; 2003: 262-284. NRCBL: 9.7; 9.5.7; 9.1. SC: le.

Manasse, Henri R., Jr. Conscientious objection and the pharmacist. *Science* 2005 June 10; 308(5728): 1558-1559. NRCBL: 9.7; 11.1; 9.5.5; 8.1; 4.1.1.

Mansfield, Peter R. Banning all drug promotion is the best option pending major reforms. *Journal of Bioethical Inquiry* 2005; 2(2): 75-81. NRCBL: 9.7; 1.3.2. SC: le.
Abstract: Drug promotion should be evaluated according to its impact on health, access to information, informed consent, and wealth. Drug promotion currently does more harm than good to each of these objectives because it is usually misleading. This is a systemic problem. Whilst improved regulation and education will address it to some degree, major reforms to payment systems for drug companies and doctors are also required. Until all these systemic reforms can be put in place, the best policy option is to ban the promotion of drugs to doctors and the public. Consequently, pending major reforms, it is appropriate for governments to restrict drug promotion as much as is politically achievable.

Mansfield, Peter R.; Mintzes, Barbara; Richards, Dee; Toop, Les. Direct to consumer advertising [editorial]. *BMJ: British Medical Journal* 2005 January 1; 330(7481): 5. NRCBL: 9.7; 1.3.2.

Marckmann, Georg. Access to essential drugs: the ethical challenge of allocating obligations. *In:* Thiele, F.; Ashcroft, R.E., eds. Bioethics in a Small World. Berlin: Springer; 2005: 111-119. NRCBL: 9.7; 21.1; 9.2. SC: an.

Markovits, Daniel. Quarantines and distributive justice. *Journal of Law, Medicine and Ethics* 2005 Summer; 33(2): 323-344. NRCBL: 9.7; 1.1; 9.1.

Maschke, Karen. Patients, patents, profits. *Hastings Center Report* 2005 July-August; 35(4): inside front cover. NRCBL: 9.7; 1.3.9; 18.6.

Mathews, Anna Wilde. An FDA reviewer battles the drug his boss approved: private letter gets Dr. Misbin pulled from diabetes case but he pursues it anyway; "I get to count the bodies". *Wall Street Journal* 2005 October 26; p. A1, A13. NRCBL: 9.7; 5.3; 9.5.1. SC: po.

Mathews, Anna Wilde. Detective work: reading fine print, insurers question studies of drugs; Kaiser's veteran sleuth scours medical-journal articles and sees marketing spin; doctors fear loss of choices. *Wall Street Journal* 2005 August 24; p. A1, A6. NRCBL: 9.7; 9.3.2; 8.1. SC: po.

Matthews, Robert. A risk we have to swallow: can we ever be sure that medicines are safe before they hit the market? [opinion]. *New Scientist* 2005 March 5-11; 185(2489): 23. NRCBL: 9.7; 18.1.

McCabe, Alison R. A precarious balancing act — the role of the FDA as protector of public health and industry wealth. *Suffolk University Law Review* 2003; 36(3): 787-819. NRCBL: 9.7; 5.3; 5.1. SC: le.

McCabe, Christopher; Claxton, Karl; Tsuchiya, Aki. Orphan drugs and the NHS: should we value rarity? *BMJ: British Medical Journal* 2005 October 29; 331(7523): 1016-1019. NRCBL: 9.7; 9.3.1; 9.4.

McHenry, Leemon. On the origin of great ideas: science in the age of big pharma. *Hastings Center Report* 2005 November-December; 35(6): 17-19. NRCBL: 9.7; 17.4; 1.3.7.

Meier, Barry. A choice for the heart: it's easier to get data on a car than on a medical device. *New York Times* 2005 June 23; p. C1, C19. NRCBL: 9.7; 1.3.12; 5.3. SC: po.

Meier, Barry. Drug industry plans release of more data about studies. *New York Times* 2005 January 7; p. C4. NRCBL: 9.7; 18.2. SC: po.

Meier, Barry. Faulty heart devices force some scary decisions; patients weigh risks of replacing unit through surgery. *New York Times* 2005 June 20; p. A1, A12. NRCBL: 9.7; 8.3.1; 8.3.4. SC: po.

Meier, Barry. Implant program for heart device was a sales spur. *New York Times* 2005 September 27; p. A1, C4. NRCBL: 9.7; 1.3.2; 9.3.1. SC: po.

NRCBL: National Reference Center for Bioethics Literature Classification Scheme   See inside front cover for terms.

153

Meier, Barry. Implants with flaws: disclosure and delay. *New York Times* 2005 June 14; p. C1, C3. NRCBL: 9.7; 5.3; 8.3.1. SC: po.

Meier, Barry. Maker of heart device kept flaw from doctors. *New York Times* 2005 May 24; p. A1, C3. NRCBL: 9.7; 8.3.1. SC: po.

Mello, Michelle M.; Brennan, Troyen A. Legal concerns and the influenza vaccine shortage [opinion]. *JAMA: The Journal of the American Medical Association* 2005 October 12; 294(14): 1817-1820. NRCBL: 9.7; 9.5.1. SC: le.

Merrills, Jon. The basis of ethics. *In:* Salek, Sam; Edgar, Andrew, eds. Pharmaceutical Ethics. New York: Wiley; 2002: 1-12. NRCBL: 9.7; 1.1; 1.3.1; 6.

Mowery, Grace-Marie. A patient's right of privacy in computerized pharmacy records. *University of Cincinnati Law Review* 1998 Winter; 66(2): 697-746. NRCBL: 9.7; 8.4; 1.3.12. SC: le.

Moynihan, Ray. The marketing of a disease: female sexual dysfunction. *BMJ: British Medical Journal* 2005 January 22; 330(7484): 192- 194. NRCBL: 9.7; 1.3.2; 1.3.9.

Murray, Elizabeth; Lo, Bernard; Pollack, Lance; Donelan, Karen. Direct-to-consumer advertising: physicians' views of its effects on quality of care and the doctor-patient relationship. *Journal of the American Board of Family Practice* 2003 November-December; 16(6): 513-524. NRCBL: 9.7; 1.3.2; 8.1; 9.8. SC: em.

Nicol, Dianne. Cross-cultural issues in balancing patent rights and consumer access to biotechnological and pharmaceutical inventions. *In:* Brannigan, Michael C., ed. Cross-Cultural Biotechnology. Lanham: Rowman and Littlefield; 2004: 155-164. NRCBL: 9.7; 5.3; 9.3.1; 21.1. SC: le.

Nortvedt, Per; Kvarstein, Gunnvald; Jønland, Ingvild. Sedation of patients in intensive care medicine and nursing: ethical issues. *Nursing Ethics* 2005 September; 12(5): 522-536. NRCBL: 9.7; 4.4; 9.5.1. SC: em.

Abstract: This article focuses on the ethical aspects of medically- induced sedation and pain relief in intensive care medicine. The study results reported are part of a larger investigation of patients' experiences of being sedated and receiving pain relief, and also families' experiences of having a close relative under controlled sedation in an intensive care unit. The study is based on qualitative in-depth interviews with nine nurses and six doctors working in intensive care and surgical units in a major Norwegian hospital. The textual data are interpreted according to Kvale's method for analyzing qualitative data. There are ethical problems regarding how to achieve an acceptable balance between a patient's subjective well-being and the medical need for reduced sedation. The authors discuss whether some medical reasons for reduced sedation are ethically justifiable, given the actual medical knowledge available. The study also addresses the ethical consequences of reducing medically-induced sedation and the demands it puts on interdisciplinary co-operation and communication, as well as the importance of improving the quality of medical and nursing care.

Oldani, Michael J. Pharma PR or medical education? [letter]. *Hastings Center Report* 2005 March-April; 35(2): 5-7. NRCBL: 9.7; 5.3; 7.2; 1.3.9; 1.3.2. Identifiers: public relations.

Panush, Richard S. Why I no longer accept pens (or other "gifts") from industry (and why you shouldn't either) [editorial]. *Journal of Rheumatology* 2004 August; 31(8): 1478-1482. NRCBL: 9.7; 1.3.2; 9.3.1.

Parmet, Wendy E.; Scott, Charity; Hodge, James G., Jr.; Nahmias, David E.; DeMaria, Alfred, Jr.; Rees, Clifford M.; Goodman, Richard A. Plenary program: Jacobson v. Massachusetts. *Journal of Law, Medicine and Ethics* 2005 Winter; 33(4, Supplement): 24-27. NRCBL: 9.7; 8.3.4; 9.1. SC: le.

Perls, Thomas T.; Reisman, Neal R.; Olshansky, S. Jay. Provision or distribution of growth hormone for "antiaging": clinical and legal issues. *JAMA: The Journal of the American Medical Association* 2005 October 26; 294(16): 2086-2090. NRCBL: 9.7; 9.5.2.

Phatak, Arun. The pharmaceutical industry and the medical profession. *Issues in Medical Ethics* 1998 October-December; 6(4): 131-132. NRCBL: 9.7; 7.2. Conference: International Conference on Ethical Values in Health Care; 2-4 January 1998; Panchgani, India.

Poe, Amy. Cancer prevention or drug promotion? Journalists mishandle the tamoxifen story. *International Journal of Health Services* 1999; 29(3): 657- 661. NRCBL: 9.7; 9.5.5; 1.3.7.

Pollack, Andrew. Justices expand rights to experiment with patented drugs. *New York Times* 2005 June 14; p. C1, C8. NRCBL: 9.7; 1.3.9. SC: po.

Pollack, Andrew. Patients in test won't get drug, Amgen decides. *New York Times* 2005 February 12; p. C1, C2. NRCBL: 9.7; 18.2. SC: po.

Popp, Richard L. Conflict of interest for the physician-inventor using a device in human subjects [editorial]. *American Heart Journal* 2005 January; 149(1): 1-3. NRCBL: 9.7; 18.2; 1.3.2; 7.3.

Preziosi, Paolo. Science, pharmacoeconomics and ethics in drug R&D: a sustainable future scenario? [opinion]. *Nature Reviews Drug Discovery* 2004 June; 3(6): 521-526. NRCBL: 9.7; 18.2; 9.3.1. Identifiers: drug research and development.

Rasmussen, Nicolas. The drug industry and clinical research in interwar America: three types of physician collaborator. *Bulletin of the History of Medicine* 2005 Spring; 79(1): 50-80. NRCBL: 9.7; 5.3; 7.1; 1.3.9; 2.2.

Ravindran, G.D. The physician and the pharmaceutical industry: both must keep the patient's interests at heart. *Issues in Medical Ethics* 1999 January-March; 7(1): 21-22. NRCBL: 9.7.

Ready, Tinker. Courts crack down on drug marketing strategies [news]. *Nature Medicine* 2004 July; 10(7): 655. NRCBL: 9.7; 1.3.2; 1.3.9; 1.3.7. SC: le.

Rentmeester, Christy A. Pharma PR or medical education? [letter]. *Hastings Center Report* 2005 March-April; 35(2): 6-7. NRCBL: 9.7; 5.3; 7.2; 1.3.9; 1.3.2. Identifiers: public relations.

Roselin, Joel M.; Koski. Pharma PR or medical education? [letter]. *Hastings Center Report* 2005 March-April; 35(2): 5-6. NRCBL: 9.7; 5.3; 7.2; 1.3.9; 1.3.2. Identifiers: public relations.

Roy, Nobhojit. Who rules the great Indian drug bazaar? [editorial]. *Indian Journal of Medical Ethics* 2004 January-March; 1(1): 2-3. NRCBL: 9.7; 1.3.2; 9.3.1.

Ryan, Michael P. Introduction: ethical responsibilities regarding drugs, patents, and health. *Business Ethics Quarterly* 2005 October; 15(4): 543-547. NRCBL: 9.7; 5.3.

Salek, Sam. Holistic approach in choice of pharmaceutical agents: ethical responsibilities. *In:* Salek, Sam; Edgar, Andrew, eds. Pharmaceutical Ethics. New York: Wiley; 2002: 123-135. NRCBL: 9.7; 8.1.

Sattar, S. Pirzada; Ahmed, Mohammed Shakeel; Madison, James; Olsen, Denise R.; Bhatia, Subhash C.; Ellahi, Shahid; Majeed, Farhan; Ramaswamy, Sriram; Petty, Frederick; Wilson, Daniel R. Patient and physician attitudes to using medications with religiously forbidden ingredients. *Annals of Pharmacotherapy* 2004 November; 38(11): 1830-1835. NRCBL: 9.7; 8.2; 8.3.1; 1.2. SC: em.

Saul, Stephanie. FDA approves a heart drug for African-Americans. *New York Times* 2005 June 24; p. C2. NRCBL: 9.7; 9.5.4. SC: po.

Schommer, Jon C. Direct-to-consumer advertising for prescription drugs. *Minnesota Medicine* 2005 March; 88(3): 32-33, 45. NRCBL: 9.7; 1.3.2; 8.1.

Seaman, Rachel M.H. The ethics and economics of consuming Canadian drugs. *Journal of the Oklahoma State Medical Association* 2005 January; 98(1): 22-26. NRCBL: 9.7; 1.3.2; 9.3.1; 21.1.

Shalev, Carmel. Access to essential drugs, human rights and global justice. *In:* Thiele, F.; Ashcroft, R.E., eds. Bioethics in a Small World. Berlin: Springer; 2005: 93-109. NRCBL: 9.7; 21.1. SC: an.

Shanmugan, Geetha. Miracle grow for children. *Ivy Journal of Ethics* 2003; 3(1): 10-13. NRCBL: 9.7; 9.5.9. SC: an.

Solomon, Daniel H.; Avorn, Jerry. Coxibs, science, and the public trust [editorial]. *Archives of Internal Medicine* 2005 January 24; 165(2): 158-160. NRCBL: 9.7; 5.3; 18.2.

Spence, Des. The age of entitlement [opinion]. *BMJ: British Medical Journal* 2005 November 26; 331(7527): 1279. NRCBL: 9.7; 9.3.1; 1.3.2.

Spier, R.E. Therapeutic vaccines. A pandoric prospect. *Advances in Experimental Medicine and Biology* 1996; 397: 183-189. NRCBL: 9.7; 18.1; 3.1; 18.1.

Steers, William D. Academic urologists and their relationships with industry [editorial]. *Journal of Urology* 2005 March; 173(3): 677-678. NRCBL: 9.7; 1.3.2; 9.3.1.

Steinbock, B. The case for physician assisted suicide: not (yet) proven. *Journal of Medical Ethics* 2005 April; 31(4): 235-241. NRCBL: 9.7; 9.5.1. SC: an; le. Identifiers: Oregon.

Abstract: The legalization of physician assisted suicide (PAS) in Oregon and physician assisted death (PAD) in The Netherlands has revitalized the debate over whether and under what conditions individuals should be able to determine the time and manner of their deaths, and whether they should be able to enlist the help of physicians in doing so. Although the change in the law is both dramatic and recent, the basic arguments for and against have not really changed since the issue was debated by Glanville Williams and Yale Kamisar nearly 50 years ago. In this paper, the author argues in favour of Kamisar's consequentialist framework. Any change in law and social policy should not be based solely on individual cases, heart wrenching though these may be. Instead, we need to assess the need for PAS, and weigh this against the risks of mistake and abuse.

Steinbrook, Robert. Financial conflicts of interest and the Food and Drug Administration's advisory committees [opinion]. *New England Journal of Medicine* 2005 July 14; 353(2): 116-118. NRCBL: 9.7; 1.3.5; 5.3.

Steinman, Michael A.; Shlipak, Michael G.; McPhee, Stephen J. Of principles and pens: attitudes and practices of medicine housestaff toward pharmaceutical industry promotions. *American Journal of Medicine* 2001 May; 110(7): 551-557. NRCBL: 9.7; 1.3.2; 7.1. SC: em.

Sullivan, Timothy M. Ethics and the physician-industry relationship [opinion]. *Annals of Vascular Surgery* 2004 May; 18(3): 263-264. NRCBL: 9.7; 4.1.2.

Sweeney, Harry A.; Elliott, Carl. Pharma PR or medical education? [letter and reply]. *Hastings Center Report* 2005 March-April; 35(2): 4-5. NRCBL: 9.7; 5.3; 7.2; 1.3.9; 1.3.2. Identifiers: public relations.

Taylor, Rosie; Giles, Jim. Cash interests taint drug advice [news]. *Nature* 2005 October 20; 437(7062): 1070-1071. NRCBL: 9.7; 9.3.1; 1.3.9.

Terry, Nicholas P. Prescriptions sans frontieres (or how I stopped worrying about Viagra on the web but grew concerned about the future of health care delivery. *Yale Journal of Health Policy, Law, and Ethics* 2004 Summer; 4(2): 183-272. NRCBL: 9.7; 1.3.12; 9.8; 8.1; 9.3.1. SC: le.

NRCBL: National Reference Center for Bioethics Literature Classification Scheme   See inside front cover for terms.

Thawani, Vijay. Drug samples are meant for advertising [opinion]. *Issues in Medical Ethics* 2001 July-September; 9(3): 91. NRCBL: 9.7; 1.3.2; 9.3.1.

Topol, Eric J. Nesiritide — not verified [opinion]. *New England Journal of Medicine* 2005 July 14; 353(2): 113-116. NRCBL: 9.7; 18.2; 5.3; 1.3.5.

Tuorto, Scott; Chan, Mei-Ki; Adusumilli, Prasad S. Drug companies, doctors and disclosures [letter]. *National Medical Journal of India* 2004 July-August; 17(4): 215-216. NRCBL: 9.7; 1.3.2.

Ubel, Peter A. Commentary: how did we get into this mess? *In:* Moore, Don A.; Cain, Daylian M.; Loewenstein, George; Bazerman, Max H., eds. Conflicts of Interest: Challenges and Solutions in Business, Law, Medicine, and Public Policy. New York: Cambridge University Press; 2005: 142-151. NRCBL: 9.7; 1.3.2; 7.3; 9.3.1.

Ulmer, Jeffrey B.; Liu, Margaret A. Ethical issues for vaccines and immunization [opinion]. *Nature Reviews Immunology* 2002 April; 2(4): 291-296. NRCBL: 9.7; 9.5.1; 21.1.

Vainiomäki, Maija; Helve, Otto; Vuorenkoski, Lauri. A national survey on the effect of pharmaceutical promotion on medical students. *Medical Teacher* 2004 November; 26(7): 630-634. NRCBL: 9.7; 1.3.2; 7.2; 9.3.1. SC: em. Identifiers: Finland.

Vallance, Patrick. Developing an open relationship with the drug industry [opinion]. *Lancet* 2005 September 24-30; 366(9491): 1062-1064. NRCBL: 9.7; 1.3.2; 9.3.1.; 1.3.7; 7.4; 7.3; 5.2.

Walker, Roger. Can we afford the medicines we need: an ethical dilemma? *In:* Salek, Sam; Edgar, Andrew, eds. Pharmaceutical Ethics. New York: Wiley; 2002: 91-95. NRCBL: 9.7; 9.3.1.

Walsh, K. The winner takes it all [opinion]. *Journal of Medical Ethics* 2005 May; 31(5): 267. NRCBL: 9.7; 1.3.2.

Waxman, Henry A. The lessons of Vioxx — drug safety and sales. *New England Journal of Medicine* 2005 June 23; 352(25): 2576-2578. NRCBL: 9.7; 18.2; 1.3.2; 1.3.9; 7.2.

Werhane, Patricia H.; Gorman, Michael. Intellectual property rights, moral imagination, and access to life-enhancing drugs. *Business Ethics Quarterly* 2005 October; 15(4): 595-613. NRCBL: 9.7; 5.3. SC: an.

Whalen, Jeanne. Valued lives: Britain stirs outcry by weighing benefits of drugs versus price; government arm finds pills for Alzheimer's too costly, angering patients, Pfizer; Ms. Dennis, 80, joins the protest. *Wall Street Journal* 2005 November 22; p. A1, A11. NRCBL: 9.7; 5.2; 1.3.5; 9.3.1. SC: po.

Wingfield, Joy; Bissell, Paul; Anderson, Claire. The scope of pharmacy ethics — an evaluation of the interna-

tional research literature, 1990-2002. *Social Science and Medicine* 2004 June; 58(12): 2383-2396. NRCBL: 9.7; 2.1; 4.1.1. SC: rv.

Yamin, Alicia Ely. Not just a tragedy: access to medications as a right under international law. *Boston University International Law Journal* 2003 Fall; 21(2): 325-371. NRCBL: 9.7; 9.2; 9.3.1; 9.4; 21.1. SC: le.

Yoo, Kristin. Self-prescribing medication: regulating prescription drug sales on the Internet. *John Marshall Journal of Computer and Information Law* 2001 Fall; 20(1): 57-89. NRCBL: 9.7; 1.3.12; 9.6. SC: le.

Zachry, Woodie M.; Ginsburg, Diane B. Patient autonomy and the regulation of direct-to-consumer advertising. *Clinical Therapeutics* 2001 December; 23(12): 2024-2037. NRCBL: 9.7; 1.3.2; 1.1; 1.3.5.

Zernike, Kate. The difference between steroids and Ritalin is . . . . *New York Times* 2005 March 20; p. WK3. NRCBL: 9.7; 4.2. SC: po.

Zimmerman, Richard Kent. Ethical analyses of vaccines grown in human cell strains derived from abortion: arguments and Internet search. *Vaccine* 2004 October 22; 22(31-32): 4238-4244. NRCBL: 9.7; 12.1; 19.5. Identifiers: moral complicity.

Zipkin, Daniella A.; Steinman, Michael A. Interactions between pharmaceutical representatives and doctors in training: a thematic review. *JGIM: Journal of General Internal Medicine* 2005 August; 20(8): 777-786. NRCBL: 9.7; 1.3.2; 7.2. SC: em.

DURABLE POWER OF ATTORNEY *See* ADVANCE DIRECTIVES

ECONOMICS *See* HEALTH CARE ECONOMICS; ORGAN AND TISSUE TRANSPLANTATION/ DONATION AND PROCUREMENT; ECONOMIC ASPECTS

EDUCATION *See* BIOETHICS AND MEDICAL ETHICS/ EDUCATION; MEDICAL EDUCATION

ELECTROCONVULSIVE THERAPY
See also BEHAVIOR CONTROL; CARE FOR SPECIFIC GROUPS/ MENTALLY DISABLED; MENTAL HEALTH THERAPIES

Turkey's disabled [editorial]. *New York Times* 2005 September 30; A28. NRCBL: 17.5; 9.5.3. SC: po.

Andrade, Chittaranjan. ECT: a measured defence. *Issues in Medical Ethics* 2003 April-June; 11(2): 44-46. NRCBL: 17.5; 4.4. Identifiers: electroconvulsive therapy.

Andrade, Chittaranjan. Unmodified ECT: ethical issues. *Issues in Medical Ethics* 2003 January-March; 11(1): 9-10. NRCBL: 17.5. Identifiers: electroconvulsive therapy.

Bhave, Sudhir. The ECT debate: a response [letter]. *Issues in Medical Ethics* 2003 April-June; 11(2): 67. NRCBL: 17.5. Identifiers: India; electroconvulsive therapy. Comments: comment on Chittaranjan Andrade, "Unmodified ECT: ethical issues," Issues in Medical Ethics 2003 January-March; 11(1): 9-10.

Dhanda, Amita. The right to treatment of persons with psychosocial disabilities and the role of the courts. *International Journal of Law and Psychiatry* 2005 March-April; 28(2): 155-170. NRCBL: 17.5; 17.7; 17.8. SC: le. Identifiers: India.

Major, Ken. Latinos and electroconvulsive therapy: implications for treatment, research, and reform in Texas and beyond. *Ethical Human Psychology and Psychiatry* 2005 Summer; 7(2): 159-166. NRCBL: 17.5; 9.5.4; 21.7; 7.1.

Raval, Nischol K.; Andrade, Chittaranjan. Unmodified ECT vs modified ECT [letter and reply]. *Issues in Medical Ethics* 2003 July-September; 11(3): 100-101. NRCBL: 17.5. Identifiers: electroconvulsive therapy. Comments: comment on Chittaranjan Andrade, "Unmodified ECT: ethical issues," Issues in Medical Ethics 2003 January-March; 11(1): 9-10.

Rose, Diana S.; Wykes, Til H.; Bindman, Jonathan P.; Fleischmann, Pete S. Information, consent and perceived coercion: patients' perspectives on electroconvulsive therapy. *British Journal of Psychiatry* 2005 January; 186: 54-59. NRCBL: 17.5; 8.3.1; 8.3.4. SC: em. Identifiers: United Kingdom (Great Britain).

Smith, Craig S. Abuse of electroshock found in Turkish mental hospitals. *New York Times* 2005 September 29; p. A3. NRCBL: 17.5; 17.8; 21.1. SC: po.

Tharyan, Prathap. Audits of electroconvulsive therapy [letter]. *Issues in Medical Ethics* 2003 July-September; 11(3): 99-100. NRCBL: 17.5. Comments: comment on Aparna Waiker et al., "ECT without anaesthesia is unethical," Issues in Medical Ethics 2003 April-June; 11(2): 41-43.

Waikar, Aparna; Davar, Bhargavi; Karhadkar, Chandra; Bansode, Darshana; Dandekar, Deepra; Kakade, Seema; Wayal, Sonali; Kulkarni, Yogita. ECT without anaesthesia is unethical. *Issues in Medical Ethics* 2003 April-June; 11(2): 41-43. NRCBL: 17.5. Identifiers: electroconvulsive therapy.

EMBRYOS *See* CARE FOR SPECIFIC GROUPS/ FETUSES; HUMAN EXPERIMENTATION/ SPECIAL POPULATIONS/ EMBRYOS AND FETUSES

ENHANCEMENT

Bailey, Ronald. Changing your own mind: the neuroethics of psychopharmacology. *In his:* Liberation Biology: The Scientific and Moral Case for the Biotech Revolution.

Amherst, NY: Prometheus Books; 2005: 223- 238. NRCBL: 4.5; 17.4; 17.1.

Bailey, Ronald. Hooray for designer babies! *In his:* Liberation Biology: The Scientific and Moral Case for the Biotech Revolution. Amherst, NY: Prometheus Books; 2005: 149- 181. NRCBL: 4.5; 15.1; 15.2; 4.4.

Bostrom, Nick. In defense of posthuman dignity. *Bioethics* 2005 June; 19(3): 202-214. NRCBL: 4.5; 15.1; 15.5; 4.4. SC: an.

Abstract: Positions on the ethics of human enhancement technologies can be (crudely) characterized as ranging from transhumanism to bioconservatism. Transhumanists believe that human enhancement technologies should be made widely available, that individuals should have broad discretion over which of these technologies to apply to themselves, and that parents should normally have the right to choose enhancements for their children-to-be. Bioconservatives (whose ranks include such diverse writers as Leon Kass, Francis Fukuyama, George Annas, Wesley Smith, Jeremy Rifkin, and Bill McKibben) are generally opposed to the use of technology to modify human nature. A central idea in bioconservativism is that human enhancement technologies will undermine our human dignity. To forestall a slide down the slippery slope towards an ultimately debased 'posthuman' state, bioconservatives often argue for broad bans on otherwise promising human enhancements. This paper distinguishes two common fears about the posthuman and argues for the importance of a concept of dignity that is inclusive enough to also apply to many possible posthuman beings. Recognizing the possibility of posthuman dignity undercuts an important objection against human enhancement and removes a distortive double standard from our field of moral vision.

Chapman, Audrey R. Should we design our descendants? *Journal of the Society of Christian Ethics* 2003 Fall-Winter; 23(2): 199-223. NRCBL: 4.5; 15.1.

Chatterjee, Anjan. Cosmetic neurology: the controversy over enhancing movement, mentation, and mood. *Neurology* 2004 September 28; 63(6): 968-974. NRCBL: 4.5; 5.1; 9.7; 4.1.2; 17.1.

Conrad, Peter; Potter, Deborah. Human growth hormone and the temptations of biomedical enhancement. *Sociology of Health and Illness* 2004 March; 26(2): 184-215. NRCBL: 4.5; 5.3. SC: rv.

DeGrazia, David. Enhancement technologies and human identity. *Journal of Medicine and Philosophy* 2005 June; 30(3): 261-283. NRCBL: 4.5; 4.4; 2.4. SC: an.

Abstract: As the President's Council on Bioethics emphasized in a recent report, rapid growth of biotechnologies creates increasingly many possibilities for enhancing human traits. This article addresses the claim that enhancement via biotechnology is inherently problematic for reasons pertaining to our identity. After clarifying the concept of enhancement, and providing a framework for understanding human identity, I examine the relationship between enhancement and identity. Then I investigate two identity-related challenges to biotechnological enhancements: (1) the charge of inauthenticity and (2) the charge of violating inviolable core characteristics. My thesis is that a lucid, plausible understanding of human identity largely neutralizes these charges, liberating our thinking from some

NRCBL: National Reference Center for Bioethics Literature Classification Scheme   See inside front cover for terms.

157

seductive yet unsound objections to enhancement via biotechnology.

DeGrazia, David. Enhancement technologies and self-creation. *In his:* Human Identity and Bioethics. New York: Cambridge University Press; 2005: 203-243. NRCBL: 4.5; 15.1; 17.4; 1.1. SC: an; rv.

Elliott, Carl. Enhancement technologies and identity ethics. *Society* 2004 July-August; 41(5): 25-31. NRCBL: 4.5; 15.4; 9.7; 4.2.

Evans, John H. Bioethical consensus and the force of good ideas. *Hastings Center Report* 2005 May-June; 35(3): 3. NRCBL: 4.5; 2.1.

Giles, Jim. Alertness drug arouses fears about 'lifestyle' misuse [news]. *Nature* 2005 August 25; 436(7054): 1076. NRCBL: 4.5; 17.4.

Hall, Stephen S. The short of it: more short children are being given growth hormone in the hope that an extra inch will protect their supposedly fragile psyches. But research suggests that their height is a problem less for them than for us. *New York Times Magazine* 2005 October 16; p. 54-59. NRCBL: 4.5; 9.5.7. SC: po.

Horrobin, S. Report on the 10th congress of the International Association of Biomedical Gerontology, the bioethicist's view. *Experimental Gerontology* 2004 March; 39(3): 285-287. NRCBL: 4.5; 18.5.7.

Lanzerath, Dirk. Enhancement: Form der Vervollkommnung des Menschen durch Medikalisierung der Lebenswelt?—Ein Werkstattbericht. *In:* Jahrbuch für Wissenschaft und Ethik. Bd. 7. Berlin: Walter de Gruyter; 2002: 319-336. NRCBL: 4.5.

Martin, Adrienne M.; Peerzada, Jehanna. The expressive meaning of enhancement [comment]. *American Journal of Bioethics* 2005 May-June; 5(3): 25-27. NRCBL: 4.5; 15.1; 14.1; 1.1; 14.3. Comments: comment on Frances M. Kamm, "Is there a problem with enhancement?" American Journal of Bioethics 2005 May-June; 5(3): 5- 14.

Miller, Franklin G.; Brody, Howard. Enhancement technologies and professional integrity [comment]. *American Journal of Bioethics* 2005 May-June; 5(3): 15-17. NRCBL: 4.5; 4.1.2. SC: an. Comments: comment on Frances M. Kamm, "Is there a problem with enhancement?" American Journal of Bioethics 2005 May-June; 5(3): 5-14.

Parens, Erik. Authenticity and ambivalence: toward understanding the enhancement debate. *Hastings Center Report* 2005 May-June; 35(3): 34-41. NRCBL: 4.5; 1.1. SC: an.

Robert, Jason Scott. Human dispossession and human enhancement [comment]. *American Journal of Bioethics* 2005 May-June; 5(3): 27-29. NRCBL: 4.5; 15.1; 14.1; 1.1; 2.1. Comments: comment on Frances M. Kamm, "Is there

a problem with enhancement?" American Journal of Bioethics 2005 May-June; 5(3): 5- 14.

Schwartz, Peter H. Defending the distinction between treatment and enhancement [comment]. *American Journal of Bioethics* 2005 May-June; 5(3): 17-19. NRCBL: 4.5; 15.1; 4.1.2; 1.1; 14.1. Comments: comment on Frances M. Kamm, "Is there a problem with enhancement?" American Journal of Bioethics 2005 May-June; 5(3): 5- 14.

Squier, Susan. Incubabies and rejuvenates: the traffic between technologies of reproduction and age extension. *In her:* Liminal Lives: Imaging the Human at the Frontiers of Biomedicine. Durham: Duke University Press; 2004: 146-167. NRCBL: 4.5; 14.1; 20.5.1.

Trachtman, Howard. A man is a man is a man [comment]. *American Journal of Bioethics* 2005 May-June; 5(3): 31-33. NRCBL: 4.5; 15.1; 14.1; 4.1.2. Comments: comment on Frances M. Kamm, "Is there a problem with enhancement?" American Journal of Bioethics 2005 May-June; 5(3): 5- 14.

Turner, Leigh. Biotechnology, bioethics and anti-aging interventions [opinion]. *Trends in Biotechnology* 2004 May; 22(5): 219-221. NRCBL: 4.5; 2.1; 5.3; 1.1.

Vince, Gaia. Rewriting your past: drugs that rid people of terrifying memories could be a lifeline for many. *New Scientist* 2005 December 3-9; 188(2528): 32-35. NRCBL: 4.5; 17.4.

ETHICISTS AND ETHICS COMMITTEES

American Psychological Association. Report of the Ethics Committee, 1998. *American Psychologist* 1999 August; 54(8): 701-710. NRCBL: 9.6; 17.1.

American Psychological Association. Report of the Ethics Committee, 2000. *American Psychologist* 2001 August; 56(8): 680-688. NRCBL: 9.6; 17.1.

American Psychologist Association. Report of the ethics committee, 2001. *American Psychologist* 2002 August; 57(8): 646-653. NRCBL: 9.6; 17.1.

Ashcroft, Richard E. Commentary: ethics committees and countries in transition: a figleaf for structural violence? *BMJ: British Medical Journal* 2005 July 23; 331(7510): 229-230. NRCBL: 9.6; 21.1.

Auckland Hospital Ethics Committee; Pinnock, Ralph; Crosthwaite, Jan. The Auckland Hospital Ethics Committee: the first 7 years. *New Zealand Medical Journal* 2004 November 5; 117(1205); 10 p. NRCBL: 9.6. SC: em.

Biiljali, Zudi. Macedonia. *Medical Ethics and Bioethics / Medicinska Etika & Bioetika* 2005; 11(Supplement): 21-22. NRCBL: 9.6; 2.3. Conference: Ethics Support in Clinical Practice: Status Quo and Perspectives in Europe; Bratislava, Slovak Republic; 18-19 November, 2004.

Bliton, Mark J. Richard Zaner's "troubled" voice in Troubled Voices: poseur, posing, possibilizing? *Theoretical Medicine and Bioethics* 2005; 26(1): 25-53. NRCBL: 9.6; 8.1; 2.1; 1.1. SC: an.

Abstract: This essay considers Richard Zaner's storytelling in Troubled Voices as a form of possibilizing which uses the stories to exemplify important moral themes such as contingency and freedom. Distinguishing between activities of moral discovery through the telling of a story and "posing" in the sense of writing to tell the "moral" of the story, I suggest that something crucial goes on for Zaner in his own tellings. Several of the more insistent implications Zaner reveals about the moral relationships encountered in the activity of clinical ethics consultation are examined in that light, especially regarding this question: is it more beneficial, or harmful, to articulate elements of core meanings and values that are entailed in individual viewpoints, which, prior to an ethics consultant's participation, may have remained unspoken and possibly unacknowledged?

Borovecki, Ana; ten Have, Henk A.M.J.; Oreškovic, Stjepan. Ethics and the structures of health care in the European countries in transition: hospital ethics committees in Croatia. *BMJ: British Medical Journal* 2005 July 23; 331(7510): 227-229. NRCBL: 9.6; 21.1.

Bosek, Marcia Sue DeWolf. What to expect from an ethics consultation. *Medsurg Nursing* 1993 October; 2(5): 408-410. NRCBL: 9.6; 7.3.

Burgess, Michael M. Public consultation on ethics: an experiment in representative ethics. *Journal of Bioethical Inquiry* 2004; 1(1): 4-13. NRCBL: 9.6; 15.1; 1.1; 5.1.

Abstract: Genome Canada has funded a research project to evaluate the usefulness of different forms of ethical analysis for assessing the moral weight of public opinion in the governance of genomics. This paper will describe a role of public consultation for ethical analysis and a contribution of ethical analysis to public consultation and the governance of genomics/biotechnology. Public consultation increases the robustness of ethical analysis with a more diverse set of moral experiences. Consultation must be carefully and respectfully designed to generate sufficiently diverse and rich accounts of moral experiences. Since dominant groups tend to define ethical or policy issues in a manner that excludes some interests or perspectives, it is important to identify the range of interests that diverse publics hold before defining the issue and scope of the discussion and the premature foreclosure of ethical dialogue. Consequently, a significant contribution of ethical dialogue strengthened by social analysis is to consider the context and non-policy use of power to govern genomics and to sustain social debate on enduring ethical issues.

Childress, James F.; Miller, Franklin G. In memoriam: John C. Fletcher [obituary]. *Hastings Center Report* 2004 July-August; 34(4): 49. NRCBL: 9.6; 2.1.

Clarke, Simon. Two models of ethics committees. *Journal of Bioethical Inquiry* 2005; 2(1): 41-47. NRCBL: 9.6; 1.1; 18.2; 8.1; 22.2; 18.5.2.

Abstract: A distinction is made between two models of ethics committees. According to the Mirror Model, ethics committees ought to reflect the values of society. The Critical Model says committees are to critically examine these standards rather than merely reflect them. It is argued that the Critical Model should be accepted because a society's ethical standards can be mistaken and a society that has Critical rather than merely Mirror ethics committees is more likely to have such mistakes revealed. Some implications of the Critical Model are discussed.

Crosthwaite, Jan. In defence of ethicists. A commentary on Christopher Cowley's paper. *Medicine, Health Care and Philosophy: A European Journal* 2005; 8(3): 281-283. NRCBL: 9.6; 2.1; 1.1.

Dalyan, Sener. Turkey. *Medical Ethics and Bioethics / Medicinska Etika & Bioetika* 2005; 11(Supplement): 22. NRCBL: 9.6; 2.3. Identifiers: Patients Rights Committees. Conference: Ethics Support in Clinical Practice: Status Quo and Perspectives in Europe; Bratislava, Slovak Republic; 18-19 November, 2004.

Demetriou, Maria. Cyprus. *Medical Ethics and Bioethics / Medicinska Etika & Bioetika* 2005; 11(Supplement): 15. NRCBL: 9.6; 2.3; 2.4. Identifiers: Cyprus National Bioethics Committee. Conference: Ethics Support in Clinical Practice: Status Quo and Perspectives in Europe; Bratislava, Slovak Republic; 18-19 November, 2004.

Doaga, Octavian. Romania. *Medical Ethics and Bioethics / Medicinska Etika & Bioetika* 2005; 11(Supplement): 17-18. NRCBL: 9.6; 2.3. Identifiers: Institutional Ethics Committee. Conference: Ethics Support in Clinical Practice: Status Quo and Perspectives in Europe; Bratislava, Slovak Republic; 18-19 November, 2004.

Dudzinski, Denise M. "Amputate my arm please — I don't want it anymore". *Journal of Clinical Ethics* 2005 Fall; 16(3): 196-201. NRCBL: 9.6; 8.1; 8.3.4. SC: cs.

Egan, Erin A. The role of ethics and ethics services in patient safety. *In:* Youngberg, Barbara J.; Hatlie, Martin J., eds. The Patient Safety Handbook. Sudbury, MA: Jones and Bartlett; 2004: 487-499. NRCBL: 9.6; 9.8; 2.1.

Ford, Paul J. Misjudging needs: a messy spiral of complexity. *Journal of Clinical Ethics* 2005 Fall; 16(3): 206-211. NRCBL: 9.6; 20.4.1; 20.3.3; 20.5.1. SC: cs.

Ford, Paul J.; Dudzinski, Denise M. Specters, traces, and regret in ethics consultation. *Journal of Clinical Ethics* 2005 Fall; 16(3): 193-195. NRCBL: 9.6; 8.1.

Førde, R.; Vandvik, I.H. Clinical ethics, information, and communication: review of 31 cases from a clinical ethics committee. *Journal of Medical Ethics* 2005 February; 31(2): 73-77. NRCBL: 9.6. SC: em; cs. Identifiers: Norway.

Gacki-Smith, Jessica; Gordon, Elisa J. Residents' access to ethics consultations: knowledge, use, and perceptions. *Academic Medicine* 2005 February; 80(2): 168-175. NRCBL: 9.6; 7.2. SC: em.

Gadd, Elaine. Ethics support in clinical practice in Europe — situation overview. *Medical Ethics and Bioethics / Medicinska Etika & Bioetika* 2005; 11(Supplement): 4-5. NRCBL: 9.6; 21.1; 2.3; 7.1. SC: em. Conference: Ethics Support in Clinical Practice: Status Quo and Perspectives

NRCBL: National Reference Center for Bioethics Literature Classification Scheme   See inside front cover for terms.

159

in Europe; Bratislava, Slovak Republic; 18-19 November, 2004.

Garanis-Papadatos, Tina. Ethics committees in Greece. *Medical Ethics and Bioethics / Medicinska Etika & Bioetika* 2005; 11(Supplement): 16-17. NRCBL: 9.6; 2.4. SC: le. Identifiers: National Committee on Deontology of Clinical Trials. Conference: Ethics Support in Clinical Practice: Status Quo and Perspectives in Europe; Bratislava, Slovak Republic; 18-19 November, 2004.

Gefenas, Eugenijus. Lithuania. *Medical Ethics and Bioethics / Medicinska Etika & Bioetika* 2005; 11(Supplement): 17. NRCBL: 9.6; 2.3; 2.4; 7.1. SC: em. Identifiers: Lithuanian Bioethics Committee. Conference: Ethics Support in Clinical Practice: Status Quo and Perspectives in Europe; Bratislava, Slovak Republic; 18-19 November, 2004.

Gilmer, Todd; Schneiderman, Lawrence J.; Teetzel, Holly; Blustein, Jeffrey; Briggs, Kathleen; Cohn, Felicia; Cranford, Ronald; Dugan, Daniel; Komatsu, Glen; Young, Ernlé. The costs of nonbeneficial treatment in the intensive care setting. *Health Affairs* 2005 July-August; 24(4): 961-971. NRCBL: 9.6; 9.3.1; 9.4; 20.5.1. SC: em.

Glasa, Jozef. Establishment and work of ethics committees in Central and Eastern European countries. *Medical Ethics and Bioethics / Medicinska Etika and Bioetika* 2002 Spring-Summer; 9(1-2): 9-12. NRCBL: 9.6; 2.4; 18.2; 21.1.

Glasa, Jozef. Slovak Republic. *Medical Ethics and Bioethics / Medicinska Etika & Bioetika* 2005; 11(Supplement): 20-21. NRCBL: 9.6; 2.3. Conference: Ethics Support in Clinical Practice: Status Quo and Perspectives in Europe; Bratislava, Slovak Republic; 18-19 November, 2004.

Glasa, Jozef; Glasová, Mária. Ethics committees and consensus in the post-totalitarian society. *Medical Ethics and Bioethics / Medicinska Etika & Bioetika* 2001 Spring-Summer; 8(1-2): 5-9. NRCBL: 9.6; 21.7; 9.1.

Godkin, M.D.; Faith, K.; Upshur, R.E.G.; MacRae, S.K.; Tracy, C.S. Project examining effectiveness in clinical ethics (PEECE): Phase 1 — descriptive analysis of nine clinical ethics services. *Journal of Medical Ethics* 2005 September; 31(9): 505-512. NRCBL: 9.6. SC: em.

Abstract: OBJECTIVE: The field of clinical ethics is relatively new and expanding. Best practices in clinical ethics against which one can benchmark performance have not been clearly articulated. The first step in developing benchmarks of clinical ethics services is to identify and understand current practices. DESIGN AND SETTING: Using a retrospective case study approach, the structure, activities, and resources of nine clinical ethics services in a large metropolitan centre are described, compared, and contrasted. RESULTS: The data yielded a unique and detailed account of the nature and scope of clinical ethics services across a spectrum of facilities. General themes emerged in four areas-variability, visibility, accountability, and complexity. There was a high degree of variability in the structures, activities, and resources across the clinical ethics services. Increasing visibility was identified as a significant challenge within organisations and externally. Although each service had a formal system for maintaining accountability and measuring performance, differences in the type, frequency, and content of reporting impacted service delivery. One of the most salient findings was the complexity inherent in the provision of clinical ethics services, which requires of clinical ethicists a broad and varied skill set and knowledge base. Benchmarks including the average number of consults/ethicist per year and the hospital beds/ethicist ratio are presented. CONCLUSION: The findings will be of interest to clinical ethicists locally, nationally, and internationally as they provide a preliminary framework from which further benchmarking measures and best practices in clinical ethics can be identified, developed, and evaluated.

Hogstel, Mildred O.; Curry, Linda C.; Walker, Charles A.; Burns, Paulette G. Ethics committees in long-term care facilities. *Geriatric Nursing* 2004 November-December; 25(6): 364-369. NRCBL: 9.6; 9.5.2; 20.5.4. SC: em.

Howe, Edmund G. When should ethics consultants risk giving their personal views? *Journal of Clinical Ethics* 2005 Fall; 16(3): 183-192. NRCBL: 9.6; 8.1; 8.2.

Iltis, Ana Smith. Bioethics consultation in the private sector. *HEC (Healthcare Ethics Committee) Forum* 2005 June; 17(2): 87- 93. NRCBL: 9.6; 1.3.2; 1.3.1.

Jaeger, Suzanne M. Ethical reasoning and the embodied, socially situated subject. *Theoretical Medicine and Bioethics* 2005; 26(1): 55-72. NRCBL: 9.6; 1.1; 8.1. SC: an.

Abstract: My discussion is concerned with how symbolic power constitutively structures our very identities in relation to one another and at the bodily level of lived experience. Although many accounts of the self and of subjectivity as socially situated have difficulties in their explanations of agency, Zaner's work suggests a basis upon which the self's independence from others can be understood. His phenomenology of embodied subjectivity explains how the emerging self presupposes presence with others. At the same time, however, "co-presence" also reveals the self's distinct perspective and capacity for "circumstantial possibilizing," that is to say, "actualizing another possible than the actual." My aim is to examine critically the intersections between Zaner's phenomenology and other theoretical accounts of the socially situated self. I also show how Zaner's work contributes to these discussions a way of understanding the possibility of agency that is rooted in embodied experience.

Kelly, David F. Ethics committees. *In his:* Contemporary Catholic Health Care Ethics. Washington, DC: Georgetown University Press; 2004: 229-244. NRCBL: 9.6; 1.2.

Kerridge, I.H.; Pearson, S.; Rolfe, I.E. Determining the function of a hospital clinical ethics committee: making ethics work. *Journal of Quality in Clinical Practice* 1998 June; 18(2): 117-124. NRCBL: 9.6; 9.8. SC: em. Identifiers: Australia.

Kerridge, Ian H.; Savulescu, Julian; Komesaroff, Paul A. Is there a future for clinical ethics services in Australia?

Medical Journal of Australia 2001 August 20; 175(4): 211-213. NRCBL: 9.6.

Lebacqz, Karen. The ethics of ethical advising: confessions of an ethical advisor. Santa Clara, CA: Markkula Center for Applied Ethics, Santa Clara University 2003 May 14; 9 p. [Online]. Available: http://www.scu.edu/ethics/practicing/events/lecture/2003/ethicala dvice.html [15 June 2005]. NRCBL: 9.6; 2.4.

Lebeer, Guy. Clinical ethics support services in Europe. *Medical Ethics and Bioethics / Medicinska Etika & Bioetika* 2005; 11(Supplement): 8-11. NRCBL: 9.6; 21.1; 2.3; 9.2. Conference: Ethics Support in Clinical Practice: Status Quo and Perspectives in Europe; Bratislava, Slovak Republic; 18-19 November, 2004.

Levee, Ellen M. IACUC replacement parts: what are the requirements? No authority. *Lab Animal* 2004 November; 33(10): 16-17. NRCBL: 9.6; 1.3.9; 22.2. SC: cs. Identifiers: Institutional Animal Care and Use Committees.

Levin, Phillip D.; Sprung, Charles L. Are ethics consultations worthwhile? *Critical Care Medicine* 2000 December; 28(12): 3942-3944. NRCBL: 9.6; 20.5.1; 4.4.

MacDonald, Chris. Corporate ethics in the life sciences: can bioethics help? Should it? *HEC (Healthcare Ethics Committee) Forum* 2005 June; 17(2): 122- 134. NRCBL: 9.6; 1.3.2; 1.3.9; 5.2; 1.3.1; 7.1.

MacRae, S.; Chidwick, P.; Berry, S.; Secker, B.; Hébert, P.; Zlotnik Shaul, R.; Faith, K.; Singer, P.A. Clinical bioethics integration, sustainability, and accountability: the Hub and Spokes Strategy. *Journal of Medical Ethics* 2005 May; 31(5): 256-261. NRCBL: 9.6.
Abstract: The "lone" clinical bioethicist working in a large, multisite hospital faces considerable challenges. While attempting to build ethics capacity and sustain a demanding range of responsibilities, he or she must also achieve an acceptable level of integration, sustainability, and accountability within a complex organisational structure. In an effort to address such inherent demands and to create a platform towards better evaluation and effectiveness, the Clinical Ethics Group at the Joint Centre for Bioethics at the University of Toronto is implementing the Hub and Spokes Strategy at seven hospitals. The goal of the Hub and Spokes Strategy is to foster an ethical climate and strengthen ethics capacity broadly throughout healthcare settings as well as create models in clinical bioethics that are excellent and effective.

Madoyan, Igor. Armenia. *Medical Ethics and Bioethics / Medicinska Etika & Bioetika* 2005; 11(Supplement): 14. NRCBL: 9.6; 2.3; 2.4. Identifiers: National Center on Bioethics of Armenia. Conference: Ethics Support in Clinical Practice: Status Quo and Perspectives in Europe; Bratislava, Slovak Republic; 18-19 November, 2004.

Mati, Jona. Albania. *Medical Ethics and Bioethics / Medicinska Etika & Bioetika* 2005; 11(Supplement): 14. NRCBL: 9.6; 2.3; 2.4. Identifiers: National Committee on Medical Ethics and Bioethics. Conference: Ethics Support in Clinical Practice: Status Quo and Perspectives in Eu-

rope; Bratislava, Slovak Republic; 18-19 November, 2004.

Mayor, Susan. Clinicians need better access to ethics advice, report says [news]. *BMJ: British Medical Journal* 2005 June 11; 330(7504): 1345. NRCBL: 9.6.

McGuire, Amy L.; Majumder, Mary A.; Cheney, J. Richard. The ethics of lawyer-ethicists. *Journal of Law, Medicine and Ethics* 2005 Fall; 33(3): 603-607. NRCBL: 9.6; 1.3.8; 7.3. SC: le.

Meulenbergs, T.; Vermylen, J.; Schotsmans, P.T. The current state of clinical ethics and healthcare ethics committees in Belgium. *Journal of Medical Ethics* 2005 June; 31(6): 318-321. NRCBL: 9.6; 2.4; 18.2.
Abstract: Ethics committees are the most important practical instrument of clinical ethics in Belgium and fulfil three tasks: the ethical review of experimental protocols, advising on the ethical aspects of healthcare practice, and ethics consultation. In this article the authors examine the current situation of ethics committees in Belgium from the perspective of clinical ethics. Firstly, the most important steps which thus far have been taken in Belgium are examined. Secondly, recent opinion by the Belgian Advisory Committee on Bioethics with regard to ethics committees is presented and the activities of Belgian ethics committees are discussed. Finally, the option to bring research ethics and clinical ethics under the roof of just one committee is criticised using a pragmatic and a methodological argument. Concomitantly, the authors build an argument in favour of the further development of ethics consultation.

Mills, Ann E.; Tereskerz, Patricia; Davis, Walt. Is evaluating ethics consultation on the basis of cost a good idea? *CQ: Cambridge Quarterly of Healthcare Ethics* 2005 Winter; 14(1): 57-64. NRCBL: 9.6; 9.8; 9.3.1.

Mishkin, Douglas B.; Povar, Gail. The District of Columbia amends its Health-Care Decisions Act: bioethics committees in the arena of public policy. *Journal of Clinical Ethics* 2005 Winter; 16(4): 292-298. NRCBL: 9.6; 20.5.1; 20.5.4; 8.3.3. SC: le.

Morgenstern, Leon. Proactive bioethics screening: a prelude to bioethics consultation. *Journal of Clinical Ethics* 2005 Summer; 16(2): 151-155. NRCBL: 9.6; 9.5.2; 9.5.3. SC: cs.

Nurock, Shirley. Commentary: patients may be less risk averse than committees. *BMJ: British Medical Journal* 2005 February 26; 330(7489): 471- 472. NRCBL: 9.6; 18.2.

Omer, Adzivic. Serbia and Montenegro. *Medical Ethics and Bioethics / Medicinska Etika & Bioetika* 2005; 11(Supplement): 19. NRCBL: 9.6; 2.3. Conference: Ethics Support in Clinical Practice: Status Quo and Perspectives in Europe; Bratislava, Slovak Republic; 18-19 November, 2004.

Orr, Robert D. Who does the ethics consultation serve? *Medical Ethics Newsletter [Lahey Clinic]* 2004 Winter; 11(1): 10-11. NRCBL: 9.6.

NRCBL: National Reference Center for Bioethics Literature Classification Scheme   See inside front cover for terms.

161

Palmer, Kim. Doing the right thing: hospital ethics committees help clinicians, families, and facilities wrestle with tough questions. *Minnesota Medicine* 2004 June; 87(6): 26-29. NRCBL: 9.6; 8.1; 9.1.

Parsi, Kayhan. Bioethics consultation in the private sector: what is an appropriate model. *HEC (Healthcare Ethics Committee) Forum* 2005 June; 17(2): 135- 145. NRCBL: 9.6; 1.3.2; 1.3.1.

Perneger, Thomas V. Why we need ethical oversight of quality improvement projects [editorial]. *International Journal for Quality in Health Care* 2004 October; 16(5): 343-344. NRCBL: 9.6; 9.8.

Pleterski-Riegler, Dusica. Slovenia. *Medical Ethics and Bioethics / Medicinska Etika & Bioetika* 2005; 11(Supplement): 20. NRCBL: 9.6; 2.3; 2.4. Identifiers: National Medical Ethics Committee of Slovenia (NMEC). Conference: Ethics Support in Clinical Practice: Status Quo and Perspectives in Europe; Bratislava, Slovak Republic; 18-19 November, 2004.

Rasmussen, Lisa M. The ethics and aesthetics of for-profit bioethics consultation. *HEC (Healthcare Ethics Committee) Forum* 2005 June; 17(2): 94- 121. NRCBL: 9.6; 1.3.2; 1.3.1.

Robley, Lois R. The benefits of serving on a hospital ethics committee: a faculty perspective. *Nurse Educator* 2005 May-June; 30(3): 123-126. NRCBL: 9.6; 7.2; 4.1.3.

Schneiderman, Lawrence J.; Gilmer, Todd; Teetzel, Holly D. Ethics consultations in the intensive care setting [letter]. *Critical Care Medicine* 2002 February; 30(2): 489. NRCBL: 9.6; 20.5.1; 20.4.1.

Schroeter, Kathryn. Expanded practice: the nurse as bioethics consultant. *Seminars in Perioperative Nursing* 2000 April; 9(2): 65-70. NRCBL: 9.6; 4.1.3.

Schroeter, Kathryn. Perioperative nurses' involvement on nursing ethics committees. *AORN Journal* 1996 October; 64(4): 588-589, 592-596. NRCBL: 9.6; 4.1.3.

Schroeter, Kathryn. A study of proactive ethics consultation for critically and terminally ill patients with extended lengths of stay. *AORN Journal* 2000 April; 71(4): 902, 904. NRCBL: 9.6; 20.5.1. SC: em.

Schwartz, John. For the end of life, hospital pairs ethics and medicine: a team effort to resolve family bedside conflicts. *New York Times* 2005 July 4; p. B1, B5. NRCBL: 9.6; 20.5.1. SC: po.

Scofield, Giles. Motion(less) in limine. *Journal of Law, Medicine and Ethics* 2005 Winter; 33(4): 821- 833. NRCBL: 9.6; 1.3.8; 2.1. SC: le. Identifiers: medical ethicists as expert witnesses.

Shkiryak-Nyzhnyk, Zoreslava. Ukraine. *Medical Ethics and Bioethics / Medicinska Etika & Bioetika* 2005; 11(Supplement): 22-23. NRCBL: 9.6; 2.3; 8.3.1; 9.5.10. Identifiers: National Bioethics Committee of the Academy of Medicine (Ukraine); National Commission on Bioethics (Ukraine). Conference: Ethics Support in Clinical Practice: Status Quo and Perspectives in Europe; Bratislava, Slovak Republic; 18-19 November, 2004.

Silverman, Jerald. IACUC replacement parts: what are the requirements? *Lab Animal* 2004 November; 33(10): 16. NRCBL: 9.6; 1.3.9; 22.2. SC: cs. Identifiers: Institutional Animal Care and Use Committees.

Slowther, Anne-Marie. Current ethical dilemmas in clinical practice in Europe. *Medical Ethics and Bioethics / Medicinska Etika & Bioetika* 2005; 11(Supplement): 5-8. NRCBL: 9.6; 21.1; 20.5.1; 9.4; 14.1; 1.2; 21.7. Identifiers: Europe; United Kingdom (Great Britain). Conference: Ethics Support in Clinical Practice: Status Quo and Perspectives in Europe; Bratislava, Slovak Republic; 18-19 November, 2004.

Sokol, Daniel K. Meeting the ethical needs of doctors [editorial]. *BMJ: British Medical Journal* 2005 April 2; 330(7494): 741-742. NRCBL: 9.6; 2.3.

Sontag, David N. Are clinical ethics consultants in danger? An analysis of the potential legal liability of individual clinical ethicists. *University of Pennsylvania Law Review* 2002 December; 151(2): 667-705. NRCBL: 9.6; 2.1. SC: le.

Spielman, Bethany. Professional independence and corporate employment in bioethics. *HEC (Healthcare Ethics Committee) Forum* 2005 June; 17(2): 146- 156. NRCBL: 9.6; 1.3.2; 1.3.1; 1.3.3.

Talvik, Tiina. Estonia. *Medical Ethics and Bioethics / Medicinska Etika & Bioetika* 2005; 11(Supplement): 15-16. NRCBL: 9.6; 2.3; 2.4. Identifiers: Estonian Council on Bioethics. Conference: Ethics Support in Clinical Practice: Status Quo and Perspectives in Europe; Bratislava, Slovak Republic; 18-19 November, 2004.

Tischenko, Pavel. Russian Federation. *Medical Ethics and Bioethics / Medicinska Etika & Bioetika* 2005; 11(Supplement): 18-19. NRCBL: 9.6; 2.3. Identifiers: Ethical Department of the Volgograd Center of Academy of Medical Sciences; Professor Natalia Sedova. Conference: Ethics Support in Clinical Practice: Status Quo and Perspectives in Europe; Bratislava, Slovak Republic; 18-19 November, 2004.

United Nations Educational, Scientific and Cultural Organization [UNESCO]. Division of Ethics of Science and Technology; ten Have, Henk A.M.J. Establishing Bioethics Committees: Guide No. 1. Paris, France: UNESCO 2005; 72 p. [[Online]. Available: http://portal. unesco.org/shs/en/ev.php-URL_ID=7771&URL_DO= DO_TOPIC&URL_SECTION=201.html [5 July 2005]. NRCBL: 9.6; 21.1; 2.1.

Vrhovac, Bozidar. Croatia. *Medical Ethics and Bioethics / Medicinska Etika & Bioetika* 2005; 11(Supplement): 14-15. NRCBL: 9.6; 2.3; 2.4. Identifiers: National Bioethics Committee. Conference: Ethics Support in Clinical Practice: Status Quo and Perspectives in Europe; Bratislava, Slovak Republic; 18-19 November, 2004.

Waisel, David B.; Truog, Robert D. How an anesthesiologist can use the ethics consultation service. *Anesthesiology* 1997 November; 87(5): 1231-1238. NRCBL: 9.6; 4.1.2.

Weber, Leonard J. Integrated ethics for the clinical systems manager. *Clinical Laboratory Management Review* 1998 September-October; 12(5): 384-388. NRCBL: 9.6; 7.1; 9.3.2.

Wharton, Mary Ann. Enhancing professional accountability: inquiry into the work of a professional ethics committee. *In:* Purtilo, Ruth B.; Jensen, Gail M.; Brasic Royeen, Charlotte, eds. Educating for Moral Action: A Sourcebook in Health and Rehabilitation Ethics. Philadelphia: F.A. Davis; 2005: 131-143. NRCBL: 9.6; 1.3.1; 6.

ETHICS COMMITTEES *See* ETHICISTS AND ETHICS COMMITTEES; HUMAN EXPERIMENTATION/ ETHICS COMMITTEES AND POLICY GUIDELINES

EUGENICS

Bankston, Carl L. Eugenics: Nazi Germany. *In:* Ness, Bryan D., ed. Encyclopedia of Genetics. Revised edition. Volume I. Pasadena, Calif.: Salem Press; 2004: 264-267. NRCBL: 15.5; 21.4.

Berez, Thomas M.; Weiss, Sheila Faith. The Nazi symbiosis: politics and human genetics at the Kaiser Wilhelm Institute. *Endeavour* 2004 December; 28(4): 172-177. NRCBL: 15.5; 1.3.9; 1.3.5.

Birn, Anne-Emanuelle; Molina, Natalia. In the name of public health [editorial]. *American Journal of Public Health* 2005 July; 95(7): 1095-1097. NRCBL: 15.5; 11.3; 8.3.4; 9.5.4; 9.1.

Boas, Franz. "Eugenics" in The Scientific Monthly 3(July-December 1916): 471-78. *In:* Ryan, Frank X., ed. Darwin's Impact: Social Evolution in America, 1880-1920. Volume 2. Race, Gender, and Supremacy. Bristol: Thoemmes; 2001: 163-170. NRCBL: 15.5.

Cavalli-Sforza, L.L.; Bodmer, W.F. Eugenics, euphenics, and human welfare. *In their:* The Genetics of Human Populations. San Francisco: Freeman; 1971: 753-804. NRCBL: 15.5.

Cooke, Kathy J. Duty or dream? Edwin G. Conklin's critique of eugenics and support for American individualism. *Journal of the History of Biology* 2002 Summer; 35(2): 365- 384. NRCBL: 15.5; 1.1.

Cornwell, John. Eugenics and psychiatry. *In his:* Hitler's Scientists: Science, War, and the Devil's Pact. New York: Penguin; 2004: 85-90. NRCBL: 15.5; 17.1; 20.5.1; 21.4.

Crook, Paul. American eugenics and the Nazis: recent historiography. *European Legacy* 2002; 7(3): 363-381. NRCBL: 15.5; 21.4; 2.2.

Davenport, Charles B. "The eugenics programme and progress in its achievement" in Eugenics, Twelve University Lectures, ed. Lucy James Wilson (1914), pp. 1-14. *In:* Ryan, Frank X., ed. Darwin's Impact: Social Evolution in America, 1880-1920. Volume 2. Race, Gender, and Supremacy. Bristol: Thoemmes; 2001: 150-157. NRCBL: 15.5.

Eggen, J.B. "The fallacy of eugenics" in Social Forces 5.1 (September 1926): 104-9. *In:* Ryan, Frank X., ed. Darwin's Impact: Social Evolution in America, 1880-1920. Volume 2. Race, Gender, and Supremacy. Bristol: Thoemmes; 2001: 171-177. NRCBL: 15.5.

Freeden, Michael. Eugenics and progressive thought: a study in ideological affinity. *Historical Journal* 1979; 22(3): 645-671. NRCBL: 15.5; 15.9. SC: rv.

Furst, Jessica. Modern eugenics. *Ivy Journal of Ethics* 2003; 3(1): 16-17. NRCBL: 15.5; 11.3; 15.1; 13.2; 9.3.1. SC: le.

Golding, Martin P. Ethical issues in biological engineering. *UCLA Law Review* 1968 February; 15(2): 443-479. NRCBL: 15.5; 5.1; 15.1; 16.1.

Greenwald, Brian H. The real "toll" of A.G. Bell: lessons about genetics. *In:* Van Cleve, John Vickery, ed. Genetics, Disability, and Deafness. Washington, DC: Gallaudet University Press; 2004: 35-41. NRCBL: 15.5; 9.5.1.

Hubbard, Ruth. Procreative autonomy versus eugenic and economic interests of the state. *In:* Krimsky, Sheldon; Shorett, Peter, eds. Rights and Liberties in the Biotech Age: Why We Need a Genetic Bill of Rights. Lanham: Rowman and Littlefield Publishers; 2005: 141-145. NRCBL: 15.5; 1.3.5; 9.3.1.

Kellicott, William E. "The sources and aims of the science of eugenics" in The Social Direction of Human Evolution (1911), pp.3-45. *In:* Ryan, Frank X., ed. Darwin's Impact: Social Evolution in America, 1880-1920. Volume 2. Race, Gender, and Supremacy. Bristol: Thoemmes; 2001: 132-149. NRCBL: 15.5.

Kennicott, Philip. The seduction of science to perfect an imperfect race. *International Journal of Health Services* 2005; 35(2): 399- 404. NRCBL: 15.5; 5.3; 21.4; 21.2. Identifiers: Holocaust Memorial Museum.

Kenny, Michael G. Racial science in social context: John R. Baker on eugenics, race, and the public role of the scientist. *Isis* 2004 September; 95(3): 394-419. NRCBL: 15.5; 15.6; 2.2.

NRCBL: National Reference Center for Bioethics Literature Classification Scheme   See inside front cover for terms.

163

Kevles, Daniel J. International eugenics. *In:* Bachrach, Susan, project director; Kuntz, Dieter, ed. Deadly Medicine: Creating the Master Race. Washington, DC: United States Holocaust Museum; 2004: 41-59. NRCBL: 15.5; 21.1.

Koch, Lene. The meaning of eugenics: reflections on the government of genetic knowledge in the past and the present. *Science in Context* 2004 September; 17(3): 315-331. NRCBL: 15.5; 15.1; 5.3; 11.3; 8.3.4; 21.1; 2.2. SC: an.

Leonard, Thomas C. "More merciful and not less effective": eugenics and American economics in the Progressive Era. *History of Political Economy* 2003; 35(4): 687-712. NRCBL: 15.5; 11.3; 2.2.

Mansell, Diana; Hibberd, Judith. 'We picked the wrong one to sterilise': the role of nursing in the eugenics movement in Alberta, 1920-1940. *International History of Nursing Journal* 1998 Summer; 3(4): 4-11. NRCBL: 15.5; 11.3; 2.2; 4.1.3. Identifiers: Canada; Sexual Sterilization Act.

Martinez, Lee Anne. Eugenics. *In:* Ness, Bryan D., ed. Encyclopedia of Genetics. Revised edition. Volume I. Pasadena, Calif.: Salem Press; 2004: 259-264. NRCBL: 15.5.

Massin, Benoit. The "science of race.". *In:* Bachrach, Susan, project director; Kuntz, Dieter, ed. Deadly Medicine: Creating the Master Race. Washington, DC: United States Holocaust Museum; 2004: 89-125. NRCBL: 15.5; 15.1; 5.1.

Micklos, David; Carlson, Elof. Engineering American society: the lesson of eugenics [opinion]. *Nature Reviews Genetics* 2000 November; 1(2): 153-158. NRCBL: 15.5.

Mitchell, David; Snyder, Sharon. The eugenic Atlantic: race, disability, and the making of an international eugenic science, 1800-1945. *Disability and Society* 2003 December; 18(7): 843-864. NRCBL: 15.5; 3.1; 15.11.

Muller, Herman J. Means and aims in human genetic betterment. *In:* Sonneborn, T.M., ed. The Control of Human Heredity and Evolution. New York: The Macmillan Company; 1965: 100-122. NRCBL: 15.5.

Müller-Hill, Benno. Reflections of a German scientist. *In:* Bachrach, Susan, project director; Kuntz, Dieter, ed. Deadly Medicine: Creating the Master Race. Washington, DC: United States Holocaust Museum; 2004: 185-199. NRCBL: 15.5; 15.1; 1.3.9; 7.4; 21.4.

Nash, Donald J. Miscegnation and antimiscegnation laws. *In:* Ness, Bryan D., ed. Encyclopedia of Genetics. Revised edition. Volume II. Pasadena, Calif.: Salem Press; 2004: 501-503. NRCBL: 15.5. SC: le.

Otsubo, Sumiko. Between two worlds: Yamanouchi Shigeo and eugenics in early twentieth-century Japan. *Annals of Science* 2005 April; 62(2): 205-231. NRCBL: 15.5; 2.2.

Pickens, Donald K. Sterilization: the search for purity in mind and body. *In his:* Eugenics and the Progressives. Nashville: Vanderbilt University Press; 1968: 86-101. NRCBL: 15.5; 11.2. SC: le.

Prusak, Bernard G. Rethinking "liberal eugenics": reflections and questions on Habermas on bioethics. *Hastings Center Report* 2005 November-December; 35(6): 31-42. NRCBL: 15.5; 10.1; 4.5; 1.1; 4.4.

Richards, Martin. Future bodies: some history and future prospects for human genetic selection. *In:* Bainham, Andrew; Sclater, Shelley Day; Richards, Martin, eds. Body Lore and Laws. Portland, OR: Hart Pub.; 2002: 289-307. NRCBL: 15.5; 15.2; 14.1; 2.2.

Ryan, Patrick J. Unnatural selection: intelligence testing, eugenics, and American political cultures. *Journal of Social History* 1997 Spring; 30(3): 669-685. NRCBL: 15.5; 2.2. SC: le.

Schuchman, John S. Deafness and eugenics in the Nazi era. *In:* Van Cleve, John Vickery, ed. Genetics, Disability, and Deafness. Washington, DC: Gallaudet University Press; 2004: 72-78. NRCBL: 15.5; 9.5.1; 21.4; 1.3.5.

Sharav, Vera Hassner. Screening for mental illness: the merger of eugenics and the drug industry. *Ethical Human Psychology and Psychiatry* 2005 Summer; 7(2): 111-124. NRCBL: 15.5; 17.4; 9.5.7; 9.5.1; 9.7.

Silver, Michael G. Eugenics and compulsory sterilization laws: providing redress for the victims of a shameful era in United States history. *George Washington Law Review* 2004 April; 72(4): 862-892. NRCBL: 15.5; 11.3; 12.4.3; 11.1; 2.2. SC: le.

Sinderbrand, Rebecca. A shameful little secret: North Carolina confronts its history of forced sterilization. Some women were sterilized for being seen as lazy or promiscuous. *Newsweek* 2005 March 28; 145(13): 33. NRCBL: 15.5; 11.3. SC: po.

Soloway, Richard A. The 'perfect contraceptive': eugenics and birth control research in Britain and America in the interwar years. *Journal of Contemporary History* 1995 October; 30(4): 637-664. NRCBL: 15.5; 11.1; 2.2.

Spektorowski, Alberto. The eugenic temptation in socialism: Sweden, Germany, and the Soviet Union. *Comparative Studies in Society and History* 2004 January; 46(1): 84-106. NRCBL: 15.5; 1.3.5; 11.3; 15.1; 2.2.

Stehney, Michael. Legacy of the American eugenics movement: implications for primary care. *Primary Care: Clinics in Office Practice* 2004 September; 31(3): 525-541, ix. NRCBL: 15.5; 2.2; 15.2. Identifiers: Germany; United States.

Testart, Jacques; Sele, Bernard. Towards an efficient medical eugenics: is the desirable always the feasible? *Hu-*

man Reproduction 1995 December; 10(12): 3086-3090. NRCBL: 15.5; 15.2; 14.4.

Weindling, Paul. International eugenics: Swedish sterilization in context. *Scandinavian Journal of History* 1991 June 1; 24(2): 179-197. NRCBL: 15.5; 11.3; 2.2.

Weiss, Sheila Faith. German eugenics, 1890-1933. *In:* Bachrach, Susan, project director; Kuntz, Dieter, ed. Deadly Medicine: Creating the Master Race. Washington, DC: United States Holocaust Museum; 2004: 15-39. NRCBL: 15.5.

Wolbring, Gregor. A disability rights approach to eugenics. *In:* Krimsky, Sheldon; Shorett, Peter, eds. Rights and Liberties in the Biotech Age: Why We Need a Genetic Bill of Rights. Lanham: Rowman and Littlefield Publishers; 2005: 146-150. NRCBL: 15.5; 15.2; 21.1.

EUTHANASIA AND ALLOWING TO DIE
See also ADVANCE DIRECTIVES; ASSISTED SUICIDE; DEATH AND DYING

Exit strategies [editorial]. *New Scientist* 2005 April 23-29; 186(2496): 5. NRCBL: 20.5.1; 20.7.

The sacred and the secular: the life and death of Terri Schiavo [editorial]. *CMAJ/JAMC: Canadian Medical Association Journal* 2005 April 26; 172(9): 1149. NRCBL: 20.5.1; 20.3.1.

A state of ignorance: severe brain damage attracts little research attention, yet science could help inform the decisions of doctors and families [editorial]. *Nature* 2005 March 31; 434(7033): 545. NRCBL: 20.5.1; 1.3.9; 18.5.6.

Terri Schiavo [editorial]. *Bioetica & Debat* 2005; 11(39): 2. NRCBL: 20.5.1.

Theresa Marie Schiavo [editorial]. *New York Times* 2005 April 1; p. A24. NRCBL: 20.5.1. SC: po.

What Schiavo taught [editorial]. *New Republic* 2005 April 11; 232(13): 7. NRCBL: 20.5.1.

Angus, Floyd; Burakoff, Robert. The percutaneous endoscopic gastrostomy tube: medical and ethical issues in placement. *American Journal of Gastroenterology* 2003 February; 98(2): 272-277. NRCBL: 20.5.1; 9.5.1; 9.5.2; 8.1.

Appel, Stanley H. Euthanasia and physician-assisted suicide in ALS: a commentary [editorial]. *American Journal of Hospice and Palliative Care* 2004 November-December; 21(6): 405-406. NRCBL: 20.5.1; 20.7; 9.5.1. Identifiers: amyotrophic lateral sclerosis.

Aumonier, Nicolas. Evaluation of the arguments. *In:* Council of Europe Publishing, ed. Euthanasia. Volume I. Ethical and Human Aspects. Strasbourg: Council of Europe; Croton-on-Hudson, NY: Manhattan Publishing Co.; 2003: 59-72. NRCBL: 20.5.1. SC: an.

Back, Anthony L.; Arnold, Robert M. Dealing with conflict in caring for the seriously ill: "it was just out of the question". *JAMA: The Journal of the American Medical Association* 2005 March 16; 293(11): 1374-1381. NRCBL: 20.5.1; 8.1.

Abstract: Physicians often assume that conflict is undesirable and destructive, yet conflict handled well can be productive, and the clarity that results can lead to clearer decision making and greater family, patient, and clinician satisfaction. We review the course of Mrs B, an 84-year-old woman with advanced dementia and an advance directive stating no artificial hydration or nutrition. Over the course of her illness, her family and physicians had conflicting opinions about the use of short-term tube feeding and intravenous hydration in her care. We describe the conflicts that arose between her physicians and family and a typology of conflicts common in care of patients who are seriously ill (family vs team, team member vs team member). Drawing from the business, psychology, and mediation literature, we describe useful communication tools and common pitfalls. We outline a step-wise approach that physicians can use to deal with conflicts and the use of treatment trials as a strategy to address conflicts about the use of life-sustaining medical interventions.

Bailey, Ronald. Forever young: the biology and politics of immortality. *In his:* Liberation Biology: The Scientific and Moral Case for the Biotech Revolution. Amherst, NY: Prometheus Books; 2005: 25-61. NRCBL: 20.5.1; 4.5.

Ballentine, Jennifer M. Pacemaker and defibrillator deactivation in competent hospice patients: an ethical consideration. *American Journal of Hospice and Palliative Medicine* 2005 January-February; 22(1): 14-19. NRCBL: 20.5.1; 20.4.1; 8.3.1.

Bandi, Venkata; Guntupalli, Kalpalatha K. Limitation and withdrawal practice patterns in India. *Critical Care Medicine* 2005 June; 33(6): 1436-1437. NRCBL: 20.5.1.

Baskett, Peter J.F.; Lim, Andy. The varying ethical attitudes towards resuscitation in Europe. *Resuscitation* 2004 September; 62(3): 267-273. NRCBL: 20.5.1; 20.3.2; 20.3.3; 21.1. SC: em.

Battin, Margaret P. Euthanasia and physician-assisted suicide. *In:* LaFollette, Hugh, ed. The Oxford Handbook of Practical Ethics. New York: Oxford University Press; 2003: 673-704. NRCBL: 20.5.1; 20.7. SC: an.

Beattie, James M.; Connolly, Michael J.; Ellershaw, John E.; Berger, Jeffrey T. Deactivating implantable cardioverter defibrillators [letter and reply]. *Annals of Internal Medicine* 2005 November 1; 143(9): 690-691. NRCBL: 20.5.1.

Bell, M.D.D. Non-heartbeating organ donation: clinical process and fundamental issues. *British Journal of Anaesthesia* 2005 April; 94(4): 474-478. NRCBL: 20.5.1; 20.2.1; 19.5. SC: cs.

Berger, Jeffrey T. The ethics of deactivating implanted cardioverter defibrillators. *Annals of Internal Medicine* 2005 April 19; 142(8): 631-634. NRCBL: 20.5.1; 8.3.4.

NRCBL: National Reference Center for Bioethics Literature Classification Scheme   See inside front cover for terms.

165

Abstract: Implantable cardioverter defibrillators are life-saving devices for many patients with cardiac disease. Recipients of these devices, nevertheless, often suffer from progressive comorbid and cardiac conditions. Therefore, physicians should anticipate situations in which the defibrillator is no longer desired by the patient or no longer medically appropriate. Near the end of life, many of these patients may decline cardiopulmonary resuscitation. The comanagement of do-not-resuscitate orders and implanted defibrillators can be confusing to patients and physicians alike since the former proscribe the use of electrical cardioversion while the latter provide this precise treatment. Although the use of implanted defibrillators has important ethical implications, few studies have examined these issues, and guidelines have not yet been developed to assist physicians in caring for patients who have received defibrillators. This paper discusses bioethical considerations in disabling implantable cardioverter defibrillators.

Bernacki, Rachelle. Not at peace. *Hastings Center Report* 2005 July-August; 35(4): 9-10. NRCBL: 20.5.1.

Blackmore, M.; Carroll, S. The do attempt resuscitation doctor [letter]. *Anaesthesia* 2000 September; 55(9): 911-912. NRCBL: 20.5.1.

Blendon, Robert J.; Benson, John M.; Herrmann, Melissa J. The American public and the Terri Schiavo case. *Archives of Internal Medicine* 2005 December 12-26; 165(22): 2580-2584. NRCBL: 20.5.1; 21.1. SC: em.
Abstract: An important question for physicians in the aftermath of the Terri Schiavo case is whether the effort of elected officials to intervene was a one-time anomaly or signals a future trend of elected officials being involved in cases where patients are in a vegetative or long-term comatose state. To try to answer this question, we used results from 12 national opinion surveys conducted in March and April 2005, when the Schiavo case was being debated. A review of these survey results showed that efforts by elected politicians to intervene in the Schiavo case were opposed by the majority of Americans. However, the public was more divided on the question of whether Schiavo's feeding tube should be removed. Opposition to removing Schiavo's feeding tube was associated with opposition to abortion. The results suggest that issues involved in cases like Schiavo's are not likely to disappear from the political agenda.

Bloche, M. Gregg. Managing conflict at the end of life [opinion]. *New England Journal of Medicine* 2005 June 9; 352(23): 2371- 2373. NRCBL: 20.5.1; 20.5.4; 8.3.3; 4.4.

Bosshard, Georg; Nilstun, Tore; Bilsen, Johan; Norup, Michael; Miccinesi, Guido; van Delden, Johannes J.M.; Faisst, Karin; van der Heide, Agnes. Forgoing treatment at the end of life in 6 European countries. *Archives of Internal Medicine* 2005 February 28; 165(4): 401- 407. NRCBL: 20.5.1; 21.1. SC: em. Identifiers: Belgium; Denmark; Italy; Netherlands; Sweden; Switzerland.
Abstract: BACKGROUND: Modern medicine provides unprecedented opportunities in diagnostics and treatment. However, in some situations at the end of a patient's life, many physicians refrain from using all possible measures to prolong life. We studied the incidence of different types of treatment withheld or withdrawn in 6 European countries and analyzed the main background characteristics. METHODS: Between June 2001 and February 2002, samples were obtained from deaths reported to registries in Belgium, Denmark, Italy, the Netherlands, Sweden, and Switzerland. The reporting physician was then sent a questionnaire about the medical decision-making process that preceded the patient's death. RESULTS: The incidence of nontreatment decisions, whether or not combined with other end-of-life decisions, varied widely from 6% of all deaths studied in Italy to 41% in Switzerland. Most frequently forgone in every country were hydration or nutrition and medication, together representing between 62% (Belgium) and 71% (Italy) of all treatments withheld or withdrawn. Forgoing treatment estimated to prolong life for more than 1 month was more common in the Netherlands (10%), Belgium (9%), and Switzerland (8%) than in Denmark (5%), Italy (3%), and Sweden (2%). Relevant determinants of treatment being withheld rather than withdrawn were older age (odds ratio [OR], 1.53; 95% confidence interval [CI], 1.31-1.79), death outside the hospital (death in hospital: OR, 0.80; 95% CI, 0.68-0.93), and greater life-shortening effect (OR, 1.75; 95% CI, 1.27- 2.39). CONCLUSIONS: In all of the participating countries, life- prolonging treatment is withheld or withdrawn at the end of life. Frequencies vary greatly among countries. Low-technology interventions, such as medication or hydration or nutrition, are most frequently forgone. In older patients and outside the hospital, physicians prefer not to initiate life-prolonging treatment at all rather than stop it later.

Bostrom, N. The fable of the dragon tyrant. *Journal of Medical Ethics* 2005 May; 31(5): 273-277. NRCBL: 20.5.1; 9.5.2.

Brett, Allan S. Futility revisited: reflections on the perspectives of families, physicians, and institutions. *HEC (Healthcare Ethics Committee) Forum* 2005 December; 17(4): 276-293. NRCBL: 20.5.1; 8.3.3; 8.1; 7.3. SC: cs.

Brink, Susan. Inside Terri's brain: she's probably not in pain. Still, doctors can't read her mind. *U.S. News and World Report* 2005 April 4; 138(12): 24-25. NRCBL: 20.5.1; 4.4; 2.2.

Busquets, Ester; Tubau, Joan Mir. Eutanasia y suicidio asistido: por que si o por que no? / Euthanasia and assisted suicide: why or why not? *Bioetica & Debat* 2005; 11(39): 8-10. NRCBL: 20.5.1; 20.7.

Callahan, Daniel. A case against euthanasia. *In:* Cohen, Andrew I.; Wellman, Christopher Heath, eds. Contemporary Debates in Applied Ethics. Malden, MA: Blackwell Pub., 2005: 179-190. NRCBL: 20.5.1; 20.7. SC: an.

Caplan, Arthur L. An unnatural process: why it is not inherently wrong to seek a cure for aging. *In:* Post, Stephen G.; Binstock, Robert H., eds. The Fountain of Youth: Cultural, Scientific, and Ethical Perspectives on a Biomedical Goal. New York: Oxford University Press; 2004: 271-286. NRCBL: 20.5.1; 9.5.2; 4.5.

Caplan, Howard. It's time we helped patients die. *RN* 1987 November; 50(11): 44-48, 50-51. NRCBL: 20.5.1.

Cardozo, Margaret. What is a good death? Issues to examine in critical care. *British Journal of Nursing* 2005 November 10-23; 14(20): 1056, 1058-1060. NRCBL: 20.5.1; 20.5.4.

Carey, Benedict. For parents, the unthinkability of letting go: the anatomy of hope. *New York Times* 2005 March 20; p. WK5. NRCBL: 20.5.1. SC: po. Identifiers: Terri Schiavo.

Carlet, Jean; Thijs, Lambertus G.; Antonelli, Massimo; Cassell, Joan; Cox, Peter; Hill, Nicholas; Hinds, Charles; Pimentel, Jorge Manuel; Reinhart, Konrad; Thompson, Boyd Taylor. Challenges in end-of-life care in the ICU. Statement of the 5th International Consensus Conference in Critical Care: Brussels, Belgium, April 2003. *Intensive Care Medicine* 2004 May; 30(5): 770-784. NRCBL: 20.5.1; 21.1. SC: rv. Conference: 5th International Consensus Conference in Critical Care; Brussels, Belgium; April 2003.

Casarett, David; Kapo, Jennifer; Caplan, Arthur. Appropriate use of artificial nutrition and hydration — fundamental principles and recommendations. *New England Journal of Medicine* 2005 December 15; 353(24): 2607-2612. NRCBL: 20.5.1; 20.4.1.

Cerminara, Kathy L. Dealing with dying: how insurers can help patients seeking last-chance therapies (even when the answer is "no"). *Health Matrix: Journal of Law-Medicine* 2005 Summer; 15(2): 285-328. NRCBL: 20.5.1; 9.4; 8.1; 9.3.1.

Chamberlain, Paul. Death after withdrawal of nutrition and hydration. *Lancet* 2005 April 23-29; 365(9469): 1446-1447. NRCBL: 20.5.1.

Chambers, John C. "Right to die" — legal view of right to life and death could threaten philosophy of palliative care [letter]. *BMJ: British Medical Journal* 2005 June 11; 330(7504): 1388. NRCBL: 20.5.1; 20.4.1; 4.4.

Charles, J. Daryl. Lebensunwertes leben: the devolution of personhood in the Weimar and pre-Weimar era. *Ethics and Medicine* 2005 Spring; 21(1): 41-54. NRCBL: 20.5.1; 4.4; 7.1; 2.2.

Chatterjee, Suhita Chopra; Mohanty, Sweta. Socio-ethical issues in the deployment of life-extending technologies. *Indian Journal of Medical Ethics* 2005 July-September; 2(3): 81-82. NRCBL: 20.5.1; 20.4.1. Identifiers: India.

Chelouche, Tessa. Some ethical dilemmas faced by Jewish doctors during the Holocaust. *Medicine and Law: World Association for Medical Law* 2005 December; 24(4): 703-716. NRCBL: 20.5.1; 20.3.2; 2.2; 9.4; 12.1.
Abstract: The discourse on physicians and ethics in the Nazi regime usually refers to the violation of medical ethics by Nazi doctors who as a guild and as individuals applied their professional knowledge, training and status in order to facilitate murder and medical "experimentation". In the introduction to this article I will give a brief outline of this vast subject. In the main article I wish to bear witness to the Jewish physicians in the ghettos and the camps who tried to the best of their ability to apply their professional training according to ethical principles in order to prolong life as best as they could, despite being forced to exist and work under the most appalling conditions. These prisoner doctors were faced with impossible existential, ethical and moral dilemmas that they had not encountered beforehand. This paper addresses some of these ethical quandaries that these prisoner doctors had to deal with in trying to help their patients despite the extreme situations they found themselves in. This is an overview of some of these ethical predicaments and does not delve into each one separately for lack of space, but rather gives the reader food for thought. Each dilemma discussed deserves an analysis of its own in the context of professionalism and medical ethics today.

Civetta, Joseph M. Futile care or caregiver frustration? A practical approach [opinion]. *Critical Care Medicine* 1996 February; 24(2): 346-351. NRCBL: 20.5.1; 4.4; 7.1; 9.4.

Cohen, Neal H. Assessing futility of medical interventions — is it futile? *Critical Care Medicine* 2003 February; 31(2): 646-648. NRCBL: 20.5.1; 9.4; 9.5.1; 4.4. SC: em.

Colabawalla, B.N. Dying with dignity: a response [letter]. *Issues in Medical Ethics* 2000 January-March; 8(1): 2. NRCBL: 20.5.1. Comments: comment on Eustace de Souza, "Dying with dignity: a response," Issues in Medical Ethics 1999 October-December; 7(4): 127.

Connors, Alfred F., Jr. The influence of prognosis on care decisions in the critically ill. *Critical Care Medicine* 1999 January; 27(1): 5-6. NRCBL: 20.5.1; 9.3.1; 9.4.

Curtis, J. Randall; Burt, Robert A. Why are critical care clinicians so powerfully distressed by family demands for futile care? [opinion]. *Journal of Critical Care* 2003 March; 18(1): 22-24. NRCBL: 20.5.1; 9.4; 8.1.

Daly, Patrick R. Point of view: who's on first? A reflection on euthanasia [opinion]. *Medicine and Health, Rhode Island* 1996 September; 79(9): 336-338. NRCBL: 20.5.1; 8.3.1; 8.3.3; 7.1.

Darr, Kurt. Terri Schindler Schiavo: an update. *Hospital Topics* 2004 Spring; 82(2): 28-31. NRCBL: 20.5.1.

Das, Abhay K.; Mulley, Graham P. The value of an ethics history? *Journal of the Royal Society of Medicine* 2005 June; 98(6): 262-266. NRCBL: 20.5.1; 8.3.3; 2.1; 20.5.4. Identifiers: United Kingdom (Great Britain).

Davis, Lennard J. Life, death, and biocultural literacy. *Chronicle of Higher Education* 2006 January 6; 52(18): B9-B10. NRCBL: 20.5.1; 20.1; 4.4; 7.1; 2.1; 5.1; 1.3.3.

de Beaufort, Inez. Patients in a persistent vegetative state — a Dutch perspective [opinion]. *New England Journal of Medicine* 2005 June 9; 352(23): 2373- 2375. NRCBL: 20.5.1; 8.3.3; 4.4.

De Gendt, Cindy; Bilsen, Johan; Vander Stichele, Robert; Lambert, Margareta; Van Den Noortgate, Nele; Deliens, Luc. Do-not-resuscitate policy on acute geriatric wards in Flanders, Belgium. *Journal of the American Geriatrics Society* 2005 December; 53(12): 2221-2226. NRCBL: 20.5.1; 9.5.2. SC: em.

NRCBL: National Reference Center for Bioethics Literature Classification Scheme   See inside front cover for terms.

167

de Grey, A.D.N.J. Life extension, human rights, and the rational refinement of repugnance. *Journal of Medical Ethics* 2005 November; 31(11): 659-663. NRCBL: 20.5.1; 4.5; 9.5.2. SC: an.

de Souza, Eustace J. Dying with dignity: a response. *Issues in Medical Ethics* 1999 October-December; 7(4): 127. NRCBL: 20.5.1. Comments: comment on Sunil Pandya, "Dying with dignity: a round-table discussion," Issues in Medical Ethics 1999 July-September; 7(3): 99.

Douglas, Claire A.; Lewis-Jones, Cathy. Cardiopulmonary resuscitation policies in northwest England hospices: a telephone survey. *International Journal of Palliative Nursing* 2004 December; 10(12): 588-591. NRCBL: 20.5.1; 20.4.1. SC: em.

Drake, Stephen. Euthanasia is out of control in the Netherlands [opinion]. *Hastings Center Report* 2005 May-June; 35(3): inside back cover. NRCBL: 20.5.1.

Dziewas, Rainer; Henningsen, Henning. Medicine, psychiatry and euthanasia: an argument against mandatory psychiatric review [letter]. *Australian and New Zealand Journal of Psychiatry* 2002 April; 36(2): 266. NRCBL: 20.5.1; 17.1; 7.1.

Edwards, Miles J. Opioids and benzodiazepines appear paradoxically to delay inevitable death after ventilator withdrawal. *Journal of Palliative Care* 2005 Winter; 21(4): 299-302. NRCBL: 20.5.1; 9.7; 9.8; 4.4. SC: cs.

Eggenberger, Sandra K.; Nelms, Tommie P. Artificial hydration and nutrition in advanced Alzheimer's disease: facilitating family decision-making. *Journal of Clinical Nursing* 2004 September; 13(6): 661-667. NRCBL: 20.5.1; 17.1; 8.1. SC: em.

Eidelman, Arthur I. The living fetus—dilemmas in treatment at the edge of viability. *In:* Blazer, Shraga; Zimmer, Etan Z., eds. The Embryo: Scientific Discovery and Medical Ethics. New York: Karger; 2005: 351-370. NRCBL: 20.5.1; 9.5.7.

Eijk, Williams Jacobus. Proportionate and disproportionate treatment, exaggerated treatment and palliative care. *Dolentium Hominum* 2005; 20(1): 79-86. NRCBL: 20.5.1; 2.2; 20.4.1. SC: rv. Conference: Proceedings of the XIX International Conference organized by the Pontifical Council for Health Pastoral Care;New Synod Hall, Vatican City; 11-13 November 2004.

Einav, Sharon; Rubinow, Alan; Avidan, Alexander; Brezis, Mayer. General medicine practitioners' attitudes towards "do not attempt resuscitation" orders. *Resuscitation* 2004 August; 62(2): 181-187. NRCBL: 20.5.1; 20.3.2. SC: em. Identifiers: Israel.

Ellis, Peter. Defining euthanasia [letter]. *Professional Nurse* 1997 May; 12(8): 600. NRCBL: 20.5.1.

Éló, Gábor; Diószeghy, Csaba; Dobos, Márta; Andorka, Mátyás. Ethical considerations behind the limitation of cardiopulmonary resuscitation in Hungary — the role of education and training. *Resuscitation* 2005 January; 64(1): 71-77. NRCBL: 20.5.1; 7.2. SC: em.

Elphick, Heather L.; Gott, Merryn; Liddle, B. Jane; Stewart, Kevin; Spice, Claire. Where now with do not attempt resuscitation decisions? [letter and reply]. *Age and Ageing* 2004 January; 33(1): 86-87. NRCBL: 20.5.1.

Fairrow, A.M.; McCallum, T.J.; Messinger-Rapport, Barbara J. Preferences of older African-Americans for long-term tube feeding at the end of life. *Aging and Mental Health* 2004 November; 8(6): 530-534. NRCBL: 20.5.1; 9.5.4. SC: em.

Farnalls, Martha. The use of limited critical care resources: an ethical dilemma. *Official Journal of the Canadian Association of Critical Care Nurses* 1997 Fall; 8(3): 23-26. NRCBL: 20.5.1; 9.4.

Favor, Christi Dawn. Puzzling cases about killing and letting die. *Res Publica* 1996; 5(1): 18-21. NRCBL: 20.5.1.

Feudtner, Chris. Control of suffering on the slippery slope of care. *Lancet* 2005 April 9-15; 365(9467): 1284-1286. NRCBL: 20.5.1; 20.5.2; 4.4.

Finlay, Ilora. Euthanasia — what it is and what it is not. *Dolentium Hominum* 2005; 20(1): 46-50. NRCBL: 20.5.1; 2.1; 7.1; 21.1. Conference: Proceedings of the XIX International Conference organized by the Pontifical Council for Health Pastoral Care;New Synod Hall, Vatican City; 11-13 November 2004.

Fins, Joseph J.; Schiff, Nicholas D. The afterlife of Terri Schiavo. *Hastings Center Report* 2005 July-August; 35(4): 8. NRCBL: 20.5.1.

Finucane, Thomas E. Choosing resuscitation late in life: problems with the paradigm [editorial]. *American Journal of Medicine* 1996 February; 100(2): 126-127. NRCBL: 20.5.1; 9.5.2; 20.3.1.

Fisher, Malcolm. Ethical issues in the intensive care unit. *Current Opinion in Critical Care* 2004 August; 10(4): 292-298. NRCBL: 20.5.1; 20.4.1.

Florin, Dominique. 'Do not resuscitate' orders: the need for a policy. *Journal of the Royal College of Physicians of London* 1993 April; 27(2): 135-138. NRCBL: 20.5.1; 2.1.

Formiga, F.; Chivite, D.; Ortega, C.; Casas, S.; Ramón, J.M.; Pujol, R. End-of-life preferences in elderly patients admitted for heart failure. *Quarterly Journal of Medicine* 2004 December; 97(12): 803-808. NRCBL: 20.5.1; 9.5.2; 8.1. SC: em. Identifiers: Spain.

Foti, Mary Ellen; Bartels, Stephen J.; Van Citters, Aricca D.; Merriman, Melanie P.; Fletcher, Kenneth E. End-of-life treatment preferences of persons with serious mental illness. *Psychiatric Services* 2005 May; 56(5): 585-591. NRCBL: 20.5.1; 17.1; 20.4.1. SC: em.

Friedman, Yaakov. Ethical issues in the critically ill patient. *Current Opinion in Critical Care* 2001 December; 7(6): 475-479. NRCBL: 20.5.1; 20.4.1; 8.1.

Fritz, Mark. Last rights: how simple device set off a fight over elderly care; invented for younger patients, feeding tube now figures in end-of-life debate; a missed box on a living will. *Wall Street Journal* 2005 December 8; p. A1, A10. NRCBL: 20.5.1; 9.5.2. SC: po.

Fry, Sara T.; Veatch, Robert M. Death and dying. *In their:* Case Studies in Nursing Ethics. Third edition. Sudbury, MA: Jones and Bartlett Publishers; 2006: 392-435. NRCBL: 20.5.1; 20.4.1.

Fry, Sara T.; Veatch, Robert M. The sanctity of human life. *In their:* Case Studies in Nursing Ethics. Third edition. Sudbury, MA: Jones and Bartlett Publishers; 2006: 192-223. NRCBL: 20.5.1; 4.4.

Gabbay, Baback B.; Matsumura, Shinji; Etzioni, Shiri; Asch, Steven M; Rosenfeld, Kenneth E.; Shiojiri, Toshiaki; Balingit, Peter P.; Lorenz, Karl A. Negotiating end-of-life decision making: a comparison of Japanese and U.S. residents' approaches. *Academic Medicine* 2005 July; 80(7): 617-621. NRCBL: 20.5.1; 7.2; 8.2; 8.3.1; 21.7. SC: em.

Gajewska, Kalina; Schroeder, Michele; De Marre, Francoise; Vincent, Jean-Louis. Analysis of terminal events in 109 successive deaths in a Belgian intensive care unit. *Intensive Care Medicine* 2004 June; 30(6): 1224-1227. NRCBL: 20.5.1. SC: em. Identifiers: Belgium.

Gannon, C. A request for hospice admission from hospital to withdraw ventilation. *Journal of Medical Ethics* 2005 July; 31(7): 383-384. NRCBL: 20.5.1; 20.4.1.
Abstract: A request to admit a hospital inpatient with motor neurone disease to the hospice generated unusual unease. Significantly, withdrawal of ventilation had already been planned. The presumption that ventilation would be withdrawn after transfer presented a dilemma. Should the hospice accept the admission? If so, should the hospice staff stop the ventilation, and then when and how? Debate centred on the continuity of best interests and the logistics of withdrawing ventilation. The factors making the request contentious identified competing interests within hospice admission decision making that could detrimentally impact on patient care.

Garrard, E.; Wilkinson, S. Passive euthanasia. *Journal of Medical Ethics* 2005 February; 31(2): 64-68. NRCBL: 20.5.1. SC: an.

Garrett, Lynnda. A response to Bilsen J.J.R., Vander Stichele R.H., Mortier F. and Deliens L. (2004), Involvement of nurses in physician-assisted dying [letter]. *Journal of Advanced Nursing* 2005 January; 49(1): 104. NRCBL: 20.5.1; 7.1.

Giacino, Joseph; Whyte, John. The vegetative and minimally conscious states: current knowledge and remaining questions. *Journal of Head Trauma and Rehabilitation* 2005 January-February; 20(1): 30-50. NRCBL: 20.5.1. SC: rv.

Giannini, Alberto; Pessina, Adriano; Tacchi, Enrico Maria. End-of-life decisions in intensive care units: attitudes of physicians in an Italian urban setting. *Intensive Care Medicine* 2003 September 11; 29: 1902-1910. NRCBL: 20.5.1; 20.3.2. SC: em.

Gigli, G.L. Persistent vegetative state: let's not blow out the candle. *Neurological Science* 2002; 23: 251-254. NRCBL: 20.5.1.

Gittelman, David K. Euthanasia and physician-assisted suicide. *Southern Medical Journal* 1999 April; 92(4): 369-374. NRCBL: 20.5.1; 20.7.

Goel, Ashish; Kalantri, S.P. When is enough enough? *Issues in Medical Ethics* 2003 January-March; 11(1): 21-22. NRCBL: 20.5.1; 7.2. SC: cs. Identifiers: decision making in medicine.

Goodnough, Abby. Behind life-and-death fight, a rift that began years ago. *New York Times* 2005 March 26; p. A1, A8. NRCBL: 20.5.1; 20.3.3. SC: po.

Goodnough, Abby. Florida steps back into fight over feeding tube in woman. *New York Times* 2005 February 24; p. A14. NRCBL: 20.5.1. SC: po.

Goodnough, Abby; Yardley, William. Federal judge condemns intervention in Schiavo case. *New York Times* 2005 March 31; p. A14. NRCBL: 20.5.1. SC: po.

Gore, D.M. Ethical, professional, and legal obligations in clinical practice: a series of discussion topics for postgraduate medical education. Topic 3: resuscitation decisions in adult patients. *Postgraduate Medical Journal* 2001 June; 77(908): 388-389. NRCBL: 20.5.1.

Gorman, Todd E.; Ahern, Stephane P.; Wiseman, Jeffrey; Skrobik, Yoanna. Residents' end-of-life decision making with adult hospitalized patients: a review of the literature. *Academic Medicine* 2005 July; 80(7): 622-633. NRCBL: 20.5.1; 7.2; 8.3.1. SC: em; rv.

Grayling, A.C. "Right to die": the moral basis of the right to die is the right to good quality life [editorial]. *BMJ: British Medical Journal* 2005 April 9; 330(7495): 799. NRCBL: 20.5.1; 20.7; 4.4.

Griffith, Lauren; Cook, Deborah; Hanna, Steven; Rocker, Graeme; Sjokvist, Peter; Dodek, Peter; Marshall, John; Levy, Mitchell; Varon, Joseph; Finfer, Simon; Jaeschke, Roman; Buckingham, Lisa; Guyatt, Gordon. Clinician discomfort with life support plans for mechanically ventilated patients. *Intensive Care Medicine* 2004 September; 30(9): 1783-1790. NRCBL: 20.5.1;

NRCBL: National Reference Center for Bioethics Literature Classification Scheme   See inside front cover for terms.

169

20.3.2. SC: em. Identifiers: Australia; Canada; Sweden; United States.

Guedj, M.; Gibert, M.; Maudet, A.; Muñoz Sastre, M.T.; Mullet, E.; Sorum, P.C. The acceptability of ending a patient's life. *Journal of Medical Ethics* 2005 June; 31(6): 311-317. NRCBL: 20.5.1; 20.7; 20.3.2. SC: em.
Abstract: OBJECTIVES: To clarify how lay people and health professionals judge the acceptability of ending the life of a terminally ill patient. DESIGN: Participants judged this acceptability in a set of 16 scenarios that combined four factors: the identity of the actor (patient or physician), the patient's statement or not of a desire to have his life ended, the nature of the action as relatively active (injecting a toxin) or passive (disconnecting life support), and the type of suffering (intractable physical pain, complete dependence, or severe psychiatric illness). PARTICIPANTS: 115 lay people and 72 health professionals (22 nurse's aides, 44 nurses, six physicians) in Toulouse, France. Main measurements: Mean acceptability ratings for each scenario for each group. RESULTS: Life ending interventions are more acceptable to lay people than to the health professionals. For both, acceptability is highest for intractable physical suffering; is higher when patients end their own lives than when physicians do so; and, when physicians are the actors, is higher when patients have expressed a desire to die (voluntary euthanasia) than when they have not (involuntary euthanasia). In contrast, when patients perform the action, acceptability for the lay people and nurse's aides does not depend on whether the patient has expressed a desire to die, while for the nurses and physicians unassisted suicide is more acceptable than physician assisted suicide. CONCLUSIONS: Lay participants judge the acceptability of life ending actions in largely the same way as do healthcare professionals.

Gunderson, Martin. A Kantian view of suicide and end-of-life treatment. *Journal of Social Philosophy* 2004 Summer; 35(2): 277-287. NRCBL: 20.5.1; 20.7.

Hall, Jacqulyn Kay. After Schiavo: next issue for nursing ethics. *JONA's Healthcare Law, Ethics, and Regulation* 2005 July- September; 7(3): 94-98. NRCBL: 20.5.1; 20.5.4; 2.1.

Hansen, Lissi; Archbold, Patricia G.; Stewart, Barbara J. Role strain and ease in decision-making to withdraw or withhold life support for elderly relatives. *Journal of Nursing Scholarship* 2004; 36(3): 233-238. NRCBL: 20.5.1; 20.3.3. SC: em.

Hanson, Stephen. How should physicians decide to resuscitate a patient? [letter]. *American Family Physician* 2004 May 15; 69(10): 2322. NRCBL: 20.5.1.

Harpes, Jean-Paul. The contemporary advocacy of euthanasia. *In:* Council of Europe Publishing, ed. Euthanasia. Volume I. Ethical and Human Aspects. Strasbourg: Council of Europe; Croton- on-Hudson, NY: Manhattan Publishing Co.; 2003: 27-36. NRCBL: 20.5.1.

Harris, D.G.; Linnane, S.J. Making do not attempt resuscitation decisions: do doctors follow the guidelines? *Hospital Medicine* 2005 January; 66(1): 43-45. NRCBL: 20.5.1. SC: em. Identifiers: United Kingdom (Great Britain).

Hartmann, Lynn C. The octogenarian's plan [opinion]. *JAMA: The Journal of the American Medical Association* 2005 January 5; 293(1): 15-16. NRCBL: 20.5.1; 20.7; 20.4.1.

Häyry, Heta. Voluntary euthanasia and medical paternalism. *In her:* Individual Liberty and Medical Control. Brookfield, VT: Ashgate Pub., 1998: 28-39. NRCBL: 20.5.1. SC: an.

Häyry, Heta. Who is to live and who is to die? *In her:* Individual Liberty and Medical Control. Brookfield, VT: Ashgate Pub., 1998: 16-27. NRCBL: 20.5.1. SC: an.

Healy, Bernadine. When life is on the line. *U.S. News and World Report* 2005 April 4; 138(12): 26. NRCBL: 20.5.1; 7.3; 1.3.5.

Hermerén, Göran. The debate about dignity. *In:* Council of Europe Publishing, ed. Euthanasia. Volume I. Ethical and Human Aspects. Strasbourg: Council of Europe; Croton-on-Hudson, NY: Manhattan Publishing Co.; 2003: 37-57. NRCBL: 20.5.1; 4.4.

Hester, D. Micah. Progressive dying: meaningful acts of euthanasia and assisted suicide. *Journal of Medical Humanities* 1998; 19(4): 279-298. NRCBL: 20.5.1; 20.7; 20.3.1.

Hijazi, Fadi; Holley, Jean L. Cardiopulmonary resuscitation and dialysis: outcome and patients' views. *Seminars in Dialysis* 2003 January-February; 16(1): 51-53. NRCBL: 20.5.1; 9.5.1; 20.4.1.

Hirsch, Joy. Raising consciousness [editorial]. *Journal of Clinical Investigation* 2005 May; 115(5): 1102- 1103. NRCBL: 20.5.1; 20.2.1. Identifiers: Terri Schiavo.

Hitchcock, James. The Schiavo case and the culture wars. *Human Life Review* 2005 Summer; 31(3): 50-60. NRCBL: 20.5.1. Identifiers: Terri Schiavo.

Ho, K.M.; Liang, J. Withholding and withdrawal of therapy in New Zealand intensive care units (ICUs): a survey of clinical directors. *Anaesthesia and Intensive Care* 2004 December; 32(6): 781-786. NRCBL: 20.5.1. SC: em.

Houts, Renate M.; Smucker, William D.; Jacobson, Jill A.; Ditto, Peter H.; Danks, Joseph H. Predicting elderly outpatients' life-sustaining treatment preferences over time: the majority rules. *Medical Decision Making* 2002 January-February; 22(1): 39-52. NRCBL: 20.5.1; 9.5.2; 20.5.4; 8.3.1; 8.3.4.

Hulse, Carl. Despite Congress, woman's feeding tube is removed: the medical turns political. *New York Times* 2005 March 19; p. A1, A12. NRCBL: 20.5.1. SC: po.

Hwang, Jessica P.; Smith, Martin L.; Flamm, Anne L. Challenges in outpatient end-of-life care: wishes to avoid resuscitation. *Journal of Clinical Oncology* 2004 November 15; 22(22): 4643-4645. NRCBL: 20.5.1. SC: cs.

Institut Borja de Bioetica. Hacia una posible despenalizacion de la eutanasia: declaracion del Institut Borja de Bioetica (URL) / Toward a possible decriminalization of euthanasia: statement of the Institut Borja de Bioetica. *Bioetica & Debat* 2005; 11(39): 1, 3-7. NRCBL: 20.5.1; 1.3.5.

Jansen-van der Weide, Marijke C.; Onwuteaka-Philipsen, Bregje D.; van der Wal, Gerrit. Granted, undecided, withdrawn, and refused requests for euthanasia and physician-assisted suicide. *Archives of Internal Medicine* 2005 August 8-22; 165(15): 1698- 1704. NRCBL: 20.5.1; 20.7; 8.1. SC: em. Identifiers: Netherlands.

Abstract: BACKGROUND: The aims of this study were to obtain information about the characteristics of requests for euthanasia and physician- assisted suicide (EAS) and to distinguish among different types of situations that can arise between the request and the physician's decision. METHODS: All general practitioners in 18 of the 23 Dutch general practitioner districts received a written questionnaire in which they were asked to describe the most recent request for EAS they received. RESULTS: A total of 3614 general practitioners responded to the questionnaire (response rate, 60%). Of all explicit requests for EAS, 44% resulted in EAS. In the other cases the patient died before the performance (13%) or finalization of the decision making (13%), the patient withdrew the request (13%), or the physician refused the request (12%). Patients' most prominent symptoms were "feeling bad," "tiredness," and "lack of appetite." The most frequently mentioned reasons for requesting EAS were "pointless suffering," "loss of dignity," and "weakness." The patients' situation met the official requirements for accepted practice best in requests that resulted in EAS and least in refused requests. A lesser degree of competence and less unbearable and hopeless suffering had the strongest associations with the refusal of a request. CONCLUSIONS: The complexity of EAS decision making is reflected in the fact that besides granting and refusing a request, 3 other situations could be distinguished. The decisions physicians make, the reasons they have for their decisions, and the way they arrived at their decisions seem to be based on patient evaluations. Physicians report compliance with the official requirements for accepted practice.

Jindal, S.K. Issues in the care of the dying. *Indian Journal of Medical Ethics* 2005 July-September; 2(3): 79-80. NRCBL: 20.5.1; 20.4.1.

John, George. Caring for a patient in a vegetative state. *Issues in Medical Ethics* 2001 July-September; 9(3): 77-78. NRCBL: 20.5.1.

Jones, James W.; McCullough, Laurence B.; Richman, Bruce W. Family-surgeon disagreements over interventions. *Journal of Vascular Surgery* 2004 October; 40(4): 831-832. NRCBL: 20.5.1; 8.3.3. SC: cs.

Jonsen, Albert R. Euthanasia. *In his:* Bioethics Beyond the Headlines: Who Lives? Who Dies? Who Decides? Lanham, MD: Rowman and Littlefield; 2005: 48-58. NRCBL: 20.5.1; 20.7.

Jonsen, Albert R. Forgoing life support: the quality of life. *In his:* Bioethics Beyond the Headlines: Who Lives?

Who Dies? Who Decides? Lanham, MD: Rowman and Littlefield; 2005: 35-39. NRCBL: 20.5.1; 4.4.

Joseph, Jay. The 1942 'euthanasia' debate in the American Journal of Psychiatry. *History of Psychiatry* 2005 June; 16(2): 171-179. NRCBL: 20.5.1; 15.5; 9.5.3; 17.1; 2.2. Identifiers: Foster Kennedy; Leo Kanner.

Kalkut, Gary; Dubler, Nancy Neveloff. The line between life and death [opinion]. *New York Times* 2005 May 10; p. A17. NRCBL: 20.5.1; 20.2.1. SC: po.

Kapadia, Farhad; Singh, Manoj; Divatia, Jigeeshu; Vaidyanathan, Priya; Udwadia, Farokh E.; Raisinghaney, Sumit J.; Limaye, Harshad S.; Karnad, Dilip R. Limitation and withdrawal of intensive therapy at the end of life: practices in intensive care units in Mumbai, India. *Critical Care Medicine* 2005 June; 33(6): 1272-1275. NRCBL: 20.5.1. SC: em.

Kaplow, Roberta. Use of nursing resources and comfort of cancer patients with and without do-not-resuscitate orders in the intensive care unit. *American Journal of Critical Care* 2000 March; 9(2): 87-95. NRCBL: 20.5.1; 4.4; 8.1; 9.8. SC: em.

Karnad, Dilip. A competent patient can decide. *Issues in Medical Ethics* 2001 January-March; 9(1): 27-28. NRCBL: 20.5.1; 8.3.4. Comments: comment on Meenal Mamdani, "When a patient has previously expressed the desire never to go on a ventilator," Issues in Medical Ethics 2000 April-June; 8(2): 65.

Kasher, Asa. At the edge of viability: philosophical, moral and ethical aspects and proposals. *In:* Blazer, Shraga; Zimmer, Etan Z., eds. The Embryo: Scientific Discovery and Medical Ethics. New York: Karger; 2005: 371-400. NRCBL: 20.5.1; 9.5.7.

Kelly, Brendan D.; McLoughlin, Declan M. Euthanasia, assisted suicide and psychiatry: a Pandora's box [editorial]. *British Journal of Psychiatry* 2002 October; 181: 278-279. NRCBL: 20.5.1; 20.7; 17.1; 7.1.

Kerkhof, Ad J.F.M. End-of-Life decisions in The Netherlands, 1990-2001 [editorial]. *Crisis* 2004; 25(3): 97-98. NRCBL: 20.5.1; 20.7; 8.1. SC: em.

Kim, Su Hyun; Kjervik, Diane. Deferred decision making: patients' reliance on family and physicians for CPR decisions in critical care. *Nursing Ethics* 2005 September; 12(5): 493-506. NRCBL: 20.5.1; 8.3.3. SC: em.

Abstract: The aim of this study was to investigate factors associated with seriously ill patients' preferences for their family and physicians making resuscitation decisions on their behalf. Using SUPPORT II data, the study revealed that, among 362 seriously ill patients who were experiencing pain, 277 (77%) answered that they would want their family and physicians to make resuscitation decisions for them instead of their own wishes being followed if they were to lose decision-making capacity. Even after controlling for other variables, patients who preferred the option of undergoing cardiopulmonary resuscitation (CPR) in the future were twice as likely, and those who had

---

NRCBL: National Reference Center for Bioethics Literature Classification Scheme   See inside front cover for terms.

171

had ventilator treatment were four-fifths less likely, to rely on their family and physicians than those who did not want CPR (odds ratio (OR) = 2.28; 95% confidence interval (CI) 1.18-4.38) or those who had not received ventilator treatment (OR = 0.23; 95% CI 0.06-0.90). Psychological variables (anxiety, quality of life, and depression), symptomatic variables (severity of pain and activities of daily living) and the existence of surrogates were not significantly associated with patients' preferences for having their family and physicians make resuscitation decisions for them. Age was not a significant factor for predicting the decision-making role after controlling for other variables.

Kimsma, Gerrit; Obstein, Keith L.; Chambers, Tod. A response to Shalowitz and Emanuel. *Journal of Clinical Ethics* 2005 Summer; 16(2): 176-178. NRCBL: 20.5.1; 20.7; 21.1; 20.5.2. Comments: comment on David Shalowitz and Ezekiel Emanuel, "Euthanasia and physician-assisted suicide: implications for physicians," Journal of Clinical Ethics 2004 Fall; 15(3): 232-236.

Kinlaw, Kathy. Ethical issues in palliative care. *Seminars in Oncology Nursing* 2005 February; 21(1): 63-68. NRCBL: 20.5.1; 20.5.4; 20.4.1; 8.1.

Kirkpatrick, David D.; Stolberg, Sheryl Gay. How family's cause reached the halls of congress; network of Christians rallied to case of Florida woman. *New York Times* 2005 March 22; p. A1, A18. NRCBL: 20.5.1; 21.1. SC: po.

Kissane, David W. The contribution of demoralization to end of life decisionmaking. *Hastings Center Report* 2004 July-August; 34(4): 21-31. NRCBL: 20.5.1; 8.3.4; 17.1; 20.7.

Koch, T. The challenge of Terri Schiavo: lessons for bioethics. *Journal of Medical Ethics* 2005 July; 31(7): 376-378. NRCBL: 20.5.1; 4.4.

> Abstract: This essay reviews a range of issues arising from the complex case of Terri Schiavo and the lessons the case raises for bioethicists. It argues that embedded in the case is a broader controversy than is immediately evident, one involving the definitions by which bioethicists judge cases of extreme physical and psychological limits, in its principled form of address. Further, it argues that bioethicists who assume the issues involved in the case are settled miss the point of the emotional responses it has brought forth.

Kollef, Marin H.; Ward, Suzanne. The influence of access to a private attending physician on the withdrawal of life-sustaining therapies in the intensive care unit. *Critical Care Medicine* 1999 October; 27(10): 2125-2132. NRCBL: 20.5.1; 9.3.1; 8.1; 9.2. SC: em.

Kornblut, Anne E. A next step: making rules to die by. Legislation. *New York Times* 2005 April 1; p. A18. NRCBL: 20.5.1; 20.4.1. SC: po.

Kothari, Manu; Mehta, Lopa. Trust her inner voice. *Issues in Medical Ethics* 2001 January-March; 9(1): 27. NRCBL: 20.5.1; 8.3.4. Comments: comment on Meenal Mamdani, "When a patient has previously expressed the desire never to go on a ventilator," Issues in Medical Ethics 2000 April-June; 8(2): 65.

Kouchner, Bernard. End-of-life reflections. *In:* Council of Europe Publishing, ed. Euthanasia. Volume I. Ethical and Human Aspects. Strasbourg: Council of Europe; Croton- on-Hudson, NY: Manhattan Publishing Co.; 2003: 97-107. NRCBL: 20.5.1; 20.4.1.

Laakkonen, Marja-Liisa; Pitkala, Kaisu H.; Strandberg, Timo E.; Tilvis, Reijo S. Physical and cognitive functioning and resuscitation preferences of aged patients [letter]. *Journal of the American Geriatrics Society* 2005 January; 53(1): 168-170. NRCBL: 20.5.1; 9.5.2. SC: em.

Lamberg, Jennifer L.; Person, Carmel J.; Kiely, Dan K.; Mitchell, Susan L. Decisions to hospitalize nursing home residents dying with advanced dementia. *Journal of the American Geriatrics Society* 2005 August; 53(8): 1396-1401. NRCBL: 20.5.1; 9.5.2; 17.1; 20.4.1. SC: em.

Lammers, Stephen E. What wasn't discussed. *Christian Century* 2005 April 19; 122(8): 11. NRCBL: 20.5.1; 9.3.1. Identifiers: Terri Schiavo; health care costs.

Larkins, Richard G.; Kerridge, Ian H.; Myser, Catherine; Mitchell, Kenneth R.; Hamblin, Julie. Guidelines for no-CPR orders [letter and reply]. *Medical Journal of Australia* 1994 December 5-19; 161(11-12): 724-725. NRCBL: 20.5.1. Identifiers: cardiopulmonary resuscitation.

Lavrijsen, Jan; van den Bosch, Hans; Koopmans, Raymond; van Weel, Chris; Froeling, Paul. Events and decision-making in the long-term care of Dutch nursing home patients in a vegetative state. *Brain Injury* 2005 January; 19(1): 67-75. NRCBL: 20.5.1; 9.5.2. SC: em; cs. Identifiers: Netherlands.

Le Conte, Philippe; Baron, Denis; Trewick, David; Touzé, Marie Dominique; Longo, Céline; Vial, Irshaad; Yatim, Danielle; Potel, Gille. Withholding and withdrawing life-support therapy in an emergency department: prospective survey. *Intensive Care Medicine* 2004 December; 30(12): 2216-2221. NRCBL: 20.5.1; 9.5.1; 9.5.2. SC: em. Identifiers: France.

Leichtentritt, Ronit D.; Rettig, Kathryn D.; Miles, Steven H. Holocaust survivors' perspectives on the euthanasia debate. *Social Science and Medicine* 1999; 48: 185-196. NRCBL: 20.5.1; 20.3.1; 21.4. SC: em.

Leo, John. End of the Affair. *U.S. News and World Report* 2005 April 11; 138(13): 46. NRCBL: 20.5.1; 4.4; 1.3.5; 7.1; 1.3.7. SC: po. Identifiers: Terri Schiavo.

Leonard, Colm; Mohindra, Vibha; Ruoss, Stephen; Doyle, Ramona L.; Raffin, Thomas A. European life-support questionnaire. *Critical Care Medicine* 1999 August; 27(8): 1686-1687. NRCBL: 20.5.1; 20.3.2; 9.4.

Letellier, Philippe. History and definition of a word. *In:* Council of Europe Publishing, ed. Euthanasia. Volume I.

Ethical and Human Aspects. Strasbourg: Council of Europe; Croton- on-Hudson, NY: Manhattan Publishing Co.; 2003: 13-24. NRCBL: 20.5.1.

Levy, Cari R.; Fish, Ronald; Kramer, Andrew. Do-not-resuscitate and do-not-hospitalize directives of persons admitted to skilled nursing facilities under the Medicare benefit. *Journal of the American Geriatrics Society* 2005 December; 53(12): 2060-2068. NRCBL: 20.5.1; 9.3.1; 9.5.2. SC: em.

Lindemann, Hilde; Callahan, Daniel. Before he wakes [case study and commentary]. *Hastings Center Report* 2005 July-August; 35(4): 15-16. NRCBL: 20.5.1; 8.3.3.

Lipman, Timothy O. Ethics and gastrointestinal artificial feeding. *Current Gastroenterology Reports* 2004 August; 6(4): 314-319. NRCBL: 20.5.1; 8.3.1; 9.4.

Lowe, Julia; Kerridge, I. Implementation of guidelines for no-CPR orders by a general medicine unit in a teaching hospital. *Australian and New Zealand Journal of Medicine* 1997 August; 27(4): 379-383. NRCBL: 20.5.1; 9.4. Identifiers: cardiopulmonary resuscitation.

Luce, John M. Physician variability in limiting life-sustaining treatment. *Critical Care Medicine* 1999 October; 27(10): 2291-2292. NRCBL: 20.5.1; 7.1.

Lucke, Jayne C.; Hall, Wayne. Who wants to live forever? [opinion]. *EMBO Reports* 2005 February; 6(2): 98-102. NRCBL: 20.5.1; 4.5; 9.5.2; 5.2.

Lynn, Joanne; Berger, Jeffrey T. Deactivating implantable cardioverter defibrillators [letter and reply]. *Annals of Internal Medicine* 2005 November 1; 143(9): 690-691. NRCBL: 20.5.1.

MacIver, Jane; Ross, Heather J. Withdrawal of ventricular assist device support. *Journal of Palliative Care* 2005 Autumn; 21(3): 151-156. NRCBL: 20.5.1; 8.3.3; 20.5.4. SC: em.

Mackay, Michael J. A time to die: is there something wrong with the way CPR is presently practised? [opinion]. *Medical Journal of Australia* 2004 December 6-20; 181(11-12): 667-668. NRCBL: 20.5.1; 20.3.1; 20.5.4. Identifiers: cardiopulmonary resuscitation.

Mamdani, Meenal. Case studies for medical ethics. *Issues in Medical Ethics* 2000 April-June; 8(2): 65. NRCBL: 20.5.1. SC: cs.

Mamdani, Meenal; Mamdani, Bashir. Follow-up: should the elderly woman have been put on a ventilator against her wishes? *Issues in Medical Ethics* 2001 January-March; 9(1): 27. NRCBL: 20.5.1; 20.1; 8.3.4. Comments: comment on Meenal Mamdani, "When a patient has previously expressed the desire never to go on a ventilator," Issues in Medical Ethics 2000 April-June; 8(2): 65.

Marckmann, Georg. Ending or extending life-sustaining treatment: ethics of the decisions. *In:* Council of Europe Publishing, ed. Euthanasia. Volume I. Ethical and Human Aspects. Strasbourg: Council of Europe; Croton- on-Hudson, NY: Manhattan Publishing Co.; 2003: 83-96. NRCBL: 20.5.1.

Marco, Catherine A.; Schears, Raquel M. Prehospital resuscitation practices: a survey of prehospital providers. *Journal of Emergency Medicine* 2003 January; 24(1): 101-106. NRCBL: 20.5.1; 9.5.1; 20.5.4. SC: em.

Maxwell, Lesley-Ann. Purposeful dehydration in a terminally ill cancer patient. *British Journal of Nursing* 2005 November 24-December 7; 14(21): 1117-1119. NRCBL: 20.5.1; 20.4.1.

McAdam, Catherine; Barton, Anna; Bull, Patricia; Rai, Gurcharan. An audit of nurses' views on DNR decisions in 1989 and 2003. *British Journal of Nursing* 2005 November 10-23; 14(20): 1061-1062, 1064-1065. NRCBL: 20.5.1. SC: em. Identifiers: do not resuscitate.

McCarthy, Michael J. After horrific burn, a wife's choice: is treatment wise? Artificial skin for Ted Fink meant pain and risks; a 7-month coma; I really didn't want to look. *Wall Street Journal* 2005 April 29; p. A1, A12. NRCBL: 20.5.1; 8.3.4. SC: po.

McCrummen, Stephanie. Brain-dead mother is taken off life support; healthy premature baby is likely to avoid cancer. *Washington Post* 2005 August 4; p. A1, A4. NRCBL: 20.5.1. SC: po. Identifiers: Susan Torres.

McCrummen, Stephanie. Brain-dead Virginia woman gives birth; baby appears healthy after 3-month ordeal. *Washington Post* 2005 August 3; p. A1, A8. NRCBL: 20.5.1; 14.1; 9.5.7. SC: po. Identifiers: Susan Torres.

McCrummen, Stephanie. Inside stricken mother, a race between life and death; cancer that felled woman now threatens fetus. *Washington Post* 2005 June 17; p. A1, A13. NRCBL: 20.5.1; 9.5.5; 9.5.8. SC: po. Identifiers: Susan Torres.

McCrummen, Stephanie. Weary father left to count the days: doctors hope technology can sustain fetus. *Washington Post* 2005 June 27; p. B1, B4. NRCBL: 20.5.1; 9.5.5; 9.5.8. SC: po. Identifiers: Susan Torres.

McCullagh, Peter. Authoritative statements. *In his:* Conscious in a Vegetative State? A Critique of the PVS Concept. Boston: Kluwer Academic; 2004: 43-57. NRCBL: 20.5.1.

McCullagh, Peter. History and context of the persistent vegetative state. *In his:* Conscious in a Vegetative State? A Critique of the PVS Concept. Boston: Kluwer Academic; 2004: 1-28. NRCBL: 20.5.1.

McCullagh, Peter. Withdrawal of hydration and nutrition from patients in vegetative states. *In his:* Conscious in a

---

NRCBL: National Reference Center for Bioethics Literature Classification Scheme   See inside front cover for terms.

173

Vegetative State? A Critique of the PVS Concept. Boston: Kluwer Academic; 2004: 233-260. NRCBL: 20.5.1.

McDougall, Rosalind. Best interests, dementia, and end of life decision-making: the case of Mrs S [case study]. *Monash Bioethics Review* 2005 July; 24(3): 36-46. NRCBL: 20.5.1; 17.1; 9.5.2; 19.3. SC: an; cs.

McHugh, Paul. Annihilating Terri Schiavo. *Human Life Review* 2005 Summer; 31(3): 67-77. NRCBL: 20.5.1.

Meilaender, Gilbert. Living life's end. *First Things* 2005 May; (153): 17-21. NRCBL: 20.5.1; 4.4; 20.4.1. SC: an. Identifiers: Paul Ramsey.

Melia, Kath M. Ethical issues and the importance of consensus for the intensive care team. *Social Science and Medicine* 2001 September; 53(6): 707-719. NRCBL: 20.5.1; 7.3; 2.1. SC: em.

Menkin, Elizabeth. Artificial nutrition and the public guardian. *Journal of Palliative Medicine* 2004 October; 7(5): 723-726. NRCBL: 20.5.1; 8.3.3; 9.5.2. SC: cs.

Millard, Peter. Euthanasia: is there a time to die? *Medico-Legal Journal* 1997; 65(4): 173-192. NRCBL: 20.5.1; 2.1.

Mirza, Ayoub; Kad, Rishi; Ellison, Neil M. Cardiopulmonary resuscitation is not addressed in the admitting medical records for the majority of patients who undergo CPR in the hospital. *American Journal of Hospice and Palliative Care* 2005 January-February; 22(1): 20-25. NRCBL: 20.5.1; 20.5.4; 8.1. SC: em.

Mitchell, Kay; Owens, Glynn. End of life decision-making by New Zealand general practitioners: a national survey. *New Zealand Medical Journal* 2004 June 18; 117(1196); 11 p. NRCBL: 20.5.1; 20.7; 7.1; 20.4.1.

Moldow, Gay; Bartels, Dianne; Brunnquell, Don; Cranford, Ron. Why address medical futility now? *Minnesota Medicine* 2004 June; 87(6): 38-44. NRCBL: 20.5.1; 9.8.

Morrison, Laura J.; Sinclair, Christian T.; Goldstein, Nathan E.; Lampert, Rachel; Krumholz, Harlan M. Next-of-kin responses and do-not-resuscitate implications for implantable cardioverter defibrillators [letter and reply]. *Annals of Internal Medicine* 2005 April 19; 142(8): 676-677. NRCBL: 20.5.1; 8.1.

Muller, David. Do NOT resuscitate: a well-orchestrated plan for death ends on a brutal note. *Health Affairs* 2005 September-October; 24(5): 1317-1322. NRCBL: 20.5.1. SC: cs.

Mystakidou, Kyriaki; Parpa, Efi; Tsilika, Eleni; Katsouda, Emmanuela; Vlahos, Lambros. The evolution of euthanasia and its perceptions in Greek culture and civilization. *Perspectives in Biology and Medicine* 2005 Winter; 48(1): 95- 104. NRCBL: 20.5.1; 20.3.1; 21.7; 7.1.

Nair, K. Rajasekharan. Clinical tales in neurology: a vegetative existence. *Issues in Medical Ethics* 2002 July-September; 10(3): 55-57. NRCBL: 20.5.1.

Narbekovas, Andrius; Meilius, Kazimieras. Letting die and mercy killing. *Medical Ethics and Bioethics / Medicinska Etika & Bioetika* 2003 Autumn-Winter; 10(3-4): 2-7. NRCBL: 20.5.1. Identifiers: double effect.

Nasraway, Stanley A. Unilateral withdrawal of life-sustaining therapy: is it time? Are we ready? *Critical Care Medicine* 2001 January; 29(1): 215-217. NRCBL: 20.5.1; 7.1; 9.4.

Neher, Jon O. A measure of success. *Hastings Center Report* 2005 March-April; 35(2): 9-10. NRCBL: 20.5.1; 9.4; 8.1.

Newman, Maria. Gov. Bush's role is ended in feeding tube dispute. *New York Times* 2005 January 25; p. A21. NRCBL: 20.5.1. SC: po. Identifiers: Terri Schiavo.

Nibert, Ainslie T. Teaching clinical ethics using a case study family presence during cardiopulmonary resuscitation. *Critical Care Nurse* 2005 February; 25(1): 38-44. NRCBL: 20.5.1; 8.1; 7.1; 7.2. SC: cs.

Niven, Elizabeth. Mortality, morality and the media [editorial]. *Nursing Ethics* 2005 September; 12(5): 429-430. NRCBL: 20.5.1; 1.3.7. Identifiers: Terri Schiavo.

Norris, Wendi M.; Nielsen, Elizabeth L.; Engelberg, Ruth A.; Curtis, J. Randall. Treatment preferences for resuscitation and critical care among homeless persons. *Chest* 2005 June; 127(6): 2180-2187. NRCBL: 20.5.1; 9.5.10. SC: em.

North Carolina Medical Society. Ethical and Judicial Affairs Committee. Guiding the decisions of physicians and families in end-of-life care: the case of long-term feeding tube placement. *North Carolina Medical Journal* 2004 July-August; 65(4): 242-245. NRCBL: 20.5.1.

Nyman, D.J.; Sprung, C.L. End-of-life decision making in the intensive care unit. *Intensive Care Medicine* 2000 October; 26(10): 1414-1420. NRCBL: 20.5.1; 9.4.

Pandya, Sunil. Dying with dignity: a round-table discussion. *Issues in Medical Ethics* 1999 July-September; 7(3): 99. NRCBL: 20.5.1. Conference: Mr Minoo Masani Memorial Programme; 29 May 1999; Mumbai, India; sponsored by the Society for the Right to Die with Dignity, the Freedom First Foundation, and the Leslie Sawhney Programme.

Pandya, Sunil K. Impact of life-prolonging technologies on end-of-life care in India [editorial]. *Indian Journal of Medical Ethics* 2005 July-September; 2(3): 76-77. NRCBL: 20.5.1; 20.4.1.

Pang, Samantha M.C.; Tse, Chun-yan.; Chan, Kin-sang; Chung, Betty P.M.; Leung, Amanda K.A.;

Leung, Edward M.F.; Ko, Stanley K.K. An empirical analysis of the decision-making of limiting life-sustaining treatment for patients with advanced chronic obstructive pulmonary disease in Hong Kong, China. *Journal of Critical Care* 2004 September; 19(3): 135-144. NRCBL: 20.5.1; 4.4. SC: em.

Parker, Malcolm. End games: euthanasia under interminable scrutiny. *Bioethics* 2005 October; 19(5-6): 523-536. NRCBL: 20.5.1. SC: an.

Abstract: It is increasingly asserted that the disagreements of abstract principle between adversaries in the euthanasia debate fail to account for the complex, particular and ambiguous experiences of people at the end of their lives. A greater research effort into experiences, meaning, connection, vulnerability, and motivation is advocated, during which the euthanasia 'question' should remain open. I argue that this is a normative strategy, which is felicitous to the status quo and further medicalises the end of life, but which masquerades as a value-neutral assertion about needing more knowledge.

Parker, Malcolm. Medicine, psychiatry and euthanasia: an argument against mandatory psychiatric review. *Australian and New Zealand Journal of Psychiatry* 2000 April; 34(2): 318-324. NRCBL: 20.5.1; 17.1; 8.1.

Parkinson, Lynne; Rainbird, Katherine; Kerridge, Ian; Carter, Gregory; Cavenagh, John; McPhee, John; Ravenscroft, Peter. Cancer patients' attitudes towards euthanasia and physician- assisted suicide: the influence of question wording and patients' own definitions on responses. *Journal of Bioethical Inquiry* 2005; 2(2): 82-89. NRCBL: 20.5.1; 20.3.1; 4.4; 20.7. SC: em.

Abstract: Objectives: The aims of this study were to: (1) investigate patients' views on euthanasia and physician-assisted suicide (PAS), and (2) examine the impact of question wording and patients' own definitions on their responses. Design: Cross-sectional survey of consecutive patients with cancer. Setting: Newcastle (Australia) Mater Hospital Outpatients Clinic. Participants: Patients over 18 years of age, attending the clinic for follow-up consultation or treatment by a medical oncologist, radiation oncologist or haematologist. Main Outcome Measures: Face-to-face patient interviews were conducted examining attitudes to euthanasia and PAS. Results: 236 patients with cancer (24% participation rate; 87% consent rate) were interviewed. Though the majority of participants supported the idea of euthanasia, patient views varied significantly according to question wording and their own understanding of the definition of euthanasia. Conclusions: Researchers need to be circumspect about framing and interpreting questions about support of 'euthanasia', as the term can mean different things to different people, and response may depend upon the specifics of the question asked.

Pasman, H. Roeline W.; Onwuteaka-Philipsen, Bregje D.; Ooms, Marcel E.; van Wigcheren, Petra T.; van der Wal, Gerrit; Ribbe, Miel W. Forgoing artificial nutrition and hydration in nursing home patients with dementia: patients, decision making, and participants. *Alzheimer Disease and Associated Disorders* 2004 July-September; 18(3): 154-162. NRCBL: 20.5.1; 17.1; 9.5.2. SC: em.

Pawlik, Timothy M.; Curley, Steven A. Ethical issues in surgical palliative care: am I killing the patient by "letting him go"? *Surgical Clinics of North America* 2005 April; 85(2): 273-286. NRCBL: 20.5.1; 20.4.1; 20.7; 7.1; 20.5.4.

Peretti-Watel, P.; Bendiane, M.K.; Moatti, J.P. Attitudes toward palliative care, conceptions of euthanasia and opinions about its legalization among French physicians. *Social Science and Medicine* 2005 April; 60(8): 1781-1793. NRCBL: 20.5.1; 7.1; 20.4.1. SC: em.

Pochard, Frédéric; Abroug, Fekri. End-of-life decisions in ICU and cultural specificities [editorial]. *Intensive Care Medicine* 2005 April; 31(4): 506-507. NRCBL: 20.5.1; 21.1; 21.7. Identifiers: intensive care unit; Lebanon.

Pochard, Frédéric; Azoulay, Elie; Chevret, Sylvie; Lemaire, François; Hubert, Philippe; Canoui, Pierre; Grassin, Marc; Zittoun, Robert; le Gall, Jean-Roger; Dhainaut, Jean François; Schlemmer, Benoît. Symptoms of anxiety and depression in family members of intensive care unit patients: ethical hypothesis regarding decision-making capacity. *Critical Care Medicine* 2001 October; 29(10): 1893-1897. NRCBL: 20.5.1; 8.3.3; 8.1; 17.1.

Pollack, Simeon; Phillips, Russell S. Near end-of-life care preferences [letter and reply]. *American Journal of Medicine* 1996 December; 101(6): 663. NRCBL: 20.5.1; 20.3.1; 8.3.1; 8.3.3.

Porter, Theresa; Johnson, Punporn; Warren, Nancy A. Bioethical issues concerning death: death, dying, and end-of-life rights. *Critical Care Nursing Quarterly* 2005 January-March; 28(1): 85-92. NRCBL: 20.5.1; 20.3.1; 20.5.4; 8.3.4; 2.2.

Powell, Tia P.; Oz, Mehmet C. Discontinuing the LVAD: ethical considerations [editorial]. *Annals of Thoracic Surgery* 1997 May; 63(5): 1223-1224. NRCBL: 20.5.1. Identifiers: left ventricular assist devices.

Prendergast, Thomas J.; Luce, John M. Increasing incidence of withholding and withdrawal of life support from the critically ill. *American Journal of Respiratory and Critical Care Medicine* 1997 January; 155(1): 15-20. NRCBL: 20.5.1; 8.3.3; 8.3.4. SC: em.

Putnam, Andrew. Do I have to resuscitate this patient against her wishes? *American Family Physician* 2003 May 1; 67(9): 2025-2028. NRCBL: 20.5.1; 20.5.4; 8.3.3. SC: cs.

Quill, Timothy E. The million dollar question. *New England Journal of Medicine* 2005 April 21; 352(16): 1632. NRCBL: 20.5.1; 20.7. Identifiers: Million Dollar Baby.

Rahman, Masoor-Ur; Arabi, Yaseen; Adhami, Naeem A.; Parker, Barbara; Al-Shimemeri, Abdullah. The practice of do-not-resuscitate orders in the Kingdom of Saudi Arabia. The experience of a tertiary care center. *Saudi Medical Journal* 2004 September; 25(9): 1278-1279. NRCBL: 20.5.1. SC: em.

NRCBL: National Reference Center for Bioethics Literature Classification Scheme   See inside front cover for terms.

175

Rastogi, Anil Kumar. End-of-life issues neglected in India. *Indian Journal of Medical Ethics* 2005 July-September; 2(3): 83-84. NRCBL: 20.5.1; 20.4.1.

Rich, Ben A. The process of dying. *In:* American College of Legal Medicine Textbook Committee, Sanbar, S. Sandy; Firestone, Marvin H.; Buckner, Fillmore; Gibofsky, Allan; LeBlang, Theodore R.; Snyder, Jack W.; Wecht, Cyril H.; Zaremski, Miles J. Legal Medicine. 6th ed. St. Louis: Mosby; 2004: 308-314. NRCBL: 20.5.1; 20.4.1.

Rivett, Andrew G. "Right to die" — no man (or woman) is an island [letter]. *BMJ: British Medical Journal* 2005 June 11; 330(7504): 1388- 1389. NRCBL: 20.5.1; 20.7.

Roberts, James A.; Brown, Douglas; Elkins, Thomas; Larson, David B. Factors influencing views of patients with gynecologic cancer about end-of-life decisions. *American Journal of Obstetrics and Gynecology* 1997 January; 176 (1, Part 1): 166-172. NRCBL: 20.5.1; 20.4.1; 8.1; 9.5.5; 9.5.1. SC: em.

Ross, Heather M.; Berger, Jeffrey T. Deactivating implantable cardioverter defibrillators [letter and reply]. *Annals of Internal Medicine* 2005 November 1; 143(9): 690-691. NRCBL: 20.5.1; 8.3.4.

Rougé, Daniel; Telmon, Norbert; Albarède, Jean-Louis; Arbus, Louis. Questions raised by artificial prolongation of life of the aged patient. *Medicine and Law: World Association for Medical Law* 1994; 13(3-4): 269-275. NRCBL: 20.5.1; 9.5.2.

Ryan, Christopher James. Velcro on the slippery slope: the role of psychiatry in active voluntary euthanasia. *Australian and New Zealand Journal of Psychiatry* 1995 December; 29: 580-585. NRCBL: 20.5.1; 17.2.

Samanta, Ash; Samanta, Jo. End of life decisions: clinical decisions are increasingly shaped by legal judgments [editorial]. *BMJ: British Medical Journal* 2005 December 3; 331(7528): 1284- 1285. NRCBL: 20.5.1; 20.5.4.

Sandman, Lars. Should people die a natural death? *Health Care Analysis: An International Journal of Health Care Philosophy and Policy* 2005 December; 13(4): 275-287. NRCBL: 20.5.1; 4.4. SC: an.

Abstract: In the article the concept of natural death as used in end-of- life decision contexts is explored. Reviewing some recent empirical studies on end-of-life decision-making, it is argued that the concept of natural death should not be used as an action-guiding concept in end-of-life decisions both for being too imprecise and descriptively open in its current use but mainly since it appears to be superfluous to the kind of considerations that are really at stake in these situations. Considerations in terms of the quality of life cost of the intervention in relation to the quality and length of life benefits of the same intervention. In referring to the concept of natural death we risk to blur these considerations and end up in difficult distinctions between what is a natural and non- or un-natural death, a distinction which it is argued is of no real moral interest.

Schneiderman, Lawrence J. The perils of hope [opinion]. *CQ: Cambridge Quarterly of Healthcare Ethics* 2005 Spring; 14(2): 235-239. NRCBL: 20.5.1; 7.1.

Schneiderman, Lawrence; Gilmer, Todd. Ethics and futility [letter]. *Health Affairs* 2005 September-October; 24(5): 1376-1377. NRCBL: 20.5.1; 9.6.

Schwartz, John. Experts say ending feeding can lead to a gentle death. *New York Times* 2005 March 20; p. A29. NRCBL: 20.5.1. SC: po.

Schwartz, John. Neither "starvation" nor the suffering it connotes applies to Schiavo, doctors say; the medical situation. *New York Times* 2005 March 25; p. A14. NRCBL: 20.5.1. SC: po.

Schwartz, John; Grady, Denise. A diagnosis with a dose of religion; the bioethicist. *New York Times* 2005 March 24; p. A20. NRCBL: 20.5.1; 2.1. SC: po.

Scott, Larry D. The PEG "consult". *American Journal of Gastroenterology* 2005 April; 100(4): 740-743. NRCBL: 20.5.1; 8.3.3. SC: cs. Identifiers: percutaneous endoscopic gastrostomy.

Seidel, Asher. Facing immortality. *International Journal of Applied Philosophy* 2005 Spring; 19(1): 85-104. NRCBL: 20.5.1; 9.5.2; 5.1; 4.4; 4.5. Identifiers: life extension.

Sessa, A. When dialysis becomes worse than death [editorial]. *Nephrology, Dialysis, Transplantation* 1995; 10(7): 1128-1130. NRCBL: 20.5.1; 19.3.

Sharma, B.R. Ethical and practical principles underlying the end of life decisions. *American Journal of Forensic Medicine and Pathology* 2004 September; 25(3): 216-219. NRCBL: 20.5.1; 20.7; 2.1.

Sheldon, Tony. Dutch murder case leads to talks with attorney general [news]. *BMJ: British Medical Journal* 2005 September 3; 331(7515): 473. NRCBL: 20.5.1; 20.4.1.

Shimoda, Motomu. "Death with dignity" in the Japanese context. *Journal International de Bioethique / International Journal of Bioethics* 2005 March-June; 16(1-2): 125-134, 197. NRCBL: 20.5.1; 8.3.4; 20.3.1; 4.4; 20.4.1. SC: an. Identifiers: Japan. Note: Abstract in English and French.

Simon, Alfred. End-of-life decision making in Germany. *In:* Blank, Robert H.; Merrick, Janna C., eds. End-of-Life Decision Making: A Cross-National Study. Cambridge, MA: MIT Press; 2005: 61-78. NRCBL: 20.5.1; 20.4.1; 20.5.4.

Singer, Peter. Making our own decisions about death: competency should be paramount. *Free Inquiry* 2005 August-September; 25(5): 36-38. NRCBL: 20.5.1; 20.7.

Slosar, John Paul. Discontinuing implantable cardiac devices and the ERDs. *Health Care Ethics USA [electronic]*

2005; 13(2); 3 p. Available: http://www.slu.edu/centers/chce/hceusa/2_2005_2.html [19 September 2005]. NRCBL: 20.5.1.

Smith, Craig S. France lets terminally ill refuse care, but still bans euthanasia. *New York Times* 2005 April 14; p. A13. NRCBL: 20.5.1. SC: po.

Sonnenblick, Moshe; Gratch, Lena; Reveh, David; Steinberg, Abraham; Yinnon, Amos M. Epidemiology of decision on life-sustaining treatment in the general internal medicine division. *Harefuah* 2003 October; 142(10): 650-653, 720. NRCBL: 20.5.1. SC: em. Note: Abstract in English.

Spinney, Laura. Last rights: if someone wants help to end their life, should the law stand in their way. *New Scientist* 2005 April 23-29; 186(2496): 46-49. NRCBL: 20.5.1; 20.7.

Stähelin, Hannes; Bondolfi, Alberto; Fischer, Johannes; Gerber, Andreas U.; Kesselring, Annemarie; Kind, Christian; Klauser, Cornelia; Ritz, Rudolf; Salathé, Michelle; de Stoutz, Noëmi; Stratenwerth, Günter; Vallotton, Michel; Zulian, Gilbert. Treatment and care of patients with chronic severe brain damage. *Swiss Medical Weekly* 2004 April 17; 134(15-16): 225-229. NRCBL: 20.5.1; 20.4.1; 8.1; 7.1.

Stephenson, Lucinda. The changing nature of death — what you need to know about OOH DNRs. *Iowa Medicine* 2004 July-August; 94(4): 24-26. NRCBL: 20.5.1. Identifiers: out-of-hospital, do not resuscitate orders.

Stevens, Lesley; Cook, Deborah; Guyatt, Gordon; Griffith, Lauren; Walter, Steven; McMullin, Joseph. Education, ethics, and end-of-life decisions in the intensive care unit. *Critical Care Medicine* 2002 February; 30(2): 290-296. NRCBL: 20.5.1; 7.2. SC: em. Identifiers: Canada.

Stolberg, Sheryl Gay. Lawmakers ready to again debate end-of-life issues. *New York Times* 2005 March 28; p. A1, A14. NRCBL: 20.5.1; 21.1. SC: po.

Sullivan, Dennis J.; Hansen-Flaschen, John. Termination of life support after major trauma. *Surgical Clinics of North America* 2000 June; 80(3): 1055-1066. NRCBL: 20.5.1; 20.5.4; 9.5.2.

Tassy, Sebastien; Gorincour, Guillaume; Le Coz, Pierre. Emotions stimulate ethical debate but must not seize it: the example of end-of-life decision-making process [letter]. *Journal of the American Geriatrics Society* 2005 December; 53(12): 2231. NRCBL: 20.5.1.

Taylor, Brigit R.; McCann, Robert M. Controlled sedation for physical and existential suffering? *Journal of Palliative Medicine* 2005 February; 8(1): 144-147. NRCBL: 20.5.1; 20.4.1; 4.4. SC: cs.

Tilden, Virginia P.; Tolle, Susan W.; Nelson, Christine A.; Fields, Jonathan. Family decision-making to withdraw life-sustaining treatments from hospitalized patients. *Nursing Research* 2001 March-April; 50(2): 105-115. NRCBL: 20.5.1; 8.3.3. SC: em.

Tonelli, Mark R. Waking the dying: must we always attempt to involve critically ill patients in end-of-life decisions? *Chest* 2005 February; 127(2): 637-642. NRCBL: 20.5.1; 8.3.3. SC: cs.

Truog, Robert D.; Waisel, David B.; Burns, Jeffrey P. Do-not-resuscitate orders in the surgical setting [opinion]. *Lancet* 2005 February 26-March 4; 365(9461): 733-735. NRCBL: 20.5.1; 7.1; 9.5.1.

Uvey, Dogan; Gokce, Ayse Nur; Basagaoglu, Ibrahim. Euthanasia: the concept and the situation in Turkey. *Medical Ethics and Bioethics / Medicinska Etika & Bioetika* 2004 Autumn-Winter; 11(3-4): 7-8. NRCBL: 20.5.1; 8.1; 20.7; 2.2.

van Leeuwen, Anna F.; Voogt, Elsbeth; Visser, Adriaan; van der Rijt, Carin C.D.; van der Heide, Agnes. Considerations of healthcare professionals in medical decision-making about treatment for clinical end-stage cancer patients. *Journal of Pain and Symptom Management* 2004 October; 28(4): 351-355. NRCBL: 20.5.1; 20.3.2. SC: em. Identifiers: Netherlands.

Veatch, Robert M. Terri Schiavo, Son Hudson, and 'nonbeneficial' medical treatments. *Health Affairs* 2005 July-August; 24(4): 976-979. NRCBL: 20.5.1; 8.3.3; 20.5.4.

Veatch, Robert M. The total artificial heart: is paying for it immoral and stopping it murder? *Medical Ethics Newsletter [Lahey Clinic]* 2004 Winter; 11(1): 1-2, 12. NRCBL: 20.5.1; 19.2; 9.4.

Vedantam, Shankar; Weiss, Rick. Medical, ethical questions largely decided, experts say. *Washington Post* 2005 March 22; p. A6. NRCBL: 20.5.4; 20.5.1; 2.1. SC: po. Identifiers: Terri Schiavo.

Vetsch, G.; Uehlinger, D.E.; Zenklusen, Regula M. Zürcher. DNR orders at a tertiary care hospital — are they appropriate? *Swiss Medical Weekly* 2002 April 20; 132(15-16): 190-196. NRCBL: 20.5.1; 8.3.1. SC: em. Identifiers: Switzerland; do not resuscitate.

Veysman, Boris. Full code: a young physician is confounded by — then learns from — a dying patient's decisions. *Health Affairs* 2005 September-October; 24(5): 1311-1316. NRCBL: 20.5.1. SC: cs.

Vis, Theodorus A.M.; Onwuteaka-Philipsen, Bregje D.; Muller, Martien T.; van der Wal, Gerrit. Euthanasia and old age [letter and reply]. *Age and Ageing* 1999 July; 28(4): 414. NRCBL: 20.5.1; 20.7. Identifiers: Netherlands.

NRCBL: National Reference Center for Bioethics Literature Classification Scheme   See inside front cover for terms.

von Gruenigen, Vivian E.; Daly, Barbara J. Futility: clinical decisions at the end-of-life in women with ovarian cancer. *Gynecologic Oncology* 2005 May; 97(2): 638-644. NRCBL: 20.5.1; 9.5.1; 9.5.5. SC: em.

Vrakking, Astrid M.; van der Heide, Agnes; van Delden, Johannes J.M.; Looman, Caspar W.N.; Visser, Michelle H.; van der Maas, Paul J. Medical decision-making for seriously ill non-elderly and elderly patients. *Health Policy* 2005 December; 75(1): 40-48. NRCBL: 20.5.1; 9.5.2; 9.5.1; 8.1; 7.1. SC: em. Identifiers: Netherlands.

Waghela, Jagruti; George, Jameela. Euthanasia: a worldwide dilemma. *Indian Journal of Medical Ethics* 2004 July-September; 1(3): 92. NRCBL: 20.5.1.

Wagle, Rinata K.; Ede, Kekoa; Craig, Jana; Bottum, Kathleen. An ethical dilemma: when the family wants the withdrawal of care. *Journal of Psychiatric Practice* 2004 September; 10(5): 334-336. NRCBL: 20.5.1; 8.3.3; 20.7. SC: cs.

Wasserman, Jason; Clair, Jeffrey Michael; Ritchey, Ferris J. A scale to assess attitudes toward euthanasia. *Omega: Journal of Death and Dying* 2005; 51(3): 229-237. NRCBL: 20.5.1. SC: rv.

Werth, James L., Jr. Incorporating end-of-life issues into psychology courses. *Teaching of Psychology* 2002 Spring; 29(2): 106-111. NRCBL: 20.5.1; 7.2; 17.1; 20.7.

Wijdicks, Eelco F.M.; Rabinstein, Alejandro A. Absolutely no hope? Some ambiguity of futility of care in devastating acute stroke. *Critical Care Medicine* 2004 November; 32(11): 2332-2342. NRCBL: 20.5.1; 9.5.1. SC: rv.

Wolf, Susan M. Assessing physician compliance with the rules for euthanasia and assisted suicide [editorial]. *Archives of Internal Medicine* 2005 August 8-22; 165(15): 1677-1679. NRCBL: 20.5.1; 20.7. Identifiers: Netherlands.

Wolf, Susan M. Death and dying in America: Schiavo's implications [opinion]. *Minnesota Medicine* 2005 June; 88(6): 34-35. NRCBL: 20.5.1; 20.4.1; 1.3.8.

Woodhouse, S.P.; Wilkinson, T.J.; Watson, D.R.; Sainsbury, R.; Kidd, J.E.; Lowe, J.; Kerridge, I. Implementation of guidelines for no-CPR orders [letters and reply]. *Australian and New Zealand Journal of Medicine* 1998 February; 28(1): 67-68. NRCBL: 20.5.1; 7.1. Identifiers: cardiopulmonary resuscitation. Comments: comment on J. Lowe, I. Kerridge, "Implementation of guidelines for no-CPR orders by a general medicine unit in a teaching hospital," Australian and New Zealand Journal of Medicine 1997 August; 27(4): 379-383.

Woods, Simon. Respect for persons, autonomy and palliative care. *Medicine, Health Care and Philosophy: A European Journal* 2005; 8(2): 243-253. NRCBL: 20.5.1; 4.4. SC: an.

Abstract: This paper explores some of the values that underpin health care and how these relate more specifically to the values and ethics of palliative care. The paper focuses on the concept of autonomy because autonomy has emerged as a foundational concept in contemporary health care ethics and because this is an opportunity to scratch the surface of this concept in order to reveal something of its complexity, a necessary precaution when applying the concept to the context of palliative care. The paper begins with a theoretical discussion of autonomy exploring an aspect of its contemporary meaning and relevance to health care. The second part of the paper focuses more closely on how the principle of respect for autonomy can be applied in the context of palliative care. In this section an ethical framework is employed to explore a practical application of this principle within a broader context of respect for persons.

Yaguchi, Arino; Truog, Robert D.; Curtis, J. Randall; Luce, John M.; Levy, Mitchell M.; Mélot, Christian; Vincent, Jean-Louis. International differences in end-of-life attitudes in the intensive care unit. *Archives of Internal Medicine* 2005 September 26; 165(17): 1970-1975. NRCBL: 20.5.1; 20.4.1; 21.1. SC: em.

Abstract: BACKGROUND: Important international differences exist in attitudes toward end-of-life issues in the intensive care unit. METHODS: A simple questionnaire survey was sent by e-mail to participants at an international meeting on intensive care medicine. Respondents were asked to choose 1 of 3 to 5 possible answers for each of 4 questions related to the treatment of a hypothetical patient in a vegetative state due to anoxic encephalopathy after cardiac arrest with no family and no advance directives. RESULTS: From 3494 valid addresses, 1961 complete questionnaires (56%) were received from 21 countries. Sixty-two percent of physicians from Northern and Central Europe said they involved nurses in end-of-life discussions compared with only 32% of physicians in Southern Europe, 38% in Brazil, 39% in Japan, and 29% in the United States (P001 for all comparisons). Written do-not-resuscitate orders were preferred in Northern and Central Europe, whereas oral orders took preference in Southern Europe, Turkey, and Brazil. One third of Japanese physicians said that they would not apply do-not-resuscitate orders. Most participants from Japan, Turkey, the United States, Southern Europe, and Brazil chose to treat the hypothetical patient with antibiotics if he/she developed septic shock, whereas in Northern Europe, Central Europe, Canada, and Australia, terminal withdrawal of mechanical ventilation and extubation were the more commonly chosen responses. CONCLUSIONS: In countries where intensive care medicine is relatively well developed, considerable differences remain in physicians' attitudes toward end-of-life care in the intensive care unit. Substantial work remains if an international consensus on these issues is to be reached.

Yazigi, Alexandre; Riachi, Moussa; Dabbar, Georges. Withholding and withdrawal of life-sustaining treatment in a Lebanese intensive care unit: a prospective observational study. *Intensive Care Medicine* 2005 April; 31(4): 562-567. NRCBL: 20.5.1; 9.5.1. SC: em. Identifiers: Lebanon.

Yin, Xiuyun; Li, Benfu; Cong, Yali. Should this 96-year-old woman be allowed to die? *Medical Ethics Newsletter [Lahey Clinic]* 2005 Winter; 12(1): 3, 12. NRCBL: 20.5.1. Identifiers: China.

SC (Subject Caption):   an=analytical   cs=case studies   em=empirical   le=legal   po=popular   rv=review

Zingmond, David S.; Wenger, Neil S. Regional and institutional variation in the initiation of early do-not-resuscitate orders. *Archives of Internal Medicine* 2005 August 8-22; 165(15): 1705-1712. NRCBL: 20.5.1; 9.1. SC: em.

Abstract: BACKGROUND: Do-not-resuscitate (DNR) orders are an important step in decision making about aggressiveness of care for patients in hospitals. The use of DNR orders is known to vary with patient characteristics, but few studies have investigated the role of hospital factors or of regional variation. We examined these influences on the use of early DNR orders (written hours after admission). METHODS: We conducted a retrospective cross-sectional study of patients 50 years and older admitted to acute-care hospitals in California in 2000 from the most prevalent medical and surgical diagnosis related groups. We performed multivariate logistic regression predicting use of DNR by hospital characteristics while accounting for patient characteristics, and estimated indirectly standardized rates of DNR use by county. RESULTS: In the selected diagnosis related groups, 819 686 persons were admitted to 386 hospitals. Early DNR orders varied from 2% (patients aged 50-59 years) to 17% (patients aged or =80 years). In multivariate analyses, the odds of having early DNR orders written were significantly lower in for-profit (vs private nonprofit) hospitals, higher in the smallest (vs the largest) hospitals, and lower in academic (vs nonacademic) hospitals. Standardized rates of DNR order use varied 10-fold across counties. The highest rates were among patients from rural areas. However, variation in use did not correspond well to county population, hospital bed availability, or population density. CONCLUSIONS: Hospital characteristics appear to be associated with the use of DNR orders, even after accounting for differences in patient characteristics. This association reflects institutional culture, technological bent, and physician practice patterns. If these factors do not match patient preferences, then improvements in care are needed.

EUTHANASIA AND ALLOWING TO DIE/ LEGAL ASPECTS

The right to require life-prolonging treatment: R (Burke) v. General Medical Council (Defendant) and Disability Rights Commission (Interested Party) and The Official Solicitor (Intervener). *Medical Law Review* 2004 Autumn; 12(3): 306-316. NRCBL: 20.5.1; 8.3.4. SC: le. Identifiers: United Kingdom (Great Britain).

The Theresa Schiavo case [news]. *Mental and Physical Disability Law Reporter* 2005 March-April; 29(2): 154-156. NRCBL: 20.5.1; 8.3.3. SC: le.

Alters, Sandra. Courts and the end of life. *In her:* Death and Dying. Who Decides? Detroit: Thomson Gale; 2005: 101-113. NRCBL: 20.5.1; 20.7. SC: le.

Alters, Sandra. Euthanasia and assisted suicide. *In her:* Death and Dying. Who Decides? Detroit: Thomson Gale; 2005: 57-78. NRCBL: 20.5.1; 20.7. SC: le.

Amarasekara, Kumar; Bagaric, Mirko. The legalisation of euthanasia in the Netherlands: lessons to be learnt. *Monash University Law Review* 2001; 27(2): 179-196. NRCBL: 20.5.1. SC: le.

Amarasekara, Kumar; Bagaric, Mirko. Moving from voluntary euthanasia to non-voluntary euthanasia: equal-

ity and compassion. *Ratio Juris* 2004 September; 17(3): 398-423. NRCBL: 20.5.1; 20.5.3; 8.3.3; 8.3.2. SC: le. Identifiers: Netherlands.

Anderson-Shaw, Lisa; Meadow, William; Leeds, Hilary S.; Lantos, John J. The fiction of futility: what to do with policy? *HEC (Healthcare Ethics Committee) Forum* 2005 December; 17(4): 294-307. NRCBL: 20.5.1. SC: cs; le.

Annas, George J. "Culture of life" politics at the bedside — the case of Terri Schiavo. *New England Journal of Medicine* 2005 April 21; 352(16): 1710-1715. NRCBL: 20.5.1. SC: le.

Ashcroft, Richard. Death policy in the United Kingdom. *In:* Blank, Robert H.; Merrick, Janna C., eds. End-of-Life Decision Making: A Cross-National Study. Cambridge, MA: MIT Press; 2005: 197-218. NRCBL: 20.5.1; 20.4.1; 20.7. SC: le.

Australia. Parliament; Cica, Natasha. Euthanasia — The Australian Law in an International Context. Part 1: Passive Voluntary Euthanasia: Research Paper 3: 1996-1997. Canberra, Australia: Law and Public Administration Group. Parliament 1996 September 9; 24 p. [Online]. Available: http://www.aph.gov.au/library/pubs/rp/1996-97/97rp3.htm [7 July 2005]. NRCBL: 20.5.1; 20.7; 21.1; 8.1. SC: le.

Australia. Parliament; Cica, Natasha. Euthanasia — The Australian Law in an International Context. Part 2: Active Voluntary Euthanasia. Research Paper 4: 1996-1997. Canberra, Australia: Law and Public Administration Group, Parliament 1996 September 9; 40 p. [Online]. Available: http://www.aph.gov.au/library/pubs/rp/1996-97/97rp4.htm [7 July 2005]. NRCBL: 20.5.1; 20.7; 21.1; 8.1; 20.5.4. SC: le.

Baxter, Mark. Time to legalise assisted dying? Use of Baxter products in figure for physician assisted suicide was inappropriate [letter]. *BMJ: British Medical Journal* 2005 October 8; 331(7520): 842. NRCBL: 20.5.1. SC: le.

Becker-Schwarze, Kathrin. Terri Schiavo: the assessment of the persistent vegetative state in accordance with German law. *European Journal of Health Law* 2005 December; 12(4): 321-334. NRCBL: 20.5.1; 20.5.4; 8.3.3. SC: le.

Belluck, Pam. Even as doctors say enough, families fight to prolong life; medical advances raise hopes of loved ones. *New York Times* 2005 March 27; p. A1, A22. NRCBL: 20.5.1; 20.5.3. SC: le; po.

Boer, Theo A. After the slippery slope: Dutch experiences on regulating active euthanasia. *Journal of the Society of Christian Ethics* 2003 Fall-Winter; 23(2): 225-242. NRCBL: 20.5.1; 2.1. SC: le.

NRCBL: National Reference Center for Bioethics Literature Classification Scheme   See inside front cover for terms.

179

Bostrom, Barry A. In the matter of Christine B. Biersack in the Ohio Court of Appeals. *Issues in Law and Medicine* 2005 Spring; 20(3): 267-270. NRCBL: 20.5.1. SC: le.

Bostrom, Barry A. In the Supreme Court of Kentucky Woods v. Commonwealth of Kentucky. *Issues in Law and Medicine* 2004 Fall; 20(2): 185-192. NRCBL: 20.5.1; 8.3.3; 9.5.3. SC: le.

Branthwaite, M.A. Taking the final step: changing the law on euthanasia and physician assisted suicide: time for change. *BMJ: British Medical Journal* 2005 September 24; 331(7518): 681-683. NRCBL: 20.5.1; 20.7; 21.1. SC: le.

Broeckaert, Bert. Belgium: towards a legal recognition of euthanasia. *European Journal of Health Law* 2001 June; 8(2): 95-107. NRCBL: 20.5.1. SC: le.

Buchanan, Maura. Assisted dying. *Nursing Standard* 2004 August 25-31; 18(50): 18. NRCBL: 20.5.1. SC: le. Identifiers: United Kingdom (Great Britain).

Cameron, Miriam E.; Park, Hyeoun-Ae. Equity versus economics in South Korea. *Journal of Nursing Law* 1999 November; 6(3): 47-54. NRCBL: 20.5.1; 9.3.1. SC: le.

Capron, Alexander Morgan. Borrowed lessons: the role of ethical distinctions in framing law on life-sustaining treatment. *Arizona State Law Journal* 1984; 1984(4): 647-660. NRCBL: 20.5.1; 8.4. SC: le.

Catholic Church. Catholic Bishops of Florida. The care of Terri Schiavo. *Origins* 2005 March 17; 34(39): 632. NRCBL: 20.5.1; 20.5.3; 1.2. SC: le.

Charatan, Fred. President Bush and Congress intervene in "right to die" case [news]. *BMJ: British Medical Journal* 2005 March 26; 330(7493): 687. NRCBL: 20.5.1; 21.1. SC: le. Identifiers: Terri Schiavo.

Charatan, Fred. US Supreme Court refuses to intervene in 'right to die' case [news]. *BMJ: British Medical Journal* 2005 April 2; 330(7494): 746. NRCBL: 20.5.1. SC: le. Identifiers: Terri Schiavo.

Cranford, Ronald. Facts, lies, and videotapes: the permanent vegetative state and the sad case of Terri Schiavo. *Journal of Law, Medicine and Ethics* 2005 Summer; 33(2): 363-371. NRCBL: 20.5.1; 20.5.4; 20.3.3; 8.3.3. SC: cs; le.

Daar, Judith F. Direct democracy and bioethical choices: voting life and death at the ballot box. *University of Michigan Journal of Law Reform* 1995 Summer; 28(4): 799-859. NRCBL: 20.5.1; 20.7; 8.1; 1.3.5; 1.1. SC: le.

Dellinger, Anne; Wall, Aimee. A brief review of North Carolina's law on dying. *North Carolina Medical Journal* 2004 July-August; 65(4): 221-225. NRCBL: 20.5.1. SC: le.

Dewan, Shaila. States taking a new look at end-of-life legislation; Schiavo case prompts flurry of activity. *New York Times* 2005 March 31; p. A14. NRCBL: 20.5.1. SC: po; le.

Didion, Joan. The case of Theresa Schiavo. *New York Review* 2005 June 9; 52(10): 60-64, 69. NRCBL: 20.5.1; 20.5.3; 1.3.5. SC: le; rv.

Downie, Jocelyn. Voluntary euthanasia in Canada. *Health Law in Canada* 1993; 14: 13-30. NRCBL: 20.5.1; 20.7; 4.4; 20.4.1; 1.1. SC: le.

Dresser, Rebecca. Schiavo's legacy: the need for an objective standard. *Hastings Center Report* 2005 May-June; 35(3): 20-22. NRCBL: 20.5.1; 20.5.4. SC: le.

Duguet, Anne-Marie. Euthanasia and assistance to end of life legislation in France. *European Journal of Health Law* 2001 June; 8(2): 109-123. NRCBL: 20.5.1; 20.7; 20.4.1. SC: le.

Dute, Joseph. The Terri Schiavo case in a comparative perspective [editorial]. *European Journal of Health Law* 2005 December; 12(4): 317-319. NRCBL: 20.5.1; 20.5.4. SC: le.

Dyer, Clare. GMC challenges court ruling on end of life decisions [news]. *BMJ: British Medical Journal* 2005 May 21; 330(7501): 1165. NRCBL: 20.5.1; 20.5.3; 4.4. SC: le. Identifiers: General Medical Council.

Dyer, Owen. Judges support doctors' decision to stop treating dying man [news]. *BMJ: British Medical Journal* 2005 September 10; 331(7516): 536. NRCBL: 20.5.1; 8.1. SC: le.

Dyer, Owen. Parents of disabled baby lose appeal against court order [news]. *BMJ: British Medical Journal* 2005 September 3; 331(7515): 472. NRCBL: 20.5.1; 20.5.2. SC: le.

Elon, Menachem; Auerbach, Bernard; Chazin, Daniel D.; Sykes, Melvin J. Euthanasia and the right to refuse treatment. *In their:* Jewish Law (Mishpat Ivri): Cases and Materials. New York: M. Bender; 1999: 637-696. NRCBL: 20.5.1; 20.5.3; 1.2. SC: le.

Emmett, Thomas H. Time to legalise assisted dying? No, thank you [letter]. *BMJ: British Medical Journal* 2005 October 8; 331(7520): 842. NRCBL: 20.5.1; 20.7. SC: le.

Florida. Circuit Court. Pinellas County. Sixth Circuit. *Schiavo v. Bush* [Date of Decision: 5 May 2004] Order Granting Petitioner's Motion for Protective Order. Civil Case No. 03-008212-CI-20. Florida: Circuit Court 2004 May 5; 5 p. NRCBL: 20.5.3; 8.3.3. SC: le. Identifiers: Terri Schiavo; Jeb Bush.

Florida. Circuit Court. Pinellas County. Sixth Circuit. *Schiavo v. Bush* [Date of Decision: 5 May 2004] Order Granting Petitioner's Motion for Summary Judgment. Civil Case No. 03-008212-CI-20. Florida: Circuit Court

2004 May 5; 23 p. NRCBL: 20.5.3; 8.3.3. SC: le. Identifiers: Terri Schiavo; Jeb Bush.

Florida. Court of Appeal. In re Guardianship of Schiavo [Date of Decision: 2001 October 17]. *Southern Reporter*, 2d Series, 2001; 800: 640-647. NRCBL: 20.5.3. SC: le.

Abstract: Court Decision: 800 *Southern Reporter*, 2d Series 640; 17 Oct 2001 (date of decision). The District Court of Appeal of Florida permitted the trial court to conduct an evidentiary hearing to determine whether a person in a persistent vegetative state would have elected to pursue new medical treatment before withdrawing life-support procedures. Theresa Marie Schiavo had been in a persistant vegetative state for ten years when her guardian (husband Michael) petitioned to have life-sustaining support withdrawn. Mrs. Schiavo's parents opposed their son-in-law's petition. The Schindlers (Mrs. Schiavo's parents) filed a motion for relief from judgment citing new evidence that (1) Mrs. Schiavo would not have chosen to withdraw life support, and (2) that Mrs. Schiavo was not in a persistent vegetative state, and because there were current accepted medical treatments that could restore Mrs. Schiavo's ability to speak and eat, she would elect to undergo the new treatment and reverse any prior decision to withdraw life support. The Florida District Court of Appeal rejected the Schindlers' first claim but allowed a trial court to conduct an evidentiary hearing regarding their second claim. Specifically, the court remanded the case for a determination of whether the new treatment provides a sufficient promise of improvement in Mrs. Schiavo's life "so that she herself would elect to undergo this treatment and would reverse the prior decision to withdraw life-prolonging procedures." [KIE/INW]

Foster, Charles A. Time to legalise assisted dying? What autonomy really means [letter]. *BMJ: British Medical Journal* 2005 October 8; 331(7520): 841- 842. NRCBL: 20.5.1; 20.7; 1.1. SC: le.

Freeland, Richard. Euthanasia and Islamic law. *Medico-Legal Journal* 1997; 65(4): 196-198. NRCBL: 20.5.1; 1.2. SC: le.

Gast, Scott. Who defines "legitimate medical practice?" Lessons learned from the Controlled Substances Act, physician-assisted suicide, and Oregon v. Ashcroft. *Virginia Journal of Social Policy and the Law* 2002 Winter; 10(2): 261-291. NRCBL: 20.5.1; 1.3.5; 9.7. SC: le.

George, R.J.D.; Finlay, I.G.; Jeffrey, David. Legalised euthanasia will violate the rights of vulnerable patients. *BMJ: British Medical Journal* 2005 September 24; 331(7518): 684-685. NRCBL: 20.5.1; 20.7; 20.4.1; 9.5.1. SC: le.

Gevers, Sjef. Withdrawing life support from patients in a persistent vegetative state: the law in the Netherlands. *European Journal of Health Law* 2005 December; 12(4): 347-355. NRCBL: 20.5.1; 8.3.3; 20.5.4. SC: le.

Godfrey, Kathryn. Assisted dying legislation must wait until after UK election [news]. *BMJ: British Medical Journal* 2005 April 9; 330(7495): 807. NRCBL: 20.5.1; 20.7; 5.3; 2.4. SC: le. Identifiers: United Kingdom (Great Britain).

Godlovitch, Glenys; Mitchell, Ian; Doig, Christopher James. Discontinuing life support in comatose patients: an example from Canadian case law. *CMAJ/JAMC: Canadian Medical Association Journal* 2005 April 26; 172(9): 1172-1173. NRCBL: 20.5.1. SC: le.

Goodnough, Abby. In Schiavo feeding-tube case, notoriety finds unlikely judge presiding. *New York Times* 2005 March 17; p. A18. NRCBL: 20.5.1. SC: po; le.

Goodnough, Abby. Judge delays feeding tube removal. *New York Times* 2005 February 23; p. A13. NRCBL: 20.5.1. SC: po; le.

Goodnough, Abby. Supreme court refuses to hear the Schiavo case; day of legal scrambling; governor rebuffed too — few options as parents return to U.S. court. *New York Times* 2005 March 25; p. A1, A14. NRCBL: 20.5.1. SC: po; le.

Goodnough, Abby. U.S. judge denies feeding-tube bid in Schiavo's case; parents quickly appeal; family cites urgency as woman enters 5th day without nutrition. *New York Times* 2005 March 23; p. A1, A14. NRCBL: 20.5.1; 21.1. SC: po; le.

Goodnough, Abby. U.S. judge hears tense testimony in Schiavo's case; no quick ruling is made; he expresses doubts that a federal review will change outcome. *New York Times* 2005 March 22; p. A1, A14. NRCBL: 20.5.1; 21.1. SC: po; le.

Goodnough, Abby; Hulse, Carl. Despite Congress, woman's feeding tube is removed: judge in Florida rejects effort by House. *New York Times* 2005 March 19; p. A1, A12. NRCBL: 20.5.1. SC: po; le.

Goodnough, Abby; Liptak, Adam. Court blocks bid; new Schiavo tack by governor Bush; appeal to supreme court; Florida judge agrees to hear new motions — neurologist in fray. *New York Times* 2005 March 24; p. A1, A20. NRCBL: 20.5.1; 21.1. SC: po; le.

Gostin, Lawrence O. Ethics, the Constitution, and the dying process: the case of Theresa Marie Schiavo. *JAMA: The Journal of the American Medical Association* 2005 May 18; 293(19): 2403-2407. NRCBL: 20.5.1. SC: le.

Grubb, Andrew. Euthanasia in England — a law lacking compassion? [editorial]. *European Journal of Health Law* 2001 June; 8(2): 89-93. NRCBL: 20.5.1. SC: le.

Guarisco, Kristen K. Managing do-not-resuscitate orders in the perianesthesia period. *Journal of Perianesthesia Nursing* 2004 October; 19(5): 300-307. NRCBL: 20.5.1; 8.3.1; 20.3.1. SC: le.

Hafemeister, Thomas L.; Robinson, Donna M. The views of the judiciary regarding life-sustaining medical treatment decisions. *Law and Psychology Review* 1994 Spring; 18: 189-246. NRCBL: 20.5.1. SC: le.

NRCBL: National Reference Center for Bioethics Literature Classification Scheme   See inside front cover for terms.

181

Hall, Mark A.; Trachtenberg, F.; Dugan, E. The impact on patient trust of legalising physician aid in dying. *Journal of Medical Ethics* 2005 December; 31(12): 693-697. NRCBL: 20.5.1; 20.7; 8.1. SC: em; le.

Abstract: OBJECTIVE: Little empirical evidence exists to support either side of the ongoing debate over whether legalising physician aid in dying would undermine patient trust. DESIGN: A random national sample of 1117 US adults were asked about their level of agreement with a statement that they would trust their doctor less if "euthanasia were legal [and] doctors were allowed to help patients die". RESULTS: There was disagreement by 58% of the participants, and agreement by only 20% that legalising euthanasia would cause them to trust their personal physician less. The remainder were neutral. These attitudes were the same in men and women, but older people and black people had more agreement that euthanasia would lower trust. However, overall, only 27% of elderly people (age 65+) and 32% of black people thought that physician aid in dying would lower trust. These views differed with physical and mental health, and also with education and income, with those having more of these attributes tending to view physician aid in dying somewhat more favourably. Again, however, overall views in most of these subgroups were positive. Views about the effect of physician aid in dying on trust were significantly correlated with participants' underlying trust in their physicians and their satisfaction with care. In a multivariate regression model, trust, satisfaction, age, and white/black race remained independently significant. CONCLUSION: Despite the widespread concern that legalising physician aid in dying would seriously threaten or undermine trust in physicians, the weight of the evidence in the USA is to the contrary, although views vary significantly.

Hampson, Lindsay A.; Emanuel, Ezekiel J. The prognosis for changes in end-of-life care after the Schiavo case. *Health Affairs* 2005 July-August; 24(4): 972-975. NRCBL: 20.5.1; 8.3.3; 20.5.4. SC: le.

Hampton, Sylvia. Should euthanasia be legalized? *British Journal of Nursing* 1993 April 22-May 12; 2(8): 429-431. NRCBL: 20.5.1; 1.3.5. SC: le.

Harper, Richard S. The withholding or withdrawal of life-sustaining treatment in relation to adults and minors. *In his:* Medical Treatment and the Law: The Protection of Adults and Minors in the Family Division. Bristol: Family Law; 1999: 33-54. NRCBL: 20.5.1; 20.5.2. SC: le.

Harris, John. The right to die lives! There is no personhood paradox [debate]. *Medical Law Review* 2005 Autumn; 13(3): 386-392. NRCBL: 20.5.1; 4.4. SC: le.

Hulse, Carl; Kirkpatrick, David D. Even death does not quiet harsh political fight. *New York Times* 2005 April 1; p. A1. A16. NRCBL: 20.5.1; 21.1. SC: po; le.

Hulse, Carl; Kirkpatrick, David D. Moving quickly, Senate approves Schiavo measure; allows review by judge; Bush rushes to capital to sign bill in clash over feeding tube case. *New York Times* 2005 March 21; p. A1, A14. NRCBL: 20.5.1; 21.1. SC: po; le.

Huxtable, Richard. Get out of jail free? The doctrine of double effect in English law. *Palliative Medicine* 2004; 18(1): 62-68. NRCBL: 20.5.1; 20.4.1; 9.7; 8.1; 1.1. SC: le.

Ishak, April; Miller, Robert T. Schiavo under the law [letter and reply]. *First Things* 2005 October; (156): 5, 6-8. NRCBL: 20.5.1. SC: le.

Jakobson, Daniel J.; Eidelman, Leonid A.; Worner, T.M.; Oppenheim, Arieh Eden; Pizov, Reuven; Sprung, Charles L. Evaluation of changes in forgoing life-sustaining treatment in Israeli ICU patients. *Chest* 2004 December; 126(6): 1969-1973. NRCBL: 20.5.1. SC: em; le.

Kapp, Marshall B. 'Ageism' and right to die litigation. *Medicine and Law: World Association for Medical Law* 1994; 13(1-2): 69-77. NRCBL: 20.5.1. SC: em; le.

Kelly, David F. Forgoing treatment, pillar three: decisions for incompetent patients. *In his:* Contemporary Catholic Health Care Ethics. Washington, DC: Georgetown University Press; 2004: 153-169. NRCBL: 20.5.1; 1.2; 8.3.3; 8.3.4. SC: le.

Kelly, David F. Physician-assisted suicide and euthanasia. *In his:* Contemporary Catholic Health Care Ethics. Washington, DC: Georgetown University Press; 2004: 196-205. NRCBL: 20.5.1; 20.7; 1.2. SC: le.

Keown, John. A futile defence of Bland: a reply to Andrew McGee [debate]. *Medical Law Review* 2005 Autumn; 13(3): 393-402. NRCBL: 20.5.1; 4.4. SC: le.

Keown, John. Dehydrating bodies: the Bland case, the Winterton bill and the importance of intention in evaluating end-of-life decision-making. *In:* Bainham, Andrew; Sclater, Shelley Day; Richards, Martin, eds. Body Lore and Laws. Portland, OR: Hart Pub.; 2002: 249-264. NRCBL: 20.5.1. SC: le.

Keown, John. Medical murder by omission? The law and ethics of withholding and withdrawing treatment and tube feeding. *Clinical Medicine* 2003 September-October; 3(5): 460-463. NRCBL: 20.5.1. SC: le. Identifiers: Tony Bland; British Medical Association.

Keown, John. No charter for assisted suicide. *Cambridge Law Journal* 1994 July; 53(2): 234-236. NRCBL: 20.5.1. SC: le. Identifiers: Sue Rodriguez.

Kovach, Kimberlee K. Neonatology life and death decisions: can mediation help? *Capital University Law Review* 2000; 28(2): 251-292. NRCBL: 20.5.1; 9.5.7; 9.4; 8.3.2. SC: le.

Lakhani, Mayur K. Time to legalise assisted dying? RCGP is not neutral: it opposes a change in legislation [letter]. *BMJ: British Medical Journal* 2005 October 8; 331(7520): 841. NRCBL: 20.5.1; 20.7. SC: le. Identifiers: Royal College of General Practitioners.

Lavi, Shai. Euthanasia and the changing ethics of the deathbed. *Theoretical Inquiries in Law* 2003 July; 4(2): 729-761. NRCBL: 20.5.1; 20.1; 20.3.1; 20.5.3. SC: le.

Leenen, H.J.J. The development of euthanasia in the Netherlands. *European Journal of Health Law* 2001 June; 8(2): 125-133. NRCBL: 20.5.1; 2.2. SC: le.

Lemaire, François J.P. A law for end of life care in France? [news]. *Intensive Care Medicine* 2004 November; 30(11): 2120. NRCBL: 20.5.1. SC: le.

Lemmens, Trudo; Dickens, Bernard. Canadian law on euthanasia: contrasts and comparisons. *European Journal of Health Law* 2001 June; 8(2): 135-155. NRCBL: 20.5.1; 20.7. SC: le.

Liaschenko, Joan. Death: can Monty Python do what philosophers can not? [editorial]. *Nursing Philosophy* 2005 July; 6(3): 159-60. NRCBL: 20.5.1; 7.1; 10. SC: le.

Linane, Marianne; Miller, Robert T. Schiavo under the law [letter and reply]. *First Things* 2005 October; (156): 5, 6-8. NRCBL: 20.5.1. SC: le.

Luce, John M.; Alpers, Ann. Legal aspects of withholding and withdrawing life support from critically ill patients in the United States and providing palliative care to them. *American Journal of Respiratory and Critical Care Medicine* 2000 December; 162(6): 2029-2032. NRCBL: 20.5.1; 20.4.1. SC: le.

Malcolm, David. The Everett Magnus Oration: euthanasia and the law: crossing the rubicon? *Australian and New Zealand Journal of Medicine* 1998 February; 28(1): 46-54. NRCBL: 20.5.1; 8.3.3; 8.3.4; 20.5.4. SC: le.

Mamdani, Bashir. The Terry Schiavo case: possible implications for India. *Indian Journal of Medical Ethics* 2005 July-September; 2(3): 97-98. NRCBL: 20.5.1. SC: le.

Mareiniss, Darren P. A comparison of Cruzan and Schiavo: the burden of proof, due process, and autonomy in the persistently vegetative patient. *Journal of Legal Medicine* 2005 June; 26(2): 233-259. NRCBL: 20.5.1; 1.1; 8.3.3. SC: le.

Mathie, William. Justice, rhetoric and law: reflections on Latimer v. The Queen. *In:* Koterski, Joseph W., ed. Life and Learning XI: Proceedings of the Eleventh University Faculty for Life Conference. Washington, DC: University Faculty for Life; 2002: 46-62. NRCBL: 20.5.1. SC: le. Identifiers: Canada; Canadian Charter of Rights and Freedoms.

Mavroforou, Anna; Michalodimitrakis, Emmanuel. Euthanasia in Greece, Hippocrates' birthplace. *European Journal of Health Law* 2001 June; 8(2): 157-162. NRCBL: 20.5.1; 1.2. SC: le.

McCullagh, Peter. Vegetative states in court. *In his:* Conscious in a Vegetative State? A Critique of the PVS Concept. Boston: Kluwer Academic; 2004: 282-314. NRCBL: 20.5.1. SC: le.

McGee, Andrew. Finding a way through the ethical and legal maze: withdrawal of medical treatment and euthanasia. *Medical Law Review* 2005 Autumn; 13(3): 357-385. NRCBL: 20.5.1; 1.1. SC: le.

McGrew, Lydia; Miller, Robert T. Schiavo under the law [letter and reply]. *First Things* 2005 October; (156): 5-8. NRCBL: 20.5.1. SC: le.

McPhee, John; Stewart, Cameron. Recent developments in law. *Journal of Bioethical Inquiry* 2005; 2(1): 4-9. NRCBL: 20.5.1; 20.4.2; 20.5.2; 20.5.4. SC: le.

Meisel, Alan. Quality of life and end-of-life decisionmaking. *Quality of Life Research* 2003; 12(Supplement 1): 91-94. NRCBL: 20.5.1; 4.4; 8.3.3. SC: le.

Merrick, Janna C. Death and dying: the American experience. *In:* Blank, Robert H.; Merrick, Janna C., eds. End-of-Life Decision Making: A Cross-National Study. Cambridge, MA: MIT Press; 2005: 219-241. NRCBL: 20.5.1; 20.7. SC: le.

Miller, Robert T. The legal death of Terri Schiavo. *First Things* 2005 May; (153): 14-16. NRCBL: 20.5.1; 1.3.5. SC: le.

Morgan, Derek; Veitch, Kenneth. Being Ms B: B, autonomy and the nature of legal regulation. *Sydney Law Review* 2004 March; 26(1): 107-130. NRCBL: 20.5.1; 1.1; 8.3.4. SC: le.

Munby, James; Francis, Robert; Taylor, Michael R.; Lester, Anthony; Saini, Pushbinder. Medical treatment — withdrawal of treatment — patient in persistent vegetative state: Airedale National Health Service Trust v. Bland [Date of Decision: 9 December 1992]. *New Law Journal* 1992 December 18; 142(6581): 1755-1758. NRCBL: 20.5.1. SC: le.

Nelson, Lawrence J. Persistent indeterminate state: reflections on the Wendland case. *Issues in Ethics* 2003 Winter; 14(1): 14-17. NRCBL: 20.5.1. SC: le.

Nespolon, Harry M.; Kuhse, Helga; Clark, Malcolm; Woollard, Keith V. Medical end-of-life decisions and legislation [opinion]. *Medical Journal of Australia* 1997 September 1; 167(5): 282-283. NRCBL: 20.5.1; 1.3.5; 7.1. SC: le.

Newnham, Helen. Should nurses act legally or ethically? *Contemporary Nurse* 1998 March; 7(1): 42-47. NRCBL: 20.5.1; 7.1; 4.1.3. SC: le.

O'Keefe, Mary E.; Crawford, Kate. End-of-life care: legal and ethical considerations. *Seminars in Oncology Nursing* 2002 May; 18(2): 143-148. NRCBL: 20.5.1; 20.5.4; 20.7; 4.1.3. SC: le.

Onwuteaka-Philipsen, Bregje D.; van der Heide, Agnes; Muller, Martien T.; Rurup, Mette; Rietjens, Judith A.C.; Georges, Jean- Jacques; Vrakking, Astrid

NRCBL: National Reference Center for Bioethics Literature Classification Scheme   See inside front cover for terms.

183

M.; **Cuperus-Bosma, Jacqueline M.; van der Wal, Gerrit; van der Maas, Paul J.** Dutch experience of monitoring euthanasia. *BMJ: British Medical Journal* 2005 September 24; 331(7518): 691-693. NRCBL: 20.5.1; 20.7; 8.4; 9.6. SC: le.

Ouellette, Alicia R. When vitalism is dead wrong: the discrimination against and torture of incompetent patients by compulsory life-sustaining treatment. *Indiana Law Journal* 2004 Winter; 79(1): 1-55. NRCBL: 20.5.1; 8.3.3. SC: le.

Patel, Kant. Euthanasia and physician-assisted suicide policy in the Netherlands and Oregon: a comparative analysis. *Journal of Health and Social Policy* 2004; 19(1): 37-55. NRCBL: 20.5.1; 20.7; 20.5.3; 8.1. SC: an; le.

Peckitt, Michael G. Time to legalise assisted dying? BMA should take an active role, whatever that may be [letter]. *BMJ: British Medical Journal* 2005 October 8; 331(7520): 841. NRCBL: 20.5.1. SC: le. Identifiers: British Medical Association.

Pence, Gregory E. Classic cases about death and dying. *In his:* Classic Cases in Medical Ethics: Accounts of Cases That Have Shaped Medical Ethics, with Philosophical, Legal, and Historical Backgrounds. Fourth edition. Boston, MA: McGraw- Hill; 2004: 27-120. NRCBL: 20.5.1; 20.7. SC: le.

Perry, Joshua E.; Churchill, Larry R.; Kirshner, Howard S. The Terri Schiavo case: legal, ethical, and medical perspectives. *Annals of Internal Medicine* 2005 November 15; 143(10): 744-748. NRCBL: 20.5.1. SC: le.
  Abstract: Although tragic, the plight of Terri Schiavo provides a valuable case study. The conflicts and misunderstandings surrounding her situation offer important lessons in medicine, law, and ethics. Despite media saturation and intense public interest, widespread confusion lingers regarding the diagnosis of persistent vegetative state, the judicial processes involved, and the appropriateness of the ethical framework used by those entrusted with Terri Schiavo's care. First, the authors review the current medical understanding of persistent vegetative state, including the requirements for patient examination, the differential diagnosis, and the practice guidelines of the American Academy of Neurology regarding artificial nutrition and hydration for patients with this diagnosis. Second, they examine the legal history, including the 2000 trial, the 2002 evidentiary hearing, and the subsequent appeals. The authors argue that the law did not fail Terri Schiavo, but produced the highest-quality evidence and provided the most judicial review of any end-of-life guardianship case in U.S. history. Third, they review alternative ethical frameworks for understanding the Terri Schiavo case and contend that the principle of respect for autonomy is paramount in this case and in similar cases. Far from being unusual, the manner in which Terri Schiavo's case was reviewed and the basis for the decision reflect a broad medical, legal, and ethical consensus. Greater clarity regarding the persistent vegetative state, less apprehension of the presumed mysteries of legal proceedings, and greater appreciation of the ethical principles at work are the chief benefits obtained from studying this provocative case.

Pessini, Leo. Ethical questions related to end-of-life decisions: the Brazilian reality. *In:* Blank, Robert H.; Merrick, Janna C., eds. End-of-Life Decision Making: A Cross-National Study. Cambridge, MA: MIT Press; 2005: 13-31. NRCBL: 20.5.1; 20.4.1; 19.5. SC: le.

Potter, C. Ann. Will the "right to die" become a license to kill? The growth of euthanasia in America. *Journal of Legislation* 1993; 19(1): 31-62. NRCBL: 20.5.1; 20.3.1; 2.2. SC: le.

Pradella, Geoffrey M. Substituting a judgment of best interests: dignity and the application of objective principles to PVS cases in the U.K. *European Journal of Health Law* 2005 December; 12(4): 335-345. NRCBL: 20.5.1; 8.3.3. SC: le. Identifiers: persistent vegetative state.

Quill, Timothy E. Terri Schiavo—a tragedy compounded [opinion]. *New England Journal of Medicine* 2005 April 21; 352(16): 1630- 1631, 1633. NRCBL: 20.5.1; 20.5.3. SC: le.

Rahdert, George K.; Lapertosa, Max. Brief of amici curiae Not Dead Yet et al., Jeb Bush v. Michael Schiavo. *Issues in Law and Medicine* 2004 Fall; 20(2): 171-181. NRCBL: 20.5.1; 8.3.3. SC: le.

Ravenstein, Christian. Discontinuation of life supporting measures in Germany. *European Journal of Health Law* 2002 December; 9(4): 321-335. NRCBL: 20.5.1; 20.5.2; 20.5.4. SC: le.

Roig-Franziza, Manuel. Court lets right-to-die ruling stand: parents at odds with husband over removing Fla. woman's feeding tube. *Washington Post* 2005 January 25; p. A7. NRCBL: 20.5.1. SC: po; le. Identifiers: Terri Schiavo.

Roig-Franzia, Manuel; Connolly, Ceci. La. investigates allegations of euthanasia at hospital; autopsies sought on 45 in post-Katrina inquiry. *Washington Post* 2005 October 15; p. A3. NRCBL: 20.5.1. SC: po; le. Identifiers: Louisiana.

Savell, Kristin. Human rights in the age of technology: can law rein in the medical juggernaut? *Sydney Law Review* 2001 September; 23(3): 423-460. NRCBL: 20.5.1; 20.5.2; 4.4. SC: le.

Schneider, Carl E. Hard cases and the politics of righteousness. *Hastings Center Report* 2005 May-June; 35(3): 24-27. NRCBL: 20.5.1; 12.4.1; 20.7. SC: le. Identifiers: Terri Schiavo.

Siegel, Shana. Can we learn anything from the tragedy that is the Schiavo case? *Health Care Law Monthly* 2004 November: 3-8. NRCBL: 20.5.1; 8.3.3; 1.3.5. SC: le.

Siegel-Itzkovich, Judy. Israelis turn to timer device to facilitate passive euthanasia [news]. *BMJ: British Medical Journal* 2005 December 10; 331(7529): 1357. NRCBL: 20.5.1; 20.5.4; 9.6; 20.4.1. SC: le.

SC (Subject Caption):   an=analytical   cs=case studies   em=empirical   le=legal   po=popular   rv=review

Skene, Loane. Disputes about the withdrawal of treatment: the role of the courts. *Journal of Law, Medicine and Ethics* 2004 Winter; 32(4): 701- 707. NRCBL: 20.5.1; 4.4; 20.5.2; 8.3.4. SC: le.

Sommerville, Ann. Changes in BMA policy on assisted dying. *BMJ: British Medical Journal* 2005 September 24; 331(7518): 686-688. NRCBL: 20.5.1; 20.7; 7.1; 21.1. SC: le. Identifiers: British Medical Association.

Stith, Richard. Death by hunger and thirst. *Ethics and Medics* 2005 June; 30(6): 1-2. NRCBL: 20.5.1; 1.2. SC: le. Identifiers: Terri Schiavo.

Stolberg, Sheryl Gay. A collision of disparate forces may be reshaping American law; the Schiavo case: looking ahead and looking back. *New York Times* 2005 April 1; p. A18. NRCBL: 20.5.1. SC: po; le.

Tak, Peter. Recent developments concerning euthanasia in the Netherlands. *Tilburg Foreign Law Review* 1999; 8(1): 43-80. NRCBL: 20.5.1; 20.7; 8.3.3; 8.3.1; 20.4.1. SC: le; em.

Talib, Norchaya. Dilemmas surrounding passive euthanasia — a Malaysian perspective. *Medicine and Law: World Association for Medical Law* 2005 September; 24(3): 605-613. NRCBL: 20.5.1; 21.7; 20.3.2. SC: le.
Abstract: In western societies where the principle of autonomy is jealously guarded, perhaps active euthanasia is more often the focus of public concern and debates rather than any other forms of euthanasia. However due to the advance in technology and its corresponding ability in prolonging life, in Malaysia passive euthanasia presents more of a dilemma. For those concerned and involved with end of life decision-making, it is generally agreed that this is an area fraught with not only medical but legal and ethical issues. In Malaysia where the society is not homogenous but is multi-cultural and multi-religious, in addition to medical, legal and ethical issues, religious principles and cultural norms further impact and play significant roles in end of life decision- making. This paper seeks to identify the issues surrounding the practice of passive euthanasia in Malaysia. It will be shown that despite applicable legal provisions, current practice of the medical profession combined with religious and cultural values together affect decision-making which involves the withholding and/or withdrawing of life-saving treatment.

ten Have, Henk A.M.J. End-of-life decision making in the Netherlands. *In:* Blank, Robert H.; Merrick, Janna C., eds. End-of-Life Decision Making: A Cross-National Study. Cambridge, MA: MIT Press; 2005: 147-168. NRCBL: 20.5.1. SC: le.

Toner, Robin; Hulse, Carl. Congress ready to approve bill in Schiavo case: look to federal courts; family's battle is forcing the public to confront end-of-life issues. *New York Times* 2005 March 20; p. A1, A19. NRCBL: 20.5.1; 21.1. SC: po; le.

Tonti-Filippini, Nicholas. Some refusals of medical treatment which changed the law of Victoria. *Medical Journal of Australia* 1992 August 17; 157(4): 277-279. NRCBL: 20.5.1; 8.3.4. SC: le; cs.

Truog, Robert D.; Cochrane, Thomas I. Refusal of hydration and nutrition: irrelevance of the "artificial" vs "natural" distinction. *Archives of Internal Medicine* 2005 December 12-26; 165(22): 2574-2576. NRCBL: 20.5.1; 8.3.4. SC: an; le.

Tur, Richard H.S. The doctor's defense. *Mount Sinai Journal of Medicine* 2002 October; 69(5): 317-328. NRCBL: 20.5.1; 1.3.5; 7.1; 8.1. SC: le.

Twisselmann, Birte. Time to legalise assisted suicide? Summary of responses [letter]. *BMJ: British Medical Journal* 2005 October 8; 331(7520): 843. NRCBL: 20.5.1; 20.7. SC: le.

Tynan, Anne. Time to legalise assisted dying? Recruiting more vulnerable doctors may be the answer [letter]. *BMJ: British Medical Journal* 2005 October 8; 331(7520): 842. NRCBL: 20.5.1. SC: le.

United States. District Court. Central District of California. *Kevorkian v. Arnett* [Date of Decision: 11 September 1996]. *West's Federal Supplement* 1996; 939: 725-732. NRCBL: 20.5.3; 20.7. SC: le.
Abstract: Court Decision: 939 *Federal Supplement*, 725; 1996 Sep 11 (date of decision). The United States District Court granted the plaintiff's motion for summary judgment on a claim that California's law against assisted suicide violated his federal due process rights and dismissed the plaintiff's claims that the law violated his privacy and equal protection rights under California's constitution. Plaintiff John Doe, a terminally ill patient, wanted to end his life with the assistance of plaintiff Jack Kevorkian. The court dismissed Kevorkian from the action because he was not licensed to practice medicine in the state of California and thereby lacked standing to challenge the constitutionality of California's Penal Code. The court applied the standard of "undue burden" in determining whether California's law against assisted suicide violated Doe's liberty interest under the due process clause of the Federal Constitution. Because the U.S. Court of Appeals for the Ninth Circuit has acknowledged a liberty interest "in controlling the time and manner of one's death," and because the California Code categorically prohibits assisted suicide, the court found the law placed a "substantial obstacle" in a "large fraction of the cases" and therefore violated the due process clause. Relying on a California appellate court decision, the court held that the law prohibiting assisted suicide does not violate the plaintiff's right to privacy. The court also held the law prohibiting assisted suicide does not violate the plaintiff's right to equal protection under California law because the law bears "some rational relationship to a conceivable legitimate state purpose." [KIE/INW]

United States. District Court. Eastern District of Michigan. *Kevorkian v. Thompson* [Date of Decision: 6 January 1997]. *Federal Supplement* 1997; 947: 1152-1179. NRCBL: 20.5.3; 20.7. SC: le.
Abstract: Court Decision: 947 *Federal Supplement*, 1152; 1997 Jan 6 (date of decision). The United States District Court for the Eastern District of Michigan held that a mentally competent patient who is terminally ill or intractably suffering does not have a liberty interest in assisted suicide under the due process clause of the Fourteenth Amendment and is not denied equal protection under the Fourteenth Amendment. Plaintiff Jack Kevorkian is a physician who advocates the right to die and as-

---

NRCBL: National Reference Center for Bioethics Literature Classification Scheme   See inside front cover for terms.

185

sists patients to commit suicide. Plaintiff Janet Good, the former president of the Michigan Hemlock Society, suffers from terminal pancreatic cancer. The plaintiffs claimed that Michigan's statute prohibiting physician-assisted suicide is unconstitutional. The District Court held there is no cognizable constitutional right to assisted suicide because the right to suicide or assisted suicide is not deeply rooted in the nation's history and traditions, and because the statute does not infringe on any fundamental right or liberty. The court also held that the plaintiff was not denied equal protection under Michigan law and first noted a difference between the withdrawal of life support and acts to hasten death by assisted suicide. The court further held that the law against physician-assisted suicide furthered legitimate state interests in denying to physicians "the role of killers of their patients," in regulating circumstances under which life may be ended, and in protecting the vulnerable but viable from "self-interested importuning of third parties." [KIE/INW]

Weber, Susan M. Court affirms relatives' right to shut off life support. *Pennsylvania Medicine* 1996 June; 99(6): 24-25. NRCBL: 20.5.1; 8.3.3. SC: le.

Weijer, Charles. A death in the family: reflections on the Terri Schiavo case [opinion]. *CMAJ/JAMC: Canadian Medical Association Journal* 2005 April 26; 172(9): 1197-1198. NRCBL: 20.5.1; 20.5.4. SC: le. Identifiers: Robert Kenneth Durksen.

Weinrib, Lorraine Eisenstat. The body and the body politic: assisted suicide under the Canadian Charter of Rights and Freedoms. *McGill Law Journal* 1994; 39(3): 618-643. NRCBL: 20.5.1; 20.7; 4.4; 1.1. SC: le.

Wolfson, Jay. Erring on the side of Theresa Schiavo: reflections of the special guardian ad litem. *Hastings Center Report* 2005 May-June; 35(3): 16-19. NRCBL: 20.5.1. SC: le.

Young, Ernlé W.D. Ethical issues at the end of life. *Stanford Law and Policy Review* 1998 Spring; 9(2): 267-288. NRCBL: 20.5.1; 20.3.1; 20.5.4; 2.1. SC: le.

Young, Robert. Should voluntary euthanasia be legally permitted? *Res Publica* 1996; 5(1): 1-7. NRCBL: 20.5.1. SC: an; le.

EUTHANASIA AND ALLOWING TO DIE/ MINORS

The right of a treatment proxy to challenge a decision to administer diamorphine to a patient. *Medical Law Review* 2004 Autumn; 12(3): 317-322. NRCBL: 20.5.2; 8.3.2. SC: le.

The Supreme Court judgment dated May 4, 2001 in the PNDT Act, 1994. *Issues in Medical Ethics* 2001 July-September; 9(3): 97-98. NRCBL: 20.5.2. Identifiers: Pre-Natal Diagnostic Techniques (Regulation and Prevention of Misuse) Act 1994; India.

Baer, Steven. Should imperfect infants survive? *National Review* 1983 September 2; 35(17): 1069, 1092-1093. NRCBL: 20.5.2; 9.5.3; 4.4. SC: le.

Belluck, Pam. Custody and abuse cases swirl around a troubled girl on life support. *New York Times* 2005 December 6; p. A18. NRCBL: 20.5.2. SC: po.

Brazier, Margot. An intractable dispute: when parents and professionals disagree. *Medical Law Review* 2005 Autumn; 13(3): 412-418. NRCBL: 20.5.2; 20.4.2; 8.3.2. SC: le. Identifiers: Re Wyatt (A Child).

British Association of Perinatal Medicine [BAPM]. Witholding or Withdrawing Life Sustaining Treatment in Children: A Framework for Practice. United Kingdom: British Association of Perinatal Medicine 2004 May; 42 p. [Online]. Available: http://www.rcpch.ac.uk/publications/recent_publications/Witholding.pdf [31 January 2006]. NRCBL: 20.5.2. Note: Second edition.

Burns, Jeffrey. Does anyone actually invoke their hospital futility policy? *Medical Ethics Newsletter [Lahey Clinic]* 2005 Fall; 12(3): 3. NRCBL: 20.5.2; 9.4. SC: cs.

Carnevale, Franco A. Ethical care of the critically ill child: a conception of a 'thick' bioethics. *Nursing Ethics* 2005 May; 12(3): 239-252. NRCBL: 20.5.2; 1.1; 2.1; 21.7. SC: cs.

Casagrande, Kathleen M. Children not meant to be: protecting the interests of the child when abortion results in live birth. *Quinnipiac Health Law Journal* 2002; 6(1): 19-55. NRCBL: 20.5.2; 12.4.2. SC: le.

Collier, Julie; Sandborg, Christy. The first step: DNAR outside the hospital and the role of pediatric medical care providers. *American Journal of Bioethics* 2005 January-February; 5(1): 85- 86. NRCBL: 20.5.2; 9.5.7. Identifiers: do-not-attempt-resuscitation. Comments: comment on Michael B. Kimberly, Amanda L. Forte, Jean M. Carroll, Chris Feudtner, "Pediatric do-not-attempt-resuscitation orders and public schools: a national assessment of policies and laws," American Journal of Bioethics 2005 January-February; 5(1): 59-65.

Crouch, Gregory. A crusade born of a suffering infant's cry: Saturday profile (Dr. Eduard Verhagen). *New York Times* 2005 March 19; p. A4. NRCBL: 20.5.2. SC: po.

Curlin, Farr A.; Verhagen, Eduard; Sauer, Pieter J.J. Euthanasia in severely ill newborns [letter and reply]. *New England Journal of Medicine* 2005 June 2; 352(22): 2354-2355. NRCBL: 20.5.2; 9.5.1; 15.1.

Davies, Michael. Selective non-treatment of the newborn: in whose best interests? In whose judgment? *Northern Ireland Legal Quarterly* 1998 Spring; 49(1): 82-93. NRCBL: 20.5.2; 8.3.4; 8.3.2. SC: le.

Diamond,Eugene F. Anencephaly and early delivery: can there ever be justification? *Ethics and Medics* 2003 October; 28(10): 2-3. NRCBL: 20.5.2.

Diekema, Douglas S. DNAR in the schools: watch your language! *American Journal of Bioethics* 2005 January-February; 5(1): 76- 78. NRCBL: 20.5.2; 9.5.7; 1.1. Identifiers: do-not-attempt-resuscitation. Comments: comment on Michael B. Kimberly, Amanda L. Forte, Jean M. Carroll, Chris Feudtner, "Pediatric do-not-attempt-re-suscitation orders and public schools: a national assess-ment of policies and laws," American Journal of Bioethics 2005 January-February; 5(1): 59-65.

Dorscheidt, Jozef H.H.M. Assessment procedures re-garding end-of-life decisions in neonatology in the Nether-lands. *Medicine and Law: World Association for Medical Law* 2005 December; 24(4): 803-829. NRCBL: 20.5.2; 4.4; 21.1. SC: le.

Abstract: This paper describes the position of Dutch law con-cerning end- of-life decisions in neonatology consequent on rulings of the Dutch appeals court in two cases. The concept of a multidisciplinary assessment committee is explored. The Euro-pean Convention on Human Rights in its articles 2 and 13 is rel-evant to this concept. The author provides a detailed discussion of the current situation and draws conclusions based on his per-ception of future developments in regulating thanatic practices in neonatology.

Dute, Joseph. ECHR 2004/9 Case of Glass v. The United Kingdom, 9 March 2004 no. 61827/00 (Fourth Section) [summary]. *European Journal of Health Law* 2004 June; 11(2): 216-220. NRCBL: 20.5.2; 8.3.2. SC: le.

Dyer, Clare. Parents fail to overturn ruling not to resusci-tate baby [news]. *BMJ: British Medical Journal* 2005 April 30; 330(7498): 985. NRCBL: 20.5.2. SC: le.

Fauriel, Isabelle; Moutel, Grégoire; Moutard, Ma-rie-Laure; Montuclard, Luc; Duchange, Nathalie; Callies, Ingrid; François, Irène; Cochat, Pierre; Hervé, Christian. Decisions concerning potentially life-sustain-ing treatments in paediatric nephrology: a multicentre study in French-speaking countries. *Nephrology, Dialysis, Transplantation* 2004 May; 19(5): 1252-1257. NRCBL: 20.5.2. SC: em. Identifiers: Europe.

Fine, Dionne Koller. Government as God: an update on federal intervention in the treatment of critically ill new-borns. *New England Law Review* 2000; 34(2): 343-362. NRCBL: 20.5.2; 1.3.5; 9.5.7; 8.3.2. SC: le.

Ford, Norman M. Early delivery of a fetus with anencephaly: the medical and moral aspects. *Ethics and Medics* 2003 July; 28(7): 1-4. NRCBL: 20.5.2.

Frader, Joel E. Surveying euthanasia practices: methods and morality [editorial]. *Journal of Pediatrics* 2005 May; 146(5): 584-585. NRCBL: 20.5.2.

Frader, Joel E. Withdrawing mechanical ventilation in children. *Critical Care Medicine* 2000 August; 28(8): 3119-3120. NRCBL: 20.5.2; 7.1; 7.3; 8.1.

Gladsjo, Julie Akiko; Breding, John; Sine, David; Wells, Robert; Kalemkiarian, Sharon; Oak, Joni; Vieira, Angela S.; Friedlander, Sheila Fallon. Termina-tion of life support after severe child abuse: the role of a

guardian ad litem. *Pediatrics* 2004 February; 113(2): e141-e145. NRCBL: 20.5.2; 9.5.7; 8.3.3; 9.1. SC: cs.

Gold, F. The Manchester Siamese twins case — a French ethical analysis. *European Journal of Obstetrics and Gy-necology, and Reproductive Biology* 2001 December 1; 99(2): 165-166. NRCBL: 20.5.2.

Goldworth, Amnon. The challenge of DNAR orders in schools. *American Journal of Bioethics* 2005 Janu-ary-February; 5(1): 71- 72. NRCBL: 20.5.2; 9.5.7. Com-ments: comment on Michael B. Kimberly, Amanda L. Forte, Jean M. Carroll, Chris Feudtner, "Pediatric do-not-attempt-resuscitation orders and public schools: a national assessment of policies and laws," American Jour-nal of Bioethics 2005 January-February; 5(1): 59-65.

Guevara, Angie L. In re K.I.: an urgent need for a uniform system in the treatment of the critically ill infant — recog-nizing the sanctity of the life of the child. *University of San Francisco Law Review* 2001 Fall; 36(1): 237-260. NRCBL: 20.5.2; 9.5.7; 8.3.2; 8.3.4. SC: le.

Hartman, Rhonda Gay. Dying young: cues from the courts. *Archives of Pediatrics and Adolescent Medicine* 2004 July; 158(7): 615-619. NRCBL: 20.5.2. SC: le.

Hill, Daniel J. The morality of the separation of the con-joined Attard twins of Manchester. *Health Care Analysis: An International Journal of Health Care Philosophy and Policy* 2005 September; 13(3): 163-176. NRCBL: 20.5.2; 1.1; 8.3.2. SC: an. Identifiers: Jodie and Mary Attard.

Abstract: I argue that the separation of the conjoined Attard twins of Manchester was not morally justified as it involved in-tentionally internally affecting ("invading") the body of the weaker twin without permission and without any advantage to her.

Holt, Jim. Euthanasia for babies? Dutch doctors have pro-posed a procedure for infant mercy killing. Is this humane or barbaric? *New York Times Magazine* 2005 July 10; p. 11,12,14. NRCBL: 20.5.2. SC: po.

International Federation of Associations of Catholic Physicians [FIAMC]. Statement on euthanasia in chil-dren. *Medical Ethics and Bioethics / Medicinska Etika & Bioetika* 2004 Autumn-Winter; 11(3-4): 22. NRCBL: 20.5.2; 8.3.2; 8.3.3; 1.2. SC: le.

Jennings, John C. Forum on ethics. Small babies and hard decisions. *Texas Medicine* 1998 August; 94(8): 24-25. NRCBL: 20.5.2; 8.3.2; 8.3.4.

Kaur, Manmeet. Female foeticide: a sociological per-spective. *Journal of Family Welfare* 1993 March; 39(1); 4 p. [Online]. Available: http://www.hsph.harvard.edu/ Organizations/healthnet/SAsia/suchana/0326/kaur.html [7 October 2005]. NRCBL: 20.5.2; 7.1; 14.3; 15.2; 4.4. Identifiers: India.

Kimberly, Michael B.; Forte, Amanda L.; Carroll, Jean M.; Feudtner, Chris. A response to selected com-

NRCBL: National Reference Center for Bioethics Literature Classification Scheme   See inside front cover for terms.

187

mentaries on "pediatric do-not- attempt-resuscitation orders and public schools: a national assessment of policies and laws" [letter]. *American Journal of Bioethics [Online]* 2005 January-February; 5(1): W19-W21. NRCBL: 20.5.2; 9.5.7; 1.1.

Kimberly, Michael B.; Forte, Amanda L.; Carroll, Jean M.; Feudtner, Chris. Pediatric do-not-attempt-resuscitation orders and public schools: a national assessment of policies and laws. *American Journal of Bioethics* 2005 January-February; 5(1): 59- 65. NRCBL: 20.5.2; 9.5.7; 1.1. SC: em; le.

Abstract: Some children living with life-shortening medical conditions may wish to attend school without the threat of having resuscitation attempted in the event of cardiopulmonary arrest on the school premises. Despite recent attention to in-school do-not- attempt-resuscitation (DNAR) orders, no assessment of state laws or school policies has yet been made. We therefore sought to survey a national sample of prominent school districts and situate their policies in the context of relevant state laws. Most (80%) school districts sampled did not have policies, regulations, or protocols for dealing with student DNARs. A similar majority (76%) either would not honor student DNARs or were uncertain about whether they could. Frequent contradictions between school policies and state laws also exist. Consequently, children living with life-shortening conditions who have DNARs may not have these orders honored if cardiopulmonary arrest were to occur on school premises. Coordinated efforts are needed to harmonize school district, state, and federal approaches in order to support children and families' right to have important medical decisions honored.

Kocis, Keith C. Pediatric cardiac extracorporeal membrane oxygenation: supporting life or prolonging death? *Critical Care Medicine* 2000 February; 28(2): 594-595. NRCBL: 20.5.2.

Kopelman, Loretta M. Are the 21-year-old Baby Doe rules misunderstood or mistaken? *Pediatrics* 2005 March; 115(3): 797-802. NRCBL: 20.5.2. SC: le.

Kopelman, Loretta M. Rejecting the Baby Doe Rules and defending a "negative" analysis of the best interests standard. *Journal of Medicine and Philosophy* 2005 August; 30(4): 331-352. NRCBL: 20.5.2. SC: le.

Abstract: Two incompatible policies exist for guiding medical decisions for extremely premature, sick, or terminally ill infants, the Best Interests Standard and the newer, 20-year old "Baby Doe" Rules. The background, including why there were two sets of Baby Doe Rules, and their differences with the Best Interests Standard, are illustrated. Two defenses of the Baby Doe Rules are considered and rejected. The first, held by Reagan, Koop, and others, is a "right- to-life" defense. The second, held by some leaders of the American Academy of Pediatrics, is that the Baby Doe Rules are benign and misunderstood. The Baby Doe Rules should be rejected since they can thwart compassionate and individualized decision-making, undercut duties to minimize unnecessary suffering, and single out one group for treatment adults would not want for themselves. In these ways, they are inferior to the older Best Interests Standard. A "negative" analysis of the Best Interests Standard is articulated and defended for decision-making for all incompetent individuals.

Krautkramer, Christian J. Pediatric resuscitation: questioning DNAR legitimacy and offering an alternative decision-making model. *American Journal of Bioethics* 2005 January-February; 5(1): 86- 88. NRCBL: 20.5.2; 9.5.7; 1.1. Identifiers: do-not-attempt-resuscitation. Comments: comment on Michael B. Kimberly, Amanda L. Forte, Jean M. Carroll, Chris Feudtner, "Pediatric do-not-attempt-resuscitation orders and public schools: a national assessment of policies and laws," American Journal of Bioethics 2005 January-February; 5(1): 59-65.

Lannon, Andrew P. Let him die with dignity or hope for a cure: the consequences of modern medicine. *Journal of Contemporary Health Law and Policy* 2002 Winter; 19(1): 279-307. NRCBL: 20.5.2; 20.5.1; 8.3.4. SC: le.

Leavitt, Frank J. Neonates must sometimes be allowed to die, but err in favour of life [letter]. *BMJ: British Medical Journal* 2005 September 24; 331(7518): 695-696. NRCBL: 20.5.2; 9.5.7.

Lerner, Barron H. Playing God with birth defects in the nursery. *New York Times* 2005 June 14; p.F5. NRCBL: 20.5.2. SC: po.

Levene, Malcolm. Is intensive care for very immature babies justified? [opinion]. *Acta Paediatrica* 2004 February; 93(2): 149-152. NRCBL: 20.5.2.

Levetown, Marcia. Ensuring that difficult decisions are honored — even in school settings. *American Journal of Bioethics* 2005 January-February; 5(1): 78- 81. NRCBL: 20.5.2; 9.5.7. Comments: comment on Michael B. Kimberly, Amanda L. Forte, Jean M. Carroll, Chris Feudtner, "Pediatric do-not-attempt-resuscitation orders and public schools: a national assessment of policies and laws," American Journal of Bioethics 2005 January-February; 5(1): 59-65.

Lightfoot, Lance. The ethical health lawyer: incompetent decisionmakers and withdrawal of life-sustaining treatment: a case study. *Journal of Law, Medicine and Ethics* 2005 Winter; 33(4): 851- 856. NRCBL: 20.5.2; 8.3.2; 8.3.3; 9.6. SC: le; cs.

Mahon, Margaret M.; Deatrick, Janet A.; McKnight, Heather J.; Mohr, Wanda K. Discontinuing treatment in children with chronic, critical illnesses. *Nurse Practitioner Forum* 2000 March; 11(1): 6-14. NRCBL: 20.5.2; 9.5.7; 8.1. SC: cs.

Mantz, Allison. Do not resuscitate decision-making: Ohio's do not resuscitate law should be amended to include a mature minor's right to initiate a DNR order. *Journal of Law and Health* 2002-2003; 17(2): 359-384. NRCBL: 20.5.2; 8.3.2; 8.3.4. SC: le.

Marcelletti, Carlo. Bioethics and medicine. *Medicine and Law: World Association for Medical Law* 1995; 14(1-2): 9-12. NRCBL: 20.5.2; 20.2.1; 4.4. SC: le.

Masek, Theodore D. CEJA reverses its stance on using anencephalic neonates as live organ donors. *Update [Loma Linda University Center for Christian Bioethics]* 1996 July; 12(2); 4 p. NRCBL: 20.5.2; 19.5. Identifiers: Council on Ethical and Judicial Affairs.

Nuffield Council on Bioethics. The Ethics of Prolonging Life in Fetuses and the Newborn: Consultation Paper. London: Nuffield Council on Bioethics 2005; 40 p. [Online]. Available: http://www.nuffieldbioethics.org/fileLibrary/pdf/NCOB_prolong_life-consult_paper.pdf [25 May 2005]. NRCBL: 20.5.2; 9.5.8; 9.5.7; 8.1; 4.4. SC: le. Note: Deadline for responses: 9 June 2005.

O'Brien, Dan. Borderline viability resuscitation cases. *Medical Ethics and Bioethics / Medicinska Etika & Bioetika* 2002 Autumn-Winter; 9(3-4): 6-10. NRCBL: 20.5.2; 8.3.4; 1.2; 4.4.

Oakley, Godfrey P., Jr.; Verhagen, Eduard; Sauer, Pieter J.J. Euthanasia in severely ill newborns [letter and reply]. *New England Journal of Medicine* 2005 June 2; 352(22): 2354- 2355. NRCBL: 20.5.2; 9.5.1; 15.1; 9.7; 20.4.2.

Paris, J.J.; Elias-Jones, A.C. "Do we murder Mary to save Jodie?" An ethical analysis of the separation of the Manchester conjoined twins [opinion]. *Postgraduate Medical Journal* 2001 September; 77(911): 593- 598. NRCBL: 20.5.2; 1.3.8; 1.1; 1.2. SC: le.

Paris, J.J.; Schreiber, M.D.; Elias-Jones, Alun. Resuscitation of the preterm infant against parental wishes. *Archives of Disease in Childhood. Fetal and Neonatal Edition* 2005 May; 90(3): F208-F210. NRCBL: 20.5.2; 8.3.2; 8.3.4. SC: le. Identifiers: Miller v. HCA; Texas.

Paris, John J.; Webster, Gregory. Back to the future: overcoming reluctance to honor in-school DNAR orders. *American Journal of Bioethics* 2005 January-February; 5(1): 67- 69. NRCBL: 20.5.2; 9.5.7. Comments: comment on Michael B. Kimberly, Amanda L. Forte, Jean M. Carroll, Chris Feudtner, "Pediatric do-not-attempt-resuscitation orders and public schools: a national assessment of policies and laws," American Journal of Bioethics 2005 January-February; 5(1): 59-65.

Peerzada, Jehanna M.; Richardson, Douglas K.; Burns, Jeffrey P. Delivery room decision-making at the threshold of viability. *Journal of Pediatrics* 2004 October; 145(4): 492-498. NRCBL: 20.5.2; 20.3.2. SC: em.

Petersen, Andrea. A new approach for the sickest babies: some hospice programs begin accepting infants; managing pain in the NICU. *Wall Street Journal* 2005 July 26; p. D1, D4. NRCBL: 20.5.2. SC: po. Identifiers: neonatal intensive care unit.

Postovsky, Sergey; Levenzon, Anna; Ofir, Ruth; Ben Arush, Myriam Weyl. "Do not resuscitate" orders among children with solid tumors at the end of life. *Pediatric He-*

matology and Oncology 2004 October-November; 21(7): 661-668. NRCBL: 20.5.2; 20.4.2. SC: em.

Provoost, Veerle; Cools, Filip; Mortier, Freddy; Bilsen, Johan; Ramet, José; Vandenplas, Yvan; Deliens, Luc. Medical end-of-life decisions in neonates and infants in Flanders. *Lancet* 2005 April 9-15; 365(9467): 1315-1320. NRCBL: 20.5.2; 7.1; 4.4. SC: em.

Abstract: BACKGROUND: Paediatricians are increasingly confronted with end-of-life decisions in critically ill neonates and infants. Little is known about the frequency and characteristics of end-of- life decisions in this population, nor about the relation with clinical and patients' characteristics. METHODS: A death- certificate study was done for all deaths of neonates and infants in the whole of Flanders over a 12 month period (August, 1999, to July, 2000). We sent an anonymous questionnaire by mail to the attending physician for each of the 292 children who died under the age of 1 year. Information on patients was obtained from national registers. An attitude study was done for all physicians who attended at least one death during the study period. FINDINGS: 253 (87%) of the 292 questionnaires were returned, and 121 (69%) of the 175 physicians involved completed the attitude questions. An end- of-life decision was possible in 194 (77%; 95% CI 70.4-82.4) of the 253 deaths studied, and such a decision was made in 143 cases (57%; 48.9-64.0). Lethal drugs were administered in 15 cases among 117 early neonatal deaths and in two cases among 77 later deaths (13%vs 3%; p=0.018). The attitude study showed that 95 (79%; 70.1-85.5) of the 121 physicians thought that their professional duty sometimes includes the prevention of unnecessary suffering by hastening death and 69 (58%; 48.1-66.5) of 120 supported legalisation of life termination in some cases. INTERPRETATION: Death of neonates and infants is commonly preceded by an end-of-life decision. The type of decision varied substantially according to the age of the child. Most physicians favour legalisation of the use of lethal drugs in some cases.

Robertson, John A. Extreme prematurity and parental rights after Baby Doe. *Hastings Center Report* 2004 July-August; 34(4): 32-39. NRCBL: 20.5.2; 9.5.7. SC: le. Identifiers: Texas; Miller v. HCA.

Rogers, Jonathan. Necessity, private defence and the killing of Mary. *Criminal Law Review* 2001 July: 515-526. NRCBL: 20.5.2; 4.4. SC: le. Identifiers: Mary and Jodie; conjoined twins.

Roy, R.; Aladangady, N.; Costeloe, K.; Larcher, V. Decision making and modes of death in a tertiary neonatal unit. *Archives of Disease in Childhood. Fetal and Neonatal Edition* 2004 November; 89(6): F527-F530. NRCBL: 20.5.2; 21.7. SC: em. Identifiers: United Kingdom (Great Britain).

Saal, Howard M. Neonatal intensive care as a locus for ethical decisions. *Cleft Palate-Craniofacial Journal* 1995 November; 32(6): 500-503. NRCBL: 20.5.2. SC: cs.

Savage, Teresa A. DNAR in schools: questions and concerns. *American Journal of Bioethics* 2005 January-February; 5(1): 72- 74. NRCBL: 20.5.2; 9.5.7. Identifiers: do-not-attempt-resuscitation. Comments: comment on Michael B. Kimberly, Amanda L. Forte, Jean M. Carroll, Chris Feudtner, "Pediatric do-not-attempt-resuscitation orders and public schools: a national assessment of policies and laws," *American Journal of Bioethics* 2005 January-February; 5(1): 59-65.

Schmitz, Michael L.; Taylor, Bonnie J.; Anand, Kanwaljeet J.S. End-of-life decisions in the neonatal intensive care unit: medical infanticide or palliative terminal care? *Critical Care Medicine* 2000 July; 28(7): 2668-2671. NRCBL: 20.5.2; 20.4.2.

Severijnen, René; Hulstijn-Dirkmaat, Ineke; Gordijn, Bert; Bakker, Leo; Bongaerts, Ger. Acute loss of the small bowel in a school-age boy. Difficult choices: to sustain life or to stop treatment? *European Journal of Pediatrics* 2003 November; 162(11): 794-798. NRCBL: 20.5.2; 19.1. SC: cs.

Sheldon, Tony. Dutch doctors adopt guidelines on mercy killing of newborns [news]. *BMJ: British Medical Journal* 2005 July 16; 331(7509): 126. NRCBL: 20.5.2; 21.1.

Sheldon, Tony. The Netherlands regulates ending the lives of severely ill neonates [news]. *BMJ: British Medical Journal* 2005 December 10; 331(7529): 1357. NRCBL: 20.5.2. SC: le.

Sheldon, Tony; Verhagen, Eduard. Killing or caring? *BMJ: British Medical Journal* 2005 March 12; 330(7491): 560. NRCBL: 20.5.2. Identifiers: Groningen protocol.

Shewchuk, Tara Rayne. The uncertain 'best interests' of neonates: decision making in the neonatal intensive care unit. *Medicine and Law: World Association for Medical Law* 1995; 14(5-6): 331-358. NRCBL: 20.5.2; 4.2; 20.4.2; 9.5.7. SC: le.

Silvers, Anita. Going to school to die: equal treatment for well and ill children. *American Journal of Bioethics* 2005 January-February; 5(1): 69- 71. NRCBL: 20.5.2; 9.5.7. Comments: comment on Michael B. Kimberly, Amanda L. Forte, Jean M. Carroll, Chris Feudtner, "Pediatric do-not-attempt-resuscitation orders and public schools: a national assessment of policies and laws," American Journal of Bioethics 2005 January-February; 5(1): 59-65.

Simeoni, Umberto; Vendemmia, Mariella; Rizzotti, Alina; Gamerre, Marc. Ethical dilemmas in extreme prematurity: recent answers; more questions. *European Journal of Obstetrics and Gynecology and Reproductive Biology* 2004 November 15; 117(Supplement 1): S33-S36. NRCBL: 20.5.2; 9.5.7.

Singh, Jaideep; Lantos, John; Meadow, William. End-of-life after birth: death and dying in a neonatal intensive care unit. *Pediatrics* 2004 December; 114(6): 1620-1626. NRCBL: 20.5.2; 20.4.2. SC: em.

Skene, L. Terminally ill infants, parents and the courts. *Medicine and Law: World Association for Medical Law* 2005 December; 24(4): 663-671. NRCBL: 20.5.2. SC: rv; le.

Abstract: Parents sometimes demand 'full active treatment' for a terminally ill child, even against medical advice. They think that they should decide their child's best interests, not medical staff, who may conclude too readily that the child's life is 'not worth living'. Only parents who know and love their child can decide that. Doctors and nurses, on the other hand, feel they have the training and experience to assess the pain and distress of heroic measures and whether they are justified in cases where a child cannot survive, or will have profound disability. This paper reviews recent case law in the United Kingdom and Australia on the role and processes of courts where a hospital (or a parent) applies for a court order regarding treatment. The author concludes that it is possible but unlikely that a court would direct medical staff to provide treatment they regard as clinically inappropriate.

Smith, Stephen W. The killing of severely disabled newborns: the spectre behind the legalisation of physician-assisted suicide and euthanasia. *Medicine and Law: World Association for Medical Law* 2005 December; 24(4): 791-802. NRCBL: 20.5.2; 4.4; 1.1; 20.5.1.

Abstract: Arguments made by those in favour of the legalisation of physician-assisted suicide (PAS) and euthanasia often rely upon the idea of the quality of life. This idea states that an individual's life is not valuable as an intrinsic good, but is only good based upon the things which it allows us to do. It thus allows the argument that it is morally permissible to kill individuals whose lives have fallen below an acceptable 'quality of life.' However, this concept may require that one accept the killing of individuals who have not expressly request to be killed such as severely disabled newborns. This paper will examine the issue of whether those who utilise a quality of life approach to justify the legalisation of PAS and euthanasia must logically accept the policy of killing severely disabled newborn children. First, there will be an examination of the concept of quality of life and its importance in the arguments for the legalisation of PAS or euthanasia. This paper will then consider how notions of personhood interact with the concept of quality of life in order to create the problem faced by those who favour the legalisation of PAS or euthanasia. Finally, this paper will consider how the notion of autonomy may be used as a way to avoid this difficulty created by the quality of life approach.

Stewart, Charles L. Making decisions about neonatal life support: respecting the views of all concerned requires coordinated communication among all parties. *Healthcare Executive* 2005 March-April; 20(2): 42-43. NRCBL: 20.5.2; 8.1; 7.3.

Suziedelis, Ann K. Conjoined twins: the ambiguity of double effect reasoning. *Medical Ethics and Bioethics / Medicinska Etika & Bioetika* 2001 Autumn-Winter; 8(3-4): 3-5. NRCBL: 20.5.2; 1.1; 1.2; 4.4. SC: an. Identifiers: Mary and Jodie.

Tarnow-Mordi, William O. "Right to die" — . . . but context of limited resources can be encountered in developed countries too [letter]. *BMJ: British Medical Journal* 2005 June 11; 330(7504): 1389. NRCBL: 20.5.2; 9.4.

Verhagen, Eduard; Sauer, Pieter J.J. The Groningen protocol — euthanasia in severely ill newborns [opinion]. *New England Journal of Medicine* 2005 March 10; 352(10): 959- 962. NRCBL: 20.5.2.

Vermeulen, Eric. Dealing with doubt: making decisions in a neonatal ward in the Netherlands. *Social Science and Medicine* 2004 November; 59(10): 2071-2085. NRCBL: 20.5.2; 20.4.2; 8.3.2. SC: em.

Viens, Adrian M.; Bibbee, Jeffrey R. Legal frameworks for addressing the well-being of terminally ill children. *American Journal of Bioethics* 2005 January-February; 5(1): 74- 76. NRCBL: 20.5.2; 9.5.7. SC: le. Comments: comment on Michael B. Kimberly, Amanda L. Forte, Jean M. Carroll, Chris Feudtner, "Pediatric do-not-attempt-resuscitation orders and public schools: a national assessment of policies and laws," American Journal of Bioethics 2005 January-February; 5(1): 59-65.

Vrakking, Astrid M.; van der Heide, Agnes; Looman, Caspar W.N.; van Delden, Johannes J.M.; Onwuteaka-Philipsen, Bregje D.; van der Maas, Paul J.; van der Wal, Gerrit. Physicians' willingness to grant requests for assistance in dying for children: a study of hypothetical cases. *Journal of Pediatrics* 2005 May; 146(5): 611-617. NRCBL: 20.5.2. SC: em. Identifiers: Netherlands.

Vrakking, Astrid M.; van der Heide, Agnes; Onwuteaka- Philipsen, Bregje D.; Keij-Deerenberg, Ingeborg M.; van der Maas, Paul J.; van der Wal, Gerrit. Medical end-of-life decisions made for neonates and infants in the Netherlands, 1995-2001. *Lancet* 2005 April 9-15; 365(9467): 1329-1331. NRCBL: 20.5.2; 7.1. SC: em.

Abstract: End-of-life decision-making for severely affected infants might be influenced by technical advances and societal debates. In 2001, we assessed the proportion of deaths of infants younger than 1 year that were preceded by end-of-life decisions, by replicating a questionnaire study from 1995. This proportion increased from 62% to 68% (weighted percentages), but the difference was not significant. Most of these decisions were to forgo life-sustaining treatment. Decisions to actively end the lives of infants not dependent on life-sustaining treatment remained stable at 1%. The practice of end-of-life decision-making in neonatology of 2001 has changed little since 1995.

Waisel, David B. Moral permissibility as a guide for decision making about conjoined twins [editorial]. *Anesthesia and Analgesia* 2005 July; 101(1): 41-43. NRCBL: 20.5.2; 8.3.2; 1.1.

Walden, Marlene; Sala, D. Jean. Controversies in the resuscitation of infants of borderline viability. *AWHONN's Clinical Issues in Perinatal and Women's Health Nursing* 1993; 4(4): 570-577. NRCBL: 20.5.2; 9.4.

Walters, Jim. AMA council's ethics overwhelmed by public sentiment. *Update [Loma Linda University Center for Christian Bioethics]* 1996 July; 12(2): 4 p. NRCBL: 20.5.2; 19.5; 4.4. Identifiers: American Medical Association.

Walters, Stacey R. Life-sustaining medical decisions involving children: father knows best. *Thomas M. Cooley*

Law Review 1998; 15(1): 115-154. NRCBL: 20.5.2; 8.3.2; 9.5.7. SC: le.

Weise, Kathryn. Finding our way. *Hastings Center Report* 2004 July-August; 34(4): 8-9. NRCBL: 20.5.2; 9.5.7.

Weise, Kathryn L. The spectrum of our obligations: DNR in public schools [case studies]. *American Journal of Bioethics* 2005 January-February; 5(1): 81- 83. NRCBL: 20.5.2; 9.5.7. Comments: comment on Michael B. Kimberly, Amanda L. Forte, Jean M. Carroll, Chris Feudtner, "Pediatric do-not-attempt-resuscitation orders and public schools: a national assessment of policies and laws," American Journal of Bioethics 2005 January-February; 5(1): 59-65.

White, Gladys. Nurses at the helm: implementing DNAR orders in the public school setting. *American Journal of Bioethics* 2005 January-February; 5(1): 83- 85. NRCBL: 20.5.2; 9.5.7; 4.1.3. Comments: comment on Michael B. Kimberly, Amanda L. Forte, Jean M. Carroll, Chris Feudtner, "Pediatric do-not-attempt-resuscitation orders and public schools: a national assessment of policies and laws," American Journal of Bioethics 2005 January-February; 5(1): 59-65.

Working Group of Intensive Care in the Delivery Room of Extremely Premature Newborns; Verlato, Giovanna; Gobber, Daniela; Drago, Donatella; Chiandetti, Lino; Drigo, Paola. Guidelines for resuscitation in the delivery room of extremely preterm infants. *Journal of Child Neurology* 2004 January; 19(1): 31-34. NRCBL: 20.5.2; 9.8. SC: le. Identifiers: Italy.

Wynn, Francine. Nursing and the concept of life: towards an ethics of testimony. *Nursing Philosophy* 2002 July; 3(2): 120-132. NRCBL: 20.5.2; 1.1; 4.1.3; 20.4.2.

Youngner, Stuart J. School DNAR in the real world. *American Journal of Bioethics* 2005 January-February; 5(1): 66- 67. NRCBL: 20.5.2; 9.5.7. Comments: comment on Michael B. Kimberly, Amanda L. Forte, Jean M. Carroll, Chris Feudtner, "Pediatric do-not-attempt-resuscitation orders and public schools: a national assessment of policies and laws," American Journal of Bioethics 2005 January-February; 5(1): 59-65.

Zetterström, Rolf. Decisions on therapeutic intervention in neonatal intensive care [editorial]. *Acta Paediatrica* 2004 February; 93(2): 148. NRCBL: 20.5.2.

EUTHANASIA AND ALLOWING TO DIE/ PHILOSOPHICAL ASPECTS

Baggini, Julian; Pym, Madeleine. End of life: the humanist view [opinion]. *Lancet* 2005 October 1-7; 366(9492): 1235-1237. NRCBL: 20.5.1; 1.1; 1.2; 7.1. SC: rv.

Berghs, M.; Dierckx de Casterlé, B.; Gastmans, C. The complexity of nurses' attitudes toward euthanasia: a re-

NRCBL: National Reference Center for Bioethics Literature Classification Scheme   See inside front cover for terms.

191

view of the literature. *Journal of Medical Ethics* 2005 August; 31(8): 441-446. NRCBL: 20.5.1; 4.1.3; 20.3.2. SC: em.

Abstract: In this literature review, a picture is given of the complexity of nursing attitudes toward euthanasia. The myriad of data found in empirical literature is mostly framed within a polarised debate and inconclusive about the complex reality behind attitudes toward euthanasia. Yet, a further examination of the content as well as the context of attitudes is more revealing. The arguments for euthanasia have to do with quality of life and respect for autonomy. Arguments against euthanasia have to do with non-maleficence, sanctity of life, and the notion of the slippery slope. When the context of attitudes is examined a number of positive correlates for euthanasia such as age, nursing specialty, and religion appear. In a further analysis of nurses' comments on euthanasia, it is revealed that part of the complexity of nursing attitudes toward euthanasia arises because of the needs of nurses at the levels of clinical practice, communication, emotions, decision making, and ethics.

Cassell, Eric J. The Schiavo case: a medical perspective. *Hastings Center Report* 2005 May-June; 35(3): 22-23. NRCBL: 20.5.1; 1.1.

Daar, Judith F. Direct democracy and bioethical choices: voting life and death at the ballot box. *University of Michigan Journal of Law Reform* 1995 Summer; 28(4): 799-859. NRCBL: 20.5.1; 20.7; 8.1; 1.3.5; 1.1. SC: le.

Davis, John K. Life-extension and the Malthusian objection. *Journal of Medicine and Philosophy* 2005 February; 30(1): 27-44. NRCBL: 20.5.1; 1.1; 4.5.

Abstract: Dramatically extending the human lifespan seems increasingly possible. Many bioethicists object that life-extension will have Malthusian consequences as new Methuselahs accumulate, generation by generation. I argue for a Life-Years Response to the Malthusian Objection. If even a minority of each generation chooses life- extension, denying it to them deprives them of many years of extra life, and their total extra life-years are likely to exceed the total life-years of a majority who do not want life-extension. This is a greater harm to those who want extended life than the Malthusian harms to those who refuse extended life, both because losing an extra year of life is worse than enduring a year of Malthusian conditions, and because the would-be Methuselahs have more life-years at stake. Therefore, even if life-extension seems likely to cause severe overcrowding and resource shortages, that threat is not sufficient to justify society in restricting the development or availability of life-extension.

Dawe, Ursula; Verhoef, Marja J.; Page, Stacey A. Treatment refusal: the beliefs and experiences of Alberta nurses. *International Journal of Nursing Studies* 2002 January; 39(1): 71-77. NRCBL: 20.5.1; 8.3.4; 7.1; 4.1.3.

Downie, Jocelyn. Voluntary euthanasia in Canada. *Health Law in Canada* 1993; 14: 13-30. NRCBL: 20.5.1; 20.7; 4.4; 20.4.1; 1.1. SC: le.

Dracup, Kathleen; Bryan-Brown, Christopher W. Nurses and euthanasia: a tale of two studies [editorial]. *American Journal of Critical Care* 1996 July; 5(4): 249-252. NRCBL: 20.5.1; 4.1.3; 8.1. SC: em.

Ellard, J. Euthanasia: over the Rubicon already? *Australian and New Zealand Journal of Medicine* 1998 February; 28(1): 57. NRCBL: 20.5.1; 1.1; 21.1. Comments: comment on Australian and New Zealand Journal of Medicine 1998 February; 28(1): 46-54.

Engelhardt, H. Tristram, Jr.; Iltis, Ana Smith. End-of-life: the traditional Christian view. *Lancet* 2005 September 17-23; 366(9490): 1045-1049. NRCBL: 20.5.1; 1.2; 4.4; 4.1.2; 8.1. SC: rv.

Fleming, David A. Futility: revisiting a concept of shared moral judgment. *HEC (Healthcare Ethics Committee) Forum* 2005 December; 17(4): 260-275. NRCBL: 20.5.1; 1.1; 8.3.3; 5.1; 8.1; 4.1.2; 2.2; 7.1.

Foster, Charles A. Time to legalise assisted dying? What autonomy really means [letter]. *BMJ: British Medical Journal* 2005 October 8; 331(7520): 841- 842. NRCBL: 20.5.1; 20.7; 1.1. SC: le.

Henke, Donald E. A history of ordinary and extraordinary means. *National Catholic Bioethics Quarterly* 2005 Autumn; 5(3): 555- 575. NRCBL: 20.5.1; 4.1.1; 1.2; 4.4.

Hermsen, Maaike; ten Have, Henk A.M.J. Decision-making in palliative care practice and the need for moral deliberation: a qualitative study. *Patient Education and Counseling* 2005 March; 56(3): 268-275. NRCBL: 20.5.1; 20.4.1; 8.1; 1.1. SC: em. Identifiers: Netherlands.

Huxtable, Richard. Get out of jail free? The doctrine of double effect in English law. *Palliative Medicine* 2004; 18(1): 62-68. NRCBL: 20.5.1; 20.4.1; 9.7; 8.1; 1.1. SC: le.

Jezuit, Deborah L. Suffering of critical care nurses with end-of-life decisions. *Medsurg Nursing* 2000 June; 9(3): 145-152. NRCBL: 20.5.1; 8.1; 4.1.3.

Kampits, Peter. Offene Ethik angesichts des Lebensendes. *In:* Baumann, Eva; Brink, Alexander; May, Arnd T.; Schröder, Peter; Schutzeichel, Corinna Iris, eds. Weltanschauliche Offenheit in der Bioethik. Berlin: Duncker & Humblot; 2004: 95-112. NRCBL: 20.5.1; 1.1; 20.4.1; 21.7.

Kelly, David F. Forgoing treatment, pillar two: killing and allowing to die. *In his:* Contemporary Catholic Health Care Ethics. Washington, DC: Georgetown University Press; 2004: 134-142. NRCBL: 20.5.1; 1.1; 1.2; 20.4.1.

Latkovic, Mark S. The morality of tube feeding PVS patients. *National Catholic Bioethics Quarterly* 2005 Autumn; 5(3): 503- 513. NRCBL: 20.5.1; 1.2; 4.1.1; 4.4. SC: an. Identifiers: persistent vegetative state.

Manias, Elizabeth. Australian nurses' experiences and attitudes in the "do not resuscitate" decision. *Research in Nursing and Health* 1998 October; 21(5): 429-441. NRCBL: 20.5.1; 8.1; 4.1.3. SC: em.

Mareiniss, Darren P. A comparison of Cruzan and Schiavo: the burden of proof, due process, and autonomy in the persistently vegetative patient. *Journal of Legal*

Medicine 2005 June; 26(2): 233-259. NRCBL: 20.5.1; 1.1; 8.3.3. SC: le.

Markwell, Hazel. End-of-life: a Catholic view [opinion]. *Lancet* 2005 September 24-30; 366(9491): 1132-1135. NRCBL: 20.5.1; 1.2; 1.1; 4.4; 8.1; 21.1. SC: rv.

McGee, Andrew. Finding a way through the ethical and legal maze: withdrawal of medical treatment and euthanasia. *Medical Law Review* 2005 Autumn; 13(3): 357-385. NRCBL: 20.5.1; 1.1. SC: le.

Millard, Peter H. Ethical decisions at the end of life. *Journal of the Royal College Physicians of London* 1999 July-August; 33(4): 365-367. NRCBL: 20.5.1; 1.1.

Milliken, Jan. One palliative care nurse's view of euthanasia: a social movement reflective of a self-serving generation. *International Journal of Palliative Nursing* 2004 June; 10(6): 308-311. NRCBL: 20.5.1; 21.1; 4.1.3.

Morgan, Derek; Veitch, Kenneth. Being Ms B: B, autonomy and the nature of legal regulation. *Sydney Law Review* 2004 March; 26(1): 107-130. NRCBL: 20.5.1; 1.1; 8.3.4. SC: le.

Narbekovas, Andrius; Meilius, Kazimieras. Why is the ethics of euthanasia wrong? *Medical Ethics and Bioethics / Medicinska Etika & Bioetika* 2004 Autumn-Winter; 11(3-4): 2-6. NRCBL: 20.5.1; 8.1; 20.7; 1.1; 4.4.

Newnham, Helen. Should nurses act legally or ethically? *Contemporary Nurse* 1998 March; 7(1): 42-47. NRCBL: 20.5.1; 7.1; 4.1.3. SC: le.

O'Keefe, Mary E.; Crawford, Kate. End-of-life care: legal and ethical considerations. *Seminars in Oncology Nursing* 2002 May; 18(2): 143-148. NRCBL: 20.5.1; 20.5.4; 20.7; 4.1.3. SC: le.

O'Rourke, Kevin D. The Catholic tradition on forgoing life support. *National Catholic Bioethics Quarterly* 2005 Autumn; 5(3): 537- 553. NRCBL: 20.5.1; 4.1.1; 1.2; 4.4.

Oderberg, David S. Euthanasia. *In his:* Applied Ethics: A Non-Consequentialist Approach. Malden, MA: Blackwell Publishers; 2000: 48-96. NRCBL: 20.5.1; 20.7; 1.1. SC: an.

Papanikitas, Andrew N. Is it historically possible for a consensus to be reached on the subject of euthanasia, voluntary or otherwise? *Catholic Medical Quarterly* 2000 February; 50(1); 12 p. [Online]. Available: http://www.catholicdoctors.org.uk/CMQ/Feb_2000/censensus_on_euthanasia.htm [4 November 2005]. NRCBL: 20.5.1; 1.1; 7.1; 15.5.

Pellegrino, Edmund D. Futility in medical decisions: the word and the concept. *HEC (Healthcare Ethics Committee) Forum* 2005 December; 17(4): 308-318. NRCBL: 20.5.1; 7.1; 2.2; 1.1.

Rieth, Katherine A. How do we withhold or withdraw life-sustaining therapy? *Nursing Management* 1999 October; 30(10): 20-25, M139. NRCBL: 20.5.1; 8.3.3; 8.3.4; 8.1; 4.1.3.

Saunders, Cicely. Care of the dying- 1: the problem of euthanasia. *Nursing Times* 1976 July 1; 72(26): 1003-1005. NRCBL: 20.5.1; 4.1.3; 1.2.

Seay, Gary. Euthanasia and physicians' moral duties. *Journal of Medicine and Philosophy* 2005 October; 30(5): 517- 533. NRCBL: 20.5.1; 20.7; 1.1. SC: an.
  Abstract: Opponents of euthanasia sometimes argue that it is incompatible with the purpose of medicine, since physicians have an unconditional duty never to intentionally cause death. But it is not clear how such a duty could ever actually be unconditional, if due consideration is given to the moral weight of countervailing duties equally fundamental to medicine. Whether physicians' moral duties are understood as correlative with patients' moral rights or construed noncorrelatively, a doctor's obligation to abstain from intentional killing cannot be more than a defeasible duty.

Sullivan, Dennis. Euthanasia versus letting die: Christian decision-making in terminal patients. *Ethics and Medicine* 2005 Summer; 21(2): 109-118. NRCBL: 20.5.1; 20.4.1; 4.4; 1.1; 1.2.

Syme, Rodney R.A.; Zalcberg, John R.; Buchanan, John D. The euthanasia controversy. Decision-making in extreme circumstances [letter and reply]. *Medical Journal of Australia* 1996 March 4; 164(5): 317-318. NRCBL: 20.5.1; 2.1; 4.1.1; 20.4.1.

Tännsjö, Torbjörn. Moral dimensions. *BMJ: British Medical Journal* 2005 September 24; 331(7518): 689-691. NRCBL: 20.5.1; 1.1.

Tooley, Michael. In defense of voluntary active euthanasia and assisted suicide. *In:* Cohen, Andrew I.; Wellman, Christopher Heath, eds. Contemporary Debates in Applied Ethics. Malden, MA: Blackwell Pub., 2005: 161-178. NRCBL: 20.5.1; 20.7; 1.1. SC: an.

van Rooyen, D.; Elfick, M.; Strümpher, J. Registered nurses' experience of the withdrawal of treatment from the critically ill patient in an intensive care unit. *Curationis* 2005 February; 28(1): 42-51. NRCBL: 20.5.1; 8.1; 4.1.3. SC: em. Identifiers: South Africa.

Vélez G., Juan R. Death of John Paul II and the basic human care for the sick and the dying. *Ethics and Medicine* 2005 Fall; 21(3): 167-177. NRCBL: 20.5.1; 15.5; 2.2; 1.1; 1.2; 21.1; 4.4.

Wainwright, Paul. Persistent vegetative state: ethical issues for nursing. *Nursing Standard* 1996 November 20; 11(9): 39-44. NRCBL: 20.5.1; 4.1.3; 1.1.

Weinrib, Lorraine Eisenstat. The body and the body politic: assisted suicide under the Canadian Charter of Rights and Freedoms. *McGill Law Journal* 1994; 39(3): 618-643. NRCBL: 20.5.1; 20.7; 4.4; 1.1. SC: le.

NRCBL: National Reference Center for Bioethics Literature Classification Scheme   See inside front cover for terms.

193

Williams, Rowan; Murphy-O'Connor, Cormac. From the right to die to the duty to die? *Dolentium Hominum* 2004; 19(3): 47-49. NRCBL: 20.5.1; 1.2; 1.1; 4.4.

Wilson, Donna M. Highlighting the role of policy in nursing practice through a comparison of "DNR" policy influences and "no CPR" decision influences. *Nursing Outlook* 1996 November-December; 44(6): 272-279. NRCBL: 20.5.1; 8.1; 9.8; 4.1.3;. Identifiers: Canada; do not resuscitate; cardiopulmonary resuscitation.

Winzelberg, Gary S.; Hanson, Laura C.; Tulsky, James A. Beyond autonomy: diversifying end-of-life decision-making approaches to serve patients and families. *Journal of the American Geriatrics Society* 2005 June; 53(6): 1046-1050. NRCBL: 20.5.1; 1.1; 8.3.3; 20.4.1.

EUTHANASIA AND ALLOWING TO DIE/ RELIGIOUS ASPECTS

Ali, Raoutsi Hadj Eddine Sari. Islam. *In:* Council of Europe Publishing, ed. Euthanasia. Volume I. Ethical and Human Aspects. Strasbourg: Council of Europe; Croton-on-Hudson, NY: Manhattan Publishing Co.; 2003: 141-144. NRCBL: 20.5.1; 1.2.

Alters, Sandra. The end of life: ethical considerations. *In her:* Death and Dying. Who Decides? Detroit: Thomson Gale; 2005: 13-20. NRCBL: 20.5.1; 20.7; 1.2.

Amidror, Tali; Leavitt, Frank J. End-of-life decision making in Israel. *In:* Blank, Robert H.; Merrick, Janna C., eds. End-of-Life Decision Making: A Cross-National Study. Cambridge, MA: MIT Press; 2005: 97-108. NRCBL: 20.5.1; 1.2; 8.3.4.

Baggini, Julian; Pym, Madeleine. End of life: the humanist view [opinion]. *Lancet* 2005 October 1-7; 366(9492): 1235-1237. NRCBL: 20.5.1; 1.1; 1.2; 7.1. SC: rv.

Baron, Jeremy Hugh. "Thou shalt not kill": some legal and linguistic problems. *Mount Sinai Journal of Medicine* 2004 October; 71(5): 355-357. NRCBL: 20.5.1; 1.2.

Barry, Robert. The papal allocution on caring for persons in a "vegetative state". *Issues in Law and Medicine* 2004 Fall; 20(2): 155-164. NRCBL: 20.5.1; 4.4; 1.2.

Basta, Lofty L. Ethical issues in the management of geriatric cardiac patients. *American Journal of Geriatric Cardiology* 2004 July-August; 13(4): 219-220. NRCBL: 20.5.1; 20.5.4; 1.2. SC: cs.

Brown, James E., Jr. The PVS patient [letter]. *Linacre Quarterly* 2005 February; 72(1): 4. NRCBL: 20.5.1; 1.2. Identifiers: persistent vegetative state.

Buchman, Alan L. Ethics and economics in nutritional support. *Nestle Nutrition Workshop Series. Clinical and Performance Programme* 2005; 10: 143-166. NRCBL: 20.5.1; 9.3.1; 20.5.4; 1.2.

Cahill, Lisa Sowle. Catholicism, death and modern medicine. *America* 2005 April 25; 192(14): 14-17. NRCBL: 20.5.1; 20.4.1; 1.2.

Catholic Church. Catholic Bishops of Florida. The care of Terri Schiavo. *Origins* 2005 March 17; 34(39): 632. NRCBL: 20.5.1; 20.5.3; 1.2. SC: le.

Cessario, Romanus. Conditional stewardship of life: a moral principle of John Paul II. *In:* McMahon, Kevin T., ed. Moral Issues in Catholic Health Care. Wynnewood, PA: Saint Charles Borromeo Seminary; 2004: 120-138. NRCBL: 20.5.1; 1.2.

Chevassut, Daniel. Buddhism. *In:* Council of Europe Publishing, ed. Euthanasia. Volume I. Ethical and Human Aspects. Strasbourg: Council of Europe; Croton-on-Hudson, NY: Manhattan Publishing Co.; 2003: 131-134. NRCBL: 20.5.1; 1.2.

Collange, Jean-François. Protestantism. *In:* Council of Europe Publishing, ed. Euthanasia. Volume I. Ethical and Human Aspects. Strasbourg: Council of Europe; Croton-on-Hudson, NY: Manhattan Publishing Co.; 2003: 153-156. NRCBL: 20.5.1; 1.2.

Dorff, Elliot N. End-of-life: Jewish perspectives [opinion]. *Lancet* 2005 September 3-9; 366(9488): 862-865. NRCBL: 20.5.1; 1.2; 8.1; 20.4.1; 4.4; 19.5. SC: rv.

Eberl, Jason T. Extraordinary care and the spiritual goal of life: a defense of the view of Kevin O'Rourke, O.P. *National Catholic Bioethics Quarterly* 2005 Autumn; 5(3): 491-501. NRCBL: 20.5.1; 1.2; 4.4.

Elon, Menachem; Auerbach, Bernard; Chazin, Daniel D.; Sykes, Melvin J. Euthanasia and the right to refuse treatment. *In their:* Jewish Law (Mishpat Ivri): Cases and Materials. New York: M. Bender; 1999: 637-696. NRCBL: 20.5.1; 20.5.3; 1.2. SC: le.

Engelhardt, H. Tristram, Jr.; Iltis, Ana Smith. End-of-life: the traditional Christian view. *Lancet* 2005 September 17-23; 366(9490): 1045-1049. NRCBL: 20.5.1; 1.2; 4.4; 4.1.2; 8.1. SC: rv.

Fenton, Kathleen. Killing versus allowing to die: examining a critical moral difference. *Ethics and Medics* 2005 March; 30(3): 1-2. NRCBL: 20.5.1; 1.2.

Firth, Shirley. End-of-life: a Hindu view [opinion]. *Lancet* 2005 August 20-26; 366(9486): 682-686. NRCBL: 20.5.1; 1.2; 4.4; 8.2. SC: rv.

Ford, Norman M. Thoughts on the papal address and MANH: reflections on post-coma unresponsiveness. *Ethics and Medics* 2005 February; 30(2): 3-4. NRCBL: 20.5.1; 1.2. Identifiers: medically administered nutrition and hydration.

Foster, Charles. What is man, that the judges are mindful of him?: lessons from the PVS cases. *Journal of Philoso-*

phy, Science and Law [electronic] 2005 September 28; 5: 1-15. Available: http://www.psljournal.com/ [24 November 2005]. NRCBL: 20.5.1; 1.2; 4.4. Identifiers: persistent vegetative state.

Freeland, Richard. Euthanasia and Islamic law. *Medico-Legal Journal* 1997; 65(4): 196-198. NRCBL: 20.5.1; 1.2. SC: le.

Furton, Edward J. A critique of the five wishes: comments in the light of a papal statement. *Ethics and Medics* 2005 March; 30(3): 3-4. NRCBL: 20.5.1; 1.2.

Furton, Edward J. On the death of Terri Schiavo. *Ethics and Medics* 2005 June; 30(6): 3-4. NRCBL: 20.5.1; 1.2.

Furton, Edward J.; Shannon, Thomas A.; Walter, James J.; Repenshek, Mark; Slosar, John Paul. Nutrition and hydration [letter and reply]. *Hastings Center Report* 2005 May-June; 35(3): 5-6. NRCBL: 20.5.1; 1.2.

Gambino, Gabriella. Catholicism. *In:* Council of Europe Publishing, ed. Euthanasia. Volume I. Ethical and Human Aspects. Strasbourg: Council of Europe; Croton- on-Hudson, NY: Manhattan Publishing Co.; 2003: 135-140. NRCBL: 20.5.1; 1.2.

Guigui, Albert. Judiasm. *In:* Council of Europe Publishing, ed. Euthanasia. Volume I. Ethical and Human Aspects. Strasbourg: Council of Europe; Croton- on-Hudson, NY: Manhattan Publishing Co.; 2003: 145-147. NRCBL: 20.5.1; 1.2.

Henke, Donald E. A history of ordinary and extraordinary means. *National Catholic Bioethics Quarterly* 2005 Autumn; 5(3): 555- 575. NRCBL: 20.5.1; 4.1.1; 1.2; 4.4.

Hildebrand, Adam J. On "vegetative" human beings. *Ethics and Medics* 2005 January; 30(1): 1-4. NRCBL: 20.5.1; 1.2.

John Paul II, Pope. Address of John Paul II to the participants at the International Congress on "Life-sustaining Treatments and the Vegetative State: Scientific Advances and Ethical Dilemmas". *Dolentium Hominum* 2004; 19(2): 20-22. NRCBL: 20.5.1; 1.2; 4.4.

John Paul II, Pope. Euthanasia must be avoided. *Dolentium Hominum* 2005; 20(1): 7-8. NRCBL: 20.5.1; 1.2; 4.4; 20.4.1. Conference: Proceedings of the XIX International Conference organized by the Pontifical Council for Health Pastoral Care;New Synod Hall, Vatican City; 11-13 November 2004.

John Paul II, Pope. Life-sustaining treatments and vegetative state: scientific advances and ethical dilemmas. *Issues in Law and Medicine* 2004 Fall; 20(2): 167-170. NRCBL: 20.5.1; 20.2.1; 4.4; 1.2.

Johnson, Kimberly S.; Elbert-Avila, Katja I.; Tulsky, James A. The influence of spiritual beliefs and practices on the treatment preferences of African Americans: a re-

view of the literature. *Journal of the American Geriatrics Society* 2005 April; 53(4): 711-719. NRCBL: 20.5.1; 1.2; 9.5.4; 20.4.1. SC: em.

Kelly, David F. Forgoing treatment, pillar one: ordinary and extraordinary means. *In his:* Contemporary Catholic Health Care Ethics. Washington, DC: Georgetown University Press; 2004: 127-133. NRCBL: 20.5.1; 1.2.

Kelly, David F. Forgoing treatment, pillar three: decisions for incompetent patients. *In his:* Contemporary Catholic Health Care Ethics. Washington, DC: Georgetown University Press; 2004: 153-169. NRCBL: 20.5.1; 1.2; 8.3.3; 8.3.4. SC: le.

Kelly, David F. Forgoing treatment, pillar two: killing and allowing to die. *In his:* Contemporary Catholic Health Care Ethics. Washington, DC: Georgetown University Press; 2004: 134-142. NRCBL: 20.5.1; 1.1; 1.2; 20.4.1.

Kelly, David F. Hydration and nutrition. *In his:* Contemporary Catholic Health Care Ethics. Washington, DC: Georgetown University Press; 2004: 183-195. NRCBL: 20.5.1; 1.2.

Kelly, David F. Medical futility. *In his:* Contemporary Catholic Health Care Ethics. Washington, DC: Georgetown University Press; 2004: 206-218. NRCBL: 20.5.1; 1.2.

Kelly, David F. Physician-assisted suicide and euthanasia. *In his:* Contemporary Catholic Health Care Ethics. Washington, DC: Georgetown University Press; 2004: 196-205. NRCBL: 20.5.1; 20.7; 1.2. SC: le.

Kenny, Robert Wade. A cycle of terms implicit in the idea of medicine: Karen Ann Quinlan as a rhetorical icon and the transvaluation of the ethics of euthanasia. *Health Communication* 2005; 17(1): 17-39. NRCBL: 20.5.1; 8.3.3; 1.2; 7.1. SC: an.

Keown, Damien. End of life: the Buddhist view [opinion]. *Lancet* 2005 September 10-16; 366(9489): 952-955. NRCBL: 20.5.1; 1.2; 4.4; 20.2.1; 20.4.1. SC: rv.

Kinzbrunner, Barry M. Jewish medical ethics and end-of-life care. *Journal of Palliative Medicine* 2004 August; 7(4): 558-573. NRCBL: 20.5.1; 20.4.1; 20.3.1; 1.2; 2.1. SC: rv.

Kunin, Joshua. Caring for the terminally ill: halachic approaches to withholding and withdrawing of therapy. *Jewish Medical Ethics and Halacha* 2005 August; 5(1): 22-28. NRCBL: 20.5.1; 1.2.

Latkovic, Mark S. The morality of tube feeding PVS patients. *National Catholic Bioethics Quarterly* 2005 Autumn; 5(3): 503- 513. NRCBL: 20.5.1; 1.2; 4.1.1; 4.4. SC: an. Identifiers: persistent vegetative state.

NRCBL: National Reference Center for Bioethics Literature Classification Scheme   See inside front cover for terms.

195

Mahawar, Kamal Kumar. End-of-life issues [letter]. *Lancet* 2005 November 26-December 2; 366(9500): 1848. NRCBL: 20.5.1; 1.2.

Markwell, Hazel. End-of-life: a Catholic view [opinion]. *Lancet* 2005 September 24-30; 366(9491): 1132-1135. NRCBL: 20.5.1; 1.2; 1.1; 4.4; 8.1; 21.1. SC: rv.

Mavroforou, Anna; Michalodimitrakis, Emmanuel. Euthanasia in Greece, Hippocrates' birthplace. *European Journal of Health Law* 2001 June; 8(2): 157-162. NRCBL: 20.5.1; 1.2. SC: le.

May, William E.; Repenshek, Mark; Slosar, John Paul. Nutrition and hydration [letter and reply]. *Hastings Center Report* 2005 May-June; 35(3): 4-6. NRCBL: 20.5.1; 1.2.

McMahon, Kevin T. Nutrition and hydration: should they be considered medical therapy? *Linacre Quarterly* 2005 August; 72(3): 229-239. NRCBL: 20.5.1; 20.4.1; 1.2.

Mulligan, James J. Caring for the unconscious. *Ethics and Medics* 2005 July; 30(7): 2-4. NRCBL: 20.5.1; 1.2; 20.2.1.

Myers, John. End-of-life decisions: ethical principles. *Origins* 2005 September 22; 35(15): 248-253. NRCBL: 20.5.1; 1.2; 20.3.1; 4.4.

O'Rourke, Kevin D. The Catholic tradition on forgoing life support. *National Catholic Bioethics Quarterly* 2005 Autumn; 5(3): 537-553. NRCBL: 20.5.1; 4.1.1; 1.2; 4.4.

Pontifical Academy for Life. Respect for the dignity of the dying person ethical observations on euthanasia. *Medical Ethics and Bioethics / Medicinska Etika & Bioetika* 2001 Spring-Summer; 8(1-2): 10-12. NRCBL: 20.5.1; 4.4; 1.2.

Ravitsky, Vardit. Timers on ventilators. *BMJ: British Medical Journal* 2005 February 19; 330(7488): 415-417. NRCBL: 20.5.1; 1.2.

Rodriguez del Pozo, Pablo; Fins, Joseph J. Death, dying and informatics: misrepresenting religion on MedLine. *BMC Medical Ethics [electronic]* 2005 July 1; 6(6); 5 p. Available: http://www.biomedcentral.com/content/pdf/1472-6939-6-6.pdf [1 February 2006]. NRCBL: 20.5.1; 1.2; 1.3.12. SC: em.
Abstract: BACKGROUND: The globalization of medical science carries for doctors worldwide a correlative duty to deepen their understanding of patients' cultural contexts and religious backgrounds, in order to satisfy each as a unique individual. To become better informed, practitioners may turn to MedLine, but it is unclear whether the information found there is an accurate representation of culture and religion. To test MedLine's representation of this field, we chose the topic of death and dying in the three major monotheistic religions. METHODS: We searched MedLine using PubMed in order to retrieve and thematically analyze fulllength scholarly journal papers or case reports dealing with religious traditions and end-of-life care. Our search consisted of a string of words that included the most common denominations of the three religions, the standard heading terms used by the National Reference Center for

Bioethics Literature (NRCBL), and the Medical Subject Headings (MeSH) used by the National Library of Medicine. Eligible articles were limited to English-language papers with an abstract. RESULTS: We found that while a bibliographic search in MedLine on this topic produced instant results and some valuable literature, the aggregate reflected a selection bias. American writers were over-represented given the global prevalence of these religious traditions. Denominationally affiliated authors predominated in representing the Christian traditions. The Islamic tradition was under-represented. CONCLUSION: MedLine's capability to identify the most current, reliable and accurate information about purely scientific topics should not be assumed to be the same case when considering the interface of religion, culture and end-of-life care.

Sachedina, Abdulaziz. End-of-life: the Islamic view [opinion]. *Lancet* 2005 August 27-September 2; 366(9487): 774-779. NRCBL: 20.5.1; 1.2; 8.3.3; 4.4; 20.7. SC: rv.

Saunders, Cicely. Care of the dying- 1: the problem of euthanasia. *Nursing Times* 1976 July 1; 72(26): 1003-1005. NRCBL: 20.5.1; 4.1.3; 1.2.

Sebastian, J. Jayakiran. A theological perspective on the withdrawal of care. *Issues in Medical Ethics* 2001 July-September; 9(3): 79-81. NRCBL: 20.5.1; 1.2.

Shannon, Thomas A. The legacy of the Schiavo case: the atmosphere around end-of- life decisions has changed. *America* 2005 June 6-13; 192(20): 17-19. NRCBL: 20.5.1; 20.5.4; 1.2; 20.3.1; 4.4.

Shannon, Thomas A.; Walter, James J. Implications of the papal allocution on feeding tubes. *Hastings Center Report* 2004 July-August; 34(4): 18-20. NRCBL: 20.5.1; 1.2.

Shannon, Thomas A.; Walter, James J.; Repenshek, Mark; Slosar, John Paul. Nutrition and hydration [letter and reply]. *Hastings Center Report* 2005 May-June; 35(3): 4-6. NRCBL: 20.5.1; 1.2.

Stavropoulos, Alexandre M. Orthodox Church. *In:* Council of Europe Publishing, ed. Euthanasia. Volume I. Ethical and Human Aspects. Strasbourg: Council of Europe; Croton- on-Hudson, NY: Manhattan Publishing Co.; 2003: 149-151. NRCBL: 20.5.1; 1.2.

Stith, Richard. Death by hunger and thirst. *Ethics and Medics* 2005 June; 30(6): 1-2. NRCBL: 20.5.1; 1.2. SC: le. Identifiers: Terri Schiavo.

Stoneking, Carole Bailey. Receiving communion: euthanasia, suicide, and letting die. *In:* Hauerwas, Stanley; Wells, Samuel eds. The Blackwell Companion to Christian Ethics. Oxford, UK: Blackwell Publishers Ltd.; 2004: 375-387. NRCBL: 20.5.1; 1.2; 20.3.1; 20.7.

Sullivan, Dennis. Euthanasia versus letting die: Christian decision-making in terminal patients. *Ethics and Medicine* 2005 Summer; 21(2): 109-118. NRCBL: 20.5.1; 20.4.1; 4.4; 1.1; 1.2.

Tolson, Jay. Wrestling with the final call: when it comes to end-of-life decisions, taking an ethical path isn't always easy. *U.S. News and World Report* 2005 April 4; 138(12): 22-23. NRCBL: 20.5.1; 1.2; 7.1; 2.2.

Vélez G., Juan R. Death of John Paul II and the basic human care for the sick and the dying. *Ethics and Medicine* 2005 Fall; 21(3): 167-177. NRCBL: 20.5.1; 15.5; 2.2; 1.1; 1.2; 21.1; 4.4.

Verhey, Allen. Necessary decisions. *Christian Century* 2005 April 19; 122(8): 9-10. NRCBL: 20.5.1; 1.2. Identifiers: Terri Schiavo.

Williams, Rowan; Murphy-O'Connor, Cormac. From the right to die to the duty to die? *Dolentium Hominum* 2004; 19(3): 47-49. NRCBL: 20.5.1; 1.2; 1.1; 4.4.

World Federation of Catholic Medical Associations [FIAMC]. Considerations of the scientific and ethical problems related to vegetative state. *Medical Ethics and Bioethics / Medicinska Etika & Bioetika* 2004 Spring-Summer; 11(1-2): 20-21. NRCBL: 20.5.1; 1.2; 4.4.

FETUSES *See* CARE FOR SPECIFIC GROUPS/ FETUSES; HUMAN EXPERIMENTATION/ SPECIAL POPULATIONS/ EMBRYOS AND FETUSES
See also TREATMENT REFUSAL

FORCE FEEDING OF PRISONERS

Gregory, Bernadette. Hunger striking prisoners: the doctors' dilemma [opinion]. *BMJ: British Medical Journal* 2005 October 15; 331(7521): 913. NRCBL: 21.5; 2.1.

Oguz, N.Y.; Miles, S.H. The physician and prison hunger strikes: reflecting on the experience in Turkey. *Journal of Medical Ethics* 2005 March; 31(3): 169-172. NRCBL: 21.5; 4.1.2; 2.1.
  Abstract: The medical ethics of a physician's relationship with a prisoner who is participating in a collective hunger strike has become a major public, professional, and governmental concern in The Republic of Turkey. This article examines the Turkish experience and debate about physician ethics during prison hunger strikes. It is hoped that this analysis will be of use to those formulating policy in similar situations.

FOREIGN NATIONALS *See* HUMAN EXPERIMENTATION/ SPECIAL POPULATIONS/ FOREIGN NATIONALS

GENE THERAPY

Anderson, W. French. Genetic therapy. *In:* Hamilton, Michael P., ed. The New Genetics and the Future of Man. Grand Rapids, MI: William B. Eerdmans Publishing Co.; 1972: 109-124. NRCBL: 15.4; 18.1.

Arkin, Lisa M.; Sondhi, Dolan; Worgall, Stefan; Suh, Lily Hyon K.; Hackett, Neil R.; Kaminsky, Stephen M.; Hosain, Syed A.; Souweidane, Mark M.; Kaplitt, Mi- chael G.; Dyke, Jonathan P.; Heier, Linda A.; Ballon, Douglas J.; Shungu, Dikoma C.; Wisniewski, Krystyna E.; Greenwald, Bruce M.; Hollmann, Charleen; Crystal, Ronald G. Confronting the issues of therapeutic misconception enrollment decisions, and personal motives in genetic medicine-based clinical research studies for fatal disorders. *Human Gene Therapy* 2005 September; 16(9): 1028-1036. NRCBL: 15.4; 18.2.
  Abstract: Genetic medicine-based therapies have unlocked the potential for ameliorating diseases previously considered inevitably fatal. Inherent in the clinical trials of genetic medicines are ethical issues of therapeutic misconception, enrollment decisions as they relate to the risks and benefits of research, and the complex relationships among funding sources, investigators, and the families of affected individuals. The purpose of this paper is to help define these complex issues relevant to the use of genetic medicines and to describe the strategy we have used to confront these issues in a phase I trial of adeno-associated virus-mediated gene transfer to the central nervous system of children with late infantile neuronal ceroid lipofuscinosis (LINCL), a fatal lysosomal storage disease associated with progressive neurodegeneration and death by mid-childhood. Our approach to these challenges should provide a useful paradigm for investigators initiating other genetic medicine- based studies to treat inevitably fatal diseases.

Ashcroft, Richard E. Gene therapy in the clinic: whose risks? *Trends in Biotechnology* 2004 November; 22(11): 560-563. NRCBL: 15.4; 18.6. SC: an.

Bailey, Ronald. Final victory over disease? Building humanity's extended immune system. *In his:* Liberation Biology: The Scientific and Moral Case for the Biotech Revolution. Amherst, NY: Prometheus Books; 2005: 63-94. NRCBL: 15.4.

Bamford, K.B.; Wood, S.; Shaw, R.J. Standards for gene therapy clinical trials based on pro-active risk assessment in a London NHS Teaching Hospital Trust. *QJM* 2005 February; 98(2): 75-86. NRCBL: 15.4; 15.7; 18.2; 18.6. Identifiers: National Health Service.

Capron, Alexander M. Genetic therapy: a lawyer's response. *In:* Hamilton, Michael P., ed. The New Genetics and the Future of Man. Grand Rapids, MI: William B. Eerdmans Publishing Co.; 1972: 133-156. NRCBL: 15.4; 18.1. SC: le.

Check, Erika. Sanctions agreed over teenager's gene-therapy death [news]. *Nature* 2005 February 17; 433(7027): 674. NRCBL: 15.4; 18.6. SC: le. Identifiers: Jesse Gelsinger; James Wilson.

Couzin, Jennifer; Kaiser, Jocelyn. As Gelsinger case ends, gene therapy suffers another blow [news]. *Science* 2005 February 18; 307(5712): 1028. NRCBL: 15.4; 18.6. SC: le.

Crofts, Christine; Krimsky, Sheldon. Emergence of a scientific and commercial research and development infrastructure for human gene therapy. *Human Gene Therapy* 2005 February; 16(2): 169-177. NRCBL: 15.4; 2.2; 18.6; 5.1. SC: rv.

NRCBL: National Reference Center for Bioethics Literature Classification Scheme   See inside front cover for terms.

197

Abstract: A research and clinical subfield known as "human gene therapy" has grown rapidly since 1990, when the first human trials were approved in the United States. Using quantitative data, this paper describes and analyzes the research and commercial infrastructure, including academic centers, publications, intellectual property, and biotechnology firms, that has developed around the goal of discovering clinical applications for the modification and transport of DNA to somatic cells. Despite setbacks and few documented successes, the subfield of human gene therapy continues to serve as an influential clinical paradigm for the treatment of inherited and noninherited diseases.

Etzioni, Amos. Gene therapy — where do we go? [editorial]. *Israel Medical Association Journal* 2003 December; 5(12): 883-884. NRCBL: 15.4; 9.5.1.

Evans, M.D.R.; Kelley, Jonathan; Zanjani, Esmail D. The ethics of gene therapy and abortion: public opinion. *Fetal Diagnosis and Therapy* 2005 May-June; 20(3): 223-234. NRCBL: 15.4; 5.2; 12.5.2. SC: em. Identifiers: Australia.

Gene Therapy Advisory Committee [GTAC]; Committee on Safety of Medicines [CSM]. Recommendations of the Gene Therapy Advisory Committee / Committee on Safety of Medicines working party on retroviruses May 2005. *Human Gene Therapy* 2005 October; 16(10): 1237-1239. NRCBL: 15.4; 18.6; 9.8.

Giangrande, Paul L.F. Gene therapy for hemophilia? No [debate]. *Journal of Thrombosis and Haemostasis* 2004 August; 2(8): 1236-1237. NRCBL: 15.4; 9.5.1.

Greenwell, Pamela. Germline gene therapy — changing future generations [opinion]. *International Journal of Biosciences and the Law* 1997; 1(3): 217-226. NRCBL: 15.4; 5.3; 14.1; 15.2; 14.4. SC: le.

Grey, William. Design constraints for the post-human future. *Monash Bioethics Review* 2005 April; 24(2): 10-19. NRCBL: 15.4. SC: an.

Harris, Gardiner. Gene therapy is facing a crucial hearing. *New York Times* 2005 March 3; p. A16. NRCBL: 15.4. SC: po.

Henderson, Gail E.; Davis, Arlene M.; King, Nancy M.P.; Easter, Michele M.; Zimmer, Catherine R.; Rothschild, Barbra Bluestone; Wilfond, Benjamin S.; Nelson, Daniel K.; Churchill, Larry R. Uncertain benefit: investigators' views and communications in early phase gene transfer trials. *Molecular Therapy* 2004 August; 10(2): 225-231. NRCBL: 15.4; 18.2; 18.3; 9.5.1.

Kaiser, Jocelyn. Panel urges limits on X-SCID trials [news]. *Science* 2005 March 11; 307(5715): 1544-1545. NRCBL: 15.4; 18.5.2. Identifiers: X-linked severe combined immunodeficiency.

Kimmelman, Jonathan. Recent developments in gene transfer: risk and ethics. *BMJ: British Medical Journal* 2005 January 8; 330(7482): 79-82. NRCBL: 15.4; 18.5.1; 18.2; 18.5.7.

Kimmelman, Jonathan; Levenstadt, Aaron. Elements of style: consent form language and the therapeutic misconception in phase 1 gene transfer trials. *Human Gene Therapy* 2005 April; 16(4): 502-508. NRCBL: 15.4; 18.3. SC: em.

Abstract: The therapeutic misconception arises wherever human subjects misinterpret the primary purpose of a clinical trial as therapeutic. Such misconceptions are particularly prevalent in trials involving severely ill subjects or novel and well-publicized investigational agents. In order to identify possible sources of the therapeutic misconception in gene transfer trials, 286 phase 1 human gene transfer consent documents were analyzed for their description of purpose, alternatives, and their use of the term gene transfer. We report that 20% of trials fail to explain their purpose as safety and dosage, only 41% of oncology trials identify comfort care as an alternative to participation, and that the term gene therapy is used with twice the frequency of the term gene transfer. Trends and coherence in consent form language were analyzed as well. Our results indicate that consent forms used in gene transfer phase 1 trials often contain language that promotes, or does little to deter, therapeutic misconceptions.

Kong, Wing May. The regulation of gene therapy research competent adult patients, today and tomorrow: implications of EU directive 2001/20/EC. *Medical Law Review* 2004 Summer; 12(2): 164-180. NRCBL: 15.4; 18.3; 18.6; 5.3; 21.1. SC: le. Identifiers: European Union.

Krimsky, Sheldon. China's gene therapy drug: do Shenzen SiBiono Gen-Tech's claims hold up? *GeneWatch* 2005 November-December; 18(6): 10-13. NRCBL: 15.4; 9.7; 18.1; 5.3.

Lapin, Eve. Public comment. *Human Gene Therapy* 2003 May 20; 14(8): 845-846. NRCBL: 15.4. Identifiers: adrenoleukodystrophy (ALD); x-linked genetic disease.

Leavitt, Wilder J. Regulating human gene therapy: legislative overreaction to human subject protection failures. *Administrative Law Review* 2001 Winter; 53(1): 315-341. NRCBL: 15.4; 18.2; 18.6. SC: le.

MacLaren, Robert E.; Ali, Robin R.; Thrasher, Adrian J. Risks of gene therapy should be weighed against lack of alternatives for many diseases [letter]. *BMJ: British Medical Journal* 2005 April 2; 330(7494): 791. NRCBL: 15.4.

Maloney, Dennis M. Federal case is settled over death of research subject. *Human Research Report* 2005 April; 20(4): 1-2. NRCBL: 15.4; 18.2; 18.3; 18.6; 20.1. SC: le. Identifiers: Jesse Gelsinger; University of Pennsylvania.

Manilla, Peter; Rebello, Tessio; Afable, Cathleen; Lu, Xiaobin; Slepushkin, Vladimir; Humeau, Laurent M.; Schonely, Kathy; Ni, Yajin; Binder, Gwendolyn K.; Levine, Bruce L.; MacGregor, Rob- Roy; June, Carl H.; Dropulic, Boro. Regulatory considerations for novel gene therapy products: a review of the process leading to the first clinical lentiviral vector. *Human Gene Therapy* 2005 January; 16(1): 17-25. NRCBL: 15.4; 18.2; 18.6. SC: rv.

Mannikko, Nancy Farm; Ness, Bryan D. Gene therapy: ethical and economic issues. *In:* Ness, Bryan D., ed. Encyclopedia of Genetics. Revised edition. Volume I. Pasadena, Calif.: Salem Press; 2004: 309-313. NRCBL: 15.4; 9.3.1.

Miah, Andy. The engineered athlete: human rights in the genetic revolution. *Culture, Sport, Society* 2000 Autumn; 3(3): 25-40. NRCBL: 15.4; 4.5; 21.1.

Miller, Henry. Cat and mouse in regulating genetic 'enhancement' [opinion]. *Nature Biotechnology* 2005 February; 23(2): 171-172. NRCBL: 15.4.

Moores, Donald F. Genetic engineering and our brave new world [editorial]. *American Annals of the Deaf* 1998 July; 143(3): 223-224. NRCBL: 15.4; 4.5.

Mulherkar, Rita. Biotechnology and medicine: ethical concerns. *Issues in Medical Ethics* 1997 October-December; 5(4): 110-111. NRCBL: 15.4; 14.5.

National Institutes of Health [NIH] (United States). Recombinant DNA Advisory Committee [RAC]. Informed Consent Working Group. NIH Guidance on informed consent for gene transfer research. Bethesda, MD: National Institutes of Health. Office of Biotechnology Activities 2004 February; 39 p. [Online]. Available: http://www4.od.nih.gov/oba/rac/ic/pdfs/temp_pdf.pdf [25 July 2005]. NRCBL: 15.4; 18.3; 5.3.

Negrier, Claude. Gene therapy for hemophilia? Yes [debate]. *Journal of Thrombosis and Haemostasis* 2004 August; 2(8): 1234-1235. NRCBL: 15.4; 9.5.1.

Pandya, S.K. Ethical aspects of clinical trials in gene therapy. *Issues in Medical Ethics* 2000 October-December; 8(4): 122-124. NRCBL: 15.4.

Ramellini, Pietro. Some critical comments on oocyte-assisted reprogramming [letter]. *National Catholic Bioethics Quarterly* 2005 Winter; 5(4): 658-660. NRCBL: 15.4; 14.4; 15.1; 22.2; 4.4.

Ramsey, Paul. Genetic therapy: a theologian's response. *In:* Hamilton, Michael P., ed. The New Genetics and the Future of Man. Grand Rapids, MI: William B. Eerdmans Publishing Co.; 1972: 157-175. NRCBL: 15.4; 18.1; 1.2.

Simonstein, Frida F. Germ-line engineering and late-onset diseases: the ethics of self-evolution [opinion]. *IMAJ: Israel Medical Association Journal* 2004 November; 6(11): 652-657. NRCBL: 15.4; 14.1.

Spink, J.; Geddes, D. Gene therapy progress and prospects: bringing gene therapy into medical practice: the evolution of international ethics and the regulatory environment. *Gene Therapy* 2004 November; 11(22): 1611-1616. NRCBL: 15.4; 18.1; 18.6; 2.2; 21.1.

Sturgis, Patrick; Cooper, Helen; Fife-Schaw, Chris. Attitudes to biotechnology: estimating the opinions of a better-informed public. *New Genetics and Society* 2005 April; 24(1): 31-56. NRCBL: 15.4; 5.1. SC: em. Identifiers: United Kingdom (Great Britain).

Trent, Ronald J.A. Oversight and monitoring of clinical research with gene therapy in Australia [editorial]. *Medical Journal of Australia* 2005 May 2; 182(9): 441-442. NRCBL: 15.4; 18.6.

United States. District Court. Pennsylvania. Eastern District. Settlement Agreement (with James M. Wilson, M.D., Ph.D.). Philadelphia, PA: United States Attorney's Office 2005; 21 p. [Online]. Available: http://www.usdoj.gov/usao/pae/News/Pr/2005/feb/Wilson5.settlement.pdf [29 August 2005]. NRCBL: 15.4; 18.2; 1.3.5. SC: le. Identifiers: Jesse Gelsinger; University of Pennsylvania; Children's National Medical Center [CNMC]; Mark L. Batshaw; Steven E. Raper.

United States. District Court. Pennsylvania. Eastern District. Settlement Agreement (with Mark L. Batshaw, M.D. and Children's National Medical Center [CNMC]). Philadelphia, PA: United States Attorney's Office 2005; 26 p. [Online]. Available: http://www.usdoj.gov/usao/pae/News/Pr/2005/feb/batshawsettlementdraft1-23-05.pdf [29 August 2005]. NRCBL: 15.4; 18.2; 1.3.5. SC: le. Identifiers: Jesse Gelsinger; University of Pennsylvania; Steven E. Raper; James M. Wilson.

United States. District Court. Pennsylvania. Eastern District. Settlement Agreement (with Steven E. Raper, M.D.). Philadelphia, PA: United States Attorney's Office 2005; 19 p. [Online]. Available: http://www.usdoj.gov/usao/pae/News/Pr/2005/feb/raper.settlement.pdf [29 August 2005]. NRCBL: 15.4; 18.2; 1.3.5. Identifiers: Jesse Gelsinger; Children's National Medical Center [CNMC]; University of Pennsylvania; Mark L. Batshaw; James M. Wilson.

United States. District Court. Pennsylvania. Eastern District. Settlement Agreement (with the Trustees of the University of Pennsylvania). Philadelphia, PA: United States Attorney's Office 2005; 11 p. [Online]. Available: http://www.usdoj.gov/usao/pae/News/Pr/2005/feb/IHGT settlement 5.pdf [29 August 2005]. NRCBL: 15.4; 18.2; 1.3.5. SC: le. Identifiers: Jesse Gelsinger; Children's National Medical Center [CNMC]; James M. Wilson; Mark L. Batshaw; Steven E. Raper.

United States. District Court. Pennsylvania. Eastern District. U.S. settles case of gene therapy study that ended with teen's death [press release]. *Philadelphia, PA: United States Attorney's Office* 2005 February 9; 4 p. [Online]. Available: http://www.usdoj.gov/usao/pae/News/Pr/2005/feb/UofPSettlement%20release.html [21 July 2005]. NRCBL: 15.4; 18.2; 1.3.5. Identifiers: Jesse Gelsinger; Steven E. Raper; James M. Wilson; Mark L. Batshaw; Children's National Medical Center [CNMC].

NRCBL: National Reference Center for Bioethics Literature Classification Scheme   See inside front cover for terms.

199

Vardy, Peter. The correction of human physical defects. *In his:* Being Human: Fulfilling Genetic and Spiritual Potential. London: Darton, Longman and Todd; 2003: 47-62. NRCBL: 15.4; 18.5.4; 4.5.

Waite, Michelle. Altering the future. *Ivy Journal of Ethics; 3(1):* 20-23. NRCBL: 15.4; 15.7; 5.2; 9.3.1; 5.2.

Walter, James. Why did Jesse die? *Update [Loma Linda University Center for Christian Bioethics]* 2001 November; 17(2): 4 p. NRCBL: 15.4; 18.5.1; 1.3.9; 9.7. Identifiers: Jesse Gelsinger.

Walters, LeRoy. Genforschung und Gesellschaft: Erwartungen, Ziele und Grenzen. *In:* Honnefelder, Ludger; Mieth, Dietmar; Propping, Peter; Siep, Ludwig; Wiesemann, Claudia, eds. Das genetische Wissen und die Zukunft des Menschen. New York: De Gruyter; 2003: 152-166. NRCBL: 15.4; 18.6.

Walters, LeRoy. Human genetic intervention: past, present, and future. *In:* Baillie, Harold W.; Casey, Timothy K., eds. Is Human Nature Obsolete? Genetics Bioengineering, and the Future of the Human Condition. Cambridge, MA: MIT Press; 2005: 367-384. NRCBL: 15.4; 18.2.

Weiss, Rick. U.S. researchers reach deal in '99 gene therapy case. *Washington Post* 2005 February 10; p. A3. NRCBL: 15.4. SC: po; le. Identifiers: Jesse Gelsinger.

GENETIC COUNSELING
See also GENETIC SCREENING; SEX DETERMINATION

Regulating preimplantation genetic diagnosis: the pathologization problem. *Harvard Law Review* 2005 June; 118(8): 2770-2791. NRCBL: 15.2; 14.4; 5.3; 9.5.1; 9.5.3. SC: le.

That little ball of cells: what we do with embryos depends on what we think they are [editorial]. *New Scientist* 2005 August 20-26; 187(2513): 5. NRCBL: 15.2; 14.4; 18.5.4; 15.1; 19.1. Identifiers: United Kingdom (Great Britain); Human Fertilisation and Embryology Authority.

Unapproved tests on a chip [editorial]. *Nature* 2005 December 8; 438(7069): 711. NRCBL: 15.2; 5.2. SC: le. Identifiers: Food and Drug Administration (FDA).

Annas, George J. Ethical aspects of non-invasive prenatal diagnosis: medical, market, or regulatory model? *Early Human Development* 1996 December 30; 47(supplement 1): S5-S11. NRCBL: 15.2; 9.1; 9.3.1. SC: le.

Asch, Adrienne; Wasserman, David. Where is the sin in synecdoche?: prenatal testing and the parent-child relationship. *In:* Wasserman, David; Bickenbach, Jerome; Wachbroit, Robert, eds. Quality of Life and Human Difference: Genetic Testing, Health Care, and Disability. New York: Cambridge University Press; 2005: 172-216. NRCBL: 15.2; 4.4.

Baetens, Patricia; Van de Velde, H.; Camus, M.; Pennings, G.; Van Steirteghem, A.; Devroey, P.; Liebaers, I. HLA-matched embryos selected for siblings requiring haematopoietic stem cell transplantation: a psychological perspective. *Reproductive BioMedicine Online [electronic]* 2005 February; 10(2): 154-163. Available: http://rbmonline.com/index.html [17 February 2006]. NRCBL: 15.2; 14.4; 19.5; 17.1. SC: em. Identifiers: human leukocyte antigen.

Baria, Farah. May be baby. *India Today* 1999 May 11-17; 24(20); 3 p. [Online]. Available: http://www.hsph.harvard.edu/Organizations/healthnet/SAsia/suchana/0300/h017.html [6 October 2005]. NRCBL: 15.2; 14.4. Identifiers: India.

Boddington, P.; Clarke, Angus. It's only teeth — limits to genetic testing? A response to Aldred, Crawford, Savarirayan, and Savulescu [letter]. *Clinical Genetics* 2004 December; 66(6): 562-564. NRCBL: 15.2; 14.1; 9.3.1. Comments: comment on M.J. Aldred et al., "It's only teeth — are there limits to genetic testing?" Clinical Genetics 2003; 63: 333-339.

Bohannon, John. Eugenics stir emotions in Germany [news]. *Christian Science Monitor* 2004 July 22; p. 11, 13. NRCBL: 15.2.

Bonnin, David C. The need for increased oversight of genetic testing: a detailed look at the genetic testing process. *Houston Journal of Health Law and Policy* 2003 Fall; 4(1): 149- 180. NRCBL: 15.2; 9.8. SC: le.

Bostrom, Barry A. Willis v. Wu in the Supreme Court of South Carolina. *Issues in Law and Medicine* 2005 Spring; 20(3): 275-278. NRCBL: 15.2; 12.4.1. SC: le.

Bouchard, Louise; Renaud, Marc. Female and male physicians' attitudes toward prenatal diagnosis: a Pan-Canadian survey. *Social Science and Medicine* 1997 February; 44(3): 381-392. NRCBL: 15.2; 12.5.2; 7.1. SC: em. Identifiers: Canada.

Byers, Tim; MacDonald, Deborah J.; Severin, Matthew J.; Fishbach, Andrea A. Cancer genetic counseling: need for confidentiality versus responsibility to notify. *Cancer Practice* 1999 March-April; 7(2): 93-95. NRCBL: 15.2; 9.5.1; 8.4.

Carmi, Rivka. Cross-cultural genetic counseling. *In:* Blazer, Shraga; Zimmer, Etan Z., eds. The Embryo: Scientific Discovery and Medical Ethics. New York: Karger; 2005: 223-236. NRCBL: 15.2; 21.7.

Carrera, Jose M. Bioethical aspects of ultrasonographic and invasive prenatal diagnosis. *In:* Carrera, Jose M.; Chervenak, Frank A.; Kurjak, Asim, eds. Controversies in Perinatal Medicine: Studies on the Fetus as a Patient. New York: Parthenon Pub. Group; 2003: 282-288. NRCBL: 15.2.

Chaplin, Julie; Schweitzer, Robert; Perkoulidis, Shelley. Experiences of prenatal diagnosis of spina bifida or hydrocephalus in parents who decide to continue with their pregnancy. *Journal of Genetic Counseling* 2005 April; 14(2): 151-162. NRCBL: 15.2; 9.5.1; 15.1. SC: em.

Chasen, S.T.; Skupski, D.W.; McCullough, L.B.; Chervenak, F.A. Ethical dimensions of nuchal translucency screening. *In:* Carrera, Jose M.; Chervenak, Frank A.; Kurjak, Asim, eds. Controversies in Perinatal Medicine: Studies on the Fetus as a Patient. New York: Parthenon Pub. Group; 2003: 289-295. NRCBL: 15.2.

Check, Erika. Screen test [news]. *Nature* 2005 December 8; 438(7069): 733-734. NRCBL: 15.2; 5.2.

Chervenak, Frank A.; McCullough, Laurence B. Implementation of first-trimester risk assessment for trisomy 21: ethical considerations. *American Journal of Obstetrics and Gynecology* 2005 June; 192(6): 1777-1781. NRCBL: 15.2; 2.1.

Crawford, Peter J.M.; Aldred, M.J; Savarirayan, R.; Savulescu, J. 'It's (not) only teeth' [letter]. *Clinical Genetics* 2004 December; 66(6): 565. NRCBL: 15.2.

Csaba, A.; Papp, Z. Decision-making in prenatal diagnosis. *In:* Carrera, Jose M.; Chervenak, Frank A.; Kurjak, Asim, eds. Controversies in Perinatal Medicine: Studies on the Fetus as a Patient. New York: Parthenon Pub. Group; 2003: 101-106. NRCBL: 15.2.

Dahl, Edgar. Babies by design: a response to Martin Johnson's moral case study on tissue typing [opinion]. *Reproductive BioMedicine Online [electronic]* 2004 December; 9(6): 597-598. Available: http://www.rbmonline.com/index.html [14 July 2005]. NRCBL: 15.2; 14.4; 19.5; 1.1. SC: an. Comments: comment on Martin H. Johnson, "A moral case study for discussion: designer babies and tissue typing," Reproductive BioMedicine Online 2004 October; 9(4): 372.

de Crespigny, L.; Chervenak, F.; Coquel, P.A.; Ville, Y.; McCullough, L. Practicing prenatal diagnosis within the law [editorial]. *Ultrasound in Obstetrics and Gynecology* 2004 October; 24(5): 489-494. NRCBL: 15.2; 12.4.1; 21.1. SC: cs; le. Identifiers: Roe v. Wade; Nicolas Perruche; Australia; France; United States.

de Wert, Guido. Preimplantation genetic diagnosis: the ethics of intermediate cases [opinion]. *Human Reproduction* 2005 December; 20(12): 3261-3266. NRCBL: 15.2; 14.4; 14.3; 4.4.

Delatycki, M. Response to Spriggs: is conceiving a child to benefit another against the interest of the new child? *Journal of Medical Ethics* 2005 June; 31(6): 343. NRCBL: 15.2; 14.4; 19.4.

Devolder, Katrien. Preimplantation HLA typing: having children to save our loved ones. *Journal of Medical Ethics* 2005 October; 31(10): 582-586. NRCBL: 15.2; 14.4; 19.5. SC: an. Identifiers: human leukocyte antigen.
Abstract: Preimplantation tissue typing has been proposed as a method for creating a tissue matched child that can serve as a haematopoietic stem cell donor to save its sick sibling in need of a stem cell transplant. Despite recent promising results, many people have expressed their disapproval of this method. This paper addresses the main concerns of these critics: the risk of preimplantation genetic diagnosis (PGD) for the child to be born; the intention to have a donor child; the limits that should be placed on what may be done to the donor child, and whether the intended recipient can be someone other than a sibling. The author will show that these concerns do not constitute a sufficient ground to forbid people to use this technique to save not only a sibling, but also any other loved one's life. Finally, the author briefly deals with two alternative scenarios: the creation of a human leukocyte antigen (HLA) matched child as an insurance policy, and the banking of HLA matched embryos.

Dickens, B.M. Preimplantation genetic diagnosis and 'savior siblings'. *International Journal of Gynecology and Obstetrics* 2005 January; 88(1): 91-96. NRCBL: 15.2; 14.4; 19.5; 8.3.2.

Doubilet, Peter M.; Copel, Joshua A.; Benson, Carol B.; Bahado-Singh, Ray O.; Platt, Lawrence D. Choroid plexus cyst and echogenic intracardiac focus in women at low risk for chromosomal anomalies: the obligation to inform the mother. *Journal of Ultrasound in Medicine* 2004 July; 23(7): 883-885. NRCBL: 15.2; 8.2.

Dugas, Robbie. Nursing and genetics: applying the American Nurses Association's Code of Ethics. *Journal of Professional Nursing* 2005 March-April; 21(2): 103- 113. NRCBL: 15.2; 6.

Durosinmi, M.A.; Odebiyi, A.I.; Akinola, N.O.; Adediran, L.A.; Aken'Ova, Y.; Okunade, M.A.; Halim, N.K.; Onwukeme, K.E.; Olatunji, P.O.; Adegoroye, D.E. Acceptability of prenatal diagnosis of sickle cell anaemia by a sample of the Nigerian population. *African Journal of Medicine and Medical Sciences* 1997 March-June; 26(1-2): 55-58. NRCBL: 15.2; 9.5.1. SC: em.

Dyer, Clare. Law lords give the go ahead for creation of "saviour siblings" [news]. *BMJ: British Medical Journal* 2005 May 7; 330(7499): 1041. NRCBL: 15.2; 14.4; 19.5. SC: le.

Edwards, Robert G. Ethics of PGD: thoughts on the consequences of typing HLA in embryos. *Reproductive BioMedicine Online [electronic]* 2004 August; 9(2): 222-224 Available: http://www.rbmonline.com/index.html [15 June 2005]. NRCBL: 15.2; 14.4; 18.5.4. Identifiers: pre-implantation genetic diagnosis.

Ekelin, Maria; Crang-Svalenius, Elizabeth. Midwives' attitudes to and knowledge about a newly introduced foetal screening method. *Scandinavian Journal of Caring Sciences* 2004 September; 18(3): 287-293. NRCBL: 15.2; 4.1.3. SC: em.

NRCBL: National Reference Center for Bioethics Literature Classification Scheme   See inside front cover for terms.

201

Feitshans, Ilise L. Legislating to preserve women's autonomy during pregnancy. *Medicine and Law: World Association for Medical Law* 1995; 14(5-6): 397-412. NRCBL: 15.2; 9.5.5; 8.3.4; 1.1. SC: le.

Fiddler, Morris; Pergament, Eugene. Medically-assisted procreation: a maturing technology or a premature fear? Response to Testart and Sele [opinion]. *Human Reproduction* 1996 April; 11(4): 708-709. NRCBL: 15.2; 14.4; 15.5.

Gillett, G. The unwitting sacrifice problem. *Journal of Medical Ethics* 2005 June; 31(6): 327-332. NRCBL: 15.2; 17.1. SC: an.
Abstract: The diagnosis of bipolar disorder has been linked to giftedness of various sorts and this raises a special problem in that it is likely that the condition has a genetic basis. Therefore it seems possible that in the near future we will be able to detect and eliminate the gene predisposing to the disorder. This may mean, however, that, as a society, we lose the associated gifts. We might then face a difficult decision either way in that it is unclear that we are preventing an unalloyed bad when we diagnose and eliminate bipolar disorder through prenatal genetic testing and yet if we allow the individual to be born we are condemning that person to being an unwitting sacrifice in that they might well suffer considerable net distress as a result of our need to keep our gene pool enriched in the relevant way.

Godard, Béatrice; Cardinal, Geneviève. Ethical implications in genetic counseling and family studies of the epilepsies. *Epilepsy and Behavior* 2004 October; 5(5): 621-626. NRCBL: 15.2; 9.7; 15.1.

Gurmankin, Andrea D.; Domchek, Susan; Stopfer, Jill; Fels, Christina; Armstrong, Katrina. Patients' resistance to risk information in genetic counseling for BRCA1/2. *Archives of Internal Medicine* 2005 March 14; 165(5): 523-529. NRCBL: 15.2; 8.1; 9.5.5. SC: em.
Abstract: BACKGROUND: Risk information from health care providers is relevant to and used in nearly all medical decisions. Patients often misunderstand their risks, yet little is known about the risk perception that patients derive from risk communications with health care providers. This study examines patients' risk perceptions following communication with health care providers during genetic counseling about the risks of breast cancer and BRCA1/2 mutations. METHODS: A prospective, longitudinal study was conducted from October 2002 to February 2004 of women who received genetic counseling. The women completed a survey before their counseling and a telephone interview in the week after the counseling. Main outcome measures included change from precounseling in risk perception and accuracy of postcounseling risk perception (relative to actual risk information communicated). RESULTS: A total of 108 women agreed to participate in the study. The women's postcounseling risk perceptions were significantly lower than their precounseling risk perceptions (breast cancer: 17%, P001; mutation: 13%, P001) but were significantly higher than the actual risk information communicated (breast cancer: 19%, P001; mutation: 24%, P001). Accuracy of breast cancer risk perception but not mutation risk perception was associated with precounseling worry (P = .04), even after adjusting for trait anxiety (P = .01). CONCLUSIONS: This research demonstrates patients' resistance to risk information. Inappropriately high risk perception derived from a risk communication with a health care provider can lead patients to make different, and potentially worse, medical decisions than they would with an accurate risk perception and to be unnecessarily distressed about their risk.

Haker, Hille. Harm as the price of liberty? Preimplantation diagnosis and reproductive freedom. *Ethical Perspectives* 2003; 10(3-4): 215-223. NRCBL: 15.2; 14.4; 14.1; 1.1. SC: an.

Hall, Stephen C. The physician's duty and role in communicating with family members regarding results of patients' genetic testing. *Journal of the Kentucky Medical Association* 2005 April; 103(4): 159-161. NRCBL: 15.2; 8.2. SC: le.

Hamamy, Hanan A.; Dahoun, Sophie. Parental decisions following the prenatal diagnosis of sex chromosome abnormalities. *European Journal of Obstetrics and Gynecology and Reproductive Biology* 2004 September 10; 116(1): 58-62. NRCBL: 15.2. SC: em. Identifiers: Switzerland.

Handyside, Alan H. Commonsense as applied to eugenics: response to Testart and Sele [opinion]. *Human Reproduction* 1996 April; 11(4): 707. NRCBL: 15.2; 14.4; 15.5.

Helén, Ilpo. Risk management and ethics in high-tech antenatal care. *In:* Bunton, Robin; Petersen, Alan, eds. Genetic Governance: Health, Risk and Ethics in the Biotech Era. New York: Routledge; 2005: 47-63. NRCBL: 15.2; 12.3; 15.3.

Hill, David L.; Li, Man. What regulations for preimplantation genetic diagnosis? *Journal of Assisted Reproduction and Genetics* 2004 January; 21(1): 11-13. NRCBL: 15.2; 14.4. SC: le.

Hodgson, Jan; Spriggs, Merle. A practical account of autonomy: why genetic counseling is especially well suited to the facilitation of informed autonomous decision making. *Journal of Genetic Counseling* 2005 April; 14(2): 89-97. NRCBL: 15.2; 1.1.

Hui, Pui Wah; Lam, Yung Hang; Chen, Min; Tang, Mary Hoi Yin; Yeung, William Shu Biu; Ng, Ernest Hung Yu; Ho, Pak Chung. Attitude of at-risk subjects towards preimplantation genetic diagnosis of (alpha)- and (beta)-thalassaemias in Hong Kong. *Prenatal Diagnosis* 2002 June; 22(6): 508-511. NRCBL: 15.2; 14.4; 9.5.1. SC: em.

Human Fertilisation and Embryology Authority [HFEA] (United Kingdom). Choices and Boundaries. Should people be able to select embryos free from an inherited suceptibility to cancer? London: Human Fertilisation and Embryology Authority 2005 November; 15 p. [Online]. Available: http://www.hfea.gov.uk/AboutHFEA/HFEAPolicy/Choicesandboundaries/Choices_Boundaries.pdf [7 February 2006]. NRCBL: 15.2; 14.4. Identifiers: preimplantation diagnosis.

Hunt, Linda M.; de Voogd, Katherine B.; Castañeda, Heide. The routine and the traumatic in prenatal genetic diagnosis: does clinical information inform patient decision-making? *Patient Education and Counseling* 2005 March; 56(3): 302-312. NRCBL: 15.2; 8.1. SC: em.

Ibrahim, Hythum; Newman, Michael. Ultrasound soft markers of chromosomal abnormalities; an ethical dilemma for obstetricians. *Human Reproduction and Genetic Ethics: An International Journal* 2005; 11(2): 25-27. NRCBL: 15.2; 9.5.5; 9.5.8.

Jallinoja, Piia. Ethics of clinical genetics: the spirit of the profession and trials of suitability from 1970 to 2000. *In:* Bunton, Robin; Petersen, Alan, eds. Genetic Governance: Health, Risk and Ethics in the Biotech Era. New York: Routledge; 2005: 31-45. NRCBL: 15.2; 15.3; 2.2.

Johnson, Martin H. A moral case study for discussion: designer babies and tissue typing. *Reproductive BioMedicine Online [electronic]* 2004 October; 9(4): 372. Available: http://www.rbmonline.com [29 June 2005]. NRCBL: 15.2; 14.4. SC: cs.

Kabra, S.G. Gender disparity: need to look beyond 'female foeticide'. *Issues in Medical Ethics* 2002 April-June; 10(2): 24. NRCBL: 15.2; 12.5.1; 10. Identifiers: Medical Termination of Pregnancy Act; India.

Kahn, Jeffrey P.; Mastroianni, Anna C. The ethics and policy issues in creating a stem cell donor: a case study in reproductive genetics. *In:* Brannigan, Michael C., ed. Cross-Cultural Biotechnology. Lanham: Rowman and Littlefield; 2004: 43-55. NRCBL: 15.2; 14.4; 19.5; 5.3.

Kaiser, Jocelyn. An earlier look at baby's genes [news]. *Science* 2005 September 2; 309(5740): 1476-1478. NRCBL: 15.2; 15.3.

Keefer, Christopher M. Bridging the gap between life insurer and consumer in the genetic testing era: the RF proposal. *Indiana Law Journal* 1999 Autumn; 74(4): 1375-1395. NRCBL: 15.2; 9.3.1; 5.3. SC: le. Identifiers: risk factor.

Keeling, Sharon L. Duty to warn of genetic harm in breach of patient confidentiality. *Journal of Law and Medicine* 2004 November; 12(2): 235-253. NRCBL: 15.2; 8.4. SC: le. Identifiers: Australia.

Kharaboyan, Linda; Avard, Denise; Knoppers, Bartha Maria. Storing newborn blood spots: modern controversies. *Journal of Law, Medicine and Ethics* 2004 Winter; 32(4): 741- 748. NRCBL: 15.2; 15.10; 1.3.12; 13.1; 8.4. SC: le.

Khoshnood, Babak; De Vigan, Catherine; Vodovar, Véronique; Goujard, Janine; Lhomme, Anne; Bonnet, Damien; Goffinet, François. Trends in prenatal diagnosis, pregnancy termination, and perinatal mortality of newborns with congenital heart disease in France, 1983-2000: a population-based evaluation. *Pediatrics* 2005 January; 115(1): 95-101. NRCBL: 15.2; 12.1; 9.5.7. SC: em.

Kodish, Eric D. Testing children for cancer genes: the rule of earliest onset. *Journal of Pediatrics* 1999 September; 135(3): 390-395. NRCBL: 15.2; 9.5.7; 8.3.2.

Krones, Tanja; Schlüter, Elmar; Manolopoulos, Konstantin; Bock, Karin; Tinneberg, Hans-Rudolf; Koch, Manuela C.; Lindner, Martin; Hoffmann, Georg F.; Mayatepek, Ertan; Huels, Gerd; Neuwohner, Elke; El Ansari, Susan; Wissner, Thomas; Richter, Gerd. Public, expert and patients' opinions on preimplantation genetic diagnosis (PGD) in Germany. *Reproductive BioMedicine Online [electronic]* 2005 January; 10(1): 116-123. Available: http://www.rbmonline.com/index.html [17 February 2006]. NRCBL: 15.2; 14.4; 21.1; 5.3. SC: em; le.

Kuntsmann, Erdmute; Maas, Ines; Epplen, Jörg T. Nicht-direktive Beratung im Rahmen prädiktiver Diagnostik bei genetischen Risiken für Kinder? *In:* Baumann, Eva; Brink, Alexander; May, Arnd T.; Schröder, Peter; Schutzeichel, Corinna Iris, eds. Weltanschauliche Offenheit in der Bioethik. Berlin: Duncker & Humblot; 2004: 259-270. NRCBL: 15.2; 9.5.2.

Lashwood, Alison. Preimplantation genetic diagnosis to prevent genetic disorders in children. *British Journal of Nursing* 2005 January 27-February 9; 14(2): 64-70. NRCBL: 15.2; 14.4.

Lavery, Stuart. Preimplantation genetic diagnosis and the welfare of the child. *Human Fertility* 2004 December; 7(4): 295-300. NRCBL: 15.2; 14.4. Identifiers: Europe.

Leung, Tse Ngong; Ching Chau, Macy Mo; Chang, Joseph Jeremy; Leung, Tak Yeung; Fung, Tak Yuen; Lau, Tze Kin. Attitudes towards termination of pregnancy among Hong Kong Chinese women attending prenatal diagnosis counselling clinic. *Prenatal Diagnosis* 2004 July; 24(7): 546-551. NRCBL: 15.2; 12.5.2; 14.3. SC: em.

Lilani, Anjali. Ethical issues and policy analysis for genetic testing: Huntington's disease as a paradigm for diseases with a late onset. *Human Reproduction and Genetic Ethics: An International Journal* 2005; 11(2): 28-34. NRCBL: 15.2; 15.1; 8.3.1; 9.3.1.

Lohmann, Georg. On the relation between moral, legal and evaluative justifications of pre-implantation genetic diagnosis (PGD). *Ethical Perspectives* 2003; 10(3-4): 196-203. NRCBL: 15.2; 14.4; 4.4. SC: le; an.

Ludwig, M. Martin Johnson's moral case study: a reply [opinion]. *Reproductive BioMedicine Online [electronic]* 2004 December; 9(6): 598-599. Available: http://www.rbmonline.com/index.html [14 July 2005]. NRCBL: 15.2; 14.4; 19.5. Comments: comment on Martin H. Johnson, "A moral case study for discussion: designer babies and tissue typing," Reproductive BioMedicine Online 2004 October; 9(4): 372.

NRCBL: National Reference Center for Bioethics Literature Classification Scheme   See inside front cover for terms.

203

Maryland. Court of Appeals. *Kassama v. Magat* [Date of Decision: 2002 February 5]. *Atlantic Reporter*, 2d Series, 2002; 792: 1102-1124. NRCBL: 15.2. SC: le.

Abstract: Court Decision: 792 *Atlantic Reporter*, 2d Series 1102; 2002 Feb 5 (date of decision). The Maryland Court of Appeals held that life cannot be an injury that gives rise to a "wrongful life" claim. At her first appointment with Dr. Aaron Magat, an ultrasound confirmed that Millicent Kassama was carrying a 17- week-old fetus. Magat referred Kassama for alpha-fetoprotein (AFP) testing to determine whether she was at an increased risk for carrying a Down's syndrome baby. The test results, received at 22 weeks, indicated an increased risk of Down's syndrome. Because abortions of Down's syndrome fetuses are not performed in Maryland after 24 weeks, Magat advised Kassama that she would likely have to go out-of-state for an abortion if amniocentesis results (usually available within two weeks of the test) were positive. Kassama gave birth to a baby with Down's syndrome. She claims she was not informed of the results or her options. Kassama, on behalf of her child, sued Magat for "wrongful life." The Maryland Court of Appeals held that an "impaired life is not worse than non-life, and, for that reason, life is not and cannot be, an injury." The court based its holding on the fact that a jury cannot issue a consistent and reasoned verdict on the value of life because that value is so intimately intertwined with individual philosophy and theology. [KIE/INW]

Maryland. Court of Special Appeals. *Kassama v. Magat* [Date of Decision: 2001 February 28]. *Atlantic Reporter*, 2d Series, 2001; 767: 348-369. NRCBL: 15.2. SC: le.

Abstract: Court Decision: 767 *Atlantic Reporter*, 2d Series 348; 28 Feb 2001 (date of decision). The Court of Special Appeals of Maryland held that wrongful life is not a recognized cause of action in Maryland. Millicent Kassama sought medical care from Dr. Magat for her pregnancy. During her first visit with Dr. Magat, an ultrasound showed that Kassama was pregnant with a 17-week-old fetus. Magat referred her for alpha fetoprotein (AFP) testing, and Kassama's results showed an increased risk for Down's syndrome. Because the AFP test was not performed until the fetus was approximately 22 weeks old, and abortions on fetuses older than 24 weeks are not performed in Maryland, Magat informed Kassama that she would likely have to travel out-of-state should she chose to abort. Kassama claimed Magat did not inform her of either the test results or her options. Subsequently, Kassama gave birth to a baby with Down's syndrome. Kassama asserted that the infant would have been aborted but for the physician's negligence, and sought damages on behalf of the child for living in a defective state. The Maryland Court of Special Appeals held that there is no cause of action for wrongful life "because it is an impossible task to calculate damages based on a comparison between life in an impaired state and no life at all." The court affirmed the trial court's judgment for Magat. [KIE/INW]

Mason, J.K. Wrongful life: the problem of causation. *Medical Law International* 2004; 6(2): 149-161. NRCBL: 15.2; 12.4.2. SC: le.

Masserman, Dean E. Preimplanation genetic testing: undivine intervention? *Journal of Assisted Reproductive Law* 1997; 3 p. [Online]. Available: http://www.vgme.com/pgd.htm [21 July 2005]. NRCBL: 15.2; 14.1.

Meister, U.; Finck, C.; Stöbel-Richter, Y.; Schmutzer, G.; Brähler, E. Knowledge and attitudes towards preimplantation genetic diagnosis in Germany. *Human Re-production* 2005 January; 20(1): 231-238. NRCBL: 15.2; 14.4. SC: em.

Michie, Susan; Allanson, Abi; Armstrong, David; Weinman, John; Bobrow, Martin; Marteau, Theresa M. Objectives of genetic counselling: differing views of purchasers, providers and users. *Journal of Public Health Medicine* 1998; 20(4): 404-408. NRCBL: 15.2; 8.1. SC: em.

Michie, Susan; Dormandy, Elizabeth; Marteau, Theresa M. Informed choice: understanding knowledge in the context of screening uptake. *Patient Education and Counseling* 2003 July; 50(3): 247-253. NRCBL: 15.2; 8.3.1; 9.5.8; 9.5.5; 17.1; 7.1. SC: em. Identifiers: United Kingdom (Great Britain).

Middleton, Anna. Deaf and hearing adults' attitudes toward genetic testing for deafness. *In:* Van Cleve, John Vickery, ed. Genetics, Disability, and Deafness. Washington, DC: Gallaudet University Press; 2004: 127- 147. NRCBL: 15.2; 15.3. SC: em.

Milner, Karen K.; Collins, Elizabeth E.; Connors, Geoffrey R.; Petty, Elizabeth M. Attitudes of young adults to prenatal screening and genetic correction for human attributes and psychiatric conditions. *American Journal of Medical Genetics* 1998 March 5; 76(2): 111-119. NRCBL: 15.2; 9.5.1; 17.1.

Morton, Newton E. Genetic aspects of population policy. *Clinical Genetics* 1999 August; 56(2): 105-109. NRCBL: 15.2; 13.3; 15.5.

Motluk, Alison. Which IVF test is best for baby? [news]. *New Scientist* 2005 October 29-November 4; 188(2523): 10. NRCBL: 15.2; 14.4.

Mulvenna, Beverley. Pre-implantation genetic diagnosis, tissue typing and beyond: the legal implications of the Hashmi case. *Medical Law International* 2004; 6(2): 163-182. NRCBL: 15.2; 14.4; 19.5; 4.4. SC: le.

Munné, Santiago; Cohen, Jacques. The status of preimplantation genetic diagnosis in Japan: a criticism [opinion]. *Reproductive BioMedicine Online [electronic]* 2004 September; 9(3): 258-259. Available: http://www.rbmonline.com/index.html [14 July 2005]. NRCBL: 15.2; 14.4; 14.3.

Patrawala, Zeenat. The Down syndrome abortion dilemma. *Ivy Journal of Ethics* 2003; 3(1): 24-27. NRCBL: 15.2; 15.3; 9.5.3; 12.1; 4.4. SC: an.

Pembrey, Marcus E. In the light of preimplantation genetic diagnosis: some ethical issues in medical genetics revisited [opinion]. *European Journal of Human Genetics* 1998 January; 6(1): 4-11. NRCBL: 15.2; 14.4; 15.5; 18.5.4.

Peterson, T.S. Just diagnosis? Preimplantation genetic diagnosis and injustices to disabled people. *Journal of Medi-*

cal Ethics 2005 April; 31(4): 231-234. NRCBL: 15.2; 14.4; 4.4; 9.5.1. SC: an.

Plachot, Michelle; Cohen, Jean. Regulations for preimplantation genetic diagnosis in France. *Journal of Assisted Reproduction and Genetics* 2004 January; 21(1): 5-6. NRCBL: 15.2; 14.4. SC: le.

Rabino, Isaac. Genetic testing and its implications: human genetics researchers grapple with ethical issues. *Science, Technology, and Human Values* 2003 Summer; 28(3): 365- 402. NRCBL: 15.2; 8.4; 15.1. SC: em.

Ratcliff, Kathryn Strother. Fetal quality control. *In her:* Women and Health: Power, Technology, Inequality, and Conflict in a Gendered World. Boston, MA: Allyn and Bacon; 2002: 245-260. NRCBL: 15.2; 9.5.8; 9.5.5.

Ray, Pierre F.; Munnich, Arnold; Nisand, Israël; Frydman, René; Vekemans, Michel; Viville, Stéphane. Is preimplantation genetic diagnosis for 'social sexing' desirable in today's and tomorrow's society? [letter]. *Human Reproduction* 2003 February; 18(2): 463-464. NRCBL: 15.2; 14.3.

Raz, Aviad. "Important to test, important to support": attitudes toward disability rights and prenatal diagnosis among leaders of support groups for genetic disorders in Israel. *Social Science and Medicine* 2004 November; 59(9): 1857-1866. NRCBL: 15.2; 12.1; 15.5; 21.1. SC: em.

Raz, Aviad E. Disability rights, prenatal diagnosis and eugenics: a cross- cultural view. *Journal of Genetic Counseling* 2005 June; 14(3): 183-187. NRCBL: 15.2; 9.5.1; 15.3.

Roberts, Christy D.; Stough, Laura M.; Parrish, Linda H. The role of genetic counseling in the elective termination of pregnancies involving fetuses with disabilities. *Journal of Special Education* 2002 Spring; 36(1): 48-55. NRCBL: 15.2; 9.5.5; 14.1; 12.5.2.

Robertson, John A. Is preimplantation genetic diagnosis for 'social sexing' desirable in today's and tomorrow's society? View of the ASRM ethics committee [letter]. *Human Reproduction* 2003 February; 18(2): 464. NRCBL: 15.2; 14.3. Identifiers: American Society of Reproductive Medicine.

Romero, Linda J.; Garry, Philip J.; Schuyler, Mark; Bennahum, David A.; Qualls, Clifford; Ballinger, Lori; Kelly, Velma; Schmitt, Cheryl; Skipper, Betty; Ortiz, Irene E.; Rhyne, Robert L. Emotional responses to APO E genotype disclosure for Alzheimer disease. *Journal of Genetic Counseling* 2005 April; 14(2): 141-150. NRCBL: 15.2; 15.3; 17.1; 9.5.2. SC: em.

Ross, Julie A. Genetics and childhood cancer. Commentary on: inherited cancer in children: practical/ethical problems and challenges. *European Journal of Cancer* 2004 November; 40(16): 2471-2472. NRCBL: 15.2; 9.5.1; 9.5.7.

Rough, Bonnie J. His genes hold gifts. Mine carry risk. *New York Times* 2005 January 30; p.ST7. NRCBL: 15.2. SC: po.

Rudolph, William C. Social issues in perinatal screening for sickle cell anemia. *Urban Health* 1983 August; 12(8): 32-34. NRCBL: 15.2; 9.5.1.

Schaap, Tamar. Confidentiality in counseling for X-linked conditions. *Clinical Genetics* 1995 March; 47(3): 155-157. NRCBL: 15.2; 8.4; 8.1; 8.2.

Scott, Rosamund. Prenatal screening, autonomy and reasons: the relationship between the law of abortion and wrongful birth. *Medical Law Review* 2003 Autumn; 11(3): 265-325. NRCBL: 15.2; 12.5.3; 1.1; 8.5. SC: le.

Scott, Rosamund. The uncertain scope of reproductive autonomy in preimplantation genetic diagnosis and selective abortion. *Medical Law Review* 2005 Autumn; 13(3): 291-327. NRCBL: 15.2; 14.4; 12.3; 1.1. SC: le.

Seif, Rony. Sex selection by preimplantation genetic diagnosis: should it be carried out for social reasons? [letter]. *Human Reproduction* 2003 February; 18(2): 461-462. NRCBL: 15.2; 14.3.

Sermon, Karen. Sex selection by preimplantation genetic diagnosis: should it be carried out for social reasons? A personal view [letter]. *Human Reproduction* 2003 February; 18(2): 462-463. NRCBL: 15.2; 14.3.

Shapira, Amos. 'Wrongful life' lawsuits for faulty genetic counselling: legal, ethical and policy aspects. *In:* Blazer, Shraga; Zimmer, Etan Z., eds. The Embryo: Scientific Discovery and Medical Ethics. New York: Karger; 2005: 340-350. NRCBL: 15.2; 8.5; 15.2. SC: le.

Sheldon, Tony. Dutch Supreme Court backs damages for child for having been born [news]. *BMJ: British Medical Journal* 2005 April 2; 330(7494): 747. NRCBL: 15.2. SC: le.

Simpson, Bob; Dissanayake, V.H.W.; Jayasekara, R.W. Contemplating choice: attitudes towards intervening in human reproduction in Sri Lanka. *New Genetics and Society* 2005 April; 24(1): 99-117. NRCBL: 15.2; 12.5.2; 14.4. SC: em.

Sjögren, Berit; Uddenberg, Nils. Attitudes towards disabled persons and the possible effects of prenatal diagnosis. An interview study among 53 women participating in prenatal diagnosis and 20 of their husbands. *Journal of Psychosomatic Obstetrics and Gynaecology* 1987; 6: 187-196. NRCBL: 15.2; 9.5.3.

Sousa, Mário; Barros, Alberto. A moral case study for discussion: designer babies and tissue typing [opinion]. *Reproductive BioMedicine Online [electronic]* 2004 December; 9(6): 596-597. Available: http://www.rbmonline.com/index.html [14 July 2005]. NRCBL: 15.2; 14.4; 19.5. SC: an. Comments: comment on Martin H. Johnson, "A

NRCBL: National Reference Center for Bioethics Literature Classification Scheme   See inside front cover for terms.

205

moral case study for discussion: designer babies and tissue typing," Reproductive BioMedicine Online 2004 October; 9(4): 372.

Spriggs, M. Is conceiving a child to benefit another against the interests of the new child? *Journal of Medical Ethics* 2005 June; 31(6): 341-342. NRCBL: 15.2; 14.4; 19.4.

Abstract: Conceiving a child by way of embryo selection and tissue matching to benefit a sick sibling is generally justified on the grounds that as well as the potential to save the sick child, there is a benefit for the new baby. The new baby is selected so he or she will not have the disease suffered by the first child. It is not possible, however, to select against conditions for which there is no test and Jamie Whitaker's birth is a case where the process of in vitro fertilisation with tissue matching is viewed as being of benefit only to a third party-the sick child. Some people object to using the technology for this purpose. There are also good reasons to argue that the technology should be used to save a sick child, and that it would be morally remiss for Jamie's parents not to consent to the use of his cord blood.

Stuck, Jamalynne; McElroy, Dough. Genetic counseling. *In:* Ness, Bryan D., ed. Encyclopedia of Genetics. Revised edition. Volume I. Pasadena, Calif.: Salem Press; 2004: 321-326. NRCBL: 15.2.

Sulmasy, Daniel P. Duty to warn about hereditary disease risks [letter]. *JAMA: The Journal of the American Medical Association* 2005 February 9; 293(6): 676. NRCBL: 15.2; 8.4.

Takeshita, Naoki; Kubo, Harumi. Regulating preimplantation genetic diagnosis — how to control PGD. *Journal of Assisted Reproduction and Genetics* 2004 January; 21(1): 19-25. NRCBL: 15.2; 14.4; 5.3; 8.3.1; 9.8. Identifiers: Japan.

Tsafrir, Avi; Shufaro, Yoel; Simon, Alex; Laufer, Neri. Preimplantation genetic diagnosis. *In:* Blazer, Shraga; Zimmer, Etan Z., eds. The Embryo: Scientific Discovery and Medical Ethics. New York: Karger; 2005: 166-201. NRCBL: 15.2; 14.3; 19.5.

van den Berg, Matthijs; Timmermans, Danielle R.M.; ten Kate, Leo P.; van Vugt, John M.G.; van der Wal, Gerrit. Are pregnant women making informed choices about prenatal screening? *Genetics in Medicine* 2005 May-June; 7(5): 332-338. NRCBL: 15.2; 9.5.5; 8.3.1. SC: em.

Venne, Vickie L.; Botkin, Jeffrey R.; Buys, Saundra S. Professional opportunities and responsibilities in the provision of genetic information to children relinquished for adoption. *American Journal of Medical Genetics* 2003 May 15; 119A(1): 41-46. NRCBL: 15.2; 8.4; 14.1. SC: cs.

Voelker, Rebecca. The business of baby pictures — controversy brews over "keepsake" fetal ultrasounds. *JAMA: The Journal of the American Medical Association* 2005 January 5; 293(1): 25-27. NRCBL: 15.2; 9.3.1; 9.5.8.

Waldschmidt, Anne. Who is normal? Who is deviant?: "normality" and "risk" in genetic diagnostics and counseling. *In:* Tremain, Shelley, ed. Foucault and the Government of Disability. Ann Arbor: University of Michigan Press; 2005: 191-207. NRCBL: 15.2; 4.2.

Ward, Linda. Whose right to choose?: the new genetics, prenatal testing and people living with learning difficulties. *In:* Bunton, Robin; Petersen, Alan, eds. Genetic Governance: Health, Risk and Ethics in the Biotech Era. New York: Routledge; 2005: 121-135. NRCBL: 15.2; 15.3; 9.5.1.

Wertz, Dorothy C. Ethical issues in the application of knowledge from molecular genetics to mental disorders. *In:* Bulyzhenkov, V.; Christen, Y.; Prilipko, L., eds. Genetic Approaches in the Prevention of Mental Disorders. New York: Springer-Verlag; 1990: 92-106. NRCBL: 15.2; 8.4; 9.3.1; 17.1. SC: em.

Wertz, Dorothy C.; Knoppers, Bartha Maria. Serious genetic disorders: can or should they be defined? *American Journal of Medical Genetics* 2002; 108: 29-35. NRCBL: 15.2; 8.2; 21.1. SC: em.

Wyszynski, Diego F.; Perandones, Claudia; Bennun, Ricardo D. Attitudes toward prenatal diagnosis, termination of pregnancy, and reproduction by parents of children with nonsyndromic oral clefts in Argentina. *Prenatal Diagnosis* 2003 September; 23(9): 722-727. NRCBL: 15.2; 12.1.

Zatz, Mayana. When science is not enough: fighting genetic disease in Brazil. *Science* 2005 April 1; 308(5718): 55-57. NRCBL: 15.2; 15.3; 18.5.4.

GENETIC RESEARCH
See also GENOME MAPPING; RECOMBINANT DNA RESEARCH

Beyond the yuck factor: revulsion isn't reason enough to close the door on controversial research [editorial]. *New Scientist* 2005 June 25-July 1; 186(2505): 5. NRCBL: 15.1; 22.1.

Anderlik, Mary R. Commercial biobanks and genetics research: banking without checks? *In:* Knoppers, Bartha Maria, ed. Populations and Genetics: Legal and Socio-Ethical Perspectives. Boston: Martinus Nijhoff; 2003: 345-376. NRCBL: 15.1; 1.3.12; 9.3.1. SC: em.

Brunger, Fern. Problematizing the notion of "community" in research ethics. *In:* Knoppers, Bartha Maria, ed. Populations and Genetics: Legal and Socio-Ethical Perspectives. Boston: Martinus Nijhoff; 2003: 245-255. NRCBL: 15.1.

Cyranoski, David. Japan's laws on recombinant DNA tie researchers' hands [news]. *Nature Medicine* 2004 June; 10(6): 557. NRCBL: 15.1. SC: le.

Davis, Dena S. Genetic research and communal narratives. *Hastings Center Report* 2004 July-August; 34(4): 40-49. NRCBL: 15.1; 15.11; 18.3.

Elger, B.; Mauron, A. A presumed-consent model for regulating informed consent of genetic research involving DNA banking. *In:* Knoppers, Bartha Maria, ed. Populations and Genetics: Legal and Socio-Ethical Perspectives. Boston: Martinus Nijhoff; 2003: 269-295. NRCBL: 15.1; 1.3.12. SC: an.

Fine, Michael J.; Ibrahim, Said A.; Thomas, Stephen B. The role of race and genetics in health disparities research [editorial]. *American Journal of Public Health* 2005 December; 95(12): 2125- 2128. NRCBL: 15.1; 9.5.4; 3.1.

Foster, Morris W.; Freeman, William L. Naming names in human genetic variation research. *Genome Research* 1998 August; 8(8): 755-757. NRCBL: 15.1; 8.4; 1.3.12.

Grizzle, William; Grody, Wayne W.; Noll, Walter W.; Sobel, Mark E.; Stass, Sanford A.; Trainer, Thomas; Travers, Henry; Weedn, Victor; Woodruff, Kay. Recommended policies for uses of human tissue in research, education, and quality control. *Archives of Pathology and Laboratory Medicine* 1999 April; 123(4): 296-300. NRCBL: 15.1; 18.1; 19.5; 18.3; 8.4. Identifiers: College of American Pathologists Ad Hoc Committee on Stored Tissues.

Guttmacher, Alan E.; Collins, Francis S. Realizing the promise of genomics in biomedical research. *JAMA: The Journal of the American Medical Association* 2005 September 21; 294(11): 1399-1402. NRCBL: 15.1; 1.3.9.

Hansson, Mats G. Building on relationships of trust in biobank research. *Journal of Medical Ethics* 2005 July; 31(7): 415-418. NRCBL: 15.1; 1.3.12; 18.3.

Abstract: Trust among current and future patients is essential for the success of biobank research. The submission of an informed consent is an act of trust by a patient or a research subject, but a strict application of the rule of informed consent may not be sensitive to the multiplicity of patient interests at stake, and could thus be detrimental to trust. According to a recently proposed law on "genetic integrity" in Sweden, third parties will be prohibited from requesting or seeking genetic information about an individual. Cumbersome restrictions on research may be lifted, thus creating a more favourable climate for medical research.

Helgesson, Gert; Johnsson, Linus. The right to withdraw consent to research on biobank samples. *Medicine, Health Care and Philosophy: A European Journal* 2005; 8(3): 315-321. NRCBL: 15.1; 1.3.12; 18.3.

Abstract: Ethical guidelines commonly state that research subjects should have a right to withdraw consent to participate. According to the guidelines we have studied, this right applies also to research on biological samples. However, research conducted on human subjects themselves differs in important respects from research on biological samples. It is therefore not obvious that the same rights should be granted research participants in the two cases. This paper investigates arguments for and against granting a right to withdraw consent to research on biobank samples. We conclude that (1) there are no explicit ar-

guments for such a right in the guidelines we have studied, (2) the arguments against such a right are inconclusive, (3) considerations of autonomy, privacy, personal integrity, and trust in medical research provide sufficient reasons for granting a right to withdraw consent to research on biobank samples, (4) in certain cases, research participants should be allowed to waive this right.

Hoeyer, Klaus. The role of ethics in commercial genetic research: notes on the notion of commodification. *Medical Anthropology* 2005 January-March; 24(1): 45-70. NRCBL: 15.1; 1.3.9; 9.3.1. SC: an. Identifiers: Sweden.

Hoeyer, Klaus; Olofsson, Bert-Ove; Mjörndal, Tom; Lynöe, Niels. The ethics of research using biobanks. *Archives of Internal Medicine* 2005 January 10; 165(1): 97-100. NRCBL: 15.1; 1.3.12; 8.3.1; 19.4; 19.5. SC: em.

Høyer, Klaus. Conflicting notions of personhood in genetic research. *Anthropology Today* 2002 October; 18(5): 9-13. NRCBL: 15.1; 4.4; 1.3.12; 1.3.2.

Juengst, Eric T. Community engagement in genetic research: the "slow code" of research ethics? *In:* Knoppers, Bartha Maria, ed. Populations and Genetics: Legal and Socio-Ethical Perspectives. Boston: Martinus Nijhoff; 2003: 181-197. NRCBL: 15.1; 5.1.

Karpowicz, Phillip; Cohen, Cynthia B.; van der Kooy, Derek. Developing human-nonhuman chimeras in human stem cell research: ethical issues and boundaries. *Kennedy Institute of Ethics Journal* 2005 June; 15(2): 107-134. NRCBL: 15.1; 18.1; 22.1; 1.1; 4.4; 18.5.4.

Abstract: The transplantation of adult human neural stem cells into prenatal non-humans offers an avenue for studying human neural cell development without direct use of human embryos. However, such experiments raise significant ethical concerns about mixing human and nonhuman materials in ways that could result in the development of human-nonhuman chimeras. This paper examines four arguments against such research, the moral taboo, species integrity, "unnaturalness," and human dignity arguments, and finds the last plausible. It argues that the transfer of human brain or retinal stem cells to nonhuman embryos would not result in the development of human-nonhuman chimeras that denigrate human dignity, provided such stem cells are dissociated. The article provides guidelines that set ethical boundaries for conducting such research that are consonant with the requirements of human dignity.

Kirsh, Nurit. Genetic research on Israel's populations: two opposite tendencies. *In:* Roelcke, Volker; Maio, Giovanni, eds. Twentieth Century Ethics of Human Subjects Research: Historical Perspectives on Values, Practices, and Regulations. Stuttgart: Franz Steiner Verlag; 2004: 309-317. NRCBL: 15.1; 15.11.

Kissell, Judith Lee. "Suspended animation," my mother's wife and cultural discernment: considerations for genetic research among immigrants. *Theoretical Medicine and Bioethics* 2005; 26(6): 515-528. NRCBL: 15.1; 21.7; 18.5.1.

Abstract: One of the most difficult contemporary issues facing the bioethics of clinical research is balancing the maintaining of a universality of ethics standards with a sensitivity to cultural is-

NRCBL: National Reference Center for Bioethics Literature Classification Scheme   See inside front cover for terms.

207

sues and differences. The concept of "vulnerability" for research subjects is especially apt for investigating the ethical and cultural issues surrounding the conduct of genetic research among new immigrants to the United States, using the Sudanese Nuer and Dinka tribes, recently settled in the Midwest, as an example. Issues of cultural vulnerability arise for some immigrants, related to relationship to the earth and to kinship issues, that threaten the narrative richness of a subject's life as well as the way she situates herself in the world.

Knoppers, Bartha Maria; Chadwick, Ruth. Human genetic research: emerging trends in ethics [opinion]. *Nature Reviews Genetics* 2005 January; 6(1): 75-79. NRCBL: 15.1; 15.3; 2.1. SC: an.

Koay, Pei P. An Icelandic (ad-)venture: new research? new subjects? new ethics? *In:* Roelcke, Volker; Maio, Giovanni, eds. Twentieth Century Ethics of Human Subjects Research: Historical Perspectives on Values, Practices, and Regulations. Stuttgart: Franz Steiner Verlag; 2004: 335-348. NRCBL: 15.1; 1.3.12.

Kothari, Manu; Mehta, Lopa. The cloning bandwagon: current discussion on the ethical consequences of genetic research is misplaced [opinion]. *Issues in Medical Ethics* 1998 January; 6(1): 17-19. NRCBL: 15.1; 14.5.

Machado, Nora; Burns, Tom R. The new genetics: a social science and humanities research agenda. *Canadian Journal of Sociology/Cahiers Canadiens de Sociologie* 2000 Autumn; 25(4): 495-506. NRCBL: 15.1; 15.3. SC: le. Identifiers: Sweden.

Majumder, Mary Anderlik. Cyberbanks and other virtual research repositories. *Journal of Law, Medicine and Ethics* 2005 Spring; 33(1): 31-39. NRCBL: 15.1; 1.3.12; 8.4; 18.3.

Merz, Jon F. On the intersection of privacy, consent, commerce and genetics research. *In:* Knoppers, Bartha Maria, ed. Populations and Genetics: Legal and Socio-Ethical Perspectives. Boston: Martinus Nijhoff; 2003: 257-268. NRCBL: 15.1; 1.3.12; 1.1; 9.3.1.

Møldrup, Claus. Medical technology assessment of the ethical, social, and legal implications of pharmacogenomics: a research proposal for an Internet citizen jury. *International Journal of Technology Assessment in Health Care* 2002 Summer; 18(3): 728-732. NRCBL: 15.1; 9.7; 5.3; 7.1. SC: em.

Rawle, Frances C. UK DNA sample collections for research. *In:* Knoppers, Bartha Maria, ed. Populations and Genetics: Legal and Socio-Ethical Perspectives. Boston: Martinus Nijhoff; 2003: 3-15. NRCBL: 15.1; 1.3.12.

Reymond, M.A.; Steinert, R.; Escourrou, J.; Fourtanier, G. Ethical, legal and economic issues raised by the use of human tissue in postgenomic research. *Digestive Diseases* 2002; 20: 257-265. NRCBL: 15.1; 19.5; 1.3.12; 21.1. SC: le.

Richards, Martin. Attitudes to genetic research and uses of genetic information support: concerns and genetic discrimination. *In:* Knoppers, Bartha Maria, ed. Populations and Genetics: Legal and Socio-Ethical Perspectives. Boston: Martinus Nijhoff; 2003: 567-578. NRCBL: 15.1; 5.1. SC: em.

Roberts, Laura Weiss; Warner, Teddy D.; Geppert, Cynthia M.A.; Rodgers, Melinda; Hammond, Katherine A. Green. Employees' perspectives on ethically important aspects of genetic research participation: a pilot study. *Comprehensive Psychiatry* 2005; 46: 27-33. NRCBL: 15.1; 16.3; 18.1. SC: em.

Schroeder, Doris; Ladikas, Miltos; Schuklenk, Udo; Diáz, Carolina Lasén; Kleinsmidt, Anita; Alvarez-Castillo, Fatima; Feinholz, Dafna. Sharing the benefits of genetic research: will the World Trade Organization act to stop the exploitation of biodiversity? [editorial]. *BMJ: British Medical Journal* 2005 December 10; 331(7529): 1351-1352. NRCBL: 15.1; 21.1; 15.8.

Wendler, David; Pace, Christine; Talisuna, Ambrose O.; Maiso, Faustine; Grady, Christine; Emanuel, Ezekiel. Research on stored biological samples: the views of Ugandans. *IRB: Ethics and Human Research* 2005 March-April; 27(2): 1-5. NRCBL: 15.1; 1.3.12; 18.1; 21.1; 18.3; 19.5. SC: em.

GENETIC SCREENING
See also DNA FINGERPRINTING; GENETIC COUNSELING; GENOME MAPPING

'Are you Jewish?' [news]. *New Scientist* 2005 July 9-15; 187(2507): 7. NRCBL: 15.3; 15.8; 9.5.4. Identifiers: Jews; Myriad Genetics.

Gene patent fight [news]. *New Scientist* 2005 June 25-July 1; 186(2505): 7. NRCBL: 15.3; 5.3; 9.5.4. Identifiers: Europe; Jews; Myriad Genetics.

Getting a grip on genetic testing [editorial]. *Nature Medicine* 2003 February; 9(2): 147. NRCBL: 15.3; 9.7.

Adams, Karen; Cain, Joanna M. The genetic revolution: new ethical issues for obstetrics and gynaecology. *Best Practice and Research in Clinical Obstetrics and Gynaecology* 2002 October; 16(5): 745-756. NRCBL: 15.3; 15.2; 14.4.

Akinwunmi, Oluwatoyin O. Genetic screening. *In:* Ness, Bryan D., ed. Encyclopedia of Genetics. Revised edition. Volume I. Pasadena, Calif.: Salem Press; 2004: 357-360. NRCBL: 15.3.

Akinwunmi, Oluwatoyin O. Genetic testing. *In:* Ness, Bryan D., ed. Encyclopedia of Genetics. Revised edition. Volume I. Pasadena, Calif.: Salem Press; 2004: 360-364. NRCBL: 15.3.

Aldhous, Peter. Victims of genetic discrimination speak up [news]. *New Scientist* 2005 November 5-11; 188(2524): 7. NRCBL: 15.3. SC: em. Identifiers: Genetic Discrimination Project (Australia).

Alex, April. Genetic discrimination: health insurance for the genetically lucky and the genetically unlucky. *Medical Trial Technique Quarterly* 2004; 50(3): 173-198. NRCBL: 15.3; 9.3.1; 8.4; 5.3; 1.1. SC: le.

Alper, Joseph S. Beyond genetic anti-discrimination legislation. *In:* Krimsky, Sheldon; Shorett, Peter, eds. Rights and Liberties in the Biotech Age: Why We Need a Genetic Bill of Rights. Lanham: Rowman and Littlefield Publishers; 2005: 167-172. NRCBL: 15.3. SC: le.

Ames, David A. The role of the church in the new genetics. *In:* Smith, David H.; Cohen, Cynthia B., eds. A Christian Response to the New Genetics: Religious, Ethical, and Social Issues. Lanham, MD: Rowman & Littlefield Publishers; 2003: 169-183. NRCBL: 15.3; 1.2.

Anido, Aimee; Carlson, Lisa M.; Taft, Lisa; Sherman, Stephanie L. Women's attitudes toward testing for fragile X carrier status: a qualitative analysis. *Journal of Genetic Counseling* 2005 August; 14(4): 295-306. NRCBL: 15.3; 15.2. SC: em.

Bayley, Carol. Cancer and genetic medicine: an ethical view. *Health Progress* 2005 September-October; 86(5): 35-37. NRCBL: 15.3; 15.1; 9.5.1; 8.4.

Beard, Tika. Advocate participation in the context of genetic testing for hereditary cancers. *Journal of the National Cancer Institute Monographs* 1995; (17): 123-124. NRCBL: 15.3; 9.1; 8.1; 9.5.1.

Beckman, Ludvig. Democracy and genetic privacy: the value of bodily integrity. *Medicine, Health Care and Philosophy: A European Journal* 2005; 8(1): 97-103. NRCBL: 15.3; 8.4; 21.7. SC: an.

Abstract: The right to genetic privacy is presently being incorporated in legal systems all over the world. It remains largely unclear however what interests and values this right serves to protect. There are many different arguments made in the literature, yet none takes into account the problem of how particular values can be justified given the plurality of moral and religious doctrines in our societies. In this article theories of public reason are used in order to explore how genetic privacy could be justified in a way that is sensitive to the "fact of pluralism". The idea of public reason is specified as the idea that governments should appeal only to values and beliefs that are acceptable to all reasonable citizens in the justification of rights. In examining prevalent arguments for genetic privacy—based on the value of autonomy or on the value of intimacy—it is concluded that they do not meet this requirement. In dealing with this deficiency in the literature, an argument is developed that genetic privacy is fundamental to the democratic participation of all citizens. By referring to the preconditions of democratic citizenship, genetic privacy can be justified in a way that respects the plurality of comprehensive doctrines of morality and religion in contemporary societies.

Bennet, Tierney. Fundamental problems and solutions concerning genetic testing (2nd part). *Alpha Omega* 2002 December; 5(3): 473-497. NRCBL: 15.3; 1.1; 8.3.1; 8.4; 15.2.

Berg, Kåre; Pettersson, Ulf; Riis, Povl; Tranøy, Knut Erik. Genetics in democratic societies — the Nordic perspective. *Clinical Genetics* 1995 October; 48(4): 199-208. NRCBL: 15.3; 1.1; 9.1; 8.3.1; 21.1.

Berry, P.J. Incidental diagnosis of genetic disease at autopsy — a point of view [editorial]. *Pediatric and Developmental Pathology* 1999 September-October; 2(5): 399-401. NRCBL: 15.3; 20.1; 8.2; 8.3.1.

Beskow, Laura M.; Gwinn, Marta; Rothstein, Mark A. Integrating genomics into public health policy and practice. *In:* Goodman, Richard A.; Rothstein, Mark A.; Hoffman, Richard E.; Lopez, Wilfredo; Matthews, Gene W., eds. Law in Public Health Practice. New York: Oxford University Press; 2003: 245-261. NRCBL: 15.3; 9.1. SC: le.

Biesecker, Leslie G. Surrendered autonomy for genetic screening [editorial]. *American Journal of Medical Genetics* 2004 August 30; 129A(2): 165. NRCBL: 15.3; 1.1; 9.1.

Black, Charles. Genetic information and insurance: some issues. *In:* Knoppers, Bartha Maria, ed. Populations and Genetics: Legal and Socio-Ethical Perspectives. Boston: Martinus Nijhoff; 2003: 579-590. NRCBL: 15.3; 9.3.1.

Bondy, Melissa; Mastromarino, Carrie. Ethical issues of genetic testing and their implications in epidemiologic studies. *Annals of Epidemiology* 1997 July; 7(5): 363-366. NRCBL: 15.3; 7.1; 8.3.1.

Bosek, Marcia Sue DeWolf. Commentary on genetic testing of children: maintaining an open future. *Pediatric Nursing* 1999 January-February; 25(1): 66-68. NRCBL: 15.3; 9.5.7; 8.3.2.

Brock, Dan W. Preventing genetically transmitted disabilities while respecting persons with disabilities. *In:* Wasserman, David; Bickenbach, Jerome; Wachbroit, Robert, eds. Quality of Life and Human Difference: Genetic Testing, Health Care, and Disability. New York: Cambridge University Press; 2005: 67-100. NRCBL: 15.3; 4.4; 1.1; 9.4. SC: an.

Burke, Wylie; Zimmern, Ron L. Ensuring the appropriate use of genetic tests. *Nature Reviews Genetics* 2004 December; 5(12): 955-959. NRCBL: 15.3; 5.3. SC: le.

Burroughs, A. Maxwell. The medical examination in United States immigration applications: the potential use of genetic testing leads to heightened privacy concerns. *Journal of Biolaw and Business* 2005; 8(4): 22-32. NRCBL: 15.3; 8.4; 18.5.9; 15.10; 1.3.12; 13.1. SC: le.

Byk, Christian. Nationale Modelle zur Regelung des Gebrauchs der Gendiagnostik. Frankreich: Ist legislativer

NRCBL: National Reference Center for Bioethics Literature Classification Scheme   See inside front cover for terms.

209

Prinzipalismus eine illusorische und abwegige Politik? *In:* Honnefelder, Ludger; Mieth, Dietmar; Propping, Peter; Siep, Ludwig; Wiesemann, Claudia, eds. Das genetische Wissen und die Zukunft des Menschen. New York: De Gruyter; 2003: 286-298. NRCBL: 15.3; 5.3. SC: le.

Calvo, Cheye; Jones, Jennifer. Protecting genetic information. *Legisbrief* 2000 June-July; 8(28): 1-2. NRCBL: 15.3; 1.3.12; 5.3; 8.4. SC: le. Note: National Conference of Sate Legislature.

Campbell, Elizabeth; Ross, Lainie Friedman. Parental attitudes and beliefs regarding the genetic testing of children. *Community Genetics* 2005 May; 8(2): 94-102. NRCBL: 15.3; 9.5.7; 8.3.2.

Carnovale, Benjamin V.; Clanton, Mark S. Genetic testing: issues related to privacy, employment, and health insurance. *Cancer Practice* 2002 March-April; 10(2): 102-104. NRCBL: 15.3; 8.4; 9.3.1.

Catz, Diana S.; Green, Nancy S.; Tobin, Jonathan N.; Lloyd- Puryear, Michele A.; Kyler, Penny; Umemoto, Ann; Cernoch, Jennifer; Brown, Roxane; Wolman, Fredericka. Attitudes about genetics in underserved, culturally diverse populations. *Community Genetics* 2005 August; 8(3): 161-172. NRCBL: 15.3; 15.1; 9.5.4. SC: em.

Caulfield, Timothy; Hirtle, Marie. Regulating the genetic revolution [opinion]. *Molecular Medicine Today* 1999 May; 5(5): 198-200. NRCBL: 15.3; 5.3; 1.3.5.

Caulfield, Timothy A.; Gold, E. Richard. Genetic testing, ethical concerns, and the role of patent law. *Clinical Genetics* 2000; 57(5): 370-375. NRCBL: 15.3; 15.8. SC: le.

Chadwick, Ruth; Ngwena, Charles. The Human Genome Project, predictive testing and insurance contracts: ethical and legal responses. *Res Publica* 1995; 1(2): 115-129. NRCBL: 15.3; 9.3.1; 15.10. SC: le.

Chapman, Elizabeth. Perceptions of the body and genetic risk. *In:* Bainham, Andrew; Sclater, Shelley Day; Richards, Martin, eds. Body Lore and Laws. Portland, OR: Hart Pub.; 2002: 309-328. NRCBL: 15.3; 15.2; 4.4.

Check, Erika. Biologists forced to reassess embryo test [news]. *Nature* 2005 October 20; 437(7062): 1075. NRCBL: 15.3; 14.4.

Cline, Heather S. Genetic testing of children: an issue of ethical and legal concern. *Pediatric Nursing* 1999 January-February; 25(1): 61-62, 65, 68. NRCBL: 15.3; 9.5.7; 8.4; 9.3.1.

Crabb, Jennifer A.; Tucker, Diane C.; Mun, Eun Young. The effect of preventability and severity levels of a genetic disorder on desire to communicate genetic testing information to family members. *Genetic Testing* 2005 Winter; 9(4): 320-327. NRCBL: 15.3; 8.2; 9.1. SC: em.

Dalpé, Robert; Bouchard, Louise; Houle, Anne-Julie; Bédard, Louis. Watching the race to find the breast cancer genes. *Science, Technology, and Human Values* 2003 Spring; 28(2): 187- 216. NRCBL: 15.3; 1.3.9; 15.8; 1.3.2.

Damm, Reinhard. Prädiktive genetische Tests: Gesellschaftliche Folgen und rechtlicher Schutz der Persönlichkeit. *In:* Honnefelder, Ludger; Mieth, Dietmar; Propping, Peter; Siep, Ludwig; Wiesemann, Claudia, eds. Das genetische Wissen und die Zukunft des Menschen. New York: De Gruyter; 2003: 203-228. NRCBL: 15.3. SC: le.

Dennis, Carina. Rugby team converts to give gene tests a try [news]. *Nature* 2005 March 17; 434(7031): 260. NRCBL: 15.3; 9.5.1. Identifiers: Australia.

Deschênes, Mylène. Optimizing safety and benefits of genetic testing: a look at the Canadian policy. *In:* Brannigan, Michael C., ed. Cross-Cultural Biotechnology. Lanham: Rowman and Littlefield; 2004: 57-70. NRCBL: 15.3. SC: le.

Di Pietro, M.L.; Giuli, A.; Spagnolo, A.G. Ethical implications of predictive DNA testing for hereditary breast cancer. *Annals of Oncology* 2004; 15(Supplement 1): I65-I70. NRCBL: 15.3; 9.5.5; 15.2.

Draper, Elaine. The screening of America: the social and legal framework of employers' use of genetic information. *Berkeley Journal of Employment and Labor Law* 1999; 20(2): 286-324. NRCBL: 15.3; 16.3; 8.4; 9.3.2; 9.3.1. SC: le.

Duncan, Rony E. Predictive genetic testing in young people: when is it appropriate? *Journal of Paediatrics and Child Health* 2004 November; 40(11): 593-595. NRCBL: 15.3; 9.5.7; 8.3.3; 8.4.

Duncan, Rony E.; Savulescu, Julian; Gillam, Lynn; Williamson, Robert; Delatycki, Martin B. An international survey of predictive genetic testing in children for adult onset conditions. *Genetics in Medicine* 2005 July-August; 7(6): 390-396. NRCBL: 15.3; 9.5.7; 21.1; 9.8. SC: em.

Ensenauer, Regina E.; Michels, Virginia V.; Reinke, Shanda S. Genetic testing: practical, ethical, and counseling considerations. *Mayo Clinic Proceedings* 2005 January; 80(1): 63-73. NRCBL: 15.3; 15.2; 1.1. SC: cs.

Estonia. Parliament. Human Genes Research Act [passed 2000 December 13]. Tallinn, Estonia: Riigi Teataja [State Gazette] I 2000, 104, 68.5, Legislation; 14 p. [Online]. Available: http://www.legaltext.ee/et/andmebaas/tekst.asp?dok=X50010&keel=en [22 July 2005]. NRCBL: 15.3; 1.3.12; 8.4. SC: le. Note: Effective date: 2001 January 8.

Ettorre, Elizabeth. The sociology of the new genetics: conceptualizing the links between reproduction, gender and bodies. *In:* Bunton, Robin; Petersen, Alan, eds. Genetic Governance: Health, Risk and Ethics in the Biotech Era. New York: Routledge; 2005: 107-120. NRCBL: 15.3; 15.2; 4.4; 10. SC: em.

Farkas, Daniel H.; Goerl, Hans S.; Hyer, Randall N. Genetic privacy legislation: two views. *Molecular Diagnosis* 1997 March; 2(1): 83-87. NRCBL: 15.3; 8.4; 1.3.5; 5.3.

French, Kyle G. The elderly and the discriminatory use of genetic information. *Elder Law Journal* 1997 Spring; 5(1); 29 p. [Online]. Available: http://web.lexis-nexis.com/universe/printdoc [22 July 2005]. NRCBL: 15.3; 9.5.2; 9.3.1. SC: le.

Friedman-Ross, Lainie. The ethics of newborn screening diabetes research. *In:* Kodish, Eric, ed. Ethics and Research with Children: A Case-Based Approach. New York: Oxford University Press; 2005: 123- 142. NRCBL: 15.3; 18.5.2.

Fukushima, Yoshimitsu; Sakurai, Akihiro. Comprehensive genetics clinic for familial tumors: proposal for a suitable system in Japan. *International Journal of Clinical Oncology* 2004 August; 9(4): 304-307. NRCBL: 15.3; 15.2. SC: cs.

Geller, Gail. The ethics of predictive genetic testing in prevention trials involving adolescents. *In:* Kodish, Eric, ed. Ethics and Research with Children: A Case-Based Approach. New York: Oxford University Press; 2005: 194-220. NRCBL: 15.3; 15.1; 15.6.

Geller, Lisa N.; Alper, Joseph S.; Billings, Paul R.; Barash, Carol I.; Beckwith, Jonathan; Natowicz, Marvin R. Individual, family, and societal dimensions of genetic discrimination: a case study analysis. *Science and Engineering Ethics* 1996; 2(1): 71-88. NRCBL: 15.3; 9.3.1; 19.4.

Glantz, Leonard H. Keeping genetic secrets. *Medical Ethics Newsletter [Lahey Clinic]* 2004 Winter; 11(1): 4, 11. NRCBL: 15.3; 8.4. SC: le.

Gollust, Sarah E.; Apse, Kira; Fuller, Barbara P.; Miller, Paul Steven; Biesecker, Barbara B. Community involvement in developing policies for genetic testing: assessing the interests and experiences of individuals affected by genetic conditions. *American Journal of Public Health* 2005 January; 95(1): 35-41. NRCBL: 15.3; 9.1.

Abstract: Because the introduction of genetic testing into clinical medicine and public health creates concerns for the welfare of individuals affected with genetic conditions, those individuals should have a role in policy decisions about testing. Mechanisms for promoting participation range from membership on advisory committees to community dialogues to surveys that provide evidence for supporting practice guidelines.Surveys can assess the attitudes and the experiences of members of an affected group and thus inform discussions about that community's concerns regarding the appropriate use of a genetic test. Results of a survey of individuals affected with inherited dwarf-ism show how data can be used in policy and clinical-practice contexts.Future research of affected communities' interests should be pursued so that underrepresented voices can be heard.

Great Britain. Human Genetics Commission. Profiling the newborn: a prospective gene technology? London: Human Genetics Commission 2005 March; 41 p. [Online]. Available: http://www.hgc.gov.uk/UploadDocs/Contents/Documents/Final%20Draft %20of%20Profiling%20 Newborn%20Report%2003%205.pdf [8 July 2005]. NRCBL: 15.3; 5.3; 9.5.7. Note: A report from a Joint Working Group of the Human Genetics Commission and the UK National Screening Committee.

Haker, Hille. Genetische Diagnostik und die Entwicklung von Gentests: Reflexionen zur ethischen Urteilsbildung. *In:* Honnefelder, Ludger; Mieth, Dietmar; Propping, Peter; Siep, Ludwig; Wiesemann, Claudia, eds. Das genetische Wissen und die Zukunft des Menschen. New York: De Gruyter; 2003: 186-202. NRCBL: 15.3.

Hall, Mark A.; McEwen, Jean E.; Barton, James C.; Walker, Ann P.; Howe, Edmund G.; Reiss, Jacob A.; Power, Tara E.; Ellis, Shellie D.; Tucker, Diane C.; Harrison, Barbara W.; McLaren, Gordon D.; Ruggiero, Andrea; Thomson, Elizabeth J. Concerns in a primary care population about genetic discrimination by insurers. *Genetics in Medicine* 2005 May-June; 7(5): 311-316. NRCBL: 15.3; 9.3.1; 7.1; 9.5.2; 9.5.4. SC: em.

Hamilton, Rebekah J.; Bowers, Barbara J.; Williams, Janet K. Disclosing genetic test results to family members. *Journal of Nursing Scholarship* 2005; 37(1): 18-24. NRCBL: 15.3; 8.1; 8.2. SC: em. Identifiers: Huntington's disease; hereditary breast and ovarian cancer.

Harmon, Amy. The problem with an almost-perfect genetic world. *New York Times* 2005 November 20; p. WK1, WK14. NRCBL: 15.3; 15.2; 9.5.3. SC: po.

Harris, Marion; Winship, Ingrid; Spriggs, Merle. Controversies and ethical issues in cancer-genetics clinics. *Lancet Oncology* 2005 May; 6(5): 301-310. NRCBL: 15.3; 8.3.1; 9.3.1; 8.4; 8.2; 9.5.1. SC: le.

Hathaway, Katherine A. Federal genetic nondiscrimination legislation: the new "right" and the race to protect DNA at the local, state, and federal level. *Catholic University Law Review* 2002 Autumn; 52(1): 133-177. NRCBL: 15.3; 15.10; 8.4; 5.3; 16.3; 9.3.1. SC: le.

Heinrichs, Bert. What should we want to know about our future? A Kantian view on predictive genetic testing. *Medicine, Health Care and Philosophy: A European Journal* 2005; 8(1): 29-37. NRCBL: 15.3; 1.1. SC: an.

Abstract: Recent advances in genomic research have led to the development of new diagnostic tools, including tests which make it possible to predict the future occurrence of monogenetic diseases (e.g. Chorea Huntington) or to determine increased susceptibilities to the future development of more complex diseases (e.g. breast cancer). The use of such tests raises a number of ethical, legal and social issues which are usu-

NRCBL: National Reference Center for Bioethics Literature Classification Scheme   See inside front cover for terms.

211

ally discussed in terms of rights. However, in the context of predictive genetic tests a key question arises which lies beyond the concept of rights, namely, What should we want to know about our future? In the following I shall discuss this question against the background of Kant's Doctrine of Virtue. It will be demonstrated that the system of duties of virtue that Kant elaborates in the second part of his Metaphysics of Morals offers a theoretical framework for addressing the question of a proper scope of future knowledge as provided by genetic tests. This approach can serve as a source of moral guidance complementary to a justice perspective. It does, however, not rest on the-rather problematic—claim to be able to define what the "good life" is.

Heinrichs, Bert. Zur Regelungsbedürftigkeit prädiktiver genetischer Tests und zur normativen Kraft des Gesundheitsbegriffs. *In:* Jahrbuch für Wissenschaft und Ethik. Bd. 7. Berlin: Walter de Gruyter; 2002: 197-215. NRCBL: 15.3; 4.2. SC: le.

Hicken, Bret L.; Foshee, Aimee; Tucker, Diane C. Perceptions and attitudes about HFE genotyping among college-age adults. *Journal of Genetic Counseling* 2005 December; 14(6): 465-472. NRCBL: 15.3. SC: em.

Hoffmann, Diane E.; Rothenberg, Karen H. When should judges admit or compel genetic tests? *Science* 2005 October 14; 310(5746): 241-242. NRCBL: 15.3; 1.3.5. SC: le.

Hogben, Susan; Boddington, Paula. Policy recommendations for carrier testing and predictive testing in childhood: a distinction that makes a real difference. *Journal of Genetic Counseling* 2005 August; 14(4): 271-281. NRCBL: 15.3.

Horner, Sharon D. Ethics and genetics: implications for CNS practice. *Clinical Nurse Specialist* 2004 September-October; 18(5): 228-231. NRCBL: 15.3; 8.4. Identifiers: clinical nurse specialist.

Humphries, S.E.; Galton, D.; Nicholls, P. Genetic testing for familial hypercholesterolaemia: practical and ethical issues. *QJM: Monthly Journal of the Association of Physicians* 1997 March; 90(3): 169-181. NRCBL: 15.3; 9.5.1; 8.1.

Hunter, Alasdair G.W.; Sharpe, Neil; Mullen, Michelle; Meschino, Wendy S. Ethical, legal, and practical concerns about recontacting patients to inform them of new information: the case in medical genetics. *American Journal of Medical Genetics* 2001; 103: 265-276. NRCBL: 15.3; 8.1. SC: le; em.

Jennings, Bruce; Heitman, Elizabeth. Genetics and genetic technology in social context. *In:* Smith, David H.; Cohen, Cynthia B., eds. A Christian Response to the New Genetics: Religious, Ethical, and Social Issues. Lanham, MD: Rowman & Littlefield Publishers; 2003: 131-146. NRCBL: 15.3; 5.1.

Johnson, Summer; Kass, Nancy E.; Natowicz, Marvin. Disclosure of personal medical information: differences among parents and affected adults for genetic and nongenetic conditions. *Genetic Testing* 2005 Fall; 9(3): 269-280. NRCBL: 15.3; 8.4; 1.3.12. SC: em.

Jones, Shirley L.; Fallon, Lee A. Reproductive options for individuals at risk for transmission of a genetic disorder. *JOGNN: Journal of Obstetric, Gynecologic and Neonatal Nursing* 2002 March-April; 31(2): 193-199. NRCBL: 15.3; 14.4; 8.1; 7.1; 4.1.3.

Keogh, Louise A.; Southey, Melissa C.; Maskiell, Judi; Young, Mary-Anne; Gaff, Clara L.; Kirk, Judy; Tucker, Katherine M.; Rosenthal, Doreen; McCredie, Margaret R.E.; Giles, Graham G.; Hopper, John L. Uptake of offer to receive genetic information about BRCA1 and BRCA2 mutations in an Australian population-based study. *Cancer Epidemiology, Biomarkers and Prevention* 2004 December; 13(12): 2258-2263. NRCBL: 15.3. SC: em.

Kinney, Anita Yeomans; Choi, Yeon-Ah; DeVellis, Brenda; Millikan, Robert; Kobetz, Erin; Sandler, Robert S. Attitudes toward genetic testing in patients with colorectal cancer. *Cancer Practice* 2000 July-August; 8(4): 178-186. NRCBL: 15.3; 9.5.1; 17.1.

Knoppers, Bartha Maria. Duty to recontact: a legal harbinger? [editorial]. *American Journal of Medical Genetics* 2001 November 1; 103(4): 277. NRCBL: 15.3; 8.1. SC: le.

Knoppers, Bartha Maria; Isasi, Rosario M. Regulatory approaches to reproductive genetic testing [opinion]. *Human Reproduction* 2004 December; 19(12): 2695-2701. NRCBL: 15.3; 15.2; 9.6. SC: le.

Koch, Lene; Svendsen, Mette Nordahl. Providing solutions — defining problems: the imperative of disease prevention in genetic counselling. *Social Science and Medicine* 2005 February; 60(4): 823-832. NRCBL: 15.3; 15.2. SC: an.

Kolata, Gina. Panel to advise tests on babies for 29 diseases. *New York Times* 2005 February 21; p. A1, A14. NRCBL: 15.3. SC: po.

Kruip, Stephan. Prädiktive genetische Tests—Eine Stellungnahme aus der Patientenperspektive. *In:* Honnefelder, Ludger; Mieth, Dietmar; Propping, Peter; Siep, Ludwig; Wiesemann, Claudia, eds. Das genetische Wissen und die Zukunft des Menschen. New York: De Gruyter; 2003: 229-234. NRCBL: 15.3. SC: le.

LaRusse, Susan; Roberts, J. Scott; Marteau, Theresa M.; Katzen, Heather; Linnenbringer, Erin L.; Barber, Melissa; Whitehouse, Peter; Quaid, Kimberly; Brown, Tamsen; Green, Robert C.; Relkin, Norman R. Genetic susceptibility testing versus family history-based risk assessment: impact on perceived risk of Alzheimer disease. *Genetics in Medicine* 2005 January; 7(1): 48-53. NRCBL: 15.3; 17.1. SC: em.

Lee, Robert C.; Kmet, Leanne; Cook, Linda S.; Lorenzetti, Diane; Godlovitch, Glenys; Einsiedel, Edna. Risk assessment for inherited susceptibility to cancer: a review of the psychosocial and ethical dimensions. *Genetic Testing* 2005 Spring; 9(1): 66-79. NRCBL: 15.3; 4.4; 15.2; 9.3.1; 8.3.1; 9.5.4. SC: em.

Leib, Jennifer R.; Gollust, Sarah E.; Hull, Sara Chandros; Wilfond, Benjamin S. Carrier screening panels for Ashkenazi Jews: is more better? *Genetics in Medicine* 2005 March; 7(3): 185-190. NRCBL: 15.3; 9.8; 7.1. SC: em.

Lemke, Thomas. From eugenics to the government of genetic risks. *In:* Bunton, Robin; Petersen, Alan, eds. Genetic Governance: Health, Risk and Ethics in the Biotech Era. New York: Routledge; 2005: 95-105. NRCBL: 15.3; 15.5.

Lerman, Caryn; Shields, Alexandra E. Genetic testing for cancer susceptibility: the promise and the pitfalls [opinion]. *Nature Reviews Cancer* 2004 March; 4(3): 235-241. NRCBL: 15.3.

Levine, David Z.; Kielstein, Rita; Sass, Hans-Martin; Wesson, Donald E.; Oberbauer, Rainer; Kurtzman, Neil A.; Aufricht, Christoph; Muehlbacher, Ferdinand; Laski, Melvin; Mannhalter, Christine; Hörl, Walter; Druml, Christiane; Jones, Brent. Genetics in kidney disease: how much do we want to know? *American Journal of Kidney Diseases* 2002 March; 39(3): 637-652. NRCBL: 15.3; 19.3; 8.1; 8.3.1; 15.2.

Levin-Epstein, Michael. Time to decipher legislation's DNA. *Managed Care* 2005 April; 14(4): 29-30. NRCBL: 15.3; 1.3.12; 8.4; 9.3.1; 5.3. SC: le.

Liebman, Jerome. Some legal, social, and ethical issues related to the genetic testing revolution, as exemplified in the Long QT Syndrome. *Journal of Electrocardiology* 2001; 34 (Supplement): 183-188. NRCBL: 15.3; 7.1; 7.3. SC: le.

Lohr, Steve. IBM to put genetic data of workers off limits. *New York Times* 2005 October 10; p. C1, C4. NRCBL: 15.3; 5.3; 1.3.12; 1.3.2. SC: po.

Lovejoy, Wendy. Ending the genetic discrimination barrier: regaining confidence in preconception, prenatal, and neonatal genetic testing. *Southern California Law Review* 2001 March; 74(3): 873-911. NRCBL: 15.3; 9.5.8; 15.2. SC: le.

Lowrey, Kerri McGowan. Legal and ethical issues in cancer genetics nursing. *Seminars in Oncology Nursing* 2004 August; 20(3): 203-208. NRCBL: 15.3; 8.3.1; 8.4. SC: le.

Ludlam, Christopher A.; Pasi, K.J.; Bolton-Maggs, P.; Collins, P.W.; Cumming, A.M.; Dolan, G.; Fryer, A.; Harrington, C.; Hill, F.G.H.; Peake, I.R.; Perry, D.J.; Skirton, H.; Smith, M. A framework for genetic service provision for haemophilia and other inherited bleeding disorders. *Haemophilia* 2005 March; 11(2): 145-163. NRCBL: 15.3; 15.2; 9.5.1; 8.3.1; 8.4; 1.3.12. Identifiers: United Kingdom (Great Britain); UK Haemophilia Centre Doctors' Organisation.

Mallia, Pierre; ten Have, Henk A.M.J. Applying theological developments to bioethical issues such as genetic screening. *Ethics and Medicine* 2005 Summer; 21(2): 95-107. NRCBL: 15.3; 1.1; 1.2; 1.3.12; 8.3.1.

Mallia, Pierre; ten Have, Henk A.M.J. Pragmatic approaches to genetic screening. *Medicine, Health Care and Philosophy: A European Journal* 2005; 8(1): 69-77. NRCBL: 15.3; 15.2. SC: an.
Abstract: Pragmatic approaches to genetic testing are discussed and appraised. Whilst there are various schools of pragmatism, the Deweyan approach seems to be the most appreciated in bioethics as it allows a historical approach indebted to Hegel. This in turn allows the pragmatist to specify and balance principles in various contexts. There are problems with where to draw a line between what is referred to here as the micro- and macro-level of doing bioethics, unless one is simply to be classified as a principlist. Whilst most discussions on genetics occur at a macro level, most specifying must be done also at a micro level - the clinical encounter. Whilst pragmatism encourages us to understand better social and scientific factors and puts into perspective statements like 'playing God', doubts are raised about the 'consensus' process and how one can put aside fundamental values such as the moral status of the embryo on which there is general disagreement. If those doing pragmatism do not endorse these values, there seems to be little ground for process and compromise with those who do. It seems therefore that pragmatism cannot ignore values, even those which are not endorsed by everyone.

Mandavilli, Apoorva. Screen savers [news]. *Nature Medicine* 2005 October; 11(10): 1020-1021. NRCBL: 15.3; 9.5.7; 18.2. SC: le. Identifiers: neonatal genetic screening.

Mandl, Kenneth D.; Feit, Shlomit; Larson, Cecilia; Kohane, Isaac S. Newborn screening program practices in the United States: notification, research and consent. *Pediatrics* 2002 February; 109(2): 269-273. NRCBL: 15.3; 1.3.12; 8.3.2; 8.4; 9.5.7. SC: em.

Mannikko, Nancy Farm; Ness, Bryan D. Insurance. *In:* Ness, Bryan D., ed. Encyclopedia of Genetics. Revised edition. Volume II. Pasadena, Calif.: Salem Press; 2004: 471-474. NRCBL: 15.3; 9.3.1.

Markman, Maurie. Genetic discrimination arising from cancer risk assessments: a societal dilemma. *Cleveland Clinic Journal of Medicine* 2004 January; 71(1): 12, 15-18. NRCBL: 15.3; 9.3.1; 1.3.2.

Marris, Emma. Unchecked by government, genetic tests sell hope and hype [news]. *Nature Medicine* 2005 June; 11(6): 584. NRCBL: 15.3; 15.2; 5.3.

Matloff, Ellen T.; Shappell, Heather; Brierley, Karina; Bernhardt, Barbara A.; McKinnon, Wendy; Peshkin, Beth N. What would you do? Specialists' perspectives on cancer genetic testing, prophylactic surgery, and insurance

NRCBL: National Reference Center for Bioethics Literature Classification Scheme   See inside front cover for terms.

213

discrimination. *Journal of Clinical Oncology* 2000 June; 18(12); 17 p. [Online]. Available: http://gateway.ut.ovid.com/gw2/ovidweb.cgi [21 July 2005]. NRCBL: 15.3; 9.5.1; 9.3.1; 7.1.

Mayor, Susan. UK insurers postpone using predictive genetic testing until 2011 [news]. *BMJ: British Medical Journal* 2005 March 19; 330(7492): 617. NRCBL: 15.3; 9.3.1.

McMahan, Jeff. Causing disabled people to exist and causing people to be disabled. *Ethics: An International Journal of Social, Political, and Legal Philosophy* 2005 October; 116(1): 77-99. NRCBL: 15.3; 4.4; 15.2; 9.5.7; 9.5.1; 9.5.3. SC: an.

McMahan, Jeff. Preventing the existence of people with disabilities. *In:* Wasserman, David; Bickenbach, Jerome; Wachbroit, Robert, eds. Quality of Life and Human Difference: Genetic Testing, Health Care, and Disability. New York: Cambridge University Press; 2005: 142-171. NRCBL: 15.3; 4.4; 1.1; 9.5.3. SC: an.

Miesfeldt, Susan; Jones, Susan M.; Cohn, Wendy; Lippert, Marguerite; Haden, Kathleen; Turner, Beverly L.; Martin-Fries, Tracee; Clark, Stephanie M. Men's attitudes regarding genetic testing for hereditary prostate cancer risk. *Urology* 2000 January; 55(1): 46-50. NRCBL: 15.3; 9.5.1; 17.1.

Miller, Jennifer. Physician-patient confidentiality and familial access to genetic information. *Health Law Journal* 1994; 2: 141-158. NRCBL: 15.3; 8.4. SC: le.

Miller, Paul Steven. Analyzing genetic discrimination in the workplace. *In:* Krimsky, Sheldon; Shorett, Peter, eds. Rights and Liberties in the Biotech Age: Why We Need a Genetic Bill of Rights. Lanham: Rowman and Littlefield Publishers; 2005: 173-177. NRCBL: 15.3; 8.4; 16.3.

Millett, Christopher; Parker, M. Informed decision making for cancer screening — not all of the ethical issues have been considered [editorial]. *Cytopathology* 2003 February; 14(1): 3-4. NRCBL: 15.3; 8.3.1.

Mitchell, Peter. UK to regulate 'serious' genetic tests [news]. *Nature Medicine* 2003 March; 9(3): 250. NRCBL: 15.3; 9.7; 5.3.

Morrison, Patrick J. Insurance, unfair discrimination, and genetic testing. *Lancet* 2005 September 10-16; 366(9489): 877-880. NRCBL: 15.3; 9.3.1; 7.1.

Mouchawar, Judy; Hensley-Alford, Sharon; Laurion, Suzanne; Ellis, Jennifer; Kulchak-Rahm, Alanna; Finucane, Melissa L.; Meenan, Richard; Axell, Lisen; Pollack, Rebecca; Ritzwoller, Debra. Impact of direct-to-consumer advertising for hereditary breast cancer testing on genetic services at a managed care organization: a naturally-occurring experiment. *Genetics in Medicine*

2005 March; 7(3): 191-197. NRCBL: 15.3; 9.5.5; 9.5.1; 1.3.2; 9.3.2. SC: em.

Ness, Bryan D. Genetic testing: ethical and economic issues. *In his : Ness, Bryan D., ed. Encyclopedia of Genetics. Revised edition. Volume I. Pasadena, Calif.: Salem Press; 2004: 364-366. NRCBL: 15.3; 9.3.1.*

Nevada. Laws. An act relating to genetic information; providing that it is an unlawful employment practice for an employer, a labor organization or an employment agency to discriminate against a person based on genetic information; and providing other matters properly relating thereto [approved: 9 July 1999]. Nevada. Senate Bill No. 16, 1999 Statutes of Nevada, Chapter 551; 3 p. NRCBL: 15.3; 16.3; 1.3.5. SC: le.

Obinata, Naomi. Genetic screening and insurance: too valuable an underwriting tool to be banned from the system. *Santa Clara Computer and High Technology Law Journal* 1992; 8(1): 145- 167. NRCBL: 15.3; 9.3.1. SC: le.

Ojha, Rohit P.; Thertulien, Raymond. Health care policy issues as a result of the genetic revolution: implications for public health. *American Journal of Public Health* 2005 March; 95(3): 385-388. NRCBL: 15.3; 8.4; 15.8; 9.1. SC: le.

Abstract: The genetic revolution has spawned 4 distinct issues of universal importance to health care policy and society: genetic privacy, regulation and standardization of genetic tests, gene patenting, and education. Adequate policy advancements for these 4 areas are lacking. Stringent controls must be placed on individual health records to prevent their misuse. Genetic testing within the clinical setting should undergo thorough evaluation before it is implemented. Regulations are needed to prevent the monopolization of DNA sequences. Society and health care professionals must be educated about the scope of genetic testing because current trends indicate that genetic and molecular assessments are destined to become a routine component of health care.

Oliver, S.; Dezateux, C.; Kavanagh, J.; Lempert, T.; Stewart, R. Disclosing to parents newborn carrier status identified by routine blood spot screening. *Cochrane Library* 2004; (4): 14 p. [Online]. Available: http://www.mrw.interscience.wiley.com/cochrane/clsysrev/articles/CD003859/frame.html [19 July 2005]. NRCBL: 15.3; 8.2. SC: em.

Ossa, Diego F.; Towse, Adrian. Genetic screening, health care and the insurance industry. Should genetic information be made available to insurers? *European Journal of Health Economics* 2004 June; 5(2): 116-121. NRCBL: 15.3; 9.3.1. Identifiers: United Kingdom (Great Britain).

Patterson, Annette R.; Robinson, Linda D.; Naftalis, Elizabeth Z.; Haley, Barbara B.; Tomlinson, Gail E. Custodianship of genetic information: clinical challenges and professional responsibility. *Journal of Clinical Oncology* 2005 March 20; 23(9): 2100-2104. NRCBL: 15.3; 15.2; 8.4; 8.2. SC: cs.

Pelias, Mary Z. Genetic testing: who decides, who informs? [opinion]. *Children's Legal Rights Journal* 1998 Spring; 18(2): 43-46. NRCBL: 15.3; 9.5.7; 8.4. SC: le.

Pentz, Rebecca D.; Peterson, Susan K.; Watts, Beatty; Vernon, Sally W.; Lynch, Patrick M.; Koehly, Laura M.; Gritz, Ellen R. Hereditary nonpolyposis colorectal cancer family members' perceptions about the duty to inform and health professionals' role in disseminating genetic information. *Genetic Testing* 2005 Fall; 9(3): 261-268. NRCBL: 15.3; 8.3.1; 8.4; 1.3.12. SC: em.

Pesonen, Lorie M. Genetic screening: an employer's tool to differentiate or to discriminate? *Journal of Contemporary Health Law and Policy* 2002 Winter; 19(1): 187-223. NRCBL: 15.3; 16.3; 8.4. SC: le.

Polzer, Jessica. Choice as responsibility: genetic testing as citizenship through familial oblation and the management of risk. *In:* Bunton, Robin; Petersen, Alan, eds. Genetic Governance: Health, Risk and Ethics in the Biotech Era. New York: Routledge; 2005: 79-92. NRCBL: 15.3. SC: em.

Poutanen, Seppo. The first genetic screening in Finland: its execution, evaluation and some possible implications for liberal government. *In:* Bunton, Robin; Petersen, Alan, eds. Genetic Governance: Health, Risk and Ethics in the Biotech Era. New York: Routledge; 2005: 65-78. NRCBL: 15.3; 5.3.

Quick, John J. Genetic discrimination and the need for federal legislation. *Journal of Biolaw and Business* 2005; 8(1): 22-26. NRCBL: 15.3. SC: le.

Rawbone, Roger G. Future impact of genetic screening in occupational and environmental medicine. *Occupational and Environmental Medicine* 1999 November; 56: 721-724. NRCBL: 15.3; 16.1; 16.3.

Reusser, Ruth. Nationale Modelle zur Regelung des Gebrauchs der Gendiagnostik. Schweiz: Die schweizerische Rechtsordnung—Ein Beispiel für Regelungsansätze in Etappen. *In:* Honnefelder, Ludger; Mieth, Dietmar; Propping, Peter; Siep, Ludwig; Wiesemann, Claudia, eds. Das genetische Wissen und die Zukunft des Menschen. New York: De Gruyter; 2003: 237-243. NRCBL: 15.3; 5.3. SC: le.

Reynolds, P. Preston; Kamei, Robert K.; Sundquist, Janet; Khanna, Niharika; Palmer, Elissa J.; Palmer, Trish. Using the PRACTICE mnemonic to apply cultural competency to genetics in medical education and patient care. *Academic Medicine* 2005 December; 80(12): 1107-1113. NRCBL: 15.3; 21.7. SC: cs. Identifiers: prevalence, risk, attitude, communication, testing, investigation, consent, empowerment.

Rizzo, Robert F. Genetic testing and therapy: a pathway to progress and/or profit? *International Journal of Social Economics* 1999; 26(1-3); 18 p. [Online]. Available: http://proquest.umi.com/pqdlink?did=116352591&sid=9&Fmt=3&clientId=5604&RQT=309&VName=PQD [21 July 2005]. NRCBL: 15.3; 15.4; 9.3.1.

Roscam Abbing, Henriette D.C. Neonatal screening, new technologies, old and new legal concerns [editorial]. *European Journal of Health Law* 2004 June; 11(2): 129-137. NRCBL: 15.3; 15.2; 8.3.2. SC: le.

Rose, Abigail L.; Peters, Nikki; Shea, Judy A.; Armstrong, Katrina. Attitudes and misconceptions about predictive genetic testing for cancer risk. *Community Genetics* 2005 August; 8(3): 145-151. NRCBL: 15.3; 15.1; 9.3.1; 8.4. SC: em.

Rosen, Ami; Wallenstein, Sylvan; McGovern, Margaret M. Attitudes of pediatric residents toward ethical issues associated with genetic testing in children. *Pediatrics* 2002 August; 110(2): 360-363. NRCBL: 15.3; 7.2; 9.5.7.

Rosenthal, M. Sara; Pierce, Heather Hanson. Inherited medullary thyroid cancer and the duty to warn: revisiting Pate v. Threlkel in light of HIPAA. *Thyroid* 2005 February; 15(2): 140-145. NRCBL: 15.3; 9.5.1; 8.4. SC: le. Identifiers: Health Insurance Portability and Accountability Act of 1996.

Roses, Allen D. Genetic testing for Alzheimer disease: practical and ethical issues. *Archives of Neurology* 1997 October; 54(10): 1226-1229. NRCBL: 15.3; 9.5.2; 17.1.

Rothstein, Mark A. Genetic testing: employability, insurability, and health reform. *Journal of the National Cancer Institute Monographs* 1995; (17): 87-90. NRCBL: 15.3; 16.3; 9.3.1.

Salkovskis, Paul M.; Dennis, Ruth; Wroe, Abigail L. An experimental study of influences on the perceived likelihood of seeking genetic testing: "nondirectiveness" may be misleading. *Journal of Psychosomatic Research* 1999 November; 47(5): 439-447. NRCBL: 15.3; 9.4; 15.2.

Sanderson, Simon; Zimmern, Ron; Kroese, Mark; Higgins, Julian; Patch, Christine; Emery, Jon. How can the evaluation of genetic tests be enhanced? Lessons learned from the ACCE framework and evaluating genetic tests in the United Kingdom. *Genetics in Medicine* 2005 September; 7(7): 495-500. NRCBL: 15.3; 9.8. Identifiers: analytic validity, clinical validity, clinical utility and ethical, legal, and social issues.

Sandor, Judit. Personal identification and genetic fingerprinting: "secrets or lies.". *In:* Actes du Colloque International AMADE-UNESCO sur Bioethique et Droits de L'enfant (Monaco, 28-30 Avril 2000) = Proceedings of the International Symposium AMADE-UNESCO on Bioethics and the Rights of the Child (Monaco, 28-30 April 2000). Paris: UNESCO, Division des Sciences Humaines, de la Philosophie et de L'ethique des Sciences et des Technologies; 2001: 69-79. NRCBL: 15.3; 15.1; 14.2; 1.3.5.

NRCBL: National Reference Center for Bioethics Literature Classification Scheme   See inside front cover for terms.

215

Scott, Larry D. Ethical issues in genetic testing. *American Journal of Gastroenterology* 2004 October; 99(10): 1871-1873. NRCBL: 15.3. SC: cs.

Seel, Klaus-M. Zum Umgang mit Information, Tests und Diagnostik im Bereich der Humangenetik. Wie müsste eine Regelung aussehen, die auch in Zukunft Bestand haben soll? *In:* Jahrbuch für Wissenschaft und Ethik. Bd. 7. Berlin: Walter de Gruyter; 2002: 217-242. NRCBL: 15.3. SC: le.

Senior, Victoria; Marteau, Theresa M.; Peters, Timothy J. Will genetic testing for predisposition for disease result in fatalism? A qualitative study of parents responses to neonatal screening for familial hypercholesterolaemia. *Social Science and Medicine* 1999 June; 48(12): 1857-1860. NRCBL: 15.3; 9.1; 9.5.7; 17.1.

Setoyama, Koichi. Privacy of genetic information. *Osaka University Law Review* 2005 February; 52: 75-105. NRCBL: 15.3; 8.4; 1.3.12; 5.3; 15.10. SC: le.

Shakespeare, Tom. The social context of individual choice. *In:* Wasserman, David; Bickenbach, Jerome; Wachbroit, Robert, eds. Quality of Life and Human Difference: Genetic Testing, Health Care, and Disability. New York: Cambridge University Press; 2005: 217-236. NRCBL: 15.3; 12.3; 4.4.

Sheldon, Sally. Saviour siblings and the discretionary power of the HFEA: Quintavalle (on behalf of Comment on Reproductive Ethics) v. Human Fertilisation and Embryology Authority. *Medical Law Review* 2005 Autumn; 13(3): 403-411. NRCBL: 15.3; 4.4; 18.6; 1.1. SC: le.

Sheldon, Sally; Wilkinson, Stephen. Hashmi and Whitaker: an unjustifiable and misguided distinction? *Medical Law Review* 2004 Summer; 12(2): 137-163. NRCBL: 15.3; 14.4; 4.4; 19.5; 8.3.2; 18.6; 5.3. SC: le.

Simonstein, Frida. Genetic screening and reproductive choice: is making a child to save another unethical? *Medicine and Law: World Association for Medical Law* 2005 December; 24(4): 775-781. NRCBL: 15.3; 14.4; 4.4. SC: le.
  Abstract: During 2002, the Human Fertilization and Embryology Authority (HFEA) in England, which regulates in vitro fertilization (IVF) clinics, agreed to allow a family to attempt to create a baby genetically selected to help treat a desperately ill child. The media reaction against this HFEA decision has shown profound outrage, expressing that having a child for the sake of the other is improper, immoral and 'against human dignity'. Other claims were, "we should protect vulnerable human life", and "human beings should not be treated 'as a means to an end'". None of these moral claims however, stand rational and coherent scrutiny. Thus, this paper maintains that making a child to save the life of his brother is not only ethically permissible but it would rather be unethical NOT to do so.

Singapore. Bioethics Advisory Committee. Ethical, legal and social issues in genetic testing and genetics research: a consultation paper. Singapore: The Bioethics Advisory Committee 2005 April 5; 55 p. [Online] Available: http://www.bioethics-singapore.org/resources/pdfg/GT%20CP%20Final.pdf [14 April 2005]. NRCBL: 15.3; 15.1; 15.2; 14.4; 2.4; 8.4; 9.2; 9.5.7; 9.8.

Slosar, John Paul. Ethical issues in genetic testing. *Health Care Ethics USA [electronic]* 2005; 13(3); E2, 3 p. Available: http://www.slu.edu/centers/chce/hceusa/3_2005_index.html [21 February 2006]. NRCBL: 15.3; 8.3.1; 15.2.

Smith, Alexander McCall. Nationale Modelle zur Regelung des Gebrauchs der Gendiagnostik. Großbritannien: Tests und Screening zur Gewinnung persönlicher genetischer Informationen: Die britische Erfahrung. *In:* Honnefelder, Ludger; Mieth, Dietmar; Propping, Peter; Siep, Ludwig; Wiesemann, Claudia, eds. Das genetische Wissen und die Zukunft des Menschen. New York: De Gruyter; 2003: 275-285. NRCBL: 15.3. SC: le.

Stein, Rob. Found on the web, with DNA: a boy's father. *Washington Post* 2005 November 13; p. A9. NRCBL: 15.3; 15.11. SC: po.

Steinberg, Karen K. Ethical challenges at the beginning of the millennium. *Statistics in Medicine* 2001 May 15; 20(9-10): 1415-1419. NRCBL: 15.3; 1.3.12; 15.1; 7.1; 18.3; 18.2. Identifiers: Third National Health and Nutrition Examination Survey (NHANES III).

Stolt, Ulrica Gustafsson; Liss, Per-Erik; Ludvigsson, Johnny. Nurses' views of longitudinal genetic screening of and research on children. *British Journal of Nursing* 2005 January 27-February 9; 14(2): 71-77. NRCBL: 15.3; 18.5.2. Identifiers: Sweden.

Strong, Louise C.; Marteau, Theresa. Evaluating children and adolescents for heritable cancer risk. *Journal of the National Cancer Institute Monographs* 1995; (17): 111-113. NRCBL: 15.3; 9.5.7; 9.5.1.

Stuhrmann, Manfred; Hoy, Ludwig; Nippert, Irmgard; Schmidtke, Jörg. Genotype-based screening for hereditary Hemochromatosis: II. Attitudes toward genetic testing and psychosocial impact — a report from a German pilot study. *Genetic Testing* 2005 Fall; 9(3): 242-254. NRCBL: 15.3. SC: em.

Takala, Tuija. Genetic knowledge and our conception of ourselves as persons. *In:* Thomasma, David C.; Weisstub, David N.; Herve, Christian eds. Personhood and Health Care. Boston: Kluwer Academic Pub.; 2001: 91-97. NRCBL: 15.3; 1.1; 4.4.

Taupitz, Jochen. Nationale Modelle zur Regelung des Gebrauchs der Gendiagnostik. Deutschland: Wie regeln wir den Gebrauch der Gendiagnostik? *In:* Honnefelder, Ludger; Mieth, Dietmar; Propping, Peter; Siep, Ludwig; Wiesemann, Claudia, eds. Das genetische Wissen und die Zukunft des Menschen. New York: De Gruyter; 2003: 244-274. NRCBL: 15.3; 5.3. SC: le.

Taylor, Jennifer R. Mixing the gene pool and the labor pool: protecting workers from genetic discrimination in employment. *Temple Environmental Law and Technology Journal* 2001 Fall; 20(1): 51-72. NRCBL: 15.3; 16.3. SC: le.

Taylor, Sandra. Gender differences in attitudes among those at risk for Huntington's disease. *Genetic Testing* 2005 Summer; 9(2): 152-157. NRCBL: 15.3; 8.2; 10.

Turney, Lyn. The incidental discovery of nonpaternity through genetic carrier screening: an exploration of lay attitudes. *Qualitative Health Research* 2005 May; 15(5): 620-634. NRCBL: 15.3; 14.1.

Urbiztondo, Ned. The economic efficiency behind genetic "discrimination". *Ivy Journal of Ethics* 2003; 3(1): 4-6. NRCBL: 15.3; 16.3; 8.4; 1.3.2. SC: an.

Wallace, Helen M. The misleading marketing of genetic tests: will the genome become the source of diagnostic miracles or potential scams? *GeneWatch* 2005 March-April; 18(2): 3-5. NRCBL: 15.3; 1.3.7; 1.3.2; 9.7.

Watson, M.; Foster, C.; Eeles, R.; Eccles, D.; Ashley, S.; Davidson, R.; Mackay, J.; Morrison, P.J.; Hopwood, P.; Evans, D.G.R. Psychosocial impact of breast/ovarian (BRCA1/2) cancer-predictive genetic testing in a UK multi-centre clinical cohort. *British Journal of Cancer* 2004 November 15; 91(10): 1787-1794. NRCBL: 15.3; 15.2; 15.1; 9.3.1. SC: em. Identifiers: United Kingdom (Great Britain); Psychosocial Study Collaborators.

Welkenhuysen, M.; Evers-Kiebooms, G.; Van den Berghe, H. Attitudes toward predictive testing for Alzheimer's disease in a student population. *Psychiatric Genetics* 1997; 7: 121-126. NRCBL: 15.3; 17.1. SC: em.

Wertz, Dorothy. "Genetic discrimination" in an international context. *In:* Knoppers, Bartha Maria, ed. Populations and Genetics: Legal and Socio-Ethical Perspectives. Boston: Martinus Nijhoff; 2003: 603-622. NRCBL: 15.3; 21.1. SC: em.

Wertz, Dorothy C. Biomedical research: genetic testing and confidentiality. *World and I* 1990 September; 543-555. NRCBL: 15.3; 8.4.

Wexler, Barbara. Genetic testing. *In her:* Genetics and Genetic Engineering. Detroit, MI: Gale Group; 2004: 71-83. NRCBL: 15.3; 15.2.

White, Mary T. The many facets of genetic testing. *In:* Smith, David H.; Cohen, Cynthia B., eds. A Christian Response to the New Genetics: Religious, Ethical, and Social Issues. Lanham, MD: Rowman & Littlefield Publishers; 2003: 27-52. NRCBL: 15.3; 1.2; 15.2.

Wiesing, Urban. Gendiagnostik und Gesundheitsversorgung. *In:* Honnefelder, Ludger; Mieth, Dietmar; Propping, Peter; Siep, Ludwig; Wiesemann, Claudia, eds. Das genetische Wissen und die Zukunft des Menschen. New York: De Gruyter; 2003: 369-374. NRCBL: 15.3; 9.3.1.

Willis, Evan. Public health and the 'new genetics': balancing individual and collective outcomes. *In:* Bunton, Robin; Petersen, Alan, eds. Genetic Governance: Health, Risk and Ethics in the Biotech Era. New York: Routledge; 2005: 155-169. NRCBL: 15.3; 9.1.

Wolbring, Gregor. Disability rights and genetic discrimination. *In:* Krimsky, Sheldon; Shorett, Peter, eds. Rights and Liberties in the Biotech Age: Why We Need a Genetic Bill of Rights. Lanham: Rowman and Littlefield Publishers; 2005: 178-182. NRCBL: 15.3; 21.1.

Zick, Cathleen D.; Mathews, Charles J.; Roberts, J. Scott; Cook-Deegan, Robert; Pokorski, Robert J.; Green, Robert C. Genetic testing for Alzheimer's disease and its impact on insurance purchasing behavior. *Health Affairs* 2005 March-April; 24(2): 483-490. NRCBL: 15.3; 9.3.1; 17.1. SC: em.

GENETICS

Genetics and ethics. *In:* Concise Routledge Encyclopedia of Philosophy. New York: Routledge; 2000: 309. NRCBL: 15.1.

Not black and white: BiDil my work best for African Americans — but do we know why? [editorial]. *New Scientist* 2005 June 11-17; 186(2503): 3. NRCBL: 15.1; 9.7; 15.11.

Abels, Gabriele. The long and winding road from Asilomar to Brussels: science, politics and the public in biotechnology regulation. *Science as Culture* 2005 December; 14(4): 339-353. NRCBL: 15.1; 5.3; 1.3.11. SC: an.

Acheson, Louise S.; Stange, Kurt C.; Zyzanski, Stephen. Clinical genetics issues encountered by family physicians. *Genetics in Medicine* 2005 September; 7(7): 501-508. NRCBL: 15.1; 9.5.1; 9.2; 9.3.1; 7.1. SC: em.

Allhoff, Fritz. Germ-line genetic enhancement and Rawlsian primary goods. *Kennedy Institute of Ethics Journal* 2005 March; 15(1): 39-56. NRCBL: 15.1; 15.4; 4.5; 1.1; 5.3.

Abstract: Genetic interventions raise a host of moral issues and, of its various species, germ-line genetic enhancement is the most morally contentious. This paper surveys various arguments against germ-line enhancement and attempts to demonstrate their inadequacies. A positive argument is advanced in favor of certain forms of germ-line enhancements, which holds that they are morally permissible if and only if they augment Rawlsian primary goods, either directly or by facilitating their acquisition.

Almarsdóttir, Anna Birna; Björnsdóttir, Ingunn; Traulsen, Janine Morgall. A lay prescription for tailor-made drugs — focus group reflections on

NRCBL: National Reference Center for Bioethics Literature Classification Scheme   See inside front cover for terms.

217

pharmacogenomics. *Health Policy* 2005 February; 71(2): 233-241. NRCBL: 15.1; 9.7; 9.3.1; 5.3; 7.1; 15.10. SC: em.

Anderlik, Mary R.; Heller, Jan C. The economics and politics of the new genetics. *In:* Smith, David H.; Cohen, Cynthia B., eds. A Christian Response to the New Genetics: Religious, Ethical, and Social Issues. Lanham, MD: Rowman & Littlefield Publishers; 2003: 147-167. NRCBL: 15.1; 9.3.1.

Anderson, Stephanie L. The Human Genome Project. *In:* American College of Legal Medicine Textbook Committee, Sanbar, S. Sandy; Firestone, Marvin H.; Buckner, Fillmore; Gibofsky, Allan; LeBlang, Theodore R.; Snyder, Jack W.; Wecht, Cyril H.; Zaremski, Miles J. Legal Medicine. 6th ed. St. Louis: Mosby; 2004: 256-263. NRCBL: 15.1; 15.10.

Andrews, Lori B. Harnessing the benefits of biobanks. *Journal of Law, Medicine and Ethics* 2005 Spring; 33(1): 22-30. NRCBL: 15.1; 1.3.12; 18.3; 4.4.

Appelbaum, Paul S. Ethical issues in psychiatric genetics. *Journal of Psychiatric Practice* 2004 November; 10(6): 343-351. NRCBL: 15.1; 15.3; 8.4; 17.1.

Ashcroft, Richard E.; Gui, Karen P. Ethics and world pictures in Kamm on enhancement [comment]. *American Journal of Bioethics* 2005 May-June; 5(3): 19-20. NRCBL: 15.1; 14.1; 4.5. Comments: comment on Frances M. Kamm, "Is there a problem with enhancement?" American Journal of Bioethics 2005 May-June; 5(3): 5- 14.

Bailey, Ronald. Biotech cornucopia: improving nature for humanity's benefit. *In his:* Liberation Biology: The Scientific and Moral Case for the Biotech Revolution. Amherst, NY: Prometheus Books; 2005: 183- 222. NRCBL: 15.1; 1.3.11.

Baillie, Harold W. Aristotle and genetic engineering: the uncertainty of excellence. *In:* Baillie, Harold W.; Casey, Timothy K., eds. Is Human Nature Obsolete? Genetics Bioengineering, and the Future of the Human Condition. Cambridge, MA: MIT Press; 2005: 209-232. NRCBL: 15.1; 1.1.

Bala, Mohan V.; Zarkin, Gary A. Pharmacogenomics and the evolution of healthcare: is it time for cost-effectiveness analysis at the individual level? [opinion]. *Pharmacoeconomics* 2004; 22(8): 495-498. NRCBL: 15.1; 9.7; 9.3.1; 9.4.

Bankston, Carl L. Genetic engineering: social and ethical issues. *In:* Ness, Bryan D., ed. Encyclopedia of Genetics. Revised edition. Volume I. Pasadena, Calif.: Salem Press; 2004: 351-354. NRCBL: 15.1; 5.1.

Bartfai, T. Pharmacogenomics in drug development: societal and technical aspects. *Pharmacogenomics Journal* 2004; 4(4): 226-232. NRCBL: 15.1; 9.7.

Beckmann, Jan P. Pharmakogenomik und Pharmakogenetik: Ethische Fragen. *In:* Jahrbuch für Wissenschaft und Ethik. Bd. 7. Berlin: Walter de Gruyter; 2002: 259-276. NRCBL: 15.1; 9.7.

Beckmann, Jan P. Pharmakogenomik und Pharmakogenetik: Ethische Fragen. *In:* Honnefelder, Ludger; Mieth, Dietmar; Propping, Peter; Siep, Ludwig; Wiesemann, Claudia, eds. Das genetische Wissen und die Zukunft des Menschen. New York: De Gruyter; 2003: 348-360. NRCBL: 15.1; 9.7.

Bereano, Philip. Biotechnology's challenge to individual privacy. *In:* Krimsky, Sheldon; Shorett, Peter, eds. Rights and Liberties in the Biotech Age: Why We Need a Genetic Bill of Rights. Lanham: Rowman and Littlefield Publishers; 2005: 159-163. NRCBL: 15.1; 8.4.

Berg, Kåre. The ethics of benefit sharing [opinion]. *Clinical Genetics* 2001 April; 59(4): 240-243. NRCBL: 15.1; 18.3; 18.2; 9.3.1.

Bernstein, Mark; Bampoe, Joseph; Daar, Abdallah S. Ethical issues in molecular medicine of relevance to surgeons. *Canadian Journal of Surgery* 2004 December; 47(6): 414-421. NRCBL: 15.1; 1.3.9; 8.4; 15.4; 18.5.4.

Berube, Michael. Disability, democracy, and the new genetics. *In:* Van Cleve, John Vickery, ed. Genetics, Disability, and Deafness. Washington, DC: Gallaudet University Press; 2004: 202- 220. NRCBL: 15.1; 9.5.1; 15.3; 15.5; 21.1.

Bioethics Advisory Committee of the Israel Academy of Sciences and Humanities. Population-based large-scale collections of DNA samples and databases of genetic information. Jerusalem: The Israel Academy of Sciences and Humanities, 2002 December; 29 p. [Online]. Available: http://www.academy.ac.il/bioethics/english/PDF/Finalized_Dna_Bank_Full.pdf [10 January 2006]. NRCBL: 15.1; 9.1; 1.3.12; 8.3.1; 8.4.

Birch, Kean. Beneficence, determinism and justice: an engagement with the argument for the genetic selection of intelligence. *Bioethics* 2005 February; 19(1): 12-28. NRCBL: 15.1; 1.1; 15.3; 15.5. SC: an.

Brooke, John Hedley. Detracting from divine power? Religious belief and the appraisal of new technologies. *In:* Deane-Drummond, Celia; Szerszynski, Bronislaw, eds. Re- ordering Nature: Theology, Society and the New Genetics. New York: T & T Clark; 2003: 43-67. NRCBL: 15.1; 1.2.

Brugger, E. Christian. Ethical commitment stimulates scientific insights. *National Catholic Bioethics Quarterly* 2005 Autumn; 5(3): 445- 446. NRCBL: 15.1; 18.5.4; 14.4. Identifiers: altered nuclear transfer (ANT).

Cahill, Lisa Sowle. Nature, sin, and society. *In:* Baillie, Harold W.; Casey, Timothy K., eds. Is Human Nature Obsolete? Genetics Bioengineering, and the Future of the Human Condition. Cambridge, MA: MIT Press; 2005: 339-365. NRCBL: 15.1; 1.2; 14.5; 15.8; 1.1.

Cambon-Thomsen, A.; Hirtzlin, I.; Preaubert, N.; Dubreuil, C.; Duchier, J.; Jansen, B.; Simon, J.; Lobato de Faria, P.; Perez- Lezaun, A.; Visser, B.; Williams, G.; Galloux, J.C. An empirical study on biobanking of human genetic material and data in six EU countries. *In:* Knoppers, Bartha Maria, ed. Populations and Genetics: Legal and Socio-Ethical Perspectives. Boston: Martinus Nijhoff; 2003: 141-167. NRCBL: 15.1; 1.3.12; 21.1. SC: em.

Cambon-Thomsen, Anne. The social and ethical issues of post-genomic human biobanks. *Nature Reviews Genetics* 2004 November; 5(11): 866-873. NRCBL: 15.1; 1.3.12.

Cameron, Nigel M. de S.; FitzGerald, Kevin T.; Flannery, Kevin; Gómez-Lobo, Alfonso; Harvey, John Collins; Kilner, John F.; May, William E.; Williams, Thomas; et al. Production of pluripotent stem cells by oocyte-assisted reprogramming: joint statement with signatories. *National Catholic Bioethics Quarterly* 2005 Autumn; 5(3): 579- 583. NRCBL: 15.1; 18.5.1; 15.4; 19.1.

Cardinal, Genevieve; Deschênes, Mylène. Surveying the population biobankers. *In:* Knoppers, Bartha Maria, ed. Populations and Genetics: Legal and Socio-Ethical Perspectives. Boston: Martinus Nijhoff; 2003: 37-94. NRCBL: 15.1; 1.3.12. SC: em.

Casey, Timothy K. Nature, technology, and the emergence of cybernetic humanity. *In:* Baillie, Harold W.; Casey, Timothy K., eds. Is Human Nature Obsolete? Genetics Bioengineering, and the Future of the Human Condition. Cambridge, MA: MIT Press; 2005: 35-65. NRCBL: 15.1; 1.1; 5.1.

Chadwick, Ruth; Berg, Kåre. Solidarity and equity: new ethical frameworks for genetic databases [opinion]. *Nature Reviews Genetics* 2001 April; 2(4): 318-321. NRCBL: 15.1; 1.3.12; 8.3.1; 21.1.

Chalmers, Don. Commercialization and benefit sharing of biotechnology: cross- cultural concerns? *In:* Brannigan, Michael C., ed. Cross-Cultural Biotechnology. Lanham: Rowman and Littlefield; 2004: 3-14. NRCBL: 15.1; 1.1; 9.3.1; 21.1.

Charafeddine, Moussa. Discrimination. *In:* Knoppers, Bartha Maria, ed. Populations and Genetics: Legal and Socio-Ethical Perspectives. Boston: Martinus Nijhoff; 2003: 591-601. NRCBL: 15.1.

Check, Erika. Synthetic biologists face up to security issues [news]. *Nature* 2005 August 18; 436(7053): 894-895. NRCBL: 15.1; 15.7; 21.3.

Cho, Mildred K.; Sankar, Pamela. Forensic genetics and ethical, legal and social implications beyond the clinic [opinion]. *Nature Genetics* 2004 November; 36(11, Supplement): S8-S12. NRCBL: 15.1; 1.3.5; 9.5.4.

Clark, Stephen R.L. Thinking about biotechnology: towards a theory of just experimentation. *In:* Deane-Drummond, Celia; Szerszynski, Bronislaw, eds. Re- ordering Nature: Theology, Society and the New Genetics. New York: T & T Clark; 2003: 165-177. NRCBL: 15.1; 22.2. SC: an.

Cohen, Cynthia B. Genetics, ethics, and the principle of subsidiarity. *Anglican Theological Review* 1999 Fall; 81(4): 621-630. NRCBL: 15.1; 1.2; 1.1; 15.3. Conference: Presiding Bishop's Consultation on Bioethics; 8-9 June 1999; College of Preachers.

Cohen, Cynthia B.; Walters, LeRoy. Gene transfer for therapy or enhancement. *In:* Smith, David H.; Cohen, Cynthia B., eds. A Christian Response to the New Genetics: Religious, Ethical, and Social Issues. Lanham, MD: Rowman & Littlefield Publishers; 2003: 53-74. NRCBL: 15.1; 1.2; 4.5; 15.4.

Cohen, Eric. The real meaning of genetics. *New Atlantis* 2005 Summer; 9: 29-41. NRCBL: 15.1; 15.4; 4.5; 15.5.

Coors, Marilyn E.; Hunter, Lawrence. Evaluation of genetic enhancement: will human wisdom properly acknowledge the value of evolution? [comment]. *American Journal of Bioethics* 2005 May-June; 5(3): 21-22. NRCBL: 15.1; 14.1; 3.2. Comments: comment on Frances M. Kamm, "Is there a problem with enhancement?" American Journal of Bioethics 2005 May-June; 5(3): 5- 14.

Copland, P. The book of life. *Journal of Medical Ethics* 2005 May; 31(5): 278-279. NRCBL: 15.1.

Abstract: It has recently been suggested that the practice of bioethics in the area of biology and genetics has been hampered by the lack of an accurate and appropriate metaphor. Beginning with previous metaphors that have compared the genome with a static blueprint or "book of life", I develop a dynamic metaphor that is compatible with our present understanding of the role of genetics in biology. The resulting metaphor is not only an accurate representation of current biology but of particular use to bioethicists and non- biologists in general.

Corrigan, O.P. Pharmacogenetics, ethical issues: review of the Nuffield Council on Bioethics report. *Journal of Medical Ethics* 2005 March; 31(3): 144-148. NRCBL: 15.1; 9.7.

Abstract: In September this year the Nuffield Council on Bioethics held a meeting to disclose and discuss the main findings of their newly published report on the ethical issues associated with developments in pharmacogenetics research. The basics of pharmacogenetics science is briefly outlined, and then the extent to which the report was successful in addressing (or at least highlighting) the attendant social, ethical, and policy implications of pharmacogenetics research is evaluated.

Corrigan, Oonagh. Informed consent: the contradictory ethical safeguards in pharmacogenetics. *In:* Tutton, Rich-

NRCBL: National Reference Center for Bioethics Literature Classification Scheme						See inside front cover for terms.

219

ard; Corrigan, Oonagh, eds. Genetic Databases: Socio-ethical Issues in the Collection and Use of DNA. New York: Routledge; 2004: 78-96. NRCBL: 15.1; 9.7; 18.3.

Corte-Real, Francisco. Forensic DNA databases. *Forensic Science International* 2004 December 2; 146(Supplement): S143-S144. NRCBL: 15.1; 1.3.5; 1.3.12; 21.1.

Cotton, Richard G.H.; Horaitis, Ourania. Mutation databases and ethical considerations. *In:* Knoppers, Bartha Maria, ed. Populations and Genetics: Legal and Socio-Ethical Perspectives. Boston: Martinus Nijhoff; 2003: 169-178. NRCBL: 15.1; 1.3.12.

Coupland, Robin; Martin, Sophie; Dutli, Maria-Teresa. Protecting everybody's genetic data. *Lancet* 2005 May 21-27; 365(9473): 1754-1756. NRCBL: 15.1; 8.3.1; 8.4; 1.3.12; 21.1.

Couzin, Jennifer. Gene bank proposal draws support — and a competitor [news]. *Science* 2005 July 29; 309(5735): 684-685. NRCBL: 15.1; 1.3.12; 18.5.8. Identifiers: Department of Veterans Affairs.

Crysdale, Cynthia S.W. Playing God? Moral agency in an emergent world. *Journal of the Society of Christian Ethics* 2003 Fall-Winter; 23(2): 243-259. NRCBL: 15.1; 4.1.1; 1.2.

Cunningham-Burley, Sarah; Boulton, Mary. The social context of the new genetics. *In:* Albrecht, Gary L.; Fitzpatrick, Ray; Scrimshaw, Susan C., eds. The Handbook of Social Studies in Health & Medicine. Thousand Oaks, CA: Sage; 2000: 173-187. NRCBL: 15.1; 15.10; 15.3.

Daar, Abdallah S.; Acharya, Tara; Filate, Isaac; Thorsteinsdottir, Halla; Singer, Peter. Beyond GM foods: genomics, biotechnology and global health equity. *In:* Thiele, F.; Ashcroft, R.E., eds. Bioethics in a Small World. Berlin: Springer; 2005: 33-44. NRCBL: 15.1; 1.3.11.

Damm, Reinhard. Individualisierte Medizin und Patientenrechte. *In:* Honnefelder, Ludger; Mieth, Dietmar; Propping, Peter; Siep, Ludwig; Wiesemann, Claudia, eds. Das genetische Wissen und die Zukunft des Menschen. New York: De Gruyter; 2003: 361-368. NRCBL: 15.1; 9.7.

Darnovsky, Marcy. Human rights in a post-human future. *In:* Krimsky, Sheldon; Shorett, Peter, eds. Rights and Liberties in the Biotech Age: Why We Need a Genetic Bill of Rights. Lanham: Rowman and Littlefield Publishers; 2005: 209-215. NRCBL: 15.1; 4.5; 21.1.

de Ortuzar, Maria Graciela. Towards a universal definition of "benefit-sharing.". *In:* Knoppers, Bartha Maria, ed. Populations and Genetics: Legal and Socio-Ethical Perspectives. Boston: Martinus Nijhoff; 2003: 473-485. NRCBL: 15.1; 13.1.

Deane-Drummond, Celia. Aquinas, wisdom ethics and the new genetics. *In:* Deane-Drummond, Celia; Szerszynski, Bronislaw, eds. Re- ordering Nature: Theology, Society and the New Genetics. New York: T & T Clark; 2003: 293-311. NRCBL: 15.1; 1.2.

Deane-Drummond, Celia E. The ethics of biotechnology. *In her:* Ethics of Nature. Malden, MA: Blackwell Pub.; 2004: 86-110. NRCBL: 15.1; 1.2; 1.3.11.

Dickenson, Donna. Einwilligung, Kommodifizierung und Vorteilsausgleich in der Genforschung. *In:* Honnefelder, Ludger; Mieth, Dietmar; Propping, Peter; Siep, Ludwig; Wiesemann, Claudia, eds. Das genetische Wissen und die Zukunft des Menschen. New York: De Gruyter; 2003: 139-151. NRCBL: 15.1; 18.3; 21.1; 9.3.1.

Diprose, Rosalyn. A "genethics" that makes sense: take two. *In:* Shildrick, Margrit; Mykitiuk, Roxanne, eds. Ethics of the Body: Postconventional Challenges. Cambridge, MA: MIT Press; 2005: 237- 258. NRCBL: 15.1; 1.1.

Elshtain, Jean Bethke. The body and the quest for control. *In:* Baillie, Harold W.; Casey, Timothy K., eds. Is Human Nature Obsolete? Genetics Bioengineering, and the Future of the Human Condition. Cambridge, MA: MIT Press; 2005: 155-175. NRCBL: 15.1; 1.2.

Farrelly, Colin. Justice in the genetically transformed society. *Kennedy Institute of Ethics Journal* 2005 March; 15(1): 91-99. NRCBL: 15.1; 15.4; 4.5; 1.1; 5.3.
Abstract: This paper explores some of the challenges raised by human genetic interventions for debates about distributive justice, focusing on the challenges that face prioritarian theories of justice and their relation to the argument advanced by Ronald Lindsay elsewhere in this issue of the Kennedy Institute of Ethics Journal. Also examined are the implications of germ-line genetic enhancements for intergenerational justice, and an argument is given against Fritz Allhoff's conclusion, found in this issue as well, that such enhancements are morally permissible if and only if they augment primary goods.

Furton, Edward J. A defense of oocyte-assisted reprogramming. *National Catholic Bioethics Quarterly* 2005 Autumn; 5(3): 465- 468. NRCBL: 15.1; 14.4; 18.5.4; 4.4.

Geller, Gail; Bernhardt, Barbara A.; Gardner, Mary; Rodgers, Joann; Holtzman, Neil A. Scientists' and science writers' experiences reporting genetic discoveries: toward an ethic of trust in science journalism. *Genetics in Medicine* 2005 March; 7(3): 198-205. NRCBL: 15.1; 1.3.7; 1.3.9; 7.1; 5.1. SC: em.

Gosline, Anna. Will DNA profiling fuel prejudice? *New Scientist* 2005 April 9-15; 186(2494): 12-13. NRCBL: 15.1; 1.3.5; 1.3.12; 15.11.

Gottweis, Herbert. Emerging forms of governance in genomics and post-genomics: structures, trends, perspectives. *In:* Bunton, Robin; Petersen, Alan, eds. Genetic Governance: Health, Risk and Ethics in the Biotech Era. New York: Routledge; 2005: 189-208. NRCBL: 15.1; 5.3.

Gottweis, Herbert. Regulating genomics in the 21st century: from logos to pathos? [opinion]. *Trends in Biotechnology* 2005 March; 23(3): 118-121. NRCBL: 15.1; 15.10; 5.3.

Gottweis, Herbert. Transnationalizing recombinant-DNA regulation: between Asilomar, EMBO, the OECD, and the European Community. *Science as Culture* 2005 December; 14(4): 325-338. NRCBL: 15.1; 5.3; 21.1. SC: rv. Identifiers: European Molecular Biology Organization; Organization for Economic Cooperation and Development.

Great Britain. Department of Health; Medical Research Council [MRC]; Wellcome Trust; Interim Advisory Group on Ethics and Governance [IAG]. Setting standards: UK Biobank ethics and governance framework [EGF] [summary]. London: UKBiobank 2003 September 24; 4 p. [Online]. Available: http://www.ukbiobank.ac.uk/ethics/efg-summary.doc [8 August 2005]. NRCBL: 15.1; 1.3.12; 18.2.

Great Britain. Department of Health; Medical Research Council [MRC]; Wellcome Trust; Interim Advisory Group on Ethics and Governance [IAG]. UK Biobank ethics and governance framework [EGF]: Version 1.0: for comment. London: UK Biobank 2003 September 24; 31 p. [Online]. Available: http://www.ukbiobank.ac.uk/ethics/efg.php [8 August2005]. NRCBL: 15.1; 1.3.12; 18.2.

Great Britain. Department of Health; Wellcome Trust; Medical Research Council [MRC]; Scottish Executive; Interim Advisory Group on Ethics and Governance [IAG]. UK Biobank Ethics and Governance Framework [EGF]: Background Document. London: UK Biobank 2003 October 10; 21 p. [Online]. Available: http://www.ukbiobank.ac.uk/ethics/efg.php [8 August 2005]. NRCBL: 15.1; 1.3.12; 18.2.

Green, Ronald M. Last word: imagining the future. *Kennedy Institute of Ethics Journal* 2005 March; 15(1): 101-106. NRCBL: 15.1; 15.4; 4.5; 1.1; 5.3.

Abstract: H.G. Wells warned, in 1895, not to allow economic injustices to become so acute that they ultimately transform human biology. Wells's warning is all the more pertinent today as society contemplates the use of biotechnologies to manipulate or "enhance" the human genome.

Gurwitz, David; Kimchi, Orit; Bonne-Tamir, Batsheva. The Israeli DNA and cell line collection: a human diversity repository. *In:* Knoppers, Bartha Maria, ed. Populations and Genetics: Legal and Socio-Ethical Perspectives. Boston: Martinus Nijhoff; 2003: 95-113. NRCBL: 15.1; 1.3.12; 15.11.

Haimes, Erica; Whong-Barr, Michael. Competing perspectives on reasons for participation and non- participation in the North Cumbria Community Genetics Project. *In:* Knoppers, Bartha Maria, ed. Populations and Genetics:

Legal and Socio-Ethical Perspectives. Boston: Martinus Nijhoff; 2003: 199-216. NRCBL: 15.1; 5.1.

Haimes, Erica; Whong-Barr, Michael. Levels and styles of participation in genetic databases: a case study of the North Cumbria Community Genetics Project. *In:* Tutton, Richard; Corrigan, Oonagh, eds. Genetic Databases: Socio-ethical Issues in the Collection and Use of DNA. New York: Routledge; 2004: 57-77. NRCBL: 15.1; 1.3.12. SC: em.

Halliday, Jane L.; Collins, Veronica R.; Aitken, Mary Ann; Richards, Martin P.M.; Olsson, Craig A. Genetics and public health — evolution, or revolution? *Journal of Epidemiology and Community Health* 2004 November; 58(11): 894-899. NRCBL: 15.1; 15.3; 9.1.

Harry, Debra. Acts of self-determination and self-defense: indigenous peoples' responses to biocolonialism. *In:* Krimsky, Sheldon; Shorett, Peter, eds. Rights and Liberties in the Biotech Age: Why We Need a Genetic Bill of Rights. Lanham: Rowman and Littlefield Publishers; 2005: 87-97. NRCBL: 15.1; 21.1; 18.5.9.

Herbert, Martha R. More than code: from genetic reductionism to complex biological systems. *In:* Bunton, Robin; Petersen, Alan, eds. Genetic Governance: Health, Risk and Ethics in the Biotech Era. New York: Routledge; 2005: 171-188. NRCBL: 15.1.

Hermerén, Göran. Der Einfluss der Humangenomeprojekte auf unser Selbstverständnis. *In:* Honnefelder, Ludger; Mieth, Dietmar; Propping, Peter; Siep, Ludwig; Wiesemann, Claudia, eds. Das genetische Wissen und die Zukunft des Menschen. New York: De Gruyter; 2003: 57-77. NRCBL: 15.1; 1.1.

Holmes, Bob. Alive! *New Scientist* 2005 February 12-18; 185(2486): 28-33. NRCBL: 15.1; 3.1. Identifiers: synthetic life form.

Hubbard, Ruth. Rights for fetuses and embryos? *In:* Krimsky, Sheldon; Shorett, Peter, eds. Rights and Liberties in the Biotech Age: Why We Need a Genetic Bill of Rights. Lanham: Rowman and Littlefield Publishers; 2005: 216-218. NRCBL: 15.1; 9.5.7.

Hunter, Katherine. A new direction on DNA? *Criminal Law Review* 1998 July: 478-480. NRCBL: 15.1; 1.3.5; 1.3.12. Identifiers: Sierra Leone.

Ida, Ryuichi. Ethical and legal aspects of biotechnology. *In:* Brannigan, Michael C., ed. Cross-Cultural Biotechnology. Lanham: Rowman and Littlefield; 2004: 25-35. NRCBL: 15.1; 4.4; 15.8; 18.5.4; 21.1.

Ilencíková, Denisa. Clinical genetics: views of ethical and legislative conclusions in the Slovak Republic. *Human Reproduction and Genetic Ethics: An International Journal* 2005; 11(2): 49-54. NRCBL: 15.1; 9.5.1; 15.2; 1.3.5.

NRCBL: National Reference Center for Bioethics Literature Classification Scheme   See inside front cover for terms.

221

Issa, Amalia M. Ethical perspectives on pharmacogenomic profiling in the drug development process. *Nature Reviews Drug Discovery* 2002 April; 1(4): 300-308. NRCBL: 15.1; 9.7; 18.2.

Joly, Y.; Knoppers, Bartha Maria; Nguyen, M.T. Stored tissue samples: through the confidentiality maze. *Pharmacogenomics Journal* 2005; 5(1): 2-5. NRCBL: 15.1; 9.7; 19.5; 8.4.

Jonsen, Albert R. Environmental ethics. *In his:* Bioethics Beyond the Headlines: Who Lives? Who Dies? Who Decides? Lanham, MD: Rowman and Littlefield Pub.; 2005: 167-176. NRCBL: 15.1; 16.1.

Jonsen, Albert R. Genetics. *In his:* Bioethics Beyond the Headlines: Who Lives? Who Dies? Who Decides? Lanham, MD: Rowman and Littlefield; 2005: 96-113. NRCBL: 15.1; 15.3; 15.5; 15.6.

Kahn, Jonathan D.; Bhopal, Raj; Rahemtulla, Taslin. Pharmacogenetics and ethnically targeted therapies: racial drugs need to be put in context; authors' reply [letter and reply]. *BMJ: British Medical Journal* 2005 June 25; 330(7506): 1508- 1509. NRCBL: 15.1; 9.7.

Kaiser, Jocelyn. Resurrected influenza virus yields secrets of deadly 1918 pandemic [news]. *Science* 2005 October 7; 310(5745): 28-29. NRCBL: 15.1; 1.3.9; 21.3.

Kamm, Frances M. Is there a problem with enhancement? [comment]. *American Journal of Bioethics* 2005 May-June; 5(3): 5-14. NRCBL: 15.1; 4.5; 14.1; 1.1. SC: an. Comments: comment on M. Sandel, "The case against perfection," Atlantic Monthly 2004; 293(3): 51-62.

Abstract: This article examines arguments concerning enhancement of human persons recently presented by Michael Sandel (2004). In the first section, I briefly describe some of his arguments. In section two, I consider whether, as Sandel claims, the desire for mastery motivates enhancement and whether such a desire could be grounds for its impermissibility. Section three considers how Sandel draws the distinction between treatment and enhancement, and the relation to nature that he thinks each expresses. The fourth section examines Sandel's views about parent/child relations and also how enhancement would affect distributive justice and the duty to aid. In conclusion, I briefly offer an alternative suggestion as to why enhancement may be troubling and consider what we could safely enhance.

Karpowicz, Phillip; Cohen, Cynthia B.; van der Kooy, Derek. It is ethical to transplant human stem cells into non-human embryos. *Nature Medicine* 2004 April; 10(4): 331-335. NRCBL: 15.1; 22.1; 18.5.1.

Kass, Leon R. Triumph or tragedy? The moral meaning of genetic technology. *American Journal of Jurisprudence* 2000; 45: 1-16. NRCBL: 15.1; 1.1; 15.4; 4.5.

Kelly, David F. Genetic engineering. *In his:* Contemporary Catholic Health Care Ethics. Washington, DC: Georgetown University Press; 2004: 260-268. NRCBL: 15.1; 1.2; 14.2; 15.4.

Kelly, Susan E. 'New' genetics meets the old underclass: findings from a study of genetic outreach services in rural Kentucky. *In:* Bunton, Robin; Petersen, Alan, eds. Genetic Governance: Health, Risk and Ethics in the Biotech Era. New York: Routledge; 2005: 137-151. NRCBL: 15.1; 9.5.10. SC: em.

Kemp, Thomas. The stem cell debate: a Veblenian perspective. *Journal of Economic Issues* 2004 June; 38(2): 421-428. NRCBL: 15.1; 18.5.4; 18.6; 1.3.2.

Kingsland, James. Colour-coded cures. *New Scientist* 2005 June 11-17; 186(2503): 42-47. NRCBL: 15.1; 9.7; 15.11.

Knoppers, Bartha Maria. Genetic information and the family: are we our brother's keeper? *Trends in Biotechnology* 2002 February; 20(2): 85-86. NRCBL: 15.1; 8.1; 8.4.

Knoppers, Bartha Maria. Of biotechnology and man [opinion]. *Community Genetics* 2005 January; 7(4): 176-181. NRCBL: 15.1; 1.1; 15.4; 18.1.

Knoppers, Bartha Maria. Of genomics and public health: building public "goods"? *CMAJ/JAMC: Canadian Medical Association Journal* 2005 November 8; 173(10): 1185-1186. NRCBL: 15.1; 15.10; 9.1.

Kohane, Isaac S.; Altman, Russ B. Health-information altruists — a potentially critical resource. *New England Journal of Medicine* 2005 November 10; 353(19): 2074-2077. NRCBL: 15.1; 1.3.12; 8.4.

Konrad, Monica. From secrets of life to the life of secrets: tracing genetic knowledge as genealogical ethics in biomedical Britain. *Journal of the Royal Anthropological Institute* 2003 June; 9(2): 339-358. NRCBL: 15.1; 1.1; 15.2; 15.3.

Korthals, Michiel. Neither golden nugget nor Frankenstein. The need to re-embed food biotechnologies in sociocultural contexts. *In:* Thiele, F.; Ashcroft, R.E., eds. Bioethics in a Small World. Berlin: Springer; 2005: 23-31. NRCBL: 15.1; 1.3.11; 5.1.

Körtner, Ulrich. The challenge of genetic engineering to medical anthropology and ethics. *Human Reproduction and Genetic Ethics: An International Journal* 2001; 7(1): 21-24. NRCBL: 15.1; 11.1; 1.2; 7.1.

Kotval, Jeroo. Genetic privacy in the health care system. *In:* Krimsky, Sheldon; Shorett, Peter, eds. Rights and Liberties in the Biotech Age: Why We Need a Genetic Bill of Rights. Lanham: Rowman and Littlefield Publishers; 2005: 153-158. NRCBL: 15.1; 8.4; 15.3.

Krentz, Christopher. Frankenstein, *Gattaca*, and the quest for perfection. *In:* Van Cleve, John Vickery, ed. Genetics, Disability, and Deafness. Washington, DC: Gallaudet University Press; 2004: 189- 201. NRCBL: 15.1; 7.1.

Krimsky, Sheldon; Shorett, Peter. The genetic bill of rights: advancing a rights platform in biotechnology. *GeneWatch* 2005 January-February; 18(1): 12-14, 18. NRCBL: 15.1; 5.3; 15.3; 15.7.

Kuehn, Bridget M. Genetic information: how much can patients handle? *JAMA: The Journal of the American Medical Association* 2005 July 20; 294(3): 295-296. NRCBL: 15.1; 15.3; 18.3.

Laberge, Claude. Why another statement from the RMGA? *In:* Knoppers, Bartha Maria, ed. Populations and Genetics: Legal and Socio-Ethical Perspectives. Boston: Martinus Nijhoff; 2003: 641-648. NRCBL: 15.1; 13.1; 9.3.1; 15.11. Identifiers: Quebec Network of Applied Genetic Medicine.

Lamb, Gregory M. A mix of mice and men [news]. *Christian Science Monitor* 2005 March 17: 13, 15. NRCBL: 15.1; 18.1; 22.1.

Landon, Melissa R. Ethics and policy perspectives on personalized medicine in the post-genomic era. *Journal of Biolaw and Business* 2005; 8(3): 28-36. NRCBL: 15.1; 9.7; 18.6; 8.4; 18.2; 18.3.

Lanzerath, Dirk. Der Vorstoß in die molekulare Dimension des Menschen— Möglichkeiten und Grenzen. *In:* Honnefelder, Ludger; Mieth, Dietmar; Propping, Peter; Siep, Ludwig; Wiesemann, Claudia, eds. Das genetische Wissen und die Zukunft des Menschen. New York: De Gruyter; 2003: 120-135. NRCBL: 15.1; 1.1; 15.2.

Leavitt, Mairi. 'Just because we can do something doesn't mean we should': young people's responses to biotechnology. *In:* Deane-Drummond, Celia; Szerszynski, Bronislaw, eds. Re- ordering Nature: Theology, Society and the New Genetics. New York: T & T Clark; 2003: 186-201. NRCBL: 15.1; 5.1. SC: em.

Lee, Sandra Soo-Jin. Racializing drug design: implications of pharmacogenomics for health disparities. *American Journal of Public Health* 2005 December; 95(12): 2133- 2138. NRCBL: 15.1; 9.7; 3.1.
Abstract: Current practices of using "race" in pharmacogenomics research demands consideration of the ethical and social implications for understandings of group difference and for efforts to eliminate health disparities. This discussion focuses on an "infrastructure of racialization" created by current trajectories of research on genetic differences among racially identified groups, the use of race as a proxy for risk in clinical practice, and increasing interest in new market niches by the pharmaceutical industry. The confluence of these factors has resulted in the conflation of genes, disease, and race. I argue that public investment in pharmacogenomics requires careful consideration of current inequities in health status and social and ethical concerns over reifying race and issues of distributive justice.

Leng, Chee Heng. Genomics and health: ethical, legal and social implications for developing countries. *Issues in Medical Ethics* 2002 January-March; 10(1): 146-149. NRCBL: 15.1; 1.1; 8.3.1; 15.5; 14.3; 21.1.

Levitt, Mairi; Häyry, Matti. Overcritical, overfriendly? A dialogue between a sociologist and a philosopher on genetic technology and its applications. *Medicine, Health Care and Philosophy: A European Journal* 2005; 8(3): 377-383. NRCBL: 15.1; 7.1; 1.1.

Levitt, Mairi; Weiner, Kate; Goodacre, John. Stimulating public debate on the ethical and social issues raised by the new genetics. *In:* Holm, Søren; Jonas, Monique F., eds. Engaging the World: The Use of Empirical Research in Bioethics and the Regulation of Biotechnology. Washington, DC: IOS Press; 2004: 109-118. NRCBL: 15.1; 5.3. SC: em.

Lewis, Graham. Tissue collection and the pharamceutical industry: investigating corporate biobanks. *In:* Tutton, Richard; Corrigan, Oonagh, eds. Genetic Databases: Socio-ethical Issues in the Collection and Use of DNA. New York: Routledge; 2004: 181-202. NRCBL: 15.1; 1.3.12; 9.7; 19.5.

Lewontin, Richard C. The fallacy of racial medicine: confusions about human races. *GeneWatch* 2005 July-August; 18(4): 5-7, 17. NRCBL: 15.1; 9.5.4; 15.11.

Liao, S. Matthew. Are 'ex ante' enhancements always permissible? [comment]. *American Journal of Bioethics* 2005 May-June; 5(3): 23-25. NRCBL: 15.1; 14.1; 1.1; 4.5. Comments: comment on Frances M. Kamm, "Is there a problem with enhancement?" American Journal of Bioethics 2005 May-June; 5(3): 5- 14.

Liao, S. Matthew. The ethics of using genetic engineering for sex selection. *Journal of Medical Ethics* 2005 February; 31(2): 116-118. NRCBL: 15.1; 14.3.

Lindsay, Ronald A. Enhancements and justice: problems in determining the requirements of justice in a genetically transformed society. *Kennedy Institute of Ethics Journal* 2005 March; 15(1): 3-38. NRCBL: 15.1; 15.4; 4.5; 1.1; 5.3. Identifiers: John Rawls.
Abstract: There is a concern that genetic engineering will exacerbate existing social divisions and inequalities, especially if only the wealthy can afford genetic enhancements. Accordingly, many argue that justice requires the imposition of constraints on genetic engineering. However, it would be unwise to decide at this time what limits should be imposed in the future. Decision makers currently lack both the theoretical tools and the factual foundation for making sound judgments about the requirements of justice in a genetically transformed society. Moreover, focusing on the uncertain inequities of the future may result in failure to give priority to more pressing inequities of the present. Especially in a country that recently has enacted tax legislation that will widen existing wealth disparities, concern about the distant threat of a genetic aristocracy appears misplaced.

Liska, Adam J. The morality of problem selection in proteomics [opinion]. *Proteomics* 2004 July; 4(7): 1929-1931. NRCBL: 15.1; 5.2; 5.3.

Lloyd-Puryear, Michele A.; Kyler, Penny; Weissman, Gloria. The engagement of consumers in genetic educa-

NRCBL: National Reference Center for Bioethics Literature Classification Scheme   See inside front cover for terms.

223

tion: lessons learned. *In:* Knoppers, Bartha Maria, ed. Populations and Genetics: Legal and Socio-Ethical Perspectives. Boston: Martinus Nijhoff; 2003: 217-230. NRCBL: 15.1; 5.1.

Loftis, J. Robert. Germ-line enhancement of humans and nonhumans. *Kennedy Institute of Ethics Journal* 2005 March; 15(1): 57-76. NRCBL: 15.1; 15.4; 4.5; 5.3; 1.1; 5.2; 1.3.11. Identifiers: Monsanto; Roundup Ready.

Abstract: The current difference in attitude toward germ-line enhancement in humans and nonhumans is unjustified. Society should be more cautious in modifying the genes of nonhumans and more bold in thinking about modifying our own genome. I identify four classes of arguments pertaining to germ-line enhancement: safety arguments, justice arguments, trust arguments, and naturalness arguments. The first three types are compelling, but do not distinguish between human and nonhuman cases. The final class of argument would justify a distinction between human and nonhuman germ-line enhancement; however, this type of argument fails and, therefore, the discrepancy in attitude toward human and nonhuman germ-line enhancement is unjustified.

Longtin, Robert. Canadian province seeks control of its genes [news]. *Journal of the National Cancer Institute* 2004 November 3; 96(21): 1567-1569. NRCBL: 15.1; 18.2.

MacDonald, Chris. Patents and benefit-sharing as a challenge for corporate ethics. *In:* Knoppers, Bartha Maria, ed. Populations and Genetics: Legal and Socio-Ethical Perspectives. Boston: Martinus Nijhoff; 2003: 505-523. NRCBL: 15.1; 15.8; 1.3.2.

Macer, Darryl. Do the ethical duties of donor, and administrators, depend on whether the database is public or private? *In:* Knoppers, Bartha Maria, ed. Populations and Genetics: Legal and Socio-Ethical Perspectives. Boston: Martinus Nijhoff; 2003: 311-321. NRCBL: 15.1; 1.3.12; 19.5.

Macer, Darryl. Ethical, legal and social issues of genetically modifying insect vectors for public health. *Insect Biochemistry and Molecular Biology* 2005 July; 35(7): 649-660. NRCBL: 15.1; 1.3.11; 22.2; 9.1; 16.1; 21.1.

Maclin, Tracey. Is obtaining an arrestee's DNA a valid special needs search under the Fourth Amendment? What should (and will) the Supreme Court do? *Journal of Law, Medicine and Ethics* 2005 Spring; 33(1): 102- 124. NRCBL: 15.1; 1.3.5.

Malin, Bradley A. An evaluation of the current state of genomic data privacy protection technology and a roadmap for the future. *Journal of the American Medical Informatics Association* 2005 January-February; 12(1): 28-34. NRCBL: 15.1; 1.3.12; 8.4. SC: an.

Malinowski, Michael J. Technology transfer in biobanking: credits, debits, and population health futures. *Journal of Law, Medicine and Ethics* 2005 Spring; 33(1): 54-69. NRCBL: 15.1; 1.3.12; 18.6; 18.2.

Marques, M.B. Pharmaceutical patents and benefit-sharing: evolution of drug accessibility in Brazil since the 1980's. *In:* Knoppers, Bartha Maria, ed. Populations and Genetics: Legal and Socio-Ethical Perspectives. Boston: Martinus Nijhoff; 2003: 525-542. NRCBL: 15.1; 9.7; 15.8.

Matsui, K.; Kita, Y.; Ueshima, H. Informed consent, participation in, and withdrawal from a population based cohort study involving genetic analysis. *Journal of Medical Ethics* 2005 July; 31(7): 385-392. NRCBL: 15.1; 18.3. SC: em. Identifiers: Japan.

Abstract: OBJECTIVE: Population based cohort studies involving genetic research have been initiated in several countries. However, research published to date provides little information on the willingness of the general population to participate in such studies. Furthermore, there is a need to discover the optimal methods for acquiring fully informed consent from the general population. We therefore examined the results of a population based genetic cohort study to identify the factors affecting the participation rate by members of the general public and also specifically to examine the impact of different consent procedures on the rate of participation by prospective candidates and their subsequent withdrawal rate from the study. DESIGN: Descriptive analyses. SETTING AND PARTICIPANTS: The study evaluated two non- genetic subcohorts comprising 3166 people attending for a health checkup during 2002, and two genetic subcohorts comprising 2195 people who underwent a checkup during 2003.Main outcome measurements: Analysis endpoints were differences in participation rates between the non-genetic and genetic subcohorts, differences between providing non-extensive and extensive preliminary information, and changes in participation status between baseline and at 6 months. RESULTS: Participation rates in the genetic subcohorts were 4.7-9.3% lower than those in the non-genetic subcohorts. The odds ratios (OR) of participation in genetic research were between 0.60 and 0.77, and the OR for withdrawal from the research was over 7.70; providing preliminary extensive information about genetic research reduced the withdrawal risks (OR 0.15 for all dependent variables) but worsened participation rates (OR 0.63-0.74). CONCLUSIONS: The general population responded sceptically towards genetic research. It is crucial that genetic researchers utilise an informative and educational consent process worthy of public trust.

McDonagh, Sean. Genetic engineering is not the answer. *America* 2005 May 2; 192(15): 8-10. NRCBL: 15.1; 1.3.11; 1.2.

McQueen, Matthew J. Ethical and legal issues in the procurement, storage and use of DNA. *Clinical Chemistry and Laboratory Medicine* 1998 August; 36(8): 545-549. NRCBL: 15.1; 8.3.1; 8.4; 15.3.

Mehlman, Maxwell J. Genetic enhancement: plan now to act later. *Kennedy Institute of Ethics Journal* 2005 March; 15(1): 77-82. NRCBL: 15.1; 15.4; 4.5; 1.1; 5.3.

Abstract: All three main articles in the issues of the Kennedy Institute of Ethics Journal endorse the view that genetic enhancement should be permitted, including human germ-line genetic enhancement. However, unregulated, wealth-based access to genetic enhancement in general, and germ-line enhancement in particular, would create intolerable risks for society. Although there are a number of practical problems raised by proposals to regulate or restrict access to genetic enhancement, which will make it difficult if not impossible to muster support for any effective restrictions until we begin to experience the societal problems that genetic enhancement will create, it is important to consider now what restrictions would be appropriate, how they would be imposed, and what changes would be needed in existing laws and institutions to facilitate them. Without this type of groundwork, there is no way society will be in a position to act in time.

Miah, Andy. Bioethics, sport and the genetically enhanced athlete. *Medical Ethics and Bioethics / Medicinska Etika & Bioetika* 2002 Autumn-Winter; 9(3-4): 2-6. NRCBL: 15.1; 4.5; 9.5.1; 9.7. SC: an.

Middleton, Carl; Biegert, Mary Elise. Planning for the age of genetics: a Denver-based system makes ethical, theological, and practical decisions about genetic medicine. *Health Progress* 2005 January-February; 86(1): 35-40, 60. NRCBL: 15.1; 4.1.2.

Mirza, Bushra. Islamic perspectives on biotechnology. *In:* Brannigan, Michael C., ed. Cross-Cultural Biotechnology. Lanham: Rowman and Littlefield; 2004: 105-114. NRCBL: 15.1; 1.2; 1.3.11; 14.1; 15.3.

Mitchell, C. Ben. The return of eugenics [editorial]. *Ethics and Medicine* 2005 Summer; 21(2): 67. NRCBL: 15.1; 4.5; 15.5; 14.1; 7.1; 5.3.

Miyazaki, Satoru; Tateno, Yoshio. DNA data bank of Japan as an indispensable public database. *In:* Knoppers, Bartha Maria, ed. Populations and Genetics: Legal and Socio-Ethical Perspectives. Boston: Martinus Nijhoff; 2003: 115-121. NRCBL: 15.1; 1.3.12.

Munthe, Christian. Selected champions: making winners in the age of genetic technology. *In:* Tannsjo, Torbjorn; Tamburrini, Claudio, eds. Values in Sport: Elitism, Nationalism, Gender Equality, and the Scientific Manufacture of Winners. New York: E & FN Spon; 2000: 217-231. NRCBL: 15.1.

Mwase, Isaac M.T. Genetic enhancement and the fate of the worse off. *Kennedy Institute of Ethics Journal* 2005 March; 15(1): 83-89. NRCBL: 15.1; 15.4; 4.5; 1.1; 5.3.

Abstract: When reflecting on arguments in the debate about genetic technologies, decision makers must try to be empathetic to those who are worse off. Disparities in health and health care in the U.S. pale when global facts are considered. Although U.S. citizens ought to be concerned about the worse off in the U.S., such concern ultimately must be balanced against the urgent imperative to address the plight of those in poor countries. It is a matter of fairness that care and concern be directed to those who are truly worse off in global terms.

Nedelcu, R.; Blazer, K.R.; Schwerin, B.U.; Gambol, P.; Mantha, P.; Uman, G.C.; Weitzel, J.N. Genetic discrimination: the clinician perspective. *Clinical Genetics* 2004 October; 66(4): 311-317. NRCBL: 15.1; 9.3.1. SC: em.

Neter, Efrat; Wolowelsky, Yael; Borochowitz, Zvi U. Attitudes of Israeli Muslims at risk of genetic disorders towards pregnancy termination. *Community Genetics* 2005 May; 8(2): 88-93. NRCBL: 15.1; 12.3.

Newman, Stuart A. The perils of human developmental modification. *In:* Krimsky, Sheldon; Shorett, Peter, eds. Rights and Liberties in the Biotech Age: Why We Need a Genetic Bill of Rights. Lanham: Rowman and Littlefield Publishers; 2005: 203-208. NRCBL: 15.1; 4.5.

Pacholczyk, Tadeusz. Ethical considerations in oocyte assisted reprogramming. *National Catholic Bioethics Quarterly* 2005 Autumn; 5(3): 446- 447. NRCBL: 15.1; 18.5.4; 14.4.

Palmer, Larry I. Should liability play a role in social control of biobanks? *Journal of Law, Medicine and Ethics* 2005 Spring; 33(1): 70-78. NRCBL: 15.1; 1.3.12; 18.3; 18.6.

Palmour, Nicole. A survey of the variability of DNA banks worldwide. *In:* Knoppers, Bartha Maria, ed. Populations and Genetics: Legal and Socio-Ethical Perspectives. Boston: Martinus Nijhoff; 2003: 123-140. NRCBL: 15.1; 1.3.12. SC: em.

Parry, Bronwyn. From the corporeal to the informational: exploring the scope of benefit sharing agreements and their applicability to sequence databases. *In:* Thiele, F.; Ashcroft, R.E., eds. Bioethics in a Small World. Berlin: Springer; 2005: 73-91. NRCBL: 15.1; 21.1; 5.1.

Patel, Kant; Rushefsky, Mark E. The politics of genetics and public health. *In their:* The Politics of Public Health in the United States. Armonk, NY: M.E. Sharpe; 2005: 176-209. NRCBL: 15.1; 9.1; 21.1.

Paul, Diane B. Genetic engineering and eugenics: the uses of history. *In:* Baillie, Harold W.; Casey, Timothy K., eds. Is Human Nature Obsolete? Genetics Bioengineering, and the Future of the Human Condition. Cambridge, MA: MIT Press; 2005: 123-151. NRCBL: 15.1; 15.5; 21.4; 13.5.

Peacocke, Arthur. Relating genetics to theology on the map of scientific knowledge. *In:* Deane-Drummond, Celia; Szerszynski, Bronislaw, eds. Re- ordering Nature: Theology, Society and the New Genetics. New York: T & T Clark; 2003: 122-137. NRCBL: 15.1; 1.2.

Pincock, Stephen. Gene doping. *Lancet* 2005 December; 366(Medicine and Sport): S18-S19. NRCBL: 15.1; 4.5.

Pullman, Daryl; Latus, Andrew. Reconciling social justice and economic opportunism: regulating the Newfoundland genome. *In:* Knoppers, Bartha Maria, ed. Populations and Genetics: Legal and Socio-Ethical Perspectives. Boston: Martinus Nijhoff; 2003: 543-564. NRCBL: 15.1; 13.1; 1.1; 18.6.

Rabinow, Paul. Life sciences: discontents and consolations. *In:* Baillie, Harold W.; Casey, Timothy K., eds. Is Human Nature Obsolete? Genetics Bioengineering, and the Future of the Human Condition. Cambridge, MA: MIT Press; 2005: 99-121. NRCBL: 15.1; 15.10; 1.3.9.

NRCBL: National Reference Center for Bioethics Literature Classification Scheme   See inside front cover for terms.

225

Rahemtulla, Taslin; Bhopal, Raj. Pharmacogenetics and ethnically targeted therapies: the new drug BiDil marks the return of biology to the debate about race and ethnicity [editorial]. *BMJ: British Medical Journal* 2005 May 7; 330(7499): 1036-1037. NRCBL: 15.1; 9.7; 9.5.4.

Rannamae, Andres. Estonian Genome Project—large scale health status description and DNA collection. *In:* Knoppers, Bartha Maria, ed. Populations and Genetics: Legal and Socio-Ethical Perspectives. Boston: Martinus Nijhoff; 2003: 17-36. NRCBL: 15.1; 1.3.12.

Ravelingien, A.; Braeckman, J. To the core of porcine matter: evaluating arguments against producing transgenic pigs. *Xenotransplantation* 2004 July; 11(4): 371-375. NRCBL: 15.1; 22.2; 22.3; 19.1. SC: an.

Reichman, Edward. Why is this gene different from all other genes? The Jewish approach to biotechnology. *In:* Brannigan, Michael C., ed. Cross-Cultural Biotechnology. Lanham: Rowman and Littlefield; 2004: 93-104. NRCBL: 15.1; 1.2; 12.3; 14.1; 15.3; 18.5.4.

Rein, Diane C. Icelandic genetic database. *In:* Ness, Bryan D., ed. Encyclopedia of Genetics. Revised edition. Volume II. Pasadena, Calif.: Salem Press; 2004: 447-449. NRCBL: 15.1; 15.3; 1.3.12.

Reisner, Avram Israel; Parens, Erik. Genetics and complexity [letter and reply]. *Hastings Center Report* 2004 July-August; 34(4): 4-5. NRCBL: 15.1; 15.6.

Reiss, Michael J. Is it right to move genes between species? A theological perspective. *In:* Deane-Drummond, Celia; Szerszynski, Bronislaw, eds. Re- ordering Nature: Theology, Society and the New Genetics. New York: T & T Clark; 2003: 138-150. NRCBL: 15.1; 1.2.

Resnik, David B. Genetic engineering and social justice: a Rawlsian approach. *Social Theory Practice* 1997 Fall; 23(3): 427-448. NRCBL: 15.1; 15.6; 1.1.

Revel, Michel. Are genes our destiny?: Implications and ethical limitations of genetic determination in medicine and behavioral sciences. *In:* Blazer, Shraga; Zimmer, Etan Z., eds. The Embryo: Scientific Discovery and Medical Ethics. New York: Karger; 2005: 143-165. NRCBL: 15.1.

Rinaldi, Andrea. A new code for life. *EMBO Reports* 2004 April; 5(4): 336-339. NRCBL: 15.1.

Roberts, Laura Weiss; Geppert, Cynthia M.A.; Warner, Teddy D.; Hammond, Katherine A. Green; Rogers, Melinda; Smrcka, Julienne; Roberts, Brian B. Perspectives on use and protection of genetic information in work settings: results of a preliminary study. *Social Science and Medicine* 2005 April; 60(8): 1855-1858. NRCBL: 15.1; 1.3.12; 8.4. SC: em. Identifiers: United Kingdom (Great Britain).

Rogers-Hayden, Tee. Asilomar's legacy in Aotearoa New Zealand. *Science as Culture* 2005 December; 14(4): 393-410. NRCBL: 15.1; 1.3.11; 5.3. SC: rv.

Rollin, Bernard E. Telos, value, and genetic engineering. *In:* Baillie, Harold W.; Casey, Timothy K., eds. Is Human Nature Obsolete? Genetics Bioengineering, and the Future of the Human Condition. Cambridge, MA: MIT Press; 2005: 317-336. NRCBL: 15.1; 1.3.1; 1.1; 22.2.

Rothschild, Joan. Bioethics discourse and reproductive practice. *In her:* The Dream of the Perfect Child. Bloomington, IN: Indiana University Press; 2005: 157-187. NRCBL: 15.1; 2.1; 15.2; 15.3; 15.4; 15.5.

Rothstein, Mark A. Genetic justice [opinion]. *New England Journal of Medicine* 2005 June 30; 352(26): 2667-2668. NRCBL: 15.1; 1.3.5; 1.3.12.

Sagoff, Mark. Nature and human nature. *In:* Baillie, Harold W.; Casey, Timothy K., eds. Is Human Nature Obsolete? Genetics Bioengineering, and the Future of the Human Condition. Cambridge, MA: MIT Press; 2005: 67-98. NRCBL: 15.1; 1.1; 1.2.

Schiermeier, Quirin. Political deadlock leaves scientists frustrated [news]. *Nature* 2005 September 29; 437(7059): 603. NRCBL: 15.1; 1.3.5; 18.5.4. Identifiers: Germany.

Schrecker, Ted. Benefit-sharing in the new genomic marketplace: expanding the ethical frame of reference. *In:* Knoppers, Bartha Maria, ed. Populations and Genetics: Legal and Socio-Ethical Perspectives. Boston: Martinus Nijhoff; 2003:. NRCBL: 15.1; 15.8; 9.3.1.

Scott, Peter. Nature, technology and the rule of God: (en)countering the disgracing of nature. *In:* Deane-Drummond, Celia; Szerszynski, Bronislaw, eds. Re- ordering Nature: Theology, Society and the New Genetics. New York: T & T Clark; 2003: 275-292. NRCBL: 15.1; 1.2.

Scott, Rosamund. Prenatal testing, reproductive autonomy, and disability interests. *CQ: Cambridge Quarterly of Healthcare Ethics* 2005 Winter; 14(1): 65-82. NRCBL: 15.2; 12.1; 1.1; 14.1; 12.4.2; 9.5.1; 4.4; 9.4; 9.5.2.

Scully, Jackie Leach; Rippberger, Christine; Rehmann-Sutter, Christoph. Additional ethical issues in genetic medicine perceived by the potential patients. *In:* Knoppers, Bartha Maria, ed. Populations and Genetics: Legal and Socio-Ethical Perspectives. Boston: Martinus Nijhoff; 2003: 623-638. NRCBL: 15.1. SC: em.

Shannon, Thomas A. Human nature in a post-human genome project world. *In:* Baillie, Harold W.; Casey, Timothy K., eds. Is Human Nature Obsolete? Genetics Bioengineering, and the Future of the Human Condition. Cambridge, MA: MIT Press; 2005: 269-316. NRCBL: 15.1; 15.10; 3.2; 1.1; 1.2.

Shapiro, Michael H. The identity of identity: moral and legal aspects of technological self-transformation. *Social Philosophy and Policy* 2005 Summer; 22(2): 308-373. NRCBL: 15.1; 4.5; 15.4; 14.1; 4.4.

Sharp, Phillip A. 1918 flu and responsible science [editorial]. *Science* 2005 October 7; 310(5745): 17. NRCBL: 15.1; 1.3.9; 21.3.

Sheremeta, Lorraine; Gold, E. Richard; Caulfield, Timothy. Harmonizing commercialisation and gene patent policy with other social goals. *In:* Knoppers, Bartha Maria, ed. Populations and Genetics: Legal and Socio-Ethical Perspectives. Boston: Martinus Nijhoff; 2003: 423-452. NRCBL: 15.1; 15.8; 9.3.1.

Shickle, Darren; Hapgood, Rhydian; Carlisle, Jane; Shackley, Phil; Morgan, Ann; McCabe, Chris. Public attitudes to participating in UK BioBank: a DNA bank, lifestyle and morbidity database on 500,000 members of the UK public aged 45-69. *In:* Knoppers, Bartha Maria, ed. Populations and Genetics: Legal and Socio-Ethical Perspectives. Boston: Martinus Nijhoff; 2003:. NRCBL: 15.1; 1.3.12; 7.1. SC: em.

Shreeve, Jamie. I, chimera. *New Scientist* 2005 June 25-July 1; 186(2505): 39-43. NRCBL: 15.1; 22.1. Identifiers: human embryonic stem-cell research; interspecies mixing.

Shreeve, Jamie. The other stem-cell debate: to test the potential curative powers of human embryonic stem cells, biologists want to inject them into lab animals. Creating such chimeras makes perfect sense, to a point: a sheep with a human liver? O.K. A mouse brain made up of human cells? Maybe. But a chimp that sobs? *New York Times Magazine* 2005 April 10; p. 42-47. NRCBL: 15.1; 18.1; 22.1. SC: po.

Siep, Ludwig. Wissen—Vorbeugen—Verändern: Über die ethischen Probleme beim gegenwärtigen Stand des Genomprojekts. *In:* Honnefelder, Ludger; Mieth, Dietmar; Propping, Peter; Siep, Ludwig; Wiesemann, Claudia, eds. Das genetische Wissen und die Zukunft des Menschen. New York: De Gruyter; 2003: 78-86. NRCBL: 15.1; 4.5. SC: an.

Silverman, Paul H.; Parens, Erik. Genetics and complexity [letter and reply]. *Hastings Center Report* 2004 July-August; 34(4): 4-5. NRCBL: 15.1; 15.6; 15.10.

Singh, S. Kumar. Responsibilities in the post genome era: are we prepared? *Issues in Medical Ethics* 2002 January-March; 10(1): 150-151. NRCBL: 15.1; 15.10.

Smith, David H.; Sedgwick, Timothy. Theological perspectives. *In:* Smith, David H.; Cohen, Cynthia B., eds. A Christian Response to the New Genetics: Religious, Ethical, and Social Issues. Lanham, MD: Rowman & Littlefield Publishers; 2003: 1-13. NRCBL: 15.1; 1.2.

Squier, Susan. The hybrid embryo and xenogenic desire. *In her:* Liminal Lives: Imaging the Human at the Frontiers of Biomedicine. Durham: Duke University Press; 2004: 89-111. NRCBL: 15.1; 18.5.4; 22.2; 18.1.

Strong, Carson. Lost in translation: religious arguments made secular [comment]. *American Journal of Bioethics* 2005 May-June; 5(3): 29-31. NRCBL: 15.1; 14.1; 1.1; 4.5. SC: an. Comments: comment on Frances M. Kamm, "Is there a problem with enhancement?" American Journal of Bioethics 2005 May-June; 5(3): 5- 14.

Surbone, A. Genetic medicine: the balance between science and morality. *Annals of Oncology* 2004; 15(Supplement 1): I60-I64. NRCBL: 15.1; 4.2; 8.1.

Tate, Sarah K.; Goldstein, David B. Will tomorrow's medicines work for everyone? [opinion]. *Nature Genetics* 2004 November; 36(11, Supplement): S34-S42. NRCBL: 15.1; 9.5.4; 9.7; 13.1.

Tauer, Carol A. Obstetrics and pediatrics: the second article in a series about the significance of genetic science for Catholic health care — an ethical view. *Health Progress* 2005 July-August; 86(4): 13-18. NRCBL: 15.1; 1.2.

Taussig, Karen-Sue. Genetics and genetic engineering. *In:* Restivo, Sal, ed. Science, Technology, and Society: An Encyclopedia. New York: Oxford University Press; 2005: 156-162. NRCBL: 15.1; 15.5; 15.10.

Taylor, Sandy. A case study of genetic discrimination: social work and advocacy within a new context. *Australian Social Work* 1998 December; 51(4): 51-57. NRCBL: 15.1; 1.3.10; 15.3.

Templeton, Alan R. When does life begin?: An evolutionary genetic answer to a central ethical question. *In:* Blazer, Shraga; Zimmer, Etan Z., eds. The Embryo: Scientific Discovery and Medical Ethics. New York: Karger; 2005: 1-20. NRCBL: 15.1; 4.4.

Thomas, James C.; Irwin, Debra E.; Zuiker, Erin Shaugnessy; Millikan, Robert C. Genomics and the public health code of ethics. *American Journal of Public Health* 2005 December; 95(12): 2139- 2143. NRCBL: 15.1; 9.1; 1.3.1.
Abstract: We consider the public health applications of genomic technologies as viewed through the lens of the public health code of ethics. We note, for example, the potential for genomics to increase our appreciation for the public health value of interdependence, the potential for some genomic tools to exacerbate health disparities because of their inaccessibility by the poor and the way in which genomics forces public health to refine its notions of prevention. The public health code of ethics sheds light on concerns raised by commercial genomic products that are not discussed in detail by more clinically oriented perspectives. In addition, the concerns raised by genomics highlight areas of our understanding of the ethical principles of public health in which further refinement may be necessary.

NRCBL: National Reference Center for Bioethics Literature Classification Scheme   See inside front cover for terms.

227

Thomas, Sandy M. Society and ethics — the genetics of disease. *Current Opinion in Genetics and Development* 2004 June; 14(3): 287-291. NRCBL: 15.1; 8.4; 9.7.

Treloar, Susan; Taylor, Sandra; Otlowski, Margaret; Barlow- Stewart, Kristine; Stranger, Mark; Chenoweth, Kellie. Methodological considerations in the study of genetic discrimination. *Community Genetics* 2005 January; 7(4): 161-168. NRCBL: 15.1; 15.3; 9.3.1; 18.1. SC: em.

Trump, Eric F. Identity crisis. *Hastings Center Report* 2004 July-August; 34(4): 2. NRCBL: 15.1; 15.11.

Tutton, Richard; Kaye, Jane; Hoeyer, Klaus. Governing UK Biobank: the importance of ensuring public trust [opinion]. *Trends in Biotechnology* 2004 June; 22(6): 284-285. NRCBL: 15.1; 1.3.12; 18.2; 18.3; 19.5. Identifiers: United Kingdom (Great Britain).

Vardy, Peter. The physical enhancement of humanity. *In his:* Being Human: Fulfilling Genetic and Spiritual Potential. London: Darton, Longman and Todd; 2003: 63-74. NRCBL: 15.1; 15.4; 4.5.

Vardy, Peter. A test case—the challenge of genetic engineering. *In his:* Being Human: Fulfilling Genetic and Spiritual Potential. London: Darton, Longman and Todd; 2003: 19-25. NRCBL: 15.1; 15.4.

von Bubnoff, Andreas. The 1918 flu virus is resurrected [news]. *Nature* 2005 October 6; 437(7060): 794-795. NRCBL: 15.1; 1.3.9; 21.3.

Wade, Nicholas. Chimeras on the horizon, but don't expect centaurs. *New York Times* 2005 May 3; p. F1, F8. NRCBL: 15.1; 22.1; 22.3. SC: po.

Wadman, Meredith. Drug targeting: is race enough? [news]. *Nature* 2005 June 23; 435(7045): 1008-1009. NRCBL: 15.1; 9.5.4; 9.7. Identifiers: BiDil.

Wenz, Peter. Engineering genetic injustice. *Bioethics* 2005 February; 19(1): 1-11. NRCBL: 15.1;; 1.1. SC: an.

Wertz, Dorothy C. International perspectives on privacy and access to genetic information. *Microbial and Comparative Genomics* 1997; 2(1): 53-61. NRCBL: 15.1; 8.4; 21.1. SC: em.

Wexler, Barbara. Ethical issues and public opinion. *In her:* Genetics and Genetic Engineering. Detroit, MI: Gale Group; 2004: 133-141. NRCBL: 15.1; 15.3; 18.5.4; 5.1.

Wheeler, Sondra. Making babies? Genetic engineering and the character of parenthood [opinion]. *Sojourners* 1999 May-June; 28(3): 14. NRCBL: 15.1; 14.1; 9.5.8; 2.1.

Williams, Garrath. Human gene banks. *Medical Ethics Newsletter [Lahey Clinic]* 2005 Winter; 12(1): 1-2. NRCBL: 15.1; 1.3.12; 13.1.

Williams-Jones, Bryn; Corrigan, Oonagh P. Rhetoric and hype: where's the 'ethics' in pharmacogenomics? *American Journal of Pharmacogenomics* 2003; 3(6): 375-383. NRCBL: 15.1; 9.7.

Willis, Evan. Public health, private genes: the social context of genetic biotechnologies. *Critical Public Health* 1998 June; 8(2): 131-139. NRCBL: 15.1; 5.3; 9.1.

Willis, Mark. Not this pig: dignity, imagination, and informed consent. *In:* Van Cleve, John Vickery, ed. Genetics, Disability, and Deafness. Washington, DC: Gallaudet University Press; 2004: 174- 185. NRCBL: 15.1; 15.5; 18.3.

Wilson, Jane. To know or not to know? Genetic ignorance, autonomy and paternalism. *Bioethics* 2005 October; 19(5-6): 492-504. NRCBL: 15.1; 8.3.1; 1.1.
Abstract: This paper examines some arguments which deny the existence of an individual right to remain ignorant about genetic information relating to oneself—often referred to as 'a right to genetic ignorance' or, more generically, as 'a right not to know'. Such arguments fall broadly into two categories: 1) those which accept that individuals have a right to remain ignorant in self-regarding matters, but deny that this right can be extended to genetic ignorance, since such ignorance may be harmful to others, particularly those to whom one is genetically related (the 'harm to others objection') and 2) those which contend that, even if genetic ignorance is only self harming, it is not something to which individuals can rationally or morally claim to have a 'right' at all, since they defend their claims on autonomy-respecting grounds and ignorance is inimical to autonomy (the 'incoherence objection'). I argue that defenders of a right not to know have some plausible responses to the 'harm to others objection', they and their opponents reach an impasse in which both sides are left voicing concerns about the paternalistic implications of the other's point of view. I conclude that defenders of a right not to know would, therefore, advance their position further by analysing it in terms of values other than those of autonomy and rights.

Winkelmann, Bernhard R.; Prickett, Katie. Pharmacogenomics, genetic testing and ethnic variability: tackling the ethical questions [interview]. *Pharmacogenomics* 2003 September; 4(5): 531-535. NRCBL: 15.1; 9.7.

Winner, Langdon. Resistance is futile: the posthuman condition and its advocates. *In:* Baillie, Harold W.; Casey, Timothy K., eds. Is Human Nature Obsolete? Genetics Bioengineering, and the Future of the Human Condition. Cambridge, MA: MIT Press; 2005: 385-411. NRCBL: 15.1; 5.1.

Wolbring, Gregor. The animal farm philosophy of genetic discrimination. *Revista de Derecho y Genoma-Humano / Law and the Human Genome Review* 2004 July-December; (21): 165-184. NRCBL: 15.1; 4.2; 15.2; 14.3. SC: em. Note: Abstract in English and Spanish.

Wyke, Alexandra. Inherited wealth. *Economist* 1988 April 30; 307: 3-18. NRCBL: 15.1; 15.7.

Wynne, Brian. Interpreting public concerns about GMOs—questions of meaning. *In:* Deane-Drummond,

Celia; Szerszynski, Bronislaw, eds. Re- ordering Nature: Theology, Society and the New Genetics. New York: T & T Clark; 2003: 221-248. NRCBL: 15.1; 1.3.11.

Yang, Huanming. Advances in science and progress of humanity: a global perspective on DNA sampling. *In:* Knoppers, Bartha Maria, ed. Populations and Genetics: Legal and Socio-Ethical Perspectives. Boston: Martinus Nijhoff; 2003: 395-404. NRCBL: 15.1; 1.3.12; 21.1.

Zaner, Richard M. Visions and re-visions: life and the accident of birth. *In:* Baillie, Harold W.; Casey, Timothy K., eds. Is Human Nature Obsolete? Genetics Bioengineering, and the Future of the Human Condition. Cambridge, MA: MIT Press; 2005: 177-207. NRCBL: 15.1; 14.5; 1.1.

GENETICS/ LEGAL ASPECTS

Adalsteinsson, Ragnar. Human genetic databases and liberty. *Juridical Review* 2004; 2004(1): 65-74. NRCBL: 15.1; 1.3.12; 13.1; 15.10; 5.3; 8.4. SC: le. Identifiers: Iceland.

Andrews, Lori B. A conceptual framework for genetic policy: comparing the medical, public health, and fundamental rights models. *Washington University Law Quarterly* 2001; 79(152): 221-285. NRCBL: 15.1; 9.1; 9.2. SC: le.

Beskow, Laura M. Ethical, legal, and social issues in the design and conduct of human genome epidemiology studies. *In:* Khoury, Muin J.; Little, Julian; Burke, Wylie, eds. Human Genome Epidemiology: A Scientific Foundation for Using Genetic Information to Improve Health and Prevent Disease. New York: Oxford University Press; 2004: 58-76. NRCBL: 15.1; 7.1. SC: le.

Brownsword, Roger. Regulating human genetics: new dilemmas for a new millennium. *Medical Law Review* 2004 Spring; 12(1): 14-39. NRCBL: 15.1; 5.3; 4.4; 18.5.4; 1.1. SC: le.

Chico, Dee Marlo E. Pharmacogenomics: a brave new world in designer drugs. *Scholar: Saint Mary's Law Review on Minority Issues* 2002 Fall; 5(1): 111-152. NRCBL: 15.1; 9.7; 5.3. SC: le.

Chorpening, Jennifer. Genetic disability: a modest proposal to modify the ADA to protect against some forms of genetic discrimination. *North Carolina Law Review* 2004 May; 82(4): 1441-1481. NRCBL: 15.1; 15.3; 16.3; 1.3.5. SC: le. Identifiers: Americans with Disabilities Act.

Clayton, Ellen Wright. Informed consent and biobanks. *Journal of Law, Medicine and Ethics* 2005 Spring; 33(1): 15-21. NRCBL: 15.1; 1.3.12; 18.2; 18.3. SC: le.

Deschênes, Mylène; Sallée, Clémentine. Accountability in population biobanking: comparative approaches. *Journal of Law, Medicine and Ethics* 2005 Spring; 33(1): 40-53. NRCBL: 15.1; 1.3.12; 8.4. SC: rv; an; le.

Deutsch, Erwin. Rights and obligations of the persons concerning their genetic data. *Revista de Derecho y Genoma Humano / Law and the Human Genome Review* 2005 January-June; (22): 75-84. NRCBL: 15.1; 1.1; 8.4; 18.3; 1.3.5. SC: le. Note: Abstract in English and Spanish.

Etzioni, Amitai. DNA tests and databases in criminal justice: individual rights and the common good. *In:* Lazer, David, ed. DNA and the Criminal Justice System: The Technology of Justice. Cambridge, MA: MIT Press; 2004: 197-223. NRCBL: 15.1; 1.3.5; 1.1; 1.3.12. SC: le.

Fernandez, Holly K. Genetic privacy, abandonment, and DNA dragnets: is Fourth Amendment jurisprudence adequate? *Hastings Center Report* 2005 January-February; 35(1): 21-23. NRCBL: 15.1; 1.3.5; 1.3.12. SC: le.

Gentry, Deborah B. Genetic technology and family conflict. *Mediation Quarterly* 2000 Fall; 18(1): 5-17. NRCBL: 15.1; 1.3.8. SC: le.

Gevers, J.K.M. Genetic databases and consent for use of medical records. *Community Genetics* 2005 January; 7(4): 173-175. NRCBL: 15.1; 1.3.12; 8.3.1. SC: le.

Gevers, J.K.M. Response of the law to developments in genetics. *Medicine and Law: World Association for Medical Law* 1995; 14(3-4): 199-206. NRCBL: 15.1; 15.3; 8.4; 13.1. SC: le.

Gibbons, Susan M.C.; Helgason, Hördur Helgi; Kaye, Jane; Nõmper, Ants; Wendel, Lotta. Lessons from European population genetic databases: comparing the law in Estonia, Iceland, Sweden and the United Kingdom. *European Journal of Health Law* 2005 June; 12(2): 103-133. NRCBL: 15.1; 1.3.12; 17.1; 18.3; 4.4; 1.3.9; 21.1. SC: le; an.

Gonzalez-Arnal, Stella. Indigenous knowledge, patenting, and the biotechnology industry. *In:* Brannigan, Michael C., ed. Cross-Cultural Biotechnology. Lanham: Rowman and Littlefield; 2004: 139-151. NRCBL: 15.1; 15.8; 21.1. SC: le.

Greely, Henry T. Banning genetic discrimination [opinion]. *New England Journal of Medicine* 2005 September 1; 353(9): 865- 867. NRCBL: 15.1; 9.5.4; 16.3; 9.3.1. SC: le.

Halliday, Samantha; Steinberg, Deborah Lynn. The regulated gene: new legal dilemmas. *Medical Law Review* 2004 Spring; 12(1): 2-13. NRCBL: 15.1; 5.3; 18.6. SC: le.

Hendriks, Aart. Genetic discrimination: how to anticipate predictable problems? [editorial]. *European Journal of Health Law* 2002 June; 9(2): 87-92. NRCBL: 15.1; 9.2; 2.4; 5.3. SC: le.

Hindmarsh, Richard. Genetic engineering regulation in Australia: an 'archaeology' of expertise and power. *Science as Culture* 2005 December; 14(4): 373-392. NRCBL: 15.1; 5.3; 18.2. SC: rv; le.

NRCBL: National Reference Center for Bioethics Literature Classification Scheme   See inside front cover for terms.

229

Hsieh, Alice. A nation's genes for a cure to cancer: evolving ethical, social and legal issues regarding population genetic databases. *Columbia Journal of Law and Social Problems* 2004 Spring; 37(3): 359-411. NRCBL: 15.1; 1.3.12; 5.3; 21.1; 18.3; 8.4; 15.10. SC: le.

Ioirysh, A.I.; Krasovskii, O.A. Legal aspects of genetic engineering. *Russian Politics and Law* 1998 July-August; 36(4): 77-83. NRCBL: 15.1; 5.3; 21.1. SC: le.

Janger, Edward J. Genetic information, privacy and insolvency. *Journal of Law, Medicine and Ethics* 2005 Spring; 33(1): 79-88. NRCBL: 15.1; 1.3.12; 8.4; 4.4; 18.6. SC: le.

Karpin, Isabel. Genetics and the legal conception of self. *In:* Shildrick, Margrit; Mykitiuk, Roxanne, eds. Ethics of the Body: Postconventional Challenges. Cambridge, MA: MIT Press; 2005: 195-216. NRCBL: 15.1; 1.1; 4.4. SC: le.

Kaye, D.H.; Smith, Michael E. DNA databases for law enforcement: the coverage question and the case for a population-wide database. *In:* Lazer, David, ed. DNA and the Criminal Justice System: The Technology of Justice. Cambridge, MA: MIT Press; 2004: 247-284. NRCBL: 15.1; 1.3.5. SC: le.

Knoppers, Bartha Maria. Biobanking: international norms. *Journal of Law, Medicine and Ethics* 2005 Spring; 33(1): 7-14. NRCBL: 15.1; 1.3.12; 21.1; 18.3; 4.4. SC: le.

Kopinski, Nicole E. Human-nonhuman chimeras: a regulatory proposal on the blurring of species lines. *Boston College Law Review* 2004 May; 45(3): 619-666. NRCBL: 15.1; 18.1; 22.1. SC: le.

Mandel, Gregory N. Gaps, inexperience, inconsistencies, and overlaps: crisis in the regulation of genetically modified plants and animals. *William and Mary Law Review* 2004 April; 45(5): 2167-2259. NRCBL: 15.1; 5.3; 16.1. SC: le.

Mandry, Tilo. Legal implications of pharmacogenomics regarding drug trials, drug labeling, and genetic testing for drug prescription: an international approach. *Food and Drug Law Journal* 2004; 59(4): 519-535. NRCBL: 15.1; 9.7; 21.1; 18.2; 5.3. SC: le.

Manson, Neil C. How not to think about genetic information [opinion]. *Hastings Center Report* 2005 July-August; 35(4): 3. NRCBL: 15.1. SC: le.

Merali, Zara; Singer, Peter A.; Boulyjenkov, Victor; Daar, Abdallah S. The ELSI genetics regulatory resource kit: a tool for policymakers in developing countries. *Journal of Law, Medicine and Ethics* 2004 Winter; 32(4): 692-700. NRCBL: 15.1; 21.1; 18.6; 5.3. SC: le. Identifiers: ethical, legal, and social issues.

Moniz, Helena. Privacy and intra-family communication of genetic information. *Revista de Derecho y Genoma-Humano / Law and the Human Genome Review*

2004 July-December; (21): 103-124. NRCBL: 15.1; 8.4; 1.1; 8.3.1; 8.1. SC: le. Note: Abstract in English and Spanish.

Noah, Lars. The coming pharmacogenomics revolution: tailoring drugs to fit patients' genetic profiles. *Jurimetrics* 2002 Fall; 43(1): 1-28. NRCBL: 15.1; 9.7; 5.3; 15.3. SC: le.

O'Connell, Karen. The devouring: genetics, abjection, and the limits of law. *In:* Shildrick, Margrit; Mykitiuk, Roxanne, eds. Ethics of the Body: Postconventional Challenges. Cambridge, MA: MIT Press; 2005: 217- 234. NRCBL: 15.1. SC: le.

Otlowski, Margaret. Exploring the concept of genetic discrimination. *Journal of Bioethical Inquiry* 2005; 2(3): 165-176. NRCBL: 15.1; 15.3; 15.6. SC: an; le. Identifiers: Australia.

Parfett, Julianne. Canada's DNA databank: public safety and private costs. *Manitoba Law Journal* 2002; 29(1): 33-79. NRCBL: 15.1; 1.3.12; 1.3.5; 8.4. SC: le.

Reilly, Phil. Legal and public policy issues in DNA forensics [opinion]. *Nature Reviews Genetics* 2001 April; 2(4): 313-317. NRCBL: 15.1; 1.3.5; 21.1. SC: le. Identifiers: National Commission on the Future of DNA Evidence.

Robertson, John A. Ethical and legal issues in genetic biobanking. *In:* Knoppers, Bartha Maria, ed. Populations and Genetics: Legal and Socio-Ethical Perspectives. Boston: Martinus Nijhoff; 2003: 297-309. NRCBL: 15.1; 1.3.12. SC: le.

Rosén, Elisabeth. Genetic information and genetic discrimination how medical records vitiate legal protection: a comparative analysis of international legislation and policies. *Scandinavian Journal of Public Health* 1999 September; 27(3): 166-172. NRCBL: 15.1; 9.1; 15.3; 9.2; 1.3.5; 21.1. SC: le.

Rothstein, Mark A. Expanding the ethical analysis of biobanks. *Journal of Law, Medicine and Ethics* 2005 Spring; 33(1): 89-101. NRCBL: 15.1; 1.3.12; 18.3; 8.4. SC: le.

Rothstein, Mark A. Genetic exceptionalism and legislative pragmatism. *Hastings Center Report* 2005 July-August; 35(4): 27-33. NRCBL: 15.1; 15.3. SC: le.

Scherer, Robert Craig. Mandatory genetic dogtags and the Fourth Amendment: the need for a new post-Skinner test. *Georgetown Law Journal* 1997 June; 85(6): 2007-2038. NRCBL: 15.1; 1.3.12. SC: le.

Simoncelli, Tania; Steinhardt, Barry. California's proposition 69: a dangerous precedent for criminal DNA databases. *Journal of Law, Medicine and Ethics* 2005 Summer; 33(2): 279- 293. NRCBL: 15.1; 1.3.5; 18.5.5; 18.3; 8.4. SC: le.

Steinhardt, Barry. Privacy and forensic DNA data banks. *In:* Lazer, David, ed. DNA and the Criminal Justice System: The Technology of Justice. Cambridge, MA: MIT Press; 2004: 173-196. NRCBL: 15.1; 15.3; 1.3.7; 8.4. SC: le.

Taitz, J.; Weekers, J.E.M.; Mosca, D.T. The last resort: exploring the use of DNA testing for family reunification. *Health and Human Rights: An International Journal* 2002; 6(1): 21-32. NRCBL: 15.1; 1.3.5; 21.1; 15.3; 8.4; 8.3.4; 1.2. SC: le.

Taylor, M.J. Problems of practice and principle if centring law reform on the concept of genetic discrimination. *European Journal of Health Law* 2004 December; 11(4): 365-380. NRCBL: 15.1; 1.1; 15.3. SC: le.

Tracy, Paul E.; Morgan, Vincent. Big brother and his science kit: DNA databases for 21st century crime control? *Journal of Criminal Law and Criminology* 2000 Winter; 90(2): 635-690. NRCBL: 15.1; 1.3.12. SC: le.

United States. Department of Labor; Department of Health and Human Services; Equal Employment Opportunity Commission; Department of Justice. Genetic information in the workplace. *Labor Law Journal* 1998 February; 49(2): 867-876. NRCBL: 15.1; 16.3; 8.4. SC: le.

Van Hoyweghen, Ine; Horstman, Klasien; Schepers, Rita. 'Genetics is not the issue': insurers on genetics and life insurance. *New Genetics and Society* 2005 April; 24(1): 79-98. NRCBL: 15.1; 9.3.1; 5.3. SC: le.

Weiman, Darryl S. Genes and the law. *In:* Ellis, C.N., ed. Inherited Cancer Syndromes: Current Clinical Management. New York: Springer-Verlag; 2004: 83-90. NRCBL: 15.1; 9.3.1; 15.3; 8.4. SC: an; le.

Whitcomb, David J. Genetic discrimination. Individual protection legislation stalls in Congress. *AWHONN Lifelines* 2004 October-November; 8(5): 414-416. NRCBL: 15.1; 9.3.1. SC: le.

GENETICS AND HUMAN ANCESTRY

Balaban, Evan. The new racial economy: making a silk purse out of the sow's ear of racial distinctions. *GeneWatch* 2005 July-August; 18(4): 8-10. NRCBL: 15.11; 9.5.4; 15.1; 7.1.

Barr, Donald A. The practitioner's dilemma: can we use a patient's race to predict genetics, ancestry, and the expected outcomes of treatment? *Annals of Internal Medicine* 2005 December 6; 143(11): 809-815. NRCBL: 15.11; 9.5.4.

Abstract: Recent research has identified genetic traits that can be used in a laboratory setting to distinguish among global population groups. In some genetic analyses, the population groups identified resemble groups that are historically categorized as "races." On the basis of these associations, some researchers have argued that a patient's race can be used to predict underlying genetic traits and from these traits, the expected outcomes of treatment. Others have questioned the use of race in this way, arguing that racially defined groups are so heterogeneous that predictions of individual characteristics derived from group averages are bound to be problematic. Practitioners today face the dilemma of translating this scientific debate into clinical decisions made 1 patient at a time. Is it or is it not appropriate to use a patient's self-identified "race" to help decide treatment? In contrast to the global population groups identified by genetic studies, the U.S. population has experienced substantial genetic admixture over time, weakening our ability to distinguish groups on the basis of meaningful genetic differences. Nonetheless, many researchers have suggested that these differences are still sufficient to identify racially specific uses for pharmaceutical and other treatments. A review of recent research on the treatment of hypertension and congestive heart failure finds that race-specific treatments of this type carry a substantial risk for treating patients—black or white—inappropriately, either by withholding a treatment that may be effective or by using a treatment that may be ineffective. Only by moving beyond historical concepts of "race" to examining a patient's individual socioeconomic, cultural, behavioral, and ancestral circumstances can a practitioner select the treatment that is most likely to be effective and in doing so, can best serve that patient's needs.

Carlson, Rick J. The case of BiDil: a policy commentary on race and genetics [opinion]. *Health Affairs* 2005 July-December; 24(Supplement 3): W5-464- W5-468. NRCBL: 15.11; 9.5.4; 9.7.

Chismark, Sacie R. Race. *In:* Ness, Bryan D., ed. Encyclopedia of Genetics. Revised edition. Volume II. Pasadena, Calif.: Salem Press; 2004: 658-663. NRCBL: 15.11.

Garte, Seymour. The racial genetics paradox in biomedical research and public health [opinion]. *Public Health Reports* 2002 September-October; 117(5): 421-425. NRCBL: 15.11; 9.5.4. Note: Erratum in: Public Health Reports 2003 January-February; 118(1): 2.

Kahn, Jonathan. BiDil: false promises: faulty statistics and reasoning have lead [sic; led] to the first "racial medicine". *GeneWatch* 2005 November-December; 18(6): 6-9, 18. NRCBL: 15.11; 9.7; 9.5.4. Identifiers: NitroMed.

Marks, Jonathan. New information, enduring questions: race, genetics, and medicine in the 21st century. *GeneWatch* 2005 July-August; 18(4): 11-16. NRCBL: 15.11; 21.1.

Sankar, Pamela; Kahn, Jonathan. BiDil: race medicine or race marketing? *Health Affairs* 2005 July-December; 24(Supplement 3): W5-455- W5-463. NRCBL: 15.11; 9.3.1; 9.5.4; 9.7.

Shields, Alexandra E.; Fortun, Michael; Hammonds, Evelynn M.; King, Patricia A.; Lerman, Caryn; Rapp, Rayna; Sullivan, Patrick F. The use of race variables in genetic studies of complex traits and the goal of reducing health disparities: a transdisciplinary perspective. *American Psychologist* 2005 January; 60(1): 77-103. NRCBL: 15.11; 9.5.4; 9.5.9; 18.5.1.

NRCBL: National Reference Center for Bioethics Literature Classification Scheme   See inside front cover for terms.

231

Singer, Emily. Race-based heart drug might stall search for better markers [news]. *Nature Medicine* 2005 August; 11(8): 812. NRCBL: 15.11; 9.5.4; 9.7.

Soo-Jin Lee, Sandra; Koenig, Barbara A. Racial profiling of DNA samples: will it affect scientific knowledge about human genetic variation? *In:* Knoppers, Bartha Maria, ed. Populations and Genetics: Legal and Socio-Ethical Perspectives. Boston: Martinus Nijhoff; 2003: 231-244. NRCBL: 15.11; 15.1; 18.5.1.

Wade, Nicholas. Genetic catalog may aid search for roots of disease. *New York Times* 2005 October 27; p. A20. NRCBL: 15.11. SC: po.

Wallbank, Julie. The role of rights and utility in instituting a child's right to know her genetic history. *Social and Legal Studies* 2004 June 1; 13(2): 245-264. NRCBL: 15.11; 8.4; 14.2. SC: le.

GENOCIDE *See* TORTURE, GENOCIDE, AND WAR CRIMES

GENOME MAPPING
See also GENETIC RESEARCH; GENETIC SCREENING; RECOMBINANT DNA RESEARCH

Baumann, Teresa K. Proxy consent and a national DNA databank: an unethical and discriminatory combination. *Iowa Law Review* 2001 January; 86(2): 667-701. NRCBL: 15.10; 1.3.12; 13.1; 8.3.2; 15.11; 18.3. SC: le.

Chadwick, Ruth; Wilson, Sarah. Genomic databases as global public goods? *Res Publica* 2004; 10(2): 123-134. NRCBL: 15.10; 1.3.12; 21.1. SC: le.

Council of Europe. Recommendation 1512 (2001): protection of the human genome by the Council of Europe. *Medical Ethics and Bioethics / Medicinska Etika & Bioetika* 2001 Spring-Summer; 8(1-2): 9-10. NRCBL: 15.10; 4.4; 21.1. SC: le.

Despoja, Natasha Stott. The Human Genome Project: how do we protect Australians? *Medical Journal of Australia* 2000 December 4-18; 173(11-12): 596-598. NRCBL: 15.10; 15.1; 15.7.

Diamond, Ian; Woodgate, Dawn. Genomics research in the UK — the social science agenda. *New Genetics and Society* 2005 August; 24(2): 239-252. NRCBL: 15.10; 4.2; 5.3. Identifiers: United Kingdom (Great Britain).

Döring, Martin. A sequence of 'factishes': the media-metaphorical knowledge dynamics structuring the German press coverage of the human genome. *New Genetics and Society* 2005 December; 24(3): 317-336. NRCBL: 15.10; 1.3.7; 5.1.

Eisenberg, Rebecca S. Genomics in the public domain: strategy and policy [opinion]. *Nature Reviews Genetics* 2000 October; 1(1): 70-74. NRCBL: 15.10; 15.8; 9.3.1; 5.3.

Gogorosi, Eleni. Untying the Gordian knot of creation: metaphors for the Human Genome Project in Greek newspapers. *New Genetics and Society* 2005 December; 24(3): 299-315. NRCBL: 15.10; 1.3.7; 5.1.

Greely, Henry T. Iceland's plan for genomics research: facts and implications. *Jurimetrics* 2000 Winter; 40: 153-191. NRCBL: 15.10; 1.3.12; 13.1. SC: le.

Hellsten, Iina. From sequencing to annotating: extending the metaphor of the book of life from genetics to genomics. *New Genetics and Society* 2005 December; 24(3): 283-297. NRCBL: 15.10; 1.3.7; 5.1.

Iceland. Supreme Court. Icelandic. Decision of the Supreme Court on the protection of privacy with regard to the processing of Health Sector Databases. *Revista de Derecho y Genoma-Humano / Law and the Human Genome Review* 2004 July-December; (21): 127-138. NRCBL: 15.10; 1.3.12; 13.1; 8.4; 1.1. SC: le. Note: Abstract in English and Spanish.

Johnston, Carolyn; Kaye, Jane. Does the UK biobank have a legal obligation to feedback individual findings to participants? *Medical Law Review* 2004 Autumn; 12(3): 239-267. NRCBL: 15.10; 1.3.12; 13.1; 8.5; 1.1. SC: le; an.

Kirby, Michael. The Human Genome Project in the dock. *Medical Journal of Australia* 2000 December 4-18; 173(11-12): 599-600. NRCBL: 15.10; 8.4; 15.8; 9.1.

Koski, Cheryl A. The Human Genome Project: an examination of its challenge to the technological imperative. *New Genetics and Society* 2005 December; 24(3): 265-281. NRCBL: 15.10; 18.6; 5.3; 2.3.

Kriari-Catranis, Ismini. Genetic data and confidentiality, the Estonian experiment. *Revista de Derecho y Genoma Humano / Law and the Human Genome Review* 2003 July-December; (19): 147-157. NRCBL: 15.10; 1.3.12; 13.1; 8.4. SC: le. Note: abstract in Spanish.

Lagay, Faith. Humanitas and the human genome: a guiding principle for decision making. *Free Inquiry* 2002-2003 Winter; 23(1): 34-37. NRCBL: 15.10; 1.1.

Magill, Gerard. Ethical perspectives on life sciences research after mapping the human genome. *Medical Ethics and Bioethics / Medicinska Etika & Bioetika* 2001 Spring-Summer; 8(1-2): 3-5. NRCBL: 15.10; 8.4; 15.4; 15.3; 15.7.

McHale, J.V. Regulating genetic databases: some legal and ethical issues. *Medical Law Review* 2004 Spring; 12(1): 70-96. NRCBL: 15.10; 1.3.12; 13.1; 5.3; 18.6; 18.3; 8.4; 2.4. SC: le.

McLochlin, Deborah L. Whose genetic information is it anyway? A legal analysis of the effects that mapping the human genome will have on privacy rights and genetic discrimination. *John Marshall Journal of Computer and Information Law* 2001 Summer; 19(4): 609-646. NRCBL: 15.10; 15.1; 8.4. SC: le.

Mowat, David. Ethical, legal and social issues surrounding the Human Genome Project. *Internal Medicine Journal* 2002 March; 32(3): 89-90. NRCBL: 15.10; 15.1.

Nerlich, Brigitte; Dingwall, Robert; Clarke, David D. The book of life: how the completion of the Human Genome Project was revealed to the public. *Health: An Interdisciplinary Journal for the Social Study of Health, Illness and Medicine* 2002; 6(4): 445-469. NRCBL: 15.10; 15.1; 1.3.7; 5.1.

Rai, Arti K. The information revolution reaches pharmaceuticals: balancing innovation incentives, cost, and access in the post-genomics era. *University of Illinois Law Review* 2001; 2001(1): 173-210. NRCBL: 15.10; 9.7; 5.1; 5.3; 1.3.12; 15.3. SC: le.

Sheremeta, Lorraine; Knoppers, Bartha Maria. Beyond the rhetoric: population genetics and benefit-sharing. *Health Law Journal* 2003; 11: 89-117. NRCBL: 15.10; 1.3.12; 13.1; 21.1. SC: le.

Sleeboom, Margaret. The Harvard case of Xu Xiping: exploitation of the people, scientific advance, or genetic theft? *New Genetics and Society* 2005 April; 24(1): 57-78. NRCBL: 15.10; 13.1; 21.1; 18.3; 18.5.9. SC: cs. Identifiers: Millennium Pharmaceuticals; China.

Sulston, John. Society and human genome [opinion]. *Revista de Derecho y Genoma Humano / Law and the Human Genome Review* 2004 January-June; (20): 25-33. NRCBL: 15.10; 1.3.9; 15.8; 9.7.

Tharien, A.K. Human values in genetics and embryo experiments. *Issues in Medical Ethics* 1997 April-June; 5(2): 46-47. NRCBL: 15.10; 1.5.3.

Uranga, Amelia Martín; Arribas, Concepción Martín; Jaeger, Cécile; Posadas, Manuel. Outstanding ethical-legal issues on biobanks. An overview on the regulations of the Member States of the EuroBiobank project. *Revista de Derecho y Genoma Humano / Law and the Human Genome Review* 2005 January-June; (22): 103-114. NRCBL: 15.10; 1.3.12; 13.1. SC: le. Note: Abstract in English and Spanish.

Webster, Andrew. Social science and a post-genomic future: alternative readings of genomic agency. *New Genetics and Society* 2005 August; 24(2): 227-238. NRCBL: 15.10; 4.2; 5.1.

Wu, Annie O. Surpassing the material: the human rights implications of informed consent in bioprospecting cells derived from indigenous people groups. *Washington University Law Quarterly* 2000 Fall; 78(3): 979-1003. NRCBL: 15.10; 13.1; 21.1. SC: le.

HEALTH CARE

See also CARE FOR SPECIFIC GROUPS; HEALTH CARE ECONOMICS; HEALTH CARE QUALITY; RESOURCE ALLOCATION; RIGHT TO HEALTH CARE

Anand, Sudhir. The concern for equity in health. *In:* Anand, Sudhir; Peter, Fabienne; Sen, Amartya, eds. Public Health, Ethics, and Equity. New York: Oxford University Press; 2004: 13-20. NRCBL: 9.1; 9.3.1; 4.2; 9.2.

Ayers, Marva; Rendleman, Neal J. In response to the August 1999 article entitled: "Mandated Tuberculosis Screening in a Community of Homeless People" [letter and reply]. *American Journal of Preventive Medicine* 2000 April; 18(3): 268. NRCBL: 9.1; 9.5.10.

Balachandran, Shreedevi. Patient autonomy, advocacy and the critical care nurse. *Issues in Medical Ethics* 2001 July-September; 9(3): 82-83. NRCBL: 9.1; 4.1.3.

Baverstock, Keith. Science, politics and ethics in the low dose debate. *Medicine, Conflict and Survival* 2005 April-June; 21(2): 88-100. NRCBL: 9.1; 16.2; 5.1; 5.2; 5.3; 9.5.1; 15.1.

Benatar, Solomon R.; Fox, Renée C. Meeting threats to global health: a call for American leadership. *Perspectives in Biology and Medicine* 2005 Summer; 48(3): 344- 361. NRCBL: 9.1; 21.1.

Bickenbach, Jerome. Disability and health systems assessment. *In:* Wasserman, David; Bickenbach, Jerome; Wachbroit, Robert, eds. Quality of Life and Human Difference: Genetic Testing, Health Care, and Disability. New York: Cambridge University Press; 2005: 237-266. NRCBL: 9.1; 1.1; 9.4; 4.4.

Bramstedt, Katrina A.; Schneider, Paul L. Saying "good-bye": ethical issues in the stewardship of bed spaces. *Journal of Clinical Ethics* 2005 Summer; 16(2): 170-175. NRCBL: 9.1; 9.4; 9.2. SC: cs.

Brehany, John. Health charities, unethical research and organizational integrity. *Health Care Ethics USA [electronic]* 2005; 13(3): E3, 3 p. Available: http://www.slu.edu/centers/chce/hceusa/3_2005_index.html [21 February 2006]. NRCBL: 9.1; 1.2; 1.3.2; 14.5; 18.5.4.

Brom, Bernard; Kiepiel, Kazalette. The ethics of fluoridation of water [letters]. *South African Medical Journal* 2002 November; 92(11): 836-837. NRCBL: 9.1.

Cassidy, Virginia R. Ethical leadership in managed care: creating a new vision. *Nursing Leadership Forum* 1998 Summer; 3(2): 52-57. NRCBL: 9.1; 9.8.

Catholic Medical Association. Task Force on Health Care; Mauceri, Joseph M. Report of the task force on health care in America. *Linacre Quarterly* 2005 May; 72(2): 92-132. NRCBL: 9.1; 1.2; 8.1; 9.3.1.

NRCBL: National Reference Center for Bioethics Literature Classification Scheme   See inside front cover for terms.

233

Cessario, Romanus. Catholic hospitals in the new evangelization. *National Catholic Bioethics Quarterly* 2005 Winter; 5(4): 675- 686. NRCBL: 9.1; 1.2; 4.4.

Chase, Anthony Tirado; Alaug, Abdul Karim. Health, human rights, and Islam: a focus on Yemen. *Health and Human Rights: An International Journal* 2004; 8(1): 115-137. NRCBL: 9.1; 21.1; 1.2; 21.7; 14.1; 1.1.

Chervenak, Frank A.; McCullough, Laurence B. The diagnosis and management of progressive dysfunction of health care organizations. *Obstetrics and Gynecology* 2005 April; 105(4): 882-887. NRCBL: 9.1; 1.3.2; 9.3.1; 7.1.

Coffin, Susan E.; Nelson, Robert M. Optimizing risks and benefits: the case of rotavirus vaccine. *In:* Kodish, Eric, ed. Ethics and Research with Children: A Case-Based Approach. New York: Oxford University Press; 2005: 46-62. NRCBL: 9.1.; 9.7; 18.5.2; 18.3. SC: le.

Cong, Yali; Hu, Linying; Dwyer, James. The VIP floors [case study and commentaries]. *Hastings Center Report* 2005 January-February; 35(1): 16-17. NRCBL: 9.1; 7.1; 9.3.1. SC: cs.

Coulter, Angela; Fitzpatrick, Ray. The patient's perspective regarding appropriate health care. *In:* Albrecht, Gary L.; Fitzpatrick, Ray; Scrimshaw, Susan C., eds. The Handbook of Social Studies in Health & Medicine. Thousand Oaks, CA: Sage; 2000: 454-464. NRCBL: 9.1; 8.1.

Daniels, Norman; Kennedy, Bruce; Kawachi, Ichiro. Health and inequality, or, why justice is good for our health. *In:* Anand, Sudhir; Peter, Fabienne; Sen, Amartya, eds. Public Health, Ethics, and Equity. New York: Oxford University Press; 2004: 63-91. NRCBL: 9.1; 1.1; 21.1; 9.4.

Deogaonkar, Milind. Day-to-day decision making as a physician in India. *Indian Journal of Medical Ethics* 2005 July-September; 2(3): 86-87. NRCBL: 9.1; 9.8.

Dignam, Paul. Ethics of community treatment orders [letter]. *Australian and New Zealand Journal of Psychiatry* 1998 December; 32(6): 890. NRCBL: 9.1; 17.1; 9.2.

Duncan, R.E.; Delatycki, M.B.; Collins, S.J.; Boyd, A.; Masters, C.L.; Savulescu, Julian. Ethical considerations in presymptomatic testing for variant CJD. *Journal of Medical Ethics* 2005 November; 31(11): 625-630. NRCBL: 9.1; 9.5.1; 15.3. SC: an.
Abstract: Variant Creutzfeldt-Jakob disease (vCJD) is a fatal, transmissible, neurodegenerative disorder for which there is currently no effective treatment. vCJD arose from the zoonotic spread of bovine spongiform encephalopathy. There is now compelling evidence for human to human transmission through blood transfusions from presymptomatic carriers and experts are warning that the real epidemic may be yet to come. Imperatives exist for the development of reliable, non-invasive presymptomatic diagnostic tests. Research into such tests is well advanced. In this article the ethical implications of the availability of these tests are elaborated and comparisons drawn with predictive genetic testing for Huntington's disease and

screening for HIV. Paramount to considerations is the issue of whom to test, weighing up respect for personal autonomy against obligations to benefit and protect society. A paradigm is proposed similar to that used for HIV screening but with unique features: compulsory testing of all blood/organ donors and individuals undergoing surgery or invasive procedures who have a significant risk of disease transmission.

Edgar, Andrew. Health care and the Habermasian public sphere. *In:* Holm, Søren; Jonas, Monique F., eds. Engaging the World: The Use of Empirical Research in Bioethics and the Regulation of Biotechnology. Washington, DC: IOS Press; 2004: 8-17. NRCBL: 9.1; 1.1.

Engelhardt, H. Tristram, Jr. The bioethics of care: widows, monastics, and a Christian presence in health care. *Christian Bioethics* 2005 April; 11(1): 1-10. NRCBL: 9.1; 1.2; 10; 9.5.5; 7.1.
Abstract: At the beginning of the twenty-first century, with vocations to the Christian religious orders of the West in marked decline, an authentic Christian presence in health care is threatened. There are no longer large numbers of women willing to offer their life labors bound in vows of poverty, chastity, and obedience, so as to provide a real preferential option for the poor through supporting an authentic Christian mission in health care. At the same time, the frequent earlier death of men leaves a large number of widows, some in need of care and some able to provide care. Drawing on the role of widows sketched in 1 Timothy 2, one can envision Christian widows entering a life of prayer and service in health care settings. As female monastics, such widows could reintroduce a salient Christian presence in health care. How one ties this response to the message of 1 Timothy 2 will depend on one's understanding of the status of Scripture, the significance of tradition, the nature of theological epistemology, the meaning of theology, the nature of the Church, and the ontology of gender. The position taken on these issues will define the character of a Christian bioethics of care.

Faden, Ruth R.; Taylor, Holly A.; Seiler, Naomi K. Consent and compensation: a social compact for smallpox vaccine policy in the event of an attack. *Clinical Infectious Diseases* 2003; 36: 1547-1551. NRCBL: 9.1; 9.7; 9.3.1.

Fallberg, Lars; Mackenney, Stephen. Patient ombudsmen in seven European countries: an effective way to implement patients' rights? *European Journal of Health Law* 2003 December; 10(4): 343-357. NRCBL: 9.1; 7.1; 21.1. SC: le.

Feldheim, Mary Ann. Health care policy evaluation: a conceptual model using medical ethics. *Journal of Health and Human Services Administration* 1998 Fall; 21(2): 181-198. NRCBL: 9.1; 9.3.1; 2.1; 21.1.

Gatter, Robert. Faith, confidence, and health care: fostering trust in medicine through law. *Wake Forest Law Review* 2004 Summer; 39(2): 395-445. NRCBL: 9.1; 8.1; 9.3.1. SC: le.

Gessert, Charles E. Daily decisions: even as new biotechnologies expand the horizons of bioethics, focus needs to be placed on the ethics of everyday practice. *Minnesota Medicine* 2004 June; 87(6): 30-31. NRCBL: 9.1; 2.1.

Gilson, Aaron M.; Maurer, Martha A.; Joranson, David E. State policy affecting pain management: recent improvements and the positive impact of regulatory health policies. *Health Policy* 2005 October; 74(2): 192-204. NRCBL: 9.1; 9.7; 4.4; 7.1. SC: em; le. Identifiers: University of Wisconsin Pain and Policy Studies Group (PPSG).

Gostin, Lawrence O. Fast and supersized: is the answer to diet by fiat? *Hastings Center Report* 2005 March-April; 35(2): 11-12. NRCBL: 9.1; 7.1. SC: le.

Gostin, Lawrence O. Jacobson v Massachusetts at 100 years: police power and civil liberties in tension. *American Journal of Public Health* 2005 April; 95(4): 576-581. NRCBL: 9.1; 1.3.5; 8.3.4. SC: le.
Abstract: A century ago, the US Supreme Court in Jacobson v Massachusetts upheld the exercise of the police power to protect the public's health. Despite intervening scientific and legal advances, public health practitioners still struggle with Jacobson's basic tension between individual liberty and the common good. In affirming Massachusetts' compulsory vaccination law, the Court established a floor of constitutional protections that consists of 4 standards: necessity, reasonable means, proportionality, and harm avoidance. Under Jacobson, the courts are to support public health matters insofar as these standards are respected. If the Court today were to decide Jacobson once again, the analysis would likely differ—to account for developments in constitutional law—but the outcome would certainly reaffirm the basic power of government to safeguard the public's health.

Gostin, Lawrence O. The negative Constitution: the duty to protect. *Hastings Center Report* 2005 September-October; 35(5): 10-11. NRCBL: 9.1. SC: le.

Grace, Pamela J. Professional advocacy: widening the scope of accountability. *Nursing Philosophy* 2001 July; 2(2): 151-162. NRCBL: 9.1; 4.1.3.

Guttman, Nurit. Ethics in health communication interventions. *In:* Thompson, Teresa L.; Dorsey, Alicia M.; Miller, Katherine I.; Parrott, Roxanne, eds. Handbook of Health Communication. Mahwah, NJ: Lawrence Erlbaum Associates; 2003: 651-679. NRCBL: 9.1; 7.1. SC: rv.

Hall, Amy Laura. Ruth's resolve: what Jesus' great-grandmother may teach about bioethics and care. *Christian Bioethics* 2005 April; 11(1): 35-50. NRCBL: 9.1; 1.2; 10; 9.5.5; 7.1.
Abstract: When thinking about the intersection of care and Christian bioethics, it is helpful to follow closely the account of Ruth, who turned away from security and walked alongside her grieving mother-in-law to Bethlehem. Remembering Ruth may help one to heed Professor Kaveny's summoning of Christians to remember "the Order of Widows" and the church's historic calling to bring "the almanah into its center rather than pushing her to its margins." Disabled, elderly and terminally ill people often seem, at least implicitly, expendable. By hearing the scriptural account of Jesus' steadfast great-grandmother, readers may recall another way. One may read Ruth's care for Naomi as a performative, prophetic act of faith. Ruth's faithful resolve, when set next to Orpah's prudent way, challenges the notion that a bioethic of care is innately feminine, and may further call women and men corporately to participate in a kind of care that is strenuous work.

Hansson, S.O. Extended antipaternalism. *Journal of Medical Ethics* 2005 February; 31(2): 97-100. NRCBL: 9.1; 9.5.9; 1.1. SC: an.
Abstract: Extended antipaternalism means the use of antipaternalist arguments to defend activities that harm (consenting) others. As an example, a smoker's right to smoke is often invoked in defence of the activities of tobacco companies. It can, however, be shown that antipaternalism in the proper sense does not imply such extended antipaternalism. We may therefore approve of Mill's antipaternalist principle (namely, that the only reason to interfere with someone's behaviour is to protect others from harm) without accepting activities that harm (consenting) others. This has immediate consequences for the ethics of public health. An antipaternalist need not refrain from interfering with activities such as the marketing of tobacco or heroin, boxing promotion, driving with unbelted passengers, or buying sex from "voluntary" prostitutes.

Hassan, Riaz. Social consequences of manufactured longevity. *Medical Journal of Australia* 2000 December 4-18; 173(11-12): 601-603. NRCBL: 9.1; 9.5.1; 9.5.2; 9.3.1.

Häyry, Heta. Does democratic might make right in health care policy-making? *In her:* Individual Liberty and Medical Control. Brookfield, VT: Ashgate Pub., 1998: 92-102. NRCBL: 9.1. SC: an.

Häyry, Heta. Health education, the ideal observer and personal autonomy. *In her:* Individual Liberty and Medical Control. Brookfield, VT: Ashgate Pub., 1998: 57-66. NRCBL: 9.1; 7.2; 1.1. SC: an.

Häyry, Heta. Preventive medicine and the welfare of the population. *In her:* Individual Liberty and Medical Control. Brookfield, VT: Ashgate Pub., 1998: 67-81. NRCBL: 9.1. SC: an.

Heller, Jan C. Discussing the theological grounds of moral principles. *Health Care Ethics USA [electronic]* 2005; 13(2); 2 p. Available: http://www.slu.edu/centers/chce/hceusa/2_2005_1.html [19 September 2005]. NRCBL: 9.1; 1.1; 1.2.

Iltis, Ana Smith. Values based decision making: organizational mission and integrity. *HEC (Healthcare Ethics Committee) Forum* 2005 March; 17(1): 6-17. NRCBL: 9.1; 1.3.2; 4.1.2.

Jalgaonkar, Mangesh. Consumer Protection Act — an introspection by a general practitioner. *Medical Ethics: Journal of Forum for Medical Ethics Society* 1994 November-December; 2(2): 12-13. NRCBL: 9.1. SC: le. Identifiers: Consumer Protection Act; India.

Jepson, R.G.; Hewison, J.; Thompson, A.G.H.; Weller, D. How should we measure informed choice? The case of cancer screening. *Journal of Medical Ethics* 2005 April; 31(4): 192-196. NRCBL: 9.1; 9.5.1; 8.3.1.
Abstract: Informed choice is increasingly recognised as important in supporting patient autonomy and ensuring that people are neither deceived nor coerced. In cancer screening the emphasis has shifted away from just promoting the benefits of screening to providing comprehensive information to enable people to make an informed choice. Cancer screening

NRCBL: National Reference Center for Bioethics Literature Classification Scheme   See inside front cover for terms.

235

programmes in the UK now have policies in place which state that it is their responsibility to ensure that individuals are making an individual informed choice. There is a need to evaluate whether such policies mean that those people invited for screening are making informed choices, and how comprehensive information affects other variables such as uptake, cost effectiveness, and satisfaction. At the present time, there is no validated measure of informed choice in cancer screening. Such a measure could be used to evaluate the effectiveness of interventions to increase informed choice and levels of informed choice in a population invited for screening. It could encourage health professionals to be accountable. Factors important when measuring informed choice in cancer screening include an individual's understanding of the limitations of screening, the ability to make an autonomous choice, and the difference between choice and behaviour.

John Paul II, Pope. To the participants in the 19th International Conference of the Pontifical Council for Pastoral Health Care. *National Catholic Bioethics Quarterly* 2005 Spring; 5(1): 153- 155. NRCBL: 9.1; 1.2.

Kaldis, Byron. Could the ethics of institutionalized health care be anything but Kantian? Collecting building blocks for a unifying metaethics. *Medicine, Health Care and Philosophy: A European Journal* 2005; 8(1): 39-52. NRCBL: 9.1; 2.1; 1.1. SC: an.

Abstract: Is a Health Care Ethics possible? Against skeptical and relativist doubts Kantian deontology may advance a challenging alternative affirming the possibility of such an ethics on the condition that deontology be adopted as a total programme or complete vision. Kantian deontology is enlisted to move us from an ethics of two-person informal care to one of institutions. It justifies this affirmative answer by occupying a commanding meta- ethical stand. Such a total programme comprises, on the one hand, a dual-aspect strategy incorporating the macro- (institutional) and micro- (person-to-person) levels while, on the other, it integrates consistently within moral epistemology a meta-ethics with lower- ground moral theories. The article describes the issues to be dealt with and the problems which have to be solved on the way to a unifying theory of that kind (Sections I-III) and indicates elements of Kantian moral philosophy which may serve as building blocks (Section IV). Among these are not only Kant's ideas concerning the moral acting of persons and his ideas concerning civil society and state but also his ideas concerning morality, schematism and religion.

Kaveny, M. Cathleen. The order of widows: what the early church can teach us about older women and health care. *Christian Bioethics* 2005 April; 11(1): 11-34. NRCBL: 9.1; 1.2; 10; 9.5.5; 7.1.

Abstract: This article argues that the early Christian "order of widows" provides a fruitful model for Christian ethicists struggling to address the medical and social problems of elderly women today. After outlining the precarious state of the "almanah"—or widow—in biblical times, it describes the emergence of the order of widows in the early Church. Turning to the contemporary situation, it argues that demographics both in the United States and around the globe suggest that meeting the needs of elderly women will become an enormous challenge in the years to come. The order of widows illustrates a three-fold conception of solidarity that has immediate implications today. That conception of solidarity encourages us: 1) to identify the unique medical needs of elderly women (e.g., osteoporosis); 2) to find ways of overcoming their societal isolation, which can increase their risk of medical and psychological

problems; and 3) to develop strategies for enabling them to remain contributing members of the community for as long as possible.

Keehan, Carol. Catholic health care's community benefit role. *Origins* 2005 June 16; 35(5): 75-79. NRCBL: 9.1; 9.8; 9.5.10; 9.3.1; 1.2.

Kotalik, Jaro. Preparing for an influenza pandemic: ethical issues. *Bioethics* 2005 August; 19(4): 422-431. NRCBL: 9.1; 9.5.1; 21.1; 9.4; 9.7.

Abstract: In the near future, experts predict, an influenza pandemic will likely spread throughout the world. Many countries have been creating a contingency plan in order to mitigate the severe health and social consequences of such an event. Examination of the pandemic plans of Canada, the United Kingdom and the United States, from an ethical perspective, raises several concerns. One: scarcity of human and material resources is assumed to be severe. Plans focus on prioritization but do not identify resources that would be optimally required to reduce deaths and other serious consequences. Hence, these plans do not facilitate a truly informed choice at the political level where decisions have to be made on how much to invest now in order to reduce scarcity when a pandemic occurs. Two: mass vaccination is considered to be the most important instrument for reducing the impact of infection, yet pandemic plans do not provide concrete estimates of the benefits and burdens of vaccination to assure everyone that the balance is highly favorable. Three: pandemic plans make extraordinary demands on health care workers, yet professional organizations and unions may not have been involved in the plans' formulation and they have not been assured that authorities will aim to protect and support health care workers in a way that corresponds to the demands made on them. Four: all sectors of society and all individuals will be affected by a pandemic and everyone's collaboration will be required. Yet, it appears that the various populations have been inadequately informed by occasional media reports. Hence, it is essential that plans are developed and communication programs implemented that will not only inform but also create an atmosphere of mutual trust and solidarity; qualities that at the time of a pandemic will be much needed.

Lichtman, Joan. Access to medical care. *In:* American College of Legal Medicine Textbook Committee, Sanbar, S. Sandy; Firestone, Marvin H.; Buckner, Fillmore; Gibofsky, Allan; LeBlang, Theodore R.; Snyder, Jack W.; Wecht, Cyril H.; Zaremski, Miles J. Legal Medicine. 6th ed. St. Louis: Mosby; 2004: 230-237. NRCBL: 9.1; 9.2.

Loewy, Erich H. In defense of paternalism. *Theoretical Medicine and Bioethics* 2005; 26(6): 445-468. NRCBL: 9.1; 8.1; 1.1; 4.1.2.

Abstract: This paper argues that we have wrongly and not for the patient's benefit made a form of stark autonomy our highest value which allows physicians to slip out from under their basic duty which has always been to pursue a particular patient's good. In general - I shall argue - it is the patient's right to select his or her own goals and the physician's duty to inform the patient of the feasibility of that goal and of the means needed to attain it. If the goal is not one that is possible, the patient, with the physician and family, must select a feasible goal and then discuss the costs/benefits of various approaches. The physician should take a leading role in helping the patient select the goal. I argue that to simply present a laundry list of means and insist that patients choose for themselves is not only abandoning patients to their autonomy but is, in fact, a crass form of violating the patient's autonomy. Freely choosing not to choose is a choice a patient with decisional capacity is entitled to make and one that needs to be respected.

Lysaught, M. Therese. Practicing the order of widows: a new call for an old vocation. *Christian Bioethics* 2005 April; 11(1): 51-68. NRCBL: 9.1; 1.2; 10; 9.5.5; 7.1.

Abstract: This essay argues for a renewed institution of an ancient Christian practice, the Order of Widows. Drawing on the Roman Catholic tradition's recent writings on the elderly, particularly the 1998 document from the Pontifical Council for the Laity entitled "The Dignity of Older People and their Mission in the Church and in the World," I argue that we find within the Roman Catholic tradition advocacy for a renewed understanding of the vocation of the elderly within the Church. Building on this, I then trace in the broadest of outlines some elements of what a renewal of the Order of Widows might look like. In doing so, it becomes clear how this new ecclesial practice addresses health issues of older women (devaluation, marginalization, loss of voice, impoverishment, debilitation, loneliness, isolation, and euthanasia). More importantly, such a practice moves beyond principles to demonstrate a concrete alternative. As such it would provide a powerful witness to the very culture the Church seeks to transform.

Macauley, Domhnall. Fair, honest, ethical, and last [editorial]. *British Journal of Sports Medicine* 1999 October; 33(5): 293-294. NRCBL: 9.1; 9.5.1; 9.7.

Macintyre, Sally. The Black Report and beyond: what are the issues? *Social Science and Medicine* 1997 March; 44(6): 723-745. NRCBL: 9.1; 9.4; 9.5.10; 2.2. Identifiers: United Kingdom (Great Britain).

McCallum, Hamish; Hocking, Barbara Ann. Reflecting on ethical and legal issues in wildlife disease. *Bioethics* 2005 August; 19(4): 336-347. NRCBL: 9.1; 22.1; 9.5.1; 2.1.

Abstract: Disease in wildlife raises a number of issues that have not been widely considered in the bioethical literature. However, wildlife disease has major implications for human welfare. The majority of emerging human infectious diseases are zoonotic: this is, they occur in humans by cross-species transmissions from animal hosts. Managing these diseases often involves balancing concerns with human health against animal welfare and conservation concerns. Many infectious diseases of domestic animals are shared with wild animals, although it is often unclear whether the infection spills over from wild animals to domestic animals or vice versa. Culling is the standard means of managing such diseases, bringing economic considerations, animal welfare and conservation into conflict. Infectious diseases are also major threatening processes in conservation biology and their appropriate management by culling, vaccination or treatment raises substantial animal ethics issues. One particular issue of great significance in Australia is an ongoing research program to develop genetically modified pathogens to control vertebrate pests including rabbits, foxes and house mice. Release of any self-replicating GMO vertebrate pathogen gives rise to a whole series of ethical questions. We briefly review current Australian legal responses to these problems. Finally, we present two unresolved problems of general importance that are exemplified by wildlife disease. First, to what extent can or should 'bioethics' be broadened beyond direct concerns with human welfare to animal welfare and environmental welfare? Second, how should the irreducible uncertainty of ecological systems be accounted for in ethical decision making?

McCartney, James J. Values based decision making in healthcare. *HEC (Healthcare Ethics Committee) Forum* 2005 March; 17(1): 1-5. NRCBL: 9.1; 1.3.2; 4.1.2.

McLachlan, H.V. Justice and the NHS: a comment on Culyer. *Journal of Medical Ethics* 2005 July; 31(7): 379-382. NRCBL: 9.1; 9.2. SC: an. Identifiers: United Kingdom (Great Britain); National Health Service. Comments: comment on A.J. Culyer, "Equity — some theory and its policy implications," Journal of Medical Ethics 2001; 27: 275-283.

Abstract: The nature and significance of equity and equality in relation to health and healthcare policy is discussed in the light of a recent article by Culyer. Culyer makes the following claims: (a) the importance of equity in relation to the provision of health care derives from the human need for health in order to flourish; and (b) for the sake of equity, equality of health among the members of particular political jurisdictions should be the aim of health policy. Both these claims are challenged in this paper. The argument put forward is that it is only when needs arise and are met in particular contexts that need and equity are fused. The state and its agents and agencies should distribute what it distributes impartially, whatever it distributes. Whether or not equity applies to the distribution of healthcare services depends on how they are provided and not on their nature as "primary goods". Contrary to what Culyer suggests, a policy of trying to produce the outcome of health equality would be inequitable. It would not be impartial and it would fail to treat persons as persons ought to be treated.

McLachlan, Hugh V. Drunks, pedestrians and hospitals in Britain and the U.S.A. *In his:* Social Justice, Human Rights and Public Policy. Glasgow, Scotland: Humming Earth; 2005: 79-86. NRCBL: 9.1; 9.2; 21.1.

McLachlan, Hugh V. Justice, health and inequality. *In his:* Social Justice, Human Rights and Public Policy. Glasgow, Scotland: Humming Earth; 2005: 65-78. NRCBL: 9.1; 9.2; 1.1.

Merianos, Angela; Peiris, Malik. International Health Regulations (2005) [opinion]. *Lancet* 2005 October 8-14; 366(9493): 1249-1251. NRCBL: 9.1; 21.1; 21.3.

Mills, Ann E.; Spencer, Edward M. Values based decision making: a tool for achieving the goals of healthcare. *HEC (Healthcare Ethics Committee) Forum* 2005 March; 17(1): 18- 32. NRCBL: 9.1; 1.3.2; 4.1.2.

Moffit, Robert E. The economic and ethical dimensions of health policy. *Journal of Contemporary Health Law and Policy* 2002 Fall; 18(3): 663-672. NRCBL: 9.1; 9.3.1; 7.1.

Natowicz, Marvin. Newborn screening — setting evidence-based policy for protection [opinion]. *New England Journal of Medicine* 2005 September 1; 353(9): 867- 870. NRCBL: 9.1; 9.5.7; 15.3; 9.8.

Oetjen, Dawn; Rotarius, Timothy. Incorporating ethics into your comprehensive organizational plan. *Health Care Manager* 2005 January-March; 24(1): 61-67. NRCBL: 9.1; 1.3.2.

NRCBL: National Reference Center for Bioethics Literature Classification Scheme   See inside front cover for terms.

237

Oliver, A.; Evans, J.G. The paradox of promoting choice in a collectivist system [editorial]. *Journal of Medical Ethics* 2005 April; 31(4): 187. NRCBL: 9.1. Identifiers: United Kingdom (Great Britain); National Health Service (NHS).

Oliver, J. Eric; Lee, Taeku. Public opinion and the politics of obesity in America. *Journal of Health Politics, Policy and Law* 2005 October; 30(5): 923-954. NRCBL: 9.1; 9.5.1. SC: em.

Abstract: Health policy experts have recently sounded the warning about the severe health and economic consequences of America's growing rates of obesity. Despite this fact, obesity has only begun to enter America's political consciousness and we have little information about what average Americans think of obesity or whether they support obesity-related policies. Using unique survey data collected by the authors, this essay examines public attitudes toward obesity and obesity policy. We find that, contrary to the views of health experts, most Americans are not seriously concerned with obesity, express relatively low support for obesity-targeted policies, and still view obesity as resulting from individual failure rather than environmental or genetic sources. Given the absence of elite discourse on this problem, we also find that typical determinants of policy preferences, such as ideology or partisanship, are not good predictors of attitudes on obesity policy. Rather, with a low-valence issue such as obesity, the public utilizes other attitudinal frameworks such as their opinions on smoking policy and the environmental culpability for obesity. The implications of these findings for obesity policy and research on health-related public opinion are discussed.

Partridge, Christina T.; Turiaso, Jennifer. Widows, women, and the bioethics of care. *Christian Bioethics* 2005 April; 11(1): 77-92. NRCBL: 9.1; 1.2; 10; 9.5.5; 7.1.

Abstract: Widows, women, and the bioethics of care must be understood within an authentic Christian ontology of gender. Men are men and women are women, and their being is ontologically marked in difference. There is an ontology of gender with important implications for the role of women in the family and the Church. The Christian Church has traditionally recognized a role for widows, deaconesses, and female monastics, which is not that of the liturgical priesthood, but one with a special relationship to care and therefore with particular implications for health care and a Christian bioethics of care in the twenty-first century. In the shadow of early male mortality, women as wives should turn to support their husbands and as widows to support those in need. Widows, in becoming authentic Christian monastics, can bring into the world an icon of rightly ordered women providing rightly ordered Christian care for those in need. They can enter the moral vacuum created by misunderstandings of the place of women and the service vacuum created by a disappearance of religious nuns in Western health care facilities with a presence that is at one with the Church of the Fathers.

Pellegrino, Edmund D. The present and future importance of Catholic health care in the United States. *In:* McMahon, Kevin T., ed. Moral Issues in Catholic Health Care. Wynnewood, PA: Saint Charles Borromeo Seminary; 2004: 1-18. NRCBL: 9.1; 1.2.

Peter, Fabienne. Health equity and social justice. *In:* Anand, Sudhir; Peter, Fabienne; Sen, Amartya, eds. Public Health, Ethics, and Equity. New York: Oxford University Press; 2004: 93-106. NRCBL: 9.1; 1.1.

Pijnenburg, Martien A.M.; Gordijn, Bert. Identity and moral responsibility on healthcare organizations. *Theoretical Medicine and Bioethics* 2005; 26(2): 141-160. NRCBL: 9.1; 1.3.2; 1.1. SC: an.

Abstract: In this paper the moral responsibility of a Healthcare Organization (HCO) is conceived as an inextricable aspect of the identity of the HCO. We attempt to show that by exploring this relation a more profound insight in moral responsibility can be gained. Referring to Charles Taylor we explore the meaning of the concept of identity. It consists of three interdependent dimensions: a moral, a dialogical, and a narrative one. In section two we develop some additional arguments to apply his concept of personal identity to organizations. The final section works out the relationship of three dimensions of identity to some actual issues in contemporary HCOs: the tension between care and justice, the importance of dialogues about the diversity of goods, and the relevance of becoming familiar with the life-story of the HCO. Identity of an HCO is established and developed in commitments to and identification with certain goods that are central for a HCO. However, many of these goods are interwoven with everyday practices and policies. Therefore, moral responsibility asks for articulation of goods that often stay implicit and should not be reduced to a merely procedural approach. However difficult this articulation may be, if it is not tried at all HCOs run the risk of drifting away from their very identity as healthcare institutions: to offer care to patients and to do this in accordance with demands of social justice.

Pogge, Thomas W. Relational conceptions of justice: responsibilities for health outcomes. *In:* Anand, Sudhir; Peter, Fabienne; Sen, Amartya, eds. Public Health, Ethics, and Equity. New York: Oxford University Press; 2004: 135-161. NRCBL: 9.1; 9.5.10; 1.1.

Pope, Thaddeus Mason. Counting the dragon's teeth and claws: the definition of hard paternalism. *Georgia State University Law Review* 2004 Spring; 20(3): 659- 722. NRCBL: 9.1; 1.1; 2.1.

Ritvo, Roger A.; Ohlsen, Joel D.; Holland, Thomas P. Exercising ethical leadership: conflicts of interest. *Trustee* 2004 October; 57(9): 27-30. NRCBL: 9.1; 1.3.2. SC: cs.

Roscam Abbing, Henriette D.C. Constitutional treaty of the European Union, health and human rights. An appraisal [editorial]. *European Journal of Health Law* 2004 December; 11(4): 337-345. NRCBL: 9.1; 21.1. SC: le.

Saguy, Abigail C.; Riley, Kevin W. Weighing both sides: morality, mortality, and framing contests over obesity. *Journal of Health Politics, Policy and Law* 2005 October; 30(5): 869-921. NRCBL: 9.1; 7.1; 9.5.1.

Abstract: Despite recent and growing media attention surrounding obesity in the United States, the so-called obesity epidemic remains a highly contested scientific and social fact. This article examines the contemporary obesity debate through systematic examination of the claims and claimants involved in the controversy. We argue that four primary groups-antiobesity researchers, antiobesity activists, fat acceptance researchers, and fat acceptance activists-are at the forefront of this controversy and that these groups are fundamentally engaged in framing contests over the nature and consequences of excess body weight. While members of the fat acceptance groups embrace a body diversity frame, presenting fatness as a natural and largely inevitable form of diversity, members of the antiobesity camp frame higher weights as risky behavior akin to smoking, implying that body weight is under personal control and that people have a moral and medical responsibility to manage their weight. Both groups sometimes frame obesity as an illness, which limits blame by suggesting that weight is biologically or genetically determined but simultaneously stigmatizes fat bodies as diseased. While the antiobesity camp frames obesity as an epidemic to increase public attention, fat acceptance activists argue that concern over obesity is distracting attention from a host of more important health issues for fat Americans. We examine the strategies claimants use to establish their own credibility or discredit their opponents, and explain how the fat acceptance movement has exploited structural opportunities and cultural resources created by AIDS activism and feminism to wield some influence over U.S. public health approaches. We conclude that notions of morality play a central role in the controversy over obesity, as in many medical disputes, and illustrate how medical arguments about body weight can be used to stymie rights claims and justify morality-based fears.

Sanson-Fisher, Rob; Turnbull, Deborah. 'To do or not do?': ethical problems for behavioural medicine. *In:* Fairbairn, Susan; Fairbairn, Gavin, eds. Psychology, Ethics and Change. New York: Routledge & Kegan Paul; 1987: 191- 211. NRCBL: 9.1; 8.1.

Sen, Amartya. Why health equity? *In:* Anand, Sudhir; Peter, Fabienne; Sen, Amartya, eds. Public Health, Ethics, and Equity. New York: Oxford University Press; 2004: 21-33. NRCBL: 9.1; 1.1; 9.4.

Shah, Ghanshyam. Doctors and the plague. *Issues in Medical Ethics* 1996 October-December; 4(4): 119-121. NRCBL: 9.1. Identifiers: India.

Sieber, William J.; Kaplan, Robert M. Informed adherence: the need for shared medical decision making. *Controlled Clinical Trials* 2000 October; 21(5 Supplement): 233S-240S. NRCBL: 9.1; 9.5.1; 9.5.5; 8.3.1; 9.4.

Simpson, Christy; Kirby, Jeffrey; Davies, Maura. Building a culture of ethics: the Capital Health Ethics Support model. *Healthcare Management Forum* 2004 Autumn; 17(3): 14-17. NRCBL: 9.1; 1.3.2. Identifiers: Canada.

Solyom, Antal E. Improving the health of the public requires changes in medical education. *Academic Medicine* 2005 December; 80(12): 1089-1093. NRCBL: 9.1; 4.4; 8.1; 7.2.

South Africa. Parliament. National Health Bill: As amended by the Portfolia Committee on Health (National Assembly) [B 32B-2003]. Pretoria, South Africa: Parliament 2003; 46 p. [Online]. Available: http://www.polity.org.za/pdf/NationalHealthB32B.pdf [9 August 2005]. NRCBL: 9.1; 8.3.1; 9.4; 9.2; 18.1; 19.1. SC: le.

Srinivasan, Sandhya. After the floods: health services' responsibilities in a crisis [editorial]. *Indian Journal of Medical Ethics* 2005 October-December; 2(4): 108-109. NRCBL: 9.1; 8.2; 9.3.1; 9.4; 9.5.10; 9.8; 1.3.7; 1.3.5. Identifiers: India.

Stone, T. Howard; Horton, Heather H.; Pestronk, Robert M. Considerations for special populations. *In:* Goodman, Richard A.; Rothstein, Mark A.; Hoffman, Richard E.; Lopez, Wilfredo; Matthews, Gene W., eds. Law in Public Health Practice. New York: Oxford University Press; 2003: 211-241. NRCBL: 9.1; 9.5.1. SC: le.

Struhkamp, Rita M. Patient autonomy: a view from the kitchen. *Medicine, Health Care and Philosophy: A European Journal* 2005; 8(1): 105-114. NRCBL: 9.1; 1.1; 8.1; 9.5.1. SC: an.

Abstract: In contemporary liberal ethics patient autonomy is often interpreted as the right to self-determination: when it comes to treatment decisions, the patient is given the right to give or withhold informed consent. This paper joins in the philosophical and ethical criticism of the liberal interpretation as it does not regard patient autonomy as a right, rule or principle, but rather as a practice. Patient autonomy, or so I will argue, is realised in the concrete activities of day-to-day health care, in the material and technological context of care, in arrangements of health care institutions, in the physical training of people with disabilities, as well as in the concrete activities of care-giving. This move from conversations in the consultation room to other sites and situations in the practice of care takes seriously the empirical reality of medical care and intends to show that patient autonomy is practically realised in a much richer and more creative way than most ethical theory seems to assume.

Thomas, George. Practicing medicine in India: some ethical dilemmas. *Indian Journal of Medical Ethics* 2005 July-September; 2(3): 88. NRCBL: 9.1; 9.8.

Thompson, Dennis F. Hospital ethics. *In his:* Restoring Responsibility: Essays on Ethics in Government, Business, and Healthcare. New York: Cambridge University Press; 2005: 278-289. NRCBL: 9.1; 1.3.2; 8.4; 9.6.; 9.8.

Thurston, Wilfreda E.; MacKean, Gail; Vollman, Ardene; Casebeer, Ann; Weber, Myron; Maloff, Bretta; Bader, Judy. Public participation in regional health policy: a theoretical framework. *Health Policy* 2005 September 8; 73(3): 237-252. NRCBL: 9.1; 7.1. SC: em.

University of Toronto Joint Centre for Bioethics. Pandemic Influenza Working Group; Upshur, Ross E.G.; Faith, Karen; Gibson, Jennifer L.; Thompson, Alison K.; Tracy, C. Shawn; Wilson, Kumanan; Singer, Peter A. Stand on Guard for Thee: Ethical considerations in preparedness planning for pandemic influenza. Toronto: University of Toronto Joint Centre for Bioethics 2005 November; 29 p. [Online]. Available: http://www.utoronto.ca/jcb/home/documents/pandemic.pdf [4 January 2006]. NRCBL: 9.1; 9.5.1.

Üstün, Cagatay; Ceber, Esin. Ethical issues for cancer screenings: five countries — four types of cancer. *Preventive Medicine* 2004 August; 39(2): 223-229. NRCBL: 9.1; 9.5.1; 21.1.

Van Detta, Jeffrey A. "Typhoid Mary" meets the ADA: a case study of the "direct threat" standard under the Americans with Disabilities Act. *Harvard Journal of Law and*

NRCBL: National Reference Center for Bioethics Literature Classification Scheme   See inside front cover for terms.

239

Public Policy 1999 Summer; 22(3): 849-958. NRCBL: 9.1; 4.2. SC: le.

Verweij, Marcel. Obligatory precautions against infection. *Bioethics* 2005 August; 19(4): 323-335. NRCBL: 9.1; 9.5.1; 1.1; 9.7. SC: an.

Abstract: If we have a duty not to infect others, how far does it go? This question is often discussed with respect to HIV transmission, but reflection on other diseases like influenza raises a number of interesting theoretical issues. I argue that a duty to avoid infection not only yields requirements for persons who know they carry a disease, but also for persons who know they are at increased risk, and even for those who definitely know they are completely healthy. Given the numerous ways in which human interaction facilitates the spread of communicable diseases, a maximum level of precaution would be very demanding—possibly unreasonably demanding. The 'over-demandingness problem' is mostly invoked as a criticism of utilitarianism, as this theory requires moral agents to always maximise general welfare, even at significant cost for themselves. However, I argue that, with respect to precautions against infectious diseases like influenza, utilitarianism is able to avoid the over-demandingness problem. A contractualist account, on the other hand, whilst able to explain how one's obligations to avoid infection can be limited, given that other persons have opportunities and responsibilities to protect themselves, in the end requires precautions that raise the over-demandingness problem.

Wagner, William Joseph. Constitutional values and the ethics of health care: a comparison of the United States and Germany. *Journal of Contemporary Health Law and Policy* 2002 Fall; 18(3): 619-632. NRCBL: 9.1; 8.1; 4.4; 2.1. SC: le.

Waller, Bruce N. Responsibility and health. *CQ: Cambridge Quarterly of Healthcare Ethics* 2005 Spring; 14(2): 177-188. NRCBL: 9.1; 1.1; 7.1; 9.2; 9.4; 8.1. Identifiers: autonomy.

Wheeler, Sondra. Contemporary ethics from an ambiguous past. *Christian Bioethics* 2005 April; 11(1): 69-76. NRCBL: 9.1; 1.2; 10; 9.5.5; 7.1.

Abstract: Kaveny recommends models drawn from the Gospel of John and the practices of the early church for modern Christians in their response to older women and their health needs. She draws upon a historical reconstruction of the early Christian Order of Widows to propose a normative standard of care for elderly women, one that attends seriously to their bodily needs but also to their needs for inclusion and engagement in the social and vocational world both as givers and recipients of care. This is also to serve as an overarching model for a bioethics that prizes the embodied existence of all women and rejects judgments of appropriate treatment based on their social utility. The following response raises questions about the exegetical and historical foundations of Kaveny's analysis. However, these caveats may not detract substantially from the normative usefulness of her work.

White, Deena. Consumer and community participation: a reassessment of process, impact, and value. *In:* Albrecht, Gary L.; Fitzpatrick, Ray; Scrimshaw, Susan C., eds. The Handbook of Social Studies in Health & Medicine. Thousand Oaks, CA: Sage; 2000: 465-480. NRCBL: 9.1.

Wikler, Daniel. Personal and social responsibility for health. *In:* Anand, Sudhir; Peter, Fabienne; Sen, Amartya, eds. Public Health, Ethics, and Equity. New York: Oxford University Press; 2004: 109-134. NRCBL: 9.1; 1.1.

Williamson, Charlotte. Withholding policies from patients restricts their autonomy. *BMJ: British Medical Journal* 2005 November 5; 331(7524): 1078- 1080. NRCBL: 9.1; 1.3.2; 8.1; 1.1.

Winkler, Eva C. The ethics of policy writing: how should hospitals deal with moral disagreement about controversial medical practices? *Journal of Medical Ethics* 2005 October; 31(10): 559-566. NRCBL: 9.1; 1.3.2; 8.3.4. SC: an.

Abstract: Every healthcare organisation (HCO) enacts a multitude of policies, but there has been no discussion as to what procedural and substantive requirements a policy writing process should meet in order to achieve good outcomes and to possess sufficient authority for those who are asked to follow it.Using, as an example, the controversy about patient's refusal of blood transfusions, I argue that a hospital wide policy is preferable to individual decision making, because it ensures autonomy, quality, fairness, and efficiency.Policy writing for morally controversial medical practices needs additional justification compared to policies on standard medical practices and secures legitimate authority for HCO members by meeting five requirements: all parties directed by the policy are represented; the deliberative process encompasses all of the HCO's obligations; the rationales for the policy are made available; there is a mechanism for criticising, and for evaluating the policy.

Winkler, Eva C.; Gruen, Russell L. First principles: substantive ethics for healthcare organizations. *Journal of Healthcare Management* 2005 March-April; 50(2): 109-119. NRCBL: 9.1; 1.3.2; 2.1.

Worth, Allison. Ethical issues in the discharge of patients from hospital to community care. *In:* Chadwick, Ruth; Levitt, Mairi, eds. Ethical Issues in Community Health Care. New York: Arnold; 1998: 135-145. NRCBL: 9.1.

HEALTH CARE ECONOMICS
See also RESOURCE ALLOCATION

Genomics and economics [editorial]. *CMAJ/JAMC: Canadian Medical Association Journal* 2005 August 16; 173(4): 329. NRCBL: 9.3.1; 15.1; 15.3; 9.5.5; 9.7.

Making health care a moral issue [news]. *Christian Century* 2005 February 22; 122(4): 18-19. NRCBL: 9.3.1; 1.2; 1.3.5.

Alexander, G. Caleb; Kurlander, Jacob; Wynia, Matthew K. Physicians in retainer ("concierge") practice. *JGIM: Journal of General Internal Medicine* 2005 December; 20(12): 1079-1083. NRCBL: 9.3.1; 9.2; 8.1. SC: em.

Armstrong, David. Lucrative operation: how some doctors turn a $90 profit from a $17 test; physician groups add markup to work done by others, despite ethics concerns; administrative costs cited. *Wall Street Journal* 2005 September 30; p. A1, A8. NRCBL: 9.3.1; 7.4. SC: po.

Armstrong, David. Skillful operation: a surgeon earns riches, enmity by plucking profitable patients;specialty hospitals go public, sparking ire in Rapid City; older facility faces losses; clash over anonymous letter. *Wall Street Journal* 2005 August 2; p. A1, A7. NRCBL: 9.3.1; 9.5.1; 7.3. SC: po.

Axtell-Thompson, Linda M. Consumer directed health care: ethical limits to choice and responsibility. *Journal of Medicine and Philosophy* 2005 April; 30(2): 207-226. NRCBL: 9.3.1; 2.1; 9.4; 9.1. SC: an.

Abstract: As health care costs continue to escalate, cost control measures will likely become unavoidable and painful. One approach is to engage external forces to allocate resources—for example, through managed care or outright rationing. Another approach is to engage consumers to make their own allocation decisions, through "self-rationing," wherein they are given greater awareness, control, and hence responsibility for their health care spending. Steadily gaining popularity in this context is the concept of "consumer directed health care" (CDHC), which is envisioned to both control cost and enhance choice, by combining financial incentives with information to help consumers make more informed health care decisions and to appreciate the economic trade-offs of those decisions. While CDHC is gaining attention in the popular press, business publications, and academic journals, it is not without controversy about its relative merits and demerits. CDHC raises questions regarding the ethical limits of consumer responsibility for their choices. While the emphasis on consumer choice implies that autonomy is the ruling ethical principle in CDHC, it must be tempered by justice and beneficence. Justice must temper autonomy to protect disadvantaged populations from further widening disparities in health care access and outcomes that could arise from health care reform efforts. Beneficence must temper autonomy to protect consumers from unintended consequences of uninformed decisions. Thoughtful paternalism suggests that CDHC plans offer choices that are comprehensible to lay consumers, limited in their range of options, and carefully structured with default rules that minimize potential error costs.

Brennan, Troyen A. Concierge care and the future of general internal medicine [editorial]. *JGIM: Journal of General Internal Medicine* 2005 December; 20(12): 1190. NRCBL: 9.3.1; 8.1.

Bristol, Nellie. Physician-owned specialty hospitals in the USA. *Lancet* 2005 July 16-22; 366(9481): 193-194. NRCBL: 9.3.1; 7.3; 1.3.2; 9.4; 9.2.

Brown, E. Richard. Why we need more studies on health insurance coverage and access [opinion]. *Medical Care Research and Review* 2000 September; 57(3): 319-325. NRCBL: 9.3.1; 9.2.

Browne, Andrew. Health crisis: Chinese doctors tell patients to pay upfront, or no treatment; parents of boy with leukemia scramble for cash to cover new chemotherapy round; threat seen to social stability. *Wall Street Journal* 2005 December 5; p. A1, A12. NRCBL: 9.3.1. SC: po.

Browne, Andrew. Policy woes: China's workers see thin protection in insurance plans; under state health program, "big sickness" is pricey; doctors demand cash ; Mr. Hu buys his chemo drugs. *Wall Street Journal* 2005 December 30; p. A1, A9. NRCBL: 9.3.1. SC: po.

Callahan, Daniel. Conservatives, liberals, and medical progress. *New Atlantis* 2005 Fall; 10: 3-16. NRCBL: 9.3.1; 4.1.2; 9.4; 20.5.1.

Capaldi, Nicholas. The ethics and economics of health care. *Journal of Medicine and Philosophy* 2005 December; 30(6): 571- 578. NRCBL: 9.3.1. SC: an.

Abstract: This essay argues that medical innovation proceeds most efficiently and effectively within a free market economy. Medical innovation is an expression of the technological project: the program through which we seek to control nature, to improve the quality and quantity of life. The Technological Project proceeds most efficiently with a free market economy because such a market both promotes competition and encourages innovation. As I argue, the market is a discovery process in which alternatives are tried, tested, and selected by consumer's choices. The alternatives to a free market-primarily central planning and a heavily regulated market-fail adequately to encourage medical innovation.

Centers for Medicare and Medicaid Services [CMS]; Health and Human Services [HHS]. Medicare and Medicaid programs; religious nonmedical health care institutions and advance directives. Final rule. *Federal Register* 2003 November 28; 68(229): 66710-66721. NRCBL: 9.3.1; 9.1.

Cherry, Mark J. The market and medical innovation: human passions and medical advancement. *Journal of Medicine and Philosophy* 2005 December; 30(6): 555- 569. NRCBL: 9.3.1; 1.3.2; 1.3.9.

Dell'Oro, Roberto. The market ethos and the integrity of health care. *Journal of Contemporary Health Law and Policy* 2002 Fall; 18(3): 641-647. NRCBL: 9.3.1; 7.1.

Dowie, Jack. Why cost-effectiveness should trump (clinical) effectiveness: the ethical economics of the South West quadrant. *Health Economics* 2004 May; 13(5): 453-459. NRCBL: 9.3.1; 9.8. SC: an. Identifiers: United Kingdom (Great Britain).

Emanuel, Ezekiel J.; Fuchs, Victory R. Health care vouchers — a proposal for universal coverage. *New England Journal of Medicine* 2005 March 24; 352(12): 1255-1260. NRCBL: 9.3.1.

Folland, Sherman. The quality of mercy: social health insurance in the charitable liberal state. *International Journal of Health Care Finance and Economics* 2005 March; 5(1): 23-46. NRCBL: 9.3.1; 1.1. SC: an.

Frist, William H. Health care in the 21st century. *New England Journal of Medicine* 2005 January 20; 352(3): 267- 272. NRCBL: 9.3.1.

Gaal, Peter; McKee, Martin. Fee-for-service or donation? Hungarian perspectives on informal payment for health care. *Social Science and Medicine* 2005 April;

NRCBL: National Reference Center for Bioethics Literature Classification Scheme   See inside front cover for terms.

241

60(7): 1445-1457. NRCBL: 9.3.1; 7.1; 8.1. SC: rv. Identifiers: Hungary.

Goyal, Venkat; Lokhandwala, Yash. Practising ethically in a high-tech specialty. *Issues in Medical Ethics* 1998 October-December; 6(4): 123-124. NRCBL: 9.3.1; 5.1; 1.3.9.

Greß, Stefan; Niebuhr, Dea; Rothgang, Heinz; Wasem, Jürgen. Criteria and procedures for determining benefit packages in health care. A comparative perspective. *Health Policy* 2005 July; 73(1): 78-91. NRCBL: 9.3.1; 9.4; 21.1. Identifiers: United Kingdom (Great Britain); Germany; Switzerland.

Gunderman, Richard B.; Hubbard, Mark Adam. The wages of healing: ethical issues in the compensation of physicians. *Medical Science Monitor* 2005 February; 11(2): SR5-SR10. NRCBL: 9.3.1; 4.1.2.

Herron, William G. Revisiting fee policies. *Psychological Reports* 1996 June; 78(3, Part 1): 881-882. NRCBL: 9.3.1; 17.2.

Hoffman, Sharona. AIDS caps, contraceptive coverage, and the law: an analysis of the federal anti-discrimination statutes' applicability to health insurance. *Cardozo Law Review* 2002 March; 23(4): 1315-1362. NRCBL: 9.3.1; 9.2; 1.3.5. SC: le.

Horwitz, Jill R. Why we need the independent sector: the behavior, law, and ethics of not-for-profit hospitals. *UCLA Law Review* 2003 August; 50(6): 1345-1411. NRCBL: 9.3.1; 9.2. SC: an.

Iglehart, John K. The emergence of physician-owned specialty hospitals. *New England Journal of Medicine* 2005 January 6; 352(1): 78-84. NRCBL: 9.3.1; 7.3; 1.3.2.

Jecker, Nancy S. Health care reform: what history doesn't teach. *Theoretical Medicine and Bioethics* 2005; 26(4): 277-305. NRCBL: 9.3.1; 9.3.2; 7.1; 4.1.2; 1.3.1.
Abstract: The paper begins by tracing the historical development of American medicine as practice, profession, and industry from the eighteenth century to the present. This historical outline emphasizes shifting conceptions of physicians and physician ethics. It lays the basis for showing, in the second section, how contemporary controversies about the physician's role in managed care take root in medicine's past. In the final two sections, I revisit both the historical analysis and its application to contemporary debates. I argue that historical narratives can function as "master narratives" that suppress or leave out historical facts. I bring to the surface what is covered up by the master narrative approach, and show its relevance to contemporary ethical debates. I conclude by proposing that preserving the integrity of medicine will require modifying the master narratives we tell about physicians. The integrity of medicine also offers new perspectives for thinking about managed care and the broader topic of health care reform.

Jesani, Amar. Calls for advertising and market reforms in health care [debate]. *Issues in Medical Ethics* 2001 January-March; 9(1): 19. NRCBL: 9.3.1; 8.1; 1.3.2; 1.3.12. Identifiers: India.

Jesilow, Paul. The effects of fraud on the evaluation of health care. *Health Care Analysis: An International Journal of Health Care Philosophy and Policy* 2005 September; 13(3): 239-245. NRCBL: 9.3.1; 9.5.2; 9.5.10.
Abstract: Studies on health care practices, financing, and organization increasingly rely on Medicare and other expanded data sets. These studies are of critical importance for public policy and for the development of strategies to contain escalating health care costs, but they often use data that have been corrupted by fraud and abuse. Mistaken conclusions, as to the effectiveness of policy and procedures, are likely being reached in studies that have used corrupted data. Researchers need to consider the suspect nature of results obtained from the corrupted data, and determine methods for making the data more valid.

Jindal, Surinder. Privatisation of health care: new ethical dilemmas. *Issues in Medical Ethics* 1998 July-September; 6(3): 85-86. NRCBL: 9.3.1.

Jones, Kenneth D., Jr. Is it ethical to offer financial incentives to staff who convince patients to consent to treatment? *Journal of the American Dental Association* 2004 November; 135(11): 1619. NRCBL: 9.3.1; 7.3; 1.3.2; 4.1.1.

Kasper, Judith D.; Giovannini, Terence A.; Hoffman, Catherine. Gaining and losing health insurance: strengthening the evidence for effects on access to care and health outcomes. *Medical Care Research and Review* 2000 September; 57(3): 298-318. NRCBL: 9.3.1; 9.2.

Kennedy, Patrick J. Why we must end insurance discrimination against mental health care. *Harvard Journal on Legislation* 2004 Summer; 41(2): 363-375. NRCBL: 9.3.1; 17.1; 9.2; 9.4.

Keshavjee, Salmaan. Medicine and money: the ethical transformation of medical practice. *Medical Education* 2004 March; 38(3): 271-275. NRCBL: 9.3.1; 9.4; 1.3.2. Identifiers: United States.

Kimsma, Gerrit K.; van Leeuwen, Evert. Shifts in the direction of Dutch bioethics: forward or backward? *CQ: Cambridge Quarterly of Healthcare Ethics* 2005 Summer; 14(3): 292-297. NRCBL: 9.3.1; 20.5.1; 20.5.2. SC: le. Identifiers: Groningen Protocol.

Kindell, Kathryn. Prescription for fairness: health insurance reimbursement for Viagra and contraceptives. *Tulsa Law Journal* 2000 Winter; 35(2): 399-419. NRCBL: 9.3.1; 11.1. SC: le.

Lucas, Peter. Perspectivism in risk management. *In:* Häyry, Matti; Takala, Tuija; Herissone-Kelly, Peter, eds. Bioethics and Social Reality. New York: Rodopi, 2005: 127-135. NRCBL: 9.3.1; 5.2. SC: an.

Macauley, Robert. The Hippocratic underground: civil disobedience and health care reform. *Hastings Center Report* 2005 January-February; 35(1): 38-45. NRCBL: 9.3.1; 5.3; 7.1; 9.2.

Majumder, Mary Anderlik. Uncharitable care? *Hastings Center Report* 2004 July-August; 34(4): 7. NRCBL: 9.3.1.

McGregor, Maurice; Chen, Jun. Should the implantable cardiac defibrillator be used for primary prevention of sudden death? A review of the issues relevant to hospital decision making [opinion]. *Canadian Journal of Cardiology* 2004 October; 20(12): 1199-1204. NRCBL: 9.3.1; 9.4; 20.5.1. SC: rv; le.

Meadowcroft, John. Health care markets, prices, and coordination: the epistemic explanation of government failure and the UK National Health Service. *HEC (Healthcare Ethics Committee) Forum* 2005 September; 17(3): 159-177. NRCBL: 9.3.1; 1.3.2.

Mehta, Lopa. Ethical basis for charging medical fees. *Issues in Medical Ethics* 2000 April-June; 8(2): 49-50. NRCBL: 9.3.1; 4.1.2; 7.1.

Mirza, Sohail K. Accountability of the accused: facing public perceptions about financial conflicts of interest in spine surgery [editorial]. *Spine Journal* 2004 September-October; 4(5): 491-494. NRCBL: 9.3.1; 7.3; 1.3.2; 1.3.9.

Morreim, E. Haavi; Macauley, Robert. Civil disobedience: the devil is in the details [letter and reply]. *Hastings Center Report* 2005 July-August; 35(4): 4, 5-6. NRCBL: 9.3.1; 4.1.2.

Murphy, Leslie C. Mandatory health insurance coverage for cancer clinical trials. *McGeorge Law Review* 2001; 33(2): 314-322. NRCBL: 9.3.1; 9.2; 9.5.1. SC: le.

Nagral, Sanjay. Sponsored medical education? [editorial]. *Issues in Medical Ethics* 1998 January; 6(1): 3. NRCBL: 9.3.1; 9.7; 7.2.

Needell, Mervin H.; Kenyon, John S. Ethical evaluation of "retainer fee" medical practice. *Journal of Clinical Ethics* 2005 Spring; 16(1): 72-84. NRCBL: 9.3.1; 9.8; 9.2; 7.4; 1.3.1.

Neumann, Peter J.; Rosen, Allison B.; Weinstein, Milton C. Medicare and cost-effectiveness analysis. *New England Journal of Medicine* 2005 October 3; 353(14): 1516- 1522. NRCBL: 9.3.1; 9.5.2; 5.2; 4.4.

Nomura, Hideki; Nakayama, Takeo. The Japanese healthcare system [editorial]. *BMJ: British Medical Journal* 2005 September 24; 331(7518): 648-649. NRCBL: 9.3.1; 7.1.

Pence, Gregory E. Classic cases about individual rights and the public good. *In his:* Classic Cases in Medical Ethics: Accounts of Cases That Have Shaped Medical Ethics, with Philosophical, Legal, and Historical Backgrounds. Fourth edition. Boston, MA: McGraw- Hill; 2004: 367-470. NRCBL: 9.3.1; 9.5.6; 15.3; 17.7.

Petratos, Pythagoras. Does the private finance initiative promote innovation in health care? The case of the British National Health Service. *Journal of Medicine and Philosophy* 2005 December; 30(6): 627- 642. NRCBL: 9.3.1. SC: an; em.

Abstract: The Private Finance Initiative (PFI) is a specific example of health care privatization within the British National Health Service. In this essay, I critically assess the ways in which various Private Finance Initiatives have increased health care efficiency and effectiveness, as well as encouraged medical innovation. Indeed, as the analysis will demonstrate, significant empirical evidence supports the conclusion that Private Finance Initiatives are a driving force of innovation within the British Health Care System.

Saver, Richard S. Squandering the gain: gainsharing and the continuing dilemma of physician financial incentives. *Northwestern University Law Review* 2003 Fall; 98(1): 145-238. NRCBL: 9.3.1; 7.3. SC: le.

Schlegel, Rainer. German health care — towards universal access: an overview of the principles of access and benefits. *Journal of Contemporary Health Law and Policy* 2002 Fall; 18(3): 673-683. NRCBL: 9.3.1; 9.2. SC: le.

Varatharajan, D. Provision of health care by the government. *Indian Journal of Medical Ethics* 2004 October-December; 1(4): 117-118. NRCBL: 9.3.1. Identifiers: India.

Varatharajan, D. Taking biotechnology to the patient: at what cost? *Issues in Medical Ethics* 2003 April-June; 11(2): 54-55. NRCBL: 9.3.1; 5.1.

Weissman, Joel S. The trouble with uncompensated hospital care [opinion]. *New England Journal of Medicine* 2005 March 24; 352(12): 1171- 1173. NRCBL: 9.3.1; 9.5.10.

HEALTH CARE/. . ./ MANAGED CARE PROGRAMS

Brewer, Albert P. Comments on the ethics of managed health care. *Cumberland Law Review* 1997-1998; 28(2): 315-319. NRCBL: 9.3.2; 1.3.2; 8.1; 2.1. SC: le.

Distelhorst, Michael. A business ethics approach to contractual good faith and fair dealing: briefly modeled in selected managed healthcare contexts. *Ohio Northern University Law Review* 2000; 26(1): 57-88. NRCBL: 9.3.2; 1.3.2. SC: le.

Dunne, Tad. Group-level ethics in managed care. *Medical Group Management Journal* 1997 May-June; 44(3): 28, 30, 32-34, 36, 38-39. NRCBL: 9.3.2; 9.8.

Erb, Christopher T.; Rich, Robert F.; Mariner, Wendy K.; Bloche, M. Gregg. The Supreme Court and managed-care liability [letter and replies]. *New England Journal of Medicine* 2005 January 13; 352(2): 201- 203. NRCBL: 9.3.2; 8.5; 9.1. SC: le.

Fentiman, Linda C. Patient advocacy and termination from managed care organizations. Do state laws protecting

---

NRCBL: National Reference Center for Bioethics Literature Classification Scheme   See inside front cover for terms.

243

health care professional advocacy make any difference? *Nebraska Law Review* 2003; 82(2): 508-574. NRCBL: 9.3.2; 9.4; 9.3.1; 9.1; 8.1; 1.3.5. SC: le.

Hadorn, David. The Chaoulli challenge: getting a grip on waiting lists [opinion]. *CMAJ/JAMC: Canadian Medical Association Journal* 2005 August 2; 173(3): 271-273. NRCBL: 9.3.2; 21.1; 9.4. SC: le. Identifiers: Chaoulli v. Quebec.

Hall, Mark A. Managed care patient protection or provider protection? A qualitative assessment. *American Journal of Medicine* 2004 December 15; 117(12): 932-937. NRCBL: 9.3.2; 9.8. SC: em; le.

Hall, Mark A.; Berenson, Robert A. The ethics of managed care: a dose of realism. *Cumberland Law Review* 1997-1998; 28(2): 287-314. NRCBL: 9.3.2; 2.1; 4.1.2; 1.3.2. SC: le.

Hurst, Samia A.; Mauron, Alex. Selective contracting of Swiss physicians: ethical issues and open questions. *Swiss Medical Weekly* 2004 October 30; 134(43-44): 632-639. NRCBL: 9.3.2; 9.4. SC: em. Identifiers: Switzerland.

Kelly, Victoria J. The effects of financial incentives on health care decisions. *Medical Trial Technique Quarterly* 2000; 46(4): 195-210. NRCBL: 9.3.2; 9.4; 8.1; 7.1. SC: le.

King, Cheryl Slagle. Managed care: is it moral? [interview]. *Advanced Practice Nursing Quarterly* 1995 Winter; 1(3): 7-11. NRCBL: 9.3.2; 15.5; 21.4. Identifiers: Nuremberg Trials; Michael J. Franzblau.

Krause, Joan H. The brief life of the gag clause: why anti-gag clause legislation isn't enough. *Tennessee Law Review* 1999 Fall; 67(1): 1-44. NRCBL: 9.3.2; 8.1; 9.4. SC: le.

Kremer, Thomas G.; Gesten, Ellis L. Confidentiality limits of managed care and clients' willingness to self-disclose. *Professional Psychology: Research and Practice* 1998 December; 29(6): 553-558. NRCBL: 9.3.2; 8.4; 17.1. SC: em.

Levinson, Wendy; Kao, Audiey; Kuby, Alma M.; Thisted, Ronald A. The effect of physician disclosure of financial incentives on trust. *Archives of Internal Medicine* 2005 March 28; 165(6): 625-630. NRCBL: 9.3.2; 8.1; 9.3.1. SC: em.
> Abstract: BACKGROUND: Many physicians receive financial incentives to limit their ordering of expensive tests and procedures. While Medicare mandates disclosure of incentives, it is not clear how to inform patients without undermining trust. METHODS: Our objective was to determine public opinion about physician disclosure of financial incentives and how this might be best communicated to patients. The 2002 General Social Survey included 2765 interviews from a probability sample of English-speaking US households. The interview included questions about financial incentives and an audiotaped scenario of a physician discussing the impact of financial incentives on ordering a magnetic resonance image. Respondents heard 1 of 6 randomly selected disclosure strategies. The measurements included ratings of trust, satisfaction, agreement with the physician's decision, and likelihood of remaining with the physician/health plan or seeking a second opinion. RESULTS: Nearly half (48.8%) of respondents had previously heard of financial incentives to limit test ordering. Of the respondents, 94.8% wanted to be told about incentives, at the time of enrollment in a health plan (80.5%), by a health plan representative (44.8%), their physician (17.1%), or both (38.1%). Of the 6 different disclosure strategies, "addressing emotions" and "negotiation" were associated with the best outcomes, while "common enemy" and "denying influences" were most negatively perceived. Black and Hispanic subjects were less likely to express satisfaction or trust and more likely to disenroll or seek a second opinion. CONCLUSIONS: The public wants information about physician financial incentives. Specific communication styles enhance how this information is conveyed to patients, increasing trust and supporting the physician-patient relationship.

Maher, Daniel P. Managed care and undividing loyalties. *Journal of Contemporary Health Law and Policy* 2002 Fall; 18(3): 703-709. NRCBL: 9.3.2; 7.3.

Mamdani, Bashir; Mamdani, Meenal. Export of managed care: Europe, Latin America and implications for India. *Issues in Medical Ethics* 2002 April-June; 10(2): 17-19. NRCBL: 9.3.2; 21.1.

Marsh, Andrea K. Sacrificing patients for profits: physician incentives to limit care and ERISA fiduciary duty. *Washington University Law Quarterly* 1999 Winter; 77(4): 1323-1342. NRCBL: 9.3.2; 7.3. SC: le. Identifiers: Employee Retirement Income Security Act.

McCabe, Helen. Financial incentives, cross-purposes, and moral motivation in health care provision. *Monash Bioethics Review* 2005 July; 24(3): 20-35. NRCBL: 9.3.2. SC: an.

McKoy, June M.; Karsjens, Kari L.; Wynia, Matthew; MacDonald-Glenn, Linda. Is ethics for sale? . . . Juggling law and ethics in managed care. *DePaul Journal of Health Care Law* 2005 Spring; 8(3): 559-613. NRCBL: 9.3.2; 7.3; 8.5; 9.8; 2.1. SC: le.

Mennemeyer, Stephen T. Response to professor Mark Hall. *Cumberland Law Review* 1997-1998; 28(2): 321-323. NRCBL: 9.3.2; 1.3.2. SC: le. Identifiers: managed health care.

Minwalla, Sherizaan. The high price of silence: requiring ERISA regulated managed care organizations to disclose financial incentives used to limit medical care. *Journal of Medicine and Law* 2001 Fall; 6(1): 1-28. NRCBL: 9.3.2; 5.3. SC: le. Identifiers: Employee Retirement Income Security Act.

Nelson, Leonard J., III. Markets and managed care ethics. *Cumberland Law Review* 1997-1998; 28(2): 325-328. NRCBL: 9.3.2; 1.3.2. SC: le.

Purtilo, Ruth B. Managed care: challenges facing interdisciplinary health care teams. *Update [Loma Linda Uni-*

versity Center for Christian Bioethics] 1995 October; 11(3); 8 p. NRCBL: 9.3.2; 9.8.

Savitz, Martin H.; Rivlin, Michael M.; Fleetwood, Janet; Caputo, Zach; Perry, Constance. Ethical differences between socialized and HMO systems. *Mount Sinai Journal of Medicine* 2004 November; 71(6): 392-400. NRCBL: 9.3.2; 9.3.1; 20.7; 20.5.1; 14.1; 9.4; 19.5; 21.1. Identifiers: health maintenance organization.

Sullivan, MaryCarroll. Ethical considerations in managed care: a commentary. *UMKC Law Review* 1998 Summer; 66(4): 757-762. NRCBL: 9.3.2; 8.1.

Talesh, Shauhin A. Breaking the learned helplessness of patients: why MCOs should be required to disclose financial incentives. *Law and Psychology Review* 2002 Spring; 26(1): 49-95. NRCBL: 9.3.2; 9.4; 9.3.1; 1.3.2; 8.2. SC: le. Identifiers: Managed Care Organizations.

Zinberg, Joel M.; Mariner, Wendy K.; Bloche, M. Gregg. The Supreme Court and managed-care liability [letter and replies]. *New England Journal of Medicine* 2005 January 13; 352(2): 201- 203. NRCBL: 9.3.2; 8.5; 9.1. SC: le.

Zoloth-Dorfman, Laurie. Standing at the gate: managed care and daily ethical choices. *Managed Care Medicine* 1994 November-December; 1: 26-27, 31- 33, 37-38. NRCBL: 9.3.2; 9.2; 9.3.1; 9.4.

HEALTH CARE/ HEALTH CARE QUALITY

Disclosure and performance: expecting more, and better [editorial]. *CMAJ/JAMC: Canadian Medical Association Journal* 2005 August 30: 173(5): 457. NRCBL: 9.8; 9.7; 5.1; 8.3.1.

Anderson, Joan M. Empowering patients: issues and strategies. *Social Science and Medicine* 1996 September; 43(5): 697-705. NRCBL: 9.8; 9.5.5; 20.7; 8.1; 9.3.1. Identifiers: Canada.

Ashmore, R. A study on how mental health practitioners address ethical issues in clinical audit. *Journal of Psychiatric and Mental Health Nursing* 2005 February; 12(1): 112-120. NRCBL: 9.8; 8.3.1; 8.4; 17.1. SC: em. Identifiers: United Kingdom (Great Britain).

Banja, John D. Disclosing medical error: how much to tell? *Journal of Healthcare Risk Management* 2003 Winter; 23(1): 11-14. NRCBL: 9.8; 8.2.

Banja, John D. Why, what, and how ought harmed parties be told? The art, mechanics, and ambiguities of error disclosure. *In:* Youngberg, Barbara J.; Hatlie, Martin J., eds. The Patient Safety Handbook. Sudbury, MA: Jones and Bartlett; 2004: 531-548. NRCBL: 9.8; 8.2.

Bauman, Adam N.; Pedersen, Craig A., Schommer, Jon C.; Griffith, Niesha L. Policies on documentation and disciplinary action in hospital pharmacies after a medi-

cation error. *American Journal of Health-System Pharmacies* 2001 June 15; 58(12): 1120-1125. NRCBL: 9.8; 7.1. SC: em.

Bayley, Carol. Medical mistakes and institutional culture. *In:* Sharpe, Virginia A., ed. Accountability: Patient Safety and Policy Reform. Washington, DC: Georgetown University Press; 2004: 99-117. NRCBL: 9.8; 7.1.

Berlinger, Nancy. "Missing the mark": medical error, forgiveness, and justice. *In:* Sharpe, Virginia A., ed. Accountability: Patient Safety and Policy Reform. Washington, DC: Georgetown University Press; 2004: 119-134. NRCBL: 9.8; 1.2; 7.1.

Bernstein, Mark; Potvin, Dawn; Martin, Douglas K. A qualitative study of attitudes toward error in patients facing brain tumour surgery. *Canadian Journal of Neurological Sciences* 2004 May; 31(2): 208-212. NRCBL: 9.8; 9.5.1; 8.1.

Bhattacharyya, Timothy; Yeon, Howard. "Doctor, was this surgery done wrong?" Ethical issues in providing second opinions. *Journal of Bone and Joint Surgery* 2005 January; 87(1): 223-225. NRCBL: 9.8; 8.2.

Brody, Howard; Miller, Franklin G.; Bogdan-Lovis, Elizabeth. Evidence-based medicine: watching out for its friends. *Perspectives in Biology and Medicine* 2005 Autumn; 48(4): 570-584. NRCBL: 9.8; 18.2; 9.7; 9.4.

Cohen, Joshua. Are clinical practice guidelines impartial? *International Journal of Technology Assessment in Health Care* 2004 Fall; 20(4): 415-420. NRCBL: 9.8; 9.4. SC: an.

De Ville, Kenneth. God, science, and history: the cultural origins of medical error. *In:* Sharpe, Virginia A., ed. Accountability: Patient Safety and Policy Reform. Washington, DC: Georgetown University Press; 2004: 143-158. NRCBL: 9.8; 7.1.

Fins, Joseph J. Everyday disasters. *CQ: Cambridge Quarterly of Healthcare Ethics* 2005 Spring; 14(2): 207-213. NRCBL: 9.8; 9.4; 9.3.1.

Freeman, Robert A. Minimizing bias in industry-sponsored outcomes research. *Medical Interface* 1994 April; 7(4): 130-134. NRCBL: 9.8; 1.3.2; 18.1; 9.7.

Gallagher, Thomas H.; Levinson, Wendy. Disclosing harmful medical errors to patients: a time for professional action. *Archives of Internal Medicine* 2005 September 12; 165(16): 1819-1824. NRCBL: 9.8; 8.2.

Gerber, A.; Lauterbach, K.W. Evidence-based medicine: why do opponents and proponents use the same arguments? *Health Care Analysis: An International Journal of Health Care Philosophy and Policy* 2005 March; 13(1): 59-71. NRCBL: 9.8; 7.1; 9.4. SC: an.
Abstract: There is quite some ethical controversy on Evidence-based Medicine (EbM) with regard to issues of physician

NRCBL: National Reference Center for Bioethics Literature Classification Scheme   See inside front cover for terms.

245

autonomy as well as its allocative implications. Yet, there are some shortcomings in the current debate. First of all, some of the arguments brought up against EbM are similarly defaults of "classical medicine" as well, for instance its negligence of social aspects of medicine. Second, it is often maintained that EbM is just a tool to attain cost containment. This argument is false in two regards for neither is there any idea of cutting costs in the roots of EbM nor does EbM once practiced necessarily lead to less costs as there can be underuse as well as overuse. Third, both opponents and proponents of EbM come up with the same arguments against each other. Both maintain that the other way of practicing medicine does not allow for physicians' autonomy and free judgment. Therefore, we are going to search for the different presuppositions on which these "reproaches" rely. In this way we can demonstrate that both opponents and proponents rely on different notions of autonomy and free judgment in their argument. Finally, we hope to show that some of the ethical criticism may be raised against classical medicine as well and that allocation in terms of costs is not primarily an aim of EbM.

Gilbert, Sandra M. Writing/righting wrong. *In:* Sharpe, Virginia A., ed. Accountability: Patient Safety and Policy Reform. Washington, DC: Georgetown University Press; 2004: 27-41. NRCBL: 9.8; 8.5; 7.1.

Goeltz, Roxanne. In memory of my brother, Mike. *In:* Sharpe, Virginia A., ed. Accountability: Patient Safety and Policy Reform. Washington, DC: Georgetown University Press; 2004: 49-57. NRCBL: 9.8; 7.1.

Goodman, Kenneth W. Ethics, evidence, and public policy. *Perspectives in Biology and Medicine* 2005 Autumn; 48(4): 548-556. NRCBL: 9.8; 2.1; 1.3.5.

Gupta, Mona. Evidence-based medicine: ethically obligatory or ethically suspect? *Evidence-Based Mental Health* 2004 November; 7(4): 96-97. NRCBL: 9.8; 1.3.9.

Healy, Bernadine. A medical-industrial complex. How about medical grand juries to oversee, analyze, and approve the experts' health guidelines? *U.S. News and World Report* 2005 January 24; 138(3): 54. NRCBL: 9.8; 5.3; 9.3.1; 7.4; 7.3. SC: po.

Hevia, Armando; Hobgood, Cherri. Medical error during residency: to tell or not to tell. *Annals of Emergency Medicine* 2003 October; 42(4): 565-570. NRCBL: 9.8; 8.2; 7.3.

Hobgood, Cherri; Hevia, Armando. Disclosing medical error: a professional standard. *Seminars in Medical Practice* 2004; 7: 12-23. NRCBL: 9.8; 7.1. SC: cs.

Hodder, Peter; Gallagher, Ann. Standard-setting. *In:* Chadwick, Ruth; Levitt, Mairi, eds. Ethical Issues in Community Health Care. New York: Arnold; 1998: 63-72. NRCBL: 9.8.

Jensen, Uffe Juul. Evidence, effectiveness and ethics: Cochrane's legacy. *In:* Kristiansen, Ivar Sonbo; Mooney, Gavin, eds. Evidence- Based Medicine: In its Place. New York: Routledge; 2004: 20-32. NRCBL: 9.8.

Jones, James W.; McCullough, Laurence B. Disclosure of intraoperative events. *Surgery* 2002 September; 133(4): 531-532. NRCBL: 9.8; 8.2. SC: cs.

Jones, James W.; McCullough, Laurence B.; Richman, Bruce W. What to tell patients harmed by other physicians. *Journal of Vascular Surgery* 2003 October; 38(4): 866-867. NRCBL: 9.8; 8.2; 7.3. SC: cs.

Kalra, Jawahar; Massey, K. Lorne; Mulla, Amith. Disclosure of medical error: policies and practice. *Journal of the Royal Society of Medicine* 2005 July; 98(7): 307-309. NRCBL: 9.8; 8.2; 21.1.

Kothari, M.L.; Mehta, L.A.; Kothari, V.M. The ethics of evidence-based therapy. *Issues in Medical Ethics* 1999 January-March; 7(1): 16-18. NRCBL: 9.8.

Lehmann, Lisa Soleymani; Puopolo, Ann Louise; Shaykevich, Shimon; Brennan, Troyen A. Iatrogenic events resulting in intensive care admission: frequency, cause, and disclosure to patients and institutions. *American Journal of Medicine* 2005 April; 118(4): 409-413. NRCBL: 9.8; 9.1; 8.2. SC: em.

Liang, Bryan A. Error disclosure for quality improvement: authenticating a team of patients and providers to promote patient safety. *In:* Sharpe, Virginia A., ed. Accountability: Patient Safety and Policy Reform. Washington, DC: Georgetown University Press; 2004: 59-82. NRCBL: 9.8; 7.1.

Lurie, Nicole. Health disparities — less talk, more action [editorial]. *New England Journal of Medicine* 2005 August 18; 353(7): 727- 729. NRCBL: 9.8; 9.5.4.

Magotra, Ratna; Dastur, F.D. Iatrogenic complications: what are doctors' and hospitals' responsibilities? [case study and commentary]. *Issues in Medical Ethics* 2001 July-September; 9(3): 95-96. NRCBL: 9.8; 9.1.

Mooney, Gavin. Evidence-based medicine: objectives and values. *In:* Kristiansen, Ivar Sonbo; Mooney, Gavin, eds. Evidence- Based Medicine: In its Place. New York: Routledge; 2004: 62-72. NRCBL: 9.8; 9.1.

Morreim, E. Haavi. Medical errors: pinning the blame versus blaming the system. *In:* Sharpe, Virginia A., ed. Accountability: Patient Safety and Policy Reform. Washington, DC: Georgetown University Press; 2004: 213-232. NRCBL: 9.8; 7.1.

Narins, Craig R.; Dozier, Ann M.; Ling, Frederick S.; Zareba, Wojciech. The influence of public reporting of outcome data on medical decision making by physicians. *Archives of Internal Medicine* 2005 January 10; 165(1): 83-87. NRCBL: 9.8; 1.3.7; 7.1; 20.1. SC: em.

Parker, M. False dichotomies: EBM, clinical freedom, and the art of medicine. *Medical Humanities* 2005 June; 31(1): 23-30. NRCBL: 9.8.

Abstract: According to numerous commentators, clinical freedom, the art of medicine, and, by implication, a degree of patient welfare, are threatened by evidence based medicine (EBM). As EBM has developed over the last fifteen years, claims about better evidence for medical treatments, and improvements in healthcare delivery, have been matched by critiques of EBM's reductionism and uniformity, its problematic application to individual patients, and its alleged denial of the continuing need for clinical interpretation, insight, and judgment. Most of these attacks on EBM and defences of clinical freedom fail. They are based on erroneous understandings of the relationships between inductive knowledge, clinical uncertainty, and action. Evidence based medicine is a necessary condition for clinical freedom, not a threat to it, and EBM is not something to be balanced with either clinical experience or patient preferences. The art and science of medicine are more conceptually and practically connected than the defenders of clinical freedom, whatever they conceive that to be, are willing to admit.

Pedersen, Kjeld Moller. Randomised controlled trials in drug policies: can the best be the enemy of the good? *In:* Kristiansen, Ivar Sonbo; Mooney, Gavin, eds. Evidence-Based Medicine: In its Place. New York: Routledge; 2004: 124-140. NRCBL: 9.8; 9.7; 18.2.

Pellegrino, Edmund D. Prevention of medical error: where professional and organizational ethics meet. *In:* Sharpe, Virginia A., ed. Accountability: Patient Safety and Policy Reform. Washington, DC: Georgetown University Press; 2004: 83-98. NRCBL: 9.8; 2.1; 7.1.

Ramsey, Gloria. Nurses, medical errors, and the culture of blame. *Hastings Center Report* 2005 March-April; 35(2): 20-21. NRCBL: 9.8; 4.1.3; 7.3.

Rich, Ben A. Medical custom and medical ethics: rethinking the standard of care. *CQ: Cambridge Quarterly of Healthcare Ethics* 2005 Winter; 14(1): 27-39. NRCBL: 9.8; 8.5; 7.3; 1.3.5; 4.4; 20.4.1; 5.2. SC: le.

Richard, Shawn A.; Rawal, Shail; Martin, Douglas K. An ethical framework for cardiac report cards: a qualitative study. *BMC Medical Ethics [electronic]* 2005; 6(3); 7 p. Available: http://www.biomedcentral.com/bmcmedethics/ [17 May 2005]. NRCBL: 9.8; 9.5.1. SC: em.

Rowe, Michael. Doctors' responses to medical errors. *Critical Reviews in Oncology/Hematology* 2004 December; 52(3): 147-163. NRCBL: 9.8; 8.2; 7.1; 7.3; 8.1.

Ruroede, Kathleen. Attitudes of risk management professionals toward disclosure of medical mistakes. *Risk: Health, Safety and Environment* 2001 Spring; 12(1 and 2): 67-90. NRCBL: 9.8; 8.2; 7.1. SC: le; em.

Sackett, David L. Participants in research: neither guinea pigs nor sacrificial lambs, but pointers to better health care [editorial]. *BMJ: British Medical Journal* 2005 May 21; 330(7501): 1164. NRCBL: 9.8; 18.1; 9.5. SC: em.

Sage, William M. Reputation, malpractice liability, and medical error. *In:* Sharpe, Virginia A., ed. Accountability: Patient Safety and Policy Reform. Washington, DC: Georgetown University Press; 2004: 159-183. NRCBL: 9.8; 8.5; 7.1.

Schwappach, David L.B.; Koeck, Christian M. What makes an error unacceptable? A factorial survey on the disclosure of medical errors. *International Journal for Quality in Health Care* 2004 August; 16(4): 317-326. NRCBL: 9.8; 8.2. SC: em. Identifiers: Germany.

Surbone, Antonella. Complexity and the future of the patient-doctor relationship [editorial]. *Critical Reviews in Oncology/Hematology* 2004 December; 52(3): 143-145. NRCBL: 9.8; 8.2; 7.1; 7.3; 8.1.

Szatmari, Peter. Response to Dr Gupta. *Evidence-Based Mental Health* 2004 November; 7(4): 97-98. NRCBL: 9.8; 17.1.

Trivedi, Amal N.; Zaslavsky, Alan M.; Schneider, Eric C.; Ayanian, John Z. Trends in the quality of care and racial disparities in Medicare managed care. *New England Journal of Medicine* 2005 August 18; 353(7): 692- 700. NRCBL: 9.8; 9.5.4; 9.5.2.

Abstract: BACKGROUND: Since 1997, all managed-care plans administered by Medicare have reported on quality-of-care measures from the Health Plan Employer Data and Information Set (HEDIS). Studies of early data found that blacks received care that was of lower quality than that received by whites. In this study, we assessed changes over time in the overall quality of care and in the magnitude of racial disparities in nine measures of clinical performance. METHODS: In order to compare the quality of care for elderly white and black beneficiaries enrolled in Medicare managed-care plans who were eligible for at least one of nine HEDIS measures, we analyzed 1.8 million individual-level observations from 183 health plans from 1997 to 2003. For each measure, we assessed whether the magnitude of the racial disparity had changed over time with the use of multivariable models that adjusted for the age, sex, health plan, Medicaid eligibility, and socioeconomic position of beneficiaries on the basis of their area of residence. RESULTS: During the seven- year study period, clinical performance improved on all measures for both white enrollees and black enrollees (P.001). The gap between white beneficiaries and black beneficiaries narrowed for seven HEDIS measures (P.01). However, racial disparities did not decrease for glucose control among patients with diabetes (increasing from 4 percent to 7 percent, P.001) or for cholesterol control among patients with cardiovascular disorders (increasing from 14 percent to 17 percent; change not significant, P=0.72). CONCLUSIONS: The measured quality of care for elderly Medicare beneficiaries in managed-care plans improved substantially from 1997 to 2003. Racial disparities declined for most, but not all, HEDIS measures we studied. Future research should examine factors that contributed to the narrowing of racial disparities on some measures and focus on interventions to eliminate persistent disparities in the quality of care.

Veterans Health Administration. National Ethics Committee; Fox, Ellen; Tulsky, James A. Recommendations for the ethical conduct of quality improvement. *Journal of Clinical Ethics* 2005 Spring; 16(1): 61-71. NRCBL: 9.8; 2.4.

NRCBL: National Reference Center for Bioethics Literature Classification Scheme   See inside front cover for terms.

247

Vist, Gunn Elisabeth; Hagen, Kåre Birger; Devereaux, P.J.; Bryant, Dianne; Kristoffersen, Doris Tove; Oxman, Andrew David. Systematic review to determine whether participation in a trial influences outcome. *BMJ: British Medical Journal* 2005 May 21; 330(7501): 1175-1179. NRCBL: 9.8; 18.1; 9.5.1. SC: em.

Abstract: OBJECTIVE: To systematically compare the outcomes of participants in randomised controlled trials (RCTs) with those in comparable non-participants who received the same or similar treatment. DATA SOURCES: Bibliographic databases, reference lists from eligible articles, medical journals, and study authors. REVIEW METHODS: RCTs and cohort studies that evaluated the clinical outcomes of participants in RCTs and comparable non-participants who received the same or similar treatment. RESULTS: Five RCTs (six comparisons) and 50 cohort studies (85 comparisons) provided data on 31,140 patients treated in RCTs and 20,380 comparable patients treated outside RCTs. In the five RCTs, in which patients were given the option of participating or not, the comparisons provided limited information because of small sample sizes (a total of 412 patients) and the nature of the questions considered. 73 dichotomous outcomes were compared, of which 59 reported no statistically significant differences. For patients treated within RCTs, 10 comparisons reported significantly better outcomes and four reported significantly worse outcomes. Significantly heterogeneity was found (I2 = 89%) among the comparisons of 73 dichotomous outcomes; none of our a priori explanatory factors helped explain this heterogeneity. The 18 comparisons of continuous outcomes showed no significant differences in heterogeneity (I2 = 0%). The overall pooled estimate for continuous outcomes of the effect of participating in an RCT was not significant (standardised mean difference 0.01, 95% confidence interval -0.10 to 0.12). CONCLUSION: No strong evidence was found of a harmful or beneficial effect of participating in RCTs compared with receiving the same or similar treatment outside such trials.

Weissman, Joel S.; Annas, Catherine L.; Epstein, Arnold M.; Schneider, Eric C.; Clarridge, Brian; Kirle, Leslie; Gatsonis, Constantine; Feibelmann, Sandra; Ridley, Nancy. Error reporting and disclosure systems: views from hospital leaders. *JAMA: The Journal of the American Medical Association* 2005 March 16; 293(11): 1359-1366. NRCBL: 9.8; 8.4. SC: le; em.

Abstract: CONTEXT: The Institute of Medicine has recommended establishing mandatory error reporting systems for hospitals and other health settings. OBJECTIVE: To examine the opinions and experiences of hospital leaders with state reporting systems. DESIGN AND SETTING: Survey of chief executive and chief operating officers (CEOs/COOs) from randomly selected hospitals in 2 states with mandatory reporting and public disclosure, 2 states with mandatory reporting without public disclosure, and 2 states without mandatory systems in 2002-2003. MAIN OUTCOME MEASURES: Perceptions of the effects of mandatory systems on error reporting, likelihood of lawsuits, and overall patient safety; attitudes regarding release of incident reports to the public; and likelihood of reporting incidents to the state or to the affected patient based on hypothetical clinical vignettes that varied the type and severity of patient injury. RESULTS: Responses were received from 203 of 320 hospitals (response rate = 63%). Most CEOs/COOs thought that a mandatory, nonconfidential system would discourage reporting of patient safety incidents to their hospital's own internal reporting system (69%) and encourage lawsuits (79%) while having no effect or a negative effect on patient safety (73%). More than 80% felt that the names of both the hospital and the involved professionals should be kept confidential, although respondents from states with mandatory public disclosure systems were more willing than respondents from the other states to release the hospital name (22% vs 4%-6%, P = .005). Based on the vignettes, more than 90% of hospital leaders said their hospital would report incidents involving serious injury to the state, but far fewer would report moderate or minor injuries, even when the incident was of sufficient consequence that they would tell the affected patient or family. CONCLUSIONS: Most hospital leaders expressed substantial concerns about the impact of mandatory, nonconfidential reporting systems on hospital internal reporting, lawsuits, and overall patient safety. While hospital leaders generally favor disclosure of patient safety incidents to involved patients, fewer would disclose incidents involving moderate or minor injury to state reporting systems.

Werner, Rachel M.; Asch, David A. The unintended consequences of publicly reporting quality information. *JAMA: The Journal of the American Medical Association* 2005 March 9; 293(10): 1239-1244. NRCBL: 9.8. SC: em.

Abstract: Health care report cards publicly report information about physician, hospital, and health plan quality in an attempt to improve that quality. Reporting quality information publicly is presumed to motivate quality improvement through 2 main mechanisms. First, public quality information allows patients, referring physicians, and health care purchasers to preferentially select high-quality physicians. Second, public report cards may motivate physicians to compete on quality and, by providing feedback and by identifying areas for quality improvement initiatives, help physicians to do so. Despite these plausible mechanisms of quality improvement, the value of publicly reporting quality information is largely undemonstrated and public reporting may have unintended and negative consequences on health care. These unintended consequences include causing physicians to avoid sick patients in an attempt to improve their quality ranking, encouraging physicians to achieve "target rates" for health care interventions even when it may be inappropriate among some patients, and discounting patient preferences and clinical judgment. Public reporting of quality information promotes a spirit of openness that may be valuable for enhancing trust of the health professions, but its ability to improve health remains undemonstrated, and public reporting may inadvertently reduce, rather than improve, quality. Given these limitations, it may be necessary to reassess the role of public quality reporting in quality improvement.

Wu, Albert W. Is there an obligation to disclose near-misses in medical care? *In:* Sharpe, Virginia A., ed. Accountability: Patient Safety and Policy Reform. Washington, DC: Georgetown University Press; 2004: 135-142. NRCBL: 9.8; 7.1.

HEALTH CARE RATIONING *See* RESOURCE ALLOCATION

HEALTH CARE RIGHTS *See* RIGHT TO HEALTH CARE

HEALTH, CONCEPT OF
See also MENTAL HEALTH, CONCEPT OF

Allmark, Peter. Health, happiness and health promotion. *Journal of Applied Philosophy* 2005; 22(1): 1-15. NRCBL: 4.2; 1.1.

Abstract: This article claims that health promotion is best practiced in the light of an Aristotelian conception of the good life for humans and of the place of health within it.

Badcott, David. Employing patient expertise: introduction to the theme [editorial]. *Medicine, Health Care and Philosophy: A European Journal* 2005; 8(2): 147-148. NRCBL: 4.2; 8.1; 9.1.

Badcott, David. The expert patient: valid recognition or false hope? *Medicine, Health Care and Philosophy: A European Journal* 2005; 8(2): 173-178. NRCBL: 8.1; 4.2; 9.1. SC: an.

Abstract: The United Kingdom Department of Health initiative on "The Expert Patient" (2001) reflects recent trends in political philosophy, ethics and health services research. The overall objective of the initiative is to encourage patients, particularly those suffering from chronic conditions to become more actively involved in decisions concerning their treatment. In doing so there would be (perhaps) an expectation of better patient compliance and (arguably) a resultant improvement in quality of life. Despite these anticipated beneficial influences on health outcomes, there may be a danger that such initiatives are being carried along by the general swell of enthusiasm for recognising and facilitating the claims of disadvantaged or discriminated against groups. What more attractive than that patients should be "liberated" from what might be seen as the oppression of medical paternalism? To a great extent the potential for success of the Expert Patient venture turns on:(a) whether and to what extent a patient can be considered truly to be an expert and (b) full acceptance by the medical and heath care professions of allowing patients a more equitable and positive role.Whilst clearly the patient is an expert in the hermeneutic sense - it is they and they alone who experience their illness - there is nevertheless a risk of confusing experience with expertise. Experience limited to an individual does not of itself give rise to the generalisations that underlie reliable clinical treatment. Neither do the vast majority of patients possess the physiological and pharmacological knowledge to fully appreciate the biological nature of their illness nor the basis, risks or limitations of therapeutic measures. Might the notion of "The Expert Patient" as informed co-decision maker become a well-meaning but rather vacuous aspiration similar to that of informed consent? Even worse, could patient "empowerment" have a deleterious effect? The paper reviews some of the major issues and concludes that the expert patient initiative could have benefits for both patients and health professionals if operated on the basis of concordance: an informed collaborative alliance that optimises the potential benefits of medical care.

Bergdolt, Klaus. History of medicine and concepts of health [editorial]. *Croatian Medical Journal* 1999 June; 40(2): 119-122. NRCBL: 4.2; 9.1; 7.1; 21.1.

Bircher, Johannes. Towards a dynamic definition of health and disease. *Medicine, Health Care and Philosophy: A European Journal* 2005; 8(3): 335-341. NRCBL: 4.2; 1.1; 4.1.2.

Abstract: A multifactorial and growing crisis of health care systems in the developed world has affected medicine. In order to provide rational responses, some central concepts of the past, such as the definitions of health and disease, need to be updated. For this purpose physicians should initiate a new debate. As a point of departure the following definitions are proposed: Health is a dynamic state of wellbeing characterized by a physical, mental and social potential, which satisfies the demands of a life commensurate with age, culture, and personal responsibil-

ity. If the potential is insufficient to satisfy these demands the state is disease. This term includes sickness, illness, ill health, and malady. The described potential is divided into a biologically given and a personally acquired partial potential. Their proportions vary throughout the life cycle. The proposed definitions render it empirically possible to diagnose persons as healthy or diseased and to apportion some of the responsibility for their state of health to individuals themselves. Treatment strategies should always consider three therapeutic routes: improvements of the biologically given and of the personally acquired partial potentials and adaptations of the demands of life. These consequences favourably contrast with those resulting from the WHO-definition of health.

Clarke, Adele E.; Shim, Janet K.; Mamo, Laura; Fosket, Jennifer Ruth; Fishman, Jennifer R. Biomedicalization: technoscientific transformations of health, illness, and U.S. biomedicine. *American Sociological Review* 2003 April; 68(2): 161-194. NRCBL: 4.2; 9.1; 7.1. SC: rv.

Davis, N. Ann. Invisible disability. *Ethics: An International Journal of Social, Political, and Legal Philosophy* 2005 October; 116(1): 153-213. NRCBL: 4.2; 4.3; 9.5.1; 17.1. SC: an.

Diedrich, Lisa. A bioethics of failure: antiheroic cancer narratives. *In:* Shildrick, Margrit; Mykitiuk, Roxanne, eds. Ethics of the Body: Postconventional Challenges. Cambridge, MA: MIT Press; 2005: 135- 150. NRCBL: 4.2; 9.5.5.

Dwyer, James. Global health and justice. *Bioethics* 2005 October; 19(5-6): 460-475. NRCBL: 4.2; 21.1; 1.1.

Abstract: In Australia, Japan, Sweden, and Switzerland, the average life expectancy is now greater than 80 years. But in Angola, Malawi, Sierra Leone, and Zimbabwe, the average life expectancy is less than 40 years. The situation is even worse than these statistics suggest because average figures tend to mask inequalities within countries. What are we to make of a world with such unequal health prospects? What does justice demand in terms of global health? To address these problems, I characterize justice at the local level, at the domestic or social level, and at the international or global level. Because social conditions, structures, and institutions have such a profound influence on the health of populations, I begin by focusing attention on the relationship between social justice and health prospects. Then I go on to discuss health prospects and the problem of global justice. Here I distinguish two views: a cosmopolitan view and a political view of global justice. In my account of global justice, I modify and use the political view that John Rawls developed in The Law of Peoples. I try to show why an adequate political account must include three duties: a duty not to harm, a duty to reconstruct international arrangements, and a duty to assist.

Edgar, Andrew. The expert patient: illness as practice. *Medicine, Health Care and Philosophy: A European Journal* 2005; 8(2): 165-171. NRCBL: 4.2; 8.1; 9.1. SC: an.

Abstract: This paper responds to the Expert Patient initiative by questioning its over-reliance on instrumental forms of reasoning. It will be suggested that expertise of the patient suffering from chronic illness should not be exclusively seen in terms of a model of technical knowledge derived from the natural sciences, but should rather include an awareness of the hermeneutic skills that the patient needs in order to make sense of their

NRCBL: National Reference Center for Bioethics Literature Classification Scheme   See inside front cover for terms.

249

illness and the impact that the illness has upon their sense of self-identity. By appealing to MacIntyre's concepts of "virtue" and "practice", as well as Frank's notion of the "wounded story-teller", it will be argued that chronic illness can be constituted as a practice, by building a culture of honest and courageous story-telling about the experience of chronic suffering. The building of such a practice will renew the cultural resources available to the patient, the physician and the rest of the community in understanding illness and patient-hood.

Engelhardt, H. Tristram, Jr. Health, disease, and persons: well-being in a post-modern world. *In:* Taboada, Paulina; Cuddeback, Kateryna Fedoryka; Donohue-White, Patricia, eds. Person, Society and Value: Towards a Personalist Concept of Health. Boston: Kluwer Academic Pub.; 2002: 147-163. NRCBL: 4.2; 1.1.

Goldworth, Amnon. Disease, illness, and ethics. *CQ: Cambridge Quarterly of Healthcare Ethics* 2005 Summer; 14(3): 346-351. NRCBL: 4.2; 4.1.1; 1.1; 4.4.

Hilhorst, Medard. 'Prosthetic fit': on personal identity and the value of bodily difference. *Medicine, Health Care and Philosophy: A European Journal* 2004; 7(3): 303-310. NRCBL: 4.2; 9.5.1; 4.4; 9.5.7; 4.1.2. SC: an.
  Abstract: It is within the context of a person's life story, we argue, that the idea of wearing a prosthesis assumes place and meaning. To develop this argument, a brightly colored hook prosthesis for children is taken as a starting point for reflection. The prosthesis can be seen as fitting this person perfectly, when the bodily difference is understood as positively adding to this person's identity. The choice for the prosthesis is normative in a moral sense, in that it is grounded in a person's fundamental convictions with respect to his being and living. This understanding of 'how to live' can best be grasped—as is suggested—in contrastive terms of 'sameness' and 'otherness'. Striving for conformity and similarity would do no justice to the experiences and ideals of unique persons, and would come at great cost. Moreover, society is not benefited by persons who merely conform, who copy and imitate others, but by those who willfully live up to their own unique standards.

Hintermair, Manfred; Albertini, John A. Ethics, deafness, and new medical technologies. *Journal of Deaf Studies and Deaf Education* 2005 Spring; 10(2): 184-192. NRCBL: 4.2; 4.4; 5.1; 9.5.7.

Hofmann, Bjørn. Simplified models of the relationship between health and disease. *Theoretical Medicine and Bioethics* 2005; 26(5): 355-377. NRCBL: 4.2; 4.1.2; 7.1.
  Abstract: The concepts of health and disease are crucial in defining the aim and the limits of modern medicine. Accordingly it is important to understand them and their relationship. However, there appears to be a discrepancy between scholars in philosophy of medicine and health care professionals with regard to these concepts. This article investigates health care professionals' concepts of health and disease and the relationship between them. In order to do so, four different models are described and analyzed: the ideal model, the holistic model, the medical model and the disjunctive model. The analysis reveals that each model has its pros and cons, and that health care professionals appear to apply more than one models. Furthermore, the models and the way health care professionals' use them may be helpful for scholars in philosophy of medicine with regard to developing theories and communicating them to health care professionals.

Holm, Søren. Justifying patient self-management — evidence based medicine or the primacy of the first person perspective. *Medicine, Health Care and Philosophy: A European Journal* 2005; 8(2): 159-164. NRCBL: 4.2; 8.1; 9.1. SC: an.
  Abstract: Patient self-management programs have become increasingly popular and are now also receiving official endorsements. This paper analyses two possible types of positive justifications for promoting patient self-management: evidence-based and patient-centred justifications. It is argued that evidence-based justifications, although important politically are deficient and that the primary justification for patient self-management must be a patient-centred justification focusing on the patient's privileged access to his or her own lived body.

Marcum, James A. Biomechanical and phenomenological models of the body, the meaning of illness and quality of care. *Medicine, Health Care and Philosophy: A European Journal* 2004; 7(3): 311-320. NRCBL: 4.2; 4.1.2; 4.4; 8.1; 9.8. SC: an.
  Abstract: The predominant model of the body in modern western medicine is the machine. Practitioners of the biomechanical model reduce the patient to separate, individual body parts in order to diagnose and treat disease. Utilization of this model has led, in part, to a quality of care crisis in medicine, in which patients perceive physicians as not sufficiently compassionate or empathic towards their suffering. Alternative models of the body, such as the phenomenological model, have been proposed to address this crisis. According to the phenomenological model, the patient is viewed as an embodied person within a lived context and through this view the physician comes to understand the disruption illness causes in the patient's everyday world of meaning. In this paper, I explore the impact these two models of the patient's body have had on modern medical practice. To that end I first examine briefly the historical origins of the biomechanical and phenomenological models, providing a historical context for the discussion of each model's main features in terms of machine-world and life-world. Next, I discuss the impact each model has had on the patient-physician relationship, and then I examine briefly the future development of each model. The meaning of illness vis-a-vis each model of the patient's body is finally examined, especially in terms of how these two models affect the patient's interpretation of illness. The paper concludes with a discussion of the biomechanical and phenomenological models, in terms of the quality of care crisis in modern western medicine.

McKee, Martin; Raine, Rosalind. Choosing health? First choose your philosophy [opinion]. *Lancet* 2005 January 29-February 4; 365(9457): 369-371. NRCBL: 4.2; 9.1; 1.1. Identifiers: United Kingdom (Great Britain).

Scully, Jackie Leach. Admitting all variations? Postmodernism and genetic normality. *In:* Shildrick, Margrit; Mykitiuk, Roxanne, eds. Ethics of the Body: Postconventional Challenges. Cambridge, MA: MIT Press; 2005: 49-68. NRCBL: 4.2; 9.5.1; 15.1.

Scully, Jackie Leach. What is a disease? Disease, disability and their definitions [opinion]. *EMBO Reports* 2004 July; 5(7): 650-653. NRCBL: 4.2; 4.4; 15.2.

Siegel, Marc. What doctors fear most. *Hastings Center Report* 2005 November-December; 35(6): 8. NRCBL: 4.2; 7.3; 8.1. Identifiers: doctors as patients.

Silvers, Anita. Predicting genetic disability while commodifying health. *In:* Wasserman, David; Bickenbach, Jerome; Wachbroit, Robert, eds. Quality of Life and Human Difference: Genetic Testing, Health Care, and Disability. New York: Cambridge University Press; 2005: 43-66. NRCBL: 4.2; 9.4; 15.3; 1.1. SC: an.

Tyreman, Stephen. An expert in what?: the need to clarify meaning and expectations in "The Expert Patient". *Medicine, Health Care and Philosophy: A European Journal* 2005; 8(2): 153-157. NRCBL: 4.2; 8.1; 9.1.

Abstract: This paper critiques particular aspects of the published UK government Department of Health's proposal to promote 'The Expert Patient' as a way of enhancing patient autonomy and reducing reliance on limited health care resources. Although the broad aims of the report are supported the detail is criticised on the basis that lack of clarity over key terms, including 'expert' 'illness' and 'disease', means that there is no clear focus for action and threatens to undermine the effectiveness of the proposals.

Tyreman, Stephen. The expert patient: outline of UK government paper. *Medicine, Health Care and Philosophy: A European Journal* 2005; 8(2): 149-151. NRCBL: 4.2; 8.1; 9.1.

Abstract: This introduction outlines key elements in a recent United Kingdom Department of Health report that, it is hoped, will change attitudes, expectations and practices in the care of patients with chronic illness [Department of Health: 2001, The Expert Patient: A New Approach to Chronic Disease Management for the 21st Century. London: Department of Health.]. The findings of the Task Force are summarised as accurately as possible and without comment. Analysis and comment can be found in the accompanying papers.

Varelius, Jukka. Health and autonomy. *Medicine, Health Care and Philosophy: A European Journal* 2005; 8(2): 221-230. NRCBL: 4.2; 4.4; 1.1. SC: an.

Abstract: Individual autonomy is a prominent value in Western medicine and medical ethics, and there it is often accepted that the only way to pay proper respect to autonomy is to let the patients themselves determine what is good for them. Adopting this approach has, however, given rise to some unwanted results, thus motivating a quest for an objective conception of health. Unfortunately, the purportedly objective conceptions of health have failed in objectivity, and if a conception of health is not acceptable for all agents, the threat of offending the patients' autonomy arises. This article sketches an objective conception of health that is able to respect individual autonomy.

Young, Katherine K. Health. *In:* Schweiker, William, ed. The Blackwell Companion to Religious Ethics. Malden, MA: Blackwell Pub.; 2005: 519-526. NRCBL: 4.2; 7.1; 1.2.

HISTORY OF BIOETHICS *See* BIOETHICS AND MEDICAL ETHICS/ HISTORY

HOSPICES *See* DEATH AND DYING/ TERMINAL CARE

HOSPITAL ETHICS COMMITTEES *See* ETHICISTS AND ETHICS COMMITTEES

HUMAN EXPERIMENTATION
See also AIDS/ HUMAN EXPERIMENTATION; BEHAVIORAL RESEARCH; BIOMEDICAL RESEARCH

Al-Sulaiman, Abdulsalam A.; Al-Gindan, Yussuf M. The dilemma of clinical research. Historical and philosophical consideration of physicians' ambitions and patients' fear. *Saudi Medical Journal* 2004 November; 25(11): 1739-1741. NRCBL: 18.1; 18.2; 1.3.9. Identifiers: Saudi Arabia.

Alvino, Lori A. Who's watching the watchdogs? Responding to the erosion of research ethics by enforcing promises. *Columbia Law Review* 2003 May; 103(4): 893-924. NRCBL: 18.1; 18.2; 9.3.1; 18.6. SC: le.

Baader, Gerhard. Jewish halachic medical ethics and human experimentation. *In:* Roelcke, Volker; Maio, Giovanni, eds. Twentieth Century Ethics of Human Subjects Research: Historical Perspectives on Values, Practices, and Regulations. Stuttgart: Franz Steiner Verlag; 2004: 51-63. NRCBL: 18.1; 1.2; 2.2.

Beck, Norbert. Proteomics in pathology, research and practice: ethical considerations. *Pathology, Research and Practice* 2004; 200(2): 179-180. NRCBL: 18.1; 18.3.

Beecher, Henry K. Human experimentation: a world problem from the standpoint of a medical investigator. *World Medical Journal* 1960 March; 8: 79-80. NRCBL: 18.1.

Beh, Hazel. Compensation for research injuries. *IRB: Ethics and Human Research* 2005 May-June; 27(3): 11-15. NRCBL: 18.1; 9.3.1. Identifiers: National Vaccine Injury Compensation Program (VICP).

Bernstein, Mark. Assessing the bioethical integrity of a clinical trial in surgery. *Canadian Journal of Surgery* 2004 October; 47(5): 329-332. NRCBL: 18.1; 18.2.

Beskow, Laura M.; Botkin, Jeffrey R.; Daly, Mary; Juengst, Eric T.; Lehmann, Lisa Soleymani; Merz, Jon F.; Pentz, Rebecca; Press, Nancy A.; Ross, Lainie Friedman; Sugarman, Jeremy; Susswein, Lisa R.; Terry, Sharon F.; Austin, Melissa A.; Burke, Wylie. Ethical issues in identifying and recruiting participants for familial genetic research. *American Journal of Medical Genetics* 2004 November 1; 130A(4): 424-431. NRCBL: 18.1; 8.1; 15.3.

Bonah, Christian; Menut, Philippe. BCG vaccination around 1930: dangerous experiment or established prevention? Debates in France and Germany. *In:* Roelcke, Volker; Maio, Giovanni, eds. Twentieth Century Ethics of Human Subjects Research: Historical Perspectives on Values,

NRCBL: National Reference Center for Bioethics Literature Classification Scheme   See inside front cover for terms.

251

Practices, and Regulations. Stuttgart: Franz Steiner Verlag; 2004: 111-127. NRCBL: 18.1; 9.5.1; 9.7; 2.2; 21.1.

Chan, David Kum-Wah. Autonomy, humane medicine, and research ethics: an East Asian perspective. *In:* Brannigan, Michael C., ed. Cross-Cultural Biotechnology. Lanham: Rowman and Littlefield; 2004: 127-137. NRCBL: 18.1; 1.1; 1.2; 1.3.9; 2.1; 21.1.

Doerflinger, Richard M. Experimentation on human subjects and stem cell research. *In:* McMahon, Kevin T., ed. Moral Issues in Catholic Health Care. Wynnewood, PA: Saint Charles Borromeo Seminary; 2004: 93-107. NRCBL: 18.1; 18.5.4; 1.2.

Edelson, Paul J. Henry K. Beecher and Maurice Pappworth: honor in the development of the ethics of human experimentation. *In:* Roelcke, Volker; Maio, Giovanni, eds. Twentieth Century Ethics of Human Subjects Research: Historical Perspectives on Values, Practices, and Regulations. Stuttgart: Franz Steiner Verlag; 2004: 219-233. NRCBL: 18.1; 2.2.

Elkeles, Barbara. The German debate on human experimentation between 1880 and 1914. *In:* Roelcke, Volker; Maio, Giovanni, eds. Twentieth Century Ethics of Human Subjects Research: Historical Perspectives on Values, Practices, and Regulations. Stuttgart: Franz Steiner Verlag; 2004: 19-33. NRCBL: 18.1; 22.2.

Elon, Menachem; Auerbach, Bernard; Chazin, Daniel D.; Sykes, Melvin J. Medical experimentation. *In their:* Jewish Law (Mishpat Ivri): Cases and Materials. New York: M. Bender; 1999: 737-741. NRCBL: 18.1; 1.2; 22.2.

Elster, Nanette R.; Hoffman, Richard E.; Livengood, John R. Public health research and health information. *In:* Goodman, Richard A.; Rothstein, Mark A.; Hoffman, Richard E.; Lopez, Wilfredo; Matthews, Gene W., eds. Law in Public Health Practice. New York: Oxford University Press; 2003: 160-174. NRCBL: 18.1; 1.3.9; 9.1. SC: le.

Emanuel, Ezekiel J.; Currie, Xolani E.; Herman, Allen. Undue inducement in clinical research in developing countries: is it a worry? [opinion]. *Lancet* 2005 July 23-29; 366(9482): 336-340. NRCBL: 18.1; 9.3.1; 18.2; 18.6; 9.5.6; 18.5.7.

Frewer, Andreas. Debates on human experimentation in Weimar and early Nazi Germany as reflected in the journal "Ethik" (1922-1938) and its context. *In:* Roelcke, Volker; Maio, Giovanni, eds. Twentieth Century Ethics of Human Subjects Research: Historical Perspectives on Values, Practices, and Regulations. Stuttgart: Franz Steiner Verlag; 2004: 137-150. NRCBL: 18.1; 1.3.7; 21.4; 15.5; 1.3.5; 2.2.

Fry, C.L.; Ritter, A.; Baldwin, S.; Bowen, K.J.; Gardiner, P.; Holt, T.; Jenkinson, R.; Johnston, J. Paying research participants: a study of current practices in Australia. *Journal of Medical Ethics* 2005 September; 31(9): 542-547. NRCBL: 18.1; 9.3.1. SC: em.

Abstract: OBJECTIVE: To examine current research payment practices and to inform development of clearer guidelines for researchers and ethics committees. DESIGN: Exploratory email based questionnaire study of current research participant reimbursement practices. A diverse sample of organisations and individuals were targeted. SETTING: Australia. PARTICIPANTS: Contacts in 84 key research organisations and select electronic listservers across Australia. A total of 100 completed questionnaires were received with representations from a variety of research areas (for example, market, alcohol and drug, medical, pharmaceutical and social research). MAIN MEASUREMENTS: Open-ended and fixed alternative questions about type of research agency; type of research; type of population under study; whether payment is standard; amounts and mechanisms of payment; factors taken into account when deciding on payment practices; and whether payment policies exist. RESULTS: Reimbursement practice is highly variable. Where it occurs (most commonly for drug dependent rather than health professional or general population samples) it is largely monetary and is for time and out-of-pocket expenses. Ethics committees were reported to be often involved in decision making around reimbursement. CONCLUSIONS: Research subject payment practices vary in Australia. Researchers who do provide payments to research participants generally do so without written policy and procedures. Ethics committees have an important role in developing guidelines in this area. Specific guidelines are needed considering existing local policies and procedures; payment models and their application in diverse settings; case study examples of types and levels of reimbursement; applied definitions of incentive and inducement; and the rationale for diverse payment practices in different settings.

Fry, Sara T.; Veatch, Robert M. Experimentation on human beings. *In their:* Case Studies in Nursing Ethics. Third edition. Sudbury, MA: Jones and Bartlett Publishers; 2006: 330-363. NRCBL: 18.1.

Gillon, John J., Jr. More subject and less human: the pain-filled journey of human subjects protection . . . and some differences in the United States and the European Union. *Medical Law International* 2005; 7(1): 65-89. NRCBL: 18.1; 2.2; 21.1. SC: le.

Giuseppe, Bosio M.; De Senarclens, Jacques; Groen, J.J. Human experimentation — a world problem from the standpoint of spiritual leaders. *World Medical Journal* 1960 March; 8: 80-83. 96. NRCBL: 18.1; 1.2.

Gradmann, Christoph. "It seemed about time to try one of those modern medicines": animal and human experimentation in the chemotherapy of sleeping sickness 1905-1908. *In:* Roelcke, Volker; Maio, Giovanni, eds. Twentieth Century Ethics of Human Subjects Research: Historical Perspectives on Values, Practices, and Regulations. Stuttgart: Franz Steiner Verlag; 2004: 83-97. NRCBL: 18.1; 2.2; 22.2.

Gulhati, C.M. Needed: closer scrutiny of clinical trials [editorial]. *Indian Journal of Medical Ethics* 2004 January-March; 1(1): 4-5. NRCBL: 18.1; 9.7.

Harris, John. Scientific research is a moral duty. *Journal of Medical Ethics* 2005 April; 31(4): 242-248. NRCBL: 18.1; 1.3.9. SC: an.

Hazelgrove, Jenny. British research ethics after the Second World War: the controversy at the British postgraduate medical school, Hammersmith Hospital. *In:* Roelcke, Volker; Maio, Giovanni, eds. Twentieth Century Ethics of Human Subjects Research: Historical Perspectives on Values, Practices, and Regulations. Stuttgart: Franz Steiner Verlag; 2004: 181-197. NRCBL: 18.1; 18.2; 2.2.

Hershey, Nathan. The clinical investigator as target. *Controlled Clinical Trials* 1996 June; 17(3): 183-190. NRCBL: 18.1; 1.3.9.

Illes, Judy; Kirschen, Matthew P.; Karetsky, Kim; Kelly, Megan; Saha, Arnold; Desmond, John E.; Raffin, Thomas A.; Glover, Gary H.; Atlas, Scott W. Discovery and disclosure of incidental findings in neuroimaging research. *Journal of Magnetic Resonance Imaging* 2004 November; 20(5): 743-747. NRCBL: 18.1; 8.2; 17.1. SC: em.

Iltis, Ana Smith. Third-party payers and the costs of biomedical research. *Kennedy Institute of Ethics Journal* 2005 June; 15(2): 135-160. NRCBL: 18.1; 9.3.1; 9.2; 5.3; 1.3.2.

Abstract: Four principal arguments have been offered in support of requiring public and private third-party payers to help fund medical research: (1) many of the costs associated with clinical trial participation are for routine care that would be reimbursed if delivered outside of a trial; (2) there is a need to promote scientific research and medical progress and lack of coverage is an impediment to enrollment; (3) to cover the costs of trials expands health care and treatment options for the sick; and (4) it is beneficial for private insurers to cover the costs associated with cancer clinical trials because doing so makes such companies more attractive to consumers. Although many see third-party-payer coverage as a victory for patients and for the future of research, requiring coverage of services provided in a trial beyond those that would be provided to a comparable patient outside the research context raises a number of concerns.

Katz, Jay. What consequences to society should affect the authority of the investigator? *In his:* Experimentation with Human Beings: The Authority of the Investigator, Subject, Professions, and State in the Human Experimentation Process. New York: Russell Sage Foundation; 1972: 435-520. NRCBL: 18.1; 18.4.

Katz, Jay. What consequences to subjects should affect the authority of the investigator? *In his:* Experimentation with Human Beings: The Authority of the Investigator, Subject, Professions, and State in the Human Experimentation Process. New York: Russell Sage Foundation; 1972: 323-434. NRCBL: 18.1; 18.4.

Kavanaugh, A. Ethical and practical issues in conducting clinical trials in psoriasis and psoriatic arthritis. *Annals of the Rheumatic Diseases* 2005 March; 64(Supplement 2): ii46-ii48. NRCBL: 18.1; 18.3; 1.1.

Khanlou, N.; Peter, E. Participatory action research: considerations for ethical review. *Social Science and Medicine* 2005 May; 60(10): 2333-2340. NRCBL: 18.1; 18.2; 9.1.

Kong, W.M. Legitimate requests and indecent proposals: matters of justice in the ethical assessment of phase I trials involving competent patients. *Journal of Medical Ethics* 2005 April; 31(4): 205-208. NRCBL: 18.1; 15.4. SC: an.

Abstract: The death of Jesse Gelsinger in 1999 during a gene therapy trial raised many questions about the ethical review of medical research. Here, the author argues that the principle of justice is interpreted too narrowly and receives insufficient emphasis and that what we permit in terms of bodily invasion affects the value we place on individuals. Medical research is a societally supported activity. As such, the author contends that justice requires that invasive medical research demonstrates sufficiently compelling societal benefit. Many consider this societal benefit to be self evident. However, medical research is a complex activity; it yields new treatments but also creates financial rewards and affects health resource allocation. As research evolves into a multibillion pound, multinational enterprise, justice requires a much broader analysis of societal benefit. Without such evaluation we risk undermining the value of bodily integrity and of research participants.

Lepicard, Etienne. The construction of human experimentation ethics: Catholic voices in context. *In:* Roelcke, Volker; Maio, Giovanni, eds. Twentieth Century Ethics of Human Subjects Research: Historical Perspectives on Values, Practices, and Regulations. Stuttgart: Franz Steiner Verlag; 2004: 35-49. NRCBL: 18.1; 1.2; 2.2.

Lertsithichai, Panuwat. Medical research ethics in Thailand: what should be the most appropriate approach? An analysis based on western ethical principles. *Journal of the Medical Association of Thailand* 2004 October; 87(10): 1253-1261. NRCBL: 18.1; 18.3; 1.3.9; 2.1. Note: Text in English and Thai.

Lock, Stephen. Fraud and misconduct in medical research. *Medico-Legal Journal* 1996; 64(Part 4): 139-152. NRCBL: 18.1; 8.5.

Löfman, Päivi; Pelkonen, Marjaana; Pietilä, Anna-Maija. Ethical issues in participatory action research. *Scandinavian Journal of Caring Sciences* 2004 September; 18(3): 333-340. NRCBL: 18.1; 18.3; 8.4.

Maio, Giovanni. Medical ethics and human experimentation in France after 1945. *In:* Roelcke, Volker; Maio, Giovanni, eds. Twentieth Century Ethics of Human Subjects Research: Historical Perspectives on Values, Practices, and Regulations. Stuttgart: Franz Steiner Verlag; 2004: 235-252. NRCBL: 18.1; 2.1; 7.2; 2.2.

Maloney, Dennis M. Critics claim even babies could be exposed to pesticides in research. *Human Research Report* 2005 August; 20(8): 1-2. NRCBL: 18.1; 16.1; 18.5.2.

Martin, Robyn. Undue inducement in clinical research. *Lancet* 2005 July 23-29; 366(9482): 275-276. NRCBL: 18.1; 9.3.1; 18.2; 18.6.

NRCBL: National Reference Center for Bioethics Literature Classification Scheme   See inside front cover for terms.

253

Merritt, Maria. Moral conflict in clinical trials. *Ethics: An International Journal of Social, Political, and Legal Philosophy* 2005 January; 115(2): 306-330. NRCBL: 18.1; 1.3.9; 18.2; 5.2.

Morreim, E. Haavi. Clinical trials litigation: practical realities as seen from the trenches. *Accountability in Research* 2005 January-March; 12(1): 47-67. NRCBL: 18.1; 8.5. SC: le.

Abstract: Litigation involving human clinical research trials has escalated rapidly in the past few years. Whereas these suits raise many important theoretical questions, they also have important practical and human dimensions of which many people are unlikely to be aware until, by some unfortunate turn, they must live the reality. From the vantage of a fairly close view on one recent lawsuit, this article offers some ground-level observations and reflections that, it is hoped, may be of use to people in clinical research who might one day find themselves in a similar position.

Nagashima, Takashi. Freedom of scientific research and human dignity: Japanese discussions following wartime human experimentation and implications for today's debates on medical ethics. *In:* Roelcke, Volker; Maio, Giovanni, eds. Twentieth Century Ethics of Human Subjects Research: Historical Perspectives on Values, Practices, and Regulations. Stuttgart: Franz Steiner Verlag; 2004: 261-273. NRCBL: 18.1; 21.1; 2.2.

Peart, Nicola; Adams, Jane; Dunckley, Catherine. Research on human tissue. *In:* Dawson, John; Peart, Nicola, eds. The Law of Research: A Guide. Dunedin, NZ: University of Otago Press; 2003: 211-230. NRCBL: 18.1. SC: le.

Pence, Gregory E. Classic cases about research and experimental treatments. *In his:* Classic Cases in Medical Ethics: Accounts of Cases That Have Shaped Medical Ethics, with Philosophical, Legal, and Historical Backgrounds. Fourth edition. Boston, MA: McGraw-Hill; 2004: 245-365. NRCBL: 18.1; 19.1; 22.2.

Pickard, John D.; Gillard, Jonathan H. Guidelines reduce the risk of brain-scan shock: responsibility for research is separate from a centre's duty of care to MRI volunteers [letter]. *Nature* 2005 May 5; 435(7038): 17. NRCBL: 18.1; 17.1. Identifiers: magnetic resonance imaging.

Pontifical Academy for Life. Ethics and biomedical research. *Medical Ethics and Bioethics / Medicinska Etika & Bioetika* 2003 Spring-Summer; 10(1-2): 13-14. NRCBL: 18.1; 1.2; 4.4.

Ramakrishna, Jayashree. Values and obligations in qualitative research. *Issues in Medical Ethics* 2001 January-March; 9(1): 5-6. NRCBL: 18.1; 18.3.

Ravindra, R.P. Ethics in human medical research: views of a non-medical person. *Medical Ethics: Journal of Forum for Medical Ethics Society* 1994 May-July; 1(4): 6-7. NRCBL: 18.1.

Rivera, Roberto; Borasky, David; Rice, Robert; Carayon, Florence. Many worlds, one ethic: design and development of a global research ethics training curriculum. *Developing World Bioethics* 2005 May; 5(2): 169-175. NRCBL: 18.1; 2.3; 21.7.

Abstract: The demand for basic research ethics training has grown considerably in the past few years. Research and education organizations face the challenge of providing this training with limited resources and training tools available. To meet this need, Family Health International (FHI), a U.S.-based international research organization, recently developed a Research Ethics Training Curriculum (RETC). It was designed as a practical, user-friendly tool that provides basic, up-to-date, standardized training on the ethics of human research. The curriculum can easily be adapted to different audiences and training requirements. The RETC was reviewed by a group of international experts and field tested in five countries. It is available in English, French, and Spanish as a three-ring binder and CD-ROM, as well as on the Web. It may be used as either an interactive self-study program or for group training.

Roberts, Laura Weiss; Warner, Teddy D.; Hammond, Katherine A. Green. Coexisting commitments to ethics and human research: a preliminary study of the perspectives of 83 medical students. *American Journal of Bioethics [Online]* 2005 November-December; 5(6): W1-W7. NRCBL: 18.1. SC: em.

Roberts, Laura Weiss; Warner, Teddy D.; Hammond, Katherine A. Green; Brody, Janet L.; Kaminsky, Alexis; Roberts, Brian B. Teaching medical students to discern ethical problems in human clinical research studies. *Academic Medicine* 2005 October; 80(10): 925-930. NRCBL: 18.1; 7.2. SC: em.

Roelcke, Volker. Human subjects research during the National Socialist era, 1933-1945: programs, practices, and motivations. *In:* Roelcke, Volker; Maio, Giovanni, eds. Twentieth Century Ethics of Human Subjects Research: Historical Perspectives on Values, Practices, and Regulations. Stuttgart: Franz Steiner Verlag; 2004: 151-166. NRCBL: 18.1; 15.5; 21.4; 1.3.5; 2.2.

Rothman, David J. Other people's bodies: human experimentation on the fiftieth anniversary of the Nuremberg Code. *In:* Longo, Lawrence D., ed. Our Lords, The Sick: McGovern Lectures on the History of Medicine and Medical Humanism. Malabar, Fla.: Krieger Pub. Co.; 2004: 125-144. NRCBL: 18.1; 18.2; 2.2; 1.3.9.

Samanta, Ash; Samanta, Jo; Price, David. Who owns my body — thee or me? The human tissue story continues. *Clinical Medicine* 2004 July-August; 4(4): 327-331. NRCBL: 18.1; 4.4; 18.3; 19.1. SC: le. Identifiers: United Kingdom (Great Britain).

Schüklenk, Udo. Module one: introduction to research ethics. *Developing World Bioethics* 2005 March; 5(1): 1-13. NRCBL: 18.1; 2.3.

Abstract: This module will introduce you to the ethical concepts underlying applied ethical decision-making in the area of research involving human participants. We will also learn what the issues are that people involved in research on research ethics are concerned with. Ethics without an understanding of historical and legal context makes arguably little sense. It is for this reason that this module will begin with a brief history of research ethics and ends with a brief overview of the relevant national and international guidelines pertaining to ethical issues in research involving human participants.

Shalowitz, David I.; Miller, Franklin G. Disclosing individual results of clinical research: implications of respect for participants. *JAMA: The Journal of the American Medical Association* 2005 August 10; 294(6): 737-740. NRCBL: 18.1; 18.2; 18.3.

Simek, Jiri. Human experimentation in the Czech Republic during the last decades. *In:* Roelcke, Volker; Maio, Giovanni, eds. Twentieth Century Ethics of Human Subjects Research: Historical Perspectives on Values, Practices, and Regulations. Stuttgart: Franz Steiner Verlag; 2004: 253-259. NRCBL: 18.1; 2.2.

Stevens, Tony; Wilson, Roger. Patients' interests: paramount in randomised trials [letter]. *BMJ: British Medical Journal* 2005 January 1; 330(7481): 44-45. NRCBL: 18.1.

Visser, H.K.A. Experimental malaria in human volunteers: ethical aspects [editorial]. *Netherlands Journal of Medicine* 2005 February; 63(2): 41-42. NRCBL: 18.1; 18.2; 18.3; 9.3.1.

Wecht, Cyril H. Research and experimentation. *In:* American College of Legal Medicine Textbook Committee, Sanbar, S. Sandy; Firestone, Marvin H.; Buckner, Fillmore; Gibofsky, Allan; LeBlang, Theodore R.; Snyder, Jack W.; Wecht, Cyril H.; Zaremski, Miles J. Legal Medicine. 6th ed. St. Louis: Mosby; 2004: 238-255. NRCBL: 18.1; 18.2; 18.5.1.

Weindling, Paul. "No mere murder trial": the discourse on human experiments at the Nuremberg medical trial. *In:* Roelcke, Volker; Maio, Giovanni, eds. Twentieth Century Ethics of Human Subjects Research: Historical Perspectives on Values, Practices, and Regulations. Stuttgart: Franz Steiner Verlag; 2004: 167-180. NRCBL: 18.1; 21.4; 15.5; 1.3.5; 2.2. SC: le.

Wertz, Dorothy C. Archived specimens: ethics concerns. *Acta Tropica* 2001 January 15; 78(Supplement): S77-S84. NRCBL: 18.1; 8.4; 9.3.1; 15.1; 18.3.

Young, Charles; Horton, Richard. Putting clinical trials into context [opinion]. *Lancet* 2005 July 9-15; 366(9480): 107-108. NRCBL: 18.1; 1.3.7; 1.3.9; 5.2.

Yudin, Boris. Human experimentation in Russia/the Soviet Union in the first half of the 20th century. *In:* Roelcke, Volker; Maio, Giovanni, eds. Twentieth Century Ethics of Human Subjects Research: Historical Perspectives on Values, Practices, and Regulations. Stuttgart: Franz Steiner Verlag; 2004: 99-110. NRCBL: 18.1; 2.2.

HUMAN EXPERIMENTATION/ ETHICS COMMITTEES AND POLICY GUIDELINES

Ethics committee gets it wrong [news]. *Bulletin of Medical Ethics* 2003 November; (193): 6. NRCBL: 18.2; 9.5.6; 8.4; 1.3.3; 20.5.1; 20.7.

EU clinical trials directive: 0% inspiration, 100% perspiration? *Lancet Neurology* 2004 June; 3(6): 321. NRCBL: 18.2; 21.1. Identifiers: European Union.

Navajo nation IRB: a unique human research review board has three primary concerns: protecting its community, its people, and its heritage. *Protecting Human Subjects* 2003 Spring; (8): 1-2. NRCBL: 18.2; 18.5.1; 21.7.

Out in the open [editorial]. *Nature Biotechnology* 2005 February; 23(2): 153. NRCBL: 18.2; 9.7; 5.3. Identifiers: clinical trial data disclosure.

The trials of tenofovir trials [editorial]. *Lancet* 2005 March 26-April 1; 365(9465): 1111. NRCBL: 18.2; 18.5.9; 21.1.

Abbasi, Kamran; Heath, Iona. Ethics review of research and audit — journals should not abdicate their responsibility [editorial]. *BMJ: British Medical Journal* 2005 February 26; 330(7489): 431- 432. NRCBL: 18.2.

Ackerman, Paul D.; Kelly, Michael L.; Walsh, Catherine A.; Ross, Lainie Friedman. Do peer guidelines or editorial policies affect the reporting and discussion of race and ethnicity in pediatric research? *Accountability in Research* 2005 January-March; 12(1): 17-31. NRCBL: 18.2; 1.3.7; 7.1; 18.5.2. SC: em.

Abstract: Objectives: Two policy statements published in pediatric journals encouraged researchers not to use race and ethnicity [R/E] to explain cohort differences without collecting and analyzing data that examine the potential underlying social mechanisms. We sought to determine if these statements had any impact on the reporting and discussion of R/E and sociodemographic markers [SM]. Methods: Articles in three general pediatric journals between July 2002 and June 2003 were reviewed, and were compared with previously collected data from July 1999-June 2000. We recorded whether the articles documented R/E or SM, or both, in the results, and whether they discussed their significance. Researchers were surveyed to determine whether and why they collected R/E data. Results: Race was reported in 156 of 228 articles (68%), but discussed in only one-third (75). Although there is wide interjournal variability, there was little change between the two periods. Seventy-two percent of respondents thought that R/E was or might be relevant to their research, and this influenced their decision to report and discuss R/E. Conclusions: Most researchers report R/E and believe it is relevant to their research. Despite policies that reject R/E as explanatory variables, most researchers do not report or discuss the underlying social mechanisms that may explain R/E differences.

Adams-Campbell, Lucile L.; Ahaghotu, Chiledum; Gaskins, Melvin; Dawkins, Fitzroy W.; Smoot, Duane; Polk, Octavius D.; Gooding, Robert; Dewitty, Robert L. Enrollment of African Americans onto clinical treatment trials: study design barriers. *Journal of Clinical On-*

NRCBL: National Reference Center for Bioethics Literature Classification Scheme   See inside front cover for terms.

255

cology 2004 February 15; 22(4): 730-734. NRCBL: 18.2; 18.5.1; 9.5.4. SC: em.

Ahmad, Aasim. Universality of care: a response. *Issues in Medical Ethics* 2001 October-December; 9(4): 117. NRCBL: 18.2; 18.5.9. Identifiers: Helsinki Declaration.

Albin, R.L. Sham surgery controls are mitigated trolleys. *Journal of Medical Ethics* 2005 March; 31(3): 149-152. NRCBL: 18.2; 18.5.1; 1.1. SC: an.

Abstract: Debate continues about the ethics of sham surgery controls. The most powerful argument for sham surgery controls is that rigorous experiments are needed to demonstrate safety and efficacy of surgical procedures. Without such experiments, there is danger of adopting worthless procedures in clinical practice. Opponents of sham surgery controls argue that sham surgery constitutes unacceptable violation of the rights of research subjects. Recent philosophical discussion has used two thought experiments-the transplant case and the trolley problem-to explore the circumstances under which individuals may be harmed to benefit a larger group. The transplant case is felt to exemplify circumstances that forbid harming some to benefit a larger group while the trolley problem exemplifies circumstances that permit harming some to benefit others. I argue that sham surgery controls satisfy criteria derived from the trolley problem and are morally permissible.

Alexander, John. Commentary: research ethics committees deserve support. *BMJ: British Medical Journal* 2005 February 26; 330(7489): 472- 473. NRCBL: 18.2; 9.6.

Allhoff, Fritz. Free-riding and research ethics. *American Journal of Bioethics* 2005 January-February; 5(1): 50- 51. NRCBL: 18.2; 18.3; 1.1. Comments: comment on Rosamond Rhodes, "Rethinking research ethics," American Journal of Bioethics 2005 January-February; 5(1): 7-28.

American College of Cardiology Foundation; American Heart Association; Popp, Richard J.; Smith, Sidney C., Jr.; Adams, Robert J.; Antman, Elliott M.; Kavey, Rae Ellen W.; DeMaria, Anthony N.; Ohman, Erik Magnus; Pitt, Bertram; Willerson, James T.; Bellande, Bruce J.; Fonarow, Gregg C.; Nishimura, Rick A.; Shah, Pravin M.; Hirshfeld, John W., Jr.; Messer, Joseph V.; Peterson, Eric D.; Prystowsky, Eric N.; Anderson, Jeffrey L.; Cheitlin, Melvin D., Goldstein, Larry B.; Grant, Augustus O.; Beller, George A.; Hines, Edward F., Jr.; Livingston, David W.; McEntee, Christine W. ACCF/AHA consensus conference report on professionalism and ethics. *Circulation* 2004 October 19; 110(16): 2506-2549. NRCBL: 18.2; 18.6; 7.3; 1.3.2. Conference: ACCF/AHA Consensus Conference; Heart House, Bethesda, MD; 2-3 June 2004; American College of Cardiology Foundation; American Heart Association.

American Physiological Society [APS]. Guiding principles for research involving animals and human beings. *American Journal of Physiology Regulatory, Integrative and Comparative Physiology* 2002 August; 283: R281-R283. NRCBL: 18.2; 22.2; 21.1; 6.

American Society for Clinical Laboratory Science. ASCLS position paper. Ethical responsibility. *Clinical Laboratory Science* 1999 March-April; 12(2): 71-72. NRCBL: 18.2; 8.1; 18.6.

Australian Health Ethics Committee; Chalmers, Donald; Pettit, Philip. Towards a consensual culture in the ethical review of research. *Medical Journal of Australia* 1998 January 19; 168(2): 79-82. NRCBL: 18.2; 18.6. SC: rv.

Avorn, Jerry. Torcetrapib and Atorvastatin — should marketing drive the research agenda? [opinion]. *New England Journal of Medicine* 2005 June 23; 352(25): 2573-2576. NRCBL: 18.2; 9.7; 1.3.2; 1.3.9; 18.6.

Bacchetti, Peter; Wolf, Leslie E.; Segal, Mark R.; McCulloch, Charles E. Bacchetti et al. respond to "ethics and sample size — another view". *American Journal of Epidemiology* 2005; 161(2): 113. NRCBL: 18.2.

Bacchetti, Peter; Wolf, Leslie E.; Segal, Mark R.; McCulloch, Charles E. Ethics and sample size. *American Journal of Epidemiology* 2005 January 15; 161(2): 105-110. NRCBL: 18.2.

Baer, Lawrence J. Influences on IRB decisionmaking [letter]. *IRB: Ethics and Human Research* 2005 May-June; 27(3): 7. NRCBL: 18.2. Identifiers: institutional review board.

Beagan, Brenda; McDonald, Michael. Evidence-based practice of research ethics review? *Health Law Review* 2005; 13(2-3): 62-68. NRCBL: 18.2; 9.8.

Beauchamp, Tom L. How not to rethink research ethics. *American Journal of Bioethics* 2005 January-February; 5(1): 31- 33. NRCBL: 18.2; 1.1; 18.3. Comments: comment on Rosamond Rhodes, "Rethinking research ethics," American Journal of Bioethics 2005 January-February; 5(1): 7-28.

Beauchamp, Tom L. The origins and evolution of the Belmont Report. *In:* Childress, James F.; Meslin, Eric M.; Shapiro, Harold T., eds. Belmont Revisited: Ethical Principles for Research with Human Subjects. Washington, DC: Georgetown University Press; 2005: 12-25. NRCBL: 18.2; 2.2; 2.4.

Beecher, Henry K. Some guiding principles for clinical investigation. *JAMA: The Journal of the American Medical Association* 1966 March 28; 195(13): 157-158. NRCBL: 18.2.

Benatar, Solomon R. Towards progress in resolving dilemmas in international research ethics. *Journal of Law, Medicine and Ethics* 2004 Winter; 32(4): 574- 582. NRCBL: 18.2; 21.7; 7.1.

Benedek, Thomas G. Gonorrhea and the beginnings of clinical research ethics. *Perspectives in Biology and Medi-*

---

cine 2005 Winter; 48(1): 54-73. NRCBL: 18.2; 9.5.1; 10; 1.3.9.

Berlin, Jesse A. Commentary: why industry should register and disclose results of clinical studies — perspective of a recovering academic. *BMJ: British Medical Journal* 2005 April 23; 330(7497): 959. NRCBL: 18.2; 9.7.

Bhatt, Arun D. Clinical trial publications. *Issues in Medical Ethics* 2000 October-December; 8(4): 119-121. NRCBL: 18.2; 1.3.7.

Blackmer, Jeff; Haddad, Henry. The Declaration of Helsinki: an update on paragraph 30 [opinion]. *CMAJ/JAMC: Canadian Medical Association Journal* 2005 October 25; 173(9): 1052-1053. NRCBL: 18.2; 21.1.

Botkin, Jeffrey R. Addressing the "petty tyranny" of IRBs. *American Journal of Medical Genetics* 2005 April 30; 134A(3): 240-241. NRCBL: 18.2. Identifiers: institutional review boards.

Bouvier, Paul. Good epidemiological practice: ethical review is essential [opinion]. *Sozial- und Praventivmedizin* 2005; 50(1): 34-35. NRCBL: 18.2; 7.1.

Bozik, Michael. He who pays the piper calls the tune: the role of the industry sponsor in acute stroke trials. *European Neurology* 2003; 49(2): 128-130. NRCBL: 18.2; 9.7; 1.3.9.

Bramstedt, Katrina A.; Kassimatis, Katy. A study of warning letters issued to institutional review boards by the United States Food and Drug Administration. *Clinical and Investigative Medicine* 2004 December; 27(6): 316-323. NRCBL: 18.2; 18.6. SC: em.

Breen, Kerry J. Multicentre research: negotiating the ethics approval obstacle course [letter]. *Medical Journal of Australia* 2004 October 18; 181(8): 460. NRCBL: 18.2.

Brody, Baruch A.; McCullough, Laurence B.; Sharp, Richard R. Consensus and controversy in clinical research ethics. *JAMA: The Journal of the American Medical Association* 2005 September 21; 294(11): 1411-1414. NRCBL: 18.2.

Brody, Howard. Should a clinical trial coordinator blow the whistle? *Medical Ethics Newsletter [Lahey Clinic]* 2004 Winter; 11(1): 3, 11. NRCBL: 18.2; 8.1.

Bromberg, Jonathan S.; Silverstein, Jeffrey H.; Kirk, Allan D. Proposal for the American Journal of Transplantation policy for review of ethical standards of clinical research involving live human subjects. *American Journal of Transplantation* 2005 April; 5(4 Part 1): 648-650. NRCBL: 18.2.

Brower, Vicki. Vulnerable groups at risk from "commercial" ethical review boards [news]. *Nature Medicine* 1997 July; 3(7): 705. NRCBL: 18.2; 18.6; 9.3.1.

Brunger, Fern; Burgess, Michael. A cultural understanding of research ethics governance. *Health Law Review* 2005; 13(2-3): 69-74. NRCBL: 18.2; 2.1; 7.1.

Bryant, J.; Powell, J. Payment to healthcare professionals for patient recruitment to trials: a systematic review. *BMJ: British Medical Journal* 2005 December 10; 331(7529): 1377-1378. NRCBL: 18.2; 9.3.1. SC: em.

Buchanan, David; Miller, Franklin G. Principles of early stopping of randomized trials for efficacy: a critique of equipoise and an alternative nonexploitation ethical framework. *Kennedy Institute of Ethics Journal* 2005 June; 15(2): 161-178. NRCBL: 18.2; 18.6; 9.8; 4.1.2; 1.1; 5.2.
Abstract: Recent controversial decisions to terminate several large clinical trials have called attention to the need for developing a sound ethical framework to determine when trials should be stopped in light of emerging efficacy data. Currently, the fundamental rationale for stopping trials early is based on the principle that equipoise has been disturbed. We present an analysis of the ethical and practical problems with the "equipoise disturbed" position and describe an alternative ethical framework based on the principle of nonexploitation. This framework acknowledges the need for balancing the dual ethical obligations of clinical research, the protection of human subjects and the generation of new medical knowledge. Based on this framework, we put forward a proposal to make early stopping guidelines more stringent under specified conditions. The temporary withholding of apparent benefits in certain circumstances is justified by achieving a fair contract with the research participants, one that protects them from undue harm and exploitation while reducing the many uncertainties surrounding new investigational treatments that arise when trials are stopped prematurely.

Burman, William; Breese, Peter; Weis, Stephen; Bock, Naomi; Bernardo, John; Vernon, Andrew. The effects of local review on informed consent documents from a multicenter clinical trials consortium. *Controlled Clinical Trials* 2003 June; 24(3): 245-255. NRCBL: 18.2; 18.3. SC: em. Identifiers: Centers for Disease Control and Prevention; Tuberculosis Trials Consortium.

Byrne, Geraldine. Ethical approval. *Professional Nurse* 2001 January; 16(4): 1052-1054. NRCBL: 18.2.

Canada. Canadian Institutes of Health Research; Natural Sciences and Engineering Research Council of Canada; Social Sciences and Humanities Research Council of Canada. Tri-Council policy statement: ethical conduct for research involving humans. Canada: Interagency Secretariat on Research Ethics 1998 August, with 2000, 2002 and 2005 amendments; 93 p. [Online]. Available: http://www.pre.ethics.gc.ca/english/pdf/TCPSOctober2005_E.pdf [10 February 2006]. NRCBL: 18.2.

Candilis, Philip J.; Arikan, Rasim; Noone, Sheila B.; Holzer, Jacob C. The new research ethic: will oversight requirements sink forensic research? *Journal of the American Academy of Psychiatry and the Law* 2005; 33(3): 361-367. NRCBL: 18.2; 18.5.6; 1.3.5.

NRCBL: National Reference Center for Bioethics Literature Classification Scheme   See inside front cover for terms.

257

Capron, Alexander M. The dog in the night-time: or, the curious relationship of the Belmont Report and the President's Commission. *In:* Childress, James F.; Meslin, Eric M.; Shapiro, Harold T., eds. Belmont Revisited: Ethical Principles for Research with Human Subjects. Washington, DC: Georgetown University Press; 2005: 29-40. NRCBL: 18.2; 2.2; 2.4.

Carlson, Robert. How then should we do medical research? *Ethics and Medicine* 2005 Spring; 21(1): 59-61. NRCBL: 18.2; 6.

Cash, Richard A. Ethical principles and health research [editorial]. *National Medical Journal of India* 2001 November-December; 14(6): 321-323. NRCBL: 18.2; 18.5.9; 18.6.

Chalmers, Don. Research involving humans: a time for change? *Journal of Law, Medicine and Ethics* 2004 Winter; 32(4): 583- 595. NRCBL: 18.2; 15.10; 1.3.12; 13.1.

Chassany, Olivier; Duracinsky, Martin; Mahe, Isabelle. Clinical trials of pharmaceuticals: ethical aspects. *In:* Salek, Sam; Edgar, Andrew, eds. Pharmaceutical Ethics. New York: Wiley; 2002: 71-90. NRCBL: 18.2; 9.7.

Christensen, James A.; Orlowski, James P. Bounty-hunting and finder's fees. *IRB: Ethics and Human Research* 2005 May-June; 27(3): 16-19. NRCBL: 18.2; 9.3.1; 18.1.

Churchill, Larry R. Towards a more robust autonomy: revisiting the Belmont Report. *In:* Childress, James F.; Meslin, Eric M.; Shapiro, Harold T., eds. Belmont Revisited: Ethical Principles for Research with Human Subjects. Washington, DC: Georgetown University Press; 2005: 111- 125. NRCBL: 18.2; 1.1; 2.2; 2.4. SC: an.

Cohen, A. More trouble with ethics committees [letter]. *British Journal of Psychiatry* 1999 October; 175: 393-394. NRCBL: 18.2; 18.3.

Collins, Beth A. Ethical issues in conducting clinical nursing research. *AWHONN's Clinical Issues in Perinatal and Women's Health Nursing* 1993; 4(4): 620-633. NRCBL: 18.2; 18.6; 4.1.3.

Council, James R.; Smith, Elizabeth J.H.; Kaster-Bundgaard, Jessica; Gladue, Brian A. Ethical evaluation of hypnosis research: a survey of investigators and their Institutional Review Boards. *American Journal of Clinical Hypnosis* 1997 April; 39(4): 258-265. NRCBL: 18.2; 17.1. SC: em.

Coyer, Sharon M.; Gallo, Agatha M. Secondary analysis of data. *Journal of Pediatric Health Care* 2005 January-February; 19(1): 60-63. NRCBL: 18.2; 18.3.

Cram, Fiona; Phillips, Hazel; Tipene-Matua, Bevan; Parsons, Murray; Taupo, Katrina. A 'parallel process'? Beginning a constructive conversation about a Maori methodology. *Journal of Bioethical Inquiry* 2004; 1(1): 14-19. NRCBL: 18.2; 21.7; 18.5.1; 5.3; 18.3.

Abstract: This paper documents the beginning of a conversation about what it means to be Maori within a larger, mainstream research project. This larger project was conceived by a team of researchers that included a Maori principal investigator, and funding was gained from a funding agency that has established criteria for Maori responsiveness. The Maori component of the project was, however, not initially conceived of as separate from the non-Maori component. Discussions about this were initiated approximately one year into the project in response to Maori team members' desires to undertake Kaupapa Maori research. This effectively means that the Maori team collects and analyses the Maori research data prior to re-engaging with the full research team. While there is a level of uncertainty about how this process will play itself out, there is a commitment to continue a constructive conversation within the team and to journey together in good faith and trust.

Crumbaker, Mary. St. Mary's hospital IRB: a small community hospital-based IRB has advantages as well as unique problems in efforts to protect human subjects. *Protecting Human Subjects* 2003 Spring; (8): 8-9. NRCBL: 18.2. Identifiers: institutional review board.

Dada, Mahomed A.; Moorad, Ruweida. A review of a South African research ethics committee. *Issues in Medical Ethics* 2001 April-June; 9(2): 58-59. NRCBL: 18.2.

Dale, O.; Salo, Malti. The Helsinki Declaration, research guidelines and regulations: present and future editorial aspects [editorial]. *Acta Anaesthesiologica Scandinavica* 1996 August; 40(7): 771-772. NRCBL: 18.2; 6; 1.3.7; 1.3.9.

Dal-Ré, R.; Ortega, R.; Morejón, E. Multicentre trials review process by research ethics committees in Spain: where do they stand before implementing the new European regulation? *Journal of Medical Ethics* 2005 June; 31(6): 344-350. NRCBL: 18.2. SC: em.

Abstract: OBJECTIVES: To review the performance of research ethics committees (RECs) in Spain in assessing multicentre clinical trial (MCT) drug protocols, and to evaluate if they would comply with the requirements of the new EU Directive to be implemented by May 2004. DESIGN AND SETTING: Prospective study of applications of MCT submitted to RECs. MAIN MEASUREMENTS: Protocol related features and evaluation process dynamics. RESULTS: 187 applications (24 protocols, 18 study drugs) to be performed in 114 centres, were reviewed by 62 RECs. RECs had a median number of 14 members, of which three were lay members. All applications were approved except four which were however approved by the other RECs involved. The median times from submission to approval and from submission to reception at the sponsor's offices were 48 and 62 days, respectively. In 55% (101/183) of all applications approved, 41 RECs raised 307 queries, 40% of these were protocol related issues, and 38% related to the patients' information sheets. RECs charging an evaluation fee in advance and applications with no queries raised were statistically significantly associated with shorter evaluation times. However, there is a gap of at least 1.5 weeks between the date of the meeting and the reception of the approval letter in the sponsor's office. CONCLUSIONS: Evaluating MCT protocols by RECs is a time consuming process. Needing 1.5 weeks for communicating the decision taken by RECs to the sponsor suggests serious administrative shortcomings within most RECs. By significantly reducing the time for communication of their decisions, the majority of RECs would comply with the Directive requirement of a maximum 60 day period for the assessment of MCT.

Dal-Ré, Rafael; Morejón, Elena; Ortega, Rafael. Nature and extent of changes in the patient's information sheets of international multicentre clinical trials as requested by Spanish Research Ethics Committees. *Medicina Clinica* 2004 December 4; 123(20): 770-774. NRCBL: 18.2; 18.3. SC: em.

Dawson, A.J. The Ad Hoc Advisory Group's proposals for research ethics committees: a mixture of the timid, the revolutionary, and the bizarre [editorial]. *Journal of Medical Ethics* 2005 August; 31(8): 435-436. NRCBL: 18.2. Identifiers: Great Britain (United Kingdom).

Decullier, Evelyne; Lhéritier, Véronique; Chapuis, François. The activity of French Research Ethics Committees and characteristics of biomedical research protocols involving humans: a retrospective cohort study. *BMC Medical Ethics [electronic].* 2005; 6(9); 10 p. Available: http://www.biomedcentral.com/bmcmedethics/ [24 November 2005]. NRCBL: 18.2. SC: em.

Decullier, Evelyne; Lhéritier, Véronique; Chapuis, François. Fate of biomedical research protocols and publication bias in France: retrospective cohort study. *BMJ: British Medical Journal* 2005 July 2; 331(7507): 19-22. NRCBL: 18.2; 1.3.7.

Abstract: OBJECTIVES: To describe the fate of protocols approved by the French research ethics committees, a national system created by the French 1988 Huriet-Serusclat Act; to assess publication bias at a national level. DESIGN: Retrospective cohort study. SETTING: Representative sample of 25/48 French research ethics committees in 1994. PROTOCOLS: 649 research protocols approved by committees, with follow-up information. MAIN OUTCOME MEASURES: Protocols' initial characteristics (design, study size, investigator) abstracted from committees' archives; follow-up information (rates of initiation, completion, and publication) obtained from mailed questionnaire to principal investigators. RESULTS: Completed questionnaires were available for 649/976 (69%) protocols. Of these, 581 (90%) studies were initiated, 501/581 (86%) were completed, and 190/501 (38%) were published. Studies with confirmatory results were more likely to be published as scientific papers than were studies with inconclusive results (adjusted odds ratio 4.59, 95% confidence interval 2.21 to 9.54). Moreover, studies with confirmatory results were published more quickly than studies with inconclusive results (hazard ratio 2.48, 1.36 to 4.55). CONCLUSION: At a national level, too many research studies are not completed, and among those completed too many are not published. We suggest capitalising on research ethics committees to register and follow all authorised research on human participants on a systematic and prospective basis.

Dent, Nigel J.; Sweatman, W.J.F. Can non-regulators audit Independent Ethic Committees (IEC), and if so, how? *Quality Assurance* 2001-2002; 9(1): 43-54. NRCBL: 18.2; 18.6.

Dhai, Ames. Module five: implementation of ethics review. *Developing World Bioethics* 2005 March; 5(1): 73-91. NRCBL: 18.2; 2.3. SC: cs.

Abstract: The objective of this module is to inform you on issues of concern for Research Ethics Committee members and investigators during the review process. The many guidelines on research ethics, including those from the South African Department of Health and the World Health Organisation, will be referred to extensively to educate you on the requirements of Research Ethics Committees. The evolution of the review process in South Africa will be detailed.

Dickert, Neal; Sugarman, Jeremy. Ethical goals of community consultation in research. *American Journal of Public Health* 2005 July; 95(7): 1123-1127. NRCBL: 18.2; 18.6; 15.1; 13.1.

Abstract: In response to the traditional emphasis on the rights, interests, and well-being of individual research subjects, there has been growing attention focused on the importance of involving communities in research development and approval. Community consultation is a particularly common method of involving communities. However, the fundamental ethical goals of community consultation have not been delineated, which makes it difficult for investigators, sponsors, and institutional review boards to design and evaluate consultation efforts. Community consultation must be tailored to the communities in which it is conducted, but the purposes of consultation-the ethical goals it is designed to achieve-should be universal. We propose 4 ethical goals that give investigators, sponsors, institutional review boards, and communities a framework for evaluating community consultation processes.

Dickson, Hugh G. Multicentre research: negotiating the ethics approval obstacle course [letter]. *Medical Journal of Australia* 2004 October 18; 181(8): 459-460. NRCBL: 18.2.

Dion, Sophie; Reizenstein, Peter. Ethical problems in clinical trials concerning minimal residual tumors. *Supplement to the Journal Medical Oncology and Tumor Pharmacotherapy* 1988; 1: 99-102. NRCBL: 18.2; 9.2; 18.6.

Dominguez, Roberto A.; Feaster, Daniel J.; Twiggs, Leo B.; Altman, Norman H. Searching for an efficient institutional review board review model: interrelationship of trainee-investigators, funding, and initial approval. *Journal of Laboratory and Clinical Medicine* 2005 February; 145(2): 65-71. NRCBL: 18.2. SC: em.

Douglas, Neil J.; Engleman, Heather M.; Faccenda, Jacqueline F.; McArdle, Nigel; Karlawish, Jason H.T.; Pack, Allan I. The science of designing ethical CPAP trials [letter and reply]. *American Journal of Respiratory and Critical Care Medicine* 2002 January 1; 165(1): 132-134. NRCBL: 18.2; 18.3. Identifiers: continous positive airway pressure.

Drazen, Jeffrey M.; Wood, Alastair J.J. Trial registration report card [editorial]. *New England Journal of Medicine* 2005 December 29; 353(26): 2809-2811. NRCBL: 18.2; 9.7; 1.3.7.

NRCBL: National Reference Center for Bioethics Literature Classification Scheme   See inside front cover for terms.

259

DuVal, Gordon; Gensler, Gary; Danis, Marion. Ethical dilemmas encountered by clinical researchers. *Journal of Clinical Ethics* 2005 Fall; 16(3): 267-276. NRCBL: 18.2; 9.6; 18.3; 8.2; 8.4; 7.1. SC: em.

Dyer, Sarah. Rationalising public participation in the health service: the case of research ethics committees. *Health and Place* 2004 December; 10(4): 339-348. NRCBL: 18.2. SC: em. Identifiers: United Kingdom (Great Britain).

Dziak, Kathleen; Anderson, Roger; Sevick, Mary Ann; Weisman, Carol S.; Levine, Douglas W.; Scholle, Sarah Hudson. Variations among institutional review board reviews in a multisite health services research study. *Health Services Research* 2005 February; 40(1): 279-290. NRCBL: 18.2; 8.4. SC: em.

Eckstein, Sue. Training for research ethics committees in the UK. *Issues in Medical Ethics* 2001 April-June; 9(2): 56-57. NRCBL: 18.2. Identifiers: United Kingdom (Great Britain).

Elwyn, Glyn; Seagrove, Anne; Thorne, Kym; Cheung, Wai Yee. Ethics and research governance in a multicentre study: add 150 days to your study protocol [letter]. *BMJ: British Medical Journal* 2005 April 9; 330(7495): 847. NRCBL: 18.2. SC: em. Identifiers: United Kingdom (Great Britain).

Enzle, Michael E.; Schmaltz, Rodney. Ethics review of multi-centre clinical trials in Canada. *Health Law Review* 2005; 13(2-3): 51-57. NRCBL: 18.2.

Faden, Ruth R.; Mastroianni, Anna C.; Kahn, Jeffrey P. Beyond Belmont: trust, openness, and the work of the Advisory Committee on Human Radiation Experiments. *In:* Childress, James F.; Meslin, Eric M.; Shapiro, Harold T., eds. Belmont Revisited: Ethical Principles for Research with Human Subjects. Washington, DC: Georgetown University Press; 2005: 41-54. NRCBL: 18.2; 2.2; 2.4; 16.2; 18.5.2.

Fauriel, I.; Moutel, G.; Duchange, N.; Callies, I.; François, I.; Huriet, C.; Hervé, C. Improving protection for research subjects in France: analysis of regional ethics committees. *Regulatory Toxicology and Pharmacology* 2004 December; 40(3): 312-318. NRCBL: 18.2. SC: em.

Featherstone, Katie; Donovan, Jenny L. "Why don't they just tell me straight, why allocate it?" The struggle to make sense of participating in a randomised controlled trial. *Social Science and Medicine* 2002 September; 55(5): 709-719. NRCBL: 18.2; 18.3. SC: cs; em.

Fisher, Celia B. Deception research involving children: ethical practices and paradoxes. *Ethics and Behavior* 2005; 15(3): 271-287. NRCBL: 18.2; 18.5.2; 1.3.9; 6; 18.3; 8.3.2; 18.4.
    Abstract: This commentary draws on the thoughtful contemplation and innovative procedures described in the special section articles as well as current professional codes and federal regulations to highlight ethical practices and paradoxes of deception research involving children. The discussion is organized around 4 key decision points for the conduct of responsible deception research involving children: (a) evaluating the scientific validity and social value of deception research within the context of alternative methodologies, (b) avoiding and minimizing experimental risk, (c) the use of child assent procedures as questionable ethical safeguards, and (d) debriefing as both remedy and risk.

Fisher, Jill A. Human subjects in medical experiments. *In:* Restivo, Sal, ed. Science, Technology, and Society: An Encyclopedia. New York: Oxford University Press; 2005: 195-201. NRCBL: 18.2; 18.5.1; 21.1.

Fitzgerald, John; Hamilton, Margaret. The consequences of knowing: ethical and legal liabilities in illicit drug research. *Social Science and Medicine* 1996 December; 43(11): 1591-1600. NRCBL: 18.2; 18.5.1; 9.5.9; 8.4.

Forbat, Liz; Henderson, Jeanette. "Stuck in the middle with you": the ethics and process of qualitative research with two people in an intimate relationship. *Qualitative Health Research* 2003 December; 13(10): 1453-1462. NRCBL: 18.2; 8.4; 8.1; 1.1; 18.4; 17.2.

Foster, Andrea L. New California law stiffens data-protection rules for research on human subjects [news]. *Chronicle of Higher Education* 2005 December 16; 52(17): 33. NRCBL: 18.2; 1.3.12.

Garrard, Eve; Dawson, A. What is the role of the research ethics committee? Paternalism, inducements, and harm in research ethics. *Journal of Medical Ethics* 2005 July; 31(7): 419-423. NRCBL: 18.2. SC: an.
    Abstract: In a recent paper Edwards, Kirchin, and Huxtable have argued that research ethics committees (RECs) are often wrongfully paternalistic in their approach to medical research. They argue that it should be left to competent potential research subjects to make judgments about the acceptability of harms and benefits relating to research, and that this is not a legitimate role for any REC. They allow an exception to their overall antipaternalism, however, in that they think RECs should have the power to prohibit the use of financial inducements to recruit research subjects into trials. In this paper it is argued that these claims are unjustified and implausible. A sketch is provided of an alternative model of the role of the REC as an expert body making judgments about the acceptability of research proposals through a consensual weighing of different moral considerations.

Geller, Alisa L. Regulations limiting medical research in prisons remains necessary. *Journal of Biolaw and Business* 2005; 8(4): 72-73. NRCBL: 18.2; 18.5.5; 18.3.

Giles, Jim. Researchers break the rules in frustration at review boards [news]. *Nature* 2005 November 10; 438(7065): 136-137. NRCBL: 18.2. SC: em.

Glantz, Leonard; Grodin, Michael. Undue inducement [letter]. *Lancet* 2005 October 15-21; 366(9494): 1356-1357. NRCBL: 18.2; 9.3.1; 18.5.9.

Glanville, Julie. Ethics of health care and research. *Journal of Health Services Research and Policy* 2004 July; 9(3): 189-190. NRCBL: 18.2; 1.3.12.

Glasa, Jozef. Training and dissemination of good practices for research ethics committees: standardization, harmonization and collaboration. *Medical Ethics and Bioethics / Medicinska Etika & Bioetika* 2005 Spring-Summer; 12(1): 7-8. NRCBL: 18.2; 7.2; 21.1. Identifiers: Europe.

Gold, Jennifer L.; Dewa, Carolyn S. Institutional review boards and multisite studies in health services research: is there a better way? *Health Services Research* 2005 February; 40(1): 291-307. NRCBL: 18.2. SC: an; rv.

Goodrum, Linda A.; Hankins, Gary D.V.; Jermain, Donna; Chanaud, Cheryl M. Conference report: complex clinical, legal, and ethical issues of pregnant and postpartum women as subjects in clinical trials. *Journal of Women's Health* 2003 October; 12(9): 857-867. NRCBL: 18.2; 18.5.3; 9.7; 14.1.

Grant, A.M.; Altman, D.G.; Babiker, A.G.; Campbell, M.K.; Clemens, F.; Darbyshire, J.H.; Elbourne, D.R.; McLeer, S.K.; Parmar, M.K.B.; Pocock, S.J.; Spiegelhalter, D.J.; Sydes, M.R.; Walker, A.E.; Wallace, S.A. A proposed charter for clinical trial data monitoring committees: helping them to do their job well. *Lancet* 2005 February 19-25; 365(9460): 711-722. NRCBL: 18.2; 6; 18.6. SC: em. Identifiers: DAMOCLES Study Group.
Abstract: Formal monitoring of data from randomised controlled trials (RCTs) is becoming more common. Wide variation exists in the structure and organisation of data monitoring committees (DMCs), with little guidance on how they should operate. We used various strategies to consider the behavioural, procedural, and organisational aspects of data monitoring in RCTs: systematic reviews of DMCs and small group processes in decision making; surveys of reports of RCTs, recently completed and ongoing RCTs, and the policies of major organisations connected with RCTs; detailed case studies of four DMCs that faced difficult decisions; and interviews with experienced DMC members. The findings aided the development of a template for a charter for DMCs. We summarise the findings and outline the key considerations at every stage of the data monitoring process. Widespread use of a charter for the structure and organisation of DMCs would promote a systematic and transparent approach, and enable them to operate more effectively and efficiently.

Greenwood, Jennifer; Holmes, Colin; Bidewell, John. Mission impossible? Developing best practice guidelines for institutional ethics committees (IECs) in Greater Sydney. *Collegian* 2001 January; 8(1): 8-13. NRCBL: 18.2. SC: em. Identifiers: institutional ethics committees; Australia.

Gupte, M.D.; Sampath, D.K. Ethical issues considered in Tamil Nadu leprosy vaccine trial. *Issues in Medical Ethics* 2000 January-March; 8(1): 10-12. NRCBL: 18.2; 18.3; 9.7.

Guz, Abraham. Hering and Breuer revisited in humans: an invasive study before the days of ethics committees. *American Journal of Respiratory and Critical Care Medicine* 2001 October 1; 164(7): 1110-1111. NRCBL: 18.2; 8.1.

Hammerschmidt, Dale E. Kibuka's umbilical cord. *Journal of Laboratory Clinical Medicine* 2005 March; 145(3): 163-164. NRCBL: 18.2; 18.3; 21.7; 19.1.

Harris, Gerald J. The privacy rule and the ophthalmic plastic surgeon as author [editorial]. *Ophthalmic Plastic and Reconstructive Surgery* 2005 March; 21(2): 85-86. NRCBL: 18.2; 18.3; 8.4.

Haug, Charlotte; Gøtzsche, Peter C.; Schroeder, Torben V. Registries and registration of clinical trials [editorial]. *New England Journal of Medicine* 2005 December 29; 353(26): 2811-2812. NRCBL: 18.2; 1.3.7; 21.1.

Hawkins, Jennifer S.; Emanuel, Ezekiel J. Clarifying confusions about coercion. *Hastings Center Report* 2005 September-October; 35(5): 16-19. NRCBL: 18.2; 18.3.

Hayward, Rodney A.; Kent, David M.; Vijan, Sandeep; Hofer, Timothy P. Reporting clinical trial results to inform providers, payers, and consumers. *Health Affairs* 2005 November-December; 24(6): 1571-1581. NRCBL: 18.2; 7.1.

Hechem, Maria I.; Gonorazky, Sergio. Looking for ways to avoid deception in the pursuit of science [letter]. *Archives of Internal Medicine* 2005 May 23; 165(10): 1199-1200. NRCBL: 18.2; 18.3.

Heckerling, Paul S. The ethics of single blind trials. *IRB: Ethics and Human Research* 2005 July-August; 27(4): 12-16. NRCBL: 18.2; 5.2.

Heenan, Andrew L.J. Research ethics [editorial]. *Professional Nurse* 1995 July; 10(10): 615. NRCBL: 18.2; 18.6.

Hill, J.; Foster, N.; Hughes, R.; Hay, E. Meeting the challenges of research governance [editorial]. *Rheumatology* 2005 May; 44(5): 571-572. NRCBL: 18.2; 18.6.

Hillbrand, Marc. Obstacles to research in forensic psychiatry [editorial]. *Journal of the American Academy of Psychiatry and the Law* 2005; 33(3): 295-298. NRCBL: 18.2; 18.5.6; 1.3.5.

Hirschfeld, Robert M.A.; Winslade, William; Krause, Todd L. Protecting subjects and fostering research: striking the proper balance [opinion]. *Archives of General Psychiatry* 1997 February; 54(2): 5 p. [Online]. Available: http://gateway.ut.ovid.com/gwl/ovidweb.cgi [6 October 2005]. NRCBL: 18.2; 18.3; 18.5.6; 8.3.3.

Hirshon, Jon Mark; Krugman, Scott D.; Witting, Michael D.; Furuno, Jon P.; Limcangco, M. Rhona; Perisse, Andre R.; Rasch, Elizabeth K. Variability in institutional review board assessment of minimal-risk re-

NRCBL: National Reference Center for Bioethics Literature Classification Scheme   See inside front cover for terms.

261

search. *Academic Emergency Medicine* 2002 December; 9(12): 1417-1420. NRCBL: 18.2; 5.2; 18.3; 18.6.

Hohmann, Elizabeth; Woodson, Jonathan. "Inefficient, arbitrary, inconsistent": a frank look at how some investigators view IRBs and a few suggestions for improvement [discussion]. *Protecting Human Subjects* 2005 Summer; (12): 12-14. NRCBL: 18.2. Identifiers: institutional review boards.

Horton, Richard. Expression of concern: Indo-Mediterranean diet heart study. *Lancet* 2005 July 30-August 5; 366(9483): 354-356. NRCBL: 18.2; 1.3.7; 7.1.

Hougham, Gavin W. Waste not, want not: cognitive impairment should not preclude research participation. *American Journal of Bioethics* 2005 January-February; 5(1): 36- 37. NRCBL: 18.2; 18.5.6; 18.3. Comments: comment on Rosamond Rhodes, "Rethinking research ethics," American Journal of Bioethics 2005 January-February; 5(1): 7-28.

Idänpään-Heikkilä, Juhana E. US exceptionalism and research ethics [letter]. *Lancet* 2005 May 7-13; 365(9471): 1617. NRCBL: 18.2; 18.6; 21.1.

Iltis, Ana Smith. Stopping trials early for commercial reasons: the risk-benefit relationship as a moral compass. *Journal of Medical Ethics* 2005 July; 31(7): 410-414. NRCBL: 18.2.

Abstract: Decisions by industry sponsors to end clinical trials early for commercial reasons have been the subject of controversy. I argue that the principal consideration in assessing these decisions ought to be the way in which the termination would affect the trial's risk-benefit relationship. If there is not yet sufficient benefit to be gained from the study to offset the risks to which participants were exposed and it is expected that important scientific information would be obtained if the trial were continued, early termination constitutes an unethical alteration of the risk-benefit relationship. This violates the grounds on which permission is given to conduct human research, patients consent to participate, and investigators agree to conduct studies. These knowable and avoidable changes in risk-benefit relationship should generally be seen as impermissible.

International Association of Cancer Registries. Guidelines on confidentiality for population-based cancer registration. *Asian Pacific Journal of Cancer Prevention* 2005 January-March; 6(1): 87-103. NRCBL: 18.2; 8.4; 1.3.12; 9.5.1.

Jansen, Lynn A. A closer look at the bad deal trial: beyond clinical equipoise. *Hastings Center Report* 2005 September-October; 35(5): 29-36. NRCBL: 18.2. SC: an.

Jansen, Lynn A. Local IRBs, multicenter trials, and the ethics of internal amendments. *IRB: Ethics and Human Research* 2005 July-August; 27(4): 7-11. NRCBL: 18.2. SC: an. Identifiers: institutional review boards.

Jenkins, Gwynne L.; Sugarman, Jeremy. The importance of cultural considerations in the promotion of ethical research with human biologic material. *Journal of Labora-*

tory *Clinical Medicine* 2005 March; 145(3): 118-124. NRCBL: 18.2; 18.3; 21.7; 19.1.

Jintarkanon, Seree; Nakapiew, Supatra; Tienudom, Nimit; Suwannawong, Paisan; Wilson, David. Unethical clinical trials in Thailand: a community reponse [letter]. *Lancet* 2005 May 7-13; 365(9471): 1617-1618. NRCBL: 18.2; 18.5.9; 21.1.

Jones, James W. Surgical databases: ethics in evolution. *Annals of Thoracic Surgery* 2002; 74: 983-985. NRCBL: 18.2; 1.3.12; 18.3.

Jones, James W.; McCullough, Laurence B.; Richman, Bruce W. The ethics of sham surgery in research. *Journal of Vascular Surgery* 2003 February; 37(2): 482-483. NRCBL: 18.2; 18.5.1. SC: cs.

Jones, Jeffrey S.; White, Lynn J.; Pool, Linda C.; Dougherty, James M. Structure and practice of institutional review boards in the United States. *Academic Emergency Medicine* 1996 August; 3(8): 804-809. NRCBL: 18.2; 18.6.

Jonsen, Albert R. On the origins and future of the Belmont Report. *In:* Childress, James F.; Meslin, Eric M.; Shapiro, Harold T., eds. Belmont Revisited: Ethical Principles for Research with Human Subjects. Washington, DC: Georgetown University Press; 2005: 3-11. NRCBL: 18.2; 2.2; 2.4.

Jonsen, Albert R. Research with humans: experimentation, autonomy, and benefits to others. *In his:* Bioethics Beyond the Headlines: Who Lives? Who Dies? Who Decides? Lanham, MD: Rowman and Littlefield; 2005: 86-95. NRCBL: 18.2; 1.1.

Justo, Luis. Trust, understanding and utopia in the research setting. *American Journal of Bioethics* 2005 January-February; 5(1): 56- 58. NRCBL: 18.2; 1.1; 1.3.9. Comments: comment on Rosamond Rhodes, "Rethinking research ethics," American Journal of Bioethics 2005 January-February; 5(1): 7-28.

Kaebnick, Gregory E. Rethinking the ethics of research. *Hastings Center Report* 2005 September-October; 35(5): 2. NRCBL: 18.2.

Keith-Spiegel, Patricia; Koocher, Gerald P. The IRB paradox: could the protectors also encourage deceit? *Ethics and Behavior* 2005; 15(4): 339-349. NRCBL: 18.2; 1.3.9; 7.3.

Abstract: The efforts of some institutional review boards (IRBs) to exercise what is viewed as appropriate oversight may contribute to deceit on the part of investigators who feel unjustly treated. An organizational justice paradigm provides a useful context for exploring why certain IRB behaviors may lead investigators to believe that they have not received fair treatment. These feelings may, in turn, lead to intentional deception by investigators that IRBs will rarely detect. Paradoxically, excessive protective zeal by IRBs may actually encourage misconduct by some investigators. The authors contend that, by fostering a climate in which investigators perceive that they receive fair and unbiased treatment, IRBs optimize the likelihood of collegial compliance with appropriate participant protections.

Kelly, P. Adam; Johnson, Michael L. Just-in-time IRB review: capitalizing on scientific merit review to improve human subjects research compliance. *IRB: Ethics and Human Research* 2005 March-April; 27(2): 6-10. NRCBL: 18.2; 18.6. SC: em; cs. Identifiers: Department of Veterans Affairs Health Services Research and Development Service (VA HSR&D).

Kerrison, S.; Pollock, A.M. The reform of UK research ethics committees: throwing the baby out with the bath water? *Journal of Medical Ethics* 2005 August; 31(8): 487-489. NRCBL: 18.2.
Abstract: On 1 May 2004 research ethics committees became legally accountable to a new government body, the United Kingdom Ethics Committee Authority. This marks the end of the self regulation of research ethics. This paper describes how this change in research ethics committee status has come about and explores the implications for research subjects, researchers, institutions, and for regulation of research.

Kimmelman, Jonathan. Medical research, risk, and bystanders. *IRB: Ethics and Human Research* 2005 July-August; 27(4): 1-6. NRCBL: 18.2; 15.1; 9.7; 1.3.9.

King, Patricia A. Justice beyond Belmont. *In:* Childress, James F.; Meslin, Eric M.; Shapiro, Harold T., eds. Belmont Revisited: Ethical Principles for Research with Human Subjects. Washington, DC: Georgetown University Press; 2005: 136-147. NRCBL: 18.2; 1.1; 2.2; 2.4.

Kirigia, Joses M.; Wambebe, Charles; Baba-Moussa, Amido. Status of national research bioethics committees in the WHO African region. *BMC Medical Ethics [electronic]* 2005; 6(10); 7 p. Available: http://www.biomedcentral.com/bmcmedethics/ [24 November 2005]. NRCBL: 18.2; 21.1. SC: em. Identifiers: Regional Committee for Africa of the World Health Organization.

Kirk, Dwayne D.; Robert, Jason Scott. Assessing commercial feasibility: a practical and ethical prerequisite for human clinical testing. *Accountability in Research* 2005 October-December; 12(4): 281- 297. NRCBL: 18.2; 1.3.2; 18.6.
Abstract: This article proposes that an assessment of commercial feasibility should be integrated as a prerequisite for human clinical testing to improve the quality and relevance of materials being investigated, as an ethical aspect for human subject protection, and as a means of improving accountability where clinical development is funded on promises of successful translational research. A commercial feasibility analysis is not currently required to justify human clinical testing, but is assumed to have been conducted by industry participants, and use of public funds for clinical trials should be defensible in the same manner. Plant-made vaccines (PMVs) are offered in this discussion as a model for evaluating the relevance of commercial feasibility before human clinical testing. PMVs have been proposed as a potential solution for global health, based on a vision of immunizing the world against many infectious diseases. Such a vision depends on translating current knowledge in plant science and immunology into a potent vaccine that can be readily manufactured and distributed to those in need. But new biologics such as PMVs may fail to be manufactured due to financial or logistical reasons—particularly for orphan diseases without sufficient revenue incentive for industry investment—regardless of the effectiveness which might be demonstrated in human clinical testing. Moreover, all potential instruments of global health depend on translational agents well beyond the lab in order to reach those in need. A model compromising five criteria for commercial feasibility is suggested for inclusion by regulators and ethics review boards as part of the review process prior to approval of human clinical testing. Use of this model may help to facilitate safe and appropriate translational research and bring more immediate benefits to those in need.

Komesaroff, Paul A. Clinical research in the emergency setting: the role of ethics committees. *Medical Journal of Australia* 2001 December 3-17; 175(11-12): 630-631. NRCBL: 18.2; 18.3; 9.5.1.

Koski, Greg; Aungst, Jessica; Kupersmith, Joel; Getz, Kenneth; Rimoin, David. Cooperative research ethics review boards: a win-win solution? *IRB: Ethics and Human Research* 2005 May-June; 27(3): 1-7. NRCBL: 18.2.

Kurzrock, Razelle; Benjamin, Robert S. Risks and benefits of phase 1 oncology trials, revisited [editorial]. *New England Journal of Medicine* 2005 March 3; 352(9): 930-932. NRCBL: 18.2.

Kvalsvig, A.J.; Unsworth, D.J. Ethics approvals and quagmires [letter]. *Clinical Medicine* 2002 November-December; 2(6): 599. NRCBL: 18.2; 18.6.

LaRosa, Judith H. Reflections: guidelines for the inclusion of women and minorities in clinical studies. *In:* Beech, Bettina; Goodman, Maurine, eds. Race & Research: Perspectives on Minority Participation in Health Studies. Washington, DC: American Public Health Association; 2004: 143-161. NRCBL: 18.2; 18.5.1; 18.5.3. SC: em.

Larson, Elaine; Bratts, Tiffany; Zwanziger, Jack; Stone, Patricia. A survey of IRB process in 68 U.S. hospitals. *Journal of Nursing Scholarship* 2004; 36(3): 260-264. NRCBL: 18.2. SC: em.

Lederer, Susan E. Research without borders: the origins of the Declaration of Helsinki. *In:* Roelcke, Volker; Maio, Giovanni, eds. Twentieth Century Ethics of Human Subjects Research: Historical Perspectives on Values, Practices, and Regulations. Stuttgart: Franz Steiner Verlag; 2004: 199-217. NRCBL: 18.2; 18.6; 2.2.

Levine, Robert J. The National Commission's ethical principles with special attention to beneficence. *In:* Childress, James F.; Meslin, Eric M.; Shapiro, Harold T., eds. Belmont Revisited: Ethical Principles for Research with Human Subjects. Washington, DC: Georgetown University Press; 2005: 126-135. NRCBL: 18.2; 1.1; 2.2; 2.4.

Levine, Robert J. Reflections on 'rethinking research ethics' [editorial]. *American Journal of Bioethics* 2005 Janu-

NRCBL: National Reference Center for Bioethics Literature Classification Scheme See inside front cover for terms.

263

ary-February; 5(1): 1-3. NRCBL: 18.2; 18.3; 18.5; 21.4; 13.5.

Levine, Robert J.; Lebacqz, Karen. Some ethical considerations in clinical trials. *Clinical Pharmacology and Therapeutics* 1979 May; 25(5 Part 2): 728-741. NRCBL: 18.2. SC: an.

Lin, Chii-Dean; Lui, Kung-Jong; Zelen, Marvin. Randomized consent designs for clinical trials: an update [letter and reply]. *Statistics in Medicine* 2002 September 15; 21(17): 2601-2605. NRCBL: 18.2; 7.1. Comments: comment on Marvin Zelen, "Randomized consent designs for clinical trials: an update," Statistics in Medicine 1990; 9: 645- 656.

List, Justin M. Histories of mistrust and protectionism: disadvantaged minority groups and human-subject research policies. *American Journal of Bioethics* 2005 January-February; 5(1): 53- 56. NRCBL: 18.2; 18.5.1; 6. Comments: comment on Rosamond Rhodes, "Rethinking research ethics," American Journal of Bioethics 2005 January-February; 5(1): 7-28.

Litton, Paul; Miller, Franklin G. A normative justification for distinguishing the ethics of clinical research from the ethics of medical care. *Journal of Law, Medicine and Ethics* 2005 Fall; 33(3): 566-574. NRCBL: 18.2; 8.1; 4.4.

LiVolsi, Virginia A. Use of human tissue blocks for research [editorial]. *American Journal of Clinical Pathology* 1996 March; 105(3): 260-261. NRCBL: 18.2; 18.3; 18.6.

Loff, Bebe; Black, Jim. Research ethics committees: what is their contribution? [opinion]. *Medical Journal of Australia* 2004 October 18; 181(8): 440-441. NRCBL: 18.2; 7.2.

Loff, Bebe; Jenkins, Carol; Ditmore, Melissa; Overs, Cheryl; Barbero, Rosanna. Unethical clinical trials in Thailand: a community response [letter]. *Lancet* 2005 May 7-13; 365(9471): 1618-1619. NRCBL: 18.2; 18.5.9; 21.1.

London, Alex John. Does research ethics rest on a mistake? The common good, reasonable risk and social justice. *American Journal of Bioethics* 2005 January-February; 5(1): 37- 39. NRCBL: 18.2; 1.1; 21.4. Comments: comment on Rosamond Rhodes, "Rethinking research ethics," American Journal of Bioethics 2005 January-February; 5(1): 7-28.

Lurie, Peter; Greco, Dirceu B. US exceptionalism comes to research ethics. *Lancet* 2005 March 26-April 1; 365(9465): 1117-1119. NRCBL: 18.2; 18.6; 21.1. Identifiers: United States.

Luu, Arlene D. The impact of the HIPAA Privacy Rule on research participation. *Journal of Biolaw and Business* 2005; 8(4): 68-69. NRCBL: 18.2; 8.4. Identifiers: The Health Insurance Portability and Accountability Act of 1996.

Macklin, Ruth. Some questionable premises about research ethics. *American Journal of Bioethics* 2005 January-February; 5(1): 29- 31. NRCBL: 18.2; 18.3; 6; 21.4; 1.3.5. Comments: comment on Rosamond Rhodes, "Rethinking research ethics," American Journal of Bioethics 2005 January-February; 5(1): 7-28.

Malfroy, Moira; Llewelyn, C.A.; Johnson, T.; Williamson, L.M. Using patient-identifiable data for epidemiological research. *Transfusion Medicine* 2004 August; 14(4): 275-279. NRCBL: 18.2; 1.3.12; 8.4. Identifiers: United Kingdom (Great Britain).

Maloney, Dennis M. Death of research subject leads to lawsuit. *Human Research Report* 2002 January; 17(1): 8. NRCBL: 18.2; 18.5.2; 20.1; 1.3.9; 9.3.1.

Maloney, Dennis M. Final rule on additional protections for women. *Human Research Report* 2002 January; 17(1): 3. NRCBL: 18.2; 18.5.3; 18.3.

Maloney, Dennis M. Institutional review boards (IRBs) and working with adverse event reports. *Human Research Report* 2005 December; 20(12): 1-3. NRCBL: 18.2; 18.6.

Maloney, Dennis M. Institutional review boards must conduct safety review. *Human Research Report* 2005 February; 20(2): 3. NRCBL: 18.2; 9.7.

Maloney, Dennis M. IRBs and human embryonic stem cell experimentation. *Human Research Report* 2002 January; 17(1): 5. NRCBL: 18.2; 18.5.4; 18.6; 15.1. Identifiers: institutional review boards.

Maloney, Dennis M. IRBs and the new rule on research with children. *Human Research Report* 2002 January; 17(1): 4. NRCBL: 18.2; 18.5.2. Identifiers: institutional review boards.

Maloney, Dennis M. IRBs, human subjects, and reporting adverse events. *Human Research Report* 2005 November; 20(11): 3. NRCBL: 18.2. Identifiers: institutional review boards.

Maloney, Dennis M. More flexibility on reporting to federal agencies about injuries to research subjects. *Human Research Report* 2002 January; 17(1): 1-2. NRCBL: 18.2; 18.6.

Maloney, Dennis M. New federal guidance adds duties for institutional review boards (IRBs). *Human Research Report* 2005 November; 20(11): 1-2. NRCBL: 18.2; 8.4.

Maloney, Dennis M. New guidance on reviews by central institutional review boards (IRBs). *Human Research Report* 2005 May; 20(5): 1-2. NRCBL: 18.2.

Maloney, Dennis M. New human subject protection regulations are being delayed. *Human Research Report* 2005 January; 20(1): 1-2. NRCBL: 18.2; 9.7; 18.3.

Maloney, Dennis M. Protection of human subjects and coded private information. *Human Research Report* 2005 February; 20(2): 1-2. NRCBL: 18.2; 8.4.

Maloney, Dennis M. Research subject complains about how she was treated by an institutional review board (IRB) [case study]. *Human Research Report* 2005 December; 20(12): 7. NRCBL: 18.2; 1.3.3.

Maloney, Dennis M. University denies that it failed to comply with special rule for subjects who are prisoners [case study]. *Human Research Report* 2002 January; 17(1): 6-7. NRCBL: 18.2; 18.5.5; 18.3; 18.6; 1.3.3.

Mamdani, Bashir. The Helsinki Declaration, 2000, and ethics of human research in developing countries. *Indian Journal of Medical Ethics* 2004 July-September; 1(3): 94-95. NRCBL: 18.2; 6.

Manaloto, Renato B.; Alvarez, Allen Andrew A.; Alvarez, Mary Ann V. Analysis of some Filipino perspectives on ethical issues in multi-country collaborative research: a case of deep listening. *Bioethics* 2005 October; 19(5-6): 550-564. NRCBL: 18.2; 21.1; 21.7.
Abstract: The discussion on ethical issues, it is said, should not be confined to experts but should be extended to patients and local communities, because of the real need to engage stakeholders and non-stakeholders alike not only in carrying out any biomedical research project, but also in the drafting and legislation of bioethics instruments. Several local and inter-country consultations have already been conducted in furtherance of this goal, but there is much left to be desired in them. The consultations may have helped in articulating local principles, but not in making the instruments embody these principles. As such, instruments turn incompossible, i.e. the principles and actions they legitimate are not performable. In an ethnographic study conducted in the Philippines, for example, paragraphs 29 and 30 of the Declaration of Helsinki and CIOMS guidelines 8 and 15 are construed as not only contradictory to one another but also to local principles. This problem can be solved by taking deliberate steps to ensure that consultations are grounded in ethnographic data about local principles, which the instruments would embody. A steering committee can be of help in gathering ethnographic data, in conducting consultations at the local level, and in providing a venue for discourse on various bioethical issues.

Manasco, Penelope K. Ethical and legal aspects of applied genomic technologies: practical solutions. *Current Molecular Medicine* 2005 February; 5(1): 23-28. NRCBL: 18.2; 18.3; 15.1; 8.4; 1.3.12.

Mann, H. Controversial choice of a control intervention in a trial of ventilator therapy in ARDS: standard of care arguments in a randomised controlled trial. *Journal of Medical Ethics* 2005 September; 31(9): 548-553. NRCBL: 18.2.
Abstract: When evaluating an innovative intervention in a randomised controlled trial (RCT), choosing an appropriate control intervention is necessary for a clinically meaningful result. An RCT reported in 2000 addressed the relative merits of two tidal volume ventilatory strategies, 6 ml/kg (innovative) and 12 ml/kg (control), in patients with acute respiratory distress syndrome. Critics claim that the 12 ml/kg volume did not represent the clinical practice standard at that time, and that lower tidal volumes had been used in some patients prior to randomisation.

The trialists responded that current practice involved the use of a broad range of tidal volumes, including 12 ml/kg. Appropriate control interventions for RCTs can be ensured by: a systematic review of the relevant literature; a formal survey of expert clinicians; and publication of the proposed research protocol to solicit critical appraisal. A global survey of experts during the RCT's design stage would have been of probative value in determining the appropriate control tidal volume. Hypothetical, but plausible, results of such a survey are presented and examined to demonstrate the value of this method.

Mann, Jim. The Indo-Mediterranean diet revisited. *Lancet* 2005 July 30-August 5; 366(9483): 353-354. NRCBL: 18.2; 1.3.7; 7.1.

Markin, Karen M. Playing it safe with research risk: if you fail to follow the rules, you could conduct an entire project and be forbidden to publish the results. *Chronicle of Higher Education* 2005 August 12; 51(49): C1, C4. NRCBL: 18.2; 18.5.1; 1.3.9; 22.2.

Maschke, Karen J. Reconciling protection with scientific progress. *Hastings Center Report* 2005 September-October; 35(5): 3. NRCBL: 18.2.

Matthews, Robert. No way to treat a patient: tens of thousands of people have been subjected to unnecessary drug trials. *New Scientist* 2005 July 9-15; 187(2507): 19. NRCBL: 18.2. Identifiers: randomized controlled trials (RCT).

Mavroforou, A.; Giannoukas, A.D.; Gaines, P.; Michalodimitrakis, E.; Beard, J.D. Ethical dilemmas regarding treatment when recruitment ends in randomized trials [editorial]. *European Journal of Vascular and Endovascular Surgery* 2004 December; 28(6): 571-572. NRCBL: 18.2.

Mavroforou, Anna; Giannoukas, Athanasios D.; Mavrophoros, Dimitrios; Michalodimitrakis, Emmanuel. Confidentiality governing surgical research practice. *World Journal of Surgery* 2005 February; 29(2): 122-123. NRCBL: 18.2; 8.4.

Maxwell, David J.; Kaye, Karen I. Multicentre research: negotiating the ethics approval obstacle course [letter]. *Medical Journal of Australia* 2004 October 18; 181(8): 460. NRCBL: 18.2.

Mayor, Susan. Drug companies agree to make clinical trial results public [news]. *BMJ: British Medical Journal* 2005 January 15; 330(7483): 109. NRCBL: 18.2; 9.7.

McEachern, Terrence P. The inducement of meaningful work: a response to Anderson and Weijer. *Theoretical Medicine and Bioethics* 2005; 26(5): 427-430. NRCBL: 18.2; 18.5.1; 9.3.1. Comments: comment on James A. Anderson and Charles Weijer, "The research subject as wage earner," Theoretical Medicine and Bioethics 2002; 23: 359-376.
Abstract: James A. Anderson and Charles Weijer take the wage payment model proposed by Neil Dickert and Christine Grady and extend the analogy of research participation to unskilled

NRCBL: National Reference Center for Bioethics Literature Classification Scheme   See inside front cover for terms.

265

wage labor to include just working conditions. Although noble in its intentions, this moral extension generates unsavory outcomes. Most notably, Anderson and Weijer distinguish between two types of research subjects: occasional and professional. The latter, in this case, receives benefits beyond the moral minima in the form of "the right to meaningful work." The problem is that meaningful work can itself be a form of inducement, and consequently, may in fact increase the incidence of inducement contrary to the intentions of the wage payment model.

McGuire, Amy L.; McCullough, Laurence B. Respect as an organizing normative category for research ethics. *American Journal of Bioethics [Online]* 2005 January-February; 5(1): W1-W2. NRCBL: 18.2; 1.1; 1.3.9.

McMillan, John; Sheehan, Mark. Commentary: ethical review and ethical behaviour. *BMJ: British Medical Journal* 2005 February 26; 330(7489): 473. NRCBL: 18.2; 9.6.

McMurray, Terry. The changing face of research ethics [editorial]. *Ulster Medical Journal* 2002 November; 71(2): 98-100. NRCBL: 18.2; 18.6; 5.3.

McNay, Laura A.; Tavel, Jorge A.; Oseekey, Karen; McDermott, Cathy M.; Mollerup, David; Bebchuk, Judith D. Regulatory approvals in a large multinational clinical trial: the ESPRIT experience. *Controlled Clinical Trials* 2002 February; 23(1): 59-66. NRCBL: 18.2; 18.6; 21.1. Identifiers: Evaluation of Subcutaneous Proleukin in a Randomized International Trial.

Mehendale, Sanjay. Ethical considerations in AIDS vaccine trials. *Issues in Medical Ethics* 2000 January-March; 8(1): 13-15. NRCBL: 18.2; 18.5.9; 9.5.6; 9.7.

Meyers, Derek H.; Komesaroff, Paul A. Whose ethics? [letter and reply]. *Medical Journal of Australia* 2001 May 21; 174(10): 546-547. NRCBL: 18.2; 9.6.

Miller, Franklin G. Does research ethics rest on a mistake? *American Journal of Bioethics* 2005 January-February; 5(1): 34- 36. NRCBL: 18.2; 18.3; 6; 21.4; 5.2. Comments: comment on Rosamond Rhodes, "Rethinking research ethics," American Journal of Bioethics 2005 January-February; 5(1): 7-28.

Miller, Robert G.; Munsat, Theodore L.; Swash, Michael; Brooks, Benjamin R. Consensus guidelines for the design and implementation of clinical trials in ALS. *Journal of Neurological Sciences* 1999 October 31; 169(1-2): 2-12. NRCBL: 18.2; 18.3; 18.6; 18.5.1. Identifiers: amyotrophic lateral sclerosis.

Miser, William F. Educational research — to IRB, or not to IRB? *Family Medicine* 2005 March; 37(3): 168-173. NRCBL: 18.2; 18.1; 7.2. Identifiers: institutional review board.

Mittra, I. Mishandling misconduct: the breast cancer trials scandal [editorial]. *National Medical Journal of India* 1994 November-December; 7(6): 255-257. NRCBL: 18.2; 18.5.3; 9.8.

Moler, Frank W. Resuscitation research and the final rule: is there an impasse? [opinion]. *Pediatrics* 2004 September; 114(3): 859-861. NRCBL: 18.2; 18.3; 18.5.2; 20.5.1.

Montori, Victor M.; Devereaux, P.J.; Adhikari, Neill K.J.; Burns, Karen E.A.; Eggert, Christoph H.; Briel, Matthias; Lacchetti, Christina; Leung, Teresa W.; Darling, Elizabeth; Bryant, Dianne M.; Bucher, Heiner C.; Schünemann, Holger J.; Meade, Maureen O.; Cook, Deborah J.; Erwin, Patricia J.; Sood, Amit; Sood, Richa; Lo, Benjamin; Thompson, Carly A.; Zhou, Qi; Mills, Edward; Guyatt, Gordon H. Randomized trials stopped early for benefit: a systematic review. *JAMA: The Journal of the American Medical Association* 2005 November 2; 294(17): 2203-2209. NRCBL: 18.2. SC: em.

Abstract: CONTEXT: Randomized clinical trials (RCTs) that stop earlier than planned because of apparent benefit often receive great attention and affect clinical practice. Their prevalence, the magnitude and plausibility of their treatment effects, and the extent to which they report information about how investigators decided to stop early are, however, unknown. OBJECTIVE: To evaluate the epidemiology and reporting quality of RCTs involving interventions stopped early for benefit. DATA SOURCES: Systematic review up to November 2004 of MEDLINE, EMBASE, Current Contents, and full-text journal content databases to identify RCTs stopped early for benefit. STUDY SELECTION: Randomized clinical trials of any intervention reported as having stopped early because of results favoring the intervention. There were no exclusion criteria. DATA EXTRACTION: Twelve reviewers working independently and in duplicate abstracted data on content area and type of intervention tested, reporting of funding, type of end point driving study termination, treatment effect, length of follow-up, estimated sample size and total sample studied, role of a data and safety monitoring board in stopping the study, number of interim analyses planned and conducted, and existence and type of monitoring methods, statistical boundaries, and adjustment procedures for interim analyses and early stopping. DATA SYNTHESIS: Of 143 RCTs stopped early for benefit, the majority (92) were published in 5 high-impact medical journals. Typically, these were industry-funded drug trials in cardiology, cancer, and human immunodeficiency virus/AIDS. The proportion of all RCTs published in high-impact journals that were stopped early for benefit increased from 0.5% in 1990-1994 to 1.2% in 2000-2004 (P001 for trend). On average, RCTs recruited 63% (SD, 25%) of the planned sample and stopped after a median of 13 (interquartile range [IQR], 3-25) months of follow-up, 1 interim analysis, and when a median of 66 (IQR, 23-195) patients had experienced the end point driving study termination (event). The median risk ratio among truncated RCTs was 0.53 (IQR, 0.28-0.66). One hundred thirty-five (94%) of the 143 RCTs did not report at least 1 of the following: the planned sample size (n = 28), the interim analysis after which the trial was stopped (n = 45), whether a stopping rule informed the decision (n = 48), or an adjusted analysis accounting for interim monitoring and truncation (n = 129). Trials with fewer events yielded greater treatment effects (odds ratio, 28; 95% confidence interval, 11-73). CONCLUSIONS: RCTs stopped early for benefit are becoming more common, often fail to adequately report relevant information about the decision to stop early, and show implausibly large treatment effects, particularly when the number of events is small. These findings suggest clinicians should view the results of such trials with skepticism.

Morreim, E. Haavi. Research versus innovation: real differences. *American Journal of Bioethics* 2005 January-February; 5(1): 42- 43. NRCBL: 18.2; 18.3; 19.2. Comments: comment on Rosamond Rhodes, "Rethinking research ethics," American Journal of Bioethics 2005 January-February; 5(1): 7-28.

Morris, Amelia D.; Zaritsky, Arno L.; LeFever, Gretchen. Evaluation of ethical conflicts associated with randomized, controlled trials in critically ill children. *Critical Care Medicine* 2000 April; 28(4): 1152-1156. NRCBL: 18.2; 18.5.2; 20.5.2; 8.3.2.

Morse, Janice M. Ethical issues in institutional research [editorial]. *Qualitative Health Research* 2005 April; 15(4): 435-437. NRCBL: 18.2.

Morse, Janice M. The paid/unpaid work of participants [editorial]. *Qualitative Health Research* 2005 July; 15(6): 727-728. NRCBL: 18.2; 9.3.1; 18.6.

Nair, V. Mohanan; Martin, Douglas K. Concerns about ethical review of health research in India. *Indian Journal of Medical Ethics* 2004 October-December; 1(4): 119-120. NRCBL: 18.2.

National Health and Medical Research Council [NHMRC] (Australia). Report of the 1999 Workshops on the National Statement on Ethical Conduct in Research Involving Humans. Canberra, ACT: The Council 2000; 46 p. [Online]. Available: http://www7.health.gov.au/nhmrc/publications/pdf/e40.pdf [31 March 2005]. NRCBL: 18.2. SC: em; cs.

National Institutes of Health [NIH] (United States). Office of Biotechnology Activities. Points to consider in the design and submission of protocols for the transfer of recombinant DNA molecules into one or more human research participants. Appendix M. Bethesda, MD: National Institutes of Health. Office of Biotechnology Activities 2002; 15 p.[Online]. Available: http://www4.od.nih.gov/oba/rac/guidelines_02/Appendix_M.htm#_Appendix_M-I._Requirements [25 July 2005]. NRCBL: 18.2; 15.4.

Newman, Robert G. US exceptionalism and research ethics [letter]. *Lancet* 2005 May 7-13; 365(9471): 1617. NRCBL: 18.2; 18.6; 21.1.

Nosé, Yukihiko. Institutional review board approval for clinical application of new medical devices rather than government agency [editorial]. *Artificial Organs* 2004 December; 28(12): 1057-1058. NRCBL: 18.2; 18.6; 21.1; 9.7. Identifiers: Japan.

O'Brien, Kylie. Commentary on C Zaslawski and S Davis, 'The ethics of complementary and alternative medicine research'. *Monash Bioethics Review* 2005 July; 24(3): 62-66. NRCBL: 18.2; 4.1.1.

O'Lonergan, Theresa. Creative solutions: research subject advocates: increase in reports of human subject protection deficiencies brings scrutiny as well as more efforts at education and support. *Protecting Human Subjects* 2003 Spring; (8): 10-11. NRCBL: 18.2.

Olde Rikkert, Marcel G.M.; Lauque, S.; Frölich, L.; Vellas, B.; Dekkers, W. The practice of obtaining approval from medical research ethics committees: a comparison within 12 European countries for a descriptive study on acetylcholinesterase inhibitors in Alzheimer's dementia. *European Journal of Neurology* 2005 March; 12(3): 212-217. NRCBL: 18.2; 18.6; 18.3; 17.1; 9.5.2; 21.1. SC: em.

Oleson, Kimberly A. Role of the industry sponsor: protection of human subjects in early device-application studies. *Journal of Laboratory and Clinical Medicine* 2005 January; 145(1): 17-20. NRCBL: 18.2; 1.3.9; 4.1.1.

Olsen, Jørn; Mulvad, Gert; Pedersen, Mille Søvndah; Christiansen, Thue; Sørensen, Paul Henrik. An ethics committee for medical research in Greenland: history and challenges. *International Journal of Circumpolar Health* 2004; 63(Supplement 2): 144-146. NRCBL: 18.2; 15.1; 1.3.12; 18.3. Conference: Proceedings of the 12th International Congress on Circumpolar Health; Nuuk, Greenland; 10-14 September 2003.

Owens, Nancy G. Human subjects — are they protected? *Plastic Surgical Nursing* 1999 Winter; 19(4): 212-217. NRCBL: 18.2; 18.5.1; 2.2.

Paasche-Orlow, Michael K.; Brancati, Frederick L. Assessment of medical school institutional review board policies regarding compensation of subjects for research-related injury. *American Journal of Medicine* 2005 February; 118(2): 175-180. NRCBL: 18.2; 18.1; 9.3.1. SC: em.

Page-Shafer, Kimberly; Saphonn, Vonthanak; Sun, Ly Penh; Vun, Mean Chhi; Cooper, David A.; Kaldor, John M. HIV prevention research in a resource-limited setting: the experience of planning a trial in Cambodia [opinion]. *Lancet* 2005 October 22-28; 366(9495): 1499-1503. NRCBL: 18.2; 18.5.9; 9.5.6; 9.3.1.

Parker, Damon B.; James, Michael; Barrett, Robert J. The practical logic of reasonableness: an ethnographic reconnaissance of a research ethics committee. *Monash Bioethics Review* 2005 October; 24(4): 7-27. NRCBL: 18.2; 9.6. SC: cs.

Parnis, Deborah; Du Mont, Janice; Gombay, Brydon. Cooperation or co-optation?: assessing the methodological benefits and barriers involved in conducting qualitative research through medical institutional settings. *Qualitative Health Research* 2005 May; 15(5): 686-697. NRCBL: 18.2; 10; 18.6; 18.5.3.

NRCBL: National Reference Center for Bioethics Literature Classification Scheme   See inside front cover for terms.

267

Partridge, Ann H.; Wong, Julia S.; Knudsen, Katherine; Gelman, Rebecca; Sampson, Ebonie; Gadd, Michele; Bishop, Karyn L.; Harris, Jay R.; Winer, Eric P. Offering participants results of a clinical trial: sharing results of a negative study. *Lancet* 2005 March 12-18; 365(9463): 963-964. NRCBL: 18.2; 18.3; 8.1; 18.5.3.

Abstract: In general, patients are not given information about the results of trials in which they have participated. We aimed to assess the process and effect of providing clinical trial participants with results of a negative study. We offered results to 135 participants in a phase II trial of breast excision alone for women with ductal carcinoma in situ, which was stopped early because of an early high rate of local recurrence. 85 (90%) of 94 respondents chose to receive results; these women were more educated (57 [67%] of 85 college graduates) than those who chose not to (two [22%] of nine, p=0.006). Most participants reported positive feelings about being offered results and about clinical trials in general. These preliminary findings from sharing clinical trial results are encouraging.

Pentz, Rebecca D.; Cohen, Cynthia B.; Wicclair, Mark; DeVita, Michael A.; Flamm, Anne Lederman; Youngner, Stuart J.; Hamric, Ann B.; McCabe, Mary S.; Glover, Jacqueline J.; Kittiko, Winona J.; Kinlaw, Kathy; Keller, James; Asch, Adrienne; Kavanagh, John J.; Arap, Wadih. Ethics guidelines for research with the recently dead. *Nature Medicine* 2005 November; 11(11): 1145-1149. NRCBL: 18.2; 18.5.1; 19.1; 20.1. SC: rv. Identifiers: Consensus Panel on Research with the Recently Dead (CPRRD).

Perlis, Roy H.; Perlis, Clifford S.; Wu, Yelena; Hwang, Cindy; Joseph, Megan; Nierenberg, Andrew A. Industry sponsorship and financial conflict of interest in the reporting of clinical trials in psychiatry. *American Journal of Psychiatry* 2005 October; 162(10): 1957- 1960. NRCBL: 18.2; 17.4; 9.7; 1.3.9; 17.1; 9.3.1. SC: em.

Pilpel, Dina; Leavitt, Frank J.; Elizur-Leiberman, Esther. Ethical and cross cultural questions concerning pediatric clinical trials. *Controlled Clinical Trials* 1996 June; 17(3): 201-208. NRCBL: 18.2; 18.5.2; 21.7; 18.3.

Pocock, Stuart J. When (not) to stop a clinical trial for benefit [editorial]. *JAMA: The Journal of the American Medical Association* 2005 November 2; 294(17): 2228-2230. NRCBL: 18.2.

Powers, John H.; Cooper, Charles K.; Lin, Daphne; Ross, David B. Sample size and the ethics of non-inferiority trials [letter]. *Lancet* 2005 July 2-8; 366(9479): 24-25. NRCBL: 18.2; 7.1.

Prentice, Ross. Invited commentary: ethics and sample size — another view. *American Journal of Epidemiology* 2005 January 15; 161(2): 111-112. NRCBL: 18.2.

Price, Linnie. Research ethics committees and conflicts of interest. *Bulletin of Medical Ethics* 2003 September; (191): 13-16. NRCBL: 18.2; 1.3.9; 7.3. Identifiers: United Kingdom (Great Britain).

Rahman, Mahbubur; Morita, Satoshi; Fukui, Tsuguya; Sakamoto, Junichi. Physicians' reasons for not entering their patients in a randomized controlled trial in Japan. *Tohoku Journal of Experimental Medicine* 2004 June; 203(2): 105-109. NRCBL: 18.2; 8.1; 18.3. SC: em.

Raja, Asad Jamil. The revised Helsinki Declaration: is it enough? *Issues in Medical Ethics* 2001 October-December; 9(4): 114-116. NRCBL: 18.2; 18.5.9; 9.7.

Rance, Susanna; Salinas, Silvia. Ethical mapping: a methodological proposal. *Issues in Medical Ethics* 2001 July-September; 9(3): 86-87. NRCBL: 18.2.

Reitsma, Angelique M.; Moreno, Jonathan D. Ethics of innovative surgery: US surgeons' definitions, knowledge, and attitudes. *Journal of the American College of Surgeons* 2005 January; 200(1): 103-110. NRCBL: 18.2; 18.3; 18.6. SC: em.

Retsas, Spyros. Treatment at random: the ultimate science or the betrayal of Hippocrates? *Journal of Clinical Oncology* 2004 December 15; 22(24): 5005-5008. NRCBL: 18.2; 8.1.

Rhodes, Rosamond. Response to commentators on "Rethinking Research Ethics" [letter]. *American Journal of Bioethics [Online]* 2005 January-February; 5(1): W15-W18. NRCBL: 18.2; 1.1; 5.3.

Rhodes, Rosamond. Rethinking research ethics. *American Journal of Bioethics* 2005 January-February; 5(1): 7-28. NRCBL: 18.2; 18.3; 21.4; 1.3.5; 1.1; 18.5.2; 18.5.6.

Abstract: Contemporary research ethics policies started with reflection on the atrocities perpetrated upon concentration camp inmates by Nazi doctors. Apparently, as a consequence of that experience, the policies that now guide human subject research focus on the protection of human subjects by making informed consent the centerpiece of regulatory attention. I take the choice of context for policy design, the initial prioritization of informed consent, and several associated conceptual missteps, to have set research ethics off in the wrong direction. The aim of this paper is to sort out these confusions and their implications and to offer instead a straightforward framework for considering the ethical conduct of human subject research. In the course of this discussion I clarify different senses of autonomy that have been confounded and present more intelligible justifications for informed consent. I also take issue with several of the now accepted dogmas that govern research ethics. These include: the primacy of informed consent, the protection of the vulnerable, the substitution of beneficence for research's social purpose, and the introduction of an untenable distinction between innovation and research.

Roberts, Laura Weiss; Geppert, Cynthia M.A.; Brody, Janet L. A framework for considering the ethical aspects of psychiatric research protocols. *Comprehensive Psychiatry* 2001 September-October; 42(5): 351-363. NRCBL: 18.2; 17.4; 18.3; 18.5.1; 18.6.

Roberts, Lynne M.; Bowyer, Lucy; Homer, Caroline S.; Brown, Mark A. Multicentre research: negotiating the ethics approval obstacle course [letter]. *Medical Journal of*

Australia 2004 February 2; 180(3): 139. NRCBL: 18.2; 18.5.3; 18.6.

Roberts, Robin S. Early closure of the Watterberg trial. *Pediatrics* 2004 December; 114(6): 1670-1671. NRCBL: 18.2.

Roehr, Bob. FDA seeks to ease burden on trial review boards [news]. *BMJ: British Medical Journal* 2005 April 2; 330(7494): 748. NRCBL: 18.2. Identifiers: Food and Drug Administration.

Rogers, Anne; Day, Jenny; Randall, Fiona; Bentall, Richard P. Patients' understanding and participation in a trial designed to improve the management of anti-psychotic medication: a qualitative study. *Social Psychiatry and Psychiatric Epidemiology* 2003 December; 38(12): 720-727. NRCBL: 18.2; 8.1; 17.4.

Rothman, Kenneth J.; Evans, Stephen. Extra scrutiny for industry funded trials: JAMA's demand for an additional hurdle is unfair — and absurd [editorial]. *BMJ: British Medical Journal* 2005 December 10; 331(7529): 1350-1351. NRCBL: 18.2; 5.3; 1.3.9; 1.3.7.

Rothwell, Peter M. External validity of randomised controlled trials: "to whom do the results of this trial apply?". *Lancet* 2005 January 1-7; 365(9453): 82-93. NRCBL: 18.2; 8.1; 9.7; 18.5.1; 18.6. SC: rv.

Roychowdhury, Debasish; Meropol, Neal J.; Weinfurt, Kevin P.; Schulman, Kevin A. Phase I trials: physician and patient perceptions [letter and reply]. *Journal of Clinical Oncology* 2003 December 15; 21(24): 4658-4660. NRCBL: 18.2; 8.1.

Saheli Women's Resource Centre. ICMR draft ethical guidelines: a critique. *Issues in Medical Ethics* 2000 January-March; 8(1): 20-21. NRCBL: 18.2; 18.3; 18.5.3; 14.1; 11.1. Identifiers: Indian Council of Medical Research.

Sarson-Lawrence, M.; Alt, C.; Mok, M.T.; Dodds, M.; Rosenthal, M.A. Trust and confidence: towards mutual acceptance of ethics committee approval of multicentre studies. *Internal Medicine Journal* 2004 November; 34(11): 598-603. NRCBL: 18.2. SC: em. Identifiers: Australia.

Saver, Richard S. What IRBs could learn from corporate boards. *IRB: Ethics and Human Research* 2005 September-October; 27(5): 1-6. NRCBL: 18.2; 1.3.2. Identifiers: institutional review boards.

Schadick, Kevin. Bioethics consultants: corporate reliance on a new field of consultation. *Health Matrix: Journal of Law-Medicine* 2005 Summer; 15(2): 433-458. NRCBL: 18.2; 9.6; 2.3; 7.3.

Schüklenk, Udo. Ethics and AIDS vaccine trials: a response [letter]. *Issues in Medical Ethics* 2000 April-June; 8(2): 37. NRCBL: 18.2; 18.5.9; 9.5.6. Comments: comment on Sanjay Mehendale, "Ethical considerations in

AIDS vaccine trials," Issues in Medical Ethics 2000 January-March; 8(1): 13-15.

Schüklenk, Udo. Helsinki Declaration revisions. *Issues in Medical Ethics* 2001 January-March; 9(1): 29. NRCBL: 18.2.

Schüklenk, Udo. International research ethics guidelines under threat: a full- scale attack on the CIOMS Guidelines and the Declaration of Helsinki is currently underway. *Issues in Medical Ethics* 1999 July-September; 7(3): 97-98. NRCBL: 18.2; 18.3; 9.5.6; 21.1. Identifiers: Council of International Organisations of Medical Sciences.

Seibold, Carmel. Qualitative research from a feminist perspective in the postmodern era: methodological, ethical and reflexive concerns. *Nursing Inquiry* 2000 September; 7(3): 147-155. NRCBL: 18.2; 10; 1.1.

Shapiro, Harold T.; Meslin, Eric M. Relating to history: the influence of the National Commission and its Belmont Report on the National Bioethics Advisory Commission. *In:* Childress, James F.; Meslin, Eric M.; Shapiro, Harold T., eds. Belmont Revisited: Ethical Principles for Research with Human Subjects. Washington, DC: Georgetown University Press; 2005: 55-76. NRCBL: 18.2; 2.1; 2.2; 2.4.

Sharp, Richard R.; Yarborough, Mark. Additional thoughts on rethinking research ethics. *American Journal of Bioethics* 2005 January-February; 5(1): 40- 42. NRCBL: 18.2; 1.1. Comments: comment on Rosamond Rhodes, "Rethinking research ethics," American Journal of Bioethics 2005 January-February; 5(1): 7-28.

Sharp, S. Michael; Pentz, Rebecca D. Issues, both ethical and practical, in the development and conduct of chemoprevention trials. *Current Problems in Cancer* 2004 July-August; 28(4): 186-200. NRCBL: 18.2; 18.5.1.

Shephard, Roy J. Ethics in exercise science research. *Sports Medicine* 2002; 32(3): 169-183. NRCBL: 18.2; 18.3; 1.3.7; 7.2.

Sherwin, Susan. Belmont revisited through a feminist lens. *In:* Childress, James F.; Meslin, Eric M.; Shapiro, Harold T., eds. Belmont Revisited: Ethical Principles for Research with Human Subjects. Washington, DC: Georgetown University Press; 2005: 148-164. NRCBL: 18.2; 10; 18.5.1; 1.1. SC: an.

Shrotri, D.S. Role of ethics committees in medical research. *Indian Journal of Medical Ethics* 2004 October-December; 1(4): 121. NRCBL: 18.2.

Simmerling, Mary; Schwegler, Brian. Beginning anew: same principles, different direction for research ethics. *American Journal of Bioethics* 2005 January-February; 5(1): 44- 46. NRCBL: 18.2; 18.3; 18.5.1; 18.6. Comments: comment on Rosamond Rhodes, "Rethinking research ethics," American Journal of Bioethics 2005 January-February; 5(1): 7-28.

NRCBL: National Reference Center for Bioethics Literature Classification Scheme   See inside front cover for terms.

Slovenko, Ralph. The evolution of standards for experimental treatment or research. *Journal of Psychiatry and Law* 2005 Spring; 33(1): 129-174. NRCBL: 18.2; 21.4; 15.1; 1.3.5.

Smith, M.; Doyle, F.; McGee, H.M.; De La Harpe, D. Ethical approval for national studies in Ireland: an illustration of current challenges. *Irish Journal of Medical Science* 2004 April-June; 173(2): 72-74. NRCBL: 18.2.

Speck, Peter. Research and ethical scrutiny: an editor's dilemma? [editorial]. *Palliative Medicine* 2001 March 1; 15(2): 89-90. NRCBL: 18.2; 18.6.

Speers, Marjorie A. Making human research safe: why we cannot afford to fail. *Science and Engineering Ethics* 2005 January; 11(1): 53-59. NRCBL: 18.2; 18.6; 21.1. Conference: 5th International Conference on Bioethics: The Ethics of Intellectual Property Rights and Patents; Warsaw, Poland; 23-24 April 2004; Minister of Science and the Minister of Health, Poland.

Spike, Jeffrey. Putting the "ethics" into "research ethics". *American Journal of Bioethics* 2005 January-February; 5(1): 51- 53. NRCBL: 18.2; 1.3.9; 1.1. Comments: comment on Rosamond Rhodes, "Rethinking research ethics," American Journal of Bioethics 2005 January-February; 5(1): 7-28.

Sporle, Andrew; Koea, Jonathan. Maori responsiveness in health and medical research: clarifying the roles of the researcher and the institution (Part 2). *New Zealand Medical Journal* 2004 August 6; 117(1199); 7 p. NRCBL: 18.2; 18.5.9; 21.7.

Sporle, Andrew; Koea, Jonathan. Maori responsiveness in health and medical research: key issues for researchers (Part 1). *New Zealand Medical Journal* 2004 August 6; 117(1199): 10 p. NRCBL: 18.2; 18.5.9; 21.7.

Srinivasan, Sandhya; Pai, Sanjay A. Research: history repeats itself [editorial]. *Issues in Medical Ethics* 2001 October-December; 9(4): 108. NRCBL: 18.2; 18.5.9.

Stair, Thomas O.; Reed, Caitlin R.; Radeos, Michael S.; Koski, Greg; Camargo, Carlos A. Variation in institutional review board responses to a standard protocol for a multicenter clinical trial. *Academic Emergency Medicine* 2001 June; 8(6): 636-641. NRCBL: 18.2; 18.3. Identifiers: Multicenter Airway Research Collaboration (MARC).

Steinbrook, Robert. Public access to NIH-funded research [opinion]. *New England Journal of Medicine* 2005 April 28; 352(17): 1739- 1741. NRCBL: 18.2; 5.1; 1.3.7; 1.3.9; 1.3.12; 18.6. Identifiers: National Institutes of Health.

Sugarman, Jeremy; Getz, Kenneth; Speckman, Jeanne L.; Byrne, Margaret M.; Gerson, Jason; Emanuel, Ezekiel J. The cost of institutional review boards in academic medical centers [letter]. *New England Journal of Medicine* 2005 April 28; 352(17): 1825- 1827. NRCBL: 18.2; 9.3.1.

Sumathipala, Athula; Siribaddana, Sisira. Research and clinical ethics after the tsunami: Sri Lanka [opinion]. *Lancet* 2005 October 22-28; 366(9495): 1418-1420. NRCBL: 18.2; 9.3.1; 18.3; 1.3.7.

Tamakoshi, Akiko. Informed consent in epidemiologic research before the implementation of ethical guidelines. *Journal of Epidemiology* 2004 November; 14(6): 177-181. NRCBL: 18.2; 18.3; 7.1. SC: em. Identifiers: Japan.

Taylor, G.J.; Wainwright, P. Open label extension studies: research or marketing? *BMJ: British Medical Journal* 2005 September 10; 331(7516): 572-574. NRCBL: 18.2; 9.7; 18.3. SC: em.

Thabane, Lehana; Childs, Aaron; Lafontaine, Amanda. Determining the level of statistician participation on Canadian-based research ethics boards. *IRB: Ethics and Human Research* 2005 March-April; 27(2): 11-14. NRCBL: 18.2. SC: em.

Touitou, Yvan; Portaluppi, Francesco; Smolensky, Michael H.; Rensing, Ludger. Ethical principles and standards for the conduct of human and animal biological rhythm research. *Chronobiology International* 2004 January; 21(1): 161-170. NRCBL: 18.2; 18.5.1; 22.2.

Toumbourou, John W.; Evans-Whipp, Tracy; Clements, Jackie; McMorris, Barbara J.; Mathers, Megan; Catalano, Richard F. Ethical guidelines for the payment of research participants should be clarified: reflections from cross-national research. *Australian and New Zealand Journal of Public Health* 2004; 28(6): 584-585. NRCBL: 18.2; 18.5.9; 9.3.1. SC: em. Identifiers: Australia; United States.

Trachtman, Howard. Does Uncle Sam really want you?: a response to "Rethinking Research Ethics" by Rosamond Rhodes (AJOB 5:1). *American Journal of Bioethics [Online]* 2005 January-February; 5(1): W22-W23. NRCBL: 18.2; 18.5.1; 1.1. Comments: comment on Rosamond Rhodes, "Rethinking Research Ethics," American Journal of Bioethics 2005 January-February; 5(1): 7-28.

Tuech, J.J.; Pessaux, P.; Moutel, G.; Thoma, V.; Schraub, S.; Herve, C. Methodological quality and reporting of ethical requirements in phase III cancer trials. *Journal of Medical Ethics* 2005 May; 31(5): 251-255. NRCBL: 18.2. SC: em.
Abstract: BACKGROUND: The approval of a research ethics committee (REC) and obtaining informed consent from patients (ICP) could be considered the main issues in the ethics of research with human beings. The aim of this study was to assess both methodological quality and ethical quality, and also to assess the relationship between these two qualities in randomised phase III cancer trials. METHOD: Methodological quality (Jadad score) and ethical quality (Berdeu score) were assessed for all randomised controlled trials (RCTs) published in 10 international journals between 1999 and 2001 (n = 231). RE-

SULTS: The mean Jadad score was 9.86 +/- 1.117. The methodological quality was poor in 75 RCTs (Jadad score). The mean Berdeu score was 0.42 +/- 0.133. The mean ethical quality score for poor methodological quality RCTs (n = 75) was 0.39 +/- 0.133; it was 0.43 +/- 0.133 for good (n = 156) methodological quality RCTs (p = 0.07). There was improvement in ethical quality according to the year of commencement of the trials (p 0.001). There was no correlation between methodological quality and the number of participating patients (R2 = 0.003, p = 0.78), between ethical quality and the number of participating patients (R2 = 0.003, p = 0.76), or between ethical quality and methodological quality (R2 = 0.012, p = 0.1). ICP and REC approval were not obtained for 21 and 77 trials respectively. CONCLUSION: The association between methodological quality and the reporting of ethical requirements probably reflects the respect shown for patients during the whole research process. These results suggest that closer attention to the conduct of clinical research, as well as the reporting of its ethical aspects, is needed.

Ulrich, Connie M.; Wallen, Gwenyth R.; Grady, Christine. Research vulnerability and patient advocacy: balance-seeking perspectives for the clinical nurse scientist? [editorial]. *Nursing Research* 2002 March-April; 51(2): 71. NRCBL: 18.2; 4.1.3.

United Kingdom. Department of Health. Report of the ad hoc advisory group on the operation of NHS research ethics committees. London: Department of Health 2005; 26 p. [Online]. Available: http://www.dh.gov.uk/assetRoot/04/11/24/17/04112417.pdf [7 March 2006]. NRCBL: 18.2. Identifiers: National Health Service.

United States. Department of Health and Human Services. Equivalent Protections Working Group. Report of the Equivalent Protections Working Group, Department of Health and Human Services. Washington, DC: Department of Health and Human Services 2003 July 17; 21 p., 4 p. appendix [Online]. Available: http://hhs.gov.ohrp/international/EPWGReport2003.pdf; http://hhs.gov/ohrp/international/EPWGFramework.pdf [2 December 2005]. NRCBL: 18.2. Note: Submitted to Dr. Bernard Schwetz, Director, Office for Human Research Protections.

United States. Food and Drug Administration [FDA]; Good Clinical Practice Program, Office of the Commissioner [OC]; Center for Drug Evaluation and Research [CDER]; Center for Biologics Evaluation and Research [CBER]; Office of Regulatory Affairs [ORA]. Guidance for industry. Using a centralized IRB review process in multicenter clinical trials. Draft guidance. Rockville, MD: Food and Drug Administration 2005 March; 10 p. [Online]. Available: http://www.fda/gov/cder/guidance/OC273dft.pdf [20 July 2005]. NRCBL: 18.2.

Valdez-Martinez; Edith; Trumbull, Bernardo; Garduño-Espinosa, Juan; Porter, John David Henley. Understanding the structure and practices of research ethics committees through research and audit: a study from Mexico. *Health Policy* 2005 September 28; 74(1): 56-68. NRCBL: 18.2; 2.2; 1.3.9; 5.3.

Van Der Weyden, Martin B. Multicentre research: negotiating the ethics approval obstacle course [letter]. *Medical Journal of Australia* 2004 October 18; 181(8): 460-461. NRCBL: 18.2.

Veatch, Robert M. Ranking, balancing, or simultaneity: resolving conflicts among the Belmont principles. *In:* Childress, James F.; Meslin, Eric M.; Shapiro, Harold T., eds. Belmont Revisited: Ethical Principles for Research with Human Subjects. Washington, DC: Georgetown University Press; 2005: 184-204. NRCBL: 18.2; 1.1; 2.1. SC: an.

Wachbroit, Robert; Wasserman, David. Research participation: are we subject to a duty? *American Journal of Bioethics* 2005 January-February; 5(1): 48- 49. NRCBL: 18.2; 1.3.9; 1.1; 18.3. Comments: comment on Rosamond Rhodes, "Rethinking research ethics," American Journal of Bioethics 2005 January-February; 5(1): 7-28.

Wade, Derick T. Ethics, audit, and research: all shades of grey. *BMJ: British Medical Journal* 2005 February 26; 330(7489): 468- 471. NRCBL: 18.2; 9.6.

Wadman, Meredith. US set to endorse human pesticide testing. *Nature* 2005 September 1; 437(7055): 24-25. NRCBL: 18.2; 16.1. Identifiers: Environmental Protection Agency.

Wagner, Richard M. Ethical review of research involving human subjects: when and why is IRB review necessary? *Muscle and Nerve* 2003 July; 28: 27-39. NRCBL: 18.2; 18.6. Identifiers: institutional review board.

Walker, Gay; de Valois, Beverley; Davies, Raten; Young, Teresa; Maher, Jane. Opinions of research participants about study paperwork [review]. *Bulletin of Medical Ethics* 2005 February; (205): 21-24. NRCBL: 18.2. SC: em.

Wallwork, Ernest. Failed community representation: does the process inhibit full IRB participation by community representatives? *Protecting Human Subjects* 2003 Fall; (9): 4, 14. NRCBL: 18.2. Identifiers: institutional review boards.

Walsh, Michael K.; McNeil, John J.; Breen, Kerry J. Improving the governance of health research. *Medical Journal of Australia* 2005 May 2; 182(9): 468-471. NRCBL: 18.2; 18.6. Identifiers: Australia.

Weijer, Charles. Is clinical research and ethics a zero-sum game? *Critical Care Medicine* 2005 April; 33(4): 912-913. NRCBL: 18.2; 18.3; 18.5.1.

Weijer, Charles. Meaningful work as due inducement. *Theoretical Medicine and Bioethics* 2005; 26(5): 431-435. NRCBL: 18.2; 9.3.1.

Weiss, Barry D.; Smith, Mindy A.; Magill, Michael K. Journal policy statement — IRB approval for educational research [policy statement]. *Family Medicine* 2005 March;

NRCBL: National Reference Center for Bioethics Literature Classification Scheme   See inside front cover for terms.

271

37(3): 219-220. NRCBL: 18.2; 18.1; 7.2. Identifiers: institutional review board.

Wendler, David. Protecting subjects who cannot give consent. *Hastings Center Report* 2005 September-October; 35(5): 37-43. NRCBL: 18.2; 18.5.1; 18.5.2.

Wieand, Samuel; Murphy, Kate. A commentary on treatment at random: the ultimate science or the betrayal of Hippocrates? *Journal of Clinical Oncology* 2004 December 15; 22(24): 5009- 5011. NRCBL: 18.2; 8.1.

Wilkes, Lesley. Ethics on the floor. *Collegian* 2003 April; 10(2): 34-39. NRCBL: 18.2. SC: em. Identifiers: Australia.

Wilkinson, Martin. Payments to research subjects. *Monash Bioethics Review* 2005 January; 24(1): 70-74. NRCBL: 18.2; 1.3.2. SC: an.

Wilson, John T.; Kearns, G.; Springer, M.A. Role of the research-subject locator (RSL) in the performance of a pediatric drug trial. *Journal of Clinical Pharmacology* 2003 November; 43(11): 1196-1202. NRCBL: 18.2; 18.5.2; 9.7.

Wilson, Mark. Vulnerable subjects and Canadian research governance. *IRB: Ethics and Human Research* 2005 November-December; 27(6): 9-11. NRCBL: 18.2; 18.5.1. Identifiers: Canada; Health Insurance Portability and Accountability Act (HIPAA).

Winship, Ingrid; Marbrook, John. Ethical considerations relating to research in human genetics. *Auckland City, New Zealand: Health Research Council of New Zealand,* 1998 December: 1-12. NRCBL: 18.2; 18.3; 15.1. Identifiers: Health Research Council of New Zealand.

Yealy, Donald M.; Paris, Paul M.; Vukmir, Rade B.; Kim, David T. Prehospital IRBs and consent . . . [letter and reply]. *Annals of Emergency Medicine* 1994 October; 24(4): 759-760. NRCBL: 18.2; 18.3. Identifiers: institutional review board.

Zaslawski, Chris; Davis, Susanna. The ethics of complementary and alternative medicine research: a case study of traditional Chinese medicine at the University of Technology, Sydney. *Monash Bioethics Review* 2005 July; 24(3): 52-60. NRCBL: 18.2; 4.1.1.

Zlotnik Shaul, Randi; Reid, Lynette; Essue, Beverley; Gibson, Julie; Marzinotto, Velma; Daneman, Denis. Dissemination to research subjects: operationalizing investigator accountability. *Accountability in Research* 2005 January-March; 12(1): 1-16. NRCBL: 18.2; 8.1; 8.4. SC: an.

Abstract: Recent articles have argued from principles of bioethics for the right of research subjects to receive the results of the studies in which they have participated. We argue that accountability is a powerful tool of meso-level analysis appropriate to reasoning about answerability in research ethics, and that it captures the responsibility of researchers to disseminate study results to research subjects. We offer the following features of the research situation as relevant to the manner of dissemination

to study subject, in addition to factors already proposed in the literature (risk and impact on health outcome): (a) features of the research subject in relation to identity, personal investment, disease, and community; (b) characteristics of the research study and field of inquiry in relation to certainty and significance; and (c) relationships among the research subjects and the healthcare workers involved in their care and in the research.

HUMAN EXPERIMENTATION/ . . . / LEGAL ASPECTS

Additional protocol to the convention for the protection of human rights and dignity of the human being with regard to the application of biology and medicine, on biomedical research. *Revista de Derecho y Genoma-Humano / Law and the Human Genome Review* 2004 July-December; (21): 201-214. NRCBL: 18.2; 18.3. SC: le.

Arford, Patricia H. Working with human research protections. *Journal of Nursing Scholarship* 2004; 36(3): 265-271. NRCBL: 18.2; 8.4; 18.6. SC: le.

Ashcroft, Richard E.; Newson, Ainsley J.; Benn, Piers M.W. Reforming research ethics committees: latest proposals are a missed opportunity for a radical review [editorial]. *BMJ: British Medical Journal* 2005 September 17; 331(7517): 587-588. NRCBL: 18.2; 21.1. SC: le.

Baeyens, A.J. Implementation of the clinical trials directive: pitfalls and benefits. *European Journal of Health Law* 2002 March; 9(1): 31-47. NRCBL: 18.2; 9.7; 18.3. SC: le.

Beh, Hazel Glenn. The role of institutional review boards in protecting human subjects: are we really ready to fix a broken system? *Law and Psychology Review* 2002 Spring; 26(1): 1-47. NRCBL: 18.2; 18.5.2; 18.1. SC: le.

Beran, Roy G. Ethical considerations within clinical research with special focus upon clinical drug trials. *Medicine and Law: World Association for Medical Law* 2005 June; 24(2): 411-436. NRCBL: 18.2; 7.3; 2.1. SC: le.

Beran, Roy G. Legal and ethical obligations to conduct a clinical drug trial in Australia as an investigator initiated and sponsored study for an overseas pharmaceutical company. *Medicine and Law: World Association for Medical Law* 2004; 23(4): 913-924. NRCBL: 18.2; 9.7; 18.5.9. SC: le.

Abstract: Most multi-centre trials are both financed and sponsored by the pharmaceutical company involved. What follows will map the path adopted for an investigator initiated and sponsored study for a new indication of an established medication. The chief investigators of a company-sponsored, investigator-initiated, multi-centre, placebo- controlled study of an established medication, Pharmaceutical Benefit Scheme (PBS) listed for treatment of one condition but trialled in the management of another condition (trial of off-label use), were approached to submit a protocol to repeat the type of study with a different compound. The new study would test a different agent, also PBS listed, for the same condition as in the initial study and with the same off-licence application. The company would finance the study, provide the medication and matched placebo but only review the investigator-initiated protocol which would be sponsored by the principal investigator. This required the investigator to implement the trial, as would normally be done by the pharmaceutical company, yet also act as its principal investigator. The principal investigator, with colleagues and a Clinical Research Organisation (CRO), developed a protocol, adapted for the new agent, and submitted it for approval. Upon acceptance a contract was negotiated with the pharmaceutical company which had to overcome jurisdictional conflicts between common law and civil law legal systems. A CRO was contracted to undertake administrative functions which dictated special contractual agreements to overcome possible conflicts of interest for a sponsor/investigator to protect patient interests. There was need to find indemnification insurance with jurisdictional problems, co-investigators, ethics committee approvals and finance management as just some of the difficulties encountered. The paper will outline how these obstacles were overcome and how ethical and legal issues were respected through compromise. The ethical and legal obligations were addressed in a fashion which allowed the conduct of a trial adopting a proven methodology but novel infrastructure such that it was a totally independent study with regards conduct and reporting of final data, irrespective of the results being either positive or negative. This may represent a more acceptable way to ensure that future clinical trials are devoid of undue influence from the pharmaceutical industry which may still fund the study.

Beyleveld, Deryck; Townend, David M.R. When is personal data rendered anonymous? Interpreting Recital 26 of Directive 95/46/EC. *Medical Law International* 2004; 6(2): 73-86. NRCBL: 18.2; 8.4. SC: le.

Canadian Institutes of Health Research. Ottawa Group; Krleza-Jeric, Karmela; Chan, An-Wen; Dickersin, Kay; Sim, Ida; Grimshaw, Jeremy; Gluud, Christian. Principles for international registration of protocol information and results from human trials of health related interventions: Ottawa statement (Part 1). *BMJ: British Medical Journal* 2005 April 23; 330(7497): 956-958. NRCBL: 18.2; 18.6; 21.1. SC: le.

Carr, David M. Pfizer's epidemic: a need for international regulation of human experimentation in developing countries. *Case Western Reserve Journal of International Law* 2003 Winter; 35(1): 15-53. NRCBL: 18.2; 21.1; 18.1; 18.3; 1.3.9; 9.7; 1.3.2. SC: le.

Coleman, Carl H. Rationalizing risk assessment in human subject research. *Arizona Law Review* 2004; 46(1): 1-51. NRCBL: 18.2; 18.6; 5.2. SC: le.

Currie, Peter M. Balancing privacy protections with efficient research: institutional review boards and the use of certificates of confidentiality. *IRB: Ethics and Human Research* 2005 September-October; 27(5): 7-12. NRCBL: 18.2; 8.4. SC: le.

Dawson, John; Foley, Mary; Peart, Nicola. Research ethics committees. *In:* Dawson, John; Peart, Nicola, eds. The Law of Research: A Guide. Dunedin, NZ: University of Otago Press; 2003: 47-60. NRCBL: 18.2. SC: le.

Dinsdale, Henry. Professional responsibility and the protection of human subjects of research in Canada. *Health*

Law Review 2005; 13(2-3): 80-85. NRCBL: 18.2; 18.6; 7.1. SC: le.

Downie, Jocelyn; McDonald, Fiona. Revisioning the oversight of research involving humans in Canada. *Health Law Journal* 2004; 12: 159-181. NRCBL: 18.2; 18.6; 2.4. SC: le.

Downie, Jocelyn; Thompson, Jon; Baird, Patricia; Dodds, Susan. The Olivieri case: lessons for Australasia. *Journal of Bioethical Inquiry* 2005; 2(2): 90-105. NRCBL: 18.2; 18.3; 18.1; 9.7; 1.3.9; 18.6. SC: le; cs. Identifiers: Australia; New Zealand.

Abstract: The case of Dr. Nancy Olivieri, the Hospital for Sick Children, the University of Toronto, and Apotex Inc. vividly illustrates many of the issues central to contemporary health research and the safety of research participants. First, it exemplifies the financial and health stakes in such research. Second, it shows deficits in the ways in which research is governed. Finally, it was and remains relevant not only in Toronto but in communities across Canada and well beyond its borders because, absent appropriate policies, what happened in Toronto could have happened (and could well still happen) elsewhere. In Part One of this paper, we review the facts of the Olivieri case relevant to the issues we wish to highlight: first, the right of participants in a clinical trial to be informed of a risk that an investigator had identified during the course of the trial and the obligation of the investigator to inform participants (both her own and those of other investigators); and second, the obligation of institutions to protect and promote the well-being of research participants as well as academic freedom and research integrity, the obligations of research sponsors to inform participants, research regulators, and others about unforeseen risks, and the obligations of research regulators to ensure that participants are informed of unforeseen risks and to otherwise protect and promote research integrity. In Part Two, we relate these facts and issues to New Zealand and Australia. We also make detailed recommendations for changes to the various instruments used for the governance of research involving humans in Australasia.

Endacott, R. Clinical research 2: legal and ethical issues in research. *Intensive and Critical Care Nursing* 2004 October; 20(5): 313-315. NRCBL: 18.2. SC: le.

European Parliament; Council of the European Union. Directive 2001/20/EC of the European Parliament and of the Council of 4 April 2001 on the approximation of the laws, regulations and administrative provisions of the member states relating to the implementation of good clinical practice in the conduct of clinical trials on medicinal products for human use. *Medical Ethics and Bioethics / Medicinska Etika and Bioetika* 2002 Spring-Summer; 9(1-2): 12-19. NRCBL: 18.2; 9.7; 18.3; 18.5.2. SC: le.

Fisher, Celia B.; Kornetsky, Susan Z. SACHRP recommendations for review of children's research requiring DHHS secretary's approval. *IRB: Ethics and Human Research* 2005 May-June; 27(3): 8-10. NRCBL: 18.2; 18.6. SC: le. Identifiers: Secretary's Advisory Commission on Human Research Protections (SACHRP); Department of Health and Human Services (DHHS); Office of Human Research Protections (OHRP).

NRCBL: National Reference Center for Bioethics Literature Classification Scheme   See inside front cover for terms.

273

Fitzgerald, Daniel W.; Wasunna, Angela. Away from exploitation and towards engagement: an ethical compass for medical researchers working in resource-poor countries. *Journal of Law, Medicine and Ethics* 2005 Fall; 33(3): 559-565. NRCBL: 18.2; 2.1; 18.5.9. SC: cs; le.

Gandhi, Rupali. Research involving children: regulations, review boards and reform. *Journal of Health Care Law and Policy* 2005; 8(2): 264-330. NRCBL: 18.2; 18.5.2; 18.3. SC: le.

Gatter, Robert. Walking the talk of trust in human subjects research: the challenge of regulating financial conflicts of interest. *Emory Law Journal* 2003 Winter; 52(1): 327-401. NRCBL: 18.2; 18.6; 1.3.9; 1.3.2; 5.3. SC: le.

Gold, Jennifer L. Watching the watchdogs: negligence liability, and research ethics boards. *Health Law Journal* 2003; 11: 153-176. NRCBL: 18.2; 8.5; 18.3. SC: le.

Hadskis, Michael; Carver, Peter. The long arm of administrative law: applying administrative law principles to research ethics boards. *Health Law Review* 2005; 13(2-3): 19-32. NRCBL: 18.2; 18.6. SC: le.

Harris, John. Ethical genetic research on human subjects. *Jurimetrics* 1999 Fall; 40: 77-91. NRCBL: 18.2; 15.1. SC: le.

Hazard, Gregory. Please, sir, I want some more: Congress' carrot-and-stick approach to pediatric testing leaves therapeutic orphans needing more protection. *Journal of Contemporary Health Law and Policy* 2004 Spring; 20(2): 467-508. NRCBL: 18.2; 18.5.2; 8.3.2; 9.7. SC: le.

Hirtle, Marie. The governance of research involving human participants in Canada. *Health Law Journal* 2003; 11: 137-152. NRCBL: 18.2; 18.6. SC: le.

Hodge, James G., Jr. An enhanced approach to distinguishing public health practice and human subjects research. *Journal of Law, Medicine and Ethics* 2005 Spring; 33(1): 125- 141. NRCBL: 18.2; 9.1; 8.4. SC: le.

Hoffman, Sharona. Continued concern: human subject protection, the institutional review board, and continuing review. *Tennessee Law Review* 2001 Summer; 68(4): 725-770. NRCBL: 18.2; 18.6. SC: le.

Ibata, Brent. Institutional review and clinical research — proactive IRBs and risk reduction. *Medical Trial Technique Quarterly* 2002; 48(3): 253-270. NRCBL: 18.2; 18.3. SC: le. Identifiers: institutional review boards.

Jordan, Karen A. Financial conflicts of interest in human subjects research: proposals for a more effective regulatory scheme. *Washington and Lee Law Review* 2003 Winter; 60(1): 15-109. NRCBL: 18.2; 1.3.9; 7.3. SC: le.

Katerberg, Robert J. Institutional review boards, research on children, and informed consent of parents: walking the tightrope between encouraging vital

experimentation and protecting subjects' rights. *Journal of College and University Law* 1998 Winter; 24(3): 545-579. NRCBL: 18.2; 18.5.2; 18.3; 8.3.2. SC: le.

Kopelman, Loretta M. What conditions justify risky nontherapeutic or "no benefit" pediatric studies: a sliding scale analysis. *Journal of Law, Medicine and Ethics* 2004 Winter; 32(4): 749- 758. NRCBL: 18.2; 18.5.2; 5.2. SC: le.

Laufer, Suzie. The regulation of medical/scientific research practices involving experimentation on human beings. *Law in Context* 1990; 8(1): 78-105. NRCBL: 18.2. SC: le. Identifiers: Australia.

Lavery, James V. Putting international research ethics guidelines to work for the benefit of developing countries. *Yale Journal of Health Policy, Law, and Ethics* 2004 Summer; 4(2): 319-336. NRCBL: 18.2; 21.1; 18.6. SC: le.

Lavery, James V.; McDonald, Michael; Meslin, Eric M. Research ethics across the 49th parallel: the potential value of pilot testing "equivalent protections" in Canadian research institutions. *Health Law Review* 2005; 13(2-3): 86-96. NRCBL: 18.2; 21.1. SC: le.

Lemmens, Trudo. Federal regulation of REB review of clinical trials: a modest but easy step towards an accountable REB review structure in Canada. *Health Law Review* 2005; 13(2-3): 39-50. NRCBL: 18.2; 18.6. SC: le. Identifiers: research ethics boards.

Lemmens, Trudo. Leopards in the temple: restoring scientific integrity to the commercialized research scene. *Journal of Law, Medicine and Ethics* 2004 Winter; 32(4): 641- 657. NRCBL: 18.2; 1.3.9; 7.3; 5.3; 18.6; 9.7. SC: le.

Levine, Robert J. International codes of research ethics: current controversies and the future. *Indiana Law Review* 2002; 35(2): 557-567. NRCBL: 18.2; 21.1. SC: le.

Maloney, Dennis M. University ordered to halt human research [case study]. *Human Research Report* 2005 April; 20(4): 6-7. NRCBL: 18.2; 1.3.3; 18.6. SC: le; cs.

Margolin, Gayla; Chien, Deborah; Duman, Sarah E.; Fauchier, Angele; Gordis, Elana B.; Oliver, Pamella H.; Ramos, Michelle C.; Vickerman, Katrina A. Ethical issues in couple and family research. *Journal of Family Psychology* 2005 March; 19(1): 157-167. NRCBL: 18.2; 18.3; 18.5.2; 17.2; 8.4; 1.3.12. SC: le.

McLean, Sheila A.M. Regulating research and experimentation: a view from the UK. *Journal of Law, Medicine and Ethics* 2004 Winter; 32(4): 604- 612. NRCBL: 18.2; 18.3; 18.6. SC: le.

Peart, Nicola; McCrimmon, Fiona; Dawson, John. Clinical trials. *In:* Dawson, John; Peart, Nicola, eds. The Law of Research: A Guide. Dunedin, NZ: University of Otago Press; 2003: 175-195. NRCBL: 18.2. SC: le.

Pullman, Daryl. Research governance, bio-politics and political will: recent lessons from Newfoundland and Labrador. *Health Law Review* 2005; 13(2-3): 75-79. NRCBL: 18.2. SC: le.

Resnik, D.B. Eliminating the daily life risks standard from the definition of minimal risk. *Journal of Medical Ethics* 2005 January; 31(1): 35-38. NRCBL: 18.2. SC: le. Identifiers: United States.

Ross, Lainie Friedman. Lessons to be learned from the 407 process. *Health Matrix: Journal of Law-Medicine* 2005 Summer; 15(2): 401-421. NRCBL: 18.2; 18.5.2. SC: le.

Schatz, Gerald S. Are the rationale and regulatory system for protecting human subjects of biomedical and behavioral research obsolete and unworkable, or ethically important but inconvenient and inadequately enforced? *Journal of Contemporary Health Law and Policy* 2003 Winter; 20(1): 1-31. NRCBL: 18.2; 18.6. SC: le.

Sharp, Richard R.; Foster, Morris W. Community involvement in the ethical review of genetic research: lessons from American Indian and Alaska Native populations. *Environmental Justice* 2002 April; 110(supplement 2): 145-148. NRCBL: 18.2; 2.4; 7.1. SC: le.

Shaul, Randi Zlotnik; Birenbaum, Shelley; Evans, Megan. Legal liabilities in research: early lessons from North America. *BMC Medical Ethics [electronic].* 2005; 6(4); 4 p. Available: http://www.biomedcentral.com/bmcmedethics/ [6 September 2005]. NRCBL: 18.2. SC: le.
Abstract: The legal risks associated with health research involving human subjects have been highlighted recently by a number of lawsuits launched against those involved in conducting and evaluating the research. Some of these cases have been fully addressed by the legal system, resulting in judgments that provide some guidance. The vast majority of cases have either settled before going to trial, or have not yet been addressed by the courts, leaving us to wonder what might have been and what guidance future cases may bring. What is striking about the lawsuits that have been commenced is the broad range of individuals/institutions that are named as defendants and the broad range of allegations that are made. The research community should take this early experience as a warning and should reflect carefully on practices where research involving human subjects is concerned.

Sheikh, Asim A. The Data Protection (Amendment) Act, 2003: the Data Protection Directive and its implications for medical research in Ireland. *European Journal of Health Law* 2005 December; 12(4): 357-372. NRCBL: 18.2; 18.3; 8.4; 1.3.12. SC: le.

Sprumont, Dominique; Gytis, Andrulionis. The importance of national laws in the implementation of European legislation of biomedical research. *European Journal of Health Law* 2005 September; 12(3): 245- 267. NRCBL: 18.2; 21.1; 18.6; 5.3. SC: le; an.

Tipene-Matua, Bevan; Dawson, John. The Treaty of Waitangi and research. *In:* Dawson, John; Peart, Nicola, eds. The Law of Research: A Guide. Dunedin, NZ: University of Otago Press; 2003: 61-79. NRCBL: 18.2. SC: le.

Zimmerman, Susan V. Translating ethics into law: duties of care in health research involving humans. *Health Law Review* 2005; 13(2-3): 13-18. NRCBL: 18.2; 18.6. SC: le.

HUMAN EXPERIMENTATION/ INFORMED CONSENT
See also INFORMED CONSENT

How volunteering for an MRI scan changed my life: discovering a serious problem not only causes shock but can have financial implications [letter]. *Nature* 2005 March 3; 434(7029): 17. NRCBL: 18.3; 17.1.

Adamis, D.; Martin, F.C.; Treloar, A.; Macdonald, A.J.D. Capacity, consent, and selection bias in a study of delirium. *Journal of Medical Ethics* 2005 March; 31(3): 137-143. NRCBL: 18.3; 18.5.7. SC: em.
Abstract: OBJECTIVES: To investigate whether different methods of obtaining informed consent affected recruitment to a study of delirium in older, medically ill hospital inpatients. DESIGN: Open randomised study. SETTING: Acute medical service for older people in an inner city teaching hospital. PARTICIPANTS: Patients 70 years or older admitted to the unit within three days of hospital admission randomised into two groups. INTERVENTION: Attempted recruitment of subjects to a study of the natural history of delirium. This was done by either (a) a formal test of capacity, followed by either a request for consent or an attempt at obtaining assent from a proxy, or (b) a combined informal capacity/consent process. MAIN OUTCOME MEASURES: Prevalence and severity of delirium, and, as case mix measures, length of hospital stay and destination on discharge. RESULTS: Recruitment of subjects through establishing formal capacity and then informed consent was less successful (43.9% v 74% of those approached) and, compared with those recruited through the usual combined capacity/consent approach, yielded a sample with less cognitive impairment, lower severity of delirium, lower probability of case note diagnosis of delirium and lower rate of entering a care home. CONCLUSIONS: Methods of obtaining informed consent may significantly influence the case mix of subjects recruited to a study of delirium. Stringent testing of capacity may exclude patients with delirium from studies, thus rendering findings less generalizable. A different method is necessary to achieve an ethical balance between respecting autonomy through obtaining adequate informed consent and avoiding sample bias.

Ågård, Anders; Herlitz, J.; Hermerén, G. Obtaining informed consent from patients in the early phase of acute myocardial infarction: physicians' experiences and attitudes. *Heart* 2004 February 1; 90(2): 208-210. NRCBL: 18.3; 7.1. SC: em. Identifiers: Sweden.

Al-Shahi, Rustam; Vousden, Céline; Warlow, Charles. Bias from requiring explicit consent from all participants in observational research: prospective, population based study. *BMJ: British Medical Journal* 2005 October 22; 331(7522): 942- 945. NRCBL: 18.3. Identifiers: Scottish Intracranial Vascular Malformation Study (SIVMS) Steering Committee.
Abstract: OBJECTIVE: To evaluate the differences between adults who consent to participate in observational research, and

---

NRCBL: National Reference Center for Bioethics Literature Classification Scheme   See inside front cover for terms.

275

those who do not. DESIGN: Prospective, population based co-hort study. SETTING: Primary and secondary care throughout Scotland. PARTICIPANTS: 187 adults (aged or = 16 years) resident in Scotland at the time of their first diagnosis of a brain arteriovenous malformation in 1999-2002. INTERVENTION: Postal consent form sent via participants' general practitioner. MAIN OUTCOME MEASURES: Differences between consenters and non-consenters in demographic and clinical features at first presentation, and outcome during follow-up. RESULTS: 111 adults (59%) consented to participate in the study. These consenters were not significantly different from non-consenters in age, sex, or socioeconomic status at first presentation. However, consenters were significantly more likely than non-consenters to present alive and independent, and with a seizure. During follow- up, consenters were significantly more likely to receive interventional treatment. Although consenters' survival was significantly better, they were more likely to have a seizure during follow-up. Presentation with intracranial haemorrhage conferred a higher risk of subsequent haemorrhage when the whole cohort was analysed, but not when it was restricted to consenters. CONCLUSIONS: We have found differences between adults who consent to participate in observational records-based research and those who do not, or cannot, consent. Blanket requirements for explicit consent for the use of individuals' identifiable data can bias disease registers, epidemiological studies, and health services research.

Andanda, Pamela. Module two: informed consent. *Developing World Bioethics* 2005 March; 5(1): 14-29. NRCBL: 18.3; 2.3.

Abstract: The objective of this module is to familiarise you with the concept of informed consent, its ethical basis, its elements, and typical problems that are encountered even by the most well intentioned researchers when trying to achieve genuine informed consent.

Baldwin, David; Broich, Karl; Fritze, Jürgen; Kasper, Siegfried; Westenberg, Herman; Möller, Hans-Jürgen. Placebo-controlled studies in depression: necessary, ethical and feasible. *European Archives of Psychiatry and Clinical Neuroscience* 2003 February; 253(1): 22-28. NRCBL: 18.3; 18.2; 17.1; 18.5.1.

Barker, Jeffrey H. Human experimentation and the double facelessness of a merciless epoch. *New York University Review of Law and Social Change* 1999; 25(4): 603-623. NRCBL: 18.3; 2.2. SC: le.

Bhutta, Zulfiqar A. Beyond informed consent. *Bulletin of the World Health Organization* 2004 October; 82(10): 771-777. NRCBL: 18.3; 18.2; 21.7.

Biros, Michelle H. Research without consent: current status, 2003. *Annals of Emergency Medicine* 2003 October; 42(4): 550-564. NRCBL: 18.3; 8.3.5.

Biros, Michelle H. Waiver of consent for emergency research [reply]. *Annals of Emergency Medicine* 2004 September; 44(3): 278-280. NRCBL: 18.3; 18.6.

Blixen, Carol E.; Agich, G.J. Stroke patients' preferences and values about emergency research. *Journal of Medical Ethics* 2005 October; 31(10): 608-611. NRCBL: 18.3; 18.5.1. SC: em.

Abstract: BACKGROUND: In the USA, the Food and Drug Administration waiver of informed consent permits certain emergency research only if community consultation occurs. However, uncertainty exists regarding how to define the community(ies) or their representatives. OBJECTIVE: To collect data on the actual preferences and values of a group-those at risk for stroke-most directly affected by the waiver of informed consent for emergency research. DESIGN: Face to face focused interviews were conducted with 12 patients who were hospitalised with a stroke diagnosis in the previous year. The interviews were audiotaped and a transcript based method was used for their analysis. RESULTS: All 12 participants felt "that it was important that new treatments for stroke be developed", but they were initially confused about the distinction between "research for stroke" and "emergency research for stroke". However, after explanation, most (n = 10; 83%) expressed willingness to participate in the latter. In the absence of a surrogate to give informed consent in a stroke emergency situation, the majority (n = 11; 92%) said they would want the physician to "go ahead and enrol them in the trial". CONCLUSIONS: This study is the first to identify the values and concerns of individuals most directly affected by stroke emergency research. Further interviews and focus groups are needed to develop and test a validated questionnaire on the preferences and values surrounding emergency research for stroke.

Bloch, Sidney; Salzberg, Michael. Informed consent in psychiatric research. *Current Opinion in Psychiatry* 2003 November; 16(6): 679-684. NRCBL: 18.3; 18.5.6.

Bramstedt, Katrina A. Failure mode and effects analysis as an informed consent tool for investigational cardiothoracic devices. *ASAIO Journal* 2002; 48: 293-295. NRCBL: 18.3; 9.7; 9.5.1.

Bramstedt, Katrina A. Informed consent documentation for total artificial heart technology. *Update [Loma Linda University Center for Christian Bioethics]* 2002 May; 17(4): 5-8. NRCBL: 18.3; 19.2.

Brender, Erin. Supporting medical research. *JAMA: The Journal of the American Medical Association* 2005 September 21; 294(11): 1454. NRCBL: 18.3. SC: po.

Brody, Howard. The welcome reassessment of research ethics: is "undue inducement" suspect? [comment]. *American Journal of Bioethics* 2005 September-October; 5(5): 15-16. NRCBL: 18.3; 9.3.1. Comments: comment on Ezekiel J. Emanuel, "Undue inducement: nonsense on stilts?" American Journal of Bioethics 2005 September-October; 5(5): 9-13.

Brown, R.F.; Butow, P.N.; Ellis, P.; Boyle, F.; Tattersall, M.H.N. Seeking informed consent to cancer clinical trials: describing current practice. *Social Science and Medicine* 2004 June; 58(12): 2445-2457. NRCBL: 18.3; 18.2. SC: em. Identifiers: Australia.

Bruinsma, Fiona; Venn, Alison; Skene, Loane. Accessing patients' records without individual consent for epidemiological research. *Journal of Law and Medicine* 2000 August; 8(1): 76-80. NRCBL: 18.3; 8.4; 1.3.12. SC: le.

Brull, Richard; McCartney, Colin J.L.; Chan, Vincent W.S.; Chung, Frances; Rawson, Regan. Are patients

---

comfortable consenting to clinical anesthesia research trials on the day of surgery? *Anesthesia and Analgesia* 2004 April; 98(4): 1106-1110. NRCBL: 18.3. SC: em. Identifiers: Canada.

Capron, Alexander Morgan. Informed consent in catastrophic disease research and treatment. *University of Pennsylvania Law Review* 1974 December; 123(2): 340-438. NRCBL: 18.3; 1.1; 2.2; 8.3.1; 19.2. SC: le. Identifiers: Haskell Karp; Denton Cooley.

Caulfield, Timothy. Legal and ethical issues associated with patient recruitment in clinical trials: the case of competitive enrolment. *Health Law Review* 2005; 13(2-3): 58-61. NRCBL: 18.3; 18.2. SC: le.

Caulfield, Timothy; Ries, Nola M. Consent, privacy and confidentiality in longitudinal, population health research: the Canadian legal context. *Health Law Journal* 2004; (Supplement): 1-65. NRCBL: 18.3; 13.1; 8.4; 21.1. SC: le.

Chen, Donna T.; Rosenstein, Donald L.; Muthappan, Palaniappan; Hilsenbeck, Susan G.; Miller, Franklin G.; Emanuel, Ezekiel J.; Wendler, David. Research with stored biological samples: what do research participants want? *Archives of Internal Medicine* 2005 March 28; 165(6): 652-655. NRCBL: 18.3; 19.5; 15.1. SC: em.
Abstract: BACKGROUND: There is widespread disagreement about the type of consent needed for research with stored biological samples. Many believe consent for each future use is required to respect individuals. Others worry this approach may block important research. METHODS: We analyzed 1670 consent forms signed by research participants at the Warren G. Magnuson Clinical Center, National Institutes of Health, between January 1, 2000, and May 31, 2002, that offer options for future research with participants' biological samples. The research participants were healthy volunteers, family members of affected individuals, and individuals with a broad range of medical conditions enrolled in clinical research studies with and without the prospect of direct medical benefit. RESULTS: Overall, 87.1% of research participants given the option chose to authorize future research on any medical condition. More than 85% permitted unlimited future research with their stored biological samples regardless of sex, age, geographic location, or whether the individual was affected by the disease being studied or a healthy volunteer. Only 6.7% of those given the option to refuse all future research did so. Although African Americans were less likely to permit future research, 75.0% of African Americans still authorized unlimited future research with their samples. CONCLUSIONS: Most research participants authorize the unlimited future research use of their biological samples when given the opportunity to do so. These findings suggest that providing research participants with a simple binary choice to authorize or refuse all future research might allow individuals to control use of their samples, simplify consent forms, and allow important research to proceed.

Corbie-Smith, Giselle; Arriola, Kimberly R. Jacob. Research and ethics: a legacy of distrust. *In:* Braithwaite, Ronald L.; Taylor, Sandra E., eds. Health Issues in the Black Community. 2nd ed. San Francisco: Jossey-Bass; 2001: 489-502. NRCBL: 18.3; 18.5.1.

Corrigan, Oonagh. Empty ethics: the problem with informed consent. *Sociology of Health and Illness* 2003 November; 25(3): 768-792. NRCBL: 18.3; 18.2; 2.1. SC: em.

CRASH Trial Management Group. Research in emergency situations: with or without relatives consent. *Emergency Medicine Journal* 2004 November; 21(6): 703. NRCBL: 18.3. SC: em.

Cyranoski, David. Consenting adults? Not necessarily . . . [news]. *Nature* 2005 May 12; 435(7039): 138-139. NRCBL: 18.3; 18.5.9; 18.6. Identifiers: China.

Dawson, A.; Spencer, S.A. Informing children and parents about research. *Archives of Disease in Childhood* 2005 March; 90(3): 233-235. NRCBL: 18.3; 18.5.2.

Dawson, Angus. What should we do about it? Implications of the empirical evidence in relation to comprehension and acceptability of randomisation. *In:* Holm, Søren; Jonas, Monique F., eds. Engaging the World: The Use of Empirical Research in Bioethics and the Regulation of Biotechnology. Washington, DC: IOS Press; 2004: 41-52. NRCBL: 18.3. SC: em.

de Souza, Eustace J. Custody, ownership and confidentiality: there are many ethical concerns regarding human tissues. *Issues in Medical Ethics* 1999 January-March; 7(1): 19-20. NRCBL: 18.3; 8.4; 9.5.6.

Devi, Sharmila. Research scandal forces Israel to tighten up supervision. *Lancet* 2005 June 4-10; 365(9475): 1915. NRCBL: 18.3; 18.5.2; 18.5.7; 18.6.

Dickert, Neal; Kass, Nancy; Paasche-Orlow, Michael; Taylor, Holly. Excluding particular information from consent forms. *Accountability in Research* 2005 January-March; 12(1): 33-45. NRCBL: 18.3; 18.2; 9.5.6; 18.5.9. SC: an.
Abstract: Although the informed consent process is crucial to protecting human research subjects, there are cases when particular information within the consent form may present risks to those subjects. In this paper, we examine a case in which including the sponsor's name on the consent form may allow the form to serve as a surrogate for subjects' HIV status. There is no literature addressing the ethical acceptability of excluding particular information from consent forms, and there exists little regulatory guidance on this issue. We argue that excluding information from the consent form is, in fact, obligatory when that information is disclosed orally during the consent process but its presence on the form poses risks to the subjects the consent process is designed to protect. Further, we argue that the regulations ought to be amended to reflect this obligation.

Dunn, Laura B.; Gordon, Nora E. Improving informed consent and enhancing recruitment for research by understanding economic behavior. *JAMA: The Journal of the American Medical Association* 2005 February 2; 293(5): 609-612. NRCBL: 18.3; 9.3.1; 18.6.

Earl, Catherine E.; Penney, Pamela J. The significance of trust in the research consent process with African Amer-

NRCBL: National Reference Center for Bioethics Literature Classification Scheme   See inside front cover for terms.

277

icans. *Western Journal of Nursing Research* 2001 November; 23(7): 753-762. NRCBL: 18.3; 9.5.4; 8.2; 8.1; 18.5.1.

Edwards, Adrian; Elwyn, Glyn. Involving patients in decision making and communicating risk: a longitudinal evaluation of doctors' attitudes and confidence during a randomized trial. *Journal of Evaluation in Clinical Practice* 2004 August; 10(3): 431-437. NRCBL: 18.3; 8.1. SC: em. Identifiers: United Kingdom (Great Britain).

Edwards, Sarah J.L. Research participation and the right to withdraw. *Bioethics* 2005 April; 19(2): 112-130. NRCBL: 18.3; 1.1. SC: an.

Abstract: Most ethics committees which review research protocols insist that potential research participants reserve unconditional or absolute 'right' of withdrawal at any time and without giving any reason. In this paper, I examine what consent means for research participation and a sense of commitment in relation to this right to withdraw. I suggest that, once consent has been given (and here I am excluding incompetent minors and adults), participants should not necessarily have unconditional or absolute rights to withdraw. This does not imply that there should be a complete absence of rights, or, indeed, an abandonment of the right to withdraw. The point of this paper is to show that the supposed unconditional or absolute nature of these rights may be self-defeating and so fail to respect the autonomy of participants. In addition, and on a more positive note, I suggest that, attaching certain conditions on the right to withdraw, may better respect the autonomy of these participants by underlining the idea that autonomy is more than mere whim or indifference to the fate of others. On the contrary, research staff are currently unable to 'push' participants, who may merely have logistical difficulties unrelated to the research itself, but who really want to stay the course, for fear of coercing them. Furthermore, researchers now try to 'screen out' people they think may be unreliable to protect the science of the study and so groups at risk of dropping out may be unfairly denied access to research treatments. I conclude that on-going negotiation between the relevant parties could be on balance the only truly acceptable way forward but concede certain important limitations to take into account.

Emanuel, Ezekiel J. Response to commentators on "Undue inducement: nonsense on stilts?" [letter]. *American Journal of Bioethics [Online]* 2005 September- October; 5(5): W8-W11. NRCBL: 18.3; 18.2; 9.3.1.

Emanuel, Ezekiel J. Undue inducement: nonsense on stilts? *American Journal of Bioethics* 2005 September-October; 5(5): 9- 13. NRCBL: 18.3; 9.3.1; 18.2.

Eriksson, S.; Helgesson, Gert. Keep people informed or leave them alone? A suggested tool for identifying research participants who rightly want only limited information. *Journal of Medical Ethics* 2005 November; 31(11): 674-678. NRCBL: 18.3. SC: em.

Abstract: People taking part in research vary in the extent to which they understand information concerning their participation. Since they may choose to limit the time and effort spent on such information, lack of understanding is not necessarily an ethical problem. Researchers who notice a lack of understanding are in the quandary of not knowing whether this is due to flaws in the information process or to participants' deliberate choices. We argue that the two explanations call for different responses. A tool for identifying those research participants who want limited information is presented. This consists of a re-stricted number of questions about trust in and appraisal of research, priority of time and privacy, and perception of a duty to participate. It is argued that an important group of participants who purposely lack understanding of the study can be identified with this tool. Some limitations to this approach are also discussed.

Evans, H.M. Response to F.G. Miller and J.D. Moreno, "The state of research ethics: a tribute to John C. Fletcher". *Journal of Clinical Ethics* 2005 Winter; 16(4): 372-375. NRCBL: 18.3; 18.2; 1.1.

Farnell, Sheila M. Informed consent — east meets west — worlds apart? [opinion]. *Medical and Pediatric Oncology* 2002 March; 38(3): 201-202. NRCBL: 18.3; 18.2; 8.3.1; 8.2; 21.7.

Fost, Norman. Gather ye shibboleths while ye may [comment]. *American Journal of Bioethics* 2005 September-October; 5(5): 14-15. NRCBL: 18.3. Comments: comment on Ezekiel J. Emanuel, "Undue inducement: nonsense on stilts?" American Journal of Bioethics 2005 September-October; 5(5): 9-13.

Gammelgaard, Anne. An empirical study of the informed consent process of a clinical trial. *In:* Holm, Søren; Jonas, Monique F., eds. Engaging the World: The Use of Empirical Research in Bioethics and the Regulation of Biotechnology. Washington, DC: IOS Press; 2004: 99-108. NRCBL: 18.3. SC: em.

Glass, Kathleen Cranley; Waring, Duff. The physician/investigator's obligation to patients participating in research: the case of placebo controlled trials. *Journal of Law, Medicine and Ethics* 2005 Fall; 33(3): 575-585. NRCBL: 18.3; 18.2; 8.2; 8.5. SC: le.

Gold, E. Richard; Adams, Wendy A. Reconciling private benefit and public risk in biotechnology: xenotransplantation as a case study in consent. *Health Law Journal* 2002; 10: 31-75. NRCBL: 18.3; 19.1; 22.2; 9.4; 5.2; 5.3. SC: cs; le.

Greaves, Claire D.; Tindale, Wendy B. Implications of the UK NHS consent policy for nuclear medicine practice. *Nuclear Medicine Communications* 2005 February; 26(2): 167-174. NRCBL: 18.3. Identifiers: United Kingdom (Great Britain); National Health Service.

Green, J.B.; Duncan, R.E.; Barnes, G.L.; Oberklaid, F. Putting the 'informed' into 'consent': a matter of plain language. *Journal of Paediatrics and Child Health* 2003 December; 39(9): 700-703. NRCBL: 18.3; 18.5.2.

Grout, Gwyn. Using negotiated consent in research and practice. *Nursing Older People* 2004 June; 16(4): 18-20. NRCBL: 18.3; 17.1; 9.5.2; 8.3.3.

Hahn, D.L.; Burge, P.S.; Lewis, S.A. Ethics of placebo controlled studies of inhaled steroids for COPD [letter and reply]. *Thorax* 2004 June; 59(6): 539-540. NRCBL: 18.3. Identifiers: chronic obstructive pulmonary disease.

Halila, Ritva; Lötjönen, Salla. Children and medical research. *Medicine and Law: World Association for Medical Law* 2005 September; 24(3): 505-513. NRCBL: 18.3; 8.3.2; 18.2. SC: le.

Abstract: A considerable proportion of medical treatments for children are based on estimates and assumptions rather than clinical evidence. Clinical research on children provokes intensive discussion internationally. While children are protected from the risks of clinical trials, they are hindered from receiving the benefits of pharmaceutical innovations obtained by adults. The recruitment of children into research trials is more complicated than that of adults for several reasons: 1) the physical size and relative water content of the body differs not just compared to adults but also amongst subgroups of children making the group of potential participants relatively small; 2) diseases common among adults may be rare among children and vice versa; 3) children's ability to understand the significance of a study varies and depends on the age and developmental stage of the child; and 4) depending on the level of understanding, differing views have been given on the degree of respect that should be paid to a child's right to consent, assent, or refuse to participate in a trial. We suggest that: 1) the number of children recruited in research trials should be kept as small as possible, but large enough to enable scientifically valid results; 2) special training should be made mandatory for researchers who study diseases of children; 3) children or adolescents should participate in decision-making that concerns them whenever possible; and 4) in minor procedures, the consent of just one parent is sufficient.

Hardy, J.R. Placebo-controlled trials in palliative care: the argument for. *Palliative Medicine* 1997 September; 11(5): 415-418. NRCBL: 18.3; 4.4; 9.5.1.

Harth, S.C.; Thong, Y.H. Parental perceptions and attitudes about informed consent in clinical research involving children. *Social Science and Medicine* 1995 December; 41(12): 1647-1651. NRCBL: 18.3; 18.5.2. SC: em. Identifiers: Australia.

Hawkins, J.S. The ethics of Zelen consent [opinion]. *Journal of Thrombosis and Haemostasis* 2004 June; 2(6): 882-883. NRCBL: 18.3; 18.2.

Helgesson, Gert; Ludvigsson, J.; Gustafsson Stolt, U. How to handle informed consent in longitudinal studies when participants have a limited understanding of the study. *Journal of Medical Ethics* 2005 November; 31(11): 670-673. NRCBL: 18.3. SC: em.

Abstract: Empirical findings from a Swedish longitudinal screening study show that many of the research subjects had a limited understanding of the study. Nevertheless they were satisfied with the understanding they had and found it sufficient for informed continued participation. Were they wrong? In this paper, it is argued that the kind of understanding that is morally required depends partly on the kind of understanding on which the research subjects want to base their decisions, and partly on what kind of knowledge they lack. Researchers must ensure that the information process is not flawed and that participants receive the information they want. To achieve this, new information efforts may be needed. Researchers must also ensure that research subjects have knowledge about aspects of importance to them. Lack of understanding may, however, be the result of conscious choices by research subjects to disregard some of the information because it is not important to them. Such choices should normally be respected.

Hoeyer, Klaus. Ambiguous gifts: public anxiety, informed consent and biobanks. *In:* Tutton, Richard; Corrigan, Oonagh, eds. Genetic Databases: Socio-ethical Issues in the Collection and Use of DNA. New York: Routledge; 2004: 97-116. NRCBL: 18.3; 15.1; 13.12; 19.4.

Hoffmann, Diane E.; Schwartz, Jack; DeRenzo, Evan G. Regulating research with decisionally impaired individuals: are we making progress? *DePaul Journal of Health Care Law* 2000 Spring-Summer; 3(3-4): 547-608. NRCBL: 18.3; 18.5.6; 18.6; 8.3.3; 2.4. SC: le.

Iltis, Ana Smith. Timing invitations to participate in clinical research: preliminary versus informed consent. *Journal of Medicine and Philosophy* 2005 February; 30(1): 89-106. NRCBL: 18.3; 2.1; 4.1.2. SC: an.

Abstract: This article addresses the impact of the potential conflict between the roles of physicians who are both clinicians and researchers on the recruitment of persons into research trials. It has been proposed (1) that a physician breaches inter-role confidentiality when he or she uses information gathered in his or her clinical role to inform patients about trials for which they may be eligible and (2) that clinician-researchers should adopt a model of preliminary consent to be approached about research prior to commencing a clinical relationship. This article argues that even if we grant the legitimacy of inter-role confidentiality (which is open to question), there are circumstances in which other obligations physicians bear override the obligation of inter-role confidentiality. Moreover, it is argued that the practice of preliminary consent is morally suspect and that such consent cannot be deemed valid. The article concludes with a series of recommendations of ways in which the legitimate concern regarding the conflicting roles of clinician-researchers can be addressed in the recruitment stage of research.

Jairath, Nalini; Ulrich, Connie M.; Ley, Cathaleen. Ethical considerations in the recruitment of research subjects from hospitalized, cardiovascular patient populations. *Journal of Cardiovascular Nursing* 2005 January-February; 20(1): 56-61. NRCBL: 18.3; 18.5.1.

Javitt, Gail H. Old legacies and new paradigms: confusing "research" and "treatment" and its consequences in responding to emergent health threats. *Journal of Health Care Law and Policy* 2005; 8(1): 38-70. NRCBL: 18.3; 18.5.8; 9.7; 18.6. SC: le.

Joffe, Steven; Simon, Christian. Informed consent from the doctor? [case study]. *Hastings Center Report* 2004 July-August; 34(4): 12-13. NRCBL: 18.3; 8.3.2; 18.5.2. SC: cs.

Jones, James W.; McCullough, Laurence B. When does conventional surgical therapy become research? *Journal of Vascular Surgery* 2002 August; 35(8): 423-424. NRCBL: 18.3; 18.2. SC: cs.

Junghans, Cornelia; Feder, Gene; Hemingway, Harry; Timmis, Adam; Jones, Melvyn. Recruiting patients to medical research: double blind randomised trial of "opt-in" versus "opt-out" strategies. *BMJ: British Medical Journal* 2005 October 22; 331(7522): 940-942. NRCBL: 18.3; 18.2.

NRCBL: National Reference Center for Bioethics Literature Classification Scheme   See inside front cover for terms.

279

Abstract: OBJECTIVE: To evaluate the effect of opt-in compared with opt-out recruitment strategies on response rate and selection bias. DESIGN: Double blind randomised controlled trial. SETTING: Two general practices in England. PARTICIPANTS: 510 patients with angina. INTERVENTION: Patients were randomly allocated to an opt-in (asked to actively signal willingness to participate in research) or opt-out (contacted repeatedly unless they signalled unwillingness to participate) approach for recruitment to an observational prognostic study of patients with angina. MAIN OUTCOME MEASURES: Recruitment rate and clinical characteristics of patients. RESULTS: The recruitment rate, defined by clinic attendance, was 38% (96/252) in the opt-in arm and 50% (128/258) in the opt-out arm (P = 0.014). Once an appointment had been made, non-attendance at the clinic was similar (20% opt-in arm v 17% opt-out arm; P = 0.86). Patients in the opt-in arm had fewer risk factors (44% v 60%; P = 0.053), less treatment for angina (69% v 82%; P = 0.010), and less functional impairment (9% v 20%; P = 0.023) than patients in the opt-out arm. CONCLUSIONS: The opt-in approach to participant recruitment, increasingly required by ethics committees, resulted in lower response rates and a biased sample. We propose that the opt-out approach should be the default recruitment strategy for studies with low risk to participants.

Kalantri, S.P. Ethics of drug trials in India [letter]. *National Medical Journal of India* 2002 May-June; 15(3): 179. NRCBL: 18.3.

Kass, Nancy E.; Maman, Suzanne; Atkinson, Joan. Motivations, understanding, and voluntariness in international randomized trials. *IRB: Ethics and Human Research* 2005 November-December; 27(6): 1-8. NRCBL: 18.3; 9.5.6; 21.1. SC: em.

Katz, Jay. What are the functions of informed consent? *In his:* Experimentation with Human Beings: The Authority of the Investigator, Subject, Professions, and State in the Human Experimentation Process. New York: Russell Sage Foundation; 1972: 523-608. NRCBL: 18.3; 8.3.1. SC: le.

Katz, Jay. What limitations are inherent in informed consent? *In his:* Experimentation with Human Beings: The Authority of the Investigator, Subject, Professions, and State in the Human Experimentation Process. New York: Russell Sage Foundation; 1972: 609-673. NRCBL: 18.3; 8.3.1.

Katz, Jay. What limitations should be imposed on informed consent? *In his:* Experimentation with Human Beings: The Authority of the Investigator, Subject, Professions, and State in the Human Experimentation Process. New York: Russell Sage Foundation; 1972: 675-724. NRCBL: 18.3; 8.2. SC: le.

Kaye, Jane. Abandoning informed consent: the case of genetic research in population collections. *In:* Tutton, Richard; Corrigan, Oonagh, eds. Genetic Databases: Socio-ethical Issues in the Collection and Use of DNA. New York: Routledge; 2004: 117-138. NRCBL: 18.3; 15.1; 13.1; 8.4; 21.1.

Kent, Gerry. Shared understandings for informed consent: the relevance of psychological research on the provision of information. *Social Science and Medicine* 1996 November; 43(10): 1517-1523. NRCBL: 18.3; 8.3.1; 17.1.

Kimmelman, J.; Palmour, N. Therapeutic optimism in the consent forms of phase 1 gene transfer trials: an empirical analysis. *Journal of Medical Ethics* 2005 April; 31(4): 209-214. NRCBL: 18.3; 15.4. SC: em.
Abstract: BACKGROUND: "Therapeutic misconception" arises when human subjects interpret a clinical trial as aimed primarily at therapy rather than producing knowledge. Therapeutic misconceptions may be more prevalent in trials enrolling gravely ill subjects or involving novel and well publicized investigational agents. OBJECTIVE: To examine the extent to which investigators express therapeutic optimism in phase 1 human gene transfer consent documents, whether highly active gene transfer researchers are more prone to expressing therapeutic optimism, and whether consent forms have grown more optimistic in their descriptions of personal benefit over the last decade. DESIGN: Content analysis was performed on 277 consent documents to measure the number of sentences describing possibility of benefit, terminology used for experimental agents, the proportion of statements describing personal versus societal benefits, and whether investigators attempted to thwart therapeutic misconceptions. RESULTS: Consent forms generally used therapeutic terminology to describe study agents, devoted more sentences to describing possible personal benefits than to describing benefits to society, and infrequently explained that a particular benefit was unlikely. Consent documents used by highly active gene transfer researchers tended to portray significantly greater optimism about personal benefit than less active investigators, though they were also significantly more cautious with agent terminology. Finally, therapeutic optimism expressed in consent forms has declined over the past decade. CONCLUSIONS: Consent documents used in phase 1 gene transfer trials, although increasingly attentive to possible therapeutic misconceptions, are inappropriately optimistic about direct benefits of trial participation. Such optimism is expressed more emphatically in trials involving highly active gene transfer researchers as principal investigators.

King, Kevin M. A proposal for the effective international regulation of biomedical research involving human subjects. *Stanford Journal of International Law* 1998 Winter; 34(1): 163-206. NRCBL: 18.3; 18.2; 21.1. SC: le.

King, Nancy M.P.; Henderson, Gail E.; Churchill, Larry R.; Davis, Arlene M.; Hull, Sara Chandros; Nelson, Daniel K.; Parham-Vetter, P. Christy; Rothschild, Barbra Bluestone; Easter, Michele M.; Wilfond, Benjamin S. Consent forms and the therapeutic misconception: the example of gene transfer research. *IRB: Ethics and Human Research* 2005 January-February; 27(1): 1-8. NRCBL: 18.3; 15.4. SC: em.

Klitzman, Robert. The importance of social, cultural, and economic contexts, and empirical research in examining "undue inducement" [comment]. *American Journal of Bioethics* 2005 September-October; 5(5): 19-21. NRCBL: 18.3; 18.2; 9.3.1. Comments: comment on Ezekiel J. Emanuel, "Undue inducement: nonsense on stilts?" American Journal of Bioethics 2005 September-October; 5(5): 9-13.

Knoppers, Bartha Maria. Consent revisited: points to consider. *Health Law Review* 2005; 13(2-3): 33-38. NRCBL: 18.3; 15.10; 8.3.3; 19.5; 8.4.

Lamb, H. Richard. Commentary: on research and forensic patients' capacity. *Journal of the American Academy of Psychiatry and the Law* 2005; 33(3): 308-309. NRCBL: 18.3; 18.5.1; 18.5.6.

Leadbeatter, Stephen; Williams, Dillwyn; Cross, Simon; Start, Roger; Cotton, Dennis; Slater, David. Human tissue research: is legislation needed? [letters and reply]. *British Journal of Hospital Medicine* 1994 February 2-15; 51(3): 132-133. NRCBL: 18.3; 8.2; 18.5.1; 15.8.

Lemmens, Trudo; Sprumont, Dominique; Nys, Herman; Singh, Jerome; Glass, Kathleen Cranley. CIOMS' placebo rule and the promotion of negligent medical practice. *European Journal of Health Law* 2004 June; 11(2): 153-174. NRCBL: 18.3; 18.2; 21.1; 18.6. SC: le; an. Identifiers: Council of International Organizations of Medical Sciences.

Lertsithichai, Panuwat. Waiver of consent in clinical observational research. *Journal of the Medical Association of Thailand* 2005 February; 88(2): 275-281. NRCBL: 18.3; 18.2; 9.5.1.

LoBiondo, Anthony R. Patient autonomy and biomedical research: judicial compromise in Moore v. Regents of the University of California. *Albany Law Journal of Science and Technology* 1991; 1: 277-305. NRCBL: 18.3; 8.2; 4.4. SC: le.

Loder, Elizabeth; Goldstein, R.; Biondi, D. Placebo effects in oral triptan trials: the scientific and ethical rationale for continued use of placebo controls. *Cephalalgia* 2005 February; 25(2): 124-131. NRCBL: 18.3. SC: em.

London, Alex John. Undue inducements and reasonable risks: will the dismal science lead to dismal research ethics? [comment]. *American Journal of Bioethics* 2005 September-October; 5(5): 29-32. NRCBL: 18.3; 9.3.1; 18.2. Comments: comment on Ezekiel J. Emanuel, "Undue inducement: nonsense on stilts?" American Journal of Bioethics 2005 September-October; 5(5): 9-13.

Luce, John M. Research ethics and consent in the intensive care unit. *Current Opinion in Critical Care* 2003 December; 9(6): 540-544. NRCBL: 18.3; 8.1; 21.1. SC: em.

Lurie, Peter; Wolfe, Sidney M. Should research ethics change at the border? [letter]. *Medical Journal of Australia* 1999 August 2; 171(3): 167-168. NRCBL: 18.3; 18.2; 9.5.6; 21.1; 18.6.

Lynöe, N.; Hoeyer, K. Quantitative aspects of informed consent: considering the dose response curve when estimating quantity of information. *Journal of Medical Ethics* 2005 December; 31(12): 736-738. NRCBL: 18.3. SC: em.
Abstract: Information is usually supposed to be a prerequisite for people making decisions on whether or not to participate in a clinical trial. Previously conducted studies and research ethics scandals indicate that participants have sometimes lacked important pieces of information. Over the past few decades the quantity of information believed to be adequate has increased significantly, and in some instances a new maxim seems to be in place: the more information, the better the ethics in terms of respecting a participant's autonomy. The authors hypothesise that the dose-response curve from pharmacology or toxicology serves as a model to illustrate that a large amount of written information does not equal optimality. Using the curve as a pedagogical analogy when teaching ethics to students in clinical sciences, and also in engaging in dialogue with research institutions, may promote reflection on how to adjust information in relation to the preferences of individual participants, thereby transgressing the maxim that more information means better ethics.

Lynöe, Niels; Näsström, Birgit; Sandlund, Mikael. Study of the quality of information given to patients participating in a clinical trial regarding chronic hemodialysis. *Scandinavian Journal of Urology and Nephrology* 2004; 38(6): 517-520. NRCBL: 18.3. SC: em. Identifiers: Sweden.

Lynöe, Niels; Sandlund, Mikael; Jacobsson, Lars; Nordberg, Gunnar; Jin, Taiyi. Informed consent in China: quality of information provided to participants in a research project. *Scandinavian Journal of Public Health* 2004; 32(6): 472-475. NRCBL: 18.3; 18.2. SC: em.

Maloney, Dennis M. Complaint alleges "coercion" and "undue influence" in IRB-approved consent form. *Human Research Report* 2005 September; 20(9): 8. NRCBL: 18.3; 18.2. SC: le. Identifiers: Diaz v. Hillsborough County Hospital Authority, d/b/a Tampa General Hospital, et al. (Part 2).

Maloney, Dennis M. Complaint alleges many deficiencies in IRB-approved informed consent form. *Human Research Report* 2005 October; 20(10): 8. NRCBL: 18.3; 18.5.3. SC: le. Identifiers: Diaz v. Hillsborough County Hospital Authority, d/b/a/ Tampa General Hospital, et al. (Part 2).

Maloney, Dennis M. Complaint alleges that informed consent procedures were used after experiment began. *Human Research Report* 2005 November; 20(11): 8. NRCBL: 18.3; 18.5.3. SC: le. Identifiers: Diaz v. Hillsborough County Hospital Authority, d/b/a Tampa General Hospital, et al. (Part 3).

Maloney, Dennis M. Congressmen say military should have the right to informed consent. *Human Research Report* 2005 March; 20(3): 9. NRCBL: 18.3; 9.7; 18.5.8; 21.3. SC: le. Identifiers: Armed Forces Voluntary Immunization and Health Justice Act (H.R. 514).

Maloney, Dennis M. Former human subjects sue over their allegations of inadequate informed consent. *Human Research Report* 2005 August; 20(8): 8. NRCBL: 18.3. SC: le. Identifiers: Diaz v. Hillsborough County Hospital Authority, d/b/a Tampa General Hospital.

NRCBL: National Reference Center for Bioethics Literature Classification Scheme   See inside front cover for terms.

281

Maloney, Dennis M. IRB opts for "user friendly" letter rather than an informed consent form. *Human Research Report* 2005 January; 20(1): 6-7. NRCBL: 18.3; 18.2.

Maloney, Dennis M. Plaintiffs claim that research subject was too drowsy to give informed consent. *Human Research Report* 2005 December; 20(12): 8. NRCBL: 18.3; 18.5.3. SC: le. Identifiers: Diaz v. Hillsborough County Hospital Authority, d/b/a Tampa General Hospital, et al. (Part 5).

Maloney, Dennis M. University says research subjects' family members are not research subjects too. *Human Research Report* 2005 February; 20(2): 6-7. NRCBL: 18.3; 1.3.3; 8.4; 18.2.

Maloney, Dennis M. University uses "implied informed consent". *Human Research Report* 2005 March; 20(3): 6-7. NRCBL: 18.3; 1.3.3; 8.4. SC: cs.

Markman, Maurie. Ethical conflict in providing informed consent for clinical trials: a problematic example from the gynecologic cancer research community. *Oncologist* 2004; 9(1): 3-7. NRCBL: 18.3; 18.2; 18.5.3.

McDermott, Barbara E.; Gerbasi, Joan B.; Quanbeck, Cameron; Scott, Charles L. Capacity for forensic patients to consent to research: the use of the MacCAT-CR. *Journal of the American Academy of Psychiatry and the Law* 2005; 33(3): 299-307. NRCBL: 18.3; 18.5.1; 18.5.6. SC: em.

McGregor, Joan. 'Undue inducement' as coercive offers [comment]. *American Journal of Bioethics* 2005 September-October; 5(5): 24-25. NRCBL: 18.3; 9.3.1; 18.2. Comments: comment on Ezekiel J. Emanuel, "Undue inducement: nonsense on stilts?" American Journal of Bioethics 2005 September-October; 5(5): 9-13.

McMillan, Gigi. What do researchers say? What do subjects hear? Not what they would like to hear. What do subjects need? More information. *Protecting Human Subjects* 2005 Summer; (12): 10-11. NRCBL: 18.3.

McNeill, Paul M. Should research ethics change at the border? [editorial]. *Medical Journal of Australia* 1998 November 16; 169(10): 509-510. NRCBL: 18.3; 18.2; 9.5.6; 21.1; 18.6.

McQuay, H.J.; Moore, R.A. Placebo. *Postgraduate Medical Journal* 2005 March; 81(953): 155-160. NRCBL: 18.3. Identifiers: ethics of placebo use in clinical trials.

McRae, Andrew D.; Weijer, Charles. Waiver of consent for emergency research [letter]. *Annals of Emergency Medicine* 2004 September; 44(3): 278-279. NRCBL: 18.3; 18.6.

Menikoff, Jerry. Full disclosure: telling patients when not being a research subject is a good choice. *Perspectives in Biology and Medicine* 2005 Winter; 48(1, Supplement): S139-S149. NRCBL: 18.3; 18.5.2; 9.5.7. Note: Special issue: Disparities and Discrimination in Health Care and Health Outcomes.

Meran, Johannes Gobertus. Consent and equipoise, the crucial ethical issues in randomised clinical trials. *Onkologie* 2003; 26(6): 524-528. NRCBL: 18.3; 18.2. SC: an. Note: Abstract in English and German.

Miller, A. Ethical issues in MS clinical trials. *Multiple Sclerosis* 2005 February; 11(1): 97-98. NRCBL: 18.3; 18.2; 18.5.1. Identifiers: multiple sclerosis.

Miller, Franklin G.; Kaptchuk, Ted J. Sham procedures and the ethics of clinical trials. *Journal of the Royal Society of Medicine* 2004 December; 97(12): 576-578. NRCBL: 18.3.

Miller, Franklin G.; Moreno, Jonathan D. Informed consent and the ethics of clinical research: reply to commentaries. *Journal of Clinical Ethics* 2005 Winter; 16(4): 376-379. NRCBL: 18.3; 18.2.

Miller, Franklin G.; Moreno, Jonathan D. The state of research ethics: a tribute to John C. Fletcher. *Journal of Clinical Ethics* 2005 Winter; 16(4): 355-364. NRCBL: 18.3; 18.2; 2.1; 2.2.

Miller, Franklin G.; Wendler, David; Kravitz, Richard L.; Franks, Peter; Epstein, Ronald M.; Feldman, Mitchell D.; Franz, Carol E. Direct-to-consumer advertising and physician prescribing [letter and reply]. *JAMA: The Journal of the American Medical Association* 2005 August 10; 294(6): 678-679. NRCBL: 18.3.

Miller, Matthew J.; Horstmann, Elizabeth; Emanuel, Ezekiel J.; Grady, Christine; Kurzrock, Razelle; Benjamin, Robert S. Phase 1 clinical trials in oncology [letter and replies]. *New England Journal of Medicine* 2005 June 9; 352(23): 2452- 2453. NRCBL: 18.3.

Miller, Victoria A.; Nelson, Robert M. Moving beyond the consent document in research on informed consent [editorial]. *Archives of Pediatric and Adolescent Medicine* 2005 April; 159(4): 396-397. NRCBL: 18.3; 18.5.2.

Millson, David S. Are consenters representative of a target population? [letter]. *BMJ: British Medical Journal* 2005 November 5; 331(7524): 1082- 1083. NRCBL: 18.3.

Molyneux, C.S.; Peshu, N.; Marsh, K. Understanding of informed consent in a low-income setting: three case studies from the Kenyan Coast. *Social Science and Medicine* 2004 December; 59(12): 2547-2559. NRCBL: 18.3; 18.5.2. SC: em; cs.

Moodley, K.; Pather, M.; Myer, L. Informed consent and participant perceptions of influenza vaccine trials in South Africa. *Journal of Medical Ethics* 2005 December; 31(12): 727-732. NRCBL: 18.3; 9.7. SC: em.
Abstract: BACKGROUND AND OBJECTIVES: There are few insights from sub- Saharan Africa on research participants' experiences of the informed consent process, particularly in the

---

context of randomised controlled trials, where issues of randomisation and the use of placebos may be confusing concepts for participants. This study investigated the knowledge and perceptions of the informed consent process among individuals participating in influenza vaccine trials in two disadvantaged communities in South Africa. METHOD: Four to 12 months after completion of the trials, participants were contacted to return to participate in the informed consent study. The semistructured questionnaire administered to assess recall of trial procedures and the informed consent process covered key issues including: purpose of the study; awareness that the study was not part of routine treatment; voluntary nature of participation and freedom to withdraw; randomisation; placebos; and remuneration. RESULTS: A total of 334 participants (93% of the original vaccine trial sample; mean age 68 years, median level of education grade 8, 69% women) completed the questionnaire. Only 21% were able to recall that they were allocated randomly to the different treatment arms. Only 19% of those involved in the placebo controlled study had interpreted the concept of placebo as an inactive medication. CONCLUSION: Although a good general recall of trial concepts was demonstrated, only a small proportion of the participants correctly interpreted and recalled the concepts of randomisation and placebos. Informed consent in this and similarly disadvantaged communities may often be inadequate and new ways to improve understanding of the research process should be explored.

Morgan, Alan. Informed consent: finding a path toward prudent policy. *Pacing and Clinical Electrophysiology* 1997 March; 20(3, Part 1): 730-731. NRCBL: 18.3; 18.6; 18.5.9.

Morris, Marilyn C.; Nadkarni, Vinay M.; Ward, Frances R.; Nelson, Robert M. Exception from informed consent for pediatric resuscitation research: community consultation for a trial of brain cooling after in-hospital cardiac arrest. *Pediatrics* 2004 September; 114(3): 776-781. NRCBL: 18.3; 18.5.2; 20.5.1. SC: em.

Moser, David J.; Reese, Rebecca L.; Schultz, Susan K.; Benjamin, Michelle L.; Arndt, Stephan; Fleming, Frank W.; Andreasen, Nancy C. Informed consent in medication-free schizophrenia research. *American Journal of Psychiatry* 2005 June; 162(6): 1209-1211. NRCBL: 18.3; 18.5.6; 20.5.1.

Muggia, Franco M.; Horstmann, Elizabeth; Emanuel, Ezekiel J.; Grady, Christine; Kurzrock, Razelle; Benjamin, Robert S. Phase 1 clinical trials in oncology [letter and replies]. *New England Journal of Medicine* 2005 June 9; 352(23): 2451- 2453. NRCBL: 18.3.

Orentlicher, David. Making research a requirement of treatment: why we should sometimes let doctors pressure patients to participate in research. *Hastings Center Report* 2005 September-October; 35(5): 20-28. NRCBL: 18.3.

Pace, Christine; Emanuel, Ezekiel J.; Chuenyam, Theshinee; Duncombe, Chris; Bebchuk, Judith D.; Wendler, David; Tavel, Jorge A.; McNay, Laura A.; Phanuphak, Praphan; Forster, Heidi P.; Grady, Christine. The quality of informed consent in a clinical research study in Thailand. *IRB: Ethics and Human Research* 2005

January-February; 27(1): 9-17. NRCBL: 18.3; 21.1. SC: em. Identifiers: Evaluation of Subcutaneous Proleukin in a Randomized International Trial.

Patel, Angira; Wilke, Hans J., II.; Mingay, David; Ellis, John E. Patient attitudes toward granting consent to participate in perioperative randomized clinical trials. *Journal of Clinical Anesthesia* 2004 September; 16(6): 426-434. NRCBL: 18.3. SC: em.

Paz, David A.; Dunn, Laura B.; Gordon, Nora E. Economic behavior and informed consent [letter and reply]. *JAMA: The Journal of the American Medical Association* 2005 May 4; 293(17): 2092. NRCBL: 18.3; 18.5.1.

Peterson, Dymphna Rees. The ethics of research into schizophrenia prevention: a carer's perspective. *Australian and New Zealand Journal of Psychiatry* 2000 November; 34 (supplement): S201-S203. NRCBL: 18.3; 18.5.6; 8.3.3.

Phillips, Michael. Coping with unsuspected findings in volunteers [letter]. *Nature* 2005 March 3; 434(7029): 17. NRCBL: 18.3.

Pilon, Susan. Protecting psychiatric patients in research [comment]. *Indian Journal of Medical Ethics* 2005 April-June; 2(2): 59. NRCBL: 18.3; 18.5.6; 18.4. Comments: comment on Renu Addlakha, "Ethical quandaries in anthropological fieldwork in psychiatric settings," Indian Journal of Medical Ethics 2005 April-June; 2(2): 55-56.

Plomer, Aurora. Non-therapeutic research: domestic remedies and convention rights. *In her:* The Law and Ethics of Medical Research: International Bioethics and Human Rights. Portland, OR: Cavendish; 2005: 43-65. NRCBL: 18.3; 18.2; 18.5.8. SC: le.

Price, Donald D. New facts and improved ethical guidelines for placebo analgesia [editorial]. *Journal of Pain* 2005 April; 6(4): 213-214. NRCBL: 18.3; 8.2; 4.4.

Public Access Defibrillation [PAD] Trial Investigators ; Mosesso, Vincent N., Jr.; Brown, Lawrence H.; Greene, H. Leon; Schmidt, Terri A.; Aufderheide, Tom P.; Sayre, Michael R.; Stephens, Shannon W.; Travers, Andrew; Craven, Richard A.; Weisfeldt, Myron L. Conducting research using the emergency exception from informed consent: the Public Access Defibrillation (PAD) Trial experience. *Resuscitation* 2004 April; 61(1): 29-36. NRCBL: 18.3; 18.6; 21.1. SC: em.

Regidor, Enrique. The use of personal data from medical records and biological materials: ethical perspectives and the basis for legal restrictions in health research. *Social Science and Medicine* 2004 November; 59(9): 1975-1984. NRCBL: 18.3; 1.3.12; 15.1; 19.5.

Reid, Lynette. Nice work if you can get it [comment]. *American Journal of Bioethics* 2005 September-October;

NRCBL: National Reference Center for Bioethics Literature Classification Scheme   See inside front cover for terms.

283

5(5): 27-29. NRCBL: 18.3; 9.3.1. Comments: comment on Ezekiel J. Emanuel, "Undue inducement: nonsense on stilts?" American Journal of Bioethics 2005 September-October; 5(5): 9-13.

Reiser, Stanley Joel. Research compensation and the monetarization of medicine. *JAMA: The Journal of the American Medical Association* 2005 February 2; 293(5): 613-614. NRCBL: 18.3; 9.3.1.

Rothschild, Barbra B.; King, Nancy M.P.; Horstmann, Elizabeth; Emanuel, Ezekiel J.; Grady, Christine; Kurzrock, Razelle; Benjamin, Robert S. Phase 1 clinical trials in oncology [letter and replies]. *New England Journal of Medicine* 2005 June 9; 352(23): 2451- 2453. NRCBL: 18.3.

Russell, F.M.; Carapetis, J.R.; Liddle, H.; Edwards, T.; Ruff, T.A.; Devitt, J. A pilot study of the quality of informed consent materials for Aboriginal participants in clinical trials. *Journal of Medical Ethics* 2005 August; 31(8): 490-494. NRCBL: 18.3; 18.5.1. SC: em. Identifiers: Australia.

Abstract: OBJECTIVE: To pilot informed consent materials developed for Aboriginal parents in a vaccine trial, and evaluate their design and the informed consent process. METHODS: Cross sectional quantitative and qualitative survey of 20 Aboriginal and 20 non- Aboriginal women in Alice Springs. Information about the proposed research was presented to Aboriginal participants by an Aboriginal researcher, using purpose designed verbal, visual, and written materials. Non-Aboriginal participants received standard materials developed by the sponsor. Questionnaires were used to evaluate recall and understanding immediately and five days later. Qualitative analysis of Aboriginal participants' interviews was performed. RESULTS: There were no differences between the groups in understanding of diseases prevented by the vaccine, the potential risks of participating, or the voluntary nature of participation. Most Aboriginal participants had difficulty with the concept of a "licensed" versus "unlicensed" vaccine. The non-Aboriginal group had a good understanding of this. Aboriginal participants identified the use of the flipchart, along with a presentation by a doctor and Aboriginal health worker, as preferred delivery modes. Group presentations were preferred rather than one-on-one discussions. The use of the questionnaire posed considerable methodological difficulties. CONCLUSIONS: A one-off oral presentation to Aboriginal participants is unlikely to produce "informed consent". Key but unfamiliar concepts require identification and particularly considered presentation.

Sabik, Lindsay; Pace, Christine A.; Forster-Gertner, Heidi P.; Wendler, David; Bebchuk, Judith D.; Tavel, Jorge A.; McNay, Laura A.; Killen, Jack; Emanuel, Ezekiel J.; Grady, Christine. Informed consent: practices and views of investigators in a multinational clinical trial. *IRB: Ethics and Human Research* 2005 September-October; 27(5): 13-18. NRCBL: 18.3; 9.5.6; 21.1. SC: em. Identifiers: Evaluation of Subcutaneous Proleukin in a Randomized International Trial [ESPRIT].

Sankar, Pamela. Communication and miscommunication in informed consent to research. *Medical Anthropology*

Quarterly 2004 December; 18(4): 429-446. NRCBL: 18.3; 18.2. SC: em.

Satin, David J. More realism about informed consent. *Journal of Laboratory and Clinical Medicine* 2005 June; 145(6): 292-294. NRCBL: 18.3; 8.3.1; 8.1.

Saunders, John; Wainwright, Paul. Risk, Helsinki 2000 and the use of placebo in medical research. *Clinical Medicine* 2003 September-October; 3(5): 435-439. NRCBL: 18.3; 18.2; 6.

Schellings, Ron; Kessels, Alfons G.; ter Riet, Gerben; Kleijnen, Jos; Leffers, Pieter; Knottnerus, J. André; Sturmans, Ferd. Members of research ethics committees accepted a modification of the randomized consent design. *Journal of Clinical Epidemiology* 2005 June; 58(6): 589-594. NRCBL: 18.3; 18.2. SC: em. Identifiers: United Kingdom (Great Britain); Netherlands.

Schmidt, Terri A. The legacy of the Tuskegee syphilis experiments for emergency exception from informed consent. *Annals of Emergency Medicine* 2003 January; 41(1): 79-81. NRCBL: 18.3; 18.5.1; 18.6.

Schneider, Carl E. Some realism about informed consent [editorial]. *Journal of Laboratory and Clinical Medicine* 2005 June; 145(6): 289-291. NRCBL: 18.3; 8.3.1; 8.1.

Schonfeld, Toby L.; Brown, Joseph S.; Gordon, Bruce G. Subject protection and the risk-benefit relationship [comment]. *American Journal of Bioethics* 2005 September-October; 5(5): 22-23. NRCBL: 18.3; 9.3.1; 18.2. Comments: comment on Ezekiel J. Emanuel, "Undue inducement: nonsense on stilts?" American Journal of Bioethics 2005 September-October; 5(5): 9-13.

Schwab, Abraham P. Would you know an undue inducement if you saw one? [letter]. *American Journal of Bioethics [Online]* 2005 September- October; 5(5): W17. NRCBL: 18.3; 18.2.

Sears, Jeanne M. Context is key for voluntary and informed consent. *American Journal of Bioethics* 2005 January-February; 5(1): 47- 48. NRCBL: 18.3; 18.2; 18.5.1. Comments: comment on Rosamond Rhodes, "Rethinking research ethics," American Journal of Bioethics 2005 January-February; 5(1): 7-28.

Sharp, S. Michael. Consent documents for oncology trials: does anybody read these things? *American Journal of Clinical Oncology* 2004 December; 27(6): 570-575. NRCBL: 18.3. SC: em.

Sheikh, Asim A. Genetic research and human biological samples: some legal and ethical considerations. *Medicine and Law: World Association for Medical Law* 2004; 23(4): 897-912. NRCBL: 18.3; 19.5; 15.1; 8.4. SC: le.

Abstract: This paper examines the medico-legal and medico-ethical issues that ethics committees and researchers will have to consider when examining proposals pertaining to non-therapeutic genetic research. This paper is limited to the examination of issues that relate to those individuals who donate bodily/DNA samples for the purposes of non-therapeutic genetic research. The issues that arise are those of (i) informed consent and those with diminished capacity (ii) the drafting of consent forms as they relate to genetic research (iii) confidentiality, genetic research with non-EU countries and the implications of the EC Directive on the Protection of Data: 95/46/EC and (iv) an examination of international ethical guidelines. The paper concludes with (i) a summary of the main points of concern that ethics committees must consider before the approval of genetic research (ii) the manner in which consent forms must be drafted and (iii) a brief look at medico-legal issues that will become important and will have to be considered in Ireland in the near future in relation to genetic research.

Silverman, Henry J.; Luce, John M.; Lanken, Paul N.; Morris, Alan H.; Harabin, Andrea L.; Oldmixon, Cathryn F.; Thompson, B. Taylor; Bernard, Gordon R. Recommendations for informed consent forms for critical care clinical trials. *Critical Care Medicine* 2005 April; 33(4): 867-882. NRCBL: 18.3; 18.5.1. Identifiers: National Heart, Lung and Blood Institute Acute Respiratory Distress Syndrome Clinical Trials Network (ARDSNet).

Simon, Christian M.; Kodish, Eric D. "Step into my zapatos, doc": understanding and reducing communication disparities in the multicultural informed consent setting. *Perspectives in Biology and Medicine* 2005 Winter; 48(1, Supplement): S123-S138. NRCBL: 18.3; 18.5.2; 8.3.2; 9.5.4; 8.1. Note: Special issue: Disparities and Discrimination in Health Care and Health Outcomes.

Simon, Christian M.; Siminoff, Laura A.; Kodish, Eric D.; Burant, Christopher. Comparison of the informed consent process for randomized clinical trials in pediatric and adult oncology. *Journal of Clinical Oncology* 2004 July 1; 22(13): 2708-2717. NRCBL: 18.3; 18.5.2. SC: em. Identifiers: United States; Canada.

Simpson, Bob. Response to Athula Sumathipala and Sisira Siribaddana, "Revisiting 'Freely Given Informed Consent' in Relation to the Developing World: the Role of an Ombudsman" (AJOB 4:3). *American Journal of Bioethics [Online]* 2005 January-February; 5(1): W24-W26. NRCBL: 18.3; 18.5.1; 18.2; 21.1. Comments: comment on American Journal of Bioethics [Online] 2004 May-June; 4(3): W1-W7.

Sivarajah, Neeraja. Neuroregenerative gene therapy: the implications for informed consent laws. *Health Law in Canada* 2005 November; 26(2): 19-28. NRCBL: 18.3; 15.4; 18.5.4; 19.1; 7.3. SC: le.

Skegg, P.D.G. Consent and information disclosure. *In:* Dawson, John; Peart, Nicola, eds. The Law of Research: A Guide. Dunedin, NZ: University of Otago Press; 2003: 233-251. NRCBL: 18.3. SC: le.

Society for Academic Emergency Medicine [SAEM]. Ethics Committee; Marco, Catherine A. The Society for Academic Emergency Medicine position on informed consent for emergency medicine research. *Academic Emer-*

gency Medicine 2004 October; 11(10): 1090-1091. NRCBL: 18.3; 18.2; 9.5.1.

Society for Academic Emergency Medicine [SAEM]. Ethics Committee; Schmidt, Terri A.; Salo, David; Hughes, Jason A.; Abbott, Jean T.; Geiderman, Joel M.; Johnson, Catherine X.; McClure, Katie B.; McKay, Mary Pat; Razzak, Junaid A.; Schears, Raquel M.; Solomon, Robert C. Confronting the ethical challenges to informed consent in emergency medicine research. *Academic Emergency Medicine* 2004 October; 11(10): 1082-1089. NRCBL: 18.3; 18.2; 9.5.1.

Spigt, M.G.; Knipschild, P.G.; van Schayck, C.P.; Knottnerus, J.A. The validity and ethics of giving placebo in a randomized nonpharmacologic trial was evaluated. *Journal of Clinical Epidemiology* 2005 April; 58(4): 350-356. NRCBL: 18.3; 18.2. SC: em. Identifiers: Netherlands.

Sreenivasan, Gopal. Informed consent and the therapeutic misconception: clarifying the challenge. *Journal of Clinical Ethics* 2005 Winter; 16(4): 369-371. NRCBL: 18.3; 18.2.

Stead, Martine; Eadie, D.; Gordon, D.; Angus, K. "Hello, hello — it's English I speak!": a qualitative exploration of patients' understanding of the science of clinical trials. *Journal of Medical Ethics* 2005 November; 31(11): 664-669. NRCBL: 18.3; 18.5.1; 21.7.

Abstract: Informed consent may be seriously compromised if patients fail to understand the experimental nature of the trial in which they are participating. Using focus groups, the authors explored how prospective trial participants interpret and understand the science of clinical trials by using patient information sheets relative to their medical condition. An opportunity was provided to hear in the patients' own words how they interpret the information and why there is variable understanding. Respondents struggled to comprehend the meaning and purpose of concepts such as randomisation and double blinding, and found them threatening to their ideas of medical care. Suggestions are made about how to improve the national guidelines on written information for trial participants and pretesting of the information sheets is advocated.

Tabak, N. Doctors' policy on explaining the implementation of novel experimental treatment to cancer patients. *Medicine and Law: World Association for Medical Law* 1994; 13(3-4): 331-355. NRCBL: 18.3; 8.3.1; 18.5.7. SC: em.

Tait, Alan R.; Voepel-Lewis, Terri; Malviya, Shobha; Philipson, Sandra J. Improving the readability and processability of a pediatric informed consent document: effects on parents' understanding. *Archives of Pediatric and Adolescent Medicine* 2005 April; 159(4): 347-352. NRCBL: 18.3; 18.5.2. SC: em.

Thomas, C. The use and control of heel prick blood samples. *Medicine and Law: World Association for Medical Law* 2005 June; 24(2): 259-277. NRCBL: 18.3; 4.4; 8.3.2; 9.5.7; 15.3. SC: le.

NRCBL: National Reference Center for Bioethics Literature Classification Scheme   See inside front cover for terms.

285

Abstract: The human body is assuming new meanings and value. When tissue, such as hair, blood and saliva is subjected to DNA analysis, detailed intimate information can be revealed about a person that may predict information about behavioural traits and future disorders. Such genetic information may lead to the development of beneficial therapeutic treatments, but it may also lead to employment or insurance discrimination. Human tissue is commonly used by law enforcement agencies to detect perpetrators of crimes and to identify corpses. There are many sources of such tissue samples. One is from samples routinely collected from newborn babies for a test known as the "Guthrie test" or heel prick test. At about two days of age the child's heel is pricked and the resultant drops of blood are applied to filter paper attached to a test card. This is dried and analysed and, in New Zealand, the cards are stored indefinitely. The potential range of research purposes using such blood samples is increasing, and expanding markets have increased their value. This paper considers the status of the samples in light of recent developments in New Zealand and suggests appropriate approaches for retention and further use of the samples, or third party access to them.

Thomson, Colin. Medical research and participants with disabilities. *Monash Bioethics Review* 2005 October; 24(4): 56-63. NRCBL: 18.3; 9.5.1. Identifiers: Australia.

Tolich, Martin; Baldwin, Kate Mary. Informing consent in New Zealand research: researchers' conflict of interest and patient vulnerability. *New Zealand Medical Journal* 2005 February 25; 118(1210); 8 p. NRCBL: 18.3; 18.2.

Torpy, Janet M. Randomized controlled trials. *JAMA: The Journal of the American Medical Association* 2005 November 2; 294(17): 2262. NRCBL: 18.3. SC: po.

Truog, Robert D. Informed consent: an end or a means? A response to Miller and Moreno. *Journal of Clinical Ethics* 2005 Winter; 16(4): 365-368. NRCBL: 18.3; 18.2.

United States. Food and Drug Administration. Protection of human subjects; informed consent; final rules. *Federal Register* 1996 October 2; 61(192): 51498-51531 [Online] Available: http://frwebgate.access.gpo.gov/cgi-bin/multidb.cgi [12 December 2005]. NRCBL: 18.3; 18.2. SC: le. Comments: See also "Waiver of Informed Consent Requirement in Certain Emergency Research".

van Kammen, Jessika. Informed consent in clinical trials. *Issues in Medical Ethics* 2000 July-September; 8(3): 84-86. NRCBL: 18.3; 18.5.3; 11.1.

Vanderpool, Harold Y. A quartet of criticisms [comment]. *American Journal of Bioethics* 2005 September-October; 5(5): 16-19. NRCBL: 18.3; 9.3.1; 18.6; 2.4. Identifiers: Belmont Report. Comments: comment on Ezekiel J. Emanuel, "Undue inducement: nonsense on stilts?" American Journal of Bioethics 2005 September-October; 5(5): 9-13.

VanderWalde, Ari. Undue inducement: the only objection to payment? [comment]. *American Journal of Bioethics* 2005 September-October; 5(5): 25-27. NRCBL: 18.3; 9.3.1; 18.2. Comments: comment on Ezekiel J. Emanuel, "Undue inducement: nonsense on stilts?" Amer-

ican Journal of Bioethics 2005 September-October; 5(5): 9-13.

Varnhagen, Connie K.; Gushta, Matthew; Daniels, Jason; Peters, Tara C.; Parmar, Neil; Law, Danielle; Hirsch, Rachel; Takach, Bonnie Sadler; Johnson, Tom. How informed is online informed consent? *Ethics and Behavior* 2005; 15(1): 37-48. NRCBL: 18.3; 1.3.12; 7.1. SC: em.

Abstract: We examined participants' reading and recall of informed consent documents presented via paper or computer. Within each presentation medium, we presented the document as a continuous or paginated document to simulate common computer and paper presentation formats. Participants took slightly longer to read paginated and computer informed consent documents and recalled slightly more information from the paginated documents. We concluded that obtaining informed consent online is not substantially different than obtaining it via paper presentation. We also provide suggestions for improving informed consent—in both face-to-face and online experiments.

Wadman, Meredith. Medicare compels heart patients to enlist in follow-up research [news]. *Nature* 2005 January 27; 433(7024): 341. NRCBL: 18.3; 5.2; 9.3.1; 9.5.2.

Weijer, Charles; Miller, Paul B. When are research risks reasonable in relation to anticipated benefits? *Nature Medicine* 2004 June; 10(6): 570-573. NRCBL: 18.3.

Weldon, Sue. 'Public consent' or 'scientific citizenship'?: what counts as public participation in population-based DNA collection? *In:* Tutton, Richard; Corrigan, Oonagh, eds. Genetic Databases: Socio-ethical Issues in the Collection and Use of DNA. New York: Routledge; 2004: 161-180. NRCBL: 18.3; 15.1; 13.1.

Wogalter, Michael S.; Howe, Julie E.; Sifuentes, Alla H.; Luginbuhl, James. On the adequacy of legal documents: factors that influence informed consent. *Ergonomics* 1999; 42(4): 593-613. NRCBL: 18.3; 8.3.1. SC: le; em.

Young, Diony. Will exercising informed consent stop "unfortunate experiments"? [editorial]. *Birth* 2005 March; 32(1): 1-3. NRCBL: 18.3; 18.2; 18.5.3; 2.2.

HUMAN EXPERIMENTATION/ REGULATION

Missed opportunity to ban reproductive cloning [editorial]. *Nature Cell Biology* 2005 April; 7(4): 323. NRCBL: 18.6; 14.5; 21.1.

Not so fast: anyone thinking of collaborations with emerging biomedical powers should test the ethical waters before jumping in [editorial]. *Nature* 2005 February 10; 433(7026): 557. NRCBL: 18.6; 18.3; 18.5.4. Identifiers: China.

Why should clinical trials be registered? [editorial]. *CMAJ/JAMC: Canadian Medical Association Journal* 2005 June 21; 172(13): 1653. NRCBL: 18.6; 1.3.7; 9.7.

Besselink, Marc G.H.; Goozen, Hein G.; Buskens, Erik; DeAngelis, Catherine D. Clinical trial registration and the ICMJE [letter and reply]. *JAMA: The Journal of the American Medical Association* 2005 January 12; 293(2): 157-158. NRCBL: 18.6; 1.3.7. Identifiers: International Committee of Medical Journal Editors.

Chase, Marilyn. AIDS researchers, activists to face off over drug studies. *Wall Street Journal* 2005 May 18; p. B7. NRCBL: 18.6; 9.5.6; 9.7; 18.5.9. SC: po.

Cuomo, Peter. Regulation of biotechnology by executive orders: questions about constitutionality, legality and overall fairness to the American public. *Journal of Biolaw and Business* 2005; 8(2): 30-42. NRCBL: 18.6; 18.2; 18.5.4; 2.4; 5.1. SC: le.

Darou, Wes G.; Hum, Andrew; Kurtness, Jacques. An investigation of the impact of psychosocial research on a native population. *Professional Psychology: Research and Practice* 1993 August; 24(3): 325-329. NRCBL: 18.6; 18.5.1; 21.7. Identifiers: Cree.

Davis, Terry. Responsible conduct in research: recent policy developments in the area of research integrity. *Canadian Journal of Cardiovascular Nursing* 1996; 7(2): 21-24. NRCBL: 18.6; 18.1; 18.2.

Dresser, Rebecca; DeAngelis, Catherine D. Clinical trial registration and the ICMJE [letter and reply]. *JAMA: The Journal of the American Medical Association* 2005 January 12; 293(2): 157-158. NRCBL: 18.6; 1.3.7. Identifiers: International Committee of Medical Journal Editors.

Dubler, Nancy; Barnes, Mark. Has compliance eclipsed ethics? Should we expect serious ethical consideration or give up and admit that regulations are the only hope? [debate]. *Protecting Human Subjects* 2005 Summer; (12): 7-9. NRCBL: 18.6. SC: le.

Fluss, Sev S. The evolution of research ethics: the current international configuration. *Journal of Law, Medicine and Ethics* 2004 Winter; 32(4): 596- 603. NRCBL: 18.6; 21.1; 17.1. SC: le.

Gennery, Brian. Academic clinical research in the new regulatory environment. *Clinical Medicine* 2005 January-February; 5(1): 39-41. NRCBL: 18.6; 18.2; 21.1. SC: le. Identifiers: European clinical trials directive.

Gold, Jennifer L.; Studdert, David M. Clinical trials registries: a reform that is past due. *Journal of Law, Medicine and Ethics* 2005 Winter; 33(4): 811- 820. NRCBL: 18.6; 1.3.9; 18.2; 8.2; 1.3.12. SC: le.

Grass, Guido. Clinical trial registration. *New England Journal of Medicine* 2005 January 13; 352(2): 198. NRCBL: 18.6; 1.3.7.

Huhn, Wilson. Three legal frameworks for regulating genetic technology. *Journal of Contemporary Health Law and Policy* 2002 Winter; 19(1): 1-36. NRCBL: 18.6; 5.3; 15.7. SC: le.

International Committee of Medical Journal Editors; De Angelis, Catherine; Drazen, Jeffrey M.; Frizelle, Frank A.; Haug, Charlotte; Joey, John; Horton, Richard; Kotzin, Sheldon; Laine, Christine; Marušic, Ana; Overbeke, John P.M.; Schroeder, Torben V.; Sox, Harold C.; Van Der Weyden, Martin B. Is This Clinical Trial Fully Registered?: A Statement from the International Committee of Medical Journal Editors. Philadelphia, PA: The Committee, 2005 May; 7 p. [Online]. Available: http://www.icmje.org/clin_trialup.htm [1 July 2005]. NRCBL: 18.6; 1.3.7; 1.3.12; 21.1. Note: This article has also been published in journals that include: JAMA 2005 June 15; 293(23): 2927-2929; NEJM 2005 June 6; 352(23): 2436-2438; Lancet 2005 May 28-June 3; 365(9474): 1827-1829.

Kaiser, Jocelyn. House would foil human pesticide studies [news]. *Science* 2005 May 27; 308(5726): 1234. NRCBL: 18.6; 16.1. SC: le. Identifiers: Environmental Protection Agency (EPA).

Khalil, Omar; Govinarajan, Rangaswamy; Safar, Mazin; Hutchins, Laura; Mehta, Paulette; DeAngelis, Catherine D. Clinical trial registration and the ICMJE [letter and reply]. *JAMA: The Journal of the American Medical Association* 2005 January 12; 293(2): 157-158. NRCBL: 18.6; 1.3.7. Identifiers: International Committee of Medical Journal Editors.

Koski, Greg. Changing the paradigm: new directions in federal oversight of human research. *Journal of Pediatric Gastroenterology and Nutrition* 2003 November-December; 37 (Supplement 1): S2-S6. NRCBL: 18.6; 18.2; 18.5.2. SC: an.

Krall, Ronald; Rockhold, Frank; Rennie, Drummond. Trial registration: ignored to irresistible [letter and reply]. *JAMA: The Journal of the American Medical Association* 2005 January 12; 293(2): 158. NRCBL: 18.6; 1.3.7; 9.7.

Kulvichit, Kittisak; Kulwichit, Wanla; Lumbiganon, Pisake. Clinical trial registration. *New England Journal of Medicine* 2005 January 13; 352(2): 198- 199. NRCBL: 18.6; 1.3.7; 21.1.

Mackenzie, Robin. Reprogenetics and pharmacogenetics: in whose best interests? *Medicine and Law: World Association for Medical Law* 2005 June; 24(2): 343-354. NRCBL: 18.6; 15.1; 9.7; 15.2. SC: le.
Abstract: Reprogenetics involves embryonic pre-implantation genetic diagnosis, provoking controversy over the creation of saviour siblings, eugenics and genetic enhancement. It will soon ascertain pharmacogenetic susceptibilities. Pharmacogenetics impacts upon public health initiatives underpinned by resource allocation constraints in that genetic epidemiological studies assist in administering health care resources and public health strategies. Knowing how likely sections of the population are to develop specific medical conditions so that lifestyle and environmental factors influencing these condi-

NRCBL: National Reference Center for Bioethics Literature Classification Scheme   See inside front cover for terms.

287

tions can be targeted has the potential to save public money and improve public health. Aligning population groups with genetic susceptibilities with specific medications would enable cost-effective prescribing. Reprogenetics and pharmacogenetics also possess great commercial potential for nation states and biotechnology companies. Hence ethical legal safeguards for members of the public whose reproductive or genetic tissue is a research or health care resource are essential. Both legal measures such as informed consent and mechanisms for including the public in policy decisions over reprogenetics and pharmacogenetics must be rethought to ensure that they provide protection rather than function as rubber stamps which preclude deeper inquiry into justifications of projects.

Maloney, Dennis M. Agency proposes major expansion of its regulations for human subjects. *Human Research Report* 2005 October; 20(10): 1-2. NRCBL: 18.6; 16.1; 18.2. Identifiers: Environmental Protection Agency (EPA).

Maloney, Dennis M. New guidance on when and how to report human research problems. *Human Research Report* 2005 July; 20(7): 1-2. NRCBL: 18.6; 18.2.

McHale, J.V. Law and clinical research — from rights to regulation? An English perspective. *Journal of Law, Medicine and Ethics* 2004 Winter; 32(4): 718- 730. NRCBL: 18.6; 18.2; 18.3; 4.4; 21.1. SC: le.

Meslin, Eric M.; Sidle, John E.; Wools-Kaloustian, Kara; Were, Edwin; Salmon, Karen; Chuani, Christine. International research ethics: a needs assessment of research ethics capacity at Moi University and Indiana University. Volume I: Final report. Indianapolis, IN; Eldoret, Kenya: Indiana University Center for Bioethics 2005 June; 31 p. [Online]. Available: http://www.bioethics.iu.edu/moi_vol1.pdf [4 January 2006]. NRCBL: 18.6; 18.5.9; 18.2.

Mudur, Ganapati. India plans to audit clinical trials [news]. *BMJ: British Medical Journal* 2005 November 5; 331(7524): 1044. NRCBL: 18.6; 18.2.

Nadav, Daniel S. The "death dance of Lubeck": Julius Moses and the German guidelines for human experimentation, 1930. *In:* Roelcke, Volker; Maio, Giovanni, eds. Twentieth Century Ethics of Human Subjects Research: Historical Perspectives on Values, Practices, and Regulations. Stuttgart: Franz Steiner Verlag; 2004: 129-135. NRCBL: 18.6; 9.5.1; 9.7; 2.2; 18.2.

Resnik, David B.; Zeldin, Darryl C.; Sharp, Richard R. Research on environmental health interventions: ethical problems and solutions. *Accountability in Research* 2005 April-June; 12(2): 69-101. NRCBL: 18.6; 16.3.

Abstract: This article reviews a variety of ethical issues one must consider when conducting research on environmental health interventions on human subjects. The paper uses the Kennedy Krieger Institute lead abatement study as well as a hypothetical asthma study to discuss questions concerning benefits and risks, risk minimization, safety monitoring, the duty to warn, the duty to report, the use of control groups, informed consent, equitable subject selection, privacy, conflicts of interest, and community consultation. Research on environmental health interventions can make an important contribution to our

understanding of human health and disease prevention, provided it is conducted in a manner that meets prevailing scientific, ethical, and legal standards for research on human subjects.

Reveiz, Ludovic; Cardona, Andres Felipe; Ospina, Edgar Guillermo. Clinical trial registration. *New England Journal of Medicine* 2005 January 13; 352(2): 198. NRCBL: 18.6; 1.3.7.

Selgelid, Michael J. Module four: standards of care and clinical trials. *Developing World Bioethics* 2005 March; 5(1): 55-72. NRCBL: 18.6; 2.3.
Abstract: This module examines ethical debates about the level of care that should be provided to human research participants. Particular attention is placed on the question of what should be considered an ethically acceptable control arm. You will also learn what relevant international and domestic regulatory documents say about standards of care.

Steinbrook, Robert. Gag clauses in clinical-trial agreements [opinion]. *New England Journal of Medicine* 2005 May 26; 352(21): 2160- 2162. NRCBL: 18.6; 18.2; 5.3; 1.3.9; 1.3.2; 9.7.

Strode, Ann; Grant, Catherine; Slack, Catherine; Mushariwa, Muriel. How well does South Africa's National Health Act regulate research involving children? *South African Medical Journal* 2005 April; 95(4): 265-268. NRCBL: 18.6; 18.5.2.

Thurston, George D. Mandating the release of health research data: issues and implications. *Tulane Environmental Law Journal* 1998 Summer; 11(2): 331-354. NRCBL: 18.6; 8.4; 1.3.9; 16.1; 5.3.

Wadman, Meredith. US Senate votes to ban pesticide tests on humans [news]. *Nature Medicine* 2005 August; 11(8): 811. NRCBL: 18.6; 16.1.

Warlow, Charles. Over-regulation of clinical research: a threat to public health. *Clinical Medicine* 2005 January-February; 5(1): 33-38. NRCBL: 18.6; 18.2; 9.3.1; 8.4; 19.1. SC: an; le. Identifiers: United Kingdom (Great Britain); European Union.

HUMAN EXPERIMENTATION/ SPECIAL POPULATIONS

Clearing the myths of time: Tuskegee revisited. *Lancet Infectious Diseases* 2005 March; 5(3): 127. NRCBL: 18.5.1; 18.3; 10; 9.5.6; 9.5.4.

Don't keep your distance: investigations that involve human subjects always require a close relationship between the researchers and those being studied [editorial]. *Nature* 2005 September 22; 437(7058): 451. NRCBL: 18.5.1.

Patient choice in clinical trials [editorial]. *Lancet* 2005 June 11-17; 365(9476): 1984. NRCBL: 18.5.1; 18.3; 9.7. Identifiers: Amgen.

Addlakha, Renu. The dilemmas of independent researchers [comment]. *Indian Journal of Medical Ethics* 2005 January-March; 2(1): 24. NRCBL: 18.5.1; 18.4. Comments: comment on Hemlata Pisal and Sunita Bandewar, "Research with transgendered people," Indian Journal of Medical Ethics 2005 January-March; 2(1): 22-23.

American Academy of Pediatrics. Committee on Native American Child Health. Committee on Community Health Services. Ethical considerations in research with socially identifiable populations [policy statement]. *Pediatrics* 2004 January; 113(1, Part 1): 148-151. NRCBL: 18.5.1; 18.2; 18.6; 18.5.2.

American Thoracic Society; Luce, John M.; Cook, Deborah J.; Martin, Thomas R.; Angus, Derek C.; Boushey, Homer A.; Curtis, J. Randall; Heffner, John E.; Lanken, Paul N.; Levy, Mitchell M.; Polite, Paula Y.; Rocker, Graeme M.; Truog, Robert D. The ethical conduct of clinical research involving critically ill patients in the United States and Canada: principles and recommendations. *American Journal of Respiratory and Critical Care Medicine* 2004 December 15; 170(12): 1375-1384. NRCBL: 18.5.1; 1.3.9; 18.2; 18.3; 21.1.

Bayoumi, Ahmed M.; Hwang, Stephen W. Methodological, practical, and ethical challenges to inner-city health research. *Journal of Urban Health: Bulletin of the New York Academy of Medicine* 2002 December; 79(4, Supplement 1): S35-S42. NRCBL: 18.5.1; 18.2; 18.3.

Beech, Derrick J.; Beech, Bettina M. For-profit clinical trials. *In:* Beech, Bettina; Goodman, Maurine, eds. Race & Research: Perspectives on Minority Participation in Health Studies. Washington, DC: American Public Health Association; 2004: 163-174. NRCBL: 18.5.1; 9.3.1; 9.7.

Caplan, Arthur L. Too hard to face. *Journal of the American Academy of Psychiatry and the Law* 2005; 33(3): 394-400. NRCBL: 18.5.1; 21.4; 2.2; 4.1.1; 7.4.

Carmeli, Daphna Birenbaum. Prevalence of Jews as subjects in genetic research: figures, explanation, and potential implications. *American Journal of Medical Genetics Part A* 2004 September 15; 130(1): 76-83. NRCBL: 18.5.1; 1.2; 15.1. SC: em.

Clark, Eileen; McCann, Terence V. Researching students: an ethical dilemma. *Nurse Researcher* 2005; 12(3): 42-51. NRCBL: 18.5.1; 18.3; 7.2; 8.4; 1.3.3.

Cornwell, John. The 'science' of racial hygiene. *In his:* Hitler's Scientists: Science, War, and the Devil's Pact. New York: Penguin; 2004: 71-84. NRCBL: 18.5.1; 1.3.9; 20.5.1.

Deutsch, Erwin. Clinical studies in the intensive care unit: ethical and legal aspects. *Victoria University of Wellington Law Review* 1997 July; 27(2): 259-272. NRCBL: 18.5.1; 18.2; 18.1; 18.3; 21.1. SC: le.

Ekouevi, Koumavi Didier; Becquet, Renaud; Viho, Ida; Bequet, Laurence; Dabis, François; Leroy, Valériane. Obtaining informed consent from HIV-infected pregnant women, Abidjan, Cote d'Ivoire [letter]. *AIDS* 2004 July 2; 18(10): 1486-1488. NRCBL: 18.5.1; 18.3; 9.5.6. Identifiers: ANRS1201/1202 Ditrame Plus Study Group.

Emanuel, Ezekiel J.; Weijer, Charles. Protecting communities in research: from a new principle to rational protections. *In:* Childress, James F.; Meslin, Eric M.; Shapiro, Harold T., eds. Belmont Revisited: Ethical Principles for Research with Human Subjects. Washington, DC: Georgetown University Press; 2005: 165-183. NRCBL: 18.5.1; 1.1; 18.2. SC: an.

Ethics Committee of the American Medical Directors Association; Boult, Lisa; Dentler, Bruce; Volicer, Ladislav; Mead, Sharon; Evans, Jonathan M. Ethics and research in long-term care: a position statement from the American Medical Directors Association. *Journal of the American Medical Directors Association* 2003 May-June; 4(3): 171-174. NRCBL: 18.5.1; 18.2.

Foster, Morris W.; Sharp, Richard R. Genetic research with minority populations. *In:* Beech, Bettina; Goodman, Maurine, eds. Race & Research: Perspectives on Minority Participation in Health Studies. Washington, DC: American Public Health Association; 2004: 113-123. NRCBL: 18.5.1; 15.1.

Gandevia, S.C. Self-experimentation, ethics and efficacy. *Monash Bioethics Review* 2005 April; 24(2): 43-48. NRCBL: 18.5.1.

Gilbert, Tony. Involving people with learning disabilities in research: issues and possibilities. *Health and Social Care in the Community* 2004 July; 12(4): 298-308. NRCBL: 18.5.1; 18.1. SC: rv. Identifiers: United Kingdom (Great Britain).

Gillam, Lynn; Weedon, Kathryn. Medical research and involuntary mental health patients: implications of proposed changes to legislation in Victoria. *Monash Bioethics Review* 2005 October; 24(4): 45-49. NRCBL: 18.5.1; 17.1. SC: le. Identifiers: Australia.

Grady, Christine. The challenge of assuring continued post-trial access to beneficial treatment. *Yale Journal of Health Policy, Law, and Ethics* 2005 Winter; 5(1): 425-435. NRCBL: 18.5.1; 9.2; 9.7. SC: le.

Grove, Natalie; Brough, Mark; Canuto, Condy; Dobson, Annette. Aboriginal and Torres Strait Islander health research and the conduct of longitudinal studies: issues for debate. *Australian and New Zealand Journal of Public Health* 2003 December; 27(6): 637-641. NRCBL: 18.5.1; 18.3.

Grulich, Andrew E.; Kaldor, John M. Individual privacy and observational health research: violating an indi-

NRCBL: National Reference Center for Bioethics Literature Classification Scheme   See inside front cover for terms.

289

vidual's privacy to benefit the health of others. *University of New South Wales Law Journal* 2001; 24(1): 298-305. NRCBL: 18.5.1; 8.4; 18.3; 18.2; 1.3.12. SC: le.

Heitman, Elizabeth; Wells, Alan L. Ethical issues and unethical conduct: race, racism, and the abuse of human subjects in research. *In:* Beech, Bettina; Goodman, Maurine, eds. Race & Research: Perspectives on Minority Participation in Health Studies. Washington, DC: American Public Health Association; 2004: 35-59. NRCBL: 18.5.1; 18.2; 18.5.9.

Hobbins, Peter Graeme. Compromised ethical principles in randomised clinical trials of distant, intercessory prayer. *Journal of Bioethical Inquiry* 2005; 2(3): 142-152. NRCBL: 18.5.1; 1.2; 18.2; 1.3.9; 18.3.
Abstract: The effects of distant, intercessory prayer on health outcomes have been studied in a range of randomised, blinded clinical trials. However, while seeking the evidentiary status accorded this 'gold standard' methodology, many prayer studies fall short of the requirements of the World Medical Association's Declaration of Helsinki for the ethical conduct of trials involving human subjects. Within a sample of 15 such studies published in the medical literature, many were found to have ignored or waived key ethical precepts, including inadequate standards of care, patient confidentiality and informed consent. Prayer was considered in most studies to pose negligible or no risk to subjects, despite the fact that no clear mechanism of action nor any safety monitoring procedures were described. As a result, many studies did not meet basic ethical standards required of clinical trials of biophysical interventions, making application of their results ethically problematic. If investigators wish their data to adequately inform the use or rejection of intercessory prayer to improve health, these shortcomings should be addressed in future studies.

Jenkins, Bill; Jones, Camara; Blumenthal, Daniel S. Public health ethics and community-based research: lessons from the Tuskegee Syphilis Study. *In:* Blumenthal, D.S.; Diclemente, R.J., eds. Community- Based Health Research: Issues and Methods. New York: Springer Publishing Company, 2004: 47-62. NRCBL: 18.5.1; 18.3; 18.6; 9.1; 10.

Kipnis, Kenneth. Vulnerability in research subjects: an analytical approach. *In:* Thomasma, David C.; Weisstub, David N., eds. The Variables of Moral Capacity. Boston: Kluwer Academic Publishers; 2004: 217- 231. NRCBL: 18.5.1. SC: an.

Krishnan, Suneeta. Dynamic relationships in community-based research [comment]. *Indian Journal of Medical Ethics* 2005 January-March; 2(1): 25. NRCBL: 18.5.1; 18.4. Comments: comment on Hemlata Pisal and Sunita Bandewar, "Research with transgendered people," Indian Journal of Medical Ethics 2005 January-March; 2(1): 22-23.

Leggon, Cheryl. Tuskegee project, the. *In:* Restivo, Sal, ed. Science, Technology, and Society: An Encyclopedia. New York: Oxford University Press; 2005: 646-648. NRCBL: 18.5.1.

Li, Nicole. Out of the armchair: a bioethics student's search for practical knowledge in Kenya. *Journal of Bioethical Inquiry* 2004; 1(1): 20-26. NRCBL: 18.5.1; 18.2; 18.3; 9.5.6.
Abstract: This paper recounts the efforts of a bioethics student to understand the experience of human subjects of medical research in Kenya. Although the endeavor resulted in more questions than answers, it served to highlight areas where the current system of protections has failed to secure the well-being of those involved. It concludes that, in addition to existing considerations, ethical review ought to include another kind of information: that which can be gained only from listening to the feelings and experiences related by subjects themselves.

Lindegger, G.; Slack, C.; Vardas, E. HIV vaccine trials in South Africa — some ethical considerations. *South African Medical Journal* 2000 August; 90(8): 769-770, 772. NRCBL: 18.5.1; 9.5.6; 18.3.

Lott, Jason P. Module three: vulnerable/special participant populations. *Developing World Bioethics* 2005 March; 5(1): 30-54. NRCBL: 18.5.1; 2.2; 2.3. SC: cs.
Abstract: This module is designed to sensitise you to the special needs of participants who belong to populations that are more vulnerable than other participant populations. These populations typically include incompetent persons, women who may or may not be pregnant, children, prisoners and refugees, impoverished people, and ethnic minorities. These and similar groups deserve special consideration for a number of important ethical and historical reasons, specifically those that surround the potential for exploitation, problems with informed consent, and concerns about respect for participant autonomy. This module introduces modus operandi that are based on national and international research guidelines for dealing with vulnerable/special participant populations, offering contextually-dependent advice and relevant ethical considerations/arguments for and against their involvement in scientific research endeavours.

Mattern, R.; Schueler, F.; Kallieris, D. Traumatology of the traffic accident — dead people for the safety in traffic. *Forensic Science International* 2004 September 10; 144(2-3): 193-200. NRCBL: 18.5.1; 20.1.

McKane, Maureen; Tolson, Debbie. Research, ethics and the data protection legislation. *Nursing Standard* 2000 February 2-8; 14(20): 36-41. NRCBL: 18.5.1; 8.4; 18.3; 4.1.3; 1.1. SC: le.

Paalman, Mark H. Stem cells and cloning: the fuss, revisited [editorial]. *Anatomical Record* 2001 June 15; 265(3): 121-122. NRCBL: 18.5.1; 15.1; 14.5; 19.1.

Pisal, Hemlata; Bandewar, Sunita. Research with transgendered people [case study]. *Indian Journal of Medical Ethics* 2005 January-March; 2(1): 22- 23. NRCBL: 18.5.1; 18.4; 18.3.

Reverby, Susan M. Rethinking the Tuskegee Syphilis Study: Nurse Rivers, silence and the meaning of treatment. *Nursing History Review* 1999; 7: 3-28. NRCBL: 18.5.1; 18.3; 10; 4.1.3; 7.1. Identifiers: Eunice Rivers Laurie.

Roberts, Laura Weiss. Evidence-based ethics and informed consent in mental illness research [opinion]. *Ar-*

chives of General Psychiatry 2000 June; 57(6): 5 p. [Online]. Available: http://gateway.ut.ovid.come/gw1/ovidweb.cgi [6 October 2005]. NRCBL: 18.5.1; 18.3; 17.1.

Rogers, Bonnie. Research with protected populations — vulnerable participants. *AAOHN Journal* 2005 April; 53(4): 156-157. NRCBL: 18.5.1.

Rothstein, Mark A. Ethical guidelines for medical research on workers. *Journal of Occupational and Environmental Medicine* 2000 December; 42(12): 1166-1171. NRCBL: 18.5.1; 18.2; 6.

Scott, Debbie A.; Valery, Patricia C.; Boyle, Frances M.; Bain, Christopher J. Does research into sensitive areas do harm? Experiences of research participation after a child's diagnosis with Ewing's sarcoma. *Medical Journal of Australia* 2002 November 4; 177(9): 507-510. NRCBL: 18.5.1; 18.5.7; 18.4; 18.5.2. SC: em.

Seedat, Soraya; Pienaar, Willem P.; Williams, David; Stein, Daniel J. Ethics of research on survivors of trauma. *Current Psychiatry Reports* 2004 August; 6(4): 262-267. NRCBL: 18.5.1.

Siegfried, Nandi; Clarke, Mike; Volmink, Jimmy. Randomised controlled trials in Africa of HIV and AIDS: descriptive study and spatial distribution. *BMJ: British Medical Journal* 2005 October 1; 331(7519): 742- 746. NRCBL: 18.5.1; 9.5.6; 21.1. SC: em.

Abstract: OBJECTIVES: To identify and describe randomised controlled trials on HIV and AIDS conducted in Africa and to map their spatial distribution using exact geographic coordinates. DESIGN: Construction and analysis of a database of trials conducted wholly or partly in Africa and reported before 2004. DATA SOURCES: CENTRAL, Medline, Embase, and LILACS. RESULTS: Our comprehensive search yielded 284 distinct records that were potentially eligible for inclusion in the database. Of these, 150 articles reported on 77 eligible trials published or reported from 1987 to 2003. Seven trials were identified exclusively from the CENTRAL database. Trials were conducted in 18 of 48 countries in sub-Saharan Africa. None were conducted in north Africa. Only 19 had a principal investigator located in an African country. Forty two trials assessed prevention and 35 assessed treatment. Most studies were funded by government agencies outside Africa (n = 43), with the pharmaceutical industry providing partial support to 16 of these. The pharmaceutical industry provided full or partial support to a further 18 trials. Only 43 trials reported conducting a power calculation for determining sample size. There was no mention of ethical approval or informed consent in 19 and 17 trials, respectively. CONCLUSION: The relatively small number of HIV/AIDS trials conducted in Africa is not commensurate with the burden of disease. Geographical mapping as an adjunct to prospective trial registration is a useful tool for researchers and decision makers to track existing and future trials.

Singer, Merrill; Huertas, Elsa; Scott, Glenn. Am I my brother's keeper?: a case study of the responsibilities of research. *Human Organization* 2000 Winter; 59(4): 389-400. NRCBL: 18.5.1; 18.2; 9.5.6; 9.5.9.

Sodeke, Stephen. Protecting vulnerable populations: Tuskegee's National Center for Bioethics in Research and Health Care is helping to pioneer participatory methods. *Protecting Human Subjects* 2003 Fall; (9): 8-9. NRCBL: 18.5.1; 18.2.

Stokstad, Erik. EPA draft rules for human subjects draw fire [news]. *Science* 2005 July 8; 309(5732): 232. NRCBL: 18.5.1; 16.1; 18.6. SC: le. Identifiers: Environmental Protection Agency.

Swift, Patricia. Ethical considerations in research from a cancer nurse's perspective. *Professional Nurse* 2002 November; 18(3): 171-175. NRCBL: 18.5.1; 18.3. SC: an.

Treschan, Tanja A.; Scheck, Thomas; Kober, Alexander; Fleischmann, Edith; Birkenberg, Beatrice; Petschnigg, Brigitte; Akça, Ozan; Lackner, Franz X.; Jandl-Jager, Elisabeth; Sessler, Daniel I. The influence of protocol pain and risk on patients' willingness to consent for clinical studies: a randomized trial. *Anesthesia and Analgesia* 2003 February; 96(2): 498-506. NRCBL: 18.5.1; 18.3; 4.4. SC: em.

Ulrich, Connie M.; Wallen, Gwenyth R.; Feister, Autumn; Grady, Christine. Respondent burden in clinical research: when are we asking too much of subjects? [case study]. *IRB: Ethics and Human Research* 2005 July-August; 27(4): 17-20. NRCBL: 18.5.1; 18.3; 18.2. SC: cs.

Weissman, Irving. Stem cell research: paths to cancer therapies and regenerative medicine. *JAMA: The Journal of the American Medical Association* 2005 September 21; 294(11): 1359-1366. NRCBL: 18.5.1; 18.5.4; 15.1; 19.1.

Abstract: Most tissues in complex metazoans contain a rare subset of cells that, at the single-cell level, can self-renew and also give rise to mature daughter cells. Such stem cells likely in development build tissues and are retained in adult life to regenerate them. Cancers and leukemias are apparently not an exception: rare leukemia stem cells and cancer stem cells have been isolated that contain all of the tumorigenicity of the whole tumor, and it is their properties that will guide future therapies. None of this was apparent just 20 years ago, yet this kind of stem cell thinking already provides new perspectives in medical science and could usher in new therapies. Today, political, religious, and ethical issues surround embryonic stem cell and patient-specific pluripotent stem cell research and are center stage in the attempts by governments to ban these fields for discovery and potential therapies. These interventions require physicians and physician- scientists to determine for themselves whether patient welfare or personal ethics will dominate in their practices, and whether all aspects of stem cell research can be pursued in a safe and regulated fashion.

White, Robert M. Misrepresentations of the Tuskegee Study of Untreated Syphilis. *Journal of the National Medical Association* 2005 April; 97(4): 564-581. NRCBL: 18.5.1; 18.3; 10; 9.5.4. SC: rv.

White, Robert M.; Schmidt, Terri. The Tuskegee Syphilis Study and informed consent [letter and reply]. *Annals of Emergency Medicine* 2003 September; 42(3): 430-431. NRCBL: 18.5.1; 18.3; 10.

NRCBL: National Reference Center for Bioethics Literature Classification Scheme   See inside front cover for terms.

291

Williams, Michael A.; Haywood, Carlton, Jr. Critical care research on patients with advance directives or do-not-resuscitate status: ethical challenges for clinician-investigators. *Critical Care Medicine* 2003 March; 31(3, Supplement): S167-S171. NRCBL: 18.5.1; 20.5.4; 20.5.1; 7.3.

Wissow, Larry. Does the journal need a special policy for ethical aspects of research in professional education? [editorial]. *Patient Education and Counseling* 2005 January; 56(1): 1-2. NRCBL: 18.5.1; 1.3.7; 1.3.9; 7.2.

HUMAN EXPERIMENTATION/ . . . / AGED AND TERMINALLY ILL

Aapro, Matti S.; Köhne, Claus-Henning; Cohen, Harvey Jay; Extermann, Martine. Never too old? Age should not be a barrier to enrollment in cancer clinical trials. *Oncologist* 2005 March; 10(3): 198-204. NRCBL: 18.5.7; 18.2.

Addington-Hall, J. Research sensitivities to palliative care patients. *European Journal of Cancer Care* 2002; 11: 220-224. NRCBL: 18.5.7.

Agich, George; Smith, David; Levine, Robert. A challenging case: how should an IRB rule when a protocol calls for using an extremely vulnerable population: the dying? [debate]. *Protecting Human Subjects* 2005 Summer; (12): 5-6. NRCBL: 18.5.7. Identifiers: institutional review board.

Cherniack, E. Paul. Informed consent for medical research by the elderly. *Experimental Aging Research* 2002; 28: 183-198. NRCBL: 18.5.7; 18.3.

Katz, Jay. Experimentation with dying subjects. *In his:* Experimentation with Human Beings: The Authority of the Investigator, Subject, Professions, and State in the Human Experimentation Process. New York: Russell Sage Foundation; 1972: 1053-1108. NRCBL: 18.5.7.

Lyttle, C. Paul. Elderly consumers' and community nurses' experience of bereavement visiting: navigating, networking and negotiating with a local research ethics committee. *Managing Clinical Nursing* 1998 June; 2(2): 41-44. NRCBL: 18.5.7; 18.2; 4.1.3.

Maas, Meridean L.; Kelley, Lisa S.; Park, Myonghwa; Specht, Janet P. Issues in conducting research in nursing homes. *Western Journal of Nursing Research* 2002 June; 24(4): 373-389. NRCBL: 18.5.7.

McMurdo, Marion E.T.; Witham, Miles D.; Gillespie, Neil D. Including older people in clinical research [editorial]. *BMJ: British Medical Journal* 2005 November 5; 331(7524): 1036- 1037. NRCBL: 18.5.7.

Stocking, Carol B.; Hougham, Gavin W.; Baron, Aliza R.; Sachs, Greg A. Are the rules for research with subjects with dementia changing?: views from the field. *Neurology* 2003 December 23; 61(12): 1649-1651. NRCBL: 18.5.7; 18.3; 18.2; 18.5.6. SC: em.

Thombs, J.; Borthwick, N.J.; Hungerford, J.L.; Cree, I.A. Recruiting donors for autopsy based cancer research. *Journal of Medical Ethics* 2005 June; 31(6): 360-361. NRCBL: 18.5.7; 20.1.

Abstract: The use of human tissue for scientific research is a highly sensitive issue. A lack of confidence in patient recruitment is one reason for the failure of many studies to be funded and it is important therefore that recruitment procedures are as effective and sympathetic as possible. The authors recruited patients with uveal melanoma into a postmortem study investigating tumour latency in this cancer. Two approaches were used—firstly a direct approach when patients attended clinic and secondly an initial approach by mail followed by telephone contact. In the first year of study the authors had a take up rate of 88.5%, significantly higher than the average rate of 40% quoted by the National Institute for Clinical Excellence (NICE). Key features are a sympathetic personal approach by experienced oncology nurses, the provision of clear information, and the inclusion of the next of kin in the recruitment procedure.

Zermansky, Arnold G. Including care home residents in clinical research is fraught [letter]. *BMJ: British Medical Journal* 2005 November 26; 331(7527): 1271-1272. NRCBL: 18.5.7; 18.3.

HUMAN EXPERIMENTATION/ . . . / EMBRYOS AND FETUSES
See also CLONING

Consultation on Human Fertilisation and Embryology Act. *Bulletin of Medical Ethics* 2005 August-September; (210): 10-13. NRCBL: 18.5.4; 14.4. SC: le.

EUROSTEM. An ethical framework for stem cell research. *Revista de Derecho y Genoma Humano / Law and the Human Genome Review* 2005 January-June; (22): 235-248. NRCBL: 18.5.4; 19.5; 15.1; 4.4; 18.3; 8.4. SC: le.

Every little helps [editorial]. *Nature* 2005 October 20; 437(7062): 1065. NRCBL: 18.5.4; 15.1; 19.1. Identifiers: human embryonic stem-cell research.

HR 810: Stem Cell Research Enhancement Act. *GeneWatch* 2005 September-October; 18(5): 13. NRCBL: 18.5.4; 14.4; 19.5. SC: le.

Lives of the embryo [opinion]. *Christian Century* 2005 June 28; 122(13): 5. NRCBL: 18.5.4; 15.1; 1.2.

Method may yield pluripotent stem cells without killing embryos: statement of thirty-five scientists and ethicists. *Origins* 2005 July 7; 35(8): 126-128. NRCBL: 18.5.4; 15.1; 18.2.

Playing the name game: stem-cell biologists should not try to change the definition of the word 'embryo' [editorial]. *Nature* 2005 July 7; 436(7047): 2. NRCBL: 18.5.4; 14.5; 19.1; 15.1.

Stem cell debacle [editorial]. *New Scientist* 2005 December 3-9; 188(2528): 3. NRCBL: 18.5.4; 14.5; 15.1; 19.1; 1.3.9; 14.4; 14.6. Identifiers: Korea.

Stem-cell lines [editorial]. *Wall Street Journal* 2005 May 26; p. A12. NRCBL: 18.5.4; 19.1. SC: po; le.

Stem-cell probe needed [editorial]. *Nature* 2005 December 1; 438(7068): 532. NRCBL: 18.5.4; 14.5; 15.1; 19.1; 1.3.9; 14.6. Identifiers: Korea.

Turn of the tide [editorial]. *Nature Medicine* 2004 April; 10(4): 317. NRCBL: 18.5.4; 15.1; 5.3. SC: le.

Will the regulator please stand up [editorial]. *Nature* 2005 November 17; 438(7066): 257. NRCBL: 18.5.4; 15.1; 14.4; 14.5; 14.6. Identifiers: Korea.

Adams, Nathan A. An unnatural assault on natural law: regulating biotechnology using a just research theory. *In:* Colson, Charles W.; de S. Cameron, Nigel M., eds. Human Dignity in the Biotech Century: a Christian Vision for Public Policy. Downers Grove, Ill.: InterVarsity Press; 2004: 160-180. NRCBL: 18.5.4; 1.2; 18.3; 1.1; 18.6.

Aksoy, S. Making regulations and drawing up legislation in Islamic countries under conditions of uncertainty, with special reference to embryonic stem cell research. *Journal of Medical Ethics* 2005 July; 31(7): 399-403. NRCBL: 18.5.4; 1.2; 15.1. SC: le.
  Abstract: Stem cell research is a newly emerging technology that promises a wide variety of benefits for humanity. It has, however, also caused much ethical, legal, and theological debate. While some forms of its application were prohibited in the beginning, they have now started to be used in many countries. This fact obliges us to discuss the regulation of stem cell research at national and international level [sic;levels]. It is obvious that in order to make regulations and to draw up legislation at national or international levels it helps to know the perspectives of different cultures and faith traditions. In this article the issue is explored from an Islamic perspective. Firstly, some basic information is given about Islam to explain how laws are drawn up and regulations made in this tradition. Secondly, the principles on which the laws and regulations are based are applied to stem cell research, and finally the permitted and prohibited methods of stem cell research are described. The discussions throughout the paper demonstrate that while some ethicists argue that stem cell research is unethical in the Islamic tradition, tradition permits it as long as such research is aimed at improving human health.

Aldhous, Peter. After the gold rush. *Nature* 2005 April 7; 434(7034): 694-696. NRCBL: 18.5.4; 9.3.1; 14.5; 19.1; 18.6; 15.1. SC: le. Identifiers: California; United States.

Allhoff, Fritz. Stem cells and the blastocyst transfer method: some concerns regarding autonomy. *American Journal of Bioethics* 2005 November-December; 5(6): 28-30. NRCBL: 18.5.4; 4.4; 1.1. Comments: comment on S. Matthew Liao, "Rescuing human embryonic stem cell research: the blastocyst transfer method," American Journal of Bioethics 2005 November-December; 5(6): 8-16.

Austriaco, Nicanor Pier Giorgio; Hurlbut, William B. Teratomas as an ANT standard [letter and reply]. *National Catholic Bioethics Quarterly* 2005 Spring; 5(1): 10-12, 19-22. NRCBL: 18.5.4; 15.4; 4.4. Identifiers: altered nuclear transfer.

Bailey, Ronald. Are stem cells babies? The ethics of making perfect transplants. *In his:* Liberation Biology: The Scientific and Moral Case for the Biotech Revolution. Amherst, NY: Prometheus Books; 2005: 95-133. NRCBL: 18.5.4; 18.5.1; 15.1; 19.1.

Baylis, Françoise. Embryological viability. *American Journal of Bioethics* 2005 November-December; 5(6): 17-18. NRCBL: 18.5.4; 4.4. Comments: comment on S. Matthew Liao, "Rescuing human embryonic stem cell research: the blastocyst transfer method," American Journal of Bioethics 2005 November-December; 5(6): 8-16.

Belew, Kara L. Stem cell division: abortion law and its influence on the adoption of radically different embryonic stem cell legislation in the United States, the United Kingdom, and Germany. *Texas International Law Journal* 2004 Spring; 39(3): 479-519. NRCBL: 18.5.4; 12.4.1; 18.6; 4.4. SC: le.

Belluck, Pam. Massachusetts legislators endorse study of stem cells. *New York Times* 2005 April 1; p. A12. NRCBL: 18.5.4; 19.1. SC: po.

Bernal, Susan Kerr. New Jersey passes law supporting stem cell research. *Journal of Andrology* 2004 May-June; 25(3): 314-316. NRCBL: 18.5.4; 15.1. SC: le.

Bortolotti, Lisa; Harris, John. Stem cell research, personhood and sentience. *Reproductive BioMedicine Online [electronic]* 2005 March; 10(Supplement 1): 68-75. Available: http://www.rbmonline.com/Article/1587 [12 September 2005]. NRCBL: 18.5.4; 15.1; 4.4.

Bosch, Xavier. Changing ethics rules land Spanish stem cell scientist in hot water [news]. *Nature Medicine* 2005 December; 11(12): 1262. NRCBL: 18.5.4; 15.1; 8.3.1.

Bosch, Xavier. Embryo research stirs up Spanish spat [news]. *Nature Medicine* 2004 April; 10(4): 320. NRCBL: 18.5.4; 15.1; 19.5. SC: le.

Bradford, Barry. Arguing about the use of stem cells [letter]. *Science* 2005 July 1; 309(5731): 51. NRCBL: 18.5.4.

Brainard, Jeffrey. House challenges Bush's limits on embryonic-stem-cell research. *Chronicle of Higher Education* 2005 June 3; 51(39): A17. NRCBL: 18.5.4; 15.1.

Brainard, Jeffrey. National academies report recommends tighter rules for stem-cell research. *Chronicle of Higher Education* 2005 May 6; 51(35): A25. NRCBL: 18.5.4; 18.2; 19.5; 22.2.

Brainard, Jeffrey. NIH sets up national stem-cell bank in Wisconsin [news]. *Chronicle of Higher Education* 2005

NRCBL: National Reference Center for Bioethics Literature Classification Scheme   See inside front cover for terms.

293

October 14; 52(8): 24. NRCBL: 18.5.4; 15.1. Identifiers: National Institutes of Health.

Braude, Peter; Minger, Stephen L.; Warwick, Ruth M. Stem cell therapy: hope or hype? Safety and quality must be assured before this treatment can really benefit patients [editorial]. *BMJ: British Medical Journal* 2005 May 21; 330(7501): 1159-1160. NRCBL: 18.5.4; 15.1; 19.5; 19.1; 18.6; 5.3; 21.1.

Brehany, John. Nontraditional sources of pluripotent stem cells: a new chapter in the debate about embryonic stem cell research. *Health Care Ethics USA [electronic]* 2005; 13(2); 3 p. Available: http://www.slu.edu/centers/chce/hceusa/2_2005_3.html [19 September 2005]. NRCBL: 18.5.4; 15.1.

British Fertility Society; Murdoch, Alison; Fleming, Richard; Hamilton, Mark; Mills, John. Human embryonic stem cell research. *Human Reproduction and Genetic Ethics: An International Journal* 2001; 7(1): 14. NRCBL: 18.5.4; 15.1.

Brogaard, Berit. The moral status of the human embryo: the twinning argument. *Free Inquiry* 2002-2003 Winter; 23(1): 45-48. NRCBL: 18.5.4; 15.1; 4.4.

Brouillet, Miriam; Turner, Leigh. Bioethics, religion, and democratic deliberation: policy formation and embryonic stem cell research. *HEC (Healthcare Ethics Committee) Forum* 2005 March; 17(1): 49- 63. NRCBL: 18.5.4; 4.4; 5.3; 1.3.5; 1.1.

Brush, Silla. Hoping to avoid brain drain, states push to finance stem-cell research. *Chronicle of Higher Education* 2005 February 4; 51(22): A22. NRCBL: 18.5.4; 1.3.9.

Burke, William J.; Pullicino, Patrick; Richard, Edward J.; Condic, Maureen. Stemming the tide of cloning [letter and reply]. *First Things* 2005 December; (158): 6-9. NRCBL: 18.5.4; 15.1. Identifiers: oocyte-assisted reprogramming (OAR); altered nuclear transfer (ANT).

Burkli, Peter. Zur Stammzelldiskussion in der Schweiz. *In:* Maio, Giovanni; Just, Hanjörg, eds. Die Forschung an embryonalen Stammzellen in ethischer und rechtlicher Perspektive. Baden-Baden: Nomos Verlagsgesellschaft; 2003: 119-123. NRCBL: 18.5.4; 15.1. SC: le.

Byravan, Sujatha; Annas, George. The year of the stem cell: George Annas talks about the future of stem cell research in America. *GeneWatch* 2005 September-October; 18(5): 12-15. NRCBL: 18.5.4; 14.4; 19.5; 8.3.1. Identifiers: Stem Cell Research Enhancement Act.

Byrnes, W. Malcom. Why human "altered nuclear transfer" is unethical: a holistic systems view. *National Catholic Bioethics Quarterly* 2005 Summer; 5(2): 271- 279. NRCBL: 18.5.4; 15.4; 4.4; 2.4. SC: an.

Cahill, Lisa Sowle; Lauritzen, Paul. Our posthuman future: discussing the consequences of biotechnological ad-

vances [letter and reply]. *Hastings Center Report* 2005 November-December; 35(6): 5-7. NRCBL: 18.5.4; 15.1; 4.5.

Callahan, Sidney; Chervenak, Frank A.; McCullough, Laurence B. Ethics and fetal research [discussion]. *Medical Ethics Newsletter [Lahey Clinic]* 2003 Spring; 10(2): 10-11. NRCBL: 18.5.4; 9.5.8; 9.5.5.

Campbell, Amy T. In search of a real "third way" in process and outcome. *American Journal of Bioethics* 2005 November-December; 5(6): 66-68. NRCBL: 18.5.4; 12.3. Comments: comment on Lawrence J. Nelson and Michael J. Meyer, "Confronting deep moral disagreement: the President's Council on Bioethics, moral status, and human embryos," American Journal of Bioethics 2005 November-December; 5(6): 33-42.

Campbell, Angela; Nycum, Gillian. Harmonizing the international regulation of embryonic stem cell research: possibilities, promises and potential pitfalls. *Medical Law International* 2005; 7(2): 113-148. NRCBL: 18.5.4; 14.5; 15.1; 18.2; 5.3; 18.6; 21.1. SC: le.

Casell, Jason H. Lengthening the stem: allowing federally funded researchers to derive human pluripotent stem cells from embryos. *University of Michigan Journal of Law Reform* 2001 Spring; 34(3): 547-572. NRCBL: 18.5.4; 15.1; 19.5; 14.4; 18.6. SC: le.

Catenhusen, Michael. Ist das Tor auf? Das Stammzellgesetz und die Zukunft des Embryonenschutzgesetzes. *In:* Maio, Giovanni; Just, Hanjörg, eds. Die Forschung an embryonalen Stammzellen in ethischer und rechtlicher Perspektive. Baden-Baden: Nomos Verlagsgesellschaft; 2003: 239-247. NRCBL: 18.5.4; 19.1; 15.1. SC: le.

Chalmers, Don; Nicol, Dianne. Embryonic stem cell research: can the law balance ethical, scientific and economic values? (Part II). *Revista de Derecho y Genoma Humano / Law and the Human Genome Review* 2003 July-December; (19): 91-108. NRCBL: 18.5.4; 19.5; 15.1; 18.2. SC: le.

Check, Erika. Altered embryos offered as solution to stem-cell rift [news]. *Nature* 2005 July 21; 436(7049): 309. NRCBL: 18.5.4; 15.1; 19.1. SC: le.

Check, Erika. UK embryo licence draws global attention [news]. *Nature* 2005 September 15; 437(7057): 305. NRCBL: 18.5.4; 14.1; 15.1. Identifiers: United Kingdom (Great Britain).

Check, Erika. US experts draw up guidelines for stem-cell research [news]. *Nature* 2005 April 28; 434(7037): 1058. NRCBL: 18.5.4; 2.4; 19.1; 15.1.

Check, Erika; Cyranoski, David. Korean scandal will have global fallout [news]. *Nature* 2005 December 22-29;

438(7071): 1056-1057. NRCBL: 18.5.4; 1.3.9; 15.1; 19.1. Identifiers: Korea.

Check, Erika; Cyranoski, David. Korea's accelerating stem-cell work prompts calls for global ethical rules [news]. *Nature* 2005 May 26; 435(7041): 393. NRCBL: 18.5.4; 19.1; 15.1.

Chervenak, F.A.; McCullough, L.B. Ethics on the frontier of fetal research. *In:* Carrera, Jose M.; Chervenak, Frank A.; Kurjak, Asim, eds. Controversies in Perinatal Medicine: Studies on the Fetus as a Patient. New York: Parthenon Pub. Group; 2003: 296-302. NRCBL: 18.5.4.

Chervenak, Frank A.; McCullough, Laurence B. An ethical framework for fetal research. *Medical Ethics Newsletter [Lahey Clinic]* 2003 Winter; 10(1): 1-2. NRCBL: 18.5.4; 9.5.8; 9.5.5.

Chervenak, Frank A.; McCullough, Laurence B.; Birnbach, David J. Ethical issues in fetal surgery research. *Best Practice and Research: Clinical Anaesthesiology* 2004 June; 18(2): 221-230. NRCBL: 18.5.4; 18.5.3; 18.3.

Cheshire, William P., Jr.; Jones, Nancy L. Can artificial techniques supply morally neutral human embryos for research? *Ethics and Medicine* 2005 Summer; 21(2): 73-88. NRCBL: 18.5.4; 15.1; 4.4; 1.1.

Clausen, Jens. Zelltherapie unter Verwendung adulter Stammzellen oder solcher aus geklonten Embyonen? *In:* Maio, Giovanni; Just, Hanjörg, eds. Die Forschung an embryonalen Stammzellen in ethischer und rechtlicher Perspektive. Baden-Baden: Nomos Verlagsgesellschaft; 2003: 196-213. NRCBL: 18.5.4; 1.1; 14.5; 19.1; 15.1.

Coghlan, Andy. Are all human embryos equal? [news]. *New Scientist* 2005 October 22-28; 188(2522): 10-11. NRCBL: 18.5.4; 14.5; 15.1; 19.1.

Cohen, Eric. Orphans by design [opinion]. *First Things* 2005 December; (158): 13-15. NRCBL: 18.5.4; 15.1; 14.4; 4.4; 2.4. Identifiers: President's Council on Bioethics.

Condic, Maureen L. Stem cells and babies. *First Things* 2005 August-September; (155): 12-13. NRCBL: 18.5.4; 15.1; 2.4. Identifiers: altered nuclear transfer- oocyte assisted reprogramming (ANT-OAR); President's Council on Bioethics.

Condic, Maureen L.; Condic, Samuel B.; Hurlbut, William B. Producing non-embryonic organisms for stem cells [letter and reply]. *National Catholic Bioethics Quarterly* 2005 Spring; 5(1): 13- 15, 19-22. NRCBL: 18.5.4; 15.4; 4.4.

Cook, Gareth. 94 new cell lines created abroad since Bush decision. *Boston Globe* 2004 May 23; p. A14. NRCBL: 18.5.4; 15.1; 1.3.5; 5.2; 21.1.

Cregan, Kate. Ethical and social issues of embryonic stem cell technology. *Internal Medicine Journal* 2005 February; 35(2): 126-127. NRCBL: 18.5.4; 15.1; 14.5; 5.1.

Crombie, H. David. Stem cell research: ethical concerns — 'great expectations'. *Connecticut Medicine* 2005 February; 69(2): 109. NRCBL: 18.5.4; 15.1; 18.6.

Cyranoski, David. Japan sets rules for stem cell research [news]. *Nature Medicine* 2004 August; 10(8): 763. NRCBL: 18.5.4; 15.1; 5.3.

Cyranoski, David. Japan's embryo experts beg for faster ethical reviews [news]. *Nature* 2005 November 17; 438(7066): 263. NRCBL: 18.5.4; 15.1; 18.2.

Cyranoski, David. Korean stem-cell crisis deepens [news]. *Nature* 2005 November 24; 438(7067): 405. NRCBL: 18.5.4; 14.5; 15.1; 19.1; 1.3.9; 14.6.

Cyranoski, David. TV tests call into question cloner's stem-cell success [news]. *Nature* 2005 December 8; 438(7069): 718. NRCBL: 18.5.4; 1.3.9; 14.5; 15.1; 19.1. Identifiers: Korea.

Cyranoski, David; Check, Erika. Clone star admits lies over eggs [news]. *Nature* 2005 December 1; 438(7068): 536-537. NRCBL: 18.5.4; 14.5; 15.1; 19.1; 1.3.9; 14.6. Identifiers: Korea.

Cyranoski, David; Check, Erika. Stem-cell brothers divide [news]. *Nature* 2005 November 17; 438(7066): 262-263. NRCBL: 18.5.4; 15.1; 14.4; 14.5; 14.6. Identifiers: Korea.

Daar, A.S.; Bhatt, A.; Court, E.; Singer, P.A. Stem cell research and transplantation: science leading ethics. *Transplantation Proceedings* 2004 October; 36(8): 2504-2506. NRCBL: 18.5.4; 15.1; 19.1.

Daley, George Q.; Sandel, Michael J.; Moreno, Jonathan D. Stem cell research: science, ethics and policy. *Medical Ethics Newsletter [Lahey Clinic]* 2005 Winter; 12(1): 5-8. NRCBL: 18.5.4; 15.1; 18.6.

Dalton, Rex. California prepares to roll out stem-cell funding [news]. *Nature* 2005 October 6; 437(7060): 800-801. NRCBL: 18.5.4; 15.1; 19.1. Identifiers: California Institute for Regenerative Medicine (CIRM).

DeBaets, Amy Michelle. Patents, royalties, and publicly funded stem cell research. *Ethics and Medicine* 2005 Fall; 21(3): 188-190. NRCBL: 18.5.4; 15.1; 15.8; 9.4.

Deckers, Jan. Why current UK legislation on embryo research is immoral. How the argument from lack of qualities and the argument from potentiality have been applied and why they should be rejected. *Bioethics* 2005 June; 19(3): 251-271. NRCBL: 18.5.4; 15.1; 19.1; 19.5. SC: le; an.
Abstract: On 22 January 2001, the UK became the first country to approve of embryonic stem cell research by passing the Human Fertilisation (Research Purposes) Regulations 2001, which legislated new research purposes for which early em-

---

NRCBL: National Reference Center for Bioethics Literature Classification Scheme   See inside front cover for terms.

295

bryos can be used, in addition to those approved by the Human Fertilisation and Embryology Act 1990. Legal advisory committees, most notably the Chief Medical Officer's Expert Group and the House of Lords' Select Committee, have offered various reasons, which can also be found in the ethics literature, to justify this change. Those examined here are the views that: 1. Early embryos lack relevant qualities (or 'the argument from lack of qualities') and 2. Early embryos only have a potentiality to become humans with moral status (or 'the argument from potentiality'). The validity of these arguments is questioned and a case is made for egalitarian speciesism. Embryos have moral status (used here in the restricted sense of the status possessed by all members of the class of beings which deserve the greatest moral significance in equal measure). They have more value than the value that should be assigned to non-human beings from the start of fertilisation. Current UK legislation on embryo research is immoral.

Dennis, Carina. Korea launches network to share cloning information [news]. *Nature* 2005 October 20; 437(7062): 1077. NRCBL: 18.5.4; 14.5; 15.1; 19.1.

Dennis, Carina; Check, Erika. 'Ethical' routes to stem cells highlight political divide [news]. *Nature* 2005 October 20; 437(7062): 1076-1077. NRCBL: 18.5.4; 15.1; 19.1.

Deutsch, Erwin. Research and use of stem cells. *Revista de Derecho y Genoma-Humano / Law and the Human Genome Review* 2004 July-December; (21): 51-65. NRCBL: 18.5.4; 19.5; 15.1; 18.3; 4.4. SC: le. Note: Abstract in English and Spanish.

Devolder, Katrien. Human embryonic stem cell research: why the discarded-created- distinction cannot be based on the potentiality argument. *Bioethics* 2005 April; 19(2): 167-186. NRCBL: 18.5.4; 15.1; 4.4. SC: an.
Abstract: Discussions about the use and derivation of pluripotent human embryonic stem cells are a stumbling block in developing public policy on stem cell research. On the one hand there is a broad consensus on the benefits of these cells for science and biomedicine; on the other hand there is the controversial issue of killing human embryos. I will focus on the compromise position that accepts research on spare embryos, but not on research embryos ('discarded-created-distinction', from now on d-c-d). I will point out that this viewpoint is hard to maintain. The main focus is that the 'revealed beliefs' of its defenders are inconsistent with their 'professed beliefs', more specifically with their main argument, i.e. the potentiality argument. I will point out that (1) the defenders of d-c-d actually grant a relative moral status to the human embryo, (2) this moral status is dependent on internal and external criteria of potentiality, (3) potentiality seen as a variable value that also depends on external criteria cannot justify d-c-d, and (4) an approach to human embryonic stem cell-research that would also allow the use of research embryos is more compatible with the feelings, attitudes and values of those who currently defend d-c-d and, therefore, could lead to a broader consensus and to actions that alleviate individual human suffering.

Devolder, K. Advance directives to protect embryos? [editorial]. *Journal of Medical Ethics* 2005 September; 31(9): 497-498. NRCBL: 18.5.4; 20.5.4.

Devolder, K. Creating and sacrificing embryos for stem cells. *Journal of Medical Ethics* 2005 June; 31(6): 366-370. NRCBL: 18.5.4; 15.1; 19.1. SC: an.
Abstract: The compromise position that accepts the use and derivation of stem cells from spare in vitro fertilisation embryos but opposes the creation of embryos for these purposes is a very weak ethical position. This paper argues that whatever the basis is on which defenders of this viewpoint accord intrinsic value to the embryo, once they accept the creation and sacrifice of embryos to benefit infertile people with a child-wish, they do not have a sound moral argument to condemn the creation and sacrifice of embryos to benefit ill and injured people.

Dhai, A.; Moodley, J.; McQuoid-Mason, D.J.; Rodeck, C. Ethical and legal controversies in cloning for biomedical research — a South African perspective. *South African Medical Journal* 2004 November; 94(11): 906-909. NRCBL: 18.5.4.

Diamond, Eugene F. Stem cells and the culture wars. *Linacre Quarterly* 2005 August; 72(3): 240-245. NRCBL: 18.5.4; 14.5; 1.2.

Doerflinger, Richard M. Washington insider. Federal funding for embryonic stem cell researcj. *National Catholic Bioethics Quarterly* 2005 Autumn; 5(3): 455- 462. NRCBL: 18.5.4; 15.1; 14.4; 19.4; 9.3.1; 2.4.

Doerflinger, Richard M. Washington insider. The elections and Congress: a continued statement on embryo research? *National Catholic Bioethics Quarterly* 2005 Spring; 5(1): 25-33. NRCBL: 18.5.4; 15.1; 14.5.

Dresser, Rebecca. Research ethics and maternal-fetal surgery. *In:* Kodish, Eric, ed. Ethics and Research with Children: A Case-Based Approach. New York: Oxford University Press; 2005: 223- 240. NRCBL: 18.5.4; 18.5.3; 9.5.8; 9.5.5.

Dresser, Rebecca. Stem cell research: the bigger picture. *Perspectives in Biology and Medicine* 2005 Spring; 48(2): 181-194. NRCBL: 18.5.4; 15.1; 19.5; 4.4; 14.4; 9.4.

Eckart, Wolfgang U. Medical experiments at the colonial periphery: the fight against sleeping sickness in German East Africa and Togo. *In:* Roelcke, Volker; Maio, Giovanni, eds. Twentieth Century Ethics of Human Subjects Research: Historical Perspectives on Values, Practices, and Regulations. Stuttgart: Franz Steiner Verlag; 2004: 65-82. NRCBL: 18.5.4; 2.2; 21.1.

Edwards, Brian E.; Gearhart, John D.; Wallach, Edward E. The human pluripotent stem cell: impact on medicine and society. *Fertility and Sterility* 2000 July; 74(1): 1-7. NRCBL: 18.5.4; 15.1; 19.5; 18.6.

Edwards, R.G. Cloning and embryo stem cells meet further but limited approvals. *Reproductive BioMedicine Online [electronic]* 2005 January; 10(1): 141. Available: http://www.rbmonline.com/index.html [17 February 2006]. NRCBL: 18.5.4; 15.1; 14.5; 21.1; 18.6.

Egan, Richard; Hurlbut, William B. The burden of proof [letter and reply]. *National Catholic Bioethics Quarterly* 2005 Spring; 5(1): 12- 13, 19-22. NRCBL: 18.5.4; 15.4; 4.4.

Ekemo, Afton. Government support for embryonic stem cell research. *Journal of Biolaw and Business* 2005; 8(4): 66-67. NRCBL: 18.5.4; 15.1; 19.5; 5.3.

European Commission. European Group on Ethics in Science and New Technologies. Ethical aspects of human stem cell research and use. *Human Reproduction and Genetic Ethics: An International Journal* 2001; 7(1): 7. NRCBL: 18.5.4; 15.1; 18.5.1.

Fabbro, Ronald. Stem cell research, cloning and Catholic moral theology. *Linacre Quarterly* 2005 November; 72(4): 294-306. NRCBL: 18.5.4; 14.5; 1.2; 4.4.

Fahr, Uwe; Reiter-Theil, Stella; Rubin, Beatrix P. Ethik, Weltanschauung, Wissenschaft. Zur Kontroverse um die Stammzellforschung. *In:* Baumann, Eva; Brink, Alexander; May, Arnd T.; Schröder, Peter; Schutzeichel, Corinna Iris, eds. Weltanschauliche Offenheit in der Bioethik. Berlin: Duncker & Humblot; 2004: 233-256. NRCBL: 18.5.4; 15.1; 21.1.

Fischbach, Gerald D.; Fischbach, Ruth L. Stem cells: science, policy, and ethics. *Journal of Clinical Investigation* 2004 November; 114(10): 1364-1370. NRCBL: 18.5.4.

Fowler, Heather L. Misapplied ethical considerations: U.S. federal stem cell mandates lack global focus and market foresight. *Cornell International Law Journal* 2004; 36(3): 521-544. NRCBL: 18.5.4; 18.6; 4.4; 15.1; 19.5. SC: le.

Fox, Cynthia. Cloning laws, policies, and attitudes worldwide. *IEEE Engineering in Medicine and Biology Magazine* 2004 March-April; 23(2): 55-61. NRCBL: 18.5.4; 15.1; 5.3.

Friedmann, Theodore. Lessons for the stem cell discourse from the gene therapy experience. *Perspectives in Biology and Medicine* 2005 Autumn; 48(4): 585-591. NRCBL: 18.5.4; 15.1; 15.4.

Fukuyama, Francis. Human biomedicine and the problem of governance. *Perspectives in Biology and Medicine* 2005 Spring; 48(2): 195-200. NRCBL: 18.5.4; 15.1; 19.5; 4.4; 5.3; 2.4.

Ganten, Detlev. Selbstkontrolle und Vertrauen in die Wissenschaft. *In:* Maio, Giovanni; Just, Hanjörg, eds. Die Forschung an embryonalen Stammzellen in ethischer und rechtlicher Perspektive. Baden-Baden: Nomos Verlagsgesellschaft; 2003: 229-238. NRCBL: 18.5.4; 15.1.

Ganthaler, Heinrich. Experimentation on human embryos: the bioethical discussion in Europe with special at-tention to Austria and Germany. *In:* Brannigan, Michael C., ed. Cross-Cultural Biotechnology. Lanham: Rowman amd Littlefield; 2004: 71-79. NRCBL: 18.5.4; 15.1; 21.1. SC: an.

Garwood-Gowers, Austen. Contemporary issues in the regulation of artificial reproduction and embryology in the UK. *Revista de Derecho y Genoma-Humano / Law and the Human Genome Review* 2004 July-December; (21): 67-101. NRCBL: 18.5.4; 14.5; 15.2; 15.5; 18.3; 8.4; 18.6; 5.3. SC: le. Identifiers: United Kingdom (Great Britain). Note: Abstract in English and Spanish.

Gilbert, David M. The future of human embryonic stem cell research: addressing ethical conflict with responsible scientific research. *Medical Science Monitor* 2004 May; 10(5): RA99-RA103. NRCBL: 18.5.4; 15.1; 1.3.9; 19.5.

Glasner, Peter. Banking on immortality? Exploring the stem cell supply chain from embryo to therapeutic application. *Current Sociology* 2005 March; 53(2): 355-366. NRCBL: 18.5.4; 1.2; 15.1; 19.5. Identifiers: United Kingdom (Great Britain).

Glenn, David. In South Korea, ethics questions prompt a stem-cell pioneer to resign a top post. *Chronicle of Higher Education* 2005 December 9; 52(16): 35. NRCBL: 18.5.4; 7.4; 19.5.

Gross, Michael. Swiss back stem-cell studies [news]. *Current Biology* 2005 January 26; 15(2): R35. NRCBL: 18.5.4; 15.1; 18.6. SC: le. Identifiers: Switzerland.

Guenin, Louis M. A failed noncomplicity scheme. *Stem Cells and Development* 2004 October; 13(5): 456-459. NRCBL: 18.5.4; 15.1; 18.6; 1.1. SC: an. Comments: comment on John A. Robertson, "Causative vs. beneficial complicity in the embryonic stem cell debate," Connecticut Law Review 2004 Summer; 36(4): 1099-1113.

Harris, John; Bortolotti, Lisa; Irving, Louise. An ethical framework for stem cell research in the European Union. *Health Care Analysis: An International Journal of Health Care Philosophy and Policy* 2005 September; 13(3): 157-162. NRCBL: 18.5.4; 15.1; 21.1.
Abstract: The European Union is a nightmare from the perspective of the ethics and regulation of science. A hitherto insoluble problem has been the task of drafting ethical principles which do not founder on the radically different attitudes taken to the question of the moral status of the human embryo. Following the conclusions reached in an international project, EUROSTEM, we suggest that this problem can be solved by concentration on the scope of principles and we emphasize that European research should be funded in a way that does not discriminate between individual states and researchers in the EU. Finally, we observe that the availability of any eventual embryonic stem cell therapies will pose a dilemma for those countries and those people that have declared stem cell research to be unacceptable.

Heilig, Steve; Blackburn, Elizabeth. Stem cell science and politics: a talk with Elizabeth Blackburn [interview]. *CQ: Cambridge Quarterly of Healthcare Ethics* 2005

NRCBL: National Reference Center for Bioethics Literature Classification Scheme   See inside front cover for terms.

297

Spring; 14(2): 214-217. NRCBL: 18.5.4; 5.3; 2.4; 1.3.5; 7.1.

Höfling, Wolfram. Die Forschung an embryonalen Stammzellen in verfassungsrechtlicher Perspektive. *In:* Maio, Giovanni; Just, Hanjörg, eds. Die Forschung an embryonalen Stammzellen in ethischer und rechtlicher Perspektive. Baden-Baden: Nomos Verlagsgesellschaft; 2003: 141-155. NRCBL: 18.5.4; 4.4; 15.1. SC: le.

Holden, Constance. California's bold $3 billion initiative hits the ground running [news]. *Science* 2005 January 14; 307(5707): 195. NRCBL: 18.5.4; 15.1; 5.3. Identifiers: California Institute for Regenerative Medicine (CIRM).

Holden, Constance. Restiveness grows at NIH over Bush research restrictions [news]. *Science* 2005 April 15; 308(5720): 334-335. NRCBL: 18.5.4; 15.1; 5.3. Identifiers: National Institutes of Health.

Holm, Søren. The blastocyst transfer method cannot rescue human embryonic stem cell research. *American Journal of Bioethics* 2005 November-December; 5(6): 20-21. NRCBL: 18.5.4. Comments: comment on S. Matthew Liao, "Rescuing human embryonic stem cell research: the blastocyst transfer method," American Journal of Bioethics 2005 November-December; 5(6): 8-16.

Huarte, Joachim; Suarez, Antoine; Hurlbut, William B. An unanswered question [letter and reply]. *National Catholic Bioethics Quarterly* 2005 Spring; 5(1): 9, 19-22. NRCBL: 18.5.4; 15.4; 4.4. Identifiers: altered nuclear transfer.

Hurlbut, William B. Altered nuclear transfer as a morally acceptable means for the procurement of human embryonic stem cells. *National Catholic Bioethics Quarterly* 2005 Spring; 5(1): 145- 151. NRCBL: 18.5.4; 15.4; 4.4.

Hurlbut, William B. Altered nuclear transfer as a morally acceptable means for the procurement of human embryonic stem cells. *Perspectives in Biology and Medicine* 2005 Spring; 48(2): 211-228. NRCBL: 18.5.4; 15.1; 19.5; 4.4; 18.5.1; 14.5.

Hurlbut, William B.; Melton, Douglas A.; Daley, George Q.; Jennings, Charles G. Altered nuclear transfer [letter and reply]. *New England Journal of Medicine* 2005 March 17; 352(11): 1153- 1154. NRCBL: 18.5.4; 15.1.

Inman, Mason. Divided committee urges less restriction on embryo research [news]. *Science* 2005 April 1; 308(5718): 30. NRCBL: 18.5.4; 15.1; 5.3. Identifiers: United Kingdom (Great Britain).

Isasi, Rosario M.; Knoppers, Bartha Maria; Singer, Peter A.; Daar, Abdallah S. Legal and ethical approaches to stem cell and cloning research: a comparative analysis of policies in Latin America, Asia, and Africa. *Journal of Law, Medicine and Ethics* 2004 Winter; 32(4): 626- 640. NRCBL: 18.5.4; 14.5; 4.4; 18.6. SC: an; le.

Jayaraman, K.S. Indian regulations fail to monitor growing stem-cell use in clinics [news]. *Nature* 2005 March 17; 434(7031): 259. NRCBL: 18.5.4; 19.1; 15.1. SC: le.

Johnson, Alissa. Stem cell research. *NCSL Legisbrief* 2005 March; 13(15): 1-2. NRCBL: 18.5.4; 15.1; 14.5; 18.6. SC: le.

Johnston, Josephine. Stem cell protocols: the NAS guidelines are a useful start. *Hastings Center Report* 2005 November-December; 35(6): 16-17. NRCBL: 18.5.4; 15.1; 18.2. Identifiers: National Academy of Sciences.

Jones, D.A. The human embryo in the Christian tradition: a reconsideration. *Journal of Medical Ethics* 2005 December; 31(12): 710-713. NRCBL: 18.5.4; 1.2; 4.4; 12.3.
Abstract: Recent claims that the Christian tradition justifies destructive research on human embryos have drawn upon an article by the late Professor Gordon Dunstan which appeared in this journal in 1984. Despite its undoubted influence, this article was flawed and seriously misrepresented the tradition of Christian reflection on the moral status of the human embryo.

Jones, Nancy L.; Cheshire, William P., Jr. Can artificial techniques supply morally neutral human embryos for research? Part I. Creating novel categories of human embryos. *Ethics and Medicine* 2005 Spring; 21(1): 29-40. NRCBL: 18.5.4; 15.1.

Jonsen, Albert R. Cloning and stem cell research. *In his:* Bioethics Beyond the Headlines: Who Lives? Who Dies? Who Decides? Lanham, MD: Rowman and Littlefield; 2005: 127-138. NRCBL: 18.5.4; 14.5; 15.1.

Kass, Leon R. A way forward on stem cells [opinion]. *Washington Post* 2005 July 12; p. A21. NRCBL: 18.5.4. SC: po.

Kavanaugh, John F. Leftover embryos: 'this is not junk science'. *America* 2005 June 20-27; 192(21): 8. NRCBL: 18.5.4; 15.1; 4.4; 1.2; 12.3.

Kelly, David F. Embryonic stem cells and the beginning of personhood. *In his:* Contemporary Catholic Health Care Ethics. Washington, DC: Georgetown University Press; 2004: 245-254. NRCBL: 18.5.4; 4.4; 15.1; 1.2.

Kerstein, Samuel J. Extra embryos. *Maryland Medicine* 2003 Summer; 4(3): 31-33. NRCBL: 18.5.4; 14.4; 4.4.

Kian, Catherine Tay Swee; Leng, Tien Sim. The Singapore approach to human stem cell research, therapeutic and reproductive cloning. *Bioethics* 2005 June; 19(3): 290-303. NRCBL: 18.5.4; 15.1; 19.1; 19.5; 14.5; 21.1. SC: le.

Kiessling, Ann A. Eggs alone — human parthenotes: an ethical source of stem cells for therapies? *Nature* 2005 March 10; 434(7030): 145. NRCBL: 18.5.4; 14.6; 19.1; 15.1.

SC (Subject Caption):   an=analytical   cs=case studies   em=empirical   le=legal   po=popular   rv=review

Klein, Robert. The next big thing [opinion]. *New Scientist* 2005 August 6-12; 187(2511): 19. NRCBL: 18.5.4; 15.1. Identifiers: California.

Koch, Hans-Georg. Vom Embryonenschutzgesetz zum Stammzellgesetz: Überlegungen zum Status des Embryos in vitro aus rechtlicher und rechtsvergleichender Sicht. *In:* Maio, Giovanni; Just, Hanjörg, eds. Die Forschung an embryonalen Stammzellen in ethischer und rechtlicher Perspektive. Baden-Baden: Nomos Verlagsgesellschaft; 2003: 97-118. NRCBL: 18.5.4; 14.4; 15.1. SC: le.

Körtner, Ulrich H.J. Forschung an embryonalen Stammzellen—Zur Diskussion und Gesetzeslage in Österreich. *In:* Maio, Giovanni; Just, Hanjörg, eds. Die Forschung an embryonalen Stammzellen in ethischer und rechtlicher Perspektive. Baden-Baden: Nomos Verlagsgesellschaft; 2003: 124-140. NRCBL: 18.5.4; 1.2; 15.1. SC: le. Identifiers: Austria.

Kostka, Ulrike. Die Reproduktionsmedizin im Kontext der Stammzellforschung. *In:* Maio, Giovanni; Just, Hanjörg, eds. Die Forschung an embryonalen Stammzellen in ethischer und rechtlicher Perspektive. Baden-Baden: Nomos Verlagsgesellschaft; 2003: 32-41. NRCBL: 18.5.4; 14.4; 15.1; 19.5.

Kuehn, Bridget M. Advances aim to ease stem cell concerns [news]. *JAMA: The Journal of the American Medical Association* 2005 November 23-20; 294(20): 2557-2558. NRCBL: 18.5.4; 15.1.

Landry, Donald W.; Zucker, Howard A. Embryonic death and the creation of human embryonic stem cells. *Journal of Clinical Investigation* 2004 November; 114(9): 1184-1186. NRCBL: 18.5.4; 19.5; 20.2.1.

Lauritzen, Paul. Stem cells, biotechnology, and human rights: implications for a posthuman future. *Hastings Center Report* 2005 March-April; 35(2): 25-33. NRCBL: 18.5.4; 15.1; 2.1; 4.4; 7.1. SC: an.

Liao, S. Matthew. Rescuing human embryonic stem cell research: the blastocyst transfer method. *American Journal of Bioethics* 2005 November-December; 5(6): 8- 16. NRCBL: 18.5.4; 18.3; 4.4; 21.1.

Abstract: Despite the therapeutic potential of human embryonic stem (HES) cells, many people believe that HES cell research should be banned. The reason is that the present method of extracting HES cells involves the destruction of the embryo, which for many is the beginning of a person. This paper examines a number of compromise solutions such as parthenogenesis, the use of defective embryos, genetically creating a "pseudo embryo" that can never form a placenta, and determining embryo death, and argues that none of these proposals are likely to satisfy embryoists, that is, those who regard the embryo as a person. This paper then proposes a method of extracting HES cells, what might be called the Blastocyst Transfer Method, that meets the ethical requirements of embryoists, and it considers some possible concerns regarding this method. It concludes by encouraging future HES cell research to investigate this method.

Liao, S. Matthew. Response to commentators on "Rescuing human embryonic stem cell research: the blastocyst transfer method". *American Journal of Bioethics [Online]* 2005 November- December; 5(6): W10-W13. NRCBL: 18.5.4; 4.4.

Lippman, Abby; Newman, Stuart A.; Testa, Giuseppe; Harris, John. The ethics of deriving gametes from ES cells [letter and reply]. *Science* 2005 January 28; 307(5709): 515, 517. NRCBL: 18.5.4; 15.1; 10; 14.4. Identifiers: embryonic stem cells.

Lougheed, Tim. New US guidelines for research on human embryos [news]. *CMAJ/JAMC: Canadian Medical Association Journal* 2005 June 21; 172(13): 1672. NRCBL: 18.5.4; 18.2. SC: le. Identifiers: National Academy of Sciences (NAS).

Mackler, Aaron L. Jewish perspectives on embryo and stem cell research. *In:* Peppin, John F.; Cherry, Mark J., eds. Religious Perspectives in Bioethics. New York: Taylor & Francis; 2004: 147- 152. NRCBL: 18.5.4; 1.2; 15.1.

Magnus, David; Cho, Mildred K. Issues in oocyte donation for stem cell research. *Science* 2005 June 17; 308(5729): 1747-1748. NRCBL: 18.5.4; 19.5; 18.5.3; 18.3; 21.1; 1.3.7. Identifiers: Korea.

Mandavilli, Apoorva. Scientists seek simple remedies to cloning conundrums [news]. *Nature Medicine* 2005 May; 11(5): 459. NRCBL: 18.5.4; 15.1.

Mandavilli, Apoorva. Woo-Suk Hwang. *Nature Medicine* 2005 May; 11(5): 464. NRCBL: 18.5.4; 15.1.

Marquis, Don. Stem cell research: the failure of bioethics. *Free Inquiry* 2002-2003 Winter; 23(1): 40-44. NRCBL: 18.5.4; 15.1.

Martin, John. Collaboration in cardiovascular stem-cell research [opinion]. *Lancet* 2005 June 18-24; 365(9477): 2070-2071. NRCBL: 18.5.4; 21.1; 18.3; 5.3; 9.3.1.

Marwick, Charles. US academy calls for new bodies to oversee stem cell research [news]. *BMJ: British Medical Journal* 2005 April 30; 330(7498): 982. NRCBL: 18.5.4; 19.1; 19.5; 15.1; 5.3.

Master, Zubin. Can we really bypass the moral debate for embryo research? *American Journal of Bioethics* 2005 November-December; 5(6): 27-28. NRCBL: 18.5.4. Comments: comment on S. Matthew Liao, "Rescuing human embryonic stem cell research: the blastocyst transfer method," American Journal of Bioethics 2005 November-December; 5(6): 8-16.

Mavroforou, Anna; Michalodimitrakis, Emmanuel. Moral arguments on the use of ovarian tissue from aborted foetuses in infertility treatment. *Human Reproduction and Genetic Ethics: An International Journal* 2005; 11(1): 6-11. NRCBL: 18.5.4; 12.4.2; 19.5.

NRCBL: National Reference Center for Bioethics Literature Classification Scheme   See inside front cover for terms.

Mayor, Susan. UK team hopes to create a human embryo from three donors [news]. *BMJ: British Medical Journal* 2005 September 17; 331(7517): 591. NRCBL: 18.5.4.

McConnaha, Scott. Blessed are the pluripotent: New Testament guidance for the embryonic stem cell debate. *National Catholic Bioethics Quarterly* 2005 Winter; 5(4): 707- 715. NRCBL: 18.5.4; 1.2; 4.4; 18.2.

McGee, Glenn; Patrizio, Pasquale; Kuhn, Vanessa; Robertson- Kraft, Claire. The ethics of stem cell therapy. *In:* Patrizio, Pasquale; Tucker, Michael J.; Guelman, Vanessa, eds. A Color Atlas for Human Assisted Reproduction: Laboratory and Clinical Insights. Philadelphia: Lippincott Williams & Wilkins; 2003: 297-309. NRCBL: 18.5.4; 19.1; 19.5; 15.1.

McGee, Glenn; Patrizio, Pasquale; Kuhn, Vanessa; Robertson- Kraft, Claire. The ethics of stem cell therapy. *In:* McGee, Glenn; Caplan, Arthur, eds. The Human Cloning Debate. 4th edition. Berkeley, CA: Berkeley Hills Books; 2004: 37- 56. NRCBL: 18.5.4; 15.1.

Meyer, John R. The brave new world of embryonic stem cell research: utilitarian consequentialism and faulty moral reasoning. *Linacre Quarterly* 2005 November; 72(4): 319-330. NRCBL: 18.5.4; 18.2; 1.1; 15.1.

Miech, Ralph; Schwarz, Stephen D.; Latimer, James S. The supposed conflict between religion and science. *National Catholic Bioethics Quarterly* 2005 Autumn; 5(3): 450- 451. NRCBL: 18.5.4; 4.4.

Mitka, Mike. Scenarios for stem cell creation debated: panel members spar over ethical and scientific issues. *JAMA: The Journal of the American Medical Association* 2005 June 22-29; 293(24): 2990-2991. NRCBL: 18.5.4; 2.4; 19.1; 15.1. Identifiers: President's Council on Bioethics.

Monastersky, Richard. Cell divisions. *Chronicle of Higher Education* 2006 January 6; 52(18): A26-A28. NRCBL: 18.5.4; 15.1; 14.4; 14.5; 1.3.9.

Moraczewski, Albert S. Stem cells: answers to three questions. *Ethics and Medics* 2003 March; 28(3): 1-2. NRCBL: 18.5.4; 15.1; 1.2.

Murphy, Timothy F. Ethical justifications for moratoriums on vanguard scientific research. *American Journal of Bioethics* 2005 November-December; 5(6): 51-52. NRCBL: 18.5.4; 14.5. Identifiers: President's Council on Bioethics. Comments: comment on Lawrence J. Nelson and Michael J. Meyer, "Confronting deep moral disagreement: the President's Council on Bioethics, moral status, and human embryos," American Journal of Bioethics 2005 November-December; 5(6): 33-42.

Murray, Thomas H. Will new ways of creating stem cells dodge the objections? *Hastings Center Report* 2005 January-February; 35(1): 8-9. NRCBL: 18.5.4; 15.1.

NARAL Pro-Choice America Foundation. Fetal tissue research: moving beyond anti-choice politics. Washington, DC: NARAL Pro-Choice America, 2004 January 1; 14 p. [Online]. Available: http://www.naral.org/facts/loader.cfm?url=commonspot/security/getfile.cfm&PageID=8080 [24 May 2005]. NRCBL: 18.5.4; 12.5.1.

National Health and Medical Research Council [NHMRC] (Australia). NHMRC statement on human experimentation and supplementary notes (No. 5). Canberra, ACT: The Council 1992; 3 p. [Online]. Available: http://www7.health.gov.au/nhmrc/issues/humanexp/supp5.htm [31 March 2005]. NRCBL: 18.5.4; 12.1; 19.5. Identifiers: "The Human Fetus and the Use of Human Fetal Tissue".

Nelson, Laura. Biosafety law brings stem-cell research to Brazil [news]. *Nature* 2005 March 10; 434(7030): 128. NRCBL: 18.5.4; 19.1; 15.1. SC: le.

Newhart, Allison B. The intersection of law and medicine: the case for providing federal funding for embryonic stem cell research. *Villanova Law Review* 2004; 49(2): 329-361. NRCBL: 18.5.4; 18.6; 15.1; 4.4. SC: le.

Nisker, Jeffrey; White, Angela. The CMA Code of Ethics and the donation of fresh embryos for stem cell research. *CMAJ/JAMC: Canadian Medical Association Journal* 2005 September 13; 173(6): 621-622. NRCBL: 18.5.4; 6.

Nuffield Council on Bioethics. Experts give go-ahead for human stem cell research but safeguards are needed. *Human Reproduction and Genetic Ethics: An International Journal* 2001; 7(1): 1. NRCBL: 18.5.4; 15.1.

Oderberg, David S. Human embryonic stem cell research: what's wrong with it? *Human Life Review* 2005 Fall; 31(4): 21-33. NRCBL: 18.5.4.

Okie, Susan. An offshore haven for human embryonic stem-cell research? [opinion]. *New England Journal of Medicine* 2005 October 20; 353(16): 1645-1649. NRCBL: 18.5.4; 15.1; 19.5; 19.1; 14.5; 21.1. SC: le.

Okie, Susan. Stem-cell research — signposts and roadblocks [opinion]. *New England Journal of Medicine* 2005 July 7; 353(1): 1-5. NRCBL: 18.5.4; 15.1; 19.1; 19.5; 18.2.

Orellana, Claudia. Mexico reverses ban on stem cell research [news]. *Nature Medicine* 2004 July; 10(7): 656. NRCBL: 18.5.4; 15.1; 5.3.

Pacholczyk, Tadeusz; Hurlbut, William B. The substantive issues raised by altered nuclear transfer [letter and reply]. *National Catholic Bioethics Quarterly* 2005 Spring; 5(1): 17- 19, 19-22. NRCBL: 18.5.4; 15.4; 4.4.

Panetta, Joe; Wetherell, John; Mehok, Michelle. California Stem Cell Research and Cures Act — what to expect from stem cell research? *Journal of Biolaw and Business* 2005; 8(4): 3-12. NRCBL: 18.5.4; 15.1; 19.5; 18.6; 5.3. SC: le.

Parfitt, Tom. Russian scientists voice concern over "stem-cell cosmetics". *Lancet* 2005 April 2-8; 365(9466): 1219-1220. NRCBL: 18.5.4; 19.5; 19.1; 15.1; 9.5.1.

Peduzzi-Nelson, Jean D. Criticism of the Hurlbut ANT proposal. *National Catholic Bioethics Quarterly* 2005 Summer; 5(2): 226. NRCBL: 18.5.4; 14.4; 14.5. Identifiers: Altered Nuclear Transfer.

Pellegrino, Edmund D. Balancing science, ethics and politics: stem cell research, a paradigm case. *Journal of Contemporary Health Law and Policy* 2002 Fall; 18(3): 591-611. NRCBL: 18.5.4; 15.1; 19.5; 4.4; 5.3.

Philpott, Sean. Eggs, lies and compromise [editorial]. *American Journal of Bioethics* 2005 November-December; 5(6): 1- 3. NRCBL: 18.5.4; 4.4.

Plomer, Aurora. Embryonic stem cell research: human dignity and the right to life. *In her:* The Law and Ethics of Medical Research: International Bioethics and Human Rights. Portland, OR: Cavendish; 2005: 67-92. NRCBL: 18.5.4; 4.4; 21.1. SC: le.

Pollack, Andrew. Moving stem cells front and center: researcher makes paralyzed rats walk and asks, why not people? *New York Times* 2005 February 23; p. C1, C10. NRCBL: 18.5.4; 19.1. SC: po.

President's Council on Bioethics (United States). The moral retrieval of ES cells: a new and promising proposal. *Ethics and Medics* 2005 July; 30(7): 1-2. NRCBL: 18.5.4; 15.1. Identifiers: embryonic stem cells.

Quintavalle, Josephine; Hurlbut, William B. The many perils that lie ahead [letter and reply]. *National Catholic Bioethics Quarterly* 2005 Spring; 5(1): 16- 17, 19-22. NRCBL: 18.5.4; 15.4; 4.4.

Rasmussen, Colin. Canada's Assisted Human Reproductive Act: is it scientific censorship, or a reasoned approach to the regulation of rapidly emerging reproductive technologies? *Saskatchewan Law Review* 2004; 67(1): 97-135. NRCBL: 18.5.4; 14.4; 21.1; 18.6; 14.1; 14.5. SC: le.

Ready, Tinker. Private donors breathe new life into US stem cell research [news]. *Nature Medicine* 2004 April; 10(4): 320. NRCBL: 18.5.4; 15.1; 5.3; 9.3.1.

Ready, Tinker. Scientists irked by ethicists' alternatives for embryo research [news]. *Nature Medicine* 2005 February; 11(2): 108. NRCBL: 18.5.4; 15.1. Identifiers: altered nuclear transfer.

Regalado, Antonio. Senators mull new ways to make stem cells. *Wall Street Journal* 2005 July 20; p. B1, B4. NRCBL: 18.5.4; 19.5. SC: po.

Regalado, Antonio; Dumcius, Gintautas. Stem-cell labs to get guidance on ethics issues. *Wall Street Journal* 2005 April 26; p. B1, B7. NRCBL: 18.5.4; 5.3. SC: po; le.

Reicin, Cheryl; McMahon, Eileen. Stem cell research in Canada: business opportunities for U.S. companies. *Journal of Biolaw and Business* 2005; 8(1): 61-64. NRCBL: 18.5.4; 15.1; 19.1. SC: le.

Richardt, Nicole. A comparative analysis of the embryological research debate in Great Britain and Germany. *Social Politics* 2003 Spring; 10(1): 86-128. NRCBL: 18.5.4; 14.1; 1.3.5; 18.6. Identifiers: Human Fertilisation and Embryology Act of 1990; Embryonenschutzgesetz [Embryo Protection Act 1990 ESchG].

Richarson, Genevra. The banking of embryonic stem cells: the legal and ethical framework in the UK. *Revista de Derecho y Genoma Humano / Law and the Human Genome Review* 2004 January-June; (20): 147-160. NRCBL: 18.5.4; 19.5; 15.1; 18.3. SC: le. Note: Abstract in Spanish.

Robert, Jason Scott; Baylis, Françoise. Stem cell politics: the NAS prohibition pack more bark than bite. *Hastings Center Report* 2005 November-December; 35(6): 15-16. NRCBL: 18.5.4; 15.1; 18.2. Identifiers: National Academy of Sciences.

Robertson, Christopher. Recent developments in the law and ethics of embryonic research: can science resolve the ethical problems it creates? *Journal of Law, Medicine and Ethics* 2005 Summer; 33(2): 384- 388. NRCBL: 18.5.4; 4.4; 18.6; 5.3. SC: le.

Robertson, John A. Blastocyst transfer (sic) is no solution. *American Journal of Bioethics* 2005 November-December; 5(6): 18-20. NRCBL: 18.5.4; 4.4. Comments: comment on S. Matthew Liao, "Rescuing human embryonic stem cell research: the blastocyst transfer method," American Journal of Bioethics 2005 November-December; 5(6): 8-16.

Robertson, John A. Human embryonic stem cell research: ethical and legal issues. *Nature Reviews Genetics* 2001 January; 2: 74-78. NRCBL: 18.5.4; 15.1. SC: le.

Romano, Gaetano. Stem cell transplantation therapy: controversy over ethical issues and clinical relevance. *Drug News and Perspectives* 2004 December; 17(10): 637-645. NRCBL: 18.5.4; 18.5.1; 15.1.

Sagoff, Mark. Extracorporeal embryos and three conceptions of the human. *American Journal of Bioethics* 2005 November-December; 5(6): 52-54. NRCBL: 18.5.4; 4.4; 1.1; 2.4. Identifiers: President's Council on Bioethics. Comments: comment on Lawrence J. Nelson and Michael J. Meyer, "Confronting deep moral disagreement: the President's Council on Bioethics, moral status, and human embryos," American Journal of Bioethics 2005 November-December; 5(6): 33-42.

Sardinia, Lisa M. Stem cells. *In:* Ness, Bryan D., ed. Encyclopedia of Genetics. Revised edition. Volume II. Pasa-

---

NRCBL: National Reference Center for Bioethics Literature Classification Scheme   See inside front cover for terms.

301

dena, Calif.: Salem Press; 2004: 710-715. NRCBL: 18.5.4; 15.1.

Saunders, William L., Jr. Embryology: inconvenient facts [opinion]. *First Things* 2004 December; (148): 13-15. NRCBL: 18.5.4; 14.5; 4.4; 15.1.

Schiller, Charity. Stem cell research and conditional federal funding: do state laws allowing more extensive research pose a problem for federalism? *Pepperdine Law Review* 2004 May; 31(4): 1017-1054. NRCBL: 18.5.4; 15.1; 18.6; 18.5.1. SC: le.

Schüklenk, Udo; Lott, Jason. Ethics, politics and embryo stem cell research in South Africa. *South African Medical Journal* 2002 October; 92(10): 782, 784-786. NRCBL: 18.5.4; 15.1; 21.1. SC: le.

Scolding, Neil. Stem-cell therapy: hope and hype [opinion]. *Lancet* 2005 June 18-24; 365(9477): 2073-2075. NRCBL: 18.5.4; 5.1; 7.1.

Sharma, B.R. Research on human embryos: issues, politics and solutions. *Medicine Science and the Law* 2004 January; 44(1): 41-46. NRCBL: 18.5.4; 2.2; 18.6.

Shenfield, Françoise. Semantics and ethics of human embryonic stem-cell research [opinion]. *Lancet* 2005 June 18-24; 365(9477): 2071-2073. NRCBL: 18.5.4; 5.3; 4.4; 21.1; 18.3.

Shoemaker, David W. Embryos, souls, and the fourth dimension. *Social Theory and Practice* 2005 January; 31(1): 51-75. NRCBL: 18.5.4; 15.1; 4.4; 1.2. SC: an.

Siep, Ludwig. Kriterien und Argumenttypen im Streit um die Embryonenforschung in Europa. *In:* Jahrbuch für Wissenschaft und Ethik. Bd. 7. Berlin: Walter de Gruyter; 2002: 179-195. NRCBL: 18.5.4; 4.4; 21.1.

Silvers, Anita; Lauritzen, Paul. Our posthuman future: discussing the consequences of biotechnological advances [letter and reply]. *Hastings Center Report* 2005 November-December; 35(6): 4-5, 6-7. NRCBL: 18.5.4; 15.1; 4.5.

Skorecki, Karl L., et al. The unborn child: scientific discovery, medical and ethical dilemmas. *In:* Blazer, Shraga; Zimmer, Etan Z., eds. The Embryo: Scientific Discovery and Medical Ethics. New York: Karger; 2005: 120-142. NRCBL: 18.5.4; 1.1; 15.1; 14.1.

Snead, O. Carter. The pedagogical significance of the Bush stem cell policy: a window into bioethical regulation in the United States. *Yale Journal of Health Policy, Law, and Ethics* 2005 Winter; 5(1): 491-504. NRCBL: 18.5.4; 15.1; 19.5; 2.4. SC: le.

Solbakk, Jan Helge. Use and abuse of empirical knowledge in contemporary bioethics: a critical analysis of empirical arguments employed in the controversy surrounding stem cell research. *In:* Holm, Søren; Jonas, Monique F., eds. Engaging the World: The Use of Empiri-

cal Research in Bioethics and the Regulation of Biotechnology. Washington, DC: IOS Press; 2004: 53-60. NRCBL: 18.5.4; 19.1; 15.1. SC: em.

Solter, Davor. Politically correct human embryonic stem cells? [opinion]. *New England Journal of Medicine* 2005 December 1; 353(22): 2321-2323. NRCBL: 18.5.4; 15.1; 19.5.

Squier, Susan; Waldby, Catherine; Lauritzen, Paul. Our posthuman future: discussing the consequences of biotechnological advances [letter and reply]. *Hastings Center Report* 2005 November-December; 35(6): 4, 6-7. NRCBL: 18.5.4; 15.1; 4.5.

St. John, Justin C.; Alderson, Jon. Stem-cell banking: the size of the task [opinion]. *Lancet* 2005 December 10-16; 366(9502): 1991-1992. NRCBL: 18.5.4; 15.1; 1.3.12; 7.1; 9.5.4; 8.3.2; 5.3.

Steinbock, Bonnie. Alternative sources of stem cells. *Hastings Center Report* 2005 July-August; 35(4): 24-26. NRCBL: 18.5.4; 15.1; 19.1.

Stolberg, Sheryl Gay. House approves a stem cell bill opposed by Bush; margin is not veto-proof; bipartisan senate support may set up showdown over federal funds. *New York Times* 2005 May 25; p. A1, A22. NRCBL: 18.5.4; 19.1; 5.3. SC: po; le.

Strong, Carson. Obtaining stem cells: moving from Scylla toward Charybdis. *American Journal of Bioethics* 2005 November-December; 5(6): 21-23. NRCBL: 18.5.4; 15.2. Comments: comment on S. Matthew Liao, "Rescuing human embryonic stem cell research: the blastocyst transfer method," American Journal of Bioethics 2005 November-December; 5(6): 8-16.

Sullivan, Lucy. Embryo experimentation and the murder prohibition: a casuistic examination of the utilitarian and pro-life positions on the moral status of the embryo. *Medicine and Law: World Association for Medical Law* 1995; 14(5-6): 369-386. NRCBL: 18.5.4; 4.4; 1.1. SC: le.

Tanne, Janice Hopkins. US Senate leader gives support to expanded stem cell research [news]. *BMJ: British Medical Journal* 2005 August 6; 331(7512): 307. NRCBL: 18.5.4; 15.1; 19.5; 14.4; 9.3.1. SC: le. Identifiers: William (Bill) H. Frist, Senate Majority Leader.

Tassy, Sebastien; Gorincour, Guillaume; Le Coz, Pierre. Prenatal research: a very sensitive field [letter]. *Lancet* 2005 October 1-7; 366(9492): 1162. NRCBL: 18.5.4; 9.5.8; 9.8. SC: em.

Taupitz, Jochen; Brewe, Manuela. Der Status des Embryos im Rechtsvergleich. *In:* Maio, Giovanni; Just, Hanjörg, eds. Die Forschung an embryonalen Stammzellen in ethischer und rechtlicher Perspektive. Baden-Baden: Nomos Verlagsgesellschaft; 2003: 85-96. NRCBL: 18.5.4. SC: le.

SC (Subject Caption): an=analytical cs=case studies em=empirical le=legal po=popular rv=review

Taylor, Craig J.; Bolton, Eleanor M.; Pocock, Susan; Sharples, Linda D.; Pedersen, Roger A.; Bradley, J. Andrew. Banking on human embryonic stem cells: estimating the number of donor cell lines needed for HLA matching. *Lancet* 2005 December 10-16; 366(9502): 2019-2025. NRCBL: 18.5.4; 15.1; 1.3.12. SC: em.

Abstract: BACKGROUND: Human embryonic stem (hES) cells are a promising source for transplantation to replace diseased or damaged tissue, but their differentiated progeny express human leucocyte antigens (HLAs) that will probably cause graft rejection. The creation of a bank of HLA-typed hES cells, from which a best match could be selected, would help reduce the likelihood of graft rejection. We investigated how many hES cell lines would be needed to make matching possible in most cases. METHODS: The number of hES cell lines needed to achieve varying degrees of HLA match was estimated by use of, as a surrogate for hES-cell donor embryos, blood group and HLA types on a series of 10,000 consecutive UK cadaveric organ donors. The degree of blood group compatibility and HLA matching for a recipient population consisting of 6577 patients registered on the UK kidney transplant waiting list was determined, assuming all donor hES cell lines could provide a transplant for an unlimited number of recipients. FINDINGS: A bank of 150 consecutive donors provided a full match at HLA-A, HLA-B, and HLA-DR for a minority of recipients (%); a beneficial match (defined as one HLA-A or one HLA-B mismatch only) or better for 37.9% (range 27.9- 47.5); and an HLA-DR match or better for 84.9% (77.5-90.0). Extending the number of donors beyond 150 conferred only a very gradual incremental benefit with respect to HLA matching. A panel of only ten donors homozygous for common HLA types selected from 10,000 donors provided a complete HLA-A, HLA-B and HLA-DR match for 37.7% of recipients, and a beneficial match for 67.4%. INTERPRETATION: Approximately 150 consecutive blood group compatible donors, 100 consecutive blood group O donors, or ten highly selected homozygous donors could provide the maximum practical benefit for HLA matching. The findings from these simulations have practical, political, and ethical implications for the establishment of hES-cell banks.

Taylor, Patrick L. The gap between law and ethics in human embryonic stem cell research: overcoming the effect of U.S. federal policy on research advances and public benefit. *Science and Engineering Ethics* 2005 October; 11(4): 589-616. NRCBL: 18.5.4; 15.1; 19.1; 9.3.1; 5.3; 18.6; 18.2. SC: rv; le.

Then, Shih-Ning. Stem cell technologies: regulation, patents and problems. *Journal of Law and Medicine* 2004 November; 12(2): 188-204. NRCBL: 18.5.4; 15.1; 15.8; 5.3. SC: le. Identifiers: United States; United Kingdom (Great Britain); Australia.

Tsai, D.F.-C. Human embryonic stem cell research debates: a Confucian argument. *Journal of Medical Ethics* 2005 November; 31(11): 635-640. NRCBL: 18.5.4; 15.1; 19.1; 1.2; 4.4.

Abstract: Human embryonic stem cell research can bring about major biomedical breakthroughs and thus contribute enormously to human welfare, yet it raises serious moral problems because it involves using human embryos for experiment. The "moral status of the human embryo" remains the core of such debates. Three different positions regarding the moral status of the human embryo can be categorised: the "all" position, the "none" position, and the "gradualist" position. The author proposes that the "gradualist" position is more plausible than the other two positions. Confucius's moral principle of jen, which proposes a unique theory of "love of gradation", and the principle of yi, which advocates "due treatment for persons", are then explored. The author then argues that our moral obligations to do good to other living organisms, persons, and our families are different. Putting together the "gradualist" position on the human embryo, and Confucius's theories of "love of gradation" and "due treatment for persons", the author concludes that the early embryo has less ethical significance than the later fetus and adult human. The moral obligation we have toward persons is clearer and stronger than that which we have toward human embryos. Embryo research is justifiable if it brings enormous welfare to human persons that cannot be otherwise achieved. The "love of gradation" requires us, however, to extend love and respect towards other entities according to their different status. We should therefore be very cautious in using human embryos for research, acknowledging the gradualist nature of their moral status.

Turnpenny, Lee. Embryo's moral status is unaffected by alteration [letter]. *Nature* 2005 September 1; 437(7055): 26. NRCBL: 18.5.4; 15.1.

Vogel, Gretchen. Abstentions scuttle drive to liberalize Italy's embryo laws [news]. *Science* 2005 June 17; 308(5729): 1722. NRCBL: 18.5.4; 5.3. SC: le.

Vogel, Gretchen. Deriving 'controversy-free' ES cells is controversial [news]. *Science* 2005 October 21; 310(5747): 416-417. NRCBL: 18.5.4; 15.1; 22.2. Identifiers: embryonic stem cells.

Vogel, Gretchen. Embryo-free techniques gain momentum [news]. *Science* 2005 July 8; 309(5732): 240-241. NRCBL: 18.5.4.

Vogel, Gretchen. Korean team speeds up creation of cloned human stem cells [news]. *Science* 2005 May 20; 308(5725): 1096-1097. NRCBL: 18.5.4.

Vogel, Gretchen. U.S. public supports stem cell research [news]. *Science* 2005 October 21; 310(5747): 416. NRCBL: 18.5.4; 15.1; 18.1; 9.1.

Wade, Nicholas. Scientists draft rules on ethics for stem cells; academy cites lack of guidelines by U.S. *New York Times* 2005 April 27; p. A1, A16. NRCBL: 18.5.4; 5.3. SC: po.

Wadman, Meredith. Licensing fees slow advance of stem cells. *Nature* 2005 May 19; 435(7040): 272-273. NRCBL: 18.5.4; 5.3; 19.1; 15.1.

Watt, Helen. Ethical aspects of use of fetal/embryonic cells in treatment and research. *Zentralblatt fur Neurochirurgie* 2005 May; 66(2): 75-78. NRCBL: 18.5.4; 15.1; 4.4; 1.1.

Weed, Matthew. Discourse on embryo science and human cloning in the United States and Great Britain: 1984-2002. *Journal of Law, Medicine and Ethics* 2005 Winter; 33(4): 802- 810. NRCBL: 18.5.4; 14.5; 18.2; 2.2. SC: le.

NRCBL: National Reference Center for Bioethics Literature Classification Scheme   See inside front cover for terms.

303

Weiss, Rick. British to clone human embryos for stem cells. *Washington Post* 2005 February 9; p. A2. NRCBL: 18.5.4; 14.5. SC: po.

Wertz, Dorothy C. Embryo and stem cell research: views from the USA. *Journal of Commercial Biotechnology* 2002; 8(3): 200-208. NRCBL: 18.5.4; 12.5.1; 21.1. SC: em.

White, Katherine. Stem cells 201: an overview of the ethics of stem cell research. *Topics in Stroke Rehabilitation* 2005 Winter; 12(1): 83-88. NRCBL: 18.5.4; 15.1; 4.4; 18.6. SC: rv.

Wiedemann, Peter M.; Simon, Judith; Schicktanz, Silke; Tannert, Christof. The future of stem-cell research in Germany: a Delphi study [opinion]. *EMBO Reports* 2004 October; 5(10): 927-931. NRCBL: 18.5.4; 15.1. SC: em.

Willard, Laura A. California makes unprecedented commitment to fund stem cell research. *Journal of Biolaw and Business* 2005; 8(2): 47-48. NRCBL: 18.5.4; 18.6; 5.3. SC: le.

Wilmut, Ian; West, Michael D.; Lanza, Robert P.; Gearhart, John D.; Smith, Austin; Colman, Alan; Trounson, Alan O.; Campbell, Keith H. Human embryonic stem cells [letter]. *Science* 2005 December 23; 310(5756): 1903. NRCBL: 18.5.4; 15.1; 1.3.9.

Wuerl, Donald. Pastoral letter on human, embryonic stem cell research. *Origins* 2005 April 7; 34(42): 674-676. NRCBL: 18.5.4; 1.2; 4.4.

Zwillich, Todd. Guidelines set ethical bar for US stem cell research. *Lancet* 2005 May 7-13; 365(9471): 1612. NRCBL: 18.5.4; 18.6; 1.3.5; 15.1; 19.1.

HUMAN EXPERIMENTATION/ . . . / FOREIGN NATIONALS

Andrews, Jason. U.S. military sponsored vaccine trials and la resistance in Nepal. *American Journal of Bioethics [Online]* 2005 May-June; 5(3): W1-W3. NRCBL: 18.5.9; 18.5.8; 9.7.

Ballantyne, Angela. HIV international clinical research: exploitation and risk. *Bioethics* 2005 October; 19(5-6): 476-491. NRCBL: 18.5.9; 9.5.6; 21.1.
Abstract: This paper aims to show that to reduce the level of exploitation present in (some) international clinical trials, research sponsors must aim to provide both an ex-ante expected gain in utility and a fair ex-post distribution of benefits for research subjects. I suggest the following principles of fair risk distribution in international research as the basis of a normative definition of fairness: (a) Persons should not be forced (by circumstance) to gamble in order to achieve or protect basic goods; (b) In cases where one party is gambling with basic goods and the other party is not, the distribution of benefits and burdens must be arranged so that they are of greatest benefit to the worst off; (c) In relationships where one party is gambling for basic goods and the other party is not, the party gambling for basic goods must be assured of some guaranteed benefits in addition to the chance of getting some practical benefits. These principles are applied to the case of HIV international research. I conclude that the research (as described) is mutually advantageous but still exploitative because the distribution of surplus benefits is unfair. It is unfair because research subjects are gambling with and for basic goods but they are not assured of a fair ex-post distribution of benefits. Principles (b) and (c) are not satisfied. Research participants are not accorded enough guaranteed benefits to outweigh the risks they undertake.

Barsdorf, Nicola Wendy; Wassenaar, Douglas Richard. Racial differences in public perceptions of voluntariness of medical research participants in South Africa. *Social Science and Medicine* 2005 March; 60(5): 1087-1098. NRCBL: 18.5.9; 18.3; 21.1. SC: em.

Borry, Pascal; Schotsmans, Paul; Dierickx, Kris. Developing countries and bioethical research [letter]. *New England Journal of Medicine* 2005 August 25; 353(8): 852- 853. NRCBL: 18.5.9.

Calman, Kenneth. Conducting research ethically in developing countries. *Drug Discovery Today* 2002 December; 7(23): 1155-1159. NRCBL: 18.5.9.

Check, Erika. US policy keeps drugs out of reach in clinical trials abroad [news]. *Nature Medicine* 2005 May; 11(5): 460. NRCBL: 18.5.9; 9.7; 5.3.

de Thé, G.; Buonaguro, F.; Charpak, N.; Hutton, J.L.; Thorstensson, R.; Valdas, E.; Zetterström, R.; Franca Junior, I. Ethical issues in research on control of the HIV/AIDS epidemic: report from a workshop of the world federation of scientists, Erice, Sicily, Italy, 22-24 August 2003 [see correction in Acta Paediatrica 2004 October; 93(10): 1407]. *Acta Paediatrica* 2004 August; 93(8): 1125-1128. NRCBL: 18.5.9; 9.5.6; 9.7.

Dhai, Amaboo; Lavery, Jim. Beyond our borders: different laws, different languages. Universal ethics? [discussion]. *Protecting Human Subjects* 2005 Summer; (12): 15-17. NRCBL: 18.5.9; 21.7.

Geller, S.E.; Patel, A.; Niak, V.A.; Goudar, S.S.; Edlavitch, S.A.; Kodkany, B.S.; Derman, R.J. Conducting international collaborative research in developing nations. *International Journal of Gynecology and Obstetrics* 2004 December; 87(3): 267-271. NRCBL: 18.5.9; 18.2; 18.3; 21.1. Identifiers: India.

Gupta, Amit Sen. Research on hire. *Issues in Medical Ethics* 2001 October-December; 9(4): 111-113. NRCBL: 18.5.9.

Hyder, Adnan A.; Dawson, Liza. Defining standard of care in the developing world: the intersection of international research ethics and health systems analysis. *Developing World Bioethics* 2005 May; 5(2): 142-152. NRCBL: 18.5.9; 9.2; 9.8. SC: an.
Abstract: In recent years there has been intense debate regarding the level of medical care provided to 'standard care' control groups in clinical trials in developing countries, particularly

when the research sponsors come from wealthier countries. The debate revolves around the issue of how to define a standard of medical care in a country in which many people are not receiving the best methods of medical care available in other settings. In this paper, we argue that additional dimensions of the standard of care have been hitherto neglected, namely, the structure and efficiency of the national health system. The health system affects locally available medical care in two important ways: first, the system may be structured to provide different levels of care at different sites with referral mechanisms to direct patients to the appropriate level of care. Second, inefficiencies in this system may influence what care is available in a particular locale. As a result of these two factors locally available care cannot be equated with a national 'standard'. A reasonable approach is to define the national standard of care as the level of care that ought to be delivered under conditions of appropriate and efficient referral in a national system. This standard is the minimum level of care that ought to be provided to a control group. There may be additional moral arguments for higher levels of care in some circumstances. This health system analysis may be helpful to researchers and ethics committees in designing and reviewing research involving standard care control groups in developing country research.

Jesus, John E.; Higgs, Elizabeth S. International research ethics: progress, but not perfection. *Trends in Molecular Medicine* 2002 February; 8(2): 93-95. NRCBL: 18.5.9; 21.1; 2.1; 18.3; 18.6.

Kelleher, Finnuala. The pharmaceutical industry's responsibility for protecting human subjects of clinical trials in developing nations. *Columbia Journal of Law and Social Problems* 2004 Fall; 38(1): 67-106. NRCBL: 18.5.9; 9.7; 18.3; 21.1; 18.2; 1.3.2. SC: le.

Kietinun, Somboon; Gupte, M.D.; Sengupta, Amit. A clinical trial in a developing country: many questions, few answers [case study and commentaries]. *Issues in Medical Ethics* 2003 July-September; 11(3): 89-90. NRCBL: 18.5.9. SC: cs.

Killen, Jack; Grady, Christine; Folkers, Gregory K.; Fauci, Anthony S. Ethics of clinical research in the developing world [opinion]. *Nature Reviews Immunology* 2002 March; 2(3): 210-215. NRCBL: 18.5.9; 9.5.6; 21.1; 9.7. Identifiers: uniform care requirement.

LaPlante, Pierre. Purity of standards: at what price? *Indian Journal of Medical Ethics* 2004 October-December; 1(4): 124. NRCBL: 18.5.9. Comments: comment on Rajan R. Patil, "Research in a tribal community," Indian Journal of Medical Ethics 2004 October-December; 1(4): 122-123.

London, Alex John. Justice and the human development approach to international research. *Hastings Center Report* 2005 January-February; 35(1): 24-37. NRCBL: 18.5.9; 1.1; 21.1.

Mamdani, Bashir; Mamdani, Meenal. Colonialism of clinical trials: discerning the positive spin offs [summary]. *Indian Journal of Medical Ethics* 2005 October-December; 2(4): 132-133. NRCBL: 18.5.9; 9.7; 18.2; 18.3; 9.3.1.

Mann, Charles C. A new skirmish in the Yanomamo wars [news]. *Science* 2005 July 8; 309(5732): 227, 229. NRCBL: 18.5.9; 18.4.

Marshall, Patricia A. Human rights, cultural pluralism, and international health research. *Theoretical Medicine and Bioethics* 2005; 26(6): 529-557. NRCBL: 18.5.9; 21.7; 21.1; 1.3.9.

Abstract: In the field of bioethics, scholars have begun to consider carefully the impact of structural issues on global population health, including socioeconomic and political factors influencing the disproportionate burden of disease throughout the world. Human rights and social justice are key considerations for both population health and biomedical research. In this paper, I will briefly explore approaches to human rights in bioethics and review guidelines for ethical conduct in international health research, focusing specifically on health research conducted in resource-poor settings. I will demonstrate the potential for addressing human rights considerations in international health research with special attention to the importance of collaborative partnerships, capacity building, and respect for cultural traditions. Strengthening professional knowledge about international research ethics increases awareness of ethical concerns associated with study design and informed consent among researchers working in resource- poor settings. But this is not enough. Technological and financial resources are also necessary to build capacity for local communities to ensure that research results are integrated into existing health systems. Problematic issues surrounding the application of ethical guidelines in resource-poor settings are embedded in social history, cultural context, and the global political economy. Resolving the moral complexities requires a commitment to engaged dialogue and action among investigators, funding agencies, policy makers, governmental institutions, and private industry.

Mills, Edward J.; Singh, Sonal; Singh, Jerome A.; Orbinski, James J.; Warren, Mitchell; Upshur, Ross E. Designing research in vulnerable populations: lessons from HIV prevention trials that stopped early. *BMJ: British Medical Journal* 2005 December 10; 331(7529): 1403-1406. NRCBL: 18.5.9; 9.5.6; 21.1; 18.6.

Mwase, Isaac M.T.; London, Alex John. Justice in research [letter and reply]. *Hastings Center Report* 2005 July-August; 35(4): 7. NRCBL: 18.5.9.

Nundy, Samiran; Gulhati, Chandra M. A new colonialism? — conducting clinical trials in India [opinion]. *New England Journal of Medicine* 2005 April 21; 352(16): 1633- 1636. NRCBL: 18.5.9; 18.2; 18.6; 18.3; 9.2.

Obyerodhyambo, Oby. Keeping medical research ethical [letter]. *Science* 2005 July 8; 309(5732): 246. NRCBL: 18.5.9; 18.3.

Pace, Christine A.; Emanuel, Ezekiel J. The ethics of research in developing countries: assessing voluntariness [opinion]. *Lancet* 2005 January 1-7; 365(9453): 11-12. NRCBL: 18.5.9; 18.1.

Page, Alice K. Ethical issues in international biomedical research: an overview. *Journal of Health Law* 2004 Fall; 37(4): 629-665. NRCBL: 18.5.9; 18.2; 18.6. SC: rv.

NRCBL: National Reference Center for Bioethics Literature Classification Scheme   See inside front cover for terms.

305

Patil, Rajan R. Research in a tribal community [case study]. *Indian Journal of Medical Ethics* 2004 October-December; 1(4): 122-123. NRCBL: 18.5.9; 18.3.

Plomer, Aurora. Research in developing countries: new ethics and new threats to human rights. *In her:* The Law and Ethics of Medical Research: International Bioethics and Human Rights. Portland, OR: Cavendish; 2005: 113-135. NRCBL: 18.5.9; 21.1.

Rai, Saritha. Drug companies cut costs with foreign clinical trials. *New York Times* 2005 February 24; p. C4. NRCBL: 18.5.9; 9.7. SC: po.

Saha, Shelley. Challenges in research in tribal communities. *Indian Journal of Medical Ethics* 2004 October-December; 1(4): 125. NRCBL: 18.5.9; 18.3. Comments: comment on Rajan R. Patil, "Research in a tribal community," Indian Journal of Medical Ethics 2004 October-December; 1(4): 122- 123.

Shah, Sonia. Globalizing clinical research. *Nation* 2002 July 1: 23-24, 26-28. NRCBL: 18.5.9; 21.1; 18.6.

Smylie, Janet; Tonelli, Marcello; Hemmelgarn, Brenda; Yeates, Karen; Gill, John; Wenman, Wanda M.; Joffres, Michel R.; Tataryn, Ivanna V.; Cass, Alan. The ethics of research involving Canada's Aboriginal populations [letters and replies]. *CMAJ/JAMC: Canadian Medical Association Journal* 2005 April 12; 172(8): 977-979. NRCBL: 18.5.9.

Srinivasan, Sandhya. Research on public health interventions in poor countries. *Issues in Medical Ethics* 2001 October-December; 9(4): 118-119. NRCBL: 18.5.9.

Sugarman, Jeremy. Should the gold rule? Assessing "equivalent protections" for research participants across international borders. *Hastings Center Report* 2005 September-October; 35(5): 12-13. NRCBL: 18.5.9.

United States. Congress. House. Highly Essential Life-saving Pharmaceuticals for Africa Act. H.R. 2700 [introduced: 4 August 1999]. United States House of Representatives, 106th Congress; 4 p. [Online]. Available: http://thomas.loc.gov/cgi-bin/query/C?c106:./temp/~c10 6ydmtuA [9 September 2005]. NRCBL: 18.5.9; 18.2; 21.1; 1.3.5; 1.3.6. Identifiers: HELP for Africa Act.

Wasunna, Angela. Researchers abroad. *Hastings Center Report* 2005 January-February; 35(1): 3. NRCBL: 18.5.9; 21.1.

Whittington, Dale. Ethical issues with contingent valuation surveys in developing countries: a note on informed consent and other concerns. *Environmental and Resource Economics* 2004 August; 28(4): 507-515. NRCBL: 18.5.9; 18.3; 18.2.

Yearby, Ruqaiijah. Good enough to use for research, but not good enough to benefit from the results of that research: are the clinical HIV vaccine trials in Africa unjust?

DePaul Law Review 2004 Spring; 53(3): 1127-1154. NRCBL: 18.5.9; 9.5.6; 2.2; 18.2. SC: le.

HUMAN EXPERIMENTATION/ . . . / MENTALLY DISABLED

Research with adults who lack capacity. *Bulletin of Medical Ethics* 2005 February; (205): 8-11. NRCBL: 18.5.6; 9.7; 19.5; 18.6. SC: le.

Addlakha, Renu. Ethical quandaries in anthropological fieldwork in psychiatric settings [case study]. *Indian Journal of Medical Ethics* 2005 April-June; 2(2): 55-56. NRCBL: 18.5.6; 18.4; 18.3.

Alzheimer's Association. Research consent for cognitively impaired adults: recommendations for institutional review boards and investigators. *Alzheimer Disease and Associated Disorders* 2004 July-September; 18(3): 171-175. NRCBL: 18.5.6; 18.3; 18.2.

Berger, Jeffrey T.; Majerovitz, S. Deborah. Do elderly persons' concerns for family burden influence their preferences for future participation in dementia research? *Journal of Clinical Ethics* 2005 Summer; 16(2): 108-115. NRCBL: 18.5.6; 18.3; 18.2; 9.5.2. SC: em.

Brigham, Lindsay. Representing the lives of women with learning difficulties: ethical dilemmas in the research process. *British Journal of Learning Disabilities* 1998 Winter; 26(4): 146-150. NRCBL: 18.5.6; 10. SC: cs.

Buckles, V.D.; Powlishta, K.K.; Palmer, J.L.; Coats, M.; Hosto, T.; Buckley, A.; Morris, J.C. Understanding of informed consent by demented individuals. *Neurology* 2003 December 23; 61(12): 1662-1666. NRCBL: 18.5.6; 18.3; 18.5.7. SC: em.

Davies, Bronwen R. Coercion or collaboration? Nurses doing research with people who have severe mental health problems. *Journal of Psychiatric and Mental Health Nursing* 2005 February; 12(1): 106-111. NRCBL: 18.5.6; 18.5.3; 18.3; 17.1. SC: em. Identifiers: United Kingdom (Great Britain).

Kim, Scott Y.H.; Karlawish, Jason H.T. Ethics and politics of research involving subjects with impaired decision-making abilities [editorial]. *Neurology* 2003 December 23; 61(12): 1645-1646. NRCBL: 18.5.6; 18.3; 18.5.7.

McCarthy, Michelle. Interviewing people with learning disabilities about sensitive topics: a discussion of ethical issues. *British Journal of Learning Disabilities* 1998 Winter; 26(4): 140-145. NRCBL: 18.5.6; 10; 18.2.

Michara, Brian L.; Weisstub, David N. Ethical and legal issues in suicide research. *International Journal of Law and Psychiatry* 2005 January- February; 28(1): 23-41. NRCBL: 18.5.6; 1.3.1; 20.7; 1.1; 18.3.

Muthappan, Palaniappan; Forster, Heidi; Wendler, David. Research advance directives: protection or obstacle? *American Journal of Psychiatry* 2005 December; 162(12): 2389- 2391. NRCBL: 18.5.6; 18.3; 20.5.4.

Pols, Jeannette. Enacting appreciations: beyond the patient perspective. *Health Care Analysis: An International Journal of Health Care Philosophy and Policy* 2005 September; 13(3): 203-221. NRCBL: 18.5.6; 18.5.7.

Abstract: The "patient perspective" serves as an analytical tool to present patients as knowing subjects in research, rather than as objects known by medicine. This paper analyses problems encountered with the concept of the patient perspective as applied to long-term mental health care. One problem is that "having a perspective" requires a perception of oneself as an individual and the ability to represent one's individual situation in language; this excludes from research patients who do not express themselves verbally. Another problem is that the idea of "talk" as a representation of the world ignores the fact that talk is also performative in the world: it requires, at least, the ability to deal with an interview situation. To think up alternative ways of including patients as subjects in research, I develop an approach that takes this performativity as a starting point. Analysing practical situations and activities, I argue that patients enact appreciations, making known what they like or dislike by verbal or non-verbal means in a given material environment, in situations that are co-produced by others. Thus, subjectivity is linked to situations and interactions, rather than just to individual characteristics; to "patient positions;" rather than "patient perspectives".

Ramakrishna, Jayashree. Rapport building and blurring identity [comment]. *Indian Journal of Medical Ethics* 2005 April-June; 2(2): 57. NRCBL: 18.5.6; 18.4; 18.3. Comments: comment on Renu Addlakha, "Ethical quandaries in anthropological fieldwork in psychiatric settings," Indian Journal of Medical Ethics 2005 April-June; 2(2): 55-56.

Roberts, Laura Weiss; Hammond, Katherine A. Green; Warner, Teddy D.; Lewis, Rae. Influence of ethical safeguards on research participation: comparison of perspectives of people with schizophrenia and psychiatrists. *American Journal of Psychiatry* 2004 December; 161(12): 2309-2311. NRCBL: 18.5.6; 18.2; 18.3. SC: em.

Silverman, Henry J.; Druml, Christiane; Lemaire, Francois; Nelson, Robert. The European Union Directive and the protection of incapacitated subjects in research: an ethical analysis. *Intensive Care Medicine* 2004 September; 30(9): 1723-1729. NRCBL: 18.5.6; 18.2; 18.3; 9.7; 21.1; 18.6. SC: an; le.

Silverman, Henry J.; Luce, John M.; Schwartz, Jack. Protecting subjects with decisional impairment in research: the need for a multifaceted approach. *American Journal of Respiratory and Critical Care Medicine* 2004 January 1; 169(1): 10-14. NRCBL: 18.5.6; 18.2; 18.6. SC: le.

von Cranach, Michael. Menschenversuche in den bayerischen Heil- und Pflegeanstalten. *In:* von Cranach, Michael; Siemen, Hans-Ludwig, eds. Psychiatrie im

Nationalsozialismus: die Bayerischen Heil- und Pflegeanstalten zwischen 1933 und 1945. München: Oldenbourg; 1999: 405-411. NRCBL: 18.5.6; 2.2; 21.4.

Walmsley, Jan. Research ethics [editorial]. *British Journal of Learning Disabilities* 1998 Winter; 26(4): 126-127. NRCBL: 18.5.6.

Winslade, William J.; Tovino, Stacey A. Research with brain-injured subjects. *Journal of Head Trauma Rehabilitation* 2004 November-December; 19(6): 513-515. NRCBL: 18.5.6; 18.3.

Wirshing, Donna A.; Sergi, Mark J.; Mintz, Jim. A videotape intervention to enhance the informed consent process for medical and psychiatric treatment research. *American Journal of Psychiatry* 2005 January; 162(1): 186-188. NRCBL: 18.5.6; 18.3; 1.3.12.

Young, John L. Comment: refusing to give up on forensic research. *Journal of the American Academy of Psychiatry and the Law* 2005; 33(3): 368-370. NRCBL: 18.5.6; 18.2.

HUMAN EXPERIMENTATION/ . . . / MILITARY PERSONNEL

Gebhardt, D.O.E. Off-label administration of drugs to healthy military personnel. Dubious ethics of preventive measures [opinion]. *Journal of Medical Ethics* 2005 May; 31(5): 268. NRCBL: 18.5.8; 9.7.

Melson, Ashley R. Bioterrorism, biodefense, and biotechnology in the military: a comparative analysis of legal and ethical issues in the research, development, and use of biotechnological products on American and British soldiers. *Albany Law Journal of Science and Technology* 2004; 14(2): 497-534 [Online]. Available: http://heinonline.org [3 May 2006]. NRCBL: 18.5.8; 5.1; 1.3.5. SC: le.

Nie, Jing-Bao. The West's dismissal of the Khabarovsk Trial as 'Communist propaganda': ideology, evidence and international bioethics. *Journal of Bioethical Inquiry* 2004; 1(1): 32-42. NRCBL: 18.5.8; 2.2; 21.2; 21.1. Identifiers: Unit 731.

Abstract: In late 1949 the former Soviet Union conducted an open trial of eight Japanese physicians and researchers and four other military servicemen in Khabarovsk, a city in eastern Siberia. Despite its strong ideological tone and many obvious shortcomings such as the lack of international participation, the trial established beyond a reasonable doubt that the Japanese army had prepared and deployed bacteriological weapons and that Japanese researchers had conducted cruel experiments on living human beings. However, the trial, together with the evidence presented to the court and its major findings—which have proved remarkably accurate—was dismissed as communist propaganda and totally ignored in the West until the 1980s. This paper reviews the 1949 Khabarovsk trial, examines the West's dismissal of the proceedings as mere propaganda and draws some moral lessons for bioethics today. As an important historical case, set in the unique socio-political context of the Cold War, the West's dismissal of the trial powerfully illustrates some perennial ethical issues such as the ambivalence of evi-

NRCBL: National Reference Center for Bioethics Literature Classification Scheme   See inside front cover for terms.

307

dence and power of ideology in making (or failing to make) cross-national and cross-cultural factual and moral judgments.

O'Connor, Michael J. Bearing true faith and allegiance? Allowing recovery for soldiers under fire in military experiments that violate the Nuremberg Code. *Suffolk Transnational Law Review* 2002 Summer; 25(3): 649-686. NRCBL: 18.5.8; 18.3; 1.3.5; 18.2. SC: le.

Pittman, Phillip R.; Norris, Sarah L.; Coonan, Kevin M.; McKee, Kelly T., Jr. An assessment of health status among medical research volunteers who served in the Project Whitecoat program at Fort Detrick, Maryland. *Military Medicine* 2005 March; 170(3): 183-187. NRCBL: 18.5.8; 21.3; 2.2. SC: em.

Sontag, Deborah. Abuses endangered veterans in cancer drug experiments. *New York Times* 2005 February 6; p. A1, A28. NRCBL: 18.5.8; 1.3.9; 7.4. SC: po.

HUMAN EXPERIMENTATION/.../ MINORS

Newborn screening grows up [editorial]. *Nature Medicine* 2005 October; 11(10): 1013. NRCBL: 18.5.2; 8.2.

Amaya-Jackson, Lisa; Socolar, Rebecca R.S.; Hunter, Wanda; Runyan, Desmond K.; Colindres, Rom. Directly questioning children and adolescents about maltreatment: a review of survey measures used. *Journal of Interpersonal Violence* 2000 July; 15(7): 725-759. NRCBL: 18.5.2; 9.5.7; 9.1. SC: em.

Ambulatory Pediatric Association [APA]. Research Committee; Etzel, Ruth A. Ambulatory Pediatric Association policy statement: ensuring integrity for research with children. *Ambulatory Pediatrics* 2005 January-February; 5(1): 3-5. NRCBL: 18.5.2; 18.2; 6.

Anderson, Barry D.; Adamson, Peter C.; Weiner, Susan L.; McCabe, Mary S.; Smith, Malcolm A. Tissue collection for correlative studies in childhood cancer clinical trials: ethical considerations and special imperatives. *Journal of Clinical Oncology* 2004 December 1; 22(23): 4794-4798. NRCBL: 18.5.2; 18.2; 18.6. Note: The December 1, 2004 print issue contains a pagination sequence error. The correct page numbers for this article are 4846-4850.

Barfield, Raymond C.; Church, Christopher. Informed consent in pediatric clinical trials. *Current Opinion in Pediatrics* 2005 February; 17(1): 20-24. NRCBL: 18.5.2; 18.3. SC: rv.

Baylis, Françoise; Downie, Jocelyn. An ethical and criminal law framework for research involving children in Canada. *Health Law Journal* 1993; 1: 39-64. NRCBL: 18.5.2; 18.3. SC: le.

Berg, Jessica Wilen. Children and placebos. *In:* Kodish, Eric, ed. Ethics and Research with Children: A Case-Based Approach. New York: Oxford University Press; 2005: 294- 309. NRCBL: 18.5.2; 18.3.

Berkowitz, Carol D. The need for a developmental approach to adolescent decision- making [comment]. *American Journal of Bioethics* 2005 September-October; 5(5): 77-78. NRCBL: 18.5.2; 18.3. Comments: comment on Jennifer M. Cohn, Kenneth R. Ginsburg, Nancy Kassam-Adams, Joel A. Fein, "Adolescent decisional autonomy regarding participation in an emergency department youth violence interview," American Journal of Bioethics 2005 September-October; 5(5): 70-74.

Black, Maureen M.; Ponirakis, Angelo. Computer-administered interviews with children about maltreatment: methodological, developmental, and ethical issues. *Journal of Interpersonal Violence* 2000 July; 15(7): 682-695. NRCBL: 18.5.2; 9.5.7; 9.1; 1.3.12.

Bluebond-Langner, Myra; DeCicco, Amy; Belasco, Jean. Involving children with life-shortening illnesses in decisions about participation in clinical research: a proposal for shuttle diplomacy and negotiation. *In:* Kodish, Eric, ed. Ethics and Research with Children: A Case-Based Approach. New York: Oxford University Press; 2005: 323- 343. NRCBL: 18.5.2; 18.5.7.

Breslow, Lauren Hammer. The Best Pharmaceuticals for Children Act of 2002: the rise of the voluntary incentive structure and congressional refusal to require pediatric testing. *Harvard Journal on Legislation* 2003 Winter; 40(1): 133-193. NRCBL: 18.5.2; 9.7; 18.6. SC: le.

British Paediatric Association. Working on Party Ethics of Research in Children. Guidelines to aid ethical committees considering research involving children. *Archives of Disease in Childhood* 1980 January; 55(1): 75-77. NRCBL: 18.5.2; 18.2.

Broome, Marion E. Researching the world of children [editorial]. *Nursing Research* 1998 November-December; 47(6): 305-306. NRCBL: 18.5.2; 18.2.

Burke, Tara M.; Abramovitch, R.; Zlotkin, S. Children's understanding of the risks and benefits associated with research. *Journal of Medical Ethics* 2005 December; 31(12): 715-720. NRCBL: 18.5.2; 18.3. SC: em.
Abstract: OBJECTIVE: The objective of the current study was to maximise the amount of information children and adolescents understand about the risks and benefits associated with participation in a biomedical research study. DESIGN: Participants were presented with one of six hypothetical research protocols describing how to fix a fractured thigh using either a "standard" cast or "new" pins procedure. Risks and benefits associated with each of the treatment options were manipulated so that for each one of the six protocols there was either a correct or ambiguous choice.Participants and SETTING: Two hundred and fifty one children, ages 6-15 (53% boys), and 237 adults (30% men) were interviewed while waiting for a clinic appointment at the Hospital for Sick Children. RESULTS: Using standardised procedures and questionnaires, it was determined that most participants, regardless of age group, were able to understand the basic purpose and procedures involved in the research, and most were able to choose the "correct" operation. The younger children, however, showed an overall preference for a cast operation, whereas the older participants were more

likely to choose the pins. CONCLUSIONS: By creating age appropriate modules of information, children as young as six years can understand potentially difficult and complex concepts such as the risks and benefits associated with participation in biomedical research. It appears, however, that different criteria were used for treatment preference, regardless of associated risks; older participants tended to opt for mobility (the pins procedure) whereas younger participants stayed with the more familiar cast operation.

Campbell, Amy T. Adolescent decisional autonomy in research: issues in translating research into policy [comment]. *American Journal of Bioethics* 2005 September-October; 5(5): 78-80. NRCBL: 18.5.2; 18.3; 18.6. Comments: comment on Jennifer M. Cohn, Kenneth R. Ginsburg, Nancy Kassam-Adams, Joel A. Fein, "Adolescent decisional autonomy regarding participation in an emergency department youth violence interview," American Journal of Bioethics 2005 September-October; 5(5): 70-74.

Caskey, John D.; Rosenthal, Susan L. Conducting research on sensitive topics with adolescents: ethical and developmental considerations. *Journal of Developmental and Behavioral Pediatrics* 2005 February; 26(1): 61-67. NRCBL: 18.5.2; 18.2.

Chang, Ann. Nurses' perceptions of phase I clinical trials in pediatric oncology: a review of the literature. *Journal of Pediatric Oncology Nursing* 2004 November-December; 21(6): 343-349. NRCBL: 18.5.2; 8.1; 18.3. SC: rv.

Chesney, Russell W. Children as clinical research subjects. *Journal of Pediatrics* 2005 May; 146(5): 579-580. NRCBL: 18.5.2; 18.2.

Church, Christopher; Santana, Victor M.; Hinds, Pamela S.; Horwitz, Edwin M. Near the boundary of research: roles, responsibilities, and resource allocation. *In:* Kodish, Eric, ed. Ethics and Research with Children: A Case-Based Approach. New York: Oxford University Press; 2005: 274- 293. NRCBL: 18.5.2; 9.5.4.

Coffey, M. Justin; Wilfond, Benjamin; Ross, Lainie Friedman. Ethical assessment of clinical asthma trials including children subjects. *Pediatrics* 2004 January; 113(1, Part 1): 87-94. NRCBL: 18.5.2. SC: em.

Cohn, Jennifer M. Response to commentary on "Adolescent decisional autonomy regarding participation in an emergency department youth violence interview" [letter]. *American Journal of Bioethics [Online]* 2005 September-October; 5(5): W14. NRCBL: 18.5.2; 18.3.

Cohn, Jennifer M.; Ginsburg, Kenneth R.; Kassam-Adams, Nancy; Fein, Joel A. Adolescent decisional autonomy regarding participation in an emergency department youth violence interview. *American Journal of Bioethics* 2005 September-October; 5(5): 70-74. NRCBL: 18.5.2; 18.3. SC: em.
Abstract: Much attention has been given to determining whether an adolescent patient has the capacity to consent to re-

search. This study explores the factors that influence adolescents' decisions to participate in a research study about youth violence and to determine positive or negative feelings elicited by being a research subject. The majority of subjects perceived their decision to participate to be free of coercion, and few felt badly about having participated. However, adolescents who were alone in the room during the assent process were more likely to report that they chose freely to be a research subject. This study may influence the ways physicians communicate with adolescent patients around research assent within a clinical care environment.

Collogan, Lauren K.; Fleischman, Alan R. Adolescent research and parental permission. *In:* Kodish, Eric, ed. Ethics and Research with Children: A Case-Based Approach. New York: Oxford University Press; 2005: 77- 99. NRCBL: 18.5.2; 18.4.

Culbert, A.; Davis, D.J. Parental preferences for neonatal resuscitation research consent: a pilot study. *Journal of Medical Ethics* 2005 December; 31(12): 721-726. NRCBL: 18.5.2; 18.3; 8.3.2. SC: em.
Abstract: OBJECTIVE: Obtaining informed consent for resuscitation research, especially in the newborn, is problematic. This study aimed to evaluate parental preferences for hypothetical consent procedures in neonatal resuscitation research. DESIGN: Mail-out survey questionnaire. Setting/PARTICIPANTS: Randomly selected parents who had received obstetrical or neonatal care at a tertiary perinatal centre. MAIN OUTCOME MEASURES: Parental levels of comfort (Likert-type scale 1-6) regarding different methods of obtaining consent in hypothetical resuscitation research scenarios. RESULTS: The response rate was 34%. The respondents were a group of highly educated women with a higher family income than would be expected in the general population. In terms of results, parents valued the impact the research would have on their baby and the importance of a positive interaction with the physicians conducting the research study. Parents felt most comfortable with prospective consent in the setting of prenatal classes or prenatal visits with a physician, but they were somewhat uncomfortable with prospective consent upon admission to hospital after labour had begun. Parents were uncomfortable with waived consent, deferred consent, and opting out, no matter when during the pregnancy consent was requested. CONCLUSION: This pilot study reports parental preferences for prenatal information and consent for such research trials of neonatal resuscitation. A low response rate and potentially skewed demographics of the respondents prevent generalisability of this result. Interview studies should be performed to better determine parental preferences for informed consent in a more representative population.

Daniels, Stephen R. Should adolescents be paid to participate in research? [opinion]. *Journal of Pediatrics* 2005 April; 146(4): A1. NRCBL: 18.5.2; 9.3.1.

Derivan, Albert T.; Leventhal, Bennett L.; March, John; Wolraich, Mark; Zito, Julie Magno. The ethical use of placebo in clinical trials involving children. *Journal of Child and Adolescent Psychopharmacology* 2004 Summer; 14(2): 169-174. NRCBL: 18.5.2; 18.3.

Diekema, Douglas S. Payments for participation of children in research. *In:* Kodish, Eric, ed. Ethics and Research with Children: A Case-Based Approach. New York: Ox-

NRCBL: National Reference Center for Bioethics Literature Classification Scheme   See inside front cover for terms.

309

ford University Press; 2005: 143- 160. NRCBL: 18.5.2; 9.3.1.

Downie, Jocelyn; Baird, Patricia; Thompson, Jon. Industry and the academy: conflicts of interest in contemporary health research. *Health Law Journal* 2002; 10: 103-122. NRCBL: 18.5.2; 19.4; 18.3; 9.7; 7.3; 18.6; 18.2. SC: cs; le.

Eder, Michelle. Testing drugs in developing countries: pediatric research ethics in an international context. *In:* Kodish, Eric, ed. Ethics and Research with Children: A Case-Based Approach. New York: Oxford University Press; 2005: 241- 261. NRCBL: 18.5.2; 18.5.7.

Edwards, S.D.; McNamee, M.J. Ethical concerns regarding guidelines for the conduct of clinical research on children. *Journal of Medical Ethics* 2005 June; 31(6): 351-354. NRCBL: 18.5.2; 6.

Abstract: In this article we examine ethical aspects of the involvement of children in clinical research, specifically those who are incapable of giving informed consent to participate. The topic is, of course, not a new one in medical ethics but there are some tensions in current guidelines that, in our view, need to be made explicit and which need to be responded to by the relevant official bodies. In particular, we focus on tensions between the World Medical Association Declaration of Helsinki, and the guidance offered by the British Medical Association, the Royal College of Paediatrics and Child Health (formerly the British Paediatric Association), and the Council for International Organizations of Medical Sciences. We conclude with a call for these organisations to make their guidance explicit in relation to the World Medical Association Declaration.

Field, Marilyn J.; Behrman, Richard E. Responsible research involving children. *Ambulatory Pediatrics* 2005 January-February; 5(1): 47-49. NRCBL: 18.5.2; 18.2; 18.3.

Fisher, Celia B. Informed consent and clinical research involving children and adolescents: implications of the revised APA ethics code and HIPAA. *Journal of Clinical Child and Adolescent Psychology* 2004 December; 33(4): 832-839. NRCBL: 18.5.2; 18.3; 8.4; 6. SC: le. Identifiers: American Psychological Association; Health Insurance Portability and Accountability Act.

Fisher, Celia B.; Hoagwood, Kimberly; Boyce, Cheryl; Duster, Troy; Frank, Deborah A.; Grisso, Thomas; Levine, Robert J.; Macklin, Ruth; Spencer, Margaret Beale; Takanishi, Ruby; Trimble, Joseph E.; Zayas, Luis H. Research ethics for mental health science involving ethnic minority children and youths. *American Psychologist* 2002 December; 57(12): 1024-1040. NRCBL: 18.5.2; 18.2; 18.5.6; 18.5.1. SC: rv. Conference: Research Ethics in Mental Health Science Involving Ethnic Minority Children and Youth Conference; Fordham University, New York; 16-17 July 2001; sponsored by the American Psychological Association, the National Institute of Mental Health, and the Fordham University Center for Ethics Education.

Golec, Lisa; Gibbins, Sharyn; Dunn, Michael S.; Hebert, Philip. Informed consent in the NICU setting: an ethically optimal model for research solicitation. *Journal of Perinatology* 2004 December; 24(12): 783-791. NRCBL: 18.5.2; 18.3; 8.1.

Hampton, Tracy. Experts ponder pediatric research ethics. *JAMA: The Journal of the American Medical Association* 2005 November 2; 294(17): 2148, 2151. NRCBL: 18.5.2; 18.2.

Helgesson, Gert. Children, longitudinal studies, and informed consent. *Medicine, Health Care and Philosophy: A European Journal* 2005; 8(3): 307-313. NRCBL: 18.5.2; 18.3.

Abstract: This paper deals with ethical issues of particular relevance to longitudinal research involving children. First some general problems concerning information and lack of understanding are discussed. Thereafter focus is shifted to issues concerning information and consent procedures in studies that include young children growing up to become autonomous persons while the project still runs. Some of the questions raised are: When is it right to include children in longitudinal studies? Is an approval from the child needed? How should information to children be handled? A general point stressed is that autonomy considerations underline the importance of adjusting the information given to meet demands. A "presumption of competence" may be needed in research involving children, in order to pay their views sufficient attention.

Hirtz, Deborah G.; Fitzsimmons, Lorraine G. Regulatory and ethical issues in the conduct of clinical research involving children. *Current Opinion in Pediatrics* 2002 December; 14(6): 669-675. NRCBL: 18.5.2; 18.6; 18.3; 8.4.

Hoehn, K.S.; Wernovsky, G.; Rychik, J.; Gaynor, J.W.; Spray, T.L.; Feudtner, C.; Nelson, R.M. What factors are important to parents making decisions about neonatal research? *Archives of Disease in Childhood. Fetal and Neonatal Edition* 2005 May; 90(3): F267-F269. NRCBL: 18.5.2; 18.3. SC: em.

Horizons; Population Council; IMPACT; Family Health International; Schenk, Katie; Williamson, Jan. Ethical approaches to gathering information from children and adolescents in international settings: guidelines and resources. Washington, DC: Population Council 2005 August; 78 p. [Online]. Available: http//www.popcouncil.org/pdfs/horizons/childrenethics.pdf [23 January 2006]. NRCBL: 18.5.2; 6; 18.2; 1.3.12.

Ijichi, Shinji; Ijichi, Naomi. The scientific establishment of a new therapeutic intervention for developmental conditions: practical and ethical principles. *Child's Nervous System* 2003 November; 19(10-11): 711-715. NRCBL: 18.5.2.

Jeffery, A.; Snaith, R.; Voss, L. Ethical dilemmas: feeding back results to members of a longitudinal cohort study. *Journal of Medical Ethics* 2005 March; 31(3): 153. NRCBL: 18.5.2; 18.3.

Katz, Jay. Experimenting with uncomprehending subjects. *In his:* Experimentation with Human Beings: The Authority of the Investigator, Subject, Professions, and State in the Human Experimentation Process. New York: Russell Sage Foundation; 1972: 955-1011. NRCBL: 18.5.2; 18.5.6.

Kim, Eunjung. Protection of child human subjects. *Journal of Wound, Ostomy, and Continence Nursing* 2004 July-August; 31(4): 161-167. NRCBL: 18.5.2; 18.3; 18.6; 2.2. SC: em.

King, Nancy M.P.; Churchill, Larry R. Ethical principles guiding research on child and adolescent subjects. *Journal of Interpersonal Violence* 2000 July; 15(7): 710-724. NRCBL: 18.5.2; 1.3.9; 9.5.7; 18.3.

Knight, Elizabeth Dawes; Runyan, Desmond K.; Dubowitz, Howard; Brandford, Carol; Kotch, Jonathan; Litrownik, Alan; Hunter, Wanda. Methodological and ethical challenges associated with child self-report of maltreatment: solutions implemented by the LongSCAN Consortium. *Journal of Interpersonal Violence* 2000 July; 15(7): 760-775. NRCBL: 18.5.2; 18.2; 18.3; 18.4.

Korenman, Stanley G. Research in children: assessing risks and benefits. *Pediatric Research* 2004 August; 56(2): 165-166. NRCBL: 18.5.2; 5.2.

Kotch, Jonathan B. Ethical issues in longitudinal child maltreatment research. *Journal of Interpersonal Violence* 2000 July; 15(7): 696-709. NRCBL: 18.5.2; 9.5.7; 9.1; 1.1.

Krugman, Saul. Experiments at the Willowbrook State School [letter]. *Lancet* 1971 May 8; 1(7706): 966-967. NRCBL: 18.5.2; 1.3.7; 18.5.6.

Lenzer, Jeanne. US teenager's parents sue school over depression screening test [news]. *BMJ: British Medical Journal* 2005 October 1; 331(7519): 714. NRCBL: 18.5.2; 17.1; 4.3; 8.3.2.

Lépine, Suzanne; Smolla, Nicole. Ethical issues concerning participants in community surveys of child and adolescent mental disorders. *Canadian Journal of Psychiatry* 2000 February; 45(1): 48-54. NRCBL: 18.5.2; 17.1.

Martin, Molly; Lantos, John. Bioethics meets the barrios: community-based research involving children. *In:* Kodish, Eric, ed. Ethics and Research with Children: A Case-Based Approach. New York: Oxford University Press; 2005: 63- 76. NRCBL: 18.5.2.

Morley, C.J.; Lau, R.; Davis, P.G.; Morse, C. What do parents think about enrolling their premature babies in several research studies? *Archives of Disease in Childhood. Fetal and Neonatal Edition* 2005 May; 90(3): F225-F228. NRCBL: 18.5.2. SC: em. Identifiers: Australia.

Muntarbhorn, Vitit. Child rights and use of the child's body. *In:* Actes du Colloque International AMADE-UNESCO sur Bioethique et Droits de L'enfant (Monaco, 28-30 Avril 2000)/Proceedings of the International Symposium AMADE-UNESCO on Bioethics and the Rights of the Child (Monaco, 28-30 April 2000). Paris: UNESCO, Division des Sciences Humaines, de la Philosophie et de L'ethique des Sciences et des Technologies; 2001: 123-139. NRCBL: 18.5.2; 19.5; 9.5.7.

Neill, Sarah J. Research with children: a critical review of the guidelines. *Journal of Child Health Care* 2005 March; 9(1): 46-58. NRCBL: 18.5.2; 18.2; 18.3. SC: rv.

Nelson, Robert M. Justice, lead, and environmental research involving children. *In:* Kodish, Eric, ed. Ethics and Research with Children: A Case-Based Approach. New York: Oxford University Press; 2005: 161- 178. NRCBL: 18.5.2; 16.1.

Olds, R. Scott. Informed-consent issues with adolescent health behavior research. *American Journal of Health Behavior* 2003 November-December; 27(Supplement 3): S248-S263. NRCBL: 18.5.2; 18.2; 18.3. SC: cs; rv; le.

Otto, Mary. Drugs tested on HIV-positive foster children; Hill investigates ethical questions raised by 1990s trials in Maryland, elsewhere. *Washington Post* 2005 May 19; p. B1, B4. NRCBL: 18.5.2; 9.7; 9.5.6. SC: po.

Peart, Nicola; Foley, Mary; Henaghan, Mark. Children as research participants. *In:* Dawson, John; Peart, Nicola, eds. The Law of Research: A Guide. Dunedin, NZ: University of Otago Press; 2003: 269-284. NRCBL: 18.5.2; 18.3.

Piercy, Hilary; Hargate, Maria. Social research on the under-16s: a consideration of the issues from a UK perspective. *Journal of Child Health Care* 2004 December; 8(4): 253-263. NRCBL: 18.5.2; 18.3. Identifiers: United Kingdom (Great Britain).

Ross, Lainie Friedman. Children as research subjects: a proposal to revise the current federal regulations using a moral framework. *Stanford Law and Policy Review* 1997 Winter; 8(1): 159-176. NRCBL: 18.5.2; 18.3. SC: le.

Runyan, Desmond K. The ethical, legal, and methodological implications of directly asking children about abuse. *Journal of Interpersonal Violence* 2000 July; 15(7): 675-681. NRCBL: 18.5.2; 9.5.7; 9.1.

Ryan, Ann E. Protecting the rights of pediatric research subjects in the International Conference on Harmonisation of Technical Requirements for Registration of Pharmaceuticals for Human Use. *Fordham International Law Journal* 2000 March; 23(3): 848-934. NRCBL: 18.5.2; 18.2; 18.3; 21.1. SC: le.

Saint Raymond, Agnès; Brasseur, Daniel. Development of medicines for children in Europe: ethical implications. *Paediatric Respiratory Reviews* 2005 March; 6(1): 45-51. NRCBL: 18.5.2; 18.6; 9.7; 21.1.

Salazar, Juan C. Pediatric clinical trial experience: government, child, parent and physician's perspective. *Pediat-*

NRCBL: National Reference Center for Bioethics Literature Classification Scheme   See inside front cover for terms.

311

ric Infectious Disease Journal 2003 December; 22(12): 1124-1127. NRCBL: 18.5.2; 18.2.

Scherer, David G.; Brody, Janet L.; Annett, Robert D.; Hetter, Jeanne; Roberts, Laura Weiss; Cofrin, Keely M.W. Financial compensation to adolescents for participation in biomedical research: adolescent and parent perspectives in seven studies. *Journal of Pediatrics* 2005 April; 146(4): 552-558. NRCBL: 18.5.2; 9.3.1. SC: em.

Scott, Janny; Kaufman, Leslie. Belated charge ignites furor over AIDS drug trial. *New York Times* 2005 July 17; p. A1, A10. NRCBL: 18.5.2; 9.5.6. SC: po.

Singhal, Nalini; Oberle, Kathleen; Darwish, Amy; Burgess, Ellen. Attitudes of health-care providers towards research with newborn babies. *Journal of Perinatology* 2004 December; 24(12): 775-782. NRCBL: 18.5.2; 18.3. SC: em. Identifiers: Canada.

Solyom, Antal E.; Moreno, Jonathan D. Protection of children and adolescents in psychiatric research: an unfinished business. *HEC (Healthcare Ethics Committee) Forum* 2005 September; 17(3): 210-226. NRCBL: 18.5.2; 18.5.6; 18.4; 17.1; 18.6; 17.4.

Stiffman, Arlene Rubin; Brown, Eddie; Striley, Catherine Woodstock; Ostmann, Emily; Chowa, Gina. Cultural and ethical issues concerning research on American Indian youth. *Ethics and Behavior* 2005; 15(1): 1-14. NRCBL: 18.5.2; 18.2; 18.3; 20.7; 8.4. SC: em.
Abstract: A study of American Indian youths illustrates competing pressures between research and ethics. A stakeholder-researcher team developed three plans to protect participants. The first allowed participants to skip potentially upsetting interview sections. The second called for participants to skip potentially upsetting interview sections. The second [sic] called for participants flagged for abuse or suicidality to receive referrals, emergency 24-hr clinical backup, or both. The third, based on the community's desire to promote service access, included giving participants a list of service resources. Interviewers gave referrals to participants flagged as having mild problems, and reported participants with serious problems to supervisors for clinical backup. Participants seldom chose to skip sections, so data integrity was not compromised. However, participants did have more problems than expected (e.g., 1 in 3 had thought about suicide, 1 in 5 had attempted suicide, and 1 in 4 reported abuse), so service agencies were not equipped to respond. Researchers must accept the competing pressures and find ethically appropriate compromises that will not undermine research integrity.

Stromberg, Daniel; Tortoriello, Tia; Adame, Tracine; Morris, Marilyn C. Waiver of prospective consent for pediatric resuscitation research [letters and reply]. *Pediatrics* 2005 March; 115(3): 828-829. NRCBL: 18.5.2; 18.3; 8.3.3.

Thomas, Karen A. Safety: when infants and parents are research subjects. *Journal of Perinatal and Neonatal Nursing* 2005 January-March; 19(1): 52-58. NRCBL: 18.5.2; 18.3; 18.2; 8.4.

Trivedi, Amar D. Rethinking adolescent assent: a triangular approach [comment]. *American Journal of Bioethics* 2005 September-October; 5(5): 75-76. NRCBL: 18.5.2; 18.3. Comments: comment on Jennifer M. Cohn, Kenneth R. Ginsburg, Nancy Kassam-Adams, Joel A. Fein, "Adolescent decisional autonomy regarding participation in an emergency department youth violence interview," American Journal of Bioethics 2005 September-October; 5(5): 70-74.

Twomey, John G., Jr. The ethics of clinical research with children with HIV infection. *Virginia Nurse* 1989 Summer; 57(3): 38-40, 42-43. NRCBL: 18.5.2; 9.5.6.

Ward Platt, M.P. Participation in multiple neonatal research studies [opinion]. *Archives of Disease in Childhood. Fetal and Neonatal Edition* 2005 May; 90(3): F191. NRCBL: 18.5.2; 18.3.

Weiss, Rick. Medical studies and the average American kid. *Washington Post* 2005 August 22; p. A5. NRCBL: 18.5.2. SC: po; em.

Wendler, David; Belsky, Leah; Thompson, Kimberly M.; Emanuel, Ezekiel J. Qualifying the federal minimal risk standard: implications for pediatric research without a prospect of direct benefit. *JAMA: The Journal of the American Medical Association* 2005 August 17; 294(7): 826-832. NRCBL: 18.5.2; 18.2. SC: em.
Abstract: United States federal regulations allow institutional review boards (IRBs) to approve pediatric research that does not offer participants a "prospect of direct" benefit only when the risks are minimal or a "minor" increase over minimal. The federal regulations define minimal risks based on the risks "ordinarily encountered in daily life or during routine physical or psychological examinations or tests." In the absence of empirical data, IRB members may assume they are familiar with the risks of daily life and with the risks of routine examinations and tests and rely on their own intuitive judgment to make these assessments. Yet intuitive judgment of risk is subject to systematic errors, highlighting the need for empirical data to guide IRB review and approval of pediatric research. Current data reveal that car trips pose the highest risk of mortality ordinarily encountered by healthy children. On average, these risks are approximately 0.06 per million for children aged 14 years and younger, and approximately 0.4 per million for children aged 15 through 19 years. Riskier, but still ordinary, car trips pose an approximately 0.6 per million chance of death for children aged 14 years and younger and an approximately 4 per million chance of death for children aged 15 through 19 years. Participation in sports represents the upper end of the range of morbidity risks for healthy children. For every million instances of playing basketball, approximately 1900 individuals will sustain injuries, including 180 broken bones and 58 permanent disabilities. These findings suggest IRBs are implementing the federal minimal risk standard too cautiously in many cases. These data also raise the question of whether the federal minimal risk standard may sometimes fail to provide sufficient protection for children, prompting the need to consider alternative standards.

Wilfond, Benjamin; Candotti, Fabio. When eligibility criteria clash with personal treatment choice: a dilemma of clinical research. *In:* Kodish, Eric, ed. Ethics and Research with Children: A Case-Based Approach. New York: Oxford University Press; 2005: 310- 322. NRCBL: 18.5.2; 18.2.

Williamson, Emma; Goodenough, Trudy; Kent, Julie; Ashcroft, Richard. Children's participation in genetic epidemiology: consent and control. *In:* Tutton, Richard; Corrigan, Oonagh, eds. Genetic Databases: Socio-ethical Issues in the Collection and Use of DNA. New York: Routledge; 2004: 139-160. NRCBL: 18.5.2; 15.1. SC: em.

HUMAN EXPERIMENTATION/ . . . / PRISONERS

Bogod, David. The Nazi hypothermia experiments: forbidden data? [editorial]. *Anaesthesia* 2004 December; 59(12): 1155-1156. NRCBL: 18.5.5; 21.4; 1.3.9.

Byrne, Mary Woods. Conducting research as a visiting scientist in a women's prison. *Journal of Professional Nursing* 2005 July-August; 21(4): 223-230. NRCBL: 18.5.5; 18.5.3.

California. Penal Code. Human experimentation: use of prisoners in biomedical and behavioural research. *International Digest of Health Legislation* 1979; 30(1): 143- 146. NRCBL: 18.5.5. SC: le.

Hoffman, Sharona. Beneficial and unusual punishment: an argument in support of prisoner participation in clinical trials. *Indiana Law Review* 2000; 33(2): 475-515. NRCBL: 18.5.5; 18.2; 17.8. SC: le.

Katz, Jay. Experimentation with captive subjects. *In his:* Experimentation with Human Beings: The Authority of the Investigator, Subject, Professions, and State in the Human Experimentation Process. New York: Russell Sage Foundation; 1972: 1013-1052. NRCBL: 18.5.5; 18.5.8.

Peternelj-Taylor, Cindy A. Conceptualizing nursing research with offenders: another look at vulnerability. *International Journal of Law and Psychiatry* 2005 July-August; 28(4): 348-359. NRCBL: 18.5.5; 4.1.3; 9.5.1; 1.3.5; 18.2; 18.3.

United States. Department of Health and Human Services. Office for Human Research Protections [OHRP]. OHRP Guidance on the Involvement of Prisoners in Research. Washington, DC: Department of Health and Human Services 2003 May 23; 8 p. [Online]. Available: http://www.hhs.gov/ohrp/humansubjects/guidance/prisoner.pdf [18 April 2005]. NRCBL: 18.5.5; 18.2.

HUMAN EXPERIMENTATION/ . . . / WOMEN

American College of Obstetricians and Gynecologists [ACOG]. Committee on Ethics. ACOG committee opinion. Ethical considerations in research involving women. *International Journal of Gynecology and Obstetrics* 2004 July; 86(1): 124-130. NRCBL: 18.5.3; 18.2; 18.3; 18.5.4.

American College of Obstetricians and Gynecologists [ACOG]. Committee on Health Care for Underserved Women. ACOG Committee Opinion No. 307. Partner consent for participation in women's reproductive health research. *Obstetrics and Gynecology* 2004 December; 104(6): 1467-1469. NRCBL: 18.5.3; 18.3; 18.2.

Baker, Lisa; Lavender, Tina; Tincello, Douglas. Factors that influence women's decisions about whether to participate in research: an exploratory study. *Birth* 2005 March; 32(1): 60-66. NRCBL: 18.5.3; 18.3. SC: em. Identifiers: United Kingdom (Great Britain).

Hatton, Diane C.; Kaiser, Lisa. Methodological and ethical issues emerging from pilot testing an intervention with women in a transitional shelter. *Western Journal of Nursing Research* 2004 February; 26(1): 129-136. NRCBL: 18.5.3; 9.5.5; 4.1.3; 18.3.

Lupton, Martin G.F.; Williams, David J. The ethics of research on pregnant women: is maternal consent sufficient? [opinion]. *BJOG: An International Journal of Obstetrics and Gynaecology* 2004 December; 111(12): 1307-1312. NRCBL: 18.5.3; 18.3; 18.5.4; 1.3.7; 18.2.

Madhiwalla, Neha. Experiences in health research with women. *Issues in Medical Ethics* 2001 January-March; 9(1): 12-14. NRCBL: 18.5.3; 18.3.

Mehra, Preeti. Of human guinea pigs. Illustrated Weekly of India 1992 May 2-8; 5 p. [Online]. Available: http://www.hsph.harvard.edu/Organizations/healthnet/SAsia/suchana/0400/h011.html [6 October 2005]. NRCBL: 18.5.3; 1.3.9; 18.2; 2.1. Identifiers: India.

Nataraj, Shyamala. Ethical considerations in research on preventing mother-to- child HIV transmission. *Monash Bioethics Review* 2005 October; 24(4): 28-39. NRCBL: 18.5.3; 18.5.2; 9.5.6. SC: cs. Identifiers: India.

Pandya, Sunil K. An unusual forum for a discussion on medical ethics [letter]. *National Medical Journal of India* 1999 March-April; 12(2): 79-81. NRCBL: 18.5.3; 18.3; 14.1. Identifiers: Mumbai.

Rentetzi, Maria. The women radium dial painters as experimental subjects (1920- 1990), or: what counts as human experimentation? *In:* Roelcke, Volker; Maio, Giovanni, eds. Twentieth Century Ethics of Human Subjects Research: Historical Perspectives on Values, Practices, and Regulations. Stuttgart: Franz Steiner Verlag; 2004: 275-291. NRCBL: 18.5.3; 2.2; 16.2.

Rentetzi, Maria. The women radium dial painters as experimental subjects (1920-1990) or what counts as human experimentation. *NTM* 2004; 12(4): 233-248. NRCBL: 18.5.3; 2.2; 18.3.

Saheli Women's Health Centre. Research on anti-fertility vaccines: serious concerns for women's health. *Issues* *in Medical Ethics* 2000 April-June; 8(2): 51-52. NRCBL: 18.5.3; 11.1; 18.3; 14.1.

Salmeron, Betty Jo. Autonomy and contraception [letter]. *IRB: Ethics and Human Research* 2005 September-October; 27(5): 20. NRCBL: 18.5.3; 11.1; 1.1.

Santelli, John; Geller, Gail; Chen, Donna T.; Speers, Marjorie A.; Botkin, Jeffrey B.; Laswell, Stacy. Recruitment of pregnant, minor adolescents and minor adolescents at risk of pregnancy into longitudinal, observational research: the case of the National Children's Study. *In:* Kodish, Eric, ed. Ethics and Research with Children: A Case-Based Approach. New York: Oxford University Press; 2005: 100- 119. NRCBL: 18.5.3; 18.5.2.

Schonfeld, Toby L.; Gordon, Bruce G. Contraception in research: a policy suggestion. *IRB: Ethics and Human Research* 2005 March-April; 27(2): 15-20. NRCBL: 18.5.3; 11.1; 18.3.

Viswanath, Kalpana; Kirbat, Preeti. Genealogy of a controversy: development of an anti-fertility vaccine. Economic and Political Weekly 2000 February 19-26; 34(8 and 9); 15 p. [Online]. Available: http://www.hsph.harvard.edu/Organizations/healthnet/SAsia/suchana/0500/h071.html [7 October 2005]. NRCBL: 18.5.3; 1.3.9; 21.1; 1.3.6; 11.1. Identifiers: India.

HUMAN RIGHTS *See* INTERNATIONAL HUMAN RIGHTS

IMMUNIZATION *See* CARE FOR SPECIFIC GROUPS; HUMAN EXPERIMENTATION/ SPECIAL POPULATIONS/ MILITARY PERSONNEL; PUBLIC HEALTH

IN VITRO FERTILIZATION
See also REPRODUCTIVE TECHNOLOGIES

Assessing the viability of a substantive due process right to in vitro fertilization. *Harvard Law Review* 2005 June; 118(8): 2792-2813. NRCBL: 14.4; 9.2. SC: le.

Ban on import of embryos in Israel [news]. *European Journal of Obstetrics, Gynecology, and Reproductive Biology* 2001 November; 99(1): 1. NRCBL: 14.4; 19.1; 14.6; 1.3.5.

Death no longer a bar to fatherhood [news]. *Bulletin of Medical Ethics* 2003 September; (191): 5. NRCBL: 14.2; 14.6; 20.1; 8.3.1. SC: le.

A fragile gift: sharing and saving life through embryo adoption. *Today's Christian Doctor* 2005 Fall; 36(3): 28-30. NRCBL: 14.4.

Adibah, I.; Bakar, W.Y. Wan Abu. Should this couple have undergone infertility treatment? [case study]. *Indian Journal of Medical Ethics* 2005 October-December; 2(4): 126. NRCBL: 14.4; 9.5.10; 14.1. SC: cs.

Andrew, Gracy. Issues are complex and need innovative solutions [case study]. *Indian Journal of Medical Ethics* 2005 October-December; 2(4): 127. NRCBL: 14.4; 8.3.1.

Belluck, Pam. It's not so easy to adopt an embryo. *New York Times* 2005 June 12; p. Wk5. NRCBL: 14.4. SC: po.

Benagiano, Giuseppe; Gianaroli, Luca. The new Italian IVF legislation [editorial]. *Reproductive BioMedicine Online [electronic]* 2004 August; 9(2): 117-125 Available: http://www.rbmonline.com/index.html [3 June 2005]. NRCBL: 14.4; 21.1; 5.3. SC: le. Identifiers: in vitro fertilization.

Bender, Leslie. Genes, parents, and assisted reproductive technologies: ARTs, mistakes, sex, race, and law. *Columbia Journal of Gender and Law* 2003; 12(1): 1-76. NRCBL: 14.4; 8.5; 15.1. SC: le; cs.

Birenbaum-Carmeli, Daphna. 'Cheaper than a newcomer': on the social production of IVF policy in Israel. *Sociology of Health and Illness* 2004 November; 26(7): 897-924. NRCBL: 14.4; 5.3. SC: le.

Blyth, Eric. Patient experiences of an "egg sharing" programme. *Human Fertility* 2004 September; 7(3): 157-162. NRCBL: 14.4; 19.5; 8.4. SC: em. Identifiers: United Kingdom (Great Britain).

Blyth, Eric; Crawshaw, Marilyn; Daniels, Ken. Policy formation in gamete donation and egg sharing in the UK — a critical appraisal. *Social Science and Medicine* 2004 December; 59(12): 2617-2626. NRCBL: 14.4; 14.2; 19.5; 5.3. Identifiers: United Kingdom (Great Britain).

Blyth, Eric; Farrand, Abigail. Anonymity in donor-assisted conception and the UN Convention on the Rights of the Child. *International Journal of Children's Rights* 2004 April; 12(2): 89-104. NRCBL: 14.4; 8.4; 21.1. SC: le. Identifiers: United Nations.

Boggio, Andrea. Italy enacts new law on medically assisted reproduction. *Human Reproduction* 2005 May; 20(5): 1153-1157. NRCBL: 14.4; 14.6; 18.5.4; 15.2; 2.4. SC: le.

Bracken, W. Jerome. Is in vitro fertilization in accord with a symbolic concept of natural law? *In:* Koterski, Joseph W., ed. Life and Learning IX: Proceedings of the Ninth University Faculty for Life Conference. Washington, DC: University Faculty for Life; 2000: 115-142. NRCBL: 14.4; 1.2.

Brownsword, Roger. Reproductive opportunities and regulatory challenges. *Modern Law Review* 2004 March; 67(2): 304-321. NRCBL: 14.4; 15.2; 18.5.4; 19.5. SC: le. Identifiers: Human Fertilisation and Embryology Authority [HFEA]; United Kingdom (Great Britain).

Brugger, E. Christian. In defense of transferring heterologous embryos. *National Catholic Bioethics Quar-*

terly 2005 Spring; 5(1): 95- 112. NRCBL: 14.4; 4.4; 14.2; 10.

Byk, C. Public and private regulation of reproductive technologies. *Medicine and Law: World Association for Medical Law* 1995; 14(3-4): 215-219. NRCBL: 14.4; 5.3. SC: le.

Cain, Joanna M. Ethical guidelines in the prevention of iatrogenic multiple pregnancy. *International Journal of Gynecology and Obstetrics* 2000 December; 71(3): 293-294. NRCBL: 14.4; 9.8; 8.3.1. SC: le.

Canestrari, Stefano. The law of February 19th 2004, No. 40: procreation and punishment. *Revista de Derecho y Genoma Humano / Law and the Human Genome Review* 2005 January-June; (22): 57-73. NRCBL: 14.4; 14.2; 4.4; 18.5.4. SC: le. Note: Abstract in English and Spanish.

Check, Erika. Gene study raises fears for three-parent babies [news]. *Nature* 2005 November 3; 438(7064): 12. NRCBL: 14.4; 15.1.

Conti, A.; Delbon, P. Medically-assisted procreation in Italy. *Medicine and Law: World Association for Medical Law* 2005 March; 24(1): 163-172. NRCBL: 14.4; 14.6; 8.3.1. SC: le.
   Abstract: In February 2004, a law was approved in Italy on medically assisted procreation. The authors attempt to discuss the main provisions of the law. In its 18 articles, the law provides access to approved assisted procreation methods for adult couples of different sex, either married or cohabiting, of a potentially fertile age, both living, and establishes that the couple must be offered the chance of reverting to adoption or foster care procedures pursuant to the law in force. The law contains numerous prohibitions and restrictions: heterologous insemination, cloning, the cryo-preservation of embryos and research on human embryos are forbidden; during an assisted reproduction cycle, the methods used must not produce a number of embryos greater than those strictly necessary for a single and simultaneous implant, and in any case never more than three. The law calls for the woman and her husband or partner to be properly informed and for their approval to be given in writing. Fairly severe sanctions have been established for persons who break the law; health workers are however entitled to object on conscientious grounds to performing certain procedures.

Cook, Rachel. Villain, hero or masked stranger: ambivalence in transactions with human gametes. *In:* Bainham, Andrew; Sclater, Shelley Day; Richards, Martin, eds. Body Lore and Laws. Portland, OR: Hart Pub.; 2002: 211-227. NRCBL: 14.4. SC: le.

Craft, Ian; Flyckt, Sofia; Heeley, Gosia; Layland, Sarah; Thornhill, Alan; Kelada, Ehab. Will removal of anonymity influence the recruitment of egg donors? A survey of past donors and recipients. *Reproductive BioMedicine Online [electronic]* 2005 March; 10(3): 325-329. Available: http://www.rbmonline.com/Article/1633 [30 September 2005]. NRCBL: 14.4; 8.4. SC: em. Identifiers: United Kingdom (Great Britain); Human Fertilisation and Embryology Authority [HFEA].

Craft, Ian; Thornhill, Alan. Would 'all-inclusive' compensation attract more gamete donors to balance their loss of anonymity? *Reproductive BioMedicine Online [electronic]* 2005 March; 10(3): 301-306. Available: http://www.rbmonline/Article/1687 [30 September 2005]. NRCBL: 14.4; 8.4. Identifiers: United Kingdom (Great Britain); Human Fertilisation and Embryology Authority [HFEA].

Daniels, Ken. Recruiting gamete donors: response to Craft and Thornhill. *Reproductive BioMedicine Online [electronic]* 2005 April; 10(4): 430-431. Available: http://www.rbmonline.com/Article/1735 [30 September 2005]. NRCBL: 14.4; 8.4; 9.3.1. Identifiers: United Kingdom (Great Britain); Human Fertilisation and Embryology Authority [HFEA]. Comments: comment on Ian Craft and Alan Thornhill, "Would 'all- inclusive' compensation attract more gamete donors to balance their loss of anonymity?" Reproductive BioMedicine Online 2005 March; 10(3): 301-306.

de Rosa, Francis M. The transfer of abandoned frozen embryos — identifying the object of the act. *National Catholic Bioethics Quarterly* 2005 Spring; 5(1): 59-62. NRCBL: 14.4; 1.2.

Dyer, Clare. Woman seeks approval to use frozen embryos [news]. *BMJ: British Medical Journal* 2005 February 19; 330(7488): 380. NRCBL: 14.4. SC: le.

Dyer, Owen. Fertility agency is to investigate single embryo transfer [news]. *BMJ: British Medical Journal* 2005 August 6; 331(7512): 308. NRCBL: 14.4; 9.3.1; 9.5.7.

European Society for Human Reproduction and Embryology [ESHRE]. Task Force on Ethics and Law; Shenfield, F.; Pennings, G.; Cohen, J.; Devroey, P.; Tarlatzis, B. Taskforce 9: the application of preimplantation genetic diagnosis for human leukocyte antigen typing of embryos. *Human Reproduction* 2005 April; 20(4): 845-847. NRCBL: 14.4; 4.4; 19.5.

Fisher, Ian. Italian vote to ease fertility law fails for want of voters. *New York Times* 2005 June 14; p. A11. NRCBL: 14.4; 14.1; 21.1. SC: po; le.

Fuscaldo, Giuliana; Savulescu, Julian. Spare embryos: 3000 reasons to rethink the significance of genetic relatedness. *Reproductive BioMedicine Online [electronic]* 2005 February; 10(2): 164-168. Available: http://www. rbmonline.com/index.html [17 February 2006]. NRCBL: 14.4; 14.6; 15.1; 19.6. Identifiers: Australia.

Ghali, R.P.; Woodside, J.L. Proposed Canadian legislation to regulate reproductive technologies and related research. *Reproductive BioMedicine Online [electronic]* 2003 January-February; 6(1): 114-116. Available: http://www.rbmonline.com/article/788 [1 September 2005]. NRCBL: 14.4; 18.5.4. SC: le. Identifiers: An Act Respecting Assisted Human Reproduction.

NRCBL: National Reference Center for Bioethics Literature Classification Scheme   See inside front cover for terms.

315

Greenfeld, Dorothy A.; Klock, Susan Caruso. Disclosure decisions among known and anonymous oocyte donation recipients. *Fertility and Sterility* 2004 June; 81(6): 1565-1571. NRCBL: 14.4. SC: em.

Heng, Boon Chin. Egg-sharing in return for subsidized fertility treatment: a possible solution for therapeutic cloning? [letter]. *Human Reproduction* 2005 November; 20(11): 3258. NRCBL: 14.4; 14.5.

Hershberger, Patricia. Recipients of oocyte donation: an integrative review. *Journal of Obstetric, Gynecologic, and Neonatal Nursing* 2004 September-October; 33(5): 610-621. NRCBL: 14.4; 19.5; 17.1. SC: em; rv.

Inhorn, Marcia C. Privacy, privatization, and the politics of patronage: ethnographic challenges to penetrating the secret world of Middle Eastern, hospital-based in vitro fertilization. *Social Science and Medicine* 2004 November; 59(10): 2095-2108. NRCBL: 14.4; 18.6; 8.4; 7.1. Identifiers: Egypt; Lebanon.

Irvine, W. Nigel. An ill-conceived conception? *Medical Law International* 2004; 6(3): 231-249. NRCBL: 14.4; 14.5; 15.2; 9.8. SC: an.

Jordan, Caren B.; Belar, Cynthia D.; Williams, R. Stan. Anonymous oocyte donation: a follow-up analysis of donors' experiences. *Journal of Psychosomatic Obstetrics and Gynecology* 2004 June; 25(2): 145-151. NRCBL: 14.4; 14.6. SC: em.

Kalb, Claudia. Ethics, eggs and embryos: thanks to medical advances, scientists are looking for a few good women to donate their oocytes to stem-cell research. *Newsweek* 2005 June 20; 145(25): 52-53. NRCBL: 14.4; 18.5.4; 19.5; 14.5. SC: po.

Kass, Leon R. New beginnings in life. *In:* Hamilton, Michael P., ed. The New Genetics and the Future of Man. Grand Rapids, MI: William B. Eerdmans Publishing Co.; 1972: 15-63. NRCBL: 14.4; 14.5. SC: an.

Kelly, Lorraine. In vitro fertilisation: the science and the ethics in the 21st century. *Human Reproduction and Genetic Ethics: An International Journal* 2001; 7(1): 15-20. NRCBL: 14.4; 14.6.

Khanijou, Siddharth. Multifetal pregnancy reduction in assisted reproductive technologies: a license to kill? *DePaul Journal of Health Care Law* 2005; 8(2): 403-430. NRCBL: 14.4; 12.3; 9.8. SC: le.

Kirkman, Maggie. Egg and embryo donation and the meaning of motherhood. *Women and Health* 2003; 38(2): 1-18. NRCBL: 14.4; 14.1; 4.4.

Kovacs, Gabor T.; Breheny, Sue A.; Dear, Melinda J. Embryo donation at an Australian university in-vitro fertilisation clinic: issues and outcomes. *Medical Journal of Australia* 2003 February 3; 178(3): 127-129. NRCBL: 14.4; 19.5. SC: em.

Kovacs, Gabor T.; Morgan, Gary; Wood, E. Carl; Forbes, Catherine; Howlett, Donna. Community attitudes to assisted reproductive technology: a 20-year trend. *Medical Journal of Australia* 2003 November 17; 179(10): 536-538. NRCBL: 14.4; 14.2; 9.3.1. SC: em. Identifiers: Australia.

Kumar, T.C. Anand. Proposed legislation for assisted reproduction technology clinics in India. *Reproductive BioMedicine Online [electronic]* 2002 November-December; 5(3): 351. Available: http://www.rbmonline.com/article/778 [1 September 2005]. NRCBL: 14.4; 21.1. SC: le.

Lal, Meena. The role of the federal government in assisted reproductive technologies. *Santa Clara Computer and High Technology Law Journal* 1997; 13(2): 517-543. NRCBL: 14.4; 14.1; 14.6; 5.3. SC: le.

Landau, Ruth. The promise of post-menopausal pregnancy (PMP). *Social Work in Health Care* 2004; 40(1): 53-69. NRCBL: 14.4; 9.5.2; 9.5.5. SC: an.

Lee, Felicia R. Driven by costs, fertility clients head overseas. *New York Times* 2005 January 25; p. A1, A14. NRCBL: 14.4. SC: po.

Majumder, Mary Anderlik; Brakman, Sarah-Vaughan. The politics of embryo transfer [discussion]. *Medical Ethics Newsletter [Lahey Clinic]* 2005 Fall; 12(3): 10-11. NRCBL: 14.4. SC: le.

Martínez, Jaime Vidal. The regulation of assisted reproduction in Spanish law. The ruling of the Spanish Constitutional Court of 17 June 1999. *European Journal of Health Law* 2002 June; 9(2): 121-137. NRCBL: 14.4; 18.5.4; 4.4; 14.5. SC: le.

May, William E. On "rescuing" frozen embryos — why the decision to do so is moral. *National Catholic Bioethics Quarterly* 2005 Spring; 5(1): 51-57. NRCBL: 14.4; 1.2; 14.6; 4.4.

Mead, Rebecca. Eggs for sale. *New Yorker* 1999 August 9: 56-65. NRCBL: 14.4; 1.3.2; 9.3.1.

Morgan, Derek; Bernat, Erwin. The reproductive waltz: the Austrian Act on Procreative Medicine 1992. *Journal of Social Welfare and Family Law* 1992; 5: 420-426. NRCBL: 14.4; 14.2; 14.1; 14.6; 18.5.4; 5.3. SC: le.

Noble-Allgire, Alice M. Switched at the fertility clinic: determining maternal rights when a child is born from stolen or misdelivered genetic material. *Missouri Law Review* 1999 Summer; 64(3): 517-594. NRCBL: 14.4; 14.1; 14.2. SC: le.

Norsigian, Judy. Egg donation dangers: additional demand for eggs leads to additional risks. *GeneWatch* 2005 September-October; 18(5): 6-8, 16. NRCBL: 14.4; 9.7; 19.5.

Onder, Robert F., Jr. Practical and moral caveats on heterologous embryo transfer. *National Catholic Bioethics Quarterly* 2005 Spring; 5(1): 75-94. NRCBL: 14.4; 14.6; 14.2; 1.1; 1.2.

Ouellette, Alicia; Caplan, Arthur; Carroll, Kelly; Fossett, James W.; Bjarnadottir, Dyrleif; Shickle, Darren; McGee, Glenn. Lessons across the pond: assisted reproductive technology in the United Kingdom and the United States. *American Journal of Law and Medicine* 2005; 31(4): 419-446. NRCBL: 14.4; 2.4; 9.8; 21.1.

Paine, Shirley J.; Moore, Patrick K.; Hill, David L. Ethical dilemmas in reproductive medicine. *Whittier Law Review* 1996 Fall; 18(1): 51-66. NRCBL: 14.4; 4.4; 8.3.1. SC: le.

Ragni, G.; Allegra, A.; Anserini, P.; Causio, F.; Ferraretti, A.P.; Greco, E.; Palermo, R.; Somigliana, E. The 2004 Italian legislation regulating assisted reproduction technology: a multicentre survey on the results of IVF cycles. *Human Reproduction* 2005 August; 20(8): 2224-2228. NRCBL: 14.4. SC: le. Identifiers: in vitro fertilization; Societa Italiana della Riproduzione (S.I.d.R.); Study group on the impact of the law 40/2004.

Randal, Asha Emsley. The personal, interpersonal, and political issues of egg donation. *Journal of Obstetrics and Gynaecology Canada* 2004 December; 26(12): 1087-1090. NRCBL: 14.4; 19.5; 9.3.1; 8.4. SC: le. Identifiers: Canada.

Saldeen, Pia; Sundström, Per. Would legislation imposing single embryo transfer be a feasible way to reduce the rate of multiple pregnancies after IVF treatment? *Human Reproduction* 2005 January; 20(1): 4-8. NRCBL: 14.4. SC: le. Identifiers: in vitro fertilization.

Schenker, Joseph G.; Laufer, Neri; Navot, Daniel; Margalioth, Ehud J.; Yarkoni, Shaul; Rabinowitz, Ron; Voss, Ruth. In vitro fertilization and embryo transfer — legal and religious aspects in Israel, patient selection, and a modified technique for oocyte collection. *Israel Journal of Medical Sciences* 1983 March; 19(3): 218-224. NRCBL: 14.4; 1.2. SC: em; le.

Schmittlein, David C.; Morrison, Donald G. A live baby or your money back: the marketing of in vitro fertilization procedures. *Management Science* 2003 December; 49(12): 1617-1635. NRCBL: 14.4; 9.3.1.

Schudt, Karl. What is chosen in the act of embryo adoption? *National Catholic Bioethics Quarterly* 2005 Spring; 5(1): 63-71. NRCBL: 14.4; 14.6; 1.2.

Seyfer, Tara L. Medical and ethical concerns over IVF: potential harms and available options. *Ethics and Medics* 2003 August; 28(8): 1-3. NRCBL: 14.4.

Sieck, William A. In vitro fertilization and the right to procreate: the right to no. *University of Pennsylvania Law Re-view* 1998 December; 147(2): 435-485. NRCBL: 14.4; 14.1; 4.4; 14.6; 8.3.1. SC: le.

Tarrant, Stella. Western Australia's persistent enforcement of an invalid law: Section 23(c) of the Human Reproductive Technology Act 1991 (WA). *Journal of Law and Medicine* 2000 August; 8(1): 92-111. NRCBL: 14.4; 10; 9.2. SC: le.

Vercellone, Paolo. Children's rights and artificial procreation. *Medicine and Law: World Association for Medical Law* 1995; 14(1-2): 13-22. NRCBL: 14.4; 14.2; 4.4.

Wallbank, Julie. "Throwing baby out with the bath water": some reflections on the evolution of reproductive technology. *Res Publica* 1999; 5(1): 47-67. NRCBL: 14.4; 14.1; 4.4; 12.4.2; 19.1. SC: le. Identifiers: United Kingdom (Great Britain).

Watt, Helen. Ethical problems in assisted conception. *In:* McMahon, Kevin T., ed. Moral Issues in Catholic Health Care. Wynnewood, PA: Saint Charles Borromeo Seminary; 2004: 57-67. NRCBL: 14.4; 1.2.

Wechter, David. Response to Catherine Althaus on heterologous embryo transfer. *National Catholic Bioethics Quarterly* 2005 Summer; 5(2): 225. NRCBL: 14.4; 10; 1.2.

Wechter, David; Althaus, Catherine. Response to Catherine Althaus on heterologous embryo transfer [article and commentary]. *National Catholic Bioethics Quarterly* 2005 Autumn; 5(3): 451- 452. NRCBL: 14.4; 4.4. Comments: comment on Catherine Althaus, "Can one 'rescue' a human embryo?" National Catholic Bioethics Quarterly 2005 Spring; 5(1): 113-141.

Williams, Thomas D. The least of my brethren: the ethics of heterologous embryo transfer. *Human Life Review* 2005 Summer; 31(3): 87-98. NRCBL: 14.4; 1.2.

INCOMPETENTS *See* INFORMED CONSENT/ INCOMPETENTS

INDIGENTS *See* CARE FOR SPECIFIC GROUPS/ INDIGENTS

INFANTICIDE *See* EUTHANASIA AND ALLOWING TO DIE/ MINORS

INFANTS *See* CARE FOR SPECIFIC GROUPS/ MINORS; EUTHANASIA AND ALLOWING TO DIE/ MINORS; HUMAN EXPERIMENTATION/ SPECIAL POPULATIONS/ MINORS

INFORMATICS *See* TELEMEDICINE AND INFORMATICS

INFORMED CONSENT
See also HUMAN EXPERIMENTATION/ INFORMED CONSENT; TREATMENT REFUSAL

NRCBL: National Reference Center for Bioethics Literature Classification Scheme   See inside front cover for terms.

317

The European Constitution establishing a core of human rights as applied to the fields of medicine and biology / La Constitucion Europea, un nucleo de los derechos humanos de la medicina y la biologia [editorial]. *Revista de Derecho y Genoma-Humano / Law and the Human Genome Review* 2004 July-December; (21): 15-26. NRCBL: 8.3.1; 18.3; 14.5; 15.5. SC: le. Note: Article in English and Spanish, English p. 15-20; Spanish p. 21-26.

What information must be disclosed and by whom? *Hospital Law Newsletter* 1999 January; 16(3): 1-4. NRCBL: 8.3.1; 9.5.6. SC: le.

When the patient changed her mind. *Hospital Law Newsletter* 1999 March; 16(5): 1-3. NRCBL: 8.3.1. SC: le. Identifiers: Wisconsin; Schreiber v. Physicians Ins. Co.

Ackerman, James L.; Proffit, William R. Communication in orthodontic treatment planning: bioethical and informed consent issues. *Angle Orthodontist* 1995; 65(4): 253-261. NRCBL: 8.3.1; 8.1; 4.1.1.

Akkad, Andrea; Jackson, Clare; Kenyon, Sara; Dixon-Woods, Mary; Taub, Nick; Habiba, Marwan. Informed consent for elective and emergency surgery: questionnaire study. *BJOG: An International Journal of Obstetrics and Gynaecology* 2004 October; 111(10): 1133-1138. NRCBL: 8.3.1; 9.5.5. SC: em.

Aveyard, Helen. Informed consent prior to nursing care procedures. *Nursing Ethics* 2005 January; 12(1): 19-29. NRCBL: 8.3.1; 8.1. SC: em. Identifiers: United Kingdom (Great Britain).
Abstract: It is largely undisputed that nurses should obtain consent prior to nursing care procedures. This article reports on a qualitative study examining the way in which nurses obtain such informed consent. Data were collected through focus group discussion and by using a critical incident technique in order to explore the way in which nurses approach consent prior to nursing care procedures. Qualified nurses in two teaching hospitals in England participated in the study. An analysis of the data provides evidence that consent was often not obtained by those who participated in the study and that refusals of care were often ignored. In addition, participants were often uncertain how to proceed with care when the patient was unable to consent. Consent prior to nursing care procedures is an essential but undeveloped concept, for which a new ethos is required.

Bal, Arun. Informed consent — legal and ethical aspects. *Issues in Medical Ethics* 1999 April-June; 7(2): 56-57. NRCBL: 8.3.1; 8.3.5. SC: le.

Barnett, G.C.; Charman, S.C.; Sizer, B.; Murray, P.A. Information given to patients about adverse effects of radiotherapy: a survey of patients' views. *Clinical Oncology* 2004 October; 16(7): 479-484. NRCBL: 8.3.1. SC: em. Identifiers: United Kingdom (Great Britain). Note: Royal College of Radiologists.

Basson, Marc D.; Gomez, Ruben; Fishman, Lisa; Panzini, Lisa. Informed consent for screening sigmoidoscopy in a Veterans Administration population. *Diseases of the Colon and Rectum* 2004 November; 47(11): 1939-1946. NRCBL: 8.3.1; 9.5.1. SC: em.

Beauchamp, Tom L.; Kukla, Rebecca. Conscientious autonomy: what patients do vs. what is done to them [letter and reply]. *Hastings Center Report* 2005 September-October; 35(5): 5-7. NRCBL: 8.3.1; 8.1.

Berry, Roberta M. Informed consent law, ethics, and practice: from infancy to reflective adolescence. *HEC (Healthcare Ethics Committee) Forum* 2005 March; 17(1): 64-81. NRCBL: 8.3.1; 2.2; 1.1; 4.1.2. SC: le.

Bielby, Philip. The conflation of competence and capacity in English medical law: a philosophical critique. *Medicine, Health Care and Philosophy: A European Journal* 2005; 8(3): 357-369. NRCBL: 8.3.1. SC: le. Identifiers: United Kingdom (Great Britain).
Abstract: Ethical and legal discourse pertaining to the ability to consent to treatment and research in England operates within a dualist framework of "competence" and "capacity". This is confusing, as while there exists in England two possible senses of legal capacity — "first person" legal capacity and "delegable" legal capacity, currently neither is formulated to bear a necessary relationship with decision-making competence. Notwithstanding this, judges and academic commentators frequently invoke competence to consent in discussions involving the validity of offering or withholding consent as a synonym for legal capacity to consent. I argue that this gives rise to a conflation, jeopardising clarity and consistency in law. This is somewhat less problematic in instances of "first-person" legal capacity that are heavily informed by criteria for decision-making competence than in the second sense of legal capacity, which is qualitatively different from decision-making competence, or with first-person legal capacity when defined in different terms from competence. The paper concludes by proposing that the soundest resolution to this problem is by making decision-making competence a necessary and sufficient condition of first-person legal capacity, affording a more scrupulous distinction between the two different forms of legal capacity that exist.

Bierig, Jack R. Informed consent in the practice of pathology. *Archives of Pathology and Laboratory Medicine* 2001 November; 125(11): 1425-1429. NRCBL: 8.3.1; 7.1.

Blankenship, James C. Ethics in interventional cardiology: combining coronary intervention with diagnostic catheterization [opinion]. *American Heart Hospital Journal* 2004 Winter; 2(1): 52-54. NRCBL: 8.3.1; 9.3.1; 1.1.

Boyd, Ann Lewis; Morioka, Masahiro. Anagogy of autonomy [article and commentary]. *Eubios Journal of Asian and International Bioethics* 2000 July; 10(4): 113-119. NRCBL: 8.3.1; 20.4.2; 20.5.1; 8.1; 1.1.

Browner, C.H.; Kukla, Rebecca. Conscientious autonomy: what patients do vs. what is done to them [letter and reply]. *Hastings Center Report* 2005 September-October; 35(5): 4-5, 6-7. NRCBL: 8.3.1; 9.5.4.

Butterworth, Cathy. Ongoing consent to care for older people in care homes. *Nursing Standard* 2005 January

26-February 1; 19(20): 40-45. NRCBL: 8.3.1; 9.5.2; 20.5.1.

Carter, H. Ballentine. Informed consent for prostate-specific antigen screening [editorial]. *Urology* 2003 January; 61(1): 13-14. NRCBL: 8.3.1.

Cassell, Eric J. Consent or obedience? Power and authority in medicine. *New England Journal of Medicine* 2005 January 27; 352(4): 328-330. NRCBL: 8.3.1; 1.1. Identifiers: Stanley Milgram.

Catalona, William J. Informed consent for prostate-specific antigen screening [editorial]. *Urology* 2003 January; 61(1): 17-19. NRCBL: 8.3.1.

Chadha, N.K.; Repanos, C. How much do healthcare professionals know about informed consent? A Bristol experience. *Surgeon* 2004 December; 2(6): 328-333, 360. NRCBL: 8.3.1; 7.2. SC: em; le. Identifiers: United Kingdom (Great Britain).

Che Ngah, Anisah. Informed consent in Malaysia: an overview. *Journal International de Bioethique / International Journal of Bioethics* 2005 March-June; 16(1-2): 143-161, 199. NRCBL: 8.3.1; 8.3.3; 9.5.5; 9.4. Note: Abstract in English and French.

Chescheir, Nancy G. A response: teaching pelvic examination on women under anesthesia [opinion]. *JAMWA: Journal of the American Medical Women's Association* 2003 Fall; 58(4): 221-222. NRCBL: 8.3.1; 9.5.5; 7.2.

Coulehan, Jack. My injury, your blood. *Hastings Center Report* 2005 January-February; 35(1): 10-11. NRCBL: 8.3.1; 9.5.1; 8.1.

Culver, Charles M.; Gert, Bernard. Competence. *In:* Radden, Jennifer, ed. The Philosophy of Psychiatry: A Companion. New York: Oxford University Press; 2004: 258-270. NRCBL: 8.3.1; 8.3.4.

Davey, Claire; White, Victoria; Gattellari, Melina; Ward, Jeanette E. Reconciling population benefits and women's individual autonomy in mammographic screening: in-depth interviews to explore women's views about 'informed choice'. *Australian and New Zealand Journal of Public Health* 2005 February; 29(1): 69-77. NRCBL: 8.3.1; 9.5.5. SC: em. Identifiers: Australia.

Davis, John K. Precedent autonomy and subsequent consent. *Ethical Theory and Moral Practice* 2004 June; 7(3): 267-291. NRCBL: 8.3.1; 1.1; 8.3.3; 4.3; 20.5.4. SC: an. Identifiers: Ulysses contract.

Dawson, Angus. Informed consent: bioethical ideal and empirical reality. *In:* Häyry, Matti; Takala, Tuija; Herissone-Kelly, Peter, eds. Bioethics and Social Reality. New York: Rodopi, 2005: 93-105. NRCBL: 8.3.1. SC: an; em.

Dimond, Bridgit. Consent to treatment records. *British Journal of Nursing* 2005 October 27-November 9; 14(19): 1024, 1026-1027. NRCBL: 8.3.1. SC: le.

Doyal, L. Informed consent: don't throw out the moral baby with the critical bath water [opinion]. *Quality and Safety in Health Care* 2004 December; 13(6): 414-415. NRCBL: 8.3.1.

Dubé-Baril, Cyndie. The personalized consent form: an optional, but useful tool! *Journal of the Canadian Dental Association* 2004 February; 70(2): 89-92. NRCBL: 8.3.1; 4.1.1.

Durfy, Sharon J.; Buchanan, Trisha E.; Burke, Wylie. Testing for inherited susceptibility to breast cancer: a survey of informed consent forms for BRCA1 and BRCA2 mutation testing. *American Journal of Medical Genetics* 1998 January 6; 75(1): 82-87. NRCBL: 8.3.1; 15.3. SC: em.

Earnest, Frank IV; Swensen, Stephen J.; Zink, Frank E. Respecting patient autonomy: screening at CT and informed consent. *Radiology* 2003 March; 226(3): 633-634. NRCBL: 8.3.1. Identifiers: computed tomographic technology.

Edwards, A.G.; Weale, A.R.; Morgan, J.D. Informed consent in renal transplantation. *Postgraduate Medical Journal* 2005 March; 81(953): 188-190. NRCBL: 8.3.1; 19.3. SC: em. Identifiers: United Kingdom (Great Britain).

Enoch, S.; Shaaban, H.; Dunn; K.W. Informed consent should be obtained from patients to use products (skin substitutes) and dressings containing biological material. *Journal of Medical Ethics* 2005 January; 31(1): 2-6. NRCBL: 8.3.1; 19.5; 19.1; 1.2. SC: em.

Abstract: BACKGROUND: Biological products (tissue engineered skin, allograft and xenograft, and biological dressings) are widely used in the treatment of burns, chronic wounds, and other forms of acute injury. However, the religious and ethical issues, including consent, arising from their use have never been addressed in the medical literature. AIMS: This study was aimed to ascertain the views of religious leaders about the acceptability of biological products and to evaluate awareness among healthcare professionals about their constituents. METHODS: The religious groups that make up about 75% of the United Kingdom population were identified and a questionnaire on 11 biological products was sent to its leaders. Another questionnaire concerning 17 products (11 biological and 6 synthetic dressings) was sent to 100 healthcare professionals working in seven specialist units in the UK. RESULTS: All religious leaders (100% response rate) replied, some after consultation with international bodies. Among them, 77% said that patients should be informed of the constituents of the biological products and consent obtained. Some leaders expressed concerns about particular products including the transmission of viral and prion diseases, cruelty to animals, and material derived from neonates. None of the healthcare professionals (73% response rate) surveyed knew the constituents of all the products correctly. CONCLUSION: Ignoring religious sensitivities and neglecting consent in the usage of biological products could have very serious implications, including litigation. Hospitals and manufacturers should take immediate measures to

NRCBL: National Reference Center for Bioethics Literature Classification Scheme   See inside front cover for terms.

319

enlighten healthcare professionals of the constituents of these products so that they can obtain informed consent from patients.

Fernie, G. Consent and the individual detained in custody. *Medicine and Law: World Association for Medical Law* 2005 September; 24(3): 515-523. NRCBL: 8.3.1; 8.1; 1.3.5. SC: le.
Abstract: It has been acknowledged that autonomy is one of the prima facie principles in modern medical practice and integral to the interchange between doctor and patient even if that meeting does not fulfil the normal criteria for a consultation. The lead having been taken by other jurisdictions, the General Medical Council, the UK national regulatory body for doctors, has now acknowledged the concept of informed consent that was first espoused in cases such as Rogers v. Whitaker. In regard to the concept of informed consent, there are three pertinent issues that the Forensic Physician should consider in deciding upon the adequacy of this: Did that person have capacity in the eyes of the law? The Forensic Physician may be asked to examine individuals whose age span ranges from the newly born to the elderly and there will be potential conflict of interest between parent and child or elderly people and their carers. Even if adequate information was imparted, did a person under the (significant) influence of alcohol or drugs understand the likely implications that would flow from their decision? Was the individual concerned given appropriate information beforehand—in other words, was the consent truly informed? Was the consent given voluntarily? Voluntariness is probably the most significant ethical worry likely to confront the doctor, particularly when examining an individual for fitness to be detained or fitness to be interviewed, both categories of which make up the main work load in this sub-specialty. The thorny ethical dilemmas faced in this specialty are considered and how the professional standard originally defined in Hunter v Hanley and reiterated in the Bolam test (with subsequent modification in Bolitho) affect the way in which the clinician deals with the problems is likely to face.

Ferrand, E.; Bachoud-Levi, A.-C.; Rodrigues, M.; Maggiore, S.; Brun-Buisson, C.; Lemaire, F. Decision-making capacity and surrogate designation in French ICU patients. *Intensive Care Medicine* 2001 August; 27(8): 1360-1364. NRCBL: 8.3.1; 8.3.3; 20.4.1; 9.4. Identifiers: intensive care unit.

Fiesta, Janine. Informed consent: what health care professionals need to know, Part 1. *Nursing Management* 1999 June; 30(6): 8-9. NRCBL: 8.3.1; 4.1.3; 8.3.3. SC: le.

Fiesta, Janine. Informed consent: what health care professionals need to know, Part 2. *Nursing Management* 1999 July; 30(7): 6-7. NRCBL: 8.3.1; 4.1.3; 8.3.3. SC: le.

Fisher, Eric S. Informed consent in Oklahoma: a search for reasonableness and predictability in the aftermath of Scott v. Bradford. *Oklahoma Law Review* 1996 Winter; 49(4): 651-675. NRCBL: 8.3.1. SC: le.

Florencio, Patrik S.; Wyatt, Brian M.; Barnes, Mark. Can informed consent be tailored for the critical care unit? *Health Law in Canada* 2004 September; 25(1): 10-16. NRCBL: 8.3.1; 8.3.3. SC: le; an.

Foëx, Bernard A. Is informed consent possible in acute myocardial infarction? [editorial]. *Heart* 2004 November; 90(11): 1237-1238. NRCBL: 8.3.1.

Froom, Paul; Barak, M. An informed consent form for treatment with oral anticoagulants [letter]. *Journal of Thrombosis and Haemostasis* 2004 January; 2(1): 196-197. NRCBL: 8.3.1.

Fry, Sara T.; Veatch, Robert M. Consent and the right to refuse treatment. *In their:* Case Studies in Nursing Ethics. Third edition. Sudbury, MA: Jones and Bartlett Publishers; 2006: 364-391. NRCBL: 8.3.1; 8.3.4.

Fuller, R.; Dudley, N.; Blacktop, J. How informed is consent? Understanding of pictorial and verbal probability information by medical inpatients. *Postgraduate Medical Journal* 2002; 78: 543-544. NRCBL: 8.3.1. SC: em. Identifiers: United Kingdom (Great Britain).

Gann, Peter H. Informed consent for prostate-specific antigen testing [editorial]. *Urology* 2003 January; 61(1): 5-6. NRCBL: 8.3.1.

Gasparini, Giulio; Boniello, Roberto; Longobardi, Gianluigi; Pelo, Sandro. Orthognathic surgery: an informed consent model. *Journal of Craniofacial Surgery* 2004 September; 15(5): 858-862. NRCBL: 8.3.1.

Gattellari, Melina; Ward, Jeanette E. Men's reactions to disclosed and undisclosed opportunistic PSA screening for prostate cancer. *Medical Journal of Australia* 2005 April 18; 182(8): 386-389. NRCBL: 8.3.1; 8.2. SC: em. Identifiers: Australia.

Geiderman, Joel M. In defense of patient privacy [letter]. *Annals of Emergency Medicine* 2002 January; 39(1): 2 p. [Online]. Available: http://home.mdconsult.com/das/article/body/51079232-2/jorg=journal&source=MI&sp=12 [5 October 2005]. NRCBL: 8.3.1; 8.4; 7.1; 1.3.7. Comments: comment on Annals of Emergency Medicine 2001 August; 38(2): 189.

Gert, Heather J.; Steinberg, David. The characteristics of information and avoiding surprises [discussion]. *Medical Ethics Newsletter [Lahey Clinic]* 2003 Winter; 10(1): 6-7. NRCBL: 8.3.1; 1.1.

Grace, Pamela J.; McLaughlin, Moriah. When consent isn't informed enough. *AJN: American Journal of Nursing* 2005 April; 105(4): 79, 81- 84. NRCBL: 8.3.1.

Groves, Trish; Croot, Jan. Using pictures in the BMJ [editorial]. *BMJ: British Medical Journal* 2005 April 23; 330(7497): 916. NRCBL: 8.3.1; 8.4; 1.3.7.

Haggerty, Lois A.; Hawkins, Joellen. Informed consent and the limits of confidentiality. *Western Journal of Nursing Research* 2000 June; 22(4): 508-514. NRCBL: 8.3.1; 8.4; 10. SC: le.

Handelsman, Mitchell M.; Galvin, Michael D. Facilitating informed consent for outpatient psychotherapy: a suggested written format. *Professional Psychology: Research and Practice* 1988; 19(2): 223-225. NRCBL: 8.3.1; 17.2.

Harris, Tess; Cook, Derek G.; Victor, Christina; Beighton, Carole; DeWilde, Stephen; Carey, Iain. Linking questionnaires to primary care records: factors affecting consent in older people. *Journal of Epidemiology and Community Health* 2005 April; 59(4): 336-338. NRCBL: 8.3.1; 9.5.2; 1.3.12. SC: em. Identifiers: United Kingdom (Great Britain).

Haslam, Darryl R.; Harris, Steven M. Informed consent documents of marriage and family therapists in private practice: a qualitative analysis. *American Journal of Family Therapy* 2004 July-September; 32(4): 359-374. NRCBL: 8.3.1; 8.1; 17.2.

Heinemann, Richard A. Pushing the limits of informed consent: Johnson v. Kokemoor and physician-specific disclosure. *Wisconsin Law Review* 1997; 5: 1079-1121. NRCBL: 8.3.1; 8.5. SC: le.

Heitz, Ruth M. Recent developments in the doctrine of informed consent. *Wisconsin Medical Journal* 1999 September-October; 98(6): 56-57. NRCBL: 8.3.1. SC: le. Identifiers: Schreiber v. Physicians Insurance Company; Brown v. Dibbell.

Heywood, Rob. Excessive risk disclosure: the effects of the law on medical practice. *Medical Law International* 2005; 7(2): 93-112. NRCBL: 8.3.1; 8.1. SC: le.

Hoffman, Jan. Awash in information, patients face a lonely, uncertain road. *New York Times* 2005 August 14; p. A1, A18, A19. NRCBL: 8.3.1; 9.5.1. SC: po.

Howlader, Mohammad H.; Dhanji, Al-Rehan; Uppal, Rakesh; Magee, Patrick; Wood, Alan J.; Anyanwu, Ani C. Patients' views of the consent process for adult cardiac surgery: questionnaire survey. *Scandinavian Cardiovascular Journal* 2004 December; 38(6): 363-368. NRCBL: 8.3.1; 9.5.1. SC: em. Identifiers: United Kingdom (Great Britain).

Hufford, David J. Authority, knowledge, and substituted judgment. *Alternative Therapies in Health and Medicine* 1996 November; 2(6): 92-94. NRCBL: 8.3.1; 8.3.3; 8.3.4; 20.5.1. SC: cs.

Humphreys, Melanie; Smallwood, Andrew. An exploration of the ethical dimensions pertinent to gaining consent for thrombolysis. *Nursing in Critical Care* 2004 November-December; 9(6): 264-270. NRCBL: 8.3.1; 4.1.3; 1.1.

Humphreys, Sally. Patient autonomy: legal and ethical issues in the post-anaesthetic care unit. *British Journal of Perioperative Nursing* 2005 January; 15(1): 35-38, 40-41, 43. NRCBL: 8.3.1; 8.3.3; 4.4; 1.1.

Ibrahim, Talal; Ong, Shong Meng; Taylor, Grahame John Saint Clair. The new consent form: is it any better? *Annals of the Royal College of Surgeons of England* 2004 May; 86(3): 206-209. NRCBL: 8.3.1. Identifiers: United Kingdom (Great Britain).

Jacobson, Peter Lars; Mann, J. Douglas. The valid informed consent-treatment contract in chronic non-cancer pain: its role in reducing barriers to effective pain management. *Comprehensive Therapy* 2004 Summer; 30(2): 101-104. NRCBL: 8.3.1; 2.1; 4.4.

Jafarey, A.M.; Farooqui, A. Informed consent in the Pakistani milieu: the physician's perspective. *Journal of Medical Ethics* 2005 February; 31(2): 93-96. NRCBL: 8.3.1. SC: em.

Jamieson, Denise J.; O'Sullivan, Mary Jo; Maupin, Robert; Cohen, Mardge; Webber, Mayris P.; Nesheim, Steven; Lampe, Margaret; Garcia, Patricia; Lindsay, Michael; Bulterys, Marc. The challenges of informed consent for rapid HIV testing in labor. *Journal of Women's Health* 2003 October; 12(9): 889-895. NRCBL: 8.3.1; 9.5.5; 9.5.6; 14.1.

Jansen, Brigitte; Simon, Juergen. Some ethical and legal issues in Germany involving informed consent and patenting. *Science and Engineering Ethics* 2005 January; 11(1): 93-96. NRCBL: 8.3.1; 15.8; 15.1; 1.3.12; 19.5. SC: an. Conference: 5th International Conference on Bioethics: The Ethics of Intellectual Property Rights and Patents; Warsaw, Poland; 23-24 April 2004; Minister of Science and the Minister of Health, Poland.

Johnson-Greene, D. Informed consent in clinical neuropsychology practice: official statement of the National Academy of Neuropsychology. *Archives of Clinical Neuropsychology* 2005 May; 20(3): 335-340. NRCBL: 8.3.1; 17.1.

Jonsen, Albert R. Autonomy of the patient. *In his: Bioethics Beyond the Headlines: Who Lives? Who Dies? Who Decides?* Lanham, MD: Rowman and Littlefield; 2005: 40-47. NRCBL: 8.3.1; 8.3.4.

Kalantri, S.P. Informed consent in public hospitals. *Issues in Medical Ethics* 2000 October-December; 8(4): 116-117. NRCBL: 8.3.1.

Kegley, Jacquelyn Ann K. Challenges to informed consent. *EMBO Reports* 2004 September; 5(9): 832-836. NRCBL: 8.3.1; 18.3; 15.1; 1.3.12.

Kelly, Bernard. The matter of informed consent: a case history. *Australian Family Physician* 1994 June; 23(6): 1047-1049, 1052-1053. NRCBL: 8.3.1; 8.1; 9.2. SC: cs.

Kelly, Gillian D.; Blunt, Cornelia; Moore, Philip A.; Lewis, Margo. Consent for regional anaesthesia in the United Kingdom: what is material risk? *International*

NRCBL: National Reference Center for Bioethics Literature Classification Scheme   See inside front cover for terms.

321

Journal of Obstetric Anesthesia 2004 April; 13(2): 71-74. NRCBL: 8.3.1; 9.5.5. SC: em.

King, Jennifer. Informed consent: does practice match conviction? *Journal of the American College of Dentists* 2005 Spring; 72(1): 27-31. NRCBL: 8.3.1; 4.1.1; 9.5.1.

Klepatsky, Arlene; Mahlmeister, Laura. Consent and informed consent in perinatal and neonatal settings. *Journal of Perinatal and Neonatal Nursing* 1997 June; 11(1): 34-51. NRCBL: 8.3.1; 8.1; 4.1.3. SC: le.

Kluge, Eike-Henner W. Informed consent to the secondary use of EHRs: informatic rights and their limitations. *Medinfo* 2004; 11(Part 1): 635-638. NRCBL: 8.3.1; 8.4; 1.3.12. Identifiers: electronic health records.

Kottkamp, Nathan A. Finding clarity in a Gray opinion: a critique of Pennsylvania's informed consent doctrine. *University of Pittsburgh Law Review* 1999 Fall; 61(1): 241-285. NRCBL: 8.3.1; 1.1. SC: le. Identifiers: Gray v. Grunnagle, 233 A.2d 663,674 (Pa. 1966); Morgan v. MacPhail, 704 A.2d 617, 619 (Pa.1997).

Kukla, Rebecca. Conscientious autonomy: displacing decisions in health care. *Hastings Center Report* 2005 March-April; 35(2): 34-44. NRCBL: 8.3.1; 1.1; 2.1. SC: an.

Kurtz, Sheldon F. The law of informed consent: from "doctor is right" to "patient has rights". *Syracuse Law Review* 2000; 50(4): 1243-1260. NRCBL: 8.3.1. SC: le.

Kyambi, J.M. Issues involved in pre-operative consent [editorial]. *East African Medical Journal* 2004 July; 81(7): 329-330. NRCBL: 8.3.1.

Lantz, Elizabeth Johnson. Life-or-death decisions and informed consent: communication key to hospital informed consent policies. *QRC Advisor* 1999 April; 15(6): 8-12. NRCBL: 8.3.1; 8.3.3; 20.5.4.

LeBlang, Theodore R. Informed consent and disclosure in the physician-patient relationship: expanding obligations for physicians in the United States. *Medicine and Law: World Association for Medical Law* 1995; 14(5-6): 429-444. NRCBL: 8.3.1; 7.3. SC: le.

Leflar, Robert B. Informed consent and patients' rights in Japan. *Houston Law Review* 1996 Spring; 33(1): 1-112. NRCBL: 8.3.1; 21.7; 8.2; 20.2.1; 19.5; 18.3; 1.1. SC: le.

Lindemann, Hilde; Kukla, Rebecca. Conscientious autonomy: what patients do vs. what is done to them [letter and reply]. *Hastings Center Report* 2005 September-October; 35(5): 4, 6-7. NRCBL: 8.3.1.

Lofft, Annette L. Informed consent for endoscopy. *Gastrointestinal Endoscopy Clinics of North America* 1995 April; 5(2): 457-470. NRCBL: 8.3.1; 9.5.1.

Lombardo, Paul A. Phantom tumors and hysterical women: revising our view of the Schloendorff case. *Journal of Law, Medicine and Ethics* 2005 Winter; 33(4): 791-801. NRCBL: 8.3.1; 8.3.5; 2.2. SC: le.

Mackenzie, R.A. Ethical considerations in epilepsy management. *Medicine and Law: World Association for Medical Law* 2004; 23(4): 781-789. NRCBL: 8.3.1; 9.5.3.

Maclean, Alasdair. Giving the reasonable patient a voice: information disclosure and the relevance of empirical evidence. *Medical Law International* 2005; 7(1): 1-40. NRCBL: 8.3.1; 8.5.

Mamdani, Meenal; Mamdani, Bashir; Pandya, Sunil K. Informed consent for brain surgery [case study]. *Issues in Medical Ethics* 2000 January-March; 8(1): 29. NRCBL: 8.3.1.

Mangal, Rambarran. Consent to medical treatment. *West Indian Law Journal* 1999 May and October; 24(2): 83-91. NRCBL: 8.3.1; 8.3.2. SC: le.

Manning, Joanna. Informed consent to medical treatment: the common law and New Zealand's Code of Patient's Rights. *Medical Law Review* 2004 Summer; 12(2): 181-216. NRCBL: 8.3.1; 18.3; 8.5. SC: le.

Marczyk, Geoffrey R.; Wertheimer, Ellen. The bitter pill of empiricism: health maintenance organizations, informed consent and the reasonable psychotherapist standard of care. *Villanova Law Review* 2001; 46(1): 33-93. NRCBL: 8.3.1; 17.2; 9.3.2; 4.1.2. SC: le.

Maruyama, Eiji. Japanese law of informed consent. *Kobe University Law Review* 1991; 25: 39-43. NRCBL: 8.3.1. SC: le.

Mayberry, Margaret K.; Mayberry, John F. Consent with understanding: a movement towards informed decisions. *Clinical Medicine* 2002 November-December; 2(6): 523-526. NRCBL: 8.3.1; 8.1.

McLeod, Carolyn; Kukla, Rebecca. Conscientious autonomy: what patients do vs. what is done to them [letter and reply]. *Hastings Center Report* 2005 September-October; 35(5): 5, 6-7. NRCBL: 8.3.1; 8.1.

McMillan, John. Commentary: doing what's best and best interests. *BMJ: British Medical Journal* 2005 May 7; 330(7499): 1069. NRCBL: 8.3.1; 9.5.3.

Mesich-Brant, Jennifer L.; Grossback, Lawrence J. Assisting altruism: evaluating legally binding consent in organ donation policy. *Journal of Health Politics, Policy and Law* 2005 August; 30(4): 687-717. NRCBL: 8.3.1; 19.5. SC: le.
Abstract: The growing need for organ and tissue transplants has led a number of states to enforce a policy that views a donor's declared intent to be an organ donor as legally binding. This allows health officials to harvest organs without the permission of the next of kin. Legally binding consent is controversial because of concerns that it may anger family members, lead to negative publicity, and discourage potential donors. We use interviews and a pooled time-series data set of cadaveric donation

rates in U.S. states to evaluate the effectiveness of this policy. Our research indicates that enforcement of legally binding consent has marginally increased cadaveric donations while not significantly affecting donor registration. We also find evidence that the effect of the policy might be greater if it were more fully implemented and coordinated with efforts to improve public acceptance and awareness.

Mistry, D.; Kelly, G. Consent for tonsillectomy. *Clinical Otolaryngology and Allied Sciences* 2004 August; 29(4): 362-368. NRCBL: 8.3.1. SC: em. Identifiers: United Kingdom (Great Britain).

Nelson, Deborah; Wright, M.; Walsh, I.; Moody, K.; Beveridge, L. The use of consent-to-treatment forms at the state hospital: an audit in 1996 and 2000. *Medicine, Science, and the Law* 2003 April; 43(2): 132-135. NRCBL: 8.3.1; 9.5.1; 1.3.5; 17.4. SC: em.

Nelson, Erin L. Informed consent in the (mis)information age. *Journal of Obstetrics and Gynaecology Canada* 2004 January; 26(1): 43-48. NRCBL: 8.3.1; 1.3.12; 8.2. SC: le. Identifiers: Canada.

Nguyen, Tuong-Nam; Silver, David; Arthurs, Bryan. Consent to cataract surgery performed by residents. *Canadian Journal of Ophthalmology* 2005 February; 40(1): 34-37. NRCBL: 8.3.1; 7.2; 9.5.1. SC: em. Identifiers: Canada.

Nisker, Jeffrey A. Ethical issues of "case" reports: what can we learn from case studies? [editorial]. *Journal of Obstetrics and Gynaecology Canada* 2004 January; 26(1): 7-13. NRCBL: 8.3.1; 8.4; 18.3; 18.5.3. Identifiers: Canada. Note: text in English and French.

O'Boyle, Donna. Informed consent: danger is ahead when staff don't know what they don't know [letter]. *BMJ: British Medical Journal* 2005 November 5; 331(7524): 1082. NRCBL: 8.3.1.

O'Neill, Onora. Informed consent and public health. *Philosophical Transactions of the Royal Society of London. Series B, Biological Sciences* 2004 July 29; 359(1447): 1133-1136. NRCBL: 8.3.1; 9.1.

Olivier, S. Informed consent and transcultural research [editorial]. *South African Medical Journal* 1995 October; 85(10): 984-985. NRCBL: 8.3.1; 21.7.

Osime, O.C.; Okojie, O.; Osadolor, F.; Mohammed, S. Current practices and medico-legal aspects of pre-operative consent. *East African Medical Journal* 2004 July; 81(7): 331-335. NRCBL: 8.3.1. SC: em. Identifiers: Nigeria.

Parmet, Wendy E. Informed consent and public health: are they compatible when it comes to vaccines? *Journal of Health Care Law and Policy* 2005; 8(1): 71-110. NRCBL: 8.3.1; 9.1; 9.7; 8.1. SC: le.

Payne, Jan. Informed consent: reconsideration of its structure and role in medicine. *In:* Salek, Sam; Edgar, An-

drew, eds. Pharmaceutical Ethics. New York: Wiley; 2002: 61-69. NRCBL: 8.3.1.

Pilotto, Franco; Badon, Pierluigi. Informed consent: between ethics and law. *Dolentium Hominum* 2002; 17(3): 29-34. NRCBL: 8.3.1; 2.2; 1.1; 4.3; 8.1. SC: le.

Plotnikoff, Gregory A. From informed consent to informed coercion? [opinion]. *Minnesota Medicine* 2005 October; 88(10): 34-35. NRCBL: 8.3.1; 8.3.4; 9.3.1; 9.4.

Plunkett, Lance R. Informed consent — more and more important in optometric practice. *Optometry* 2004 November; 75(11): 723-725. NRCBL: 8.3.1; 9.5.1.

Pomerantz, Andrew M. Increasingly informed consent: discussing distinct aspects of psychotherapy at different points in time. *Ethics and Behavior* 2005; 15(4): 351-360. NRCBL: 8.3.1; 17.2; 8.4; 1.3.1; 7.1. SC: em.

Abstract: Psychologists are ethically obligated to obtain informed consent to psychotherapy "as early as is feasible" (American Psychological Association, 2002, p.1072). However, the range of topics to be addressed includes both information that may be immediately and uniformly applicable to most clients policy or rule, as well as information that is not immediately presentable because it varies widely across clients or emerges over time. In this study, licensed psychologists were surveyed regarding the earliest feasible point at which they could provide information regarding specific aspects of psychotherapy. Results indicate that, although psychologists believe that they are capable of presenting some information, such as payment and confidentiality policies, at the outset, they believe that a discussion of more substantive issues, such as psychotherapy duration, goals, orientation, and activities, can take place only after some therapy has transpired. Implications are discussed regarding the process and event models of informed consent.

Pothier, David D. Many patients may not understand consent forms [letter]. *BMJ: British Medical Journal* 2005 May 14; 330(7500): 1151. NRCBL: 8.3.1.

Raab, Edward L. The parameters of informed consent. *Transactions of the American Ophthalmological Society* 2004; 102: 225-232. NRCBL: 8.3.1; 8.3.2; 8.3.3; 18.3. SC: le.

Rosenbaum, Julie R.; Bravata, Dawn M.; Concato, John; Brass, Lawrence M.; Kim, Nancy; Fried, Terri R. Informed consent for thrombolytic therapy for patients with acute ischemic stroke treated in routine clinical practice. *Stroke* 2004 September; 35(9): e353-e355. NRCBL: 8.3.1; 9.5.1. SC: em.

Sadan, Batami; Chajek-Shaul, Tova. Attitudes and practices of patients and physicians towards patient autonomy: a survey conducted prior to the enactment of the Patients' Rights Bill in Israel. *Eubios Journal of Asian and International Bioethics* 2000 July; 10(4): 119-125. NRCBL: 8.3.1; 1.1; 8.1. SC: em; cs.

Sanders, Tom; Skevington, Suzanne. Participation as an expression of patient uncertainty: an exploration of bowel cancer consultations. *Psycho-Oncology* 2004 October;

NRCBL: National Reference Center for Bioethics Literature Classification Scheme   See inside front cover for terms.

323

13(10): 675-688. NRCBL: 8.3.1; 18.3; 8.1; 9.5.1. SC: em. Identifiers: United Kingdom (Great Britain).

Schouten, Barbara C.; Hoogstraten, Johan; Eijkman, Michiel A.J. Dutch dentists' views of informed consent: a replication study. *Patient Education and Counseling* 2004 February; 52(2): 165-168. NRCBL: 8.3.1; 4.1.1. SC: em. Identifiers: Netherlands.

Schwartz, Kevin O. Uninformed consent: the undisclosed risk rooted in our current informed consent framework. *Medical Trial Technique Quarterly* 2002; 48(3): 311-347. NRCBL: 8.3.1; 1.3.5; 18.3; 9.5.1; 9.8; 4.1.2; 1.3.1. SC: le.

Scott, Jennifer A.; Campos-Outcalt, Doug. Non-consented IUD placement reported by Mexican immigrants: a caution for caregivers in the US? *Journal of Family Practice* 2005 March; 54(3): 263-264. NRCBL: 8.3.1; 11.1; 21.1. SC: em. Identifiers: intrauterine device.

Segest, Erling. The legal position with regard to informed consent in Denmark. *Medicine and Law: World Association for Medical Law* 1995; 14(3-4): 245-254. NRCBL: 8.3.1; 8.2. SC: le.

Shalowitz, David I.; Wolf, Michael S. Shared decision-making and the lower literate patient. *Journal of Law, Medicine and Ethics* 2004 Winter; 32(4): 759- 764. NRCBL: 8.3.1; 8.1; 7.2.

Shaw, Alexander S.J. Do we really know the law about students and patient consent? [opinion]. *BMJ: British Medical Journal* 2005 September 3; 331(7515): 522. NRCBL: 8.3.1.

Sheth, Arun. Informed consent — a view from the trenches [letter]. *Indian Journal of Medical Ethics* 2004 January-March; 1(1): 33. NRCBL: 8.3.1. Comments: comment on Neha Dangayach and Nikhil Joshi, "Informed consent: consent with a view," Issues in Medical Ethics 2003 July- September; 11(3): 86.

Singleton, Peter D. Informed consent: talking with patients, not at them [letter]. *BMJ: British Medical Journal* 2005 November 5; 331(7524): 1082. NRCBL: 8.3.1.

Siotia, A.K.; Chaudhuri, A.; Muzulu, S.I.; Harling, D.; Muthusamy, R. Postoperative hypoxia in a woman with Down's syndrome: case outcome. *BMJ: British Medical Journal* 2005 May 7; 330(7499): 1068. NRCBL: 8.3.1; 9.5.3.

Soler-González, J.; Ruiz, M.C. Patients' written consent when photographed could suffice for journals [letter]. *BMJ: British Medical Journal* 2005 June 25; 330(7506): 1509. NRCBL: 8.3.1; 1.3.7.

Sosis, Mitchel B.; McCartney, Colin J.L.; Brull, Richard; Chan, Vincent; Chung, Frances. Proper consent for clinical anesthesia research may be difficult to obtain on the day of surgery [letter and reply]. *Anesthesia and Analgesia* 2004 October; 99(4): 1272. NRCBL: 8.3.1.

Steer, Philip. The bioethics of preterm labour. *BJOG: An International Journal of Obstetrics and Gynaecology* 2005 March; 112(Supplement 1): 109-112. NRCBL: 8.3.1; 8.4; 1.3.12; 9.5.5.

Stewart, Douglas O.; DeMarco, Joseph P. An economic theory of patient decision-making. *Journal of Bioethical Inquiry* 2005; 2(3): 153-164. NRCBL: 8.3.1; 8.1; 9.3.1.

Abstract: Patient autonomy, as exercised in the informed consent process, is a central concern in bioethics. The typical bioethicist's analysis of autonomy centers on decisional capacity—finding the line between autonomy and its absence. This approach leaves unexplored the structure of reasoning behind patient treatment decisions. To counter that approach, we present a microeconomic theory of patient decision-making regarding the acceptable level of medical treatment from the patient's perspective. We show that a rational patient's desired treatment level typically departs from the level yielding an absence of symptoms, the level we call ideal. This microeconomic theory demonstrates why patients have good reason not to pursue treatment to the point of absence of physical symptoms. We defend our view against possible objections that it is unrealistic and that it fails to adequately consider harm a patient may suffer by curtailing treatment. Our analysis is fruitful in various ways. It shows why decisions often considered unreasonable might be fully reasonable. It offers a theoretical account of how physician misinformation may adversely affect a patient's decision. It shows how billing costs influence patient decision-making. It indicates that health care professionals' beliefs about the 'unreasonable' attitudes of patients might often be wrong. It provides a better understanding of patient rationality that should help to ensure fuller information as well as increased respect for patient decision-making.

Stirrat, G.M.; Gill, R. Autonomy in medical ethics after O'Neill. *Journal of Medical Ethics* 2005 March; 31(3): 127-130. NRCBL: 8.3.1; 8.1. SC: an.

Abstract: Following the influential Gifford and Reith lectures by Onora O'Neill, this paper explores further the paradigm of individual autonomy which has been so dominant in bioethics until recently and concurs that it is an aberrant application and that conceptions of individual autonomy cannot provide a sufficient and convincing starting point for ethics within medical practice. We suggest that revision of the operational definition of patient autonomy is required for the twenty first century. We follow O'Neill in recommending a principled version of patient autonomy, which for us involves the provision of sufficient and understandable information and space for patients, who have the capacity to make a settled choice about medical interventions on themselves, to do so responsibly in a manner considerate to others. We test it against the patient-doctor relationship in which each fully respects the autonomy of the other based on an unspoken covenant and bilateral trust between the doctor and patient. Indeed we consider that the dominance of the individual autonomy paradigm harmed that relationship. Although it seems to eliminate any residue of medical paternalism we suggest that it has tended to replace it with an equally (or possibly even more) unacceptable bioethical paternalism. In addition it may, for example, lead some doctors to consider mistakenly that unthinking acquiescence to a requested intervention against their clinical judgement is honouring "patient autonomy" when it is, in fact, abrogation of their duty as doctors.

Stringer, Mark D. Informed consent and choice in cholecystectomy. *Pediatric Surgery International* 2004

October; 20(10): 741-743. NRCBL: 8.3.1; 8.3.2; 9.5.7. SC: em.

Takasugi, Miyuki; Iwamoto, Eriko; Akashi-Tanaka, Sadako; Kinoshita, Takayuki; Fukutomi, Takashi; Kubouchi, Kohichi. General aspects and specific issues of informed consent on breast cancer treatments. *Breast Cancer* 2005 January; 12(1): 39-44. NRCBL: 8.3.1; 9.5.5; 9.5.1.

Talcott, James A. What patients should be told before agreeing to a blood test that could change their lives [editorial]. *Urology* 2003 January; 61(1): 7-9. NRCBL: 8.3.1.

Taylor, Rodney J.; Chiu, Alexander G.; Palmer, James N.; Schofield, Kim; O'Malley, Bert W., Jr.; Wolf, Jeffrey S. Informed consent in sinus surgery: link between demographics and patient desires. *Laryngoscope* 2005 May; 115(5): 826-831. NRCBL: 8.3.1; 9.5.4. SC: em.

Thompson, Ian M. Informed consent for prostate cancer screening — a call for equity in medical interventions [editorial]. *Urology* 2003 January; 61(1): 15-16. NRCBL: 8.3.1.

Tranberg, H.A.; Rous, B.A.; Rashbass, J. Legal and ethical issues in the use of anonymous images in pathology teaching and research. *Histopathology* 2003 February; 42(2): 104-109. NRCBL: 8.3.1; 7.2; 8.4; 18.3. SC: le.

Ubel, P.A.; Loewenstein, G. The role of decision analysis in informed consent: choosing between intuition and systematicity. *Social Science and Medicine* 1997; 44(5): 647-656. NRCBL: 8.3.1; 8.1; 1.1.

Vallance, James H.; Ahmed, Mehra; Dhillon, Baljean. Cataract surgery and consent: recall, anxiety, and attitude toward trainee surgeons preoperatively and postoperatively. *Journal of Cataract and Refractive Surgery* 2004 July; 30(7): 1479-1483. NRCBL: 8.3.1; 9.5.1. SC: em. Identifiers: United Kingdom (Great Britain).

Verweij, M.F.; van den Hoven, M.A. Influenza vaccination in Dutch nursing homes: is tacit consent morally justified? *Medicine, Health Care and Philosophy: A European Journal* 2005; 8(1): 89-95. NRCBL: 8.3.1; 9.1; 9.5.2; 9.7. SC: em. Identifiers: Netherlands.

Abstract: OBJECTIVES: Efficient procedures for obtaining informed (proxy) consent may contribute to high influenza vaccination rates in nursing homes. Yet are such procedures justified? This study's objective was to gain insight in informed consent policies in Dutch nursing homes; to assess how these may affect influenza vaccination rates and to answer the question whether deviating from standard informed consent procedures could be morally justified. DESIGN: A survey among nursing home physicians. SETTING & PARTICIPANTS: We sent a questionnaire to all (356) nursing homes in the Netherlands, to be completed by one of the physicians. RESULTS: We received 245 completed questionnaires. As 21 institutions appeared to be closed or merged into other institutions, the response was 73.1% (245/335). Of all respondents 81.9% reported a vaccination rate above 80%. Almost 50% reported a vaccination rate above 90%. Most respondents considered herd

immunity to be an important consideration for institutional policy. Freedom of choice for residents was considered important by almost all. Nevertheless, 106 out of 245 respondents follow a tacit consent procedure, according to which vaccination will be administered unless the resident or her proxy refuses. These institutions show significantly higher vaccination rates (p 0.03). CONCLUSIONS: In our discussion we focus on the question whether tacit consent procedures can be morally justifiable. Such procedures assume that vaccination is good for residents either as individuals or as a group. Even though this assumption may be true for most residents, there are good reasons for preferring express consent procedures.

Waisel, David B.; Truog, Robert D. Informed consent. *Anesthesiology* 1997 October; 87(4): 968-978. NRCBL: 8.3.1; 8.3.3; 8.1. SC: le.

Webb, Jane; Siotia, A.K. Commentary: patient's perspective. *BMJ: British Medical Journal* 2005 May 7; 330(7499): 1069. NRCBL: 8.3.1; 9.5.3.

Werkö, Lars. Informed consent in routine healthcare. *Scandinavian Cardiovascular Journal* 2004 December; 38(6): 323-324. NRCBL: 8.3.1; 21.1.

Westberg, Katarina; Duchek, Miloš; Sandlund, Mikael; Lynöe, Niels. Informed consent for clinical education: randomized study of two different strategies at a urology surgery. *Scandinavian Journal of Urology and Nephrology* 2004; 38(6): 490-494. NRCBL: 8.3.1; 7.2. SC: em. Identifiers: Sweden.

Wheat, Kay. Progress of the prudent patient: consent after Chester v Afshar [editorial]. *Anaesthesia* 2005 March; 60(3): 217-219. NRCBL: 8.3.1. SC: le. Identifiers: United Kingdom (Great Britain).

Wilson, Robin Fretwell. Autonomy suspended: using female patients to teach intimate exams without their knowledge or consent. *Journal of Health Care Law and Policy* 2005; 8(2): 240-263. NRCBL: 8.3.1; 19.5.5; 7.2.

Wilson, Robin Fretwell. Unauthorized practice: teaching pelvic examination on women under anesthesia [opinion]. *JAMWA: Journal of the American Medical Women's Association* 2003 Fall; 58(4): 217-220. NRCBL: 8.3.1; 9.5.5; 7.2.

Wolf, Jeffrey S.; Chiu, Alexander G.; Palmer, James N.; O'Malley, Bert W., Jr.; Schofield, Kimberly; Taylor, Rodney J. Informed consent in endoscopic sinus surgery: the patient perspective. *Laryngoscope* 2005 March; 115(3): 492-494. NRCBL: 8.3.1; 9.5.1. SC: em.

Wolfberg, Jennifer. Two kinds of statistics, the kind you look up and the kind you make up: a critical analysis of comparative provider statistics and the doctrine of informed consent. *Pepperdine Law Review* 2002; 29(3): 585-608. NRCBL: 8.3.1; 1.3.12; 7.1; 8.1. SC: le.

Wollin, David A.; Avanzato, Joseph. Informed consent: a primer for health care practitioners [opinion]. *Medicine*

NRCBL: National Reference Center for Bioethics Literature Classification Scheme   See inside front cover for terms.

325

and Health, Rhode Island 1996 April; 79(4): 155-157. NRCBL: 8.3.1; 18.3. SC: le.

Wood, Christopher P.J.; Blackburn, Simon C. Informed consent: is frightening patients really in their best interests? [letter]. *BMJ: British Medical Journal* 2005 November 5; 331(7524): 1082. NRCBL: 8.3.1.

Woodsong, Cynthia; Karim, Quarraisha Abdool. A model designed to enhance informed consent: experiences from the HIV Prevention Trials Network. *American Journal of Public Health* 2005 March; 95(3): 412-419. NRCBL: 8.3.1; 9.5.6; 18.5.1.

Abstract: HIV prevention research in developing countries has resulted in increased attention to and discussion of ethical issues, particularly the issue of the quality of informed consent. We present a conceptual framework for an enhanced informed consent process, drawing on experiences garnered from domestic and international studies conducted by the HIV Prevention Trials Network, funded by the National Institutes of Health. This framework guides the development of an informed consent process designed to help ensure initial and continued comprehension of research participation, with an emphasis on HIV prevention research. Attention is focused at the individual and community levels and on 3 study phases: preenrollment, enrollment, and postenrollment.

Woolf, Steven H.; Chan, Evelyn C.Y.; Harris, Russell; Sheridan, Stacey L.; Braddock, Clarence H., III; Kaplan, Robert M.; Krist, Alex; O'Connor, Annette M.; Tunis, Sean. Promoting informed choice: transforming health care to dispense knowledge for decision making. *Annals of Internal Medicine* 2005 August 16; 143(4): 293-300. NRCBL: 8.3.1; 8.1.

Abstract: Ours is an era in which patients seek greater engagement in health care choices, increasing the demand for high-quality information about clinical options. Providing support for informed choice is not straightforward, however, because of challenges faced by clinicians, health systems, and consumers. Greater use of written or electronic tools can help to clarify choices for patients, but decision aids cannot replace the human element in facilitating informed choice. The ideal solution is to couple information with high-quality decision counseling to help patients understand the potential risks, benefits, and uncertainties of clinical options and to assist them in selecting the option that best accommodates their personal preferences. Decision counseling can be offered by 3 types of providers: clinicians who lack formal informed-choice training ("usual care"), clinicians with formal informed-choice training, or trained third parties who function as impartial decision counselors. Controlled studies are needed to determine which model is best, but none appears to be ideal. The health care system cannot truly support informed decision making without correcting the underlying obstacles that impede patient access to needed information. New information technology solutions, training programs, and reimbursement schemes are necessary. Patient demand for guidance will only increase as clinical options multiply and the world of information continues its rapid growth. Today's health care system is unprepared for the convergence of these 2 burgeoning domains, and the need to address systemic deficiencies will grow more urgent over time.

INFORMED CONSENT/ INCOMPETENTS

Azoulay, Élie; Pochard, Frédéric; Chevret, Sylvie; Adrie, Christophe; Bollaert, Pierre-Edouard; Brun, Frédéric; Dreyfuss, Didier; Garrouste-Orgeas, Maité; Goldgran-Toledano, Dany; Jourdain, Mercé; Wolff, Michel; Le Gall, Jean-Roger; Schlemmer, Benoît. Opinions about surrogate designation: a population survey in France. *Critical Care Medicine* 2003 June; 31(6): 1711-1714. NRCBL: 8.3.3. SC: em.

Azoulay, Élie; Sprung, Charles L. Family-physician interactions in the intensive care unit. *Critical Care Medicine* 2004 November; 32(11): 2323-2328. NRCBL: 8.3.3; 8.1.

Baumrucker, Steven J.; Davis, Mellar P.; Stolick, Matt; Morris, Gerald M.; Sheldon, Joanne. Sisters to the end: the rights of the mentally retarded to refuse treatment [case study]. *American Journal of Hospice and Palliative Care* 2005 January-February; 22(1): 61-65. NRCBL: 8.3.3; 8.3.4; 9.5.3; 9.6. SC: le; cs.

Bernal, Susan Kerr. Twin autonomy. *Journal of Andrology* 2004 January-February; 25(1): 2-4. NRCBL: 8.3.3; 1.1. SC: cs.

Bramstedt, Katrina A. Questioning the decision-making capacity of surrogates. *Internal Medicine Journal* 2003 June; 33(5-6): 257-259. NRCBL: 8.3.3; 20.5.4; 9.6. SC: cs.

Breslin, Jonathan M. Autonomy and the role of the family in making decisions at the end of life. *Journal of Clinical Ethics* 2005 Spring; 16(1): 11-19. NRCBL: 8.3.3; 20.3.3; 1.1.

Cantor, Norman L. The bane of surrogate decision-making: defining the best interests of never-competent persons. *Journal of Legal Medicine* 2005 June; 26(2): 155-205. NRCBL: 8.3.3; 4.4; 8.3.2.

Chambers-Evans, Jane; Carnevale, Franco A. Dawning of awareness: the experience of surrogate decision making at the end of life. *Journal of Clinical Ethics* 2005 Spring; 16(1): 28-45. NRCBL: 8.3.3; 20.5.1; 20.3.3. SC: em.

Demarquay, Geneviève; Derex, Laurent; Nighoghossian, Norbert; Adeleine, Patrice; Philippeau, Frédéric; Honnorat, Jérôme; Trouillas, Paul. Ethical issues of informed consent in acute stroke: analysis of the modalities of consent in 56 patients enrolled in urgent therapeutic trials. *Cerebrovascular Diseases* 2005; 19(2): 65-68. NRCBL: 8.3.3; 9.5.1. SC: em. Identifiers: France.

Dimond, Bridgit. The long-awaited Mental Capacity Bill has arrived [opinion]. *British Journal of Nursing* 2005 January 13-26; 14(1): 6. NRCBL: 8.3.3. SC: le. Identifiers: United Kingdom (Great Britain).

Dudzinski, Denise M.; Sullivan, Mark. When agreeing with the patient is not enough: a schizophrenic woman requests pregnancy termination. *General Hospital Psychiatry* 2004 November-December; 26(6): 475-480. NRCBL: 8.3.3; 12.5.3; 9.5.5; 9.5.9; 17.1. SC: cs.

Elliott, Carl. Caring about risks: are severely depressed patients competent to consent to research? *Archives of General Psychiatry* 1997 February; 54(2): 113-116. NRCBL: 8.3.3; 18.2; 18.5.6; 18.3; 4.3.

Goldblatt, David. Conflicting roles for the physician. *Medical Ethics Newsletter [Lahey Clinic]* 2003 Spring; 10(2): 3, 12. NRCBL: 8.3.3; 8.1.

Gore, D.M. Ethical, professional, and legal obligations in clinical practice: a series of discussion topics for postgraduate medical education. Topic 2: consent and legal competence. *Postgraduate Medical Journal* 2001 May; 77(907): 318-319. NRCBL: 8.3.3; 8.3.2; 8.1.

Gropelli, Theresa. A decision for Sam. *Journal of Gerontological Nursing* 2005 January; 31(1): 45-48. NRCBL: 8.3.3; 20.4.1; 20.5.1. SC: cs.

Haddad, Amy. Deciding for others. *RN* 2004 July; 67(7): 25-26, 28. NRCBL: 8.3.3; 4.1.3.

Haddad, Amy. Ethics in action. Durable power of attorney. *RN* 1999 September; 62(9): 25-26, 28. NRCBL: 8.3.3; 8.1; 7.1.

Kirk, Linda. Dialysis decisions: should everyone be dialyzed? *Nephrology Nursing Journal* 2005 January-February; 32(1): 96. NRCBL: 8.3.3; 8.3.4; 20.5.4. SC: cs.

Marcus, E-L.; Wasserstein Fassberg, C.; Namestnik, J.; Guedj, D.; Caine, Y. Strict vegan, low-calorie diet administered by care-giving daughter to elderly mother — is this elder abuse? *Medicine and Law: World Association for Medical Law* 2005 June; 24(2): 279-296. NRCBL: 8.3.3; 9.5.2; 8.3.4. SC: le.

Abstract: We present a case in which a 40 year old woman, who was the primary care-giver of her 78 year-old mother, provided a strict vegan diet which caused the mother severe malnutrition. The mother was hospitalized with severe functional deterioration and, while eating a proper diet during hospitalization, gained weight and her condition improved. The case was reported to the Welfare Officer and the mother was released under the supervision of the Welfare Officer. Cases of severe malnutrition and even death of infants who were fed a strict vegan diet have been reported. This case raises some ethical and legal issues. Should a guardian or a caregiver be allowed to make decisions regarding the way of life and medical treatment of the person in his/her charge which are likely to endanger that person's health and when is it appropriate for society to intervene in individual freedom? The paper includes a review of some reported cases of child and elder abuse or neglect which illustrate these issues.

McCormack, Brendan. The person of the voice: narrative identities in informed consent. *Nursing Philosophy* 2002 July; 3(2): 114-119. NRCBL: 8.3.3; 9.5.2; 17.1.

Morag, Rumm M.; DeSouza, Sylvie; Steen, Petter A.; Salem, Ashraf; Harris, Mark; Ohnstad, Oyvind; Fosen, Jan T.; Brenner, Barry E. Performing procedures on the newly deceased for teaching purposes: what if we were to ask? *Archives of Internal Medicine* 2005 January 10; 165(1): 82-96. NRCBL: 8.3.3; 7.2; 20.3.3; 21.1. SC: em.

Mueller, Eric; Mondragón, Delfi. Ethical implications of type I, type II error in patient competency assessment. *Nebraska Medical Journal* 1996 November; 81(11): 356-358. NRCBL: 8.3.3; 1.1; 17.1.

Rhodes, Rosamond; Holzman, Ian. Surrogate decision making: a case for boundaries. *In:* Thomasma, David C.; Weisstub, David N., eds. The Variables of Moral Capacity. Boston: Kluwer Academic Publishers; 2004: 173- 185. NRCBL: 8.3.3. SC: an.

Roberts, Laura Weiss. Mental illness and informed consent: seeking an empirically derived understanding of voluntarism. *Current Opinion in Psychiatry* 2003 September; 16(5): 543-545. NRCBL: 8.3.3. SC: em.

Roupie, E.; Santin, A.; Boulme, R.; Wartel, J.S.; Lepage, E.; Lemaire, F.; Lejonc, J.L.; Montagne, O. Patients' preferences concerning medical information and surrogacy: results of a prospective study in a French emergency department. *Intensive Care Medicine* 2000 January; 26(1): 52-56. NRCBL: 8.3.3; 8.3.1; 20.5.1; 7.1. SC: em.

Schwarz, Judith Kennedy. Revisiting New York State's proposed surrogate decision-making legislation. *Journal of the New York State Nurses Association* 1995 September; 26(3): 18-23. NRCBL: 8.3.3; 1.3.5. SC: le.

Sherman, Heather B.; McGaghie, William C.; Unti, Sharon M.; Thomas, John X. Teaching pediatrics residents how to obtain informed consent. *Academic Medicine* 2005 October; 80(10, Supplement): S10-S13. NRCBL: 8.3.3; 9.5.7; 7.2. SC: em.

Silberfeld, Michel. Vulnerable persons. *In:* Thomasma, David C.; Weisstub, David N.; Herve, Christian eds. Personhood and Health Care. Boston: Kluwer Academic Pub.; 2001: 299-316. NRCBL: 8.3.3; 4.4.

Silberfeld, Michel. Vulnerable persons: measuring moral capacity. *In:* Thomasma, David C.; Weisstub, David N., eds. The Variables of Moral Capacity. Boston: Kluwer Academic Publishers; 2004: 203- 215. NRCBL: 8.3.3; 4.3. SC: an.

Silberfeld, Michel; Finstad, Mary; Stephens, Derek. Agreement between professions on ethical decisions: an empirical demonstration. *Medicine and Law: World Association for Medical Law* 1995; 14(3-4): 191-197. NRCBL: 8.3.3; 4.3; 1.1. SC: em.

NRCBL: National Reference Center for Bioethics Literature Classification Scheme   See inside front cover for terms.

327

Sullivan, Ellen E. Issues of informed consent in the geriatric population. *Journal of Perianesthesia Nursing* 2004 December; 19(6): 430-432. NRCBL: 8.3.3; 4.1.3. SC: cs.

Sundram, Clarence J.; Stavis, Paul F. Obtaining informed consent for treatment of mentally incompetent patients: a decade under New York's innovative approach. *International Journal of Law and Psychiatry* 1999 March-April; 22(2): 107-123. NRCBL: 8.3.3. SC: le.

Van Leeuwen, Evert; Vellinga, Astrid. Knowing well or living well: is competence relevant to moral experience and capacity in clinical decision-making? *In:* Thomasma, David C.; Weisstub, David N., eds. The Variables of Moral Capacity. Boston: Kluwer Academic Publishers; 2004: 187- 202. NRCBL: 8.3.3; 18.5.6. SC: an; em.

Vellinga, A.; Smit, J.H.; Van Leeuwen, E.; Van Tilburg, W.; Jonker, C. Competence to consent to treatment of geriatric patients: judgements of physicians, family members and the vignette method. *International Journal of Geriatric Psychiatry* 2004 July; 19(7): 645-654. NRCBL: 8.3.3; 9.5.2. SC: em.

Welie, Sander P.K.; Dute, Joseph; Nys, Herman; van Wijman, Frans C.B. Patient incompetence and substitute decision-making: an analysis of the role of the health care professional in Dutch law. *Health Policy* 2005 July; 73(1): 21-40. NRCBL: 8.3.3; 4.3; 1.1. SC: le.

INFORMED CONSENT/ MINORS

Court can make parental decisions [news]. *Bulletin of Medical Ethics* 2003 November; (193): 4. NRCBL: 8.3.2; 8.1; 9.5.7. SC: le.

Texas judge orders treatment for a 13-year-old with cancer. *New York Times* 2005 September 10; p. A15. NRCBL: 8.3.2. SC: po; le.

Alderson, Priscilla. Complications within consent. *Bulletin of Medical Ethics* 2005 August-September; (210): 15-19. NRCBL: 8.3.2; 9.5.7. SC: rv; em.

Baker, Hannah. MMR: medicine, mothers and rights. *Cambridge Law Journal* 2004 March; 63(1): 49-52. NRCBL: 8.3.2; 8.3.5; 9.5.7. SC: le. Identifiers: Re C (A Child) (Immunisation: Parental Rights) [2003] EWCA Civ 1148 2 F.L.R. 1095.

Beh, Hazel; Diamond, Milton. Ethical concerns related to treating gender noncomformity in childhood and adolescence: lessons from the family court of Australia. *Health Matrix: Journal of Law-Medicine* 2005 Summer; 15(2): 239-283. NRCBL: 8.3.2; 10; 9.5.7. SC: le.

Blondeau, M.J.C.E. Legal protection or legal threat? Ethical conflicts in the process of medical decision making. *Medicine and Law: World Association for Medical Law* 1995; 14(5-6): 325-329. NRCBL: 8.3.2; 9.6. SC: le.

British Association of Perinatal Medicine [BAPM]. Consent in neonatal clinical care: good practice framework. United Kingdom: British Association of Perinatal Medicine 2004 October; 3 p. [Online] Available: http://www.bapm.org/media/documents/publications/Staff-leaflet.pdf [31 January 2006]. NRCBL: 8.3.2. Identifiers: staff leaflet.

Busby, Araceli; Ritvanen, Annukka; Dolk, Helen; Armstrong, Nicola; De Walle, Hermien; Riaño-Galán, Isolina; Gatt, Miriam; McDonnell, Robert; Nelen, Vera; Stone, David. Survey of informed consent for registration of congenital anomalies in Europe. *BMJ: British Medical Journal* 2005 July 16; 331(7509): 140-141. NRCBL: 8.3.2; 8.4; 1.3.12; 21.1.

Confederation of European Specialists in Paediatrics [CESP]. Ethics Working Group; De Lourdes Levy, Maria; Larcher, Victor; Kurz, Ronald. Informed consent/assent in children. Statement of the Ethics Working Group of the Confederation of European Specialists in Paediatrics (CESP). *European Journal of Pediatrics* 2003 September; 162(9): 629-633. NRCBL: 8.3.2; 21.1.

Cooke, Richard W.I. Good practice in consent. *Seminars in Fetal and Neonatal Medicine* 2005 February; 10(1): 63-71. NRCBL: 8.3.2; 15.3; 20.5.2; 21.1.

Crockin, Susan L. Adam Nash: legally speaking, a happy ending or slippery slope? [opinion]. *Reproductive BioMedicine Online [electronic]* 2001 January-February; 2(1): 6-7 Available: http://www.rbmonline.com/index.html [3 June 2005]. NRCBL: 8.3.2; 14.4; 19.5; 15.2.

Dickey, Susan B.; Kiefner, Jeanne; Beidler, Susan M. Consent and confidentiality issues among school-age children and adolescents. *Journal of School Nursing* 2002 June; 18(3): 179-186. NRCBL: 8.3.2; 8.4; 9.5.7. SC: le.

Fraser, John J., Jr.; McAbee, Gary N. Dealing with the parent whose judgment is impaired by alcohol or drugs: legal and ethical considerations. *Pediatrics* 2004 September; 114(3): 869-873. NRCBL: 8.3.2; 9.5.9; 8.1; 9.5.7.

Griffith, Richard. Childhood immunization: public health or parental choice? *British Journal of Community Nursing* 2004 September; 9(9): 379-382. NRCBL: 8.3.2; 9.5.1; 9.5.7; 9.7. SC: le. Identifiers: United Kingdom (Great Britain).

Hallström, Inger; Elander, Gunnel. Decision making in paediatric care: an overview with reference to nursing care. *Nursing Ethics* 2005 May; 12(3): 223-238. NRCBL: 8.3.2; 9.5.7. SC: em.
Abstract: The purpose of this overview of published articles on decision making in paediatric care was to identify important aspects of its possible use in clinical practice and to obtain a base for future research. A literature review was undertaken utilizing snowball sampling to identify articles because of the diversity present within the area of decision making in paediatric care. The databases PubMed and CINAHL were used. The search was limited to articles published in English during the period

---

SC (Subject Caption):   an=analytical   cs=case studies   em=empirical   le=legal   po=popular   rv=review

1994-2004. The analysis entailed a series of comparisons across articles, focusing on major areas of enquiry and patterns of results. Various levels of decision making are described because these seem to form a basis for how decisions are made. Concepts found to be of importance for decision making are described under the following headings: competence, the child's best interests, knowledge, values and attitudes, roles and partnership, power, and economy. Further research is suggested.

Huang, M-C; Lee, C-K; Lin, S-J; Lu, I-C. Parental consent for newborn screening in southern Taiwan. *Journal of Medical Ethics* 2005 November; 31(11): 621-624. NRCBL: 8.3.2; 9.5.7; 15.3. SC: em.
Abstract: OBJECTS: With the advent of genetic technologies, many genetic/metabolic disorders can be detected asymptomatically but might be untreatable, and the benefits and risks of screening for them are not fully known. The purpose of this study is to explore current practice with regard to the parental consent process in newborn screening (NBS). DESIGN: Staff in 23 obstetric clinics/hospitals that conduct NBS in one city of southern Taiwan were interviewed. Using content analysis, 15 interview transcripts, eight completed questionnaires, and other relevant documents from the 23 clinics/hospitals were analysed to reveal the framework of the parental consent process in NBS in southern Taiwan. MAIN MEASURES: Three categories-informed consent, informed dissent, and no informed/consent-were developed to analyse the parental consent process in NBS. RESULTS: The parental consent procedures in NBS and the quality of the information provided before obtaining consent vary widely. Because the traditional NBS was incorporated into routine paediatric practices in most clinics/hospitals, the most frequently encountered consent model is "informed dissent" (60.9%) and "no informed/consent" (30.4%); while an "informed consent" model (45.5%) is the frequent model for screening rare metabolic/genetic disorders. CONCLUSIONS: Specific guidelines to regulate the parental consent process for NBS are essential. Further studies should investigate parental responses to NBS, taking these as the basis on which to establish an informed consent model in Taiwan.

Huxtable, Richard. Re M (medical treatment: consent): time to remove the 'flak jacket'? *Child and Family Law Quarterly* 2000; 12(1): 83-88. NRCBL: 8.3.2; 8.3.4; 9.5.7; 19.6; 8.3.5. SC: le.

Kennedy, Sheila Suess. The muffled voice of the child: American health care and children's rights. *Journal of Medicine and Law* 2001 Fall; 6(1): 51-64. NRCBL: 8.3.2; 4.4. SC: le.

Kuther, Tara L. Medical decision-making and minors: issues of consent and assent. *Adolescence* 2003 Summer; 38(150): 343-358. NRCBL: 8.3.2.

Larcher, Vic. Consent, competence, and confidentiality. *BMJ: British Medical Journal* 2005 February 12; 330(7487): 353- 356. NRCBL: 8.3.2; 8.4; 4.3; 8.3.4; 9.5.7.

Lareau, Alyssa Connell. Who decides? Genital-normalizing surgery on intersexed infants. *Georgetown Law Journal* 2003 November; 92(1): 129-151. NRCBL: 8.3.2; 10. SC: le.

Manning, Donal. Proxy consent in neonatal care — goal-directed or procedure- specific? *Health Care Analysis: An International Journal of Health Care Philosophy and Policy* 2005 March; 13(1): 1-9. NRCBL: 8.3.2; 9.5.7; 20.4.2; 20.5.2. SC: em. Identifiers: United Kingdom (Great Britain).
Abstract: The prescription of practice guidelines for consent in neonatal care that are appropriate for all interventions faces substantial problems. Current practice varies widely. Consent in neonatal care is compromised by postnatal constraints on information sharing and decision-making. Empirical research shows marked individual and cultural variation in the degree to which parents want to contribute to decision-making on behalf of their infants. Conflict between the parents' wishes and the infant's best interests could arise if consent for a recommended intervention were refused, and parental refusal of consent may have to be overridden. Consent to an appropriate package of care (such as special, intensive or palliative care) may be morally preferable to a universal requirement to seek consent for all individual interventions entailed by that package.

Mathews, Catherine; Guttmacher, Sally J.; Flisher, Alan J.; Mtshizana, Yolisa; Hani, Andiswa; Zwarenstein, Merrick. Written parental consent in school-based HIV/AIDS prevention research. *American Journal of Public Health* 2005 July; 95(7): 1266-1269. NRCBL: 8.3.2; 9.5.6; 9.1; 18.4; 18.5.2. SC: em.
Abstract: OBJECTIVES: We examined the process of obtaining "active," written parental consent for a school-based HIV/AIDS prevention project in a South African high school by investigating (1) parental consent form return rates, (2) parents' recall and knowledge of the research, and (3) the extent to which this consent procedure represented parents' wishes about their child's involvement in the research. METHODS: This cross-sectional descriptive study comprised interviews with parents of children in grades eight and nine in a poor, periurban settlement in Cape Town. RESULTS: Within 2 weeks, 94% of 258 parents responded to a letter requesting written consent and of those, 93% consented, but subsequent interviews showed that 65% remembered seeing the consent form. At the end of the interview, 99% consented to their child's participation. CONCLUSIONS: These findings challenge many of the assumptions underlying active written parental consent. However, they should not be used to deny adolescents at high risk of HIV infection the opportunity to participate in prevention trials. Rather, researchers together with the communities in which the research is undertaken need to decide on appropriate informed consent strategies.

McKinney, Patricia A.; Jones, Samantha; Parslow, Roger; Davey, Nicola; Darowski, Mark; Chaudhry, Bill; Stack, Charles; Parry, Gareth; Draper, Elizabeth S. A feasibility study of signed consent for the collection of patient identifiable information for a national paediatric clinical audit database. *BMJ: British Medical Journal* 2005 April 16; 330(7496): 877-879. NRCBL: 8.3.2; 8.4; 1.3.12. SC: em.
Abstract: OBJECTIVES: To investigate the feasibility of obtaining signed consent for submission of patient identifiable data to a national clinical audit database and to identify factors influencing the consent process and its success. DESIGN: Feasibility study. SETTING: Seven paediatric intensive care units in England. PARTICIPANTS: Parents/guardians of patients, or patients aged 12-16 years old, approached consecutively over three months for signed consent for submission of patient iden-

NRCBL: National Reference Center for Bioethics Literature Classification Scheme   See inside front cover for terms.

329

tifiable data to the national clinical audit database the Paediatric Intensive Care Audit Network (PICANet). MAIN OUTCOME MEASURES: The numbers and proportions of admissions for which signed consent was given, refused, or not obtained (form not returned or form partially completed but not signed), by age, sex, level of deprivation, ethnicity (South Asian or not), paediatric index of mortality score, length of hospital stay (days in paediatric intensive care). RESULTS: One unit did not start and one did not fully implement the protocol, so analysis excluded these two units. Consent was obtained for 182 of 422 admissions (43%) (range by unit 9% to 84%). Most (101/182; 55%) consents were taken by staff nurses. One refusal (0.2%) was received. Consent rates were significantly better for children who were more severely ill on admission and for hospital stays of six days or more, and significantly poorer for children aged 10-14 years. Long hospital stays and children aged 10-14 years remained significant in a stepwise regression model of the factors that were significant in the univariate model. CONCLUSION: Systematically obtaining individual signed consent for sharing patient identifiable information with an externally located clinical audit database is difficult. Obtaining such consent is unlikely to be successful unless additional resources are specifically allocated to training, staff time, and administrative support.

Mitchell, John. Who knows best? *Medico-Legal Journal* 2005; 73(Part 1): 34-38. NRCBL: 8.3.2; 8.3.4; 9.7; 9.5.7. SC: le. Identifiers: United Kingdom (Great Britain).

Molin, Ronald; Palmer, Sally. Consent and participation: ethical issues in the treatment of children in out-of-home care. *American Journal of Orthopsychiatry* 2005 January; 75(1): 152-157. NRCBL: 8.3.2; 17.1; 1.3.10.

Olusanya, B.O.; Luxon, L.M.; Wirz, S.L. Infant hearing screening: route to informed choice. *Archives of Disease in Childhood* 2004 November; 89(11): 1039-1040. NRCBL: 8.3.2; 9.1.

Pace, Christine; Talisuna, Ambrose; Wendler, David; Maiso, Faustin; Wabwire-Mangen, Fred; Bakyaita, Nathan; Okiria, Edith; Garrett-Mayer, Elizabeth S.; Emanuel, Ezekiel; Grady, Christine. Quality of parental consent in Ugandan malaria study. *American Journal of Public Health* 2005 July; 95(7): 1184-1189. NRCBL: 8.3.2; 18.5.2; 21.1. SC: em.
Abstract: OBJECTIVES: We surveyed Ugandan parents who enrolled their children in a randomized pediatric malaria treatment trial to evaluate the parents' levels of understanding about the treatment trial and the quality of the parents' consents to allow their children to participate in the study. METHODS: We conducted 347 interviews immediately following enrollment at 4 Ugandan sites. RESULTS: A majority (78%) of the parents, most of whom where mothers (86%) had at most a primary school education. Of the participating mothers, a substantial percentage reported that they remembered being told about the study's purpose (77%), the required number of visits (88%), the risks involved (61%), treatment allocation (84%), and their ability to discontinue their children's participation (64%). In addition, most reported knowing the trial's purpose (80%) and the required number of visits (78%); however, only 18% could name possible side effects from the drugs being administered, and only 19% knew that children would not all be administered identical treatments. Ninety-four percent reported that they made the enrollment decision themselves, but 58% said they felt pressure to participate because of their child's illness, and 15% said they felt some type of pressure to participate from others; 41% reported knowing that they did not have to participate. CONCLUSIONS: The consent Ugandan parents provided to allow their children to participate in the malaria study was of mixed quality. Parents understood many of the study details, but they were not very aware of the risks involved or of randomization. Many parents felt that they could not have refused to participate because their child was sick and they either did not know or did not believe that their child would receive treatment outside of the study. Our results indicate that further debate is needed about informed consent in treatment studies of emergent illnesses in children.

Park, Shellie K. Severing the bond of life: when conflicts of interest fail to recognize the value of two lives. *University of Hawai'i Law Review* 2002 Winter; 25(1): 157-198. NRCBL: 8.3.2; 20.5.2; 4.4; 9.5.7. SC: le.

Pretzlaff, Robert K. Should age be a deciding factor in ethical decision-making? *Health Care Analysis: An International Journal of Health Care Philosophy and Policy* 2005 June; 13(2): 119-128. NRCBL: 8.3.2.
Abstract: The question of age as a factor in ethical decision-making takes two forms. The first form considers age as a factor at the societal, or policy, level, and the second as a factor in determining the capacity of the individual patient to make decisions regarding their own care. This article satisfies itself with a consideration of only the latter question. The issue of whether age is a contributing factor in medical decision-making is frequently posited when one considers ethically charged instances of medical decision making at the end of life. Few would argue that the person who has the capacity for decision-making should be denied the ability to exercise that facility and so, it is when a person has lost their ability for making those choices that the question of age as a contributing factor in ethical decision making is raised. The question therefore becomes one of capacity more than age, with age as a useful, but inexact, gauge of that capacity. The inexactitude of age as a surrogate of capacity is a contributing factor to the problem posed in this series of articles. Therefore, to define the relative contribution of age to the capacity for ethical decision-making this article will focus not on the loss of that ability, but rather on the factors that define the realization of that faculty. To do this it will be necessary to define how that faculty is to be measured and what are the characteristics of an ethical decision that define it apart from other decisions. Since at the beginning of life, if age is the only variable (adjusting for other co-morbid states) then the issue of surrogacy is a temporary one and is unlike the adult where the presumption is that the person is unlikely to regain decision-making capacity as they slip further into their morbid state.

Ranganathan, M.; Raghuraman, G. Ethical considerations in obtaining consent under anaesthesia [letter]. *Anaesthesia* 2003 December; 58(12): 1250-1251. NRCBL: 8.3.2.

Rushforth, Kay; McKinney, Patricia A. Issues of patient consent: a study of paediatric high- dependency care. *British Journal of Nursing* 2005 May 12-25; 14(9): 519-523. NRCBL: 8.3.2; 8.4; 18.3; 18.5.2. SC: le.

Scott, Elizabeth S.; Reppucci, N. Dickon; Woolard, Jennifer L. Evaluating adolescent decision making in legal contexts. *Law and Human Behavior* 1995 June; 19(3): 221-244. NRCBL: 8.3.2. SC: le.

Shah, Sapan S. Medical decision-making in non-life threatening situations for minor children. *Medical Trial Technique Quarterly* 2003; 49(3): 189-216. NRCBL: 8.3.2; 1.3.5; 8.3.4; 1.2. SC: le.

Stevens, Patricia E.; Pletsch, Pamela K. Ethical issues of informed consent: mothers' experiences enrolling their children in bone marrow transplantation research. *Cancer Nursing* 2002 April; 25(2): 81-87. NRCBL: 8.3.2; 9.5.7; 9.5.1; 19.1; 18.2.

Tagliabue, John. Discovery of stored fetuses and stillborns roils France. *New York Times* 2005 August 4; p. A10. NRCBL: 8.3.2; 19.5; 18.5.4. SC: po.

Tilden, Samuel J. Ethical and legal aspects of using an identical twin as a skin transplant donor for a severely burned minor. *American Journal of Law and Medicine* 2005; 31(1): 87-116. NRCBL: 8.3.2; 19.5; 8.3.3; 4.4. SC: le; cs.

Trahan, Jennifer. Constitutional law: parental denial of a child's medical treatment for religious reasons. *Annual Survey of American Law* 1989; 1989(1): 307-341. NRCBL: 8.3.2; 8.3.4; 1.2. SC: le.

Turkoski, Beatrice B. When a child's treatment decisions conflict with the parents'. *Home Healthcare Nurse* 2005 February; 23(2): 123-126. NRCBL: 8.3.2; 8.3.4; 20.5.2; 8.1. SC: cs.

Vukadinovich, David M. Minors' rights to consent to treatment: navigating the complexity of state laws. *Journal of Health Law* 2004 Fall; 37(4): 667-691. NRCBL: 8.3.2; 8.4. SC: le.

Wijnberg, Bart. Consent of children and minors. *In:* Actes du Colloque International AMADE-UNESCO sur Bioethique et Droits de L'enfant (Monaco, 28-30 Avril 2000)/Proceedings of the International Symposium AMADE-UNESCO on Bioethics and the Rights of the Child (Monaco, 28-30 April 2000). Paris: UNESCO, Division des Sciences Humaines, de la Philosophie et de L'ethique des Sciences et des Technologies; 2001: 105-110. NRCBL: 8.3.2.

Wise, M.E. Jan. Understanding, not wisdom, needed for capacity [letter]. *BMJ: British Medical Journal* 2005 July 30; 331(7511): 294. NRCBL: 8.3.2; 11.3.

INSTITUTIONAL REVIEW BOARDS *See* HUMAN EXPERIMENTATION/ ETHICS COMMITTEES

INTERNATIONAL HUMAN RIGHTS
See also TORTURE, GENOCIDE AND WAR CRIMES; WAR AND TERRORISM

Ashcroft, Richard E. Standing up for the medical rights of asylum seekers [editorial]. *Journal of Medical Ethics* 2005 March; 31(3): 125-126. NRCBL: 21.1; 9.2.

Brownscombe, J. Crisis in humanitarianism? *Journal of Medical Ethics* 2005 March; 31(3): 182-183. NRCBL: 21.1; 21.2.

Chirwa, Danwood Mzikenge. The right to health in international law: its implications for the obligations of state and non-state actors in ensuring access to essential medicine. *South African Journal on Human Rights* 2003; 19(4): 541-566. NRCBL: 21.1; 9.2. SC: le.

Dyer, Owen. Article removed after US complains it could help terrorists [news]. *BMJ: British Medical Journal* 2005 June 18; 330(7505): 1406. NRCBL: 21.1; 1.3.7; 1.3.5. SC: le. Identifiers: Food and Drug Administration; milk distribution.

Faunce, T.A. Will international human rights subsume medical ethics? Intersections in the UNESCO universal bioethics declaration. *Journal of Medical Ethics* 2005 March; 31(3): 173-178. NRCBL: 21.1; 2.1; 6. Identifiers: United Nations Educational, Scientific and Cultural Organization.

Abstract: The International Bioethics Committee (IBC) of the United Nations Educational, Scientific and Cultural Organisation (UNESCO) is currently drafting a Universal Bioethics Declaration ("the declaration"). The content and even the name of the declaration has yet to be finalized, but it is expected to range widely over human and non-human bioethics. It appears likely to include many articles directly related to medical ethics. The declaration may well evolve, like the Universal Declaration of Human Rights, into a component of international customary law, or be the precursor to an International Convention on Bioethics. This article discusses whether this process will facilitate bioethics and, in particular, medical ethics, being subsumed by the normative system of international human rights.

Fidler, David P. Mission impossible? International law and infectious diseases. *Temple International and Comparative Law Journal* 1996 Fall; 10(2): 493-502. NRCBL: 21.1. SC: le.

Griffith, Richard. Human rights and district nursing practice. *British Journal of Community Nursing* 2005 February; 10(2): 86-91. NRCBL: 21.1; 4.1.3. SC: le. Identifiers: United Kingdom (Great Britain).

Hammonds, Rachel; Ooms, Gorik. World Bank policies and the obligation of its members to respect, protect and fulfill the right to health. *Health and Human Rights: An International Journal* 2004; 8(1): 27-60. NRCBL: 21.1; 1.3.6; 9.3.1.

Jasanoff, Sheila. In the democracies of DNA: ontological uncertainty and political order in three states. *New Genetics and Society* 2005 August; 24(2): 139-155. NRCBL: 21.1; 12.4.1; 14.4; 18.5.4; 5.1. SC: le.

London, Leslie. Health and human rights: what can ten years of democracy in South Africa tell us? *Health and Human Rights: An International Journal* 2004; 8(1): 1-25. NRCBL: 21.1; 8.1; 7.1.

NRCBL: National Reference Center for Bioethics Literature Classification Scheme   See inside front cover for terms.

331

Pai, Sanjay A. The medical profession and human rights [editorial]. *Issues in Medical Ethics* 1998 October-December; 6(4): 107. NRCBL: 21.1; 21.4.

Peel, Michael. Human rights and medical ethics. *Journal of the Royal Society of Medicine* 2005 April; 98(4): 171-173. NRCBL: 21.1; 2.1; 2.2.

Sharma, Shridhar. Human rights of mental patients in India: a global perspective. *Current Opinion in Psychiatry* 2003 September; 16(5): 547-551. NRCBL: 21.1; 17.1. SC: le.

Sommerville, Ann. Recommendations concerning human rights for the medical profession. *Issues in Medical Ethics* 2003 January-March; 11(1): 19-20. NRCBL: 21.1; 7.1. Identifiers: British Medical Association.

United Nations Educational, Scientific and Cultural Organization [UNESCO]. Universal Declaration on Bioethics and Human Rights. Paris, France: UNESCO 2005 October 19; 9 p. [Online]. Available: http://portal. unesco.org/shs/en/file_download.php/46133e1f4691e4c 6e57566763d474a4dBioethicsDeclaration_EN.pdf [3 January 2006]. NRCBL: 21.1; 6; 2.1. Note: Adopted by acclamation on 19 October 2005 by the 33rd session of the General Conference of UNESCO.

Zion, Deborah. Caring for detained asylum seekers, human rights and bioethics [editorial]. *Australian and New Zealand Journal of Public Health* 2004 December; 28(6): 510-512. NRCBL: 21.1; 2.1.

INTERNATIONAL MIGRATION OF HEALTH CARE PROFESSIONALS

Ahmad, Omar B. Managing medical migration from poor countries. *BMJ: British Medical Journal* 2005 July 2; 331(7507): 43-45. NRCBL: 21.6; 21.1.

Chaguturu, Sreekanth; Vallabhaneni, Snigdha. Aiding and abetting — nursing crises at home and abroad [opinion]. *New England Journal of Medicine* 2005 October 27; 353(17): 1761-1763. NRCBL: 21.6; 21.1; 4.1.3.

Chen, Lincoln C.; Boufford, Jo Ivey. Fatal flows — doctors on the move [editorial]. *New England Journal of Medicine* 2005 October 27; 353(17): 1850-1852. NRCBL: 21.6; 21.1; 9.4.

Hutton, John. Hutton announces strengthened code of practice covering recruitment of overseas healthcare staff. London: Department of Health 2004 December 8; 2 p. [Online]. Available: http://www.dh.gov.uk/Publications AndStatistics/PressReleases/PressReleasesNotic es/ fs/en?CONTENT_ID=4097747&chk=GiuK6D [5 July 2005]. NRCBL: 21.6.

Mullan, Fitzhugh. The metrics of the physician brain drain. *New England Journal of Medicine* 2005 October 27; 353(17): 1810-1818. NRCBL: 21.6; 9.4; 21.1. SC: em.

Abstract: BACKGROUND: There has been substantial immigration of physicians to developed countries, much of it coming from lower- income countries. Although the recipient nations and the immigrating physicians benefit from this migration, less developed countries lose important health capabilities as a result of the loss of physicians. METHODS: Data on the countries of origin, based on countries of medical education, of international medical graduates practicing in the United States, the United Kingdom, Canada, and Australia were obtained from sources in the respective countries and analyzed separately and in aggregate. With the use of World Health Organization data, I computed an emigration factor for the countries of origin of the immigrant physicians to provide a relative measure of the number of physicians lost by emigration. RESULTS: International medical graduates constitute between 23 and 28 percent of physicians in the United States, the United Kingdom, Canada, and Australia, and lower-income countries supply between 40 and 75 percent of these international medical graduates. India, the Philippines, and Pakistan are the leading sources of international medical graduates. The United Kingdom, Canada, and Australia draw a substantial number of physicians from South Africa, and the United States draws very heavily from the Philippines. Nine of the 20 countries with the highest emigration factors are in sub-Saharan Africa or the Caribbean. CONCLUSIONS: Reliance on international medical graduates in the United States, the United Kingdom, Canada, and Australia is reducing the supply of physicians in many lower- income countries.

Scott, Mark L.; Whelan, Anna; Dewdney, John; Zwi, Anthony B. "Brain drain" or ethical recruitment? Solving health workforce shortages with professionals from developing countries. *Medical Journal of Australia* 2004 February 16; 180(4): 174-176. NRCBL: 21.6. Identifiers: Australia.

Xu, Yu; Zhang, Jianhui. One size doesn't fit all: ethics of international nurse recruitment from the conceptual framework of stakeholder interests. *Nursing Ethics* 2005 November; 12(6): 571-581. NRCBL: 21.6; 4.1.3.

Abstract: This theoretical study examines the ethics of international nurse recruitment from the conceptual framework of stakeholder interests. It argues that there are stakeholders at individual, institutional, national and international levels, with overlapping but, more often, different or even conflicting interests. Depending on the interests of given stakeholders, different conclusions regarding the ethics of international nurse recruitment may be reached. There is no right or wrong with these varying ethical positions because they reflect different beliefs and philosophies that are not amenable to value judgment. To illustrate and support this line of argument, this article analyzes the underpinnings of two ethical standards published by the International Council of Nurses and the UK Department of Health. In addition, a case study on China augments the argument by demonstrating limitations of the one-size-fits-all approach to the issue. The most important question in understanding and evaluating the ethical standards of international nurse recruitment is to know whose interests they are designed to represent and protect.

INVOLUNTARY COMMITMENT

Compulsory community treatment of mentally disordered patients. *Medical Law Review* 2003 Autumn; 11(3): 381-384. NRCBL: 17.7; 9.5.3. SC: le.

Constraint and coercion in psychiatry [news]. *Bulletin of Medical Ethics* 2003 September; (191): 4-5. NRCBL: 17.7; 8.1; 9.8. Identifiers: Netherlands.

Allan, Alfred. The past, present and future of mental health law: a therapeutic jurisprudence analysis. *Law in Context* 2003; 20(2): 24-53. NRCBL: 17.7; 17.1; 17.8; 8.3.4. SC: le.

Andrews, Jonathan. The politics of committal to early modern Bethlem. *Clio Medica* 1995; 29: 6-63. NRCBL: 17.7; 4.3. SC: rv.

Appelbaum, Paul S. Dangerous severe personality disorders: England's experiment in using psychiatry for public protection. *Psychiatric Services* 2005 April; 56(4): 397-399. NRCBL: 17.7; 4.3. SC: le.

Balevre, Park. Is it legal to be crazy: an ethical dilemma. *Archives of Psychiatric Nursing* 2001 October; 15(5): 241-244. NRCBL: 17.7; 17.3; 8.1. SC: cs.

Bauer, Arie; Rosca, Paula; Grinshpoon, Alex; Khawalled, Razak; Mester, Roberto. Regional psychiatric boards in Israel: expectations and realities. *International Journal of Law and Psychiatry* 2005 November-December; 28(6): 661-669. NRCBL: 17.7; 9.5.3. SC: em.

Bonsack, Charles; Borgeat, François. Perceived coercion and need for hospitalization related to psychiatric admission. *International Journal of Law and Psychiatry* 2005 July- August; 28(4): 342-347. NRCBL: 17.7; 17.8; 8.1; 8.3.4; 8.3.3. SC: em.

Bosanac, Sanja Babic. Involuntary hospitalization and the rights of mental patients in Croatia. *Medicine and Law: World Association for Medical Law* 1995; 14(5-6): 457-461. NRCBL: 17.7; 7.1; 1.3.5. SC: le.

Brooks, William. The privatization of the civil commitment process and the state action doctrine: have the mentally ill been systematically stripped of their Fourteenth Amendment rights? *Duquesne Law Review* 2001 Fall; 40(1): 1-75. NRCBL: 17.7; 1.3.5. SC: le.

Catalano, Ralph A.; Kessell, Eric; Christy, Annette; Monahan, John. Involuntary psychiatric examinations for danger to others in Florida after the attacks of September 11, 2001. *Psychiatric Services* 2005 July; 56(7): 858-862. NRCBL: 17.7; 1.3.5; 21.1. SC: em; le.

Clark, Colleen; Becker, Marion; Giard, Julienne; Mazelis, Ruta; Savage, Andrea; Vogel, Wendy. The role of coercion in the treatment of women with co-occurring disorders and histories of abuse. *Journal of Behavioral Health Services and Research* 2005 April-June; 32(2): 167-181. NRCBL: 17.7; 9.5.5; 9.5.9. SC: em.

Cohen, David A.; Ben-David, Sarah. Halachic perspective on involuntary psychiatric care of the mentally ill. *Medicine and Law: World Association for Medical Law*

1995; 14(5-6): 463-469. NRCBL: 17.7; 8.3.4; 1.2; 9.5.3. SC: le.

Council of Europe. Recommendation Rec (2004) 10 of the Committee of Ministers of the Council of Europe to member states concerning the protection of the human rights and dignity of persons with mental disorder. *European Journal of Health Law* 2004 December; 11(4): 407-425. NRCBL: 17.7; 9.5.3; 4.4. SC: le.

Curtis, Laurie C.; Diamond, Ronald. Power and coercion in mental health practice. *In:* Blackwell, Barry, ed. Treatment compliance and the therapeutic alliance. Australia: Harwood Academic Publishers; 1997: 97-122. NRCBL: 17.7.

Dhir, Aaron A. The maelstrom of civil commitment in Ontario: using examinations conducted during periods of unlawful detention to form the basis of subsequent involuntary detention under Ontario's Mental Health Act. *Health Law in Canada* 2003 November; 24(2): 9-18. NRCBL: 17.7; 1.1. SC: le.

Dósa, Ágnes. New legislation on civil commitment in Hungary. *Medicine and Law: World Association for Medical Law* 1995; 14(7-8): 581-587. NRCBL: 17.7. SC: le.

Dressing, Harald; Salize, Hans Joachim. Compulsory admission of mentally ill patients in European Union Member States. *Social Psychiatry and Psychiatric Epidemiology* 2004 October; 39(10): 797-803. NRCBL: 17.7; 21.1. SC: le; em.

Elbogen, Eric B.; Soriano, Catherine; Van Dorn, Richard; Swartz, Marvin S.; Swanson, Jeffrey W. Consumer views of representative payee use of disability funds to leverage treatment adherence. *Psychiatric Services* 2005 January; 56(1): 45-49. NRCBL: 17.7; 17.8; 9.3.1. SC: em.

Greenberg, David; Mazar, Joseph; Brom, Danny; Barel, Yair Carlos. Involuntary outpatient commitment: a naturalistic study of its use and a consumer survey at one community mental health center in Israel. *Medicine and Law: World Association for Medical Law* 2005 March; 24(1): 95-110. NRCBL: 17.7. SC: em.

Abstract: The following study assessed the efficacy of involuntary outpatient commitment in promoting treatment adherence and preventing hospitalization during and after a period of compulsory treatment in one community mental health center in Israel and evaluated the attitudes of patients and psychiatrists. All patients referred for involuntary outpatient commitment over a two year period (N = 26) were followed up for 3-5 years. After the termination of the commitment, the patient and psychiatrist were interviewed. Although only three patients had been in regular outpatient treatment before the commitment, fourteen remained in regular care during the commitment's duration and ten remained for a further two years. Comparing the follow-up period with the identical duration before the commitment, the number of hospitalizations and number of days hospitalized were significantly reduced. Fifteen were rehospitalized during follow-up. Thirteen patients were interviewed at the termination of the commitment, and nearly all perceived the commitment in negative terms, although eight did not think it had a

NRCBL: National Reference Center for Bioethics Literature Classification Scheme   See inside front cover for terms.

333

negative effect on their relationship with the psychiatrist and six thought their opinions were respected. Six of the psychiatrists considered they were not giving optimum treatment. Despite the presence of the commitment, psychiatrists were often sensitive to patients' wishes and the involuntary aspect of the care was often not pursued. While half of the sample were lost to community care, half remained for several years. The study reflects the delicate nature of involuntary care in the community, so that in practice it is often not involuntary, not for outpatients and not a commitment.

Gutheil, Thomas G.; Simon, Robert I.; Hilliard, James T. "The wrong handle": flawed fixes of medicolegal problems in psychiatry and the law [editorial]. *Journal of the American Academy of Psychiatry and the Law* 2005; 33(4): 432-436. NRCBL: 17.7; 17.8; 7.3; 1.3.5; 1.3.8; 8.4. SC: le.

Hiday, Virginia Aldigé. Civil commitment: a review of empirical research. *Behavioral Sciences and the Law* 1988; 6(1): 15-43. NRCBL: 17.7; 17.8; 4.3. SC: le; em; rv.

Houston, R.A. Rights and wrongs in the confinement of the mentally incapable in eighteenth-century Scotland. *Continuity and Change* 2003 December; 18(3): 373-394. NRCBL: 17.7; 17.1; 4.3. SC: le. Identifiers: United Kingdom (Great Britain).

Huss, Matthew T.; Zeiss, Robert A. You have the right not to have a hearing: an evaluation of the impact of fully advising civilly committed patients on their rights. *International Journal of Law and Psychiatry* 2005 July- August; 28(4): 334-341. NRCBL: 17.7; 17.8; 8.1; 8.3.3; 8.3.4. SC: em.

Jennings, Elaine Marie. And some grow mad, and all grow bad: prisoners constitutional right to receive psychiatric treatment. *New England Journal on Criminal and Civil Confinement* 1985 Winter; 11(1): 160-185. NRCBL: 17.7; 17.8. SC: le.

Klein, Dora W. Involuntary treatment of the mentally ill: autonomy is asking the wrong question. *Specialty Law Digest: Health Care Law* 2004 August; (304): 9-40. NRCBL: 17.7; 1.1. SC: le.

Krieg, Randall G. A social contract for deinstitutionalization. *Journal of Social Philosophy* 2003 Fall; 34(3): 475-486. NRCBL: 17.7; 1.1. SC: an.

Krongard, Mara Lynn. A population at risk: civil commitment of substance abusers after Kansas v. Hendricks. *California Law Review* 2002 January; 90(1): 111-163. NRCBL: 17.7; 1.3.5; 9.5.9. SC: le.

Lecompte, D. The paradoxical increase in involuntary admissions after the revision of the Civil Commitment Law in Belgium. *Medicine and Law: World Association for Medical Law* 1995; 14(1-2): 53-57. NRCBL: 17.7; 4.3. SC: le.

Leong, Gregory B. Sell v. U.S.: involuntary treatment case or catalyst for change? [editorial]. *Journal of the*

American Academy of Psychiatry and the Law 2005; 33(3): 292-294. NRCBL: 17.7; 17.4; 1.3.5. SC: le.

Mela, Mansfield. Folie a trois in a multilevel security forensic treatment center: forensic and ethics-related implications. *Journal of the American Academy of Psychiatry and the Law* 2005; 33(3): 310-316. NRCBL: 17.7; 17.4; 1.3.5. SC: cs.

Mester, Roberto; Pinals, Debra. Comparing aspects of mental health legislation of Israel and Massachusetts. *Israel Journal of Psychiatry and Related Sciences* 2004; 41(2): 133-139. NRCBL: 17.7; 9.5.9; 21.1. SC: le.

Mihanovic, Mate; Restek-Petrovic, Branka; Babic, Goran; Sain, Ivica; Telarovic, Sinisa; Zilic-Dzeba, Jadranka. Involuntary hospitalizations in the psychiatric hospital "Jankomir" before and following the alterations and amendments made to ZZODS. *Collegium Antropologicum* 2004 June; 28(1): 385-391. NRCBL: 17.7; 9.5.9. SC: le; em. Identifiers: Croatia.

Monahan, John; Redlich, Allison D.; Swanson, Jeffrey; Robbins, Pamela Clark; Appelbaum, Paul S.; Petrila, John; Steadman, Henry J.; Swartz, Marvin; Angell, Beth; McNiel, Dale E. Use of leverage to improve adherence to psychiatric treatment in the community. *Psychiatric Services* 2005 January; 56(1): 37-44. NRCBL: 17.7; 17.8. SC: em.

Perlin, Michael L. "May you stay forever young": Robert Sadoff and the history of Mental Disability Law. *Journal of the American Academy of Psychiatry and the Law* 2005; 33(2): 236-244. NRCBL: 17.7; 17.8; 8.3.4. SC: le.

Romans, Sarah; Dawson, John; Mullen, Richard; Gibbs, Anita. How mental health clinicians view community treatment orders: a national New Zealand survey. *Australian and New Zealand Journal of Psychiatry* 2004 October; 38(10): 836-841. NRCBL: 17.7; 7.1. SC: em.

Schmidt, Winsor C., Jr. Critique of the American Psychiatric Association's guidelines for state legislation on civil commitment of the mentally ill. *New England Journal on Criminal and Civil Confinement* 1985 Winter; 11(1): 11-43. NRCBL: 17.7. SC: le.

Slovenko, Ralph. Civil commitment [opinion]. *Medicine and Law* 1982; 1: 217-226. NRCBL: 17.7. SC: le.

Stone, Donald H. The benefits of voluntary inpatient psychiatric hospitalization: myth or reality? *Boston University Public Interest Law Journal* 1999 Fall; 9(1): 25-52. NRCBL: 17.7; 8.3.1; 17.1. SC: le.

Szasz, Thomas. Protecting patients against psychiatric intervention [opinion]. *Society* 2004 March-April; 41(3): 7-9. NRCBL: 17.7; 17.8; 8.3.1; 9.5.3.

Tavcar, Rok; Dernovsek, Mojca Z.; Grubic, Virginija Novak. Use of coercive measures in a psychiatric intensive care unit in Slovenia [letter]. *Psychiatric Services* 2005 April; 56(4): 491-492. NRCBL: 17.7; 17.3. SC: em.

Tuohimäki, C.; Kaltiala-Heino, R.; Korkeila, J.; Tuori, T.; Lehtinen, V.; Joukamaa, M. The use of harmful to others-criterion for involuntary treatment in Finland. *European Journal of Health Law* 2003 June; 10(2): 183-199. NRCBL: 17.7; 4.3. SC: em.

Vuckovich, Paula K.; Artinian, Barbara M. Justifying coercion. *Nursing Ethics* 2005 July; 12(4): 370-380. NRCBL: 17.7; 17.4; 8.1. SC: em.

Abstract: A grounded theory study of psychiatric nurses' experiences of administering medication to involuntary psychiatric patients revealed a basic social process of justifying coercion. Although the 17 nurses interviewed all reported success at avoiding the use of coercion, each had an individual approach to using the nurse- patient relationship to do this. However, all the nurses used the same process to reconcile themselves to using coercion when it became necessary. This has three stages: assessment of need; negotiation; and justifying and taking coercive action. Two critical junctures—decision to engage and impasse - determine the progression from one stage to the next. The process of justifying coercion allows a nurse to engage in behavior generally disapproved of while retaining a self-image of a 'good' nurse.

Wallsten, Tuula; Kjellin, Lars. Involuntarily and voluntarily admitted patients' experiences of psychiatric admission and treatment — a comparison before and after changed legislation in Sweden. *European Psychiatry* 2004 December; 19(8): 464-468. NRCBL: 17.7. SC: em; le.

JOURNALISM AND PUBLISHING
See also BIOMEDICAL RESEARCH

Clamp down on copycats: plagiarism is on the rise, thanks to the Internet. Universities and journals need to take action [editorial]. *Nature* 2005 November 3; 438(7064): 2. NRCBL: 1.3.7; 1.3.9.

Manipulating a journal article [editorial]. *New York Times* 2005 December 11; p. WK11. NRCBL: 1.3.7; 9.7. SC: po.

Afifi, Mustafa M. Authorship. Credit and disputes. *Saudi Medical Journal* 2004 November; 25(11): 1742-1743. NRCBL: 1.3.7; 1.3.9; 7.3.

Albert, Daniel M.; Liesegang, Thomas J.; Schachat, Andrew P. Meeting our ethical obligations in medical publishing: responsibilities of editors, authors, and readers of peer-reviewed journals [editorial]. *Archives of Ophthalmology* 2005 May; 123(5): 684-686. NRCBL: 1.3.7; 1.3.9.

Arshinoff, Steve; Choi, Stephen. Excluding the experts? [letter and reply]. *CMAJ/JAMC: Canadian Medical Association Journal* 2005 October 11; 173(8): 849. NRCBL: 1.3.7; 1.3.9.

Baggs, Judith Gedney; Schmitt, Madeline H. Editors and conflict of interest [editorial]. *Research in Nursing and Health* 2003 April; 26(2): 87-89. NRCBL: 1.3.7; 1.3.9; 7.3.

Baillie, J. On writing (5): fabrication, falsification and plagerism [sic; plagiarism] in medical research and publishing. *Endoscopy* 2004 November; 36(11): 1008-1010. NRCBL: 1.3.7; 1.3.9.

Bakalar, Nicholas. Potential conflicts cited in process for new drugs. *New York Times* 2005 October 25; p. F7. NRCBL: 1.3.7; 1.3.9; 9.7. SC: po.

Benninger, Michael S.; Jackler, Robert K.; Johns, Michael M.E.; Johnson, Jonas T.; Kennedy, David W.; Ruben, Robert J.; Sataloff, Robert T.; Smith, Richard J.H.; Weber, Peter C.; Weber, Randal S.; Young, Eric D. Consortium of otolaryngology-head and neck surgery journals to collaborate in maintenance of high ethical standards [editorial]. *Archives of Otolaryngology-Head and Neck Surgery* 2005 May; 131(5): 381-382. NRCBL: 1.3.7; 1.3.9.

Benninger, Michael S.; Jackler, Robert K.; Johnson, Jonas T.; Johns, Michael M.; Kennedy, David W.; Ruben, Robert J.; Sataloff, Robert T.; Smith, Richard J.H.; Weber, Peter C.; Weber, Randal S.; Young, Eric D. Consortium of otolaryngology — head and neck surgery journals to collaborate in maintenance of high ethical standards [editorial]. *Laryngoscope* 2005 May; 115(5): 761-762. NRCBL: 1.3.7; 1.3.9.

Berenson, Alex. Medical journal criticizes Merck over Vioxx data. *New York Times* 2005 December 9; p. A1, C13. NRCBL: 1.3.7; 1.3.9; 9.7. SC: po.

Block, Barry H. Ethical and legal issues in medical writing. *Journal of the American Podiatric Medical Association* 1998 January; 88(1): 45-46. NRCBL: 1.3.7. SC: le.

Brand, Richard A.; Heckman, James D.; Scott, James. Changing ethical standards in scientific publication [editorial]. *Journal of the American Academy of Orthopaedic Surgeons* 2004 September-October; 12(5): 296-297. NRCBL: 1.3.7; 1.3.9.

Brand, Richard A.; Heckman, James D.; Scott, James. Changing ethical standards in scientific publication [editorial]. *Journal of Bone and Joint Surgery: American Volume* 2004 September; 86-A(9): 1855-1856. NRCBL: 1.3.7; 1.3.9.

Brice, Julie; Bligh, John. Author misconduct: not just the editors' responsibility. *Medical Education* 2004 January; 39(1): 83-89. NRCBL: 1.3.7; 1.3.9. SC: em; cs.

Burda, David. The rules we follow. An updated ethics code for our staff. *Modern Healthcare* 2004 November 1; 34(44): 20. NRCBL: 1.3.7; 6.

Cohn, Felicia; Manetta, Alberto. A teachable moment: research ethics revisited. *American Journal of Obstetrics and Gynecology* 2003 January; 188(1): 2. NRCBL: 1.3.7; 1.3.9; 18.3.

NRCBL: National Reference Center for Bioethics Literature Classification Scheme   See inside front cover for terms.

335

Coleman, Renita; May, Thomas. Professional-client relationships: rethinking confidentiality, harm, and journalists' public health duties. *Journal of Mass Media Ethics* 2004; 19(3-4): 276-292. NRCBL: 1.3.7; 8.4; 7.1; 6. SC: an.

Coyne, James. Reply to letter to the editor [letter]. *American Journal of Bioethics [Online]* 2005 May-June; 5(3): W13-W15. NRCBL: 1.3.7; 1.3.9; 9.7; 1.3.2. Identifiers: comment on Jeffrey P. Kahn, "To the editor," American Journal of Bioethics [Online] 2005 May-June; 5(3): W13.

Dubben, Hans-Hermann; Beck-Bornholdt, Hans-Peter. Systematic review of publication bias in studies on publication bias. *BMJ: British Medical Journal* 2005 August 20-27; 331(7514): 433-434. NRCBL: 1.3.7; 18.2. SC: em.

Eedy, D.J.; Graham-Brown, R.A.C. Ethics and conflicts of interest in the BJD [editorial]. *British Journal of Dermatology* 2004 July; 151(1): 1-2. NRCBL: 1.3.7; 1.3.9; 9.7.

Elliott, Carl. To the editor [letter]. *American Journal of Bioethics [Online]* 2005 May-June; 5(3): W16. NRCBL: 1.3.7; 1.3.2. Comments: comment on James Coyne, "Lessons in conflict of interest: the construction of the martyrdom of David Healy and the dilemma of bioethics," American Journal of Bioethics [Online] 2005 Winter; 5(1): W3-W14.

Flanagin, Annette. Fraudulent publication [editorial]. *Orthopaedic Nursing* 1994 March-April; 13(2): 7. NRCBL: 1.3.7; 1.3.9.

Fugh-Berman, Adriane. The corporate coauthor [opinion]. *JGIM: Journal of General Internal Medicine* 2005 June; 20(6): 546-548. NRCBL: 1.3.7; 1.3.9; 9.7.

Garne, David; Watson, Megan; Chapman, Simon; Byrne, Fiona. Environmental tobacco smoke research published in the journal Indoor and Built Environment and associations with the tobacco industry. *Lancet* 2005 February 26-March 4; 365(9461): 804-809. NRCBL: 1.3.7; 16.1; 1.3.2; 9.5.9; 9.3.1.

Abstract: In the late 1980s, the international tobacco industry assisted in the establishment of the International Society of the Built Environment, which published the journal Indoor and Built Environment. Using evidence from tobacco industry documents, we examine the industry associations of the Society's executive, the journal's editor and board, and the extent to which the journal publishes papers on environmental tobacco smoke that would be deemed favourable by the tobacco industry. The society's executive has been dominated by paid consultants to the tobacco industry: all six members in 1992 and seven of eight members in 2002 had financial associations through industry lawyers. 67% of the editorial board in 1992 and 66% in 2002 had histories of financial associations with the tobacco industry. 61% (40/66) of papers related to environmental tobacco smoke published in Indoor and Built Environment in the study period reached conclusions that could be judged to be industry-positive. Of these, 90% (36/40) had at least one author with a history of association with the tobacco industry. The executive of the International Society of the Built Environment and the editorial board of Indoor and Built Environment are in large part consisted of people with histories of consultancies to the to-bacco industry. On the basis of the evidence presented in this paper, there is a serious concern the tobacco industry may have been unduly influential on the content of the journal.

Gavey, Nicola; Braun, Virginia. Ethics and the publication of clinical case material. *Professional Psychology: Research and Practice* 1997 August; 28(4): 399-404. NRCBL: 1.3.7; 17.1; 8.3.1.

Giles, Jim. Journals lack explicit policies for separating eds from ads [news]. *Nature* 2005 March 31; 434(7033): 549. NRCBL: 1.3.7; 9.7; 1.3.9.

Grace, Mike. A cautionary tale [opinion]. *British Dental Journal* 2003 November 22; 195(10): 549. NRCBL: 1.3.7; 7.3.

Hadjistavropoulos, Thomas; Bieling, Peter J. When reviews attack: ethics, free speech, and the peer review process. *Canadian Psychology/Psychologie Canadienne* 2000 August; 41(3): 152-159. NRCBL: 1.3.7; 17.1.

Halsted, Charles H. Responsibilities of authors [editorial]. *American Journal of Clinical Nutrition* 2002 January; 75(1): 1. NRCBL: 1.3.7; 7.1; 9.3.1; 7.3.

Hamilton, Cindy W.; Mallia-Hughes, Marianne; Mitrany, Devora; Foote, MaryAnn; Fugh-Berman, Adriane. Comments on "the corporate author" [letter and reply]. *JGIM: Journal of General Internal Medicine* 2005 October; 20(10): 972-973. NRCBL: 1.3.7; 1.3.9.

Hampton, Tracy. Biomedical journals probe peer review [news]. *JAMA: The Journal of the American Medical Association* 2005 November 9; 294(18): 2287-2288. NRCBL: 1.3.7; 1.3.9.

Holden, Constance. Withdrawn parasite paper stirs criticism of Cell [news]. *Science* 2005 October 7; 310(5745): 34. NRCBL: 1.3.7; 1.3.9.

Johnson, Jonas T. Conflicts of interest in medical publishing [editorial]. *Laryngoscope* 2004 October; 114(10): 1685. NRCBL: 1.3.7; 1.3.9.

Kahn, Jeffrey P. To the editor [letter]. *American Journal of Bioethics [Online]* 2005 May-June; 5(3): W13. NRCBL: 1.3.7; 1.3.9; 9.7. Identifiers: University of Minnesota; Institute for Applied and Basic Research in Surgery (IABRS). Comments: comment on James Coyne, "Lessons in conflict of interest: the construction of the martyrdom of David Healy and the dilemma of bioethics," American Journal of Bioethics [Online] 2005 Winter; 5(1): W3-W14.

Kempers, Roger D. Ethical issues in biomedical publications. *Fertility and Sterility* 2002 May; 77(5): 883-888. NRCBL: 1.3.7; 7.3; 1.3.9.

Krane, Vikki. Conversing about ethics [editorial]. *Sport Psychologist* 2003 December; 17(4): 387-390. NRCBL: 1.3.7; 1.3.9.

Laine, Christine; Mulrow, Cynthia D. Exorcising ghosts and unwelcome guests [editorial]. *Annals of Internal Medicine* 2005 October 18; 143(8): 611-612. NRCBL: 1.3.7; 1.3.9.

Lazar, R. Up for grabs — authors are a dime a dozen: the problem of multiple authors [opinion]. *Acta Paediatrica* 2004 May; 93(5): 589-591. NRCBL: 1.3.7; 1.3.9.

Lefebvre, Carol A.; Lang, Brien R. The Journal of Prosthetic Dentistry publication standards of ethical conduct. *Journal of Prosthetic Dentistry* 2005 April; 93(4): 311-314. NRCBL: 1.3.7; 1.3.9.

Lehman-Wilzig, Sam N. Political ill-health coverage: professional-ethical questions regarding news reporting of leaders' ailments. *Journal of Health Communication* 2003 January-February; 8(1): 59-77. NRCBL: 1.3.7; 8.4; 1.3.5; 1.1.

Lloyd, Stanley J.; Whitney, Harvey. Publishing ethics: duplication indiscretion [editorial]. *Annals of Pharmacotherapy* 2003 January; 37(1): 147. NRCBL: 1.3.7; 1.3.9.

Mackie, Phil; Sim, Fiona. Publishing ethics and public health [editorial]. *Public Health* 2005 April; 119(4): 223-224. NRCBL: 1.3.7; 9.1.

Marušic, Ana. Author misconduct: editors as educators of research integrity [opinion]. *Medical Education* 2005 January; 39(1): 7-8. NRCBL: 1.3.7; 1.3.9.

Mathews, Anna Wilde. Ghost story: at medical journals, writers paid by industry play big role; articles appear under name of academic researchers, but they often get help; J & J receives a positive "spin". *Wall Street Journal* 2005 December 13; p. A1, A8. NRCBL: 1.3.7; 1.3.9. SC: po.

Mathews, Anna Wilde. Worrisome ailment in medicine: misleading journal articles; editors demand more data to ensure full disclosure of drug risks, trial gaps; Sarbanes-Oxley for professors. *Wall Street Journal* 2005 May 10; p. A1, A9. NRCBL: 1.3.7; 1.3.9. SC: po.

McKenna, Jeffrey W.; Pechacek, Terry F.; Stroup, Donna F. Health communication ethics and CDC quality-control guidelines for information. *Public Health Reports* 2003 May-June; 118(3): 193-196. NRCBL: 1.3.7; 1.3.12; 5.1. Identifiers: Centers for Disease Control and Prevention.

Ngai, Stephanie; Gold, Jennifer L.; Gill, Sudeep S.; Rochon, Paula A. Haunted manuscripts: ghost authorship in the medical literature. *Accountability in Research* 2005 April-June; 12(2): 103-114. NRCBL: 1.3.7; 1.3.9.
Abstract: Ghost authorship occurs when an individual who contributed substantially to a manuscript is not named in the byline or acknowledgments. Ghost authors may be employed by industry to prepare clinical trial results for publication. An expert is then "hired" as author so as to lend an air of credibility and neutrality to the manuscript. Ghost authorship is difficult to de-

tect, and most articles that have been identified as ghostwritten were revealed as such only after investigative work by lawyers, journalists, or scientists. Ghost authorship is ethically questionable in that it may be used to mask conflicts of interest with industry. As it has been demonstrated that industry sponsorship of clinical trials may be associated with outcomes favorable to industry, this is problematic. Evidence-based medicine requires that clinical decisions be based on empirical evidence published in peer-reviewed medical journals. If physicians base their decisions on dubious research data, this can have negative consequences for patients. Ghost authorship also compromises academic integrity. A "film credit" concept of authority is one solution to the problems posed by ghost authorship. Other approaches have been taken by the United Kingdom and Denmark. A solution is necessary, as the relationship between authorship and accountability must be maintained.

Pai, Sanjay A. Publication ethics policies for medical journals. *Indian Journal of Medical Ethics* 2004 July-September; 1(3): 93. NRCBL: 1.3.7.

Pitkin, Roy M. Ethical and quasi-ethical issues in medical editing and publishing [editorial]. *Croatian Medical Journal* 1998 June; 39(2): 95-101. NRCBL: 1.3.7; 1.3.9; 9.8.

Rier, David A. Publication visibility of sensitive public health data: when scientists bury their results. *Science and Engineering Ethics* 2004 October; 10(4): 597-613. NRCBL: 1.3.7; 5.1; 7.1; 9.1; 16.1. SC: em.

Roy, Nobhojit. Medical ethics: funding the discourse. *Issues in Medical Ethics* 2002 April-June; 10(2): 20-21. NRCBL: 1.3.7.

Savulescu, Julian; Viens, A.M. What makes the best medical ethics journal? A North American perspective. *Journal of Medical Ethics* 2005 October; 31(10): 591-597. NRCBL: 1.3.7; 2.1; 7.3. SC: em.
Abstract: BACKGROUND: There currently exist no data on the factors that contribute to determining why medical ethicists choose to review for and submit articles to medical ethics journals. OBJECTIVE: To establish which factors contribute to medical ethicists reviewing articles for or submitting them to medical ethics journals by consulting those who are active in this capacity. METHODS: Medical ethicists were surveyed to determine their incentives and disincentives for reviewing articles for or submitting them to medical ethics journals. Survey participants were chosen based on a review of the academic and research record of medical ethicists working in North America in higher education institutions. RESULTS: The most frequent incentives to reviewing journal articles were: an opportunity to contribute to the field/profession, the good reputation of the journal, the high impact factor of the journal, and to keep up to date on current research. The most frequent disincentives to reviewing journal articles were: time constraints due to academic commitments, the poor reputation of the journal, and time constraints caused by other editorial commitments (for example, reviewing for other journals/publishers). The most important incentives to submitting journal articles were: the good reputation of the journal, the quality of scholarship previously published in the journal, the impact factor of the journal, and a fast turn-around from acceptance to publication. The most important disincentives to submitting journal articles were: the poor reputation of the journal, the poor quality of work previously published in the journal, and a slow turn-around from acceptance to publication. CONCLUSION: A series of factors that medical ethics journals should strive to employ to

NRCBL: National Reference Center for Bioethics Literature Classification Scheme   See inside front cover for terms.

337

encourage reviewing and submission of articles are recommended.

Smith, G. Ethics and research in anaesthesia [letter]. *Anaesthesia* 1998 September; 53(9): 930. NRCBL: 1.3.7; 1.3.9.

Spear, Hila J. On ethical peer review and publication: the importance of professional conduct and communication. *Nurse Author and Editor* 2004 Fall; 14(4): 1-3. NRCBL: 1.3.7; 7.3.

Stein, C. Michael. Publishing work sponsored by the tobacco industry. *Clinical Pharmacology and Therapeutics* 2004 December; 76(6): 517-518. NRCBL: 1.3.7; 1.3.9; 1.3.2; 9.5.9.

Supe, Avinash. Ethical considerations in medical photography. *Issues in Medical Ethics* 2003 July-September; 11(3): 83-84. NRCBL: 1.3.7.

Thomas, Carol. Doctors for Life abortion on demand survey [letter]. *South African Medical Journal* 1996 December; 86(12): 1561-1562. NRCBL: 1.3.7; 12.3.

Tierney, William M.; Gerrity, Martha S. Scientific discourse, corporate ghostwriting, journal policy, and public trust [editorial]. *JGIM: Journal of General Internal Medicine* 2005 June; 20(6): 550-551. NRCBL: 1.3.7; 1.3.9; 1.3.2.

von Bubnoff, Andreas. Spanish flu papers put spotlight on 'dual use' decisions [news]. *Nature Medicine* 2005 November; 11(11): 1130. NRCBL: 1.3.7; 21.3.

Wagena, Edwin J.; Knipschild, P. Do drug firms hoodwink medical journals? Or is something wrong with the contribution and integrity of declared authors? *Journal of Medical Ethics* 2005 May; 31(5): 307. NRCBL: 1.3.7; 1.3.9; 9.7.

Wager, Elizabeth; Jacobs, Adam. Response to "The Corporate Coauthor" [letter]. *JGIM: Journal of General Internal Medicine* 2005 July; 20(7): 672. NRCBL: 1.3.7; 1.3.9; 9.3.1.

Wells, Michael. Policy on ethics and patient consent [editorial]. *Histopathology* 2003 February; 42(2): 103. NRCBL: 1.3.7; 18.3; 6.

Wharton, Barbara. Ethical issues in the publication of clinical material. *Journal of Analytical Psychology* 2005 February; 50(1): 83-89. NRCBL: 1.3.7; 8.4; 17.2.

World Association of Medical Editors [WAME]. Ghost writing initiated by commercial companies. *JGIM: Journal of General Internal Medicine* 2005 June; 20(6): 549. NRCBL: 1.3.7; 1.3.9; 1.3.2.

Young, Simon N.; Joffe, Russell T. Ethical conduct of journal editors [editorial]. *Journal of Psychiatry and Neuroscience* 2004 September; 29(5): 334-336. NRCBL: 1.3.7; 6; 1.3.9.

JUSTICE *See* RESOURCE ALLOCATION; RIGHT TO HEALTH CARE

LEGAL ASPECTS *See* ABORTION/ LEGAL ASPECTS; BIOETHICS AND MEDICAL ETHICS/ LEGAL ASPECTS; CLONING/ LEGAL ASPECTS; EUTHANASIA AND ALLOWING TO DIE/ LEGAL ASPECTS; GENETICS/ LEGAL ASPECTS; HUMAN EXPERIMENTATION/ ETHICS COMMITTEES AND POLICY GUIDELINES/ LEGAL ASPECTS; ORGAN AND TISSUE TRANSPLANTATION/ DONATION AND PROCUREMENT/ LEGAL ASPECTS

LIVING WILLS *See* ADVANCE DIRECTIVES

MALPRACTICE AND PROFESSIONAL MISCONDUCT
See also BIOMEDICAL RESEARCH/ RESEARCH ETHICS AND SCIENTIFIC MISCONDUCT

Appel, Jacob M. May physicians date their patients' relatives? Rethinking sexual misconduct and disclosure after Long v. Ostroff. *Medicine and Health, Rhode Island* 2004 May; 87(5): 159-161. NRCBL: 7.4; 8.1; 10; 8.2. SC: le.

Bayer, Timothy; Coverdale, John; Chiang, Elizabeth. A national survey of physicians' behaviors regarding sexual contact with patients. *Southern Medical Journal* 1996 October; 89(10): 977-982. NRCBL: 7.4; 8.1; 10. SC: em. Identifiers: United States.

Bleich, J. David. Medical malpractice and Jewish law. *Tradition* 2005 Spring; 39(1): 72-117. NRCBL: 8.5; 1.2.

Bloche, M. Gregg; Marks, Jonathan H. Doctors and interrogators at Guantanamo Bay [opinion]. *New England Journal of Medicine* 2005 July 7; 353(1): 6-8. NRCBL: 7.4; 21.4; 17.1; 1.3.5; 9.5.1; 8.4.

Bonner, Raymond. Deaths and a doctor's past transfix Australians. *New York Times* 2005 June 19; p. A1, A14. NRCBL: 7.4. SC: po.

Bottis, Maria Canellopoulou Vrachliotis. Return to basics: the cases of informed consent and lost chances of living [editorial]. *European Journal of Health Law* 2002 December; 9(4): 287-291. NRCBL: 8.5; 8.3.1. SC: le.

Castledine, George. Case of the deputy ward manager who broke patient confidentiality. *British Journal of Nursing* 2005 October 27-November 9; 14(19): 1033. NRCBL: 7.4; 8.4. SC: cs.

Crausman, Robert S. Sexual boundary violations in the physician-patient relationship. *Medicine and Health, Rhode Island* 2004 August; 87(8): 255-256. NRCBL: 7.4; 8.1; 10. SC: le.

Dauer, Edward A. Ethical misfits: mediation and medical malpractice litigation. *In:* Sharpe, Virginia A., ed. Accountability: Patient Safety and Policy Reform. Washington, DC: Georgetown University Press; 2004: 185-201. NRCBL: 8.5; 9.8; 7.1.

Donohoe, Martin. Urine trouble: practical, legal, and ethical issues surrounding mandated drug testing of physicians. *Journal of Clinical Ethics* 2005 Spring; 16(1): 85-96. NRCBL: 7.4; 9.5.9; 8.4.

Galletly, Cherrie A. Crossing professional boundaries in medicine: the slippery slope to patient sexual exploitation. *Medical Journal of Australia* 2004 October 4; 181(7): 380-383. NRCBL: 7.4; 8.1; 10.

Gallop, Ruth. Abuse of power in the nurse-client relationship. *Nursing Standard* 1998 June 3-9; 12(37): 43-47. NRCBL: 7.4; 8.1; 4.1.3; 10; 1.3.5.

Glater, Jonathan D. In a surgery capital, a swirl of fraud charges. *New York Times* 2005 July 10; p. BU1, BU4. NRCBL: 7.4; 9.3.1. SC: po.

Hoffman, David N. The medical malpractice insurance crisis, again. *Hastings Center Report* 2005 March-April; 35(2): 15-19. NRCBL: 8.5; 9.3.1; 9.8.

Horton, Richard. A dismal and dangerous verdict against Roy Meadow. *Lancet* 2005 July 23-29; 366(9482): 277-278. NRCBL: 7.4; 7.3; 1.3.5.

Johnstone, Megan-Jane; Kanitsaki, Olga. Processes for disciplining nurses for unprofessional conduct of a serious nature: a critique. *Journal of Advanced Nursing* 2005 May; 50(4): 363-371. NRCBL: 7.4; 7.1. SC: em; le. Identifiers: Australia.

Jones, James W.; McCullough, Laurence B.; Richman, Bruce W. Ethical nuances of combining romance with medical practice. *Journal of Vascular Surgery* 2005 January; 41(1): 174-175. NRCBL: 7.4; 8.1; 10. SC: cs.

Marshall, Eliot. Flawed statistics in murder trial may cost expert his medical license [news]. *Science* 2005 July 22; 309(5734): 543. NRCBL: 7.4; 9.5.7. SC: le. Identifiers: Roy Meadow.

Neal, Joseph M. Author misconduct — a continuing saga [editorial]. *Regional Anesthesia and Pain Medicine* 2004 March-April; 29(2): 90-91. NRCBL: 7.4; 1.3.7; 1.3.9.

Norcross, William A.; Ganiats, Theodore G. Illness and secrecy on the Supreme Court [letter]. *New England Journal of Medicine* 2005 March 31; 352(13): 1388. NRCBL: 7.4.

Papdakis, Maxine A.; Teherani, Arianne; Banach, Mary A.; Knettler, Timothy R.; Rattner, Susan L.; Stern, David T.; Veloski, J. Jon; Hodgson, Carol S. Disciplinary action by medical boards and prior behavior in medical school. *New England Journal of Medicine* 2005 December 22; 353(25): 2673-2682. NRCBL: 7.4; 7.2. SC: em.

Abstract: BACKGROUND: Evidence supporting professionalism as a critical measure of competence in medical education is limited. In this case-control study, we investigated the association of disciplinary action against practicing physicians with prior unprofessional behavior in medical school. We also examined the specific types of behavior that are most predictive of disciplinary action against practicing physicians with unprofessional behavior in medical school. METHODS: The study included 235 graduates of three medical schools who were disciplined by one of 40 state medical boards between 1990 and 2003 (case physicians). The 469 control physicians were matched with the case physicians according to medical school and graduation year. Predictor variables from medical school included the presence or absence of narratives describing unprofessional behavior, grades, standardized-test scores, and demographic characteristics. Narratives were assigned an overall rating for unprofessional behavior. Those that met the threshold for unprofessional behavior were further classified among eight types of behavior and assigned a severity rating (moderate to severe). RESULTS: Disciplinary action by a medical board was strongly associated with prior unprofessional behavior in medical school (odds ratio, 3.0; 95 percent confidence interval, 1.9 to 4.8), for a population attributable risk of disciplinary action of 26 percent. The types of unprofessional behavior most strongly linked with disciplinary action were severe irresponsibility (odds ratio, 8.5; 95 percent confidence interval, 1.8 to 40.1) and severely diminished capacity for self-improvement (odds ratio, 3.1; 95 percent confidence interval, 1.2 to 8.2). Disciplinary action by a medical board was also associated with low scores on the Medical College Admission Test and poor grades in the first two years of medical school (1 percent and 7 percent population attributable risk, respectively), but the association with these variables was less strong than that with unprofessional behavior. CONCLUSIONS: In this case-control study, disciplinary action among practicing physicians by medical boards was strongly associated with unprofessional behavior in medical school. Students with the strongest association were those who were described as irresponsible or as having diminished ability to improve their behavior. Professionalism should have a central role in medical academics and throughout one's medical career.

Pogash, Carol. A California murder case raises troubling issues. *New York Times* 2005 September 18; p. A14. NRCBL: 7.4; 8.1; 10. 17.2. SC: po.

Rice, Berkeley. Publishing physician profiles: what's fair? *Medical Economics* 2004 December 17; 81(24): 16-19. NRCBL: 7.4; 1.3.12; 1.3.7.

Shavit, Natalie; Bucky, Steven; Danielian, Jack. Sexual contact between psychologists and their former therapy patients: psychoanalytic perspectives and professional implications. *American Journal of Psychoanalysis* 2004 September; 64(3): 229-251. NRCBL: 7.4; 8.1; 17.2; 10. SC: em.

Somer, Eli; Saadon, Meir. Therapist-client sex: clients' retrospective reports. *Professional Psychology: Research and Practice* 1999 October; 30(5): 504-509. NRCBL: 7.4; 17.2. SC: em.

Studdert, David M. On selling "no-fault.". *In:* Sharpe, Virginia A., ed. Accountability: Patient Safety and Policy

NRCBL: National Reference Center for Bioethics Literature Classification Scheme   See inside front cover for terms.

339

Reform. Washington, DC: Georgetown University Press; 2004: 203-212. NRCBL: 8.5; 9.8; 7.1.

ter Heerdt, J. Ethics and medical liability: a minefield for physicians? *Acta Clinica Belgica* 2002 June-July; 57(3): 117-125. NRCBL: 8.5; 8.3.1; 9.8; 7.1. SC: le. Identifiers: Belgium.

Thompson, Richard E. Misbehaving physicians and professional ethics. *Physician Executive* 2004 September-October; 30(5): 32-34. NRCBL: 7.4; 7.3. SC: cs.

Vogel, Gretchen. Collaborators split over ethics allegations [news]. *Science* 2005 November 19; 310(5751): 1100. NRCBL: 7.4; 1.3.9; 14.5; 18.5.4; 19.1; 19.5. Identifiers: Woo-Suk Hwang; Gerald Schatten.

Waldinger, Robert J. Boundary crossings and boundary violations: thoughts on navigating a slippery slope. *Harvard Review of Psychiatry* 1994 November-December; 2(4): 225-227. NRCBL: 7.4; 17.2; 8.1; 1.1. SC: cs.

Watson, Donald C., Jr.; Robicsek, Francis; Sade, Robert M. Are thoracic surgeons ethically obligated to serve as expert witnesses for the plaintiff? [debate]. *Annals of Thoracic Surgery* 2004 October; 78(4): 1137-1141. NRCBL: 8.5; 7.3. SC: cs; le.

Wilcoxon, Kimberly D. Statutory remedies for judicial torts: the need for wrongful birth legislation. *University of Cincinnati Law Review* 2001 Spring; 69(3): 1023-1053. NRCBL: 8.5; 11.4; 15.2. SC: le.

MASS SCREENING *See* PUBLIC HEALTH

MEDICAL EDUCATION
See also BIOETHICS AND MEDICAL ETHICS/ EDUCATION

Al-Dwairi, Ziad Nawaf; Al-Waheidi, E.M. Cheating behaviors of dental students. *Journal of Dental Education* 2004 November; 68(11): 1192-1195. NRCBL: 7.2; 4.1.1. SC: em. Identifiers: Jordan.

Ananthakrishnan, N. The ethics of live operative workshops [letter]. *National Medical Journal of India* 2003 November-December; 16(6): 340. NRCBL: 7.2; 2.1.

Ananthakrishnan, N. The ethics of live operative workshops [reply]. *National Medical Journal of India* 2004; 17(4): 224-225. NRCBL: 7.2; 2.1.

Anderson, Rebecca Cogwell; Fox, Robert. Ethical issues in health promotion and health education. *AAOHN Journal* 1987 May; 35(5): 220-223, 246-248. NRCBL: 7.2; 2.3; 1.1.

Atlas, Michel C. Ethics and access to teaching materials in the medical library: the case of the Pernkopf atlas. *Bulletin of the Medical Library Association* 2001 January; 89(1): 51-58. NRCBL: 7.2; 1.3.12.

Benatar, Solomon R. The humanities in medicine at UCT [editorial]. *South African Medical Journal* 1997 December; 87(12): 1662-1664. NRCBL: 7.2. Identifiers: University of Cape Town.

Bertolami, Charles N. Further dialogue on ethics in dental education: a response to the Koerber et al. and Jenson articles. *Journal of Dental Education* 2005 February; 69(2): 229-231. NRCBL: 7.2; 4.1.1.

Bishop, M.G.H.; Gelbier, S. Ethics: how the Apothecaries Act of 1815 shaped the dental profession. Part 1. The apothecaries and the emergence of the profession of dentistry. *British Dental Journal* 2002 December 7; 193(11): 627-631. NRCBL: 7.2; 4.1.1.

Bishop, Malcolm G.H.; Gelbier, S. Ethics: how the Apothecaries Act of 1815 shaped the dental profession. Part 2. The chemist-dentists and the education of dentists. *British Dental Journal* 2002 December 21; 193(12): 683-686. NRCBL: 7.2; 4.1.1.

Bore, Miles; Munro, Don; Kerridge, Ian; Powis, David. Selection of medical students according to their moral orientation. *Medical Education* 2005 March; 39(3): 266-275. NRCBL: 7.2; 1.1. SC: em.

Borman, Karen R. Professionalism in the match process: the rules and ethics of recruitment. *Surgical Clinics of North America* 2004 December; 84(6): 1511-1523, ix. NRCBL: 7.2; 4.1.2.

Breen, Kerry J. Professional development and ethics for today's and tomorrow's doctors [editorial]. *Medical Journal of Australia* 2001 August 20; 175(4): 183-184. NRCBL: 7.2; 2.3; 4.1.2.

Burazeri, Genc; Civljak, Marta; Ilakovac, Vesna; Jankovic, Slobodan; Majica-Kovacevic, Tanja; Nedera, Olesea; Roshi, Enver; Sava, Valeriu; Šimunovic, Vladimir; Marušic, Ana; Marušic, Matko. Survey of attitudes and knowledge about science in medical students in southeast Europe. *BMJ: British Medical Journal* 2005 July 23; 331(7510): 195-196. NRCBL: 7.2; 18.1; 21.1. SC: em.

Caan, Woody. A testing time for ethical standards [letter]. *BMJ: British Medical Journal* 2005 June 25; 330(7506): 1510. NRCBL: 7.2; 2.3.

Carek, Peter J.; Anderson, Kimberly D.; Blue, Amy V.; Mavis, Brian E. Recruitment behavior and program directors: how ethical are their perspectives about the match process? *Family Medicine* 2000 April; 32(4): 258-260. NRCBL: 7.2; 1.3.2; 7.3. SC: em.

Cash, Richard. Ethical issues in health workforce development. *Bulletin of the World Health Organization* 2005 April; 83(4): 280-284. NRCBL: 7.2; 21.1.

Catton, Michelle. Medical schools tackle conflict of interest [news]. *CMAJ/JAMC: Canadian Medical Association*

Journal 2005 November 8; 173(10): 1143. NRCBL: 7.2; 9.7; 7.3.

Ceaser, Mike. Sun, sand, and an M.D. [news]. *Chronicle of Higher Education* 2005 October 28; 52(10): 55-60. NRCBL: 7.2; 1.3.2; 1.3.3; 21.1.

Chambers, Tod; Watson, Katie; Verkerk, Marian. Enhancing reflection [letter and reply]. *Hastings Center Report* 2005 July-August; 35(4): 6, 7. NRCBL: 7.2.

Colvin, Brian T. Why we do not need a Hippocratic Oath. *Medical Education* 2003 December; 37(12): 1125-1126. NRCBL: 7.2; 6; 7.1.

Cooper, Richard A.; Tauber, Alfred I. New physicians for a new century [opinion]. *Academic Medicine* 2005 December; 80(12): 1086-1088. NRCBL: 7.2; 4.1.2; 2.3.

Coward, Harold; Hartrick, Gwen. Perspectives on health and cultural pluralism: ethics in medical education. *Clinical and Investigative Medicine/ Medecine Clinique et Experimentale* 2000 August; 23(4): 261-265. NRCBL: 7.2; 9.1; 21.7.

Coxe, Mattie Fincher; Ubel, Peter A.; Silver-Isenstadt, Ari. A change in medical student attitudes of obstetrics-gynecology clerkships toward seeking consent for pelvic examinations on an anesthetized patient [letter and reply]. *American Journal of Obstetrics and Gynecology* 2003 December; 189(6): 1808-1809. NRCBL: 7.2; 9.5.5; 8.3.1.

Davidson, Graham; Garton, Alison F.; Joyce, Marie. Survey of ethics education in Australian university schools and departments of psychology. *Australian Psychologist* 2003 November; 38(3): 216-222. NRCBL: 7.2; 17.1.

Dickinson, George E.; Field, David. Teaching end-of-life issues: current status in United Kingdom and United States medical schools. *American Journal of Hospice and Palliative Care* 2002 May-June; 19(3): 181-186. NRCBL: 7.2; 20.4.1; 20.5.1. SC: em.

Dutra, Margarida Maria Dantas; Bonfim, T.A.S.; Pereira, I.S.; Figueiredo, I.C.; Dutra, A.M.D.; Lopes, A.A. Knowledge about transplantation and attitudes toward organ donation: a survey among medical students in Northeast Brazil. *Transplantation Proceedings* 2004 May; 36(4): 818-820. NRCBL: 7.2; 19.1; 19.5; 7.1. SC: em.

Eidelman, Leonid A.; Jakobson, Daniel J.; Worner, T.M.; Pizov, Reuven; Geber, Debora; Sprung, Charles L. End-of-life intensive care unit decisions, communication, and documentation: an evaluation of physician training. *Journal of Critical Care* 2003 March; 18(1): 11-16. NRCBL: 7.2; 20.5.1. SC: em. Identifiers: Israel.

Evans, Bronwynne C.; Bendel, Robert. Cognitive and ethical maturity in baccalaureate nursing students: did a class using Narrative Pedagogy make a difference? *Nursing Education Perspectives* 2004 July-August; 25(4): 188-195. NRCBL: 7.2; 4.1.3. SC: em.

Fitzgerald, Faith. An academic clinician's perspective on the care of the geriatric patient. *Health Care Analysis: An International Journal of Health Care Philosophy and Policy* 2005 June; 13(2): 95-100. NRCBL: 7.2; 9.5.2; 2.2.

Abstract: This paper discusses the role that the personal history plays in a patient's perception of his or her own illness in the light of the patient's own personal history. It demonstrates the regrettable modern tendency to regards the patient as the "bearer of a disease" rather than as a human being with personal values and experiences into which their current illness needs to be integrated. I illustrate my point by an exchange between a student and an "attending" and the "attending" and the patient. It represents only one out of unfortunately many such instances in which the pressures of "managed care" and "efficiency" have made truly knowing the patient as an individual with life experiences and personal values much more difficult.

Fitzgerald, Paul. Sex, lies and training programs: the ethics of consensual sexual relationships between psychiatrists and trainee psychiatrists [letter]. *Australian and New Zealand Journal of Psychiatry* 1999 February; 33(1): 119-120. NRCBL: 7.2; 10; 17.1.

Fleetwood, Janet; Novack, Dennis; Templeton, Bryce. Bringing medical ethics to life: an educational programme using standardised patients. *Medical Education* 2002 November; 36(11): 1100-1101. NRCBL: 7.2; 2.3; 8.1.

Fox, Renée C. Cultural competence and the culture of medicine [opinion]. *New England Journal of Medicine* 2005 September 29; 353(13): 1316-1319. NRCBL: 7.2; 7.1; 21.7.

Ginsburg, Shiphra; Kachan, Natasha; Lingard, Lorelei. Before the white coat: perceptions of professional lapses in the pre-clerkship. *Medical Education* 2005 January; 39(1): 12-19. NRCBL: 7.2; 7.3. SC: em. Identifiers: Canada.

Goel, Ashish. Consent for intimate examinations [letter]. *Issues in Medical Ethics* 2003 October-December; 11(4): 134. NRCBL: 7.2; 8.3.1.

Goldie, John G.S. The detrimental ethical shift towards cynicism: can medical educators help prevent it? [opinion]. *Medical Education* 2004 March; 38(3): 232-234. NRCBL: 7.2; 8.1; 4.1.2.

Goldie, John; Schwartz, Lisa; McConnachie, Alex; Morrison, Jillian. The impact of three years' ethics teaching, in an integrated medical curriculum, on students' proposed behaviour on meeting ethical dilemmas. *Medical Education* 2002 May; 36(5): 489-497. NRCBL: 7.2; 2.3.

Grover, Michael; Dharamshi, Farah; Goveia, Crystal. Deception by applicants to family practice residencies. *Family Medicine* 2001 June; 33(6): 441-446. NRCBL: 7.2; 1.3.2; 7.3. SC: em.

Grudzen, Corita R. One resident perspective: resident education and the pharmaceutical industry. *Annals of Emergency Medicine* 2005 January; 45(1): 27-31. NRCBL: 7.2; 9.7; 1.3.2; 9.3.1.

NRCBL: National Reference Center for Bioethics Literature Classification Scheme   See inside front cover for terms.

341

Hassenfeld, Irwin N. Ethics and the role of the supervisor of psychotherapy. *Journal of Psychiatric Education* 1987; 11(2): 73-77. NRCBL: 7.2; 8.1; 17.2.

Holt, Janet; Long, Tony. Moral guidance, moral philosophy, and moral issues in practice. *Nurse Education Today* 1999 April; 19(3): 246-249. NRCBL: 7.2; 2.3; 4.1.3.

Hoop, Jinger G. Hidden ethical dilemmas in psychiatric residency training: the psychiatry resident as dual agent. *Academic Psychiatry* 2004 Fall; 28(3): 183-189. NRCBL: 7.2; 7.3; 17.1.

Hope, Tony; Frith, Peggy; Craze, Janet; Mussai, Francis; Chadha-Gupta, Ambika; Noble, Douglas. Developing guidelines for medical students about the examination of patients under 18 years old. *BMJ: British Medical Journal* 2005 December 10; 331(7529): 1384-1386. NRCBL: 7.2; 9.5.7.

Hrabak, Maja; Vujaklija, Ana; Vodopivec, Ivana; Hren, Darko; Marušic, Matko; Marušic, Ana. Academic misconduct among medical students in a post-communist country. *Medical Education* 2004 March; 38(3): 276-285. NRCBL: 7.2. Identifiers: Croatia.

Jenson, Larry E. Why our ethics curricula do work. *Journal of Dental Education* 2005 February; 69(2): 225-228. NRCBL: 7.2; 4.1.1.

Karmarkar, Santosh J. Learning 'on' patients: medical education cannot be at the patient's expense. *Issues in Medical Ethics* 1999 January-March; 7(1): 23-24. NRCBL: 7.2; 8.3.1.

Karseth, Berit. Curriculum changes and moral issues in nursing education. *Nurse Education Today* 2004 November; 24(8): 638-643. NRCBL: 7.2; 4.1.3. Identifiers: Norway.

Kirk, Lynne M.; Blank, Linda L. Professional behavior — a learner's permit for licensure [editorial]. *New England Journal of Medicine* 2005 December 22; 353(25): 2709-2711. NRCBL: 7.2; 7.4.

Kocieniewski, David. New Jersey med school board faces ethics charges. *New York Times* 2005 September 23; p. B1, B7. NRCBL: 7.2; 1.3.1; 9.3.1. SC: po.

Koerber, Anne; Botto, Ronald W.; Pendleton, Darryl D.; Albazzaz, Michael B.; Doshi, Siddhi J.; Rinando, Victoria A. Enhancing ethical behavior: views of students, administrators, and faculty. *Journal of Dental Education* 2005 February; 69(2): 213-224. NRCBL: 7.2; 4.1.1.

Landro, Laura. Teaching doctors to be nicer; new accreditation rules spur medical schools to beef up interpersonal-skills training. *Wall Street Journal* 2005 September 28; p. D1, D4. NRCBL: 7.2; 8.1. SC: po.

Le Morvan, Pierre; Stock, B. Medical learning curves and the Kantian ideal. *Journal of Medical Ethics* 2005 September; 31(9): 513-518. NRCBL: 7.2; 8.1; 1.1. SC: an.
Abstract: A hitherto unexamined problem for the "Kantian ideal" that one should always treat patients as ends in themselves, and never only as a means to other ends, is explored in this paper. The problem consists of a prima facie conflict between this Kantian ideal and the reality of medical practice. This conflict arises because, at least presently, medical practitioners can only acquire certain skills and abilities by practising on live, human patients, and given the inevitability and ubiquity of learning curves, this learning requires some patients to be treated only as a means to this end. A number of ways of attempting to establish the compatibility of the Kantian Ideal with the reality of medical practice are considered. Each attempt is found to be unsuccessful. Accordingly, until a way is found to reconcile them, we conclude that the Kantian ideal is inconsistent with the reality of medical practice.

Lewenson, Sandra B.; Truglio-Londrigan, Marie; Singleton, Joanne. Practice what you teach: a case study of ethical conduct in the academic setting. *Journal of Professional Nursing* 2005 March-April; 21(2): 89-96. NRCBL: 7.2; 4.1.3.

Linck, Jeanette C. Confidentiality, professionalism, ethics and the student. *Journal of AHIMA* 1993 December; 64(12): 67-68. NRCBL: 7.2; 8.4; 1.3.12.

Magotra, Ratna. Sponsorships for medical specialists. *Issues in Medical Ethics* 1997 October-December; 5(4): 122-125. NRCBL: 7.2; 9.3.1; 1.3.2; 9.7.

Mamdani, Meenal B.; Mamdani, Bashir. Commercial support for continuing medical education. *Issues in Medical Ethics* 1997 April-June; 5(2): 43-45. NRCBL: 7.2; 1.3.2; 9.3.1; 9.7.

Marco, Catherine A. Ethics seminars: teaching professionalism to "problem" residents. *Academic Emergency Medicine* 2002 October; 9(10): 1001-1006. NRCBL: 7.2; 1.3.1. SC: em.

Martin, Jonathan; Lloyd, Margaret; Singh, Surinder. Professional attitudes: can they be taught and assessed in medical education? *Clinical Medicine* 2002 May-June; 2(3): 217-223. NRCBL: 7.2; 4.1.2.

Marušic, Ana. Commentary: ethics in health care and research in European transition countries: reality and future prospects. *BMJ: British Medical Journal* 2005 July 23; 331(7510): 230. NRCBL: 7.2; 1.3.3; 21.1.

Mayeda, Mayumi; Takase, Kozo. Need for enforcement of ethicolegal education — an analysis of the survey of postgraduate clinical trainees. *BMC Medical Ethics [electronic]* 2005; 6(8); 12 p. Available: http://www.biomedcentral.com/bmcmedethics/ [6 September 2005]. NRCBL: 7.2; 8.5. SC: em.
Abstract: BACKGROUND: The number of medical lawsuits in Japan was between 14 and 21 each year before 1998, but increased to 24 to 35 per year after 1999. There were 210 lawsuits during this 10-year period. There is a need for skills and knowledge related to ethics, which is as fundamental to the practice of

---

medicine as basic sciences or clinical skills. In Japan education in ethics is relatively rare and its importance is not yet recognized. Establishing ethics education using legal precedents, which has already been achieved in Western countries, will be a very important issue in Japan. In the present study, a questionnaire survey was conducted among graduate intern doctors, in order to investigate whether ethics education using precedents might have a positive effect in Japan. METHODS: In 2002, a questionnaire survey entitled Physicians' Clinical Ethics was carried out in a compulsory orientation lecture given to trainees before they started clinical practice in our hospital. The attendees at this lecture were trainees who came from colleges in various districts of Japan. During the lecture, 102 questionnaires were distributed, completed by attendees and collected. The recovery rate was 100%. The questionnaire consisted of 22 questions (in three categories), of which 20 were answered by multiple choices, and the other two were answered by description. The time required to complete the questionnaire was about 10 minutes. RESULTS: The recovered questionnaires were analyzed using statistical analysis software (SPSS for Windows, Release 10.07J-1/June/2000), in addition to simple statistical analysis. Answers using multiple choices for the 20 questions in the questionnaire were input into SPSS. The principal component analysis was performed for each question. As a result, the item that came to the fore was "legal precedent". Since many intern doctors were interested in understanding laws and precedents, learning about ethical considerations through education using precedents might better meet with their needs and interests. CONCLUSION: We applied a new method in which the results of principal component analysis and frequencies of answers to other questions were combined. From this we deduced that the precedent education used in Western countries was useful to help doctors acquire ethical sensitivity and was not against their will. A relationship was found between reading precedents and the influence of lawsuits, and it was thought that student participation-type precedent education would be useful for doctors in order to acquire ethical sensitivity.

Notzer, Netta; Abramovitch, Henry; Dado-Harari, Roni; Abramovitz, Ruth; Rudnick, Abraham. Medical students' ethical, legal and cross-cultural experiences during their clinical studies. *Israel Medical Association Journal* 2005 January; 7(1): 58-61. NRCBL: 7.2; 2.3; 21.7. SC: em.

O'Brien, Eoin. Human rights and the making of a good doctor. *In:* Cahill, Kevin M., ed. Traditions, Values, and Humanitarian Action. New York: Fordham University Press and The Center for International Health and Cooperation; 2003: 136-152. NRCBL: 7.2; 2.1; 21.1.

O'Flynn, Norma; Rymer, Janice. Consent for teaching: the experience of women attending a gynaecology clinic. *Medical Education* 2003 December; 37(12): 1109-1114. NRCBL: 7.2; 9.5.5; 8.1.

Overby, Philip. The moral education of doctors. *New Atlantis* 2005 Fall; 10: 17-26. NRCBL: 7.2; 4.1.2.

Parker, Lisa M. What's wrong with the dead body? Use of the human cadaver in medical education [opinion]. *Medical Journal of Australia* 2002 January 21; 176(2): 74-76. NRCBL: 7.2; 20.1.

Peraud, Peter J.; Kulstad, Erik B. Another resident perspective: resident education and the pharmaceutical indus-

try. *Annals of Emergency Medicine* 2005 January; 45(1): 32-36. NRCBL: 7.2; 9.7; 1.3.2; 9.3.1.

Piccoli, Giorgina Barbara; Soragna, G.; Mezza, E.; Putaggio, S.; Garelli, G.; Bermond, F.; Burdese, M.; Jeantet, A.; Vercellone, F.; Segoloni, G.P.; Piccoli, G. Ethics of transplantation in the medical school: a pilot study. *International Journal of Artificial Organs* 2004 November; 27(11): 1003-1004. NRCBL: 7.2; 19.1. SC: em. Identifiers: Italy.

Pronchik, David J.; Melanson, Scott W.; Sexton, Joseph. Practicing emergency procedures on recently deceased patients [letter]. *Prehospital and Disaster Medicine* 1996 April-June; 11(2): 121-122. NRCBL: 7.2; 8.3.1; 20.1. SC: em.

Radstone, S.J.J. Practising on the poor? Healthcare workers' beliefs about the role of medical students during their elective. *Journal of Medical Ethics* 2005 February; 31(2): 109-110. NRCBL: 7.2; 9.5.10; 21.7. SC: em.

Ramesh, H. Live operative workshops: ethical issues [letter]. *National Medical Journal of India* 2004; 17(4): 224. NRCBL: 7.2; 2.1. Identifiers: India.

Rogers, Wendy A.; Mansfield, Peter R.; Braunack-Mayer, Annette J.; Jureidini, Jon N. The ethics of pharmaceutical industry relationships with medical students. *Medical Journal of Australia* 2004 April 19; 180: 411-414. NRCBL: 7.2; 9.7.

Rosner, Fred. Research and training on the newly dead [letter]. *Archives of Pathology and Laboratory Medicine* 1997 October; 121(10): 1029. NRCBL: 7.2; 20.3.2.

Rubens, Arthur J.; Wimberley, Edward T. Contrasting the American College of Healthcare Executives' code of ethics with undergraduate health administration students' values and ethical decision choices. *Hospital Topics* 2004 Summer; 82(3): 10-17. NRCBL: 7.2; 4.1.1; 6. SC: em.

Santen, Sally A.; Hemphill, Robin R.; Spanier, Cindy M.; Fletcher, Nicholas D. 'Sorry, it's my first time!' Will patients consent to medical students learning procedures? *Medical Education* 2005 April; 39(4): 365-369. NRCBL: 7.2; 8.3.1; 8.1. SC: em.

Schaffer, Marjorie A.; Juárez, Maureen. An ethical analysis of student-faculty interactions. *Nurse Educator* 1993 May-June; 18(3): 25-28. NRCBL: 7.2; 4.1.3.

Schneider, Gregory W.; Snell, Laura. C.A.R.E.: an approach for teaching ethics in medicine. *Social Science and Medicine* 2000 November 16; 51(10): 1563-1567. NRCBL: 7.2; 2.3.

Schuh, Lori A.; Burdette, David E. Initiation of an effective neurology resident ethics curriculum. *Neurology* 2004 May 25; 62(10): 1897-1898. NRCBL: 7.2; 2.3; 17.1.

NRCBL: National Reference Center for Bioethics Literature Classification Scheme   See inside front cover for terms.

343

Shannon, Sarah E.; Verkerk, Marian. Enhancing reflection [letter and reply]. *Hastings Center Report* 2005 July-August; 35(4): 6-7. NRCBL: 7.2.

Snelling, Paul C.; Lipscomb, Martin. Academic freedom, analysis, and the Code of Professional Conduct. *Nurse Education Today* 2004 November; 24(8): 615-621. NRCBL: 7.2; 1.3.3.

Society for Academic Emergency Medicine [SAEM]. Board of Directors; Schmidt, Terri A.; Abbott, Jean T.; Geiderman, Joel M.; Hughes, Jason A.; Johnson, Catherine X.; McClure, Katie B.; McKay, Mary P.; Razzak, Junaid A.; Salo, David; Schears, Raquel M.; Solomon, Robert C. Ethics seminars: the ethical debate on practicing procedures on the newly dead. *Academic Emergency Medicine* 2004 September; 11(9): 962-966. NRCBL: 7.2; 8.3.3; 20.1.

Steinbrook, Robert. Commercial support and continuing medical education [opinion]. *New England Journal of Medicine* 2005 February 10; 352(6): 534- 535. NRCBL: 7.2; 9.7.

Sulmasy, Daniel P.; Ferris, Robert E.; Ury, Wayne A. Confidence and knowledge of medical ethics among interns entering residency in different specialties. *Journal of Clinical Ethics* 2005 Fall; 16(3): 230-235. NRCBL: 7.2; 2.1. SC: em.

Talukder, Md Humayun Kabir; Chowdhury, Fatima Parveen; Shuvra Muhammad Mizanur Rashid. Teachers' views of WHO teaching guidelines on health ethics for undergraduate medical education in Bangladesh. *Indian Journal of Medical Ethics* 2005 April-June; 2(2): 54. NRCBL: 7.2; 2.3. Identifiers: World Health Organization.

Tervo, Raymond C.; Palmer, Glen; Redinius, Pat. Health professional student attitudes towards people with disability. *Clinical Rehabilitation* 2004 December; 18(8): 908-915. NRCBL: 7.2; 9.5.1; 8.1. SC: em.

Thomas, James C. Teaching ethics in schools of public health. *Public Health Reports* 2003 May-June; 118(3): 279-286. NRCBL: 7.2; 2.1; 1.1; 9.1.

Udwadia, F.E. Ethical problems in medical education. *Issues in Medical Ethics* 1997 April-June; 5(2): 37-39. NRCBL: 7.2.

Watson, Peter Y.; Khandelwal, Akshay K.; Musial, Joseph L.; Buckley, John D. Brief report: resident and faculty perceptions of conflict of interest in medical education. *JGIM: Journal of General Internal Medicine* 2005 April; 20(4): 357-359. NRCBL: 7.2; 7.3; 9.7. SC: em.

Weissman, Joel S.; Betancourt, Joseph; Campbell, Eric G.; Park, Elyse R.; Kim, Minah; Clarridge, Brian; Blumenthal, David; Lee, Karen C.; Maina, Angela W. Resident physicians' preparedness to provide cross-cultural care. *JAMA: The Journal of the American Medical Association* 2005 September 7; 294(9): 1058-1067. NRCBL: 7.2; 9.5.4; 21.7. SC: em.

Abstract: CONTEXT: Two recent reports from the Institute of Medicine cited cross-cultural training as a mechanism to address racial and ethnic disparities in health care, but little is known about residents' educational experience in this area. OBJECTIVE: To assess residents' attitudes about cross-cultural care, perceptions of their preparedness to deliver quality care to diverse patient populations, and educational experiences and educational climate regarding cross-cultural training. DESIGN, SETTING, AND PARTICIPANTS: A survey was mailed in the winter of 2003 to a stratified random sample of 3435 resident physicians in their final year of training in emergency medicine, family practice, internal medicine, obstetrics/gynecology, pediatrics, psychiatry, or general surgery at US academic health centers. RESULTS: Responses were obtained from 2047 (60%) of the sample. Virtually all (96%) of the residents indicated that it was moderately or very important to address cultural issues when providing care. The number of respondents who indicated that they believed they were not prepared to care for diverse cultures in a general sense was only 8%. However, a larger percentage of respondents believed they were not prepared to provide specific components of cross-cultural care, including caring for patients with health beliefs at odds with Western medicine (25%), new immigrants (25%), and patients whose religious beliefs affect treatment (20%). In addition, 24% indicated that they lacked the skills to identify relevant cultural customs that impact medical care. In contrast, only a small percentage of respondents (1%-2%) indicated that they were not prepared to treat clinical conditions or perform procedures common in their specialty. Approximately one third to half of the respondents reported receiving little or no instruction in specific areas of cross-cultural care beyond what was learned in medical school. Forty-one percent (family medicine) to 83% (surgery and obstetrics/gynecology) of respondents reported receiving little or no evaluation in cross-cultural care during their residencies. Barriers to delivering cross-cultural care included lack of time (58%) and lack of role models (31%). CONCLUSIONS: Resident physicians' self-reported preparedness to deliver cross-cultural care lags well behind preparedness in other clinical and technical areas. Although cross-cultural care was perceived to be important, there was little clinical time allotted during residency to address cultural issues, and there was little training, formal evaluation, or role modeling. These mixed educational messages indicate the need for significant improvement in cross-cultural education to help eliminate racial and ethnic disparities in health care.

Yentis, S.M. The use of patients for learning and maintaining practical skills. *Journal of the Royal Society of Medicine* 2005 July; 98(7): 299-302. NRCBL: 7.2; 9.8; 8.3.1.

MEDICAL ERRORS *See* HEALTH CARE QUALITY

MEDICAL ETHICS *See* BIOETHICS AND MEDICAL ETHICS

MENTAL HEALTH, CONCEPT OF
See also MENTAL HEALTH THERAPIES

Bartlett, Peter. The test of compulsion in mental health law: capacity, therapeutic benefit and dangerousness as possible criteria. *Medical Law Review* 2003 Autumn; 11(3): 326-352. NRCBL: 4.3; 17.7; 9.5.3. SC: le.

Grover, Sonja. Reification of psychiatric diagnoses as defamatory: implications for ethical clinical practice. *Ethical Human Psychology and Psychiatry* 2005 Spring; 7(1): 77-86. NRCBL: 4.3; 17.1; 8.4.

Hauerwas, Stanley. Should suffering be eliminated?: what the retarded have to teach us. *In:* Berkman, John; Cartwright, Michael, eds. The Hauerwas Reader. Durham, NC: Duke University Press; 2001: 556-576. NRCBL: 4.3; 9.5.3; 4.4. SC: an.

Parikh, Michelle. Burning the candle at both ends, and there is nothing left for proof: the Americans with Disabilities Act's disservice to persons with mental illness. *Cornell Law Review* 2004 March; 89(3): 721-762. NRCBL: 4.3; 17.1; 1.3.5. SC: le.

Prior, Pauline M. Dangerous lunacy: the misuse of mental health law in nineteenth-century Ireland. *Journal of Forensic Psychiatry and Psychology* 2003 December; 14(3): 525-541. NRCBL: 4.3; 17.7.

Reynolds, Carson; Picard, Rosalind. Ethical evaluation of displays that adapt to affect. *Cyberpsychology and Behavior* 2004 December; 7(6): 662-666. NRCBL: 4.3; 1.3.12; 5.2.

Rosenman, Stephen. Mental health law: an idea whose time has passed. *Australia and New Zealand Journal of Psychiatry* 1994 December; 28(4): 560-565. NRCBL: 4.3; 17.1. SC: le; an.

Ross, Patricia A. Sorting out the concept disorder. *Theoretical Medicine and Bioethics* 2005; 26(2): 115-140. NRCBL: 4.3. SC: an.

Abstract: Current debates concerning the concept of mental disorder involve many different philosophical issues. However, it is not always clear from these discussions how, or whether, these issues relate to one another, or in exactly what way they are important for the definition of disorder. This article aims to sort through some of the philosophical issues that arise in the current literature and provide a clarification of how these issues are related to one another and whether they are necessary for defining disorder. I argue that the main concern in defining disorder, namely demarcation, is obscured by a number of these other philosophical issues and that a focus on demarcation gives us a means of placing these other issues in a clarifying context.

Silberfeld, Michel. Vulnerable persons: measuring moral capacity. *In:* Thomasma, David C.; Weisstub, David N., eds. The Variables of Moral Capacity. Boston: Kluwer Academic Publishers; 2004: 203-215. NRCBL: 8.3.3; 4.3. SC: an.

Szasz, T. "Idiots, infants, and the insane": mental illness and legal incompetence. *Journal of Medical Ethics* 2005 February; 31(2): 78-81. NRCBL: 4.3. SC: an; le.

United Kingdom. Law Commission. Mental Incapacity Bill (draft). *Bulletin of Medical Ethics* 2003 October; (192): 22-24. NRCBL: 4.3; 17.1; 8.3.3; 20.5.1; 8.3.4; 20.5.4. SC: le.

Vollmann, Jochen; Bauer, A.; Danker-Hopfe, H.; Helmchen, H. Competence of mentally ill patients: a comparative empirical study. *Psychological Medicine* 2003 November; 33(8): 1463-1471. NRCBL: 4.3; 17.1; 8.3.3. SC: em.

Zigmond, A.; Holland, A.J. Unethical mental health law; history repeats itself. *Journal of Mental Health Law* 2000 February: 50-57. NRCBL: 4.3; 8.3.3. SC: le.

MENTAL HEALTH THERAPIES

See also BEHAVIOR CONTROL; CARE FOR SPECIFIC GROUPS/ MENTALLY DISABLED; ELECTROCONVULSIVE THERAPY; HUMAN EXPERIMENTATION/ SPECIAL POPULATIONS/ MENTALLY DISABLED; INVOLUNTARY COMMITMENT; MENTAL HEALTH, CONCEPT OF; PSYCHOPHARMACOLOGY; PSYCHOTHERAPY

Albee, George W. Call to revolution in the prevention of emotional disorders. *Ethical Human Psychology and Psychiatry* 2005 Spring; 7(1): 37-44. NRCBL: 17.1; 7.1; 17.2; 9.1. SC: an.

American Psychological Association. Presidential Task Force. Report of the American Psychological Association Presidential Task Force on Psychological Ethics and National Security. Washington, DC: The Association 2005 June; 12 p. [Online]. Available: http://www.apa.org/releases/PENSTaskForceReportFinal.pdf [2 March 2006]. NRCBL: 17.1; 1.3.5.

Appelbaum, Paul S. Assessing Kendra's law: five years of outpatient commitment in New York. *Psychiatric Services* 2005 July; 56(7): 791-792. NRCBL: 17.1; 8.3.4. SC: le.

Baldwin, Clive; Hughes, Julian; Hope, Tony; Jacoby, Robin; Ziebland, Sue. Ethics and dementia: mapping the literature by bibliometric analysis. *International Journal of Geriatric Psychiatry* 2003 January; 18(1): 41-54. NRCBL: 17.1; 9.5.2; 18.1. SC: rv.

Biernacki, Claire. Should dementia patients be informed about their diagnosis? *Professional Nurse* 2003 December; 19(4): 198-202. NRCBL: 17.1; 8.2; 8.1; 9.5.2.

Boire, Richard G. Searching the brain: the Fourth Amendment implications of brain-based deception detection devices. *American Journal of Bioethics* 2005 March-April; 5(2): 62-63. NRCBL: 17.1; 5.3; 1.1; 1.3.5. SC: le. Comments: comment on Paul Root Wolpe, Kenneth R. Foster, and Daniel D. Langleben, "Emerging neurotechnologies for lie-detection: promises and perils," American Journal of Bioethics 2005 March-April; 5(2): 39-49.

Buelow, George D.; Chafetz, Michael D. Proposed ethical practice guidelines for clinical pharmacopsychology: sharpening a new focus in psychology. *Professional Psy-*

NRCBL: National Reference Center for Bioethics Literature Classification Scheme   See inside front cover for terms.

345

chology: Research and Practice 1996 February; 27(1): 53-58. NRCBL: 17.1; 9.7; 17.4; 6.

Buford, Chris; Allhoff, Fritz. Neuroscience and metaphysics. *American Journal of Bioethics* 2005 March-April; 5(2): 34-36. NRCBL: 17.1; 15.1. Comments: comment on Judy Illes and Eric Racine, "Imaging or imagining? A neuroethics challenge informed by genetics," American Journal of Bioethics 2005 March-April; 5(2): 5-18.

Buller, Tom. Can we scan for truth in a society of liars? *American Journal of Bioethics* 2005 March-April; 5(2): 58-60. NRCBL: 17.1; 5.1. Comments: comment on Paul Root Wolpe, Kenneth R. Foster, and Daniel D. Langleben, "Emerging neurotechnologies for lie-detection: promises and perils," American Journal of Bioethics 2005 March-April; 5(2): 39-49.

Canvin, K.; Bartlett, A.; Pinfold, V. Acceptability of compulsory powers in the community: the ethical considerations of mental health service users on supervised discharge and guardianship. *Journal of Medical Ethics* 2005 August; 31(8): 457-462. NRCBL: 17.1; 17.7. SC: le; em. Identifiers: United Kingdom (Great Britain).

Abstract: OBJECTIVES: To explore mental health service users' views of existing and proposed compulsory powers. DESIGN: A qualitative study employing in-depth interviews. Participants were asked to respond to hypothetical questions regarding the application of compulsory powers under the Mental Health Act 1983 for people other than themselves. SETTING: Community setting in Southeast England. PARTICIPANTS: Mental health service users subject to Supervised Discharge/Guardianship. RESULTS: Participants considered that the use of compulsory powers was justified if there were some ultimate benefit, and if there was evidence of mental health problems, dangerousness, or a lack of insight. However, participants rejected intrusions into their autonomy and privacy. CONCLUSIONS: This paper's participants indicated that the proposed CTO may be unacceptable because it would threaten service users' autonomy. Service users' acceptance of proposed changes is conditional and they emphasised the importance of consent; there is no suggestion that consent will be required for the CTO. The findings also have implications for the exploration of mental health service users' views and how they might contribute to policy, service planning, and research.

Caplan, Arthur L. Is better best? A noted ethicist argues in favor of brain enhancement. *Scientific American* 2003 September; 289(3): 104-105. NRCBL: 17.1; 4.5.

Caplan, Arthur; Mobley, William. No brainer — can we cope with the ethical ramifications of new knowledge of the human brain? *Cerebrum: The Dana Forum on Brain Science* 2002 Summer; 4(3): 63. NRCBL: 17.1; 2.1. Conference: Neuroethics: Mapping the Field; San Francisco; 13-14 May 2002; Stanford University, University of California, the Dana Foundation.

Chadwick, Ruth; Aindow, Gordon. Treatment and research ethics. *In:* Radden, Jennifer, ed. The Philosophy of Psychiatry: A Companion. New York: Oxford University Press; 2004: 282-295. NRCBL: 17.1; 9.5.3; 18.5.6.

Chadwick, Ruth; Levitt, Mairi. The ethics of community mental health care. *In their:* Chadwick, Ruth; Levitt, Mairi, eds. Ethical Issues in Community Health Care. New York: Arnold; 1998: 102-114. NRCBL: 17.1.

Check, Erika. Brain-scan ethics come under the spotlight [news]. *Nature* 2005 January 20; 433(7023): 185. NRCBL: 17.1; 5.1.

Check, Erika. Ethicists urge caution over emotive power of brain scans [news]. *Nature* 2005 May 19; 435(7040): 254-255. NRCBL: 17.1; 5.1.

Chiswick, Derek. Commentary: test of capacity has little practical benefit. *BMJ: British Medical Journal* 2005 December 17; 331(7530): 1469-1470. NRCBL: 17.1; 4.3; 17.8; 17.7; 1.1. SC: le.

Corcoran, Cheryl; Malaspina, Dolores; Hercher, Laura. Prodromal interventions for schizophrenia vulnerability: the risks of being "at risk". *Schizophrenia Research* 2005 March 1; 73(2-3): 173-184. NRCBL: 17.1; 9.5.7; 9.1.

Corrigan, Patrick W.; Watson, Amy C.; Warpinski, Amy C.; Gracia, Gabriela. Stigmatizing attitudes about mental illness and allocation of resources to mental health services. *Community Mental Health Journal* 2004 August; 40(4): 297-307. NRCBL: 17.1; 9.4. SC: em.

Crepaz-Keay, David. Who benefits from the new act? [comment]. *BMJ: British Medical Journal* 2005 December 17; 331(7530): 1470-1471. NRCBL: 17.1; 17.7; 8.3.4. SC: le. Identifiers: mental health legislation; competency.

Crowden, Andrew. Ethically sensitive mental health care: is there a need for a unique ethics for psychiatry? *Australian and New Zealand Journal of Psychiatry* 2003 April; 37(2): 143-149. NRCBL: 17.1; 4.1.2; 1.3.1; 1.1.

Dallos, Rudi. Ethics and family therapy. *In:* Fairbairn, Susan; Fairbairn, Gavin, eds. Psychology, Ethics and Change. New York: Routledge & Kegan Paul; 1987: 136-160. NRCBL: 17.1; 8.1; 17.3.

De Vries, Raymond. Framing neuroethics: a sociological assessment of the neuroethical imagination. *American Journal of Bioethics* 2005 March-April; 5(2): 25-27. NRCBL: 17.1; 15.1; 2.1. Comments: comment on Judy Illes and Eric Racine, "Imaging or imagining? A neuroethics challenge informed by genetics," American Journal of Bioethics 2005 March-April; 5(2): 5-18.

DiPasquale, Tony; Gluck, John P. Psychologists, psychiatrists, and physician-assisted suicide: the relationship between underlying beliefs and professional behavior. *Professional Psychology: Research and Practice* 2001 October; 32(5): 501-506. NRCBL: 17.1; 20.7; 7.1.

Dolin, Gregory. A healer or an executioner? The proper role of a psychiatrist in a criminal justice system. *Journal of Law and Health* 2002-2003; 17(2): 169-216. NRCBL: 17.1; 7.3; 1.3.5. SC: le.

Doucet, Hubert. Imagining a neuroethics which would go further than genetics. *American Journal of Bioethics* 2005 March-April; 5(2): 29-31. NRCBL: 17.1; 15.1; 2.1. Comments: comment on Judy Illes and Eric Racine, "Imaging or imagining? A neuroethics challenge informed by genetics," American Journal of Bioethics 2005 March-April; 5(2): 5-18.

Downie, Jocelyn; Hadskis, Michael. Finding the right compass for issue-mapping in neuroimaging. *American Journal of Bioethics* 2005 March-April; 5(2): 27-29. NRCBL: 17.1; 15.1; 15.3; 17.4; 4.5; 18.2. Comments: comment on Judy Illes and Eric Racine, "Imaging or imagining? A neuroethics challenge informed by genetics," American Journal of Bioethics 2005 March-April; 5(2): 5-18.

Doyal, Len; Sheather, Julian. Mental health legislation should respect decision making capacity. *BMJ: British Medical Journal* 2005 December 17; 331(7530): 1467-1469. NRCBL: 17.1; 1.1; 4.3; 8.3.3; 8.3.4; 17.8. SC: le.

Dudley, Michael; Gale, Fran. Psychiatrists as a moral community? Psychiatry under the Nazis and its contemporary relevance. *Australian and New Zealand Journal of Psychiatry* 2002 October; 36(5): 585-594. NRCBL: 17.1; 7.1; 15.5; 21.4.

Erard, Robert E. "A raw deal" reheated: reply to comments by Rogers, Fischer, and Smith and Evans. *Journal of Personality Assessment* 2004 February; 82(1): 44-47. NRCBL: 17.1; 8.3.1.

Evers, Kathinka. Neuroethics: a philosophical challenge. *American Journal of Bioethics* 2005 March-April; 5(2): 31-32. NRCBL: 17.1; 2.1; 5.1. Comments: comment on Judy Illes and Eric Racine, "Imaging or imagining? A neuroethics challenge informed by genetics," American Journal of Bioethics 2005 March-April; 5(2): 5-18.

Farah, Martha J. Neuroethics: the practical and the philosophical. *Trends in Cognitive Sciences* 2005 January; 9(1): 34-40. NRCBL: 17.1; 17.4; 8.4; 4.5.

Faunce, Thomas Alured. Collaborative research trials: a strategy for fostering mental health protections in developing nations. *International Journal of Law and Psychiatry* 2005 March-April; 28(2): 171-181. NRCBL: 17.1; 21.1; 17.8; 17.7; 18.5.6; 18.2. SC: le. Identifiers: Sri Lanka.

Feldman, Tamara; Blass, Rachel. On the patient's right to tell [letter and reply]. *Journal of the American Psychoanalytic Association* 2004 Summer; 52(3): 903-907. NRCBL: 17.1; 8.1; 8.2; 8.4; 7.2.

Fins, Joseph J. The Orwellian threat to emerging neurodiagnostic technologies. *American Journal of Bioethics* 2005 March-April; 5(2): 56-58. NRCBL: 17.1; 20.5.1; 5.1; 18.4. Comments: comment on Paul Root Wolpe, Kenneth R. Foster, and Daniel D. Langleben, "Emerging neurotechnologies for lie-detection: promises and perils," American Journal of Bioethics 2005 March-April; 5(2): 39-49.

Fins, Joseph J. Rethinking disorders of consciousness: new research and its implications. *Hastings Center Report* 2005 March-April; 35(2): 22-24. NRCBL: 17.1; 20.5.1.

Fischbach, Ruth L.; Fischbach, Gerald D. The brain doesn't lie. *American Journal of Bioethics* 2005 March-April; 5(2): 54-55. NRCBL: 17.1; 5.1. Comments: comment on Paul Root Wolpe, Kenneth R. Foster, and Daniel D. Langleben, "Emerging neurotechnologies for lie-detection: promises and perils," American Journal of Bioethics 2005 March-April; 5(2): 39-49.

Ford, Paul J.; Kubu, Cynthia S. Caution in leaping from functional imaging to functional neurosurgery. *American Journal of Bioethics* 2005 March-April; 5(2): 23-25. NRCBL: 17.1; 8.3.1; 15.3. Comments: comment on Judy Illes and Eric Racine, "Imaging or imagining? A neuroethics challenge informed by genetics," American Journal of Bioethics 2005 March-April; 5(2): 5-18.

Foulks, Edward F. Advocating for persons who are mentally ill: a history of mutual empowerment of patients and profession. *Administration and Policy in Mental Health* 2000 May; 27(5): 353-367. NRCBL: 17.1; 8.3.3; 4.3.

Friedrich, M.J. Neuroscience becomes image conscious as brain scans raise ethical issues. *JAMA: The Journal of the American Medical Association* 2005 August 17; 294(7): 781-783. NRCBL: 17.1.

Frueh, B. Christopher; Knapp, Rebecca G.; Cusack, Karen J.; Grubaugh, Anouk L.; Sauvageot, Julie A.; Cousins, Victoria C.; Yim, Eunsil; Robins, Cynthia S.; Monnier, Jeannine; Hiers, Thomas G. Patients' reports of traumatic or harmful experiences within the psychiatric setting. *Psychiatric Services* 2005 September; 56(9): 1123-1133. NRCBL: 17.1. SC: em.

Fry, Sara T.; Veatch, Robert M. Psychiatry and the control of human behavior. *In their:* Case Studies in Nursing Ethics. Third edition. Sudbury, MA: Jones and Bartlett Publishers; 2006: 281-298. NRCBL: 17.1.

Ganzini, Linda; Prigerson, Holly. The other side of the slippery slope. *Hastings Center Report* 2004 July-August; 34(4): 3. NRCBL: 17.1; 20.5.1; 20.7.

Gazzaniga, Michael S. What's on your mind? [opinion]. *New Scientist* 2005 June 11-17; 186(2503): 48-50. NRCBL: 17.1; 9.5.8; 14.1; 15.1.

Gibson, S. On judgment and judgmentalism: how counselling can make people better. *Journal of Medical Ethics* 2005 October; 31(10): 575-577. NRCBL: 17.1; 1.1; 4.1.1. SC: an.
   Abstract: Counsellors, like other members of the caring professions, are required to practise within an ethical framework, at least in so far as they seek professional accreditation. As such,

---

NRCBL: National Reference Center for Bioethics Literature Classification Scheme   See inside front cover for terms.

347

the counsellor is called upon to exercise her moral agency. In most professional contexts this requirement is, in itself, unproblematic. It has been suggested, however, that counselling practice does present a problem in this respect, in so far as the counsellor is expected to take a non-judgemental stance and an attitude of "unconditional positive regard" toward the client. If, as might appear to be the case, this stance and attitude are at odds with the making of moral judgments, the possibility of an adequate ethics of counselling is called into question. This paper explores the nature and extent of the problem suggesting that, understood in a Kantian context, non-judgmentalism can be seen to be at odds with neither the moral agency of the counsellor nor that of the client. Instead, it is argued, the relationship between the non-judgmental counsellor and her client is a fundamentally moral relationship, based on respect for the client's unconditional worth as a moral agent.

Glen, Sally. Dangerous and severe personality disorder: an ethical concept? *Nursing Philosophy* 2005 April; 6(2): 98-105. NRCBL: 17.1; 1.1.

Glenn, Linda MacDonald. Keeping an open mind: what legal safeguards are needed? *American Journal of Bioethics* 2005 March-April; 5(2): 60-61. NRCBL: 17.1; 5.3; 1.3.5. Comments: comment on Paul Root Wolpe, Kenneth R. Foster, and Daniel D. Langleben, "Emerging neurotechnologies for lie-detection: promises and perils," American Journal of Bioethics 2005 March-April; 5(2): 39-49.

Gray, John E.; O'Reilly, Richard L. Canadian compulsory community treatment laws: recent reforms. *International Journal of Law and Psychiatry* 2005 January-February; 28(1): 13-22. NRCBL: 17.1; 17.7; 8.3.1; 8.3.3. SC: le.

Grazier, Kyle L.; Mowbray, Carol T.; Holter, Mark C. Rationing psychosocial treatments in the United States. *International Journal of Law and Psychiatry* 2005 September- October; 28(5): 545-560. NRCBL: 17.1; 9.3.2; 9.4; 17.2; 17.3.

Great Britain. Department of Health. Secretary of State for Health. Government response to the report of the Joint Committee on the draft Mental Health Bill 2004. London: Department of Health 2005 July; 52 p. [Online]. Available: http://www.dh.gov.uk/assetRoot/04/11/52/ 68/04115268.pdf [14 September 2005]. NRCBL: 17.1; 4.3; 1.3.5. SC: le.

Greely, Henry T. Premarket approval regulation for lie detections: an idea whose time may be coming. *American Journal of Bioethics* 2005 March-April; 5(2): 50-52. NRCBL: 17.1; 5.3; 9.7; 17.4. SC: le. Identifiers: Food and Drug Administration (FDA). Comments: comment on Paul Root Wolpe, Kenneth R. Foster, and Daniel D. Langleben, "Emerging neurotechnologies for lie-detection: promises and perils," American Journal of Bioethics 2005 March-April; 5(2): 39-49.

Green, Ronald M. Spy versus spy. *American Journal of Bioethics* 2005 March-April; 5(2): 53-54. NRCBL: 17.1; 5.1; 15.3. Comments: comment on Paul Root Wolpe, Ken-

neth R. Foster, and Daniel D. Langleben, "Emerging neurotechnologies for lie-detection: promises and perils," American Journal of Bioethics 2005 March-April; 5(2): 39-49.

Hadjistavropoulos, Thomas; Malloy, David Cruise. Making ethical choices: a comprehensive decision-making model for Canadian psychologists. *Canadian Psychology/Psychologie Canadienne* 2000 May; 41(2): 104-115. NRCBL: 17.1; 7.1; 9.4; 4.3.

Hall, Zach W. Mapping the future. *Cerebrum: The Dana Forum on Brain Science* 2002 Summer; 4(3): 72-76. NRCBL: 17.1; 2.1. Conference: Neuroethics: Mapping the Field; San Francisco; 13-14 May 2002; Stanford University, University of California, the Dana Foundation.

Harper, Richard S. Medical treatment and the mentally ill. *In his:* Medical Treatment and the Law: The Protection of Adults and Minors in the Family Division. Bristol: Family Law; 1999: 69-79. NRCBL: 17.1; 8.3.3; 8.3.4. SC: le.

Harre, Rom. Rights to display: the masking of competence. *In:* Fairbairn, Susan; Fairbairn, Gavin, eds. Psychology, Ethics and Change. New York: Routledge & Kegan Paul; 1987: 58-73. NRCBL: 17.1.

Henderson, Jeannette. The challenge of relationship boundaries in mental health. *Nursing Management* 2004 October; 11(6): 28-32. NRCBL: 17.1; 4.1.3; 8.1.

Högberg, Torbjörn; Magnusson, Annabella; Lützén, Kim. To be a nurse or a neighbour? A moral concern for psychiatric nurses living next door to individuals with a mental illness. *Nursing Ethics* 2005 September; 12(5): 468-478. NRCBL: 17.1; 8.1. SC: em. Identifiers: Sweden.
Abstract: Several studies reveal that positive attitudes towards individuals with a mental illness are correlated with knowledge about mental illness. The aim of this study was to explore and describe psychiatric nurses' experiences of living next to people with mental health problems. In addition, it sought to identify and describe how they handle situations arising in a neighbourhood where people with a mental illness live. Two men and seven women participated in the study. The constant comparative method of grounded theory was used for data collection and analysis. The process of 'behaving as a nurse or not' was identified as a core category. Four subcategories were identified: 'receiving involuntary information', 'to take action or not', 'behaving as a mediator in the neighbourhood' and 'the freedom of choice'. The findings show that psychiatric nurses with professional knowledge about mental illness have moral concerns about their role as nurses during their leisure time. In conclusion, it is not obvious that psychiatric nurses want to live in the same neighbourhood as persons with a mental illness. However, this study shows that their knowledge about mental illness creates for them a moral dilemma consisting of a conflict between whether to care for these mentally ill persons or to preserve their own leisure time.

Hundert, Edward M. Ethical issues in the practice of psychiatry. *In:* Nicholi, Armand M., ed. The Harvard Guide to Psychiatry. 3rd ed. Cambridge, MA: Belknap Press of Harvard University; 1999: 744-751. NRCBL: 17.1; 2.1; 6.

Illes, Judy. Neuroethics in a new era of neuroimaging [editorial]. *AJRN: American Journal of Neuroradiology* 2003 October; 24(9): 1739-1741. NRCBL: 17.1; 5.1.

Illes, Judy; Blakemore, Colin; Gazzaniga, Michael S.; Kotulak, Ron; Mobley, William. Brain science and public discourse. *Cerebrum: The Dana Forum on Brain Science* 2002 Summer; 4(3): 68-70. NRCBL: 17.1; 1.3.7. Conference: Neuroethics: Mapping the Field; San Francisco; 13-14 May 2002; Stanford University, University of California, the Dana Foundation.

Illes, Judy; Racine, E. Neuroethics: dialogue on a continuum from tradition to innovation [letter]. *American Journal of Bioethics [Online]* 2005 March-April; 5(2): W3-W4. NRCBL: 17.1.

Illes, Judy; Racine, Eric. Imaging or imagining? A neuroethics challenge informed by genetics. *American Journal of Bioethics* 2005 March-April; 5(2): 5-18. NRCBL: 17.1; 15.1; 5.1; 18.4; 8.4; 2.1.

Abstract: From a twenty-first century partnership between bioethics and neuroscience, the modern field of neuroethics is emerging, and technologies enabling functional neuroimaging with unprecedented sensitivity have brought new ethical, social and legal issues to the forefront. Some issues, akin to those surrounding modern genetics, raise critical questions regarding prediction of disease, privacy and identity. However, with new and still-evolving insights into our neurobiology and previously unquantifiable features of profoundly personal behaviors such as social attitude, value and moral agency, the difficulty of carefully and properly interpreting the relationship between brain findings and our own self-concept is unprecedented. Therefore, while the ethics of genetics provides a legitimate starting point—even a backbone—for tackling ethical issues in neuroimaging, they do not suffice. Drawing on recent neuroimaging findings and their plausible real-world applications, we argue that interpretation of neuroimaging data is a key epistemological and ethical challenge. This challenge is two-fold. First, at the scientific level, the sheer complexity of neuroscience research poses challenges for integration of knowledge and meaningful interpretation of data. Second, at the social and cultural level, we find that interpretations of imaging studies are bound by cultural and anthropological frameworks. In particular, the introduction of concepts of self and personhood in neuroimaging illustrates the interaction of interpretation levels and is a major reason why ethical reflection on genetics will only partially help settle neuroethical issues. Indeed, ethical interpretation of such findings will necessitate not only traditional bioethical input but also a wider perspective on the construction of scientific knowledge.

Illes, Judy; Raffin, Thomas A. No child left without a brain scan? Toward a pediatric neuroethics. *Cerebrum: The Dana Forum on Brain Science* 2005 Summer; 7(3): 33-46. NRCBL: 17.1; 9.5.7; 9.5.8.

Johnston, Josephine; Elliott, Carl. Healthy limb amputation: ethical and legal aspects. *Clinical Medicine* 2002 September-October; 2(5): 431-435. NRCBL: 17.1; 4.3; 9.5.1; 8.3.1. SC: le.

Johnstone, Julie. Ethics, identity, and new social movements in mental health services. *Res Publica* 2005; 14(2): 6-10. NRCBL: 17.1; 9.8; 4.4; 8.1.

Jonsen, Albert R. Neuroscience. *In his:* Bioethics Beyond the Headlines: Who Lives? Who Dies? Who Decides? Lanham, MD: Rowman and Littlefield; 2005: 114-126. NRCBL: 17.1; 1.1.

Jonsen, Albert R. What it means to "map" the field of neuroethics. *Cerebrum: The Dana Forum on Brain Science* 2002 Summer; 4(3): 71-72. NRCBL: 17.1; 2.1; 1.1. Conference: Neuroethics: Mapping the Field; San Francisco; 13-14 May 2002; Stanford University, University of California, the Dana Foundation.

Jonsen, Albert R.; Churchland, Patricia S.; Damasio, Antonio R.; Moreno, Jonathan; Schaffner, Kenneth F.; Mobley, William. Brain science and the self. *Cerebrum: The Dana Forum on Brain Science* 2002 Summer; 4(3): 56-58. NRCBL: 17.1; 2.1. Conference: Neuroethics: Mapping the Field; San Francisco; 13-14 May 2002; Stanford University, University of California, the Dana Foundation.

Jotkowitz, Alan B.; Clarfield, A. Mark; Glick, Shimon. The care of patients with dementia: a modern Jewish ethical perspective. *Journal of the American Geriatrics Society* 2005 May; 53(5): 881-884. NRCBL: 17.1; 1.2; 8.2; 9.5.2; 20.5.1.

Kalis, Annemarie; Schermer, Maartje H.N.; van Delden, Johannes J.M. Ideals regarding a good life for nursing home residents with dementia: views of professional caregivers. *Nursing Ethics* 2005 January; 12(1): 30-42. NRCBL: 17.1; 4.4; 9.5.2. SC: em. Identifiers: Netherlands.

Abstract: This study investigates what professional caregivers working in nursing homes consider to be a good life for residents suffering from dementia. Ten caregivers were interviewed; special attention was paid to the way in which they deal with conflicting values. Transcripts of the interviews were analysed qualitatively according to the method of grounded theory. The results were compared with those from a similar, earlier study on ideals found in mission statements of nursing homes. The concepts that were mentioned by most interviewed participants as important for a good life were 'peace and quiet', 'going along with subjective experience' and 'no enforcement: the way the resident wants it'. A considerable overlap was found between the interviews and the mission statements; however, when compared with the mission statements, the interviews put less emphasis on individuality and on giving meaning, and more on offering residents pleasant activities. When faced with conflicting values, caregivers tend to make pragmatic and more or less intuitive decisions. Although this has its merits, it may be desirable to stimulate conscious reflection regarding conflict between different values.

Kennedy, Donald. Neuroimaging: revolutionary research tool or a post-modern phrenology? *American Journal of Bioethics* 2005 March-April; 5(2): 19. NRCBL: 17.1; 15.1. Comments: comment on Judy Illes and Eric Racine, "Imaging or imagining? A neuroethics challenge informed by genetics," American Journal of Bioethics 2005 March-April; 5(2): 5-18.

Kennedy, Donald; Mobley, William. Are there things we'd rather not know? *Cerebrum: The Dana Forum on*

NRCBL: National Reference Center for Bioethics Literature Classification Scheme   See inside front cover for terms.

349

Brain Science 2002 Summer; 4(3): 67-68. NRCBL: 17.1. Conference: Neuroethics: Mapping the Field; San Francisco; 13-14 May 2002; Stanford University, University of California, the Dana Foundation.

Kennett, Jeanette; Matthews, Steve. Seeing the self: the moral goals of service provision in the mental health sector. *Res Publica* 2005; 14(2): 1-5. NRCBL: 17.1; 7.1; 9.8; 8.1; 17.8. SC: an. Identifiers: Australia.

Kier, Frederick J.; Molinari, Victor. Do-it-yourself testing for mental illness: ethical issues, concerns, and recommendations. *Professional Psychology: Research and Practice* 2004 June; 35(3): 261-267. NRCBL: 17.1; 5.1.

Kingdon, David; Jones, Roland; Lönnqvist, Jouko. Protecting the human rights of people with mental disorder: new recommendations emerging from the Council of Europe [editorial]. *British Journal of Psychiatry* 2004 October; 185: 277-279. NRCBL: 17.1; 6. SC: le.

Kmietowicz, Zosia. Plan aims to end discrimination in mental health services [news]. *BMJ: British Medical Journal* 2005 January 15; 330(7483): 113. NRCBL: 17.1; 9.5.4.

Knoppers, Bartha Maria. Neuroethics, new ethics? *American Journal of Bioethics* 2005 March-April; 5(2): 33. NRCBL: 17.1; 15.1; 5.1. Comments: comment on Judy Illes and Eric Racine, "Imaging or imagining? A neuroethics challenge informed by genetics," American Journal of Bioethics 2005 March-April; 5(2): 5-18.

Koenig, Barbara A.; Greely, Henry; Schacter, Daniel L.; Winslade, William J.; Mobley, William. Brain science and social policy. *Cerebrum: The Dana Forum on Brain Science* 2002 Summer; 4(3): 59-62. NRCBL: 17.1; 2.1. Conference: Neuroethics: Mapping the Field; San Francisco; 13-14 May 2002; Stanford University, University of California, the Dana Foundation.

Korr, Wynne S.; Encandela, John A.; Brieland, Donald. Independence or autonomy: which is the goal? *International Journal of Law and Psychiatry* 2005 May-June; 28(3): 290-299. NRCBL: 17.1; 8.1; 1.1; 9.5.3.

Lally, Matthew C.; Freeman, Scott A. The struggle to maintain neutrality in the treatment of a patient with pedophilia. *Ethics and Behavior* 2005; 15(2): 182-190. NRCBL: 17.1; 10; 8.1; 17.8; 20.7. SC: cs.
Abstract: This article explores the ethical concept of neutrality through use of a psychiatric clinical vignette. In this case a psychiatry resident is faced with the treatment of a patient who was found by the FBI to be in possession of child pornography. Although not accused of any other crimes, the patient was a fugitive from the law and requesting treatment for pedophilia. Faced with the pressures of limited resources and anxiety about the patient's dangerousness to others, the resident and his supervisor tried to strike a balance between the ethical principles of neutrality and beneficence. Through this vignette, the importance of neutrality, as well as how it can be compromised by other pressures such as expediency and anxiety, is explored.

Lazzarini, Ivelisse. Neuroethics: the new millennium view. *In:* Purtilo, Ruth B.; Jensen, Gail M.; Brasic Royeen, Charlotte, eds. Educating for Moral Action: A Sourcebook in Health and Rehabilitation Ethics. Philadelphia: F.A. Davis; 2005: 145-157. NRCBL: 17.1.

Lerner, Barron H. Last-ditch medical therapy — revisiting lobotomy [opinion]. *New England Journal of Medicine* 2005 July 14; 353(2): 119-121. NRCBL: 17.1; 17.6; 7.4.

Leshner, Alan I. It's time to go public with neuroethics [editorial]. *American Journal of Bioethics* 2005 March-April; 5(2): 1-2. NRCBL: 17.1.

Liégeois, A.; Van Audenhove, C. Ethical dilemmas in community mental health care. *Journal of Medical Ethics* 2005 August; 31(8): 452-456. NRCBL: 17.1. SC: an.
Abstract: Ethical dilemmas in community mental health care is the focus of this article. The dilemmas are derived from a discussion of the results of a qualitative research project that took place in five countries of the European Union. The different stakeholders are confronted with the following dilemmas: community care versus hospital care (clients); a life with care versus a life without care (informal carers); stimulation of the client toward greater responsibility versus protection against such responsibility (professionals); budgetary control versus financial incentives (policy makers), and respect for the client versus particular private needs (neighbourhood residents). These dilemmas are interpreted against the background of a value based ethical model. This model offers an integral approach to the dilemmas and can be used to determine policy. The dilemmas are discussed here as the result of conflicting values-namely autonomy and privacy, support and safety, justice and participation, and trust and solidarity.

Lo, Bernard; Albert, Marilyn S.; Hyman, Steven; Parens, Erik; Wolpe, Paul Root. Ethics and the practice of brain science. *Cerebrum: The Dana Forum on Brain Science* 2002 Summer; 4(3): 64-66. NRCBL: 17.1; 2.1. Conference: Neuroethics: Mapping the Field; San Francisco; 13-14 May 2002; Stanford University, University of California, the Dana Foundation.

Lorence, Daniel P. Confidentiality measures in mental health delivery settings: report of US health information managers. *Journal of Behavioral Health Services and Research* 2004 April-June; 31(2): 199-207. NRCBL: 17.1; 8.4; 1.3.12. SC: em.

Martens, W. Harmful and unethical pressure on psychiatrists as a consequence of governments' policies [letter]. *Medicine and Law: World Association for Medical Law* 2005 December; 24(4): 853-854. NRCBL: 17.1; 7.1.

McClure, Andy. Psychiatric ethics and forensic assessments [letter]. *Australian and New Zealand Journal of Psychiatry* 1999 October; 33(5): 770. NRCBL: 17.1; 7.1; 1.3.5.

McKechnie, Ron. The moral context of therapy. *In:* Fairbairn, Susan; Fairbairn, Gavin, eds. Psychology, Ethics and Change. New York: Routledge & Kegan Paul; 1987: 161- 172. NRCBL: 17.1; 9.5.9; 17.3.

Melton, Gary B. Mental health and social justice: a vision for the 21st century. *American Journal of Orthopsychiatry* 2003 July; 73(3): 245-247. NRCBL: 17.1; 1.1; 9.2; 21.1.

Misak, Cheryl. ICU psychosis and patient autonomy: some thoughts from the inside. *Journal of Medicine and Philosophy* 2005 August; 30(4): 411-430. NRCBL: 17.1; 8.2; 1.1.

Abstract: I shall draw on my experience of being an ICU patient to make some practical, ethical, and philosophical points about the care of the critically ill. The recurring theme in this paper is ICU psychosis. I suggest that discharged patients ought to be educated about it; I discuss the obstacles in the way of accurately measuring it; I argue that we must rethink autonomy in light of it; and I suggest that the self disintegrates in the face of it.

Mixon, Don. Deception, self-deception and self-determination. *In:* Fairbairn, Susan; Fairbairn, Gavin, eds. Psychology, Ethics and Change. New York: Routledge & Kegan Paul; 1987: 44-57. NRCBL: 17.1; 18.4.

Moore, Zella E. Ethical dilemmas in sport psychology: discussion and recommendations for practice. *Professional Psychology: Research and Practice* 2003 December; 34(6): 601-610. NRCBL: 17.1; 8.4; 8.3.1; 6.

Moreno, Jonathan D. Neuroethics: an agenda for neuroscience and society. *Nature Reviews Neuroscience* 2003 February; 4(2): 149-153. NRCBL: 17.1; 3.1; 4.4.

Moreno, Jonathan David. Dual use and the "moral taint" problem. *American Journal of Bioethics* 2005 March-April; 5(2): 52-53. NRCBL: 17.1; 5.3. Comments: comment on Paul Root Wolpe, Kenneth R. Foster, and Daniel D. Langleben, "Emerging neurotechnologies for lie-detection: promises and perils," American Journal of Bioethics 2005 March-April; 5(2): 39-49.

Nelson, Janet R. Bioethics and the marginalization of mental illness. *Journal of the Society of Christian Ethics* 2003 Fall-Winter; 23(2): 179-197. NRCBL: 17.1; 2.1.

Nicolai, Katherine M.; Scott, Norman A. Provision of confidentiality information and its relation to child abuse reporting. *Professional Psychology: Research and Practice* 1994 May; 25(2): 154-160. NRCBL: 17.1; 8.4; 9.5.7. SC: em.

Olson, Steve. Brain scans raise privacy concerns. *Science* 2005 March 11; 307(5715): 1548-1550. NRCBL: 17.1; 8.4.

Orme, Daniel R.; Doerman, Alan L. Ethical dilemmas and U.S. Air Force clinical psychologists: a survey. *Professional Psychology: Research and Practice* 2001 June; 32(3): 305-311. NRCBL: 17.1; 6; 7.1; 1.3.5.

Paradis, Emily K. Feminist and community psychology ethics in research with homeless women. *American Journal of Community Psychology* 2000 December; 28(6): 839-858. NRCBL: 17.1; 10; 9.5.5; 9.5.10.

Pathare, Soumitra. Beyond ECT: priorities in mental health care in India. *Issues in Medical Ethics* 2003 January-March; 11(1): 11-12. NRCBL: 17.1; 17.5. Identifiers: electroconvulsive therapy.

Potter, Nancy. Liberatory psychiatry and an ethics of the in-between. *In:* Shildrick, Margrit; Mykitiuk, Roxanne, eds. Ethics of the Body: Postconventional Challenges. Cambridge, MA: MIT Press; 2005: 113- 133. NRCBL: 17.1; 1.1.

Raj, Kirath. The presidents' mental health. *American Journal of Law and Medicine* 2005; 31(4): 509-524. NRCBL: 17.1; 1.3.5; 4.3; 8.4.

Reid, Lynette; Baylis, Françoise. Brains, genes, and the making of the self. *American Journal of Bioethics* 2005 March-April; 5(2): 21-23. NRCBL: 17.1; 15.1; 8.4. Comments: comment on Judy Illes and Eric Racine, "Imaging or imagining? A neuroethics challenge informed by genetics," American Journal of Bioethics 2005 March-April; 5(2): 5-18.

Richardson, G. The European convention and mental health law in England and Wales: moving beyond process? *International Journal of Law and Psychiatry* 2005 March-April; 28(2): 127-139. NRCBL: 17.1; 21.1; 1.3.5; 17.7; 1.1; 17.8. SC: le. Identifiers: European Convention on Human Rights.

Roberts, Laura W.; Warner, Teddy D.; Hammond, Katherine Green. Ethical challenges of mental health clinicians in rural and frontier areas [letter]. *Psychiatric Services* 2005 March; 56(3): 358-359. NRCBL: 17.1; 8.1. SC: em.

Roberts, M. Psychiatric ethics; a critical introduction for mental health nurses. *Journal of Psychiatric and Mental Health Nursing* 2004 October; 11(5): 583-588. NRCBL: 17.1; 2.1; 4.1.3.

Robins, Cynthia S.; Sauvageot, Julie A.; Cusack, Karen J.; Suffoletta-Maierle, Samantha; Frueh, B. Christopher. Consumers' perceptions of negative experiences and "sanctuary harm" in psychiatric settings. *Psychiatric Services* 2005 September; 56(9): 1134-1138. NRCBL: 17.1. SC: em.

Sachdev, Perminder; Sachdev, Jagdeep. Sixty years of psychosurgery: its present status and its future. *Australian and New Zealand Journal of Psychiatry* 1997 August; 31(4): 457-464. NRCBL: 17.1; 17.6; 7.1.

Safire, William. Our new Promethean gift. *Cerebrum: The Dana Forum on Brain Science* 2002 Summer; 4(3): 54-55. NRCBL: 17.1; 2.1. Conference: Neuroethics: Mapping the Field; San Francisco; 13-14 May 2002; Stanford University, University of California, the Dana Foundation.

Saks, Samuel J. Call 911: psychiatry and the new Emergency Medical Treatment and Active Labor Act

---

NRCBL: National Reference Center for Bioethics Literature Classification Scheme   See inside front cover for terms.

351

(EMTALA) regulations. *Journal of Psychiatry and Law* 2004 Winter; 32(4): 483-512. NRCBL: 17.1; 9.2; 9.3.1; 17.8. SC: le.

Santora, Marc; Carey, Benedict. Depressed? New York screens for people at risk. *New York Times* 2005 April 13; p. A1, A16. NRCBL: 17.1. SC: po.

Schick, Ari. Neuro exceptionalism? *American Journal of Bioethics* 2005 March-April; 5(2): 36-38. NRCBL: 17.1; 15.1; 5.1; 2.1. Comments: comment on Judy Illes and Eric Racine, "Imaging or imagining? A neuroethics challenge informed by genetics," American Journal of Bioethics 2005 March-April; 5(2): 5-18.

Srebnik, Debra S.; Rutherford, Lindsay T.; Peto, Tracy; Russo, Joan; Zick, Ellen; Jaffe, Craig; Holtzheimer, Paul. The content and clinical utility of psychiatric advance directives. *Psychiatric Services* 2005 May; 56(5): 592-598. NRCBL: 17.1; 8.3.3; 8.3.4. SC: em.

Stone, Alan A. Psychiatry and the law. *In:* Nicholi, Armand M., ed. The Harvard Guide to Psychiatry. 3rd ed. Cambridge, MA: Belknap Press of Harvard University; 1999: 798-823. NRCBL: 17.1; 1.3.5. SC: le.

van Willigenburg, Theo. Protecting autonomy as authenticity using Ulysses contracts. *Journal of Medicine and Philosophy* 2005 August; 30(4): 395-409. NRCBL: 17.1; 1.1; 8.3.3; 8.3.4; 17.7. SC: an.
   Abstract: Pre-commitment directives or Ulysses contracts are often defended as instruments that may strengthen the autonomous self- control of episodically disordered psychiatric patients. Autonomy is understood in this context in terms of sovereignty ("governing" or "managing" oneself). After critically analyzing this idea of autonomy in the context of various forms of self-commitment and pre-commitment, we argue that what is at stake in using Ulysses contracts in psychiatry is not autonomy as sovereignty, but autonomy as authenticity. Pre-commitment directives do not function to protect autonomous self-control. They serve in upholding the guidance that is provided by one's deepest identity conferring concerns. We elucidate this concept of autonomy as authenticity, by showing how Ulysses contracts protect the possibility of being "a self."

Varekamp, I. Ulysses directives in the Netherlands: opinions of psychiatrists and clients. *Health Policy* 2004 December; 70(3): 291-301. NRCBL: 17.1; 8.3.3; 8.3.4; 7.1. SC: em. Identifiers: crisis card; Ulysses contract.

Varma, Anjali; Appelbaum, Paul S. Advance directives for persons with serious mental illness [letter and reply]. *Psychiatric Services* 2005 July; 56(7): 874-875. NRCBL: 17.1; 8.3.3; 8.3.4. SC: le.

Walter, Garry; Bloch, Sidney. Publishing ethics in psychiatry. *Australian and New Zealand Journal of Psychiatry* 2001 February; 35(1): 28-35. NRCBL: 17.1; 1.3.7; 7.1.

Watchirs, Helen. Human rights audit of mental health legislation — results of an Australian pilot. *International Journal of Law and Psychiatry* 2005 March- April; 28(2): 99-125. NRCBL: 17.1; 21.1; 17.8. SC: le.

Wig, N.N. Ethical issues in psychiatry. *Indian Journal of Medical Ethics* 2004 July-September; 1(3): 83-84. NRCBL: 17.1; 18.5.6; 17.5.

Wilfond, Benjamin S.; Ravitsky, Vardit. On the proliferation of bioethics sub-disciplines: do we really need "genethics" and "neuroethics"? *American Journal of Bioethics* 2005 March-April; 5(2): 20-21. NRCBL: 17.1; 15.1; 2.1. Comments: comment on Judy Illes and Eric Racine, "Imaging or imagining? A neuroethics challenge informed by genetics," American Journal of Bioethics 2005 March-April; 5(2): 5-18.

Wolpe, Paul Root; Foster, Kenneth R.; Langleben, Daniel D. Emerging neurotechnologies for lie-detection: promises and perils. *American Journal of Bioethics* 2005 March-April; 5(2): 39-49. NRCBL: 17.1; 8.4; 5.1.
   Abstract: Detection of deception and confirmation of truth telling with conventional polygraphy raised a host of technical and ethical issues. Recently, newer methods of recording electromagnetic signals from the brain show promise in permitting the detection of deception or truth telling. Some are even being promoted as more accurate than conventional polygraphy. While the new technologies raise issues of personal privacy, acceptable forensic application, and other social issues, the focus of this paper is the technical limitations of the developing technology. Those limitations include the measurement validity of the new technologies, which remains largely unknown. Another set of questions pertains to the psychological paradigms used to model or constrain the target behavior. Finally, there is little standardization in the field, and the vulnerability of the techniques to countermeasures is unknown. Premature application of these technologies outside of research settings should be resisted, and the social conversation about the appropriate parameters of its civil, forensic, and security use should begin.

Wolpe, Paul Root; Foster, Kenneth R.; Langleben, Daniel D. Response to commentators on "Emerging Neurotechnologies for Lie-Detection: Promises and Perils?" [letter]. *American Journal of Bioethics [Online]* 2005 March-April; 5(2): W5. NRCBL: 17.1.

Yip, Kam-shing. Political dominance of mental health services in the People's Republic of China [opinion]. *Administration and Policy in Mental Health* 2004 July; 31(6): 495-502. NRCBL: 17.1; 9.1; 21.1.

Zayas, Luis H.; Torres, Luis R.; Malcolm, Joan; DesRosiers, Fabiana S. Clinicians' definitions of ethnically sensitive therapy. *Professional Psychology: Research and Practice* 1996 February; 27(1): 78-82. NRCBL: 17.1; 21.7; 9.5.4.

MENTALLY DISABLED *See* CARE FOR SPECIFIC GROUPS/ MENTALLY DISABLED; HUMAN EXPERIMENTATION/ SPECIAL POPULATIONS/ MENTALLY DISABLED; INFORMED CONSENT/ INCOMPETENTS

MENTALLY HANDICAPPED *See* CARE FOR SPECIFIC GROUPS/ MENTALLY DISABLED; HUMAN EXPERIMENTATION/ SPECIAL POP-

ULATIONS/ MENTALLY DISABLED; IN-
FORMED CONSENT/ INCOMPETENTS

MENTALLY ILL *See* CARE FOR SPECIFIC
GROUPS/ MENTALLY DISABLED; HUMAN
EXPERIMENTATION/ SPECIAL POPULA-
TIONS/ MENTALLY DISABLED; INFORMED
CONSENT/ INCOMPETENTS

MERCY KILLING *See* EUTHANASIA AND
ALLOWING TO DIE

MILITARY PERSONNEL *See* HUMAN EXPER-
IMENTATION/ SPECIAL POPULATIONS/ MILI-
TARY PERSONNEL

MINORITIES *See* CARE FOR SPECIFIC
GROUPS/ MINORITIES

MINORS *See* CARE FOR SPECIFIC GROUPS/
MINORS; DEATH AND DYING/ TERMINAL
CARE FOR MINORS; EUTHANASIA AND AL-
LOWING TO DIE/ MINORS; HUMAN EXPERI-
MENTATION/ SPECIAL POPULATIONS/
MINORS; INFORMED CONSENT/ MINORS

MISCONDUCT *See* BIOMEDICAL RESEARCH/
RESEARCH ETHICS AND SCIENTIFIC MIS-
CONDUCT; MALPRACTICE AND PROFES-
SIONAL MISCONDUCT

MORAL AND RELIGIOUS ASPECTS *See*
ABORTION/ MORAL AND RELIGIOUS AS-
PECTS

**NONTHERAPEUTIC HUMAN EXPERIMEN-
TATION** *See* HUMAN EXPERIMENTATION

NURSE PATIENT RELATIONSHIP *See* NURS-
ING ETHICS AND PHILOSOPHY; PROFES-
SIONAL PATIENT RELATIONSHIP

NURSING CARE *See* CARE FOR SPECIFIC
GROUPS; DEATH AND DYING/ TERMINAL
CARE; NURSING ETHICS AND PHILOSOPHY

NURSING ETHICS AND PHILOSOPHY
See also BIOETHICS AND MEDICAL ETHICS;
CODES OF ETHICS; PROFESSIONAL ETHICS

Nursing ethics. *In:* Concise Routledge Encyclopedia of
Philosophy. New York: Routledge; 2000: 638. NRCBL:
4.1.3.

Andrews, Diane R. Fostering ethical competency: an ongoing staff development process that encourages professional growth and staff satisfaction. *Journal of Continuing*

Education in Nursing 2004 January-February; 35(1):
27-33, 44-45. NRCBL: 4.1.3; 2.3; 1.3.1.

Annals, Geoff; O'Malley, Jane. In that case. Response
[case study]. *Journal of Bioethical Inquiry* 2005; 2(1):
53-54. NRCBL: 4.1.3; 8.1; 16.3. SC: cs. Identifiers: duty to
treat; occupational health. Comments: comment on Ian
Kerridge and Nicole Gilroy, "In that case." Journal of
Bioethical Inquiry 2005; 2(1): 51.

Armstrong, Alan E.; Parsons, S.; Barker, P.J. An inquiry into moral virtues, especially compassion, in psychiatric nurses: findings from a Delphi study. *Journal of
Psychiatric and Mental Health Nursing* 2000 August;
7(4): 297-306. NRCBL: 4.1.3; 8.1; 17.2. SC: em. Identifiers: United Kingdom (Great Britain).

Aroskar, Mila Ann. Envisioning nursing as a moral community. *Nursing Outlook* 1995 May-June; 43(3): 134-138.
NRCBL: 4.1.3; 7.1; 7.3.

**Austin, Wendy; Lemermeyer, Gillian; Goldberg, Lisa;
Bergum, Vangie; Johnson, Melissa S.** Moral distress in
healthcare practice: the situation of nurses. *HEC
(Healthcare Ethics Committee) Forum* 2005 March; 17(1):
33- 48. NRCBL: 4.1.3; 1.1. SC: em.

**Auvinen, Jaana; Suominen, Tarja; Leino-Kilpi, Hel-
ena; Helkama, Klaus.** The development of moral judgment during nursing education in Finland. *Nurse
Education Today* 2004 October; 24(7): 538-546. NRCBL:
4.1.3. SC: em.

Begley, Ann Marie. Practising virtue: a challenge to the
view that a virtue centred approach to ethics lacks practical
content. *Nursing Ethics* 2005 November; 12(6): 622-637.
NRCBL: 4.1.3; 1.1.

Abstract: A virtue centred approach to ethics has been criticized
for being vague owing to the nature of its central concept, the
paradigm person. From the perspective of the practitioner the
most damaging charge is that virtue ethics fails to be action
guiding and, in addition to this, it does not offer any means of
act appraisal. These criticisms leave virtue ethics in a weak position vis-a-vis traditional approaches to ethics. The criticism
is, however, challenged by Hursthouse in her analysis of the accounts of right action offered by deontology, utilitarianism and
virtue ethics. It is possible to defend the action guiding nature of
virtue ethics: there are virtue rules and exemplars to guide action. Insights from Aristotle's practical approach to ethics are
considered alongside Hursthouse's analysis and it is suggested
that virtue ethics is also capable of facilitating action appraisal.
It is at the same time acknowledged that approaches to virtue
ethics vary widely and that the challenges offered here would be
rejected by those who embrace a radical replacement virtue
approach.

Bekemeier, Betty; Butterfield, Patricia. Unreconciled
inconsistencies: a critical review of the concept of social
justice in 3 national nursing documents. *ANS: Advances in
Nursing Science* 2005 April-June; 28(2): 152-162.
NRCBL: 4.1.3; 6; 1.1.

NRCBL: National Reference Center for Bioethics Literature Classification Scheme   See inside front cover for terms.

353

Benner, Patricia. Honoring the good behind rights and justice in healthcare when more than justice is needed. *American Journal of Critical Care* 2005 March; 14(2): 152-156. NRCBL: 4.1.3; 1.1; 4.1.1.

Benner, Patricia. Relational ethics of comfort, touch, and solace — endangered arts? *American Journal of Critical Care* 2004 July; 13(4): 346-349. NRCBL: 4.1.3; 8.1. SC: cs.

Berggren, Ingela; Barbosa da Silva, António; Severinsson, Elisabeth. Core ethical issues of clinical nursing supervision. *Nursing and Health Sciences* 2005 March; 7(1): 21-28. NRCBL: 4.1.3; 4.1.1; 1.1.

Bergren, Martha Dewey. Privacy questions from practicing school nurses. *Journal of School Nursing* 2004 October; 20(5): 296-301. NRCBL: 4.1.3; 8.4.

Blondeau, Danielle. Nursing art as a practical art: the necessary relationship between nursing art and nursing ethics. *Nursing Philosophy* 2002 October; 3(3): 252-259. NRCBL: 4.1.3.

Buchman, Debra E.; Porock, Davina. A response to C. Varcoe, G. Doane, B. Pauly, P. Rodney, J.L. Storch, K. Mahony, G. McPherson, H. Brown and R. Starzomski (2004) 'Ethical practice in nursing: working the in-betweens'. Journal of Advanced Nursing 45(3), 316-325. *Journal of Advanced Nursing* 2005 September; 51(6): 658-659. NRCBL: 4.1.3; 8.1.

Cleary, Michelle; Jordan, Raighne; Horsfall, Jan. Ethical practice guidelines: an evaluation. *International Journal of Mental Health Nursing* 2002 September; 11(3): 199-202. NRCBL: 4.1.3; 17.1; 6. SC: em.

Cooper, Robert W.; Frank, Garry L.; Gouty, Carol Ann; Hansen, Mary Mincer. Ethical helps and challenges faced by nurse leaders in the healthcare industry. *Journal of Nursing Administration* 2003 January; 33(1): 17-23. NRCBL: 4.1.3; 7.2; 2.1. SC: em.

Corley, Mary C.; Minick, Ptlene; Elswick, R.K.; Jacobs, Mary. Nurse moral distress and ethical work environment. *Nursing Ethics* 2005 July; 12(4): 381-390. NRCBL: 4.1.3; 1.3.2; 9.1. SC: em.

Abstract: This study examined the relationship between moral distress intensity, moral distress frequency and the ethical work environment, and explored the relationship of demographic characteristics to moral distress intensity and frequency. A group of 106 nurses from two large medical centers reported moderate levels of moral distress intensity, low levels of moral distress frequency, and a moderately positive ethical work environment. Moral distress intensity and ethical work environment were correlated with moral distress frequency. Age was negatively correlated with moral distress intensity, whereas being African American was related to higher levels of moral distress intensity. The ethical work environment predicted moral distress intensity. These results reveal a difference between moral distress intensity and frequency and the importance of the environment to moral distress intensity.

Corley, Mary C.; Raines, Deborah A. Environments that support ethical nursing practice. *AWHONN's Clinical Issues in Perinatal and Women's Health Nursing* 1993; 4(4): 611-619. NRCBL: 4.1.3; 9.4; 7.1.

Curtin, Leah L.; Arnold, Lauren. A framework for analysis, Part I. *Nursing Administration Quarterly* 2005 April-June; 29(2): 183-187. NRCBL: 4.1.3; 2.1; 7.3.

Dalby, Jan. Nurse participation in ethical decision making in the clinical setting. *AWHONN's Clinical Issues in Perinatal and Women's Health Nursing* 1993; 4(4): 606-610. NRCBL: 4.1.3; 8.1; 9.6.

Davis, Mardell; Johnston, Sarah R.; DiMicco, Wendy; Findlay, Margaret P.; Taylor, Judy A. The case for a student honor code and beyond. *Journal of Professional Nursing* 1996 January-February; 12(1): 24-30. NRCBL: 4.1.3; 7.2; 1.3.3.

Dormire, Sharon L. Ethical models: facilitating clinical practice. *AWHONN's Clinical Issues in Perinatal and Women's Health Nursing* 1993; 4(4): 526-532. NRCBL: 4.1.3; 2.1; 9.4.

Fahrenwald, Nancy L.; Bassett, Susan D.; Tschetter, Lois; Carson, Paula P.; White, Lani; Winterboer, Venita J. Teaching core nursing values. *Journal of Professional Nursing* 2005 January-February; 21(1): 46-51. NRCBL: 4.1.3; 2.3; 7.2.

Forrester, Kim. Nursing ethics. *Medicine and Law: World Association for Medical Law* 2005 March; 24(1): 125-136. NRCBL: 4.1.3; 2.1.

Fry, Sara T.; Veatch, Robert M. Benefiting the patient and others: the duty to produce good and avoid harm. *In their:* Case Studies in Nursing Ethics. Third edition. Sudbury, MA: Jones and Bartlett Publishers; 2006: 65-93. NRCBL: 4.1.3.

Groenhout, Ruth; Hotz, Kendra; Joldersma, Clarence. Embodiment, nursing practice, and religious faith: a perspective from one tradition. *Journal of Religion and Health* 2005 Summer; 44(2): 147-160. NRCBL: 4.1.3; 1.2; 8.1.

Hardingham, Lorraine B. Integrity and moral residue: nurses as participants in a moral community. *Nursing Philosophy* 2004 July; 5(2): 127-134. NRCBL: 4.1.3; 8.1; 7.3.

Harris, Marcelline R. Codes of ethics and scientific integrity: what relevance to outcomes activities? *Advanced Practical Nursing Quarterly* 1997 Winter; 3(3): 36-43. NRCBL: 4.1.3; 6; 1.3.9; 7.3; 9.8.

Hart, Sara Elizabeth. Hospital ethical climates and registered nurses' turnover intentions. *Journal of Nursing Scholarship* 2005; 37(2): 173-177. NRCBL: 4.1.3; 9.1; 1.3.2; 7.3. SC: em.

Hek, Gill. Ethical issues in community health care district nursing. *In:* Chadwick, Ruth; Levitt, Mairi, eds. Ethical Issues in Community Health Care. New York: Arnold; 1998: 125-134. NRCBL: 4.1.3; 9.1.

Hess, Joanne D. Gadow's relational narrative: an elaboration. *Nursing Philosophy* 2003 July; 4(2): 137-148. NRCBL: 4.1.3; 8.1.

Husted, Gladys L.; Husted, James H. Is a return to a caring perspective desirable? *Advanced Practice Nursing Quarterly* 1997 Summer; 3(1): 14-17. NRCBL: 4.1.3; 1.1; 2.1. SC: cs.

Jacobs, Barbara Bennett. Respect for human dignity in nursing: philosophical and practical perspectives. *Canadian Journal of Nursing Research* 2000 September; 32(2): 15-33. NRCBL: 4.1.3; 1.1; 4.4; 8.1.

Jacobson, Joy. When providing care is amoral issue: is nurses' first priority protecting the patient or their own moral convictions? *AJN: American Journal of Nursing* 2005 October; 105(10): 27- 28. NRCBL: 4.1.3.

Jameton, Andrew. Dilemmas of moral distress: moral responsibility and nursing practice. *AWHONN's Clinical Issues in Perinatal and Women's Health Nursing* 1993; 4(4): 542-551. NRCBL: 4.1.3; 1.1; 7.1.

Jesani, Amar. Ethics, rights and strike of health workers [editorial]. *Issues in Medical Ethics* 1998 July-September; 6(3): 73, 103. NRCBL: 4.1.3; 9.8.

Jormsri, Pantip; Kunaviktikul, Wipada; Ketefian, Shaké; Chaowalit, Aranya. Moral competence in nursing practice. *Nursing Ethics* 2005 November; 12(6): 582-594. NRCBL: 4.1.3; 1.1.

Abstract: This article presents the derivation of moral competence in nursing practice by identifying its attributes founded on Thai culture. In this process moral competence is formed and based on the Thai nursing value system, including personal, social and professional values. It is then defined and its three dimensions (moral perception, judgment and behavior) are also identified. Additionally, eight attributes as indicators of moral competence are identified and selected from three basic values. The eight attributes are loving kindness, compassion, sympathetic joy, equanimity, responsibility, discipline, honesty, and respect for human values, dignity and rights. All attributes are discussed by addressing the three moral dimensions in order to present how to deal with ethical issues in nursing practice. As a summary, a model of moral competence is presented to demonstrate moral competence in nursing practice in Thailand.

Kellen, Joyce C.; Oberle, Kathleen; Girard, Francine; Falkenberg, Loren. Exploring ethical perspectives of nurses and nurse managers. *Canadian Journal of Nursing Leadership* 2004 March; 17(1): 78-87. NRCBL: 4.1.3; 7.3. Identifiers: Canada.

Kendrick, Kevin. Accountability in practice: professional codes and accountable practice. *Professional Nurse* 1995 April; 10(7): supplement 1-4. NRCBL: 4.1.3; 6; 7.1.

Kilpatrick, Shelley Dean; Weaver, Andrew J.; McCullough, Michael E.; Puchalski, Christina; Larson, David B.; Hays, Judith C.; Farran, Carol J.; Flannelly, Kevin J. A review of spiritual and religious measures in nursing research journals: 1995-1999. *Journal of Religion and Health* 2005 Spring; 44(1): 55-66. NRCBL: 4.1.3; 1.2; 17.1; 7.1. SC: em.

Kim, Yong-Soon; Park, Jee-Won; You, Mi-Ae; Seo, Ye-Suk; Han, Sung-Suk. Sensitivity to ethical issues confronted by Korean hospital staff nurses. *Nursing Ethics* 2005 November; 12(6): 595-605. NRCBL: 4.1.3. SC: em.

Abstract: This descriptive study was undertaken to identify the degree of ethical sensitivity of staff nurses and to analyze the differences in ethical sensitivity in terms of both general and ethics-related characteristics. Participants were 236 staff nurses working in general hospitals in Korea. Ethical sensitivity was measured by means of an instrument developed by the researchers. The results showed that the mean score for the degree of ethical sensitivity was 0.71 out of a possible maximum score of 1 (range 0.30 to 0.97). For general characteristics, there was a significant difference in ethical sensitivity according to age (F (df 2233) = 3.99, P = 0.02). For characteristics related to ethics, there was a significant difference in ethical sensitivity according to attitude towards the nursing profession (F (df 4231) = 2.94, P = 0.03). It is therefore recommended that a training program reflecting these variables be developed to enhance staff nurses' ethical sensitivity.

Kopala, Beverly. The influence of pressure on nurses' moral capacity. *In:* Thomasma, David C.; Weisstub, David N., eds. The Variables of Moral Capacity. Boston: Kluwer Academic Publishers; 2004: 159- 171. NRCBL: 4.1.3.

Krishnasamy, Meinir. Nursing, mortality, and emotions: Phase I and phase II clinical trials and patients with cancer. *Cancer Nursing* 1999 August; 22(4): 15 p. [Online]. Available: http://gateway.ut.ovid.com/gw1/ovidweb.cgi [3 November 2005]. NRCBL: 4.1.3; 1.1; 9.5.1; 18.2.

Laabs, Carolyn A. Moral problems and distress among nurse practitioners in primary care. *Journal of the American Academy of Nurse Practitioners* 2005 February; 17(2): 76-84. NRCBL: 4.1.3; 9.1; 8.1. SC: em.

Lee, Won-Hee; Pope, Marion; Han, Sung-Suk; Yang, Soon-Ok. Korean nurses' perceptions of ethical problems: toward a new code of ethics for nursing. *Nursing and Health Sciences* 2000 December; 2(4): 217-224. NRCBL: 4.1.3; 6. SC: em.

Leino-Kilpi, Helena. Editorial comment. *Nursing Ethics* 2005 January; 12(1): 3-4. NRCBL: 4.1.3. Identifiers: nursing ethics researcher.

Manning, Georgina. Care ethics in pediatric critical care nursing. *Update [Loma Linda University Center for Christian Bioethics]* 2002 March; 17(3): 8-11. NRCBL: 4.1.3; 9.5.7; 8.1.

Mathes, Michele. Ethical decision making and nursing. *MEDSURG Nursing* 2004 December; 13(6): 429-431. NRCBL: 4.1.3; 7.3; 8.1.

NRCBL: National Reference Center for Bioethics Literature Classification Scheme   See inside front cover for terms.

355

May, Thomas; Craig, J.M.; May, Carol; Tomkowiak, John. Quality of life, justice, and the demands of hospital-based nursing. *Public Affairs Quarterly* 2005 July; 19(3): 213-225. NRCBL: 4.1.3; 7.1; 9.8; 4.4.

Millette, Brenda E. Client advocacy and the moral orientation of nurses. *Western Journal of Nursing Research* 1993 October; 15(5): 607-618. NRCBL: 4.1.3; 1.1; 9.1; 8.1.

Milton, Constance L. Ethics content in nursing education: pondering with the possible. *Nursing Science Quarterly* 2004 October; 17(4): 308-311. NRCBL: 4.1.3; 7.2.

Milton, Constance L. Scholarship in nursing: ethics of a practice doctorate. *Nursing Science Quarterly* 2005 April; 18(2): 113-116. NRCBL: 4.1.3; 7.2.

Minicucci, Daryl Sharp; Schmitt, Madeline H.; Dombeck, Mary T.; Williams, Geoffrey C. Actualizing Gadow's moral framework for nursing through research. *Nursing Philosophy* 2003 July; 4(2): 92-103. NRCBL: 4.1.3; 1.1; 8.1; 9.5.9.

Neumann, Joyce L. Ethical issues confronting oncology nurses. *Nursing Clinics of North America* 2001 December; 36(4): 827- 841. NRCBL: 4.1.3; 9.5.1; 8.3.1; 9.8; 4.4; 20.5.1; 20.5.4.

Penas, Cheri D.; Barkley, Thomas W., Jr. Ethical theory and principles of decision making for the acute care nurse practitioner. *Nurse Practitioner Forum* 2001 September; 12(3): 161-165. NRCBL: 4.1.3; 9.5.1; 8.1; 20.5.4.

Penticuff, Joy Hinson; Walden, Marlene. Influence of practice environment and nurse characteristics on perinatal nurses' responses to ethical dilemmas. *Nursing Research* 2000 March-April; 49(2): 64-72. NRCBL: 4.1.3. SC: em.

Price-Hoskins, Pam. The right thing — for the right reason. *Journal of Christian Nursing* 2004 Fall; 21(4): 6-13. NRCBL: 4.1.3; 1.2; 6. SC: cs.

Proctor, S.E. School nurses and ethical dilemmas: are schools short on ethics? [editorial]. *Journal of School Nursing* 1998 April; 14(2): 3. NRCBL: 4.1.3; 9.5.7.

Raines, Deborah A. Ethical reflection and resolution. *AWHONN's Clinical Issues in Perinatal and Women's Health Nursing* 1993; 4(4): 641-647. NRCBL: 4.1.3; 6; 7.1; 9.4.

Rushton, Cindy Hylton. Creating an ethical practice environment: a focus on advocacy. *Critical Care Nursing Clinics of North America* 1995 June; 7(2): 387-397. NRCBL: 4.1.3; 8.1; 9.1.

Scott, P. Anne. Emotion, moral perception, and nursing practice. *Nursing Philosophy* 2000 October; 1(2): 123-133. NRCBL: 4.1.3; 8.1.

Shirey, Maria R. Ethical climate in nursing practice: the leader's role. *JONA's Healthcare Law, Ethics, and Regulation* 2005 April-June; 7(2): 59-67. NRCBL: 4.1.3; 2.1; 7.1.
Abstract: Clarity in an organization's mission, vision, and values is key to effective management in today's complex healthcare work environment. To clearly articulate mission, vision, and values, employees must experience consistency between what is espoused and what is lived. The purpose of this article is to discuss the nurse leader's role in ensuring congruence between caring missions and caring practices. Ethical principles are discussed as the foundation necessary for creating an ethical climate for nursing practice. Components of ethical climate are presented and strategies to create a positive ethical climate for nursing practice are provided.

Simpson, Roy L. e-Ethics: new dilemmas emerge alongside new technologies. *Nursing Administration Quarterly* 2005 April-May; 29(2): 179-182. NRCBL: 4.1.3; 1.3.12; 8.4.

Smith, Pam; Lorentzon, Maria. Is emotional labour ethical? *Nursing Ethics* 2005 November; 12(6): 638-642. NRCBL: 4.1.3.

Sorrell, Jeanne Merkle; Silva, Mary Cipriano. Unethical behaviors of student nurses: implications for nursing education and practice. *NursingConnections* 1991 Fall; 4(3): 25-28. NRCBL: 4.1.3; 7.2; 7.4.

Strachan, Heather. Ethics. *Research and Theory for Nursing Practice* 2004 Summer-Fall; 18(2-3): 123-126. NRCBL: 4.1.3; 1.3.12; 8.4; 9.1. Identifiers: United Kingdom (Great Britain).

Sturm, Bonnie A. Ethics and care: an ethnographic study of psychiatric community health nursing practice. *Archives of Psychiatric Nursing* 2004 June; 18(3): 106-115. NRCBL: 4.1.3; 17.1. SC: em.

Toiviainen, Leila. Can practical nursing ethics be taught? [editorial]. *Nursing Ethics* 2005 July; 12(4): 335-336. NRCBL: 4.1.3; 7.2.

Trevizan, Maria Auxiliadora; Mendes, Isabel Amélia Costa; Lourenço, Maria Regina; de Godoy, Simone; Rodriguez, Eliana Llapa. Spirituality: the basis for nurses' ethics. *Medicine and Law: World Association for Medical Law* 2004; 23(4): 791-796. NRCBL: 4.1.3; 1.2.
Abstract: A social crisis in both the labor and ecological systems constitutes a problem that requires the formulation of a new ethics for humanity. The social crisis is a result of the organizational model used by modern societies in the production of wealth and its unequal distribution. This intense inequality in wealth distribution contributes to a schism between populations. On one side an opulent and privileged society exists, and on the other a poor and downtrodden humanity. This crisis in the labor system stems from automated production methods, which devalue man's work and exclude him from contemporary society. The ecological crisis emerges from the dominance with which men have subjugated the Earth and its resources. Man has not acknowledged Earth's permutations and, therefore, has not taken the necessary caution of such changeability nor respected its effects. Such crises affect all populations and cry out for attention. Contemporary societies demand solutions to these questions. Nursing is a part and parcel of this yearning. In this

setting, the nurse should be able to offer collaboration and solidarity with a project of creating a world ethos based on a minimum consensus amongst humans. Understanding and believing that spirituality is invaluable in this process, the authors of this work aim at addressing it as an essential dimension for nurses' ethics.

Ulrich, Connie M.; Soeken, Karen L. A path analytic model of ethical conflict in practice and autonomy in a sample of nurse practitioners. *Nursing Ethics* 2005 May; 12(3): 305-316. NRCBL: 4.1.3; 1.1. SC: em.

Abstract: The purpose of this study was to test a causal model of ethical conflict in practice and autonomy in a sample of 254 nurse practitioners working in the primary care areas of family health, pediatrics, adult health and obstetrics/gynecology in the state of Maryland. A test of the model was conducted using a path analytic approach with LISREL 8.30 hypothesizing individual, organizational and societal/market factors influencing ethical conflict in practice and autonomy. Maximum likelihood estimation was used to estimate the parameters most likely to have generated the data. Forty-five percent of the total variance in ethical conflict was explained by the variables of ethical environment and ethical concern. Ethical concern, idealistic philosophy, ethics education in continuing education, percentage of client population enrolled in managed care, and market penetration explained 15% of the total variance in autonomy. The findings of this study indicate that the causal model of ethical conflict in practice and autonomy is consistent with the data and contributed to a fuller understanding of clinical decision making associated with practicing in a managed care environment. The final model supported a conceptual framework that is inclusive of three domains: individual, organizational and societal/market variables.

van Hooft, Stan. Kuhse on caring. *Nursing Inquiry* 1999 June; 6(2): 112-122. NRCBL: 4.1.3; 4.1.1; 1.1.

Winch, Sarah. Ethics, government and sexual health: insights from Foucault. *Nursing Ethics* 2005 March; 12(2): 177-186. NRCBL: 4.1.3; 1.1; 10.

Abstract: The work of Michel Foucault, the French philosopher who was interested in power relationships, has resonated with many nurses who seek a radically analytical view of nursing practice. The purpose of this article is to explore 'ethics' through a Foucauldian lens, in a conceptual and methodological sense. The intention is to provide a useful framework that will help researchers critically to explore aspects of nursing practice that relate to the construction of the self, morality and identity, be that nurse or patient related. The fundamentals of the research method of genealogy and the methods of ethics are reviewed. Using an example taken from the sexual health practice area, advice is given on how to structure data collection, incorporate interview data, avoid discourse determinism and measure resistance.

Woods, Martin. Nursing ethics education: are we really delivering the good(s)? *Nursing Ethics* 2005 January; 12(1): 5-18. NRCBL: 4.1.3; 7.2.

Abstract: The vast majority of research in nursing ethics over the last decade indicates that nurses may not be fully prepared to 'deliver the good(s)' for their patients, or to contribute appropriately in the wider current health care climate. When suitable research projects were evaluated for this article, one key question emerged: if nurses are educationally better prepared than ever before to exercise their ethical decision-making skills, why does research still indicate that the expected practice-based improvements remain elusive? Hence, a number of ideas gleaned from recent research about the current nature of nursing ethics, and especially teaching nursing ethics to student nurses, are analysed and critiqued in this article, which concludes with a cluster of ideas and conclusions based on that analysis. It is hoped that such a review may serve as a catalyst for nurse educators to re-examine their teaching practices with a view to enhancing good (i.e. ethical) nursing practice through educational means.

OCCUPATIONAL HEALTH

American Occupational Therapy Association [AOTA]. Enforcement procedures for Occupational Therapy Code of Ethics (2004). *American Journal of Occupational Therapy* 2004 November-December; 58(6): 655-662. NRCBL: 16.3; 6.

Ashford, Nicholas A. Monitoring the worker and the community for chemical exposure and disease: legal and ethical considerations in the US. *Clinical Chemistry* 1994 July; 40(7 Part 2): 1426-1437. NRCBL: 16.3; 9.5.1; 9.1. SC: le.

Aw, T.C. Ethical issues in occupational medicine practice: knowledge and attitudes of occupational physicians. *Occupational Medicine* 1997 August; 47(6): 371-376. NRCBL: 16.3; 4.1.2; 1.3.1; 21.1. SC: em. Identifiers: United Kingdom (Great Britain); Netherlands; Singapore.

Egilman, David; Fehnel, Corey; Bohme, Susanna Rankin. Exposing the "myth" of ABC, "anything but chrysotile": a critique of the Canadian asbestos mining industry and McGill University chrysotile studies. *American Journal of Industrial Medicine* 2003 November; 44(5): 540-557. NRCBL: 16.3; 1.3.9. SC: le; rv. Identifiers: Quebec.

Fallon, L. Fleming, Jr. Ethics in the practice of occupational medicine. *Occupational Medicine* 2001 July-September; 16(3): 517-524. NRCBL: 16.3; 4.1.2; 1.1; 7.3.

Guidotti, Tee L. Ethics and skeptics: what lies behind ethical codes in occupational health. *Journal of Occupational and Environmental Medicine* 2005 February; 47(2): 168-175. NRCBL: 16.3; 6.

Keown, Rebecca. In that case. Response [case study]. *Journal of Bioethical Inquiry* 2005; 2(1): 56. NRCBL: 16.3; 8.1; 9.5.1; 9.7. SC: cs. Identifiers: Ribavirin; occupational health; duty to treat. Comments: comment on Ian Kerridge and Nicole Gilroy "In that case, " Journal of Bioethical Inquiry 2005; 2(1): 51.

London, Leslie. Dual loyalties and the ethical and human rights obligations of occupational health professionals. *American Journal of Industrial Medicine* 2005 April; 47(4): 322-332. NRCBL: 16.3; 7.3; 21.1.

Samuels, Sheldon W. Occupational medicine and its moral discontents [editorial]. *Journal of Occupational and Environmental Medicine* 2003 December; 45(12): 1226-1233. NRCBL: 16.3.

NRCBL: National Reference Center for Bioethics Literature Classification Scheme   See inside front cover for terms.

357

Seabrook, Robert; Collins, Ben. The duty of care of the occupational physician in assessing job applicants. *Occupational Medicine* 1999 April; 49(3): 189-192. NRCBL: 16.3; 9.1; 8.1. SC: le.

Torda, Adrienne. In that case. Response [case study]. *Journal of Bioethical Inquiry* 2005; 2(1): 54-55. NRCBL: 16.3; 8.1; 9.5.1. SC: cs. Identifiers: occupational health; duty to treat; ribavirin. Comments: comment on Ian Kerridge and Nicole Gilroy, "In that case," Journal of Bioethical Inquiry 2005; 2(1): 51.

Van Damme, Karel; Vineis, Paolo; Sorsa, Marja; Casteleyn, Ludwine. Ethical issues in genetic screening and genetic monitoring of employees. *Annals of the New York Academy of Sciences* 1997 December 26; 837: 554-565. NRCBL: 16.3; 15.3; 9.1; 2.1; 21.1.

van den Hoven, Mariëtte A.; Verweij, Marcel F. Should we promote influenza vaccination of health care workers in nursing homes? Some ethical arguments in favour of immunization. *Age and Ageing* 2003 September; 32(5): 487-489. NRCBL: 16.3; 9.7.

ORGAN AND TISSUE TRANSPLANTATION
See also BLOOD DONATION AND TRANSFUSION

The first facial transplant [editorial]. *Lancet* 2005 December 10-16; 366(9502): 1984. NRCBL: 19.1; 5.2.

Agich, G.J.; Siemionow, M. Until they have faces: the ethics of facial allograft transplantation. *Journal of Medical Ethics* 2005 December; 31(12): 707-709. NRCBL: 19.1; 9.5.1; 18.1. SC: an.

Altman, Lawrence K. French, in first, use a transplant to repair a face. *New York Times* 2005 December 1; p. A1, A6. NRCBL: 19.1; 4.1.1. SC: po.

Altman, Lawrence K. A pioneering transplant, and now an ethical storm. *New York Times* 2005 December 6; p. F1, F4. NRCBL: 19.1; 4.1.2. SC: po. Identifiers: Jean-Michel Dubernard.

Appel, Jacob M. Wanted dead or alive? Kidney transplantation in inmates awaiting execution. *Journal of Clinical Ethics* 2005 Spring; 16(1): 58-60. NRCBL: 19.3; 20.6; 9.2; 9.5.1.

Ariss, Rachel. Theorizing waste in abortion and fetal ovarian tissue use. *Canadian Journal of Women and the Law* 2003; 15(2): 255-281. NRCBL: 19.1; 18.5.4; 12.1; 14.4; 4.4. SC: le.

Boggi, U.; Vistoli, F.; Del Chiaro, M.; Croce, C.; Signori, S.; Marchetti, P.; Del Prato, S.; Rizzo, G.; Mosca, F. Kidney and pancreas transplants in Jehovah's Witnesses: ethical and practical implications. *Transplantation Proceedings* 2004 April; 36(3): 601-602. NRCBL: 19.1; 8.3.4; 1.2; 19.4.

Bramstedt, Katrina A. Informed consent documentation for total artificial heart technology. *Journal of Artificial Organs* 2001; 4: 273-277. NRCBL: 19.2; 8.3.1.

Bruzzone, Paolo; Pretagostini, Renzo; Rossi, Massimo; Berloco, Pasquale B. Ethical considerations on kidney transplantation from living donors. *Annals of Transplantation* 2004; 9(2): 46-47. NRCBL: 19.3; 19.5. SC: em.

Butler, Peter E.M.; Clarke, Alex; Hettiaratchy, Shehan. Facial transplantation: a new option in reconstruction of severe facial injury [editorial]. *BMJ: British Medical Journal* 2005 December 10; 331(7529): 1349-1350. NRCBL: 19.1; 8.3.1.

Caplan, Arthur L. Transplantation at any price? *American Journal of Transplantation* 2004 December; 4(12): 1933-1934. NRCBL: 19.1; 19.3; 9.3.1.

Clark, Peter A. Face transplantation: Part II — an ethical perspective. *Medical Science Monitor* 2005 February; 11(2): RA41-RA47. NRCBL: 19.1; 18.1.

Colabawalla, B.N. Issues in organ transplantation. *Issues in Medical Ethics* 2001 July-September; 9(3): 88-90. NRCBL: 19.1.

Crawford, Michael. Live donor liver transplantation: where does it stand in Australia and New Zealand? [opinion]. *Internal Medicine Journal* 2003 November; 33(11): 482-483. NRCBL: 19.1; 19.5; 21.1.

Dekkers, Wim; Uerz, Inez; Wils, Jean-Pierre. Living well with end stage renal disease: patients' narratives interpreted from a virtue perspective. *Ethical Theory and Moral Practice* 2005 November; 8(5): 485-506. NRCBL: 19.3; 7.1; 1.1. SC: em. Identifiers: Aristotle.

Gibbons, Robert D. Racial disparities in liver transplantation [editorial]. *Liver Transplantation* 2004 July; 10(7): 842-843. NRCBL: 19.1; 19.6; 9.5.4; 9.4.

Golmakani, Mohammad Mehdi; Niknam, Mohammad Hussein; Hedayat, Kamyar M. Transplantation ethics from the Islamic point of view. *Medical Science Monitor* 2005 April; 11(4): RA105-RA109. NRCBL: 19.1; 1.2; 21.1. Identifiers: Iran.

Goodman, Neville W. Poor worth the sum of their parts. *British Journal of Hospital Medicine* 1994 January 19-February 1; 51(1- 2): 61. NRCBL: 19.3; 9.3.1; 9.5.10; 21.1.

Great Britain. Department of Health; National Health Service. Central Office for Research Ethics Committees [COREC]; Welsh AssemblyGovernment. The Use of Human Organs and Tissue: An Interim Statement. London: Department of Health [31520], 2003 April; 19 p. NRCBL: 19.1; 8.3.1; 18.2.

SC (Subject Caption):   an=analytical   cs=case studies   em=empirical   le=legal   po=popular   rv=review

Hansson, S.O. Implant ethics. *Journal of Medical Ethics* 2005 September; 31(9): 519-525. NRCBL: 19.1; 5.1; 9.7; 20.5.1.

Abstract: Implant ethics is defined here as the study of ethical aspects of the lasting introduction of technological devices into the human body. Whereas technological implants relieve us of some of the ethical problems connected with transplantation, other difficulties arise that are in need of careful analysis. A systematic approach to implant ethics is proposed. The major specific problems are identified as those concerning end of life issues (turning off devices), enhancement of human capabilities beyond normal levels, mental changes and personal identity, and cultural effects.

Hilhorst, Medard T. Directed altruistic living organ donation: partial but not unfair. *Ethical Theory and Moral Practice* 2005 April; 8(1-2): 197-215. NRCBL: 19.3; 19.5; 8.4; 1.1.

Hippen, Benjamin E. In defense of a regulated market in kidneys from living vendors. *Journal of Medicine and Philosophy* 2005 December; 30(6): 593- 626. NRCBL: 19.3; 19.5; 9.3.1. SC: an.

Abstract: The current system of organ procurement which relies on donation is inadequate to the current and future need for transplantable kidneys. The growing disparity between demand and supply is accompanied by a steep human cost. I argue that a regulated market in organs from living vendors is the only plausible solution, and that objections common to opponents of organ markets are de-feasible. I argue that a morally defensible market in kidneys from living vendors includes four characteristics: (1) the priority of safety for both vendors and recipients, (2) transparency regarding the risks to vendors and recipients, (3) institutional integrity regarding guidelines for cooperating with kidney vendors, and (4) operation under a rule of law. I conclude with some remarks on remaining problems with this account, and offer some suggestions as to how these problems might be addressed.

Huxtable, Richard; Woodley, Julie. Gaining face or losing face? Framing the debate on face transplants. *Bioethics* 2005 October; 19(5-6): 505-522. NRCBL: 19.1; 1.1.

Abstract: An American surgical team has announced its intention to perform the first human facial transplantation. The team has, however, invited further analysis of the ethical issues before it proceeds and in this paper we take up that challenge in seeking to frame the debate with a particular focus on the recipients of the transplant. We address seven related areas of concern and identify numerous questions that require answers or, perhaps, better answers. We start by examining the nature of the procedure and its intended benefits, why the procedure is being developed, and whether or not this should be viewed as experimental. Having concluded that this is experimental in nature, we then consider the broad question, who is the patient? Here we perceive difficulties in terms of the autonomy of the recipient, the unpredictable effects of receiving the transplant, and the role and influence of society. We conclude by asking whether the question should be 'whether or not?' rather than 'when?', particularly while the risks of losing face appear to far outweigh the likelihood of gaining face.

Jayakrishnan, T.; Jeeja, M.C. Human organ sale: the Kerala story. *Issues in Medical Ethics* 2003 July-September; 11(3): 81-82. NRCBL: 19.3; 9.3.1; 19.5.

Jonsen, Albert R. Organ transplantation. *In his:* Bioethics Beyond the Headlines: Who Lives? Who Dies? Who Decides? Lanham, MD: Rowman and Littlefield; 2005: 59-66. NRCBL: 19.1; 19.5; 19.6.

Kaczor, Christopher. Could artificial wombs end the abortion debate? *National Catholic Bioethics Quarterly* 2005 Summer; 5(2): 283- 301. NRCBL: 19.1; 12.1; 1.2.

Knoll, Greg; Cockfield, Sandra; Blydt-Hansen, Tom; Baran, Dana; Kiberd, Bryce; Landsberg, David; Rush, David; Cole, Edward. Canadian Society of Transplantation consensus guidelines on eligibility for kidney transplantation. *CMAJ/JAMC: Canadian Medical Association Journal* 2005 November 8; 173(10): 1181-1184. NRCBL: 19.3; 9.4.

Kraco, K. Body bequest programs in Minnesota. *Minnesota Medicine* 2004 June; 87(6): 8-9. NRCBL: 19.1; 20.1.

Le Melle, Stephanie M.; Entelis, Charles. Heart transplant in a young man with schizophrenia. *American Journal of Psychiatry* 2005 March; 162(3): 453-457. NRCBL: 19.2; 9.5.3; 9.4; 9.2; 8.1. SC: cs.

Mason, Michael. A new face. *New York Times* 2005 July 26; p. F1, F6. NRCBL: 19.1. SC: po. Identifiers: face transplants.

Mason, Michael; Altman, Lawrence K. Ethical concerns on face transplant grow; American scientists raise medical and psychological issues. *New York Times* 2005 December 6; p. A12. NRCBL: 19.1; 4.1.1. SC: po.

Nagral, Sanjay. The kidney trade again [editorial]. *Indian Journal of Medical Ethics* 2004 April-June; 1(2): 36-37. NRCBL: 19.3; 19.5; 9.3.1. Identifiers: Transplantation of Human Organs Act; India.

Nagral, Sanjay. Organ transplantation: ethical issues and the Indian scenario. *Issues in Medical Ethics* 2001 April-June; 9(2): 41-43. NRCBL: 19.1; 1.2.

Ngah, Anisah Che. Organ transplantation in Malaysia: a socio-legal study. *Formosan Journal of Medical Humanities* 2005 September; 6(1-2): 39-48. NRCBL: 19.1; 19.3; 21.1. SC: le.

Nolan, Marie T.; Walton-Moss, Benita; Taylor, Laura; Dane, Kathryn. Living kidney donor decision making: state of the science and directions for future research. *Progress in Transplantation* 2004 September; 14(3): 201-209. NRCBL: 19.3; 19.1. SC: rv.

Oreopoulos, D.G. Should we let them die? *In:* Parsons, Frank M.; Ogg, Chisholm S., eds. Renal Failure — Who Cares? Boston: MTP Press; 1983: 65-73. NRCBL: 19.3; 20.5.1; 9.4.

Orfali, Kristina; Anderson-Shaw, Lisa. When medical cure is not an unmitigated good. *Perspectives in Biology*

NRCBL: National Reference Center for Bioethics Literature Classification Scheme   See inside front cover for terms.

359

and Medicine 2005 Spring; 48(2): 282-292. NRCBL: 19.1; 19.3; 4.2; 4.4; 17.1.

Pancevski, Bojan. Swiss hospital investigates heart transplant "experiment". *Lancet* 2005 August 20-26; 366(9486): 624. NRCBL: 19.2; 7.4.

Petit, François; Paraskevas, Antonis; Minns, Alicia B.; Lee, W.P. Andrew; Lantieri, Laurent A. Face transplantation: where do we stand? *Plastic and Reconstructive Surgery* 2004 April 15; 113(5): 1429-1433. NRCBL: 19.1; 19.6.

Sarteschi, L.M. Jehovah's witnesses, blood transfusions and transplantations. *Transplantation Proceedings* 2004 April; 36(3): 499-501. NRCBL: 19.1; 8.3.4; 1.2; 19.4.

Sidley, Pat. South African doctors arrested in kidney sale scandal [news]. *BMJ: British Medical Journal* 2005 September 3; 331(7515): 473. NRCBL: 19.3; 19.5; 9.3.1; 7.4. SC: le.

Smith, Craig S. As a face transplant heals, flurries of questions arise; doctors differ on ethics and patient's mental state. *New York Times* 2005 December 14; p A1, A14. NRCBL: 19.1; 4.2. SC: po.

Smith, Craig S. Dire wounds, a new face, a glimpse in a mirror: doctors describe and defend transplant for Frenchwoman. *New York Times* 2005 December 3; p. A1, A8. NRCBL: 19.1; 9.5.1; 4.1.1. SC: po.

Springen, Karen. The ultimate transplant: surgeons are ready to offer burn victims entire faces from donors, but there are risks. *Newsweek* 2005 December 12; 146(24): 60-61. NRCBL: 19.1; 8.3.1. SC: po.

Spurgeon, Brad. Surgeons pleased with patient's progress after face transplant [news]. *BMJ: British Medical Journal* 2005 December 10; 331(7529): 1359. NRCBL: 19.1. Identifiers: France.

Squier, Susan. Transplant medicine and transformative narrative. *In her:* Liminal Lives: Imaging the Human at the Frontiers of Biomedicine. Durham: Duke University Press; 2004: 168-213. NRCBL: 19.1; 19.5.

Taylor, James Stacey. Why not a kidney market? An obvious solution to the organ shortage. *Free Inquiry* 2005 August-September; 25(5): 42-43. NRCBL: 19.3; 9.3.1.

Van Vlierberghe, H.; Colle, I.; Troisi, R.; de Hemptinne, B.; De Vos, M. Liver transplantation and mental retardation. *Acta Gastro-Enterologica Belgica* 2002 April-June; 65(2): 131-132. NRCBL: 19.1; 9.5.3.

Veatch, Robert M. Organs on the Internet [letter]. *Hastings Center Report* 2005 May-June; 35(3): 6. NRCBL: 19.1; 1.3.12; 9.3.1.

ORGAN AND TISSUE TRANSPLANTATION/ ALLOCATION

Bernat, Erwin. Marketing of human organs? *Medicine and Law: World Association for Medical Law* 1995; 14(3-4): 181-190. NRCBL: 19.6; 4.4; 19.5. SC: le.

Bollinger, R. Randal; Cho, Won-Hyun. Organ allocation for transplantation in the USA and Korea: the changing roles of equity and utility. *Yonsei Medical Journal* 2004 December 31; 45(6): 1035-1042. NRCBL: 19.6; 19.5; 2.2; 21.1. Identifiers: United Network for Organ Sharing [UNOS]; Korean Network for Organ Sharing [KONOS].

Bramstedt, Katrina A. Ethical issues associated with the determination of patient selection criteria for total artificial heart technology. *Cardiovascular Engineering* 2001; 6(1): 58-61. NRCBL: 19.6; 19.2.

Cohen, Lloyd R. UNOS: the faithless trustee. *American Journal of Bioethics* 2005 July-August; 5(4): 13-14. NRCBL: 19.6; 19.5. Identifiers: United Network for Organ Sharing. Comments: comment on Sheldon Zink et al., "Examining the potential exploitation of UNOS policies," American Journal of Bioethics 2005 July-August; 5(4): 6-10.

Egan, Thomas M. Ethical issues in thoracic organ distribution for transplant. *American Journal of Transplantation* 2003 April; 3(4): 366-372. NRCBL: 19.6. SC: em.

Evans, Roger W.; Kitzmann, Daniel J. The "arithmetic" of donor liver allocation. *Clinical Transplantation* 1996: 338-342. NRCBL: 19.6; 9.3.1; 9.3.2; 19.5.

Ferguson, Melissa E.; Ferguson, Ronald M. Rescuing Prometheus: a policy proposal to alleviate excess demand for liver transplantation. *Clinical Transplantation* 1997 February; 11(1): 49-55. NRCBL: 19.6; 19.5.

Fung, John J.; Roberts, John P. The rationale for equitable liver allocation. *Clinical Transplantation* 1996: 325-332. NRCBL: 19.6; 9.3.1; 5.3.

Gordon, Elisa J. Make it so!: advocating for UNOS policy change. *American Journal of Bioethics* 2005 July-August; 5(4): 21-22. NRCBL: 19.6; 19.5. Identifiers: United Network for Organ Sharing. Comments: comment on Sheldon Zink et al., "Examining the potential exploitation of UNOS policies," American Journal of Bioethics 2005 July-August; 5(4): 6-10.

Hackler, Chris; Hester, D. Micah. Age and the allocation of organs for transplantation: a case study. *Health Care Analysis: An International Journal of Health Care Philosophy and Policy* 2005 June; 13(2): 129-136. NRCBL: 19.6; 9.4; 9.5.2.

Abstract: What role should age play in the allocation of organs for transplantation? Historically, older patients have not been listed as candidates for transplantation on the assumption that greater benefit could be obtained by favoring younger candidates, raising questions of equity and age discrimination. At the

---

same time, organs offered for donation by the very old are frequently rejected because of concerns about length of viability. We examine a local case that challenges these practices: the liver from an elderly donor was successfully transplanted into an older patient. After exploring some of the potential problems with such a solution, we propose creating a second pool of organs from the very old for transplantation into older candidates, thus expanding the number of organs available, saving additional lives, and including the elderly more visibly in our transplant system.

Howard, David H. Dynamic analysis of liver allocation policies. *Medical Decision Making* 2001; 21: 257-266. NRCBL: 19.6. SC: em.

Howard, David H. Hope versus efficiency in organ allocation. *Transplantation* 2001 September 27; 72(6): 1169-1173. NRCBL: 19.6.

Johannes, Laura. Double standard: for some transplant patients, diseased hearts are lifesavers. Surgeons enlist elderly, sick to receive inferior organs; the new ethical issues; facing a risk of hepatitis C. *Wall Street Journal* 2005 April 14; p. A1,A8. NRCBL: 19.6; 9.4; 19.2. SC: po.

Morreim, E. Haavi. Another kind of end-run: status upgrade. *American Journal of Bioethics* 2005 July-August; 5(4): 11-12. NRCBL: 19.6; 19.5; 7.4. SC: le. Identifiers: Riley v. St. Luke's Episcopal Hospital; False Claims Act (FCA). Comments: comment on Sheldon Zink et al., "Examining the potential exploitation of UNOS policies," American Journal of Bioethics 2005 July-August; 5(4): 6-10.

Norman, Douglas J. Allocation of livers for liver transplantation: ethics and politics. *Clinics in Liver Disease* 1997 August; 1(2): 281-286, viii. NRCBL: 19.6; 19.1. SC: an.

Piccoli, G.B.; Soragna, G.; Putaggio, S.; Burdese, M.; Longo, P.; Rinaldi, D.; Bergamo, D.; Mezza, E.; Consiglio, V.; Novaresio, C.; Gai, M.; Motta, D.; Malfi, B.; Giacchino, F.; Jeantet, A.; Segoloni, G.P. How many organs should one patient receive? The ethics of transplantation in the medical school. *Transplantation Proceedings* 2004 April; 36(3): 444-445. NRCBL: 19.6. SC: em. Identifiers: Italy.

Prottas, Jeffrey. Ethics of allocation: lessons from organ procurement history. *In:* Youngner, Stuart J.; Anderson, Martha W.; Schapiro, Renie, eds. Transplanting Human Tissue: Ethics, Policy, and Practice. New York: Oxford University Press; 2004: 120-136. NRCBL: 19.6.

Ravelingien, An; Krom, André. Earning points for moral behavior: organ allocation based on reciprocity. *International Journal of Applied Philosophy* 2005 Spring; 19(1): 73-83. NRCBL: 19.6; 19.5. SC: an.

Schmidt, Volker H.; Lim, Chee Han. Organ transplantation in Singapore: history, problems, and policies. *Social Science and Medicine* 2004 November; 59(10): 2173-2182. NRCBL: 19.6. SC: em.

Sequist, Thomas D.; Narva, Andrew S.; Stiles, Sharon K.; Karp, Shelley K.; Cass, Alan; Ayanian, John Z. Access to renal transplantation among American Indians and Hispanics. *American Journal of Kidney Diseases* 2004 August; 44(2): 344-352. NRCBL: 19.6; 9.5.4; 19.3. SC: em.

Siegal, Gil; Bonnie, Richard J. Reflections on fairness in UNOS allocation policies. *American Journal of Bioethics* 2005 July-August; 5(4): 28-29. NRCBL: 19.6; 19.5; 1.1. Identifiers: United Network for Organ Sharing. Comments: comment on Sheldon Zink et al., "Examining the potential exploitation of UNOS policies," American Journal of Bioethics 2005 July-August; 5(4): 6-10.

Siegler, Jessica; Siegler, Mark; Cronin, David C., II. Recipient death during a live donor liver transplantation: who gets the "orphan" graft? *Transplantation* 2004 November 15; 78(9): 1241-1244. NRCBL: 19.6; 19.5; 20.1. SC: em.

Truog, Robert D. Are organs personal property or a societal resource? *American Journal of Bioethics* 2005 July-August; 5(4): 14-16. NRCBL: 19.6; 19.5; 9.3.1; 1.3.12. Identifiers: United Network for Organ Sharing (UNOS). Comments: comment on Sheldon Zink et al., "Examining the potential exploitation of UNOS policies," American Journal of Bioethics 2005 July-August; 5(4): 6-10.

Valapour, Maryam. Ethics of organ distribution in lung transplantation. *Minnesota Medicine* 2004 June; 87(6): 36-37. NRCBL: 19.6.

Vulchev, Anntim; Roberts, John P.; Stock, Peter G. Ethical issues in split versus whole liver transplantation. *American Journal of Transplantation* 2004 November; 4(11): 1737-1740. NRCBL: 19.6.

Whitford, Ben. Who gets the organs? Experts say transplant medicine has a race problem. *Newsweek* 2005 November 28; 146(22): 49. NRCBL: 19.6; 9.5.4. SC: po.

Wright, Jessica. Medically necessary organ transplants for prisoners: who is responsible for payment? *Boston College Law Review* 1998 September; 39(5): 1251-1292. NRCBL: 19.6; 18.5.5; 9.3.1. SC: le.

Zink, Sheldon; Wertlieb, Stacey. Response to commentators on "Examining the potential exploitation of UNOS policies" [letter]. *American Journal of Bioethics [Online]* 2005 September- October; 5(5): W15-W16. NRCBL: 19.6; 19.5. Identifiers: United Network for Organ Sharing.

Zink, Sheldon; Wertlieb, Stacey; Catalano, John; Marwin, Victor. Examining the potential exploitation of UNOS policies. *American Journal of Bioethics* 2005 July-August; 5(4): 6-10. NRCBL: 19.6; 19.5.
  Abstract: The United Network for Organ Sharing (UNOS) waiting list was designed as a just and equitable system through which the limited number of organs is allocated to the millions of Americans in need of a transplant. People have trusted the

---

NRCBL: National Reference Center for Bioethics Literature Classification Scheme   See inside front cover for terms.

361

system because of the belief that everyone on the list has an equal opportunity to receive an organ and also that allocation is blind to matters of financial standing, celebrity or political power. Recent events have revealed that certain practices and policies have the potential to be exploited. The policies addressed in this paper enable those on the list with the proper resources to gain an advantage over other less fortunate members, creating a system that benefits not the individual most in medical need, but the one with the best resources. These policies are not only unethical but threaten the balance and success of the entire UNOS system. This paper proposes one possible solution, which seeks to balance the concepts of justice and utility.

ORGAN AND TISSUE TRANSPLANTATION/ DONATION AND PROCUREMENT

Appendix B: Bill of rights for donor families. *In:* Youngner, Stuart J.; Anderson, Martha W.; Schapiro, Renie, eds. Transplanting Human Tissue: Ethics, Policy, and Practice. New York: Oxford University Press; 2004: 199-202. NRCBL: 19.5.

Appendix C: informed consent policy for tissue donation. *In:* Youngner, Stuart J.; Anderson, Martha W.; Schapiro, Renie, eds. Transplanting Human Tissue: Ethics, Policy, and Practice. New York: Oxford University Press; 2004: 203. NRCBL: 19.5; 8.3.1.

Abbud-Filho, Mario; Garcia, V.D.; Campos, H.H.; Pestana, J.O.M. Do we need living unrelated organ donation in Brazil? *Transplantation Proceedings* 2004 May; 36(4): 805-807. NRCBL: 19.5; 20.1.

Al Sebayel, M.I.M.; Khalaf, H. Knowledge and attitude of intensivists toward organ donation in Riyadh, Saudi Arabia. *Transplantation Proceedings* 2004 September; 36(7): 1883-1884. NRCBL: 19.5; 7.1. SC: em.

Al-Khader, A.A. A model for scoring and grading willingness of a potential living related donor. *Journal of Medical Ethics* 2005 June; 31(6): 338-340. NRCBL: 19.5. SC: em.
Abstract: There are few examples in the literature of objective measures for the assessment of donor willingness. The author describes the scoring system in use at his own renal transplant unit which has brought objectivity to the process of determining the willingness of living related donors. In this system, a total score to determine the degree of willingness or unwillingness is calculated based on responses to a series of questions. The author believes that with minor modifications this system could be implemented by transplant units in different countries and cultures to screen out donors who are acting under duress.

American Association of Tissue Banks; Association of Organ Procurement Organizations; Eye Bank Association of America. Appendix A: model elements of informed consent for organ and tissue donation. *In:* Youngner, Stuart J.; Anderson, Martha W.; Schapiro, Renie, eds. Transplanting Human Tissue: Ethics, Policy, and Practice. New York: Oxford University Press; 2004: 195-197. NRCBL: 19.5; 8.3.1.

Andersen, Marit Helen; Mathisen, Lars; Øyen, Ole; Wahl, Astrid Klopstad; Hanestad, Berit Rokne; Fosse, Erik. Living donors' experiences 1 wk after donating a kidney. *Clinical Transplantation* 2005 February; 19(1): 90-96. NRCBL: 19.5; 19.3. SC: em. Identifiers: Norway.

Anderson, Martha W.; Schapiro, Renie. From donor to recipient: the pathway and business of donated tissues. *In:* Youngner, Stuart J.; Anderson, Martha W.; Schapiro, Renie, eds. Transplanting Human Tissue: Ethics, Policy, and Practice. New York: Oxford University Press; 2004: 3-13. NRCBL: 19.5; 1.3.2.

Anderson-Shaw, Lisa; Schmidt, Mary Lou; Elkin, Jeanine; Chamberlin, William; Benedetti, Enrico; Testa, Guiliano. Evolution of a living donor liver transplantation advocacy program. *Journal of Clinical Ethics* 2005 Spring; 16(1): 46-57. NRCBL: 19.5; 19.6; 8.3.1.

Appel, Jacob M.; Fox, Mark D. Organ solicitation on the Internet: every man for himself? [case study and commentaries]. *Hastings Center Report* 2005 May-June; 35(3): 14-15. NRCBL: 19.5; 1.3.12.

Ashley, Benedict M. Organ donation and implantation. *In:* McMahon, Kevin T., ed. Moral Issues in Catholic Health Care. Wynnewood, PA: Saint Charles Borromeo Seminary; 2004: 153- 167. NRCBL: 19.5; 1.2.

Azarow, Kenneth S.; Olmstead, Francis L.; Hume, Roderick F.; Myers, Jerome; Calhoun, Bryon C.; Martin, Laura S. Ethical use of tissue samples in genetic research. *Military Medicine* 2003 June; 168(6): 437-441. NRCBL: 19.5; 15.1; 18.6; 18.3.

Bagheri, Alizera; Shoji, Shin'ichi. The model and moral justification for organ procurement in Japan. *Journal International de Bioethique / International Journal of Bioethics* 2005 March-June; 16(1-2): 79-90, 194-195. NRCBL: 19.5; 20.2.1; 8.3.1. Note: Abstract in English and French.

Beecham, Linda. Donors and relatives must place no conditions on organ use [news]. *BMJ: British Medical Journal* 2000 February 26; 320(7234): 534. NRCBL: 19.5. Note: See correction in BMJ 2000 March 4; 320(7235): 602.

Boey, Kam Weng. A cross-validation study of nurses' attitudes and commitment to organ donation in Hong Kong. *International Journal of Nursing Studies* 2002 January; 39(1): 95-104. NRCBL: 19.5; 7.1; 4.1.3.

Bos, Michael A. Ethical and legal issues in non-heart-beating organ donation. *Transplantation* 2005 May 15; 79(9): 1143-1147. NRCBL: 19.5; 20.2.1. Identifiers: Netherlands.

Bramstedt, Katrina A.; Stowe, Judy; Kotz, Margaret. Shopping for a transplant: when noncompliant patients seek wait listing at multiple hospitals. *Progress in Transplantation* 2004 September; 14(3): 217-221. NRCBL: 19.5; 9.5.9; 19.6. SC: cs.

Coleman, Stephen. The developing human as a source of donor organs. *In his:* The Ethics of Artificial Uteruses: Implications for Reproduction and Abortion. Burlington, VT: Ashgate Pub.; 2004: 151- 165. NRCBL: 19.5; 18.5.4; 12.1; 14.1. SC: an.

Council of Europe. Additional protocol to the Convention on Human Rights and Biomedicine, on transplantation of organs and tissues of human origin. *Medical Ethics and Bioethics / Medicinska Etika & Bioetika* 2003 Spring-Summer; 10(1-2): 10-13. NRCBL: 19.5; 8.3.1; 8.4; 1.3.2.

Cyranoski, David. Paper chase [news]. *Nature* 2005 October 6; 437(7060): 810-811. NRCBL: 19.5; 18.5.4; 18.1. Identifiers: China; Hongyun Huang.

Daar, A.S. Non-heart-beating donation: ten evidence-based ethical recommendations. *Transplantation Proceedings* 2004 September; 36(7): 1885-1887. NRCBL: 19.5; 20.2.1.

Dahlke, Marc H.; Popp, Felix C.; Eggert, Nadine; Hoy, Ludwig; Tanaka, Hideaki; Sasaki, Katsunori; Piso, Pompiliu; Schlitt, Hans J. Differences in attitude toward living and postmortal liver donation in the United States, Germany, and Japan. *Psychosomatics* 2005 January-February; 46(1): 58-64. NRCBL: 19.5; 19.1; 21.1. SC: em.

De Vise, Daniel. Years after giving marrow, the return gift of meeting: Alabama donor goes to Arundel (county) to see the young girl he saved. *Washington Post* 2005 July 11; p. B1, B7. NRCBL: 19.5; 8.4. SC: po.

Delmonico, Francis L.; Harmon, William E. The use of a minor as a live kidney donor. *American Journal of Transplantation* 2002; 2: 333-336. NRCBL: 19.5; 9.5.7. SC: em. Identifiers: United States.

Deshmukh, Harsha. Cadaver transplantation: ground realities. *Issues in Medical Ethics* 2001 April-June; 9(2): 53. NRCBL: 19.5; 20.1.

Dyer, Owen. Alder Hey pathologist is struck off medical register [news]. *BMJ: British Medical Journal* 2005 June 25; 330(7506): 1464. NRCBL: 19.5; 18.1; 8.3.2; 18.3; 7.4; 8.5.

Fitzgerald, R.D.; Fitzgerald, A.; Shaheen, F.A.M.; DuBois, J.M. Support for organ procurement: national, professional, and religious correlates among medical personnel in Austria and the Kingdom of Saudi Arabia. *Transplantation Proceedings* 2002 December; 34(8): 3042-3044. NRCBL: 19.5; 21.1. SC: em.

Ford, Norman M. Newborns and organ donation: some guidelines for decision making. *Ethics and Medics* 2003 September; 28(9): 2-4. NRCBL: 19.5; 9.5.7.

Ford, Paul J.; Nicoletti, Toni Ann. My organs, my choice. *American Journal of Bioethics* 2005 July-August; 5(4): 30-31. NRCBL: 19.5; 19.6. Identifiers: United Network for Organ Sharing (UNOS). Comments: comment on Sheldon Zink et al., "Examining the potential exploitation of UNOS policies," *American Journal of Bioethics* 2005 July-August; 5(4): 6-10.

Forsberg, Anna; Nilsson, Madeleine; Krantz, Marie; Olausson, Michael. The essence of living parental liver donation — donors' lived experiences of donation to their children. *Pediatric Transplantation* 2004 August; 8(4): 372-380. NRCBL: 19.5; 19.1; 9.5.7; 8.3.1; 20.3.3. SC: em.

Fost, Norman. Developing hospital policy: the University of Wisconsin experience. *In:* Youngner, Stuart J.; Anderson, Martha W.; Schapiro, Renie, eds. Transplanting Human Tissue: Ethics, Policy, and Practice. New York: Oxford University Press; 2004: 160-167. NRCBL: 19.5; 19.1.

Fox, Mark D.; Allee, Margaret R. Values, policies, and the public trust [editorial]. *American Journal of Bioethics* 2005 July-August; 5(4): 1-3. NRCBL: 19.5; 19.6. Identifiers: United Network for Organ Sharing (UNOS).

Fryer, Jonathan; Angelos, Peter. Is there a role for living donor intestine transplants? *Progress in Transplantation* 2004 December; 14(4): 321-329. NRCBL: 19.5; 19.1.

Garcia, V.D.; Garcia, C.D.; Keitel, E.; Santos, A.F.; Bianco, P.D.; Bittar, A.E.; Neumann, J.; Campos, H.H.; Pestana, J.O.M.; Abbud-Filho, M. Expanding criteria for the use of living donors: what are the limits? *Transplantation Proceedings* 2004 May; 36(4): 808-810. NRCBL: 19.5; 19.3.

Gilbert, James C.; Brigham, Lori; Batty, D. Scott, Jr.; Veatch, Robert M. The nondirected living donor program: a model for cooperative donation, recovery and allocation of living donor kidneys. *American Journal of Transplantation* 2005 January; 5(1): 167-174. NRCBL: 19.5; 19.3; 19.6. SC: em.

Giles, S. An antidote to the emerging two tier organ donation policy in Canada: the Public Cadaveric Organ Donation Program. *Journal of Medical Ethics* 2005 April; 31(4): 188-191. NRCBL: 19.5; 19.3.

Abstract: In Canada, as in many other countries, there exists an organ procurement/donation crisis. This paper reviews some of the most common kidney procurement and allocation programmes, analyses them in terms of public and private administration, and argues that privately administered living donor models are an inequitable stopgap measure, the good intentions of which are misplaced and opportunistic. Focusing on how to improve the publicly administered equitable cadaveric donation programme, and at the same time offering one possible explanation for its current failure, it is suggested that the simple moral principle of "give and you shall receive", already considered by some, be extended further. This would allow for those who are willing to sign up to be a public cadaveric donor be given a priority for receiving an organ donation should they ever require it. It is argued that this priority may provide the motivation to give that is so far lacking in Canada. This model is called the Public Cadaveric Organ Donation Program.

NRCBL: National Reference Center for Bioethics Literature Classification Scheme   See inside front cover for terms.

363

Giordano, Simona. Is the body a republic? *Journal of Medical Ethics* 2005 August; 31(8): 470-475. NRCBL: 19.5; 20.1; 4.4.

Abstract: The ethics of post-mortem organ retention and use is widely debated in bioethics and law. However, the fundamental ethical issues have often been inadequately treated. According to one argument, dead bodies are no longer "persons". Given the great benefits dead bodies offer to human kind, they should be automatically treated as public property: when the person dies, the body becomes a public thing (a res publica, a republic). This paper articulates the ethical issues involved in organ and tissue retention and use, both in the case in which the deceased's wishes are known and in the case in which the wishes are not known. It contends that a dead body is not a republic. The state should maximise availability of organs and tissues by inviting or requiring citizens to make an informed and responsible choice on the matter.

Glannon, Walter; Ross, Lainie Friedman. Motivation, risk, and benefit in living organ donation: a reply to Aaron Spital. *CQ: Cambridge Quarterly of Healthcare Ethics* 2005 Spring; 14(2): 191-194. NRCBL: 19.5; 1.1; 5.2.

Goodson, M.L.; Vernon, B.G. A study of public opinion on the use of tissue samples from living subjects for clinical research. *Journal of Clinical Pathology* 2004 February; 57(2): 135-138. NRCBL: 19.5; 18.1. SC: em. Identifiers: United Kingdom (Great Britain).

Gundle, Kenneth. Presumed consent: an international comparison and possibilities for change in the United States. *CQ: Cambridge Quarterly of Healthcare Ethics* 2005 Winter; 14(1): 113-118. NRCBL: 19.5; 8.3.1.

Harris, Richard Jackson; Jasper, John David; Shanteau, James; Smith, Stacy A. Organ donation consent decisions by the next of kin: an experimental simulation approach. *In:* Shanteau, James; Harris, Richard Jackson, eds. Organ Donation and Transplantation: Psychological and Behavioral Factors. Washington, DC: American Psychological Association, 1990: 13-24. NRCBL: 19.5.

Hilhorst, Medard T.; Kranenburg, Leonieke W.; Zuidema, Willij; Weimar, Willem; IJzermans, Jan N.M.; Passchier, Jan; Busschbach, Jan J.V. Altruistic living kidney donation challenges psychosocial research and policy: a response to previous articles. *Transplantation* 2005 June 15; 79(11): 1470-1474. NRCBL: 19.5; 1.3.9.

Ingelfinger, Julie R. Risks and benefits to the living donor [opinion]. *New England Journal of Medicine* 2005 August 4; 353(5): 447-449. NRCBL: 19.5; 5.2.

Janssen, Anke; Gevers, Sjef. Explicit or presumed consent and organ donation post-mortem: does it matter? *Medicine and Law: World Association for Medical Law* 2005 September; 24(3): 575-583. NRCBL: 19.5; 21.1. SC: em.

Abstract: In the last 25 years almost every West European country has enacted a transplantation law. During the preparation of these laws an important issue was whether to base the transplantation law on explicit or presumed consent regarding organ donation post-mortem. A common view of supporters of the presumed consent system is that it will result in more organ donors than the rule of explicit consent. In this article the difference between the different systems is further explored. For that purpose, the systems for post mortem donation in 10 West European countries will be discussed. Focus will be on the legal role of relatives within the consent process and finally on the role of relatives in practice. It will be argued that the difference between the two types of systems is less important than it seems to be at first sight.

John Paul II, Pope. Address of John Paul II to the 18th International Congress of the Transplantation Society. *Medical Ethics and Bioethics / Medicinska Etika & Bioetika* 2001 Spring-Summer; 8(1-2): 12-14. NRCBL: 19.5; 1.2; 4.4; 8.3.1; 19.4; 22.2.

Johnson, Eric J.; Goldstein, Daniel G. Defaults and donation decisions. *Transplantation* 2004 December 27; 78(12): 1713-1716. NRCBL: 19.5; 21.1. SC: em.

Kielstein, Rita. Differenzierte Selbstbestimmung bei der Organspende—ethische und rechtliche Konsequenzen einer empirischen Umfrage. *In:* Baumann, Eva; Brink, Alexander; May, Arnd T.; Schröder, Peter; Schutzeichel, Corinna Iris, eds. Weltanschauliche Offenheit in der Bioethik. Berlin: Duncker & Humblot; 2004: 271-290. NRCBL: 19.5; 20.2.1. SC: em.

Kulik, Ellen Gottmann. The gift of tissue: a donor mom's perspective. *In:* Youngner, Stuart J.; Anderson, Martha W.; Schapiro, Renie, eds. Transplanting Human Tissue: Ethics, Policy, and Practice. New York: Oxford University Press; 2004: 91-98. NRCBL: 19.5; 8.1.

Langat, Simon K. Reuse of samples: ethical issues encountered by two institutional ethics review committees in Kenya. *Bioethics* 2005 October; 19(5-6): 537-549. NRCBL: 19.5; 18.2; 18.3; 21.1. SC: em.

Abstract: There is growing concern about the reuse and exploitation of biological materials (human tissues) for use in research worldwide. Most discussions about samples have taken place in developed countries, where genetic manipulation techniques have greatly advanced in recent years. There is very little discussion in developing countries, although collaborative research with institutions from developed countries is on the increase. The study sought to identify and describe ethical issues arising in the storage, reuse and exportation of samples in a developing country. Research protocols presented to two Ethics Review Committees in Kenya during a period of two years were reviewed. A record was made of the protocol title, sample collected, request for storage, reuse or exportation and whether or not subject consent was sought. The findings indicated that about 25% out of the 388 protocols sought permission for reuse and only half of those actually informed subjects of the contemplated re-use. Less than 20% requested storage and again, about half of them sought consent from subjects. There is an indication that investigators do not see the need to seek consent for storage, reuse and exportation of samples. It is proposed that these issues should be addressed through policy interventions at both the national and global levels.

Lennerling, Annette; Nyberg, Gudrun. Written information for potential living kidney donors. *Transplant In-*

ternational 2004 September; 17(8): 449-452. NRCBL: 19.5; 19.3. SC: em.

Manzelli, Antonio; Fisichella, P. Marco; Bonfrate, Giuseppe; Gaspari, Achille Lucio. When living related organ donation does not entail a healthy organ: moral implications for both the donor and the recipient [opinion]. *Archives of Surgery* 2004 November; 139(11): 1259. NRCBL: 19.5; 4.4.

Matas, Arthur J.; Sutherland, David E.R. The importance of innovative efforts to increase organ donation [editorial]. *JAMA: The Journal of the American Medical Association* 2005 October 5; 294(13): 1691-1693. NRCBL: 19.5; 19.3.

McGee, Ellen M. Using personal narratives to encourage organ donation. *American Journal of Bioethics* 2005 July-August; 5(4): 19-20. NRCBL: 19.5; 1.1. Comments: comment on Sheldon Zink et al., "Examining the potential exploitation of UNOS policies," American Journal of Bioethics 2005 July-August; 5(4): 6-10.

McKenney, Elizabeth; Parker, Bridgette. Legal and ethical issues related to nonheart beating organ donation. *AORN: Association of Operating Room Nurses Journal* 2003 May; 77(5): 973-976. NRCBL: 19.5; 20.2.1.

McNally, Stephen J.; Harrison, E.M.; Wigmore, S.J. Ethical considerations in the application of preconditioning to solid organ transplantation. *Journal of Medical Ethics* 2005 November; 31(11): 631-634. NRCBL: 19.5; 19.1.

Abstract: The shortage of organs for transplantation has led researchers to look for new techniques to expand the donor pool. Preconditioning strategies have the potential to protect organs from transplant associated injury or may improve the function of substandard organs so that they become suitable for transplantation. Translating this type of technology to the clinical setting raises ethical issues, particularly relating to the deceased donor. It is important that society has the opportunity to discuss the issues raised by implementation of preconditioning strategies before they are implemented rather than as a reaction to them.

Meslin, Eric M.; Quaid, Kimberly A. Ethical issues in the collection, storage, and research use of human biological materials. *Journal of Laboratory and Clinical Medicine* 2004 November; 144(5): 229-234. NRCBL: 19.5; 15.1; 18.3.

Miyasaka, Michio. Resourcifying human bodies — Kant and bioethics. *Medicine, Health Care and Philosophy: A European Journal* 2005; 8(1): 19-27. NRCBL: 19.5; 2.1; 1.1; 9.4. SC: an.

Abstract: This essay roughly sketches two major conceptions of autonomy in contemporary bioethics that promote the resourcification of human body parts: (1) a narrow conception of autonomy as self-determination; and (2) the conception of autonomy as dissociated from human dignity. In this paper I will argue that, on the one hand, these two conceptions are very different from that found in the modern European tradition of philosophical inquiry, because bioethics has concentrated on an external account of patient's self-determination and on dissociating dignity from internal human nature. However, on the other hand, they are consistent with more recent European philosophy. In this more recent tradition, human dignity has gradually been dissociated from contextual values, and human subjectivity has been dissociated from objectivity and absolutized as never to be objectified. In the concluding part, I will give a speculative sketch in which Kant's internal inquiry of maxim of ends, causality and end, and dignity as irreplaceability is recombined with bioethics' externalized one and used to support an extended human resourcification.

Mizukami, Akiyasu; Peterson, C. Matthew; Huang, Ivan; Cook, Christopher; Boyack, Lisa M.; Emery, Benjamin R.; Carrell, Douglas T. The acceptability of posthumous human ovarian tissue donation in Utah. *Human Reproduction* 2005 December; 20(12): 3560-3565. NRCBL: 19.5; 8.3.3; 20.1; 4.4. SC: em.

Mokotedi, S.; Modiba, M.C.M.; Ndlovu, S.R. Attitudes of black South Africans to living related kidney transplantation. *Transplantation Proceedings* 2004 September; 36(7): 1896-1897. NRCBL: 19.5; 19.3. SC: em.

Molzahn, Anita E.; Starzomski, Rosalie; McDonald, Michael; O'Loughlin, Chloe. Chinese Canadian beliefs toward organ donation. *Qualitative Health Research* 2005 January; 15(1): 82-98. NRCBL: 19.5; 21.7; 20.3.1; 1.2. SC: em.

Morton, John. In support of the consent process for organ donation from deceased persons. *New Zealand Medical Journal* 2004 September 10; 117(1201); 3 p. NRCBL: 19.5; 8.3.3; 20.2.1.

Mosimann, François. Procurement of organs from executed prisoners [letter]. *Lancet* 2005 March 5-11; 365(9462): 843-844. NRCBL: 19.5; 1.3.5; 20.6.

Motta, Elizabeth D. The ethics of heparin administration to the potential non- heart-beating organ donor. *Journal of Professional Nursing* 2005 March-April; 21(2): 97- 102. NRCBL: 19.5; 9.7; 8.3.1; 20.2.1.

Murphy, Timothy F. Gay and lesbian exceptions to the heterosexual rule. *American Journal of Bioethics* 2005 July-August; 5(4): 18. NRCBL: 19.5; 10. Comments: comment on Sheldon Zink et al., "Examining the potential exploitation of UNOS policies," American Journal of Bioethics 2005 July-August; 5(4): 6-10.

National Health and Medical Research Council [NHMRC] (Australia). Recommendations for the donation of cadaveric organs and tissues for transplantation. Canberra, ACT: The Council [NHMRC], 1996; 33 p. NRCBL: 19.5; 8.3.3.

Nelson, James Lindemann. Trust and transplants. *American Journal of Bioethics* 2005 July-August; 5(4): 26-28. NRCBL: 19.5; 19.6; 1.1. Identifiers: United Network for Organ Sharing (UNOS). Comments: comment on Sheldon Zink et al., "Examining the potential exploitation of UNOS policies," American Journal of Bioethics 2005 July-August; 5(4): 6-10.

NRCBL: National Reference Center for Bioethics Literature Classification Scheme   See inside front cover for terms.

Ngahooro, Jennifer; Gillett, Grant. Over my dead body: the ethics of organ donation in New Zealand. *New Zealand Medical Journal* 2004 September 10; 117(1201); 6 p. NRCBL: 19.5.

Otte, Jean-Bernard; Janssen, Magda; Rosati, Maria-Rita; Gonze, Dominique. Parental experience with living-related donor liver transplantation [editorial]. *Pediatric Transplantation* 2004 August; 8(4): 317-321. NRCBL: 19.5; 9.5.7; 8.3.1; 8.1; 20.3.3. SC: em.

Ozdag, Nurten. Public awareness and acceptance of tissue and organ donation. *EDTNA/ERCA Journal* 2004 October-December; 30(4): 188-195. NRCBL: 19.5; 20.2.1. SC: em. Identifiers: Turkey.

Papachristou, Christina; Walter, Marc; Dietrich, Kerstin; Danzer, Gerhard; Klupp, Jochen; Klapp, Burghard F.; Frommer, Jörg. Motivation for living-donor liver transplantation from the donor's perspective: an in-depth qualitative research study. *Transplantation* 2004 November 27; 78(10): 1506-1514. NRCBL: 19.5; 19.1. SC: em. Identifiers: Germany.

Park, Jong-Hyun; Park, Joong-Won; Koo, Young-Mo; Kim, Jang Han. Relay kidney transplantation in Korea — legal, ethical and medical aspects. *Legal Medicine* 2004 July; 6(3): 178-181. NRCBL: 19.5; 19.6; 19.3.

Patil, Rajan. Discussion on transplant ethics. *Issues in Medical Ethics* 2002 July-September; 10(3): 62. NRCBL: 19.5.

Pearson, Yvette E. What's blood got to do with it? It's time to say goodbye to directed cadaveric donation. *American Journal of Bioethics* 2005 July-August; 5(4): 31-33. NRCBL: 19.5; 19.6. Identifiers: United Network for Organ Sharing (UNOS).

Pennings, Guido. Gamete donation in a system of need-adjusted reciprocity [opinion]. *Human Reproduction* 2005 November; 20(11): 2990-2993. NRCBL: 19.5; 14.2; 14.6; 4.4.

Peron, A.L.; Rodrigues, A.B.; Leite, D.A.; Lopes, J.L.; Ceschim, P.C.; Alter, R.; Roza, B.A.; Pestana, J.O.; Schirmer, J. Organ donation and transplantation in Brazil: university students' awareness and opinions. *Transplantation Proceedings* 2004 May; 36(4): 811-813. NRCBL: 19.5; 19.1; 7.1. SC: em.

Pham, Hien; Spigner, Clarence. Knowledge and opinions about organ donation and transplantation among Vietnamese Americans in Seattle, Washington: a pilot study. *Clinical Transplantation* 2004 December; 18(6): 707-715. NRCBL: 19.5; 19.6; 9.5.4; 21.7. SC: em.

Piccoli, G.B.; Soragna, G.; Putaggio, S.; Burdese, M.; Bergamo, D.; Mezza, E.; Gai, M.; Motta, D.; Rossetti, M.; Malfi, B.; Anania, P.; Marchetti, P.; Vistoli, F.; Barsotti, M.; Bianchi, A.M.; Longo, P.; Rinaldi, D.;

Giacchino, F.; Jeantet, A.; Boggi, U.; Segoloni, G.P. To give or to receive? Opinions of teenagers on kidney donation. *Transplantation Proceedings* 2004 April; 36(3): 448-449. NRCBL: 19.5; 19.3. SC: em. Identifiers: Italy.

Piccoli, Giuseppe; Segoloni, Giuseppe Paolo; Soragna, Giorgio; Mezza, Elisabetta; Burdese, Manuel; Tognarelli, Giuliana; Putaggio, Stefania; Bergamo, Daniela; Consiglio, Valentina; Vespertino, Elisa; Bonetto, Antonella; Jeantet, Alberto; Piccoli, Giorgina Barbara. Teenagers' point of view on living donor kidney transplantation: Cinderella or princess? *Journal of Nephrology* 2004 November-December; 17(Supplement 8): S47-S54. NRCBL: 19.5; 19.3; 9.5.7. SC: em. Identifiers: Italy.

Plomer, Aurora. The rights of the dead: research on human tissue and body parts after Bristol and Alder Hey. *In her:* The Law and Ethics of Medical Research: International Bioethics and Human Rights. Portland, OR: Cavendish; 2005: 93-112. NRCBL: 19.5; 18.1.

Potts, M.; Evans, D.W. Does it matter that organ donors are not dead? Ethical and policy implications. *Journal of Medical Ethics* 2005 July; 31(7): 406-409. NRCBL: 19.5; 20.2.1. SC: an.
Abstract: The "standard position" on organ donation is that the donor must be dead in order for vital organs to be removed, a position with which we agree. Recently, Robert Truog and Walter Robinson have argued that (1) brain death is not death, and (2) even though "brain dead" patients are not dead, it is morally acceptable to remove vital organs from those patients. We accept and defend their claim that brain death is not death, and we argue against both the US "whole brain" criterion and the UK "brain stem" criterion. Then we answer their arguments in favour of removing vital organs from "brain dead" and other classes of comatose patients. We dispute their claim that the removal of vital organs is morally equivalent to "letting nature take its course", arguing that, unlike "allowing to die", it is the removal of vital organs that kills the patient, not his or her disease or injury. Then, we argue that removing vital organs from living patients is immoral and contrary to the nature of medical practice. Finally, we offer practical suggestions for changing public policy on organ transplantation.

Prasad, M. Veera. Response: living donor liver transplantation [comment]. *Indian Journal of Medical Ethics* 2005 July-September; 2(3): 91-93. NRCBL: 19.5; 19.3; 18.8. Comments: comment on A.V. Srinivas, "Living donor liver transplantation," Indian Journal of Medical Ethics 2005 July- September; 2(3): 89-90.

Rajput, Vijay. Addressing the organ shortage: presumed consent and xenotransplants. *Issues in Medical Ethics* 2001 April-June; 9(2): 54-55. NRCBL: 19.5; 8.3.1; 19.1; 22.2.

Rassin, Michal; Lowenthal, Miri; Silner, Dina. Fear, ambivalence, and liminality: key concepts in refusal to donate an organ after brain death. *JONA's Healthcare Law, Ethics, and Regulation* 2005 July- September; 7(3): 79-85. NRCBL: 19.5; 8.1; 20.2.1; 2.1; 21.7.

Abstract: The refusal to donate an organ is a phenomenon in need of exploration and explanation. This article refers to the major fear of becoming an organ donor in relation to a global culture perspective and to the Halacha (Jewish law). A theoretical critique about the ambivalence demonstrated by health care providers and families will discuss these concepts in relation to brain death, from the stages of hospitalization, through the period prior to the assertion of brain death, ending with brain death, and its perspective as a liminal situation.Finally, we conclude that nursing practices during the care of the "brain dead" patient, and toward the patient's family, should convey an unequivocal message. That is, brain death describes irreversible cessation of all brain function, and therefore, the patient becomes a dead body and can be treated as a potential organ donor.

Raza, Mohsin; Hedayat, K.M. Some sociocultural aspects of cadaver organ donation: recent rulings from Iran. *Transplantation Proceedings* 2004 December; 36(10): 2888-2890. NRCBL: 19.5; 1.2. SC: rv. Identifiers: Islam.

Reynolds, Gretchen. Will any organ do? Transplant surgeons are increasingly using organs from drug users, the obese and the very ill. But with little known for certain about the consequences, doctors are confronting complex medical and ethical questions. *New York Times Magazine* 2005 July 10; p. 36-41. NRCBL: 19.5; 19.6. SC: po.

Robertson, Christopher. Organ advertising: desperate patients solicit volunteers. *Journal of Law, Medicine and Ethics* 2005 Spring; 33(1): 170- 174. NRCBL: 19.5; 4.4; 9.4.

Robertson, Christopher. Who is really hurt anyway? The problem of soliciting designated organ donations. *American Journal of Bioethics* 2005 July-August; 5(4): 16-17. NRCBL: 19.5; 19.6; 1.1. Identifiers: United Network for Organ Sharing (UNOS). Comments: comment on Sheldon Zink et al., "Examining the potential exploitation of UNOS policies," American Journal of Bioethics 2005 July-August; 5(4): 6-10.

Ross, Lainie Friedman; Zenios, Stefanos. Practical and ethical challenges to paired exchange programs [editorial]. *American Journal of Transplantation* 2004 October; 4(10): 1553-1554. NRCBL: 19.5.

Salvatierra, Oscar, Jr. Transplant physicians bear full responsibility for the consequences of kidney donation by a minor [editorial]. *American Journal of Transplantation* 2002 April; 2(4): 297- 298. NRCBL: 19.5. SC: em. Identifiers: United States.

Sanner, Margareta A. A Swedish survey of young people's views on organ donation and transplantation. *Transplant International* 2002 December; 15(12): 641-648. NRCBL: 19.5; 19.1. SC: em.

Schlessinger, Shirley; Crook, Errol D.; Black, Ruth; Barber, Henry. Case studies in ethics from the G.V. "Sonny" Montgomery VA Medical Center and the University of Mississippi Medical Center: ethical issues in transplantation: living related donation in the setting of severe

neurological damage without brain death. *American Journal of the Medical Sciences* 2002 October; 324(4): 232-236. NRCBL: 19.5; 19.3; 8.3.3. SC: cs.

Seale, Clive; Kirk, Debbie; Tobin, Martin; Burton, Paul; Grundy, Richard; Pritchard-Jones, Kathy; Dixon-Woods, Mary. Effect of media portrayals of removal of children's tissue on UK tumour bank. *BMJ: British Medical Journal* 2005 August 13; 331(7513): 401-403. NRCBL: 19.5; 18.1; 1.3.7. Identifiers: United Kingdom (Great Britain).

Shaheen, Faissal A.M.; Al-Jondeby, Mohammad; Kurpad, Ramprasad; Al-Khader, Abdullah A. Social and cultural issues in organ transplantation in Islamic countries. *Annals of Transplantation* 2004; 9(2): 11-13. NRCBL: 19.5; 1.2; 20.2.1; 20.3.1.

Shapiro, Carla. Organ transplantation in infants and children — necessity or choice: the case of K'aila Paulette. *Pediatric Nursing* 2005 March-April; 31(2): 121-122. NRCBL: 19.5; 20.5.2; 8.3.3; 1.2. SC: cs.

Siminoff, Laura A.; Burant, Christopher; Youngner, Stuart J. Death and organ procurement: public beliefs and attitudes. *Social Science and Medicine* 2004 December; 59(11): 2325-2334. NRCBL: 19.5; 20.2.1; 20.3.1.

Singh, P.; Kumar, A.; Sharma, R.K. Factors influencing refusal by relatives of brain-dead patients to give consent for organ donation: experience at a transplant centre. *Journal of the Indian Medical Association* 2004 November; 102(11): 630, 632, 643. NRCBL: 19.5; 20.2.1; 1.2. SC: em. Identifiers: India.

Snyder, David. A dispute over brain donations: families allege improper consent in lawsuits against Bethesda institute. *Washington Post* 2005 June 30; p. B1, B5. NRCBL: 19.5. SC: po.

Soin, A.S. Ethical dilemmas in living donor liver transplantation [editorial]. *Issues in Medical Ethics* 2003 October-December; 11(4): 104-105. NRCBL: 19.5; 19.6.

Soragna, G.; Carrano, R.; Putaggio, S.; Bergamo, D.; Burdese, M.; Mezza, E.; Motta, D.; Gai, M.; Bermond, F.; Jeantet, A.; Stefoni, S.; Federico, S.; Segoloni, G.P.; Piccoli, G.B. Opinions on renal transplantation and organ donation in high school students in two large northern (Torino) and southern (Napoli) Italian cities. *Transplantation Proceedings* 2004 April; 36(3): 428-430. NRCBL: 19.5; 19.3. SC: em. Identifiers: Italy.

Spielman, Bethany J. Non-family directed donation: the perils of policy-making. *American Journal of Bioethics* 2005 July-August; 5(4): 24-26. NRCBL: 19.5; 19.6. Identifiers: United Network for Organ Sharing (UNOS). Comments: comment on Sheldon Zink et al., "Examining the potential exploitation of UNOS policies," American Journal of Bioethics 2005 July-August; 5(4): 6-10.

NRCBL: National Reference Center for Bioethics Literature Classification Scheme   See inside front cover for terms.

367

Spital, Aaron. Conscription of cadaveric organs for transplantation: a stimulating idea whose time has not yet come. *CQ: Cambridge Quarterly of Healthcare Ethics* 2005 Winter; 14(1): 107-112. NRCBL: 19.5; 8.3.1; 7.1.

Spital, Aaron. Reply to Glannon and Ross: may parent to child organ donation be altruistic? *CQ: Cambridge Quarterly of Healthcare Ethics* 2005 Spring; 14(2): 195-198. NRCBL: 19.5; 1.1; 5.2.

Spital, Aaron. Should people who commit themselves to organ donation be granted preferred status to receive organ transplants? *Clinical Transplantation* 2005 April; 19(2): 269-272. NRCBL: 19.5; 19.6.

Sque, Magi; Payne, Sheila A. Dissonant loss: the experiences of donor relatives. *Social Science and Medicine* 1996 November; 43(9): 1359-1370. NRCBL: 19.5; 20.3.3. SC: em. Identifiers: United Kingdom (Great Britain).

Srinivas, A.V. Living donor liver transplantation. *Indian Journal of Medical Ethics* 2005 July-September; 2(3): 89-90. NRCBL: 19.5; 19.3; 19.8. Identifiers: India.

Steinberg, David. Exchanging kidneys: how much unfairness is justified by an extra kidney and who decides? [editorial]. *American Journal of Kidney Diseases* 2004 December; 44(6): 1115-1120. NRCBL: 19.5; 19.6; 19.3.

Steinberg, David. Response to "Special section on children as organ donors": a critique. *CQ: Cambridge Quarterly of Healthcare Ethics* 2005 Summer; 14(3): 301-305. NRCBL: 19.5; 9.5.7; 8.3.2; 1.1. Comments: comment on "Special section on children as organ donors," CQ: Cambridge Quarterly of Healthcare Ethics 2004 Spring; 13(2).

Surman, Owen S.; Fukunishi, Isao; Allen, Terre; Hertl, Martin. Live organ donation: social context, clinical encounter, and the psychology of communication. *Psychosomatics* 2005 January-February; 46(1): 1-6. NRCBL: 19.5; 2.2; 8.1.

Tettamanti, Massimo; Tralamazza, Sara; Berati, Marina; Molteni, Max; Gamba, Natascia. Human research tissue banks: the ATRA Project for establishing a human research tissue bank in Switzerland. *ATLA: Alternatives to Laboratory Animals* 2005 February; 33(1): 29-36. NRCBL: 19.5; 22.2; 1.3.9.

Truog, Robert D. The ethics of organ donation by living donors [opinion]. *New England Journal of Medicine* 2005 August 4; 353(5): 444-446. NRCBL: 19.5; 19.3.

Truog, Robert D. Organ donation without brain death? *Hastings Center Report* 2005 November-December; 35(6): 3. NRCBL: 19.5; 20.2.1.

Truog, Robert D.; Lowney, Jeremiah; Hanto, Douglas; Caplan, Arthur; Brock, Dan. Soliciting organs on the Internet [forum]. *Medical Ethics Newsletter [Lahey Clinic]* 2005 Fall; 12(3): 5-8. NRCBL: 19.5; 1.3.12.

Tutton, Richard. Person, property and gift: exploring languages of tissue donation to biomedical research. *In:* Tutton, Richard; Corrigan, Oonagh, eds. Genetic Databases: Socio-ethical Issues in the Collection and Use of DNA. New York: Routledge; 2004: 19-38. NRCBL: 19.5; 15.1; 1.3.9; 4.4.

Undis, David J. LifeSharers: increasing organ supply through directed donation. *American Journal of Bioethics* 2005 July-August; 5(4): 22-24. NRCBL: 19.5; 19.6. Identifiers: LifeSharers; United Network for Organ Sharing (UNOS). Comments: comment on Sheldon Zink et al., "Examining the potential exploitation of UNOS policies," American Journal of Bioethics 2005 July-August; 5(4): 6-10.

Vanfraussen, K.; Ponjaert-Kristoffersen, I.; Brewaeys, A. Why do children want to know more about the donor? The experience of youngsters raised in lesbian families. *Journal of Psychosomatic Obstetrics and Gynecology* 2003 March; 24(1): 31-38. NRCBL: 19.5; 14.2; 8.2; 8.4; 9.5.7. SC: em.

Veatch, Robert M. Tissue issues: the ethical dilemmas of collecting human tissues for research. *Formosan Journal of Medical Humanities* 2005 September; 6(1-2): 3-13. NRCBL: 19.5; 1.3.9; 4.4; 18.1; 18.6.

Wilkinson, T.M. Individual and family consent to organ and tissue donation: is the current position coherent? *Journal of Medical Ethics* 2005 October; 31(10): 587-590. NRCBL: 19.5; 8.3.3. SC: an.
Abstract: The current position on the deceased's consent and the family's consent to organ and tissue donation from the dead is a double veto-each has the power to withhold and override the other's desire to donate. This paper raises, and to some extent answers, questions about the coherence of the double veto. It can be coherently defended in two ways: if it has the best effects and if the deceased has only negative rights of veto. Whether the double veto has better effects than other policies requires empirical investigation, which is not undertaken here. As for rights, the paper shows that it is entirely possible that individuals have a negative right of veto but no positive right to compel acceptance of their offers. Thus if intensivists and transplant teams turn down the deceased's offer, they do not thereby violate the deceased's right. This leaves it open whether non-rights based reasons-such as avoiding bad publicity or distress -require intensivists and transplant teams to turn down or accept the deceased's offer. This, however, is beyond the scope of this paper. The current position may or may not be wrong, but it is at least coherent.

Wright, Linda; Faith, Karen; Richardson, Robert; Grant, David. Ethical guidelines for the evaluation of living organ donors. *Canadian Journal of Surgery* 2004 December; 47(6): 408-413. NRCBL: 19.5.

Youngner, Stuart J. Informed consent. *In:* Youngner, Stuart J.; Anderson, Martha W.; Schapiro, Renie, eds. Transplanting Human Tissue: Ethics, Policy, and Practice. New York: Oxford University Press; 2004: 168-185. NRCBL: 19.5; 8.3.1.

Ziaja, Jacek; Cierpka, Lech; Król, Robert; Szczepanski, Marek S.; Tyrybon, Malgorzata; Sekta, Sylwia. Transplantation procedures in social awareness opinion poll of Silesian Province citizens on living donor organ transplantation. *Annals of Transplantation* 2003; 8(4): 43-45. NRCBL: 19.5; 19.3. SC: em. Identifiers: Poland.

ORGAN AND TISSUE TRANSPLANTATION/ . . . / ECONOMIC ASPECTS

Bass, David. Kidneys for cash and egg safaris — can we allow 'transplant tourism' to flourish in South Africa? [opinion]. *South African Medical Journal* 2005 January; 95(1): 42-44. NRCBL: 19.5; 14.4; 19.3; 19.1; 9.3.1; 21.1.

Benatar, S.R. A response to J S Taylor. *Journal of Medical Ethics* 2005 March; 31(3): 180-181. NRCBL: 19.5; 19.3; 9.3.1.

Boyd, S. Gregory. Comment: considering a market in human organs. *North Carolina Journal of Law and Technology* 2003 Spring; 4(2): 417-473. NRCBL: 19.5; 4.4; 19.1; 9.3.1. SC: le.

Campbell, Courtney S. The gift and the market: cultural symbolic perspectives. *In:* Youngner, Stuart J.; Anderson, Martha W.; Schapiro, Renie, eds. Transplanting Human Tissue: Ethics, Policy, and Practice. New York: Oxford University Press; 2004: 139-159. NRCBL: 19.5; 9.3.1. SC: an.

Chang, Wesley. Arrested development: patent laws, embryonic stem cell research, and the organ black market. *Southwestern Journal of Law and Trade in the Americas* 2004; 10(2): 407-432. NRCBL: 19.5; 9.3.1; 4.4; 15.8; 18.5.4. SC: le.

Cherry, Mark. Cash and compassion. *New Scientist* 2005 August 13-19; 187(2512): 20. NRCBL: 19.5; 9.3.1.

Cosimi, Benedict. Position of the Transplantation Society on paid organ donation. *In:* Terasaki, Paul I.; Cecka, J. Michael, eds. Clinical Transplants 1998. Los Angeles, CA: UCLA Tissue Typing Laboratory; 1998: 344-345. NRCBL: 19.5; 9.3.1.

Crespi, Gregory S. Overcoming the legal obstacles to the creation of a futures market in bodily organs. *Ohio State Law Journal* 1994; 55(1): 1-77. NRCBL: 19.5; 19.6; 9.3.1. SC: le.

Daar, A.S. Paid organ procurement: pragmatic and ethical viewpoints. *Transplantation Proceedings* 2004 September; 36(7): 1876-1877. NRCBL: 19.5; 9.3.1.

Estonia. Parliament. Transplantation of Organs and Tissues Act [passed 30 January 2002; effective date: 4 March 2002]. Talinn, Estonia: Riigi Teataja [State Gazette] I 2002, 21, 118; 6 p. [Online]. Available: http://www.legaltext.ee/text/en/X60017K2.htm [11 July 2005].

NRCBL: 19.5; 19.6; 8.3.1; 9.3.1. SC: le. Note: Amended 5 June 2002, effective 1 July 2002; Amended 19 June 2002, effective 1 September 2002; Amended 18 December 2002, effective 31 December 2002.

Friedlaender, Michael M. A protocol for paid kidney donation in Israel. *IMAJ* 2003 September; 5: 611-614. NRCBL: 19.5; 19.3; 9.3.1.

George, Thomas. The case against kidney sales. *Issues in Medical Ethics* 2001 April-June; 9(2): 49-50. NRCBL: 19.5; 19.3; 9.3.1.

Goodwin, Michele. Altruism's limits: law, capacity, and organ commodification. *Rutgers Law Review* 2004 Winter; 56(2): 305-407. NRCBL: 19.5; 9.3.1; 1.3.2; 19.6; 9.5.4. SC: le.

Herring, Jonathan. Giving, selling and sharing bodies. *In:* Bainham, Andrew; Sclater, Shelley Day; Richards, Martin, eds. Body Lore and Laws. Portland, OR: Hart Pub.; 2002: 43-61. NRCBL: 19.5; 9.3.1. SC: le.

Ionescu, Carmiola. Donor charged in Romania's first organ trafficking trial. *Lancet* 2005 June 4-10; 365(9475): 1918. NRCBL: 19.5; 9.3.1; 21.1. SC: le.

Irving, Louise. The problem of intangibles. *In:* Häyry, Matti; Takala, Tuija; Herissone-Kelly, Peter, eds. Bioethics and Social Reality. New York: Rodopi, 2005: 67-76. NRCBL: 19.5; 9.3.1; 19.3. SC: an.

Israni, Ajay K.; Halpern, Scott D.; Zink, Sheldon; Sidhwani, Sonal A.; Caplan, Arthur. Incentive models to increase living kidney donation: encouraging without coercing [opinion]. *American Journal of Transplantation* 2005 January; 5(1): 15-20. NRCBL: 19.5; 19.3; 9.3.1.

Kishore, R.R. Human organs, scarcities, and sale: morality revisited. *Journal of Medical Ethics* 2005 June; 31(6): 362-365. NRCBL: 19.5; 9.3.1; 4.4. SC: an.
Abstract: Despite stringent and fine tuned laws most jurisdictions are not able to curb organ trafficking. Nor are they able to provide organs to the needy. There are reports of the kidnapping and murder of children and adults to "harvest" their organs. Millions of people are suffering, not because the organs are not available but because "morality" does not allow them to have access to the organs. Arguments against organ sale are grounded in two broad considerations: (1) sale is contrary to human dignity, and (2) sale violates equity. Both these objections are examined in this article and it is concluded that they reflect a state of moral paternalism rather than pragmatism. It is argued that a live human body constitutes a vital source of supply of organs and tissues and that the possibilities of its optimum utilisation should be explored. Commercialisation should be curbed not by depriving a needy person of his genuine requirements but by making the enforcement agencies efficient.

Kondro, Wayne. Debate over online recruitment of organ donors. *CMAJ/JAMC: Canadian Medical Association Journal* 2005 January 18; 172(2): 165-166. NRCBL: 19.5; 9.3.1; 19.3.

NRCBL: National Reference Center for Bioethics Literature Classification Scheme   See inside front cover for terms.

369

Kunin, J.D. The search for organs: halachic perspectives on altruistic giving and the selling of organs. *Journal of Medical Ethics* 2005 May; 31(5): 269-272. NRCBL: 19.5; 9.3.1; 1.2.

Abstract: Altruistic donation of organs from living donors is widely accepted as a virtue and even encouraged as a duty. Selling organs, on the other hand, is highly controversial and banned in most countries. What is the Jewish legal (halachic) position on these issues? In this review it is explained that altruistic donation is praiseworthy but in no way obligatory. Selling organs is a subject of rabbinic dispute among contemporary authorities.

Kyriazi, Harold. The ethics of organ selling: a libertarian perspective. *Issues in Medical Ethics* 2001 April-June; 9(2): 44-46. NRCBL: 19.5; 9.3.1; 1.1.

Matas, Arthur J. The case for living kidney sales: rationale, objections and concerns. *American Journal of Transplantation* 2004 December; 4(12): 2007-2017. NRCBL: 19.5; 19.3; 9.3.1.

Mayrhofer-Reinhartshuber, David; Fitzgerald, Robert. Financial incentives for cadaveric organ donation. *Annals of Transplantation* 2004; 9(1): 25-27. NRCBL: 19.5; 9.3.1.

Nagral, Sanjay. Ethics of organ transplantation. *Medical Ethics: Journal of Forum for Medical Ethics Society* 1995 April-June; 3(2): 19-22. NRCBL: 19.5; 19.3; 9.3.1. Identifiers: India.

Piccoli, G.B.; Putaggio, S.; Soragna, G.; Mezza, E.; Burdese, M.; Bergamo, D.; Longo, P.; Rinaldi, D.; Bermond, F.; Gai, M.; Motta, D.; Novaresio, C.; Jeantet, A.; Segoloni, G.P. Kidney vending: opinions of the medical school students on this controversial issue. *Transplantation Proceedings* 2004 April; 36(3): 446-447. NRCBL: 19.5; 19.3; 9.3.1; 7.2. SC: em. Identifiers: Italy.

Richards, Janet Radcliffe. Organs for sale. *Issues in Medical Ethics* 2001 April-June; 9(2): 47-48. NRCBL: 19.5; 9.3.1.

Sanal, Aslihan. "Robin Hood" of techno-Turkey or organ trafficking in the state of ethical beings. *Culture, Medicine and Psychiatry* 2004 September; 28(3): 281-309. NRCBL: 19.5; 9.3.1; 1.3.7; 19.3.

Sells, Robert. Incentives for organ donation: some ethical issues. *Annals of Transplantation* 2004; 9(1): 23-24. NRCBL: 19.5; 19.3; 9.3.1.

Steinbrook, Robert. Public solicitation of organ donors [opinion]. *New England Journal of Medicine* 2005 August 4; 353(5): 441-444. NRCBL: 19.5; 1.3.2; 9.3.1; 19.3.

Taylor, J. Blinkered objections to bioethics: a response to Benatar. *Journal of Medical Ethics* 2005 March; 31(3): 179-180. NRCBL: 19.5; 19.3; 9.3.1.

Abstract: In a recent commentary, S R Benatar criticised the debates over organ donation and kidney selling for being located within a "narrow and inadequate framework". Benatar levels four charges against those who engage in the current organs debate: that they myopically focus on saving lives; that they accept the dominance of market orientated approaches to health care; that they reify individualism, and that they engage in limited moral arguments. Given the importance of the organs debate it is imperative that the misunderstandings of it on which Benatar's criticisms are based are dispelled. Accordingly, I will consider and reject each of his objections in turn.

Wilkinson, Dominic J.C. Selling organs and souls: should the state prohibit 'demeaning' practices? *Journal of Bioethical Inquiry* 2004; 1(1): 27-31. NRCBL: 19.5; 1.1; 4.4; 9.3.1.

Abstract: It is sometimes argued that practices such as organ-selling should be prohibited because they are demeaning to the individuals involved. In this article the plausibility of such an argument is questioned. I will examine what it means to demean or be demeaned, and suggest that the mere fact that an individual is demeaning themselves does not provide sufficient justification for legal prohibition. On the contrary, such laws might be argued to be demeaning.

Young, Emma. Laws fail to stop India's organ trade [news]. *New Scientist* 2005 October 22-28; 188(2522): 20. NRCBL: 19.5; 9.3.1. SC: le.

ORGAN AND TISSUE TRANSPLANTATION/ . . . / LEGAL ASPECTS

Aigner, Gerhard. An overview of legal aspects in organ transplantation — what are the family rights? *Annals of Transplantation* 2004; 9(1): 11-14. NRCBL: 19.5; 21.1. SC: le. Identifiers: Austria; Europe.

Altman, Jason. Organ transplantations: the need for an international open organ market. *Touro International Law Review* 1994; 5: 161-183. NRCBL: 19.5; 19.6; 19.1; 21.1. SC: le.

American College of Legal Medicine. Editorial Committee. Organ donation and transplantation. *In:* American College of Legal Medicine Textbook Committee, Sanbar, S. Sandy; Firestone, Marvin H.; Buckner, Fillmore; Gibofsky, Allan; LeBlang, Theodore R.; Snyder, Jack W.; Wecht, Cyril H.; Zaremski, Miles J. Legal Medicine. 6th ed. St. Louis: Mosby; 2004: 271-299. NRCBL: 19.5; 19.1. SC: le.

Boyd, S. Gregory. Comment: considering a market in human organs. *North Carolina Journal of Law and Technology* 2003 Spring; 4(2): 417-473. NRCBL: 19.5; 4.4; 19.1; 9.3.1. SC: le.

Brazier, Margaret; Squier, Waney; Duyckaerts, Charles; Seilhean, Danielle; Hauw, Jean-Jacques; Adamson, Robert. The Human Tissue Bill. *Lancet Neurology* 2004 November; 3(11): 685-690. NRCBL: 19.5; 18.2; 18.3. SC: le. Identifiers: United Kingdom (Great Britain).

Chang, Wesley. Arrested development: patent laws, embryonic stem cell research, and the organ black market. *Southwestern Journal of Law and Trade in the Americas*

2004; 10(2): 407-432. NRCBL: 19.5; 9.3.1; 4.4; 15.8; 18.5.4. SC: le.

Charo, R. Alta. Legal characterizations of human tissue. *In:* Youngner, Stuart J.; Anderson, Martha W.; Schapiro, Renie, eds. Transplanting Human Tissue: Ethics, Policy, and Practice. New York: Oxford University Press; 2004: 101-119. NRCBL: 19.5; 20.1. SC: le.

Crespi, Gregory S. Overcoming the legal obstacles to the creation of a futures market in bodily organs. *Ohio State Law Journal* 1994; 55(1): 1-77. NRCBL: 19.5; 19.6; 9.3.1. SC: le.

Dimond, Bridgit. Law concerning organ transplants and dead donors in the UK. *British Journal of Nursing* 2005 January 13-26; 14(1): 47-48. NRCBL: 19.5; 8.3.1. SC: le. Identifiers: United Kingdom (Great Britain).

Dimond, Bridgit. Removal, retention and storage of organs and tissue in the UK. *British Journal of Nursing* 2005 January 27-February 9; 14(2): 107-108. NRCBL: 19.5; 8.3.2; 20.1. SC: le. Identifiers: United Kingdom (Great Britain).

Elon, Menachem; Auerbach, Bernard; Chazin, Daniel D.; Sykes, Melvin J. Organ transplantation. *In their:* Jewish Law (Mishpat Ivri): Cases and Materials. New York: M. Bender; 1999: 697-731. NRCBL: 19.5; 20.2.2; 1.2. SC: le.

Estonia. Parliament. Transplantation of Organs and Tissues Act [passed 30 January 2002; effective date: 4 March 2002]. Talinn, Estonia: Riigi Teataja [State Gazette] I 2002, 21, 118; 6 p. [Online]. Available: http://www.legaltext.ee/text/en/X60017K2.htm [11 July 2005]. NRCBL: 19.5; 19.6; 8.3.1; 9.3.1. SC: le. Note: Amended 5 June 2002, effective 1 July 2002; Amended 19 June 2002, effective 1 September 2002; Amended 18 December 2002, effective 31 December 2002.

Gevers, Sjef; Janssen, Anke; Friele, Roland. Consent systems for post mortem organ donation in Europe. *European Journal of Health Law* 2004 June; 11(2): 175-186. NRCBL: 19.5; 8.3.3; 21.1. SC: le.

Goodwin, Michele. Altruism's limits: law, capacity, and organ commodification. *Rutgers Law Review* 2004 Winter; 56(2): 305-407. NRCBL: 19.5; 9.3.1; 1.3.2; 19.6; 9.5.4. SC: le.

Great Britain. Department of Health; Welsh Assembly Government; Donaldson, Liam; Hall, Ruth. Proposals for new legislation on human organs and tissue: why we need new laws. London: Department of Health 2003 September; 8 p. [Online]. Available: http://www.dh.gov.uk/assetRoot/04/07/02/97/04070297.pdf [25 July 2005]. NRCBL: 19.5. SC: le. Note: United Kingdom.

Great Britain. Parliament. House of Commons. Human Tissue Act 2004 (Amendment) Bill. London: The Statio-

nery Office, Ltd. 2005 January 12; 9 p. [Online]. Available: http://www.publications.parliament.uk/pa/cm200405/cmbills/032/2005032.pdf [25 July 2005]. NRCBL: 19.5; 1.3.5. SC: le. Identifiers: organ procurement and transplantation.

Herring, Jonathan. Giving, selling and sharing bodies. *In:* Bainham, Andrew; Sclater, Shelley Day; Richards, Martin, eds. Body Lore and Laws. Portland, OR: Hart Pub.; 2002: 43-61. NRCBL: 19.5; 9.3.1. SC: le.

Ionescu, Carmiola. Donor charged in Romania's first organ trafficking trial. *Lancet* 2005 June 4-10; 365(9475): 1918. NRCBL: 19.5; 9.3.1; 21.1. SC: le.

Jasper, J.D.; Nickerson, Carol A.E.; Ubel, Peter A.; Asch, David A. Altruism, incentives, and organ donation: attitudes of the transplant community. *Medical Care* 2004 April; 42(4): 378-386. NRCBL: 19.5. SC: le; em.

Kassim, Puteri Nemie Jahn. Organ transplantation in Malaysia: a need for a comprehensive legal regime. *Medicine and Law: World Association for Medical Law* 2005 March; 24(1): 173-189. NRCBL: 19.5; 4.4; 19.6. SC: le.
Abstract: Organ transplantation has become increasingly routine as a means of saving and improving the quality of lives of thousands of people each year. However, transplant activity is increasingly constrained by the shortage of organs. The major impediment in procuring organs for transplant in Malaysia is the lack of cadaveric donors. The lack of cadaveric donors has encouraged patients to go to countries like India and China to purchase organs especially kidneys for transplantation. The inadequacies of the existing Malaysian Human Tissues Act 1974 has also contributed to this problem. For instance, the word 'tissue" is not defined under the Act. This raises complex and ethical questions as to the scope of the definition for "tissue". There is also no definition of "the person lawfully in possession of the body." This is significant as he is the person who is empowered by the Act to authorise removal of tissue. Further, there is also no articulation of a hierarchy of relatives who are deemed the next of kin. In a situation involving a large number of relatives, asserting different opinions, this may pose a problem. The articulation of a priority list is particularly difficult in Malaysia as it is a multi-cultural society where the hierarchy of relatives with the right to claim decision-making powers may vary in different cultures. Furthermore, there is also a pressing need for a legislation to ensure that the rights of potential live donors are protected. At the moment, the Human Tissues Act 1974 only relates to cadaveric donors whereas live donors fall within the purview of the common law. The system of "opting out" should be considered in Malaysia whereby every individual is presumed to be a donor unless he or she registers an objection. But this system can only be fair if every person in the community is given notice of the law and understands its implications. For the system to work, there must also exist a simple and effective way of registering objections. There is a need for continuous intensive public education and counselling. A nationally co-ordinated mechanism must be in place to ensure effectiveness of identifying potential donors and recipients.

Katz, Robert A. Who should capture the value of donated tissue? *Medical Ethics Newsletter [Lahey Clinic]* 2005 Fall; 12(3): 4, 9. NRCBL: 19.5; 1.3.2. SC: le.

NRCBL: National Reference Center for Bioethics Literature Classification Scheme   See inside front cover for terms.

371

Klaiman, M.H. Whose brain is it anyway? The comparative law of post-mortem organ retention. *Journal of Legal Medicine* 2005 December; 26(4): 475-490. NRCBL: 19.5; 20.1; 18.3; 21.1. SC: le.

Kolber, Adam J. A matter of priority: transplanting organs preferentially to registered donors. *Rutgers Law Review* 2003 Spring; 55(3): 671-740. NRCBL: 19.5; 19.6; 4.4. SC: le.

Kondo, Kazuya. The organ transplant law of Japan — the past, the present, and the future. *Journal International de Bioethique / International Journal of Bioethics* 2005 March-June; 16(1-2): 91-102, 195. NRCBL: 19.5; 20.2.1; 8.3.1. SC: le. Note: Abstract in English and French.

Kuramochi, Takeshi. Applications for human rights relief and the recommendations of the Japan Federation of bar associations. *Journal International de Bioethique / International Journal of Bioethics* 2005 March-June; 16(1-2): 103-116, 195-196. NRCBL: 19.5; 20.2.1; 21.1. SC: le. Note: Abstract in English and French.

Kwan, Eva. Organ donation: Alabama uses common law to uphold healthcare providers' duty to secure consent from next of kin — George H. Lanier Memorial Hospital v. Andrews. *Journal of Law, Medicine and Ethics* 2005 Fall; 33(3): 620-622. NRCBL: 19.5; 8.3.1. SC: le.

Liddell, Kathleen; Hall, Alison. Beyond Bristol and Alder Hey: the future regulation of human tissue. *Medical Law Review* 2005 Summer; 13(2): 170-223. NRCBL: 19.5; 18.3; 8.3.2; 8.3.3; 4.4; 8.4; 18.6. SC: le.

Liddy, Maryellen. The "new body snatchers": analyzing the effect of presumed consent organ donation laws on privacy, autonomy, and liberty. *Fordham Urban Law Journal* 2001 February; 28(3): 815-853. NRCBL: 19.5; 8.3.1; 8.3.3; 1.1. SC: le.

Mackey, Denise; Kjerulf, Maria. The ethics of organ donation: examining consent policies and donor criteria. *University of Toronto Medical Journal* 2000 December; 78(1): 51-54. NRCBL: 19.5; 20.2.1. SC: le.

Maclean, Mavis. Letting go: parents, professionals and the law in the retention of human material after post mortem. *In:* Bainham, Andrew; Sclater, Shelley Day; Richards, Martin, eds. Body Lore and Laws. Portland, OR: Hart Pub.; 2002: 79-89. NRCBL: 19.5; 8.3.2. SC: le.

Manaouil, C.; Chatelain, D.; Montpellier, D.; Graser, M.; Jardé, O. New French legislation governing organ removals for therapeutic and scientific purposes. *Medicine and Law: World Association for Medical Law* 2005 September; 24(3): 585-603. NRCBL: 19.5; 8.3.4; 8.3.2; 4.4. SC: le.
Abstract: In France the general principles of organ donation are: consent, absence of financial gain, anonymity, advertising is prohibited, healthcare safety. As regards organ removals from living persons, a panel of experts is required to give approval. The recipient's spouse, brothers or sisters, sons or daughters, grandparents, uncles or aunts and first cousins may be authorised to donate organs, as well as the spouse of the recipient's father or mother. The donor may also be any person who provides proof of having lived with the recipient for at least two years. As regards organ removals from Deceased Persons for Therapeutic Purposes, removals may be practised if the deceased did not make known their refusal during their lifetime (this may be recorded in the national registry set up for this purpose). The doctor must not seek the family's opinion, but rather ensure that the deceased did not express opposition to organ donation during his lifetime. The rule of presumed consent should apply, unless there is any danger to the health of the general public. This paper describes and discusses in detail the new legislation and its relationship to existing French legal codes.

Morrison, Doug. A holistic approach to clinical and research decision- making: lessons from the UK organ-retention scandals. *Medical Law Review* 2005 Spring; 13(1):45-79. NRCBL: 19.5; 18.3; 1.1; 8.2; 8.3.2. SC: an; le.

Nadel, Mark S.; Nadel, Carolina A. Using reciprocity to motivate organ donations. *Yale Journal of Health Policy, Law, and Ethics* 2005 Winter; 5(1): 293-325. NRCBL: 19.5; 19.6; 9.4; 4.4. SC: le.

Northup, Patrick Grant; Berg, Carl Lansing. Living donor liver transplantation: the historical and cultural basis of policy decisions and ongoing ethical questions. *Health Policy* 2005 May; 72(2): 175-185. NRCBL: 19.5; 19.1; 9.4; 19.6; 7.1. SC: le. Identifiers: A2ALL study.

Pampilly, Varghese Sebastian. Cadavers for anatomical dissection. *Indian Journal of Medical Ethics* 2005 January-March; 2(1): 16- 17. NRCBL: 19.5. SC: le. Identifiers: India; Karnataka Anatomy Act (KAA).

Powhida, Alexander. Forced organ donation: the presumed consent to organ donation laws of the various states and the United States Constitution. *Albany Law Journal of Science and Technology* 1999; 9(2): 349-374. NRCBL: 19.5; 8.3.1; 4.4. SC: le.

Roscam Abbing, Henriette D.C. A Council of Europe protocol on transplantation of organs and tissues of human origin. *European Journal of Health Law* 2002 March; 9(1): 63-76. NRCBL: 19.5; 19.6; 9.8; 9.4. SC: le.

Slabbert, Magda; Oosthuizen, Hennie. Commercialization of human organs for transplantation: a view from South Africa. *Medicine and Law: World Association for Medical Law* 2005 March; 24(1): 191-201. NRCBL: 19.5; 4.4. SC: le.
Abstract: The Human Tissue Act 65 of 1983 regulates all aspects regarding organ transplants. This Act was last amended in 1989. Since then medical science has developed tremendously and to such an extent that organ transplants today are almost routine operations in many hospitals. Unfortunately the current methods of procuring human organs are not supplying the demand. A new approach, the commercialization of human organs for transplantation is a possibility with the potential to supply one hundred per cent of the demand for organs. There are however many arguments against the commercialization of human organs, but not one of these arguments is without criticism. Eth-

ical aspects concerning commercialization of human organs also need to be investigated, in order to reach a conclusion that it is not unethical and is worth being investigated.

Snell, Gregory I.; Levvey, B.J.; Williams, T.J. Non-heart beating organ donation. *Internal Medicine Journal* 2004 August; 34(8): 501-503. NRCBL: 19.5; 20.2.1. SC: le. Identifiers: Australia.

Terry, Louise M.; Campbell, Anne. Protecting the interests of the child bone marrow donor. *Medicine and Law: World Association for Medical Law* 2004; 23(4): 805-819. NRCBL: 19.5; 8.3.2; 4.4; 19.2. SC: le.
Abstract: At a time when designer babies have been created to act as cord blood donors to sick siblings, ethical debate has focused predominantly on the extent to which it is acceptable to create one human being to assist another. However, children are frequently used this way, by their families and doctors who extract their bone marrow, to try to save the life of another, usually a sibling. With any life-threatening illness, there is the possibility that the urgency of the sick sibling's need means that the short-term welfare of the donor child receives less attention than it should by parents and doctors. This article suggests ways to protect the interests of such children and empower them within the decision- making process and concludes that the drive to save life must be tempered by recognition of the intrinsic worth of donor children and their rights not to be exploited.

Young, Emma. Laws fail to stop India's organ trade [news]. *New Scientist* 2005 October 22-28; 188(2522): 20. NRCBL: 19.5; 9.3.1. SC: le.

ORGAN AND TISSUE TRANSPLANTATION/ XENOTRANSPLANTATION

Baines, Lyndsay S.; Jindal, Rahul M. Religious beliefs and opinions on clinical xenotransplantation — a survey of university students from Kenya, Sweden and Texas [letter]. *Clinical Transplantation* 2002 August; 16(4): 314. NRCBL: 19.1; 22.2; 2.1; 21.1.

Canada. Health Canada. Survey on human organ donation and xenotransplantation. Ottawa, Ontario, Canada: Health Canada 1999 December 19; 5 p. [Online]. Available: http://www.hc-sc.gc.ca/hpfb-dgpsa/bgtd-dpbtg/xeno_survey_e.pdf [2 May 2005]. NRCBL: 19.1; 22.2. SC: em.

Canada. Health Canada/Santé Canada. Proposed Canadian Standard for Xenotransplantation, Draft No. 14. Ottawa, Ontario, Canada: Health Canada 1999 July; 48 p. [Online]. Available: http://www.hc-sc.gc.ca/dhp-mps/alt_formats/hpfb-dgpsa/pdf/brgtherap/xeno_std-norme_e .pdf [1 December 2005]. NRCBL: 19.1; 22.2. Note: Draft No. 14.

Cooke, David Tom; Caffarelli, Anthony D.; Robbins, Robert C. The road to clinical xenotransplantation: a worthwhile journey. *Transplantation* 2004 October 27; 78(8): 1108-1109. NRCBL: 19.1; 22.2.

Council of Europe. Committee of Ministers. Recommendation Rec (2003) 10 of the Committee of Ministers to member states on xenotransplantation. *Medical Ethics and Bioethics / Medicinska Etika & Bioetika* 2003 Autumn-Winter; 10(3-4): 12-16. NRCBL: 19.1; 22.2.

De Bona, M.; Canova, D.; Rumiati, R.; Russo, F.P.; Ermani, M.; Ancona, E.; Naccarato, R.; Burra, P. Understanding of and attitudes to xenotransplantation: a survey among Italian university students. *Xenotransplantation* 2004 March; 11(2): 133-140. NRCBL: 19.1; 22.2. SC: em.

Deschamps, Jack-Yves; Roux, Françoise A.; Gouin, Edouard; Saï, Pierre. Reluctance of French patients with type 1 diabetes to undergo pig pancreatic islet xenotransplantation. *Xenotransplantation* 2005 May; 12(3): 175-180. NRCBL: 19.1; 22.2; 5.2; 9.5.1. SC: em. Identifiers: France.

Einsiedel, Edna F. Commentary: on the position paper of the Ethics Committee of the International Xenotransplantation Association. *Transplantation* 2004 October 27; 78(8): 1110-1111. NRCBL: 19.1; 22.2; 18.6.

Guerra Gonzalez, Jorge. Prevention of the xenogenic infection risk and the Spanish and German constitutions. *Revista de Derecho y Genoma Humano / Law and the Human Genome Review* 2004 January-June; (20): 123-146. NRCBL: 19.1; 22.2; 18.6. SC: le. Note: abstract in Spanish.

Hagelin, Joakim. Public opinion surveys about xenotransplantation. *Xenotransplantation* 2004 November; 11(6): 551-558. NRCBL: 19.1; 22.2. SC: em.

Hagelin, Joakim; Hau, Jann; Schapiro, Steven J.; Suleman, Mbaruk A.; Carlsson, Hans-Erik. Religious beliefs and opinions on clinical xenotransplantation — a survey of university students from Kenya, Sweden and Texas [reply]. *Clinical Transplantation* 2002 August; 16(4): 315. NRCBL: 19.1; 22.2; 2.1.

International Xenotransplantation Association [IXA]. Ethics Committee.; Sykes, Megan; d'Apice, Anthony; Sandrin, Mauro. Position paper of the Ethics Committee of the International Xenotransplantation Association. *Transplantation* 2004 October 27; 78(8): 1101-1107. NRCBL: 19.1; 22.2; 18.6; 1.2.

McLean, Margaret R. Xenotransplantation: weighting individual benefit and risks to the public. Santa Clara, CA: Markkula Center for Applied Ethics, Santa Clara University 2004 February; 3 p. [Online]. Available: http://www. scu.edu/ethics/publications/ethicalperspectives/ xenotransplant.html [15 June 2005]. NRCBL: 19.1; 22.2; 5.2.

Michael, Mike; Brown, Nik. Scientific citizenships: self-representations of xenotransplantation's publics. *Science as Culture* 2005 March; 14(1): 39-57. NRCBL: 19.1; 22.2; 5.1. SC: an.

NRCBL: National Reference Center for Bioethics Literature Classification Scheme   See inside front cover for terms.

373

Michie, Colin. Xenotransplantation, endogenous pig retroviruses and the precautionary principle [opinion]. *Trends in Molecular Medicine* 2001 February; 7(2): 62-63. NRCBL: 19.1; 22.2.

Morris, Peter J.; Monaco, Anthony P. Ethical issues and xenotransplantation. *Transplantation* 2004 October 27; 78(8): 1099-1100. NRCBL: 19.1; 22.2.

Ravelingien, An. The world is my patient: a discussion of Martine Rothblatt's Your Life or Mine: how geoethics can resolve the conflict between public and private interests in xenotransplantation [opinion]. *Xenotransplantation* 2005 March; 12(2): 88-90. NRCBL: 19.1; 22.2; 21.1.

Ravelingien, An; Braeckman, Johan. The patients' perspective: comments on 'Reluctance of French patients with type 1 diabetes to undergo pig pancreatic islet xenotransplantation' [opinion]. *Xenotransplantation* 2005 May; 12(3): 173-174. NRCBL: 19.1; 22.2.

Rothblatt, Martine. Of pigs and men: issues of speciesism and chimerism. *In her:* Your Life or Mine: How Geoethics Can Resolve the Conflict Between Public and Private Interests in Xenotransplantation. Burlington, VT: Ashgate; 2004: 71-95. NRCBL: 19.1; 22.2; 1.1.

Rothblatt, Martine. The right to life: society's obligation to provide health care and xenotransplantation. *In her:* Your Life or Mine: How Geoethics Can Resolve the Conflict Between Public and Private Interests in Xenotransplantation. Burlington, VT: Ashgate; 2004: 97-116. NRCBL: 19.1; 22.2; 1.1; 9.2.

Swiss Academy of Medical Sciences. Medical-ethical principles on xenotransplantation. *Swiss Medical Weekly* 2001 June 30; 131(25-26): 388-394. NRCBL: 19.1; 22.2; 1.3.9; 18.2.

United Kingdom Xenotransplantation Interim Regulatory Authority [UKXIRA]. Guidance on Making Proposals to Conduct Xenotransplantation on Human Subjects. London: The Authority 1998; 14 p., 9 p. annexes [Online]. Available: http://www.advisorybodies.doh.gov.uk/pub/docs/doh/ukxirag.pdf; http://www.advisorybodies.doh.gov.uk/pub/docs/doh/ukxiraa.pdf [15 April 2005]. NRCBL: 19.1; 22.2. Note: Includes annexes A - E.

Welchman, Jennifer. Xenografting, species loyalty, and human solidarity. *Journal of Social Philosophy* 2003 Summer; 34(2): 244-255. NRCBL: 19.1; 22.2; 1.1. SC: an.

Wright, James R., Jr. Public consultation on xenotransplantation. *Transplantation* 2004 October 27; 78(8): 1112-1113. NRCBL: 19.1; 22.2; 18.6. Identifiers: Canada.

ORGAN DONATION *See* ORGAN AND TISSUE TRANSPLANTATION/ DONATION AND PROCUREMENT

OVUM DONORS *See* REPRODUCTIVE TECHNOLOGIES

PALLIATIVE CARE *See* DEATH AND DYING/ TERMINAL CARE

PARENTAL CONSENT *See* EUTHANASIA AND ALLOWING TO DIE/ MINORS; CARE FOR SPECIFIC GROUPS/ MINORS; HUMAN EXPERIMENTATION/ SPECIAL POPULATIONS/ MINORS; INFORMED CONSENT/ MINORS

PATIENT CARE *See* CARE FOR SPECIFIC GROUPS

PATENTS

Abbott, Alison. Europe pares down double patents on breast-cancer gene [news]. *Nature* 2005 January 27; 433(7024): 344. NRCBL: 15.8. SC: le. Identifiers: European Patent Office.

Abbott, Alison. Genetic patent singles out Jewish women [news]. *Nature* 2005 July 7; 436(7047): 12. NRCBL: 15.8; 15.3; 5.3; 9.5.4; 9.5.5. Identifiers: Europe; Jews; Myriad Genetics.

Albright, Matthew. Life patents and democratic values. *In:* Krimsky, Sheldon; Shorett, Peter, eds. Rights and Liberties in the Biotech Age: Why We Need a Genetic Bill of Rights. Lanham: Rowman and Littlefield Publishers; 2005: 29-39. NRCBL: 15.8.

Andrews, Lori B.; Paradise, Jordan. Gene patents: the need for bioethics scrutiny and legal change. *Yale Journal of Health Policy, Law, and Ethics* 2005 Winter; 5(1): 403-412. NRCBL: 15.8. SC: le.

Avisar, Solomon R. The ethics of biotechnology — the argument in favour of patents. *Canadian Intellectual Property Review* 1993 September; 10(1): 209-217. NRCBL: 15.8; 5.3; 5.1; 21.1. SC: le. Identifiers: Canada; Canadian Patent Office.

Beadle, Libby. Selling the stem cell short? An assessment of the patentability of the results of human stem cell research in New Zealand. *Canterbury Law Review* 2004; 10: 1-35. NRCBL: 15.8; 18.5.4; 15.1; 5.3; 9.1; 4.4. SC: le.

Bhutkar, Arjun. Synthetic biology: navigating the challenges ahead. *Journal of Biolaw and Business* 2005; 8(2): 19-29. NRCBL: 15.8; 4.4; 15.7.

Budds, Brian. Toward a just model of alienability of human tissue. *University of San Francisco Law Review* 2003 Spring; 37(3): 757-782. NRCBL: 15.8; 4.4; 19.5; 18.3; 18.1; 5.3. SC: le.

Caulfield, Timothy. Gene patents, human clones, and biotechnology policy: the challenges created by globalization.

Alberta Law Review 2003 December; 41(3): 713-724. NRCBL: 15.8; 14.5; 21.1; 5.3. SC: le.

Caulfield, Timothy. Policy conflicts: gene patents and health care in Canada. *Community Genetics* 2005 October; 8(4): 223-227. NRCBL: 15.8; 9.1; 9.3.1.

Caulfield, Timothy A.; Gold, E. Richard. Whistling in the wind: patents on genetic research are a reality. It's time to reframe the debate. *Forum for Applied Research and Public Policy* 2000 Spring; 15(1): 75-79. NRCBL: 15.8; 1.3.2.

Caulfield, Timothy A.; Knoppers, Bartha Maria; Gold, E.R.; Sheremeta, L.E.; Bridge, P.J. Genetic technologies, health care policy and the patent bargain [opinion]. *Clinical Genetics* 2003 January; 63(1): 15-18. NRCBL: 15.8; 5.3.

Caulfield, Timothy; Gold, E. Richard; Cho, Mildred K. Patenting human genetic material: refocusing the debate [opinion]. *Nature Reviews Genetics* 2000 December; 1(3): 227-231. NRCBL: 15.8; 5.3.

Cook-Deegan, Robert; Walters, LeRoy; Pressman, Lori; Pau, Derrick; McCormack, Stephen; Gatchalian, Janella; Burges, Richard. Preliminary data on U.S. DNA-based patents and plans for a survey of licensing practices. *In:* Knoppers, Bartha Maria, ed. Populations and Genetics: Legal and Socio-Ethical Perspectives. Boston: Martinus Nijhoff; 2003: 453-471. NRCBL: 15.8; 15.1. SC: em.

Crespi, R. Stephen. Ethico-legal issues in biomedicine patenting: a patent professional viewpoint. *Science and Engineering Ethics* 2005 January; 11(1): 117-136. NRCBL: 15.8; 5.3. SC: le.

Dillen, Jeffrey S. DNA patentability — anything but obvious. *Wisconsin Law Review* 1997; 5: 1023-1046. NRCBL: 15.8. SC: le.

Eisenberg, Rebecca S. Patents, product exclusivity, and information dissemination: how law directs biopharmaceutical research and development. *Fordham Law Review* 2003 December; 72(3): 477-491. NRCBL: 15.8; 9.7; 18.6; 5.3. SC: le.

EPO [European Patent Office] Opposition Division. Patentability of test animals — the British Union for the abolition of vivisection et al. v. the President and Fellows of Harvard College — "Onco-Mouse". *International Review of Intellectual Property and Competition Law* 2004; 35(1): 72-78. NRCBL: 15.8; 22.2; 22.3; 5.3. SC: le.

Everett, Margaret. Response to Rich's letter regarding "the social life of genes: privacy, property and the new genetics" [letter]. *Social Science and Medicine* 2003 December; 57(12): 2473. NRCBL: 15.8; 18.3; 15.1; 5.3; 4.4. SC: le.

Everett, Margaret. The social life of genes: privacy, property and the new genetics. *Social Science and Medicine* 2003 January; 56(1): 53-65. NRCBL: 15.8; 15.1; 5.3; 8.4; 4.4. Identifiers: Oregon Genetic Privacy Act of 1995.

Faye, David J. Bioprospecting, genetic patenting and indigenous populations: challenges under a restructured information commons. *Journal of World Intellectual Property* 2004 May; 7(3): 401-428. NRCBL: 15.8; 5.3; 21.1. SC: le; em.

Ford, Richard. The morality of biotech patents: differing legal obligations in Europe? *European Intellectual Property Review* 1997 June; 19(6): 315-318. NRCBL: 15.8; 5.3; 21.1. SC: le.

Girsberger, Martin A. Transparency measures under patent law regarding genetic resources and traditional knowledge: disclosure of source and evidence of prior informed consent and benefit-sharing. *Journal of World Intellectual Property* 2004 July; 7(4): 451-489. NRCBL: 15.8; 5.3; 8.3.1; 21.1. SC: le.

Goldberg, Steven. Gene patents and the death of dualism. *South California Interdisciplinary Law Journal* 1996 Winter; 5(1): 25-40. NRCBL: 15.8; 3.1; 1.1.

Gottweis, Herbert. Governing genomics in the 21st century: between risk and uncertainty. *New Genetics and Society* 2005 August; 24(2): 175-193. NRCBL: 15.8; 5.3.

Hinojosa, John Paul. The human genome, property of all: opportunities under the ALRC inquiry into gene patenting and human health. *Sydney Law Review* 2004 September; 26(3): 447-455. NRCBL: 15.8; 15.1. Identifiers: Australian Law Reform Commission.

Ho, Cynthia M. Patents, patients, and public policy: an incomplete intersection at 35 U.S.C. Section 287(c). *University of California Davis Law Review* 2000 Spring; 33(3): 601-675. NRCBL: 15.8; 9.1; 21.1. SC: le.

Hofmeyer, Timothy G. Everybody's got something to hide except me and my patented monkey: patentability of cloned organisms. *John Marshall Journal of Computer and Information Law* 1998 Summer; 16(4): 971-995. NRCBL: 15.8; 14.5. SC: le.

Holman, Molly A.; Munzer, Stephen R. Intellectual property rights in genes and gene fragments: a registration solution for expressed sequence tags. *Iowa Law Review* 2000 March; 85(3): 735-848. NRCBL: 15.8; 15.1; 5.3; 1.1. SC: le.

Jensen, Kyle; Murray, Fiona. Intellectual property landscape of the human genome. *Science* 2005 October 14; 310(5746): 239-240. NRCBL: 15.8. SC: em.

King, Jonathan; Stabinsky, Doreen. Life patents undermine the exchange of technology and scientific ideas. *In:* Krimsky, Sheldon; Shorett, Peter, eds. Rights and Liberties in the Biotech Age: Why We Need a Genetic Bill of Rights.

NRCBL: National Reference Center for Bioethics Literature Classification Scheme   See inside front cover for terms.

375

Lanham: Rowman and Littlefield Publishers; 2005: 49-54. NRCBL: 15.8; 15.1.

Lekovic, Gregory P. Genetic diagnosis and intellectual property rights: a proposal to amend "the Physician Immunity Statute". *Yale Journal of Health Policy, Law, and Ethics* 2004 Summer; 4(2): 275-304. NRCBL: 15.8; 15.3; 9.3.1; 1.3.9. SC: le.

Leute, Kirsten. Patenting and licensing of university-based genetic inventions — a view from experience at Stanford University's Office of Technology Licensing. *Community Genetics* 2005 October; 8(4): 217-222. NRCBL: 15.8; 1.3.3.

Lievrouw, Leah A. Biotechnology, intellectual property, and the prospects for scientific communication. *In:* Braman, Sandra, ed. Biotechnology and Communication: The Meta-Technologies of Information. Mahwah, NJ: Lawrence Erlbaum Associates; 2004: 145-172. NRCBL: 15.8; 1.3.7; 1.3.9; 15.1.

Marshall, Eliot. BRCA2 claim faces new challenge [news]. *Science* 2005 June 24; 308(5730): 1851. NRCBL: 15.8; 21.1.

May, Christopher. Justifying enclosure? Intellectual property and meta- technologies. *In:* Braman, Sandra, ed. Biotechnology and Communication: The Meta-Technologies of Information. Mahwah, NJ: Lawrence Erlbaum Associates; 2004: 119-143. NRCBL: 15.8; 1.3.12; 15.1.

McKay, Daniel L. Patent law and human genome research at the crossroads: the need for Congressional action. *Santa Clara Computer and High Technology Law Journal* 1994; 10(2): 465-498. NRCBL: 15.8; 15.10; 15.1. SC: le.

Merges, Robert P. Intellectual property in higher life forms: the patent system and controversial technologies. *Maryland Law Review* 1988 Summer; 47(4): 1051-1075. NRCBL: 15.8; 22.3; 5.3. SC: le.

Merz, Jon F.; Cho, Mildred K. What are gene patents and why are people worried about them? *Community Genetics* 2005 October; 8(4): 203-208. NRCBL: 15.8; 18.1.

Minwalla, Sherizaan. A modest proposal to amend the Patent Code 35 U.S.C. Section 287(c) to allow health care providers to examine their patients' DNA. *Southern Illinois University Law Journal* 2002 Spring; 26(3): 471-504. NRCBL: 15.8; 5.3. SC: le.

Mitchell, Peter. Europe dithers over stem cell patents [news]. *Nature Medicine* 2003 February; 9(2): 154. NRCBL: 15.8; 5.3; 18.5.1; 15.1; 21.1.

Nicol, Dianne. Balancing innovation and access to healthcare through the patent system — an Australian perspective. *Community Genetics* 2005 October; 8(4): 228-234. NRCBL: 15.8; 1.3.5; 9.2.

Nunnally, Allen C.; Webster, Christopher J.; Brown, Scott A.; Cohen, Gary A. Genetic patent protection in the pharmaceutical and biotechnology industries. *Community Genetics* 2005 October; 8(4): 209-216. NRCBL: 15.8; 9.7; 5.1; 1.3.2.

Ong, Burton T. Patenting the biological bounty: re-examining the status of organic inventions as patentable subject matter. *Marquette Intellectual Property Law Review* 2004 Winter; 8(1): 1-62. NRCBL: 15.8; 1.1; 5.3; 4.4. SC: le.

Paradise, Jordan; Andrews, Lori; Holbrook, Timothy. Patents on human genes: an analysis of scope and claims. *Science* 2005 March 11; 307(5715): 1566-1567. NRCBL: 15.8. SC: le.

Parthasarathy, Shobita. The patent is political: the consequences of patenting the BRCA genes in Britain. *Community Genetics* 2005 October; 8(4): 235-242. NRCBL: 15.8; 1.3.5.

Putnam, Jonathan D. Costs and benefits of genomics patents. *American Journal of Pharmacogenomics* 2004; 4(5): 277-292. NRCBL: 15.8. SC: rv.

Radick, Gregory. Discovering and patenting human genes. *In:* Bainham, Andrew; Sclater, Shelley Day; Richards, Martin, eds. Body Lore and Laws. Portland, OR: Hart Pub.; 2002: 63-78. NRCBL: 15.8. SC: le.

Rich, Leigh. Letter response to Margaret Everett (2003) "the social life of genes: privacy, property and the new genetics" Social Science and Medicine, 56:1 [letter]. *Social Science and Medicine* 2003 December; 57(12): 2471-2472. NRCBL: 15.8; 18.3. SC: le.

Sagoff, Mark. Patented genes: an ethical appraisal. *Issues in Science and Technology* 1998 Spring; 14(3): 37-41. NRCBL: 15.8. SC: le.

Shand, Hope. New enclosures: why civil society and governments should look beyond life patents. *In:* Krimsky, Sheldon; Shorett, Peter, eds. Rights and Liberties in the Biotech Age: Why We Need a Genetic Bill of Rights. Lanham: Rowman and Littlefield Publishers; 2005: 40-48. NRCBL: 15.8; 5.3.

Siegel-Itzkovich, Judy. Israeli doctors want to stop European patent for genetic test [news]. *BMJ: British Medical Journal* 2005 July 2; 331(7507): 8. NRCBL: 15.8; 15.3; 9.3.1.

Smith, George P., II. The promise of abundant life: patenting a magnificent obsession. *Utah Journal of Contemporary Law* 1982; 8: 85-96. NRCBL: 15.8. SC: le.

Spier, Raymond. Observations on a meeting on the ethics of intellectual property rights and patents. *Science and Engineering Ethics* 2005 January; 11(1): 151-158. NRCBL: 15.8; 5.3; 1.3.9. SC: le. Conference: 5th International Conference on Bioethics: The Ethics of Intellectual Property

Rights and Patents; Warsaw, Poland; 23-24 April 2004; Minister of Science and the Minister of Health, Poland.

Straus, Joseph. Patents on biomaterial—a new colonialism or a means for technology transfer and benefit-sharing? *In:* Thiele, F.; Ashcroft, R.E., eds. Bioethics in a Small World. Berlin: Springer; 2005: 45-72. NRCBL: 15.8; 21.1; 5.1.

Suter, Sonia M. Disentangling privacy from property: toward a deeper understanding of genetic privacy. *George Washington Law Review* 2004 April; 72(4): 737-814. NRCBL: 15.8; 15.3; 8.4; 4.4; 16.3. SC: le.

Terry, Patrick F. PXE International: harnessing intellectual property law for benefit-sharing. *In:* Knoppers, Bartha Maria, ed. Populations and Genetics: Legal and Socio-Ethical Perspectives. Boston: Martinus Nijhoff; 2003: 377-393. NRCBL: 15.8; 15.1; 9.3.1. SC: le.

Thorsteinsdottir, Halla; Daar, Abdallah S.; Smith, Richard D.; Singer, Peter A. Do patents encourage or inhibit genomics as a global public good? *In:* Knoppers, Bartha Maria, ed. Populations and Genetics: Legal and Socio-Ethical Perspectives. Boston: Martinus Nijhoff, 2003: 487-504. NRCBL: 15.8; 15.1; 5.1.

Tischauser, Leslie V.; Ness, Bryan D. Patents on life-forms. *In:* Ness, Bryan D., ed. Encyclopedia of Genetics. Revised edition. Volume II. Pasadena, Calif.: Salem Press; 2004: 594-596. NRCBL: 15.8.

Van Overwalle, Geertrui. Bio-patents, law and ethics. Critical analysis of the EU Biotechnology Directive. *Revista de Derecho y Genoma Humano / Law and the Human Genome Review* 2003 July-December; (19): 187-203. NRCBL: 15.8; 21.1; 18.3. SC: le.

Vanguri, Swathi Sri; Rajput, Vijay. Patents and biotechnology. *Issues in Medical Ethics* 2002 January-March; 10(1): 152-153. NRCBL: 15.8; 5.1.

Walpole, Ian R.; Dawkins, Hugh J.S.; Sinden, Peter D.; O'Leary, Peter C. Human gene patents: the possible impacts on genetic services healthcare [opinion]. *Medical Journal of Australia* 2003 August 18; 179(4): 203-205. NRCBL: 15.8; 15.3; 9.3.1; 9.1; 5.3. Identifiers: BRCA; Australia.

Warren-Jones, Amanda. Patenting DNA: a lot of controversy over a little intangibility. *Medical Law Review* 2004 Spring; 12(1): 97-124. NRCBL: 15.8; 1.3.9. SC: an; le.

Weiss, Rick. U.S. denies patent for a too-human hybrid: scientist sought legal precedent to keep others from profiting from similar "inventions". *Washington Post* 2005 February 13; p. A3. NRCBL: 15.8. SC: le; po.

Witek, Rafal. Ethics and patentability in biotechnology. *Science and Engineering Ethics* 2005 January; 11(1): 105-111. NRCBL: 15.8; 1.1. SC: le. Conference: 5th International Conference on Bioethics: The Ethics of Intellec-

tual Property Rights and Patents; Warsaw, Poland; 23-24 April 2004; Minister of Science and the Minister of Health, Poland.

Zimmer, Franz-Josef; Sethmann, Svenja. The immoral gene: does it really exist? *Science and Engineering Ethics* 2005 January; 11(1): 97-104. NRCBL: 15.8; 1.1. SC: le. Conference: 5th International Conference on Bioethics: The Ethics of Intellectual Property Rights and Patents; Warsaw, Poland; 23-24 April 2004; Minister of Science and the Minister of Health, Poland.

PATERNALISM *See* PROFESSIONAL PATIENT RELATIONSHIP

PATIENT ACCESS TO RECORDS *See* CONFIDENTIALITY; TRUTH DISCLOSURE

PATIENT CARE *See* CARE FOR SPECIFIC GROUPS; DEATH AND DYING/ TERMINAL CARE; PROFESSIONAL PATIENT RELATIONSHIP

PATIENTS' RIGHTS *See* CARE FOR SPECIFIC GROUPS; CONFIDENTIALITY; INFORMED CONSENT; RIGHT TO HEALTH CARE; TREATMENT REFUSAL; TRUTH DISCLOSURE

PERSONHOOD *See* QUALITY AND VALUE OF LIFE

PHILOSOPHY *See* BIOETHICS AND MEDICAL ETHICS/ PHILOSOPHICAL PERSPECTIVES; EUTHANASIA AND ALLOWING TO DIE/ PHILOSOPHICAL ASPECTS; NURSING ETHICS AND PHILOSOPHY; PHILOSOPHY OF MEDICINE

PHILOSOPHY OF MEDICINE

Association of Clinical Embryologists [ACE]. Code of Professional Conduct for Clinical Embryologists. *Human Fertility* 2004 December; 7(4): 301-303. NRCBL: 4.1.2; 14.1; 6. Identifiers: United Kingdom (Great Britain).

Berger, William L.; Griner, Paul. Health care costs [letters]. *Annals of Internal Medicine* 2005 December 6; 143(11): 844. NRCBL: 4.1.2; 9.3.1.

Bloche, M. Gregg; Marks, Jonathan H. When doctors go to war [opinion]. *New England Journal of Medicine* 2005 January 6; 352(1): 3-6. NRCBL: 4.1.2; 21.2; 7.4; 21.4; 1.3.5.

Braunack-Mayer, A. What makes a good GP? An empirical perspective on virtue in general practice. *Journal of Medical Ethics* 2005 February; 31(2): 82-87. NRCBL: 4.1.2; 2.1. SC: em. Identifiers: general practitioner.

NRCBL: National Reference Center for Bioethics Literature Classification Scheme   See inside front cover for terms.

377

Cheever, Kerry H.; Jubilan, Boyce; Dailey, Thomas; Ehrhardt, Kathleen; Blumenstein, Robert; Morin, Christopher J.; Lewis, Charles. Surgeons and the spirit: a study on the relationship of religiosity to clinical practice. *Journal of Religion and Health* 2005 Spring; 44(1): 67-80. NRCBL: 4.1.2; 1.2; 7.1. SC: em.

Chervenak, Frank A.; McCullough, Laurence B. A group practice disagrees about offering contraception. *American Family Physician* 2002 March 15; 65(6): 1230, 1233. NRCBL: 4.1.2; 7.3; 11.1; 1.2. SC: cs.

Clark, Chalmers C.; Macauley, Robert. Civil disobedience: the devil is in the details [letter and reply]. *Hastings Center Report* 2005 July-August; 35(4): 5-6. NRCBL: 4.1.2; 9.3.1.

Coombes, Rebecca. Do vets and doctors face similar ethical challenges? [news]. *BMJ: British Medical Journal* 2005 November 26; 331(7527): 1227. NRCBL: 4.1.2; 22.1.

Coulehan, Jack. Today's professionalism: engaging the mind but not the heart [opinion]. *Academic Medicine* 2005 October; 80(10): 892-898. NRCBL: 4.1.2; 1.3.1; 7.2.

Dekkers, Wim. Medical philosophy and medical ethics [editorial]. *Medicine, Health Care and Philosophy: A European Journal* 2004; 7(3): 241-242. NRCBL: 4.1.2; 2.1; 1.1.

Fredriksen, Ståle. Limits to doubt. *Theoretical Medicine and Bioethics* 2005; 26(5): 379-395. NRCBL: 4.1.2; 1.1.
Abstract: Supported by Ian Hacking's concept of "intervention," and Charles Taylor's concept of "intentionality," this article argues that doubting is acting, and that doubting is therefore subject to the same demands of responsibility as any other action. The argument is developed by using medical practice as a test-case. The central suggestion is that the demand of acting responsibly limits doubt in medicine. The article focuses on two such limitations to doubt. Firstly, the article argues that it is irresponsible to doubt that our actions can harm other people. Secondly, the article argues that it is irresponsible not to strive for coherence between our utterances of doubt and our other actions. Incoherence here can cause "cultural impoverishment." In a larger context this article also argues that medicine can enrich our epistemology, because medical knowledge displays important traits of knowledge that are downplayed in traditional epistemology derived from mathematics and physics. In particular, medicine makes it possible to get the relation between ethics and epistemology into sharper focus. The endpoint in medical epistemology is "responsible action," and not certainty in and of itself.

Fredriksen, Ståle. Luck, risk, and blame. *Journal of Medicine and Philosophy* 2005 October; 30(5): 535- 553. NRCBL: 4.1.2; 1.1; 4.2.
Abstract: In this article, I defend luck at the expense of risk. Or, more precisely, I try to make a distinction that gives both concepts fair treatment. I start by making it clear that luck stands in opposition to control and not to causation. Both luck and risk are related to causal uncertainty. But it is warranted to talk about risk only when the uncertainty involved is brought under control, as it is in some familiar forms of fair gambling such as dicing and roulette. Life is however not a fair gamble. We rarely have the kind of control over the preconditions of life that we have over the preconditions of say dicing. Luck therefore has profound influence on our lives and our health. This means that the standard conception of responsibility-that is, that we stand responsible only for consequences that we control - breaks down far more often than what is usually acknowledged. I therefore end the article by arguing that the standard conception of responsibility ought to be supplemented with a different conception that I have called "responsibility because of social involvement."

Garrett, Robert E. Why philosophy matters. *Family Medicine* 2002 April; 34(4): 247-249. NRCBL: 4.1.2; 1.1.

Gisondi, Michael A.; Smith-Coggins, Rebecca; Harter, Phillip M.; Soltysik, Robert C.; Yarnold, Paul R. Assessment of resident professionalism using high-fidelity simulation of ethical dilemmas. *Academic Emergency Medicine* 2004 September; 11(9): 931-937. NRCBL: 4.1.2; 2.1; 7.2. SC: em.

Guinan, Patrick. The Christian origin of medical compassion. *National Catholic Bioethics Quarterly* 2005 Summer; 5(2): 243- 248. NRCBL: 4.1.2; 1.2; 7.1; 8.1.

Harper, C. Mark. Philosophy for physicians. *Journal of the Royal Society of Medicine* 2003 January; 96(1): 40-45. NRCBL: 4.1.2; 1.1; 5.1.

Hauser, Stephen L. The shape of things to come [editorial]. *Neurology* 2004 September 28; 63(6): 948-950. NRCBL: 4.1.2; 5.1.

Hawkins, Anne Hunsaker. Epiphanic knowledge and medicine. *CQ: Cambridge Quarterly of Healthcare Ethics* 2005 Winter; 14(1): 40-46. NRCBL: 4.1.2; 7.1.

Huddle, Thomas S. Teaching professionalism: is medical morality a competency? [opinion]. *Academic Medicine* 2005 October; 80(10): 885-891. NRCBL: 4.1.2; 1.3.1; 7.2.

Jacobs, Alice K.; Smith, Sidney C., Jr.; Popp, Richard L.; Joscalzo, Joseph. Ethics and professionalism: can there be consensus? An editorial comment on the report of the ACCF/AHA consensus conference on professionalism and ethics. *Circulation* 2004 October 19; 110(16): 2278-2279. NRCBL: 4.1.2; 2.1; 1.1. Identifiers: American College of CardiologyFoundation; American Heart Association.

Jotkowitz, A.B.; Glick, S. The physician charter on medical professionalism: a Jewish ethical perspective. *Journal of Medical Ethics* 2005 July; 31(7): 404-405. NRCBL: 4.1.2; 2.1; 1.2.
Abstract: The physician charter on medical professionalism creates standards of ethical behaviour for physicians and has been endorsed by professional organisations worldwide. It is based on the cardinal principles of the primacy of patient welfare, patient autonomy, and social welfare. There has been little discussion in the bioethics community of the doctrine of the charter and none from a Jewish ethical perspective. In this essay the authors discuss the obligations of the charter from a Jewish ethical viewpoint and call on other cultures to develop their own unique perspectives on this important document.

Kodner, Ira J. Surgeons' ethics? You bet! [editorial]. *Surgery* 2002 May; 131(5): 581-582. NRCBL: 4.1.2.

Larriviere, Dan. Duty hours vs professional ethics: ACGME rules create conflicts. *Neurology* 2004 July 13; 63(1): E4-E5. NRCBL: 4.1.2; 1.3.1; 7.1; 6. Identifiers: Accreditation Council for Graduate Medical Education.

Launer, John. All doctors are liars. *QJM: An International Journal of Medicine* 2003 January; 96(1): 85-86. NRCBL: 4.1.2; 1.1.

Lazarus, Arthur. The moral obligations of physician executives. *Physician Executive* 2004 November-December; 30(6): 40-43. NRCBL: 4.1.2; 1.3.1; 6.

Lynöe, Niels; Mattsson, Bengt. Doctor for patients or doctor for society? Comparative study of GPs' and psychiatrists' assessments of clinical practice. *Scandinavian Journal of Primary Health Care* 2004 December; 22(4): 228-232. NRCBL: 4.1.2; 7.3; 8.1. SC: em. Identifiers: general practitioners; Sweden.

Mackenbach, Johan P. On the survival of the altruistic trait in medicine: is there a link with the placebo effect? [opinion]. *Journal of Clinical Epidemiology* 2005 May; 58(5): 433-435. NRCBL: 4.1.2; 8.2; 1.1; 2.2.

Medical Professionalism Project; Brennan, Troy; Blank, Linda; Cohen, Jordan; Kimball, Harry; Smelser, Neil; Copeland, Robert; Lavizzo-Mourey, Risa; McDonald, Walter; Brenning, Gunilla; Davidson, Christopher; Jaeger, Philippe; Malliani, Alberto; Muller, Hein; Sareni, Daniel; Sutorius, Eugene; Cruess, Richard; Cruess, Sylvia; Merino, Jaime. Medical professionalism in the new millennium: a physicians' charter. *Clinical Medicine* 2002 March-April; 2(2): 116-118. NRCBL: 4.1.2; 8.1.

Meir, Asher. Ethics at the doctor's office. *In his:* The Jewish Ethicist: Everyday Ethics for Business and Life. Jersey City, NJ: KTAV; 2005: 125-144. NRCBL: 4.1.2; 1.2; 2.1; 8.2; 19.4.

Merideth, Philip. Medical ethics: charting a new course [editorial]. *Journal of the Mississippi State Medical Association* 2004 September; 45(9): 275. NRCBL: 4.1.2.

Morain, William D. Primum non nocere [editorial]. *Annals of Plastic Surgery* 2004 November; 53(5): 513-514. NRCBL: 4.1.2; 1.3.1.

Nathanson, Vivienne. Why we need a new Hippocratic Oath [opinion]. *Medical Education* 2003 December; 37(12): 1123-1124. NRCBL: 4.1.2; 6.

Needham, Charles W. Pride, shame, and the oath. *Connecticut Medicine* 2005 February; 69(2): 113-114. NRCBL: 4.1.2; 6.

Panicek, David M.; Schwartz, Lawrence H.; Dershaw, D. David; Ercolani, Matthew C.; Castellino, Ronald A. Misrepresentation of publications by applicants for radiology fellowships: is it a problem? *AJR: American Journal of Roentgenology* 1998 March; 170(3): 577-581. NRCBL: 4.1.2; 7.2. SC: em.

Perkoff, Gerald T. The boundaries of medicine. *Journal of Chronic Diseases* 1985; 38(3): 271-278. NRCBL: 4.1.2.

Pingle, Suhas. Medical ethics in paediatric practice: a GP's viewpoint. *Issues in Medical Ethics* 2000 April-June; 8(2): 46. NRCBL: 4.1.2. Identifiers: general practitioner.

Ronco, Claudio. The morality of medicine. *International Journal of Artificial Organs* 2004 August; 27(8): 647-648. NRCBL: 4.1.2.

Sharp, Helen M. Ethical decision-making in interdisciplinary team care. *Cleft Palate-Craniofacial Journal* 1995 November; 32(6): 495-499. NRCBL: 4.1.2; 1.3.1. SC: cs.

Smith, Wilbur L. Re: misrepresentation of publications by applicants for radiology fellowships. *AJR: American Journal of Roentgenology* 1998 March; 170(3): 582-583. NRCBL: 4.1.2; 7.2. Comments: comment on David M. Panicek, et al, "Misrepresentation of publications by applicants for radiology fellowships: is it a problem?," AJR: American Journal Roentgenology 1998 March; 170(3): 577-581.

Stahnisch, Frank W. Historical and philosophical perspectives on experimental practice in medicine and the life sciences. *Theoretical Medicine and Bioethics* 2005; 26(5): 397-425. NRCBL: 4.1.2; 18.1; 7.1.
Abstract: The aim of this paper is to discuss a key question in the history and philosophy of medicine, namely how scholars should treat the practices and experimental hypotheses of modern life science laboratories. The paper seeks to introduce some prominent historiographical methods and theoretical approaches associated with biomedical research. Although medical scientists need no convincing that experimentation has a significant function in their laboratory work, historians, philosophers, and sociologists long neglected its importance when examining changes in medical theories or progress in scientific knowledge. The reason appears to have been the academic influence of the then dominant tradition in the history of ideas, but was also due to a misconception of what could usefully be termed the view on "historical ontology." During the last two decades, there have been many books and research articles that have turned towards the subject, so that the study of experimental practice has become a major trend in the contemporary history and philosophy of medicine. A closer look at the issue of laboratory research shows that concepts in medicine and the life sciences cannot be understood as historically constant, free-standing ideas, but have to be regarded as dependent on local research settings. They often carry particular "social memories" with them and thus acquire important ethical implications.

Stempsey, William E. The philosophy of medicine: development of a discipline. *Medicine, Health Care and Philosophy: A European Journal* 2004; 7(3): 243-251. NRCBL: 4.1.2; 2.1; 1.1. SC: an.
Abstract: This paper is a critical examination of the development of the philosophy of medicine as a discipline. It highlights two major themes in the contemporary debate about the philos-

NRCBL: National Reference Center for Bioethics Literature Classification Scheme   See inside front cover for terms.

379

ophy of medicine: the scope of the discipline and the relation of the discipline to its cognate disciplines. A broad view of the philosophy of medicine is defended and the philosophy of medicine is seen as a philosophical sub-discipline. These views depend in important ways on three factors: a general metaphysical world view, particular understandings of the cognate disciplines, and the perspective from which one asks the questions about the nature of the discipline. It is proposed that the future of the philosophy of medicine may follow the philosophy of science in that philosophical, sociological and historical studies may combine in a mutually enriching way to form "medicine studies."

Sulmasy, Daniel P. "Diseases and natural kinds". *Theoretical Medicine and Bioethics* 2005; 26(6): 487-513. NRCBL: 4.1.2; 2.1.

Abstract: David Thomasma called for the development of a medical ethics based squarely on the philosophy of medicine. He recognized, however, that widespread anti-essentialism presented a significant barrier to such an approach. The aim of this article is to introduce a theory that challenges these anti-essentialist objections. The notion of natural kinds presents a modest form of essentialism that can serve as the basis for a foundationalist philosophy of medicine. The notion of a natural kind is neither static nor reductionistic. Disease can be understood as making necessary reference to living natural kinds without invoking the claim that diseases themselves are natural kinds. The idea that natural kinds have a natural disposition to flourish as the kinds of things that they are provides a telos to which to tether the notion of disease - an objective telos that is broader than mere survival and narrower than subjective choice. It is argued that while nosology is descriptive and may have therapeutic implications, disease classification is fundamentally explanatory. Sickness and illness, while referring to the same state of affairs, can be distinguished from disease phenomenologically. Scientific and diagnostic fallibility in making judgments about diseases do not diminish the objectivity of this notion of disease. Diseases are things, not kinds. Injury is a concept parallel to disease that also makes necessary reference to living natural kinds. These ideas provide a new possibility for the development of a philosophy of medicine with implications for medical ethics.

Tai, Michael Cheng-tek. The death of a little girl exposes an ethical hole [editorial]. *Formosan Journal of Medical Humanities* 2005 September; 6(1-2): 1-2. NRCBL: 4.1.2; 2.1; 7.4.

Töpfer, F.; Wiesing, U. The medical theory of Richard Koch I: theory of science and ethics. *Medicine, Health Care and Philosophy: A European Journal* 2005; 8(2): 207-219. NRCBL: 4.1.2; 2.1; 4.2.

Abstract: Richard Koch first made his appearance in the 1920s with works published on the foundations of medicine. These publications describe the character of medicine as an action and the status of medicine within the theory of science. One of his conclusions is that medicine is not a science in the original sense of the word, but a practical discipline. It serves a practical purpose: to heal the sick. All medical knowledge is oriented towards this purpose, which also defines the physician's role. One kind of knowledge is diagnosis, which is strictly understood in relation to therapy, and is at the core of medical thinking. Diagnosis is not the assignment of a term of a species to a patient's disease: this would not do justice to the individuality of a clinical manifestation and would fail to provide a reason for individual therapy. Nevertheless, the terms assigned to diseases, although fictitious, are not useless, but assist in differentiating

various phenomena. These conclusions carry ethical consequences. Because the task of helping the sick constitutes medicine, morals not only set ethical limits: medicine originates in a moral decision. If there are no diseases but only individual sick people, disease can not be defined as an abnormality. The individual benefit to the patient must not necessarily be the complete restoration of health. With its object being incalculable, medicine cannot guarantee its own success. Here the physician has to develop principles that allow for the best possible response to the challenges faced in varying situations of conduct.

Wann, Samuel. Conflicts of interest, integrity, and public respect: challenges to the professional standing of modern cardiologists [opinion]. *American Heart Hospital Journal* 2003 Summer; 1(3): 236-239. NRCBL: 4.1.2; 7.1; 9.3.1; 9.8.

Wasnick, John D. Virtue, ethics, and anesthesia [letter]. *Anesthesiology* 1998 August; 89(2): 537. NRCBL: 4.1.2; 2.1.

Wynia, Matthew K.; Macauley, Robert. Civil disobedience: the devil is in the details [letter and reply]. *Hastings Center Report* 2005 July-August; 35(4): 4-6. NRCBL: 4.1.2; 9.3.1.

PHILOSOPHY OF NURSING *See* NURSING ETHICS AND PHILOSOPHY

PHYSICIAN PATIENT RELATIONSHIP *See* BIOETHICS AND MEDICAL ETHICS; PROFESSIONAL PATIENT RELATIONSHIP

POPULATION POLICY
See also CONTRACEPTION; STERILIZATION

Chatterjee, Patralekha. Doctors' group proposes one-child policy for India. *Lancet* 2005 May 7-13; 365(9471): 1609. NRCBL: 13.3; 7.1; 9.3.1.

Chayanika. Maharashtra's coercive population policy. *Issues in Medical Ethics* 2001 January-March; 9(1): 22-23. NRCBL: 13.3.

Das, Abhijit. The ethical implications of the targeted population programme proposed by the UPA. *Indian Journal of Medical Ethics* 2005 January-March; 2(1): 10-11. NRCBL: 13.3; 15.5. Identifiers: United Progressive Alliance.

Gangoli, Geetanjali. Reproduction, abortion and women's health. *Social Scientist* 1998 November-December; 26(11-12): 83-105. [Online]. Available: http://www.hsph.harvard.edu/Organizations/healthnet/SAsia/suchana/1299/h030.html [27 May 2005]. NRCBL: 13.3; 11.3; 15.2; 12.1. SC: le.

Hesketh, Therese; Lu, Li; Xing, Zhu Wei. The effect of China's one-child family policy after 25 years. *New England Journal of Medicine* 2005 September 15; 353(11): 1171-1176. NRCBL: 13.3; 13.2; 11.1; 12.4.1; 11.3.

Jalsevac, Paul. The inherent racism of population control. *LifeSiteNews.com* 2004: i-iv, 1-54 [Online]. Available: http://www.lifesite.net/waronfamily/Population_control/Inherentracism.pdf [28 July 2005]. NRCBL: 13.3; 15.5; 11.1; 21.4; 2.2. SC: an.

Pan, Philip P. China terse about action on abuses of one-child policy. *Washington Post* 2005 September 20; p. A17. NRCBL: 13.3; 1.3.5. SC: po.

Sen, Amartya. Population policy: authoritarianism versus cooperation. *Social Change* 1994 September-December; 24(3-4); 17 p. [Online]. Available: http://www.hsph.harvard.edu/Organizations/healthnet/SAsia/suchana/9999/rh080.html [7 October 2005]. NRCBL: 13.3; 10; 1.3.5; 21.1. Identifiers: China; India.

Su, Baoqi; Macer, Darryl R.J. A sense of autonomy is preserved under Chinese reproductive policies. *New Genetics and Society* 2005 April; 24(1): 15-29. NRCBL: 13.3; 1.1; 15.2; 21.7; 12.5.1; 15.5. SC: em.

Vermij, Peter. Scientists charged with choosing publication over public health [news]. *Nature Medicine* 2005 May; 11(5): 461. NRCBL: 13.9; 1.3.7; 18.6; 9.5.1; 10; 9.1; 21.1.

Watts, Jonathan. Chinese officials accused of forcing abortions in Shandong. *Lancet* 2005 October 8-14; 366(9493): 1253. NRCBL: 13.3; 11.1; 12.1; 1.3.5. SC: le.

PRENATAL DIAGNOSIS *See* GENETIC COUNSELING; GENETIC SCREENING; SEX DETERMINATION

PRIORITIES IN HEALTH CARE *See* RESOURCE ALLOCATION

PRISONERS *See* FORCE FEEDING OF PRISONERS; HUMAN EXPERIMENTATION/ SPECIAL POPULATIONS/ PRISONERS

PRIVILEGED COMMUNICATION *See* CONFIDENTIALITY

PROCUREMENT *See* ORGAN AND TISSUE TRANSPLANTATION/ DONATION AND PROCUREMENT

PROFESSIONAL ETHICS
See also BIOETHICS AND MEDICAL ETHICS; CODES OF ETHICS; NURSING ETHICS AND PHILOSOPHY

Adams, Vincanne. Equity of the ineffable: cultural and political constraints on ethnomedicine as a health problem in contemporary Tibet. *In:* Anand, Sudhir; Peter, Fabienne; Sen, Amartya, eds. Public Health, Ethics, and Equity. New York: Oxford University Press; 2004: 283-305. NRCBL: 4.1.1; 9.1.

Almond, Brenda. Reasonable partiality in professional relationships. *Ethical Theory and Moral Practice* 2005 April; 8(1-2): 155-168. NRCBL: 1.3.1; 8.4; 17.2; 9.5.6; 8.3.2; 19.5.

American College of Healthcare Executives [ACHE]. Board of Governors. American College of Healthcare Executives Code of Ethics. *American College of Healthcare* 2003 November 10; 2 p. [Online] Available: http://www.ache.org/ABT_ACHE/CodeofEthics.pdf [5 August 2005]. NRCBL: 4.1.1; 6.

Atwell, Barbara L. Mainstreaming complementary and alternative medicine in the face of uncertainty. *UMKC Law Review* 2004 Spring; 72(3): 593-630. NRCBL: 4.1.1; 9.3.1. SC: le.

Atwood-Harvey, Dana. Death or declaw: dealing with moral ambiguity in a veterinary hospital. *Society and Animals: Journal of Human-Animal Studies* 2005; 13(4): 315-342. NRCBL: 4.1.1; 22.1; 1.1. SC: em.

Banja, John. Moral absolutes and cultural influences on case management. *Case Manager* 2005 March-April; 16(2): 20-23. NRCBL: 4.1.1; 1.1; 21.7.

Biller-Andorno, Nikola. "Fürsorge" in der Medizinethik: Prinzip oder Perspektive? *In:* Jahrbuch für Wissenschaft und Ethik. Bd. 7. Berlin: Walter de Gruyter; 2002: 101-115. NRCBL: 4.1.1; 1.1.

Boissier, Marie-Christophe. Pondering the precautionary principle [editorial]. *Joint, Bone, Spine* 2003 September; 70(5): 318-320. NRCBL: 4.1.1; 1.1.

Bowden, Peta. An 'ethic of care' in clinical settings: encompassing 'feminine' and 'feminist' perspectives. *Nursing Philosophy* 2000 July; 1(1): 36-49. NRCBL: 4.1.1; 4.1.3; 10.

Bowden, Peter. Philosophy's dilemma: the institutionalising of ethics. University of Western Sydney, Department of Philosophy: 11 p. [Online]. Available: http://www.uws.edu.au/download.php?file_id=8683&filename=philosophys_dilemma.pdf&mimetype=application/pdf [12 September 2005]. NRCBL: 1.3.1; 1.3.2; 1.1.

Chambers, David W. Distributive justice in dentistry [editorial]. *Journal of the American College of Dentists* 2005 Spring; 72(1): 2-3. NRCBL: 4.1.1; 9.4.

Cherniack, E. Paul. The use of alternative medicine by the elderly and the doctor-patient relationship. *In:* Cherniack, P.; Cherniack, N., eds. Alternative Medicine for the Elderly. Berlin: Springer-Verlag; 2003: 27-45. NRCBL: 4.1.1; 8.1; 9.5.2.

Churchill, Jack L. What's a dentist to do? Is participating in a "Top 200 Dentists" survey unethical? *Northwest Dentistry* 2004 July-August; 83(4): 41. NRCBL: 4.1.1.

NRCBL: National Reference Center for Bioethics Literature Classification Scheme   See inside front cover for terms.

381

Crigger, Nancy J. The trouble with caring: a review of eight arguments against an ethic of care. *Journal of Professional Nursing* 1997 July-August; 13(4): 217-221. NRCBL: 4.1.1; 1.1; 4.1.3; 10. SC: an.

Darr, Kurt. Going, going , . . all but gone. *Hospital Topics* 2004 Winter; 82(1): 30-32. NRCBL: 4.1.1; 6. Identifiers: American College of Healthcare Executives [ACHE].

Davey, Monica. Illinois pharmacies ordered to provide birth control. *New York Times* 2005 April 2; p. A10. NRCBL: 4.1.1; 11.1; 9.7. SC: po; le.

Davidovitch, Nadav. From a "humble humbug" to the "powerful placebo": the image of the placebo in the orthodox-alternative medicine debate. *In:* Roelcke, Volker; Maio, Giovanni, eds. Twentieth Century Ethics of Human Subjects Research: Historical Perspectives on Values, Practices, and Regulations. Stuttgart: Franz Steiner Verlag; 2004: 293-307. NRCBL: 4.1.1; 18.1; 8.2.

Epstein, Ernst. Are we consultants or peddlers? [letter]. *Archives of Dermatology* 1998 April; 134(4): 508-509. NRCBL: 4.1.1; 7.3; 8.1; 1.3.2.

Ernst, E. Informed consent: a potential dilemma for complementary medicine [opinion]. *Journal of Manipulative and Physiological Therapeutics* 2004 July-August; 27(6): 428-429. NRCBL: 4.1.1; 8.3.1. Identifiers: United Kingdom (Great Britain).

European Communities Confederation of Clinical Chemistry and Laboratory Medicine (EC4); Sanders, Gerard; Opp, Matthias; McMurray, Janet; Koeller, Ursula; Blaton, Vic; Lund, Erik; Harmoinen, Aimo; Zerah, Simone; Baum, Hannsjoerg; Rizos, Demetrios; Kenny, Desmond; Pazzagli, Mario; Hoffman, Hans; Reguengo, Henrique; Queraltó, Jose M.; Wallinder, Hans; Jansen, Rob; Hallworth, Michael; Schuff-Werner, Peter. The European Register for Specialists in Clinical Chemistry and Laboratory Medicine: code of conduct. *Clinical Chemistry and Laboratory Medicine* 2004 May; 42(5): 563-565. NRCBL: 1.3.1; 6; 21.1.

Finder, Stuart G. Moral experience and technicians of the heart: reflections on the practice of perfusionists. *Journal of Extra-Corporeal Technology* 2004 March; 36(1): 4-9. NRCBL: 4.1.1; 5.1.

Glazer, James. The ethics of alternative medicine: an alternative standard? [editorial]. *Family Practice Management* 2005 April; 12(4): 13-14. NRCBL: 4.1.1; 21.7.

Gold, Steven A. When nobody's looking. *Journal of the American College of Dentists* 2005 Spring; 72(1): 32-33. NRCBL: 4.1.1; 1.3.1; 7.2.

Guinn, David E. Ethics and integrative medicine: moving beyond the biomedical model. *Alternative Therapies in Health and Medicine* 2001 November- December; 7(6); 68-72. NRCBL: 4.1.1; 2.1; 1.1.

Hodge, Belinda. Uncovering the ethic of care. *Nursing Praxis in New Zealand* 1993 July; 8(2): 13-22. NRCBL: 4.1.1; 4.1.3; 2.1.

Husted, Gladys L.; Husted, James H. A modest proposal concerning policies. *Advanced Practical Nursing Quarterly* 1997 Winter; 3(3): 17- 19. NRCBL: 4.1.1; 9.1; 8.1. SC: cs.

Jacobs, Frans. Reasonable partiality in professional ethics: the moral division of labour. *Ethical Theory and Moral Practice* 2005 April; 8(1-2): 141-154. NRCBL: 1.3.1.

Jotkowitz, Alan B.; Porath, Avi; Glick, Shimon. The professionalism movement. *IMAJ: Israel Medical Association Journal* 2004 November; 6(11): 661-664. NRCBL: 1.3.1; 1.2. Identifiers: Israel.

Kaptchuk, Ted J.; Miller, Franklin G. What is the best and most ethical model for the relationship between mainstream and alternative medicine: opposition, integration, or pluralism? *Academic Medicine* 2005 March; 80(3): 286-290. NRCBL: 4.1.1; 4.1.2; 7.3; 2.2.

Kasher, Asa. Professional ethics and collective professional autonomy: a conceptual analysis. *Ethical Perspectives* 2005 March; 12(1): 67-97. NRCBL: 1.3.1; 1.3.4; 6. SC: an.

Kinsella, Elizabeth Anne. Constructions of self: ethical overtones in surprising locations. *Medical Humanities* 2005 December; 31(2): 67-71. NRCBL: 4.1.1; 1.1; 8.1.
Abstract: Little discussion has occurred in the health profession literature with respect to how the "self" is constructed, despite the imagination and attention it has garnered from philosophers and theorists in various other disciplines. Yet this subject has surprisingly ethical overtones for health professional education and practice. In this paper notions of the self are briefly considered and it is suggested that a narrative and dialogic view of self can contribute to insights about ethical practice in the health professions. Subtle issues with respect to how relationship and language may be used to wield power are revealed and discussed; and awareness about how such power is used in practice is highlighted as a crucial issue. The assumptions practitioners make with respect to constructions of self are ethically important and this topic warrants consideration in the medical humanities.

Knoll, Andrew M. The reawakening of complementary and alternative medicine at the turn of the twenty-first century: filling the void in conventional biomedicine. *Journal of Contemporary Health Law and Policy* 2004 Spring; 20(2): 329-366. NRCBL: 4.1.1; 2.2; 7.1. SC: le.

Komesaroff, Paul A. Use of complementary medicines: scientific and ethical issues [editorial]. *Medical Journal of Australia* 1998 August 17; 169(4): 180-181. NRCBL: 4.1.1; 9.3.1; 9.1. Comments: comment on G. Easthope, J.J. Beilby, G.F. Gill, B.K. Tranter, "Acupuncture in Australian general practice: practitioner characteristics," Medical Journal of Australia 1998; 169: 195-198.

Kottow, Michael H. Between caring and curing. *Nursing Philosophy* 2001 April; 2(1): 53-61. NRCBL: 4.1.1; 4.1.3; 8.1; 10.

Linker, Beth. The business of ethics: gender, medicine, and the professional codification of the American Physiotherapy Association, 1918-1935. *Journal of the History of Medicine and Allied Sciences* 2005 July; 60(3): 320-354. NRCBL: 4.1.1; 2.2; 6; 10; 7.3. SC: an.

Opacich, Karin J. Moral tensions and obligations of occupational therapy practitioners providing home care. *American Journal of Occupational Therapy* 1997 June; 51(6): 430-435. NRCBL: 4.1.1; 2.1; 9.5.1.

Ornish, Steven A. Psychiatry and police interrogations [letter]. *AAPL (American Academy of Psychiatry and the Law) Newsletter* 2005 September; 30(3): 26. NRCBL: 1.3.1; 1.3.5; 17.1.

Paley, John. Virtues of autonomy: the Kantian ethics of care. *Nursing Philosophy* 2002 July; 3(2): 133-143. NRCBL: 4.1.1; 1.1; 4.1.3.

Peltier, Bruce N. White coat principles. *Journal of the American College of Dentists* 2004 Winter; 71(4): 53-56. NRCBL: 4.1.1; 1.3.1.

Phillips, Robert T.M. Expanding the role of the forensic consultant. *AAPL Newsletter (American Acaedemy of Psychiatry and the Law Newsletter)* 2005 January; 30(1): 4-5. NRCBL: 1.3.1; 1.3.5; 17.1.

Rickert, Kevin G. Alternative medicine and the duty to employ ordinary means. *National Catholic Bioethics Quarterly* 2005 Autumn; 5(3): 481- 489. NRCBL: 4.1.1; 1.2.

Rothstein, David A. Practice of medicine? [letter]. *AAPL (American Academy of Psychiatry and the Law) Newsletter* 2005 September; 30(3): 28-29. NRCBL: 1.3.1; 1.3.5; 21.4; 6; 17.1.

Ruethling, Gretchen. Illinois pharmacist sues over contraceptive rule. *New York Times* 2005 June 10; p. A18. NRCBL: 4.1.1; 9.7. SC: po; le.

Schoenholtz, Jack C. Psychiatry and police interrogations [letter]. *AAPL (American Academy of Psychiatry and the Law) Newsletter* 2005 September; 30(3): 26-27. NRCBL: 1.3.1; 1.3.5; 17.1.

Sudzina, Michael R. Industry support for dental education. *Journal of the American College of Dentists* 2005 Summer; 72(2): 12-14. NRCBL: 4.1.1; 7.2; 7.3.

Vaidya, Ashok. Ethics in the clinical practice of integral medicine: there are many ethical, legal and technical problems resulting from 'mixopathy'. *Issues in Medical Ethics* 1999 January-March; 7(1): 9-10. NRCBL: 4.1.1.

Weisstub, David N.; Thomasma, David C. Moral capacity: the tension between professional nurture and universal nature. *In their:* Thomasma, David C.; Weisstub, David N., eds. The Variables of Moral Capacity. Boston: Kluwer Academic Publishers; 2004: 139- 149. NRCBL: 1.3.1; 4.1.1; 1.1. SC: an.

Wettstein, Robert M. Ethical practice [letter]. *AAPL (American Academy of Psychiatry and the Law) Newsletter* 2005 September; 30(3): 29-30. NRCBL: 1.3.1; 1.3.5; 4.1.1.

PROFESSIONAL MISCONDUCT *See* BIO-MEDICAL RESEARCH/ RESEARCH ETHICS AND SCIENTIFIC MISCONDUCT; MALPRACTICE AND PROFESSIONAL MISCONDUCT

PROFESSIONAL PATIENT RELATIONSHIP
See also CARE FOR SPECIFIC GROUPS; PROFESSIONAL ETHICS

Will consumerism lead to better health? [editorial]. *Lancet* 2005 July 30-August 5; 366(9483): 343. NRCBL: 8.1; 7.4; 7.1.

Abma, Tineke A.; Oeseburg, Barth; Widdershoven, Guy A.M.; Goldsteen, Minke; Verkerk, Marian A. Two women with multiple sclerosis and their caregivers: conflicting normative expectations. *Nursing Ethics* 2005 September; 12(5): 479-492. NRCBL: 8.1; 9.5.1.

Abstract: It is not uncommon that nurses are unable to meet the normative expectations of chronically ill patients. The purpose of this article is to describe and illustrate Walker's expressive-collaborative view of morality to interpret the normative expectations of two women with multiple sclerosis. Both women present themselves as autonomous persons who make their own choices, but who also have to rely on others for many aspects of their lives, for example, to find a new balance between work and social contacts or to find work. We show that their narratives of identity, relationship and value differ from the narratives that others use to understand and identify them. Since identities, relationships and values give rise to normative expectations, in both cases there is a conflict between what the women expect of their caregivers and vice-versa. The narratives also show that two similar persons with multiple sclerosis may need very different care. This implies that nurses caring for such persons should listen carefully to their stories and reflect on their own perceptions of self.

Adamjee, Ashi; Alfi, David; Agarwal, Divya; Braithwaite, Yetunde; Chan, Judy; Chey, Marshall; Cho, Hyung; Choi, Christopher. What does the fact of advertising convey to patients? *Journal of the American College of Dentists* 2005 Fall; 72(3): 22-23. NRCBL: 8.1; 1.3.2; 4.1.1.

Alexander, John K. Promising, professional obligations, and the refusal to provide service. *HEC (Healthcare Ethics Committee) Forum* 2005 September; 17(3): 178-195. NRCBL: 8.1; 1.1; 4.1.1; 1.3.1; 12.4.3; 12.3. SC: cs.

Allen, David; Hardin, Pamela K. Discourse analysis and the epidemiology of meaning. *Nursing Philosophy* 2001 July; 2(2): 163-176. NRCBL: 8.1; 1.1.

NRCBL: National Reference Center for Bioethics Literature Classification Scheme   See inside front cover for terms.

383

Back, Anthony L.; Arnold, Robert M.; Tulsky, James A.; Baile, Walter F.; Fryer-Edwards, Kelly A. On saying goodbye: acknowledging the end of the patient- physician relationship with patients who are near death. *Annals of Internal Medicine* 2005 April 19; 142(8): 682-685. NRCBL: 8.1; 20.4.1.

Baker, Richard. Placing principle before expediency: the Shipman inquiry [opinion]. *Lancet* 2005 March 12-18; 365(9463): 919-921. NRCBL: 8.1; 7.1; 4.1.2; 1.3.5.

Basta, Lofty L. Ethical issues in the management of geriatric cardiac patients. How do you deal with a difficult patient? *American Journal of Geriatric Cardiology* 2005 January-February; 14(1): 39-40. NRCBL: 8.1; 4.1.2; 9.5.1. SC: cs.

Berger, Jeffrey T. Patients' interests in their family members' well-being: an overlooked, fundamental consideration within substituted judgments. *Journal of Clinical Ethics* 2005 Spring; 16(1): 3-10. NRCBL: 8.1; 8.3.3.

Berlinger, Norman. Patient trust: trust remains fundamental to the ethical practice of medicine even in the age of the patient as consumer. *Minnesota Medicine* 2004 June; 87(6): 32-34. NRCBL: 8.1.

Berndt, Ernst R. To inform or persuade? Direct-to-consumer advertising of prescription drugs. *New England Journal of Medicine* 2005 January 27; 352(4): 325- 328. NRCBL: 8.1; 9.7.

Beste, Jennifer. Instilling hope and respecting patient autonomy: reconciling apparently conflicting duties. *Bioethics* 2005 June; 19(3): 215-231. NRCBL: 8.1; 1.1; 8.3.1; 4.2; 8.2. SC: an.

Abstract: In contemporary American medical practice, certain physicians are critical and wary of the current emphasis on patient autonomy in medicine, questioning whether it really serves the complex needs of severely ill patients. Physicians such as Eric Cassell and Thomas Duffy argue that the duty of beneficence should override the duty to respect autonomy when conflicts arise in clinical situations. After evaluating their claim that severe illness robs patients of their autonomy, I will argue that this perceived conflict between beneficence and autonomy is ill-conceived, resting on misperceptions about both the capacity for autonomy and the meaning of hope. Considering insights on hope from phenomenologist Gabriel Marcel and theologian William Lynch, as well as drawing upon a case study involving a bone marrow patient, I claim that respecting and nurturing patients' capacity for autonomy is a necessary condition for acting beneficently and fostering authentic hope.

Blanchard, Janice; Lurie, Nicole. R-E-S-P-E-C-T: patient reports of disrespect in the health care setting and its impact on care. *Journal of Family Practice* 2004 September; 53(9): 721-730. NRCBL: 8.1; 9.5.4; 21.7.

Bloche, M. Gregg. Trust and betrayal in the medical marketplace. *Stanford Law Review* 2002 December; 55(2): 919-954. NRCBL: 8.1; 9.1; 9.3.1. SC: cs; le.

Bloche, M. Gregg; Quinn, Kevin P. Professionalism and personhood. *In:* Thomasma, David C.; Weisstub, David N.; Herve, Christian eds. Personhood and Health Care. Boston: Kluwer Academic Pub.; 2001: 347-354. NRCBL: 8.1; 4.4.

Bloss, Thomas. Medicine following the HCFA 'guidelines': what will be left of the patient-physician encounter? [editorial]. *Postgraduate Medicine* 1998 April; 103(4): 13-15. NRCBL: 8.1; 9.3.1. Identifiers: Health Care Financing Administration.

Braddock, Clarence H., III; Snyder, Lois. The doctor will see you shortly: the ethical significance of time for the patient-physician relationship. *JGIM: Journal of General Internal Medicine* 2005 November; 20(11): 1057-1062. NRCBL: 8.1; 1.1.

Bramstedt, Katrina A.; Molnar, Marcia; Carlson, Kirste; Bilyeu, Susan M. When families complicate patient care: a case study with guidelines for approaching ethical dilemmas [case study]. *Medsurg Nursing* 2005 April; 14(2): 122-125. NRCBL: 8.1; 7.1. SC: cs.

Brett, Allan S.; Zuger, Abigail. The run on Tamiflu — should physicians prescribe on demand? [opinion]. *New England Journal of Medicine* 2005 December 22; 353(25): 2636-2637. NRCBL: 8.1; 9.4; 9.1; 9.7.

Brody, Howard. Patient ethics and evidence-based medicine — the good healthcare citizen. *CQ: Cambridge Quarterly of Healthcare Ethics* 2005 Spring; 14(2): 141-146. NRCBL: 8.1; 1.3.1; 9.8.

Burnard, Philip. Why care? Ethical and spiritual issues in caring in nursing. *In:* Brykczynska, Gosia, ed. Caring: The Compassion and Wisdom of Nursing. New York: Arnold; 1997: 32-44. NRCBL: 8.1; 4.1.3; 1.2.

Bury, Michael. Doctors, patients and interaction in health care. *In his:* Health and Illness in a Changing Society. New York: Routledge; 1997: 77-109. NRCBL: 8.1.

Capozzi, James D.; Rhodes, Rosamond. Gifts from patients. *Journal of Bone and Joint Surgery: American Volume* 2004 October; 86-A(10): 2339-2340. NRCBL: 8.1. SC: cs.

Carter, Michele A. Patient-provider relationship in the context of genetic testing for hereditary cancers. *Journal of the National Cancer Institute Monographs* 1995; (17): 119-121. NRCBL: 8.1; 15.3; 9.5.1.

Cassel, Christine K. The patient-physician covenant: an affirmation of Asklepios. *Connecticut Medicine* 1996 May; 60(5): 291-293. NRCBL: 8.1; 4.1.2.

Cassell, Eric J. The principles of the Belmont Report: how have respect for persons, beneficence, and justice been applied in clinical medicine? *In:* Childress, James F.; Meslin, Eric M.; Shapiro, Harold T., eds. Belmont Revisited: Ethical Principles for Research with Human Subjects. Washington, DC: Georgetown University Press; 2005: 77-95. NRCBL: 8.1; 1.1.

Castro, Oswaldo; Lombardo, Frederic A.; Gordeuk, Victor R.; Charo, R. Alta. The celestial fire of conscience [letter and reply]. *New England Journal of Medicine* 2005 September 22; 353(12): 1301-1302. NRCBL: 8.1; 9.6; 1.2.

Ceci, Christine; McIntyre, Marjorie. A 'quiet' crisis in health care: developing our capacity to hear. *Nursing Philosophy* 2001 July; 2(2): 122-130. NRCBL: 8.1; 1.1; 4.1.3.

Charles, Cathy; Gafni, Amiram; Whelan, Tim. Shared decision-making in the medical encounter: what does it mean? (or it takes at least two to tango). *Social Science and Medicine* 1997 March; 44(5): 681-692. NRCBL: 8.1; 8.3.1.

Charo, R. Alta. The celestial fire of conscience — refusing to deliver medical care [opinion]. *New England Journal of Medicine* 2005 June 16; 352(24): 2471- 2473. NRCBL: 8.1; 9.6; 1.2.

Clark, Chalmers C. In harm's way: AMA physicians and the duty to treat. *Journal of Medicine and Philosophy* 2005 February; 30(1): 65-87. NRCBL: 8.1; 2.1; 4.1.2; 6. SC: an. Identifiers: American Medical Association.
  Abstract: In June 2001, the American Medical Association (AMA) issued a revised and expanded version of the Principles of Medical Ethics (last published in 1980). In light of the new and more comprehensive document, the present essay is geared to consideration of a longstanding tension between physician's autonomy rights and societal obligations in the AMA Code. In particular, it will be argued that a duty to treat overrides AMA autonomy rights in social emergencies, even in cases that involve personal risk to physicians (e.g., bioterrorist attack, HIV infection, SARS). The argument will be made by way of the logic and language of the AMA Code through its history, commentaries, and precedents. It also will be shown that there are substantial reasons to believe that the logic of the Code is sound in morally relevant ways. The essay will conclude with some philosophical proposals suggesting a framework for the duty to render aid and the extension of those duties to physicians facing personal risks.

Cohen, Charlotte; McLean, Ken; Barton, Simon. Use of chaperones in general practice: chaperones protect both parties [letter]. *BMJ: British Medical Journal* 2005 April 9; 330(7495): 846-847. NRCBL: 8.1; 10; 9.5.5. SC: em.

Connelly, Julia E. Narrative possibilities: using mindfulness in clinical practice. *Perspectives in Biology and Medicine* 2005 Winter; 48(1): 84-94. NRCBL: 8.1; 1.1.

Corke, C.F.; Stow, P.J.; Green, D.T.; Agar, J.W.; Henry, M.J. How doctors discuss major interventions with high risk patients: an observational study. *BMJ: British Medical Journal* 2005 January 22; 330(7484): 182- 184. NRCBL: 8.1. SC: em.
  Abstract: OBJECTIVE: To investigate the difficulties doctors face in discussing treatment options with patients with acute, life threatening illness and major comorbidities. DESIGN: Observational study of doctor-patient interviews based on a standardised clinical scenario involving high risk surgery in a hypothetical patient (played by an actor) with serious comorbidities. PARTICIPANTS: 30 trainee doctors 3-5 years after graduation. MAIN OUTCOME MEASURES: Adequacy of coverage of various aspects was scored from 3 (good) to 0 (not discussed). RESULTS: The medical situation was considered to be well described (median score 2.7 (interquartile range 2.1-3.0)), whereas the patient's functional status, values, and fears were poorly or minimally addressed (scores 0.5 (0.0-1.0), 0.5 (0.0-1.0), and 0.0 (0.0-1.5), respectively; all P 0.001 v score for describing the medical situation). Twenty nine of the doctors indicated that they wished to include the patient's family in the discussion, but none identified a preferred surrogate decision maker. Six doctors suggested that the patient alone should speak with his family to reach a decision without the doctor being present. The doctors were reluctant to give advice, despite it being directly requested: two doctors stated that a doctor could not give advice, while 17 simply restated the medical risks, without advocating any particular course. Of the 11 who did offer advice, eight advocated intervention. CONCLUSIONS: Doctors focused on technical medical issues and placed much less emphasis on patient issues such as functional status, values, wishes, and fears. This limits doctors' ability to offer suitable advice about treatment options. Doctors need to improve their communication skills in this difficult but common clinical situation.

Crausman, Robert S.; Baruch, Jay M. Abandonment in the physician-patient relationship. *Medicine and Health, Rhode Island* 2004 May; 87(5): 154-156. NRCBL: 8.1; 9.8.

Croatian Association for Promotion of Patients' Rights. Work group for Creation of the Law on Rights, Obligations and Responsibilities of Patients. Law on Patients' Rights, Obligations and Responsibilities: proposal. Split, Croatia: Croatian Association for Patients' Rights 2002 December; 21 p. [Online]. Available: http://www.pravapacijenata.hr/oren1.pdf [2 December 2005]. NRCBL: 8.1; 8.3.1; 8.4. SC: le. Note: proposal for formation of law.

Crosby, John F. Karol Wojtyla on treating patients as persons. *In:* Tollefsen, Christopher, ed. John Paul II's Contribution to Catholic Bioethics. Norwell, MA: Springer; 2004: 151-168. NRCBL: 8.1; 1.2.

Curlin, Farr A.; Hall, Daniel E. Strangers or friends? A proposal for a new spirituality-in- medicine ethic [opinion]. *JGIM: Journal of General Internal Medicine* 2005 April; 20(4): 370-374. NRCBL: 8.1; 1.1; 1.2.

Curlin, Farr A.; Roach, Chad J.; Gorawara-Bhat, Rita; Lantos, John D.; Chin, Marshall H. When patients choose faith over medicine. *Archives of Internal Medicine* 2005 January 10; 165(1): 88-91. NRCBL: 8.1; 1.2. SC: em.

De Dijn, Herman. Care, communication and conversation. *Ethical Perspectives* 2005 September; 12(3): 357-370. NRCBL: 8.1. SC: an.

de Raeve, Louise. Trust and trustworthiness in nurse-patient relationships. *Nursing Philosophy* 2002 July; 3(2): 152-162. NRCBL: 8.1.

Dobbs, David; Charo, R. Alta. The celestial fire of conscience [letter and reply]. *New England Journal of Medi-*

NRCBL: National Reference Center for Bioethics Literature Classification Scheme   See inside front cover for terms.

385

cine 2005 September 22; 353(12): 1301-1302. NRCBL: 8.1; 9.6; 1.2.

Dresser, Rebecca. Professionals, conformity, and conscience. *Hastings Center Report* 2005 November-December; 35(6): 9-10. NRCBL: 8.1; 1.2; 7.1; 9.7.

Dvoskin, Joel A. Commentary: two sides to every story — the need for objectivity and evidence. *Journal of the American Academy of Psychiatry and the Law* 2005; 33(4): 482-483. NRCBL: 8.1; 8.5; 17.2; 7.4; 10. SC: cs.

Dyer, Clare. Court rules in favour of GMC's guidance on withholding treatment [news]. *BMJ: British Medical Journal* 2005 August 6; 331(7512): 309. NRCBL: 8.1; 4.4; 20.5.1. SC: le. Identifiers: General Medical Council.

Dysart-Gale, Deborah. Communication models, professionalization, and the work of medical interpreters. *Health Communication* 2005; 17(1): 91-103. NRCBL: 8.1; 7.3; 21.7. SC: em.

Edgar, Andrew. Physician choice or patient choice: ethical dilemmas in science and politics. *In:* Salek, Sam; Edgar, Andrew, eds. Pharmaceutical Ethics. New York: Wiley; 2002: 97-109. NRCBL: 8.1.

Edgar, Andrew. Principles of ethics focusing on the patient. *In:* Salek, Sam; Edgar, Andrew, eds. Pharmaceutical Ethics. New York: Wiley; 2002: 13-25. NRCBL: 8.1; 2.1.

Ellis, Mark R.; Campbell, James D. Concordant spiritual orientations as a factor in physician- patient spiritual discussions: a qualitative study. *Journal of Religion and Health* 2005 Spring; 44(1): 39-53. NRCBL: 8.1; 1.2; 21.7; 7.1. SC: em.

English, Dan C. Moral obligations of patients: a clinical view. *Journal of Medicine and Philosophy* 2005 April; 30(2): 139-152. NRCBL: 8.1; 1.1. SC: an.

Abstract: After a unilateral focus on medical professional obligations to patients in most of the 20th century, there is a growing, if modest, interest in patient responsibility. This article critiques some public assertions, explores the ethics literature, and attempts to find some consensus and moral grounds for positions taken on the question, "Does a patient have moral obligations in the process of interactions with medical and other professional caregivers?" There is widespread agreement on a few responsibilities, such as "truth telling" and "avoiding harm to others," but no apparent consensus either on the list of duties or on the appropriate justification for such duties. The context and clinical realities of patient interactions are noted to suggest that feasibility is important in making judgments of patient obligations.

Erlen, Judith A. Moral distress: a pervasive problem. *Orthopaedic Nursing* 2001 March-April; 20(2): 76-80. NRCBL: 8.1; 7.1; 1.1; 9.3.2.

Fallone, Sue. What is the responsibility of the nephrology nurse when the patient is chronically late? Nephrology nurses deserve respect [debate]. *Nephrology Nursing Journal* 2004 July-August; 31(4): 445-446. NRCBL: 8.1; 19.3.

Fernandez, Richard; Gao, Connie; Genkin, William; Ghandi, Toral; Graham, Roseanna; Hou, Judy; Hsu, Eugenia; Hwang, JungSun. Changing perspectives on dental advertising. *Journal of the American College of Dentists* 2005 Fall; 72(3): 24-26. NRCBL: 8.1; 1.3.2; 4.1.1.

Fins, Joseph J. The physician-patient relationship in managed care: a tale of two prescriptions. *Seminars in Medical Practice* 1998 August; 1(1): 22-26. NRCBL: 8.1; 9.3.2; 9.5.2; 9.4. SC: cs.

Fondacaro, Mark; Frogner, Bianca; Moos, Rudolf. Justice in health care decision-making: patients' appraisals of health care providers and health plan representatives. *Social Justice Research* 2005 March; 18(1): 63-81. NRCBL: 8.1; 9.4; 9.3.2; 1.1; 9.8. SC: em.

Fournier, Veronique. The balance between beneficence and respect for patient autonomy in clinical medical ethics in France. *CQ: Cambridge Quarterly of Healthcare Ethics* 2005 Summer; 14(3): 281-286. NRCBL: 8.1; 1.1; 9.6; 21.1.

Fry, Sara T.; Veatch, Robert M. Fidelity. *In their:* Case Studies in Nursing Ethics. Third edition. Sudbury, MA: Jones and Bartlett Publishers; 2006: 167-191. NRCBL: 8.1.

Fry, Sara T.; Veatch, Robert M. The principle of autonomy. *In their:* Case Studies in Nursing Ethics. Third edition. Sudbury, MA: Jones and Bartlett Publishers; 2006: 119-141. NRCBL: 8.1; 4.1.3.

Gallagher, Thomas H.; Levinson, Wendy. A prescription for protecting the doctor-patient relationship. *American Journal of Managed Care* 2004 February; 10(2, Part 1): 61-68. NRCBL: 8.1; 9.1. SC: an.

Gambino, Gabriella; Spagnolo, Antonio G. Ethical and juridical foundations of conscientious objection for health care workers. *Medical Ethics and Bioethics / Medicinska Etika and Bioetika* 2002 Spring-Summer; 9(1-2): 3-5. NRCBL: 8.1; 6; 12.4.3.

Gauthier, Candace Cummins. The virtue of moral responsibility and the obligations of patients. *Journal of Medicine and Philosophy* 2005 April; 30(2): 153-166. NRCBL: 8.1; 1.1. SC: an.

Abstract: The American Medical Association has provided a list of patient responsibilities, said to be derived from patient autonomy, without providing any justification for this derivation. In this article, the virtue of moral responsibility is proposed as a way to justify these kinds of limits on respect for individual autonomy. The need for such limits is explained by examining the traditional principles of health care ethics. What is missing in health care decision making, and can be provided by the virtue of moral responsibility, is a careful consideration of the impact of individual decisions on particular others and the community, as a whole. The concept of moral responsibility as a virtue is then developed and examples of its application to health care decision making are provided. Finally, the roles of both physicians and health care ethicists in promoting the morally responsible exercise of individual autonomy are explored.

Gill, Fiona; Kroese, B. Stenfert; Rose, J. General practitioners' attitudes to patients who have learning disabilities. *Psychological Medicine* 2002 November; 32(8): 1445-1455. NRCBL: 8.1; 9.5.3; 9.8; 8.3.3. SC: em. Identifiers: United Kingdom (Great Britain).

Gready, Paul; de Gruchy, Jeanelle. District surgeons in apartheid South Africa: a case study of dual obligations. *Health and Human Rights: An International Journal* 2003; 7(1): 113-143. NRCBL: 8.1; 4.1.1; 7.1; 21.1; 8.4. SC: em.

Gutheil, Thomas G. Boundaries, blackmail, and double binds: a pattern observed in malpractice consultation. *Journal of the American Academy of Psychiatry and the Law* 2005; 33(4): 476-481. NRCBL: 8.1; 8.5; 17.2; 1.3.8; 7.4; 10. SC: cs.

Hack, Thomas F.; Degner, Lesley F.; Dyck, Dennis G. Relationship between preferences for decisional control and illness information among women with breast cancer: a quantitative and qualitative analysis. *Social Science and Medicine* 1994 July; 39(2): 279-289. NRCBL: 8.1; 9.5.1; 9.5.5. SC: em.

Haddad, Amy. Ethics in action. A violent patient. *RN* 2004 May; 67(5): 21-23. NRCBL: 8.1; 17.8; 4.1.3. SC: cs.

Hall, Mark A. The importance of trust for ethics, law, and public policy. *CQ: Cambridge Quarterly of Healthcare Ethics* 2005 Spring; 14(2): 156-167. NRCBL: 8.1; 1.1; 7.1.

Hall, Mark A.; Zheng, Beiyao; Dugan, Elizabeth; Camacho, Fabian; Kidd, Kristin E.; Mishra, Aneil; Balkrishnan, Rajesh. Measuring patients' trust in their primary care providers. *Medical Care Research and Review* 2002 September; 59(3): 293-318. NRCBL: 8.1; 7.1; 9.3.2. SC: em.

Hanna, N.J. Challenging medical decision-making: professional dominance, patient rights or collaborative autonomy? *Oxford Journal of Legal Studies* 1998 Spring; 18(1): 143-152. NRCBL: 8.1; 8.3.1; 1.1. SC: le.

Hanssen, Ingrid. From human ability to ethical principle: an intercultural perspective on autonomy. *Medicine, Health Care and Philosophy: A European Journal* 2004; 7(3): 269-279. NRCBL: 8.1; 21.7; 8.2; 8.3.1; 4.1.3.
Abstract: Based on an empirical study regarding ethical challenges within intercultural health care, the focus of this article is upon autonomy and disclosure, discussed in light of philosophy and anthropology. What are the consequences for patients if the patient's right to be autonomous and to participate in treatment and care decisions by health care workers is interpreted as an obligation to participate? To force a person to make independent choices who is socio-culturally unprepared to do so, may violate his/her integrity. This may in turn jeopardise the respect, integrity and human worth the principle of autonomy was meant to ensure, and if so, may damage any relationship of trust that may exist between patient and health care worker. There is necessarily a link between autonomy and disclosure. Western disclosure practices may make the relationship between pa-

tients and health care workers difficult—even distrustful. To confront a patient with a very serious diagnosis may be seen not only as a tactless action, but also an unforgivable one. Hence, among many ethnic groups it is a family member's duty to shield patients from bad or disquieting news, e.g., a cancer diagnosis. If a family member is used to interpret in such situations, will the information given equal the information communicated by that interpreter? Even though respect for a person's autonomy is part of the respect for a person, one's respect for the person in question should not depend on his/her ability or aptitude to act autonomously.

Hardart, George E.; Truog, Robert D. Practicing physicians and the role of family surrogate decision making. *Journal of Clinical Ethics* 2005 Winter; 16(4): 345-354. NRCBL: 8.1; 20.4.1; 9.4; 7.1. SC: em.

Hasegawa, Thomas K., Jr.; Matthews, Merrill; Wakefield, Charles W. Ethical dilemma #49: "extreme makeover: we want her to be a winner". *Texas Dental Journal* 2004 October; 121(10): 995-998. NRCBL: 8.1; 9.5.1; 9.5.7.

Häyry, Heta. Wrongful medical authoritarianism. *In her: Individual Liberty and Medical Control.* Brookfield, VT: Ashgate Pub., 1998: 40-56. NRCBL: 8.1; 9.1. SC: an.

Iltis, Ana Smith. Professional promises and limits on the scope of practice. *HEC (Healthcare Ethics Committee) Forum* 2005 September; 17(3): 196-209. NRCBL: 8.1; 1.1; 4.1.1; 1.3.1; 12.4.3; 12.3.

Iltis, Ana Smith; Rasmussen, Lisa M. Patient ethics and responsibilities. *Journal of Medicine and Philosophy* 2005 April; 30(2): 131-137. NRCBL: 8.1.

Jerrold, Laurance. Right to refuse treatment. *American Journal of Orthodontics and Dentofacial Orthopedics* 2005 April; 127(4): 520-522. NRCBL: 8.1; 4.1.1. SC: cs.

Jones, James W.; McCullough, Laurence B. Futility and surgical intervention. *Journal of Vascular Surgery* 2002 June; 35(6): 1305. NRCBL: 8.1; 20.4.1. SC: cs.

Jones, James W.; McCullough, Laurence B.; Richman, Bruce W. Ethics of refusal to treat patients as a social statement. *Journal of Vascular Surgery* 2004 November; 40(5): 1057-1059. NRCBL: 8.1; 8.5. SC: cs.

Jones, Kenneth D., Jr. Extreme makeovers. *Journal of the American Dental Association* 2005 March; 136(3): 395-396. NRCBL: 8.1; 9.5.1; 4.5; 4.1.1.

Kaldjian, Lauris C.; Weir, Robert F.; Duffy, Thomas P. A clinician's approach to clinical ethical reasoning. *JGIM: Journal of General Internal Medicine* 2005 March; 20(3): 306-311. NRCBL: 8.1; 1.1.

Kaplowitz, Stan A.; Campo, Shelly; Chiu, Wai Tat. Cancer patients' desires for communication of prognosis information. *Health Communication* 2002; 14(2): 221-241. NRCBL: 8.1; 9.5.1; 17.1. SC: em.

NRCBL: National Reference Center for Bioethics Literature Classification Scheme See inside front cover for terms.

387

Kärkkäinen, Oili; Bondas, Terese; Eriksson, Katie. Documentation of individualized patient care: a qualitative metasynthesis. *Nursing Ethics* 2005 March; 12(2): 123-132. NRCBL: 8.1. SC: em.

Abstract: The aim of this study was to increase understanding of how individual patient care and the ethical principles prescribed for nursing care are implemented in nursing documentation. The method used was a metasynthesis of the results of 14 qualitative research reports. The results indicate that individualized patient care is not visible in nurses' documentation of care. It seems that nurses describe their tasks more frequently than patients' experiences of their care. The results also show that the structure of nursing documentation and the forms or manner of recording presupposed by the organization may prevent individual recording of patient care. In order to obtain visibility for good patient-centred and ethical nursing care, an effort should be made to influence how the content of nursing care is documented and made an essential part of individual patient care. If the content of this documentation does not give an accurate picture of care, patients' right to receive good nursing care may not be realized.

Kolata, Gina. When the doctor is in, but you wish he wasn't. *New York Times* 2005 November 30; p. A1, A28. NRCBL: 8.1. SC: po. Identifiers: Series — Being a patient: difficult doctors.

Larson, Eric B.; Yao, Xin. Clinical empathy as emotional labor in the patient-physician relationship. *JAMA: The Journal of the American Medical Association* 2005 March 2; 293(9): 1100-1106. NRCBL: 8.1.

Abstract: Empathy should characterize all health care professions. Despite advancement in medical technology, the healing relationship between physicians and patients remains essential to quality care. We propose that physicians consider empathy as emotional labor (ie, management of experienced and displayed emotions to present a certain image). Since the publication of Hochschild's The Managed Heart in 1983, researchers in management and organization behavior have been studying emotional labor by service workers, such as flight attendants and bill collectors. In this article, we focus on physicians as professionals who are expected to be empathic caregivers. They engage in such emotional labor through deep acting (ie, generating empathy-consistent emotional and cognitive reactions before and during empathic interactions with the patient, similar to the method-acting tradition used by some stage and screen actors), surface acting (ie, forging empathic behaviors toward the patient, absent of consistent emotional and cognitive reactions), or both. Although deep acting is preferred, physicians may rely on surface acting when immediate emotional and cognitive understanding of patients is impossible. Overall, we contend that physicians are more effective healers—and enjoy more professional satisfaction—when they engage in the process of empathy. We urge physicians first to recognize that their work has an element of emotional labor and, second, to consciously practice deep and surface acting to empathize with their patients. Medical students and residents can benefit from long-term regular training that includes conscious efforts to develop their empathic abilities. This will be valuable for both physicians and patients facing the increasingly fragmented and technological world of modern medicine.

Leavitt, F.J.; Peleg, R.; Peleg, A. Informal medicine: ethical analysis. *Journal of Medical Ethics* 2005 December; 31(12): 689-692. NRCBL: 8.1; 4.1.2; 2.1. SC: an.

Abstract: CONTEXT: Doctors have been known to treat or give consultation to patients informally, with none of the usual record keeping or follow up. They may wish to know whether this practice is ethical. OBJECTIVE: To determine whether this practice meets criteria of medical ethics. DESIGN: Informal medicine is analysed according to standard ethical principles: autonomy, beneficence and non-maleficence, distributive and procedural justice, and caring. SETTING: Hospital, medical school, and other settings where patients may turn to physicians for informal help. CONCLUSION: No generalisation can be made to the effect that informal medicine is or is not ethical. Each request for informal consultation must be considered on its own merits. GUIDELINES: Informal medicine may be ethical if no payment is involved, and when the patient is fully aware of the benefits and risks of a lack of record keeping. When an informal consultation does not entail any danger to the patient or others, the physician may agree to the request. If, however, any danger to the patient or others is foreseen, then the physician must insist on professional autonomy, and consider refusing the request and persuading the patient to accept formal consultation. If a reportable infectious disease, or other serious danger to the community, is involved, the physician should refuse informal consultation or treatment, or at least make a proper report even if the consultation was informal. If agreeing to the request will result in an unfair drain on the physician's time or energy, he or she should refuse politely.

Lee, Matthew; Charo, R. Alta. The celestial fire of conscience [letter and reply]. *New England Journal of Medicine* 2005 September 22; 353(12): 1301-1302. NRCBL: 8.1; 9.6; 1.2.

Leggett, Andrew. Origins and development of the injunction prohibiting sexual relationships with patients. *Australian and New Zealand Journal of Psychiatry* 1995 December; 29(4): 586-590. NRCBL: 8.1; 10; 7.1; 9.5.1; 9.5.7.

Levinson, Wendy; Kao, Audiey; Kuby, Alma; Thisted, Ronald A. Not all patients want to participate in decision making: a national study of public preferences. *JGIM: Journal of General Internal Medicine* 2005 June; 20(6): 531-535. NRCBL: 8.1. SC: em.

Levy, Joe S. Medical ethics. *Allergy and Asthma Proceedings* 2003 July-August; 24(4): 295-297. NRCBL: 8.1; 7.3.

Luckhaupt, Sara E.; Yi, Michael, S.; Mueller, Caroline V.; Mrus, Joseph M.; Peterman, Amy H.; Puchalski, Christina M.; Tsevat, Joel. Beliefs of primary care residents regarding spirituality and religion in clinical encounters with patients: a study at a Midwestern U.S. teaching institution. *Academic Medicine* 2005 June; 80(6): 560-570. NRCBL: 8.1; 1.2; 7.2. SC: em.

Malpani, Aniruddha. Doctors should be allowed to advertise [debate]. *Issues in Medical Ethics* 2001 January-March; 9(1): 16-17. NRCBL: 8.1; 1.3.2; 1.3.12. Identifiers: India.

Malterud, Kirsti. Humiliation instead of care? [opinion]. *Lancet* 2005 September 3-9; 366(9488): 785-786. NRCBL: 8.1; 21.7; 7.1. SC: em.

Mamdani, Bashir. He's ethical but has bad taste . . . . *Issues in Medical Ethics* 2003 January-March; 11(1): 24. NRCBL: 8.1; 1.3.2.

Mamdani, Bashir; Mamdani, Meenal. Ethics of professional advertising [debate]. *Issues in Medical Ethics* 2001 January-March; 9(1): 18. NRCBL: 8.1; 1.3.2; 1.3.12. Identifiers: India.

Marcellus, Lenora. The ethics of relation: public health nurses and child protection clients. *Journal of Advanced Nursing* 2005 August; 51(4): 414-420. NRCBL: 8.1; 9.1; 9.5.7.

McCauley, Jeanne; Jenckes, Mollie W.; Tarpley, Margaret J.; Koenig, Harold G.; Yanek, Lisa R.; Becker, Diane M. Spiritual beliefs and barriers among managed care practitioners. *Journal of Religion and Health* 2005 Summer; 44(2): 137-146. NRCBL: 8.1; 1.2; 9.3.2; 7.2; 7.1. SC: em.

McCord, Gary; Gilchrist, Valerie J.; Grossman, Steven D.; King, Bridget D.; McCormick, Kenelm F.; Oprandi, Allison M.; Schrop, Susan Labuda; Selius, Brian A.; Smucker, William D.; Weldy, David L.; Amorn, Melissa; Carter, Melissa A.; Deak, Andrew J.; Hefzy, Hebah; Srivastava, Mohit. Discussing spirituality with patients: a rational and ethical approach. *Annals of Family Medicine* 2004 July-August; 2(4): 356-361. NRCBL: 8.1; 1.2. SC: em.

McGuire, Amy L.; McCullough, Laurence B.; Weller, Susan C.; Whitney, Simon N. Missed expectations? Physicians' views of patients' participation in medical decision-making. *Medical Care* 2005 May; 43(5): 466-470. NRCBL: 8.1; 8.3.1. SC: em.

Morreim, E. Haavi. The clinical investigator as fiduciary: discarding a misguided idea. *Journal of Law, Medicine and Ethics* 2005 Fall; 33(3): 586-598. NRCBL: 8.1; 18.1; 18.2. SC: le.

Myhrvold, Trine. The exclusion of the other: challenges to the ethics of closeness. *Nursing Philosophy* 2003 April; 4(1): 33-43. NRCBL: 8.1; 4.1.3.

Mytton, O. Should doctors talk to relatives without a competent patient's consent? [opinion]. *Journal of Medical Ethics* 2005 May; 31(5): 266. NRCBL: 8.1; 8.4.

Nadoolman, Wolffe; Charo, R. Alta. The celestial fire of conscience [letter and reply]. *New England Journal of Medicine* 2005 September 22; 353(12): 1301-1302. NRCBL: 8.1; 9.6; 1.2.

Nelson, James Lindemann. Families and bioethics: old problems, new themes. *Journal of Clinical Ethics* 2005 Winter; 16(4): 299-302. NRCBL: 8.1; 2.1; 9.1.

Nessa, John. Autonomy and dialogue: about the patient-doctor relationship. *In:* Thomasma, David C.; Weisstud, David N.; Herve, Christian eds. Personhood and

Health Care. Boston: Kluwer Academic Pub.; 2001: 355-362. NRCBL: 8.1; 1.1.

Nortvedt, Per. Needs, closeness and responsibilities. An inquiry into some rival moral considerations in nursing care. *Nursing Philosophy* 2001 July; 2(2): 112-121. NRCBL: 8.1; 1.1; 4.1.3; 9.4; 4.1.1.

O'Connor, Tom; Kelly, Billy. Bridging the gap: a study of general nurses' perceptions of patient advocacy in Ireland. *Nursing Ethics* 2005 September; 12(5): 453-467. NRCBL: 8.1; 7.1. SC: em.

Abstract: Advocacy has become an accepted and integral attribute of nursing practice. Despite this adoption of advocacy, confusion remains about the precise nature of the concept and how it should be enacted in practice. The aim of this study was to investigate general nurses' perceptions of being patient advocates in Ireland and how they enact this role. These perceptions were compared with existing theory and research on advocacy in order to contribute to the knowledge base on the subject. An inductive, qualitative approach was used for this study. Three focus group interviews with a total of 20 practising nurses were conducted with a sample representing different grades in a general hospital setting. Data analysis was carried out using elements of Strauss and Corbins' approach to concept development. The findings indicate that the principal role of the nurse advocate is to act as an intermediary between the patient and the health care environment. The results highlight that advocacy did, however, result in nurses becoming involved in conflict and confrontation with others and that it could be detrimental to nurses both professionally and personally. It was also clear that when enacting advocacy, nurses distinguished between 'clinical advocacy' (acting directly for patients in the clinical environment) and organizational advocacy (acting on an organizational level for one or more patients).

O'Flynn, Norma; Britten, Nicky. Use of chaperones in general practice: GPs try to balance doctors' and patients' needs [letter]. *BMJ: British Medical Journal* 2005 April 9; 330(7495): 846. NRCBL: 8.1; 10; 9.5.5.

Olive, Kenneth E. Physician religious beliefs and the physician-patient relationship: a study of devout physicians. *Southern Medical Journal* 1995 December; 88(12): 1249-1255. NRCBL: 8.1; 1.2; 7.1.

Pandya, Sunil K. Advertising remains unethical even in the digital age [debate]. *Issues in Medical Ethics* 2001 January-March; 9(1): 15. NRCBL: 8.1; 1.3.2; 1.3.12. Identifiers: India.

Pandya, Sunil K. Doctor-patient relationship. *Medical Ethics: Journal of Forum for Medical Ethics Society* 1995 April-June; 3(2): 23-24. NRCBL: 8.1; 8.3.4.

Pask, Elizabeth J. Nursing responsibility and conditions of practice: are we justified in holding nurses responsible for their behaviour in situations of patient care? *Nursing Philosophy* 2001 April; 2(1): 42-52. NRCBL: 8.1; 4.1.3.

Pellegrino, Edmund D. Some things ought never be done: moral absolutes in clinical ethics. *Theoretical Medicine and Bioethics* 2005; 26(6): 469-486. NRCBL: 8.1; 1.1; 4.1.2.

NRCBL: National Reference Center for Bioethics Literature Classification Scheme   See inside front cover for terms.

389

Abstract: Moral absolutes have little or no moral standing in our morally diverse modern society. Moral relativism is far more palatable for most ethicists and to the public at large. Yet, when pressed, every moral relativist will finally admit that there are some things which ought never be done. It is the rarest of moral relativists that will take rape, murder, theft, child sacrifice as morally neutral choices. In general ethics, the list of those things that must never be done will vary from person to person. In clinical ethics, however, the nature of the physician-patient relationship is such that certain moral absolutes are essential to the attainment of the good of the patient - the end of the relationship itself. These are all derivatives of the first moral absolute of all morality: Do good and avoid evil. In the clinical encounter, this absolute entails several subsidiary absolutes - act for the good of the patient, do not kill, keep promises, protect the dignity of the patient, do not lie, avoid complicity with evil. Each absolute is intrinsic to the healing and helping ends of the clinical encounter.

Pennachio, Dorothy L. Caring for your Muslim patients: stereotypes and misunderstandings affect the care of patients from the Middle East and other parts of the Islamic world. *Medical Economics* 2005 May 6; 82(9): 46-50. NRCBL: 8.1; 9.1; 1.2.

Pilgaokar, Anil. The doctor, the patient and the relative [case study]. *Issues in Medical Ethics* 2000 October-December; 8(4): 129-130. NRCBL: 8.1; 9.7.

Pomerantz, Anita; Rintel, E. Sean. Practices for reporting and responding to test results during medical consultations: enacting the roles of paternalism and independent expertise. *Discourse Studies* 2004 February; 6(1): 9-26. NRCBL: 8.1; 9.1. SC: em.

Ramfelt, Ethel; Lützén, Kim. Patients with cancer: their approaches to participation in treatment plan decisions. *Nursing Ethics* 2005 March; 12(2): 143-155. NRCBL: 8.1; 9.5.1. SC: em. Identifiers: Sweden.
Abstract: The aim of this study was to explore experiences of participation in treatment planning decisions from the perspective of patients recently treated for colorectal cancer. Ten patients were purposively selected and interviewed. Constant comparative analysis, the core concept of grounded theory, was used. The dimensions were developed and organized into the main theme of 'compliant participation in serious decisions', which was composed of the two variations: complying with participation; and complying without participation. Complying with participation was characterized by feelings of self-confidence and self-competence and by open dialogue between the participants, significant others and the physician. Complying without participation was characterized by participants' feelings of uncertainty and distress, and of being rushed into submitting to decisions without having time to reflect on the information provided or the opportunity to influence the treatment and care process. To participate (or choosing not to participate) builds on open and affirming dialogue, information and knowledge about the illness. Patient participation in treatment and care decision making is interpreted as a health promoting way of coping with illness.

Reid, Lynette. Diminishing returns? Risk and the duty to care in the SARS epidemic. *Bioethics* 2005 August; 19(4): 348-361. NRCBL: 8.1; 5.2; 9.5.6; 1.1. SC: an. Identifiers: severe acute respiratory syndrome.
Abstract: The seriousness of the risk that healthcare workers faced during SARS, and their response of service in the face of this risk, brings to light unrealistic assumptions about duty and risk that informed the debate on duty to care in the early years of HIV/AIDS. Duty to care is not based upon particular virtues of the health professions, but arises from social reflection on what response to an epidemic would be consistent with our values and our needs, recognizing our shared vulnerability to disease and death. Such reflection underwrites a strong duty of care, but one not to be borne solely by the altruism and heroism of individual healthcare workers.

Riley, Joan M.; Fry, Sara T. Nurses report widespread ethical conflicts. *Reflections on Nursing Leadership* 2000; 26(2): 35-36, 45. NRCBL: 8.1; 4.1.3; 9.1.

Sandman, Lars. On the autonomy turf. Assessing the value of autonomy to patients. *Medicine, Health Care and Philosophy: A European Journal* 2004; 7(3): 261-268. NRCBL: 8.1; 1.1; 8.3.1; 4.1.2. SC: an.
Abstract: Within the western health-care context autonomy is a central value. Still, as it is used within this context it is far from clear what we are actually talking about. In this article the author outlines four different uses or aspects of autonomy: self-determination, freedom, desire-fulfilment and independence. One important conclusion will be that in order to be able to respect autonomy in a way that actually brings value to the patient's life we need to clearly assess what aspect of autonomy the patient values and for what reason it is valued by the patient.

Sayers, G.M.; Bethell, H.W.L. Pacing extremely old patients: who decides — the doctor, the patient, or the relatives? *Heart* 2004 February 1; 90(2): 134-135. NRCBL: 8.1; 9.5.2; 8.3.3. SC: le. Identifiers: United Kingdom (Great Britain).

Scheurich, Neil. Spirituality, medicine, and the possibility of wisdom [editorial]. *JGIM: Journal of General Internal Medicine* 2005 April; 20(4): 379-380. NRCBL: 8.1; 1.2; 17.2.

Schwartz, Marlene B.; Chambliss, Heather O'Neal; Brownell, Kelly D.; Blair, Steven N.; Billington, Charles. Weight bias among health professionals specializing in obesity. *Obesity Research* 2003 September; 11(9): 1033-1039. NRCBL: 8.1; 9.5.4. SC: em.

Scopelliti, Joseph; Judd, Fiona; Grigg, Margaret; Hodgins, Gene; Fraser, Cait; Hulbert, Carol; Endacott, Ruth; Wood, Anita. Dual relationships in mental health practice: issues for clinicians in rural settings. *Australian and New Zealand Journal of Psychiatry* 2004 November-December; 38(11-12): 953-959. NRCBL: 8.1; 17.1; 17.2. SC: em. Identifiers: Australia.

Shenolikar, Rahul A.; Balkrishnan, Rajesh; Hall, Mark A. How patient-physician encounters in critical medical situations affect trust: results of a national survey. *BMC Health Services Research [electronic]* 2004 September 7; 4: 24-29. Available: http://www.biomedcentral.com/ [8 September 2005]. NRCBL: 8.1; 1.1.

Silbert, M. The patient-physician relationship [letter]. *South African Medical Journal* 2001 August; 91(8): 616-617. NRCBL: 8.1; 1.1.

Silveira, Maria J.; Feudtner, Chris; McNutt, Robert A. Shared medical decision making. *JAMA: The Journal of the American Medical Association* 2005 March 2; 293(9): 1058-1059. NRCBL: 8.1.

Sims, Mary. On-line physician-patient care: the future of electronic medicine. *Ethics and Medics* 2005 February; 30(2): 1-3. NRCBL: 8.1; 1.2; 1.3.12; 5.2; 8.4.

Smith, Carole. Understanding trust and confidence: two paradigms and their significance for health and social care. *Journal of Applied Philosophy* 2005; 22(3): 299-316. NRCBL: 8.1; 1.1; 9.8. SC: an. Identifiers: United Kingdom (Great Britain).

Abstract: Trusting agents characteristically anticipate beneficial outcomes, under conditions of uncertainty, in their engagement with others. However, debates about trust incorporate different interpretations of risk, uncertainty, calculation, affect, morality and motivation in explaining when trust is appropriate and how it operates. This article argues that discussions about trust have produced a concept without coherent boundaries and with little operational value. Two paradigms are identified, which distinguish the characteristics of trust and confidence. It is argued that a reliance on confidence in human affairs makes trust redundant and that this has undesirable moral consequences. Discussion is illustrated by the UK Government's 'modernisation' policy in health and social care, which privileges confidence in systems over trust in moral agents.

Smith, Jennifer A. Terminating the provider-patient relationship. *Nurse Practitioner* 2005 May; 30(5): 58-60. NRCBL: 8.1. SC: le.

Sørlie, Venke; Kihlgren, Annica; Kihlgren, Mona. Meeting ethical challenges in acute nursing care as narrated by registered nurses. *Nursing Ethics* 2005 March; 12(2): 133-142. NRCBL: 8.1; 7.1. SC: em. Identifiers: Sweden.

Spiegel, W.; Colella, T.; Lupton, P. Private or intimate relations between doctor and patient: is zero tolerance warranted? *Journal of Medical Ethics* 2005 January; 31(1): 27-28. NRCBL: 8.1; 10; 7.4. SC: rv.

Abstract: This article reviews and comments on the five categories of arguments used to defend zero tolerance with regard to sexual contacts resulting from the physician-patient relationship as summarised by Cullen. In addition it puts forward a hypothesis- "fear of loss by third party"-as a psychological explanation for the collective insistence on a zero tolerance policy.

Steckmann, Ulrich. Patientenautonomie und Paternalismus in der Medizinethik. *In:* Jahrbuch für Wissenschaft und Ethik. Bd. 7. Berlin: Walter de Gruyter; 2002: 73-100. NRCBL: 8.1; 1.1.

Stevenson, Fiona; Scambler, Graham. The relationship between medicine and the public: the challenge of concordance. *Health (London)* 2005 January; 9(1): 5-21. NRCBL: 8.1; 4.1.2; 7.1. SC: an.

Steward, Caroline. What is the responsibility of the nephrology nurse when the patient is chronically late? Nephrology nurses must follow the Nightingale Pledge. *Nephrology Nursing Journal* 2004 July-August; 31(4): 445-446. NRCBL: 8.1; 19.3.

Suziedelis, Ann. Requests for inappropriate treatment: can a doctor "just say 'no'"? *Health Care Ethics USA* [electronic] 2005; 13(1); 2 p. Available: http://www.slu.edu/centers/chce/hceusa/1_2005_3.html [19 September 2005]. NRCBL: 8.1; 9.4; 20.5.1.

Thorne, Sally E.; Robinson, Carol A. Reciprocal trust in health care relationships. *Journal of Advanced Nursing* 1988 November; 13(6): 782-789. NRCBL: 8.1; 4.1.1; 1.1.

Tolich, Martin; Baldwin, Kate Mary. Unequal protection for patient rights: the divide between university and health ethics committees. *Journal of Bioethical Inquiry* 2005; 2(1): 34-40. NRCBL: 8.1; 9.6; 18.3; 8.3.1; 6.

Abstract: Despite recommendations from the Cartwright Report ethical review by health ethics committees has continued in New Zealand without health practitioners ever having to acknowledge their dual roles as health practitioners researching their own patients. On the other hand, universities explicitly identify doctor/research-patient relations as potentially raising conflict of role issues. This stems from the acknowledgement within the university sector itself that lecturer/research-student relations are fraught with such conflicts. Although similar unequal relationships are seen to exist between health research-ers and their patients, the patient/subjects are not afforded the levels of protection that are afforded student/subjects. In this paper we argue that the difference between universities and health research is a result of the failure of the Operational Standard Code for Ethics Committees to explicitly acknowledge the vulnerability of the patient and conflict of interests in the dual roles of health practitioner/researcher. We end the paper recommending the Ministry of Health consider the rewriting of the Operational Standard Code for Ethics Committees, in particular in the rewriting of section 26 of the Operational Standard Code for Ethics Committees. We also identify the value of comparative ethical review and suggest the New Zealand's Health Research Council's trilateral relationship with Australia's NHMRC (National Health and Medical Research Council) and Canada's CIHR (Canadian Institute of Health Research) as a useful starting point for such a process.

Toombs, S.K. 'Is she experiencing any pain?': disability and the physician-patient relationship. *Internal Medicine Journal* 2004 November; 34(11): 645-647. NRCBL: 8.1; 4.4; 9.5.1.

Trotter, Griffin. Of lotteries lost and partnerships forged: the perils and promises of patient ethics [editorial]. *CQ: Cambridge Quarterly of Healthcare Ethics* 2005 Spring; 14(2): 131-139. NRCBL: 8.1; 1.3.1; 1.1; 8.2; 9.8; 7.1; 9.4.

Välimäki, Maritta; Leino-Kilpi, Helena; Grönroos, Matti; Dassen, Theo; Gasull, Maria; Lemonidou, Chryssoula; Scott, P. Anne; Arndt, Marianne Benedicta. Self-determination in surgical patients in five European countries. *Journal of Nursing Scholarship* 2004; 36(4): 305-311. NRCBL: 8.1; 8.3.1; 1.1. SC: em. Identifiers: Finland; Spain; Greece; Germany; Scotland.

NRCBL: National Reference Center for Bioethics Literature Classification Scheme　　　　　See inside front cover for terms.

391

Victoroff, Michael S. We don't serve your kind! *Managed Care* 2004 August; 13(8): 14, 16. NRCBL: 8.1; 8.5.

Waggoner, Jeffrey R.; McNutt, Robert A. Shared medical decision making [letter and reply]. *JAMA: The Journal of the American Medical Association* 2005 March 2; 293(9): 1058-1059. NRCBL: 8.1.

Walter, Fiona M.; Emery, Jon D.; Rogers, Margaret; Britten, Nicky. Women's views of optimal risk communication and decision making in general practice consultations about the menopause and hormone replacement therapy. *Patient Education and Counseling* 2004 May; 53(2): 121-128. NRCBL: 8.1; 8.3.1; 9.5.5. SC: em.

Weber, Leonard J.; Bissell, Michael G. Reporting lab results directly to the patient. *Clinical Leadership and Management Review* 2004 September-October; 18(5): 291-292. NRCBL: 8.1. SC: cs.

Welchman, Jennifer; Griener, Glenn G. Patient advocacy and professional associations: individual and collective responsibilities. *Nursing Ethics* 2005 May; 12(3): 296-304. NRCBL: 8.1; 1.3.5; 4.1.3; 9.5.1. SC: cs.

Wigder, Herbert N.; Propp, Douglas; Leslie, Kim. Patients' perception of the physician-patient relationship [letter]. *American Journal of Emergency Medicine* 2003 November; 21(7): 607. NRCBL: 8.1. SC: em.

Wildes, Kevin Wm. Patients: the Rosetta Stone in the crisis of medicine. *CQ: Cambridge Quarterly of Healthcare Ethics* 2005 Spring; 14(2): 168-176. NRCBL: 8.1; 1.3.1; 4.1.2; 7.1; 5.1.

Williams, Tricia. Paternalism and autonomy in dentistry. *Update [Loma Linda University Center for Christian Bioethics]* 2002 March; 17(3): 2-7. NRCBL: 8.1; 4.1.1; 9.1.

Woods, Simon. Moral progress. *In:* Häyry, Matti; Takala, Tuija; Herissone-Kelly, Peter, eds. Bioethics and Social Reality. New York: Rodopi, 2005: 137-148. NRCBL: 8.1; 1.3.1.

Wynn, Francine; Peter, Elizabeth. Nurses and quarantine: reflections upon the SARS crisis in Toronto [editorial]. *Nursing Inquiry* 2003 December; 10(4): 207-208. NRCBL: 8.1; 4.1.3; 9.1. Identifiers: severe acute respiratory syndrome.

PROFESSIONAL PROFESSIONAL RELATIONSHIP

Physicians and advocacy [editorial]. *CMAJ/JAMC: Canadian Medical Association Journal* 2005 May 24; 172(11): 1413. NRCBL: 7.3; 9.8.

Abelson, Reed. Possible conflicts for doctors are seen on medical devices. *New York Times* 2005 September 22; p. A1, C6. NRCBL: 7.3; 9.7. SC: po.

American College of Emergency Physicians [ACEP]. ACEP Board of Directors. Conflict of interest policy [policy statement]. *Annals of Emergency Medicine* 1998 January; 31(1): 150-152. NRCBL: 7.3; 6.

Beckstead, Jason W. Reporting peer wrongdoing in the healthcare profession: the role of incompetence and substance abuse information. *International Journal of Nursing Studies* 2005 March; 42(3): 325-331. NRCBL: 7.3; 9.8; 9.5.9. SC: em.

Bolsin, Stephen; Faunce, T.; Oakley, J. Practical virtue ethics: healthcare whistleblowing and portable digital technology. *Journal of Medical Ethics* 2005 October; 31(10): 612-618. NRCBL: 7.3; 9.8; 1.1. SC: an.

Abstract: Medical school curricula and postgraduate education programmes expend considerable resources teaching medical ethics. Simultaneously, whistleblowers' agitation continues, at great personal cost, to prompt major intrainstitutional and public inquiries that reveal problems with the application of medical ethics at particular clinical "coalfaces". Virtue ethics, emphasising techniques promoting an agent's character and instructing their conscience, has become a significant mode of discourse in modern medical ethics. Healthcare whistleblowers, whose complaints are reasonable, made in good faith, in the public interest, and not vexatious, we argue, are practising those obligations of professional conscience foundational to virtue based medical ethics. Yet, little extant virtue ethics scholarship seriously considers the theoretical foundations of healthcare whistleblowing. The authors examine whether healthcare whistleblowing should be considered central to any medical ethics emphasising professional virtues and conscience. They consider possible causes for the paucity of professional or academic interest in this area and examine the counterinfluence of a continuing historical tradition of guild mentality professionalism that routinely places relationships with colleagues ahead of patient safety. Finally, it is proposed that a virtue based ethos of medical professionalism, exhibiting transparency and sincerity with regard to achieving uniform quality and safety of health care, may be facilitated by introducing a technological imperative using portable computing devices. Their use by trainees, focused on ethical competence, provides the practical face of virtue ethics in medical education and practice. Indeed, it assists in transforming the professional conscience of whistleblowing into a practical, virtue based culture of self reporting and personal development.

Brown, Hannah. Clinician expert witnesses take the stand. *Lancet* 2005 July 2-8; 366(9479): 16-17. NRCBL: 7.3; 1.3.5; 7.4.

Chinoy, R.F. Some ethical issues in histopathology. *Issues in Medical Ethics* 2000 January-March; 8(1): 22-23. NRCBL: 7.3; 1.3.9.

Chren, Mary-Margaret. Interactions between physicians and drug company representatives [editorial]. *American Journal of Medicine* 1999 August; 107(2): 182-183. NRCBL: 7.3; 9.7.

Cilla, Dana. Physicians and pharmaceutical companies: financial conflicts of interests. *Medical Trial Technique Quarterly* 2003; 50(2): 109-144. NRCBL: 7.3; 9.7; 1.3.2; 9.3.1; 1.3.5; 18.1. SC: le.

Drew, Melinda; Garrahan, Katherine. Whistleblower protection for nurses and other health care professionals. *Journal of Nursing Law* 2005 Summer; 10(2): 79-87. NRCBL: 7.3; 9.8; 4.1.3.

Egilman, David S. Suppression bias at the Journal of Occupational and Environmental Medicine. *International Journal of Occupational and Environmental Health* 2005 April-June; 11(2): 202-204. NRCBL: 7.3; 1.3.7.

Faunce, Thomas. Coherence and healthcare whistle-blowing: a response to Parker. *Monash Bioethics Review* 2005 January; 24(1): 47-49. NRCBL: 7.3; 9.8; 1.1; 7.2. SC: an.

Friedman, Lee; Richter, Elihu D. Conflicts of interest and scientific integrity. *International Journal of Occupational and Environmental Health* 2005 April-June; 11(2): 205-206. NRCBL: 7.3; 1.3.7.

Frye, Carla B. Disclosing conflicts of interest involving clinicians who prepare therapeutic guidelines. *American Journal of Health System Pharmacy* 2005 February 15; 62(4): 361-362. NRCBL: 7.3; 9.7.

Gale, Edwin A.M. Between two cultures: the expert clinician and the pharmaceutical industry. *Clinical Medicine* 2003 November-December; 3(6): 538-541. NRCBL: 7.3; 9.7; 1.3.2.

Garity, Joan. Relationship of the ANA Code of Ethics to nurses' collaborative efforts. *Online Journal of Issues in Nursing [electronic]* 2005; 10(3); E9, 3 p. Available: http://www.nursingworld.org/ojin/ [23 November 2005]. NRCBL: 7.3; 8.1; 4.1.3; 6. Identifiers: American Nurses Association.

Gearon, Christopher J.; Fields, Helen. Medicine's turf wars: specialists without M.D.'s are pushing for more medical power. Are they ready — and are you? *U.S. News and World Report* 2005 January 31-February 7; 138(4): 57-60, 62, 64. NRCBL: 7.3; 9.3.1; 9.3.2; 8.1. SC: po.

Gillett, Grant. The ethical status of whistle-blowers. *Monash Bioethics Review* 2005 January; 24(1): 59-64. NRCBL: 7.3; 9.8; 7.2; 1.1. SC: an.

Goodwin, Guy. Conflict of interest is not just about advising pharmaceutical companies [editorial]. *Journal of Psychopharmacology* 2004 December; 18(4): 447-448. NRCBL: 7.3; 9.7; 1.3.2.

Hampson, Lindsay A.; Emanuel, Ezekiel, J.; Topol, Eric J.; Blumenthal, David. Physicians advising investment firms [letter and reply]. *JAMA: The Journal of the American Medical Association* 2005 October 19; 294(15): 1897-1898. NRCBL: 7.3.

Hirsch, Jules. A first brush with professional courtesy. *Annals of Internal Medicine* 2005 October 18; 143(8): 613. NRCBL: 7.3; 8.1.

Huston, Janis L.; Brox, Georg A. Professional ethics at the bottom line. *Health Care Manager* 2004 July-September; 23(3): 267-272. NRCBL: 7.3; 7.4. SC: cs.

Irvine, Robert; Kerridge, I.; McPhee, J. Towards a dialogical ethics of interprofessionalism. *Journal of Postgraduate Medicine* 2004 October-December; 50(4): 278-280. NRCBL: 7.3; 1.1.

Jacobson, Peter D.; Bloche, M. Gregg. Improving relations between attorneys and physicians. *JAMA: The Journal of the American Medical Association* 2005 October 26; 294(16): 2083-2085. NRCBL: 7.3; 1.3.8.

Jormsri, Pantip. Moral conflict and collaborative mode as moral conflict resolution in health care. *Nursing and Health Sciences* 2004 September; 6(3): 217-221. NRCBL: 7.3; 8.1; 4.1.3.

Keim, Twila. Physicians for professional sports teams: health care under the pressure of economic and commercial interests. *Seton Hall Journal of Sports Law* 1999 February; 97(4): 196-225. NRCBL: 7.3; 8.1; 9.5.1. SC: le.

Kim, Scott Y.H. Commentary: financial conflicts of interest and the identity of academic medicine. *In:* Moore, Don A.; Cain, Daylian M.; Loewenstein, George; Bazerman, Max H., eds. Conflicts of Interest: Challenges and Solutions in Business, Law, Medicine, and Public Policy. New York: Cambridge University Press; 2005: 181-186. NRCBL: 7.3; 1.3.2; 1.3.9; 5.1; 9.3.1; 9.7.

Krause, Joan H.; Saver, Richard S. Ethics in the practice of health law. *Journal of Law, Medicine and Ethics* 2004 Winter; 32(4): 766-769. NRCBL: 7.3; 9.6; 1.3.8. SC: le.

Larkin, Gregory L.; Marco, Catherine A. Ethics seminars: beyond authorship requirements — ethical considerations in writing letters of recommendation. *Academic Emergency Medicine* 2001 January; 8(1): 70-73. NRCBL: 7.3; 7.1; 1.3.1.

LeCraw, Linda L.; Roble, Daniel T. Physicians on the board: competitive conflicts of interest. *Trustee* 2005 January; 58(1): 27-28. NRCBL: 7.3; 9.3.1.

Levi, Benjamin H. Ethical conflicts between residents and attending physicians. *Clinical Pediatrics* 2002 November-December; 41(9): 659-667. NRCBL: 7.3; 20.5.2. SC: cs.

London, Leslie. Dual loyalties and HIV policy in South Africa — a challenge to the institutions of our professions [editorial]. *South African Medical Journal* 2002 November; 92(11): 882-883. NRCBL: 7.3; 4.1.2; 9.5.6.

McSweeny, A. John. Regarding ethics in forensic neuropsychological consultation: a comment on Guilmette and Hagan. *Clinical Neuropsychologist* 1997 August; 11(3): 291-293. NRCBL: 7.3; 1.3.5; 17.1; 6. SC: le. Comments: comment on T.J. Guilmette, L.D. Hagan, "Ethical

NRCBL: National Reference Center for Bioethics Literature Classification Scheme   See inside front cover for terms.

393

consideration in forensic neuropsychological consultation," *Clinical Neuropsychologist* 1997; 11: 287-290.

Orr, Robert D. When it's hard to please everybody: etiquette serving ethics when you disagree with a colleague. Opinion #3: professional autonomy. *Pain Medicine* 2001 March; 2(1): 83, 85-86. NRCBL: 7.3; 8.1. SC: cs.

Palermo, George B. Forensic mental health experts in the court—an ethical dilemma [editorial]. *International Journal of Offender Therapy and Comparative Criminology* 2003 April; 47(2): 122-125. NRCBL: 7.3; 1.3.5.

Palmer, Nigel; Rogers, Wendy A. Whistle-blowing in the medical curriculum: a response to Faunce. *Monash Bioethics Review* 2005 January; 24(1): 50-58. NRCBL: 7.3; 9.8; 7.2; 1.1. SC: an.

Pandya, Sunil K. Taking a second look: some opinions on the second opinion [discussion]. *Issues in Medical Ethics* 1998 January; 6(1): 9-16. NRCBL: 7.3; 9.3.1; 9.8.

Patmas, Michael A.; Topol, Eric J.; Blumenthal, David. Physicians advising investment firms [letter and reply]. *JAMA: The Journal of the American Medical Association* 2005 October 19; 294(15): 1897-1898. NRCBL: 7.3.

Peota, Carmen. Expertly stated. *Minnesota Medicine* 2005 June; 88(6): 12-14. NRCBL: 7.3; 1.3.5; 20.5.1.

Robertson, R.G. Rumours: constructive or corrosive. *Journal of Medical Ethics* 2005 September; 31(9): 540-541. NRCBL: 7.3.
Abstract: There is an ever-greater emphasis on the maintenance of professional standards in communication among medical professionals. Much of the focus to date revolves around discourse between patients and families in the clinical arena and reflects standards developed by accrediting agencies and the government. Little has been written about the communication among professionals occurring in the administrative milieu that is largely unseen by those not engaged in the direct provision of or receipt of medical care. That rumours are a part of the interactive discourse is likely not unfamiliar to most in academia. Their potential for damage to the workplace and individuals is very real and requires recognition and in some situations, corporate action. There are options to reduce the likelihood of these kinds of communications and to manage them actively when they occur. What may result is an environment that leads to greater organisational confidence and individual productivity.

Sawa, Russell J. Foundations of interdisciplinarity: a Lonergan perspective. *Medicine, Health Care and Philosophy: A European Journal* 2005; 8(1): 53-61. NRCBL: 7.3; 4.1.2.
Abstract: The postmodern enterprise, with its foundationlessness, fragmentariness, constructivism, and neopragmatism challenges interdisciplinarity. This paper discusses functional specialization and interdisciplinary method which provides a basis for interdisciplinary collaboration. In functional specialization, successive stages in the process of coming to know are distinguished. These stages correspond to Lonergan's four levels of consciousness, namely experiencing the data, coming to understanding through addressing questions which arise from the data, and judgment about which hypothe-sis best fits the data. Authenticity, which involves genuine attentiveness, intelligence, reasonableness, and responsibility, guides the appropriate attitude in interdisciplinary work.

Sierles, Frederick S.; Brodkey, Amy C.; Cleary, Lynn M.; McCurdy, Frederick A.; Mintz, Matthew; Frank, Julia; Lynn, D. Joanne; Chao, Jason; Morgenstern, Bruce Z.; Shore, William; Woodard, John L. Medical students' exposure to and attitudes about drug company interactions: a national survey. *JAMA: The Journal of the American Medical Association* 2005 September 7; 294(9): 1034-1042. NRCBL: 7.3; 9.7; 1.3.2; 7.2; 9.3.1. SC: em.
Abstract: CONTEXT: While exposure to and attitudes about drug company interactions among residents have been studied extensively, relatively little is known about relationships between drug companies and medical students. OBJECTIVE: To measure third-year medical students' exposure to and attitudes about drug company interactions. DESIGN, SETTING, AND PARTICIPANTS: In 2003, we distributed a 64-item anonymous survey to 1143 third-year students at 8 US medical schools, exploring their exposure and response to drug company interactions. The schools' characteristics included a wide spectrum of ownership types, National Institutes of Health funding, and geographic locations. In 2005, we conducted a national survey of student affairs deans to measure the prevalence of school-wide policies on drug company-medical student interactions. MAIN OUTCOME MEASURES: Monthly frequency of students' exposure to various activities and gifts during clerkships, and attitudes about receiving gifts. RESULTS: Overall response rate was 826/1143 (72.3%), with range among schools of 30.9%-90.7%. Mean exposure for each student was 1 gift or sponsored activity per week. Of respondents, 762/818 (93.2%) were asked or required by a physician to attend at least 1 sponsored lunch. Regarding attitudes, 556/808 (68.8%) believed gifts would not influence their practices and 464/804 (57.7%) believed gifts would not affect colleagues' practices. Of the students, 553/604 (80.3%) believed that they were entitled to gifts. Of 183 students who thought a gift valued at less than $50 was inappropriate, 158 (86.3%) had accepted one. The number of students who simultaneously believed that sponsored grand rounds are educationally helpful and are likely to be biased was 452/758 (59.6%). Students at 1 school who had attended a seminar about drug company-physician relationships were no more likely than the nonattending classmates to show skepticism. Of the respondents, 704/822 (85.6%) did not know if their school had a policy on these relationships. In a national survey of student affairs deans, among the 99 who knew their policy status, only 10 (10.1%) reported having school-wide policies about these interactions. CONCLUSIONS: Student experiences and attitudes suggest that as a group they are at risk for unrecognized influence by marketing efforts. Research should focus on evaluating methods to limit these experiences and affect the development of students' attitudes to ensure that physicians' decisions are based solely on helping each patient achieve the greatest possible benefit.

Society of Obstetricians and Gynaecologists of Canada [SOGC]; International Women's Health Programme Committee. Conflict of interest [policy statement]. *JOGC: Journal of Obstetrics and Gynaecology Canada* 2003 December; 25(12): 1044-1045. NRCBL: 7.3.

Stark, Andrew. Why are (some) conflicts of interest in medicine so uniquely vexing? *In:* Moore, Don A.; Cain, Daylian M.; Loewenstein, George; Bazerman, Max H., eds. Conflicts of Interest: Challenges and Solutions in

Business, Law, Medicine, and Public Policy. New York: Cambridge University Press; 2005: 152-180. NRCBL: 7.3; 1.3.2; 1.3.9; 5.1; 9.3.1; 9.7.

Tatara, Kozo. Prescribing and dispensing in Japan: conflict of interest? *Clinical Medicine* 2003 November-December; 3(6): 555. NRCBL: 7.3; 9.7; 4.1.2.

Thawani, Vijay. The doctor-doctor relationship: professional criticism. *Issues in Medical Ethics* 2000 July-September; 8(3): 82-83. NRCBL: 7.3.

Thomson, Alan B.R. Perhaps the time has come [editorial]. *Canadian Journal of Gastroenterology* 2003 October; 17(10): 613-615. NRCBL: 7.3; 9.7.

Topol, Eric J.; Blumenthal, David. Physicians and the investment industry. *JAMA: The Journal of the American Medical Association* 2005 June 1; 293(21): 2654-2657. NRCBL: 7.3; 1.3.2.

Vinten, Gerald. Whistleblowing in the health-related professions. *Issues in Medical Ethics* 1996 October-December; 4(4): 108-111. NRCBL: 7.3; 9.8.

Wales, Steven D. The Stark Law: boon or boondoggle? An analysis of the prohibition on physician self-referrals. *Law and Psychology Review* 2003 Spring; 27: 1-28. NRCBL: 7.3; 9.3.1; 1.3.5. SC: le.

Williams, Kevin W. Managing physician financial conflicts of interest in clinical trials conducted in the private practice setting. *Food and Drug Law Journal* 2004; 59(1): 45-77. NRCBL: 7.3; 9.3.1; 1.3.2; 18.5.1; 18.3; 8.1. SC: le.

Wlasienko, Pawel. Ethical and legal aspects in teaching students of medicine. *Science and Engineering Ethics* 2005 January; 11(1): 75-80. NRCBL: 7.3; 2.3. SC: le. Conference: 5th International Conference on Bioethics: The Ethics of Intellectual Property Rights and Patents; Warsaw, Poland; 23-24 April 2004; Minister of Science and the Minister of Health, Poland.

Wright, Scott M.; Carrese, Joseph A. Which values do attending physicians try to pass on to house officers? *Medical Education* 2001 October; 35(10): 941-945. NRCBL: 7.3; 7.2; 1.1; 4.1.2.

PROLONGATION OF LIFE See EUTHANASIA AND ALLOWING TO DIE

PROXY DECISION MAKING See ADVANCE DIRECTIVES; EUTHANASIA AND ALLOWING TO DIE; INFORMED CONSENT/ INCOMPETENTS; INFORMED CONSENT/ MINORS

PSYCHOPHARMACOLOGY
See also BEHAVIOR CONTROL; CARE FOR SPECIFIC GROUPS/ MENTALLY DISABLED; MENTAL HEALTH THERAPIES

Anijar, Karen; Gabbard, David. Authentic faux diamonds and attention deficit disorder [comment]. *American Journal of Bioethics* 2005 May-June; 5(3): 67-70. NRCBL: 17.4; 9.5.7; 9.7; 1.3.3; 1.3.5. Comments: comment on Ilina Singh, "Will the 'real boy' please behave: dosing dilemmas for parents of boys with ADHD," American Journal of Bioethics 2005 May-June; 5(3): 34-47.

Appelbaum, Paul S. Psychopharmacology and the power of narrative [comment]. *American Journal of Bioethics* 2005 May-June; 5(3): 48-49. NRCBL: 17.4; 9.5.7. Comments: comment on Ilina Singh, "Will the 'real boy' please behave: dosing dilemmas for parents of boys with ADHD," American Journal of Bioethics 2005 May-June; 5(3): 34-47.

Bjorklund, Pamela. Can there be a 'cosmetic' psychopharmacology? Prozac unplugged: the search for an ontologically distinct cosmetic psychopharmacology. *Nursing Philosophy* 2005 April; 6(2): 131-143. NRCBL: 17.4; 4.5.

Breithaupt, Holger; Weigmann, Katrin. Manipulating your mind: what will science discover about our brains, and how are we going to deal with it? *EMBO Reports* 2004 March; 5(3): 230-232. NRCBL: 17.4; 4.5.

Chen, Tammy; Herbert, Paul B. Involuntary medications allowed to restore competence to stand trial. *Journal of the American Academy of Psychiatry and the Law* 2005; 33(4): 553-554. NRCBL: 17.4; 1.3.5. SC: le.

Cohan, John Alan. Psychiatric ethics and emerging issues of psychopharmacology in the treatment of depression. *Journal of Contemporary Health Law and Policy* 2003 Winter; 20(1): 115-172. NRCBL: 17.4; 7.3; 4.5; 4.4; 9.7.

Frank, Richard G.; Conti, Rena M.; Goldman, Howard H. Mental health policy and psychotropic drugs. *Milbank Quarterly* 2005; 83(2): 271-298. NRCBL: 17.4; 9.5.3; 9.3.1.

Abstract: The pace of innovation in psychotropic drugs has been rapid over the past 15 years. There also have been unprecedented increases in spending on prescription drugs generally and psychotropic medications specifically. Psychotropic medications are playing a more central role in treatment. They also are receiving close scrutiny from health insurers, state budget makers, and ordinary citizens. Public policy actions regarding prescription drugs have the potential to significantly affect clinical care for mental disorders, the costs of this care to individuals and society at large, and the prospects for future scientific advances. This article outlines the policy issues related to psychotropic drugs with respect to their role in determining access to mental health treatment and the cost and quality of mental health care.

Griggins, Cynthia. Dosing dilemmas: are you rich and white or poor and black? [comment]. *American Journal of Bioethics* 2005 May-June; 5(3): 55-57. NRCBL: 17.4; 9.5.7; 7.1. Comments: comment on Ilina Singh, "Will the 'real boy' please behave: dosing dilemmas for parents of

NRCBL: National Reference Center for Bioethics Literature Classification Scheme   See inside front cover for terms.

395

boys with ADHD," American Journal of Bioethics 2005 May-June; 5(3): 34-47.

Hall, Amy Laura. Welcome to ordinary? Marketing better boys [comment]. *American Journal of Bioethics* 2005 May-June; 5(3): 59-60. NRCBL: 17.4; 9.5.9; 1.3.2. Comments: comment on Ilina Singh, "Will the 'real boy' please behave: dosing dilemmas for parents of boys with ADHD," American Journal of Bioethics 2005 May-June; 5(3): 34-47.

Hensl, Kursten B. Restored to health to be put to death: reconciling the legal and ethical dilemmas of medicating to execute in Singleton v. Norris. *Villanova Law Review* 2004; 49(2): 291-328. NRCBL: 17.4; 17.8; 8.3.4; 1.3.5; 20.6. SC: le.

Hoffmaster, Barry. 'Real' ethics for 'real' boys: context and narrative in bioethics [comment]. *American Journal of Bioethics* 2005 May-June; 5(3): 50-51. NRCBL: 17.4; 9.5.7; 2.1. Comments: comment on Ilina Singh, "Will the 'real boy' please behave: dosing dilemmas for parents of boys with ADHD," American Journal of Bioethics 2005 May-June; 5(3): 34-47.

Horton, Richard. In defence of Roy Meadow [opinion]. *Lancet* 2005 July 2-8; 366(9479): 3-5. NRCBL: 17.4; 17.3; 1.3.5; 7.1; 5.2; 1.3.7; 9.5.7; 9.1. Identifiers: sudden infant death syndrome; Sally Clark.

Kramer, Peter D. Real impairments, real treatments [comment]. *American Journal of Bioethics* 2005 May-June; 5(3): 62-63. NRCBL: 17.4; 9.5.7. Comments: comment on Ilina Singh, "Will the 'real boy' please behave: dosing dilemmas for parents of boys with ADHD," American Journal of Bioethics 2005 May-June; 5(3): 34-47.

Krautkramer, Christian J. Beyond creativity: ADHD drug therapy as a moral damper on a child's future success [comment]. *American Journal of Bioethics* 2005 May-June; 5(3): 52-53. NRCBL: 17.4; 9.5.7; 4.4. Identifiers: attention-deficit hyperactivity disorder. Comments: comment on Ilina Singh, "Will the 'real boy' please behave: dosing dilemmas for parents of boys with ADHD," American Journal of Bioethics 2005 May-June; 5(3): 34-47.

Lacasse, Jeffrey R. Consumer advertising of psychiatric medications biases the public against nonpharmacological treatment [editorial]. *Ethical Human Psychology and Psychiatry* 2005 Fall-Winter; 7(3): 175-179. NRCBL: 17.4; 1.3.2; 9.3.1; 17.2; 1.3.5.

Lilja, John; Larsson, Sam; Hamilton, David; Bauer, Mia. Ethical values in the treatment of depression and anxiety. *In:* Salek, Sam; Edgar, Andrew, eds. Pharmaceutical Ethics. New York: Wiley; 2002: 137-160. NRCBL: 17.4.

Liokis, Michelle Garriga; Herbert, Paul B. Involuntary medications not allowed to restore competence to stand

trial. *Journal of the American Academy of Psychiatry and the Law* 2005; 33(4): 554-555. NRCBL: 17.4; 1.3.5. SC: le.

Litton, Paul. ADHD, values, and the self [comment]. *American Journal of Bioethics* 2005 May-June; 5(3): 65-67. NRCBL: 17.4; 9.5.7; 4.4. Identifiers: attention-deficit hyperactivity disorder. Comments: comment on Ilina Singh, "Will the 'real boy' please behave: dosing dilemmas for parents of boys with ADHD," American Journal of Bioethics 2005 May-June; 5(3): 34-47.

Noroian, Paul. Ethical issues in surreptitious prescribing [letter]. *Psychiatric Services* 2005 August; 56(8): 1023. NRCBL: 17.4.

Perring, Christian. Expanding the repertoire of bioethics: what next? [comment]. *American Journal of Bioethics* 2005 May-June; 5(3): 63-65. NRCBL: 17.4; 9.5.7; 2.1. Comments: comment on Ilina Singh, "Will the 'real boy' please behave: dosing dilemmas for parents of boys with ADHD," American Journal of Bioethics 2005 May-June; 5(3): 34-47.

Quinlan, Megan. Forcible medication and personal autonomy: the case of Charles Thomas Sell. *Boston University Law Review* 2004 February; 84(1): 275-299. NRCBL: 17.4; 8.3.4. SC: le.

Sabini, John; Monterosso, John. Judgments of the fairness of using performance enhancing drugs. *Ethics and Behavior* 2005; 15(1): 81-94. NRCBL: 17.4; 1.3.3; 1.3.1; 9.7; 7.1. SC: em.

Abstract: Undergraduates (total N=185) were asked about performance-affecting drugs. Some drugs supposedly affected athletic performance, others memory, and other attention. Some improved performance for anyone who took them, others for the top 10% of performers, others for the bottom 10%, and finally, yet other drugs worked only on the bottom 10% who also showed physical abnormalities. Participants were asked about the fairness of allowing the drug to be used, about banning it, and about whether predictions of future performance based on testing with or without the drug were better. The study found that participants appreciated the "interaction effect," that they felt it was less unfair to allow the drug if it affected the bottom 10% than if it affected everyone, and they were more eager to have the drug banned if it affected everyone. Participants were least tolerant of drugs that affected athletic performance and most tolerant of those that affected attention.

Siegel, David M.; Grudzinskas, Albert J.; Pinals, Debra A. Old law meets new medicine: revisiting involuntary psychotropic medication of the criminal defendant. *Wisconsin Law Review* 2001; 2: 307-380. NRCBL: 17.4; 8.3.4; 1.3.5. SC: le.

Singh, Ilina. Will the "real boy" please behave: dosing dilemmas for parents of boys with ADHD. *American Journal of Bioethics* 2005 May-June; 5(3): 34-47. NRCBL: 17.4; 4.2; 9.5.7; 8.1. SC: em. Identifiers: attention-deficit hyperactivity disorder.

Abstract: The use of Ritalin and other stimulant drug treatments for attention-deficit hyperactivity disorder (ADHD) raises distinctive moral dilemmas for parents; these moral dilemmas have not been adequately addressed in the bioethics literature. This paper draws upon data from a qualitative empirical study to investigate parents' use of the moral ideal of authenticity as part of their narrative justifications for dosing decisions and actions. I show that therapeutic decisions and actions are embedded in valued cultural ideals about masculinity, self-actualization and success, as well as in moral conceptions of authenticity and personal freedom. I argue that this investigation of parents' moral justifications and dosing dilemmas raises questions about the validity of authenticity as a transcendent moral principle. Moreover, this study demonstrates that in order to be relevant, bioethical analysis of neurocognitive enhancement must engage with ground-up studies of moral principles and decision-making in context.

Taylor, Eric. To the editor [letter]. *American Journal of Bioethics [Online]* 2005 May-June; 5(3): W17. NRCBL: 17.4; 9.5.7; 9.7. Comments: comment on Ilina Singh, "Will the 'real boy' please behave: dosing dilemmas for parents of boys with ADHD," American Journal of Bioethics [Online] 2005 May-June; 5(3): 34-47.

White, Gladys B. Splitting the self: the not-so-subtle consequences of medicating boys for ADHD [comment]. *American Journal of Bioethics* 2005 May-June; 5(3): 57-59. NRCBL: 17.4; 4.4; 9.5.7. Identifiers: attention-deficit hyperactivity disorder. Comments: comment on Ilina Singh, "Will the 'real boy' please behave: dosing dilemmas for parents of boys with ADHD," American Journal of Bioethics 2005 May-June; 5(3): 34-47.

Wong, J.G.W.S.; Poon, Y.; Hui, E.C. "I can put the medicine in his soup, doctor!" [case study]. *Journal of Medical Ethics* 2005 May; 31(5): 262-265. NRCBL: 17.4; 8.3.4; 8.2. SC: an; cs.
  Abstract: The practice of covertly administering medication is controversial. Although condemned by some as overly paternalistic, others have suggested that it may be acceptable if patients have permanent mental incapacity and refuse needed treatment. Ethical, legal, and clinical considerations become more complex when the mental incapacity is temporary and when the medication actually serves to restore autonomy. We discuss these issues in the context of a young man with schizophrenia. His mother had been giving him antipsychotic medication covertly in his soup. Should the doctor continue to provide a prescription, thus allowing this to continue? We discuss this case based on the "four principles" ethical framework, addressing the conflict between autonomy and beneficence/non-maleficence, the role of antipsychotics as an autonomy restoring agent, truth telling and the balance between individual versus family autonomy.

PSYCHOTHERAPY

See also CARE FOR SPECIFIC GROUPS/ MENTALLY DISABLED; INVOLUNTARY COMMITMENT; MENTAL HEALTH THERAPIES

Adler, Robert. To tell or not to tell: the psychiatrist and child abuse. *Australian and New Zealand Journal of Psychiatry* 1995 June; 29(2): 190-197. NRCBL: 17.2; 8.1; 9.5.7; 8.2.

Austin, Wendy; Rankel, Marlene; Kagan, Leon; Bergum, Vangie; Lemermeyer, Gillian. To stay or to go, to speak or stay silent, to act or not to act: moral distress as experienced by psychologists. *Ethics and Behavior* 2005; 15(3): 197-212. NRCBL: 17.2; 7.3; 6.
  Abstract: The moral distress of psychologists working in psychiatric and mental health care settings was explored in an interdisciplinary, hermeneutic phenomenological study situated at the University of Alberta, Canada. Moral distress is the state experienced when moral choices and actions are thwarted by constraints. Psychologists described specific incidents in which they felt their integrity had been compromised by such factors as institutional and interinstitutional demands, team conflicts, and interdisciplinary disputes. They described dealing with the resulting moral distress by such means as silence, taking a stance, acting secretively, sustaining themselves through work with clients, seeking support from colleagues, and exiting. Recognizing moral distress can lead to a significant shift in the way we perceive moral choices and understand the moral context of practice.

Blass, Rachel B. On the question of the patient's right to tell and the ethical reality of psychoanalysis. *Journal of the American Psychoanalytic Association* 2003 Fall; 51(4): 1283-1304. NRCBL: 17.2; 8.1; 8.2.

Bloche, M. Gregg. Law, theory, and politics: the dilemma of Soviet psychiatry. *Yale Journal of International Law* 1986 Spring; 11(2): 297-361. NRCBL: 17.2; 1.3.5; 17.4; 17.7; 21.1. SC: le. Identifiers: Soviet Union.

Chiang, H.-H.; Lu, Z.-Y,; Wear, S.E. To have or to be: ways of caregiving identified during recovery from the earthquake disaster in Taiwan. *Journal of Medical Ethics* 2005 March; 31(3): 154-158. NRCBL: 17.2; 8.1. SC: em.
  Abstract: The aim of this article is to report the results of therapy sessions conducted with survivors of an earthquake that struck Luku Township in Nantou County, central Taiwan, in September 1999. The sessions explored survivors' feelings, interactions, and interpretations of the crisis, as well as their roles in post- earthquake relief efforts. The participants were teachers and administrators from four primary schools. The results indicated three distinct forms of caring, namely: encumbered caring, connected caring, and reflected caring. The findings were used to construct a framework for caregiver self-monitoring. They also suggest that therapy groups provide an inner space that self- regulates the frustrations arising from this type of experience, for both caregivers and survivors. The intrasubjective and intersubjective dialogues within the groups are essentially reflective practices for improving services and generating new knowledge about medical ethics.

Croarkin, Paul; Berg, Jennifer; Spira, James. Informed consent for psychotherapy: a look at therapists' understanding, opinions, and practices. *American Journal of Psychotherapy* 2003; 57(3): 384-400. NRCBL: 17.2; 8.3.1. SC: em.

Fay, Allen. Ethical implications of charging for missed sessions. *Psychological Reports* 1995 December; 77(3, Part 2): 1251-1259. NRCBL: 17.2; 9.3.1; 8.1.

Fennig, Silvana; Secker, Aya; Levkovitz, Yechiel; Barak, Vered; Benyakar, Motty; Farina, Jorje; Roe, David; Treves, Ilan; Fennig, Shmuel. Are psychothera-

NRCBL: National Reference Center for Bioethics Literature Classification Scheme   See inside front cover for terms.

397

pists consistent in their ethical attitude to patient confidentiality? *Israel Journal of Psychiatry and Related Sciences* 2004; 41(2): 82-89. NRCBL: 17.2; 8.4. SC: em. Identifiers: Argentina; Israel.

Fischman, Yael. Metaclinical issues in the treatment of psychopolitical trauma. *American Journal of Orthopsychiatry* 1998 January; 68(1): 27-38. NRCBL: 17.2; 9.5.1; 21.1; 21.7; 21.4.

Lindley, Richard. Psychotherapy as essential care. *In:* Fairbairn, Susan; Fairbairn, Gavin, eds. Psychology, Ethics and Change. New York: Routledge & Kegan Paul; 1987: 212- 230. NRCBL: 17.2; 9.4; 1.1.

Llewelyn, Sue. Ethical issues in psychology for women. *In:* Fairbairn, Susan; Fairbairn, Gavin, eds. Psychology, Ethics and Change. New York: Routledge & Kegan Paul; 1987: 115- 135. NRCBL: 17.2; 9.5.5; 10.

Miller, William R. The ethics of motivational interviewing revisited. *Behavioural and Cognitive Psychotherapy* 1995; 23: 345-348. NRCBL: 17.2; 17.1; 9.5.9.

Miller, William R. Motivational interviewing: III. On the ethics of motivational intervention. *Behavioral and Cognitive Psychotherapy* 1994; 22: 111-123. NRCBL: 17.2; 17.1; 9.5.9. SC: em.

Minnes, Patricia M. Ethical issues in supervision. *Canadian Psychology/Psychologie Canadienne* 1987 August; 28(3): 285-290. NRCBL: 17.2.

Pomerantz, A.M.; Pettibone, J.C. The influence of client characteristics on psychologists' ethical beliefs: an empirical investigation. *Journal of Clinical Psychology* 2005 April; 61(4): 517-528. NRCBL: 17.2; 8.1. SC: em.

Popov, Hristo. Psychotherapy ethics with violence victims. *Medicine and Law: World Association for Medical Law* 2005 March; 24(1): 81-93. NRCBL: 17.2; 9.5.5; 9.1.
Abstract: There are many special issues that therapists will face while providing psychotherapy services for victims of violence. The primary goal of such intervention must be to reempower the victim so that she perceives herself as the survivor she must become. To do this, she has to deal with the trauma, integrate it into her past, and then, get on with her life. Various problems could occur during custody evaluations, forensic consultations and media exposure. Monitoring confidentiality issues when working with this kind of victim may be crucial to prevent placing them in any further danger. Given the special vulnerability of violence victims, it is essential for the therapist to act in an ethical manner at all times.

Shuman, Daniel W.; Greenberg, Stuart; Heilbrun, Kirk; Foote, William E. Special perspective: an immodest proposal: should treating mental health professionals be barred from testifying about their patients? *Behavioral Sciences and the Law* 1998 Autumn; 16(4): 509-523. NRCBL: 17.2; 8.1.

Simon, Laurence. Psychotherapy as civics: the patient and therapist as citizens. *Ethical Human Psychology and Psychiatry* 2005 Spring; 7(1): 57- 64. NRCBL: 17.2; 4.3; 1.3.5.

Somer, Eli; Nachmani, Irit. Constructions of therapist-client sex: a comparative analysis of retrospective victim reports. *Sexual Abuse* 2005 January; 17(1): 47-62. NRCBL: 17.2; 8.1; 10. SC: em. Identifiers: Israel.

Steinberg, Karen L.; Levine, Murray; Doueck, Howard J. Effects of legally mandated child-abuse reports on the therapeutic relationship: a survey of psychotherapists. *American Journal of Orthopsychiatry* 1997 January; 67(1): 112-122. NRCBL: 17.2; 8.1; 8.4; 1.3.5; 9.5.7; 9.1. SC: em.

Strasburger, Larry H.; Jorgenson, Linda; Sutherland, Pamela. The prevention of psychotherapist sexual misconduct: avoiding the slippery slope. *American Journal of Psychotherapy* 1992 October; 46(4): 544-555. NRCBL: 17.2; 7.4; 10; 1.1.

Tylim, Isaac. Ethical notes on disrupted frames and violated boundaries. *Psychoanalytic Psychology* 2004 Fall; 21(4): 609-613. NRCBL: 17.2; 1.1.

Zanotti, Barbara J.; Becker, Rick A. Marching to the beat of a different drummer: is military law and mental health out-of-step after Jaffee v. Redmond? *Air Force Law Review* 1997; 41: 1-82. NRCBL: 17.2; 18.5.8; 8.4. SC: le. Note: 116 S.Ct. 1923 (1996).

PUBLIC HEALTH
See also AIDS; HEALTH CARE

Coker, Richard. Civil liberties and public good: detention of tuberculous patients and the Public Health Act 1984. *Medical History* 2001 July; 45(3): 341-358. NRCBL: 9.1. SC: le.

Colgrove, James; Bayer, Ronald. Manifold restraints: liberty, public health, and the legacy of Jacobson v Massachusetts. *American Journal of Public Health* 2005 April; 95(4): 571-576. NRCBL: 9.1; 1.3.5; 9.5.1; 9.7. SC: le.
Abstract: February 2005 marks the centenary of one of the most important pieces of public health jurisprudence, the US Supreme Court case of Jacobson v Massachusetts, which upheld the authority of states to pass compulsory vaccination laws. The Court's decision articulated the view that the freedom of the individual must sometimes be subordinated to the common welfare. We examined the relationship between the individual and society in 20th-century public health practice and law and the ways that compulsory measures have been used to constrain personal liberty for the sake of protecting the public health.

Cottam, Rachel. Is public health coercive health? [opinion]. *Lancet* 2005 November 5-11; 366(9497): 1592-1594. NRCBL: 9.1; 4.2; 1.3.5; 1.3.2; 7.1; 1.1. SC: le. Identifiers: Children's Food Bill; nanny state.

da Lomba, Sylvie; Martin, Robyn. Public health powers in relation to infectious tuberculosis in England and

France: a comparison of approaches. *Medical Law International* 2004; 6(2): 117-147. NRCBL: 9.1; 21.7. SC: le.

Denier, Yvonne. Public health, well-being and reciprocity. *Ethical Perspectives* 2005 March; 12(1): 41-66. NRCBL: 9.1; 4.2; 1.1.

Gostin, Lawrence O. Law and the public's health. *Issues in Science and Technology* 2005 Spring; 21(3): 71-77. NRCBL: 9.1. SC: le.

Gostin, Lawrence O. Pandemic influenza: public health preparedness for the next global health emergency. *Journal of Law, Medicine and Ethics* 2004 Winter; 32(4): 565-573. NRCBL: 9.1; 21.1. SC: le.

Gostin, Lawrence O.; Hodge, James G.,Jr. Public health emergencies and legal reform: implications for public health policy and practice. *Public Health Reports* 2003 September-October; 118(3): 477-479. NRCBL: 9.1; 21.1; 1.3.5. SC: le. Identifiers: Model State Emergency Health Powers Act.

Grill, K.; Hansson, S.O. Epistemic paternalism in public health. *Journal of Medical Ethics* 2005 November; 31(11): 648-653. NRCBL: 9.1; 1.1.

Abstract: Receiving information about threats to one's health can contribute to anxiety and depression. In contemporary medical ethics there is considerable consensus that patient autonomy, or the patient's right to know, in most cases outweighs these negative effects of information. Worry about the detrimental effects of information has, however, been voiced in relation to public health more generally. In particular, information about uncertain threats to public health, from-for example, chemicals-are said to entail social costs that have not been given due consideration. This criticism implies a consequentialist argument for withholding such information from the public in their own best interest. In evaluating the argument for this kind of epistemic paternalism, the consequences of making information available must be compared to the consequences of withholding it. Consequences that should be considered include epistemic effects, psychological effects, effects on private decisions, and effects on political decisions. After giving due consideration to the possible uses of uncertain information and rebutting the claims that uncertainties imply small risks and that they are especially prone to entail misunderstandings and anxiety, it is concluded that there is a strong case against withholding of information about uncertain threats to public health.

Horner, J. Stuart. Ethics and public health. *In:* Chadwick, Ruth; Levitt, Mairi, eds. Ethical Issues in Community Health Care. New York: Arnold; 1998: 34-50. NRCBL: 9.1.

Kersh, Rogan; Morone, James A. Obesity, courts, and the new politics of public health. *Journal of Health Politics, Policy and Law* 2005 October; 30(5): 839-868. NRCBL: 9.1; 9.5.1. SC: le.

Abstract: Health care politics are changing. They increasingly focus not on avowedly public projects (such as building the health care infrastructure) but on regulating private behavior. Examples include tobacco, obesity, abortion, drug abuse, the right to die, and even a patient's relationship with his or her managed care organization. Regulating private behavior intro-

duces a distinctive policy process; it alters the way we introduce (or frame) political issues and shifts many important decisions from the legislatures to the courts. In this article, we illustrate the politics of private regulation by following a dramatic case, obesity, through the political process. We describe how obesity evolved from a private matter to a political issue. We then assess how different political institutions have responded and conclude that courts will continue to take the leading role.

Kutty, V. Raman. Ethics in public health practice. *Issues in Medical Ethics* 2000 October-December; 8(4): 111-112. NRCBL: 9.1; 13.3; 9.5.6.

Leeder, Stephen R. Ethics and public health. *Internal Medicine Journal* 2004 July; 34(7): 435-439. NRCBL: 9.1; 7.2.

Lo, Bernard; Katz, Mitchell H. Clinical decision making during public health emergencies: ethical considerations. *Annals of Internal Medicine* 2005 October 4; 143(7): 493-498. NRCBL: 9.1; 9.5.1.

Abstract: Recent public health emergencies involving anthrax, the severe acute respiratory syndrome (SARS), and shortages of influenza vaccine have dramatized the need for restrictive public health measures such as quarantine, isolation, and rationing. Front-line physicians will face ethical dilemmas during public health emergencies when patients disagree with these measures. Patients might request interventions that are not recommended or for which they are not eligible, or they might object to intrusive or restrictive measures. The physician's primary responsibility in such emergencies is to the public rather than to the individual patient. In public health emergencies, physicians need to address the patient's needs and concerns, recognize their changed roles, and work closely with public health officials. Physicians can still work on behalf of patients by advocating for changes in policies and exceptions when warranted and by mitigating the adverse consequences of public health measures. Before an emergency occurs, physicians should think through how they will respond to foreseeable dilemmas arising when patients disagree with public health recommendations.

Loff, Bebe; Black, Jim. Principles for public health action on infectious diseases. *Issues in Medical Ethics* 2003 October-December; 11(4): 113-115. NRCBL: 9.1; 8.1.

Mariner, Wendy K.; Annas, George J.; Glantz, Leonard H. Jacobson v Massachusetts: it's not your great-great- grandfather's public health law. *American Journal of Public Health* 2005 April; 95(4): 581-590. NRCBL: 9.1; 1.3.5; 8.3.4; 1.3.1. SC: le.

Abstract: Jacobson v Massachusetts, a 1905 US Supreme Court decision, raised questions about the power of state government to protect the public's health and the Constitution's protection of personal liberty. We examined conceptions about state power and personal liberty in Jacobson and later cases that expanded, superseded, or even ignored those ideas. Public health and constitutional law have evolved to better protect both health and human rights. States' sovereign power to make laws of all kinds has not changed in the past century. What has changed is the Court's recognition of the importance of individual liberty and how it limits that power. Preserving the public's health in the 21st century requires preserving respect for personal liberty.

Misrahi, James J.; Matthews, Gene W.; Hoffman, Richard E. Legal authorities for interventions during pub-

NRCBL: National Reference Center for Bioethics Literature Classification Scheme   See inside front cover for terms.

399

lic health emergencies. *In:* Goodman, Richard A.; Rothstein, Mark A.; Hoffman, Richard E.; Lopez, Wilfredo; Matthews, Gene W., eds. Law in Public Health Practice. New York: Oxford University Press; 2003: 195-210. NRCBL: 9.1; 21.3. SC: le.

Nagral, Sanjay. SARS: infectious diseases, public health and medical ethics [editorial]. *Issues in Medical Ethics* 2003 July-September; 11(3): 70-71. NRCBL: 9.1. Identifiers: severe acute respiratory syndrome.

Nieburg, Phillip; Bernheim, Ruth Gaare; Bonnie, Richard J. Ethics and the practice of public health. *In:* Goodman, Richard A.; Rothstein, Mark A.; Hoffman, Richard E.; Lopez, Wilfredo; Matthews, Gene W., eds. Law in Public Health Practice. New York: Oxford University Press; 2003: 43-62. NRCBL: 9.1.

Parmet, Wendy E.; Goodman, Richard A.; Farber, Amy. Individual rights versus the public's health — 100 years after Jacobson v. Massachusetts [opinion]. *New England Journal of Medicine* 2005 February 17; 352(7): 652-654. NRCBL: 9.1; 9.5.1; 9.7; 8.3.4.

Patel, Kant; Rushefsky, Mark E. The politics of genetics and public health. *In their:* The Politics of Public Health in the United States. Armonk, NY: M.E. Sharpe; 2005: 176-209. NRCBL: 15.1; 9.1; 21.1.

Porter, John D.H.; Ogden, Jessica A. Public health, ethics, and tuberculosis: is DOTs a breakthrough or inappropriate strategy in the Indian context? *Issues in Medical Ethics* 1999 July-September; 7(3): 79-84. NRCBL: 9.1; 9.5.1; 1.1. Identifiers: directly observed therapy short course.

Rane, Wishwas; Deodhar, N.S. The ethics of public health: how can equity, social justice and human rights be incorporated into public health programmes? *Issues in Medical Ethics* 1998 October-December; 6(4): 119-120. NRCBL: 9.1.

Richards, Edward P.; Burris, Scott; McNelis, Richard P.; Hargan, Eric. Quarantine laws and public health realities. *Journal of Law, Medicine and Ethics* 2005 Winter; 33(4, Supplement): 69-72. NRCBL: 9.1; 1.3.8. SC: le.

Rogers, W.A. Ethical issues in public health: a qualitative study of public health practice in Scotland. *Journal of Epidemiology and Community Health* 2004; 58: 446-450. NRCBL: 9.1; 7.1. SC: em.

Rosenau, Pauline Vaillancourt; Roemer, Ruth. Ethical issues in public health and health services. *In:* Andersen, Ronald M.; Rice, Thomas H.; Kominski, Gerald F., eds. Changing the U.S. Health Care System: Key Issues in Health Services, Policy, and Management. 2nd ed. San Francisco: Jossey-Bass; 2001: 503-535. NRCBL: 9.1.

Stadtländer, Christian T.K.-H.; Dickens, Bernard. Challenges and opportunities for ethics in public health

[letter and reply]. *American Journal of Public Health* 2005 December; 95(12): 2122. NRCBL: 9.1.

VanderPlaat, Madine; Teles, Nair. Mainstreaming social justice: human rights and public health. *Canadian Journal of Public Health / Revue Canadienne de Sante Publique* 2005 January-February; 96(1): 34-36. NRCBL: 9.1; 1.1; 21.1.

Wikler, Daniel; Cash, Richard. Ethical issues in global public health. *In:* Beaglehole, Robert, ed. Global Public Health: A New Era. New York: Oxford University Press; 2003: 226-242. NRCBL: 9.1; 21.1.

Wynia, Matthew K. Oversimplifications I: physicians don't do public health. *American Journal of Bioethics* 2005 July-August; 5(4): 4-5. NRCBL: 9.1; 7.1; 2.1.

Wynia, Matthew K. Oversimplifications II: public health ethics ignores individual rights. *American Journal of Bioethics* 2005 September-October; 5(5): 6-8. NRCBL: 9.1; 1.3.1; 1.1; 9.5.6.

Wynia, Matthew K. Public health principlism: the precautionary principle and beyond. *American Journal of Bioethics* 2005 May-June; 5(3): 3-4. NRCBL: 9.1; 2.1.

Yamin, Alicia Ely. Promising but elusive engagements: combining human rights and public health to promote women's well-being. *Health and Human Rights: An International Journal* 2004; 8(1): 63-92. NRCBL: 9.1; 21.1; 1.1; 7.1; 14.1; 9.5.5. Conference: International Conference on Population and Development; Cairo; 1994.

PUBLISHING *See* JOURNALISM AND PUBLISHING

QUALITY AND VALUE OF LIFE

Alonso, Carlos. An ontological view of the human embryo. A paradigm. *European Journal of Endocrinology* 2004 November; 151 (Supplement 3): U17-U24. NRCBL: 4.4; 18.5.4; 15.1. SC: an.

Amundson, Ron. Disability, ideology, and quality of life. *In:* Wasserman, David; Bickenbach, Jerome; Wachbroit, Robert, eds. Quality of Life and Human Difference: Genetic Testing, Health Care, and Disability. New York: Cambridge University Press; 2005: 101-124. NRCBL: 4.4; 1.1; 4.2.

Anand, Sudhir; Hanson, Kara. Disability-adjusted life years: a critical review. *In:* Anand, Sudhir; Peter, Fabienne; Sen, Amartya, eds. Public Health, Ethics, and Equity. New York: Oxford University Press; 2004: 183-199. NRCBL: 4.4; 9.1.

Atkins, Chloë G.K. The failure of formal rights and equality in the clinic: a critique of bioethics. *Ethics and Medicine* 2005 Fall; 21(3): 139-162. NRCBL: 4.4; 7.1; 1.1; 8.1; 2.2; 20.5.1. SC: an.

Austriaco, Nicanor Pier Giorgio. Are teratomas embryos or non-embryos? *National Catholic Bioethics Quarterly* 2005 Winter; 5(4): 697- 706. NRCBL: 4.4; 15.4; 14.4.

Awaya, Tsuyoshi. Common ethical issues in regenerative medicine. *Journal International de Bioethique / International Journal of Bioethics* 2005 March-June; 16(1-2): 69-75, 192-193. NRCBL: 4.4; 19.1; 4.5; 18.5.4. Note: Abstract in English and French.

Baker, Lynne Rudder. When does a person begin? *Social Philosophy and Policy* 2005 Summer; 22(2): 25-48. NRCBL: 4.4; 22.1; 12.3. SC: an.

Ball, Carlos A. Autonomy, justice, and disability. *UCLA Law Review* 2000 February; 47(3): 599-651. NRCBL: 4.4; 1.1.

Banja, John. When it's hard to please everybody: etiquette serving ethics when you disagree with a colleague. Opinion #1: negotiating uncertainty: "Let's talk . . .". *Pain Medicine* 2001 March; 2(1): 83-85. NRCBL: 4.4; 7.3; 7.1; 1.1.

Barilan, Y. Michael. The story of the body and the story of the person: towards an ethics of representing human bodies and body-parts. *Medicine, Health Care and Philosophy: A European Journal* 2005; 8(2): 193-205. NRCBL: 4.4. SC: an.

Abstract: Western culture has a few traditions of representing the human body - among them mortuary art (gisants), the freak show, the culture of the relics, renaissance art and pre-modern and modern anatomy. A historical analysis in the spirit of Norbert Elias is offered with regard to body - person relationship in anatomy. Modern anatomy is characterized by separating the story of the person from the story of the body, a strategy that is incompatible with the bio-psycho-social paradigm of clinical medicine. The paper discusses different aspects of the above traditions and how they might bear on this conflict and on contemporary bioethics and bedside practice.

Bayertz, Kurt. Die Wahrheit über den moralischen Status menschlicher Embryonen. *In:* Maio, Giovanni; Just, Hanjörg, eds. Die Forschung an embryonalen Stammzellen in ethischer und rechtlicher Perspektive. Baden-Baden: Nomos Verlagsgesellschaft; 2003: 178-195. NRCBL: 4.4; 1.1.

Bayne, Tim; Levy, Neil. Amputees by choice: Body Integrity Identity Disorder and the ethics of amputation. *Journal of Applied Philosophy* 2005; 22(1): 75-86. NRCBL: 4.4; 4.3; 9.5.1; 8.1. SC: an.

Abstract: Should surgeons be permitted to amputate healthy limbs if patients request such operations? We argue that if such patients are experiencing significant distress as a consequence of the rare psychological disorder named Body Integrity Identity Disorder (BIID), such operations might be permissible. We examine rival accounts of the origins of the desire for healthy limb amputations and argue that none are as plausible as the BIID hypothesis. We then turn to the moral arguments against such operations, and argue that on the evidence available, none is compelling. BIID sufferers meet reasonable standards for rationality and autonomy: so as long as no other effective treatment for their disorder is available, surgeons ought to be allowed to accede to their requests.

Beckwith, F.J. Of souls, selves, and cerebrums: a reply to Himma. *Journal of Medical Ethics* 2005 January; 31(1): 56-60. NRCBL: 4.4; 12.3; 20.5.2; 1.1. SC: an.

Abstract: Ken Himma argues that a human being becomes a moral person at the commencement of brain activity. In response to Himma, the author offers (1) brief comments on Himma's project, (2) an alternative account of the human person that maintains that a human being is a human person by nature as long as it exists, and (3) a counterexample to Himma's position that shows it cannot account for the wrongness of the purposeful creation of anencephalic-like children. The author concludes with replies to two challenges to his position.

Belshaw, Chris. Death, brains, and persons. *In:* Fisher, Robert N.; Primozic, Daniel T.; Day, Peter A.; Thompson, Joel A., eds. Suffering, Death, and Identity. New York: Rodopi; 2002: 141-154. NRCBL: 4.4; 20.2.1; 1.1. SC: an.

Benaroyo, Lazare. Suffering, time, narrative, and the self. *In:* Thomasma, David C.; Weisstub, David N.; Herve, Christian eds. Personhood and Health Care. Boston: Kluwer Academic Pub.; 2001: 373-381. NRCBL: 4.4; 1.1; 8.1.

Bernstein, Mark. Neo-speciesism. *Journal of Social Philosophy* 2004 Fall; 35(3): 380-390. NRCBL: 4.4; 22.1; 1.1.

Bonzo, Matthew. The category of "personhood" and access to health care. *In:* Fisher, Robert N.; Primozic, Daniel T.; Day, Peter A.; Thompson, Joel A., eds. Suffering, Death, and Identity. New York: Rodopi; 2002: 119-126. NRCBL: 4.4; 9.4; 9.2; 20.2.1. SC: an.

Bormann, Franz-Josef. Der Status des Embryos aus der Sicht der katholischen Moraltheologie. *In:* Maio, Giovanni; Just, Hanjörg, eds. Die Forschung an embryonalen Stammzellen in ethischer und rechtlicher Perspektive. Baden-Baden: Nomos Verlagsgesellschaft; 2003: 214-228. NRCBL: 4.4; 1.1; 1.2.

Bosek, Marcia Sue DeWolf. The ethics of pain management. *Medsurg Nursing* 1993 June; 2(3): 218-220. NRCBL: 4.4; 9.2; 8.1. SC: cs.

Bosek, Marcia Sue DeWolf; Cochran, Lynn L. Ethics in practice: moral distress at 3 am. *JONA's Healthcare Law, Ethics, and Regulation* 2005 January- March; 7(1): 4-9. NRCBL: 4.4; 9.2; 9.6; 7.3. SC: cs.

Brahams, Diana. Body parts as property [editorial]. *Medico-Legal Journal* 1998; 66(Part 2): 45-47. NRCBL: 4.4; 18.3. SC: le.

Breck, John. Procreation and "the beginning of life". *St. Vladimir's Theological Quarterly* 1995; 39(3): 215-232. NRCBL: 4.4; 1.2. SC: an.

Byrnes, W. Malcolm; Elliott, Kevin C. Holistic systems and "delayed hominization" are incompatible [article and commentary]. *National Catholic Bioethics Quarterly* 2005 Autumn; 5(3): 447- 450. NRCBL: 4.4; 1.2.

NRCBL: National Reference Center for Bioethics Literature Classification Scheme   See inside front cover for terms.

401

Calabresi, Guido. An introduction to legal thought: four approaches to law and to the allocation of body parts. *Stanford Law Review* 2003 June; 55(6): 2113-2151. NRCBL: 4.4; 19.5; 1.1. SC: le.

Calhoun, Samuel W. An alarming pre-Roe view of personhood: the 1972 Byrn decision. [Byrn v. New York City Health and Hospitals Corp.]. *In:* Koterski, Joseph W., ed. Life and Learning XI: Proceedings of the Eleventh University Faculty for Life Conference. Washington, DC: University Faculty for Life; 2002: 98-110. NRCBL: 4.4; 1.2; 12.4. SC: le.

Calhoun, Samuel W. Valuing intrauterine life. *Regent University Law Review* 1997 Spring; 8: 69-81. NRCBL: 4.4; 12.4.2. SC: le. Comments: comment on Julia E. Hanigsberg, "Homologizing pregnancy and motherhood: a consideration of abortion," Michigan Law Review 1995; 94: 371.

Cameron, C.; Williamson, R. In the world of Dolly, when does a human embryo acquire respect? *Journal of Medical Ethics* 2005 April; 31(4): 215-220. NRCBL: 4.4; 14.5; 18.5.4. SC: an.

Abstract: For most of the 20th century, it was possible to regard fertilisation as the identifiable point when life begins, because this moment could be defined unequivocally and was thought to be the single most essential biological step in the establishment of a new human entity. Since the successful reproductive cloning of Dolly and other mammals, it is clear that any human cell has the potential to supply the full genome of an embryo, and hence a person, without going through fertilisation. At what point in time do such embryos acquire the respect accorded to human beings? The authors argue that the time of implantation is the most useful point at which the potential and the intention to create a new person are translated into reality, because from that point a new life develops. Implantation differentiates a somatic cell in culture (which is not due respect) from a human entity that has acquired its own identity and developmental potential. The authors examine the value of quickening or viability as alternative developmental stages in the process of acquiring respect for the Dolly embryo.

Cohen, Cynthia B. The moral status of early embryos and new genetic interventions. *In:* Smith, David H.; Cohen, Cynthia B., eds. A Christian Response to the New Genetics: Religious, Ethical, and Social Issues. Lanham, MD: Rowman & Littlefield Publishers; 2003: 105-130. NRCBL: 4.4; 1.2; 15.1.

Colombo, Roberto. The status and rights of the human embryo and fetus: a Catholic perspective on the unborn child. *In:* Blazer, Shraga; Zimmer, Etan Z., eds. The Embryo: Scientific Discovery and Medical Ethics. New York: Karger; 2005: 40-52. NRCBL: 4.4; 18.5.4; 1.2.

Condic, Maureen L.; Condic, Samuel B. Defining organisms by organization. *National Catholic Bioethics Quarterly* 2005 Summer; 5(2): 331- 353. NRCBL: 4.4; 18.5.4.

Cordner, Christopher. Life and death matters: losing a sense of the value of human beings. *Theoretical Medicine and Bioethics* 2005; 26(3): 207-226. NRCBL: 4.4; 20.5.2; 20.5.1; 1.1. SC: an. Identifiers: Peter Singer.

Abstract: The essay combines a specific and a more general theme. In attacking 'the doctrine of the sanctity of human life' Singer takes himself thereby to be opposing the conviction that human life has special value. I argue that this conviction goes deep in our lives in many ways that do not depend on what Singer identifies as central to that 'doctrine', and that his attack therefore misses its main target. I argue more generally that Singer's own moral philosophy affords only an impoverished and distorted sense of the value of human life and human beings. In purporting to dig below the supposedly illusion-ridden surface of our thinking about value, Singer in fact often leads us away from the robust terrain of our lived experience into rhetorical, and sometimes brutal, fantasy.

Cox, Neville. Causation, responsibility and foetal personhood. *Northern Ireland Legal Quarterly* 2000 Winter; 51(4): 579-596. NRCBL: 4.4; 12.4.2. SC: le.

Cushing, Simon. Against "humanism": speciesism, personhood, and preference. *Journal of Social Philosophy* 2003 Winter; 34(4): 556-571. NRCBL: 4.4; 1.1; 22.1. SC: an.

Dekkers, Wim; Hoffer, Cor; Wils, Jean-Pierre. Bodily integrity and male and female circumcision. *Medicine, Health Care and Philosophy: A European Journal* 2005; 8(2): 179-191. NRCBL: 4.4; 9.5.1; 9.5.5; 9.5.7; 10; 1.1. SC: an.

Abstract: This paper explores the ambiguous notion of bodily integrity, focusing on male and female circumcision. In the empirical part of the study we describe and analyse the various meanings that are given to the notion of bodily integrity by people in their daily lives. In the philosophical part we distinguish (1) between a person-oriented and a body-oriented approach and (2) between four levels of interpretation, i.e. bodily integrity conceived of as a biological wholeness, an experiential wholeness, an intact wholeness, and as an inviolable wholeness. We argue that bodily integrity is a prima facie principle in its own right, closely connected with, but still fundamentally different from, the principle of personal autonomy, that is, autonomy over the body.

Dickenson, Donna. The new French resistance: commodification rejected? *Medical Law International* 2005; 7(1): 41-63. NRCBL: 4.4; 19.5; 9.3.1. SC: le.

DiSilvestro, Russell. Human embryos in the original position? *Journal of Medicine and Philosophy* 2005 June; 30(3): 285-304. NRCBL: 4.4; 1.1. SC: an. Identifiers: John Rawls.

Abstract: Two different discussions in John Rawls' A Theory of Justice lead naturally to a rather conservative position on the moral status of the human embryo. When discussing paternalism, he claims that the parties in the original position would seek to protect themselves in case they end up as incapacitated or undeveloped human beings when the veil of ignorance is lifted. Since human embryos are examples of such beings, the parties in the original position would seek to protect themselves from their embryonic stages onward. When discussing the basis of equality, Rawls claims that the parties in the original position would guarantee basic rights for all those with the capacity to take part in this original position. To guarantee the basic rights of infants and young children, he goes on to interpret this capacity as a "potentiality that is ordinarily realized in due course."

Since human embryos have this potentiality, they too should have basic rights.

Doucet, Hubert. The concept of person in bioethics: impasse and beyond. *In:* Thomasma, David C.; Weisstud, David N.; Herve, Christian eds. Personhood and Health Care. Boston: Kluwer Academic Pub.; 2001: 121-128. NRCBL: 4.4; 2.1.

Drgonec, Ján. The status of the foetus. *Medicine and Law: World Association for Medical Law* 1994; 13(3-4): 215-239. NRCBL: 4.4; 12.4.1; 18.5.4; 19.5. SC: le.

Dubois, Michel Y.;Lipman, Arthur; Gitlin, Melvin C.; FeBornstein, Marcos; Passik, Steve. The case(from Dr. Edwards, University of Washington) :of "blind dosing" and detoxification: justifiable or ill conceived? [forum]. *Pain Medicine* 2001 September; 2(3): 234-237. NRCBL: 4.4; 9.7; 7.1; 9.8.

Dute, Joseph. ECHR 2004/16 Case of Vo v. France, 8 July 2004, no. 53924/00 (Grand Chamber) [summary]. *European Journal of Health Law* 2004 December; 11(4): 432-437. NRCBL: 4.4; 12.4.2; 8.5. SC: le.

Eberl, Jason T. Aquinas's account of human embryogenesis and recent interpretations. *Journal of Medicine and Philosophy* 2005 August; 30(4): 379-394. NRCBL: 4.4; 1.1; 12.3; 14.1; 18.5.4.

Abstract: In addressing bioethical issues at the beginning of human life, such as abortion, in vitro fertilization, and embryonic stem cell research, one primary concern regards establishing when a developing human embryo or fetus can be considered a person. Thomas Aquinas argues that an embryo or fetus is not a human person until its body is informed by a rational soul. Aquinas's explicit account of human embryogenesis has been generally rejected by contemporary scholars due to its dependence upon medieval biological data, which has been far surpassed by current scientific research. A number of scholars, however, have attempted to combine Aquinas's basic metaphysical account of human nature with current embryological data to develop a contemporary Thomistic account of a human person's beginning. In this article, I discuss two recent interpretations in which it is argued that a human person does not begin to exist until a fetus has developed a functioning cerebral cortex.

Elliott, Kevin C. Developmental systems theory and human embryos: a response to Austriaco. *National Catholic Bioethics Quarterly* 2005 Summer; 5(2): 249- 259. NRCBL: 4.4; 1.2. SC: an.

Fairbairn, Gavin J. Brain transplants and the orthodox view of personhood. *In:* Fisher, Robert N.; Primozic, Daniel T.; Day, Peter A.; Thompson, Joel A., eds. Suffering, Death, and Identity. New York: Rodopi; 2002: 127-139. NRCBL: 4.4; 19.1; 1.1. SC: an.

Foley, Teresa. Dobson v. Dobson: tort liability for expectant mothers? *Saskatchewan Law Review* 1998; 61(1): 177-198. NRCBL: 4.4; 9.5.8; 1.1. SC: le.

Ford, Mary. The personhood paradox and the "right to die". *Medical Law Review* 2005 Spring; 13(1): 80-101. NRCBL: 4.4; 20.5.1; 1.1. SC: le.

Frank, Arthur W. Surgical body modification and altruistic individualism: a case for cyborg ethics and methods. *Qualitative Health Research* 2003 December; 13(10): 1407-1418. NRCBL: 4.4; 1.1; 5.1; 9.5.7; 10. Conference: Fourth Advances in Qualitative Methods Conference; Banff, Alberta, Canada; 2-5 May 2003.

Frey, Christopher. Person oder empirisch verstandenes Faktum? Zum Bild vom Menschen in seinen Anfängen. *In:* Baumann, Eva; Brink, Alexander; May, Arnd T.; Schröder, Peter; Schutzeichel, Corinna Iris, eds. Weltanschauliche Offenheit in der Bioethik. Berlin: Duncker & Humblot; 2004: 147-161. NRCBL: 4.4; 1.1; 1.2.

Gamble, Denise. Potentialism and the value of an embryo. *Public Affairs Quarterly* 2005 October; 19(4): 265-299. NRCBL: 4.4; 1.1.

Gazzaniga, Michael S. The thoughtful distinction between embryo and human. *Chronicle of Higher Education* 2005 April 8; 51(31): B10-B12. NRCBL: 4.4; 2.1; 14.1; 20.2.1; 18.5.4.

George, Robert P.; Gómez-Lobo, Alfonso. The moral status of the human embryo. *Perspectives in Biology and Medicine* 2005 Spring; 48(2): 201-210. NRCBL: 4.4; 2.4. SC: an.

Gómez-Lobo, Alfonso. On potentiality and respect for embryos: a reply to Mary Mahowald. *Theoretical Medicine and Bioethics* 2005; 26(2): 105-110. NRCBL: 4.4. SC: an.

Abstract: In order to understand the nature of human embryos I first distinguish between active and passive potentiality, and then argue that the former is found in human gametes and embryos (even in embryos in vitro that may fail to be implanted) because they all have an indwelling power or capacity to initiate certain changes. Implantation provides necessary conditions for the actualization of that prior, active potentiality. This does not imply that embryos are potential persons that do not deserve the same respect as actual persons. To claim that embryos "become persons" is to understand the predicate "person" as a phase sortal, roughly equivalent to "adult person." This entails that we would not be essentially persons. In order to explain the traditional understanding of "person" as a proper sortal rather than a phase sortal, the author distinguishes between proximate and remote potentiality, and shows that, unlike feline embryos, human embryos, by their genetic constitution, possess the remote potentiality to later exercise the typically human activities. It follows that they are already persons essentially.

Gordijn, Bert; Dekkers, Wim. Autonomy, integrity and the human body [editorial]. *Medicine, Health Care and Philosophy: A European Journal* 2005; 8(2): 145-146. NRCBL: 4.4.

Gordin, Vitaly. A lucrative routine, short on pain management. Outcome studies help ethics. *Pain Medicine* 2002 December; 3(4): 349-350. NRCBL: 4.4; 9.5.1; 9.8; 7.1.

NRCBL: National Reference Center for Bioethics Literature Classification Scheme   See inside front cover for terms.

403

Grabowski, John S. Contraception, sterilization, abortion and the ethical and religious directives. *In:* McMahon, Kevin T., ed. Moral Issues in Catholic Health Care. Wynnewood, PA: Saint Charles Borromeo Seminary; 2004: 68-92. NRCBL: 4.4; 11.1; 11.3; 12.3; 1.2.

Green, Ronald. Toward a full theory of moral status. *American Journal of Bioethics* 2005 November-December; 5(6): 44-46. NRCBL: 4.4; 18.5.4. Comments: comment on Lawrence J. Nelson and Michael J. Meyer, "Confronting deep moral disagreement: the President's Council on Bioethics, moral status, and human embryos," American Journal of Bioethics 2005 November-December; 5(6): 33-42.

Hamaty, Daniel. Pain medicine's role in the restoration and reformation of medical ethics. *Pain Medicine* 2000 December; 1(4): 362-365. NRCBL: 4.4; 9.7; 7.1; 9.8.

Hamaty, Daniel. When it's hard to please everybody: etiquette serving ethics when you disagree with a colleague. Opinion #2: return to the sources: AMA guidelines. *Pain Medicine* 2001 March; 2(1): 83, 85. NRCBL: 4.4; 7.3; 7.1; 1.1. Identifiers: American Medical Association.

Harris, John. Four legs good, personhood better! *Res Publica* 1998; 4(1): 51-58. NRCBL: 4.4. SC: le.

Harris, John. Nice and not so nice [editorial]. *Journal of Medical Ethics* 2005 December; 31(12): 685-688. NRCBL: 4.4; 9.1. Identifiers: United Kingdom (Great Britain); National Institute for Health and Clinical Excellence; quality adjusted life year (QALY).

Hartman, Rhonda Gay. Face value: challenges of transplant technology. *American Journal of Law and Medicine* 2005; 31(1): 7-46. NRCBL: 4.4; 19.5; 8.3.1; 5.3. SC: le.

Hershenov, David. Do dead bodies pose a problem for biological approaches to personal identity? *Mind* 2005 January; 114(453): 31-59. NRCBL: 4.4; 20.2.1; 1.1.

Hoehner, Paul J. "Altered nuclear transfer": probing the nature of being human. *National Catholic Bioethics Quarterly* 2005 Summer; 5(2): 261- 269. NRCBL: 4.4; 14.4; 18.5.4; 1.2; 1.1.

Hope, Donald. The hand as emblem of human identity: a solution to the abortion controversy based on science and reason. *University of Toledo Law Review* 2001 Winter; 32(2): 205-228. NRCBL: 4.4; 12.4.1; 12.3. SC: le.

Howard, Joseph. The moral status of the human embryo according to Peter Singer: individuality, humanity, and personhood. *Linacre Quarterly* 2005 August; 72(3): 212-228. NRCBL: 4.4; 18.5.4; 22.1; 1.2.

Ilkilic, Ilhan. Der moralische Status des Embryos im Islam und die wertplurale Gesellschaft. *In:* Baumann, Eva; Brink, Alexander; May, Arnd T.; Schröder, Peter; Schutzeichel, Corinna Iris, eds. Weltanschauliche

Offenheit in der Bioethik. Berlin: Duncker & Humblot; 2004: 163-176. NRCBL: 4.4; 1.2; 21.7.

Johnson, Sandra H. The social, professional, and legal framework for the problem of pain management in emergency medicine. *Journal of Law, Medicine and Ethics* 2005 Winter; 33(4): 741- 760. NRCBL: 4.4; 20.4.1; 8.3.1; 9.5.6. SC: le.

Kamm, F.M. Moral status and personal identity: clones, embryos, and future generations. *Social Philosophy and Policy* 2005 Summer; 22(2): 283-307. NRCBL: 4.4; 14.5; 15.1. SC: an.

Kavanaugh, John F. Brainism: 'we are not our brains; we are embodied persons'. *America* 2005 August 15-22; 193(4): 8. NRCBL: 4.4; 1.2.

Kelly, David F. Pain and pain management. *In his:* Contemporary Catholic Health Care Ethics. Washington, DC: Georgetown University Press; 2004: 220-228. NRCBL: 4.4; 1.2; 9.5.1; 20.4.1.

Kissell, Judith Lee. The procedural morphing of the person: from self to property. *In:* Thomasma, David C.; Weisstub, David N.; Herve, Christian eds. Personhood and Health Care. Boston: Kluwer Academic Pub.; 2001: 191-202. NRCBL: 4.4; 1.1.

Kittay, Eva Feder. At the margins of moral personhood. *Ethics: An International Journal of Social, Political, and Legal Philosophy* 2005 October; 116(1): 100-131. NRCBL: 4.4; 9.5.3; 15.5. SC: an.

Klitzman, Robert; Siragusa, Joseph. Contexts, anyone? The need for contextualization in the debate about the moral status of embryos. *American Journal of Bioethics* 2005 November-December; 5(6): 56-58. NRCBL: 4.4; 18.5.4. Comments: comment on Lawrence J. Nelson and Michael J. Meyer, "Confronting deep moral disagreement: the President's Council on Bioethics, moral status, and human embryos," American Journal of Bioethics 2005 November-December; 5(6): 33-42.

Koppelman-White, Elysa. On the nature and purpose of public discourse. *American Journal of Bioethics* 2005 November-December; 5(6): 48-51. NRCBL: 4.4; 18.5.4; 1.1. Comments: comment on Lawrence J. Nelson and Michael J. Meyer, "Confronting deep moral disagreement: the President's Council on Bioethics, moral status, and human embryos," American Journal of Bioethics 2005 November-December; 5(6): 33-42.

Kovitz, Jodi. Property in potential human life? Predicting a Canadian approach. *Health Law in Canada* 2003 August; 24(1): 1-8. NRCBL: 4.4; 14.6. SC: le.

Kowalik, Monika. A brief study about the dignity of man. *Annales Universitatis Marie Curie-Sklodowska. Sectio D: Medicina* 2003; 58(2): 459-461. NRCBL: 4.4; 4.1.2; 1.3.1; 1.2; 8.1.

Kramer, Matthew H. Do animals and dead people have legal rights? *Canadian Journal of Law and Jurisprudence* 2001 January; 14(1): 29-54. NRCBL: 4.4; 1.1; 22.1; 20.1. SC: le.

Kurjak, Asim; Tripalo, Ana. The facts and doubts about beginning of the human life and personality. *Bosnian Journal of Basic Medical Sciences* 2004 February; 4(1): 5-14. NRCBL: 4.4; 1.2.

Laing, Jacqueline A.; Oderberg, David S. Artificial reproduction, the 'welfare principle' and the common good. *Medical Law Review* 2005 Autumn; 13(3): 328-356. NRCBL: 4.4; 14.1; 5.3; 1.1. SC: le.

Lammers, Stephen E. Deep disagreement, respect, and the role of women: some room for development. *American Journal of Bioethics* 2005 November-December; 5(6): 63-64. NRCBL: 4.4; 18.5.4. Comments: comment on Lawrence J. Nelson and Michael J. Meyer, "Confronting deep moral disagreement: the President's Council on Bioethics, moral status, and human embryos," American Journal of Bioethics 2005 November-December; 5(6): 33-42.

Leland, John. Did Descartes doom Terri Schiavo? [opinion]. *New York Times* 2005 March 27; Sec 4, p. 1, 3. NRCBL: 4.4; 20.5.1; 1.1. SC: po.

Lewis, Penney. The necessary implications of wrongful life claims: lessons from France. *European Journal of Health Law* 2005 June; 12(2): 135-152. NRCBL: 4.4; 12.4.2; 8.5; 20.5.1; 1.1. SC: le.

Lindsay, Ronald A. Slaves, embryos, and nonhuman animals: moral status and the limitations of common morality theory. *Kennedy Institute of Ethics Journal* 2005 December; 15(4): 323-346. NRCBL: 4.4; 1.1; 9.5.8; 22.1; 7.1; 2.2.
  Abstract: Common morality theory must confront apparent counterexamples from the history of morality, such as the widespread acceptance of slavery in prior eras, that suggest core norms have changed over time. A recent defense of common morality theory addresses this problem by drawing a distinction between the content of the norms of the common morality and the range of individuals to whom these norms apply. This distinction is successful in reconciling common morality theory with practices such as slavery, but only at the cost of underscoring the limits of common morality theory, in particular its inability to resolve disputes about the moral status of entities. Given that many controversies in bioethics center on the disputed status of various entities, such as embryos and nonhuman animals, this is an important limitation. Nonetheless, common morality theory still can be a useful resource in diminishing moral conflict on issues that do not involve disputes over moral status.

Lizza, John P. Defining death: a biological or cultural matter? *In:* Fisher, Robert N.; Primozic, Daniel T.; Day, Peter A.; Thompson, Joel A., eds. Suffering, Death, and Identity. New York: Rodopi; 2002: 155-166. NRCBL: 4.4; 20.2.1; 1.1; 21.7. SC: an.

Lomanno, Matthew P. Politics and protecting human life: "private" versus "public" actions. *Ethics and Medics* 2003 October; 28(10): 1-2. NRCBL: 4.4; 1.2; 21.1.

Longley, Clifford. Is the fetus a person? [opinion]. *Conscience* 2004 Summer-Autumn; 25(2): 45. NRCBL: 4.4; 1.2; 12.4.2.

Lugosi, Charles I. Respecting human life in 21st century America: a moral perspective to extend civil rights to the unborn from creation to natural death. *Issues in Law and Medicine* 2005 Spring; 20(3): 211-258. NRCBL: 4.4; 12.3; 18.5.4; 14.5; 1.2. SC: le.

MacReady, Norra. Criticism of US fetal pain study escalates [news]. *BMJ: British Medical Journal* 2005 September 10; 331(7516): 532. NRCBL: 4.4; 12.1; 1.3.7; 1.3.9.

Magnusson, Roger S. The recognition of proprietary rights in human tissue in common law jurisdictions. *Melbourne University Law Review* 1992 June; 18: 601-629. NRCBL: 4.4; 19.5; 14.1; 5.3; 18.1. SC: le.

Mahowald, Mary B. Another view of potentiality and human embryos. *Theoretical Medicine and Bioethics* 2005; 26(2): 111-113. NRCBL: 4.4. SC: an.

Maio, Giovanni. Zur Begründung der Schutzwürdigkeit des Embryos e contrario. *In:* Maio, Giovanni; Just, Hanjörg, eds. Die Forschung an embryonalen Stammzellen in ethischer und rechtlicher Perspektive. Baden-Baden: Nomos Verlagsgesellschaft; 2003: 168-177. NRCBL: 4.4; 1.1.

Marquis, Don. How not to argue that embryos lack full moral status. *American Journal of Bioethics* 2005 November-December; 5(6): 54-56. NRCBL: 4.4; 18.5.4. Comments: comment on Lawrence J. Nelson and Michael J. Meyer, "Confronting deep moral disagreement: the President's Council on Bioethics, moral status, and human embryos," American Journal of Bioethics 2005 November-December; 5(6): 33-42.

Mazzoni, Cosimo Marco. Real protection for the embryo. *Revista de Derecho y Genoma Humano / Law and the Human Genome Review* 2005 January-June; (22): 115-132. NRCBL: 4.4. Note: Abstract in English and Spanish.

McLeod, Carolyn. "Embryo autonomy?" What about the autonomy of infertility patients. *American Journal of Bioethics* 2005 November-December; 5(6): 25-26. NRCBL: 4.4; 18.5.4; 14.4. Comments: comment on S. Matthew Liao, "Rescuing human embryonic stem cell research: the blastocyst transfer method," American Journal of Bioethics 2005 November-December; 5(6): 8-16.

Mifflin, Pauline. 'Personhood' and the right to life. *Practising Midwife* 2004 September; 7(8): 25-26. NRCBL: 4.4.

Milton, Constance L. The ethics of respect in nursing. *Nursing Science Quarterly* 2005 January; 18(1): 20-23. NRCBL: 4.4; 8.1.

NRCBL: National Reference Center for Bioethics Literature Classification Scheme   See inside front cover for terms.

405

Mississippi. Supreme Court. *66 Federal Credit Union v. Tucker* [Date of Decision: 21 August 2003]. *West's Southern Reporter*, 2d Series, 2003; 853: 104-122. NRCBL: 4.4. SC: le.

Abstract: Court Decision: 853 *Southern Reporter*, 2d Series 104; 2003 Aug 21 (date of decision). The Supreme Court of Mississippi held that Mississippi's wrongful death statute includes a nonviable, unborn child that is "quick" in the womb as a "person." At the time of the attempted repossession of a vehicle financed by defendant 66 Federal Credit Union, Tracy Tucker was five months pregnant. On the evening of the attempted repossession, Tucker experienced abdominal pain and miscarried three days later. Tucker filed a lawsuit against the defendants for wrongful death. The court found support in its holding from criminal statutes and property law which similarly consider an unborn "quick" child a person. The court did not consider viability to be an appropriate criterion for determining whether an unborn child is a person. [KIE/INW]

Morris, Caroline. Technology and the legal discourse of fetal autonomy. *UCLA Women's Law Journal* 1997 Fall-Winter; 8(1): 47-97. NRCBL: 4.4; 1.2. SC: le.

Müller, Carola. The status of the extracorporeal embryo in German law (Part 1). *Revista de Derecho y Genoma Humano / Law and the Human Genome Review* 2005 January-June; (22): 133-151. NRCBL: 4.4; 14.4; 14.6; 12.5.1. SC: le. Note: Abstract in English and Spanish.

Natour, Ahmad; Bakri, Baha'eddin; Rispler-Chaim, Vardit. An Islamic perspective. *In:* Blazer, Shraga; Zimmer, Etan Z., eds. The Embryo: Scientific Discovery and Medical Ethics. New York: Karger; 2005: 53-73. NRCBL: 4.4; 18.5.4; 1.2.

Nelson, Lawrence J.; Meyer, Michael J. Confronting deep moral disagreement: the President's Council on Bioethics, moral status, and human embryos. *American Journal of Bioethics* 2005 November-December; 5(6): 33-42. NRCBL: 4.4; 18.5.4; 1.1; 2.4; 14.5.

Abstract: The report of the President's Council on Bioethics, Human Cloning and Human Dignity, addresses the central ethical, political, and policy issue in human embryonic stem cell research: the moral status of extracorporeal human embryos. The Council members were in sharp disagreement on this issue and essentially failed to adequately engage and respectfully acknowledge each others' deepest moral concerns, despite their stated commitment to do so. This essay provides a detailed critique of the two extreme views on the Council (i.e., embryos have full moral status or they have none at all) and then gives theoretical grounding for our judgment about the intermediate moral status of embryos. It also supplies an account of how to address profound moral disagreements in the public arena, especially by way of constructing a middle ground that deliberately pays sincere respect to the views of those with whom it has deep disagreements.

Nelson, Lawrence J.; Meyer, Michael J. Response to commentators on "Confronting deep moral disagreement: the President's Council on Bioethics, moral status, and human embryos". *American Journal of Bioethics [Online]* 2005 November- December; 5(6): W14-W16. NRCBL: 4.4; 18.5.4.

Nelson, Thomas. Is the human zygote a person? *Linacre Quarterly* 2005 November; 72(4): 281-293. NRCBL: 4.4; 1.2; 18.5.4.

Nord, Erik. Values for health states in QALYs and DALYs: desirability versus well-being and worth. *In:* Wasserman, David; Bickenbach, Jerome; Wachbroit, Robert, eds. Quality of Life and Human Difference: Genetic Testing, Health Care, and Disability. New York: Cambridge University Press; 2005: 125-141. NRCBL: 4.4; 4.2.

Obasi, Annissa R. Protecting our vital organs: the case for fetal homicide laws in Texas. *Texas Wesleyan Law Review* 1998 Spring; 4(2): 207-230. NRCBL: 4.4. SC: le.

Olthuis, Gert; Dekkers, Wim. Quality of life considered as well-being: views from philosophy and palliative care practice. *Theoretical Medicine and Bioethics* 2005; 26(4): 307-337. NRCBL: 4.4; 20.4.1; 4.1.2; 8.1. SC: em.

Abstract: The main measure of quality of life is well-being. The aim of this article is to compare insights about well-being from contemporary philosophy with the practice-related opinions of palliative care professionals. In the first part of the paper two philosophical theories on well-being are introduced: Sumner's theory of authentic happiness and Griffin's theory of prudential perfectionism. The second part presents opinions derived from interviews with 19 professional palliative caregivers. Both the well-being of patients and the well-being of the carers themselves are considered in this empirical exploration. In the third part the attention shifts from the description of "well-being" to prescriptions for the promotion of well-being. Our interview data are analysed in light of the theories of Sumner and Griffin for clues to the promotion of "well-being." The analysis (1) underscores the subject-relativity of well-being, (2) points out that values that are considered important in every life still seem to be relevant (at least in palliative care practice), and (3) shows the importance of living a certain sort of life when aiming to enhance dying patients' well-being.

Pintos, Guillermo Diaz. The medical interpretation of pain and the concept of a person. *In:* Thomasma, David C.; Weisstub, David N.; Herve, Christian eds. Personhood and Health Care. Boston: Kluwer Academic Pub.; 2001: 363-371. NRCBL: 4.4; 1.1.

Plourde, Simonne. A key term in ethics: the person and his dignity. *In:* Thomasma, David C.; Weisstub, David N.; Herve, Christian eds. Personhood and Health Care. Boston: Kluwer Academic Pub.; 2001: 137-148. NRCBL: 4.4; 2.1.

Priaulx, Nicolette. Health, disability and parental interests: adopting a contextual approach in the reproductive torts. *European Journal of Health Law* 2005 September; 12(3): 213- 243. NRCBL: 4.4; 4.2; 4.3; 11.4; 15.2; 8.5. SC: le.

Price, Bob. Demonstrating respect for patient dignity. *Nursing Standard* 2004 December 1-7; 19(12): 45-52. NRCBL: 4.4; 8.1; 7.2.

Raines, Deborah A. Values: a guiding force. *AWHONN's Clinical Issues in Perinatal and Women's Health Nursing* 1993; 4(4): 533-541. NRCBL: 4.4; 9.4; 7.1; 1.3.1.

Rao, Radhika. Property, privacy, and the human body. *Boston University Law Review* 2000 April; 80(2): 359-460. NRCBL: 4.4; 19.5. SC: le.

Rappaport, Aaron J. Beyond personhood and autonomy: moral theory and the premises of privacy. *Utah Law Review* 2001; 2001(2): 441-507. NRCBL: 4.4; 1.1; 20.7; 20.5.1; 10. SC: le.

Rich, Ben A. Oregon versus Ashcroft: pain relief, physician-assisted suicide, and the Controlled Substances Act. *Pain Medicine* 2002 December; 3(4): 353-360. NRCBL: 4.4; 20.7; 20.5.1.

Rich, Ben A. The politics of pain: rhetoric or reform? *DePaul Journal of Health Care Law* 2005 Spring; 8(3): 519-558. NRCBL: 4.4; 7.2. SC: le.

Richardson, Eileen H.; Turner, Bryan S. Bodies as property: from slavery to DNA maps. *In:* Bainham, Andrew; Sclater, Shelley Day; Richards, Martin, eds. Body Lore and Laws. Portland, OR: Hart Pub.; 2002: 29-42. NRCBL: 4.4; 2.1; 1.1; 9.3.1. SC: le.

Robertson, John A. Special respect redux. *American Journal of Bioethics* 2005 November-December; 5(6): 46-48. NRCBL: 4.4; 18.5.4; 2.4. Identifiers: President's Council on Bioethics. Comments: comment on Lawrence J. Nelson and Michael J. Meyer, "Confronting deep moral disagreement: the President's Council on Bioethics, moral status, and human embryos," American Journal of Bioethics 2005 November-December; 5(6): 33-42.

Roden, Gregory J. Prenatal tort law and the personhood of the unborn child: a separate legal existence. *St. Thomas Law Review* 2003 Fall; 16(1): 207-286. NRCBL: 4.4; 8.5. SC: le.

Rodotà, Stefano. Body transformations [opinion]. *Revista de Derecho y Genoma-Humano / Law and the Human Genome Review* 2004 July-December; (21): 29-47. NRCBL: 4.4; 15.1; 1.3.12. SC: le.

Ryan, Peter F. The value of life and its bearing on three issues of medical ethics. *In:* Koterski, Joseph W., ed. Life and Learning IX: Proceedings of the Ninth University Faculty for Life Conference. Washington, DC: University Faculty for Life; 2000: 41-57. NRCBL: 4.4; 12.3; 1.2; 20.5.1; 20.7.

Scaldo, Stacy A. The Born-Alive Infants Protection Act: baby steps toward the recognition of life after birth. *Nova Law Review* 2002 Winter; 26(2): 485-510. NRCBL: 4.4; 12.4.2. SC: le.

Scott, Rosamund. The English fetus and the right to life. *European Journal of Health Law* 2004 December; 11(4): 347-364. NRCBL: 4.4; 12.4.2; 15.2. SC: le.

Seelmann, Kurt. Menschenwürde und Embryonen. *In:* Maio, Giovanni; Just, Hanjörg, eds. Die Forschung an embryonalen Stammzellen in ethischer und rechtlicher

Perspektive. Baden-Baden: Nomos Verlagsgesellschaft; 2003: 156-167. NRCBL: 4.4; 1.1.

Segal, Thalia. A lucrative routine, short on pain management. Good ethical decision is akin to good medical decision. *Pain Medicine* 2002 December; 3(4): 349-350. NRCBL: 4.4; 9.5.1; 9.8; 7.1.

Sgreccia, Elio. The embryo: a sign of contradiction. *Medical Ethics and Bioethics / Medicinska Etika & Bioetika* 2001 Autumn-Winter; 8(3-4): 13. NRCBL: 4.4; 1.2; 11.1; 12.3.

Shabanowitz, Robert. The disposer's dilemma. *American Journal of Bioethics* 2005 November-December; 5(6): 60-61. NRCBL: 4.4; 18.5.4; 14.6. Comments: comment on Lawrence J. Nelson and Michael J. Meyer, "Confronting deep moral disagreement: the President's Council on Bioethics, moral status, and human embryos," American Journal of Bioethics 2005 November-December; 5(6): 33-42.

Shah, Mamta K. Inconsistencies in the legal status of an unborn child: recognition of a fetus as potential life. *Hofstra Law Review* 2001; 29(3): 931-969. NRCBL: 4.4. SC: le.

Shannon, Thomas A. The moral status of the early human embryo: is a via media possible? *American Journal of Bioethics* 2005 November-December; 5(6): 43-44. NRCBL: 4.4; 18.5.4. Comments: comment on Lawrence J. Nelson and Michael J. Meyer, "Confronting deep moral disagreement: the President's Council on Bioethics, moral status, and human embryos," American Journal of Bioethics 2005 November-December; 5(6): 33-42.

Sheehan, Katherine C. The hand that rocks the cradle. *University of Toledo Law Review* 2001 Winter; 32(2): 229-247. NRCBL: 4.4; 12.4.1. SC: le.

Smith, Richard D.; Richardson, Jeff. Can we estimate the 'social' value of a QALY? Four core issues to resolve. *Health Policy* 2005 September 28; 74(1): 77-84. NRCBL: 4.4; 9.4; 9.3.1; 7.1. Identifiers: quality adjusted life year.

Spahn, Elizabeth; Andrade, Barbara. Mis-conceptions: the moment of conception in religion, science, and law. *University of San Francisco Law Review* 1998 Winter; 32(2): 261-333. NRCBL: 4.4; 12.4.1; 1.2. SC: le.

Stanford, Joseph B. Mormon bioethics [letter]. *First Things* 2005 October; (156): 8. NRCBL: 4.4; 1.2; 2.1.

Stanton, Catherine; Harris, John. The moral status of the embryo post-Dolly. *Journal of Medical Ethics* 2005 April; 31(4): 221-225. NRCBL: 4.4; 14.5; 18.5.4. SC: an.
Abstract: Cameron and Williamson have provided a provocative and timely review of the ethical questions prompted by the birth of Dolly. The question Cameron and Williamson seek to address is "In the world of Dolly, when does a human embryo acquire respect?". Their initial discussion sets the scene by providing a valuable overview of attitudes towards the embryo, summarising various religious, scientific, and philosophical

NRCBL: National Reference Center for Bioethics Literature Classification Scheme   See inside front cover for terms.

407

viewpoints. They then ask, "What has Dolly changed?" and identify five changes, the first being that fertilisation is no longer required to create an embryo. Following this analysis they then ask when an embryo created other than by fertilisation begins to acquire respect. This paper explores the ethical and legal issues highlighted by Cameron and Williamson's paper.

Steinberg, Avraham. Jewish perspectives. *In:* Blazer, Shraga; Zimmer, Etan Z., eds. The Embryo: Scientific Discovery and Medical Ethics. New York: Karger; 2005: 21-39. NRCBL: 4.4; 1.2.

Steineck, Christian. Japanese discussions on the concept of "person" and its function in bioethics. *Journal International de Bioethique / International Journal of Bioethics* 2005 March-June; 16(1-2): 29-40, 190. NRCBL: 4.4; 2.2; 2.1; 21.1. SC: an. Note: Abstract in English and French.

Steinvorth, Ulrich. Über den Anfang des menschlichen Individuums. *In:* Jahrbuch für Wissenschaft und Ethik. Bd. 7. Berlin: Walter de Gruyter; 2002: 165-178. NRCBL: 4.4.

Stolk, Elly A.; Pickee, Stefan J.; Ament, André H.J.A.; Busschbach, Jan J.V. Equity in health care prioritisation: an empirical inquiry into social value. *Health Policy* 2005 November; 74(3): 343-355. NRCBL: 4.4; 9.4; 7.1. SC: em. Identifiers: quality adjusted life years (QALY).

Strasberg-Cohen, Tova. The status of the embryo under Israeli law. *In:* Blazer, Shraga; Zimmer, Etan Z., eds. The Embryo: Scientific Discovery and Medical Ethics. New York: Karger; 2005: 329-339. NRCBL: 4.4. SC: le.

Streiffer, Robert. At the edge of humanity: human stem cells, chimeras, and moral status. *Kennedy Institute of Ethics Journal* 2005 December; 15(4): 347- 370. NRCBL: 4.4; 1.1; 15.1; 18.1; 22.1; 18.5.4.

Abstract: Experiments involving the transplantation of human stem cells and their derivatives into early fetal or embryonic nonhuman animals raise novel ethical issues due to their possible implications for enhancing the moral status of che chimeric individual. Although status-enhancing research is not necessarily objectionable from the perspective of the chimeric individual, there are grounds for objecting to it in the conditions in which it is likely to occur. Translating this ethical conclusion into a policy recommendation, however, is complicated by the fact that substantial empirical and ethical uncertainties remain about which transplants, if any, would significantly enhance the chimeric individual's moral status. Considerations of moral status justify either an early-termination policy on chimeric embryos, or, in the absence of such a policy, restrictions on the introduction of pluripotent human stem cells into early-stage developing animals, pending the resolution of those uncertainties.

Sugunasiri, S.H.J. The Buddhist view concerning the dead body. *Transplantation Proceedings* 1990 June; 22(3): 947-949. NRCBL: 4.4; 1.2; 19.1; 20.3.1.

Sullivan, Mark. Ethical principles in pain management. *Pain Medicine* 2000 September; 1(3): 274-279. NRCBL: 4.4; 1.1; 2.1.

Sullivan, Mark; Ferrell, Betty. Ethical challenges in the management of chronic nonmalignant pain: negotiating through the cloud of doubt. *Journal of Pain* 2005 January; 6(1): 2-9. NRCBL: 4.4; 9.5.1. SC: cs.

Susanne, Charles; Casado, María; Buxo, María Jesús. What challenges offers nanotechnology to bioethics? [opinion]. *Revista de Derecho y Genoma Humano / Law and the Human Genome Review* 2005 January-June; (22): 27-45. NRCBL: 4.4; 2.1; 3.1. Note: Abstract in English and Spanish.

Tallacchini, Mariachiara. Rhetoric of anonymity and property rights in human biological materials (HBMs). *Revista de Derecho y Genoma Humano / Law and the Human Genome Review* 2005 January-June; (22): 153-175. NRCBL: 4.4; 19.5; 18.3; 8.4; 15.8. SC: le. Note: Abstract in English and Spanish.

te Braake, Trees A.M. Does a fetus have a right to life? The case of Vo v. France. *European Journal of Health Law* 2004 December; 11(4): 381-389. NRCBL: 4.4; 12.4.2; 8.5. SC: le.

ter Meulen, Ruud H.J. Towards a social concept of the person. *In:* Thomasma, David C.; Weisstub, David N.; Herve, Christian eds. Personhood and Health Care. Boston: Kluwer Academic Pub.; 2001: 129-135. NRCBL: 4.4; 1.1; 2.1.

Trachtman, Howard. Is the middle ground vanishing? *American Journal of Bioethics* 2005 November-December; 5(6): 68-70. NRCBL: 4.4; 18.5.4; 1.2. Comments: comment on Lawrence J. Nelson and Michael J. Meyer, "Confronting deep moral disagreement: the President's Council on Bioethics, moral status, and human embryos," American Journal of Bioethics 2005 November-December; 5(6): 33-42.

Trapp, Mark. Created equal: how the Declaration of Independence recognizes and guarantees the right to life for the unborn. *Pepperdine Law Review* 2001; 28(4): 819-847. NRCBL: 4.4; 12.4.2; 1.3.5. SC: le.

van Leeuwen, Evert. On the origin, use and destination of human embryos. *European Journal of Endocrinology* 2004 November; 151 (Supplement 3): U13-U16. NRCBL: 4.4; 18.5.4; 1.1. SC: an.

Vélez G., Juan R. Immediate animation: Thomistic principles applied to Norman Ford's objections. *Ethics and Medicine* 2005 Spring; 21(1): 11-28. NRCBL: 4.4; 1.2.

Vick, Katherine. Judge declares pre-embryo is human. *Journal of Biolaw and Business* 2005; 8(3): 52-53. NRCBL: 4.4; 14.4; 14.6. SC: le.

Wachbroit, Robert. Assessing quality of life: clinical versus health policy uses. *In:* Wasserman, David; Bickenbach, Jerome; Wachbroit, Robert, eds. Quality of Life and Human Difference: Genetic Testing, Health Care, and Disability. New York: Cambridge University Press; 2005: 27-42. NRCBL: 4.4; 9.1.

Wasserman, David. The nonidentity problem, disability, and the role morality of prospective parents. *Ethics: An International Journal of Social, Political, and Legal Philosophy* 2005 October; 116(1): 132-152. NRCBL: 4.4; 9.5.7; 15.2. SC: an.

Wasserman, David. What qualifies as a live embryo? *American Journal of Bioethics* 2005 November-December; 5(6): 23-25. NRCBL: 4.4; 18.5.4. Comments: comment on S. Matthew Liao, "Rescuing human embryonic stem cell research: the blastocyst transfer method," American Journal of Bioethics 2005 November-December; 5(6): 8-16.

Weisstub, David N.; Thomasma, David C. Human dignity, vulnerability, personhood. *In:* Thomasma, David C.; Weisstub, David N.; Herve, Christian eds. Personhood and Health Care. Boston: Kluwer Academic Pub.; 2001: 317-332. NRCBL: 4.4; 1.1.

Williams, Clare. Framing the fetus in medical work: rituals and practices. *Social Science and Medicine* 2005 May; 60(9): 2085-2095. NRCBL: 4.4; 9.5.8; 9.5.5; 15.2; 12.1.

Wisser, Josef. Der menschliche Embryo vor der Implantation—Gedanken aus der vorgeburtlichen Medizin. *In:* Maio, Giovanni; Just, Hanjörg, eds. Die Forschung an embryonalen Stammzellen in ethischer und rechtlicher Perspektive. Baden-Baden: Nomos Verlagsgesellschaft; 2003: 42-51. NRCBL: 4.4; 18.5.4.

Woods, Simon. Persons and personal identity. *Nursing Philosophy* 2000 October; 1(2): 169-172. NRCBL: 4.4; 1.1; 20.4.1.

Woolhead, Gillian; Calnan, Michael; Dieppe, Paul; Tadd, Win. Dignity in older age: what do older people in the United Kingdom think? *Age and Ageing* 2004; 33(2): 165-170. NRCBL: 4.4; 9.5.2. SC: em.

Yeung, Patrick, Jr. When does human life begin? [opinion]. *Ethics and Medicine* 2005 Summer; 21(2): 69-71. NRCBL: 4.4; 3.1; 18.5.4. Identifiers: clonote.

Zinser, Jason. The public's role in science policy. *American Journal of Bioethics* 2005 November-December; 5(6): 58-59. NRCBL: 4.4; 18.5.4; 2.1. Identifiers: President's Council on Bioethics. Comments: comment on Lawrence J. Nelson and Michael J. Meyer, "Confronting deep moral disagreement: the President's Council on Bioethics, moral status, and human embryos," American Journal of Bioethics 2005 November-December; 5(6): 33-42.

RATIONING OF HEALTH CARE *See* RESOURCE ALLOCATION

RECOMBINANT DNA RESEARCH
See also GENETIC RESEARCH; GENOME MAPPING

Bereano, Phil. Without a trace: how a lack of U.S. domestic LMO regulations is undermining international control. *GeneWatch* 2005 May-June; 18(3): 3-5, 16. NRCBL: 15.7; 16.1; 5.3. Identifiers: Cartagena Biosafety Protocol; living modified organisms.

Cook-Deegan, Robert M.; Berkelman, Ruth; Davidson, E. Megan; Finder, Stuart; Heitman, Elizabeth; Kelley, Maureen C.; King, Nancy M.P.; Moseley, Ray; Thomas, James C.; Tilden, Samuel J.; Vangsnes, Nikki M. Issues in biosecurity and biosafety [letter]. *Science* 2005 June 24; 308(5730): 1867-1868. NRCBL: 15.7; 21.3; 5.3. Identifiers: Institutional Biosafety Committees.

Hindmarsh, Richard; Gottweis, Herbert. Recombinant regulation: the Asilomar legacy 30 years on [editorial]. *Science as Culture* 2005 December; 14(4): 299-307. NRCBL: 15.7; 2.2; 21.1; 5.3. SC: rv.

Kilpi, Jukka. On corporate ethical responsibility, stakeholder value, and strict liability in biotechnology. *In:* Häyry, Matti; Takala, Tuija; Herissone-Kelly, Peter, eds. Bioethics and Social Reality. New York: Rodopi, 2005: 113-125. NRCBL: 15.7; 1.1; 1.3.2; 1.3.11. SC: le.

Krimsky, Sheldon. From Asilomar to industrial biotechnology: risks, reductionism and regulation. *Science as Culture* 2005 December; 14(4): 309-323. NRCBL: 15.7; 2.2; 5.3. SC: an; rv; le.

Morton, Oliver. Biology's new forbidden fruit [opinion]. *New York Times* 2005 February 11; p. A25. NRCBL: 15.7; 15.4; 4.4. SC: po.

Petersen, Alan; Anderson, Alison; Allan, Stuart. Science fiction/science fact: medical genetics in news stories. *New Genetics and Society* 2005 December; 24(3): 337-353. NRCBL: 15.7; 4.4; 18.5.4; 15.2; 1.3.7.

Spranger, Tade Matthias. Patent protection for stem cell procedures under the law of the European Union. *Medical Ethics and Bioethics / Medicinska Etika & Bioetika* 2003 Spring-Summer; 10(1-2): 4-8. NRCBL: 15.7; 18.5.1; 18.5.4. SC: le.

St. Amand, Paul C. Genetic engineering: risks. *In:* Ness, Bryan D., ed. Encyclopedia of Genetics. Revised edition. Volume I. Pasadena, Calif.: Salem Press; 2004: 347-350. NRCBL: 15.7.

Tanaka, Yutaka. Major psychological factors affecting acceptance of gene-recombination technology. *Risk Analysis* 2004 December; 24(6): 1575-1583. NRCBL: 15.7; 5.1. SC: em. Identifiers: Japan.

REGULATION *See* ABORTION/ LEGAL ASPECTS; BIOETHICS AND MEDICAL ETHICS/

NRCBL: National Reference Center for Bioethics Literature Classification Scheme   See inside front cover for terms.

LEGAL ASPECTS; CLONING/ LEGAL ASPECTS; EUTHANASIA AND ALLOWING TO DIE/ LEGAL ASPECTS; GENETICS/ LEGAL ASPECTS; HUMAN EXPERIMENTATION/ ETHICS COMMITTEES AND POLICY GUIDELINES/ LEGAL ASPECTS; HUMAN EXPERIMENTATION/ REGULATION; ORGAN AND TISSUE TRANSPLANTATION/ DONATION AND PROCUREMENT/ LEGAL ASPECTS

RELIGIOUS ASPECTS *See* ABORTION/ MORAL AND RELIGIOUS ASPECTS; BIOETHICS AND MEDICAL ETHICS/ RELIGIOUS PERSPECTIVES; EUTHANASIA AND ALLOWING TO DIE/ RELIGIOUS ASPECTS

REPRODUCTION *See* REPRODUCTIVE TECHNOLOGIES

REPRODUCTIVE TECHNOLOGIES
See also ARTIFICIAL INSEMINATION/ SURROGATE MOTHERS; CLONING; CRYOBANKING OF SPERM, OVA, AND EMBRYOS; IN VITRO FERTILIZATION; SEX DETERMINATION

Adventist guidelines on assisted procreation. *Update [Loma Linda University Center for Christian Bioethics]* 1996 February; 12(1); 3 p. NRCBL: 14.1; 1.2.

Reproduction and ethics. *In:* Concise Routledge Encyclopedia of Philosophy. New York: Routledge; 2000: 766-767. NRCBL: 14.1.

Spain's constitutional court and assisted reproduction techniques [editorial]. *Law and the Human Genome Review* 1999 July-December; 11: 15-17. NRCBL: 14.1; 19.5. SC: le.

Al-Inany, Hesham G. Guest editorial from abroad: pregnancy in the postmenopause: how far can assisted reproductive technology be trusted? [editorial]. *Obstetrical and Gynecological Survey* 2000 February; 55(2): 67-68. NRCBL: 14.1; 9.5.5; 1.2.

Allan, Helen; Barber, Debbie. Emotional boundary work in advanced fertility nursing roles. *Nursing Ethics* 2005 July; 12(4): 391-400. NRCBL: 14.1; 8.1. SC: em.
  Abstract: In this article we examine the nature of intimacy and knowing in the nurse-patient relationship in the context of advanced nursing roles in fertility care. We suggest that psychoanalytical approaches to emotions may contribute to an increased understanding of how emotions are managed in advanced nursing roles. These roles include nurses undertaking tasks that were formerly performed by doctors. Rather than limiting the potential for intimacy between nurses and fertility patients, we argue that such roles allow nurses to provide increased continuity of care. This facilitates the management of emotions where a feeling of closeness is created while at the same time maintaining a distance or safe boundary with which both nurses and patients are comfortable. We argue that this dis-

tanced or 'bounded' relationship can be understood as a defence against the anxiety of emotions raised in the nurse-fertility patient relationship.

American Society for Reproductive Medicine. Ethics Committee. Fertility treatment when the prognosis is very poor or futile. *Fertility and Sterility* 2004 October; 82(4): 806-810. NRCBL: 14.1.

Anderson, Bebe J.; Wilcox, Lynne S. Reproductive health. *In:* Goodman, Richard A.; Rothstein, Mark A.; Hoffman, Richard E.; Lopez, Wilfredo; Matthews, Gene W., eds. Law in Public Health Practice. New York: Oxford University Press; 2003: 348-370. NRCBL: 14.1; 11.1; 12.4.1. SC: le.

Appleton, Susan Frelich. Adoption in the age of reproductive technology. *University of Chicago Legal Forum* 2004; 2004: 393-451. NRCBL: 14.1; 4.4. SC: le.

Arrhenius, Gustaf. The person-affecting restriction, comparativism, and the moral status of potential people. *Ethical Perspectives* 2003; 10(3-4): 185-195. NRCBL: 14.1; 1.1. SC: an.

Bacchi, Carol; Beasley, Chris. Reproductive technology and the political limits of care. *In:* Shildrick, Margrit; Mykitiuk, Roxanne, eds. Ethics of the Body: Postconventional Challenges. Cambridge, MA: MIT Press; 2005: 175- 194. NRCBL: 14.1; 1.1.

Barlow, David H.; Beard, H.K.; Williams, A.C. Assisted reproductive technologies in Europe encompass diverse and complex ethical viewpoints: issues to be considered in reporting research in human reproduction. *Annals of the New York Academy of Sciences* 2004 December; 1034: 110-116. NRCBL: 14.1; 5.3; 1.3.7.

Bernal, Susan Kerr. Ethical offspring? *Journal of Andrology* 2004 September-October; 25(5): 667-670. NRCBL: 14.1; 14.4; 19.5; 15.2; 1.1.

Bozza, Steven. The morality of ovarian transplants: good and bad uses of a new technology. *Ethics and Medics* 2005 September; 30(9): 1-2. NRCBL: 14.1; 1.2; 19.5.

Braun, Kathrin. Not just for experts: the public debate about reprogenetics in Germany. *Hastings Center Report* 2005 May-June; 35(3): 42-49. NRCBL: 14.1; 15.1; 5.2; 5.3; 21.1.

Callahan, Daniel. New beginnings in life: a philosopher's response. *In:* Hamilton, Michael P., ed. The New Genetics and the Future of Man. Grand Rapids, MI: William B. Eerdmans Publishing Co.; 1972: 90-106. NRCBL: 14.1.

Campbell, Alastair V. Britain's HFEA is caught in the middle. *Hastings Center Report* 2005 May-June; 35(3): 8. NRCBL: 14.1. SC: le. Identifiers: Human Fertilisation and Embryology Authority.

Castro, Roberto; Erviti, Joaquina. Violations of reproductive rights during hospital births in Mexico. *Health and*

Human Rights: An International Journal 2003; 7(1): 91-110. NRCBL: 14.1; 11.1; 8.3.1; 4.4; 9.1; 21.1. SC: em.

Catholics for a Free Choice. A long way from the Vatican: Catholic attitudes towards reproductive rights, church-state and related issues in Bolivia, Colombia and Mexico. *Conscience* 2004 Summer-Autumn; 25(2): 39-40. NRCBL: 14.1; 1.2; 11.1; 12.5.2; 21.1. SC: em.

Cohen, Cynthia B.; Anderlik, Mary R. Creating and shaping future children. *In:* Smith, David H.; Cohen, Cynthia B., eds. A Christian Response to the New Genetics: Religious, Ethical, and Social Issues. Lanham, MD: Rowman & Littlefield Publishers; 2003: 75-103. NRCBL: 14.1; 1.2; 15.1.

Coleman, Carl H.; DeBuono, Barbara A. Developing public policy on assisted reproductive technologies: reflections on the work of the New York State Task Force on life and the law. *Fertility and Sterility* 2000 January; 73(1): 21-23. NRCBL: 14.1; 1.3.5; 9.3.1; 5.3. SC: le.

Cole-Turner, Ronald. Trust common sense [response]. *Conscience* 2003-2004 Winter; 24(4): 17. NRCBL: 14.1; 15.1.

Collins, Rebecca. Posthumous reproduction and the presumption against consent in cases of death caused by sudden trauma. *Journal of Medicine and Philosophy* 2005 August; 30(4): 431-442. NRCBL: 14.1; 20.1; 8.3.1; 8.3.3. SC: an.
Abstract: The deceased's prior consent to posthumous reproduction is a common requirement in many common law jurisdictions. This paper critically evaluates four arguments advanced to justify the presumption against consent. It is argued that, in situations where death is caused by sudden trauma, not only is there inadequate justification for the presumption against consent, but there are good reasons to reverse the presumption. The article concludes that the precondition of prior consent may be inappropriate in these situations.

David, Rina Jimenez. Living with sin: the Catholic hierarchy and reproductive rights in the Philippines. *Conscience* 2003 Summer; 24(2): 18-21. NRCBL: 14.1; 1.2; 11.1; 12.3; 13.3.

Dobson, Roger. UK government responds to call for change in reproduction technology [news]. *BMJ: British Medical Journal* 2005 August 20-27; 331(7514): 421. NRCBL: 14.1; 1.3.12; 15.1. Identifiers: United Kingdom (Great Britain).

Doyal, Len; McLean, Sheila. Choosing children: intergenerational justice? (Supplement 1). *Reproductive BioMedicine Online [electronic]* 2005 March; 10: 119-124 Available: http://www.rbmonline.com/index.html [1 September 2005]. NRCBL: 14.1; 14.3; 21.1; 1.1; 4.4.

Fineschi, V.; Neri, M.; Turillazzi, E. The new Italian law on assisted reproduction technology (Law 40/2004). *Jour-nal of Medical Ethics* 2005 September; 31(9): 536-539. NRCBL: 14.1; 14.4; 15.3. SC: le. Identifiers: Italy.
Abstract: The Italian parliament passed the law on assisted reproduction after a heated debate. The promulgation of this law (Law 40/2004) is the end point of a long and troubled journey that has seen many bills come and go, all of which have failed. The law consists of a whole set of regulations that will have a great impact on health and on society in general. The law is against many of the technical practices of assisted reproduction; several such practices are banned. This paper outlines ethical and medicolegal issues arising in connection with the law. The law states that no more than three embryos must be created at any one time and all the embryos created must be transferred together even if the couple does not need all the embryos. Embryo cryopreservation is also forbidden, as is assisted reproductive technology (ART), which uses a third party in any way, and the screening of embryos for genetic defects.

Fisher, Ian; Povoleod, Elisabetta. In political step, Pope joins fray on fertility law. *New York Times* 2005 May 31; p. A1, A11. NRCBL: 14.1; 1.2; 21.1. SC: po.

Flamigni, Carlo. Science and biotechnology: attempts of reconciliation. *Annals of the New York Academy of Sciences* 2004 December; 1034: 101-109. NRCBL: 14.1; 4.4; 5.3; 1.2. SC: an; le. Identifiers: Italy.

Fletcher, Joseph. New beginnings in life: a theologian's perspective. *In:* Hamilton, Michael P., ed. The New Genetics and the Future of Man. Grand Rapids, MI: William B. Eerdmans Publishing Co.; 1972: 78-89. NRCBL: 14.1; 1.2.

Frasca, Tim. Gaining ground: despite political and religious opposition, Latin American activists force advances in reproductive rights. *Conscience* 2003 Summer; 24(2): 22-24. NRCBL: 14.1; 1.2; 11.1; 12.3; 21.1.

Fry, Sara T.; Veatch, Robert M. Genetics, birth, and the biological revolution. *In their:* Case Studies in Nursing Ethics. Third edition. Sudbury, MA: Jones and Bartlett Publishers; 2006: 246-280. NRCBL: 14.1; 15.1.

Garcia, Laura L. Protecting persons. *In:* Tollefsen, Christopher, ed. John Paul II's Contribution to Catholic Bioethics. Norwell, MA: Springer; 2004: 93-105. NRCBL: 14.1; 1.2.

Gillott, John. 'Reprogenetics': hype, phobia and choice. *Conscience* 2003-2004 Winter; 24(4): 10-14. NRCBL: 14.1; 15.1; 2.4.

Goodman, Neville W. Whose life is it anyway? *British Journal of Hospital Medicine* 1996 September 4-17; 56(5): 240. NRCBL: 14.1; 14.4; 12.1.

Goold, Imogen. Should older and postmenopausal women have access to assisted reproductive technology? *Monash Bioethics Review* 2005 January; 24(1): 27-46. NRCBL: 14.1; 9.5.5; 9.5.2. SC: le. Identifiers: Australia.

Grad, Frank P. New beginnings in life: a lawyer's response. *In:* Hamilton, Michael P., ed. The New Genetics and the Future of Man. Grand Rapids, MI: William B.

NRCBL: National Reference Center for Bioethics Literature Classification Scheme   See inside front cover for terms.

411

Eerdmans Publishing Co.; 1972: 64-77. NRCBL: 14.1. SC: le.

Grazi, Richard V. Assisted reproduction. *In:* Overcoming Infertility: A Guide for Jewish Couples. New Milford, Conn.: Toby, 2005: 311-364. NRCBL: 14.1; 1.2.

Grazi, Richard V.; Wolowelsky, Joel B. New ethical issues. *In:* Grazi, Richard V. Overcoming Infertility: A Guide for Jewish Couples. New Milford, Conn.: Toby, 2005: 409-424. NRCBL: 14.1; 14.3; 1.2; 12.3.

Häyry, Matti. If you must make babies, then at least make the best babies you can? *Human Fertility* 2004 June; 7(2): 105-112. NRCBL: 14.1; 1.1; 15.2; 14.4. SC: an.

Häyry, Matti. The rational cure for prereproductive stress syndrome revised. *Journal of Medical Ethics* 2005 October; 31(10): 606-607. NRCBL: 14.1. SC: an.

Hohl, M.K. Restrictive ART laws sense or non sense? *Journal of Assisted Reproduction and Genetics* 2004 January; 21(1): 1. NRCBL: 14.1. SC: le. Identifiers: Switzerland; assisted reproductive technology.

Hudson, Kathy. Something old and something new. *Hastings Center Report* 2004 July-August; 34(4): 14-15. NRCBL: 14.1; 2.4; 15.1. Identifiers: President's Council on Bioethics.

Hudson, Kathy. The vagaries of government regulation [response]. *Conscience* 2003-2004 Winter; 24(4): 18. NRCBL: 14.1; 15.1.

International Federation of Gynecology and Obstetrics [FIGO]. Committee for the Ethical Aspects of Human Reproduction and Women's Health; Schenker, J.G.; Cain, J.M. International medical ethics: the FIGO Committee for the Ethical Aspects of Human Reproduction and Women's Health. *International Journal of Gynecology and Obstetrics* 2004 August; 86(2): 267-275. NRCBL: 14.1; 2.4; 9.5.5; 21.1.

Jonsen, Albert R. Assisted reproduction. *In his:* Bioethics Beyond the Headlines: Who Lives? Who Dies? Who Decides? Lanham, MD: Rowman and Littlefield; 2005: 67-76. NRCBL: 14.1.

Kalbian, Aline H. Narrative ARTifice and women's agency. *Bioethics* 2005 April; 19(2): 93-111. NRCBL: 14.1; 1.1. SC: an.
Abstract: The choice to pursue fertility treatments is a complex one. In this paper I explore the issues of choice, agency, and gender as they relate to assisted reproductive technologies (ARTs). I argue that narrative approaches to bioethics such as those by Arthur Frank and Hilde Lindemann Nelson clarify judgments about autonomy and fertility medicine. More specifically, I propose two broad narrative categories that help capture the experience of encounters with fertility medicine: narratives of hope and narratives of resistance. This narrative typology captures the inevitable conflict that women feel when they become subjects of fertility medicine. On the one hand, they must remain hopeful; on the other, they must not surrender themselves completely. Nelson's account of counterstories as narratives of resistance helps us see how women can reconcile the experience of a strong desire to have children with the desire to remain authentic and whole.

Kirchhof, Paul. Ethik und Recht als Maßstabe fur medizinisches und biotechnologisches Handeln. *In:* Jahrbuch für Wissenschaft und Ethik. Bd. 7. Berlin: Walter de Gruyter; 2002: 5-21. NRCBL: 14.1; 4.4; 15.2; 18.5.4. SC: le.

Larson, David; Winslow, Gerald; Corselli, Johanna; Whitney, Elvonne; Orr, Robert; Brock, Brian. Adventism and assisted procreation: excerpts from a panel discussion at LLU. *Update [Loma Linda University Center for Christian Bioethics]* 1996 February; 12(1): 14 p. NRCBL: 14.1; 1.2.

Lebner, Ashley. Genetic "mysteries" and international adoption: the cultural impact of biomedical technologies on the adoptive family experience. *Family Relations* 2000 October; 49(4): 371-377. NRCBL: 14.1; 15.1.

Levy, Neil. Let life shape personality, not genetics [response]. *Conscience* 2003-2004 Winter; 24(4): 15-16. NRCBL: 14.1; 15.1.

Little, Margaret O.; Moczynski, Walter V.; Richardson, Paul G.; Joffe, Steven. Dana-Farber Cancer Institute ethics rounds: life-threatening illness and the desire to adopt. *Kennedy Institute of Ethics Journal* 2005 December; 15(4): 385- 393. NRCBL: 14.1; 7.1; 1.1; 9.5.5; 9.5.1; 5.2; 8.1; 8.2.
Abstract: Originally presented during Ethics Rounds at the Dana-Farber Cancer Institute, this commentary on the case of a patient treated for life-threatening cancer explores the responsibilities of health care providers when addressing the patient's desire to adopt a child.

Matorras, Roberto; Pennings, Guido. Reproductive exile versus reproductive tourism [letter and reply]. *Human Reproduction* 2005 December; 20(12): 3571-3572. NRCBL: 14.1; 21.1; 9.1.

Meyer, Lukas H. Reproductive rights [editorial]. *Ethical Perspectives* 2003; 10(3-4): 173-175. NRCBL: 14.1; 15.2; 14.4.

Mills, Claudia. Are there morally problematic reasons for having children? *Philosophy and Public Policy Quarterly* 2005 Fall; 25(4): 2-9. NRCBL: 14.1; 19.5; 14.4; 1.1.

Mullin, Amy. The ethical significance of pregnancy. *In her:* Reconceiving Pregnancy and Childcare: Ethics, Experience, and Reproductive Labor. New York: Cambridge University Press; 2005: 72-105. NRCBL: 14.1; 9.5.5.

Mullin, Amy. What about birth? *In her:* Reconceiving Pregnancy and Childcare: Ethics, Experience, and Reproductive Labor. New York: Cambridge University Press; 2005: 106-118. NRCBL: 14.1; 9.5.5.

Murphy, Timothy F.; White, Gladys B. Dead sperm donors or world hunger: are bioethicists studying the right stuff? [opinion]. *Hastings Center Report* 2005 March-April; 35(2): inside back cover. NRCBL: 14.1; 19.5; 20.1; 21.1.

Mykitiuk, Roxanne. Beyond conception: legal determinations of filiation in the context of assisted reproductive technologies. *Osgoode Hall Law Journal* 2001 Winter; 39(4): 771-815. NRCBL: 14.1. SC: le.

Nedelsky, Jennifer. Property in potential life? A relational approach to choosing legal categories. *Canadian Journal of Law and Jurisprudence* 1993; 6(2): 343- 365. NRCBL: 14.1; 10; 14.4; 9.3.1. SC: le.

Newson, A.J.; Smajdor, A.C. Artificial gametes: new paths to parenthood? *Journal of Medical Ethics* 2005 March; 31(3): 184-186. NRCBL: 14.1; 15.1; 19.1; 18.5.4.

Parker, Malcolm H. Posthumous conception and the need for consent [letter]. *Medical Journal of Australia* 1999 May 3; 170(9): 452-453. NRCBL: 14.1; 20.1; 8.3.1.

Pennings, G. Philosophical and ethical considerations regarding assisted reproductive technologies. *In:* Gerris, Jan; Olivennes, Francois; De Sutter, Petra, eds. Assisted Reproductive Technologies: Quality and Safety. Boca Raton: Taylor & Francis; 2004: 267-276. NRCBL: 14.1.

Pennings, Guido. Legal harmonization and reproductive tourism in Europe [opinion]. *Human Reproduction* 2004 December; 19(12): 2689-2694. NRCBL: 14.1; 21.1; 9.1. SC: le.

Petersen, Kerry; Baker, H.W.G.; Pitts, Marian; Thorpe, Rachel. Assisted reproductive technologies: professional and legal restrictions in Australian clinics. *Journal of Law and Medicine* 2005 February; 12(3): 373-385. NRCBL: 14.1; 5.3. SC: le.

Peterson, M.M. Assisted reproductive technologies and equity of access issues. *Journal of Medical Ethics* 2005 May; 31(5): 280-285. NRCBL: 14.1; 9.4; 9.5.5; 9.2.

Abstract: In Australia and other countries, certain groups of women have traditionally been denied access to assisted reproductive technologies (ARTs). These typically are single heterosexual women, lesbians, poor women, and those whose ability to rear children is questioned, particularly women with certain disabilities or who are older. The arguments used to justify selection of women for ARTs are most often based on issues such as scarcity of resources, and absence of infertility (in lesbians and single women), or on social concerns: that it "goes against nature"; particular women might not make good mothers; unconventional families are not socially acceptable; or that children of older mothers might be orphaned at an early age. The social, medical, legal, and ethical reasoning that has traditionally promoted this lack of equity in access to ARTs, and whether the criteria used for client deselection are ethically appropriate in any particular case, are explored by this review. In addition, the issues of distribution and just "gatekeeping" practices associated with these sensitive medical services are examined.

Potts, Malcolm. A retreat from reason? The Catholic church and scientific progress. *Conscience* 2003 Spring; 24(1): 16-19. NRCBL: 14.1; 1.2; 18.5.4.

Ragone, Helena; Willis, Sharla K. Reproduction and assisted reproductive technologies. *In:* Albrecht, Gary L.; Fitzpatrick, Ray; Scrimshaw, Susan C., eds. The Handbook of Social Studies in Health & Medicine. Thousand Oaks, CA: Sage; 2000: 308-322. NRCBL: 14.1; 9.5.5.

Rao, Kamini A. Infertility treatment is a human right [case study]. *Indian Journal of Medical Ethics* 2005 October-December; 2(4): 128. NRCBL: 14.1; 14.4; 9.5.10.

Ravindra, R.P. New reproductive technologies and the Indian woman. *In:* Shankar, Jogan, ed. Social Problems and Welfare in India. Delhi: Ashish Publ. 1992; 14 p. [Online]. Available: http://www.hsph.harvard.edu/Organizations/healthnet/SAsia/suchana/0400b/h022.html [3 October 2005]. NRCBL: 14.1; 15.2; 14.3.

Rosato, Jennifer L. The children of ART (assisted reproductive technology): should the law protect them from harm? *Utah Law Review* 2004; 2004(1): 57-110. NRCBL: 14.1; 14.5; 14.4; 5.3; 4.4. SC: le.

Rothman, Barbara Katz. What if I just say "a pox on both your houses"? [response]. *Conscience* 2003-2004 Winter; 24(4): 14-15. NRCBL: 14.1; 15.1.

Savulescu, Julian. Reproductive technology, efficiency and equality. *Medical Journal of Australia* 1999 December 6-20; 171(11-12): 668-670. NRCBL: 14.1; 9.2.

Schneider, Keith. Repro madness. *New Age Journal* 1986 January; 3: 34-39, 72-74. NRCBL: 14.1. SC: po.

Shannon, Thomas. The genetic fallacy: perfect genes do not eliminate schmucks [response]. *Conscience* 2003-2004 Winter; 24(4): 16-17. NRCBL: 14.1; 15.1.

Shenfield, Françoise. To know or not to know the identity of gametes donors? The UK and European legal context. *Journal of Assisted Reproduction and Genetics* 2004 April; 21(4): 95-96. NRCBL: 14.1; 8.4; 19.5.

Simonstein, F. A rational cure for prereproductive stress syndrome — a perspective from Israel: a rejoinder to Häyry, Bennet, Holm, and Aksoy. *Journal of Medical Ethics* 2005 September; 31(9): 557. NRCBL: 14.1; 9.5.5.

Spar, Debora. Reproductive tourism and the regulatory map [opinion]. *New England Journal of Medicine* 2005 February 10; 352(6): 531- 533. NRCBL: 14.1; 21.1; 5.3.

Standish, Dominic. Italy: fertile ground for reform. *Conscience* 2005 Spring; 26(1): 24-26. NRCBL: 14.1; 1.2; 12.4.2. SC: le.

Stanley, Lauren. Storm clouds gathering: while the number of mergers wanes, the threats from the Catholic hierarchy to reproductive health care continue. *Conscience*

NRCBL: National Reference Center for Bioethics Literature Classification Scheme   See inside front cover for terms.

413

2004-2005 Winter; 25(3): 40-41. NRCBL: 14.1; 1.2; 9.5.5; 11.1; 12.4.3; 18.5.4.

Statman, Daniel. The right to parenthood: an argument for a narrow interpretation. *Ethical Perspectives* 2003; 10(3-4): 224-235. NRCBL: 14.1. SC: an.

Stephens, Kevin U., Sr. Reproductive capacity: what does the embryo get? *Southern University Law Review* 1997 Spring; 24(2): 263-291. NRCBL: 14.1; 14.6; 21.1; 14.4; 4.4. SC: le.

Strong, Carson. Harming by conceiving: a review of misconceptions and a new analysis. *Journal of Medicine and Philosophy* 2005 October; 30(5): 491- 516. NRCBL: 14.1; 1.1; 4.4; 14.5; 15.2. SC: an.

Abstract: An objection often is raised against the use of reproductive technology to create "nontraditional families," as in ovum donation for postmenopausal women or postmortem artificial insemination. The objection states that conceiving children in such circumstances is harmful to them because of adverse features of these nontraditional families. A similar objection is raised when parents, through negligence or willful disregard of risks, create children with serious genetic diseases or other developmental handicaps. It is claimed that such reproduction harms the children who are created. In reply to this Harm to the Child Argument, it has been pointed out that the procreative acts that supposedly harm the child are the very acts that create the child. This reply has been developed into an argument that, in most of the types of cases under consideration, creating the child does not harm her. This reply, the No Harm Argument, has been stated in three main ways, and it is one of the most misunderstood arguments in bioethics. This paper examines the main rebuttals that have been made to the No Harm Argument and argues that none of them is successful.

Syrett, Keith. Impotence or importance? Judicial review in an era of explicit NHS rationing. *Modern Law Review* 2004 March; 67(2): 289-304. NRCBL: 14.1. SC: le. Identifiers: United Kingdom (Great Britain); National Health Service.

Taylor, Graham P.; Pennings, Guido. Ethics of assisted reproduction for HIV concordant couples [letter and reply]. *Human Reproduction* 2005 May; 20(5): 1430-1431. NRCBL: 14.1; 9.5.6.

ten Have, Henk A.M.J. Horror regulationum. *Hastings Center Report* 2004 July-August; 34(4): 16-17. NRCBL: 14.1; 2.4; 15.1; 18.5.4. Identifiers: President's Council on Bioethics.

Thomas, Sandy. Paradoxes and political problems: the U.S. approach to ART as seen from the UK. *Hastings Center Report* 2004 July-August; 34(4): 15-16. NRCBL: 14.1; 2.4; 18.5.4; 15.1. Identifiers: President's Council on Bioethics; assisted reproductive technologies.

Tindall, Gillian. Mixed blessings: ethical issues in assisted conception. *Journal of the Royal Society of Medicine* 2003 January; 96(1): 34-35. NRCBL: 14.1; 9.8.

Turone, Fabio. Italians fail to overturn restrictive reproduction law [news]. *BMJ: British Medical Journal* 2005 June 18; 330(7505): 1405. NRCBL: 14.1; 21.1; 1.2. SC: le.

van Bogaert, Louis-Jacques. The right to procreate — freedom and necessity [opinion]. *South African Medical Journal* 2005 January; 95(1): 32-34. NRCBL: 14.1; 13.2; 21.1.

Vayena, Effy; Rowe, Patrick J.; Peterson, Herbert B. Assisted reproductive technology in developing countries: why should we care? *Fertility and Sterility* 2002 July; 78(1): 13-15. NRCBL: 14.1; 21.1.

Wachbroit, Robert; Wasserman, David. Reproductive technology. *In:* LaFollette, Hugh, ed. The Oxford Handbook of Practical Ethics. New York: Oxford University Press; 2003: 136-160. NRCBL: 14.1; 15.1; 1.1. SC: an.

Walker, Kristen. 1950s family values vs human rights: in vitro fertilisation, donor insemination and sexuality in Victoria. *Public Law Review* 2000 December; 11(4): 292-307. NRCBL: 14.1; 10; 14.4; 14.2. SC: le.

Welin, Stellan. Reproductive ectogenesis: the third era of human reproduction and some moral consequences. *Science and Engineering Ethics* 2004 October; 10(4): 615-626. NRCBL: 14.1; 1.1.

Wolowelsky, Joel B.; Grazi, Richard V. Future directions. *In:* Grazi, Richard V. Overcoming Infertility: A Guide for Jewish Couples. New Milford, Conn.: Toby, 2005: 425-440. NRCBL: 14.1; 14.5; 14.6; 1.2.

Zhang, Heather Xiaoquan; Locke, Catherine. Interpreting reproductive rights: institutional responses to the agenda in the 1990s. *Public Administration and Development* 2004 February; 24(1): 41-50. NRCBL: 14.1; 21.1. Identifiers: Women's Global Network for Reproductive Rights; International Federation of Family Planning Association; United Kingdom's Department for International Development.

Zupancic, Karel; Meden, Helena; Tomazevic, Tomaz; Žnidaršic, Viktorija. The future law on infertility treatment and on biomedically assisted procreation in Slovenia. *Journal of Assisted Reproduction and Genetics* 2000 October; 17(9): 496-497. NRCBL: 14.1; 14.4. SC: le.

RESEARCH *See* BEHAVIORAL RESEARCH; BIOMEDICAL RESEARCH; GENETIC RESEARCH; HUMAN EXPERIMENTATION

RESEARCH ETHICS *See* ANIMAL EXPERIMENTATION; BIOMEDICAL RESEARCH/ RESEARCH ETHICS AND SCIENTIFIC MISCONDUCT; HUMAN EXPERIMENTATION

RESEARCH ETHICS COMMITTEES *See* HUMAN EXPERIMENTATION/ ETHICS COMMITTEES

RESOURCE ALLOCATION
See also HEALTH CARE ECONOMICS

Code of ethics of nurses: making enlightened decisions about overtime. *Perspective Infirmiere* 2004 September-October; 2(1, Supplement): 7. NRCBL: 9.4; 4.1.3; 6; 9.8.

Alejandro, Patricia. Bioetica, justicia y asignacion de recursos / Bioethics, justice and the allocation of resources. *Bioetica. Un Delsafio del Tercer Milenio* 2002-2003; 4(4): 32-37. NRCBL: 9.4; 1.1.

Anand, P. Capabilities and health. *Journal of Medical Ethics* 2005 May; 31(5): 299-303. NRCBL: 9.4; 9.3.1; 9.5.2. SC: an.
   Abstract: Sen's capabilities approach offers a radical generalisation of the conventional approach to welfare economics. It has been highly influential in development and many researchers are now beginning to explore its implications for health care. This paper contributes to the emerging debate by discussing two examples of such applications: first, at the individual decision making level, namely the right to die, and second, at the social choice level. For the first application, which draws on Nussbaum's list of capabilities, it is argued that many capabilities are ambiguously or indirectly related to the right to die, but the ability to form a concept of the good life and plan one's own life provides a direct justification for such a right. In the second application, the focus is specifically on healthcare rationing and it is argued that, although not committed to age based rationing, the capabilities approach provides a more natural justification of age related access to health care than the fair innings argument, which is often used to justify the alleged ageism inherent in quality adjusted life years (QALY) maximisation.

Baines, Darrin L.; Tolley, Keith H.; Whynes, David K. The ethics of resource allocation: the views of general practitioners in Lincolnshire, U.K. *Social Science and Medicine* 1998; 47(10): 1555-1564. NRCBL: 9.4. SC: em.

Bell, Nora Kizer. Responsibilities and rights in the promotion of health: differing positions of the individual and the state. *Social Science and Medicine* 1996 September; 43(5): 775-782. NRCBL: 9.4; 4.1.1; 1.1.

Beyleveld, Deryck. Individualrechte und soziale Gerechtigkeit. *In:* Honnefelder, Ludger; Mieth, Dietmar; Propping, Peter; Siep, Ludwig; Wiesemann, Claudia, eds. Das genetische Wissen und die Zukunft des Menschen. New York: De Gruyter; 2003: 375-387. NRCBL: 9.4; 4.5; 14.1; 20.5.1; 1.1. SC: an.

Bloche, M. Gregg; Jungman, Elizabeth R. The "r" word. *Journal of Contemporary Health Law and Policy* 2002 Fall; 18(3): 633-639. NRCBL: 9.4; 9.3.2. SC: le.

Brand, Gordon S.; Munoz, Gisela M.; Nichols, Michael G.; Okata, Maritza U.; Pitt, Jonathan B.; Seager, Susan. The two faces of gag provisions: patients and physicians in a bind. *Yale Law and Policy Review* 1998; 17: 249-280. NRCBL: 9.4; 9.3.2; 7.3; 9.4; 8.1; 9.8. SC: le.

Brock, Dan W. Ethical issues in the use of cost effectiveness analysis for the prioritisation of health care resources.
In: Anand, Sudhir; Peter, Fabienne; Sen, Amartya, eds. Public Health, Ethics, and Equity. New York: Oxford University Press; 2004: 201-223. NRCBL: 9.4; 4.4.

Cappelen, A.W.; Norheim, Ole Frithjof. Responsibility in health care: a liberal egalitarian approach. *Journal of Medical Ethics* 2005 August; 31(8): 476-480. NRCBL: 9.4; 9.1. SC: an.
   Abstract: Lifestyle diseases constitute an increasing proportion of health problems and this trend is likely to continue. A better understanding of the responsibility argument is important for the assessment of policies aimed at meeting this challenge. Holding individuals accountable for their choices in the context of health care is, however, controversial. There are powerful arguments both for and against such policies. In this article the main arguments for and the traditional arguments against the use of individual responsibility as a criterion for the distribution of scarce health resources will be briefly outlined. It is argued that one of the most prominent contemporary normative traditions, liberal egalitarianism, presents a way of holding individuals accountable for their choices that avoids most of the problems pointed out by the critics. The aim of the article is to propose a plausible interpretation of liberal egalitarianism with respect to responsibility and health care and assess it against reasonable counter-arguments.

Childress, James F. Just care: rationing in a public health crisis. *Update [Loma Linda University Center for Christian Bioethics]* 2005 September; 20(3): 1-7. NRCBL: 9.4; 9.1; 21.1.

Churchill, Larry R. Age-rationing in health care: flawed policy, personal virtue. *Health Care Analysis: An International Journal of Health Care Philosophy and Policy* 2005 June; 13(2): 137-146. NRCBL: 9.4; 9.5.2.
   Abstract: The age-rationing debate of fifteen years ago will inevitably reemerge as health care costs escalate. All age-rationing proposals should be judged in light of the current system of rationing health care by price in the U.S., and the resulting pattern of excess and deprivation. Age-rationing should be rejected as public policy, but recognized as a personal virtue of stewardship among the elderly.

Collins, Jody C. Experimental medical treatments: who should decide coverage? *Seattle University Law Review* 1997 Winter; 20(2): 451-487. NRCBL: 9.4; 9.3.2; 9.2; 9.3.1; 18.5.1. SC: le.

Cornell, John; Milner, Philip. Is health a matter of choice? [editorial]. *Journal of Public Health Medicine* 1996 June; 18(2): 127-128. NRCBL: 9.4; 9.5.9; 9.5.1; 4.2.

Cross, Elizabeth; Goodacre, S.; O'Cathain, A.; Arnold, J. Rationing in the emergency department: the good, the bad, and the unacceptable. *Emergency Medicine Journal* 2005 March; 22(3): 171-176. NRCBL: 9.4; 9.5.1. SC: em. Identifiers: United Kingdom (Great Britain).

Dew, Kevin; Cumming, Jacqueline; McLeod, Deborah; Morgan, Sonya; McKinlay, Eileen; Dowell, Anthony; Love, Tom. Explicit rationing of elective services: implementing the New Zealand reforms. *Health Policy* 2005 September 28; 74(1): 1-12. NRCBL: 9.4;

NRCBL: National Reference Center for Bioethics Literature Classification Scheme   See inside front cover for terms.

415

9.5.1. Identifiers: clinical priority assessment criteria (CPAC).

Doughton, Susan D. Response to professor Mark Hall. *Cumberland Law Review* 1997-1998; 28(2): 329-332. NRCBL: 9.4; 9.3.1; 9.3.2; 2.1. SC: le.

Elcioglu, Omur; Unluoglu, Ilhami. Triage in terms of medicine and ethics. *Saudi Medical Journal* 2004 December; 25(12): 1815-1819. NRCBL: 9.4; 1.2. Identifiers: Turkey; Islam.

Frezza, Eldo Ermenegildo; Squillario, Denise M.; Smith, Thomas J. The ethical challenge and the futile treatment in the older population admitted to the intensive care unit. *American Journal of Medical Quality* 1998 Fall; 13(3): 121-126. NRCBL: 9.4; 9.5.2; 9.5.1; 20.5.1. SC: em.

Fry, Sara T.; Veatch, Robert M. Justice: the allocation of health resources. *In their:* Case Studies in Nursing Ethics. Third edition. Sudbury, MA: Jones and Bartlett Publishers; 2006: 94-118. NRCBL: 9.4.

Fulton, Jane. Cooperative approaches to health-care rationing [editorial]. *Humane Health Care International* 1997 Summer; 13(2): 9-10. NRCBL: 9.4; 9.3.1; 21.1.

Gibson, Jennifer L.; Martin, Douglas K.; Singer, Peter A. Evidence, economics and ethics: resource allocation in health services organizations. *Healthcare Quarterly* 2005; 8(2): 50-59. NRCBL: 9.4; 1.3.2; 9.1. SC: cs. Identifiers: Canada.

Girod, Jennifer; Beckman, A.W. Just allocation and team loyalty: a new virtue ethic for emergency medicine. *Journal of Medical Ethics* 2005 October; 31(10): 567-570. NRCBL: 9.4; 7.3; 9.5.1. SC: an.

Abstract: When traditional virtue ethics is applied to clinical medicine, it often claims as its goal the good of the individual patient, and focuses on the dyadic relationship between one physician and one patient. An alternative model of virtue ethics, more appropriate to the practice of emergency medicine, will be outlined by this paper. This alternative model is based on the assumption that the appropriate goal of the practice of emergency medicine is a team approach to the medical wellbeing of individual patients, constrained by the wellbeing of the patient population served by a particular emergency department. By defining boundaries and using the key virtues of justice and team loyalty, this model fits emergency practice well and gives care givers the conceptual clarity to apply this model to various conflicts both within the department and with those outside the department.

Goold, Susan Dorr; Biddle, Andrea K.; Klipp, Glenn; Hall, Charles N.; Danis, Marion. Choosing healthplans all together: a deliberative exercise for allocating limited health care resources. *Journal of Health Politics, Policy and Law* 2005 August; 30(4): 563-602. NRCBL: 9.4; 9.3.1; 9.1.

Abstract: CHAT (Choosing Healthplans All Together) is an exercise in participatory decision making designed to engage the public in health care priority setting. Participants work individually and then in groups to distribute a limited number of pegs on a board as they select from a wide range of insurance options. Randomly distributed health events illustrate the consequences of insurance choices. In 1999-2000, the authors conducted fifty sessions of CHAT involving 592 residents of North Carolina. The exercise was rated highly regarding ease of use, informativeness, and enjoyment. Participants found the information believable and complete, thought the group decision-making process was fair, and were willing to abide by group decisions. CHAT holds promise as a tool to foster group deliberation, generate collective choices, and incorporate the preferences and values of consumers into allocation decisions. It can serve to inform and stimulate public dialogue about limited health care resources.

Graber, M.A.; Tansey, J.F. Autonomy, consent, and limiting healthcare costs. *Journal of Medical Ethics* 2005 July; 31(7): 424-426. NRCBL: 9.4; 8.3.1; 9.7.

Abstract: While protection of autonomy is crucial to the practice of medicine, there is the persistent risk of a disconnect between the notion of self-determination and the need for a socially responsible medical system. An example of unbridled autonomy is the preferential use of costly medications without an appreciation of the impact of using these more expensive drugs on the resource pool of others. In the USA, costly medications of questionable incremental benefit are frequently prescribed with the complicity of both doctors and patients. Limiting self-determination in medication choices via an appreciation of the principle of justice reaches a better moral balance, while at the same time acknowledging the goals of doing good and avoiding harm in patient care.

Greß, Stefan; Niebuhr, Dea; Rothgang, Heinz; Wasem, Jürgen. Criteria and procedures for determining benefit packages in health care: a comparative perspective. *Health Policy* 2005 July; 73(1): 78-91. NRCBL: 9.4; 5.2; 9.3.1; 9.1; 7.1. Identifiers: United Kingdom (Great Britain); Germany; Switzerland.

Gross, Michael; Latimer, Eric A.; Battista, Renaldo N.; Wright, Charles J.; Pelletier, L. Conrad; McMurtry, Robert Y. The ethical allocation of scarce resources in surgery: implants and cost [article and commentaries]. *Canadian Journal of Surgery* 1997 December; 40(6): 421-429. NRCBL: 9.4; 9.5.1. Note: Abstract in French and English.

Gyrd-Hansen, Dorte. Investigating the social value of health changes. *Journal of Health Economics* 2004 November; 23(6): 1101-1116. NRCBL: 9.4; 4.4. SC: em. Identifiers: Denmark.

Ham, Chris; Coulter, Angela. Explicit and implicit rationing: taking responsibility and avoiding blame for health care choices. *Journal of Health Services Research and Policy* 2001 July; 6(3): 163-169. NRCBL: 9.4; 21.1.

Harris, John. The age-indifference principle and equality. *CQ: Cambridge Quarterly of Healthcare Ethics* 2005 Winter; 14(1): 93-99. NRCBL: 9.4; 9.5.2; 1.1; 9.3.1; 9.8.

Harris, John. It's not NICE to discriminate [editorial]. *Journal of Medical Ethics* 2005 July; 31(7): 373-375. NRCBL: 9.4; 4.4; 9.2; 9.5.1. Identifiers: United Kingdom (Great Britain); National Institute for Health and Clinical Excellence.

Harrison, Stephen; Moran, Michael. Resources and rationing: managing supply and demand in health care. *In:* Albrecht, Gary L.; Fitzpatrick, Ray; Scrimshaw, Susan C., eds. The Handbook of Social Studies in Health & Medicine. Thousand Oaks, CA: Sage; 2000: 493-508. NRCBL: 9.4; 21.1.

Hartshorne, Johan; Hasegawa, Thomas K., Jr. Overservicing in dental practice — ethical perspectives. *SADJ: Journal of the South African Dental Association* 2003 October; 58(9): 364-365, 367-369. NRCBL: 9.4; 7.4; 4.1.1; 1.3.1. SC: rv.

Hasman, Andreas; Holm, Søren. Accountability for reasonableness: opening the black box of process. *Health Care Analysis: An International Journal of Health Care Philosophy and Policy* 2005 December; 13(4): 261-273. NRCBL: 9.4; 1.1; 9.3.1. SC: an.

Abstract: Norman Daniels' and James Sabin's theory of "accountability for reasonableness" (A4R) is a much discussed account of due process for decision-making on health care priority setting. Central to the theory is the acceptance that people may justifiably disagree on what reasons it is relevant to consider when priorities are made, but that there is a core set of reasons, that all centre on fairness, on which there will be no disagreement. A4R is designed as an institutional decision process which will ensure that only those reasons which everybody will agree are relevant and appropriate form part of decision-making. The argument which we will put forward in this paper questions whether it is a simple matter to delineate the core set of reasons and claims that it is a potential problem in A4R that it does not provide an indication of the exact content of this process. The paper first briefly outlines the content of A4R. It is argued that disagreement on what services should be high priorities cannot be resolved solely with a reference to "due process." In order to retain consistency over time, decision-makers are required to agree and articulate what reasons qualify as relevant and how conflicting reasons are to be balanced in the course of the process. The second and main part of the paper then considers how the reason of "solidarity" can be handled within the A4R framework, and it is shown that deciding whether solidarity should be admitted to the core set of allowable reasons is not a simple matter.

Hongladarom, Tongchan. Ethical decision-making and its teaching. *Journal of the Medical Association of Thailand* 1998 August; 81(8): 647-651. NRCBL: 9.4; 7.1; 2.1. Note: article in both English and Thai.

Hughes, David; Griffiths, Lesley. "Ruling in" and "ruling out": two approaches to the micro-rationing of health care. *Social Science and Medicine* 1997 March; 44(5): 589-599. NRCBL: 9.4; 9.2. SC: em. Identifiers: United Kingdom (Great Britain).

James, Chris; Carrin, Guy; Savedoff, William; Hanvoravongchai, Piya. Clarifying efficiency-equity tradeoffs through explicit criteria, with a focus on developing countries. *Health Care Analysis: An International Journal of Health Care Philosophy and Policy* 2005 March; 13(1): 33-51. NRCBL: 9.4; 1.1; 21.1.

Abstract: Expenditures on health in many developing countries are being disproportionately spent on health services that have a low overall health impact, and that disproportionately benefit the rich. Without explicit consideration of priority setting, this situation is likely to remain unchanged: resource allocation is too often dictated by historical patterns, and maintains vested interests. This paper explores how prioritization between different health interventions can be rationalised by the use of clearly defined criteria. A number of key efficiency and equity criteria are examined, in particular analysing how potential tradeoffs could be incorporated into the decision making process.

Jayasinghe, K.S.A.; De Silva, D.; Mendis, N.; Lie, R.K. Ethics of resource allocation in developing countries: the case of Sri Lanka. *Social Science and Medicine* 1998 November; 47(10): 1619-1625. NRCBL: 9.4; 21.1; 9.3.1.

Jonsen, Albert R. Bioethics and the health care system. *In his:* Bioethics Beyond the Headlines: Who Lives? Who Dies? Who Decides? Lanham, MD: Rowman and Littlefield; 2005: 141-153. NRCBL: 9.4; 9.2; 9.3.1.

Jost, Timothy Stoltzfus. The role of the courts in health care rationing: the German model. *Journal of Contemporary Health Law and Policy* 2002 Fall; 18(3): 613-617. NRCBL: 9.4; 1.3.8. SC: le.

Kamm, Frances M. Deciding whom to help, health-adjusted life years and disabilities. *In:* Anand, Sudhir; Peter, Fabienne; Sen, Amartya, eds. Public Health, Ethics, and Equity. New York: Oxford University Press; 2004: 225-242. NRCBL: 9.4; 4.4.

Kelly, David F. Allocating health care resources. *In his:* Contemporary Catholic Health Care Ethics. Washington, DC: Georgetown University Press; 2004: 270-282. NRCBL: 9.4; 9.3.1; 1.2.

Kelly, David F. The use and misuse of the allocation argument. *In his:* Contemporary Catholic Health Care Ethics. Washington, DC: Georgetown University Press; 2004: 286-296. NRCBL: 9.4; 1.2.

Loewy, Erich H. Age discrimination at its best: should chronological age be a prime factor in medical decision making? *Health Care Analysis: An International Journal of Health Care Philosophy and Policy* 2005 June; 13(2): 101-117. NRCBL: 9.4; 9.5.2; 9.5.7; 9.3.1.

Abstract: This paper briefly reviews the papers in this special section of HCA and makes the point—a point which should be obvious—that statistics are useful only as guidelines but tell one nothing about the individual patient in front of you. Chronological age merely shows what is true of most but decidedly not of all patients in a particular age group. To ration on the basis of age alone is unfair to the individual denied treatment and damaging to the community because it disturbs the solidarity which comes about because most members of the community feel that the community has obligations beyond those of not directly harming them; indeed, what produces solidarity is the feeling that members of a community will do their best to come to each other's help. Rationing on the basis of age alone denies people of equal treatment under the law and—when it comes to the elderly—is a type of age discrimination. It is pointed out that what matters is a patient's disease and not his/her age. A permanently vegetative person 8 years of age is a much sadder occurrence than it would be at age 90—but the critical fact is that both are permanently vegetative. Age cuts both ways— it is

NRCBL: National Reference Center for Bioethics Literature Classification Scheme   See inside front cover for terms.

417

irrational to spend hundreds of thousands of dollars, untold amounts of time, energy and devotion to the 520 gm infant with a gr IV diffuse haemorrhage whose chance of leading a sentient life is close to zero and to hesitate before using a diagnostic MRI on a patient who is 90 but fully alert and enjoying life. It is concluded that age as an independent variable in the allocation of resources is ethically highly problematic.

Loewy, Roberta Springer. Ageisms. *Health Care Analysis: An International Journal of Health Care Philosophy and Policy* 2005 June; 13(2): 147-156. NRCBL: 9.4; 9.5.2.
Abstract: In this paper some very fundamental attitudes we have and assumptions we make in the US about persons, what they owe and what they are owed, are scrutinized and found to be indefensibly ageist. It is argued that these assumptions and the attitudes they engender are supported by logically and ethically suspect methods and conclusions. These errors are summarized and some remedial steps by which we might better protect against such illicit and unwarranted methods and conclusions in the future are suggested.

Lomas, Jonathan. Reluctant rationers: public input to health care priorities. *Journal of Health Services Research Policy* 1997 April; 2(2): 103-111. NRCBL: 9.4; 9.1.

Manning, Joanna; Paterson, Ron. "Prioritization": rationing health care in New Zealand. *Journal of Law, Medicine and Ethics* 2005 Winter; 33(4): 681- 697. NRCBL: 9.4. SC: le.

Matschinger, Herbert; Angermeyer, Matthias C. The public's preferences concerning the allocation of financial resources to health care: results from a representative population survey in Germany. *European Psychiatry* 2004 December; 19(8): 478-482. NRCBL: 9.4; 17.1. SC: em.

McCullagh, Peter. Some economic considerations. *In his:* Conscious in a Vegetative State? A Critique of the PVS Concept. Boston: Kluwer Academic; 2004: 261-281. NRCBL: 9.4; 20.5.1.

McGough, Laura J.; Reynolds, Steven J.; Quinn, Thomas C.; Zenilman, Jonathan M. Which patients first? Setting priorities for antiretroviral therapy where resources are limited. *American Journal of Public Health* 2005 July; 95(7): 1173-1180. NRCBL: 9.4; 9.5.6; 9.7; 21.1.
Abstract: The availability of limited funds from international agencies for the purchase of antiretroviral (ARV) treatment in developing countries presents challenges, especially in prioritizing who should receive therapy. Public input and the protection of human rights are crucial in making treatment programs equitable and accountable. By examining historical precedents of resource allocation, we aim to provoke and inform debate about current ARV programs.Through a critical review of the published literature, we evaluate 4 precedents for key lessons: the discovery of insulin for diabetes in 1922, the release of penicillin for civilian use in 1943, the development of chronic hemodialysis programs in 1961, and current allocation of liver transplants. We then describe current rationing mechanisms for ARVs.

Melnick, Alan; Kaplowitz, Lisa; Lopez, Wilfredo; Murphy, Anne M.; Bernheim, Ruth Gaare. Public health ethics in action: flu vaccine and drug allocation

strategies. *Journal of Law, Medicine and Ethics* 2005 Winter; 33(4, Supplement): 102-105. NRCBL: 9.4; 9.7; 9.1. SC: le.

Miller, Alfred E. Social ethics and organizational structures influencing the allocation of health care in Germany and the United States. *Journal of Contemporary Health Law and Policy* 2002 Fall; 18(3): 649-661. NRCBL: 9.4; 9.3.1; 7.1.

Mooney, Gavin; Jan, Stephen; Wiseman, Virginia. Staking a claim for claims: a case study of resource allocation in Australian Aboriginal health care. *Social Science and Medicine* 2002 June; 54(11): 1657-1667. NRCBL: 9.4; 9.3.1; 9.5.4.

Nadolski, Heidi. Budgeting and rationing in the German health care system. *Journal of Contemporary Health Law and Policy* 2002 Fall; 18(3): 697-702. NRCBL: 9.4; 9.3.1.

National Health and Medical Research Council [NHMRC] (Australia). Ethical considerations relating to health care resource allocation decisions. Canberra, ACT: The Council 1993; 7 p. [Online]. Available: http://www7. health.gov.au/nhmrc/publications/pdf/e24.pdf [31 March 2005]. NRCBL: 9.4. Note: Reprinted in January 1999 as originally released in November 1993.

Newdick, Christopher. Accountability for rationing — theory into practice. *Journal of Law, Medicine and Ethics* 2005 Winter; 33(4): 660- 668. NRCBL: 9.4. SC: le.

Øhrstrom, Peter; Albretsen, Jørgen; Holm, Søren. The use of computer simulation and artificial intelligence in the study of ethical components of medical decision-making. *In:* Holm, Søren; Jonas, Monique F., eds. Engaging the World: The Use of Empirical Research in Bioethics and the Regulation of Biotechnology. Washington, DC: IOS Press; 2004: 119-128. NRCBL: 9.4; 9.5.1; 1.3.12; 5.1.

Persing, John A. Craniofacial surgery and the ethics of decision-making. *Cleft Palate-Craniofacial Journal* 1995 November; 32(6): 504-506. NRCBL: 9.4; 4.1.2. SC: cs.

Plantak, Zdravko. Universal access to health care and religious basis of human rights. *Update [Loma Linda University Center for Christian Bioethics]* 2005 June; 20(2): 1-12. NRCBL: 9.4; 21.1; 1.2.

Pleat, Jonathon M.; Dunkin, Chris S.J.; Davies, Charlotte; Adams, Titus. Breast augmentation should be on the NHS: a discussion of the ethics of rationing [letter]. *Annals of the Royal College of Surgeons in England* 2003 March; 85(2): 145-146. NRCBL: 9.4; 4.5; 9.2. Identifiers: National Health Service.

Rhodes, Rosamond. Justice in medicine and public health. *CQ: Cambridge Quarterly of Healthcare Ethics* 2005 Winter; 14(1): 13-26. NRCBL: 9.4; 1.1; 9.1.

Ries, Nola M. The uncertain state of the law regarding health care and section 15 of the Charter. *Health Law Jour-*

nal 2003; 11: 217-239. NRCBL: 9.4; 4.4. SC: le. Identifiers: Canadian Charter of Rights and Freedoms; publicly funded health care.

Rosner, Fred. Allocation or misallocation of limited medical resources [editorial]. *Cancer Investigation* 2004; 22(5): 810-812. NRCBL: 9.4; 9.5.7; 19.6.

Schäfer, Christof; Nelson, Kristin; Herbst, Manfred. Waiting for radiotherapy: a national call for ethical discourse on waiting lists in radiotherapy: findings from a preliminary survey. *Strahlentherapie und Onkologie* 2005 January; 181(1): 9-19. NRCBL: 9.4; 9.5.1;. SC: em. Identifiers: Germany.

Schmidt, Volker H. Rationing health care in the welfare state: three policies. *Journal of Health and Social Policy* 2004; 19(1): 57-76. NRCBL: 9.4; 9.2; 9.3.2. Identifiers: United Kingdom (Great Britain); Oregon; Singapore.

Schwappach, David L.B.; Koeck, Christian M. Preferences for disclosure: the case of bedside rationing. *Social Science and Medicine* 2004 November; 59(9): 1891-1897. NRCBL: 9.4; 8.2. SC: em. Identifiers: Germany.

Segev, Re'em. Well-being and fairness in the distribution of scarce health resource. *Journal of Medicine and Philosophy* 2005 June; 30(3): 231-260. NRCBL: 9.4. SC: an.

Abstract: Based on a general thesis regarding the proper resolution of interpersonal conflicts, this paper suggests a normative framework for the distribution of scarce health resources. The proposed thesis includes two basic ideas. First, individual well-being is the fundamental value. Second, interpersonal conflicts affecting well-being should be resolved in light of several conceptions of fairness, reflecting the independent value of persons and the moral significance of responsibility of individuals for the existence of interpersonal conflicts. These ideas are elaborated in several principles that are applied with respect to the distribution of scarce health resources.

Shickle, Darren. Rationing of health care: why do acute hospital services have higher priority? *In:* Chadwick, Ruth; Levitt, Mairi, eds. Ethical Issues in Community Health Care. New York: Arnold; 1998: 51-62. NRCBL: 9.4; 9.3.1.

Silva, Mary Cipriano; Lewis, Carolyn K. Ethics, policy, and allocation of scarce resources in nursing service administration: a pilot study. *NursingConnections* 1991 Summer; 4(2): 44-52. NRCBL: 9.4; 1.1; 9.3.1; 7.1. SC: rv.

Syrett, K. Deference or deliberation: rethinking the judicial role in the allocation of healthcare resources. *Medicine and Law: World Association for Medical Law* 2005 June; 24(2): 309-322. NRCBL: 9.4. SC: le.

Abstract: The development of strategies by which healthcare resources are explicitly rationed has created significant challenges for many governments. In particular, those undertaking allocative decisions may struggle to establish sufficient legitimacy to enable them to make choices which are morally and politically controversial without generating distrust and resistance, which could jeopardise the effectiveness of the decision-making regime. This article considers possible means of addressing this difficulty from the perspective of public law.

The mechanism which is currently favoured, most clearly seen in the UK, is to establish regulatory agencies which apply scientific and social-scientific methodologies to priority-setting questions. This has not been entirely successful. Accordingly, the article will propose a more developed role for courts, which can require that reasoned, relevant justifications for allocative choices are offered and thus provide a foundation for broad public deliberation on rationing. However, in order to fulfil such a function, the judiciary will need to modify its traditionally deferential stance on issues of this type. South African and Canadian cases illustrate how such a change may come about.

Syrett, Keith. "Child B": reasons, rationing and the right to life. *Personal Injury Law and Medical Review* 1995 Summer; 2(2): 156-170. NRCBL: 9.4; 9.3.1. SC: le.

Tauber, Alfred I. A philosophical approach to rationing. *Medical Journal of Australia* 2003 May 5; 178(9): 454-456. NRCBL: 9.4; 1.1.

Taylor, Bettina; Burns, Derrick. Can medical scheme reform lead to fairer distribution of limited resources? A funding perspective. *South African Medical Journal* 2005 March; 95(3): 175-179. NRCBL: 9.4; 9.3.1; 9.3.2; 9.8.

United States. National Conference of Commissioners on Uniform State Laws. Uniform Health Care Decisions Act. [approved by the American Bar Association, Kansas City, Missouri, February 7, 1994]. Charleston, South Carolina: Annual Conference, National Conference of Commissioners on Uniform State Laws 1993 July 30-August 6; 36 p. [Online]. Available: http://www.law.upenn.edu/bll/ulc/fnact99/1990s/uhcda93.pdf [25 January 2006]. NRCBL: 9.4; 8.1. SC: le.

Van Parijs, Philippe. Just health care in a pluri-national country. *In:* Anand, Sudhir; Peter, Fabienne; Sen, Amartya, eds. Public Health, Ethics, and Equity. New York: Oxford University Press; 2004: 163-180. NRCBL: 9.4; 1.1.

VanGeest, Jonathan B.; Wynia, Matthew K.; Cummins, Deborah S.; Wilson, Ira B. Measuring deception: test-retest reliability of physicians' self-reported manipulation of reimbursement rules for patients. *Medical Care Research and Review* 2002 June; 59(2): 184-196. NRCBL: 9.4; 8.1; 7.1; 9.3.1; 9.8.

Vijayashankara, Nanjegowda. "Right to die" — situation is different in developing countries . . . [letter]. *BMJ: British Medical Journal* 2005 June 11; 330(7504): 1389. NRCBL: 9.4; 20.5.1.

Walter, Nicholas; Schillinger, Dean. Front-line bureaucracies and the moral mechanics of US health care [editorial]. *Medical Care* 2004 April; 42(4): 303-305. NRCBL: 9.4; 9.5.10; 9.3.1; 9.2; 8.3.1.

Weiner, Saul J.; Laporte, Margaret; Abrams, Richard I.; Moswin, Arthur; Warnecke, Richard. Rationing access to care to the medically uninsured: the role of bureaucratic front-line discretion at large healthcare institutions.

NRCBL: National Reference Center for Bioethics Literature Classification Scheme   See inside front cover for terms.

419

Medical Care 2004 April; 42(4): 306-312. NRCBL: 9.4; 9.3.1; 8.3.1; 9.5.10. SC: em.

Wirtz, Veronika; Cribb, Alan; Barber, Nick. Reimbursement decisions in health policy — extending our understanding of the elements of decision-making. *Health Policy* 2005 September 8; 73(3): 330-338. NRCBL: 9.4; 9.3.1; 9.7; 7.1. SC: em. Identifiers: United Kingdom (Great Britain).

RESUSCITATION ORDERS *See* EUTHANASIA AND ALLOWING TO DIE

RIGHT TO DIE *See* ASSISTED SUICIDE; EUTHANASIA AND ALLOWING TO DIE

RIGHT TO HEALTH CARE

Abbing, Henriette D.C. Roscam. The right to care for health: the contribution of the European Social Charter [editorial]. *European Journal of Health Law* 2005 September; 12(3): 183- 191. NRCBL: 9.2; 21.1. SC: le.

Anwar, Katharina; O'Mahony, Fidelma. Patient access to their records: rights or risks? *British Journal of Obstetrics and Gynaecology* 2000 January; 107(1): 141-142. NRCBL: 9.2; 8.1; 7.1.

Ashcroft, Richard E. Access to essential medicines: a Hobbesian social contract approach. *Developing World Bioethics* 2005 May; 5(2): 121-141. NRCBL: 9.2; 5.3; 9.7; 9.5.6; 21.1; 1.1. SC: an.

Abstract: Medicines that are vital for the saving and preserving of life in conditions of public health emergency or endemic serious disease are known as essential medicines. In many developing world settings such medicines may be unavailable, or unaffordably expensive for the majority of those in need of them. Furthermore, for many serious diseases (such as HIV/AIDS and tuberculosis) these essential medicines are protected by patents that permit the patent-holder to operate a monopoly on their manufacture and supply, and to price these medicines well above marginal cost. Recent international legal doctrine has placed great stress on the need to globalise intellectual property rights protections, and on the rights of intellectual property rights holders to have their property rights enforced. Although international intellectual property rights law does permit compulsory licensing of protected inventions in the interests of public health, the use of this right by sovereign states has proved highly controversial. In this paper I give an argument in support of states' sovereign right to expropriate private intellectual property in conditions of public health emergency. This argument turns on a social contract argument for the legitimacy of states. The argument shows, further, that under some circumstances states are not merely permitted compulsory to [sic] license inventions, but are actually obliged to do so, on pain of failure of their legitimacy as sovereign states. The argument draws freely on a loose interpretation of Thomas Hobbes's arguments in his Leviathan, and on an analogy between his state of War and the situation of public health disasters.

Attaran, Amir. Human rights and biomedical research funding for the developing world: discovering state obligations under the right to health. *Health and Human Rights: An International Journal* 1999; 4(1): 27-58. NRCBL: 9.2; 21.1; 1.3.6; 1.3.9; 9.3.1; 9.4. SC: le.

Bane, Ellie Paukert. Mandatory insurance coverage for infertility treatment: difficult to conceive? *Medical Trial Technique Quarterly* 2001; 48(1): 215-242. NRCBL: 9.2; 14.1; 9.4; 9.3.1. SC: le.

Bell, Sylvia. What does the "right to health" have to offer mental health patients? *International Journal of Law and Psychiatry* 2005 March- April; 28(2): 141-153. NRCBL: 9.2; 17.1; 21.1. SC: le. Identifiers: New Zealand.

Blum, J.; Carstens, P.; Talib, N. The impact of immigration on health systems: a legal analysis from a three-country perspective. *Medicine and Law: World Association for Medical Law* 2005 June; 24(2): 323-336. NRCBL: 9.2; 9.5.10; 21.1.

Abstract: The focus of this paper will be on how health care systems in three countries, Malaysia, South Africa and the United States, are responding to the health needs of immigrants with a strong focus on the legal aspects of the respective national responses. The Malaysia portion emphasizes legal immigration and analyses as to how the country's Ministry of Health and the delivery system itself is responding to the demands of immigrant's health. In the context of South Africa, the paper explores implications of the South African Constitution, which establishes a right to access health care, and explores whether such a right can be extended to non- citizens, or can be tempered by economic constraints. In the American discussion the focus is on whether publicly supported health care programs can be accessed to provide coverage for undocumented residents, and highlights recent constraints in using government monies in this area.

Bodenheimer, Thomas. The political divide in health care: a liberal perspective. *Health Affairs* 2005 November-December; 24(6): 1426-1435. NRCBL: 9.2; 9.3.1; 21.1.

Braveman, P.; Gruskin, S. Defining equity in health. *Journal of Epidemiology and Community Health* 2003 April; 57(4): 254-258. NRCBL: 9.2; 9.1; 1.1; 21.1.

Büken, Nüket Örnek; Büken, Erhan. The legal and ethical aspects of medical malpractice in Turkey. *European Journal of Health Law* 2003 June; 10(2): 201-213. NRCBL: 9.2; 8.5; 8.3.1. SC: le.

Carey, Benedict. In the hospital, a degrading shift from person to patient (Being a patient: a loss of dignity). *New York Times* 2005 August 16; p. A1, A12. NRCBL: 9.2; 4.4. SC: po.

Catholic Church. Catholic Bishops of Kentucky. Health care coverage: whose responsibility? *Origins* 2005 December 22; 35(28): 465-469. NRCBL: 9.2; 9.3.1; 1.2; 9.5.10.

den Exter, André. Access to health care in the Netherlands: the influence of (European) treaty law. *Journal of Law, Medicine and Ethics* 2005 Winter; 33(4): 698- 710. NRCBL: 9.2; 9.3.1; 21.1. SC: le.

Denier, Yvonne. On personal responsibility and the human right to health care. *CQ: Cambridge Quarterly of Healthcare Ethics* 2005 Spring; 14(2): 224-234. NRCBL: 9.2; 21.1; 1.1; 9.4; 7.1; 5.2.

Dyck, Arthur J. Justice and nurture: rescue and health care as rights and responsibilities. *In his:* Rethinking Rights and Responsiblities: The Moral Bonds of Community. Revised edition. Washington, DC: Georgetown University Press; 2005: 280-326. NRCBL: 9.2; 9.3.1; 1.1. SC: an.

Ervin, Naomi E.; Bell, Sue Ellen. Social justice issues related to uneven distribution of resources. *Journal of the New York State Nurses Association* 2004 Spring-Summer; 35(1): 8-13. NRCBL: 9.2; 1.1; 9.1.

Flood, Colleen M. Just medicare: the role of Canadian courts in determining health care rights and access. *Journal of Law, Medicine and Ethics* 2005 Winter; 33(4): 669-680. NRCBL: 9.2; 9.3.1. SC: le.

Flood, Colleen M.; Gable, Lance; Gostin, Lawrence O. Legislating and litigating health care rights around the world. *Journal of Law, Medicine and Ethics* 2005 Winter; 33(4): 636- 640. NRCBL: 9.2; 21.1. SC: le.

Forman, Lisa. Ensuring reasonable health: health rights, the judiciary, and South African HIV/AIDS policy. *Journal of Law, Medicine and Ethics* 2005 Winter; 33(4): 711-724. NRCBL: 9.2; 9.5.6. SC: le.

Giesen, Dieter. Health care as a right: some practical implications. *Medicine and Law: World Association for Medical Law* 1994; 13(3-4): 285-296. NRCBL: 9.2; 1.1.

Goodman, Timothy. Is there a right to health? *Journal of Medicine and Philosophy* 2005 December; 30(6): 643-662. NRCBL: 9.2; 9.7. SC: an.
Abstract: This article challenges the widespread contention-promoted by the World Health Organization, the U.N. Human Rights Commission, and certain non-governmental organizations-that health care should be regarded as an individual human right. Like other "post-modern" rights, the asserted individual right to health care is a positive claim on the resources of others; it is unlimited by corresponding responsibilities; and it pertains exclusively to the individual. In fact, an individual human right to health, enforceable against either governments or corporations, does not currently exist in law. If established, such a right would portend a dramatic expansion of government control over health care, with negative consequences for efficiency and patient welfare. Voluntary efforts based on partnership, rather than the imposition of legal requirements, are the most productive means of expanding access to health care while preserving incentives for continued development of innovative health technologies.

Gulliford, Martin; Figueroa-Munoz, Jose; Morgan, Myfanwy,; Hughes, David; Gibson, Barry; Beech, Roger; Hudson, Meryl. What does 'access to health care' mean? [opinion]. *Journal of Health Services Research and Policy* 2002 July; 7(3): 186-188. NRCBL: 9.2; 9.3.1; 9.4.

Hunt, Paul. The UN special rapporteur on the right to health: key objectives, themes, and interventions. *Health and Human Rights: An International Journal* 2003; 7(1): 1-27. NRCBL: 9.2; 21.1; 7.1; 17.1; 5.3. Identifiers: United Nations.

Jacobi, John V. Prison health, public health: obligations and opportunities. *American Journal of Law and Medicine* 2005; 31(4): 447-478. NRCBL: 9.2; 17.8; 9.1; 18.5.5.

Jacobson, Peter D. Health law 2005: an agenda. *Journal of Law, Medicine and Ethics* 2005 Winter; 33(4): 725- 738. NRCBL: 9.2; 7.3. SC: le.

Khajawi, Fei. Personal autonomy when deciding on medical treatment: placental and umbilical cord blood stem cell transplantation. *Medical Trial Technique Quarterly* 2002; 48(4): 347-373. NRCBL: 9.2; 1.3.5; 19.1; 9.1; 5.3. SC: le.

Kinney, Eleanor D. The international human right to health: what does this mean for our nation and world? *Indiana Law Review* 2001; 34(4): 1457-1475. NRCBL: 9.2; 21.1. SC: le.

Kirby, Michael. The right to health fifty years on: still skeptical? *Health and Human Rights: An International Journal* 1999; 4(1): 7-25. NRCBL: 9.2; 21.1; 7.1; 9.5.6. SC: le.

Kleinman, Arthur. Ethics and experience: an anthropological approach to health equity. *In:* Anand, Sudhir; Peter, Fabienne; Sen, Amartya, eds. Public Health, Ethics, and Equity. New York: Oxford University Press; 2004: 269-282. NRCBL: 9.2; 20.7; 7.1.

Kristan, Ivan. Constitutional aspects of the right to health care in Slovenia. *Medicine and Law: World Association for Medical Law* 1995; 14(3-4): 239-244. NRCBL: 9.2; 9.3.1; 12.4.3. SC: le.

Labonte, Ronald. Global right to health campaign launched [news]. *BMJ: British Medical Journal* 2005 July 30; 331(7511): 252. NRCBL: 9.2; 21.1.

Levy, Sharon. Asserting the right to life — a challenge to medical guidance on withdrawing treatment. *Medicine and Law: World Association for Medical Law* 2005 March; 24(1): 11-20. NRCBL: 9.2; 20.5.1; 20.5.4. SC: le.
Abstract: This paper analyses the English High Court decision of R (on the application of Burke) v General Medical Council and considers its implications for the future. Mr. Burke, relying on common law and the European Convention on Human Rights, succeeded in a challenge to the General Medical Council's Guidance on Withholding and Withdrawing Life-prolonging Treatment. He asserted his right to choose to be given treatment so as to live and condemned the Guidance as centred on the right to refuse treatment.

Littell, Amanda. Can a constitutional right to health guarantee universal health care coverage or improved health outcomes?: a survey of selected states. *Connecticut Law Review* 2002 Fall; 35(1): 289-318. NRCBL: 9.2; 9.3.1; 9.1; 21.1; 1.1. SC: le.

NRCBL: National Reference Center for Bioethics Literature Classification Scheme   See inside front cover for terms.

421

Mathiharan, K. The fundamental right to health care. *Issues in Medical Ethics* 2003 October-December; 11(4): 123. NRCBL: 9.2. Identifiers: India.

McLachlan, Hugh V. Health, health care, justice and rights. *In his:* Social Justice, Human Rights and Public Policy. Glasgow, Scotland: Humming Earth; 2005: 57-64. NRCBL: 9.2; 9.1; 1.1.

Molinari, Patrick A. Trends in health legislation and human rights. *Medicine and Law: World Association for Medical Law* 1995; 14(7-8): 589-599. NRCBL: 9.2; 21.1. SC: le.

Mongan, James J.; Lee, Thomas H. Do we really want broad access to health care? *New England Journal of Medicine* 2005 March 24; 352(12): 1260- 1263. NRCBL: 9.2; 9.3.1; 9.4.

Myers, Nancy A; London, Andrew S. Health care, access to. *In:* Restivo, Sal, ed. Science, Technology, and Society: An Encyclopedia. New York: Oxford University Press; 2005: 183-188. NRCBL: 9.2; 9.3.1; 9.4.

Nord, Erik. The use of cost-value analysis to judge patients' right to treatment. *Medicine and Law: World Association for Medical Law* 1995; 14(7-8): 553-558. NRCBL: 9.2; 9.4; 9.3.1. SC: em.

Norheim, Ole Frithjof. Rights to specialized health care in Norway: a normative perspective. *Journal of Law, Medicine and Ethics* 2005 Winter; 33(4): 641- 649. NRCBL: 9.2. SC: le.

Putsch, Robert W.; Pololi, Linda. Distributive justice in American healthcare: institutions, power, and the equitable care of patients. *American Journal of Managed Care* 2004 September; 10(Special Issue): SP45-SP53. NRCBL: 9.2; 7.1; 9.3.1; 9.5.1. SC: rv.

Rich, Robert F. Health policy, health insurance and the social contract. *Comparative Labor Law and Policy Journal* 2000 Winter; 21(2): 397-421. NRCBL: 9.2; 9.1; 1.1; 9.3.1; 9.3.2. SC: le.

Richardson, Lynne D.; Hwang, Ula. Access to care: a review of the emergency medicine literature. *Academic Emergency Medicine* 2001 November; 8(11): 1030-1036. NRCBL: 9.2; 9.3.1; 9.3.2.

Roche, James B. After Bragdon v. Abbott: why legislation is still needed to mandate infertility insurance. *Boston University Public Interest Law Journal* 2002 Spring- Summer; 11(2-3): 215- 228. NRCBL: 9.2; 14.1; 14.4; 1.3.5; 9.3.1. SC: le.

Shalev, Carmel; Chinitz, David. Joe Public v. the general public: the role of the courts in Israeli health care policy. *Journal of Law, Medicine and Ethics* 2005 Winter; 33(4): 650- 659. NRCBL: 9.2. SC: le.

Sharzer, Leonard A. Tradition, obligation, and healthcare. *Sh'ma* 2005 October; 36(624): 5-6. NRCBL: 9.2; 9.3.1; 1.2.

Shinn, Carolynne. The right to the highest attainable standard of health: public health's opportunity to reframe a human rights debate in the United States. *Health and Human Rights: An International Journal* 1999; 4(1): 115-133. NRCBL: 9.2; 21.1; 4.2; 7.1; 4.4.

Smith, George P., II. Human rights and bioethics: formulating a universal right to health, health care or health protection? *Vanderbilt Journal of Transnational Law* 2005 November; 38(5): 1295-1321. NRCBL: 9.2; 21.1. SC: an; le; rv. Identifiers: U.S. Declaration on Human Rights; International Covenant on Economic, Social and Cultural Rights; International Covenant on Civil and Political Rights; European Convention on Human Rights; UNESCO's Draft Declaration on Universal Norms on Bioethics.

Vaughn, Michael S. Penal harm medicine: state tort remedies for delaying and denying health care to prisoners. *Crime, Law, and Social Change* 1999; 31(4): 273-302. NRCBL: 9.2; 1.3.5; 9.5.1; 8.1. SC: le.

Wilson, Elisabeth; Grumbach, Kevin; Huebner, Jeffrey; Agrawal, Jaya; Bindman, Andrew B. Medical student, physician, and public perceptions of health care disparities. *Family Medicine* 2004 November-December; 36(10): 715-721. NRCBL: 9.2; 9.5.1; 9.5.4; 9.5.10; 7.2. SC: em.

Wood, John. The challenge of individual rights: mental health review tribunals [editorial]. *British Journal of Psychiatry* 1995 April; 166(4): 417-420. NRCBL: 9.2; 17.1; 1.3.5. SC: le.

Yamin, Alicia Ely. Challenges and possibilities for innovative praxis in health and human rights: reflections from Peru. *Health and Human Rights: An International Journal* 2002; 6(1): 35-62. NRCBL: 9.2; 9.1; 21.1; 8.3.1; 11.3; 7.1.

Yamin, Alicia Ely. The right to health under international law and its relevance to the United States. *American Journal of Public Health* 2005 July; 95(7): 1156-1161. NRCBL: 9.2; 21.1. SC: le.

Abstract: In recent years, there have been considerable developments in international law with respect to the normative definition of the right to health, which includes both health care and healthy conditions. These norms offer a framework that shifts the analysis of issues such as disparities in treatment from questions of quality of care to matters of social justice.Building on work in social epidemiology, a rights paradigm explicitly links health with laws, policies, and practices that sustain a functional democracy and focuses on accountability. In the United States, framing a well-documented problem such as health disparities as a "rights violation" attaches shame and blame to governmental neglect. Further, international law offers standards for evaluating governmental conduct as well as mechanisms for establishing some degree of accountability.

RIGHTS *See* INTERNATIONAL HUMAN RIGHTS; RIGHT TO HEALTH CARE

SCIENCE AND TECHNOLOGY *See* BIOMEDICAL RESEARCH/ SOCIAL CONTROL OF SCIENCE AND TECHNOLOGY

SCIENTIFIC MISCONDUCT *See* BIOMEDICAL RESEARCH/ RESEARCH ETHICS AND SCIENTIFIC MISCONDUCT

SEX DETERMINATION

See also GENETIC COUNSELING; GENETIC SCREENING

Sydney fertility clinics ban sex-selection [news brief]. *Monash Bioethics Review* 2005 April; 24(2): 3. NRCBL: 14.3. Identifiers: Australia.

Arora, Dolly. The victimizing discourse: sex-determination technologies and policy. Economic and Political Weekly 1996 February 17; 31(7); 11 p. [Online]. Available: http://www.hsph.harvard.edu/Organizations/healthnet/SAsia/suchana/1210/arora.html [6 October 2005]. NRCBL: 14.3; 1.3.5; 10; 20.5.2. Identifiers: India.

Baldwin, T. Reproductive liberty and elitist contempt: reply to John Harris. *Journal of Medical Ethics* 2005 May; 31(5): 288-290. NRCBL: 14.3. Identifiers: United Kingdom (Great Britain); Human Fertilisation and Embryology Authority.

Bardia, A.; Paul, E.; Kapoor, S.K.; Anand, K. Declining sex ratio: role of society, technology and government regulation in Faridabad district, Haryana. *National Medical Journal of India* 2004 July-August; 17(4): 207-211. NRCBL: 14.3. SC: em; le. Identifiers: India.

Belgium. Comite Consultatif de Bioethique. Avis No. 22 du 19 mai 2003 relatif au choix du sexe pour des raisons non medicales / Advice no. 22 of 19 May 2003 concerning the choice of sex for non-medical reasons. *Journal International de Bioethique / International Journal of Bioethics* 2005 March-June; 16(1-2): 165-167. NRCBL: 14.3.

Bhagat, Rasheeda. Where the end comes before birth. Hindu Business Line 1999 July 20; 4 p. [Online]. Available: http://www.hsph.harvard.edu/Organizations/healthnet/SAsia/suchana/0500/h007.html [6 October 2005]. NRCBL: 14.3; 20.5.2; 10; 4.4. SC: le. Identifiers: India.

Chander, Vineet. "It's (still) a boy . . .": making the Pre-natal Diagnostic Techniques Act an effective weapon in India's struggle to stamp out female feticide. *George Washington International Law Review* 2004; 36(2): 453-475. NRCBL: 14.3; 1.3.5; 13.3. SC: le.

Check, Erika. Trial aims to measure social effects of choosing babies' sex [news]. *Nature* 2005 October 27; 437(7063): 1214-1215. NRCBL: 14.3; 15.2; 14.2.

Dahl, Edgar. Sex selection: laissez faire or family balancing? *Health Care Analysis: An International Journal of Health Care Philosophy and Policy* 2005 March; 13(1): 87-90. NRCBL: 14.3.

Abstract: In a recent comment on the HFEA's public consultation on sex selection, Soren Holm claimed that proponents of family balancing are committed to embrace a laissez faire approach. Given that arguments in support of sex selection for family balancing also support sex selection for other social reasons, advocates of family balancing, he asserts, are simply inconsistent when calling for a limit on access to sex selection. In this paper, I argue that proponents of family balancing are in no way inconsistent. Provided their advocacy of family balancing is aimed at preventing a severe distortion of the natural sex ratio, they are entirely justified in insisting on restrictions to sex selection. The real question is whether a concern for the sex ratio does indeed call for a limit on sex selection. Based on a recent survey on gender preferences and data from several Gender Clinics, I argue that a restriction on sex selection to family balancing is unwarranted. In the absence of any evidence for a pending sex ratio distortion, we are actually required to adopt a laissez faire approach to sex selection.

Dahl, Edgar; Hinsch, K.D.; Brosig, B.; Beutel, M. Attitudes towards preconception sex selection: a representative survey from Germany. *Reproductive BioMedicine Online [electronic]* 2004 December; 9(6): 600-603. Available: http://www.rbmonline.com/index.html [14 July 2005]. NRCBL: 14.3. SC: em.

Dickens, Bernard M. Conflicts between protecting and respecting women: the prohibition of sex-selected birth. *Humane Health Care International* 1997 Summer; 13(2): 14-15. NRCBL: 14.3; 15.2; 14.4.

Downing, Kimberly Kristin. A feminist is a person who answers "yes" to the question, "are women human?": an argument against the use of preimplantation genetic diagnosis for gender selection. *DePaul Journal of Health Care Law* 2005; 8(2): 431-460. NRCBL: 14.3; 21.7. SC: le.

Dyer, Clare. Parents should have right to choose sex of child, say MPs [news]. *BMJ: British Medical Journal* 2005 April 2; 330(7494): 745. NRCBL: 14.3; 15.1; 22.1; 18.1; 14.1; 14.5; 2.4.

Engelen, Bart; Vandevelde, Antoon. A defence of common sense: a reply to David Heyd's "The ethics of sex selection for non-medical reasons". *Ethical Perspectives* 2004; 11(1): 84-87. NRCBL: 14.3. SC: an.

George, Sabu M.; Dahiya, Ranbir S. Female foeticide in rural Haryana. Economic and Political Weekly 1998 August 8-14; 33(32); 18 p. [Online]. Available: http://www.hsph.harvard.edu/Organizations/healthnet/SAsia/suchana/0628/george_dahiya.html [6 October 2005]. NRCBL: 14.3; 20.5.2; 10; 4.4. SC: cs. Identifiers: India.

NRCBL: National Reference Center for Bioethics Literature Classification Scheme   See inside front cover for terms.

423

Goodkind, Daniel. Sex-selective abortion, reproductive rights, and the greater locus of gender discrimination in family formation: Cairo's unresolved questions. *PSC [Population Studies Center] Research Report Series* 1997 March; No. 97-383; 35 p. [Online]. Available: http://www. psc.lrs.umich.edu/pubs/papers/rr97-383.pdf [3 October 2005. NRCBL: 14.3; 10; 21.1; 4.4.

Grayling, A.C. The power to choose. *New Scientist* 2005 April 9-15; 186(2494): 17. NRCBL: 14.3; 14.4; 15.1.

Harris, John. No sex selection please, we're British. *Journal of Medical Ethics* 2005 May; 31(5): 286-288. NRCBL: 14.3. Identifiers: United Kingdom (Great Britain); Human Fertilisation and Embryology Authority.

Harris, John. Sex selection and regulated hatred. *Journal of Medical Ethics* 2005 May; 31(5): 291-294. NRCBL: 14.3. Identifiers: United Kingdom (Great Britain); Human Fertilisation and Embryology Authority.
Abstract: This paper argues that the HFEA's recent report on sex selection abdicates its responsibility to give its own authentic advice on the matters within its remit, that it accepts arguments and conclusions that are implausible on the face of it and where they depend on empirical claims, produces no empirical evidence whatsoever, but relies on reckless speculation as to what the "facts" are likely to be. Finally, having committed itself to what I call the "democratic presumption", that human freedom will not be constrained unless very good and powerful reasons can be produced to justify such infringement of liberty, the HFEA simply reformulates the democratic presumption as saying the opposite— namely that freedom may only be exercised if powerful justifications are produced for any exercise of liberty.

Heyd, David. Male or female, we will create them: the ethics of sex selection for non-medical reasons. *Ethical Perspectives* 2003; 10(3-4): 204-214. NRCBL: 14.3; 14.4; 15.2. SC: an.

Hollingsworth, Leslie Doty. Ethical considerations of prenatal sex selection. *Health and Social Work* 2005 May; 30(2): 126-134. NRCBL: 14.3; 1.3.10; 6; 15.2.

Holm, Søren. Laissez faire sex selection — a response to Edgar Dahl. *Health Care Analysis: An International Journal of Health Care Philosophy and Policy* 2005 March; 13(1): 91-93. NRCBL: 14.3. Identifiers: United Kingdom (Great Britain); Human Fertilisation and Embryology Authority.
Abstract: In a recent comment on the HFEA's public consultation on sex selection, Soren Holm claimed that proponents of family balancing are committed to embrace a laissez faire approach. Given that arguments in support of sex selection for family balancing also support sex selection for other social reasons, advocates of family balancing, he asserts, are simply inconsistent when calling for a limit on access to sex selection. In this paper, I argue that proponents of family balancing are in no way inconsistent. Provided their advocacy of family balancing is aimed at preventing a severe distortion of the natural sex ratio, they are entirely justified in insisting on restrictions to sex selection. The real question is whether a concern for the sex ratio does indeed call for a limit on sex selection. Based on a recent survey on gender preferences and data from several

Gender Clinics, I argue that a restriction on sex selection to family balancing is unwarranted. In the absence of any evidence for a pending sex ratio distortion, we are actually required to adopt a laissez faire approach to sex selection.

Human Fertilisation and Embryology Authority [HFEA] (United Kingdom). Sex Selection: Choice and Responsibility in Human Reproduction Consultation Document. London: Human Fertilisation and Embryology Authority 2002 October; 37 p. NRCBL: 14.3; 5.3. Note: Produced for consultation from 22 October, 2002 to 22 January, 2003; includes 3 p. questionnaire.

Human Fertilisation and Embryology Authority [HFEA] (United Kingdom). Sex Selection - Policy and Regulatory Review: A Report on the Key Findings from a Qualitative Research Study. London: Human Fertilisation and Embryology Authority [HFEA], [CPR825] 2002 October; 38 p. [Online]. Available: http://www.hfea.gov.uk/AboutHFEA/Consultations/AppendixE-Qualitative Research Findings report of research conducted by Counterpoint (UK) Ltd.pdf [6 October 2004]. NRCBL: 14.3. SC: em. Note: Prepared for: Human Fertilisation & Embryology Authority.

Human Fertilisation and Embryology Authority [HFEA] (United Kingdom). Sex Selection — Public Consultation. Research Study Conducted for Human Fertilisation and Embryology Authority. London: Human Fertilisation and Embryology Authority [HFEA] 2003 January; 70 p. [Online]. Available: http://www.hfea.gov.uk/AboutHFEA/Consultations/Appendix F - Quantitative Research Findings report of research conducted by Market and Opinion Research International (MORI).pdf [6 October 2004]. NRCBL: 14.3. SC: em. Note: Summary of Findings, 5 p. and Appendices, various pagings.

Human Genetics Alert [HGA]. The case against sex selection. *Human Reproduction and Genetic Ethics: An International Journal* 2005; 11(1): 3-5. NRCBL: 14.3.

Jesani, Amar. Banning pre-natal sex determination: the scope and the limits of the Maharashtra legislation. *In:* Lingam, Lakshmi, ed. Understanding Women's Health Issues: A Reader 1998; 6 p. [Online]. Available: http://www.hsph.harvard.edu/Organizations/healthnet/SAsia/suchana/0804/rh345.html [7 October 2005]. NRCBL: 14.3; 1.3.5; 10. SC: le. Identifiers: India.

Jones, Owen D. Sex selection: regulating technology enabling the predetermination of a child's gender. *Harvard Journal of Law and Technology* 1992 Fall; 6(1): 1-62. NRCBL: 14.3; 10; 5.3. SC: le.

Karkal, Malini. Sex selection and the population policy: the medical profession's responsibilities. *Issues in Medical Ethics* 2002 April-June; 10(2): 25. NRCBL: 14.3; 15.2; 13.3.

Kohm, Lynne Marie. Sex selection abortion and the boomerang effect of a woman's right to choose: a paradox of the skeptics. *William and Mary Journal of Women and the Law* 1997 Winter; 4(1): 91-128. NRCBL: 14.3; 10; 12.5.1; 1.1. SC: le.

Kulkarni, Sanjeev. Sex determination tests in India: a survey report. *Reprinted from: Radical Journal of Health* 1986; 1(3); 4 p. [Online]. Available: http://www.hsph.harvard.edu/Organizations/healthnet/SAsia/suchana/9999sexdetermination2.html [7 October 2005]. NRCBL: 14.3; 10; 1.3.5. SC: em; le.

Löfstedt, Petra; Shusheng, Luo; Johansson, Annika. Abortion patterns and reported sex ratios at birth in rural Yunnan, China. *Reproductive Health Matters* 2004 November; 12(24): 86-95. NRCBL: 14.3; 12.5.2; 13.1. SC: em.

Madhiwalla, Neha. Sex selection: ethics in the context of development. *Issues in Medical Ethics* 2001 October-December; 9(4): 125-126. NRCBL: 14.3.

Mamdani, Bashir. In support of sex selection. *Indian Journal of Medical Ethics* 2005 January-March; 2(1): 26-27. NRCBL: 14.3; 13.3. Comments: comment on B.M. Dickens, "Can sex selection be ethically tolerated?" Journal of Medical Ethics 2002; 28: 335-336.

McDougall, R. Acting parentally: an argument against sex selection. *Journal of Medical Ethics* 2005 October; 31(10): 601-605. NRCBL: 14.3. SC: an.
Abstract: The Human Fertilisation and Embryology Authority's (HFEA) recent restrictive recommendations on sex selection have highlighted the need for consideration of the plausibility of ethical arguments against sex selection. In this paper, the author suggests a parental virtues approach to some questions of reproductive ethics (including sex selection) as a superior alternative to an exclusively harm focused approach such as the procreative liberty framework. The author formulates a virtue ethics argument against sex selection based on the idea that acceptance is a character trait of the good parent. It is concluded that, because the argument presented posits a wrong in the sex selecting agent's action that is not a harm, the argument could not function as a justification of the HFEA's restrictive position in light of their explicit commitment to procreative liberty; it does, however, suggest that ethical approaches focused exclusively on harm fail to capture all the relevant moral considerations and thus that we should look beyond such approaches.

McLean, Sheila A.M. Sex selection: intergenerational justice or injustice? *Medicine and Law: World Association for Medical Law* 2005 December; 24(4): 761-773. NRCBL: 14.3; 15.2. SC: le.
Abstract: Arguments surrounding the issue of sex selection focus on the potential, negative outcomes of permitting such choices. In this article, it is argued that—rather than being negative—sex selection (particularly for, but not confined to, family balancing reasons) can be a positive reflection of the reproductive liberties which have been won over the last century. It is accepted that this argument applies most clearly in cultures where there is no overt preference for one sex over another, but in those societies where this does not apply, it is equally unlikely that the concept of reproductive choice is valued. The article argues that permitting intending parents to choose the sex of their child—while likely to be a relatively rare event—is in line with

the concept of intergenerational justice, in that it may serve not just the interests of intending parents but also those of the children to be born.

Ravindra, R.P. The campaign against sex determination tests. *In:* Datar, Chhaya, ed. The Struggle Against Violence. Calcutta: Shree Pub. 1993; 27 p. [Online]. Available: http://www.hsph.harvard.edu/Organizations/healthnet/SAsia/suchana/0400b/h060.html [7 October 2005]. NRCBL: 14.3; 1.3.5; 10. SC: le. Identifiers: India.

Ravindra, R.P. Myths about sex determination tests. *Facts Against Myths* 1995 June; 2(3): 1-6. [Online]. Available: http://www.hsph.harvard.edu/Organizations/healthnet/Sasia/suchana/0500/h003.html [27 May 2005]. NRCBL: 14.3; 12.1. SC: em.

Sauer, Mark V. Gender selection: pressure from patients and industry should not alter our adherence to ethical guidelines. *American Journal of Obstetrics and Gynecology* 2004 November; 191(5): 1543-1545. NRCBL: 14.3; 9.8.

Waldby, Catherine. Literature Review and Annotated Bibliography: Social and Ethical Aspects of Sex Selection. London: Human Fertilisation and Embryology Authority [HFEA] undated; 18 p. [Online]. Available: http://www.hfea.gov.uk/AboutHFEA/Consultations/Appendix D - Social and Ethical Literature Review.pdf [6 October 2004]. NRCBL: 14.3.

Wertz, Dorothy C.; Fletcher, John C. Ethical and social issues in prenatal sex selection: a survey of geneticists in 37 nations. *Social Science and Medicine* 1998 January; 46(2): 255-273. NRCBL: 14.3; 8.1; 21.1. SC: em.

Williamson, Shanti. Sex(ist) selection? *Medical Law International* 2004; 6(3): 185-206. NRCBL: 14.3; 19.5; 15.2; 14.4. SC: le.

SEX PRESELECTION *See* SEX DETERMINATION

SEXUALITY
See also MALPRACTICE AND PROFESSIONAL MISCONDUCT

Catlin, Anita J. Ethical commentary on gender reassignment: a complex and provocative modern issue. *Pediatric Nursing* 1998 January-February; 24(1): 63-65, 99. NRCBL: 10; 8.3.2; 8.1. SC: cs.

Cherry, April L. Choosing substantive justice: a discussion of "choice," "rights" and the new reproductive technologies. *Wisconsin Women's Law Journal* 1997 Summer; 11(3): 431-441. NRCBL: 10; 1.1; 12.1. SC: le.

Cherry, April L. Nurturing in the service of white culture: racial subordination, gestational surrogacy, and the ideology of motherhood. *Texas Journal of Women and the Law*

NRCBL: National Reference Center for Bioethics Literature Classification Scheme   See inside front cover for terms.

425

2001 Spring; 10(2): 83-128. NRCBL: 10; 14.2; 9.5.4. SC: le.

Dasti, Jerry L. Advocating a broader understanding of the necessity of sex- reassignment surgery under Medicaid. *New York University Law Review* 2002 December; 77(6): 1738-1775. NRCBL: 10; 9.2; 9.3.1; 9.5.10; 1.3.5. SC: le.

Davis, Peggy Cooper; Gilligan, Carol. A woman decides: Justice O'Connor and due process rights of choice. *McGeorge Law Review* 2001; 32(3): 895-914. NRCBL: 10; 12.4.1; 12.4.2; 20.5.1; 1.1. SC: le.

Fitzgibbons, Richard P. The desire for a sex change: clinical observations and advice. *Ethics and Medics* 2005 October; 30(10): 1-2. NRCBL: 10.

Gormally, Luke. Marriage and the prophylactic use of condoms. *National Catholic Bioethics Quarterly* 2005 Winter; 5(4): 735- 749. NRCBL: 10; 11.1; 1.2; 14.1.

Guevin, Benedict M. Sex reassignment surgery for transsexuals: an ethical conundrum? *National Catholic Bioethics Quarterly* 2005 Winter; 5(4): 719- 734. NRCBL: 10; 9.5.1; 9.5.5; 17.2; 1.2.

Guevin, Benedict; Rhonheimer, Martin. On the use of condoms to prevent acquired immune deficiency syndrome [debate]. *National Catholic Bioethics Quarterly* 2005 Spring; 5(1): 37-48. NRCBL: 10; 9.5.6; 1.2.

Harish, Dasari; Sharma, B.R. Medical advances in transsexualism and the legal implications. *American Journal of Forensic Medicine and Pathology* 2003; 24(1): 100-105. NRCBL: 10. SC: le.

Kirtane, Jyotsna. Ethics in intersex disorders. *Issues in Medical Ethics* 2000 April-June; 8(2): 47-48. NRCBL: 10; 9.5.7.

Levkovitz, Alon. A halachic approach to transgender. *CCAR Journal: A Reform Jewish Quarterly* 2005 Fall; 52(4): 84- 93. NRCBL: 10; 9.5.7; 1.2.

Lupton, Deborah. Feminisms and medicine. *In her:* Medicine as Culture: Illness, Disease and the Body in Western Societies. Second ed. Thousand Oaks, CA: Sage Publications; 2003: 142-172. NRCBL: 10; 4.2; 9.5.5.

Lupton, Deborah. Power relations and the medical encounter. *In her:* Medicine as Culture: Illness, Disease and the Body in Western Societies. Second ed. Thousand Oaks, CA: Sage Publications; 2003: 113-141. NRCBL: 10; 9.5.5; 4.2.

Magid, Julie Manning. Contraception and contractions: a divergent decade following Johnson controls. *American Business Law Journal* 2003 Fall; 41(1); 26 p. [Online]. Available: http://web.lexis-nexis.com/universe/printdoc [3 June 2005]. NRCBL: 10; 11.1; 9.5.8; 9.5.5; 16.3. SC: le.

Roen, Katrina. Intersex embodiment: when health care means maintaining binary sexes [editorial]. *Sexual Health* 2004; 1(3): 127-130. NRCBL: 10; 9.5.7; 9.8.

Roen, Katrina. Queer kids: toward ethical clinical interactions with intersex people. *In:* Shildrick, Margrit; Mykitiuk, Roxanne, eds. Ethics of the Body: Postconventional Challenges. Cambridge, MA: MIT Press; 2005: 259- 278. NRCBL: 10; 1.1.

Rosik, Christopher H. Motivational, ethical, and epistemological foundations in the treatment of unwanted homoerotic attraction. *Journal of Marital and Family Therapy* 2003 January; 29(1): 13-28. NRCBL: 10; 17.3; 17.2.

Spack, Norman. Transgenderism. *Medical Ethics Newsletter [Lahey Clinic]* 2005 Fall; 12(3): 1- 2, 12. NRCBL: 10.

Whittaker, Rosemary. Re-framing the representation of women in advertisements for hormone replacement therapy. *Nursing Inquiry* 1998 June; 5(2): 77-86. NRCBL: 10; 9.7; 1.3.2.

SOCIAL JUSTICE *See* RESOURCE ALLOCATION; RIGHT TO HEALTH CARE

SOCIOLOGY OF MEDICINE

Anderson, Sharon K.; Kitchener, Karen S. Nonsexual posttherapy relationships: a conceptual framework to assess ethical risks. *Professional Psychology: Research and Practice* 1998 February; 29(1): 91-99. NRCBL: 7.1; 8.1; 17.1; 4.1.2. SC: cs.

Beach, Mary Catherine; Saha, Somnath. Free to be you and me? Balancing professionalism, culture, and self-expression [editorial]. *JGIM: Journal of General Internal Medicine* 2005 March; 20(3): 312-313. NRCBL: 7.1; 8.1.

Bennett, John; Collins, John. The relationship between physicians and the biomedical industries: advice from the Royal College of Physicians. *Clinical Medicine* 2002 July-August; 2(4): 320-322. NRCBL: 7.1; 1.3.2; 7.3.

Bernstein, Mark; Jürgens, Ralf. Disclosure dilemma: should doctors reveal their own medical histories? Pro: patients have a right to know. Con: no need to divulge. *Parkhurst Exchange* 2004 April; 12(4): 36-37. NRCBL: 7.1; 8.1; 9.8.6.

Boylan, Michael; Grant, Richard E. Diversity and professional excellence [editorial]. *Journal of the National Medical Association* 2004 October; 96(10): 1354-1362. NRCBL: 7.1; 1.1; 21.7. SC: an.

Carney, Bridget. The ethics of recruiting foreign nurses: how should Catholic organizations approach this troubling question? *Health Progress* 2005 November-December; 86(6): 31-35. NRCBL: 7.1; 9.8; 1.3.2; 21.1.

Carter, Brian S. Ethical concerns for physicians deployed to Operation Desert Storm. *Military Medicine* 1994 January; 159(1): 55-59. NRCBL: 7.1; 4.1.2; 21.2; 9.4; 9.2.

Doyle, Peter. The ethical dilemmas of general practice. *Australian Family Physician* 1994 June; 23(6): 1028-1029, 1032. NRCBL: 7.1; 7.3.

Edwards, R.G. British disciplinary or legal actions proliferate in IVF. *Reproductive BioMedicine Online [electronic]* 2001; 3(3): 263. Available: http://www.rbmonline.com/index.html [1 September 2005]. NRCBL: 7.1; 14.4; 9.8. Identifiers: in vitro fertilization.

Elger, Bernice S.; Harding, Timothy W. Compliance with the wishes of competent patients among future physicians and lawyers: is paternalism a predictable individual or group-specific trait? *Medical Teacher* 2004 August; 26(5): 458-462. NRCBL: 7.1; 9.1; 8.1. SC: em.

Fry, Frank. Certificates. *Australian Family Physician* 1994 June; 23(6): 1092-1093, 1095. NRCBL: 7.1; 8.3.1; 16.3. Identifiers: doctor verification of illness and injury.

Gaynor, Brian. A different dilemma every day. *Australian Family Physician* 1994 June; 23(6): 1038, 1040- 1041. NRCBL: 7.1; 8.1; 9.5.9; 11.3.

George, Thomas. Should medical students resort to a strike? *Issues in Medical Ethics* 2000 April-June; 8(2): 59. NRCBL: 7.1; 7.2.

Grenfell, Leigh. To strike or not to strike: is striking ethical, according to the code of ethics developed by NZNO? One nurse examines her own decision to strike. *Nursing New Zealand* 1994 March; 2(2): 16-18. NRCBL: 7.1; 4.1.3. Identifiers: New Zealand Nurses Organisation.

Griffith, Ezra E.H. Personal narrative and an African-American perspective on medical ethics. *Journal of the American Academy of Psychiatry and the Law* 2005; 33(3): 371-381. NRCBL: 7.1; 2.1; 1.3.5; 1.1.

Henderson, R.; Keiding, N. Individual survival time prediction using statistical models. *Journal of Medical Ethics* 2005 December; 31(12): 703-706. NRCBL: 7.1; 8.2; 20.4.1.

Abstract: Doctors' survival predictions for terminally ill patients have been shown to be inaccurate and there has been an argument for less guesswork and more use of carefully constructed statistical indices. As statisticians, the authors are less confident in the predictive value of statistical models and indices for individual survival times. This paper discusses and illustrates a variety of measures which can be used to summarise predictive information available from a statistical model. The authors argue that models and statistical indices can be useful at the group or population level, but that human survival is so uncertain that even the best statistical analysis cannot provide single-number predictions of real use for individual patients.

Hurst, S.A.; Hull, S.C.; DuVal, G.; Danis, M. How physicians face ethical difficulties: a qualitative analysis. *Journal of Medical Ethics* 2005 January; 31(1): 7-14. NRCBL: 7.1; 2.1. SC: em.

Abstract: BACKGROUND: Physicians face ethical difficulties daily, yet they seek ethics consultation infrequently. To date, no systematic data have been collected on the strategies they use to resolve such difficulties when they do so without the help of ethics consultation. Thus, our understanding of ethical decision making in day to day medical practice is poor. We report findings from the qualitative analysis of 310 ethically difficult situations described to us by physicians who encountered them in their practice. When facing such situations, the physicians sought to avoid conflict, obtain assistance, and protect the integrity of their conscience and reputation, as well as the integrity of the group of people who participated in the decisions. These goals could conflict with each other, or with ethical goals, in problematic ways. Being aware of these potentially conflicting goals may help physicians to resolve ethical difficulties more effectively. This awareness should also contribute to informing the practice of ethics consultation. OBJECTIVE: To identify strategies used by physicians in dealing with ethical difficulties in their practice. DESIGN, SETTING, AND PARTICIPANTS: National survey of internists, oncologists, and intensive care specialists by computer assisted telephone interviews (n = 344, response rate = 64%). As part of this survey, we asked physicians to tell us about a recent ethical dilemma they had encountered in their medical practice. Transcripts of their open-ended responses were analysed using coding and analytical elements of the grounded theory approach. MAIN MEASUREMENTS: Strategies and approaches reported by respondents as part of their account of a recent ethical difficulty they had encountered in their practice. RESULTS: When faced with ethical difficulties, the physicians avoided conflict and looked for assistance, which contributed to protecting, or attempting to protect, the integrity of their conscience and reputation, as well as the integrity of the group of people who participated in the decisions. These efforts sometimes reinforced ethical goals, such as following patients' wishes or their best interests, but they sometimes competed with them. The goals of avoiding conflict, obtaining assistance, and protecting the respondent's integrity and that of the group of decision makers could also compete with each other. CONCLUSION: In resolving ethical difficulties in medical practice, internists entertained competing goals that they did not always successfully achieve. Additionally, the means employed were not always the most likely to achieve those aims. Understanding these aspects of ethical decision making in medical practice is important both for physicians themselves as they struggle with ethical difficulties and for the ethics consultants who wish to help them in this process.

Jones, James W.; McCullough, Laurence B.; Crigger, Nancy A.; Richman, Bruce W. The ethics of administrative credentialing. *Journal of Vascular Surgery* 2005 April; 41(4): 729-731. NRCBL: 7.1; 9.3.1. SC: cs.

Jones, James W.; McCullough, Laurence B.; Richman, Bruce W. Ethics of the new economic credentialing: conflicted leadership roles. *Journal of Vascular Surgery* 2005 February; 41(2): 366-368. NRCBL: 7.1; 9.3.1. SC: cs.

Komesaroff, Paul A.; Kerridge, Ian H. Ethical issues concerning the relationships between medical practitioners and the pharmaceutical industry. *Medical Journal of Australia* 2002 February 4; 176(3): 118-121. NRCBL: 7.1; 7.3; 9.7; 1.3.2; 9.3.1.

NRCBL: National Reference Center for Bioethics Literature Classification Scheme   See inside front cover for terms.

427

Landow, Laurence; Truog, Robert D. Financial disclosure is needed at the lectern, as well as in print [letter and reply]. *Critical Care Medicine* 1998 December; 26(12): 2093-2094. NRCBL: 7.1; 1.3.2; 9.3.1; 7.3.

Latessa, Robyn; Ray, Lisa. Should you treat yourself, family or friends? *Family Practice Management* 2005 March; 12(3): 41-44. NRCBL: 7.1; 7.3; 8.1.

Leach, Joan. Perspectives on medicine and society. *In:* Restivo, Sal, ed. Science, Technology, and Society: An Encyclopedia. New York: Oxford University Press; 2005: 379-387. NRCBL: 7.1; 18.6; 15.3; 9.7.

Ledger, Sylvia Dianne. The duty of nurses to meet patients' spiritual and/or religious needs. *British Journal of Nursing* 2005 February 24-March 9; 14(4): 220-225. NRCBL: 7.1; 1.2; 8.1.

Martinez, Richard; Candilis, Philip J. Commentary: toward a unified theory of personal and professional ethics. *Journal of the American Academy of Psychiatry and the Law* 2005; 33(3): 382-385. NRCBL: 7.1; 1.3.1; 1.3.5; 4.1.1.

Morgan, John M.; Marco, J.; Stockx, L.; Zannad, F. Educational governance for the regulation of industry sponsored continuing medical education in interventional and device based therapies [editorial]. *Heart* 2005 June; 91(6): 710-712. NRCBL: 7.1; 7.2; 9.7; 21.1.

Newman, Alison W.; Wright, Seth W.; Wrenn, Keith D.; Bernard, Aline. Should physicians have facial piercings? *JGIM: Journal of General Internal Medicine* 2005 March; 20(3): 213-218. NRCBL: 7.1; 8.1. SC: em.

Norko, Michael A. Comment: compassion at the core of forensic ethics. *Journal of the American Academy of Psychiatry and the Law* 2005; 33(3): 386-389. NRCBL: 7.1; 1.3.5; 1.1.

Perneger, Thomas V.; Martin, Diane P.; Bovier, Patrick A. Physicians' attitudes toward health care rationing. *Medical Decision Making* 2002 January-February; 22(1): 65-70. NRCBL: 7.1; 9.4; 9.3.1; 9.2.

Powers, Bethel Ann. Ethnographic analysis of everyday ethics in the care of nursing home residents with dementia: a taxonomy. *Nursing Research* 2001 November-December; 50(6): 332-339. NRCBL: 7.1; 9.5.2; 9.5.3; 4.4.

Ryan, Christopher James; Anderson, Josephine. Sleeping with the past: the ethics of post-termination patient-therapist sexual contact [opinion]. *Australian and New Zealand Journal of Psychiatry* 1996 April; 30(2): 171-178. NRCBL: 7.1; 8.1; 10.

Santora, Marc. Cardiologists say rankings affect surgical decisions. *New York Times* 2005 January 11; p. B3. NRCBL: 7.1; 9.4; 8.1. SC: po.

Stein, Rob. Pharmacists' rights at front of new debate; because of beliefs, some refuse to fill birth control prescriptions. *Washington Post* 2005 March 28; p. A1, A10. NRCBL: 7.1; 9.7; 11.1; 12.1;. SC: po.

SPECIAL POPULATIONS *See* CARE FOR SPECIFIC GROUPS; HUMAN EXPERIMENTATION/ SPECIAL POPULATIONS

STEM CELL RESEARCH *See* HUMAN EXPERIMENTATION/ SPECIAL POPULATIONS/ EMBRYOS AND FETUSES

STERILIZATION
See also CONTRACEPTION; POPULATION POLICY

Removing the uterus from mentally handicapped women: some ethical considerations. *Medical Ethics: Journal of the Forum for Medical Ethics Society* 1994 February-April; 1(3): 10. NRCBL: 11.3; 9.5.3.

Suggested guidelines for hysterectomy in mentally handicapped women. *Medical Ethics: Journal of the Forum for Medical Ethics Society* 1994 May-July; 1(4): 1-3. NRCBL: 11.3; 9.5.3.

Benn, Piers; Lupton, Martin. Sterilisation of young, competent, and childless adults. *BMJ: British Medical Journal* 2005 June 4; 330(7503): 1323-1325. NRCBL: 11.3.

Bock, Gisela. Nazi sterilization and reproductive policies. *In:* Bachrach, Susan, project director; Kuntz, Dieter, ed. Deadly Medicine: Creating the Master Race. Washington, DC: United States Holocaust Museum; 2004: 61-87. NRCBL: 11.3; 14.1; 21.4.

Branigin, William. Va. apologizes to the victims of sterilizations [news]. *Washington Post* 2002 May 3; p. B1, B9. NRCBL: 11.3; 8.3.4; 15.5.

Brazier, Margaret. Sterilisation: down the slippery slope? *Professional Negligence* 1990 March; 6(1): 25-28. NRCBL: 11.3; 1.1; 14.1; 9.5.3. SC: le.

Center for Reproductive Rights. The Slovak Government's Response to Reproductive Rights Violations against Romani Women: Analysis and Recommendations. New York: Center for Reproductive Rights 2003 May; 16 p. NRCBL: 11.3; 8.3.1; 9.5.4; 21.4. Identifiers: Poradna pre obcianske a l'udské prßva; Slovakia; Roma. Comments: comment on Body and Soul: Forced Sterilization and Other Assults on Roma Reproductive Freedom in Slovakia.

Crain, Lucy S.; Sassaman, Edward; Mulick, James A.; Freeman, John M.; Vining, Eileen P.G. Sterilization and the retarded female: another perspective [letters and reply]. *Pediatrics* 1980 October; 66(4): 650-652. NRCBL: 11.3; 9.5.3.

Das, Abhijit. Ensuring quality of care in sterilisation services. *Indian Journal of Medical Ethics* 2004 July-September; 1(3): 79-80. NRCBL: 11.3; 9.8.

Donnelly, Mary. Non-consensual sterilisation of mentally disabled people: the law in Ireland. *Irish Jurist* 1997; 32: 297-322. NRCBL: 11.3; 9.5.3. SC: le.

EngenderHealth. Law and policy. *In its: Contraceptive Sterilization: Global Issues and Trends.* New York, NY: EngenderHealth; 2002: 87-106. NRCBL: 11.3. SC: le.

Holt, Ed. Roma women reveal that forced sterilisation remains. *Lancet* 2005 March 12-18; 365(9463): 927-928. NRCBL: 11.3; 9.5.5; 9.1.

Hughes, James E. Eugenic sterilization in the United States: a comparative summary of statutes and review of court decisions. *Washington, DC: United States Government Printing Office, Supplement No. 162 to the Public Health Reports,* 1940; 45 p. NRCBL: 11.3; 15.5.

Hyatt, Stephanie. A shared history of shame: Sweden's four-decade policy of forced sterilization and the eugenics movement in the United States. *Indiana International and Comparative Law Review* 1998; 8(2): 475-503. NRCBL: 11.3; 15.5; 2.2. SC: le.

Kosner, Katka. Gypsy women launch claim following sterilisation [news]. *BMJ: British Medical Journal* 2005 February 5; 330(7486): 275. NRCBL: 11.3; 8.3.4. SC: le.

Mulay, Shree. Quinacrine non-surgical sterilisation: troubling questions. *Issues in Medical Ethics* 2000 July-September; 8(3): 87-88. NRCBL: 11.3; 21.1.

Myerson, Abraham. Sterilization. *In his:* Speaking of Man. New York: Alfred A. Knopf; 1958: 164- 190. NRCBL: 11.3; 15.5.

Nash, Donald J. Sterilization laws. *In:* Ness, Bryan D., ed. Encyclopedia of Genetics. Revised edition. Volume II. Pasadena, Calif.: Salem Press; 2004: 715-717. NRCBL: 11.3. SC: le.

PARYAY. Hysterectomy in the mentally handicapped: an abridged version of the statement issued by PARYAY. *Medical Ethics: Journal of Forum for Medical Ethics Society* 1994 August-October; 2(1): 6-7. NRCBL: 11.3; 9.5.3. Note: PARYAY is a group in India fostering humane alternatives to hysterectomy in the mentally handicapped.

Ralstin-Lewis, D. Marie. The continuing struggle against genocide: indigenous women's reproductive rights. *Wicazo SA Review* 2005 Spring; 20(1): 71-95. NRCBL: 11.3; 11.1; 21.4; 9.5.4; 2.2.

Rao, Mohan. Neo-eugenics: the quinacrine sterilisation of women in India. *Women's Link* 1997 July-September; 3(3): 12-15. [Online]. Available: http://www.hsph.harvard.edu/Organizations/healthnet/SAsia/suchana/0200/h024.html [27 May 2005]. NRCBL: 11.3; 8.3.4.

Rao, Mohan. Quinacrine sterilisation trials: a scientific scandal? *Reprinted from: Economic and Political Weekly* 1998 March 28; 33(13); 7 p. [Online]. Available: http://www.hsph.harvard.edu/Organizations/healthnet/SAsia/suchana/9999/quinacrine.html [7 October 2005]. NRCBL: 11.3; 8.3.4; 21.1; 8.3.1; 13.1; 1.3.9; 9.7.

Rao, Mohan. Quinacrine sterilisations banned. Health for Millions 1998 May-June; 2 p. [Online]. Available: http://www.hsph.harvard.edu/Organizations/healthnet/SAsia/suchana/0719/rh189.html [7 October 2005]. NRCBL: 11.3; 8.3.4; 21.1. SC: le. Identifiers: India.

Rao, Mohan. Supreme Court judgement on sterilisations [editorial]. *Indian Journal of Medical Ethics* 2005 April-June; 2(2): 40-41. NRCBL: 11.3; 9.5.5. Identifiers: India.

Savell, Kristin. Sex and the sacred: sterilization and bodily integrity in English and Canadian law. *McGill Law Journal* 2004 October; 49(4): 1093-1141. NRCBL: 11.3; 9.5.3; 10; 14.1. SC: le.

Schoen, Johanna. Nothing is removed except the possibility of parenthood: women and the politics of sterilization. *In her:* Choice and Coercion: Birth Control, Sterilization and Abortion in Public Health and Welfare. Chapel Hill: University of North Carolina Press; 2005: 75-138. NRCBL: 11.3; 15.5; 21.1.

Smith, J. David. The Bell Curve and Carrie Buck: eugenics revisited. *Mental Retardation* 1995 February; 33(1): 60-61. NRCBL: 11.3; 15.5; 15.6; 2.2.

Stern, Alexandra Minna. Sterilized in the name of public health: race, immigration, and reproductive control in modern California. *American Journal of Public Health* 2005 July; 95(7): 1128-1138. NRCBL: 11.3; 15.5; 15.3; 13.2; 9.5.3; 9.5.5; 9.5.4.

Abstract: In exploring the history of involuntary sterilization in California, I connect the approximately 20,000 operations performed on patients in state institutions between 1909 and 1979 to the federally funded procedures carried out at a Los Angeles County hospital in the early 1970s. Highlighting the confluence of factors that facilitated widespread sterilization abuse in the early 1970s, I trace prosterilization arguments predicated on the protection of public health. This historical overview raises important questions about the legacy of eugenics in contemporary California and relates the past to recent developments in health care delivery and genetic screening.

SUBSTANCE ABUSERS *See* CARE FOR SPECIFIC GROUPS/ SUBSTANCE ABUSERS

SUICIDE *See* ASSISTED SUICIDE

SURROGATE DECISION MAKING *See* EUTHANASIA AND ALLOWING TO DIE; INFORMED CONSENT

SURROGATE MOTHERS *See* ARTIFICIAL INSEMINATION AND SURROGATE MOTHERS

NRCBL: National Reference Center for Bioethics Literature Classification Scheme   See inside front cover for terms.

429

TECHNOLOGIES, BIOMEDICAL *See* ORGAN AND TISSUE TRANSPLANTATION; REPRODUCTIVE TECHNOLOGIES

TELEMEDICINE AND INFORMATICS

Callens, S. Telemedicine and the e-commerce directive. *European Journal of Health Law* 2002 June; 9(2): 93-109. NRCBL: 1.3.12; 9.1; 8.4. SC: le.

Gostin, Lawrence O.; Lazarini, Zita; Flaherty, Kathleen M. Legislative survey of state confidentiality laws, with specific emphasis on HIV and immunization. Final Report presented to the U.S. Centers for Disease Control and Prevention [CDC], the Council of State and Territorial Epidemiologists and the Task force for Child Survival and Development Carter Presidential Center. Washington, DC: Epic Privacy Information Center 1997; 69 p. [Online]. Available: http://www.epic.org/privacy/medical/cdc_survey.html [30 November 2005]. NRCBL: 1.3.12; 8.4. Identifiers: Public Health Information Privacy Project.

Hyler, Steven E.; Gangure, Dinu P. Legal and ethical challenges in telepsychiatry. *Journal of Psychiatric Practice* 2004 July; 10(4): 272-276. NRCBL: 1.3.12; 17.2; 8.3.1; 8.4; 8.5. SC: cs.

Irvine, R. Mediating telemedicine: ethics at a distance. *Internal Medicine Journal* 2005 January; 35(1): 56-58. NRCBL: 1.3.12; 9.1; 8.1; 1.1.

Kind, Terry; Silber, Tomas Jose. Ethical issues in pediatric e-health. *Clinical Pediatrics* 2004 September; 43(7): 593-599. NRCBL: 1.3.12; 8.1; 9.8; 8.4; 9.5.7.

McAlpine, Heather; Lockerbie, Linda; Ramsay, Deyanne; Beaman, Sue. Evaluating a web-based graduate level nursing ethics course: thumbs up or thumbs down? *Journal of Continuing Education in Nursing* 2002 January-February; 33(1): 12-18. NRCBL: 1.3.12; 2.3; 7.2; 4.1.3. SC: em. Identifiers: Canada.

Mossialos, Elias; Thomson, Sarah; Ter Linden, Annemarie. Information technology law and health systems in the European Union. *International Journal of Technology Assessment in Health Care* 2004 Fall; 20(4): 498-508. NRCBL: 1.3.12; 9.1; 8.4; 5.3; 1.3.2; 21.1. SC: le.

Pyper, Cecilia; Amery, Justin; Watson, Marion; Crook, Claire. Access to electronic health records in primary care — a survey of patients' views. *Medical Science Monitor* 2004 November; 10(11): SR17-SR22. NRCBL: 1.3.12; 8.4. SC: em. Identifiers: United Kingdom (Great Britain).

Recupero, Patricia R. E-mail and the psychiatrist-patient relationship. *Journal of the American Academy of Psychiatry and the Law* 2005; 33(4): 465-475. NRCBL: 1.3.12; 8.1; 17.2; 1.3.8. SC: le.

Schulenberg, Stefan E.; Yutrzenka, Barbara A. Ethical issues in the use of computerized assessment. *Computers in Human Behavior* 2004 July; 20(4): 477-490. NRCBL: 1.3.12; 17.1; 7.1.

TERMINAL CARE *See* DEATH AND DYING/ TERMINAL CARE

TERRORISM *See* WAR AND TERRORISM

TERMINALLY ILL *See* DEATH AND DYING/ TERMINAL CARE; HUMAN EXPERIMENTATION/ SPECIAL POPULATIONS/ AGED AND TERMINALLY ILL

TEST TUBE FERTILIZATION *See* IN VITRO FERTILIZATION

THERAPEUTIC RESEARCH *See* HUMAN EXPERIMENTATION

THIRD PARTY CONSENT *See* HUMAN EXPERIMENTATION/ INFORMED CONSENT; INFORMED CONSENT

TISSUE DONATION *See* ORGAN AND TISSUE TRANSPLANTATION/ DONATION AND PROCUREMENT

TRANSPLANTATION *See* ORGAN AND TISSUE TRANSPLANTATION

TORTURE, GENOCIDE, AND WAR CRIMES

Doctors and detention [editorial]. *Washington Post* 2005 July 13; p. A20. NRCBL: 21.4. SC: po.

Don't mention the syndrome. *New Scientist* 2005 October 22-28; 188(2522): 6. NRCBL: 21.4; 7.1. Identifiers: Hans Reiter; Reiter syndrome.

Adam, Yehuda G. Aide memoire—the role of the German medical establishment in the Holocaust: a retrospective on the 60th anniversary of the liberation of Auschwitz. *Israel Medical Association Journal* 2005 March; 7(3): 139-142. NRCBL: 21.4; 1.3.5; 2.2; 20.5.1; 4.1.2; 7.1.

Annas, George J. Unspeakably cruel — torture, medical ethics, and the law [editorial]. *New England Journal of Medicine* 2005 May 19; 352(20): 2127- 2132. NRCBL: 21.4; 7.4; 21.2; 2.1; 1.3.5; 21.1. SC: le.

Benzenhöfer, Udo. Zur juristischen debatte um die "euthanasie" in der NS-zeit / The legal debate on "euthanasia" in National Socialist Germany. *Recht und Psychiatrie* 2000; 18(3): 112-121. NRCBL: 21.4; 1.3.5; 2.2; 15.5; 20.5.1. SC: le. Note: Abstract in English and German.

Bloche, M. Gregg; Marks, Jonathan H. Triage at Abu Ghraib [opinion]. *New York Times* 2005 February 4; p. A19. NRCBL: 21.4; 17.8. SC: po.

Burleigh, Michael. Nazi "euthanasia" programs. *In:* Bachrach, Susan, project director; Kuntz, Dieter, ed. Deadly Medicine: Creating the Master Race. Washington, DC: United States Holocaust Museum; 2004: 127-153. NRCBL: 21.4; 20.5.1; 15.5.

Caplan, Arthur L. Misusing the Nazi analogy [editorial]. *Science* 2005 July 22; 309(5734): 535. NRCBL: 21.4; 2.1.

Cohen, Steven P.; Bloche, M. Gregg; Marks, Jonathan H. Doctors and interrogation [letter and reply]. *New England Journal of Medicine* 2005 October 13; 353(15): 1633-1634. NRCBL: 21.4; 21.2; 21.1; 1.3.5; 2.1.

Cornwell, John. The 'science' extermination and human experiment. *In his:* Hitler's Scientists: Science, War, and the Devil's Pact. New York: Penguin; 2004: 348-366. NRCBL: 21.4; 1.3.9; 18.5; 15.5.

Farberman, Rhea. A stain on medical ethics [letter]. *Lancet* 2005 August 27-September 2; 366(9487): 712. NRCBL: 21.4; 17.1; 7.4.

Friedlander, Henry. From "euthanasia" to the "final solution.". *In:* Bachrach, Susan, project director; Kuntz, Dieter, ed. Deadly Medicine: Creating the Master Race. Washington, DC: United States Holocaust Museum; 2004: 155-183. NRCBL: 21.4; 20.5.1; 15.5.

Grau, Günter. "Unschuldige" Täter: Mediziner als Vollstrecker der nationalsozialistischen Homosexuellenpolitik. *In:* Jellonnek, Burkhard; Lautmann, Rüdiger, eds. Nationalsozialistischer Terror gegen Homosexuelle: verdrängt und ungesühnt. Paderborn: Schöningh; 2002: 209-235. NRCBL: 21.4; 1.3.5; 2.2; 9.5.1; 10; 15.5.

Hall, Peter; Tornberg, David N. A stain on medical ethics [letters]. *Lancet* 2005 October 8-14; 366(9493): 1263-1264. NRCBL: 21.4; 7.3; 7.4; 1.3.7.

Henderson, Mark. German doctors urged to shake off Nazi horrors [news]. *Times (London, Home section)* 2004 June 28; p. 4. NRCBL: 21.4; 15.5; 15.1; 7.1; 18.1.

Hoskins, Sylvia Anne. Nurses and national socialism—a moral dilemma: one historical example of a route to euthanasia. *Nursing Ethics* 2005 January; 12(1): 79-91. NRCBL: 21.4; 1.3.5; 2.2; 4.1.3; 15.5; 20.5.1. Identifiers: Germany.

Abstract: If euthanasia were to be made legal in other countries apart from The Netherlands and Belgium, nurses would be faced with ethical dilemmas that could impact on their professional accountability and their personal moral beliefs. As a part of history has demonstrated, the introduction of the practice of euthanasia could also significantly change the relationship between nurses and patients. In Germany between 1940 and 1945, in response to a government directive, nurses participated in the practice of euthanasia and as a result many innocent German people were killed by what were considered to be 'mercy deaths'. It is important to try and understand the moral thinking and examine the complex issues at this historical junction that led German nurses to participate in the killing of thousands of innocent people. Such reflection may help to stimulate an awareness of the moral issues that nurses in the twenty-first century could confront if euthanasia were to be made legal in their own country. This has implications for future nursing practice.

Jones, James W.; McCullough, Laurence B.; Richman, Bruce W. The military physician's ethical response to evidence of torture. *Surgery* 2004 November; 136(5): 1090-1093. NRCBL: 21.4; 21.1; 4.1.2. SC: cs.

LaMonica, Jay. Compulsory sterilization, euthanasia, and propaganda: the Nazi experience. *In:* Koterski, Joseph W., ed. Life and Learning VII: Proceedings of the Seventh University Faculty for Life Conference. Washington, DC: University Faculty for Life; 1998: 187-197. NRCBL: 21.4; 11.3; 15.5.

Lee, Philip R.; Conant, Marcus; Heilig, Steve. Participation of health care personnel in torture and interrogation [letter]. *New England Journal of Medicine* 2005 October 13; 353(15): 1634-1635. NRCBL: 21.4; 21.1; 2.1; 1.3.5; 1.3.6.

Lewin, Simon; Meyer, Ilan H. Torture and ill-treatment based on sexual identity: the roles and responsibilities of health professionals and their institutions. *Health and Human Rights: An International Journal* 2002; 6(1): 161-176. NRCBL: 21.4; 10; 17.3; 21.1.

Lewis, Neil A. Guantanamo tour focuses on medical ethics. *New York Times* 2005 November 13; p. A34. NRCBL: 21.4. SC: po.

Lewis, Neil A. Head of hospital at Guantanamo faces complaint. *New York Times* 2005 July 15; p. A13. NRCBL: 21.4. SC: po.

Lewis, Neil A. Interrogators cite doctors' aid at Guantanamo; ethics questions raised; Pentagon says personnel are advisers who do not treat patients. *New York Times* 2005 June 24; p. A1, A19. NRCBL: 21.4. SC: po.

Lewis, Neil A. Psychologists warned on role in detentions. *New York Times* 2005 July 6; p. A14. NRCBL: 21.4; 17.1. SC: po.

London, Leslie; Rangaka, Thabo; Ratamane, Solly; Orr, Wendy; Holland, Erroll; McCarthy, Greg; van Heerden, Judith; Wadee, Shabbir; Daniels, Letticia; Bruning, Axel; Dada, Mahomed; Baqwa, Zanele; Ramlakan, Vijay. Medical complicity in torture — healing the past [editorial]. *South African Medical Journal* 1996 September; 86(9): 1069-1070. NRCBL: 21.4; 4.1.2.

Mandler, George. Psychologists and the National Socialist access to power. *History of Psychology* 2002 May; 5(2): 190-200. NRCBL: 21.4; 17.1; 1.3.5; 7.1.

Marks, Jonathan H. Doctors of interrogation. *Hastings Center Report* 2005 July-August; 35(4): 17-22. NRCBL: 21.4; 4.1.2.

NRCBL: National Reference Center for Bioethics Literature Classification Scheme   See inside front cover for terms.

431

Mathiharan, K. The medical profession and human rights. *Issues in Medical Ethics* 1998 October-December; 6(4): 117-118. NRCBL: 21.4; 21.1.

Maugh, Thomas H., II. Ethics violations by medical staff at Abu Ghraib alleged [news]. *Los Angeles Times* 2004 August 20; p. A8. NRCBL: 21.4; 1.3.5. SC: po.

Rubenstein, Leonard; Pross, Christian; Davidoff, Frank; Iacopino, Vincent. Coercive US interrogation policies: a challenge to medical ethics. *JAMA: The Journal of the American Medical Association* 2005 September 28; 294(12): 1544-1549. NRCBL: 21.4; 21.2; 7.4.

Schlenzka, Hans J. The role of health personnel in the protection of prisoners against torture and inhuman treatment. *Acta Medicinae Legalis et Sociales* 1980; 30(1): 19-24. NRCBL: 21.4.

Schweikardt, Christoph. "You gained honor for your profession as a Brown nurse" : the career of a Nationalist Socialist nurse mirrored by her letters home. *Nursing History Review* 2004; 12: 121-138. NRCBL: 21.4; 7.2; 4.1.3; 1.3.5; 7.1.

Seeman, Mary V. Psychiatry in the Nazi era. *Canadian Journal of Psychiatry/Revue Canadienne de Psychiatrie* 2005 March; 50(4): 218-225. NRCBL: 21.4; 17.1; 1.3.5.

Shields, Linda. Report on: Complicity and Compassion: the First International Conference on Nursing and Midwifery in the Third Reich, 10-11 June 2004, Limerick, Republic of Ireland. *Nursing Ethics* 2005 January; 12(1): 106-107. NRCBL: 21.4; 1.3.5; 2.2; 4.1.3; 15.5; 20.5.1.

Sommerville, Ann; Reyes, Hernan; Peel, Michael. Doctors and torture. *In:* Peel, Michael; Iacopino, Vincent, eds. The Medical Documentation of Torture. San Francisco: Greenwich Medical Media; 2002: 63-76. NRCBL: 21.4; 4.1.2.

Wiesel, Elie. Without conscience [opinion]. *New England Journal of Medicine* 2005 April 14; 352(15): 1511- 1513. NRCBL: 21.4; 20.5.1; 18.5.5; 1.3.5; 4.1.2; 7.2; 2.2.

Wilks, Michael. A stain on medical ethics [opinion]. *Lancet* 2005 August 6-12; 366(9484): 429-431. NRCBL: 21.4; 7.4; 7.3; 2.2; 2.4; 1.3.6.

Wynia, Matthew K. Consequentialism and harsh interrogations. *American Journal of Bioethics* 2005 January-February; 5(1): 4-6. NRCBL: 21.4; 21.2; 9.1.

Xenakis, Stephen N. From the medics, unhealthy silence. *Washington Post* 2005 February 6; p. B4. NRCBL: 21.4; 17.8; 7.1. SC: po.

TREATMENT REFUSAL

See also ADVANCE DIRECTIVES; EUTHANASIA AND ALLOWING TO DIE; INFORMED CONSENT

Ackermann, Deonna; Chapman, Simon; Leask, Julie. Media coverage of anthrax vaccination refusal by Australian Defence Force personnel. *Vaccine* 2004 December 2; 23(3): 411-417. NRCBL: 8.3.4; 9.7; 1.3.7; 1.3.5. SC: em.

Allen, Michael P. The Constitution at the threshold of life and death: a suggested approach to accommodate an interest in life and a right to die. *American University Law Review* 2004 June; 53(5): 971-1020. NRCBL: 8.3.4; 20.5.1. SC: le.

American College of Obstetricians and Gynecologists [ACOG]. Committee on Professional Liability. ACOG Committee Opinion No. 306. Informed refusal. *Obstetrics and Gynecology* 2004 December; 104(6): 1465-1466. NRCBL: 8.3.4.

Anderson, Janet June. Capital punishment of kids: when courts permit parents to act on their religious beliefs at the expense of their children's lives. *Vanderbilt Law Review* 1993 April; 46(3): 755-777. NRCBL: 8.3.4; 8.3.2; 1.3.5; 1.2. SC: le.

Bender, Denise G. Do Fourteenth Amendment considerations outweigh a potential state interest in mandating cochlear implantation for deaf children? *Journal of Deaf Studies and Deaf Education* 2004 Winter; 9(1): 104-111. NRCBL: 8.3.4; 8.3.3; 9.5.7. SC: le; an.

Blank, Arnold. Respecting the autonomy of irrational patients [letter]. *Archives of Internal Medicine* 2005 March 14; 165(5): 590. NRCBL: 8.3.4; 8.3.3.

Blumenthal, Ralph. Hodgkin's returns to girl whose parents fought state: standoff ends as court hears test results. *New York Times* 2005 June 11; p. A8. NRCBL: 8.3.4; 8.3.2. SC: po; le.

Briggs, Catherine A. Informed refusal and patient autonomy: using reflection to examine how nursing knowledge and theory affect attitudes. *Intensive and Critical Care Nursing* 1995 December; 11(6): 314-317. NRCBL: 8.3.4; 1.2; 8.1; 7.1.

Carney, T.; Tait, D.; Wakefield, A.; Ingvarson, M.; Touyz, S. Coercion in the treatment of anorexia nervosa: clinical, ethical and legal implications. *Medicine and Law: World Association for Medical Law* 2005 March; 24(1): 21-40. NRCBL: 8.3.4; 8.3.2. SC: em.

Abstract: Because of its high mortality and treatment resistance, clinicians sometimes invoke the law in aid of retaining their most acutely ill-patients in treatment or re-feeding programs. Depending on the jurisdiction, various laws, including mental health and adult guardianship laws, have been invoked to achieve this objective (Carney, Tait, Saunders, Touyz & Beumont, 2003). Until recently, little was known about the therapeutic impact of coercion on patients (Saunders, 2001, Carney & Saunders 2003), or the relative advantages of different avenues of coercion (Carney, Saunders, Tait, Touyz & Ingvarson 2004). Most obscure of all, however, has been our understanding of the factors influencing clinical decisions within specialist anorexia treatment units regarding which in-patients will be selected for coerced treatment. This paper reports legal and ethical implications of findings from analysis of data gathered from a major Australian specialist anorexia treatment facility over nearly 5 years.

Crosswait, Anne Riegle. Comment: "do not resuscitate order" allowed for an infant with AIDS: In the Interest of C.A. *Journal of Health and Hospital Law* 1993 January; 26(1): 11-19. NRCBL: 8.3.4; 8.3.2; 20.5.2; 9.5.6. SC: le.

DeRenzo, Evan G.; Panzarella, Philip; Selinger, Steve; Schwartz, Jack. Emancipation, capacity, and the difference between law and ethics [case study and commentary]. *Journal of Clinical Ethics* 2005 Summer; 16(2): 144-150. NRCBL: 8.3.4; 9.5.5; 17.1; 8.3.3; 9.5.8; 9.6. SC: cs; le.

DiDio, Arthur S. The right to refuse treatment during pregnancy: where maternal and fetal rights conflict. *Medical Trial Technique Quarterly* 1999; 45(3): 225-269. NRCBL: 8.3.4; 9.5.5; 9.5.8; 4.4; 1.1. SC: le.

Ekblad, Michele. The patient's right to refuse medical care: Michigan and federal law. *Journal of Medicine and Law* 2001 Fall; 6(1): 29-50. NRCBL: 8.3.4; 8.3.2; 20.5.1. SC: le.

Fleming, Sheena. The pregnant woman's right to say no: a personal reflection [opinion]. *RCM Midwives* 2005 March; 8(3): 106-107. NRCBL: 8.3.4; 9.5.5; 9.5.8; 4.1.1.

Georgia. Supreme Court. *Adams v. State* [Date of Decision: 4 May 1998]. *West's South Eastern Reporter*, 2d Series, 1998; 498: 268-274. NRCBL: 8.3.4; 9.5.6; 1.3.5. SC: le.
Abstract: Court Decision: 498 *South Eastern Reporter*, 2d Series 268; 1998 May 4 (date of decision). The Supreme Court of Georgia held that a state statute permitting a crime victim who is significantly exposed to HIV to request an HIV blood test on the person charged with the crime and arrested does not violate the Fourth Amendment right against unreasonable searches, nor does it violate privacy or equal protection rights. Malik Adams attacked and struggled with police officers during arrest. In the struggle, Adams's and an officer's hands, on which there were bleeding wounds, came in contact. Even though Adams did not have any outward AIDS symptoms, the state filed a motion to compel HIV testing. The Supreme Court of Georgia held that, because the statute compelling HIV testing serves the compelling state interest of preventing the public's exposure to HIV, the search, in this case the taking and sampling of blood, is reasonable. [KIE/INW]

Glasgow, Richard. Forced medication of criminal defendants and the unintended consequences of Sell v. United States. *Journal of Contemporary Health Law and Policy* 2005 Summer; 21(2): 235-258. NRCBL: 8.3.4; 1.3.5; 9.5.3. SC: le.

Gomez, Paul A. Promises and pitfalls: an analysis of the shifting constitutional interests involved in the context of demanding a right to treatment in health care. *Albany Law Review* 2000; 64(1): 361-396. NRCBL: 8.3.4; 9.2; 20.5.1; 1.1. SC: le.

Goodman, Benny. Ms. B and legal competence: interprofessional collaboration and nurse autonomy. *Nurs-*

ing in Critical Care 2004 November-December; 9(6): 271-276. NRCBL: 8.3.4; 7.3; 1.1. SC: le. Identifiers: United Kingdom (Great Britain).

Great Britain. England. High Court of Justice. Family Division; Lloyd, Huw; Munby, James; Brown, Stephen P. Medical treatment — refusal of medical treatment — adult - - refusal on religious grounds: re S. (refusal of medical treatment) [Date of Decision: 12 October 1992]. *New Law Journal* 1992 October 23; 142(6573): 1450-1451. NRCBL: 8.3.4; 1.2; 9.5.5; 9.5.8. SC: le.

Gross, M.L. Treating competent patients by force: the limits and lessons of Israel's Patient's Rights Act. *Journal of Medical Ethics* 2005 January; 31(1): 29-34. NRCBL: 8.3.4; 8.3.1. SC: cs; le.
Abstract: Competent patients who refuse life saving medical treatment present a dilemma for healthcare professionals. On one hand, respect for autonomy and liberty demand that physicians respect a patient's decision to refuse treatment. However, it is often apparent that such patients are not fully competent. They may not adequately comprehend the benefits of medical care, be overly anxious about pain, or discount the value of their future state of health. Although most bioethicists are convinced that partial autonomy or marginal competence of this kind demands the same respect as full autonomy, Israeli legislators created a mechanism to allow ethics committees to override patients' informed refusal and treat them against their will. To do so, three conditions must be satisfied: physicians must make every effort to ensure the patient understands the risks of non-treatment, the treatment physicians propose must offer a realistic chance of significant improvement, and there are reasonable expectations that the patient will consent retroactively. Although not all of these conditions are equally cogent, they offer a way forward to assure care for certain classes of competent patients without abandoning the principle of autonomy altogether. These concerns reach past Israel and should engage healthcare professionals wary that respect for autonomy may sometimes cause avoidable harm.

Gross, Michael L. Dilemma over forced treatment [letter]. *Lancet* 2005 June 25-July 1; 365(9478): 2177. NRCBL: 8.3.4; 8.3.3.

Harper, Richard S. Adult refusal of medical treatment: non-consensual treatment. *In his:* Medical Treatment and the Law: The Protection of Adults and Minors in the Family Division. Bristol: Family Law; 1999: 55-67. NRCBL: 8.3.4. SC: le.

Howe, Edmund G. Why are they boxing us in like this? *Journal of Clinical Ethics* 2005 Summer; 16(2): 99-107. NRCBL: 8.3.4; 9.5.5; 17.1; 8.3.3; 8.1.

Hughes, Richard A. The death of children by faith-based medical neglect. *Journal of Law and Religion* 2004-2005; 20(1): 247-265. NRCBL: 8.3.4; 8.3.2; 4.4; 9.5.7; 1.2; 20.5.2. SC: em; le.

Jones, James W.; McCullough, Laurence B.; Richman, Bruce W. A surgeon's obligations to a Jehovah's Witness child. *Surgery* 2003 January; 133(1): 110-111. NRCBL: 8.3.4; 8.3.2; 1.2. SC: cs. Note: In a column titled "Ethical

NRCBL: National Reference Center for Bioethics Literature Classification Scheme   See inside front cover for terms.

433

Dilemmas in Surgery.". Comments: See reply in Surgery 2003 January; 133(1): 123.

Justus, Kelly. Oral aversion: a case and discussion. *Pediatric Nursing* 1998 September-October; 24(5): 474, 478. NRCBL: 8.3.4; 9.5.7. SC: cs.

Kelley, Maureen. Limits on patient responsibility. *Journal of Medicine and Philosophy* 2005 April; 30(2): 189-206. NRCBL: 8.3.4; 8.1; 1.1. SC: an.

Abstract: The medical profession and medical ethics currently place a greater emphasis on physician responsibility than patient responsibility. This imbalance is not due to accident or a mistake but, rather is motivated by strong moral reasons. As we debate the nature and extent of patient responsibility it is important to keep in mind the reasons for giving a relatively minimal role to patient responsibility in medical ethics. It is argued that the medical profession ought to be characterized by two moral asymmetries: (1) Even if some degree of responsible behavior from patients is called for, placing the dominant emphasis on professional responsibility over patient responsibility is largely correct. The value of protecting the right to refuse treatment and arguments against paternalism block a more expansive account of patient responsibility and support a strong notion of professional responsibility. (2) Insofar as we do want to encourage an increase in patient responsibility, we have good reasons to emphasize prospective rather than retrospective notions of responsibility in clinical practice. Concerns about patient vulnerability along with the determined factors in disease leave little room for blame at the bedside. These two asymmetries generate normative limits on any positive account of patient responsibility.

Kelly, David F. Forgoing treatment, pillar three: decisions by competent patients. *In his:* Contemporary Catholic Health Care Ethics. Washington, DC: Georgetown University Press; 2004: 143-152. NRCBL: 8.3.4; 1.2. SC: le.

Kennedy, Wendy. Beneficence and autonomy in nursing: a moral dilemma. *British Journal of Perioperative Nursing* 2004 November; 14(11): 500-506. NRCBL: 8.3.4; 8.3.1; 1.1. SC: cs.

Kohrs, Brendon. Bioterrorism defense: are state mandated compulsory vaccination programs an infringement upon a citizen's constitutional rights? *Journal of Law and Health* 2002-2003; 17(2): 241-270. NRCBL: 8.3.4; 9.7; 21.3. SC: le.

Lerner, Barron H. From careless consumptives to recalcitrant patients: the historical construction of noncompliance. *Social Science and Medicine* 1997 November; 45(9): 1423-1431. NRCBL: 8.3.4; 9.1; 2.2.

Linnard-Palmer, Luanne; Kools, Susan. Parents' refusal of medical treatment based on religious and/or cultural beliefs: the law, ethical principles, and clinical implications. *Journal of Pediatric Nursing* 2004 October; 19(5): 351-356. NRCBL: 8.3.4; 8.3.2; 1.2; 21.7. SC: le.

Linnard-Palmer, Luanne; Kools, Susan. Parents' refusal of medical treatment for cultural or religious beliefs: an ethnographic study of health care professionals' experiences. *Journal of Pediatric Oncology Nursing* 2005 January-February; 22(1): 48-57. NRCBL: 8.3.4; 8.3.2; 1.2; 8.1; 21.7. SC: em.

Luce, John M. New standards for patient rights and medical competence. *Critical Care Medicine* 2000 August; 28(8): 3114-3115. NRCBL: 8.3.4; 9.2; 8.1; 7.1.

Lyng, Kristin; Syse, Aslak; Børdahl, Per E. Can cesarean section be performed without the woman's consent? *Acta Obstetricia et Gynecologica Scandinavica* 2005 January; 84(1): 39-42. NRCBL: 8.3.4; 9.5.5. SC: cs. Identifiers: Norway.

McInroy, Ally. Blood transfusion and Jehovah's Witnesses: the legal and ethical issues. *British Journal of Nursing* 2005 March 10-23; 14(5): 270-274. NRCBL: 8.3.4; 19.4; 1.2. SC: le.

McQuoid-Mason, David. Parental refusal of blood transfusions for minor children solely on religious grounds — the doctor's dilemma resolved. *South African Medical Journal* 2005 January; 95(1): 29-30. NRCBL: 8.3.4; 8.3.2; 19.4; 1.2.

Miller, Kevin E. Ending renal dialysis: ethical issues in refusing life- sustaining treatment. *In:* Koterski, Joseph W., ed. Life and Learning IX: Proceedings of the Ninth University Faculty for Life Conference. Washington, DC: University Faculty for Life; 2000: 59-78. NRCBL: 8.3.4; 1.2; 20.5.1; 19.3.

Murphy, Peter. Are patients' decisions to refuse treatment binding on health care professionals? *Bioethics* 2005 June; 19(3): 189-201. NRCBL: 8.3.4; 1.1. SC: an.

Abstract: When patients refuse to receive medical treatment, the consequences of honouring their decisions can be tragic. This is no less true of patients who autonomously decide to refuse treatment. I distinguish three possible implications of these autonomous decisions. According to the Permissibility Claim, such a decision implies that it is permissible for the patient who has made the autonomous decision to forego medical treatment. According to the Anti-Paternalism Claim, it follows that health-care professionals are not morally permitted to treat that patient. According to the Binding Claim it follows that these decisions are binding on health-care professionals. My focus is the last claim. After arguing that it is importantly different from each of the first two claims, I give two arguments to show that it is false. One argument against the Binding Claim draws a comparison with cases in which patients autonomously choose perilous positive treatments. The other argument appeals to considered judgments about cases in which disincentives are used to deter patients from refusing sound treatments.

Nash, Michael J.; Cohen, Hannah. Management of Jehovah's Witness patients with haematological problems. *Blood Reviews* 2004 September; 18(3): 211-217. NRCBL: 8.3.4; 1.2; 8.3.2; 9.5.4; 19.4. Identifiers: United Kingdom (Great Britain).

Oliver, Samuel L.; Baumrucker, Steven J.; Rousseau, Paul; Stolick, Matt; Morris, Gerald M.; Ufema, Joy. Case study: death or damnation — refusing life-prolonging therapy on religious grounds. *American Journal of*

Hospice and Palliative Medicine 2004 November-December; 21(6): 469-473. NRCBL: 8.3.4; 19.4; 1.2; 8.3.2. SC: cs.

Orr, Robert D.; Cranston, Robert; Beals, Daniel. Ethics and medicine: clinical ethics dilemmas [case study and commentary]. *Ethics and Medicine* 2005 Summer; 21(2): 89-93. NRCBL: 8.3.4; 8.3.2; 19.4; 1.2. SC: le. Identifiers: Jehovah's Witness.

Pishchita, A. The practice of applying compulsory treatment to mentally disturbed people: a view from Russia. *Medicine and Law: World Association for Medical Law* 2005 December; 24(4): 717-725. NRCBL: 8.3.4; 17.1; 9.5.3; 17.8. SC: le.
Abstract: The author describes the development of current legislation in Russia relative to compulsory medical treatment for mentally ill persons. He discusses these laws in relation to criminality and its prevention.

Pollitt, Rodney J. Compliance with science: consent or coercion in newborn screening [editorial]. *European Journal of Pediatrics* 2004 December; 163(12): 757-758. NRCBL: 8.3.4; 9.5.7; 15.3.

Ravitsky, Vardit; Wendler, David. Dissolving the dilemma over forced treatment. *Lancet* 2005 April 30-May 6; 365(9470): 1525-1526. NRCBL: 8.3.4; 8.3.3.

Resnik, David B. The patient's duty to adhere to prescribed treatment: an ethical analysis. *Journal of Medicine and Philosophy* 2005 April; 30(2): 167-188. NRCBL: 8.3.4; 8.1; 1.1. SC: an.
Abstract: This article examines the ethical basis for the patient's duty to adhere to the physician's treatment prescriptions. The article argues that patients have a moral duty to adhere to the physician's treatment prescriptions, once they have accepted treatment. Since patients still retain the right to refuse medical treatment, their duty to adhere to treatment prescriptions is a prima facie duty, which can be overridden by their other ethical duties. However, patients do not have the right to refuse to adhere to treatment prescriptions if their non-adherence poses a significant threat to other people. This paper also discusses the use of written agreements between physicians and patients as a strategy for promoting patient adherence.

Rougé-Maillart, C.; Jousset, J.; Gaches, T.; Gaudin, A.; Penneau, M. Patients refusing medical attention: the case of Jehovah's Witnesses in France. *Medicine and Law: World Association for Medical Law* 2004; 23(4): 715-723. NRCBL: 8.3.4; 1.2. SC: le.
Abstract: Respect for the wishes of a patient is internationally accepted as standard medical practice. In French law, this principle is enshrined in the Civil Code of 1994 which concerns bioethics. More recently in 2002, we find it included in the Code of Public Health (in the law concerning patient's rights). According to these texts, the patient's wishes must always be respected even when his life is at stake, so long as the patient has been informed of the risk. The refusal by Jehovah's Witnesses to receive blood transfusion always poses a problem. When, in full consciousness, a patient refuses a blood transfusion his life depends on, what should the doctor do? In June 1998, the Paris Administrative Court of Appeals ruled on such a case. The judges found that. In October 2001, the State Council decided in this particular case, that given the critical situation and the ab-

sence of a therapeutic alternative, the doctor had not committed an error. But it also clearly reiterated that the doctor is required to respect the wishes of the patient and that this obligation does not override the duty of saving a life. Two emergency interim rulings by the Lille Administration Court (25th August, 2002,) and by the State Council (6th August, 2002) confirm the position of the judges. Not respecting the patient's wishes is a great infringement of individual freedom. The doctor will not err only under extreme and precise conditions. Should the doctor go against those wishes? Should the wishes of the patient be respected when their life is at stake? The authors will discuss these two questions.

Salmon, Daniel A.; Moulton, Lawrence H.; Omer, Saad B.; deHart, M. Patricia; Stokley, Shannon; Halsey, Neal A. Factors associated with refusal of childhood vaccines among parents of school-aged children: a case-control study. *Archives of Pediatric and Adolescent Medicine* 2005 May; 159(5): 470-476. NRCBL: 8.3.4; 9.7; 8.3.2; 1.2. SC: em.

Savulescu, Julian. Should all patients who attempt suicide be treated? *Monash Bioethics Review* 1995 October; 14(4): 33-40. NRCBL: 8.3.4; 20.7. SC: cs.

Sewell, Adrian C.; Gebhardt, Boris; Herwig, Jürgen; Rauterberg, Ernst W. Acceptance of extended newborn screening: the problem of parental non-compliance. *European Journal of Pediatrics* 2004 December; 163(12): 755-756. NRCBL: 8.3.4; 9.5.7; 15.3.

Spike, Jeffrey. Personhood and a paradox about capacity. *In:* Thomasma, David C.; Weisstub, David C.; Herve, Christian eds. Personhood and Health Care. Boston: Kluwer Academic Pub.; 2001: 243-251. NRCBL: 8.3.4; 9.6; 4.4.

Stewart, Cameron; Lynch, Andrew. Undue influence, consent and medical treatment. *Journal of the Royal Society of Medicine* 2003 December; 96(12): 598-601. NRCBL: 8.3.4; 8.3.1; 9.2; 8.1. SC: le.

van Kleffens, T.; van Leeuwen, E. Physicians' evaluations of patients' decisions to refuse oncological treatment. *Journal of Medical Ethics* 2005 March; 31(3): 131-136. NRCBL: 8.3.4; 7.1. SC: em.
Abstract: OBJECTIVE: To gain insight into the standards of rationality that physicians use when evaluating patients' treatment refusals. DESIGN OF THE STUDY: Qualitative design with in depth interviews. PARTICIPANTS: The study sample included 30 patients with cancer and 16 physicians (oncologists and general practitioners). All patients had refused a recommended oncological treatment. RESULTS: Patients base their treatment refusals mainly on personal values and/or experience. Physicians mainly emphasise the medical perspective when evaluating patients' treatment refusals. From a medical perspective, a patient's treatment refusal based on personal values and experience is generally evaluated as irrational and difficult to accept, especially when it concerns a curative treatment. Physicians have a different attitude towards non-curative treatments and have less difficulty accepting a patient's refusal of these treatments. Thus, an important factor in the physician's evaluation of a treatment refusal is whether the treatment refused is curative or non-curative. CONCLUSION: Physicians mainly use goal oriented and patients mainly value oriented ra-

NRCBL: National Reference Center for Bioethics Literature Classification Scheme   See inside front cover for terms.

435

tionality, but in the case of non-curative treatment refusal, physicians give more emphasis to value oriented rationality. A consensus between the value oriented approaches of patient and physician may then emerge, leading to the patient's decision being understood and accepted by the physician. The physician's acceptance is crucial to his or her attitude towards the patient. It contributes to the patient's feeling free to decide, and being understood and respected, and thus to a better physician-patient relationship.

Wilborn, S. Elizabeth. The right to refuse medical treatment: where there is a right, there ought to be a remedy. *Northern Kentucky Law Review* 1998 Summer; 25(4): 649-673. NRCBL: 8.3.4; 1.1; 20.5.1; 20.5.4. SC: le.

Wilson, Phil. Jehovah's Witness children: when religion and the law collide. *Paediatric Nursing* 2005 April; 17(3): 34-37. NRCBL: 8.3.4; 8.3.2; 1.2. SC: le.

TRUTH DISCLOSURE

Health and Social Care (Community Health and Standards) Bill. *Bulletin of Medical Ethics* 2003 October; (192): 2. NRCBL: 8.2. SC: le. Identifiers: United Kingdom (Great Britain).

Aaraas, Ivar J.; Jones, Barbara; Gupta, Tarun Sen. Reactions to adverse events among Australian and Norwegian doctors. *Australian Family Physician* 2004 December; 33(12): 1045-1046. NRCBL: 8.2; 9.8; 7.3. SC: em.

Berger, Jeffrey T. Ignorance is bliss? Ethical considerations in therapeutic nondisclosure. *Cancer Investigation* 2005; 23(1): 94-98. NRCBL: 8.2.

Best, John. The matter of disclosure — worth talking about? [editorial]. *Medical Journal of Australia* 1995 August 21; 163(4): 172. NRCBL: 8.2; 9.1.

Black, Andrew. SUDEP — whether to tell and when? *Medicine and Law: World Association for Medical Law* 2005 March; 24(1): 41-49. NRCBL: 8.2; 20.3.2. Identifiers: sudden and unexpected death in people with epilepsy.

Bramstedt, Katrina A.; Macauley, Robert. A case of deception? [case study]. *Hastings Center Report* 2005 November-December; 35(6): 13-14. NRCBL: 8.2; 8.1; 19.5. SC: cs.

Browne, Natasha. Truth-telling in palliative care. *European Journal of Oncology Nursing* 1998 December; 2(4): 218-224. NRCBL: 8.2; 20.4.1; 9.5.1.

Byk, Christian. Truth telling and informed consent: is "primum docere" the new motto of clinical practice? *Formosan Journal of Medical Humanities* 2005 September; 6(1-2): 31-38. NRCBL: 8.2; 8.3.1; 18.3.

Cantor, Michael D.; Barach, Paul; Derse, Arthur; Maklan, Claire W.; Wlody, Ginger Schafer; Fox, Ellen. Disclosing adverse events to patients. *Joint Commission Journal on Quality and Patient Safety* 2005 January; 31(1): 5-12. NRCBL: 8.2; 9.8.

Cheyne, Colin. Exploiting placebo effects for therapeutic benefit. *Health Care Analysis: An International Journal of Health Care Philosophy and Policy* 2005 September; 13(3): 177-188. NRCBL: 8.2; 18.3. SC: an.
  Abstract: It is widely believed that medically inert treatments ("placebos") can bring about therapeutic benefits. There is also evidence that medically active treatments may also have "placebo" effects. Since anything that has the potential to benefit patients ought to be exploited, subject to appropriate ethical standards, it has been suggested that more should be done to investigate and exploit the power of the placebo for therapeutic benefit. I explore the acute epistemic and ethical constraints that such exploitation is likely to face, and conclude that effective exploitation is unlikely.

Chiò, Adriano; Borasio, Gian Domenico. Breaking the news in amyotrophic lateral sclerosis. *Amyotrophic Lateral Sclerosis and Other Motor Neuron Disorders* 2004 December; 5(4): 195-201. NRCBL: 8.2; 9.5.1; 21.1. SC: rv.

Cochella, Susan E.W.; Pedersen, Donald M. Negotiating a request for nondisclosure [case study and commentary]. *American Family Physician* 2003 January 1; 67(1): 209-211. NRCBL: 8.2; 21.7. SC: cs.

Conn, Jennifer; Gillam, Lynn; Conway, Gerard S. Revealing the diagnosis of androgen insensitivity syndrome in adulthood. *BMJ: British Medical Journal* 2005 September 17; 331(7517): 628-630. NRCBL: 8.2; 10; 15.1.

De Lepeleire, J.; Buntinx, F.; Aertgeerts, B. Disclosing the diagnosis of dementia: the performance of Flemish general practitioners. *International Psychogeriatrics* 2004 December; 16(4): 421-428. NRCBL: 8.2; 17.1; 9.5.2. SC: em. Identifiers: Belgium.

Dimond, Bridgit. Rights to information access under the Data Protection Act. *British Journal of Nursing* 2005 July 28-August 10; 14(4): 774-776. NRCBL: 8.2; 8.4. SC: le.

Friedman, Joseph H. Ignorance is bliss? An ethical question [opinion]. *Medicine and Health, Rhode Island* 2004 May; 87(5): 126. NRCBL: 8.2; 15.3.

Fry, Sara T.; Veatch, Robert M. Veracity. *In their:* Case Studies in Nursing Ethics. Third edition. Sudbury, MA: Jones and Bartlett Publishers; 2006: 142-166. NRCBL: 8.2.

Gilliotti, Catherine M. Medical disclosure and decision-making: excavating complexities of physician-patient information exchange. *In:* Thompson, Teresa L.; Dorsey, Alicia M.; Miller, Katherine I.; Parrott, Roxanne, eds. Handbook of Health Communication. Mahwah, NJ: Lawrence Erlbaum Associates; 2003: 163-181. NRCBL: 8.2; 8.1. SC: rv.

Gold, Michelle. Is honesty always the best policy? Ethical aspects of truth telling. *Internal Medicine Journal* 2004

September-October; 34(9-10): 578-580. NRCBL: 8.2; 8.3.1; 21.7; 1.1. SC: cs.

Goldie, J.; Schwartz, L.; Morrison, J. Whose information is it anyway? Informing a 12-year-old patient of her terminal prognosis. *Journal of Medical Ethics* 2005 July; 31(7): 427-434. NRCBL: 8.2; 20.4.2. SC: em.

Abstract: OBJECTIVE: To examine students' attitudes and potential behaviour towards informing a 12-year-old patient of her terminal prognosis in a situation in which her parents do not wish her to be told, as they pass through a modern medical curriculum. DESIGN: A cohort study of students entering Glasgow University's new medical curriculum in October 1996. METHODS: Students' responses obtained before year 1 and at the end of years 1, 3, and 5 to the "childhood leukaemia" vignette of the Ethics in Health Care Survey Instrument (EHCI) were examined quantitatively and qualitatively. Analysis of the students' multichoice answers enabled measurement of the movement towards professional consensus opinion. An analysis of their written justifications for their answers helped to determine whether their reasoning was consistent with professional consensus and enabled measurement of changes in knowledge content and recognition of the values inherent in the vignette. Themes on the students' reasoning behind their decision to tell the patient or not were also identified. RESULTS: Unlike other vignettes of the EHCI in which autonomy was a main theme, few students chose the consensus answer before year 1 and there was no significant movement towards consensus at any point during the course. In defence of their decision to withhold information, the students expressed strong paternalistic opinions. The patient's age was seen as a barrier to respecting her autonomy. CONCLUSIONS: It is important to identify students' perceptions on entry to medical school. Transformative learning theory may provide the basis for an approach to foster doctors who consider the rights of young people. Small-group teaching is most conducive to this approach. The importance of positive role modelling is also emphasised.

Groopman, Jerome E. A strategy for hope: a commentary on necessary collusion. *Journal of Clinical Oncology* 2005 May 1; 23(13): 3151-3152. NRCBL: 8.2; 9.5.1.

Hagerty, Rebecca G.; Butow, Phyllis N.; Ellis, Peter M.; Lobb, Elizabeth A.; Pendlebury, Susan C.; Leighl, Natasha; MacLeod, Craig; Tattersall, Martin H.N. Communicating with realism and hope: incurable cancer patients' views on the disclosure of prognosis. *Journal of Clinical Oncology* 2005 February 20; 23(6): 1278-1288. NRCBL: 8.2; 9.5.1; 20.1. SC: em. Identifiers: Australia.

Haroun, Ansar M.; Morris, Grant H. Weaving a tangled web: the deceptions of psychiatrists. *Journal of Contemporary Legal Issues* 1999; 10: 227-246. NRCBL: 8.2; 17.2. SC: le.

Helft, Paul R. Necessary collusion: prognostic communication with advanced cancer patients. *Journal of Clinical Oncology* 2005 May 1; 23(13): 3146-3150. NRCBL: 8.2; 9.5.1.

Hertogh, Cees M.P.M.; The, B. Anne Mei; Miesen, Bere M.L.; Eefsting, Jan A. Truth telling and truthfulness in the care for patients with advanced dementia: an ethnographic study in Dutch nursing homes. *Social Sci-*

ence and Medicine 2004 October; 59(8): 1685-1693. NRCBL: 8.2; 4.1.3; 17.1; 9.5.2. SC: cs; le. Identifiers: Netherlands.

Hird, Crystal. A call for education [letter]. *Nursing Ethics* 2005 March; 12(2): 196-197. NRCBL: 8.2; 7.2.

Honeyman, Alasdair; Cox, Benita; Fisher, Brian. Potential impacts of patient access to their electronic care records. *Informatics in Primary Care* 2005; 13(1): 55-60. NRCBL: 8.2; 8.4; 1.3.12. SC: em. Identifiers: United Kingdom (Great Britain).

Jones, James W.; McCullough, Laurence B.; Richman, Bruce W. Truth-telling about terminal diseases. *Surgery* 2005 March; 137(3): 380-382. NRCBL: 8.2; 20.4.1; 9.5.1. SC: cs.

Jones, R.B.; Hedley, A.J.; Allison, S.P.; Tattersall, R.B. Censoring of patient-held records by doctors. *Journal of the Royal College of General Practitioners* 1988 March; 38(308): 117-118. NRCBL: 8.2; 8.4.

LeGros, Nancy; Pinkall, Jason D. The new JCAHO patient safety standards and the disclosure of unanticipated outcomes. *Journal of Health Law* 2002 Spring; 35(2): 189-210. NRCBL: 8.2; 9.6; 8.5. SC: le. Identifiers: Joint Commission on Accreditation of Healthcare Organizations.

Lowenstein, Jerome K. The weight of shared lives: truth telling and family caregiving. *In:* Levine, Carol; Murray, Thomas H., eds. The Cultures of Caregiving: Conflict and Common Ground among Families, Health Professionals, and Policy Makers. Baltimore: Johns Hopkins University Press; 2004: 47-53. NRCBL: 8.2.

Maithel, Shishir Kumar. Iatrogenic error and truth telling: a comparison of the United States and India. *Issues in Medical Ethics* 1998 October-December; 6(4): 125-127. NRCBL: 8.2; 9.8. SC: em.

Manship, Greg. Hope and the ethics of disclosure for terminally ill cancer patients. *Health Care Ethics USA [electronic]* 2005; 13(3): E4, 3 p. Available: http://www.slu.edu/centers/chce/hceusa/3_2005_index.html [21 February 2006]. NRCBL: 8.2; 8.1; 9.5.1.

Maynard, Douglas W. On predicating a diagnosis as an attribute of a person. *Discourse Studies* 2004 February; 6(1): 53-76. NRCBL: 8.2; 8.1. SC: em.

Meredith, Barbara. Data protection and freedom of information: the law is only a catalyst for changing the culture in the NHS [editorial]. *BMJ: British Medical Journal* 2005 March 5; 330(7490): 490-491. NRCBL: 8.2; 8.4; 1.3.12.

Miyata, Hioraki; Takahashi, M.; Saito, T.; Tachimori, H.; Kai, I. Disclosure preferences regarding cancer diagnosis and prognosis: to tell or not to tell? *Journal of Medi-*

NRCBL: National Reference Center for Bioethics Literature Classification Scheme   See inside front cover for terms.

437

cal Ethics 2005 August; 31(8): 447-451. NRCBL: 8.2. SC: em. Identifiers: Japan.

Abstract: Telling people that they have cancer has a great impact on their lives, so many doctors are concerned about how they should inform patients about a cancer diagnosis and its prognosis. We conducted a general population survey in Japan to investigate people's preferences on receiving this information. There were no significant differences in respondents' preferences according to the seriousness of the cancer. Full disclosure of the diagnosis was preferred by 86.1% of the respondents, while 2.7% wanted non- disclosure. As for the initial provision of information, the majority preferred partial disclosure concerning the prospects of complete recovery (64.5%) and the expected length of survival (64.1%). Those who responded negatively to the statement, "If I am close to the end of my life, I want to be informed of the fact so I can choose my own way of life", were more likely to want non- disclosure on diagnosis. The results suggest that, at the first opportunity of providing information, a disclosure policy of giving patients full details of their diagnosis and some information on prognosis can satisfy the preferences of most patients. Contrary to popular belief, the seriousness of the cancer and people's demographic characteristics displayed little impact in this study.

Moore, Dale L. Recurrent issues in the review of medical research on human subjects. *Albany Law Journal of Science and Technology* 1991; 1: 1-33. NRCBL: 8.2. SC: le.

Mulholland, Daniel. Unanticipated consequences of unanticipated outcomes disclosures. *Journal of Health Law* 2002 Spring; 35(2): 211-226. NRCBL: 8.2; 9.6. SC: le.

Nichols, Polly S.; Winslow, Gerald. Transparent truthfulness. *General Dentistry* 2005 January-February; 53(1): 15-16. NRCBL: 8.2; 9.3.1; 4.1.1. SC: cs.

Ofri, Danielle. They sent me here [opinion]. *New England Journal of Medicine* 2005 April 28; 352(17): 1746- 1748. NRCBL: 8.2; 8.1.

Ouimet, Marie-Andrée; Dendukuri, Nandini; Dion, Dominique; Belzile, Eric; Élie, Michel. Disclosure of Alzheimer's disease: senior citizens' opinions. *Canadian Family Physician* 2004 December; 50: 1671-1677. NRCBL: 8.2; 17.1; 9.5.2. SC: em.

Peretti-Watel, P.; Bendiane, M.K.; Obadia, Y.; Lapiana, J.M.; Galinier, A.; Pegliasco, H.; Favre, R.; Moatti, J.P. Disclosure of prognosis to terminally ill patients: attitudes and practices among French physicians. *Journal of Palliative Medicine* 2005 April; 8(2): 280-290. NRCBL: 8.2; 20.4.1. SC: em.

Peters, Catherine; Kantaris, Xenya; Barnes, Jacqueline; Sutcliffe, Alastair. Parental attitudes toward disclosure of the mode of conception to their child conceived by in vitro fertilization. *Fertility and Sterility* 2005 April; 83(4): 914-919. NRCBL: 8.2; 14.2. SC: em. Identifiers: United Kingdom (Great Britain).

Rosner, Fred. Informing the patient about a fatal disease: from paternalism to autonomy — the Jewish view. *Cancer Investigation* 2004; 22(6): 949-953. NRCBL: 8.2; 1.2.

Sass, Hans-Martin. Narrative approaches in patient information and communication. *Formosan Journal of Medical Humanities* 2005 September; 6(1-2): 15-29. NRCBL: 8.2; 15.1.

Slingsby, Brian Taylor. The nature of relative subjectivity: a reflexive mode of thought. *Journal of Medicine and Philosophy* 2005 February; 30(1): 9-25. NRCBL: 8.2; 1.1.

Abstract: Ethical principles including autonomy, justice and equality function in the same paradigm of thought, that is, logocentrism—an epistemological predilection that relies on the analytic power of deciphering between binary oppositions. By studying observable behavior with an analytical approach, however, one immediately limits any recognition and possible understanding of modes of thought based on separate epistemologies. This article seeks to reveal an epistemological predilection that diverges from logocentrism yet continues to function as a fundamental component of ethical behavior. The issue of cancer disclosure in Japan is used to exemplify the nature of relative subjectivity (kankeiteki- shukansei), a term I define and believe to be an epistemological predisposition fundamental to ethical behavior. Relative subjectivity denotes an epistemology quintessential to the behavior of individuals who attend to the respective tides of each particular situation, each interpersonal relationship or, in the context of clinical medicine, to the needs and values of each patient.

Sokol, Daniel K. Calling a spade a spade [opinion]. *BMJ: British Medical Journal* 2005 September 3; 331(7515): 523. NRCBL: 8.2; 8.3.1.

Sullivan, Mark; Paice, Judith A.; Benedetti, Fabrizio. Placebos and treatment of pain [case study and commentary]. *Pain Medicine* 2004 September; 5(3): 325-328. NRCBL: 8.2. SC: cs.

Surbone, Antonella; Ritossa, Claudio; Spagnolo, Antonio G. Evolution of truth-telling attitudes and practices in Italy. *Critical Reviews in Oncology/Hematology* 2004 December; 52(3): 165-172. NRCBL: 8.2; 8.3.1; 2.2.

Takayesu, James Kimo; Hutson, H. Range. Communicating life-threatening diagnoses to patients in the emergency department. *Annals of Emergency Medicine* 2004 June; 43(6): 749-755. NRCBL: 8.2; 20.4.1; 20.4.2.

Wang, Shing-Yaw; Chen, Chung-Hey; Chen, Yong-Shing; Huang, Huei-Lin. The attitude toward truth telling of cancer in Taiwan. *Journal of Psychosomatic Research* 2004 July; 57(1): 53-58. NRCBL: 8.2. SC: em.

Yun, Young Ho; Lee, Chang Geol; Kim, Si-young; Lee, Sang- wook; Heo, Dae Seog; Kim, Jun Suk; Lee, Keun Seok; Hong, Young Seon; Lee, Jung Suk; You, Chang Hoon. The attitudes of cancer patients and their families toward the disclosure of terminal illness. *Journal of Clinical Oncology* 2004 January 15; 22(2): 307-314. NRCBL: 8.2; 20.3.1. SC: em.

VALUE OF LIFE *See* QUALITY AND VALUE OF LIFE

WAR AND TERRORISM
See also TORTURE, GENOCIDE, AND WAR CRIMES

A gift to pharma? [editorial]. *Nature Medicine* 2005 July; 11(7): 693. NRCBL: 21.3; 9.7.

Editors' statement on considerations of biodefence and biosecurity [editorial]. *Nature Medicine* 2003 March; 9(3): 240. NRCBL: 21.3; 1.3.7; 1.3.9.

Agre, Peter C.; Altman, Sidney; Curl, Robert F.; Wiesel, Torsten N.; West-Eberhard, Mary Jane; Somerville, Margaret A.; Atlas, Ronald M. Using ethics to fight bioterrorism [letter and reply]. *Science* 2005 August 12; 309(5737): 1013-1015, 1017. NRCBL: 21.3; 1.3.9.

Allhoff, Fritz. On economic justifications of bioterrorism defense spending. *American Journal of Bioethics* 2005 July-August; 5(4): 52-54. NRCBL: 21.3; 9.3.1. Comments: comment on Thomas May, "Funding agendas: has bioterror defense been over-prioritized?" American Journal of Bioethics 2005 July-August; 5(4): 34-44.

Buhmann, Caecilie Böck. The role of health professionals in preventing and mediating conflict. *Medicine, Conflict and Survival* 2005 October-December; 21(4): 299-311. NRCBL: 21.2; 21.1; 9.1.

Eckenwiler, Lisa. Ethics and the underpinnings of policy in biodefense and emergency preparedness. *CQ: Cambridge Quarterly of Healthcare Ethics* 2005 Summer; 14(3): 306-315. NRCBL: 21.3; 1.1; 7.1; 9.1; 16.1.

Egan, Erin A. Bioterrorism defense education: prioritizing public health education. *American Journal of Bioethics* 2005 July-August; 5(4): 47-48. NRCBL: 21.3; 7.2; 9.1. Comments: comment on Thomas May, "Funding agendas: has bioterror defense been over-prioritized?," American Journal of Bioethics 2005 July-August; 5(4): 34-44.

Frankel, Mark S.; Somerville, Margaret A.; Atlas, Ronald M. Using ethics to fight bioterrorism [letter and reply]. *Science* 2005 August 12; 309(5737): 1012, 1014-1015, 1017. NRCBL: 21.3; 1.3.9.

Gostin, Lawrence O. Finding a space for the public's health in bioterrorism funding: a commentary. *American Journal of Bioethics* 2005 July-August; 5(4): 45-46. NRCBL: 21.3; 9.1; 9.3.1. Comments: comment on Thomas May, "Funding agendas: has bioterror defense been over-prioritized?," American Journal of Bioethics 2005 July-August; 5(4): 34-44.

Green, Shane K.; Morin, Karine. Biodefense: spend, but spend wisely. *American Journal of Bioethics* 2005 July-August; 5(4): 50-52. NRCBL: 21.3; 9.1; 9.3.1; 1.3.9. Comments: comment on Thomas May, "Funding agendas:

has bioterror defense been over-prioritized?," American Journal of Bioethics 2005 July-August; 5(4): 34-44.

Green, Shane K.; Somerville, Margaret A.; Atlas, Ronald M. Using ethics to fight bioterrorism [letter and reply]. *Science* 2005 August 12; 309(5737): 1012, 1014-1015, 1017. NRCBL: 21.3; 1.3.9.

Gross, Michael L. Physician-assisted draft evasion: civil disobedience, medicine, and war. *CQ: Cambridge Quarterly of Healthcare Ethics* 2005 Fall; 14(4): 444-454. NRCBL: 21.2; 8.1; 1.1.

Holdstock, Douglas; Gross, Michael. Wartime medical ethics [letter and reply]. *Hastings Center Report* 2005 May-June; 35(3): 6-7. NRCBL: 21.2; 2.1.

Kennedy, Donald. Better never than late [editorial]. *Science* 2005 October 14; 310(5746): 195. NRCBL: 21.3; 1.3.7; 1.3.9.

King, Nicholas B. The ethics of biodefense. *Bioethics* 2005 August; 19(4): 432-446. NRCBL: 21.3; 21.1; 1.3.5; 1.3.6; 5.1; 5.2.
  Abstract: This essay reviews major areas of ethical debate with regard to biodefense, focusing on cases in which biodefense presents ethical problems that diverge from those presented by naturally-occurring outbreaks of infectious disease. It concludes with a call for ethicists to study not only the ethical issues raised in biodefense programs, but also the ethics of biodefense more generally.

Lantz, Göran. War, nursing and morality. *Nursing Ethics* 2005 March; 12(2): 193-195. NRCBL: 21.2; 1.1; 4.1.3.

Li, Lewyn; Somerville, Margaret A.; Atlas, Ronald M. Using ethics to fight bioterrorism [letter and reply]. *Science* 2005 August 12; 309(5737): 1012, 1014-1015, 1017. NRCBL: 21.3; 1.3.9.

Lim, Meng-Kin. Hostile use of the life sciences [opinion]. *New England Journal of Medicine* 2005 November 24; 353(21): 2214-2215. NRCBL: 21.3; 1.3.9; 5.1.

May, Thomas. Funding agendas: has bioterror defense been over-prioritized? *American Journal of Bioethics* 2005 July-August; 5(4): 34-44. NRCBL: 21.3; 9.1; 9.3.1; 1.3.9; 1.1. SC: an.
  Abstract: Post-9/11, concern about bioterrorism has transformed public health from unappreciated to a central component of national security. Within the War on Terror, bioterrorism preparedness has taken a back seat only to direct military action in terms of funding. Domestically, homelessness, joblessness, crime, education, and race relations are just a few of a litany of pressing issues requiring government attention. Even within the biomedical sciences and healthcare, issues surrounding the fact that more than 40 million Americans lack health insurance, the rising cost of prescription medications, and the use of government funds for research using embryonic stem cells remain unresolved. Should we prioritize a hypothetical threat (bioterrorism), or existing conditions that have implications for identifiable individuals? Even more fundamentally, should we prioritize research aimed at defense from bioterrorism (or even terrorism in general) when there are so many pressing social problems that affect the U.S. population?

NRCBL: National Reference Center for Bioethics Literature Classification Scheme   See inside front cover for terms.

439

Meacham, Katharine R.; Croom, Jo Ann T. Tricksters, The Plague, and mirrors: biotechnology, bioterrorism, and justice. *In:* Brannigan, Michael C., ed. Cross-Cultural Biotechnology. Lanham: Rowman and Littlefield; 2004: 177-191. NRCBL: 21.3; 1.1; 1.3.9; 15.1.

Moreno, Jonathan D.; Gross, Michael. Wartime medical ethics [letter and reply]. *Hastings Center Report* 2005 May-June; 35(3): 7. NRCBL: 21.2; 8.3.1; 9.7.

Perman, Ben; Somerville, Margaret A.; Atlas, Ronald M. Using ethics to fight bioterrorism [letter and reply]. *Science* 2005 August 12; 309(5737): 1013, 1014-1015, 1017. NRCBL: 21.3; 1.3.9.

Rath, Johannes; Jank, Bernhard; Somerville, Margaret A.; Atlas, Ronald M. Using ethics to fight bioterrorism [letter and reply]. *Science* 2005 August 12; 309(5737): 1012-1013, 1014-1015, 1017. NRCBL: 21.3; 1.3.9.

Rosner, David; Markowitz, Gerald. The states and the war against bioterrorism: reactions to the federal smallpox campaign and the Model State Emergency Health Powers Act. *In:* Kleinman, Daniel Lee; Kinchy, Abby J.; Handelsman, J. eds. Controversies in Science and Technology: From Maize to Menopause. Madison, Wis.: University of Wisconsin Press; 2005: 297-310. NRCBL: 21.3; 9.1. SC: le.

Schwab, Abe. The biases of bioterror funding. *American Journal of Bioethics* 2005 July-August; 5(4): 54-56. NRCBL: 21.3; 9.1.

Selgelid, Michael J. Democratic defense spending in an age of bioterrorism. *American Journal of Bioethics* 2005 July-August; 5(4): 49-50. NRCBL: 21.3; 9.1. Comments: comment on Thomas May, "Funding agendas: has bioterror defense been over-prioritized?," American Journal of Bioethics 2005 July-August; 5(4): 34-44.

Somerville, Margaret A.; Atlas, Ronald M. Ethics: a weapon to counter bioterrorism. *Science* 2005 March 25; 307(5717): 1881-1882. NRCBL: 21.3; 6; 1.3.9; 18.2; 21.1.

Steinbrook, Robert. Biomedical research and biosecurity [opinion]. *New England Journal of Medicine* 2005 November 24; 353(21): 2212-2214. NRCBL: 21.3; 1.3.7; 1.3.9; 5.1.

Stone, Lesley; Gostin, Lawrence O.; Hodge, James G. The Model State Emergency Health Powers Act: a tool for public health preparedness. *In:* Kleinman, Daniel Lee; Kinchy, Abby J.; Handelsman, eds. Controversies in Science and Technology: From Maize to Menopause. Madison, Wis.: University of Wisconsin Press; 2005: 283-296. NRCBL: 21.3; 9.1. SC: le.

Tobin, J. The challenges and ethical dilemmas of a military medical officer serving with a peacekeeping operation in regard to the medical care of the local population. *Journal of Medical Ethics* 2005 October; 31(10): 571-574. NRCBL: 21.2; 4.1.2; 9.4. SC: an.
  Abstract: Medical Officers serving with their national contingents in peacekeeping operations are faced with difficult ethical decisions in regard to their obligations to the local civilian population. Such populations may be under-resourced in regard to medical care, and vulnerable to abuse and exploitation. Though the medical officer may support the local medical services, he/she should never undermine these resources. Adopting a human rights approach and observing the requirements of ethical medicine, aids the doctor in prioritising his/her duties. At times there may be conflict with one's own military superiors. It is wise to discuss potential difficulties prior to setting out on the mission. Human rights abuses cannot be ignored. The medical officer has a duty to do his/her best to report their observations so as to prevent abuse or to bring it to an end.

Trotter, Griffin. What jurisdiction? Whose justice? A response to Eckenwiler. *CQ: Cambridge Quarterly of Healthcare Ethics* 2005 Summer; 14(3): 316-321. NRCBL: 21.3; 1.1; 7.1; 9.1. Comments: comment on Lisa Eckenwiler, "Ethics and the underpinnings of policy in biodefense and emergency preparedness," CQ: Cambridge Quarterly of Healthcare Ethics 2005 Summer; 14(3): 306-315.

Wells, Robert J.; Gross, Michael. Wartime medical ethics [letter and reply]. *Hastings Center Report* 2005 May-June; 35(3): 7. NRCBL: 21.2; 2.1.

WITHHOLDING TREATMENT *See* EUTHANASIA AND ALLOWING TO DIE

WOMEN *See* CARE FOR SPECIFIC GROUPS/ WOMEN; HUMAN EXPERIMENTATION/ SPECIAL POPULATIONS/ WOMEN

WRONGFUL BIRTH *See* CONTRACEPTION

XENOTRANSPLANTATION *See* ORGAN AND TISSUE TRANSPLANTATION/ XENOTRANSPLANTATION

SECTION II:
PERIODICAL LITERATURE
AND ESSAYS

AUTHOR INDEX

Section II: Periodical Literature and Essays
Author Index

A

Aakvaag, Ruth Kleppe. The possibilities of human cloning: the American discussion. *In:* Ostnor, Lars, ed. Bioethics and Cloning: Report from a Workshop Arranged by the Nordic Theological Network for Bioethics in Arhus, September 25-27, 1998. Oslo: Nordic Theological Network for Bioethics; 1998: 24-34. Subject: 14.5

Aapro, Matti S.; Köhne, Claus-Henning; Cohen, Harvey Jay; Extermann, Martine. Never too old? Age should not be a barrier to enrollment in cancer clinical trials. *Oncologist* 2005 March; 10(3): 198-204. Subject: 18.5.7

Aaraas, Ivar J.; Jones, Barbara; Gupta, Tarun Sen. Reactions to adverse events among Australian and Norwegian doctors. *Australian Family Physician* 2004 December; 33(12): 1045-1046. Subject: 8.2

Abadee, Alister. The medical duty of confidentiality and prospective duty of disclosure: can they co-exist? *Journal of Law and Medicine* 1995 August; 3(1): 75-91. Subject: 8.4

Abbasi, Kamran; Heath, Iona. Ethics review of research and audit — journals should not abdicate their responsibility [editorial]. *BMJ: British Medical Journal* 2005 February 26; 330(7489): 431- 432. Subject: 18.2

Abbing, Henriette D.C. Roscam. The right to care for health: the contribution of the European Social Charter [editorial]. *European Journal of Health Law* 2005 September; 12(3): 183- 191. Subject: 9.2

Abbott, Alison. Europe pares down double patents on breast-cancer gene [news]. *Nature* 2005 January 27; 433(7024): 344. Subject: 15.8

Abbott, Alison. Genetic patent singles out Jewish women [news]. *Nature* 2005 July 7; 436(7047): 12. Subject: 15.8

Abbott, Alison. German oncology research shaken by fraud case [news]. *Annals of Oncology* 1998 January; 9(1): 1-2. Subject: 1.3.9

Abbott, Alison. More than a cosmetic change [news]. *Nature* 2005 November 10; 438(7065): 144-146. Subject: 22.2

Abbud-Filho, Mario; Garcia, V.D.; Campos, H.H.; Pestana, J.O.M. Do we need living unrelated organ donation in Brazil? *Transplantation Proceedings* 2004 May; 36(4): 805-807. Subject: 19.5

Abels, Gabriele. The long and winding road from Asilomar to Brussels: science, politics and the public in biotechnology regulation. *Science as Culture* 2005 December; 14(4): 339-353. Subject: 15.1

Abelson, Reed. Possible conflicts for doctors are seen on medical devices. *New York Times* 2005 September 22; p. A1, C6. Subject: 7.3

Abelson, Reed; Pollack, Andrew. Patient care vs. corporate connections: Cleveland Clinic wants to change but won't cut ties to industry. *New York Times* 2005 January 25; p. C1, C4. Subject: 1.3.9

Abma, Tineke A. Struggling with the fragility of life: a relational-narrative approach to ethics in palliative nursing. *Nursing Ethics* 2005 July; 12(4): 337-348. Subject: 20.4.1

Abma, Tineke A.; Oeseburg, Barth; Widdershoven, Guy A.M.; Goldsteen, Minke; Verkerk, Marian A. Two women with multiple sclerosis and their caregivers: conflicting normative expectations. *Nursing Ethics* 2005 September; 12(5): 479-492. Subject: 8.1

Abou Shabana, K.; El-Shiek, M.; El-Nazer, M.; Samir, N. Women's perceptions and practices regarding their rights to reproductive health. *Eastern Mediterranean Health Journal* 2003 May; 9(3): 296-308. Subject: 9.5.5

Abraham, Joy. Unethical practices. *Issues in Medical Ethics* 2002 October-December; 10(4): 85-86. Subject: 9.5.6

Abraham, Leena. Ethical and methodological conflicts in sexuality research. *Issues in Medical Ethics* 2001 January-March; 9(1): 9-11. Subject: 18.4

Abushama, Mandy; Ahmed, Badreldeen. Cesarean section on request. *Saudi Medical Journal* 2004 December; 25(12): 1820-1823. Subject: 9.5.5

Acheson, Louise S.; Stange, Kurt C.; Zyzanski, Stephen. Clinical genetics issues encountered by family physicians. *Genetics in Medicine* 2005 September; 7(7): 501-508. Subject: 15.1

Ackerman, James L.; Proffit, William R. Communication in orthodontic treatment planning: bioethical and informed consent issues. *Angle Orthodontist* 1995; 65(4): 253-261. Subject: 8.3.1

Ackerman, Paul D.; Kelly, Michael L.; Walsh, Catherine A.; Ross, Lainie Friedman. Do peer guidelines or editorial policies affect the reporting and discussion of race and ethnicity in pediatric research? *Accountability in Research* 2005 January-March; 12(1): 17-31. Subject: 18.2

Ackermann, Deonna; Chapman, Simon; Leask, Julie. Media coverage of anthrax vaccination refusal by Australian Defence Force personnel. *Vaccine* 2004 December 2; 23(3): 411-417. Subject: 8.3.4

Adalsteinsson, Ragnar. Human genetic databases and liberty. *Juridical Review* 2004; 2004(1): 65-74. Subject: 15.1

Adam, Yehuda G. Aide memoire—the role of the German medical establishment in the Holocaust: a retrospective on the 60th anniversary of the liberation of Auschwitz. *Israel Medical Association Journal* 2005 March; 7(3): 139-142. Subject: 21.4

Adamis, D.; Martin, F.C.; Treloar, A.; Macdonald, A.J.D. Capacity, consent, and selection bias in a study of delirium. *Journal of Medical Ethics* 2005 March; 31(3): 137-143. Subject: 18.3

Adamjee, Ashi; Alfi, David; Agarwal, Divya; Braithwaite, Yetunde; Chan, Judy; Chey, Marshall; Cho, Hyung; Choi, Christopher. What does the fact of advertising convey to patients? *Journal of the American College of Dentists* 2005 Fall; 72(3): 22-23. Subject: 8.1

Adams, Douglas; Pimple, Kenneth D. Research misconduct and crime lessons from criminal science on preventing misconduct and promoting integrity. *Accountability in Research* 2005 July-September; 12(3): 225- 240. Subject: 1.3.9

Adams, James G. Opening a dialogue on ethics [opinion]. *Academic Emergency Medicine* 2000 June; 7(6): 689-690. Subject: 9.5.1

Adams, Karen E. Gestational surrogacy for a human immunodeficiency virus seropositive sperm donor: what are the ethics? *JAMWA: Journal of the American Medical Women's Association* 2003 Summer; 58(3): 138-140. Subject: 14.2

Adams, Karen E. Moral diversity among physicians and conscientious refusal of care in the provision of abortion services. *JAMWA: Journal of the American Medical Women's Association* 2003 Fall; 58(4): 223-226. Subject: 12.3

Adams, Karen; Cain, Joanna M. The genetic revolution: new ethical issues for obstetrics and gynaecology. *Best Practice and Research in Clinical Obstetrics and Gynaecology* 2002 October; 16(5): 745-756. Subject: 15.3

Adams, Maurice; Nys, Herman. Comparative reflections on the Belgian Euthanasia Act 2002. *Medical Law Review* 2003 Autumn; 11(3): 353-376. Subject: 20.7

Adams, Nathan A. An unnatural assault on natural law: regulating biotechnology using a just research theory. *In:* Colson, Charles W.; de S. Cameron, Nigel M., eds. Human Dignity in the Biotech Century: a Christian Vision for Public Policy. Downers Grove, Ill.: InterVarsity Press; 2004: 160-180. Subject: 18.5.4

Adams, Vincanne. Equity of the ineffable: cultural and political constraints on ethnomedicine as a health problem in contemporary Tibet. *In:* Anand, Sudhir; Peter, Fabienne; Sen, Amartya, eds. Public Health, Ethics, and Equity. New York: Oxford University Press; 2004: 283-305. Subject: 4.1.1

Adams-Campbell, Lucile L.; Ahaghotu, Chiledum; Gaskins, Melvin; Dawkins, Fitzroy W.; Smoot, Duane; Polk, Octavius D.; Gooding, Robert; Dewitty, Robert L. Enrollment of African Americans onto clinical treatment trials: study design barriers. *Journal of Clinical Oncology* 2004 February 15; 22(4): 730-734. Subject: 18.2

Aday, Lu Ann. An expanded conceptual framework of equity: implications for assessing health policy. *In:* Albrecht, Gary L.; Fitzpatrick, Ray; Scrimshaw, Susan C., eds. The Handbook of Social Studies in Health & Medicine. Thousand Oaks, CA: Sage; 2000: 481-492. Subject: 1.1

Addington-Hall, J. Research sensitivities to palliative care patients. *European Journal of Cancer Care* 2002; 11: 220-224. Subject: 18.5.7

Addlakha, Renu. Ethical quandaries in anthropological fieldwork in psychiatric settings [case study]. *Indian Journal of Medical Ethics* 2005 April-June; 2(2): 55-56. Subject: 18.5.6

Addlakha, Renu. The dilemmas of independent researchers [comment]. *Indian Journal of Medical Ethics* 2005 January-March; 2(1): 24. Subject: 18.5.1

Adelman, Elizabeth. Video surveillance in nursing homes. *Albany Law Journal of Science and Technology* 2002; 12(3): 821-838. Subject: 9.5.2

Adhikari, M. Caring for babies who survive an abortion attempt — an ethical dilemma [letter]. *South African Medical Journal* 1998 May; 88(5): 578. Subject: 9.5.7

Adibah, I.; Bakar, W.Y. Wan Abu. Should this couple have undergone infertility treatment? [case study]. *Indian Journal of Medical Ethics* 2005 October-December; 2(4): 126. Subject: 14.4

Adler, Nancy E.; Ozer, Emily J.; Tschann, Jeanne. Abortion among adolescents. *American Psychologist* 2003 March; 58(3): 211-217. Subject: 12.4.2

Adler, Robert. To tell or not to tell: the psychiatrist and child abuse. *Australian and New Zealand Journal of Psychiatry* 1995 June; 29(2): 190-197. Subject: 17.2

Aeschleman, Heather K. The White world of nursing homes: the myriad barriers to access facing today's elderly minorities. *Elder Law Journal* 2000; 8(2): 367-391. Subject: 9.5.2

Afifi, Mustafa M. Authorship. Credit and disputes. *Saudi Medical Journal* 2004 November; 25(11): 1742-1743. Subject: 1.3.7

Afonso, R.C.; Buttros, D.A.B.; Sakabe, D.; Paranhos, G.C.; Garcia, L.M.C.; Resende, M.B.; Ferraz-Neto, Ben-Hur. Future doctors and brain death: what is the prognosis? *Transplantation Proceedings* 2004 May; 36(4): 816-817. Subject: 20.2.1

Ågård, Anders; Herlitz, J.; Hermerén, G. Obtaining informed consent from patients in the early phase of acute myocardial infarction: physicians' experiences and attitudes. *Heart* 2004 February 1; 90(2): 208-210. Subject: 18.3

Agarwal, Dinesh. Public health, human rights and HIV. *Issues in Medical Ethics* 2002 October-December; 10(4): 87. Subject: 9.5.6

Agarwal, Rajeev. Palliative care — Hinduism. *Dolentium Hominum* 2005; 20(1): 91-93. Subject: 20.4.1

Agich, G.J.; Siemionow, M. Until they have faces: the ethics of facial allograft transplantation. *Journal of Medical Ethics* 2005 December; 31(12): 707-709. Subject: 19.1

Agich, George J. Implications of aging paradigms for bioethics. *In:* Weisstub, David N.; Thomasma, David C.; Gauthier, Serge; Tomossy, George F., eds. Aging: Culture, Health, and Social Change. Boston: Kluwer Academic Publishers; 2001: 15-28. Subject: 9.5.2

Agich, George J. What kind of doing is clinical ethics? *Theoretical Medicine and Bioethics* 2005; 26(1): 7-24. Subject: 2.1

Agich, George; Smith, David; Levine, Robert. A challenging case: how should an IRB rule when a protocol calls for using an extremely vulnerable population: the dying? [debate]. *Protecting Human Subjects* 2005 Summer; (12): 5-6. Subject: 18.5.7

Agre, Peter C.; Altman, Sidney; Curl, Robert F.; Wiesel, Torsten N.; West-Eberhard, Mary Jane; Somerville, Margaret A.; Atlas, Ronald M. Using ethics to fight bioterrorism [letter and reply]. *Science* 2005 August 12; 309(5737): 1013-1015, 1017. Subject: 21.3

Ahmad, Aasim. Universality of care: a response. *Issues in Medical Ethics* 2001 October-December; 9(4): 117. Subject: 18.2

Ahmad, Omar B. Managing medical migration from poor countries. *BMJ: British Medical Journal* 2005 July 2; 331(7507): 43-45. Subject: 21.6

Ahuja, Anjana. Could the cure for all diseases be banned? [news]. *Times (London, Features section)* 2004 June 17; p. 8-9. Subject: 14.5

Aigner, Gerhard. An overview of legal aspects in organ transplantation — what are the family rights? *Annals of Transplantation* 2004; 9(1): 11-14. Subject: 19.5

Akabayashi, Akira; Slingsby, Brian Taylor; Takimoto, Yoshiyuki. Conflict of interest: a Japanese perspective. *CQ: Cambridge Quarterly of Healthcare Ethics* 2005 Summer; 14(3): 277-280. Subject: 1.3.9

Akeson, Nancy; Robertson, John A. Neonatal care for premature infants [letter and reply]. *Hastings Center Report* 2005 January-February; 35(1): 6, 7. Subject: 9.5.7

Akinwunmi, Oluwatoyin O. Genetic screening. *In:* Ness, Bryan D., ed. Encyclopedia of Genetics. Revised edition. Volume I. Pasadena, Calif.: Salem Press; 2004: 357-360. Subject: 15.3

Akinwunmi, Oluwatoyin O. Genetic testing. *In:* Ness, Bryan D., ed. Encyclopedia of Genetics. Revised edition. Volume I. Pasadena, Calif.: Salem Press; 2004: 360-364. Subject: 15.3

Akkad, Andrea; Jackson, Clare; Kenyon, Sara; Dixon-Woods, Mary; Taub, Nick; Habiba, Marwan. Informed consent for elective and emergency surgery: questionnaire study. *BJOG: An International Journal of Obstetrics and Gynaecology* 2004 October; 111(10): 1133-1138. Subject: 8.3.1

Akpunonu, Basil E.; Mutgi, Anand B.; Khuder, Sadik A.; Vaccarino, Viola; Jha, Ashish K.; Epstein, Arnold M.; Orav, E. John. Trends in racial disparities in care [letter and reply]. *New England Journal of Medicine* 2005 November 10; 353(19): 2083-2085. Subject: 9.5.4

Akrami, S.M.; Osati, Z.; Zahedi, F.; Raza, M. Brain death: recent ethical and religious considerations in Iran. *Transplantation Proceedings* 2004 December; 36(10): 2883-2887. Subject: 20.2.1

Aksoy, S. Making regulations and drawing up legislation in Islamic countries under conditions of uncertainty, with special reference to embryonic stem cell research. *Journal of Medical Ethics* 2005 July; 31(7): 399-403. Subject: 18.5.4

Aksoy, Sahin. End-of-life decision making in Turkey. *In:* Blank, Robert H.; Merrick, Janna C., eds. End-of-Life Decision Making: A Cross-National Study. Cambridge, MA: MIT Press; 2005: 183-195. Subject: 20.4.1

Al Sebayel, M.I.M.; Khalaf, H. Knowledge and attitude of intensivists toward organ donation in Riyadh, Saudi Arabia. *Transplantation Proceedings* 2004 September; 36(7): 1883-1884. Subject: 19.5

Albar, Mohammed A. Induced abortion from an Islamic perspective: is it criminal or just elective? *Journal of Family and Community Medicine* 2001 December; 8(3): 25-35. Subject: 12.3

Albee, George W. Call to revolution in the prevention of emotional disorders. *Ethical Human Psychology and Psychiatry* 2005 Spring; 7(1): 37- 44. Subject: 17.1

Albert, Daniel M.; Liesegang, Thomas J.; Schachat, Andrew P. Meeting our ethical obligations in medical publishing: responsibilities of editors, authors, and readers of peer-reviewed journals [editorial]. *Archives of Ophthalmology* 2005 May; 123(5): 684-686. Subject: 1.3.7

Albin, R.L. Sham surgery controls are mitigated trolleys. *Journal of Medical Ethics* 2005 March; 31(3): 149-152. Subject: 18.2

Albright, Matthew. Life patents and democratic values. *In:* Krimsky, Sheldon; Shorett, Peter, eds. Rights and Liberties in the Biotech Age: Why We Need a Genetic Bill of Rights. Lanham: Rowman and Littlefield Publishers; 2005: 29-39. Subject: 15.8

Alderson, Priscilla. Complications within consent. *Bulletin of Medical Ethics* 2005 August-September; (210): 15-19. Subject: 8.3.2

Aldhous, Peter. After the gold rush. *Nature* 2005 April 7; 434(7034): 694-696. Subject: 18.5.4

Aldhous, Peter. Victims of genetic discrimination speak up [news]. *New Scientist* 2005 November 5-11; 188(2524): 7. Subject: 15.3

Alejandro, Patricia. Bioetica, justicia y asignacion de recursos / Bioethics, justice and the allocation of resources. *Bioetica. Un Delsafio del Tercer Milenio* 2002-2003; 4(4): 32-37. Subject: 9.4

Aleksandrova, Silviya. Comparative analysis of the code of professional ethics in Bulgaria and the Hippocratic Oath, Declaration of Geneva and International Code of Medical Ethics. *Medicine and Law: World Association for Medical Law* 2005 September; 24(3): 495-503. Subject: 6

Alesch, Jill. The Americans with Disabilities Act: an end to discrimination against HIV/AIDS patients or simply another loophole to bypass? *Drake Law Review* 2004; 52(3): 523-551. Subject: 9.5.6

Alex, April. Genetic discrimination: health insurance for the genetically lucky and the genetically unlucky. *Medical Trial Technique Quarterly* 2004; 50(3): 173-198. Subject: 15.3

Alexander, G. Caleb; Kurlander, Jacob; Wynia, Matthew K. Physicians in retainer ("concierge") practice. *JGIM: Journal of General Internal Medicine* 2005 December; 20(12): 1079-1083. Subject: 9.3.1

Alexander, John. Commentary: research ethics committees deserve support. *BMJ: British Medical Journal* 2005 February 26; 330(7489): 472- 473. Subject: 18.2

Alexander, John K. Promising, professional obligations, and the refusal to provide service. *HEC (Healthcare Ethics Committee) Forum* 2005 September; 17(3): 178-195. Subject: 8.1

Alexander, Marc. The problems with physician-assisted suicide. *Origins* 2005 April 7; 34(42): 676-680. Subject: 20.7

Alexander, William; Berlin, Joshua; Cyr, Philip; Schofield, Andrew; Platt, Leslie. Realities at the leading edge of research [opinion]. *EMBO Reports* 2004 April; 5(4): 324-329. Subject: 1.3.9

Alghrani, Amel. Deciding the fate of frozen embryos: Natalie Evans v. Amicus Healthcare Ltd and Others. *Medical Law Review* 2005 Summer; 13(2): 244-256. Subject: 14.6

Ali, Raoutsi Hadj Eddine Sari. Islam. *In:* Council of Europe Publishing, ed. Euthanasia. Volume I. Ethical and Human Aspects. Strasbourg: Council of Europe; Croton-on-Hudson, NY: Manhattan Publishing Co.; 2003: 141-144. Subject: 20.5.1

Allan, Alfred. The past, present and future of mental health law: a therapeutic jurisprudence analysis. *Law in Context* 2003; 20(2): 24-53. Subject: 17.7

Allan, Helen; Barber, Debbie. Emotional boundary work in advanced fertility nursing roles. *Nursing Ethics* 2005 July; 12(4): 391-400. Subject: 14.1

Allen, Anne. Right to die, freedom of choice, and assisted death: implications for nurses. *Journal of Post Anesthesia Nursing* 1991 April; 6(2): 150-151. Subject: 20.7

Allen, David; Hardin, Pamela K. Discourse analysis and the epidemiology of meaning. *Nursing Philosophy* 2001 July; 2(2): 163-176. Subject: 8.1

Allen, Michael P. The Constitution at the threshold of life and death: a suggested approach to accommodate an interest in life and a right to die. *American University Law Review* 2004 June; 53(5): 971-1020. Subject: 8.3.4

Allen, Rose; Ventura, Nestor. Advance directives use in acute care hospitals. *JONA's Healthcare Law, Ethics, and Regulation* 2005 July- September; 7(3): 86-91. Subject: 20.5.4

Alleva, Enrico; Scattoni, Maria Luisa. Introductory keynote. The state of the art in animal experimentation. *Annali dell Istituto Superiore di Sanita* 2004; 40(2): 151-155. Subject: 22.2

Allhoff, Fritz. Free-riding and research ethics. *American Journal of Bioethics* 2005 January-February; 5(1): 50- 51. Subject: 18.2

Allhoff, Fritz. Germ-line genetic enhancement and Rawlsian primary goods. *Kennedy Institute of Ethics Journal* 2005 March; 15(1): 39-56. Subject: 15.1

Allhoff, Fritz. On economic justifications of bioterrorism defense spending. *American Journal of Bioethics* 2005 July-August; 5(4): 52-54. Subject: 21.3

Allhoff, Fritz. Stem cells and the blastocyst transfer method: some concerns regarding autonomy. *American*

Journal of Bioethics 2005 November-December; 5(6): 28-30. Subject: 18.5.4

Allison, John R.; Cooper, William W. Data disclosure and data sharing in scientific research. *Accountability in Research* 1992; 2(2): 93-132. Subject: 1.3.9

Allmark, Peter. Can the study of ethics enhance nursing practice? *Journal of Advanced Nursing* 2005 September; 51(6): 618-624. Subject: 2.1

Allmark, Peter. Health, happiness and health promotion. *Journal of Applied Philosophy* 2005; 22(1): 1-15. Subject: 4.2

Almarsdóttir, Anna Birna; Björnsdóttir, Ingunn; Traulsen, Janine Morgall. A lay prescription for tailor-made drugs — focus group reflections on pharmacogenomics. *Health Policy* 2005 February; 71(2): 233-241. Subject: 15.1

Almond, Brenda. Reasonable partiality in professional relationships. *Ethical Theory and Moral Practice* 2005 April; 8(1-2): 155-168. Subject: 1.3.1

Alonso, Carlos. An ontological view of the human embryo. A paradigm. *European Journal of Endocrinology* 2004 November; 151 (Supplement 3): U17-U24. Subject: 4.4

Alper, Joseph S. Beyond genetic anti-discrimination legislation. *In:* Krimsky, Sheldon; Shorett, Peter, eds. Rights and Liberties in the Biotech Age: Why We Need a Genetic Bill of Rights. Lanham: Rowman and Littlefield Publishers; 2005: 167-172. Subject: 15.3

Alper, Joseph; Beckwith, Jonathan. Genetic fatalism and social policy: the implications of behavior genetics research. *Yale Journal of Biology and Medicine* 1993 November-December; 66(6): 511-524. Subject: 15.6

Alpert, Joseph S. Doctors and the drug industry: how can we handle potential conflicts of interest? [editorial]. *American Journal of Medicine* 2005 February; 118(2): 99-100. Subject: 9.7

Alters, Sandra. Advance directives. *In her:* Death and Dying. Who Decides? Detroit: Thomson Gale; 2005: 79-99. Subject: 20.5.4

Alters, Sandra. Courts and the end of life. *In her:* Death and Dying. Who Decides? Detroit: Thomson Gale; 2005: 101-113. Subject: 20.5.1

Alters, Sandra. The end of life: ethical considerations. *In her:* Death and Dying. Who Decides? Detroit: Thomson Gale; 2005: 13-20. Subject: 20.5.1

Alters, Sandra. Euthanasia and assisted suicide. *In her:* Death and Dying. Who Decides? Detroit: Thomson Gale; 2005: 57-78. Subject: 20.5.1

Althaus, Catherine. Can one "rescue" a human embryo? — the moral object of the acting woman. *National Catholic Bioethics Quarterly* 2005 Spring; 5(1): 113- 141. Subject: 14.6

Altman, Jason. Organ transplantations: the need for an international open organ market. *Touro International Law Review* 1994; 5: 161-183. Subject: 19.5

Altman, Lawrence K. French, in first, use a transplant to repair a face. *New York Times* 2005 December 1; p. A1, A6. Subject: 19.1

Altman, Lawrence K. A pioneering transplant, and now an ethical storm. *New York Times* 2005 December 6; p. F1, F4. Subject: 19.1

Altman, Lawrence; Broad, William J. Global trend: more science, more fraud. *New York Times* 2005 December 20; p. F1, F6. Subject: 1.3.9

Alvino, Lori A. Who's watching the watchdogs? Responding to the erosion of research ethics by enforcing promises. *Columbia Law Review* 2003 May; 103(4): 893-924. Subject: 18.1

Alzheimer's Association. Research consent for cognitively impaired adults: recommendations for institutional review boards and investigators. *Alzheimer Disease and Associated Disorders* 2004 July-September; 18(3): 171-175. Subject: 18.5.6

Al-Damegh, Saleh A. Emerging issues in medical imaging. *Indian Journal of Medical Ethics* 2005 October-December; 2(4): 123-125. Subject: 9.5.1

Al-Dwairi, Ziad Nawaf; Al-Waheidi, E.M. Cheating behaviors of dental students. *Journal of Dental Education* 2004 November; 68(11): 1192-1195. Subject: 7.2

Al-Inany, Hesham G. Guest editorial from abroad: pregnancy in the postmenopause: how far can assisted reproductive technology be trusted? [editorial]. *Obstetrical and Gynecological Survey* 2000 February; 55(2): 67-68. Subject: 14.1

Al-Khader, A.A. A model for scoring and grading willingness of a potential living related donor. *Journal of Medical Ethics* 2005 June; 31(6): 338-340. Subject: 19.5

Al-Marzouki, Sanaa; Evans, Stephen; Marshall, Tom; Roberts, Ian. Are these data real? Statistical methods for the detection of data fabrication in clinical trials. *BMJ: British Medical Journal* 2005 July 30; 331(7511): 267-270. Subject: 1.3.9

Al-Shahi, Rustam; Vousden, Céline; Warlow, Charles. Bias from requiring explicit consent from all participants in observational research: prospective, population based study. *BMJ: British Medical Journal* 2005 October 22; 331(7522): 942- 945. Subject: 18.3

Al-Sulaiman, Abdulsalam A.; Al-Gindan, Yussuf M. The dilemma of clinical research. Historical and philosophical consideration of physicians' ambitions and patients' fear. *Saudi Medical Journal* 2004 November; 25(11): 1739-1741. Subject: 18.1

Amarasekara, Kumar; Bagaric, Mirko. Moving from voluntary euthanasia to non-voluntary euthanasia: equality and compassion. *Ratio Juris* 2004 September; 17(3): 398-423. Subject: 20.5.1

Amarasekara, Kumar; Bagaric, Mirko. The legalisation of euthanasia in the Netherlands: lessons to be learnt. *Monash University Law Review* 2001; 27(2): 179-196. Subject: 20.5.1

Amaya-Jackson, Lisa; Socolar, Rebecca R.S.; Hunter, Wanda; Runyan, Desmond K.; Colindres, Rom. Directly questioning children and adolescents about maltreatment: a review of survey measures used. *Journal of Interpersonal Violence* 2000 July; 15(7): 725-759. Subject: 18.5.2

Ambulatory Pediatric Association [APA]. Research Committee; Etzel, Ruth A. Ambulatory Pediatric Association policy statement: ensuring integrity for research with children. *Ambulatory Pediatrics* 2005 January-February; 5(1): 3-5. Subject: 18.5.2

Amdur, Robert J.; Speers, Marjorie A. A practical guideline for identifying research intent with projects that collect private, identifiable health information. *American Journal of Clinical Oncology* 2003 June; 26(3): e7-e12. Subject: 5.3

American Academy of Pain Medicine; American Pain Society; American Society of Addiction Medicine. Public policy statement on the rights and responsibilities of health care professionals in the use of opioids for the treatment of pain: a consensus document from the American Academy of Pain Medicine, the American Pain Society, and the American Society of Addiction Medicine. *Pain Medicine* 2004 September; 5(3): 301-302. Subject: 9.7

American Academy of Pediatrics. Committee on Native American Child Health. Committee on Community Health Services. Ethical considerations in research with socially identifiable populations [policy statement]. *Pediatrics* 2004 January; 113(1, Part 1): 148-151. Subject: 18.5.1

American Association of Neuromuscular and Electrodiagnostic Medicine [AANEM]; Mackin, Glenn A.; Horowitz, Steven H.; Leonard, James A., Jr.; Musick, David W. Guidelines for ethical behavior relating to clinical practice issues in electrodiagnostic medicine [policy statement]. *Muscle and Nerve* 2005 March; 31(3): 400-405. Subject: 6

American Association of Tissue Banks; Association of Organ Procurement Organizations; Eye Bank Association of America. Appendix A: model elements of informed consent for organ and tissue donation. *In:* Youngner, Stuart J.; Anderson, Martha W.; Schapiro, Renie, eds. Transplanting Human Tissue: Ethics, Policy, and Practice. New York: Oxford University Press; 2004: 195-197. Subject: 19.5

American College of Cardiology Foundation; American Heart Association; Popp, Richard J.; Smith, Sidney C., Jr.; Adams, Robert J.; Antman, Elliott M.; **Kavey, Rae Ellen W.; DeMaria, Anthony N.; Ohman, Erik Magnus; Pitt, Bertram; Willerson, James T.; Bellande, Bruce J.; Fonarow, Gregg C.; Nishimura, Rick A.; Shah, Pravin M.; Hirshfeld, John W., Jr.; Messer, Joseph V.; Peterson, Eric D.; Prystowsky, Eric N.; Anderson, Jeffrey L.; Cheitlin, Melvin D., Goldstein, Larry B.; Grant, Augustus O.; Beller, George A.; Hines, Edward F., Jr.; Livingston, David W.; McEntee, Christine W.** ACCF/AHA consensus conference report on professionalism and ethics. *Circulation* 2004 October 19; 110(16): 2506-2549. Subject: 18.2

American College of Emergency Physicians [ACEP]. ACEP Board of Directors. Conflict of interest policy [policy statement]. *Annals of Emergency Medicine* 1998 January; 31(1): 150-152. Subject: 7.3

American College of Emergency Physicians. Ethics Committee. Financial conflicts of interest in biomedical research [policy statement]. *Annals of Emergency Medicine* 2002; 40(5): 546-547. Subject: 6

American College of Healthcare Executives [ACHE]. Board of Governors. American College of Healthcare Executives Code of Ethics. *American College of Healthcare* 2003 November 10; 2 p. [Online] Available: http://www.ache.org/ABT_ACHE/CodeofEthics.pdf [5 August 2005]. Subject: 4.1.1

American College of Legal Medicine. Editorial Committee. Organ donation and transplantation. *In:* American College of Legal Medicine Textbook Committee, Sanbar, S. Sandy; Firestone, Marvin H.; Buckner, Fillmore; Gibofsky, Allan; LeBlang, Theodore R.; Snyder, Jack W.; Wecht, Cyril H.; Zaremski, Miles J. Legal Medicine. 6th ed. St. Louis: Mosby; 2004: 271-299. Subject: 19.5

American College of Obstetricians and Gynecologists [ACOG]. Committee on Ethics. ACOG committee opinion. Surgery and patient choice: the ethics of decision making. Number 289, November 2003. *International Journal of Gynecology and Obstetrics* 2004 February; 84(2): 188-193. Subject: 9.5.5

American College of Obstetricians and Gynecologists [ACOG]. Committee on Ethics. ACOG committee opinion. Ethical considerations in research involving women. *International Journal of Gynecology and Obstetrics* 2004 July; 86(1): 124-130. Subject: 18.5.3

American College of Obstetricians and Gynecologists [ACOG]. Committee on Health Care for Underserved Women. ACOG Committee Opinion No. 307. Partner consent for participation in women's reproductive health research. *Obstetrics and Gynecology* 2004 December; 104(6): 1467-1469. Subject: 18.5.3

American College of Obstetricians and Gynecologists [ACOG]. Committee on Professional Liability. ACOG Committee Opinion No. 306. Informed refusal. *Obstetrics and Gynecology* 2004 December; 104(6): 1465-1466. Subject: 8.3.4

Subject = NRCBL Primary Classification Number; See inside front cover

American College of Occupational and Environmental Medicine [ACOEM]. ACOEM position on the confidentiality of medical information in the workplace. *Journal of Occupational and Environmental Medicine* 1995 May; 37(5): 594-596. Subject: 8.4

American College of Physicians [ACP]. Ethics and Human Rights Committee; Snyder, Lois; Leffler, Cathy. Ethics manual. *Annals of Internal Medicine* 2005 April 5; 142(7): 560-582. Subject: 2.1

American College of Physicians [ACP]. Ethics and Human Rights Committee; Snyder, Lois; Leffler, Cathy. Ethics manual. Philadelphia, PA: American College of Physicians 2005; 66 p. Subject: 2.1

American College of Surgeons. Statement on principles guiding care at the end of life. *Journal of the American College of Surgeons* 2005 January; 200(1): 114. Subject: 20.4.1

American College of Toxicology. Animals in Research Committee. American College of Toxicology: policy statement on the use of animals in toxicology. *International Journal of Toxicology* 2004 March-April; 23(2): n.p. Subject: 22.2

American Health Information Management Association [AHIMA]. American Health Information Management Association. Position statement. Issue: disclosure of health information relating to alcohol and drug abuse. *Journal of AHIMA* 1993 December; 64(12): 99. Subject: 6

American Health Information Management Association [AHIMA]. American Health Information Management Association. Position statement. Issue: disclosure of health information. *Journal of AHIMA* 1993 December; 64(12): 101-102. Subject: 6

American Health Information Management Association [AHIMA]. American Health Information Management Association. Position statement. Issue: redisclosure of health information. *Journal of AHIMA* 1993 December; 64(12): 103. Subject: 6

American Hospital Association [AHA]. Put It in Writing: Questions and Answers on Advance Directives. Chicago, Illinois: American Hospital Association 1994 October; 9 p. Subject: 20.5.4

American Hospital Association [AHA]; National Association of Police Organizations [NAPO]. Guidelines for releasing patient information to law enforcement. Chicago,IL: American Hospital Association 2005 July; 8p. [Online]. Available: http://www.aha.org/aha/key_issues/hipaa/content/guidelines.pdf [6 March 2006]. Subject: 8.4

American Indian Law Center. Model tribal research code: with materials for tribal regulation for research and checklist for Indian health boards. Albuquerque, New Mexico: American Indian Law Center 1999 September; 28 p. Subject: 6

American Occupational Therapy Association [AOTA]. Enforcement procedures for Occupational Therapy Code of Ethics (2004). *American Journal of Occupational Therapy* 2004 November-December; 58(6): 655-662. Subject: 16.3

American Occupational Therapy Association [AOTA]; Arnold, Melba; Nashiro, Nancy; Hill, Diane; Slater, Deborah Y.; Morris, John; Withers, Linda; Kyler, Penny. Occupational therapy code of ethics (2000). *American Journal of Occupational Therapy* 2000 November-December; 54(6): 614-616. Subject: 6

American Physiological Society [APS]. Guiding principles for research involving animals and human beings. *American Journal of Physiology Regulatory, Integrative and Comparative Physiology* 2002 August; 283: R281-R283. Subject: 18.2

American Psychological Association. Ethical principles of psychologists and code of conduct. *American Psychologist* 2002 December; 57(12): 1060-1073. Subject: 6

American Psychological Association. Report of the Ethics Committee, 1998. *American Psychologist* 1999 August; 54(8): 701-710. Subject: 9.6

American Psychological Association. Report of the Ethics Committee, 2000. *American Psychologist* 2001 August; 56(8): 680-688. Subject: 9.6

American Psychological Association. Presidential Task Force. Report of the American Psychological Association Presidential Task Force on Psychological Ethics and National Security. Washington, DC: The Association 2005 June; 12 p. [Online]. Available: http://www.apa.org/releases/PENSTaskForceReportFinal.pdf [2 March 2006]. Subject: 17.1

American Psychologist Association. Report of the ethics committee, 2001. *American Psychologist* 2002 August; 57(8): 646-653. Subject: 9.6

American Society for Blood and Marrow Transplantation; American Association of Blood Banks; Foundation for the Accreditation of Cellular Therapy; International Bone Marrow Transplant Registry/Autologous Blood and Marrow Transplant Registry; International Society for Cellular Therapy; National Marrow Donor Program. ASBMT Position Statement: joint public policy on legislative and regulatory affairs. *Biology of Blood and Marrow Transplantation* 2004 April; 10(4): 283-284. Subject: 19.4

American Society for Clinical Laboratory Science. ASCLS position paper. Ethical responsibility. *Clinical Laboratory Science* 1999 March-April; 12(2): 71-72. Subject: 18.2

American Society for Reproductive Medicine. Ethics Committee. Fertility treatment when the prognosis is very poor or futile. *Fertility and Sterility* 2004 October; 82(4): 806-810. Subject: 14.1

American Thoracic Society; Luce, John M.; Cook, Deborah J.; Martin, Thomas R.; Angus, Derek C.; Boushey, Homer A.; Curtis, J. Randall; Heffner, John E.; Lanken, Paul N.; Levy, Mitchell M.; Polite, Paula Y.; Rocker, Graeme M.; Truog, Robert D. The ethical conduct of clinical research involving critically ill patients in the United States and Canada: principles and recommendations. *American Journal of Respiratory and Critical Care Medicine* 2004 December 15; 170(12): 1375-1384. Subject: 18.5.1

Amering, Michaela; Stastny, Peter; Hopper, Kim. Psychiatric advance directives: qualitative study of informed deliberations by mental health service users. *British Journal of Psychiatry* 2005 March; 186: 247-252. Subject: 20.5.4

Ames, David A. The role of the church in the new genetics. *In:* Smith, David H.; Cohen, Cynthia B., eds. A Christian Response to the New Genetics: Religious, Ethical, and Social Issues. Lanham, MD: Rowman & Littlefield Publishers; 2003: 169-183. Subject: 15.3

Amidror, Tali; Leavitt, Frank J. End-of-life decision making in Israel. *In:* Blank, Robert H.; Merrick, Janna C., eds. End-of-Life Decision Making: A Cross-National Study. Cambridge, MA: MIT Press; 2005: 97-108. Subject: 20.5.1

Amundson, Ron. Disability, ideology, and quality of life. *In:* Wasserman, David; Bickenbach, Jerome; Wachbroit, Robert, eds. Quality of Life and Human Difference: Genetic Testing, Health Care, and Disability. New York: Cambridge University Press; 2005: 101-124. Subject: 4.4

Anand, Geeta. Lucrative niches:how drugs for rare diseases became lifeline for companies;federal law gives monopoly for seven years, fueling surge in biotech profits;a teen's $360,000 treatment. *Wall Street Journal* 2005 November 15; p. A1, A18. Subject: 9.7

Anand, Geeta. Support system: through charities, drug makers help people — and themselves; by donating money firms keep patients insured and medicine prices high; Mrs. Gushwa's $2000 pills. *Wall Street Journal* 2005 December 1; p. A1, A10. Subject: 9.7

Anand, Geeta. Uncertain miracle: a biotech drug extends a life, but at what price? For Ms. Lees, treatment bill now totals $7 million; her bones keep crumbling; guilt of another $1400 day. *Wall Street Journal* 2005 November 16; p. A1, A15. Subject: 9.7

Anand, Geeta. Why Genzyme can charge so much for Cerezyme. *Wall Street Journal* 2005 November 16; p. A15. Subject: 9.7

Anand, P. Capabilities and health. *Journal of Medical Ethics* 2005 May; 31(5): 299-303. Subject: 9.4

Anand, Sudhir. The concern for equity in health. *In:* Anand, Sudhir; Peter, Fabienne; Sen, Amartya, eds. Public Health, Ethics, and Equity. New York: Oxford University Press; 2004: 13-20. Subject: 9.1

Anand, Sudhir; Hanson, Kara. Disability-adjusted life years: a critical review. *In:* Anand, Sudhir; Peter, Fabienne; Sen, Amartya, eds. Public Health, Ethics, and Equity. New York: Oxford University Press; 2004: 183-199. Subject: 4.4

Ananthakrishnan, N. The ethics of live operative workshops [letter]. *National Medical Journal of India* 2003 November-December; 16(6): 340. Subject: 7.2

Ananthakrishnan, N. The ethics of live operative workshops [reply]. *National Medical Journal of India* 2004; 17(4): 224-225. Subject: 7.2

Anchustegui, A.T. Biocentric ethics and animal prosperity. *International Journal of Applied Philosophy* 2005 Spring; 19(1): 105-119. Subject: 22.1

Andanda, Pamela. Module two: informed consent. *Developing World Bioethics* 2005 March; 5(1): 14-29. Subject: 18.3

Anderlik, Mary R. Commercial biobanks and genetics research: banking without checks? *In:* Knoppers, Bartha Maria, ed. Populations and Genetics: Legal and Socio-Ethical Perspectives. Boston: Martinus Nijhoff; 2003: 345-376. Subject: 15.1

Anderlik, Mary R.; Heller, Jan C. The economics and politics of the new genetics. *In:* Smith, David H.; Cohen, Cynthia B., eds. A Christian Response to the New Genetics: Religious, Ethical, and Social Issues. Lanham, MD: Rowman & Littlefield Publishers; 2003: 147-167. Subject: 15.1

Andersen, Marit Helen; Mathisen, Lars; Øyen, Ole; Wahl, Astrid Klopstad; Hanestad, Berit Rokne; Fosse, Erik. Living donors' experiences 1 wk after donating a kidney. *Clinical Transplantation* 2005 February; 19(1): 90-96. Subject: 19.5

Andersen, Svend. Chance and equality: Habermas on human cloning. *In:* Ostnor, Lars, ed. Bioethics and Cloning: Report from a Workshop Arranged by the Nordic Theological Network for Bioethics in Arhus, September 25-27, 1998. Oslo: Nordic Theological Network for Bioethics; 1998: 51-55. Subject: 14.5

Anderson, Barry D.; Adamson, Peter C.; Weiner, Susan L.; McCabe, Mary S.; Smith, Malcolm A. Tissue collection for correlative studies in childhood cancer clinical trials: ethical considerations and special imperatives. *Journal of Clinical Oncology* 2004 December 1; 22(23): 4794-4798. Subject: 18.5.2

Anderson, Bebe J.; Wilcox, Lynne S. Reproductive health. *In:* Goodman, Richard A.; Rothstein, Mark A.; Hoffman, Richard E.; Lopez, Wilfredo; Matthews, Gene W., eds. Law in Public Health Practice. New York: Oxford University Press; 2003: 348-370. Subject: 14.1

Anderson, Janet June. Capital punishment of kids: when courts permit parents to act on their religious beliefs at the expense of their children's lives. *Vanderbilt Law Review* 1993 April; 46(3): 755-777. Subject: 8.3.4

Anderson, Joan M. Empowering patients: issues and strategies. *Social Science and Medicine* 1996 September; 43(5): 697-705. Subject: 9.8

Anderson, Lynley; Cunningham, Nikki. In that case. *Journal of Bioethical Inquiry* 2005; 2(2): 109. Subject: 9.5.7

Anderson, L.C.; Gerrard, D.F. Ethical issues concerning New Zealand sports doctors. *Journal of Medical Ethics* 2005 February; 31(2): 88-92. Subject: 9.5.1

Anderson, Martha W.; Schapiro, Renie. From donor to recipient: the pathway and business of donated tissues. *In:* Youngner, Stuart J.; Anderson, Martha W.; Schapiro, Renie, eds. Transplanting Human Tissue: Ethics, Policy, and Practice. New York: Oxford University Press; 2004: 3-13. Subject: 19.5

Anderson, Mikeisha T. Criminal penalties for women engaging in substance abuse during pregnancy. *Women's Rights Law Reporter* 2000 Summer; 21(3): 181-188. Subject: 9.5.5

Anderson, Rebecca Cogwell; Fox, Robert. Ethical issues in health promotion and health education. *AAOHN Journal* 1987 May; 35(5): 220-223, 246-248. Subject: 7.2

Anderson, Ron J. Holistic healers and physician-assisted suicide. *Alternative Therapies in Health and Medicine* 1996 November; 2(6): 77-83. Subject: 20.7

Anderson, Sharon K.; Kitchener, Karen S. Nonsexual posttherapy relationships: a conceptual framework to assess ethical risks. *Professional Psychology: Research and Practice* 1998 February; 29(1): 91-99. Subject: 7.1

Anderson, Stephanie L. The Human Genome Project. *In:* American College of Legal Medicine Textbook Committee, Sanbar, S. Sandy; Firestone, Marvin H.; Buckner, Fillmore; Gibofsky, Allan; LeBlang, Theodore R.; Snyder, Jack W.; Wecht, Cyril H.; Zaremski, Miles J. Legal Medicine. 6th ed. St. Louis: Mosby; 2004: 256-263. Subject: 15.1

Anderson, W. French. Genetic therapy. *In:* Hamilton, Michael P., ed. The New Genetics and the Future of Man. Grand Rapids, MI: William B. Eerdmans Publishing Co.; 1972: 109-124. Subject: 15.4

Anderson-Shaw, Lisa; Meadow, William; Leeds, Hilary S.; Lantos, John J. The fiction of futility: what to do with policy? *HEC (Healthcare Ethics Committee) Forum* 2005 December; 17(4): 294-307. Subject: 20.5.1

Anderson-Shaw, Lisa; Schmidt, Mary Lou; Elkin, Jeanine; Chamberlin, William; Benedetti, Enrico; Testa, Guiliano. Evolution of a living donor liver transplantation advocacy program. *Journal of Clinical Ethics* 2005 Spring; 16(1): 46-57. Subject: 19.5

Andrade, Chittaranjan. ECT: a measured defence. *Issues in Medical Ethics* 2003 April-June; 11(2): 44-46. Subject: 17.5

Andrade, Chittaranjan. Unmodified ECT: ethical issues. *Issues in Medical Ethics* 2003 January-March; 11(1): 9-10. Subject: 17.5

Andrew, Gracy. Issues are complex and need innovative solutions [case study]. *Indian Journal of Medical Ethics* 2005 October-December; 2(4): 127. Subject: 14.4

Andrew, Louise. Punishing experts, or protecting the courts? *Journal of Philosophy, Science and Law [electronic]* 2005 May 18; 5; 6 p. Available: http://www.psljournal.com/archives/index.cfm [25 May 2005]. Subject: 5.1

Andrews, Diane R. Fostering ethical competency: an ongoing staff development process that encourages professional growth and staff satisfaction. *Journal of Continuing Education in Nursing* 2004 January-February; 35(1): 27-33, 44-45. Subject: 4.1.3

Andrews, Jason. U.S. military sponsored vaccine trials and la resistance in Nepal. *American Journal of Bioethics [Online]* 2005 May-June; 5(3): W1-W3. Subject: 18.5.9

Andrews, Jonathan. The politics of committal to early modern Bethlem. *Clio Medica* 1995; 29: 6-63. Subject: 17.7

Andrews, Lori B. A conceptual framework for genetic policy: comparing the medical, public health, and fundamental rights models. *Washington University Law Quarterly* 2001; 79(152): 221-285. Subject: 15.1

Andrews, Lori B. Harnessing the benefits of biobanks. *Journal of Law, Medicine and Ethics* 2005 Spring; 33(1): 22-30. Subject: 15.1

Andrews, Lori B.; Paradise, Jordan. Gene patents: the need for bioethics scrutiny and legal change. *Yale Journal of Health Policy, Law, and Ethics* 2005 Winter; 5(1): 403-412. Subject: 15.8

Anees, Munawar Ahmad. Human clones and God's trust: the Islamic view. *In:* McGee, Glenn; Caplan, Arthur, eds. The Human Cloning Debate. 4th edition. Berkeley, CA: Berkeley Hills Books; 2004: 277-281. Subject: 14.5

Angus, Floyd; Burakoff, Robert. The percutaneous endoscopic gastrostomy tube: medical and ethical issues in placement. *American Journal of Gastroenterology* 2003 February; 98(2): 272-277. Subject: 20.5.1

Anido, Aimee; Carlson, Lisa M.; Taft, Lisa; Sherman, Stephanie L. Women's attitudes toward testing for fragile X carrier status: a qualitative analysis. *Journal of Genetic Counseling* 2005 August; 14(4): 295-306. Subject: 15.3

Anijar, Karen; Gabbard, David. Authentic faux diamonds and attention deficit disorder [comment]. *American Journal of Bioethics* 2005 May-June; 5(3): 67-70. Subject: 17.4

Annals, Geoff; O'Malley, Jane. In that case. Response [case study]. *Journal of Bioethical Inquiry* 2005; 2(1): 53-54. Subject: 4.1.3

Annas, George J. American Bioethics after Nuremberg: Pragmatism, Politics, and Human Rights. Boston, MA: Boston University, University Lecture, 2005; 26 p. Subject: 2.1

Annas, George J. American bioethics and human rights: the end of all our exploring. *Journal of Law, Medicine and Ethics* 2004 Winter; 32(4): 658- 663. Subject: 2.1

Annas, George J. "Culture of life" politics at the bedside — the case of Terri Schiavo. *New England Journal of Medicine* 2005 April 21; 352(16): 1710- 1715. Subject: 20.5.1

Annas, George J. Ethical aspects of non-invasive prenatal diagnosis: medical, market, or regulatory model? *Early Human Development* 1996 December 30; 47(supplement 1): S5-S11. Subject: 15.2

Annas, George J. Family privacy and death — Antigone, war, and medical research. *New England Journal of Medicine* 2005 February 3; 352(5): 501- 505. Subject: 8.4

Annas, George J. Jumping frogs, endangered toads, and California's medical- marijuana law. *New England Journal of Medicine* 2005 November 24; 353(21): 2291-2296. Subject: 9.5.9

Annas, George J. Unspeakably cruel — torture, medical ethics, and the law [editorial]. *New England Journal of Medicine* 2005 May 19; 352(20): 2127- 2132. Subject: 21.4

Anwar, Katharina; O'Mahony, Fidelma. Patient access to their records: rights or risks? *British Journal of Obstetrics and Gynaecology* 2000 January; 107(1): 141-142. Subject: 9.2

Apfel, Howard David; Isaacson, Shimon. Halachic and medical perspectives on banking umbilical cord stem cells. *Journal of Halacha and Contemporary Society* 2005 Fall; (50): 5-37. Subject: 19.4

Appel, Jacob M. Defining death: when physicians and families differ. *Journal of Medical Ethics* 2005 November; 31(11): 641-642. Subject: 20.2.1

Appel, Jacob M. In defense of tongue splitting. *Journal of Clinical Ethics* 2005 Fall; 16(3): 236-238. Subject: 9.5.1

Appel, Jacob M. May physicians date their patients' relatives? Rethinking sexual misconduct and disclosure after Long v. Ostroff. *Medicine and Health, Rhode Island* 2004 May; 87(5): 159-161. Subject: 7.4

Appel, Jacob M. Wanted dead or alive? Kidney transplantation in inmates awaiting execution. *Journal of Clinical Ethics* 2005 Spring; 16(1): 58-60. Subject: 19.3

Appel, Jacob M.; Fox, Mark D. Organ solicitation on the Internet: every man for himself? [case study and commentaries]. *Hastings Center Report* 2005 May-June; 35(3): 14-15. Subject: 19.5

Appel, Stanley H. Euthanasia and physician-assisted suicide in ALS: a commentary [editorial]. *American Journal of Hospice and Palliative Care* 2004 November-December; 21(6): 405-406. Subject: 20.5.1

Appelbaum, Judith C.; Davis, Virginia S. Insurance coverage of contraceptives: narrowing the gender gap in health care coverage. *In:* Barnes, Andrea, ed. The Handbook of Women, Psychology, and the Law. San Francisco: Jossey-Bass; 2005: 178-191. Subject: 11.1

Appelbaum, Paul S. Assessing Kendra's law: five years of outpatient commitment in New York. *Psychiatric Services* 2005 July; 56(7): 791-792. Subject: 17.1

Appelbaum, Paul S. Comments: a crisis in the ethical and moral behavior of psychiatrists [forum]. *Current Opinion in Psychiatry* 1998 January; 11(1); 2 p. [Online]. Available: http://gateway.ut.ovid.com/gw1/ovidweb.cgi [24 May 2005]. Subject: 20.6

Appelbaum, Paul S. Dangerous severe personality disorders: England's experiment in using psychiatry for public protection. *Psychiatric Services* 2005 April; 56(4): 397-399. Subject: 17.7

Appelbaum, Paul S. Ethical issues in psychiatric genetics. *Journal of Psychiatric Practice* 2004 November; 10(6): 343-351. Subject: 15.1

Appelbaum, Paul S. Legalism, postmodernism, and the vicissitudes of teaching ethics [opinion]. *Academic Psychiatry* 2004 Fall; 28(3): 164-167. Subject: 2.1

Appelbaum, Paul S. Psychopharmacology and the power of narrative [comment]. *American Journal of Bioethics* 2005 May-June; 5(3): 48-49. Subject: 17.4

Appleton, Susan Frelich. Adoption in the age of reproductive technology. *University of Chicago Legal Forum* 2004; 2004: 393-451. Subject: 14.1

Appleton, Tim. Emotional aspects of surrogacy: a case for effective counselling and support. *In:* Cook, Rachel; Sclater, Shelley Day; Kaganas, Felicity, eds. Surrogate Motherhood: International Perspectives. Portland, OR: Hart; 2003: 199-207. Subject: 14.2

Aranibar, Fernando Antezana. Legal aspects of forms of palliative care for pain. *Dolentium Hominum* 2005; 20(1): 51-53. Subject: 20.4.1

Araujo, Robert John. The legal order and the common good: abortion rights as contradiction of constitutional purposes. *In:* Koterski, Joseph W., ed. Life and Learning XI: Proceedings of the Eleventh University Faculty for Life Conference. Washington, DC: University Faculty for Life; 2002: 65-84. Subject: 12.4.1

Arbit, Ehud; Stossel, Thomas P. Academic-industrial relationships [letter and reply]. *New England Journal of Medicine* 2005 December 22; 353(25): 2720-2722. Subject: 5.3

Archer, Colette. Scrambled eggs: defining parenthood and inheritance rights of children born of reproductive

---

Subject = NRCBL Primary Classification Number; See inside front cover

technology. *Loyola Journal of Public Interest Law* 2002 Spring; 3(2): 152-173. Subject: 14.2

Archibald, Kathy. Test people, not animals [letter]. *New Scientist* 2005 September 24-30; 187(2518): 24. Subject: 22.2

Arends, L.A.P. Legal status of incompetent patients in psychogeriatric settings from a Dutch perspective. *Medicine and Law: World Association for Medical Law* 2004; 23(4): 821-831. Subject: 9.5.3

Arford, Patricia H. Working with human research protections. *Journal of Nursing Scholarship* 2004; 36(3): 265-271. Subject: 18.2

Arie, Sophie. Crusading for change [news]. *BMJ: British Medical Journal* 2005 April 23; 330(7497): 926. Subject: 9.5.6

Ariss, Rachel. Theorizing waste in abortion and fetal ovarian tissue use. *Canadian Journal of Women and the Law* 2003; 15(2): 255-281. Subject: 19.1

Arkin, Lisa M.; Sondhi, Dolan; Worgall, Stefan; Suh, Lily Hyon K.; Hackett, Neil R.; Kaminsky, Stephen M.; Hosain, Syed A.; Souweidane, Mark M.; Kaplitt, Michael G.; Dyke, Jonathan P.; Heier, Linda A.; Ballon, Douglas J.; Shungu, Dikoma C.; Wisniewski, Krystyna E.; Greenwald, Bruce M.; Hollmann, Charleen; Crystal, Ronald G. Confronting the issues of therapeutic misconception enrollment decisions, and personal motives in genetic medicine-based clinical research studies for fatal disorders. *Human Gene Therapy* 2005 September; 16(9): 1028-1036. Subject: 15.4

Arking, Robert. A new age for aging? Ethical questions, scientific insights, and societal outcomes. *Rejuvenation Research* 2004 Spring; 7(1): 53-60. Subject: 9.5.2

Armstrong, Alan E.; Parsons, S.; Barker, P.J. An inquiry into moral virtues, especially compassion, in psychiatric nurses: findings from a Delphi study. *Journal of Psychiatric and Mental Health Nursing* 2000 August; 7(4): 297-306. Subject: 4.1.3

Armstrong, David. Delicate operation: how a famed hospital invests in device it uses and promotes; Cleveland Clinic set up fund that has stock in maker of heart-surgery system; Dr. Cosgrove's multiple roles. *Wall Street Journal* 2005 December 12; p. A1, A16. Subject: 9.7

Armstrong, David. Lucrative operation: how some doctors turn a $90 profit from a $17 test; physician groups add markup to work done by others, despite ethics concerns; administrative costs cited. *Wall Street Journal* 2005 September 30; p. A1, A8. Subject: 9.3.1

Armstrong, David. Skillful operation: a surgeon earns riches, enmity by plucking profitable patients;specialty hospitals go public, sparking ire in Rapid City; older facility faces losses; clash over anonymous letter. *Wall Street Journal* 2005 August 2; p. A1, A7. Subject: 9.3.1

Armstrong, David. Surgery journal threatens ban for authors' hidden conflicts. *Wall Street Journal* 2005 December 28; p. B1, B2. Subject: 1.3.9

Armstrong, David; Kline-Rogers, Eva; Jani, Sandeep M.; Goldman, Edward B.; Fang, Jianming; Mukherjee, Debabrata; Nallamothu, Brahmajee K.; Eagle, Kim A. Potential impact of the HIPAA privacy rule on data collection in a registry of patients with acute coronary syndrome. *Archives of Internal Medicine* 2005 May 23; 165(10): 1125-1129. Subject: 8.4

Armstrong, Elizabeth M. Drug and alcohol use during pregnancy: we need to protect, not punish, women [editorial]. *Women's Health Issues* 2005 March-April; 15(2): 45-47. Subject: 9.5.5

Árnason, Vilhjálmur. Sensible discussion in bioethics: reflections on interdisciplinary research. *CQ: Cambridge Quarterly of Healthcare Ethics* 2005 Summer; 14(3): 322-328. Subject: 2.1

Arnold, Kendra D. The right to live: a constitutional argument for mandatory preventative health care for female prisoners. *William and Mary Journal of Women and the Law* 2004 Winter; 10(2): 343-366. Subject: 9.5.5

Arons, Jessica R. Misconceived laws: the irrationality of parental involvement requirements for contraception. *William and Mary Law Review* 2000 March; 41(3): 1093-1131. Subject: 11.2

Arora, Dolly. The victimizing discourse: sex-determination technologies and policy. Economic and Political Weekly 1996 February 17; 31(7); 11 p. [Online]. Available: http://www.hsph.harvard.edu/Organizations/healthnet/SAsia/suchana /1210/arora.html [6 October 2005]. Subject: 14.3

Aroskar, Mila Ann. Envisioning nursing as a moral community. *Nursing Outlook* 1995 May-June; 43(3): 134-138. Subject: 4.1.3

Arrhenius, Gustaf. The person-affecting restriction, comparativism, and the moral status of potential people. *Ethical Perspectives* 2003; 10(3-4): 185-195. Subject: 14.1

Arshinoff, Steve; Choi, Stephen. Excluding the experts? [letter and reply]. *CMAJ/JAMC: Canadian Medical Association Journal* 2005 October 11; 173(8): 849. Subject: 1.3.7

Arthur, Joyce. Fetal pain: a red herring in the abortion debate. *Free Inquiry* 2005 August-September; 25(5): 44-47. Subject: 12.1

Artnak, Kathryn E.; Benson, Margaret. Evaluating HIPAA compliance: a guide for researchers, privacy boards, and IRBs. *Nursing Outlook* 2005 March-April; 53(2): 79-87. Subject: 8.4

Asai, Atsushi; Oe, Sachi. A valuable up-to-date compendium of bioethical knowledge. *Developing World Bioethics* 2005 September; 5(3): 216-219. Subject: 2.1

See SUBJECT HEADING KEY FOR SECTION II on inside back cover

Asch, Adrienne. Big tent bioethics: toward an inclusive and reasonable bioethics. *Hastings Center Report* 2005 November-December; 35(6): 11-12. Subject: 2.1

Asch, Adrienne; Wasserman, David. Where is the sin in synecdoche?: prenatal testing and the parent-child relationship. *In:* Wasserman, David; Bickenbach, Jerome; Wachbroit, Robert, eds. Quality of Life and Human Difference: Genetic Testing, Health Care, and Disability. New York: Cambridge University Press; 2005: 172-216. Subject: 15.2

Ashby, Michael A.; Mendelson, Danuta. Gardner; re BWV: Victorian Supreme Court makes landmark Australian ruling on tube feeding. *Medical Journal of Australia* 2004 October 18; 181(8): 442-445. Subject: 20.4.1

Ashcroft, Richard. Death policy in the United Kingdom. *In:* Blank, Robert H.; Merrick, Janna C., eds. End-of-Life Decision Making: A Cross-National Study. Cambridge, MA: MIT Press; 2005: 197-218. Subject: 20.5.1

Ashcroft, Richard E. Access to essential medicines: a Hobbesian social contract approach. *Developing World Bioethics* 2005 May; 5(2): 121-141. Subject: 9.2

Ashcroft, Richard E. Commentary: ethics committees and countries in transition: a figleaf for structural violence? *BMJ: British Medical Journal* 2005 July 23; 331(7510): 229-230. Subject: 9.6

Ashcroft, Richard E. Gene therapy in the clinic: whose risks? *Trends in Biotechnology* 2004 November; 22(11): 560-563. Subject: 15.4

Ashcroft, Richard E. Standing up for the medical rights of asylum seekers [editorial]. *Journal of Medical Ethics* 2005 March; 31(3): 125-126. Subject: 21.1

Ashcroft, Richard E.; Gui, Karen P. Ethics and world pictures in Kamm on enhancement [comment]. *American Journal of Bioethics* 2005 May-June; 5(3): 19-20. Subject: 15.1

Ashcroft, Richard E.; Newson, Ainsley J.; Benn, Piers M.W. Reforming research ethics committees: latest proposals are a missed opportunity for a radical review [editorial]. *BMJ: British Medical Journal* 2005 September 17; 331(7517): 587-588. Subject: 18.2

Ashford, Nicholas A. Monitoring the worker and the community for chemical exposure and disease: legal and ethical considerations in the US. *Clinical Chemistry* 1994 July; 40(7 Part 2): 1426-1437. Subject: 16.3

Ashley, Benedict M. Organ donation and implantation. *In:* McMahon, Kevin T., ed. Moral Issues in Catholic Health Care. Wynnewood, PA: Saint Charles Borromeo Seminary; 2004: 153- 167. Subject: 19.5

Ashmore, R. A study on how mental health practitioners address ethical issues in clinical audit. *Journal of Psychiatric and Mental Health Nursing* 2005 February; 12(1): 112-120. Subject: 9.8

Asia Pacific Network of People Living with HIV/AIDS [APN+]. AIDS discrimination in Asia. Auckland, New Zealand: Asia Pacific Network of People Living with HIV/AIDS 2004; 56 p. [Online]. Available: http://www. gnpplus.net/regions/files/AIDS-asia.pdf [24 May 2005]. Subject: 9.5.6

Aspen Health and Compliance Center; Aspen Reference Group; Aspen Communications and Data Group. Patient record documentation and confidentiality. *Pharmacy Practice Management Quarterly* 1999 April; 19(1): 57-62. Subject: 8.4

Aspinall, Peter. Language matters: the vocabulary of racism in health care. *Journal of Health Services Research and Policy* 2005 January; 10(1): 57-59. Subject: 9.5.4

Association of American Medical Colleges [AAMC]. Institutional Oversight of Individual Financial Interests in Human Subjects Resarch: Assessing Policies and Practices. Washington, DC: The Association 2003; 8 p. [Online]. Available: http://www.aamc.org/members/coitf/ coisurvey2003.pdf [2 August 2005]. Subject: 1.3.9

Association of Clinical Embryologists [ACE]. Code of Professional Conduct for Clinical Embryologists. *Human Fertility* 2004 December; 7(4): 301-303. Subject: 4.1.2

Atkins, Chloë G.K. The failure of formal rights and equality in the clinic: a critique of bioethics. *Ethics and Medicine* 2005 Fall; 21(3): 139-162. Subject: 4.4

Atlas, Michel C. Ethics and access to teaching materials in the medical library: the case of the Pernkopf atlas. *Bulletin of the Medical Library Association* 2001 January; 89(1): 51-58. Subject: 7.2

Attaran, Amir. Human rights and biomedical research funding for the developing world: discovering state obligations under the right to health. *Health and Human Rights: An International Journal* 1999; 4(1): 27-58. Subject: 9.2

Atwell, Barbara L. Mainstreaming complementary and alternative medicine in the face of uncertainty. *UMKC Law Review* 2004 Spring; 72(3): 593-630. Subject: 4.1.1

Atwood-Harvey, Dana. Death or declaw: dealing with moral ambiguity in a veterinary hospital. *Society and Animals: Journal of Human-Animal Studies* 2005; 13(4): 315-342. Subject: 4.1.1

Auckland Hospital Ethics Committee; Pinnock, Ralph; Crosthwaite, Jan. The Auckland Hospital Ethics Committee: the first 7 years. *New Zealand Medical Journal* 2004 November 5; 117(1205); 10 p. Subject: 9.6

Aumonier, Nicolas. Evaluation of the arguments. *In:* Council of Europe Publishing, ed. Euthanasia. Volume I. Ethical and Human Aspects. Strasbourg: Council of Europe; Croton- on-Hudson, NY: Manhattan Publishing Co.; 2003: 59-72. Subject: 20.5.1

Austin, Wendy; Lemermeyer, Gillian; Goldberg, Lisa; Bergum, Vangie; Johnson, Melissa S. Moral distress in

---

healthcare practice: the situation of nurses. *HEC (Healthcare Ethics Committee) Forum* 2005 March; 17(1): 33- 48. Subject: 4.1.3

Austin, Wendy; Rankel, Marlene; Kagan, Leon; Bergum, Vangie; Lemermeyer, Gillian. To stay or to go, to speak or stay silent, to act or not to act: moral distress as experienced by psychologists. *Ethics and Behavior* 2005; 15(3): 197-212. Subject: 17.2

Australian Health Ethics Committee; Chalmers, Donald; Pettit, Philip. Towards a consensual culture in the ethical review of research. *Medical Journal of Australia* 1998 January 19; 168(2): 79-82. Subject: 18.2

Australia. Parliament; Cica, Natasha. Euthanasia — The Australian Law in an International Context. Part 1: Passive Voluntary Euthanasia: Research Paper 3: 1996-1997. Canberra, Australia: Law and Public Administration Group. Parliament 1996 September 9; 24 p. [Online]. Available: http://www.aph.gov.au/library/pubs/rp/ 1996-97/97rp3.htm [7 July 2005]. Subject: 20.5.1

Australia. Parliament; Cica, Natasha. Euthanasia — The Australian Law in an International Context. Part 2: Active Voluntary Euthanasia. Research Paper 4: 1996-1997. Canberra, Australia: Law and Public Administration Group, Parliament 1996 September 9; 40 p. [Online]. Available: http://www.aph.gov.au/library/pubs/rp/ 1996-97/97rp4.htm [7 July 2005]. Subject: 20.5.1

Australia. Parliament. Law and Bills Digest Group; Cica, Natasha. Abortion law in Australia: Research Paper 1: 1998-1999. Australia: Parliamentary Library 1998-1999; 42 p. [Online] Available: http://www.aph.gov. au/library/pubs/rp/1998-99/99rp01.htm [13 September 2005]. Subject: 12.4.1

Austriaco, Nicanor Pier Giorgio. Are teratomas embryos or non-embryos? *National Catholic Bioethics Quarterly* 2005 Winter; 5(4): 697- 706. Subject: 4.4

Austriaco, Nicanor Pier Giorgio; Hurlbut, William B. Teratomas as an ANT standard [letter and reply]. *National Catholic Bioethics Quarterly* 2005 Spring; 5(1): 10- 12, 19-22. Subject: 18.5.4

Auvinen, Jaana; Suominen, Tarja; Leino-Kilpi, Helena; Helkama, Klaus. The development of moral judgment during nursing education in Finland. *Nurse Education Today* 2004 October; 24(7): 538-546. Subject: 4.1.3

Avanzini, G. Discussing "the limits of scientific research" [opinion]. *Neurological Sciences* 2005 February; 25(6): 305-306. Subject: 1.3.9

Aveyard, Helen. Informed consent prior to nursing care procedures. *Nursing Ethics* 2005 January; 12(1): 19-29. Subject: 8.3.1

Aveyard, Helen; Edwards, Sarah; West, Sharon. Core topics of health care ethics. The identification of core topics for interprofessional education. *Journal of Interprofessional Care* 2005 January; 19(1): 63-69. Subject: 2.3

Avisar, Solomon R. The ethics of biotechnology — the argument in favour of patents. *Canadian Intellectual Property Review* 1993 September; 10(1): 209-217. Subject: 15.8

Avorn, Jerry. Torcetrapib and Atorvastatin — should marketing drive the research agenda? [opinion]. *New England Journal of Medicine* 2005 June 23; 352(25): 2573-2576. Subject: 18.2

Aw, T.C. Ethical issues in occupational medicine practice: knowledge and attitudes of occupational physicians. *Occupational Medicine* 1997 August; 47(6): 371-376. Subject: 16.3

Awaya, Tsuyoshi. Common ethical issues in regenerative medicine. *Journal International de Bioethique / International Journal of Bioethics* 2005 March-June; 16(1-2): 69-75, 192-193. Subject: 4.4

Axtell-Thompson, Linda M. Consumer directed health care: ethical limits to choice and responsibility. *Journal of Medicine and Philosophy* 2005 April; 30(2): 207-226. Subject: 9.3.1

Ayers, Marva; Rendleman, Neal J. In response to the August 1999 article entitled: "Mandated Tuberculosis Screening in a Community of Homeless People" [letter and reply]. *American Journal of Preventive Medicine* 2000 April; 18(3): 268. Subject: 9.1

Ayres, Ian. Three tests for measuring unjustified disparate impacts in organ transplantation: the problem of "included variable" bias. *Perspectives in Biology and Medicine* 2005 Winter; 48(1, Supplement): S68-S87. Subject: 9.5.4

Azarow, Kenneth S.; Olmstead, Francis L.; Hume, Roderick F.; Myers, Jerome; Calhoun, Bryon C.; Martin, Laura S. Ethical use of tissue samples in genetic research. *Military Medicine* 2003 June; 168(6): 437-441. Subject: 19.5

Azevedo, David. Should you help patients die? *Medical Economics* 1997 January 13; 74(1): 137-140, 143-144, 147-149. Subject: 20.7

Azoulay, Élie; Pochard, Frédéric; Chevret, Sylvie; Adrie, Christophe; Bollaert, Pierre-Edouard; Brun, Frédéric; Dreyfuss, Didier; Garrouste-Orgeas, Maité; Goldgran-Toledano, Dany; Jourdain, Mercé; Wolff, Michel; Le Gall, Jean-Roger; Schlemmer, Benoît. Opinions about surrogate designation: a population survey in France. *Critical Care Medicine* 2003 June; 31(6): 1711-1714. Subject: 8.3.3

Azoulay, Élie; Sprung, Charles L. Family-physician interactions in the intensive care unit. *Critical Care Medicine* 2004 November; 32(11): 2323-2328. Subject: 8.3.3

B

Baader, Gerhard. Jewish halachic medical ethics and human experimentation. *In:* Roelcke, Volker; Maio, Giovanni, eds. Twentieth Century Ethics of Human Subjects Research: Historical Perspectives on Values, Practices, and Regulations. Stuttgart: Franz Steiner Verlag; 2004: 51-63. Subject: 18.1

Bacchetti, Peter; Wolf, Leslie E.; Segal, Mark R.; McCulloch, Charles E. Bacchetti et al. respond to "ethics and sample size — another view". *American Journal of Epidemiology* 2005; 161(2): 113. Subject: 18.2

Bacchetti, Peter; Wolf, Leslie E.; Segal, Mark R.; McCulloch, Charles E. Ethics and sample size. *American Journal of Epidemiology* 2005 January 15; 161(2): 105-110. Subject: 18.2

Bacchi, Carol; Beasley, Chris. Reproductive technology and the political limits of care. *In:* Shildrick, Margrit; Mykitiuk, Roxanne, eds. Ethics of the Body: Postconventional Challenges. Cambridge, MA: MIT Press; 2005: 175- 194. Subject: 14.1

Back, Anthony L.; Arnold, Robert M. Dealing with conflict in caring for the seriously ill: "it was just out of the question". *JAMA: The Journal of the American Medical Association* 2005 March 16; 293(11): 1374-1381. Subject: 20.5.1

Back, Anthony L.; Arnold, Robert M.; Tulsky, James A.; Baile, Walter F.; Fryer-Edwards, Kelly A. On saying goodbye: acknowledging the end of the patient- physician relationship with patients who are near death. *Annals of Internal Medicine* 2005 April 19; 142(8): 682-685. Subject: 8.1

Backmeyer, E. Renee. Lack of insurance coverage for prescription contraception by an otherwise comprehensive plan as a violation of Title VII as amended by the Pregnancy Discrimination Act — stretching the statute too far. *Indiana Law Review* 2004; 37(2): 437-466. Subject: 11.1

Badcott, David. Employing patient expertise: introduction to the theme [editorial]. *Medicine, Health Care and Philosophy: A European Journal* 2005; 8(2): 147-148. Subject: 4.2

Badcott, David. The expert patient: valid recognition or false hope? *Medicine, Health Care and Philosophy: A European Journal* 2005; 8(2): 173-178. Subject: 4.2

Baer, Lawrence J. Influences on IRB decisionmaking [letter]. *IRB: Ethics and Human Research* 2005 May-June; 27(3): 7. Subject: 18.2

Baer, Steven. Should imperfect infants survive? *National Review* 1983 September 2; 35(17): 1069, 1092-1093. Subject: 20.5.2

Baetens, Patricia; Van de Velde, H.; Camus, M.; Pennings, G.; Van Steirteghem, A.; Devroey, P.; Liebaers, I. HLA-matched embryos selected for siblings requiring haematopoietic stem cell transplantation: a psy-chological perspective. *Reproductive BioMedicine Online [electronic]* 2005 February; 10(2): 154-163. Available: http://rbmonline.com/index.html [17 February 2006]. Subject: 15.2

Baeyens, A.J. Implementation of the clinical trials directive: pitfalls and benefits. *European Journal of Health Law* 2002 March; 9(1): 31-47. Subject: 18.2

Baggini, Julian; Pym, Madeleine. End of life: the humanist view [opinion]. *Lancet* 2005 October 1-7; 366(9492): 1235-1237. Subject: 20.5.1

Baggs, Judith Gedney; Schmitt, Madeline H. Editors and conflict of interest [editorial]. *Research in Nursing and Health* 2003 April; 26(2): 87-89. Subject: 1.3.7

Bagheri, Alizera; Shoji, Shin'ichi. The model and moral justification for organ procurement in Japan. *Journal International de Bioethique / International Journal of Bioethics* 2005 March-June; 16(1-2): 79-90, 194-195. Subject: 19.5

Bahadur, G. Ethics of testicular stem cell medicine [opinion]. *Human Reproduction* 2004 December; 19(12): 2702-2710. Subject: 14.6

Bahadur, Gulam; Nielsen, H. Ingolf. The human embryo, embryonic stem cells, cloning, legal and political precepts [opinion]. *Reproductive BioMedicine Online [electronic]* 2001; 2(2): 81- 83. Available: http://www.rbmonline.com/index.html [1 September 2005]. Subject: 14.5

Bailey, Donald B., Jr.; Skinner, Debra; Warren, Steven F. Newborn screening for developmental disabilities: reframing presumptive benefit. *American Journal of Public Health* 2005 November; 95(11): 1889- 1893. Subject: 9.5.7

Bailey, Ronald. Are stem cells babies? The ethics of making perfect transplants. *In his:* Liberation Biology: The Scientific and Moral Case for the Biotech Revolution. Amherst, NY: Prometheus Books; 2005: 95- 133. Subject: 18.5.4

Bailey, Ronald. Biotech cornucopia: improving nature for humanity's benefit. *In his:* Liberation Biology: The Scientific and Moral Case for the Biotech Revolution. Amherst, NY: Prometheus Books; 2005: 183- 222. Subject: 15.1

Bailey, Ronald. Changing your own mind: the neuroethics of psychopharmacology. *In his:* Liberation Biology: The Scientific and Moral Case for the Biotech Revolution. Amherst, NY: Prometheus Books; 2005: 223- 238. Subject: 4.5

Bailey, Ronald. Cloning babies is not inherently immoral. *In:* McGee, Glenn; Caplan, Arthur, eds. The Human Cloning Debate. 4th edition. Berkeley, CA: Berkeley Hills Books; 2004: 211- 219. Subject: 14.5

Bailey, Ronald. Final victory over disease? Building humanity's extended immune system. *In his:* Liberation Biology: The Scientific and Moral Case for the Biotech

Revolution. Amherst, NY: Prometheus Books; 2005: 63-94. Subject: 15.4

Bailey, Ronald. Forever young: the biology and politics of immortality. *In his:* Liberation Biology: The Scientific and Moral Case for the Biotech Revolution. Amherst, NY: Prometheus Books; 2005: 25-61. Subject: 20.5.1

Bailey, Ronald. Hooray for designer babies! *In his:* Liberation Biology: The Scientific and Moral Case for the Biotech Revolution. Amherst, NY: Prometheus Books; 2005: 149- 181. Subject: 4.5

Bailey, Ronald. Who's afraid of human cloning? *In his:* Liberation Biology: The Scientific and Moral Case for the Biotech Revolution. Amherst, NY: Prometheus Books; 2005: 135- 147. Subject: 14.5

Bailey, Susan; O'Connell, Bev; Pearce, Julian. The transition from paediatric to adult health care services for young adults with a disability: an ethical perspective. *Australian Health Review* 2003; 26(1): 64-69. Subject: 9.5.1

Baillie, Harold W. Aristotle and genetic engineering: the uncertainty of excellence. *In:* Baillie, Harold W.; Casey, Timothy K., eds. Is Human Nature Obsolete? Genetics Bioengineering, and the Future of the Human Condition. Cambridge, MA: MIT Press; 2005: 209-232. Subject: 15.1

Baillie, J. On writing (5): fabrication, falsification and plagerism [sic; plagiarism] in medical research and publishing. *Endoscopy* 2004 November; 36(11): 1008-1010. Subject: 1.3.7

Baines, Darrin L.; Tolley, Keith H.; Whynes, David K. The ethics of resource allocation: the views of general practitioners in Lincolnshire, U.K. *Social Science and Medicine* 1998; 47(10): 1555-1564. Subject: 9.4

Baines, Lyndsay S.; Jindal, Rahul M. Religious beliefs and opinions on clinical xenotransplantation — a survey of university students from Kenya, Sweden and Texas [letter]. *Clinical Transplantation* 2002 August; 16(4): 314. Subject: 19.1

Baird, Keith A.; Rupert, Patricia A. Clinical management of confidentiality: a survey of psychologists in seven states. *Professional Psychology: Research and Practice* 1987 August; 18(4): 347-352. Subject: 8.4

Bakalar, Nicholas. Potential conflicts cited in process for new drugs. *New York Times* 2005 October 25; p. F7. Subject: 1.3.7

Baker, Hannah. MMR: medicine, mothers and rights. *Cambridge Law Journal* 2004 March; 63(1): 49-52. Subject: 8.3.2

Baker, Hunter. Storming the gates of a massive cultural investment: reconsidering Roe in light of its flawed foundation and undesirable consequences. *Regent University Law Review* 2002; 14: 35-65. Subject: 12.4.1

Baker, Lisa; Lavender, Tina; Tincello, Douglas. Factors that influence women's decisions about whether to partici-

pate in research: an exploratory study. *Birth* 2005 March; 32(1): 60-66. Subject: 18.5.3

Baker, Lynne Rudder. When does a person begin? *Social Philosophy and Policy* 2005 Summer; 22(2): 25-48. Subject: 4.4

Baker, Robert. A draft model aggregated code of ethics for bioethicists. *American Journal of Bioethics* 2005 September-October; 5(5): 33-41. Subject: 6

Baker, Richard. Placing principle before expediency: the Shipman inquiry [opinion]. *Lancet* 2005 March 12-18; 365(9463): 919-921. Subject: 8.1

Baker, Robert. Response to commentators on "A draft model aggregated code of ethics for bioethicists" [letter]. *American Journal of Bioethics [Online]* 2005 September-October; 5(5): W12-W13. Subject: 6

Bal, Arun. Can the medical profession and the pharmaceutical industry work ethically for better health care? *Indian Journal of Medical Ethics* 2004 January-March; 1(1): 17. Subject: 9.7

Bal, Arun. Diabetes: ethical, social and economic aspects. *Issues in Medical Ethics* 2000 July-September; 8(3): 77-78. Subject: 9.5.1

Bal, Arun. Informed consent — legal and ethical aspects. *Issues in Medical Ethics* 1999 April-June; 7(2): 56-57. Subject: 8.3.1

Bala, Mohan V.; Zarkin, Gary A. Pharmacogenomics and the evolution of healthcare: is it time for cost-effectiveness analysis at the individual level? [opinion]. *Pharmacoeconomics* 2004; 22(8): 495-498. Subject: 15.1

Balaban, Evan. The new racial economy: making a silk purse out of the sow's ear of racial distinctions. *GeneWatch* 2005 July-August; 18(4): 8-10. Subject: 15.11

Balachandran, Shreedevi. Patient autonomy, advocacy and the critical care nurse. *Issues in Medical Ethics* 2001 July-September; 9(3): 82-83. Subject: 9.1

Balasubramaniam, K. Improving access to essential drugs for people living with HIV/AIDS. *Issues in Medical Ethics* 2000 January-March; 8(1): 26-27. Subject: 9.5.6

Baldwin, Clive; Hughes, Julian; Hope, Tony; Jacoby, Robin; Ziebland, Sue. Ethics and dementia: mapping the literature by bibliometric analysis. *International Journal of Geriatric Psychiatry* 2003 January; 18(1): 41-54. Subject: 17.1

Baldwin, David; Broich, Karl; Fritze, Jürgen; Kasper, Siegfried; Westenberg, Herman; Möller, Hans-Jürgen. Placebo-controlled studies in depression: necessary, ethical and feasible. *European Archives of Psychiatry and Clinical Neuroscience* 2003 February; 253(1): 22-28. Subject: 18.3

Baldwin, T. Reproductive liberty and elitist contempt: reply to John Harris. *Journal of Medical Ethics* 2005 May; 31(5): 288-290. Subject: 14.3

See SUBJECT HEADING KEY FOR SECTION II on inside back cover

Bale, Harvey E., Jr. Industry, innovation and social values. *Science and Engineering Ethics* 2005 January; 11(1): 31-40. Subject: 9.5.6

Balevre, Park. Is it legal to be crazy: an ethical dilemma. *Archives of Psychiatric Nursing* 2001 October; 15(5): 241-244. Subject: 17.7

Ball, Carlos A. Autonomy, justice, and disability. *UCLA Law Review* 2000 February; 47(3): 599-651. Subject: 4.4

Ballantyne, Angela. HIV international clinical research: exploitation and risk. *Bioethics* 2005 October; 19(5-6): 476-491. Subject: 18.5.9

Ballentine, Jennifer M. Pacemaker and defibrillator deactivation in competent hospice patients: an ethical consideration. *American Journal of Hospice and Palliative Medicine* 2005 January-February; 22(1): 14-19. Subject: 20.5.1

Bamford, K.B.; Wood, S.; Shaw, R.J. Standards for gene therapy clinical trials based on pro-active risk assessment in a London NHS Teaching Hospital Trust. *QJM* 2005 February; 98(2): 75-86. Subject: 15.4

Bandewar, Sunita. Cultural barriers, 'competence' and informed consent in population-based surveys. *Issues in Medical Ethics* 2003 April-June; 11(2): 49-51. Subject: 12.5.2

Bandewar, Sunita. Exploring the ethics of induced abortion. *Indian Journal of Medical Ethics* 2005 January-March; 2(1): 18- 21. Subject: 12.3

Bandi, Venkata; Guntupalli, Kalpalatha K. Limitation and withdrawal practice patterns in India. *Critical Care Medicine* 2005 June; 33(6): 1436-1437. Subject: 20.5.1

Bane, Ellie Paukert. Mandatory insurance coverage for infertility treatment: difficult to conceive? *Medical Trial Technique Quarterly* 2001; 48(1): 215-242. Subject: 9.2

Banja, John. Moral absolutes and cultural influences on case management. *Case Manager* 2005 March-April; 16(2): 20-23. Subject: 4.1.1

Banja, John. When it's hard to please everybody: etiquette serving ethics when you disagree with a colleague. Opinion #1: negotiating uncertainty: "Let's talk . . .". *Pain Medicine* 2001 March; 2(1): 83-85. Subject: 4.4

Banja, John D. Disclosing medical error: how much to tell? *Journal of Healthcare Risk Management* 2003 Winter; 23(1): 11-14. Subject: 9.8

Banja, John D. Why, what, and how ought harmed parties be told? The art, mechanics, and ambiguities of error disclosure. *In:* Youngberg, Barbara J.; Hatlie, Martin J., eds. The Patient Safety Handbook. Sudbury, MA: Jones and Bartlett; 2004: 531-548. Subject: 9.8

Bankston, Carl L. Eugenics: Nazi Germany. *In:* Ness, Bryan D., ed. Encyclopedia of Genetics. Revised edition. Volume I. Pasadena, Calif.: Salem Press; 2004: 264-267. Subject: 15.5

Bankston, Carl L. Genetic engineering: social and ethical issues. *In:* Ness, Bryan D., ed. Encyclopedia of Genetics. Revised edition. Volume I. Pasadena, Calif.: Salem Press; 2004: 351-354. Subject: 15.1

Barai-Jaitly, Tejal. Use the data but take consent [case study]. *Indian Journal of Medical Ethics* 2005 October-December; 2(4): 131. Subject: 18.4

Bard, Jennifer. Standing together: how bioethics and public health can join forces to provide equitable health care. *American Journal of Bioethics [Online]* 2005 September-October; 5(5): W20-W22. Subject: 2.1

Bardia, A.; Paul, E.; Kapoor, S.K.; Anand, K. Declining sex ratio: role of society, technology and government regulation in Faridabad district, Haryana. *National Medical Journal of India* 2004 July-August; 17(4): 207-211. Subject: 14.3

Barfield, Raymond C.; Church, Christopher. Informed consent in pediatric clinical trials. *Current Opinion in Pediatrics* 2005 February; 17(1): 20-24. Subject: 18.5.2

Baria, Farah. May be baby. *India Today* 1999 May 11-17; 24(20); 3 p. [Online]. Available: http://www.hsph.harvard.edu/Organizations/healthnet/SAsia/suchana/0300/h017.html [6 October 2005]. Subject: 15.2

Barilan, Y. Michael. The story of the body and the story of the person: towards an ethics of representing human bodies and body-parts. *Medicine, Health Care and Philosophy: A European Journal* 2005; 8(2): 193-205. Subject: 4.4

Barker, Ellen; Saulino, Michael F. Life care planning: ethical and legal issues. *In:* American College of Legal Medicine Textbook Committee, Sanbar, S. Sandy; Firestone, Marvin H.; Buckner, Fillmore; Gibofsky, Allan; LeBlang, Theodore R.; Snyder, Jack W.; Wecht, Cyril H.; Zaremski, Miles J. Legal Medicine. 6th ed. St. Louis: Mosby; 2004: 300-307. Subject: 9.5.2

Barker, Jeffrey H. Human experimentation and the double facelessness of a merciless epoch. *New York University Review of Law and Social Change* 1999; 25(4): 603-623. Subject: 18.3

Barlow, David H.; Beard, H.K.; Williams, A.C. Assisted reproductive technologies in Europe encompass diverse and complex ethical viewpoints: issues to be considered in reporting research in human reproduction. *Annals of the New York Academy of Sciences* 2004 December; 1034: 110-116. Subject: 14.1

Barnes, Andrea. Update on abortion law. *In her:* Barnes, Andrea, ed. The Handbook of Women, Psychology, and the Law. San Francisco: Jossey-Bass; 2005: 147-177. Subject: 12.4.1

Barnes, David W. Imwinkelried's argument for normative ethical testimony. *Journal of Law, Medicine and Ethics* 2005 Summer; 33(2): 234- 241. Subject: 2.1

Barnes, Mark. Legal and ethical issues in revising human immunodeficiency virus postexposure protocols. *Ameri-*

can Journal of Medicine 1997 May 19; 102(5B): 111-112. Subject: 9.5.6

Barnett, G.C.; Charman, S.C.; Sizer, B.; Murray, P.A. Information given to patients about adverse effects of radiotherapy: a survey of patients' views. *Clinical Oncology* 2004 October; 16(7): 479-484. Subject: 8.3.1

Baron, Jeremy Hugh. "Thou shalt not kill": some legal and linguistic problems. *Mount Sinai Journal of Medicine* 2004 October; 71(5): 355-357. Subject: 20.5.1

Barr, Donald A. The practitioner's dilemma: can we use a patient's race to predict genetics, ancestry, and the expected outcomes of treatment? *Annals of Internal Medicine* 2005 December 6; 143(11): 809-815. Subject: 15.11

Barragán, Javier Lozano. Challenges for Christians in Europe in medicine and health care. *Dolentium Hominum* 2004; 19(2): 24-29. Subject: 2.1

Barragán, Javier Lozano. Fundamentos filosoficos y teologicos de la bioetica / Philosophical and theological foundations of bioethics. *Vida y Etica* 2003 December; 4(2): 5-43. Subject: 2.1

Barrett, Kirsten A.; Funk, Carolyn L.; Macrina, Francis L. Awareness of publication guidelines and the responsible conduct of research. *Accountability in Research* 2005 July-September; 12(3): 193-206. Subject: 1.3.9

Barretto, Zulica. Ethical issues in palliative care. *Issues in Medical Ethics* 2003 October-December; 11(4): 118-119. Subject: 20.4.1

Barry, Robert. The papal allocution on caring for persons in a "vegetative state". *Issues in Law and Medicine* 2004 Fall; 20(2): 155-164. Subject: 20.5.1

Barsdorf, Nicola Wendy; Wassenaar, Douglas Richard. Racial differences in public perceptions of voluntariness of medical research participants in South Africa. *Social Science and Medicine* 2005 March; 60(5): 1087-1098. Subject: 18.5.9

Bartfai, T. Pharmacogenomics in drug development: societal and technical aspects. *Pharmacogenomics Journal* 2004; 4(4): 226-232. Subject: 15.1

Bartlett, Peter. The test of compulsion in mental health law: capacity, therapeutic benefit and dangerousness as possible criteria. *Medical Law Review* 2003 Autumn; 11(3): 326-352. Subject: 4.3

Barton, John H.; Emanuel, Ezekiel J. The patents-based pharmaceutical development process: rationale, problems, and potential reforms. *JAMA: The Journal of the American Medical Association* 2005 October 26; 294(16): 2075-2082. Subject: 9.7

Baskett, Peter J.F.; Lim, Andy. The varying ethical attitudes towards resuscitation in Europe. *Resuscitation* 2004 September; 62(3): 267-273. Subject: 20.5.1

Bass, David. Kidneys for cash and egg safaris — can we allow 'transplant tourism' to flourish in South Africa?

[opinion]. *South African Medical Journal* 2005 January; 95(1): 42-44. Subject: 19.5

Basson, Marc D.; Gomez, Ruben; Fishman, Lisa; Panzini, Lisa. Informed consent for screening sigmoidoscopy in a Veterans Administration population. *Diseases of the Colon and Rectum* 2004 November; 47(11): 1939-1946. Subject: 8.3.1

Basta, Lofty L. Ethical issues in the management of geriatric cardiac patients. *American Journal of Geriatric Cardiology* 2004 July-August; 13(4): 219-220. Subject: 20.5.1

Basta, Lofty L. Ethical issues in the management of geriatric cardiac patients. How do you deal with a difficult patient? *American Journal of Geriatric Cardiology* 2005 January-February; 14(1): 39-40. Subject: 8.1

Basta, Lofty L. Ethical issues in the management of geriatric cardiac patients. When referred to hospice care the treating cardiologist believed that his patient would die in a few days. *American Journal of Geriatric Cardiology* 2005 March-April; 14(2): 95-97. Subject: 20.4.1

Bastable, Ruth; Sheather, Julian. Mandatory reporting to the police of all sexually active under-13s [editorial]. *BMJ: British Medical Journal* 2005 October 22; 331(7522): 918- 919. Subject: 8.4

Batchelor, Paul. Ensuring ethical standards in an international scientific journal: an evolutionary process [editorial]. *Community Dental Health* 2005 March; 22(1): 2-3. Subject: 1.3.9

Bates, Benjamin R.; Poirot, Kristan; Harris, Tina M.; Condit, Celeste M.; Achter, Paul J. Evaluating direct-to-consumer marketing of race-based pharmacogenomics: a focus group study of public understandings of applied genomic medication. *Journal of Health Communication* 2004 November-December; 9(6): 541-559. Subject: 9.7

Batmanabane, Gitanjali. ICMJE statement on compulsory clinical trial registration: should Indian journals follow suit? [editorial]. *Indian Journal of Medical Ethics* 2005 July-September; 2(3): 74-75. Subject: 1.3.9

Battin, Margaret P. Euthanasia and physician-assisted suicide. *In:* LaFollette, Hugh, ed. The Oxford Handbook of Practical Ethics. New York: Oxford University Press; 2003: 673-704. Subject: 20.5.1

Batzer, Frances R.; Hurwitz, Joshua M.; Caplan, Arthur. Postmortem parenthood and the need for a protocol with posthumous sperm procurement. *Fertility and Sterility* 2003 June; 79(6): 1263-1269. Subject: 14.6

Bauer, Arie; Rosca, Paula; Grinshpoon, Alex; Khawalled, Razak; Mester, Roberto. Regional psychiatric boards in Israel: expectations and realities. *International Journal of Law and Psychiatry* 2005 November-December; 28(6): 661-669. Subject: 17.7

Bauman, Adam N.; Pedersen, Craig A., Schommer, Jon C.; Griffith, Niesha L. Policies on documentation and disciplinary action in hospital pharmacies after a medication error. *American Journal of Health-System Pharmacies* 2001 June 15; 58(12): 1120-1125. Subject: 9.8

Baumann, Teresa K. Proxy consent and a national DNA databank: an unethical and discriminatory combination. *Iowa Law Review* 2001 January; 86(2): 667-701. Subject: 15.10

Baumans, V. Use of animals in experimental research: an ethical dilemma? *Gene Therapy* 2004 October; 11(Supplement 1): S64-S66. Subject: 22.2

Baumgardner, Jennifer. Giving women room to exhale: listening to women who have had abortions. *Conscience* 2005 Autumn; 26(3): 28-30. Subject: 12.5.1

Baumrucker, Steven J.; Davis, Mellar P.; Stolick, Matt; Morris, Gerald M.; Sheldon, Joanne. Sisters to the end: the rights of the mentally retarded to refuse treatment [case study]. *American Journal of Hospice and Palliative Care* 2005 January-February; 22(1): 61-65. Subject: 8.3.3

Baumrucker, Steven J.; Stolick, Matt; Morris, Gerald M.; Sheldon, Joanne. Case study: denying admission of a suicidal patient to a nursing home. *American Journal of Hospice and Palliative Medicine* 2004 September-October; 21(5): 395-397. Subject: 9.5.1

Baverstock, Keith. Science, politics and ethics in the low dose debate. *Medicine, Conflict and Survival* 2005 April-June; 21(2): 88-100. Subject: 9.1

Baxter, Mark. Time to legalise assisted dying? Use of Baxter products in figure for physician assisted suicide was inappropriate [letter]. *BMJ: British Medical Journal* 2005 October 8; 331(7520): 842. Subject: 20.5.1

Bayer, Timothy; Coverdale, John; Chiang, Elizabeth. A national survey of physicians' behaviors regarding sexual contact with patients. *Southern Medical Journal* 1996 October; 89(10): 977-982. Subject: 7.4

Bayertz, Kurt. Die Wahrheit über den moralischen Status menschlicher Embryonen. *In:* Maio, Giovanni; Just, Hanjörg, eds. Die Forschung an embryonalen Stammzellen in ethischer und rechtlicher Perspektive. Baden-Baden: Nomos Verlagsgesellschaft; 2003: 178-195. Subject: 4.4

Bayertz, Kurt. Dissens in Fragen von Leben und Tod: Konnen wir damit leben? *In:* Baumann, Eva; Brink, Alexander; May, Arnd T.; Schröder; Peter; Schutzeichel, Corinna Iris, eds. Weltanschauliche Offenheit in der Bioethik. Berlin: Duncker & Humblot; 2004: 23-36. Subject: 2.1

Bayley, Carol. Cancer and genetic medicine: an ethical view. *Health Progress* 2005 September-October; 86(5): 35-37. Subject: 15.3

Bayley, Carol. Medical mistakes and institutional culture. *In:* Sharpe, Virginia A., ed. Accountability: Patient Safety and Policy Reform. Washington, DC: Georgetown University Press; 2004: 99-117. Subject: 9.8

Baylis, Françoise. Embryological viability. *American Journal of Bioethics* 2005 November-December; 5(6): 17-18. Subject: 18.5.4

Baylis, Françoise; Beagan, Brenda; Johnston, Josephine; Ram, Natalie. Cryopreserved human embryos in Canada and their availability for research. *JOGC: Journal of Obstetrics and Gynaecology Canada* 2003 December; 25(12): 1026-1031. Subject: 14.6

Baylis, Françoise; Downie, Jocelyn. An ethical and criminal law framework for research involving children in Canada. *Health Law Journal* 1993; 1: 39-64. Subject: 18.5.2

Bayne, Tim; Levy, Neil. Amputees by choice: Body Integrity Identity Disorder and the ethics of amputation. *Journal of Applied Philosophy* 2005; 22(1): 75-86. Subject: 4.4

Bayoumi, Ahmed M.; Hwang, Stephen W. Methodological, practical, and ethical challenges to inner-city health research. *Journal of Urban Health: Bulletin of the New York Academy of Medicine* 2002 December; 79(4, Supplement 1): S35-S42. Subject: 18.5.1

Bazzelle, Roslyn Y. Mazurek v. Armstrong: should states be allowed to restrict the performance of abortions to licensed physicians only? *Thurgood Marshall Law Review* 1998 Fall; 24(1): 149-182. Subject: 12.4.3

Ba-Thike, Katherine. Abortion: a public health problem in Myanmar. *Reproductive Health Matters* 1997 May; (9): 7 p. [Online]. Available: http://www.hsph.harvard.edu/Organizations/healthnet/SAsia/suchana /9999/rh141.html [7 October 2005]. Subject: 12.1

Beach, Mary Catherine; Saha, Somnath. Free to be you and me? Balancing professionalism, culture, and self-expression [editorial]. *JGIM: Journal of General Internal Medicine* 2005 March; 20(3): 312-313. Subject: 7.1

Beadle, Libby. Selling the stem cell short? An assessment of the patentability of the results of human stem cell research in New Zealand. *Canterbury Law Review* 2004; 10: 1-35. Subject: 15.8

Beagan, Brenda; McDonald, Michael. Evidence-based practice of research ethics review? *Health Law Review* 2005; 13(2-3): 62-68. Subject: 18.2

Beard, Tika. Advocate participation in the context of genetic testing for hereditary cancers. *Journal of the National Cancer Institute Monographs* 1995; (17): 123-124. Subject: 15.3

Beardwood, John P.; Kerr, J. Alexis. Coming soon to a health sector near you: an advance look at the new Ontario Personal Health Information Protection Act (PHIPA): Part II. *Healthcare Quarterly* 2005; 8(1): 76-83. Subject: 8.4

Beattie, James M.; Connolly, Michael J.; Ellershaw, John E.; Berger, Jeffrey T. Deactivating implantable cardioverter defibrillators [letter and reply]. *Annals of Internal Medicine* 2005 November 1; 143(9): 690-691. Subject: 20.5.1

Beauchamp, Tom L. How not to rethink research ethics. *American Journal of Bioethics* 2005 January-February; 5(1): 31- 33. Subject: 18.2

Beauchamp, Tom L. The origins and evolution of the Belmont Report. *In:* Childress, James F.; Meslin, Eric M.; Shapiro, Harold T., eds. Belmont Revisited: Ethical Principles for Research with Human Subjects. Washington, DC: Georgetown University Press; 2005: 12-25. Subject: 18.2

Beauchamp, Tom L. Reflections on the appointment of Edmund Pellegrino to the President's Council on Bioethics. *American Journal of Bioethics [Online]* 2005 September- October; 5(5): W23-W24. Subject: 2.4

Beauchamp, Tom L. What can a model professional code for bioethics hope to achieve? [comment]. *American Journal of Bioethics* 2005 September-October; 5(5): 42-43. Subject: 6

Beauchamp, Tom L. Who deserves autonomy, and whose autonomy deserves respect? *In:* Taylor, James Stacey, ed. Personal Autonomy: New Essays on Personal Autonomy and Its Role in Contemporary Moral Philosophy. New York: Cambridge University Press; 2005: 310-329. Subject: 2.1

Beauchamp, Tom L.; Kukla, Rebecca. Conscientious autonomy: what patients do vs. what is done to them [letter and reply]. *Hastings Center Report* 2005 September-October; 35(5): 5-7. Subject: 8.3.1

Beck, Norbert. Proteomics in pathology, research and practice: ethical considerations. *Pathology, Research and Practice* 2004; 200(2): 179-180. Subject: 18.1

Beck, Philip. The confidentiality of psychiatric records and the patient's right to privacy. *Canadian Journal of Psychiatry-Revue Canadiene de Psychiatrie* 2001 April; 46(3, Insert): 6. Subject: 8.4

Becker, Lawrence C. Reciprocity, justice, and disability. *Ethics: An International Journal of Social, Political, and Legal Philosophy* 2005 October; 116(1): 9-39. Subject: 9.5.1

Becker-Schwarze, Kathrin. Legal restrictions of physician-assisted suicide. *European Journal of Health Law* 2005 March; 12(1): 11-24. Subject: 20.7

Becker-Schwarze, Kathrin. Terri Schiavo: the assessment of the persistent vegetative state in accordance with German law. *European Journal of Health Law* 2005 December; 12(4): 321-334. Subject: 20.5.1

Beckman, Ludvig. Democracy and genetic privacy: the value of bodily integrity. *Medicine, Health Care and Philosophy: A European Journal* 2005; 8(1): 97-103. Subject: 15.3

Beckmann, Jan P. Pharmakogenomik und Pharmakogenetik: Ethische Fragen. *In:* Jahrbuch für Wissenschaft und Ethik. Bd. 7. Berlin: Walter de Gruyter; 2002: 259-276. Subject: 15.1

Beckmann, Jan P. Pharmakogenomik und Pharmakogenetik: Ethische Fragen. *In:* Honnefelder, Ludger; Mieth, Dietmar; Propping, Peter; Siep, Ludwig; Wiesemann, Claudia, eds. Das genetische Wissen und die Zukunft des Menschen. New York: De Gruyter; 2003: 348-360. Subject: 15.1

Beckstead, Jason W. Reporting peer wrongdoing in the healthcare profession: the role of incompetence and substance abuse information. *International Journal of Nursing Studies* 2005 March; 42(3): 325-331. Subject: 7.3

Beckwith, F.J. Of souls, selves, and cerebrums: a reply to Himma. *Journal of Medical Ethics* 2005 January; 31(1): 56-60. Subject: 4.4

Beech, Derrick J.; Beech, Bettina M. For-profit clinical trials. *In:* Beech, Bettina; Goodman, Maurine, eds. Race & Research: Perspectives on Minority Participation in Health Studies. Washington, DC: American Public Health Association; 2004: 163-174. Subject: 18.5.1

Beecham, Linda. Donors and relatives must place no conditions on organ use [news]. *BMJ: British Medical Journal* 2000 February 26; 320(7234): 534. Subject: 19.5

Beecher, Henry K. Human experimentation: a world problem from the standpoint of a medical investigator. *World Medical Journal* 1960 March; 8: 79-80. Subject: 18.1

Beecher, Henry K. Some guiding principles for clinical investigation. *JAMA: The Journal of the American Medical Association* 1966 March 28; 195(13): 157-158. Subject: 18.2

Begley, Ann Marie. Practising virtue: a challenge to the view that a virtue centred approach to ethics lacks practical content. *Nursing Ethics* 2005 November; 12(6): 622-637. Subject: 4.1.3

Begley, Sharon. Fluoridation, cancer: did researchers ask the right questions? *Wall Street Journal* 2005 July 22; p. B1. Subject: 1.3.9

Beh, Hazel. Compensation for research injuries. *IRB: Ethics and Human Research* 2005 May-June; 27(3): 11-15. Subject: 18.1

Beh, Hazel Glenn. The role of institutional review boards in protecting human subjects: are we really ready to fix a broken system? *Law and Psychology Review* 2002 Spring; 26(1): 1-47. Subject: 18.2

Beh, Hazel; Diamond, Milton. Ethical concerns related to treating gender noncomformity in childhood and adolescence: lessons from the family court of Australia. *Health Matrix: Journal of Law-Medicine* 2005 Summer; 15(2): 239-283. Subject: 8.3.2

Bekemeier, Betty; Butterfield, Patricia. Unreconciled inconsistencies: a critical review of the concept of social justice in 3 national nursing documents. *ANS: Advances in Nursing Science* 2005 April-June; 28(2): 152-162. Subject: 4.1.3

Belden, Nancy; Wade, Alexis. Caveat lector: the true results of polling are in the small print. *Conscience* 2004 Spring; 25(1): 34-35. Subject: 12.5.2

Belew, Kara L. Stem cell division: abortion law and its influence on the adoption of radically different embryonic stem cell legislation in the United States, the United Kingdom, and Germany. *Texas International Law Journal* 2004 Spring; 39(3): 479-519. Subject: 18.5.4

Belgium. Comite Consultatif de Bioethique. Avis No. 22 du 19 mai 2003 relatif au choix du sexe pour des raisons non medicales / Advice no. 22 of 19 May 2003 concerning the choice of sex for non-medical reasons. *Journal International de Bioethique / International Journal of Bioethics* 2005 March-June; 16(1-2): 165-167. Subject: 14.3

Bell, M.D.D. Non-heartbeating organ donation: clinical process and fundamental issues. *British Journal of Anaesthesia* 2005 April; 94(4): 474-478. Subject: 20.5.1

Bell, Nora Kizer. Responsibilities and rights in the promotion of health: differing positions of the individual and the state. *Social Science and Medicine* 1996 September; 43(5): 775-782. Subject: 9.4

Bell, Sylvia. What does the "right to health" have to offer mental health patients? *International Journal of Law and Psychiatry* 2005 March- April; 28(2): 141-153. Subject: 9.2

Bellieni, Carlo. Pain definitions revised: newborns not only feel pain, they also suffer. *Ethics and Medicine* 2005 Spring; 21(1): 5-9. Subject: 9.5.7

Belling, Catherine. Imaginary fathers: a sentimental perspective on the question of identifying sperm donors. *Journal of Clinical Ethics* 2005 Winter; 16(4): 321-328. Subject: 14.2

Belling, Catherine. The purchase of fruitfulness: assisted conception and reproductive disability in a seventeenth-century comedy. *Journal of Medical Humanities* 2005 Fall; 26(2-3): 79-96. Subject: 14.2

Bellinger, Michael. The constitutional right to therapeutic cloning. *Journal of Medicine and Law* 2002 Fall; 7(1): 37-53. Subject: 14.5

Belluck, Pam. Custody and abuse cases swirl around a troubled girl on life support. *New York Times* 2005 December 6; p. A18. Subject: 20.5.2

Belluck, Pam. Even as doctors say enough, families fight to prolong life; medical advances raise hopes of loved ones. *New York Times* 2005 March 27; p. A1, A22. Subject: 20.5.1

Belluck, Pam. From stem cell opponents, an embryo crusade. *New York Times* 2005 June 2; p. A1, A22. Subject: 14.6

Belluck, Pam. It's not so easy to adopt an embryo. *New York Times* 2005 June 12; p. Wk5. Subject: 14.4

Belluck, Pam. Massachusetts legislators endorse study of stem cells. *New York Times* 2005 April 1; p. A12. Subject: 18.5.4

Belshaw, Chris. Death, brains, and persons. *In:* Fisher, Robert N.; Primozic, Daniel T.; Day, Peter A.; Thompson, Joel A., eds. Suffering, Death, and Identity. New York: Rodopi; 2002: 141-154. Subject: 4.4

Benagiano, Giuseppe; Gianaroli, Luca. The new Italian IVF legislation [editorial]. *Reproductive BioMedicine Online [electronic]* 2004 August; 9(2): 117-125 Available: http://www.rbmonline.com/index.html [3 June 2005]. Subject: 14.4

Benaroyo, Lazare. Suffering, time, narrative, and the self. *In:* Thomasma, David C.; Weisstub, David N.; Herve, Christian eds. Personhood and Health Care. Boston: Kluwer Academic Pub.; 2001: 373-381. Subject: 4.4

Benatar, David. The trouble with universal declarations. *Developing World Bioethics* 2005 September; 5(3): 220-224. Subject: 2.1

Benatar, S.R. A response to J S Taylor. *Journal of Medical Ethics* 2005 March; 31(3): 180-181. Subject: 19.5

Benatar, Solomon R. The humanities in medicine at UCT [editorial]. *South African Medical Journal* 1997 December; 87(12): 1662-1664. Subject: 7.2

Benatar, Solomon R. Towards progress in resolving dilemmas in international research ethics. *Journal of Law, Medicine and Ethics* 2004 Winter; 32(4): 574- 582. Subject: 18.2

Benatar, Solomon R.; Fox, Renée C. Meeting threats to global health: a call for American leadership. *Perspectives in Biology and Medicine* 2005 Summer; 48(3): 344- 361. Subject: 9.1

Bender, Denise G. Do Fourteenth Amendment considerations outweigh a potential state interest in mandating cochlear implantation for deaf children? *Journal of Deaf Studies and Deaf Education* 2004 Winter; 9(1): 104-111. Subject: 8.3.4

Bender, Leslie. Genes, parents, and assisted reproductive technologies: ARTs, mistakes, sex, race, and law. *Columbia Journal of Gender and Law* 2003; 12(1): 1-76. Subject: 14.4

Benedek, Thomas G. Gonorrhea and the beginnings of clinical research ethics. *Perspectives in Biology and Medicine* 2005 Winter; 48(1): 54-73. Subject: 18.2

Benn, Piers; Lupton, Martin. Sterilisation of young, competent, and childless adults. *BMJ: British Medical Journal* 2005 June 4; 330(7503): 1323-1325. Subject: 11.3

Benner, Patricia. Honoring the good behind rights and justice in healthcare when more than justice is needed. *American Journal of Critical Care* 2005 March; 14(2): 152-156. Subject: 4.1.3

Benner, Patricia. Relational ethics of comfort, touch, and solace — endangered arts? *American Journal of Critical Care* 2004 July; 13(4): 346-349. Subject: 4.1.3

Bennet, Tierney. Fundamental problems and solutions concerning genetic testing (2nd part). *Alpha Omega* 2002 December; 5(3): 473-497. Subject: 15.3

Bennett, Jo Anne. Nurses' attitudes about acquired immunodeficiency syndrome care: what research tells us. *Journal of Professional Nursing* 1995 November-December; 11(6): 339-350. Subject: 9.5.6

Bennett, John; Collins, John. The relationship between physicians and the biomedical industries: advice from the Royal College of Physicians. *Clinical Medicine* 2002 July-August; 2(4): 320-322. Subject: 7.1

Benninger, Michael S.; Jackler, Robert K.; Johns, Michael M.E.; Johnson, Jonas T.; Kennedy, David W.; Ruben, Robert J.; Sataloff, Robert T.; Smith, Richard J.H.; Weber, Peter C.; Weber, Randal S.; Young, Eric D. Consortium of otolaryngology — head and neck surgery journals to collaborate in maintenance of high ethical standards [editorial]. *Archives of Otolaryngology-Head and Neck Surgery* 2005 May; 131(5): 381-382. Subject: 1.3.7

Benninger, Michael S.; Jackler, Robert K.; Johnson, Jonas T.; Johns, Michael M.; Kennedy, David W.; Ruben, Robert J.; Sataloff, Robert T.; Smith, Richard J.H.; Weber, Peter C.; Weber, Randal S.; Young, Eric D. Consortium of otolaryngology — head and neck surgery journals to collaborate in maintenance of high ethical standards [editorial]. *Laryngoscope* 2005 May; 115(5): 761-762. Subject: 1.3.7

Benzenhöfer, Udo. Zur juristischen debatte um die "euthanasie" in der NS-zeit / The legal debate on "euthanasia" in National Socialist Germany. *Recht und Psychiatrie* 2000; 18(3): 112-121. Subject: 21.4

Beran, Roy G. Ethical considerations within clinical research with special focus upon clinical drug trials. *Medicine and Law: World Association for Medical Law* 2005 June; 24(2): 411-436. Subject: 18.2

Beran, Roy G. Legal and ethical obligations to conduct a clinical drug trial in Australia as an investigator initiated and sponsored study for an overseas pharmaceutical company. *Medicine and Law: World Association for Medical Law* 2004; 23(4): 913-924. Subject: 18.2

Bereano, Phil. Without a trace: how a lack of U.S. domestic LMO regulations is undermining international control. *GeneWatch* 2005 May-June; 18(3): 3-5, 16. Subject: 15.7

Bereano, Philip. Biotechnology's challenge to individual privacy. *In:* Krimsky, Sheldon; Shorett, Peter, eds. Rights and Liberties in the Biotech Age: Why We Need a Genetic Bill of Rights. Lanham: Rowman and Littlefield Publishers; 2005: 159-163. Subject: 15.1

Berenson, Alex. Cancer drugs offer hope, but a huge expense. *New York Times* 2005 July 12; p. A1, C3. Subject: 9.7

Berenson, Alex. Despite vow drug makers still withhold data. *New York Times* 2005 May 31; p. A1, C3. Subject: 9.7

Berenson, Alex. Evidence in Vioxx suits shows intervention by Merck officials. *New York Times* 2005 April 24; p. A1, A32. Subject: 5.3

Berenson, Alex. Medical journal criticizes Merck over Vioxx data. *New York Times* 2005 December 9; p. A1, C13. Subject: 1.3.7

Berez, Thomas M.; Weiss, Sheila Faith. The Nazi symbiosis: politics and human genetics at the Kaiser Wilhelm Institute. *Endeavour* 2004 December; 28(4): 172-177. Subject: 15.5

Berezuk, Gregory P.; McCarty, Garland E. Investigational drugs and vaccines fielded in support of Operation Desert Storm. *Military Medicine* 1992 August; 157(8): 404-406. Subject: 9.7

Berg, Abbey L.; Herb, Alice; Hurst, Marsha. Cochlear implants in children: ethics, informed consent, and parental decision making. *Journal of Clinical Ethics* 2005 Fall; 16(3): 239-250. Subject: 9.5.7

Berg, Jessica. Grave secrets: legal and ethical analysis of postmortem confidentiality. *Connecticut Law Review* 2001 Fall; 34(1): 81-122. Subject: 8.4

Berg, Jessica Wilen. Children and placebos. *In:* Kodish, Eric, ed. Ethics and Research with Children: A Case-Based Approach. New York: Oxford University Press; 2005: 294-309. Subject: 18.5.2

Berg, Kåre. The ethics of benefit sharing [opinion]. *Clinical Genetics* 2001 April; 59(4): 240-243. Subject: 15.1

Berg, Kåre; Pettersson, Ulf; Riis, Povl; Tranøy, Knut Erik. Genetics in democratic societies — the Nordic perspective. *Clinical Genetics* 1995 October; 48(4): 199-208. Subject: 15.3

Bergdolt, Klaus. History of medicine and concepts of health [editorial]. *Croatian Medical Journal* 1999 June; 40(2): 119-122. Subject: 4.2

Berger, Jeffrey T. The ethics of deactivating implanted cardioverter defibrillators. *Annals of Internal Medicine* 2005 April 19; 142(8): 631-634. Subject: 20.5.1

Berger, Jeffrey T. Ignorance is bliss? Ethical considerations in therapeutic nondisclosure. *Cancer Investigation* 2005; 23(1): 94-98. Subject: 8.2

Berger, Jeffrey T. Patients' interests in their family members' well-being: an overlooked, fundamental consideration within substituted judgments. *Journal of Clinical Ethics* 2005 Spring; 16(1): 3-10. Subject: 8.1

Berger, Jeffrey T.; Majerovitz, S. Deborah. Do elderly persons' concerns for family burden influence their preferences for future participation in dementia research? *Jour-*

See SUBJECT HEADING KEY FOR SECTION II on inside back cover

nal of Clinical Ethics 2005 Summer; 16(2): 108-115. Subject: 18.5.6

Berger, Jeffrey T.; Rosner, Fred; Bennett, Allen J. Current events and bioethical concerns in physician-assisted death. *Mount Sinai Journal of Medicine* 1998 September; 65(4): 257-264. Subject: 20.7

Berger, K. Protecting the unborn clone: can law and science evolve together? *Medicine and Law: World Association for Medical Law* 2005 September; 24(3): 561-574. Subject: 14.5

Berger, William L.; Griner, Paul. Health care costs [letters]. *Annals of Internal Medicine* 2005 December 6; 143(11): 844. Subject: 4.1.2

Bergeron, L. Rene; Gray, Betsey. Ethical dilemmas of reporting suspected elder abuse. *Social Work* 2003 January; 48(1): 96-105. Subject: 9.5.2

Berggren, Ingela; Barbosa da Silva, António; Severinsson, Elisabeth. Core ethical issues of clinical nursing supervision. *Nursing and Health Sciences* 2005 March; 7(1): 21-28. Subject: 4.1.3

Berghs, M.; Dierckx de Casterlé, B.; Gastmans, C. The complexity of nurses' attitudes toward euthanasia: a review of the literature. *Journal of Medical Ethics* 2005 August; 31(8): 441-446. Subject: 20.5.1

Bergren, Martha Dewey. Privacy questions from practicing school nurses. *Journal of School Nursing* 2004 October; 20(5): 296-301. Subject: 4.1.3

Berkowitz, Carol D. The need for a developmental approach to adolescent decision- making [comment]. *American Journal of Bioethics* 2005 September-October; 5(5): 77-78. Subject: 18.5.2

Berkowitz, Peter. The pathos of the Kass report [review of Human Cloning and Human Dignity: An Ethical Inquiry, a report issued by the President's Council on Bioethics]. *Policy Review* 2002 October-November; 115; 7 p. [Online]. Available: http://www.policyreview.org/OCT02/berkowitz_print.html [14 September 2005]. Subject: 14.5

Berkowitz, Richard L. Should refusal to undergo a Cesarean delivery be a criminal offense? *Obstetrics and Gynecology* 2004 December; 104(6): 1220-1221. Subject: 9.5.5

Berlin, Jesse A. Commentary: why industry should register and disclose results of clinical studies — perspective of a recovering academic. *BMJ: British Medical Journal* 2005 April 23; 330(7497): 959. Subject: 18.2

Berlinger, N.; Wu, A.W. Subtracting insult from injury: addressing cultural expectations in the disclosure of medical error. *Journal of Medical Ethics* 2005 February; 31(2): 106-108. Subject: 21.7

Berlinger, Nancy. The ethics of facilitating sausage-making. *Hastings Center Report* 2005 September-October; 35(5): inside front cover. Subject: 2.1

Berlinger, Nancy. "Missing the mark": medical error, forgiveness, and justice. *In:* Sharpe, Virginia A., ed. Accountability: Patient Safety and Policy Reform. Washington, DC: Georgetown University Press; 2004: 119-134. Subject: 9.8

Berlinger, Norman. Patient trust: trust remains fundamental to the ethical practice of medicine even in the age of the patient as consumer. *Minnesota Medicine* 2004 June; 87(6): 32-34. Subject: 8.1

Berman, Jennifer. Using the doctrine of informed consent to improve HIV vaccine access in the post-TRIPS era. *Wisconsin International Law Journal* 2004 Spring; 22(2): 273-321. Subject: 9.5.6

Berman, Saul J.; Bulka, Reuven; Landes, Daniel; Woolf, Jeffrey R. Rabbis condemn smoking. *Jewish Medical Ethics and Halacha* 2005 August; 5(1): 56-59. Subject: 9.5.9

Bernacki, Rachelle. Not at peace. *Hastings Center Report* 2005 July-August; 35(4): 9-10. Subject: 20.5.1

Bernal, Susan Kerr. Ethical offspring? *Journal of Andrology* 2004 September-October; 25(5): 667-670. Subject: 14.1

Bernal, Susan Kerr. New Jersey passes law supporting stem cell research. *Journal of Andrology* 2004 May-June; 25(3): 314-316. Subject: 18.5.4

Bernal, Susan Kerr. Twin autonomy. *Journal of Andrology* 2004 January-February; 25(1): 2-4. Subject: 8.3.3

Bernat, Erwin. Marketing of human organs? *Medicine and Law: World Association for Medical Law* 1995; 14(3-4): 181-190. Subject: 19.6

Berndt, Ernst R. To inform or persuade? Direct-to-consumer advertising of prescription drugs. *New England Journal of Medicine* 2005 January 27; 352(4): 325- 328. Subject: 8.1

Bernstein, Alan. New ethical requirements at the NIH: implications for CIHR and Canada. *CMAJ/JAMC: Canadian Medical Association Journal* 2005 August 16; 173(4): 353-354. Subject: 1.3.9

Bernstein, Mark. Assessing the bioethical integrity of a clinical trial in surgery. *Canadian Journal of Surgery* 2004 October; 47(5): 329-332. Subject: 18.1

Bernstein, Mark. Marginal cases and moral relevance. *Journal of Social Philosophy* 2002 Winter; 33(4): 523-539. Subject: 22.2

Bernstein, Mark. Neo-speciesism. *Journal of Social Philosophy* 2004 Fall; 35(3): 380-390. Subject: 4.4

Bernstein, Mark H. Animal experimentation. *In his:* Without a Tear: Our Tragic Relationship with Animals. Urbana: University of Illinois Press; 2004: 129-149. Subject: 22.2

Bernstein, Mark; Bampoe, Joseph; Daar, Abdallah S. Ethical issues in molecular medicine of relevance to surgeons. *Canadian Journal of Surgery* 2004 December; 47(6): 414-421. Subject: 15.1

Bernstein, Mark; Jürgens, Ralf. Disclosure dilemma: should doctors reveal their own medical histories? Pro: patients have a right to know. Con: no need to divulge. *Parkhurst Exchange* 2004 April; 12(4): 36-37. Subject: 7.1

Bernstein, Mark; Potvin, Dawn; Martin, Douglas K. A qualitative study of attitudes toward error in patients facing brain tumour surgery. *Canadian Journal of Neurological Sciences* 2004 May; 31(2): 208-212. Subject: 9.8

Bero, Lisa A. Managing financial conflicts of interest in research. *Journal of the American College of Dentists* 2005 Summer; 72(2): 4-9. Subject: 1.3.9

Bero, Lisa A. Tobacco industry manipulation of research. *Public Health Reports* 2005 March-April; 120(2): 200-208. Subject: 1.3.9

Bero, Lisa A.; Glantz, S.; Hong, M.-K. The limits of competing interest disclosures. *Tobacco Control* 2005 April; 14(2): 118-126. Subject: 1.3.9

Berry, P.J. Incidental diagnosis of genetic disease at autopsy — a point of view [editorial]. *Pediatric and Developmental Pathology* 1999 September-October; 2(5): 399-401. Subject: 15.3

Berry, Roberta M. Informed consent law, ethics, and practice: from infancy to reflective adolescence. *HEC (Healthcare Ethics Committee) Forum* 2005 March; 17(1): 64- 81. Subject: 8.3.1

Berry, Roberta M. Three stages in the lifecycle of bioethics: observations on "bioethics as co-PI". *American Journal of Bioethics* 2005 November-December; 5(6): 30-32. Subject: 2.1

Bertolami, Charles N. Further dialogue on ethics in dental education: a response to the Koerber et al. and Jenson articles. *Journal of Dental Education* 2005 February; 69(2): 229-231. Subject: 7.2

Berube, Michael. Disability, democracy, and the new genetics. *In:* Van Cleve, John Vickery, ed. Genetics, Disability, and Deafness. Washington, DC: Gallaudet University Press; 2004: 202- 220. Subject: 15.1

Beskow, Laura M. Ethical, legal, and social issues in the design and conduct of human genome epidemiology studies. *In:* Khoury, Muin J.; Little, Julian; Burke, Wylie, eds. Human Genome Epidemiology: A Scientific Foundation for Using Genetic Information to Improve Health and Prevent Disease. New York: Oxford University Press; 2004: 58-76. Subject: 15.1

Beskow, Laura M.; Botkin, Jeffrey R.; Daly, Mary; Juengst, Eric T.; Lehmann, Lisa Soleymani; Merz, Jon F.; Pentz, Rebecca; Press, Nancy A.; Ross, Lainie Friedman; Sugarman, Jeremy; Susswein, Lisa R.; Terry, Sharon F.; Austin, Melissa A.; Burke, Wylie. Ethical issues in identifying and recruiting participants for familial genetic research. *American Journal of Medical Genetics* 2004 November 1; 130A(4): 424-431. Subject: 18.1

Beskow, Laura M.; Gwinn, Marta; Rothstein, Mark A. Integrating genomics into public health policy and practice. *In:* Goodman, Richard A.; Rothstein, Mark A.; Hoffman, Richard E.; Lopez, Wilfredo; Matthews, Gene W., eds. Law in Public Health Practice. New York: Oxford University Press; 2003: 245-261. Subject: 15.3

Besselink, Marc G.H.; Goozen, Hein G.; Buskens, Erik; DeAngelis, Catherine D. Clinical trial registration and the ICMJE [letter and reply]. *JAMA: The Journal of the American Medical Association* 2005 January 12; 293(2): 157-158. Subject: 18.6

Best, John. The matter of disclosure — worth talking about? [editorial]. *Medical Journal of Australia* 1995 August 21; 163(4): 172. Subject: 8.2

Best, Steven; Kellner, Douglas. Biotechnology, democracy, and the politics of cloning. *In:* Braman, Sandra, ed. Biotechnology and Communication: The Meta-Technologies of Information. Mahwah, NJ: Lawrence Erlbaum Associates; 2004: 197-226. Subject: 14.5

Beste, Jennifer. Instilling hope and respecting patient autonomy: reconciling apparently conflicting duties. *Bioethics* 2005 June; 19(3): 215-231. Subject: 8.1

Betancourt, Joseph R. Unequal treatment: the Institute of Medicine report and its public health implications [editorial]. *Public Health Reports* 2003 July-August; 118(3): 287-292. Subject: 9.5.4

Beyleveld, Deryck. Individualrechte und soziale Gerechtigkeit. *In:* Honnefelder, Ludger; Mieth, Dietmar; Propping, Peter; Siep, Ludwig; Wiesemann, Claudia, eds. Das genetische Wissen und die Zukunft des Menschen. New York: De Gruyter; 2003: 375-387. Subject: 9.4

Beyleveld, Deryck; Townend, David M.R. When is personal data rendered anonymous? Interpreting Recital 26 of Directive 95/46/EC. *Medical Law International* 2004; 6(2): 73-86. Subject: 18.2

Bhagat, Rasheeda. Where the end comes before birth. Hindu Business Line 1999 July 20; 4 p. [Online]. Available: http://www.hsph.harvard.edu/Organizations/healthnet/SAsia/suchana /0500/h007.html [6 October 2005]. Subject: 14.3

Bhatt, Arun D. Clinical trial publications. *Issues in Medical Ethics* 2000 October-December; 8(4): 119-121. Subject: 18.2

Bhattacharya, Kaushik; Cathrine, A. Neela. Ethical considerations in laparoscopic surgery. *Indian Journal of Medical Ethics* 2004 January-March; 1(1): 22- 23. Subject: 5.2

Bhattacharya, S.K. The cloning bandwagon: a hysterical outburst [comment]. *Issues in Medical Ethics* 1998 July-September; 6(3): 92-96. Subject: 14.5

Bhattacharyya, Timothy; Yeon, Howard. "Doctor, was this surgery done wrong?" Ethical issues in providing second opinions. *Journal of Bone and Joint Surgery* 2005 January; 87(1): 223-225. Subject: 9.8

Bhave, Sudhir. The ECT debate: a response [letter]. *Issues in Medical Ethics* 2003 April-June; 11(2): 67. Subject: 17.5

Bhogal, Nirmala; Hudson, Michelle; Balls, Michael; Combes, Robert D. The use of non-human primates in biological and medical research: evidence submitted by FRAME to the Academy of Medical Sciences/Medical Research Council/Royal Society/Wellcome Trust Working Group. *ATLA: Alternatives to Laboratory Animals* 2005 October; 33(5): 519-527. Subject: 22.2

Bhutkar, Arjun. Synthetic biology: navigating the challenges ahead. *Journal of Biolaw and Business* 2005; 8(2): 19-29. Subject: 15.8

Bhutta, Zulfiqar A. Beyond informed consent. *Bulletin of the World Health Organization* 2004 October; 82(10): 771-777. Subject: 18.3

Bickenbach, Jerome. Disability and health systems assessment. *In:* Wasserman, David; Bickenbach, Jerome; Wachbroit, Robert, eds. Quality of Life and Human Difference: Genetic Testing, Health Care, and Disability. New York: Cambridge University Press; 2005: 237-266. Subject: 9.1

Bickenbach, Jerome E. The perils of human genetics. *Ethics and Intellectual Disability Newsletter* 1996 Winter; 1(2): 1-3. Subject: 9.5.3

Biegler, Paul; Stewart, Cameron; Savulescu, Julian; Skene, Loane. Determining the validity of advance directives. *Medical Journal of Australia* 2000 June 5; 172(11): 545-548. Subject: 20.5.4

Bielby, Philip. The conflation of competence and capacity in English medical law: a philosophical critique. *Medicine, Health Care and Philosophy: A European Journal* 2005; 8(3): 357-369. Subject: 8.3.1

Bierig, Jack R. Informed consent in the practice of pathology. *Archives of Pathology and Laboratory Medicine* 2001 November; 125(11): 1425-1429. Subject: 8.3.1

Biernacki, Claire. Should dementia patients be informed about their diagnosis? *Professional Nurse* 2003 December; 19(4): 198-202. Subject: 17.1

Biesecker, Leslie G. Surrendered autonomy for genetic screening [editorial]. *American Journal of Medical Genetics* 2004 August 30; 129A(2): 165. Subject: 15.3

Biggs, Hazel M. The Assisted Dying for the Terminally Ill Bill 2004: will English law soon allow patients the choice to die? *European Journal of Health Law* 2005 March; 12(1): 43-56. Subject: 20.7

Biiljali, Zudi. Macedonia. *Medical Ethics and Bioethics / Medicinska Etika & Bioetika* 2005; 11(Supplement): 21-22. Subject: 9.6

Biller-Andorno, Nikola. "Fürsorge" in der Medizinethik: Prinzip oder Perspektive? *In:* Jahrbuch für Wissenschaft und Ethik. Bd. 7. Berlin: Walter de Gruyter; 2002: 101-115. Subject: 4.1.1

Biller-Andorno, Nikola. It's cloning again! [editorial]. *Journal of Medical Ethics* 2005 February; 31(2): 63. Subject: 14.5

Billingsley, Barbara; Caulfield, Timothy. The regulation of science and the Charter of Rights: would a ban on non-reproductive human cloning unjustifiably violate freedom of expression? *Queen's Law Journal* 2004 Spring; 29(2): 647-679. Subject: 14.5

Bilsen, Johan; Bauwens, Marc; Bernheim, Jan; Stichele, Robert Vander; Deliens, Luc. Physician-assisted death: attitudes and practices of community pharmacists in East Flanders, Belgium. *Palliative Medicine* 2005 February; 19(2): 151-157. Subject: 20.7

Binetti, Paola. Biotechnology and the birth of a third culture. *Journal of Biological Regulators and Homeostatic Agents* 2004 July-December; 18(3-4): 255-260. Subject: 5.1

Binion, Gayle. Feminist theory confronts US Supreme Court rhetoric: the case of abortion rights. *International Journal of Law, Policy and Family* 1997; 11(1): 63-85. Subject: 12.3

Bioethics Advisory Committee of the Israel Academy of Sciences and Humanities. Population-based large-scale collections of DNA samples and databases of genetic information. Jerusalem: The Israel Academy of Sciences and Humanities, 2002 December; 29 p. [Online]. Available: http://www.academy.ac.il/bioethics/english/ PDF/Finalized_Dna_Bank _Full.pdf [10 January 2006]. Subject: 15.1

Birch, Kean. Beneficence, determinism and justice: an engagement with the argument for the genetic selection of intelligence. *Bioethics* 2005 February; 19(1): 12-28. Subject: 15.1

Bircher, Johannes. Towards a dynamic definition of health and disease. *Medicine, Health Care and Philosophy: A European Journal* 2005; 8(3): 335-341. Subject: 4.2

Bird, Stephanie J.; Spier, Raymond E. The complexity of competing and conflicting interests [editorial]. *Science and Engineering Ethics* 2005 October; 11(4): 515-517. Subject: 1.3.9

Birenbaum, Anna. Shielding the masses: how litigation changed the face of birth control. *Southern California Review of Law and Women's Studies* 2001 Spring; 10(2): 411-449. Subject: 11.1

Subject = NRCBL Primary Classification Number; See inside front cover

Birenbaum-Carmeli, Daphna. 'Cheaper than a newcomer': on the social production of IVF policy in Israel. *Sociology of Health and Illness* 2004 November; 26(7): 897-924. Subject: 14.4

Birn, Anne-Emanuelle; Molina, Natalia. In the name of public health [editorial]. *American Journal of Public Health* 2005 July; 95(7): 1095-1097. Subject: 15.5

Birnbacher, Dieter. Das Dilemma des bioethischen Pluralismus. *In:* Baumann, Eva; Brink, Alexander; May, Arnd T.; Schröder; Peter; Schutzeichel, Corinna Iris, eds. Weltanschauliche Offenheit in der Bioethik. Berlin: Duncker & Humblot; 2004: 51-64. Subject: 2.1

Biros, Michelle H. Research without consent: current status, 2003. *Annals of Emergency Medicine* 2003 October; 42(4): 550-564. Subject: 18.3

Biros, Michelle H. Waiver of consent for emergency research [reply]. *Annals of Emergency Medicine* 2004 September; 44(3): 278-280. Subject: 18.3

Bishop, Malcolm G.H.; Gelbier, S. Ethics: how the Apothecaries Act of 1815 shaped the dental profession. Part 2. The chemist-dentists and the education of dentists. *British Dental Journal* 2002 December 21; 193(12): 683-686. Subject: 7.2

Bishop, M.G.H.; Gelbier, S. Ethics: how the Apothecaries Act of 1815 shaped the dental profession. Part 1. The apothecaries and the emergence of the profession of dentistry. *British Dental Journal* 2002 December 7; 193(11): 627-631. Subject: 7.2

Bjorklund, Pamela. Can there be a 'cosmetic' psychopharmacology? Prozac unplugged: the search for an ontologically distinct cosmetic psychopharmacology. *Nursing Philosophy* 2005 April; 6(2): 131-143. Subject: 17.4

Black, Andrew. SUDEP — whether to tell and when? *Medicine and Law: World Association for Medical Law* 2005 March; 24(1): 41-49. Subject: 8.2

Black, Charles. Genetic information and insurance: some issues. *In:* Knoppers, Bartha Maria, ed. Populations and Genetics: Legal and Socio-Ethical Perspectives. Boston: Martinus Nijhoff; 2003: 579-590. Subject: 15.3

Black, Maureen M.; Ponirakis, Angelo. Computer-administered interviews with children about maltreatment: methodological, developmental, and ethical issues. *Journal of Interpersonal Violence* 2000 July; 15(7): 682-695. Subject: 18.5.2

Blackall, George F.; Green, Michael J.; Simms, Steve. Application of systems principles to resolving ethical dilemmas in medicine. *Journal of Clinical Ethics* 2005 Spring; 16(1): 20-27. Subject: 20.4.1

Blackburn, Elizabeth. Thoughts of a former council member. *Perspectives in Biology and Medicine* 2005 Spring; 48(2): 172-180. Subject: 2.4

Blackburn, Elizabeth; Rowley, Janet. Reason as our guide. *PLoS Biology* 2004 April; 2(4): 0420-0422 [electronic] Available: http://biology.plosjournals.org [2005 July 5]. Subject: 2.4

Blackburn, William Ross. Abortion and the voice of scripture. *Human Life Review* 2005 Spring; 31(2): 67-85. Subject: 12.3

Blackford, Russell. Human cloning and 'posthuman' society. *Monash Bioethics Review* 2005 January; 24(1): 10-26. Subject: 14.5

Blackmer, Jeff; Haddad, Henry. The Declaration of Helsinki: an update on paragraph 30 [opinion]. *CMAJ/JAMC: Canadian Medical Association Journal* 2005 October 25; 173(9): 1052-1053. Subject: 18.2

Blackmore, M.; Carroll, S. The do attempt resuscitation doctor [letter]. *Anaesthesia* 2000 September; 55(9): 911-912. Subject: 20.5.1

Blanchard, Janice; Lurie, Nicole. R-E-S-P-E-C-T: patient reports of disrespect in the health care setting and its impact on care. *Journal of Family Practice* 2004 September; 53(9): 721-730. Subject: 8.1

Blank, Arnold. Respecting the autonomy of irrational patients [letter]. *Archives of Internal Medicine* 2005 March 14; 165(5): 590. Subject: 8.3.4

Blankenship, James C. Ethics in interventional cardiology: combining coronary intervention with diagnostic catheterization [opinion]. *American Heart Hospital Journal* 2004 Winter; 2(1): 52-54. Subject: 8.3.1

Blass, Rachel B. On the question of the patient's right to tell and the ethical reality of psychoanalysis. *Journal of the American Psychoanalytic Association* 2003 Fall; 51(4): 1283-1304. Subject: 17.2

Blasszauer, Bela; Palfi, Ilona. Moral dilemmas of nursing in end-of-life care in Hungary: a personal perspective. *Nursing Ethics* 2005 January; 12(1): 92-105. Subject: 20.4.1

Bleich, J. David. Choosing between therapies: a painful dilemma. *Tradition* 2004 Fall; 38(3): 96-102. Subject: 9.5.1

Bleich, J. David. Medical malpractice and Jewish law. *Tradition* 2005 Spring; 39(1): 72-117. Subject: 8.5

Blendon, Robert J.; Benson, John M.; Herrmann, Melissa J. The American public and the Terri Schiavo case. *Archives of Internal Medicine* 2005 December 12-26; 165(22): 2580-2584. Subject: 20.5.1

Bliton, Mark J. Richard Zaner's "troubled" voice in Troubled Voices: poseur, posing, possibilizing? *Theoretical Medicine and Bioethics* 2005; 26(1): 25-53. Subject: 9.6

Blixen, Carol E.; Agich, G.J. Stroke patients' preferences and values about emergency research. *Journal of Medical Ethics* 2005 October; 31(10): 608-611. Subject: 18.3

Blizzard, Deborah. Patients' rights. *In:* Restivo, Sal, ed. Science, Technology, and Society: An Encyclopedia. New York: Oxford University Press; 2005: 374-379. Subject: 2.1

Bloch, Sidney; Salzberg, Michael. Informed consent in psychiatric research. *Current Opinion in Psychiatry* 2003 November; 16(6): 679-684. Subject: 18.3

Bloche, M. Gregg. American medicine and the politics of race. *Perspectives in Biology and Medicine* 2005 Winter; 48(1, Supplement): S54-S67. Subject: 9.5.4

Bloche, M. Gregg. Comments: a crisis in the ethical and moral behavior of psychiatrists [forum]. *Current Opinion in Psychiatry* 1998 January; 11(1); 3 p. [Online]. Available: http://gateway.ut.ovid.com/gw1/ovidweb.cgi [24 May 2005]. Subject: 20.6

Bloche, M. Gregg. Law, theory, and politics: the dilemma of Soviet psychiatry. *Yale Journal of International Law* 1986 Spring; 11(2): 297-361. Subject: 17.2

Bloche, M. Gregg. Managing conflict at the end of life [opinion]. *New England Journal of Medicine* 2005 June 9; 352(23): 2371-2373. Subject: 20.5.1

Bloche, M. Gregg. Trust and betrayal in the medical marketplace. *Stanford Law Review* 2002 December; 55(2): 919-954. Subject: 8.1

Bloche, M. Gregg; Jungman, Elizabeth R. The "r" word. *Journal of Contemporary Health Law and Policy* 2002 Fall; 18(3): 633-639. Subject: 9.4

Bloche, M. Gregg; Marks, Jonathan H. Doctors and interrogators at Guantanamo Bay [opinion]. *New England Journal of Medicine* 2005 July 7; 353(1): 6-8. Subject: 7.4

Bloche, M. Gregg; Marks, Jonathan H. Triage at Abu Ghraib [opinion]. *New York Times* 2005 February 4; p. A19. Subject: 21.4

Bloche, M. Gregg; Marks, Jonathan H. When doctors go to war [opinion]. *New England Journal of Medicine* 2005 January 6; 352(1): 3-6. Subject: 4.1.2

Bloche, M. Gregg; Quinn, Kevin P. Professionalism and personhood. *In:* Thomasma, David C.; Weisstub, David N.; Herve, Christian eds. Personhood and Health Care. Boston: Kluwer Academic Pub.; 2001: 347-354. Subject: 8.1

Block, Barry H. Ethical and legal issues in medical writing. *Journal of the American Podiatric Medical Association* 1998 January; 88(1): 45-46. Subject: 1.3.7

Block, Susan; Ganzini, Linda; Burt, Robert; Christakis, Nicholas; Krakauer, Eric. Why Oregon matters: death, assisted suicide and the principle of double effect [discussion]. *Medical Ethics Newsletter [Lahey Clinic]* 2003 Spring; 10(2): 4-7. Subject: 20.5.7

Blondeau, Danielle. Nursing art as a practical art: the necessary relationship between nursing art and nursing ethics.

Nursing Philosophy 2002 October; 3(3): 252-259. Subject: 4.1.3

Blondeau, Danielle; Roy, Louis; Dumont, Serge; Godin, Gaston; Martineau, Isabelle. Physicians' and pharmacists' attitudes toward the use of sedation at the end of life: influence of prognosis and type of suffering. *Journal of Palliative Care* 2005 Winter; 21(4): 238-245. Subject: 20.4.1

Blondeau, M.J.C.E. Legal protection or legal threat? Ethical conflicts in the process of medical decision making. *Medicine and Law: World Association for Medical Law* 1995; 14(5-6): 325-329. Subject: 8.3.2

Bloss, Thomas. Medicine following the HCFA `guidelines': what will be left of the patient-physician encounter? [editorial]. *Postgraduate Medicine* 1998 April; 103(4): 13-15. Subject: 8.1

Bluebond-Langner, Myra; DeCicco, Amy; Belasco, Jean. Involving children with life-shortening illnesses in decisions about participation in clinical research: a proposal for shuttle diplomacy and negotiation. *In:* Kodish, Eric, ed. Ethics and Research with Children: A Case-Based Approach. New York: Oxford University Press; 2005: 323-343. Subject: 18.5.2

Blum, J.; Carstens, P.; Talib, N. The impact of immigration on health systems: a legal analysis from a three-country perspective. *Medicine and Law: World Association for Medical Law* 2005 June; 24(2): 323-336. Subject: 9.2

Blumenthal, Ralph. Hodgkin's returns to girl whose parents fought state: standoff ends as court hears test results. *New York Times* 2005 June 11; p. A8. Subject: 8.3.4

Blyth, Eric. Patient experiences of an "egg sharing" programme. *Human Fertility* 2004 September; 7(3): 157-162. Subject: 14.4

Blyth, Eric; Crawshaw, Marilyn; Daniels, Ken. Policy formation in gamete donation and egg sharing in the UK — a critical appraisal. *Social Science and Medicine* 2004 December; 59(12): 2617-2626. Subject: 14.4

Blyth, Eric; Farrand, Abigail. Anonymity in donor-assisted conception and the UN Convention on the Rights of the Child. *International Journal of Children's Rights* 2004 April; 12(2): 89-104. Subject: 14.4

Blyth, Eric; Potter, Claire. Paying for it? Surrogacy, market forces and assisted conception. *In:* Cook, Rachel; Sclater, Shelley Day; Kaganas, Felicity, eds. Surrogate Motherhood: International Perspectives. Portland, OR: Hart; 2003: 227-242. Subject: 14.2

Boas, Franz. "Eugenics" in The Scientific Monthly 3(July-December 1916): 471-78. *In:* Ryan, Frank X., ed. Darwin's Impact: Social Evolution in America, 1880-1920. Volume 2. Race, Gender, and Supremacy. Bristol: Thoemmes; 2001: 163-170. Subject: 15.5

Bochatey, Alberto G. La importancia de la sociedad civil ante el proceso de desarrollo de la investigacion cientifica /

The importance of civil society to the process of scientific research. *Vida y Etica* 2003 December; 4(2): 97-108. Subject: 5.3

Bock, Gisela. Nazi sterilization and reproductive policies. *In:* Bachrach, Susan, project director; Kuntz, Dieter, ed. Deadly Medicine: Creating the Master Race. Washington, DC: United States Holocaust Museum; 2004: 61-87. Subject: 11.3

Boddington, P.; Clarke, Angus. It's only teeth — limits to genetic testing? A response to Aldred, Crawford, Savarirayan, and Savulescu [letter]. *Clinical Genetics* 2004 December; 66(6): 562-564. Subject: 15.2

Bodenheimer, Thomas. The political divide in health care: a liberal perspective. *Health Affairs* 2005 November-December; 24(6): 1426-1435. Subject: 9.2

Boer, Theo A. After the slippery slope: Dutch experiences on regulating active euthanasia. *Journal of the Society of Christian Ethics* 2003 Fall-Winter; 23(2): 225-242. Subject: 20.5.1

Boey, Kam Weng. A cross-validation study of nurses' attitudes and commitment to organ donation in Hong Kong. *International Journal of Nursing Studies* 2002 January; 39(1): 95-104. Subject: 19.5

Bogardus, Sidney T., Jr.; Bradley, Elizabeth H.; Williams, Christianna S.; Maciejewski, Paul K.; van Doorn, Carol; Inouye, Sharon K. Goals for the care of frail older adults: do caregivers and clinicians agree? *American Journal of Medicine* 2001 February 1; 110: 97-102. Subject: 9.5.2

Boggi, U.; Vistoli, F.; Del Chiaro, M.; Croce, C.; Signori, S.; Marchetti, P.; Del Prato, S.; Rizzo, G.; Mosca, F. Kidney and pancreas transplants in Jehovah's Witnesses: ethical and practical implications. *Transplantation Proceedings* 2004 April; 36(3): 601-602. Subject: 19.1

Boggio, Andrea. Italy enacts new law on medically assisted reproduction. *Human Reproduction* 2005 May; 20(5): 1153-1157. Subject: 14.4

Bogod, David. The Nazi hypothermia experiments: forbidden data? [editorial]. *Anaesthesia* 2004 December; 59(12): 1155-1156. Subject: 18.5.5

Bohannon, John. Eugenics stir emotions in Germany [news]. *Christian Science Monitor* 2004 July 22; p. 11, 13. Subject: 15.2

Boire, Richard G. Searching the brain: the Fourth Amendment implications of brain-based deception detection devices. *American Journal of Bioethics* 2005 March-April; 5(2): 62-63. Subject: 17.1

Boissier, Marie-Christophe. Pondering the precautionary principle [editorial]. *Joint, Bone, Spine* 2003 September; 70(5): 318-320. Subject: 4.1.1

Bolletino, Ruth Cohn. The need for a new ethical model in medicine: a challenge for conventional, alternative, and complementary practitioners. *Advances in Mind-Body Medicine* 1998 Winter; 14(1): 11 p. [Online]. Available: http://weblinks3.epnet.com/DeliveryPrintSave.asp?tb=1 &_ua=bo+B_+s hn+1_db+aphjnh+ [23 September 2005]. Subject: 2.1

Bollinger, R. Randal; Cho, Won-Hyun. Organ allocation for transplantation in the USA and Korea: the changing roles of equity and utility. *Yonsei Medical Journal* 2004 December 31; 45(6): 1035-1042. Subject: 19.6

Bolsin, Stephen; Faunce, T.; Oakley, J. Practical virtue ethics: healthcare whistleblowing and portable digital technology. *Journal of Medical Ethics* 2005 October; 31(10): 612-618. Subject: 7.3

Bolton, Roger G. The ethics of the drug discovery and development process. *In:* Salek, Sam; Edgar, Andrew, eds. Pharmaceutical Ethics. New York: Wiley; 2002: 45-60. Subject: 9.7

Bonah, Christian; Menut, Philippe. BCG vaccination around 1930: dangerous experiment or established prevention? Debates in France and Germany. *In:* Roelcke, Volker; Maio, Giovanni, eds. Twentieth Century Ethics of Human Subjects Research: Historical Perspectives on Values, Practices, and Regulations. Stuttgart: Franz Steiner Verlag; 2004: 111-127. Subject: 18.1

Bondy, Melissa; Mastromarino, Carrie. Ethical issues of genetic testing and their implications in epidemiologic studies. *Annals of Epidemology* 1997 July; 7(5): 363-366. Subject: 15.3

Bonkovsky, F.E. Resistance and biotechnology debates. *In:* Stone, Richard H.; Stivers, Robert L. Resistance and Theological Ethics. Lanham, MD: Rowan and Littlefield Publishers; 2004: 97-116. Subject: 5.1

Bonner, Raymond. Deaths and a doctor's past transfix Australians. *New York Times* 2005 June 19; p. A1, A14. Subject: 7.4

Bonnie, Richard J. Comments: a crisis in the ethical and moral behavior of psychiatrists [forum]. *Current Opinion in Psychiatry* 1998 January; 11(1): 3 p. [Online]. Available: http://gateway.ut.ovid.com/gw1/ovidweb.cgi [24 May 2005]. Subject: 20.6

Bonnin, David C. The need for increased oversight of genetic testing: a detailed look at the genetic testing process. *Houston Journal of Health Law and Policy* 2003 Fall; 4(1): 149- 180. Subject: 15.2

Bonsack, Charles; Borgeat, François. Perceived coercion and need for hospitalization related to psychiatric admission. *International Journal of Law and Psychiatry* 2005 July- August; 28(4): 342-347. Subject: 17.7

Bonzo, Matthew. The category of "personhood" and access to health care. *In:* Fisher, Robert N.; Primozic, Daniel T.; Day, Peter A.; Thompson, Joel A., eds. Suffering, Death, and Identity. New York: Rodopi; 2002: 119-126. Subject: 4.4

Booth, Joan M.; Garrett, Jinnie M. Instructors' practices in and attitudes toward teaching ethics in the genetics classroom. *Genetics* 2004 November; 168(3): 1111-1117. Subject: 2.3

Bootman, J. Lyle; Grizzle, Amy J. The economics of drug-related morbidity and mortality: ethical considerations. *In:* Salek, Sam; Edgar, Andrew, eds. Pharmaceutical Ethics. New York: Wiley; 2002: 111-122. Subject: 9.7

Bore, Miles; Munro, Don; Kerridge, Ian; Powis, David. Selection of medical students according to their moral orientation. *Medical Education* 2005 March; 39(3): 266-275. Subject: 7.2

Borman, Karen R. Professionalism in the match process: the rules and ethics of recruitment. *Surgical Clinics of North America* 2004 December; 84(6): 1511-1523, ix. Subject: 7.2

Bormann, Franz-Josef. Der Status des Embryos aus der Sicht der katholischen Moraltheologie. *In:* Maio, Giovanni; Just, Hanjörg, eds. Die Forschung an embryonalen Stammzellen in ethischer und rechtlicher Perspektive. Baden-Baden: Nomos Verlagsgesellschaft; 2003: 214-228. Subject: 4.4

Bornstein, Brian H. Seize this urine test: the implications of Ferguson v. City of Charleston for drug testing during pregnancy. *Journal of Medicine and Law* 2001 Fall; 6(1): 65-79. Subject: 9.5.5

Bornstein, Stephanie. The undue burden: parental notification requirements for publicly funded contraception. *Berkeley Women's Law Journal* 2000; 15: 40-75. Subject: 11.2

Borovecki, Ana; ten Have, Henk A.M.J.; Oreškovic, Stjepan. Ethics and the structures of health care in the European countries in transition: hospital ethics committees in Croatia. *BMJ: British Medical Journal* 2005 July 23; 331(7510): 227-229. Subject: 9.6

Borrego, Anne Marie. Politics, culture, and the lab: public attitudes toward animals and human embryonic stem cells have fostered different research agendas in Britain and the United States. *Chronicle of Higher Education* 2005 March 11; 51(27): A43-A45. Subject: 22.1

Borry, Pascal; Schotsmans, Paul; Dierickx, Kris. Developing countries and bioethical research [letter]. *New England Journal of Medicine* 2005 August 25; 353(8): 852- 853. Subject: 18.5.9

Borry, Pascal; Schotsmans, Paul; Dierickx, Kris. The birth of the empirical turn in bioethics. *Bioethics* 2005 February; 19(1): 49-71. Subject: 2.1

Bortolotti, Lisa; Harris, John. Stem cell research, personhood and sentience. *Reproductive BioMedicine Online [electronic]* 2005 March; 10(Supplement 1): 68-75. Available: http://www.rbmonline.com/Article/1587 [12 September 2005]. Subject: 18.5.4

Bos, Michael A. Ethical and legal issues in non-heart-beating organ donation. *Transplantation* 2005 May 15; 79(9): 1143-1147. Subject: 19.5

Bosanac, Sanja Babic. Involuntary hospitalization and the rights of mental patients in Croatia. *Medicine and Law: World Association for Medical Law* 1995; 14(5-6): 457-461. Subject: 17.7

Bosch, Xavier. Changing ethics rules land Spanish stem cell scientist in hot water [news]. *Nature Medicine* 2005 December; 11(12): 1262. Subject: 18.5.4

Bosch, Xavier. Embryo research stirs up Spanish spat [news]. *Nature Medicine* 2004 April; 10(4): 320. Subject: 18.5.4

Bosek, Marcia Sue DeWolf. Commentary on genetic testing of children: maintaining an open future. *Pediatric Nursing* 1999 January-February; 25(1): 66-68. Subject: 15.3

Bosek, Marcia Sue DeWolf. The ethics of pain management. *Medsurg Nursing* 1993 June; 2(3): 218-220. Subject: 4.4

Bosek, Marcia Sue DeWolf. The use of restraints: ethical considerations. *Medsurg Nursing* 1993 April; 2(2): 154-156. Subject: 17.3

Bosek, Marcia Sue DeWolf. What to expect from an ethics consultation. *Medsurg Nursing* 1993 October; 2(5): 408-410. Subject: 9.6

Bosek, Marcia Sue DeWolf; Cochran, Lynn L. Ethics in practice: moral distress at 3 am. *JONA's Healthcare Law, Ethics, and Regulation* 2005 January- March; 7(1): 4-9. Subject: 4.4

Bosek, Marcia Sue DeWolf; Fitzpatrick, Joyce. A nursing perspective on advance directives. *Medsurg Nursing* 1992 September; 1(1): 33-38. Subject: 20.5.4

Bosshard, Georg; Nilstun, Tore; Bilsen, Johan; Norup, Michael; Miccinesi, Guido; van Delden, Johannes J.M.; Faisst, Karin; van der Heide, Agnes. Forgoing treatment at the end of life in 6 European countries. *Archives of Internal Medicine* 2005 February 28; 165(4): 401- 407. Subject: 20.5.1

Bostrom, Barry A. In the matter of Christine B. Biersack in the Ohio Court of Appeals. *Issues in Law and Medicine* 2005 Spring; 20(3): 267-270. Subject: 20.5.1

Bostrom, Barry A. In the Supreme Court of Kentucky Woods v. Commonwealth of Kentucky. *Issues in Law and Medicine* 2004 Fall; 20(2): 185-192. Subject: 20.5.1

Bostrom, Barry A. Pettis v. Smith and Braddock in the Louisiana Court of Appeal. *Issues in Law and Medicine* 2005 Spring; 20(3): 271-273. Subject: 20.5.4

Bostrom, Barry A. Willis v. Wu in the Supreme Court of South Carolina. *Issues in Law and Medicine* 2005 Spring; 20(3): 275-278. Subject: 15.2

Bostrom, N. The fable of the dragon tyrant. *Journal of Medical Ethics* 2005 May; 31(5): 273-277. Subject: 20.5.1

Bostrom, Nick. In defense of posthuman dignity. *Bioethics* 2005 June; 19(3): 202-214. Subject: 4.5

Botkin, Jeffrey R. Addressing the "petty tyranny" of IRBs. *American Journal of Medical Genetics* 2005 April 30; 134A(3): 240-241. Subject: 18.2

Bottis, Maria Canellopoulou Vrachliotis. Return to basics: the cases of informed consent and lost chances of living [editorial]. *European Journal of Health Law* 2002 December; 9(4): 287-291. Subject: 8.5

Bouchard, Louise; Renaud, Marc. Female and male physicians' attitudes toward prenatal diagnosis: a Pan-Canadian survey. *Social Science and Medicine* 1997 February; 44(3): 381-392. Subject: 15.2

Boulware, L. Ebony; Cooper, Lisa A.; Ratner, Lloyd E.; LaVeist, Thomas A.; Powe, Neil R. Race and trust in the health care system. *Public Health Reports* 2003 July-August; 118(3): 358-365. Subject: 9.5.4

Bourne, Richard W. Abortion in 1938 and today: plus ca change, plus c'est la meme chose. *Southern California Review of Law and Women's Studies* 2003 Spring; 12(2): 225-275. Subject: 12.4.1

Bouvier, Paul. Good epidemiological practice: ethical review is essential [opinion]. *Sozial- und Praventivmedizin* 2005; 50(1): 34-35. Subject: 18.2

Bowden, Peta. An 'ethic of care' in clinical settings: encompassing 'feminine' and 'feminist' perspectives. *Nursing Philosophy* 2000 July; 1(1): 36-49. Subject: 4.1.1

Bowden, Peter. Philosophy's dilemma: the institutionalising of ethics. University of Western Sydney, Department of Philosophy: 11 p. [Online]. Available: http://www.uws.edu.au/download.php?file_id=8683&filename=philosophys_dilemma.pdf&mimetype=application/pdf [12 September 2005]. Subject: 1.3.1

Bowman, James. Bioethics at the movies. *New Atlantis* 2005 Spring; 8: 93-100. Subject: 5.3

Bowman, Kerry. Bioethics and cultural pluralism. *Humane Health Care International* 1997 Summer; 13(2): 31-34. Subject: 2.1

Bowman, Kerry. What are the limits of bioethics in a culturally pluralistic society? *Journal of Law, Medicine and Ethics* 2004 Winter; 32(4): 664- 669. Subject: 21.7

Bowser, René. Race as a proxy for drug response: the dangers and challenges of ethnic drugs. *DePaul Law Review* 2004 Spring; 53(3): 1111-1126. Subject: 9.5.4

Bowser, René. Racial bias in medical treatment. *Dickinson Law Review* 2001 Spring; 105(3): 365-383. Subject: 9.5.4

Boyd, Andrew J. Medical marijuana and personal autonomy. *John Marshall Law Review* 2004 Summer; 37(4): 1253-1288. Subject: 9.5.1

Boyd, Ann Lewis; Morioka, Masahiro. Anagogy of autonomy [article and commentary]. *Eubios Journal of Asian and International Bioethics* 2000 July; 10(4): 113-119. Subject: 8.3.1

Boyd, K.M. Medical ethics: principles, persons, and perspectives: from controversy to conversation. *Journal of Medical Ethics* 2005 August; 31(8): 481-486. Subject: 2.1

Boyd, S. Gregory. Comment: considering a market in human organs. *North Carolina Journal of Law and Technology* 2003 Spring; 4(2): 417-473. Subject: 19.5

Boylan, Michael; Grant, Richard E. Diversity and professional excellence [editorial]. *Journal of the National Medical Association* 2004 October; 96(10): 1354-1362. Subject: 7.1

Boyle, Brian. The Oregon Death with Dignity Act: a successful model or a legal anomaly vulnerable to attack? *Houston Law Review* 2004 Spring; 40(5): 1387-1421. Subject: 20.7

Boyte, W. Richard; Blackston, Joseph W.; Douglas, Sharon; Crook, Errol D. Case studies in ethics from the G.V. "Sonny" Montgomery VA Medical Center and the University of Mississippi Medical Center: caring for adolescent family members of physician colleagues. *American Journal of the Medical Sciences* 2002 January; 323(1): 49-53. Subject: 9.5.7

Bozik, Michael. He who pays the piper calls the tune: the role of the industry sponsor in acute stroke trials. *European Neurology* 2003; 49(2): 128-130. Subject: 18.2

Bozza, Steven. The morality of ovarian transplants: good and bad uses of a new technology. *Ethics and Medics* 2005 September; 30(9): 1-2. Subject: 14.1

Bozzette, Samuel A. Routine screening for HIV infection — timely and cost- effective [editorial]. *New England Journal of Medicine* 2005 February 10; 352(6): 620- 621. Subject: 9.5.6

Bracken, W. Jerome. Is in vitro fertilization in accord with a symbolic concept of natural law? *In:* Koterski, Joseph W., ed. Life and Learning IX: Proceedings of the Ninth University Faculty for Life Conference. Washington, DC: University Faculty for Life; 2000: 115-142. Subject: 14.4

Braddock, Clarence H., III; Snyder, Lois. The doctor will see you shortly: the ethical significance of time for the patient-physician relationship. *JGIM: Journal of General Internal Medicine* 2005 November; 20(11): 1057-1062. Subject: 8.1

Bradford, Barry. Arguing about the use of stem cells [letter]. *Science* 2005 July 1; 309(5731): 51. Subject: 18.5.4

Brahams, Diana. Body parts as property [editorial]. *Medico-Legal Journal* 1998; 66(Part 2): 45-47. Subject: 4.4

Brainard, Jeffrey. House challenges Bush's limits on embryonic-stem-cell research. *Chronicle of Higher Education* 2005 June 3; 51(39): A17. Subject: 18.5.4

Brainard, Jeffrey. Most researchers favor NIH policy that requires less information, survey finds. *Chronicle of Higher Education* 2005 August 12; 51(49): A22. Subject: 1.3.9

Brainard, Jeffrey. National academies report recommends tighter rules for stem- cell research. *Chronicle of Higher Education* 2005 May 6; 51(35): A25. Subject: 18.5.4

Brainard, Jeffrey. NIH consultant finds little evidence of bias against clinical researchers. *Chronicle of Higher Education* 2005 March 18; 51(28): A23. Subject: 1.3.9

Brainard, Jeffrey. NIH sets up national stem-cell bank in Wisconsin [news]. *Chronicle of Higher Education* 2005 October 14; 52(8): 24. Subject: 18.5.4

Brainard, Jeffrey. Report knocks agriculture department's protection of research animals. *Chronicle of Higher Education* 2005 November 11; 52(12): 27. Subject: 22.2

Bramstedt, Katrina A. Age-based health care allocation as a wedge separating the person from the patient and commodifying medicine. *Reviews in Clinical Gerontology* 2001; 11: 185-188. Subject: 9.5.2

Bramstedt, Katrina A. Aortic valve replacement in the elderly: frequently indicated yet frequently denied. *Gerontology* 2003; 49: 46-49. Subject: 9.5.2

Bramstedt, Katrina A. Ethical issues associated with the determination of patient selection criteria for total artificial heart technology. *Cardiovascular Engineering* 2001; 6(1): 58-61. Subject: 19.6

Bramstedt, Katrina A. Failure mode and effects analysis as an informed consent tool for investigational cardiothoracic devices. *ASAIO Journal* 2002; 48: 293-295. Subject: 18.3

Bramstedt, Katrina A. Informed consent documentation for total artificial heart technology. *Journal of Artificial Organs* 2001; 4: 273-277. Subject: 19.1

Bramstedt, Katrina A. Informed consent documentation for total artificial heart technology. *Update [Loma Linda University Center for Christian Bioethics]* 2002 May; 17(4): 5-8. Subject: 18.3

Bramstedt, Katrina A. Left ventricular assist devices and the slippery slope of ageism. *International Journal of Cardiology* 2001; 81: 201-203. Subject: 9.5.2

Bramstedt, Katrina A. Questioning the decision-making capacity of surrogates. *Internal Medicine Journal* 2003 June; 33(5-6): 257-259. Subject: 8.3.3

Bramstedt, Katrina A. Scientific breakthroughs: cause or cure of the aging `problem'. *Gerontology* 2001; 47: 52-54. Subject: 9.5.2

Bramstedt, Katrina A.; Kassimatis, Katy. A study of warning letters issued to institutional review boards by the United States Food and Drug Administration. *Clinical and Investigative Medicine* 2004 December; 27(6): 316-323. Subject: 18.2

Bramstedt, Katrina A.; Macauley, Robert. A case of deception? [case study]. *Hastings Center Report* 2005 November-December; 35(6): 13-14. Subject: 8.2

Bramstedt, Katrina A.; Molnar, Marcia; Carlson, Kirste; Bilyeu, Susan M. When families complicate patient care: a case study with guidelines for approaching ethical dilemmas [case study]. *Medsurg Nursing* 2005 April; 14(2): 122-125. Subject: 8.1

Bramstedt, Katrina A.; Morris, Harold H.; Tanner, Adriana. Now we lay them down to sleep: ethical issues with the use of pharmacologic coma for adult status epilepticus. *Epilepsy and Behavior* 2004 October; 5(5): 752-755. Subject: 9.5.1

Bramstedt, Katrina A.; Schneider, Paul L. Saying "good-bye": ethical issues in the stewardship of bed spaces. *Journal of Clinical Ethics* 2005 Summer; 16(2): 170-175. Subject: 9.1

Bramstedt, Katrina A.; Stowe, Judy; Kotz, Margaret. Shopping for a transplant: when noncompliant patients seek wait listing at multiple hospitals. *Progress in Transplantation* 2004 September; 14(3): 217-221. Subject: 19.5

Brand, Gordon S.; Munoz, Gisela M.; Nichols, Michael G.; Okata, Maritza U.; Pitt, Jonathan B.; Seager, Susan. The two faces of gag provisions: patients and physicians in a bind. *Yale Law and Policy Review* 1998; 17: 249-280. Subject: 9.4

Brand, Richard A.; Buckwalter, Joseph A.; Talman, Charlotte L.; Happe, Daniel G. Industrial support of orthopaedic research in the academic setting. *Clinical Orthopaedics and Related Research* 2003 July; (412): 45-53. Subject: 5.3

Brand, Richard A.; Heckman, James D.; Scott, James. Changing ethical standards in scientific publication [editorial]. *Journal of the American Academy of Orthopaedic Surgeons* 2004 September-October; 12(5): 296-297. Subject: 1.3.7

Brand, Richard A.; Heckman, James D.; Scott, James. Changing ethical standards in scientific publication [editorial]. *Journal of Bone and Joint Surgery: American Volume* 2004 September; 86-A(9): 1855-1856. Subject: 1.3.7

Brandt, Mary. Confidentiality today: where do you stand? *Journal of AHIMA* 1993 December; 64(12): 59-63. Subject: 8.4

Branigin, William. Va. apologizes to the victims of sterilizations [news]. *Washington Post* 2002 May 3; p. B1, B9. Subject: 11.3

Brannigan, Vincent M. Protecting the privacy of patient information in clinical networks: regulatory effectiveness analysis. *Annals of the New York Academy of Sciences* 1992 December 17; 670: 190-201. Subject: 8.4

Branthwaite, M.A. Taking the final step: changing the law on euthanasia and physician assisted suicide: time for change. *BMJ: British Medical Journal* 2005 September 24; 331(7518): 681-683. Subject: 20.5.1

Braude, Peter; Minger, Stephen L.; Warwick, Ruth M. Stem cell therapy: hope or hype? Safety and quality must be assured before this treatment can really benefit patients [editorial]. *BMJ: British Medical Journal* 2005 May 21; 330(7501): 1159-1160. Subject: 18.5.4

Braun, Kathrin. Not just for experts: the public debate about reprogenetics in Germany. *Hastings Center Report* 2005 May-June; 35(3): 42-49. Subject: 14.1

Braunack-Mayer, A. What makes a good GP? An empirical perspective on virtue in general practice. *Journal of Medical Ethics* 2005 February; 31(2): 82-87. Subject: 4.1.2

Braveman, P.; Gruskin, S. Defining equity in health. *Journal of Epidemiology and Community Health* 2003 April; 57(4): 254-258. Subject: 9.2

Brazier, Margaret. Sterilisation: down the slippery slope? *Professional Negligence* 1990 March; 6(1): 25-28. Subject: 11.3

Brazier, Margaret; Squier, Waney; Duyckaerts, Charles; Seilhean, Danielle; Hauw, Jean-Jacques; Adamson, Robert. The Human Tissue Bill. *Lancet Neurology* 2004 November; 3(11): 685-690. Subject: 19.5

Brazier, Margot. An intractable dispute: when parents and professionals disagree. *Medical Law Review* 2005 Autumn; 13(3): 412-418. Subject: 20.5.2

Breck, John. Procreation and "the beginning of life". *St. Vladimir's Theological Quarterly* 1995; 39(3): 215-232. Subject: 4.4

Breckenridge, Alasdair. For the good of the patient: risks and benefits of medicines. *Pharmacoepidemiology and Drug Safety* 2003 March; 12(2): 145-150. Subject: 9.7

Breen, Kerry J. Multicentre research: negotiating the ethics approval obstacle course [letter]. *Medical Journal of Australia* 2004 October 18; 181(8): 460. Subject: 18.2

Breen, Kerry J. Professional development and ethics for today's and tomorrow's doctors [editorial]. *Medical Journal of Australia* 2001 August 20; 175(4): 183-184. Subject: 7.2

Brehany, John. Health charities, unethical research and organizational integrity. *Health Care Ethics USA [electronic]* 2005; 13(3); E3, 3 p. Available: http://www.slu.edu/centers/chce/hceusa/3_2005_index.html [21 February 2006]. Subject: 9.1

Brehany, John. Nontraditional sources of pluripotent stem cells: a new chapter in the debate about embryonic stem cell research. *Health Care Ethics USA [electronic]* 2005; 13(2); 3 p. Available: http://www.slu.edu/centers/chce/hceusa/2_2005_3.html [19 September 2005]. Subject: 18.5.4

Breithaupt, Holger; Hadley, Caroline; Caplan, Arthur. Building stairs into slippery slopes. An interview with Arthur Caplan, director of the Center for Bioethics at the University of Pennsylvania (Philadelphia, PA, USA) [interview]. *EMBO Reports* 2005 January; 6(1): 8-12. Subject: 2.1

Breithaupt, Holger; Weigmann, Katrin. Manipulating your mind: what will science discover about our brains, and how are we going to deal with it? *EMBO Reports* 2004 March; 5(3): 230-232. Subject: 17.4

Brender, Alan. A nation's pride turns to shame. *Chronicle of Higher Education* 2006 January 6; 52(18): A27-A29. Subject: 1.3.9

Brender, Erin. Palliative sedation. *JAMA: The Journal of the American Medical Association* 2005 October 12; 294(14): 1850. Subject: 20.4.1

Brender, Erin. Supporting medical research. *JAMA: The Journal of the American Medical Association* 2005 September 21; 294(11): 1454. Subject: 18.3

Brennan, Troyen A. Concierge care and the future of general internal medicine [editorial]. *JGIM: Journal of General Internal Medicine* 2005 December; 20(12): 1190. Subject: 9.3.1

Breslin, Jonathan M. Autonomy and the role of the family in making decisions at the end of life. *Journal of Clinical Ethics* 2005 Spring; 16(1): 11-19. Subject: 8.3.3

Breslow, Lauren Hammer. The Best Pharmaceuticals for Children Act of 2002: the rise of the voluntary incentive structure and congressional refusal to require pediatric testing. *Harvard Journal on Legislation* 2003 Winter; 40(1): 133-193. Subject: 18.5.2

Brett, Allan S. Futility revisited: reflections on the perspectives of families, physicians, and institutions. *HEC (Healthcare Ethics Committee) Forum* 2005 December; 17(4): 276-293. Subject: 20.5.1

Brett, Allan S.; Zuger, Abigail. The run on Tamiflu — should physicians prescribe on demand? [opinion]. *New England Journal of Medicine* 2005 December 22; 353(25): 2636-2637. Subject: 8.1

Brettingham, Madeleine. Committee calls for more guidance on animal experiments [news]. *BMJ: British Medical Journal* 2005 May 28; 330(7502): 1226. Subject: 22.2

Brewaeys, A.; de Bruyn, J.K.; Louwe, L.A.; Helmerhorst, F.M. Anonymous or identity-registered sperm donors? A study of Dutch recipients' choices. *Human Reproduction* 2005 March; 20(3): 820-824. Subject: 14.2

Brewer, Albert P. Comments on the ethics of managed health care. *Cumberland Law Review* 1997-1998; 28(2): 315-319. Subject: 9.3.2

Brice, Julie; Bligh, John. Author misconduct: not just the editors' responsibility. *Medical Education* 2004 January; 39(1): 83-89. Subject: 1.3.7

Bridge, Caroline. Religion, culture and the body of the child. *In:* Bainham, Andrew; Sclater, Shelley Day; Richards, Martin, eds. Body Lore and Laws. Portland, OR: Hart Pub.; 2002: 265-287. Subject: 9.5.7

Brierley, Joe. "Right to die" — changing "right" to "duty" may focus debate [letter]. *BMJ: British Medical Journal* 2005 June 11; 330(7504): 1388. Subject: 20.4.1

Briggs, Catherine A. Informed refusal and patient autonomy: using reflection to examine how nursing knowledge and theory affect attitudes. *Intensive and Critical Care Nursing* 1995 December; 11(6): 314-317. Subject: 8.3.4

Briggs, Linda; Colvin, Elaine. The nurse's role in end-of-life decision-making for patients and families. *Geriatric Nursing* 2002 November; 23(6): 302-310. Subject: 20.4.1

Brigham, Lindsay. Representing the lives of women with learning difficulties: ethical dilemmas in the research process. *British Journal of Learning Disabilities* 1998 Winter; 26(4): 146-150. Subject: 18.5.6

Brind, Joel. The abortion-breast cancer connection. *National Catholic Bioethics Quarterly* 2005 Summer; 5(2): 303- 329. Subject: 12.1

Brindis, Claire D.; English, Abigail. Measuring public costs associated with loss of confidentiality for adolescents seeking confidential reproductive health care:how high the costs? How heavy the burden? [editorial]. *Archives of Pediatrics and Adolescent Medicine* 2004 December; 158(12): 1182-1184. Subject: 11.2

Brink, Susan. Inside Terri's brain: she's probably not in pain. Still, doctors can't read her mind. *U.S. News and World Report* 2005 April 4; 138(12): 24-25. Subject: 20.5.1

Brinsden, Peter R. Clinical aspects of IVF surrogacy in Britain. *In:* Cook, Rachel; Sclater, Shelley Day; Kaganas, Felicity, eds. Surrogate Motherhood: International Perspectives. Portland, OR: Hart; 2003: 99-112. Subject: 14.2

Bristol, Nellie. Physician-owned specialty hospitals in the USA. *Lancet* 2005 July 16-22; 366(9481): 193-194. Subject: 9.3.1

Bristow, Lonnie. Physician's role as healer: American Medical Association's opposition to physician-assisted suicide. *St. John's Journal of Legal Commentary* 1997 Summer; 12(3): 653-658. Subject: 20.7

British Association of Perinatal Medicine [BAPM]. Consent in neonatal clinical care: good practice framework. United Kingdom: British Association of Perinatal Medicine 2004 October; 3 p. [Online] Available: http://www.bapm.org/media/documents/publications/Staff-leaflet.pd f [31 January 2006]. Subject: 8.3.2

British Association of Perinatal Medicine [BAPM]. Witholding or Withdrawing Life Sustaining Treatment in Children: A Framework for Practice. United Kingdom: British Association of Perinatal Medicine 2004 May; 42 p. [Online]. Available: http://www.rcpch.ac.uk/publications/recent_publications/Witholdin g.pdf [31 January 2006]. Subject: 20.5.2

British Association of Perinatal Medicine [BAPM]. Thames Regional Perinatal Group. Guidelines relating to the birth of extremely immature babies (22-25 weeks gestation). United Kingdom: British Association of Perinatal Medicine 2000 March; 5 p. [Online]. Available: http://www.bapm.org/media/documents/publications/immature.pdf [31 January 2006]. Subject: 9.5.7

British Fertility Society; Murdoch, Alison; Fleming, Richard; Hamilton, Mark; Mills, John. Human embryonic stem cell research. *Human Reproduction and Genetic Ethics: An International Journal* 2001; 7(1): 14. Subject: 18.5.4

British Paediatric Association. Working on Party Ethics of Research in Children. Guidelines to aid ethical committees considering research involving children. *Archives of Disease in Childhood* 1980 January; 55(1): 75-77. Subject: 18.5.2

Brock, Dan W. Discrimination against the elderly within a consequentialist approach to health care resource allocation. *In:* Weisstub, David N.; Thomasma, David C.; Gauthier, Serge; Tomossy, George F., eds. Aging: Culture, Health, and Social Change. Boston: Kluwer Academic Publishers; 2001: 65-82. Subject: 9.5.2

Brock, Dan W. Ethical issues in the use of cost effectiveness analysis for the prioritisation of health care resources. *In:* Anand, Sudhir; Peter, Fabienne; Sen, Amartya, eds. Public Health, Ethics, and Equity. New York: Oxford University Press; 2004: 201-223. Subject: 9.4

Brock, Dan W. Preventing genetically transmitted disabilities while respecting persons with disabilities. *In:* Wasserman, David; Bickenbach, Jerome; Wachbroit, Robert, eds. Quality of Life and Human Difference: Genetic Testing, Health Care, and Disability. New York: Cambridge University Press; 2005: 67-100. Subject: 15.3

Brody, Baruch A. The ethics of cost-benefit analysis in ob/gyn practice. *Female Patient* 1986 August; 11: 23-24, 27, 30, 33, 37, 40. Subject: 9.3

Brody, Baruch A.; McCullough, Laurence B.; Sharp, Richard R. Consensus and controversy in clinical research ethics. *JAMA: The Journal of the American Medical Association* 2005 September 21; 294(11): 1411-1414. Subject: 18.2

Brody, Howard. Patient ethics and evidence-based medicine — the good healthcare citizen. *CQ: Cambridge Quarterly of Healthcare Ethics* 2005 Spring; 14(2): 141-146. Subject: 8.1

Brody, Howard. Should a clinical trial coordinator blow the whistle? *Medical Ethics Newsletter [Lahey Clinic]* 2004 Winter; 11(1): 3, 11. Subject: 18.2

Subject = NRCBL Primary Classification Number; See inside front cover

Brody, Howard. The welcome reassessment of research ethics: is "undue inducement" suspect? [comment]. *American Journal of Bioethics* 2005 September-October; 5(5): 15-16. Subject: 18.3

Brody, Howard; Miller, Franklin G.; Bogdan-Lovis, Elizabeth. Evidence-based medicine: watching out for its friends. *Perspectives in Biology and Medicine* 2005 Autumn; 48(4): 570-584. Subject: 9.8

Brody, Howard; Miller, Franklin G.; Stossel, Thomas P. Academic-industrial relationships [letter and reply]. *New England Journal of Medicine* 2005 December 22; 353(25): 2720-2722. Subject: 5.3

Broeckaert, Bert. Belgium: towards a legal recognition of euthanasia. *European Journal of Health Law* 2001 June; 8(2): 95-107. Subject: 20.5.1

Brogaard, Berit. The moral status of the human embryo: the twinning argument. *Free Inquiry* 2002-2003 Winter; 23(1): 45-48. Subject: 18.5.4

Brom, Bernard; Kiepiel, Kazalette. The ethics of fluoridation of water [letters]. *South African Medical Journal* 2002 November; 92(11): 836-837. Subject: 9.1

Bromberg, Jonathan S.; Silverstein, Jeffrey H.; Kirk, Allan D. Proposal for the American Journal of Transplantation policy for review of ethical standards of clinical research involving live human subjects. *American Journal of Transplantation* 2005 April; 5(4 Part 1): 648-650. Subject: 18.2

Brooke, James. Korean leaves cloning center in ethics furor; admits lying on source of donated eggs. *New York Times* 2005 November 25; p. A1, A8. Subject: 1.3.9

Brooke, John Hedley. Detracting from divine power? Religious belief and the appraisal of new technologies. *In:* Deane-Drummond, Celia; Szerszynski, Bronislaw, eds. Re- ordering Nature: Theology, Society and the New Genetics. New York: T & T Clark; 2003: 43-67. Subject: 15.1

Brooks, Jay P. The rights of blood recipients should supersede any asserted rights of blood donors. *Vox Sanguinis* 2004 November; 87(4): 280-286. Subject: 19.4

Brooks, Michael. Not by the book [opinion]. *New Scientist* 2005 November 19-25; 188(2526): 22. Subject: 2.1

Brooks, Sharon L. Is it ethical not to . . .? [editorial]. *Oral Surgery, Oral Medicine, Oral Pathology, Oral Radiology and Endodontics* 2001 May; 91(5): 493. Subject: 9.5.1

Brooks, William. The privatization of the civil commitment process and the state action doctrine: have the mentally ill been systematically stripped of their Fourteenth Amendment rights? *Duquesne Law Review* 2001 Fall; 40(1): 1-75. Subject: 17.7

Broome, Annabel. Psychology in medical settings. *In:* Fairbairn, Susan; Fairbairn, Gavin, eds. Psychology, Ethics and Change. New York: Routledge & Kegan Paul; 1987: 173- 190. Subject: 17.3

Broome, Marion E. Researching the world of children [editorial]. *Nursing Research* 1998 November-December; 47(6): 305-306. Subject: 18.5.2

Broome, Marion E.; Pryor, Erica; Habermann, Barbara; Pulley, Leavonne; Kincaid, Harold. The scientific misconduct questionnaire — revised (SMQ-R): validation and psychometric testing. *Accountability in Research* 2005 October-December; 12(4): 263- 280. Subject: 1.3.9

Brouillet, Miriam; Turner, Leigh. Bioethics, religion, and democratic deliberation: policy formation and embryonic stem cell research. *HEC (Healthcare Ethics Committee) Forum* 2005 March; 17(1): 49- 63. Subject: 18.5.4

Brower, Vicki. Vulnerable groups at risk from "commercial" ethical review boards [news]. *Nature Medicine* 1997 July; 3(7): 705. Subject: 18.2

Brown, E. Richard. Why we need more studies on health insurance coverage and access [opinion]. *Medical Care Research and Review* 2000 September; 57(3): 319-325. Subject: 9.3.1

Brown, Hannah. Clinician expert witnesses take the stand. *Lancet* 2005 July 2-8; 366(9479): 16-17. Subject: 7.3

Brown, James E., Jr. The PVS patient [letter]. *Linacre Quarterly* 2005 February; 72(1): 4. Subject: 20.5.1

Brown, Jennifer. A troublesome maternal-fetal conflict: legal, ethical, and social issues surrounding mandatory AZT treatment of HIV positive pregnant women. *Buffalo Public Interest Law Journal* 1999-2000; 18: 67-94. Subject: 9.5.5

Brown, Margaret. The law and practice associated with advance directives in Canada and Australia: similarities, differences and debates. *International Journal of the Sociology of Law* 2002 December; 30(4): 59-76. Subject: 20.5.4

Brown, Margaret; Grbich, Carol; Maddocks, Ian; Parker, Deborah; Connellan, Penny Roe; Willis, Eileen. Documenting end of life decisions in residential aged care facilities in South Australia. *Australian and New Zealand Journal of Public Health* 2005 February; 29(1): 85-90. Subject: 20.5.4

Brown, R.F.; Butow, P.N.; Ellis, P.; Boyle, F.; Tattersall, M.H.N. Seeking informed consent to cancer clinical trials: describing current practice. *Social Science and Medicine* 2004 June; 58(12): 2445-2457. Subject: 18.3

Browne, Alister; Sullivan, Bill. Abortion in Canada. *CQ: Cambridge Quarterly of Healthcare Ethics* 2005 Summer; 14(3): 287-291. Subject: 12.4.1

Browne, Andrew. Health crisis: Chinese doctors tell patients to pay upfront, or no treatment; parents of boy with leukemia scramble for cash to cover new chemotherapy round; threat seen to social stability. *Wall Street Journal* 2005 December 5; p. A1, A12. Subject: 9.3.1

Browne, Andrew. Policy woes: China's workers see thin protection in insurance plans; under state health program, "big sickness" is pricey; doctors demand cash ; Mr. Hu buys his chemo drugs. *Wall Street Journal* 2005 December 30; p. A1, A9. Subject: 9.3.1

Browne, Natasha. Truth-telling in palliative care. *European Journal of Oncology Nursing* 1998 December; 2(4): 218-224. Subject: 8.2

Browner, C.H.; Kukla, Rebecca. Conscientious autonomy: what patients do vs. what is done to them [letter and reply]. *Hastings Center Report* 2005 September-October; 35(5): 4-5, 6-7. Subject: 8.3.1

Brownrigg, Alissa. Mother still knows best: cancer-related gene mutations, familial privacy, and a physician's duty to warn. *Fordham Urban Law Journal* 1999 January; 26(2): 247-279. Subject: 8.4

Brownscombe, J. Crisis in humanitarianism? *Journal of Medical Ethics* 2005 March; 31(3): 182-183. Subject: 21.1

Brownsword, Roger. Regulating human genetics: new dilemmas for a new millennium. *Medical Law Review* 2004 Spring; 12(1): 14-39. Subject: 15.1

Brownsword, Roger. Reproductive opportunities and regulatory challenges. *Modern Law Review* 2004 March; 67(2): 304-321. Subject: 14.4

Broyles, Lauren M.; Colbert, Alison M.; Erlen, Judith A. Medication practice and feminist thought: a theoretical and ethical response to adherence in HIV/AIDS. *Bioethics* 2005 August; 19(4): 362-378. Subject: 9.5.6

Bruce, Donald. Human embryonic cloning. *Human Reproduction and Genetic Ethics: An International Journal* 2001; 7(1): 3-7. Subject: 14.5

Bruce, Donald. Making the world better? *New Scientist* 2005 June 11-17; 186(2503): 21. Subject: 5.1

Brugger, E. Christian. Ethical commitment stimulates scientific insights. *National Catholic Bioethics Quarterly* 2005 Autumn; 5(3): 445- 446. Subject: 15.1

Brugger, E. Christian. In defense of transferring heterologous embryos. *National Catholic Bioethics Quarterly* 2005 Spring; 5(1): 95- 112. Subject: 14.4

Bruinsma, Fiona; Venn, Alison; Skene, Loane. Accessing patients' records without individual consent for epidemiological research. *Journal of Law and Medicine* 2000 August; 8(1): 76-80. Subject: 18.3

Brull, Richard; McCartney, Colin J.L.; Chan, Vincent W.S.; Chung, Frances; Rawson, Regan. Are patients comfortable consenting to clinical anesthesia research trials on the day of surgery? *Anesthesia and Analgesia* 2004 April; 98(4): 1106-1110. Subject: 18.3

Brunger, Fern. Problematizing the notion of "community" in research ethics. *In:* Knoppers, Bartha Maria, ed. Populations and Genetics: Legal and Socio-Ethical Per-

spectives. Boston: Martinus Nijhoff; 2003: 245-255. Subject: 15.1

Brunger, Fern; Burgess, Michael. A cultural understanding of research ethics governance. *Health Law Review* 2005; 13(2-3): 69-74. Subject: 18.2

Brunner, S. Dresden. Cultural feminism: it sounds good, but will it work? Application to a husband's interest in his wife's abortion decision. *University of Dayton Law Review* 1996 Fall; 22(1): 101-123. Subject: 12.4.2

Brush, Silla. Hoping to avoid brain drain, states push to finance stem-cell research. *Chronicle of Higher Education* 2005 February 4; 51(22): A22. Subject: 18.5.4

Bruzzone, Paolo; Pretagostini, Renzo; Rossi, Massimo; Berloco, Pasquale B. Ethical considerations on kidney transplantation from living donors. *Annals of Transplantation* 2004; 9(2): 46-47. Subject: 19.3

Bryan, Bradley. Biotechnology, bioethics and liberalism: problematizing risk, consent and law. *Health Law Journal* 2003; 11: 119-135. Subject: 2.1

Bryan, Debra M. It's my body and I'll die if I want to: a plan for keeping personal autonomy from spinning out of control. *Journal of Medicine and Law* 2003 Fall-2004 Spring; 8(1-2): 45-67. Subject: 20.5.4

Bryant, J.; Powell, J. Payment to healthcare professionals for patient recruitment to trials: a systematic review. *BMJ: British Medical Journal* 2005 December 10; 331(7529): 1377-1378. Subject: 18.2

Buchanan, David; Miller, Franklin G. Principles of early stopping of randomized trials for efficacy: a critique of equipoise and an alternative nonexploitation ethical framework. *Kennedy Institute of Ethics Journal* 2005 June; 15(2): 161-178. Subject: 18.2

Buchanan, Maura. Assisted dying. *Nursing Standard* 2004 August 25-31; 18(50): 18. Subject: 20.5.1

Buchman, Alan L. Ethics and economics in nutritional support. *Nestle Nutrition Workshop Series. Clinical and Performance Programme* 2005; 10: 143-166. Subject: 20.5.1

Buchman, Debra E.; Porock, Davina. A response to C. Varcoe, G. Doane, B. Pauly, P. Rodney, J.L. Storch, K. Mahony, G. McPherson, H. Brown and R. Starzomski (2004) 'Ethical practice in nursing: working the in-betweens'. Journal of Advanced Nursing 45(3), 316-325. *Journal of Advanced Nursing* 2005 September; 51(6): 658-659. Subject: 4.1.3

Buchstein, Fred. Bioethics. *In:* Ness, Bryan D., ed. Encyclopedia of Genetics. Revised edition. Volume I. Pasadena, Calif.: Salem Press; 2004: 73-77. Subject: 2.1

Buckle, Stephen. Peter Singer's argument for utilitarianism. *Theoretical Medicine and Bioethics* 2005; 26(3): 175-194. Subject: 2.1

Buckles, V.D.; Powlishta, K.K.; Palmer, J.L.; Coats, M.; Hosto, T.; Buckley, A.; Morris, J.C. Understanding of informed consent by demented individuals. *Neurology* 2003 December 23; 61(12): 1662-1666. Subject: 18.5.6

Budds, Brian. Toward a just model of alienability of human tissue. *University of San Francisco Law Review* 2003 Spring; 37(3): 757-782. Subject: 15.8

Buelow, George D.; Chafetz, Michael D. Proposed ethical practice guidelines for clinical pharmacopsychology: sharpening a new focus in psychology. *Professional Psychology: Research and Practice* 1996 February; 27(1): 53-58. Subject: 17.1

Buetow, S. High need patients receiving targeted entitlements: what responsibilities do they have in primary health care? *Journal of Medical Ethics* 2005 May; 31(5): 304-306. Subject: 9.5.1

Buford, Chris; Allhoff, Fritz. Neuroscience and metaphysics. *American Journal of Bioethics* 2005 March-April; 5(2): 34-36. Subject: 17.1

Bühler, Karl-Ernst. Euphoria, ecstacy, inebriation, abuse, dependence, and addiction: a conceptual analysis. *Medicine, Health Care and Philosophy: A European Journal* 2005; 8(1): 79-87. Subject: 9.5.9

Buhmann, Caecilie Böck. The role of health professionals in preventing and mediating conflict. *Medicine, Conflict and Survival* 2005 October-December; 21(4): 299-311. Subject: 21.2

Büken, Nüket Örnek; Büken, Erhan. The legal and ethical aspects of medical malpractice in Turkey. *European Journal of Health Law* 2003 June; 10(2): 201-213. Subject: 9.2

Buller, Tom. Can we scan for truth in a society of liars? *American Journal of Bioethics* 2005 March-April; 5(2): 58-60. Subject: 17.1

Burazeri, Genc; Civljak, Marta; Ilakovac, Vesna; Jankovic, Slobodan; Majica-Kovacevic, Tanja; Nedera, Olesea; Roshi, Enver; Sava, Valeriu; Šimunovic, Vladimir; Marušic, Ana; Marušic, Matko. Survey of attitudes and knowledge about science in medical students in southeast Europe. *BMJ: British Medical Journal* 2005 July 23; 331(7510): 195-196. Subject: 7.2

Burda, David. The rules we follow. An updated ethics code for our staff. *Modern Healthcare* 2004 November 1; 34(44): 20. Subject: 1.3.7

Burdette, Amy M.; Hill, Terrence D.; Moulton, Benjamin E. Religion and attitudes toward physician-assisted suicide and terminal palliative care. *Journal for the Scientific Study of Religion* 2005 March; 44(1): 79-93. Subject: 20.3.1

Burgess, Michael M. Public consultation on ethics: an experiment in representative ethics. *Journal of Bioethical Inquiry* 2004; 1(1): 4-13. Subject: 9.6

Burke, Tara M.; Abramovitch, R.; Zlotkin, S. Children's understanding of the risks and benefits associated with research. *Journal of Medical Ethics* 2005 December; 31(12): 715-720. Subject: 18.5.2

Burke, William J.; Pullicino, Patrick; Richard, Edward J.; Condic, Maureen. Stemming the tide of cloning [letter and reply]. *First Things* 2005 December; (158): 6-9. Subject: 18.5.4

Burke, Wylie; Zimmern, Ron L. Ensuring the appropriate use of genetic tests. *Nature Reviews Genetics* 2004 December; 5(12): 955-959. Subject: 15.3

Burkett, Teresa Meinders; Weyrauch, Samantha. An Oklahoma perspective: end of life decision-making and termination of treatment. *Tulsa Law Journal* 2000 Spring-Summer; 35(3-4): 565-581. Subject: 20.5.4

Burkli, Peter. Zur Stammzelldiskussion in der Schweiz. *In:* Maio, Giovanni; Just, Hanjörg, eds. Die Forschung an embryonalen Stammzellen in ethischer und rechtlicher Perspektive. Baden-Baden: Nomos Verlagsgesellschaft; 2003: 119-123. Subject: 18.5.4

Burleigh, Michael. Nazi "euthanasia" programs. *In:* Bachrach, Susan, project director; Kuntz, Dieter, ed. Deadly Medicine: Creating the Master Race. Washington, DC: United States Holocaust Museum; 2004: 127-153. Subject: 21.4

Burman, William; Breese, Peter; Weis, Stephen; Bock, Naomi; Bernardo, John; Vernon, Andrew. The effects of local review on informed consent documents from a multicenter clinical trials consortium. *Controlled Clinical Trials* 2003 June; 24(3): 245-255. Subject: 18.2

Burnard, Philip. Why care? Ethical and spiritual issues in caring in nursing. *In:* Brykczynska, Gosia, ed. Caring: The Compassion and Wisdom of Nursing. New York: Arnold; 1997: 32-44. Subject: 8.1

Burns, Jeffrey. Does anyone actually invoke their hospital futility policy? *Medical Ethics Newsletter [Lahey Clinic]* 2005 Fall; 12(3): 3. Subject: 20.5.2

Burroughs, A. Maxwell. The medical examination in United States immigration applications: the potential use of genetic testing leads to heightened privacy concerns. *Journal of Biolaw and Business* 2005; 8(4): 22-32. Subject: 15.3

Burstein, Paul D.; Greene, Michael F.; Drazen, Jeffrey M.; Wood, Alastair J.J. A sad day for science at the FDA [letter and reply]. *New England Journal of Medicine* 2005 December 15; 353(24): 2619-2621. Subject: 11.1

Burt, John G. Compliance with advance directives: a legal view. *Critical Care Nursing Quarterly* 1999 November; 22(3): 72-74. Subject: 20.5.4

Burton, Kelli Whitlock. Cloning in America: The Genetics and Public Policy Center surveys the nation. *GeneWatch* 2005 November-December; 18(6): 13-18. Subject: 14.5

Bury, Michael. Doctors, patients and interaction in health care. *In his:* Health and Illness in a Changing Society. New York: Routledge; 1997: 77-109. Subject: 8.1

Busby, Araceli; Ritvanen, Annukka; Dolk, Helen; Armstrong, Nicola; De Walle, Hermien; Riaño-Galán, Isolina; Gatt, Miriam; McDonnell, Robert; Nelen, Vera; Stone, David. Survey of informed consent for registration of congenital anomalies in Europe. *BMJ: British Medical Journal* 2005 July 16; 331(7509): 140-141. Subject: 8.3.2

Busby, Helen. Blood donation for genetic research: what can we learn from donors' narratives? *In:* Tutton, Richard; Corrigan, Oonagh, eds. Genetic Databases: Socio-ethical Issues in the Collection and Use of DNA. New York: Routledge; 2004: 39-56. Subject: 19.4

Busquets, Ester; Tubau, Joan Mir. Eutanasia y suicidio asistido: por que si o por que no? / Euthanasia and assisted suicide: why or why not? *Bioetica & Debat* 2005; 11(39): 8-10. Subject: 20.5.1

Butler, Declan. Conclave kindles hope for bioethical reform [news]. *Nature* 2005 April 21; 434(7036): 944. Subject: 2.1

Butler, Peter E.M.; Clarke, Alex; Hettiaratchy, Shehan. Facial transplantation: a new option in reconstruction of severe facial injury [editorial]. *BMJ: British Medical Journal* 2005 December 10; 331(7529): 1349-1350. Subject: 19.1

Butterworth, Cathy. Ongoing consent to care for older people in care homes. *Nursing Standard* 2005 January 26-February 1; 19(20): 40-45. Subject: 8.3.1

Buzzee, Sarah E.M. The Pain Relief Promotion Act: Congress's misguided intervention into end-of-life care. *University of Cincinnati Law Review* 2001 Autumn; 70(1): 217-249. Subject: 20.4.1

Byers, Tim; MacDonald, Deborah J.; Severin, Matthew J.; Fishbach, Andrea A. Cancer genetic counseling: need for confidentiality versus responsibility to notify. *Cancer Practice* 1999 March-April; 7(2): 93-95. Subject: 15.2

Byk, C. Public and private regulation of reproductive technologies. *Medicine and Law: World Association for Medical Law* 1995; 14(3-4): 215-219. Subject: 14.4

Byk, Christian. Euthanasia and the right to life—the Pretty case. *In:* Council of Europe Publishing, ed. Euthanasia. Volume I. Ethical and Human Aspects. Strasbourg: Council of Europe; Croton- on-Hudson, NY: Manhattan Publishing Co.; 2003: 109-127. Subject: 20.7

Byk, Christian. Nationale Modelle zur Regelung des Gebrauchs der Gendiagnostik. Frankreich: Ist legislativer Prinzipalismus eine illusorische und abwegige Politik? *In:* Honnefelder, Ludger; Mieth, Dietmar; Propping, Peter; Siep, Ludwig; Wiesemann, Claudia, eds. Das genetische

Wissen und die Zukunft des Menschen. New York: De Gruyter; 2003: 286-298. Subject: 15.3

Byk, Christian. Truth telling and informed consent: is "primum docere" the new motto of clinical practice? *Formosan Journal of Medical Humanities* 2005 September; 6(1-2): 31-38. Subject: 8.2

Byravan, Sujatha; Annas, George. The year of the stem cell: George Annas talks about the future of stem cell research in America. *GeneWatch* 2005 September-October; 18(5): 12-15. Subject: 18.5.4

Byrd, Conswella M.; Baulch, Michael N. Crossing the rubicon on HIV confidentiality: medical information security in the 90's and beyond. *Progress in Cardiovascular Nursing* 1995 Spring; 10(2): 41-44. Subject: 9.5.6

Byrne, Geraldine. Ethical approval. *Professional Nurse* 2001 January; 16(4): 1052-1054. Subject: 18.2

Byrne, Mary Woods. Conducting research as a visiting scientist in a women's prison. *Journal of Professional Nursing* 2005 July-August; 21(4): 223-230. Subject: 18.5.5

Byrnes, W. Malcom. Why human "altered nuclear transfer" is unethical: a holistic systems view. *National Catholic Bioethics Quarterly* 2005 Summer; 5(2): 271- 279. Subject: 18.5.4

Byrnes, W. Malcolm; Elliott, Kevin C. Holistic systems and "delayed hominization" are incompatible [article and commentary]. *National Catholic Bioethics Quarterly* 2005 Autumn; 5(3): 447- 450. Subject: 4.4

C

Caan, Woody. A testing time for ethical standards [letter]. *BMJ: British Medical Journal* 2005 June 25; 330(7506): 1510. Subject: 7.2

Cahana, Michael Z. "Who shall live . . .": a report from the CCAR Task Force on Assisted Suicide. *CCAR Journal: A Reform Jewish Quarterly* 2005 Winter; 52(1): 42-58. Subject: 20.7

Cahill, Lisa Sowle. Catholicism, death and modern medicine. *America* 2005 April 25; 192(14): 14-17. Subject: 20.5.1

Cahill, Lisa Sowle. Nature, sin, and society. *In:* Baillie, Harold W.; Casey, Timothy K., eds. Is Human Nature Obsolete? Genetics Bioengineering, and the Future of the Human Condition. Cambridge, MA: MIT Press; 2005: 339-365. Subject: 15.1

Cahill, Lisa Sowle; Lauritzen, Paul. Our posthuman future: discussing the consequences of biotechnological advances [letter and reply]. *Hastings Center Report* 2005 November-December; 35(6): 5-7. Subject: 18.5.4

Cain, Harry I.; Harkness, Jennifer L.; Smith, Angela L.; Markowski, Edward Mel. Protecting persons in family therapy research: an overview of ethical and regulatory standards. *Journal of Marital and Family Therapy* 2003 January; 29(1): 47- 57. Subject: 18.4

Cain, Joanna M. Ethical guidelines in the prevention of iatrogenic multiple pregnancy. *International Journal of Gynecology and Obstetrics* 2000 December; 71(3): 293-294. Subject: 14.4

Calabresi, Guido. An introduction to legal thought: four approaches to law and to the allocation of body parts. *Stanford Law Review* 2003 June; 55(6): 2113-2151. Subject: 4.4

Caldicott, Catherine V.; Faber-Langendoen, Kathy. Deception, discrimination, and fear of reprisal: lessons in ethics from third-year medical students. *Academic Medicine* 2005 September; 80(9): 866-873. Subject: 2.3

Calhoun, Byron C. The fetus as our patient: the confluence of faith and science in the care of the unborn. *Linacre Quarterly* 2005 August; 72(3): 189-211. Subject: 9.5.8

Calhoun, Samuel W. An alarming pre-Roe view of personhood: the 1972 Byrn decision. [Byrn v. New York City Health and Hospitals Corp.]. *In:* Koterski, Joseph W., ed. Life and Learning XI: Proceedings of the Eleventh University Faculty for Life Conference. Washington, DC: University Faculty for Life; 2002: 98-110. Subject: 4.4

Calhoun, Samuel W. Valuing intrauterine life. *Regent University Law Review* 1997 Spring; 8: 69-81. Subject: 4.4

California Dental Association [CDA]. CDA code of ethics. *Journal of the California Dental Association* 2005 January; 33(1): 65-71. Subject: 6

California. Penal Code. Human experimentation: use of prisoners in biomedical and behavioural research. *International Digest of Health Legislation* 1979; 30(1): 143- 146. Subject: 18.5.5

Calis, Karim Anton; Pucino, Frank, Jr.; Restrepo, Maria L.; Cantor, Julie; Baum, Ken. Pharmacists and emergency contraception [letter and reply]. *New England Journal of Medicine* 2005 March 3; 352(9): 942-944. Subject: 11.1

Callahan, Daniel. Bioethics and the culture wars. *CQ: Cambridge Quarterly of Healthcare Ethics* 2005 Fall; 14(4): 424-431. Subject: 2.1

Callahan, Daniel. A case against euthanasia. *In:* Cohen, Andrew I.; Wellman, Christopher Heath, eds. Contemporary Debates in Applied Ethics. Malden, MA: Blackwell Pub., 2005: 179-190. Subject: 20.5.1

Callahan, Daniel. Conservatives, liberals, and medical progress. *New Atlantis* 2005 Fall; 10: 3-16. Subject: 9.3.1

Callahan, Daniel. New beginnings in life: a philosopher's response. *In:* Hamilton, Michael P., ed. The New Genetics and the Future of Man. Grand Rapids, MI: William B. Eerdmans Publishing Co.; 1972: 90-106. Subject: 14.1

Callahan, Sidney; Chervenak, Frank A.; McCullough, Laurence B. Ethics and fetal research [discussion]. *Medi-*

cal Ethics Newsletter [Lahey Clinic] 2003 Spring; 10(2): 10-11. Subject: 18.5.4

Callens, S. Telemedicine and the e-commerce directive. *European Journal of Health Law* 2002 June; 9(2): 93-109. Subject: 1.3.12

Calman, Kenneth. Conducting research ethically in developing countries. *Drug Discovery Today* 2002 December; 7(23): 1155-1159. Subject: 18.5.9

Calvo, Cheye. Insurance information privacy. *Legisbrief* 2001 March; 9(13): 1-2. Subject: 8.4

Calvo, Cheye; Jones, Jennifer. Protecting genetic information. *Legisbrief* 2000 June-July; 8(28): 1-2. Subject: 15.3

Cambon-Thomsen, Anne. The social and ethical issues of post-genomic human biobanks. *Nature Reviews Genetics* 2004 November; 5(11): 866-873. Subject: 15.1

Cambon-Thomsen, A.; Hirtzlin, I.; Preaubert, N.; Dubreuil, C.; Duchier, J.; Jansen, B.; Simon, J.; Lobato de Faria, P.; Perez- Lezaun, A.; Visser, B.; Williams, G.; Galloux, J.C. An empirical study on biobanking of human genetic material and data in six EU countries. *In:* Knoppers, Bartha Maria, ed. Populations and Genetics: Legal and Socio-Ethical Perspectives. Boston: Martinus Nijhoff; 2003: 141-167. Subject: 15.1

Cameron, C.; Williamson, R. In the world of Dolly, when does a human embryo acquire respect? *Journal of Medical Ethics* 2005 April; 31(4): 215-220. Subject: 4.4

Cameron, Martin J.; Penney, Gillian C. Are national recommendations regarding examination and disposal of products of miscarriage being followed? A need for revised guidelines? *Human Reproduction* 2005 February; 20(2): 531-535. Subject: 9.5.5

Cameron, Miriam E.; Park, Hyeoun-Ae. Equity versus economics in South Korea. *Journal of Nursing Law* 1999 November; 6(3): 47-54. Subject: 20.5.1

Cameron, Nigel M. de S.; FitzGerald, Kevin T.; Flannery, Kevin; Gómez-Lobo, Alfonso; Harvey, John Collins; Kilner, John F.; May, William E.; Williams, Thomas; et al. Production of pluripotent stem cells by oocyte-assisted reprogramming: joint statement with signatories. *National Catholic Bioethics Quarterly* 2005 Autumn; 5(3): 579- 583. Subject: 15.1

Campanella, James J. Cloning: ethical issues. *In:* Ness, Bryan D., ed. Encyclopedia of Genetics. Revised edition. Volume I. Pasadena, Calif.: Salem Press; 2004: 170-174. Subject: 14.5

Campbell, Alastair V. Britain's HFEA is caught in the middle. *Hastings Center Report* 2005 May-June; 35(3): 8. Subject: 14.1

Campbell, Amy T. Adolescent decisional autonomy in research: issues in translating research into policy [comment]. *American Journal of Bioethics* 2005 September-October; 5(5): 78-80. Subject: 18.5.2

Campbell, Amy T. In search of a real "third way" in process and outcome. *American Journal of Bioethics* 2005 November-December; 5(6): 66-68. Subject: 18.5.4

Campbell, Angela. Ethos and economics: examining the rationale underlying stem cell and cloning research policies in the United States, Germany, and Japan. *American Journal of Law and Medicine* 2005; 31(1): 47-86. Subject: 14.5

Campbell, Angela. A place for criminal law in the regulation of reproductive technologies. *Health Law Journal* 2002; 10: 77-101. Subject: 14.5

Campbell, Angela; Glass, Kathleen Cranley. The legal status of clinical and ethics policies, codes, and guidelines in medical practice and research. *McGill Law Journal* 2001 February; 46(2): 473-489. Subject: 6

Campbell, Angela; Nycum, Gillian. Harmonizing the international regulation of embryonic stem cell research: possibilities, promises and potential pitfalls. *Medical Law International* 2005; 7(2): 113-148. Subject: 18.5.4

Campbell, Courtney. Buddhism and cloning. *In:* McGee, Glenn; Caplan, Arthur, eds. The Human Cloning Debate. 4th edition. Berkeley, CA: Berkeley Hills Books; 2004: 283- 287. Subject: 14.5

Campbell, Courtney S. Authority and agency: policies and principles in Latter-day Saints bioethics. *In:* Peppin, John F.; Cherry, Mark J., eds. Religious Perspectives in Bioethics. New York: Taylor & Francis; 2004: 109- 130. Subject: 2.1

Campbell, Courtney S. The gift and the market: cultural symbolic perspectives. *In:* Youngner, Stuart J.; Anderson, Martha W.; Schapiro, Renie, eds. Transplanting Human Tissue: Ethics, Policy, and Practice. New York: Oxford University Press; 2004: 139-159. Subject: 19.5

Campbell, Deborah A. Physician-assisted suicide: experience and controversy [editorial]. *Medical Journal of Australia* 2001 April 2; 174(7): 325-326. Subject: 20.7

Campbell, Elizabeth; Ross, Lainie Friedman. Parental attitudes and beliefs regarding the genetic testing of children. *Community Genetics* 2005 May; 8(2): 94-102. Subject: 15.3

Campbell, Eric G.; Koski, Greg; Zinner, Darren E.; Blumenthal, David. Managing the triple helix in the life sciences. *Issues in Science and Technology* 2005 Winter; 21(2): 48-54. Subject: 5.3

Campion, Bridget. An argument for continuing a pregnancy where the fetus is discovered to be anencephalic. *In:* Koterski, Joseph W., ed. Life and Learning IX: Proceedings of the Ninth University Faculty for Life Conference. Washington, DC: University Faculty for Life; 2000: 319-329. Subject: 9.5.8

Canada. Canadian Institutes of Health Research; Natural Sciences and Engineering Research Council of Canada; Social Sciences and Humanities Research

Council of Canada. Tri-Council policy statement: ethical conduct for research involving humans. Canada: Interagency Secretariat on Research Ethics 1998 August, with 2000, 2002 and 2005 amendments; 93 p. [Online]. Available: http://www.pre.ethics.gc.ca/english/pdf/ TCPSOctober 2005_E.pdf [10 February 2006]. Subject: 18.2

Canada. Health Canada. Survey on human organ donation and xenotransplantation. Ottawa, Ontario, Canada: Health Canada 1999 December 19; 5 p. [Online]. Available: http://www.hc-sc.gc.ca/hpfb-dgpsa/bgtd-dpbtg/ xeno_survey_e.pdf [2 May 2005]. Subject: 19.1

Canada. Health Canada/Santé Canada. Proposed Canadian Standard for Xenotransplantation, Draft No. 14. Ottawa, Ontario, Canada: Health Canada 1999 July; 48 p. [Online]. Available: http://www.hc-sc.gc.ca/dhp-mps/ alt_formats/hpfb-dgpsa/pdf/brgtherap/xeno_std-norme_e.pdf [1 December 2005]. Subject: 19.1

Canadian Institutes of Health Research. Ottawa Group; Krleza-Jeric, Karmela; Chan, An-Wen; Dickersin, Kay; Sim, Ida; Grimshaw, Jeremy; Gluud, Christian. Principles for international registration of protocol information and results from human trials of health related interventions: Ottawa statement (Part 1). *BMJ: British Medical Journal* 2005 April 23; 330(7497): 956-958. Subject: 18.2

Canadian Medical Association [CMA]. CMA code of ethics. *CMAJ/JAMC: Canadian Medical Association Journal* 2005 April 12; 172(8): 1053-1055. Subject: 6

Câncio, Fernanda. When abortion is a crime: the reality that rhetoric ignores. *Conscience* 2004-2005 Winter; 25(3): 28-31. Subject: 12.4.2

Candilis, Philip J.; Arikan, Rasim; Noone, Sheila B.; Holzer, Jacob C. The new research ethic: will oversight requirements sink forensic research? *Journal of the American Academy of Psychiatry and the Law* 2005; 33(3): 361-367. Subject: 18.2

Canestrari, Stefano. The law of February 19th 2004, No. 40: procreation and punishment. *Revista de Derecho y Genoma Humano / Law and the Human Genome Review* 2005 January-June; (22): 57-73. Subject: 14.4

Caniano, D.A.; Baylis, F. Ethical considerations in prenatal surgical consultation. *Pediatric Surgery International* 1999 July; 15(5-6): 303-309. Subject: 9.5.8

Cantor, Michael D.; Barach, Paul; Derse, Arthur; Maklan, Claire W.; Wlody, Ginger Schafer; Fox, Ellen. Disclosing adverse events to patients. *Joint Commission Journal on Quality and Patient Safety* 2005 January; 31(1): 5-12. Subject: 8.2

Cantor, Norman L. The bane of surrogate decision-making: defining the best interests of never-competent persons. *Journal of Legal Medicine* 2005 June; 26(2): 155-205. Subject: 8.3.3

Cantor, Norman L. Glucksberg, the putative right to adequate pain relief, and death with dignity. *Journal of Health Law* 2001 Summer; 34(3): 301-333. Subject: 20.4.1

Cantor, Norman L. On Kamisar, killing, and the future of physician-assisted death. *Michigan Law Review* 2004 August; 102(8): 1793-1842. Subject: 20.7

Canvin, K.; Bartlett, A.; Pinfold, V. Acceptability of compulsory powers in the community: the ethical considerations of mental health service users on supervised discharge and guardianship. *Journal of Medical Ethics* 2005 August; 31(8): 457-462. Subject: 17.1

Capaldi, Nicholas. The ethics and economics of health care. *Journal of Medicine and Philosophy* 2005 December; 30(6): 571- 578. Subject: 9.3.1

Caplan, Arthur L. Arthur Caplan on the future of bioethics [interview]. *Free Inquiry* 2002-2003 Winter; 23(1): 28-29. Subject: 2.1

Caplan, Arthur L. Attack of the anti-cloners: what the government should do. *Free Inquiry* 2002-2003 Winter; 23(1): 30-31. Subject: 14.5

Caplan, Arthur L. Free the National Bioethics Commission. *Issues in Science and Technology* 2003 Summer; 19(4): 85-87. Subject: 2.4

Caplan, Arthur L. Is better best? A noted ethicist argues in favor of brain enhancement. *Scientific American* 2003 September; 289(3): 104-105. Subject: 17.1

Caplan, Arthur L. Misusing the Nazi analogy [editorial]. *Science* 2005 July 22; 309(5734): 535. Subject: 21.4

Caplan, Arthur L. Reports of bioethics' demise are premature [letter]. *Lancet* 2005 February 19-25; 365(9460): 654-655. Subject: 2.1

Caplan, Arthur L. Too hard to face. *Journal of the American Academy of Psychiatry and the Law* 2005; 33(3): 394-400. Subject: 18.5.1

Caplan, Arthur L. Transplantation at any price? *American Journal of Transplantation* 2004 December; 4(12): 1933-1934. Subject: 19.1

Caplan, Arthur L. An unnatural process: why it is not inherently wrong to seek a cure for aging. *In:* Post, Stephen G.; Binstock, Robert H., eds. The Fountain of Youth: Cultural, Scientific, and Ethical Perspectives on a Biomedical Goal. New York: Oxford University Press; 2004: 271-286. Subject: 20.5.1

Caplan, Arthur L. "Who lost China?" A foreshadowing of today's ideological disputes in bioethics. *Hastings Center Report* 2005 May-June; 35(3): 12-13. Subject: 2.1

Caplan, Arthur; Mobley, William. No brainer — can we cope with the ethical ramifications of new knowledge of the human brain? *Cerebrum: The Dana Forum on Brain Science* 2002 Summer; 4(3): 63. Subject: 17.1

Caplan, Howard. It's time we helped patients die. *RN* 1987 November; 50(11): 44-48, 50-51. Subject: 20.5.1

Capozzi, James D.; Rhodes, Rosamond. Gifts from patients. *Journal of Bone and Joint Surgery: American Volume* 2004 October; 86-A(10): 2339-2340. Subject: 8.1

Cappelen, A.W.; Norheim, Ole Frithjof. Responsibility in health care: a liberal egalitarian approach. *Journal of Medical Ethics* 2005 August; 31(8): 476-480. Subject: 9.4

Capron, Alexander M. The dog in the night-time: or, the curious relationship of the Belmont Report and the President's Commission. *In:* Childress, James F.; Meslin, Eric M.; Shapiro, Harold T., eds. Belmont Revisited: Ethical Principles for Research with Human Subjects. Washington, DC: Georgetown University Press; 2005: 29-40. Subject: 18.2

Capron, Alexander M. Genetic therapy: a lawyer's response. *In:* Hamilton, Michael P., ed. The New Genetics and the Future of Man. Grand Rapids, MI: William B. Eerdmans Publishing Co.; 1972: 133-156. Subject: 15.4

Capron, Alexander Morgan. Borrowed lessons: the role of ethical distinctions in framing law on life-sustaining treatment. *Arizona State Law Journal* 1984; 1984(4): 647-660. Subject: 20.5.1

Capron, Alexander Morgan. Informed consent in catastrophic disease research and treatment. *University of Pennsylvania Law Review* 1974 December; 123(2): 340-438. Subject: 18.3

Capron, Alexander Morgan; Biller-Andorno, Nikola. Ethics and health at the World Health Organization. *Issues in Medical Ethics* 2003 April-June; 11(2): 47-48. Subject: 2.1

Cardinal, Genevieve; Dêschenes, Mylène. Surveying the population biobankers. *In:* Knoppers, Bartha Maria, ed. Populations and Genetics: Legal and Socio-Ethical Perspectives. Boston: Martinus Nijhoff; 2003: 37-94. Subject: 15.1

Cardozo, Margaret. What is a good death? Issues to examine in critical care. *British Journal of Nursing* 2005 November 10-23; 14(20): 1056, 1058-1060. Subject: 20.5.1

Carek, Peter J.; Anderson, Kimberly D.; Blue, Amy V.; Mavis, Brian E. Recruitment behavior and program directors: how ethical are their perspectives about the match process? *Family Medicine* 2000 April; 32(4): 258-260. Subject: 7.2

Carey, Benedict. For parents, the unthinkability of letting go: the anatomy of hope. *New York Times* 2005 March 20; p. WK5. Subject: 20.5.1

Carey, Benedict. In the hospital, a degrading shift from person to patient (Being a patient: a loss of dignity). *New York Times* 2005 August 16; p. A1, A12. Subject: 9.2

Carlet, Jean; Thijs, Lambertus G.; Antonelli, Massimo; Cassell, Joan; Cox, Peter; Hill, Nicholas; Hinds, Charles; Pimentel, Jorge Manuel; Reinhart, Konrad; Thompson, Boyd Taylor. Challenges in end-of-life care in the ICU. Statement of the 5th International Consensus Conference in Critical Care: Brussels, Belgium, April 2003. *Intensive Care Medicine* 2004 May; 30(5): 770-784. Subject: 20.5.1

Carlisle, John R. Ethics and bioethics. *In:* American College of Legal Medicine Textbook Committee, Sanbar, S. Sandy; Firestone, Marvin H.; Buckner, Fillmore; Gibofsky, Allan; LeBlang, Theodore R.; Snyder, Jack W.; Wecht, Cyril H.; Zaremski, Miles J. Legal Medicine. 6th ed. St. Louis: Mosby; 2004: 221-229. Subject: 2.1

Carlisle, John R. Mandatory reporting of gunshot wounds to police . . . not as simple as it seems. *Health Law in Canada* 2004 September; 25(1): 1-10. Subject: 8.4

Carlson, Rick J. The case of BiDil: a policy commentary on race and genetics [opinion]. *Health Affairs* 2005 July-December; 24(Supplement 3): W5-464- W5-468. Subject: 15.11

Carlson, Robert. How then should we do medical research? *Ethics and Medicine* 2005 Spring; 21(1): 59-61. Subject: 18.2

Carmeli, Daphna Birenbaum. Prevalence of Jews as subjects in genetic research: figures, explanation, and potential implications. *American Journal of Medical Genetics Part A* 2004 September 15; 130(1): 76-83. Subject: 18.5.1

Carmeli, Yoram S.; Birenbaum-Carmeli, Daphna; Madgar, Igael; Weissenberg, Ruth. Donor insemination in Israel: recipients' choice of donor. *Journal of Reproductive Medicine* 2001 August; 46(8): 757-762. Subject: 14.2

Carmen, Ira H. Should human cloning be criminalized? *Journal of Law and Politics* 1997 Fall; 13(4): 745-758. Subject: 14.5

Carmi, Rivka. Cross-cultural genetic counseling. *In:* Blazer, Shraga; Zimmer, Etan Z., eds. The Embryo: Scientific Discovery and Medical Ethics. New York: Karger; 2005: 223-236. Subject: 15.2

Carmody, Allison R. Legal protection at birth: resolving the maternal-fetal conflict in the context of medical decision-making. *Medical Trial Technique Quarterly* 2001; 48(1): 165-214. Subject: 9.5.5

Carnahan, Mike. In that case. Response [case study]. *Journal of Bioethical Inquiry* 2005; 2(2): 110-111. Subject: 9.5.7

Carnevale, Franco A. Ethical care of the critically ill child: a conception of a 'thick' bioethics. *Nursing Ethics* 2005 May; 12(3): 239-252. Subject: 20.5.2

Carney, Bridget. The ethics of recruiting foreign nurses: how should Catholic organizations approach this troubling question? *Health Progress* 2005 November-December; 86(6): 31-35. Subject: 7.1

Carney, T.; Tait, D.; Wakefield, A.; Ingvarson, M.; Touyz, S. Coercion in the treatment of anorexia nervosa: clinical, ethical and legal implications. *Medicine and Law:*

World Association for Medical Law 2005 March; 24(1): 21-40. Subject: 8.3.4

Carnovale, Benjamin V.; Clanton, Mark S. Genetic testing: issues related to privacy, employment, and health insurance. *Cancer Practice* 2002 March-April; 10(2): 102-104. Subject: 15.3

Carolan, Bruce. US Supreme Court confronts 'right to die'. *Medico-Legal Journal* 1998; 66(2): 65-69. Subject: 20.7

Carpenter, Alan F.; Neher, Jon O. In defense of living wills [letter and reply]. *Hastings Center Report* 2004 July-August; 34(4): 5-6. Subject: 20.5.4

Carpenter, Betsy; Fagerlin Angela; Schnieder, Carl E. In defense of living wills [letter and reply]. *Hastings Center Report* 2004 July-August; 34(4): 6. Subject: 20.5.4

Carr, David M. Pfizer's epidemic: a need for international regulation of human experimentation in developing countries. *Case Western Reserve Journal of International Law* 2003 Winter; 35(1): 15-53. Subject: 18.2

Carrera, Jose M. Bioethical aspects of ultrasonographic and invasive prenatal diagnosis. *In:* Carrera, Jose M.; Chervenak, Frank A.; Kurjak, Asim, eds. Controversies in Perinatal Medicine: Studies on the Fetus as a Patient. New York: Parthenon Pub. Group; 2003: 282-288. Subject: 15.2

Carse, Alisa L. The moral contours of empathy. *Ethical Theory and Moral Practice* 2005 April; 8(1-2): 169-195. Subject: 1.1

Carter, Alan. Animals, pain and morality. *Journal of Applied Philosophy* 2005; 22(1): 17-22. Subject: 22.1

Carter, Brian S. Ethical concerns for physicians deployed to Operation Desert Storm. *Military Medicine* 1994 January; 159(1): 55-59. Subject: 7.1

Carter, Brian S.; Merenstein, Gerald B.; Robertson, John A. Neonatal care for premature infants [letter and reply]. *Hastings Center Report* 2005 January-February; 35(1): 4-5, 7. Subject: 9.5.7

Carter, H. Ballentine. Informed consent for prostate-specific antigen screening [editorial]. *Urology* 2003 January; 61(1): 13-14. Subject: 8.3.1

Carter, Ivan E. Canadian Psychiatric Association guidelines in relating to the pharmaceutical industry. *Canadian Journal of Psychiatry* 1987 August; 32(6): 476-480. Subject: 9.7

Carter, Meredith. Integrated electronic health records and patient privacy: possible benefits but real dangers. *Medical Journal of Australia* 2000 January 3; 172(1): 28-30. Subject: 8.4

Carter, Michele A. Patient-provider relationship in the context of genetic testing for hereditary cancers. *Journal of the National Cancer Institute Monographs* 1995; (17): 119-121. Subject: 8.1

Subject = NRCBL Primary Classification Number; See inside front cover

Cartwright, Colleen M.; Parker, Malcolm H. Advance care planning and end of life decision making. *Australian Family Physician* 2004 October; 33(10): 815-817, 819. Subject: 20.5.4

Carver, Neil; Ashmore, Russell. Anything to declare? Competing interests in mental health nursing journals [opinion]. *Journal of Psychiatric and Mental Health Nursing* 2004 October; 11(5): 620-622. Subject: 1.3.9

Casagrande, Kathleen M. Children not meant to be: protecting the interests of the child when abortion results in live birth. *Quinnipiac Health Law Journal* 2002; 6(1): 19-55. Subject: 20.5.2

Casarett, David; Crowley, Roxane; Stevenson, Carolyn; Xie, Sharon; Teno, Joan. Making difficult decisions about hospice enrollment: what do patients and families want to know? *Journal of the American Geriatrics Society* 2005 February; 53(2): 249-254. Subject: 20.4.1

Casarett, David; Kapo, Jennifer; Caplan, Arthur. Appropriate use of artificial nutrition and hydration — fundamental principles and recommendations. *New England Journal of Medicine* 2005 December 15; 353(24): 2607-2612. Subject: 20.5.1

Casarett, David J.; Crowley, Roxane L.; Hirschman, Karen B. How should clinicians describe hospice to patients and families? *Journal of the American Geriatrics Society* 2004 November; 52(11): 1923-1928. Subject: 20.4.1

Casell, Jason H. Lengthening the stem: allowing federally funded researchers to derive human pluripotent stem cells from embryos. *University of Michigan Journal of Law Reform* 2001 Spring; 34(3): 547-572. Subject: 18.5.4

Casey, Timothy K. Nature, technology, and the emergence of cybernetic humanity. *In:* Baillie, Harold W.; Casey, Timothy K., eds. Is Human Nature Obsolete? Genetics Bioengineering, and the Future of the Human Condition. Cambridge, MA: MIT Press; 2005: 35-65. Subject: 15.1

Cash, Richard. Ethical issues in health workforce development. *Bulletin of the World Health Organization* 2005 April; 83(4): 280-284. Subject: 7.2

Cash, Richard A. Ethical principles and health research [editorial]. *National Medical Journal of India* 2001 November-December; 14(6): 321-323. Subject: 18.2

Caskey, John D.; Rosenthal, Susan L. Conducting research on sensitive topics with adolescents: ethical and developmental considerations. *Journal of Developmental and Behavioral Pediatrics* 2005 February; 26(1): 61-67. Subject: 18.5.2

Casper, Edward. Doe v. Mutual of Omaha: do insurance policy caps on AIDS treatments violate the Americans with Disabilities Act? *Notre Dame Law Review* 2000 May; 75(4): 1539-1569. Subject: 9.5.6

Cassel, Christine K. The patient-physician covenant: an affirmation of Asklepios. *Connecticut Medicine* 1996 May; 60(5): 291-293. Subject: 8.1

Cassell, Eric J. Consent or obedience? Power and authority in medicine. *New England Journal of Medicine* 2005 January 27; 352(4): 328- 330. Subject: 8.3.1

Cassell, Eric J. The principles of the Belmont Report: how have respect for persons, beneficence, and justice been applied in clinical medicine? *In:* Childress, James F.; Meslin, Eric M.; Shapiro, Harold T., eds. Belmont Revisited: Ethical Principles for Research with Human Subjects. Washington, DC: Georgetown University Press; 2005: 77-95. Subject: 8.1

Cassell, Eric J. The Schiavo case: a medical perspective. *Hastings Center Report* 2005 May-June; 35(3): 22-23. Subject: 20.5.1

Cassidy, Keith. The road to Roe: cultural change and the growth of acceptance of abortion prior to 1973. *In:* Koterski, Joseph W., ed. Life and Learning VII: Proceedings of the Seventh University Faculty for Life Conference. Washington, DC: University Faculty for Life; 1998: 231-245. Subject: 12.5.2

Cassidy, Virginia R. Ethical leadership in managed care: creating a new vision. *Nursing Leadership Forum* 1998 Summer; 3(2): 52-57. Subject: 9.1

Castledine, George. Case of the deputy ward manager who broke patient confidentiality. *British Journal of Nursing* 2005 October 27-November 9; 14(19): 1033. Subject: 7.4

Castro, Arachu; Farmer, Paul. Understanding and addressing AIDS-related stigma: from anthropological theory to clinical practice in Haiti. *American Journal of Public Health* 2005 January; 95(1): 53-59. Subject: 9.5.6

Castro, Oswaldo; Lombardo, Frederic A.; Gordeuk, Victor R.; Charo, R. Alta. The celestial fire of conscience [letter and reply]. *New England Journal of Medicine* 2005 September 22; 353(12): 1301-1302. Subject: 8.1

Castro, Roberto; Erviti, Joaquina. Violations of reproductive rights during hospital births in Mexico. *Health and Human Rights: An International Journal* 2003; 7(1): 91-110. Subject: 14.1

Catalano, Ralph A.; Kessell, Eric; Christy, Annette; Monahan, John. Involuntary psychiatric examinations for danger to others in Florida after the attacks of September 11, 2001. *Psychiatric Services* 2005 July; 56(7): 858-862. Subject: 17.7

Cataldo, Peter J. The USCCB and rape protocols. *Linacre Quarterly* 2005 August; 72(3): 255-259. Subject: 9.5.5

Catalona, William J. Informed consent for prostate-specific antigen screening [editorial]. *Urology* 2003 January; 61(1): 17-19. Subject: 8.3.1

Catalona, William J.; Hakimian, Rina; Korn, David. Ownership and use of tissue specimens for research [letter and reply]. *JAMA: The Journal of the American Medical Association* 2005 March 16; 293(11): 1325-1326. Subject: 1.3.9

Cateforis, Elizabeth Seale. Surrogate motherhood: an argument for regulation and a blueprint for legislation in Kansas. *Kansas Journal of Law and Public Policy* 1995; 4(2): 101-114. Subject: 14.2

Catenhusen, Michael. Ist das Tor auf? Das Stammzellgesetz und die Zukunft des Embryonenschutzgesetzes. *In:* Maio, Giovanni; Just, Hanjörg, eds. Die Forschung an embryonalen Stammzellen in ethischer und rechtlicher Perspektive. Baden-Baden: Nomos Verlagsgesellschaft; 2003: 239-247. Subject: 18.5.4

Catholic Church. Catholic Bishops of Florida. The care of Terri Schiavo. *Origins* 2005 March 17; 34(39): 632. Subject: 20.5.1

Catholic Church. Catholic Bishops of Kentucky. Health care coverage: whose responsibility? *Origins* 2005 December 22; 35(28): 465-469. Subject: 9.2

Catholic Medical Association. Task Force on Ethical and Religious Directives. Report of the task force on ethical and religious directives. *Linacre Quarterly* 2005 May; 72(2): 174-188. Subject: 6

Catholic Medical Association. Task Force on Health Care; Mauceri, Joseph M. Report of the task force on health care in America. *Linacre Quarterly* 2005 May; 72(2): 92-132. Subject: 9.1

Catholic Medical Association. Task Force on Issues of Conscience. Report of the task force on issues of conscience. *Linacre Quarterly* 2005 May; 72(2): 133-173. Subject: 12.4.3

Catholics for a Free Choice. A long way from the Vatican: Catholic attitudes towards reproductive rights, church-state and related issues in Bolivia, Colombia and Mexico. *Conscience* 2004 Summer-Autumn; 25(2): 39-40. Subject: 14.1

Catholics for a Free Choice. Respecting women's rights and fetal value: reflections on the question of female anesthesia. *Conscience* 2005 Autumn; 26(3): 39-40. Subject: 9.5.8

Catlin, Anita J. Ethical commentary on gender reassignment: a complex and provocative modern issue. *Pediatric Nursing* 1998 January-February; 24(1): 63-65, 99. Subject: 10

Caton, Donald. Medical science and social values. *International Journal of Obstetric Anesthesia* 2004 July; 13(3): 167-173. Subject: 2.2

Catton, Michelle. Medical schools tackle conflict of interest [news]. *CMAJ/JAMC: Canadian Medical Association Journal* 2005 November 8; 173(10): 1143. Subject: 7.2

Catz, Diana S.; Green, Nancy S.; Tobin, Jonathan N.; Lloyd- Puryear, Michele A.; Kyler, Penny; Umemoto,

Ann; Cernoch, Jennifer; Brown, Roxane; Wolman, Fredericka. Attitudes about genetics in underserved, culturally diverse populations. *Community Genetics* 2005 August; 8(3): 161-172. Subject: 15.3

Caulfield, Timothy. Commentary: an independent voice?: Conflicts of interest and research on ethical, legal and social issues. *Health Law Review* 2005; 13(2-3): 114-116. Subject: 1.3.9

Caulfield, Timothy. Gene patents, human clones, and biotechnology policy: the challenges created by globalization. *Alberta Law Review* 2003 December; 41(3): 713-724. Subject: 15.8

Caulfield, Timothy. Legal and ethical issues associated with patient recruitment in clinical trials: the case of competitive enrolment. *Health Law Review* 2005; 13(2-3): 58-61. Subject: 18.3

Caulfield, Timothy. Policy conflicts: gene patents and health care in Canada. *Community Genetics* 2005 October; 8(4): 223-227. Subject: 15.8

Caulfield, Timothy A.; Gold, E. Richard. Genetic testing, ethical concerns, and the role of patent law. *Clinical Genetics* 2000; 57(5): 370-375. Subject: 15.3

Caulfield, Timothy A.; Gold, E. Richard. Whistling in the wind: patents on genetic research are a reality. It's time to reframe the debate. *Forum for Applied Research and Public Policy* 2000 Spring; 15(1): 75-79. Subject: 15.8

Caulfield, Timothy A.; Knoppers, Bartha Maria; Gold, E.R.; Sheremeta, L.E.; Bridge, P.J. Genetic technologies, health care policy and the patent bargain [opinion]. *Clinical Genetics* 2003 January; 63(1): 15-18. Subject: 15.8

Caulfield, Timothy; Gold, E. Richard; Cho, Mildred K. Patenting human genetic material: refocusing the debate [opinion]. *Nature Reviews Genetics* 2000 December; 1(3): 227-231. Subject: 15.8

Caulfield, Timothy; Hirtle, Marie. Regulating the genetic revolution [opinion]. *Molecular Medicine Today* 1999 May; 5(5): 198-200. Subject: 15.3

Caulfield, Timothy; Ries, Nola M. Consent, privacy and confidentiality in longitudinal, population health research: the Canadian legal context. *Health Law Journal* 2004; (Supplement): 1-65. Subject: 18.3

Cavalli-Sforza, L.L.; Bodmer, W.F. Eugenics, euphenics, and human welfare. *In their:* The Genetics of Human Populations. San Francisco: Freeman; 1971: 753-804. Subject: 15.5

Ceaser, Mike. Sun, sand, and an M.D. [news]. *Chronicle of Higher Education* 2005 October 28; 52(10): 55-60. Subject: 7.2

Cecchi, Rossana; Del Vecchio, Simona. Diagnosis of brain death in anencephalic infants: medicolegal and ethical aspects. *Medicine and Law: World Association for Medical Law* 1995; 14(1-2): 3-8. Subject: 20.2.1

Subject = NRCBL Primary Classification Number; See inside front cover

Ceci, Christine; McIntyre, Marjorie. A 'quiet' crisis in health care: developing our capacity to hear. *Nursing Philosophy* 2001 July; 2(2): 122-130. Subject: 8.1

Center for Reproductive Rights. Pregnant Women Living with HIV/AIDS: Protecting Human Rights in Programs to Prevent Mother-to-Child Transmission of HIV. Briefing Paper. New York: Center for Reproductive Rights 2005 August; 16 p. [Online]. Available: http://www.crlp.org/pdf/pub_bp_HIV.pdf [27 September 2005]. Subject: 9.5.6

Center for Reproductive Rights. The Slovak Government's Response to Reproductive Rights Violations against Romani Women: Analysis and Recommendations. New York: Center for Reproductive Rights 2003 May; 16 p. Subject: 11.3

Centers for Medicare and Medicaid Services [CMS]; Health and Human Services [HHS]. Medicare and Medicaid programs; religious nonmedical health care institutions and advance directives. Final rule. *Federal Register* 2003 November 28; 68(229): 66710-66721. Subject: 9.3.1

Centre for Enquiry into Health and Allied Themes. Ethics in social sciences and health research: a draft code of conduct. *Issues in Medical Ethics* 2000 April-June; 8(2): 53-57. Subject: 18.4

Cerminara, Kathy L. Dealing with dying: how insurers can help patients seeking last-chance therapies (even when the answer is "no"). *Health Matrix: Journal of Law-Medicine* 2005 Summer; 15(2): 285-328. Subject: 20.5.1

Cerny, T.; Cerny, E.H. Reply to: Hasman A and Holm S. Nicotine conjugate vaccine: is there a right to a smoking future? [letter]. *Journal of Medical Ethics* 2005 September; 31(9): 558. Subject: 9.5.9

Cessario, Romanus. Catholic hospitals in the new evangelization. *National Catholic Bioethics Quarterly* 2005 Winter; 5(4): 675-686. Subject: 9.1

Cessario, Romanus. Conditional stewardship of life: a moral principle of John Paul II. *In:* McMahon, Kevin T., ed. Moral Issues in Catholic Health Care. Wynnewood, PA: Saint Charles Borromeo Seminary; 2004: 120-138. Subject: 20.5.1

Cha, Ariana Eunjung. A struggling science experiment: states closely watch California's stem cell research initiative. *Washington Post* 2005 February 13; p. A1, A18. Subject: 5.3

Chadha, N.K.; Repanos, C. How much do healthcare professionals know about informed consent? A Bristol experience. *Surgeon* 2004 December; 2(6): 328-333, 360. Subject: 8.3.1

Chadwick, Ruth; Aindow, Gordon. Treatment and research ethics. *In:* Radden, Jennifer, ed. The Philosophy of Psychiatry: A Companion. New York: Oxford University Press; 2004: 282-295. Subject: 17.1

Chadwick, Ruth; Berg, Kåre. Solidarity and equity: new ethical frameworks for genetic databases [opinion]. *Nature Reviews Genetics* 2001 April; 2(4): 318-321. Subject: 15.1

Chadwick, Ruth; Levitt, Mairi. The ethics of community mental health care. *In their:* Chadwick, Ruth; Levitt, Mairi, eds. Ethical Issues in Community Health Care. New York: Arnold; 1998: 102-114. Subject: 17.1

Chadwick, Ruth; Ngwena, Charles. The Human Genome Project, predictive testing and insurance contracts: ethical and legal responses. *Res Publica* 1995; 1(2): 115-129. Subject: 15.3

Chadwick, Ruth; Schüklenk, Udo. Sleeping with the enemy? Where to draw the line on research funding? [editorial]. *Bioethics* 2005 April; 19(2): iii-iv. Subject: 5.3

Chadwick, Ruth; Wilson, Sarah. Genomic databases as global public goods? *Res Publica* 2004; 10(2): 123-134. Subject: 15.10

Chaguturu, Sreekanth; Vallabhaneni, Snigdha. Aiding and abetting — nursing crises at home and abroad [opinion]. *New England Journal of Medicine* 2005 October 27; 353(17): 1761-1763. Subject: 21.6

Chahal, Devinder Singh. Sikh perspectives on bioethics. *In:* Peppin, John F.; Cherry, Mark J., eds. Religious Perspectives in Bioethics. New York: Taylor & Francis; 2004: 211-220. Subject: 2.1

Chaitin, Julia. "I wish he hadn't told me that": methodological and ethical issues in social trauma and conflict research. *Qualitative Health Research* 2003 October; 13(8): 1145-1154. Subject: 18.4

Chalmers, Don. Commercialization and benefit sharing of biotechnology: cross-cultural concerns? *In:* Brannigan, Michael C., ed. Cross-Cultural Biotechnology. Lanham: Rowman and Littlefield; 2004: 3-14. Subject: 15.1

Chalmers, Don. Research involving humans: a time for change? *Journal of Law, Medicine and Ethics* 2004 Winter; 32(4): 583-595. Subject: 18.2

Chalmers, Don; Nicol, Dianne. Embryonic stem cell research: can the law balance ethical, scientific and economic values? (Part II). *Revista de Derecho y Genoma Humano / Law and the Human Genome Review* 2003 July-December; (19): 91-108. Subject: 18.5.4

Chamberlain, Paul. Death after withdrawal of nutrition and hydration. *Lancet* 2005 April 23-29; 365(9469): 1446-1447. Subject: 20.5.1

Chambers, David W. Distributive justice in dentistry [editorial]. *Journal of the American College of Dentists* 2005 Spring; 72(1): 2-3. Subject: 4.1.1

Chambers, John C. "Right to die" — legal view of right to life and death could threaten philosophy of palliative care [letter]. *BMJ: British Medical Journal* 2005 June 11; 330(7504): 1388. Subject: 20.5.1

Chambers, Tod. The art of bioethics. *Hastings Center Report* 2005 March-April; 35(2): 3. Subject: 2.1

Chambers, Tod; Watson, Katie; Verkerk, Marian. Enhancing reflection [letter and reply]. *Hastings Center Report* 2005 July-August; 35(4): 6, 7. Subject: 7.2

Chambers-Evans, Jane; Carnevale, Franco A. Dawning of awareness: the experience of surrogate decision making at the end of life. *Journal of Clinical Ethics* 2005 Spring; 16(1): 28-45. Subject: 8.3.3

Chan, David Kum-Wah. Autonomy, humane medicine, and research ethics: an East Asian perspective. *In:* Brannigan, Michael C., ed. Cross-Cultural Biotechnology. Lanham: Rowman and Littlefield; 2004: 127-137. Subject: 18.1

Chan, Evelyn C.Y.; Haynes, Michelle C.; O'Donnell, Frederick T.; Bachino, Carolyn; Vernon, Sally W. Cultural sensitivity and informed decision making about prostate cancer screening. *Journal of Community Health* 2003 December; 28(6): 393-405. Subject: 9.5.4

Chan, Jonathan. Daoism and bioethics: Daode Jin's doctrine of naturalness and the principle of non-action. *In:* Peppin, John F.; Cherry, Mark J., eds. Religious Perspectives in Bioethics. New York: Taylor & Francis; 2004: 221-231. Subject: 2.1

Chander, Vineet. "It's (still) a boy . . .": making the Pre-natal Diagnostic Techniques Act an effective weapon in India's struggle to stamp out female feticide. *George Washington International Law Review* 2004; 36(2): 453-475. Subject: 14.3

Chang, Ann. Nurses' perceptions of phase I clinical trials in pediatric oncology: a review of the literature. *Journal of Pediatric Oncology Nursing* 2004 November-December; 21(6): 343-349. Subject: 18.5.2

Chang, Wesley. Arrested development: patent laws, embryonic stem cell research, and the organ black market. *Southwestern Journal of Law and Trade in the Americas* 2004; 10(2): 407-432. Subject: 19.5

Chaplin, Julie; Schweitzer, Robert; Perkoulidis, Shelley. Experiences of prenatal diagnosis of spina bifida or hydrocephalus in parents who decide to continue with their pregnancy. *Journal of Genetic Counseling* 2005 April; 14(2): 151-162. Subject: 15.2

Chapman, Audrey R. Should we design our descendants? *Journal of the Society of Christian Ethics* 2003 Fall-Winter; 23(2): 199-223. Subject: 4.5

Chapman, Audrey R. The social and justice implications of extending the human life span. *In:* Post, Stephen G.; Binstock, Robert H., eds. The Fountain of Youth: Cultural, Scientific, and Ethical Perspectives on a Biomedical Goal. New York: Oxford University Press; 2004: 340-361. Subject: 9.5.2

Chapman, Elizabeth. Perceptions of the body and genetic risk. *In:* Bainham, Andrew; Sclater, Shelley Day; Rich-

ards, Martin, eds. Body Lore and Laws. Portland, OR: Hart Pub.; 2002: 309-328. Subject: 15.3

Charafeddine, Moussa. Discrimination. *In:* Knoppers, Bartha Maria, ed. Populations and Genetics: Legal and Socio-Ethical Perspectives. Boston: Martinus Nijhoff; 2003: 591-601. Subject: 15.1

Charatan, Fred. President Bush and Congress intervene in "right to die" case [news]. *BMJ: British Medical Journal* 2005 March 26; 330(7493): 687. Subject: 20.5.1

Charatan, Fred. US Supreme Court refuses to intervene in 'right to die' case [news]. *BMJ: British Medical Journal* 2005 April 2; 330(7494): 746. Subject: 20.5.1

Charchuk, Margo; Simpson, Christy. Hope, disclosure, and control in the neonatal intensive care unit. *Health Communication* 2005; 17(2): 191-203. Subject: 9.5.7

Charles, Cathy; Gafni, Amiram; Whelan, Tim. Shared decision-making in the medical encounter: what does it mean? (or it takes at least two to tango). *Social Science and Medicine* 1997 March; 44(5): 681-692. Subject: 8.1

Charles, J. Daryl. Lebensunwertes leben: the devolution of personhood in the Weimar and pre-Weimar era. *Ethics and Medicine* 2005 Spring; 21(1): 41-54. Subject: 20.5.1

Charlesworth, Max. Don't blame the `bio' — blame the `ethics': varieties of (bio)ethics and the challenge of pluralism. *Journal of Bioethical Inquiry* 2005; 2(1): 10-17. Subject: 2.1

Charlton, Bruce G. Conflicts of interest in medical science: peer usage, peer review and `CoI consultancy' [editorial]. *Medical Hypotheses* 2004; 63(2): 181-186. Subject: 1.3.9

Charo, R. Alta. The celestial fire of conscience — refusing to deliver medical care [opinion]. *New England Journal of Medicine* 2005 June 16; 352(24): 2471- 2473. Subject: 8.1

Charo, R. Alta. Legal characterizations of human tissue. *In:* Youngner, Stuart J.; Anderson, Martha W.; Schapiro, Renie, eds. Transplanting Human Tissue: Ethics, Policy, and Practice. New York: Oxford University Press; 2004: 101-119. Subject: 19.5

Charo, R. Alta. Realbioethik. *Hastings Center Report* 2005 July-August; 35(4): 13-14. Subject: 2.1

Chartier, Gary. The rule of double effect: a valuable contemporary resource. *Update [Loma Linda University Center for Christian Bioethics]* 2000 December; 16(4): 3-7. Subject: 2.1

Chase, Anthony Tirado; Alaug, Abdul Karim. Health, human rights, and Islam: a focus on Yemen. *Health and Human Rights: An International Journal* 2004; 8(1): 115-137. Subject: 9.1

Chase, Marilyn. AIDS researchers, activists to face off over drug studies. *Wall Street Journal* 2005 May 18; p. B7. Subject: 18.6

Subject = NRCBL Primary Classification Number; See inside front cover

Chasen, S.T.; Skupski, D.W.; McCullough, L.B.; Chervenak, F.A. Ethical dimensions of nuchal translucency screening. *In:* Carrera, Jose M.; Chervenak, Frank A.; Kurjak, Asim, eds. Controversies in Perinatal Medicine: Studies on the Fetus as a Patient. New York: Parthenon Pub. Group; 2003: 289-295. Subject: 15.2

Chassany, Olivier; Duracinsky, Martin; Mahe, Isabelle. Clinical trials of pharmaceuticals: ethical aspects. *In:* Salek, Sam; Edgar, Andrew, eds. Pharmaceutical Ethics. New York: Wiley; 2002: 71-90. Subject: 18.2

Chater, Keri. Risk and representation: older people and noncompliance. *Nursing Inquiry* 1999 June; 6(2): 132-138. Subject: 9.5.2

Chatterjee, Anjan. Cosmetic neurology: the controversy over enhancing movement, mentation, and mood. *Neurology* 2004 September 28; 63(6): 968-974. Subject: 4.5

Chatterjee, Patralekha. Doctors' group proposes one-child policy for India. *Lancet* 2005 May 7-13; 365(9471): 1609. Subject: 13.3

Chatterjee, Suhita Chopra; Mohanty, Sweta. Socio-ethical issues in the deployment of life-extending technologies. *Indian Journal of Medical Ethics* 2005 July-September; 2(3): 81-82. Subject: 20.5.1

Chaudhari, Bimal P.; Grodin, Michael A. What about proxies? [letter]. *Health Affairs* 2005 November-December; 24(6): 1686-1687. Subject: 20.5.4

Chaudhry, Samena. Fighting for justice [news]. *BMJ: British Medical Journal* 2005 January 15; 330(7483): 114. Subject: 9.5.4

Chayanika. Maharashtra's coercive population policy. *Issues in Medical Ethics* 2001 January-March; 9(1): 22-23. Subject: 13.3

Che Ngah, Anisah. Informed consent in Malaysia: an overview. *Journal International de Bioethique / International Journal of Bioethics* 2005 March-June; 16(1-2): 143-161, 199. Subject: 8.3.1

Check, Erika. Altered embryos offered as solution to stem-cell rift [news]. *Nature* 2005 July 21; 436(7049): 309. Subject: 18.5.4

Check, Erika. Biologists forced to reassess embryo test [news]. *Nature* 2005 October 20; 437(7062): 1075. Subject: 15.3

Check, Erika. Brain-scan ethics come under the spotlight [news]. *Nature* 2005 January 20; 433(7023): 185. Subject: 17.1

Check, Erika. Ethicists urge caution over emotive power of brain scans [news]. *Nature* 2005 May 19; 435(7040): 254-255. Subject: 17.1

Check, Erika. Gene study raises fears for three-parent babies [news]. *Nature* 2005 November 3; 438(7064): 12. Subject: 14.4

Check, Erika. Sanctions agreed over teenager's gene-therapy death [news]. *Nature* 2005 February 17; 433(7027): 674. Subject: 15.4

Check, Erika. Screen test [news]. *Nature* 2005 December 8; 438(7069): 733-734. Subject: 15.2

Check, Erika. Synthetic biologists face up to security issues [news]. *Nature* 2005 August 18; 436(7053): 894-895. Subject: 15.1

Check, Erika. Trial aims to measure social effects of choosing babies' sex [news]. *Nature* 2005 October 27; 437(7063): 1214-1215. Subject: 14.3

Check, Erika. UK embryo licence draws global attention [news]. *Nature* 2005 September 15; 437(7057): 305. Subject: 18.5.4

Check, Erika. US experts draw up guidelines for stem-cell research [news]. *Nature* 2005 April 28; 434(7037): 1058. Subject: 18.5.4

Check, Erika. US policy keeps drugs out of reach in clinical trials abroad [news]. *Nature Medicine* 2005 May; 11(5): 460. Subject: 18.5.9

Check, Erika. US progressives fight for a voice in bioethics [news]. *Nature* 2005 October 13; 437(7061): 932-933. Subject: 2.1

Check, Erika. Where now for stem-cell cloners? [news]. *Nature* 2005 December 22-29; 438(7071): 1058-1059. Subject: 14.5

Check, Erika; Cyranoski, David. Korea's accelerating stem-cell work prompts calls for global ethical rules [news]. *Nature* 2005 May 26; 435(7041): 393. Subject: 18.5.4

Check, Erika; Cyranoski, David. Korean scandal will have global fallout [news]. *Nature* 2005 December 22-29; 438(7071): 1056-1057. Subject: 18.5.4

Cheever, Kerry H.; Jubilan, Boyce; Dailey, Thomas; Ehrhardt, Kathleen; Blumenstein, Robert; Morin, Christopher J.; Lewis, Charles. Surgeons and the spirit: a study on the relationship of religiosity to clinical practice. *Journal of Religion and Health* 2005 Spring; 44(1): 67-80. Subject: 4.1.2

Chelouche, Tessa. Some ethical dilemmas faced by Jewish doctors during the Holocaust. *Medicine and Law: World Association for Medical Law* 2005 December; 24(4): 703-716. Subject: 20.5.1

Chen, Donna T.; Rosenstein, Donald L.; Muthappan, Palaniappan; Hilsenbeck, Susan G.; Miller, Franklin G.; Emanuel, Ezekiel J.; Wendler, David. Research with stored biological samples: what do research participants want? *Archives of Internal Medicine* 2005 March 28; 165(6): 652-655. Subject: 18.3

Chen, Lincoln C.; Boufford, Jo Ivey. Fatal flaws — doctors on the move [editorial]. *New England Journal of Medicine* 2005 October 27; 353(17): 1850-1852. Subject: 21.6

Chen, Tammy; Herbert, Paul B. Involuntary medications allowed to restore competence to stand trial. *Journal of the American Academy of Psychiatry and the Law* 2005; 33(4): 553-554. Subject: 17.4

Chenneville, Tiffany. HIV, confidentiality, and duty to protect: a decision-making model. *Professional Psychology: Research and Practice* 2000 December; 31(6): 661-670. Subject: 9.5.6

Cherniack, E. Paul. Informed consent for medical research by the elderly. *Experimental Aging Research* 2002; 28: 183-198. Subject: 18.5.7

Cherniack, E. Paul. The use of alternative medicine by the elderly and the doctor-patient relationship. *In:* Cherniack, P.; Cherniack, N., eds. Alternative Medicine for the Elderly. Berlin: Springer-Verlag; 2003: 27-45. Subject: 4.1.1

Cherry, April L. Choosing substantive justice: a discussion of "choice," "rights" and the new reproductive technologies. *Wisconsin Women's Law Journal* 1997 Summer; 11(3): 431-441. Subject: 10

Cherry, April L. Nurturing in the service of white culture: racial subordination, gestational surrogacy, and the ideology of motherhood. *Texas Journal of Women and the Law* 2001 Spring; 10(2): 83-128. Subject: 10

Cherry, Mark. Cash and compassion. *New Scientist* 2005 August 13-19; 187(2512): 20. Subject: 19.5

Cherry, Mark J. Bioethics in the ruins of Christendom: why John Paul II's diagnosis requires a more radical cure than May and Colvert provide. *In:* Tollefsen, Christopher, ed. John Paul II's Contribution to Catholic Bioethics. Norwell, MA: Springer; 2004: 73-92. Subject: 2.1

Cherry, Mark J. The market and medical innovation: human passions and medical advancement. *Journal of Medicine and Philosophy* 2005 December; 30(6): 555- 569. Subject: 9.3.1

Chervenak, F.A.; McCullough, L.B. Ethics on the frontier of fetal research. *In:* Carrera, Jose M.; Chervenak, Frank A.; Kurjak, Asim, eds. Controversies in Perinatal Medicine: Studies on the Fetus as a Patient. New York: Parthenon Pub. Group; 2003: 296-302. Subject: 18.5.4

Chervenak, Frank A.; McCullough, Laurence B. The diagnosis and management of progressive dysfunction of health care organizations. *Obstetrics and Gynecology* 2005 April; 105(4): 882-887. Subject: 9.1

Chervenak, Frank A.; McCullough, Laurence B. An ethical critique of boutique fetal imaging: a case for the medicalization of fetal imaging. *American Journal of Obstetrics and Gynecology* 2005 January; 192(1): 31-33. Subject: 9.5.8

Chervenak, Frank A.; McCullough, Laurence B. An ethical framework for fetal research. *Medical Ethics Newsletter [Lahey Clinic]* 2003 Winter; 10(1): 1-2. Subject: 18.5.4

Chervenak, Frank A.; McCullough, Laurence B. A group practice disagrees about offering contraception. *American Family Physician* 2002 March 15; 65(6): 1230, 1233. Subject: 4.1.2

Chervenak, Frank A.; McCullough, Laurence B. Implementation of first-trimester risk assessment for trisomy 21: ethical considerations. *American Journal of Obstetrics and Gynecology* 2005 June; 192(6): 1777-1781. Subject: 15.2

Chervenak, Frank A.; McCullough, Laurence B. Should all pregnant women have an ultrasound examination? *Croatian Medical Journal* 1998 June; 39(2): 102-106. Subject: 9.5.5

Chervenak, Frank A.; McCullough, Laurence B.; Birnbach, David J. Ethical issues in fetal surgery research. *Best Practice and Research: Clinical Anaesthesiology* 2004 June; 18(2): 221-230. Subject: 18.5.4

Chervenak, Frank A.; McCullough, Laurence B.; Knapp, Robert C.; Caputo, Thomas A.; Barber, Hugh R.K. A clinically comprehensive ethical framework for offering and recommending cancer treatment before and during pregnancy. *Cancer* 2004 January 15; 100(2): 215-222. Subject: 9.5.5

Chescheir, Nancy G. A response: teaching pelvic examination on women under anesthesia [opinion]. *JAMWA: Journal of the American Medical Women's Association* 2003 Fall; 58(4): 221-222. Subject: 8.3.1

Cheshire, William P., Jr.; Jones, Nancy L. Can artificial techniques supply morally neutral human embryos for research? *Ethics and Medicine* 2005 Summer; 21(2): 73-88. Subject: 18.5.4

Chesney, Russell W. Children as clinical research subjects. *Journal of Pediatrics* 2005 May; 146(5): 579-580. Subject: 18.5.2

Chester, Ronald. Freezing the heir apparent: a dialogue on postmortem conception, parental responsibility, and inheritance. *Houston Law Review* 1996 Winter; 33(4): 967-1025. Subject: 14.2

Chevassut, Daniel. Buddhism. *In:* Council of Europe Publishing, ed. Euthanasia. Volume I. Ethical and Human Aspects. Strasbourg: Council of Europe; Croton- on-Hudson, NY: Manhattan Publishing Co.; 2003: 131-134. Subject: 20.5.1

Cheyne, Colin. Exploiting placebo effects for therapeutic benefit. *Health Care Analysis: An International Journal of Health Care Philosophy and Policy* 2005 September; 13(3): 177-188. Subject: 8.2

Chiang, H.-H.; Lu, Z.-Y,; Wear, S.E. To have or to be: ways of caregiving identified during recovery from the earthquake disaster in Taiwan. *Journal of Medical Ethics* 2005 March; 31(3): 154-158. Subject: 17.2

Subject = NRCBL Primary Classification Number; See inside front cover

Chico, Dee Marlo E. Pharmacogenomics: a brave new world in designer drugs. *Scholar: Saint Mary's Law Review on Minority Issues* 2002 Fall; 5(1): 111-152. Subject: 15.1

Childress, James F. Epilogue: looking back to look forward. *In:* Childress, James F.; Meslin, Eric M.; Shapiro, Harold T., eds. Belmont Revisited: Ethical Principles for Research with Human Subjects. Washington, DC: Georgetown University Press; 2005: 244-251. Subject: 2.1

Childress, James F. Just care: rationing in a public health crisis. *Update [Loma Linda University Center for Christian Bioethics]* 2005 September; 20(3): 1-7. Subject: 9.4

Childress, James F.; Miller, Franklin G. In memoriam: John C. Fletcher [obituary]. *Hastings Center Report* 2004 July-August; 34(4): 49. Subject: 9.6

Chimonas, Susan; Rothman, David J. New federal guidelines for physician-pharmaceutical industry relations: the politics of policy formation. *Health Affairs* 2005 July-August; 24(4): 949-960. Subject: 9.7

Chin, Marshall H. The patient's role in choice of medications: direct-to-consumer advertising and patient decision aids. *Yale Journal of Health Policy, Law, and Ethics* 2005 Summer; 5(2): 771-784. Subject: 9.7

Ching, Bruce. Inverting the viability test for abortion law. *Women's Rights Law Reporter* 2000 Fall-Winter; 22(1): 37-45. Subject: 12.4.1

Chinoy, R.F. Medical ethics: relationships between doctors. *Issues in Medical Ethics* 1997 October-December; 5(4): 105-109. Subject: 2.1

Chinoy, R.F. Some ethical issues in histopathology. *Issues in Medical Ethics* 2000 January-March; 8(1): 22-23. Subject: 7.3

Chiò, Adriano; Borasio, Gian Domenico. Breaking the news in amyotrophic lateral sclerosis. *Amyotrophic Lateral Sclerosis and Other Motor Neuron Disorders* 2004 December; 5(4): 195-201. Subject: 8.2

Chiong, Winston. Brain death without definitions. *Hastings Center Report* 2005 November-December; 35(6): 20-30. Subject: 20.2.1

Chipeur, Gerald D. Blood testing without consent: the right to privacy versus the right to know (Part 2). *Medicine and Law: World Association for Medical Law* 1994; 13(1-2): 55-67. Subject: 9.5.6

Chirwa, Danwood Mzikenge. The right to health in international law: its implications for the obligations of state and non-state actors in ensuring access to essential medicine. *South African Journal on Human Rights* 2003; 19(4): 541-566. Subject: 21.1

Chisholm, Nick; Gillett, Grant. The patient's journey: living with locked-in syndrome [review]. *BMJ: British Medical Journal* 2005 July 9; 331(7508): 94-97. Subject: 9.5.1

Chismark, Sacie R. Race. *In:* Ness, Bryan D., ed. Encyclopedia of Genetics. Revised edition. Volume II. Pasadena, Calif.: Salem Press; 2004: 658-663. Subject: 15.11

Chiswick, Derek. Commentary: test of capacity has little practical benefit. *BMJ: British Medical Journal* 2005 December 17; 331(7530): 1469-1470. Subject: 17.1

Chiu, Tai-Yuan. End-of-life decision making in Taiwan. *In:* Blank, Robert H.; Merrick, Janna C., eds. End-of-Life Decision Making: A Cross-National Study. Cambridge, MA: MIT Press; 2005: 169-181. Subject: 20.4.1

Cho, Mildred K.; Sankar, Pamela. Forensic genetics and ethical, legal and social implications beyond the clinic [opinion]. *Nature Genetics* 2004 November; 36(11, Supplement): S8-S12. Subject: 15.1

Chorpening, Jennifer. Genetic disability: a modest proposal to modify the ADA to protect against some forms of genetic discrimination. *North Carolina Law Review* 2004 May; 82(4): 1441-1481. Subject: 15.1

Chren, Mary-Margaret. Interactions between physicians and drug company representatives [editorial]. *American Journal of Medicine* 1999 August; 107(2): 182-183. Subject: 7.3

Christensen, James A.; Orlowski, James P. Bounty-hunting and finder's fees. *IRB: Ethics and Human Research* 2005 May-June; 27(3): 16-19. Subject: 18.2

Church, Christopher; Santana, Victor M.; Hinds, Pamela S.; Horwitz, Edwin M. Near the boundary of research: roles, responsibilities, and resource allocation. *In:* Kodish, Eric, ed. Ethics and Research with Children: A Case-Based Approach. New York: Oxford University Press; 2005: 274-293. Subject: 18.5.2

Churchill, Jack L. What's a dentist to do? Is participating in a "Top 200 Dentists" survey unethical? *Northwest Dentistry* 2004 July-August; 83(4): 41. Subject: 4.1.1

Churchill, Larry R. Age-rationing in health care: flawed policy, personal virtue. *Health Care Analysis: An International Journal of Health Care Philosophy and Policy* 2005 June; 13(2): 137-146. Subject: 9.4

Churchill, Larry R. Towards a more robust autonomy: revisiting the Belmont Report. *In:* Childress, James F.; Meslin, Eric M.; Shapiro, Harold T., eds. Belmont Revisited: Ethical Principles for Research with Human Subjects. Washington, DC: Georgetown University Press; 2005: 111-125. Subject: 18.2

Churchill, Larry R.; Schenck, David. One cheer for bioethics: engaging the moral experiences of patients and practitioners beyond the big decisions. *CQ: Cambridge Quarterly of Healthcare Ethics* 2005 Fall; 14(4): 389-403. Subject: 2.1

Cilla, Dana. Physicians and pharmaceutical companies: financial conflicts of interests. *Medical Trial Technique Quarterly* 2003; 50(2): 109-144. Subject: 7.3

Civetta, Joseph M. Futile care or caregiver frustration? A practical approach [opinion]. *Critical Care Medicine* 1996 February; 24(2): 346-351. Subject: 20.5.1

Claerhout, B.; DeMoor, G.J.E. Privacy protection for clinical and genomic data. The use of privacy-enhancing techniques in medicine. *International Journal of Medical Informatics* 2005 March; 74(2-4): 257-265. Subject: 8.4

Clark, Annette E. Autonomy and death. *Tulane Law Review* 1996 November; 71(1): 45-137. Subject: 20.7

Clark, Chalmers C. In harm's way: AMA physicians and the duty to treat. *Journal of Medicine and Philosophy* 2005 February; 30(1): 65-87. Subject: 8.1

Clark, Chalmers C.; Macauley, Robert. Civil disobedience: the devil is in the details [letter and reply]. *Hastings Center Report* 2005 July-August; 35(4): 5-6. Subject: 4.1.2

Clark, Colleen; Becker, Marion; Giard, Julienne; Mazelis, Ruta; Savage, Andrea; Vogel, Wendy. The role of coercion in the treatment of women with co-occurring disorders and histories of abuse. *Journal of Behavioral Health Services and Research* 2005 April-June; 32(2): 167-181. Subject: 17.7

Clark, Eileen; McCann, Terence V. Researching students: an ethical dilemma. *Nurse Researcher* 2005; 12(3): 42-51. Subject: 18.5.1

Clark, Peter. Confidentiality and the physician-patient relationship — ethical reflections from a surgical waiting room. *Medical Science Monitor* 2002 November; 8(11): SR31-SR34. Subject: 8.4

Clark, Peter A. Face transplantation: Part II — an ethical perspective. *Medical Science Monitor* 2005 February; 11(2): RA41-RA47. Subject: 19.1

Clark, Stephen R.L. Thinking about biotechnology: towards a theory of just experimentation. *In:* Deane-Drummond, Celia; Szerszynski, Bronislaw, eds. Re- ordering Nature: Theology, Society and the New Genetics. New York: T & T Clark; 2003: 165-177. Subject: 15.1

Clarke, Adele E.; Shim, Janet K.; Mamo, Laura; Fosket, Jennifer Ruth; Fishman, Jennifer R. Biomedicalization: technoscientific transformations of health, illness, and U.S. biomedicine. *American Sociological Review* 2003 April; 68(2): 161-194. Subject: 4.2

Clarke, Simon. Two models of ethics committees. *Journal of Bioethical Inquiry* 2005; 2(1): 41-47. Subject: 9.6

Clausen, Jens. Zelltherapie unter Verwendung adulter Stammzellen oder solcher aus geklonten Embyonen? *In:* Maio, Giovanni; Just, Hanjörg, eds. Die Forschung an embryonalen Stammzellen in ethischer und rechtlicher Perspektive. Baden-Baden: Nomos Verlagsgesellschaft; 2003: 196-213. Subject: 18.5.4

Claxton, Larry D. Scientific authorship. Part 1. A window into scientific fraud? *Mutation Research* 2005 January; 589(1): 17-30. Subject: 1.3.9

Claxton, Larry D. Scientific authorship. Part 2. History, recurring issues, practices, and guidelines. *Mutation Research* 2005 January; 589(1): 31-45. Subject: 1.3.9

Clayton, Ellen Wright. Informed consent and biobanks. *Journal of Law, Medicine and Ethics* 2005 Spring; 33(1): 15-21. Subject: 15.1

Clayton, Ellen Wright. What should the law say about disclosure of genetic information to relatives? *Journal of Health Care Law and Policy* 1998; 1(2): 373-390. Subject: 8.4

Clayton, Paul D. Confidentiality and medical information. *Annals of Emergency Medicine* 2001 September; 38(3): 312-316. Subject: 8.4

Cleary, Michelle; Jordan, Raighne; Horsfall, Jan. Ethical practice guidelines: an evaluation. *International Journal of Mental Health Nursing* 2002 September; 11(3): 199-202. Subject: 4.1.3

Clement, Paul D.; Keisler, Peter D.; Kneedler, Edwin S.; Katsas, Gregory G.; Hallward-Driemeier, Douglas; Stern, Mark B.; Levy, Jonathan H. Brief for the petitioners Gonzales v. State of Oregon. *Issues in Law and Medicine* 2005 Summer; 21(1): 59-75. Subject: 9.5.1

Cline, Heather S. Genetic testing of children: an issue of ethical and legal concern. *Pediatric Nursing* 1999 January-February; 25(1): 61-62, 65, 68. Subject: 15.3

Cochella, Susan E.W.; Pedersen, Donald M. Negotiating a request for nondisclosure [case study and commentary]. *American Family Physician* 2003 January 1; 67(1): 209-211. Subject: 8.2

Coffey, M. Justin; Wilfond, Benjamin; Ross, Lainie Friedman. Ethical assessment of clinical asthma trials including children subjects. *Pediatrics* 2004 January; 113(1, Part 1): 87-94. Subject: 18.5.2

Coffin, Susan E.; Nelson, Robert M. Optimizing risks and benefits: the case of rotavirus vaccine. *In:* Kodish, Eric, ed. Ethics and Research with Children: A Case-Based Approach. New York: Oxford University Press; 2005: 46-62. Subject: 9.1

Coghlan, Andy. Are all human embryos equal? [news]. *New Scientist* 2005 October 22-28; 188(2522): 10-11. Subject: 18.5.4

Coghlan, Andy; Young, Emma. Why fetuses don't feel pain [news]. *New Scientist* 2005 September 3-9; 187(2515): 8-9. Subject: 9.5.8

Coghlan, Peter. The prodigal and his brother: impartiality and the equal consideration of interests. *Theoretical Medicine and Bioethics* 2005; 26(3): 195-206. Subject: 2.1

Cohan, John Alan. Psychiatric ethics and emerging issues of psychopharmacology in the treatment of depression.

Subject = NRCBL Primary Classification Number; See inside front cover

Journal of Contemporary Health Law and Policy 2003 Winter; 20(1): 115-172. Subject: 17.4

Cohen, A. More trouble with ethics committees [letter]. *British Journal of Psychiatry* 1999 October; 175: 393-394. Subject: 18.2

Cohen, Charlotte; McLean, Ken; Barton, Simon. Use of chaperones in general practice: chaperones protect both parties [letter]. *BMJ: British Medical Journal* 2005 April 9; 330(7495): 846-847. Subject: 8.1

Cohen, Cynthia B. Genetics, ethics, and the principle of subsidiarity. *Anglican Theological Review* 1999 Fall; 81(4): 621-630. Subject: 15.1

Cohen, Cynthia B. The moral status of early embryos and new genetic interventions. *In:* Smith, David H.; Cohen, Cynthia B., eds. A Christian Response to the New Genetics: Religious, Ethical, and Social Issues. Lanham, MD: Rowman & Littlefield Publishers; 2003: 105-130. Subject: 4.4

Cohen, Cynthia B. Promises and perils of public deliberation: contrasting two national bioethics commissions on embryonic stem cell research. *Kennedy Institute of Ethics Journal* 2005 September; 15(3): 269-288. Subject: 2.4

Cohen, Cynthia B.; Anderlik, Mary R. Creating and shaping future children. *In:* Smith, David H.; Cohen, Cynthia B., eds. A Christian Response to the New Genetics: Religious, Ethical, and Social Issues. Lanham, MD: Rowman & Littlefield Publishers; 2003: 75-103. Subject: 14.1

Cohen, Cynthia B.; Smith, David H. Bioethics in the Episcopal tradition. *In:* Peppin, John F.; Cherry, Mark J., eds. Religious Perspectives in Bioethics. New York: Taylor & Francis; 2004: 31-51. Subject: 2.1

Cohen, Cynthia B.; Walters, LeRoy. Gene transfer for therapy or enhancement. *In:* Smith, David H.; Cohen, Cynthia B., eds. A Christian Response to the New Genetics: Religious, Ethical, and Social Issues. Lanham, MD: Rowman & Littlefield Publishers; 2003: 53-74. Subject: 15.1

Cohen, David A.; Ben-David, Sarah. Halachic perspective on involuntary psychiatric care of the mentally ill. *Medicine and Law: World Association for Medical Law* 1995; 14(5-6): 463-469. Subject: 17.7

Cohen, Eric. A Jewish-Catholic bioethics? *First Things* 2005 June-July; (154): 7-10. Subject: 2.1

Cohen, Eric. Orphans by design [opinion]. *First Things* 2005 December; (158): 13-15. Subject: 18.5.4

Cohen, Eric. The real meaning of genetics. *New Atlantis* 2005 Summer; 9: 29-41. Subject: 15.1

Cohen, Joshua. Are clinical practice guidelines impartial? *International Journal of Technology Assessment in Health Care* 2004 Fall; 20(4): 415-420. Subject: 9.8

Cohen, Lloyd R. UNOS: the faithless trustee. *American Journal of Bioethics* 2005 July-August; 5(4): 13-14. Subject: 19.6

Cohen, Neal H. Assessing futility of medical interventions — is it futile? *Critical Care Medicine* 2003 February; 31(2): 646-648. Subject: 20.5.1

Cohen, Philip M. Toward a methodology of Reform Jewish bioethics. *CCAR Journal: A Reform Jewish Quarterly* 2005 Summer; 52(3): 3- 21. Subject: 2.1

Cohen, Sharon R. The invisible man. Artificial insemination by donor and the legislation on donor anonymity: a review. *Journal of Family Planning and Reproductive Health Care* 2004 October; 30(4): 270-273. Subject: 14.2

Cohen, Steven P.; Bloche, M. Gregg; Marks, Jonathan H. Doctors and interrogation [letter and reply]. *New England Journal of Medicine* 2005 October 13; 353(15): 1633-1634. Subject: 21.4

Cohen-Almagor, Raphael; Hartman, Monica G. The Oregon Death with Dignity Act: review and proposals for improvement. *Journal of Legislation* 2001; 27(2): 269-298. Subject: 20.7

Cohn, Felicia G. Growing pains: the debate begins [comment]. *American Journal of Bioethics* 2005 September-October; 5(5): 52-53. Subject: 2.1

Cohn, Felicia; Manetta, Alberto. A teachable moment: research ethics revisited. *American Journal of Obstetrics and Gynecology* 2003 January; 188(1): 2. Subject: 1.3.7

Cohn, Jennifer M. Response to commentary on "Adolescent decisional autonomy regarding participation in an emergency department youth violence interview" [letter]. *American Journal of Bioethics [Online]* 2005 September-October; 5(5): W14. Subject: 18.5.2

Cohn, Jennifer M.; Ginsburg, Kenneth R.; Kassam-Adams, Nancy; Fein, Joel A. Adolescent decisional autonomy regarding participation in an emergency department youth violence interview. *American Journal of Bioethics* 2005 September-October; 5(5): 70-74. Subject: 18.5.2

Coker, Richard. Civil liberties and public good: detention of tuberculous patients and the Public Health Act 1984. *Medical History* 2001 July; 45(3): 341-358. Subject: 9.1

Colabawalla, B.N. Dying with dignity: a response [letter]. *Issues in Medical Ethics* 2000 January-March; 8(1): 2. Subject: 20.5.1

Colabawalla, B.N. Issues in organ transplantation. *Issues in Medical Ethics* 2001 July-September; 9(3): 88-90. Subject: 19.1

Colaizzi, Janet. Seclusion and restraint: a historical perspective. *Journal of Psychosocial Nursing and Mental Health Services* 2005 February; 43(2): 31-37. Subject: 17.3

Coleman, Carl H. Procreative liberty and contemporaneous choice: an inalienable rights approach to frozen embryo disputes. *Minnesota Law Review* 1999 November; 84(1): 55-127. Subject: 14.6

Coleman, Carl H. Rationalizing risk assessment in human subject research. *Arizona Law Review* 2004; 46(1): 1-51. Subject: 18.2

Coleman, Carl H.; DeBuono, Barbara A. Developing public policy on assisted reproductive technologies: reflections on the work of the New York State Task Force on life and the law. *Fertility and Sterility* 2000 January; 73(1): 21-23. Subject: 14.1

Coleman, Phyllis. Privilege and confidentiality in 12-step self-help programs: believing the promises could be hazardous to an addict's freedom. *Journal of Legal Medicine* 2005 December; 26(4): 435-474. Subject: 8.4

Coleman, Renita; May, Thomas. Professional-client relationships: rethinking confidentiality, harm, and journalists' public health duties. *Journal of Mass Media Ethics* 2004; 19(3-4): 276-292. Subject: 1.3.7

Coleman, Stephen. Abortion and the foetus as non-person. *In his:* The Ethics of Artificial Uteruses: Implications for Reproduction and Abortion. Burlington, VT: Ashgate Pub.; 2004: 117- 149. Subject: 12.3

Coleman, Stephen. Abortion, ectogenesis and the foetus as person. *In his:* The Ethics of Artificial Uteruses: Implications for Reproduction and Abortion. Burlington, VT: Ashgate Pub.; 2004: 57- 83. Subject: 12.3

Coleman, Stephen. The developing human as a source of donor organs. *In his:* The Ethics of Artificial Uteruses: Implications for Reproduction and Abortion. Burlington, VT: Ashgate Pub.; 2004: 151- 165. Subject: 19.5

Coleman, Stephen. The status of the embryo and foetus. *In his:* The Ethics of Artificial Uteruses: Implications for Reproduction and Abortion. Burlington, VT: Ashgate Pub.; 2004: 85- 115. Subject: 12.3

Coletta, Raymond R. Biotechnology and the creation of ethics. *McGeorge Law Review* 2000; 32(1): 89-110. Subject: 15.6

Cole-Turner, Ronald. Trust common sense [response]. *Conscience* 2003-2004 Winter; 24(4): 17. Subject: 14.1

Colgrove, James; Bayer, Ronald. Manifold restraints: liberty, public health, and the legacy of Jacobson v Massachusetts. *American Journal of Public Health* 2005 April; 95(4): 571-576. Subject: 9.1

Collange, Jean-François. Bioethics and sin. *Christian Bioethics* 2005 August; 11(2): 175-182. Subject: 2.1

Collange, Jean-François. Protestantism. *In:* Council of Europe Publishing, ed. Euthanasia. Volume I. Ethical and Human Aspects. Strasbourg: Council of Europe; Croton-on-Hudson, NY: Manhattan Publishing Co.; 2003: 153-156. Subject: 20.5.1

Collier, Julie; Sandborg, Christy. The first step: DNAR outside the hospital and the role of pediatric medical care providers. *American Journal of Bioethics* 2005 January-February; 5(1): 85- 86. Subject: 20.5.2

Collins, Beth A. Ethical issues in conducting clinical nursing research. *AWHONN's Clinical Issues in Perinatal and Women's Health Nursing* 1993; 4(4): 620-633. Subject: 18.2

Collins, Jody C. Experimental medical treatments: who should decide coverage? *Seattle University Law Review* 1997 Winter; 20(2): 451-487. Subject: 9.4

Collins, Pauline. Restraining children for painful procedures. *Paediatric Nursing* 1999 April; 11(3): 14-16. Subject: 17.3

Collins, Rebecca. Posthumous reproduction and the presumption against consent in cases of death caused by sudden trauma. *Journal of Medicine and Philosophy* 2005 August; 30(4): 431-442. Subject: 14.1

Collins, Suzanne Edgett. Rethinking the Patient Self Determination Act: implementation without effectiveness. *Journal of Nursing Law* 1999 November; 6(3): 29-46. Subject: 2.1

Collogan, Lauren K.; Fleischman, Alan R. Adolescent research and parental permission. *In:* Kodish, Eric, ed. Ethics and Research with Children: A Case-Based Approach. New York: Oxford University Press; 2005: 77- 99. Subject: 18.5.2

Colombo, Roberto. The status and rights of the human embryo and fetus: a Catholic perspective on the unborn child. *In:* Blazer, Shraga; Zimmer, Etan Z., eds. The Embryo: Scientific Discovery and Medical Ethics. New York: Karger; 2005: 40-52. Subject: 4.4

Colombo, Sylviane. Not just euthanasia: recognizing a legal positive right to palliative care. *Medicine and Law: World Association for Medical Law* 2005 March; 24(1): 203-210. Subject: 20.4.1

Colvert, Gavin T. Liberty and responsibility: John Paul II, ethics and the law. *In:* Tollefsen, Christopher, ed. John Paul II's Contribution to Catholic Bioethics. Norwell, MA: Springer; 2004: 51-72. Subject: 2.1

Colvin, Brian T. Why we do not need a Hippocratic Oath. *Medical Education* 2003 December; 37(12): 1125-1126. Subject: 7.2

Combes, Robert. "Europe goes alternative" — what's all the fuss about? [editorial]. *ATLA: Alternatives to Laboratory Animals* 2005 December; 33(6): 549-552. Subject: 22.2

Condic, Maureen L. Stem cells and babies. *First Things* 2005 August-September; (155): 12-13. Subject: 18.5.4

Condic, Maureen L.; Condic, Samuel B. Defining organisms by organization. *National Catholic Bioethics Quarterly* 2005 Summer; 5(2): 331- 353. Subject: 4.4

Subject = NRCBL Primary Classification Number; See inside front cover

Condic, Maureen L.; Condic, Samuel B.; Hurlbut, William B. Producing non-embryonic organisms for stem cells [letter and reply]. *National Catholic Bioethics Quarterly* 2005 Spring; 5(1): 13- 15, 19-22. Subject: 18.5.4

Confederation of European Specialists in Paediatrics [CESP]. Ethics Working Group; De Lourdes Levy, Maria; Larcher, Victor; Kurz, Ronald. Informed consent/assent in children. Statement of the Ethics Working Group of the Confederation of European Specialists in Paediatrics (CESP). *European Journal of Pediatrics* 2003 September; 162(9): 629-633. Subject: 8.3.2

Cong, Yali; Hu, Linying; Dwyer, James. The VIP floors [case study and commentaries]. *Hastings Center Report* 2005 January-February; 35(1): 16-17. Subject: 9.1

Congress, Elaine P. Cultural and ethical issues in working with culturally diverse patients and their families: the use of the culturagram to promote cultural competent practice in health care settings. *Social Work in Health Care* 2004; 39(3-4): 249-262. Subject: 21.7

Conk, George W. Reactions and overreactions: smallpox vaccination, complications, and compensation. *Fordham Environmental Law Journal* 2003 Summer; 14(3): 439-498. Subject: 9.7

Conn, Jennifer; Gillam, Lynn; Conway, Gerard S. Revealing the diagnosis of androgen insensitivity syndrome in adulthood. *BMJ: British Medical Journal* 2005 September 17; 331(7517): 628-630. Subject: 8.2

Connelly, Julia E. Narrative possibilities: using mindfulness in clinical practice. *Perspectives in Biology and Medicine* 2005 Winter; 48(1): 84-94. Subject: 8.1

Connelly, Robert. Assisted suicide is consistent with the ideals of holistic healing. *Alternative Therapies in Health and Medicine* 1996 November; 2(6): 77-82. Subject: 20.7

Connolly, Ceci. Access to abortion pared at state level. *Washington Post* 2005 August 29; p. A1, A4. Subject: 12.4.1

Connolly, Erin Lynn. Constitutional issues raised by states' exclusion of fertility drugs from Medicaid coverage in light of mandated coverage of Viagra. *Vanderbuilt Law Review* 2001 March; 54(2): 451-480. Subject: 9.3.1

Connors, Alfred F., Jr. The influence of prognosis on care decisions in the critically ill. *Critical Care Medicine* 1999 January; 27(1): 5-6. Subject: 20.5.1

Conrad, Peter; Potter, Deborah. Human growth hormone and the temptations of biomedical enhancement. *Sociology of Health and Illness* 2004 March; 26(2): 184-215. Subject: 4.5

Conti, A.; Delbon, P. Medically-assisted procreation in Italy. *Medicine and Law: World Association for Medical Law* 2005 March; 24(1): 163-172. Subject: 14.4

Cook, David; Owens, Gary; Jacobs, Michael. Human growth hormone treatment in adults: balancing economics and ethics. *American Journal of Managed Care* 2004 October; 10(13, Supplement): S417-S419. Subject: 9.7

Cook, Gareth. 94 new cell lines created abroad since Bush decision. *Boston Globe* 2004 May 23; p. A14. Subject: 18.5.4

Cook, Rachel. Safety in the multitude of counsellors: do we need counselling in surrogacy? *In:* Cook, Rachel; Sclater, Shelley Day; Kaganas, Felicity, eds. Surrogate Motherhood: International Perspectives. Portland, OR: Hart; 2003: 179-197. Subject: 14.2

Cook, Rachel. Villain, hero or masked stranger: ambivalence in transactions with human gametes. *In:* Bainham, Andrew; Sclater, Shelley Day; Richards, Martin, eds. Body Lore and Laws. Portland, OR: Hart Pub.; 2002: 211-227. Subject: 14.4

Cooke, David Tom; Caffarelli, Anthony D.; Robbins, Robert C. The road to clinical xenotransplantation: a worthwhile journey. *Transplantation* 2004 October 27; 78(8): 1108-1109. Subject: 19.1

Cooke, Kathy J. Duty or dream? Edwin G. Conklin's critique of eugenics and support for American individualism. *Journal of the History of Biology* 2002 Summer; 35(2): 365- 384. Subject: 15.5

Cooke, Richard W.I. Good practice in consent. *Seminars in Fetal and Neonatal Medicine* 2005 February; 10(1): 63-71. Subject: 8.3.2

Cook-Deegan, Robert M.; Berkelman, Ruth; Davidson, E. Megan; Finder, Stuart; Heitman, Elizabeth; Kelley, Maureen C.; King, Nancy M.P.; Moseley, Ray; Thomas, James C.; Tilden, Samuel J.; Vangsnes, Nikki M. Issues in biosecurity and biosafety [letter]. *Science* 2005 June 24; 308(5730): 1867-1868. Subject: 15.7

Cook-Deegan, Robert; Walters, LeRoy; Pressman, Lori; Pau, Derrick; McCormack, Stephen; Gatchalian, Janella; Burges, Richard. Preliminary data on U.S. DNA-based patents and plans for a survey of licensing practices. *In:* Knoppers, Bartha Maria, ed. Populations and Genetics: Legal and Socio-Ethical Perspectives. Boston: Martinus Nijhoff; 2003: 453-471. Subject: 15.8

Coombes, Rebecca. Do vets and doctors face similar ethical challenges? [news]. *BMJ: British Medical Journal* 2005 November 26; 331(7527): 1227. Subject: 4.1.2

Coombes, Rebecca. Drug industry's new code criticised for lacking teeth [news]. *BMJ: British Medical Journal* 2005 November 26; 331(7527): 1225. Subject: 9.7

Cooper, Michael; Santora, Marc. Bill allows sales of pill over counter: broader distribution of after-sex pill. *New York Times* 2005 June 23; p. B1, B8. Subject: 11.1

Cooper, Richard A.; Tauber, Alfred I. New physicians for a new century [opinion]. *Academic Medicine* 2005 December; 80(12): 1086-1088. Subject: 7.2

Cooper, Richelle J.; Schriger, David L. The availability of references and the sponsorship of original research cited in pharmaceutical advertisements. *CMAJ/JAMC: Canadian Medical Association Journal* 2005 February 15; 172(4): 487-491. Subject: 9.7

Cooper, Robert W.; Frank, Garry L.; Gouty, Carol Ann; Hansen, Mary Mincer. Ethical helps and challenges faced by nurse leaders in the healthcare industry. *Journal of Nursing Administration* 2003 January; 33(1): 17-23. Subject: 4.1.3

Coors, Marilyn E.; Hunter, Lawrence. Evaluation of genetic enhancement: will human wisdom properly acknowledge the value of evolution? [comment]. *American Journal of Bioethics* 2005 May-June; 5(3): 21-22. Subject: 15.1

Copland, P. The book of life. *Journal of Medical Ethics* 2005 May; 31(5): 278-279. Subject: 15.1

Corbie-Smith, Giselle; Arriola, Kimberly R. Jacob. Research and ethics: a legacy of distrust. *In:* Braithwaite, Ronald L.; Taylor, Sandra E., eds. Health Issues in the Black Community. 2nd ed. San Francisco: Jossey-Bass; 2001: 489-502. Subject: 18.3

Corcoran, Cheryl; Malaspina, Dolores; Hercher, Laura. Prodromal interventions for schizophrenia vulnerability: the risks of being "at risk". *Schizophrenia Research* 2005 March 1; 73(2-3): 173-184. Subject: 17.1

Cordner, Christopher. Life and death matters: losing a sense of the value of human beings. *Theoretical Medicine and Bioethics* 2005; 26(3): 207-226. Subject: 4.4

Corfield, Lorraine; Granne, Ingrid. Treating non-competent patients: England's new act imposes new obligations but also makes things clearer [editorial]. *BMJ: British Medical Journal* 2005 December 10; 331(7529): 1353-1354. Subject: 9.5.3

Corinaldi, Michael. Towards the practice of surrogacy in Israel. *Medicine and Law: World Association for Medical Law* 1995; 14(5-6): 425-427. Subject: 14.2

Corke, C.F.; Stow, P.J.; Green, D.T.; Agar, J.W.; Henry, M.J. How doctors discuss major interventions with high risk patients: an observational study. *BMJ: British Medical Journal* 2005 January 22; 330(7484): 182- 184. Subject: 8.1

Corley, Mary C.; Minick, Ptlene; Elswick, R.K.; Jacobs, Mary. Nurse moral distress and ethical work environment. *Nursing Ethics* 2005 July; 12(4): 381-390. Subject: 4.1.3

Corley, Mary C.; Raines, Deborah A. Environments that support ethical nursing practice. *AWHONN's Clinical Issues in Perinatal and Women's Health Nursing* 1993; 4(4): 611-619. Subject: 4.1.3

Cornell, John; Milner, Philip. Is health a matter of choice? [editorial]. *Journal of Public Health Medicine* 1996 June; 18(2): 127-128. Subject: 9.4

Cornwell, John. Against holy orders: will the papacy ever come to terms with progress in reproductive science? *New Scientist* 2005 April 23-29; 186(2496): 23. Subject: 2.1

Cornwell, John. Eugenics and psychiatry. *In his:* Hitler's Scientists: Science, War, and the Devil's Pact. New York: Penguin; 2004: 85-90. Subject: 15.5

Cornwell, John. The 'science' extermination and human experiment. *In his:* Hitler's Scientists: Science, War, and the Devil's Pact. New York: Penguin; 2004: 348-366. Subject: 21.4

Cornwell, John. The 'science' of racial hygiene. *In his:* Hitler's Scientists: Science, War, and the Devil's Pact. New York: Penguin; 2004: 71-84. Subject: 18.5.1

Correa, Francisco Javier León. La bioetica: de la etica clinica a una bioetica social / Bioethics: from clinical ethics to social bioethics. *Vida y Etica* 2003 December; 4(2): 109-115. Subject: 2.1

Corrigan, Oonagh. Empty ethics: the problem with informed consent. *Sociology of Health and Illness* 2003 November; 25(3): 768- 792. Subject: 18.3

Corrigan, Oonagh. Informed consent: the contradictory ethical safeguards in pharmacogenetics. *In:* Tutton, Richard; Corrigan, Oonagh, eds. Genetic Databases: Socio-ethical Issues in the Collection and Use of DNA. New York: Routledge; 2004: 78-96. Subject: 15.1

Corrigan, O.P. Pharmacogenetics, ethical issues: review of the Nuffield Council on Bioethics report. *Journal of Medical Ethics* 2005 March; 31(3): 144-148. Subject: 15.1

Corrigan, Patrick W.; Watson, Amy C.; Warpinski, Amy C.; Gracia, Gabriela. Stigmatizing attitudes about mental illness and allocation of resources to mental health services. *Community Mental Health Journal* 2004 August; 40(4): 297-307. Subject: 17.1

Corte-Real, Francisco. Forensic DNA databases. *Forensic Science International* 2004 December 2; 146(Supplement): S143-S144. Subject: 15.1

Corvalán, Andrea. Fatherhood after death: a legal and ethical analysis of posthumous reproduction. *Albany Law Journal of Science and Technology* 1997; 7(2): 335-365. Subject: 14.6

Cosimi, Benedict. Position of the Transplantation Society on paid organ donation. *In:* Terasaki, Paul I.; Cecka, J. Michael, eds. Clinical Transplants 1998. Los Angeles, CA: UCLA Tissue Typing Laboratory; 1998: 344-345. Subject: 19.5

Cottam, Rachel. Is public health coercive health? [opinion]. *Lancet* 2005 November 5-11; 366(9497): 1592-1594. Subject: 9.1

Cotton, Richard G.H.; Horaitis, Ourania. Mutation databases and ethical considerations. *In:* Knoppers, Bartha Maria, ed. Populations and Genetics: Legal and Socio-Ethical Perspectives. Boston: Martinus Nijhoff; 2003: 169-178. Subject: 15.1

Coulehan, Jack. My injury, your blood. *Hastings Center Report* 2005 January-February; 35(1): 10-11. Subject: 8.3.1

Coulehan, Jack. Today's professionalism: engaging the mind but not the heart [opinion]. *Academic Medicine* 2005 October; 80(10): 892-898. Subject: 4.1.2

Coulson, Brett S.; Fenner, Stephen G.; Almeida, Osvaldo P. Successful treatment of behavioural problems in dementia using a cholinesterase inhibitor: the ethical questions. *Australian and New Zealand Journal of Psychiatry* 2002 April; 36(2): 259-262. Subject: 9.5.2

Coulter, Angela; Fitzpatrick, Ray. The patient's perspective regarding appropriate health care. *In:* Albrecht, Gary L.; Fitzpatrick, Ray; Scrimshaw, Susan C., eds. The Handbook of Social Studies in Health & Medicine. Thousand Oaks, CA: Sage; 2000: 454-464. Subject: 9.1

Council for International Organizations of Medical Sciences [CIOMS]; World Health Organization [WHO]; Islamic Organization for Medical Sciences [IOMS]. International Ethical Guidelines for Biomedical Research Involving Human Subjects (An Islamic Perspective). Geneva: The Council 2004; 74 p. [Online]. Available: http://www.islamset.com/ioms/Code2004/index.html [5 August 20055]. Subject: 2.1

Council of Europe. Additional protocol to the Convention on Human Rights and Biomedicine, on transplantation of organs and tissues of human origin. *Medical Ethics and Bioethics / Medicinska Etika & Bioetika* 2003 Spring-Summer; 10(1-2): 10-13. Subject: 19.5

Council of Europe. Recommendation Rec (2004) 10 of the Committee of Ministers of the Council of Europe to member states concerning the protection of the human rights and dignity of persons with mental disorder. *European Journal of Health Law* 2004 December; 11(4): 407-425. Subject: 17.7

Council of Europe. Recommendation 1512 (2001): protection of the human genome by the Council of Europe. *Medical Ethics and Bioethics / Medicinska Etika & Bioetika* 2001 Spring-Summer; 8(1-2): 9-10. Subject: 15.10

Council of Europe. Committee of Ministers. Recommendation Rec (2003) 10 of the Committee of Ministers to member states on xenotransplantation. *Medical Ethics and Bioethics / Medicinska Etika & Bioetika* 2003 Autumn-Winter; 10(3-4): 12-16. Subject: 19.1

Council, James R.; Smith, Elizabeth J.H.; Kaster-Bundgaard, Jessica; Gladue, Brian A. Ethical evaluation of hypnosis research: a survey of investigators and their Institutional Review Boards. *American Journal of Clinical Hypnosis* 1997 April; 39(4): 258-265. Subject: 18.2

Coupland, Robin; Martin, Sophie; Dutli, Maria-Teresa. Protecting everybody's genetic data. *Lancet* 2005 May 21-27; 365(9473): 1754-1756. Subject: 15.1

Couzin, Jennifer. Gene bank proposal draws support — and a competitor [news]. *Science* 2005 July 29; 309(5735): 684-685. Subject: 15.1

Couzin, Jennifer. Plan B: a collision of science and politics [news]. *Science* 2005 October 7; 310(5745): 38-39. Subject: 11.1

Couzin, Jennifer; Kaiser, Jocelyn. As Gelsinger case ends, gene therapy suffers another blow [news]. *Science* 2005 February 18; 307(5712): 1028. Subject: 15.4

Coverdale, John H.; McCullough, Laurence B.; Chervenak, Frank A. Assisted and surrogate decision making for pregnant patients who have schizophrenia. *Schizophrenia Bulletin* 2004; 30(3): 659-664. Subject: 9.5.5

Coward, Harold; Hartrick, Gwen. Perspectives on health and cultural pluralism: ethics in medical education. *Clinical and Investigative Medicine / Medecine Clinique et Experimentale* 2000 August; 23(4): 261-265. Subject: 7.2

Cowley, C. The dangers of medical ethics. *Journal of Medical Ethics* 2005 December; 31(12): 739-742. Subject: 2.1

Cowley, Christopher. A new rejection of moral expertise. *Medicine, Health Care and Philosophy: A European Journal* 2005; 8(3): 273-279. Subject: 2.1

Cox, Neville. Causation, responsibility and foetal personhood. *Northern Ireland Legal Quarterly* 2000 Winter; 51(4): 579-596. Subject: 4.4

Coxe, Mattie Fincher; Ubel, Peter A.; Silver-Isenstadt, Ari. A change in medical student attitudes of obstetrics-gynecology clerkships toward seeking consent for pelvic examinations on an anesthetized patient [letter and reply]. *American Journal of Obstetrics and Gynecology* 2003 December; 189(6): 1808-1809. Subject: 7.2

Coyer, Sharon M.; Gallo, Agatha M. Secondary analysis of data. *Journal of Pediatric Health Care* 2005 January-February; 19(1): 60-63. Subject: 18.2

Coyle, Nessa; Sculco, Lois. Expressed desire for hastened death in seven patients living with advanced cancer: a phenomenologic inquiry. *Oncology Nursing Forum* 2004 July 13; 31(4): 699-709. Subject: 20.3.1

Coyne, James. Lessons in conflict of interest: the construction of the martyrdom of David Healy and the dilemma of bioethics. *American Journal of Bioethics [Online]* 2005 January-February; 5(1): W3-W14. Subject: 5.3

Coyne, James. Reply to letter to the editor [letter]. *American Journal of Bioethics [Online]* 2005 May-June; 5(3): W13-W15. Subject: 1.3.7

Coyne, James C.; Tsai, Alexander C. Industry-funded bioethics articles [letters]. *Lancet* 2005 September 24-30; 366(9491): 1077-1078. Subject: 2.1

See SUBJECT HEADING KEY FOR SECTION II on inside back cover

Cozby, Dimitri. Notes on "Bioethics and Sin" by Jean-Francois Collange. *Christian Bioethics* 2005 August; 11(2): 183-188. Subject: 2.1

Cozby, Dimitri. So finally, what is Christian about Christian bioethics? *Christian Bioethics* 2005 December; 11(3): 255-267. Subject: 2.1

Crabb, Jennifer A.; Tucker, Diane C.; Mun, Eun Young. The effect of preventability and severity levels of a genetic disorder on desire to communicate genetic testing information to family members. *Genetic Testing* 2005 Winter; 9(4): 320-327. Subject: 15.3

Craft, Ian; Flyckt, Sofia; Heeley, Gosia; Layland, Sarah; Thornhill, Alan; Kelada, Ehab. Will removal of anonymity influence the recruitment of egg donors? A survey of past donors and recipients. *Reproductive BioMedicine Online [electronic]* 2005 March; 10(3): 325-329. Available: http://www.rbmonline.com/Article/1633 [30 September 2005]. Subject: 14.4

Craft, Ian; Thornhill, Alan. Would 'all-inclusive' compensation attract more gamete donors to balance their loss of anonymity? *Reproductive BioMedicine Online [electronic]* 2005 March; 10(3): 301-306. Available: http://www.rbmonline/Article/1687 [30 September 2005]. Subject: 14.4

Craig, Debra. Mechanically restraining the ill and elderly: ethical problems and proposals. *Update [Loma Linda University Center for Christian Bioethics]* 1999 December; 15(4): 12 p. Subject: 17.3

Crain, Lucy S.; Sassaman, Edward; Mulick, James A.; Freeman, John M.; Vining, Eileen P.G. Sterilization and the retarded female: another perspective [letters and reply]. *Pediatrics* 1980 October; 66(4): 650-652. Subject: 11.3

Cram, Fiona; Phillips, Hazel; Tipene-Matua, Bevan; Parsons, Murray; Taupo, Katrina. A 'parallel process'? Beginning a constructive conversation about a Maori methodology. *Journal of Bioethical Inquiry* 2004; 1(1): 14-19. Subject: 18.2

Cranford, Ronald. Facts, lies, and videotapes: the permanent vegetative state and the sad case of Terri Schiavo. *Journal of Law, Medicine and Ethics* 2005 Summer; 33(2): 363- 371. Subject: 20.5.1

CRASH Trial Management Group. Research in emergency situations: with or without relatives consent. *Emergency Medicine Journal* 2004 November; 21(6): 703. Subject: 18.3

Crausman, Robert S. Sexual boundary violations in the physician-patient relationship. *Medicine and Health, Rhode Island* 2004 August; 87(8): 255-256. Subject: 7.4

Crausman, Robert S.; Baruch, Jay M. Abandonment in the physician-patient relationship. *Medicine and Health, Rhode Island* 2004 May; 87(5): 154-156. Subject: 8.1

Crawford, Cromwell. Hindu bioethics. *In:* Peppin, John F.; Cherry, Mark J., eds. Religious Perspectives in Bioethics. New York: Taylor & Francis; 2004: 189- 209. Subject: 2.1

Crawford, Gail W. A practical application for a framework for ethical decision making [opinion]. *Dimensions of Critical Care Nursing* 2005 March-April; 24(2): 80-81. Subject: 2.1

Crawford, Michael. Live donor liver transplantation: where does it stand in Australia and New Zealand? [opinion]. *Internal Medicine Journal* 2003 November; 33(11): 482-483. Subject: 19.1

Crawford, Peter J.M.; Aldred, M.J; Savarirayan, R.; Savulescu, J. 'It's (not) only teeth' [letter]. *Clinical Genetics* 2004 December; 66(6): 565. Subject: 15.2

Cregan, Kate. Ethical and social issues of embryonic stem cell technology. *Internal Medicine Journal* 2005 February; 35(2): 126-127. Subject: 18.5.4

Crepaz-Keay, David. Who benefits from the new act? [comment]. *BMJ: British Medical Journal* 2005 December 17; 331(7530): 1470-1471. Subject: 17.1

Crespi, Gregory S. Overcoming the legal obstacles to the creation of a futures market in bodily organs. *Ohio State Law Journal* 1994; 55(1): 1-77. Subject: 19.5

Crespi, R. Stephen. Ethico-legal issues in biomedicine patenting: a patent professional viewpoint. *Science and Engineering Ethics* 2005 January; 11(1): 117-136. Subject: 15.8

Crigger, Bette-Jane. The curious saga of Congress, the NIH, and conflict of interest. *Hastings Center Report* 2005 March-April; 35(2): 13-14. Subject: 1.3.9

Crigger, Nancy J. The trouble with caring: a review of eight arguments against an ethic of care. *Journal of Professional Nursing* 1997 July-August; 13(4): 217-221. Subject: 4.1.1

Croarkin, Paul; Berg, Jennifer; Spira, James. Informed consent for psychotherapy: a look at therapists' understanding, opinions, and practices. *American Journal of Psychotherapy* 2003; 57(3): 384-400. Subject: 17.2

Croatian Association for Promotion of Patients' Rights. Work group for Creation of the Law on Rights, Obligations and Responsibilities of Patients. Law on Patients' Rights, Obligations and Responsibilities: proposal. Split, Croatia: Croatian Association for Patients' Rights 2002 December; 21 p. [Online]. Available: http://www.pravapacijenata.hr/oren1.pdf [2 December 2005]. Subject: 8.1

Crockin, Susan L. Adam Nash: legally speaking, a happy ending or slippery slope? [opinion]. *Reproductive BioMedicine Online [electronic]* 2001 January-February; 2(1): 6-7 Available: http://www.rbmonline.com/index. html [3 June 2005]. Subject: 8.3.2

Crockin, Susan L. Legal issues related to parenthood after cancer. *Journal of the National Cancer Institute Monographs* 2005; (34): 111-113. Subject: 14.6

Crofts, Christine; Krimsky, Sheldon. Emergence of a scientific and commercial research and development infrastructure for human gene therapy. *Human Gene Therapy* 2005 February; 16(2): 169-177. Subject: 15.4

Crombie, H. David. Contrasts and challenges. *Connecticut Medicine* 2004 September; 68(8): 537. Subject: 9.5.3

Crombie, H. David. Stem cell research: ethical concerns — 'great expectations'. *Connecticut Medicine* 2005 February; 69(2): 109. Subject: 18.5.4

Crombie, H. David. Technology and bioethics: two interviews and a forum. *Connecticut Medicine* 2004 October; 68(9): 595-597. Subject: 2.1

Crook, Paul. American eugenics and the Nazis: recent historiography. *European Legacy* 2002; 7(3): 363-381. Subject: 15.5

Crosby, John F. Karol Wojtyla on treating patients as persons. *In:* Tollefsen, Christopher, ed. John Paul II's Contribution to Catholic Bioethics. Norwell, MA: Springer; 2004: 151-168. Subject: 8.1

Cross, Alan W.; Churchill, Larry R.; Sharp, Michael C.; King, Nancy M.P. Ethical issues in the health care of children with developmental handicaps. *In:* Schopler, Eric; Mesibov, Gary B., eds. Neurobiological Issues in Autism. New York: Plenum Press; 1987: 63-79. Subject: 9.5.7

Cross, Elizabeth; Goodacre, S.; O'Cathain, A.; Arnold, J. Rationing in the emergency department: the good, the bad, and the unacceptable. *Emergency Medicine Journal* 2005 March; 22(3): 171-176. Subject: 9.4

Cross, Michael. UK patients can refuse to let their data be shared across networks [news]. *BMJ: British Medical Journal* 2005 May 28; 330(7502): 1226. Subject: 8.4

Crosswait, Anne Riegle. Comment: "do not resuscitate order" allowed for an infant with AIDS: In the Interest of C.A. *Journal of Health and Hospital Law* 1993 January; 26(1): 11-19. Subject: 8.3.4

Crosthwaite, Jan. In defence of ethicists. A commentary on Christopher Cowley's paper. *Medicine, Health Care and Philosophy: A European Journal* 2005; 8(3): 281-283. Subject: 9.6

Crouch, Gregory. A crusade born of a suffering infant's cry: Saturday profile (Dr. Eduard Verhagen). *New York Times* 2005 March 19; p. A4. Subject: 20.5.2

Crowden, Andrew. Ethically sensitive mental health care: is there a need for a unique ethics for psychiatry? *Australian and New Zealand Journal of Psychiatry* 2003 April; 37(2): 143-149. Subject: 17.1

Crumbaker, Mary. St. Mary's hospital IRB: a small community hospital-based IRB has advantages as well as unique problems in efforts to protect human subjects. *Protecting Human Subjects* 2003 Spring; (8): 8-9. Subject: 18.2

Crysdale, Cynthia S.W. Playing God? Moral agency in an emergent world. *Journal of the Society of Christian Ethics* 2003 Fall-Winter; 23(2): 243-259. Subject: 15.1

Csaba, A.; Papp, Z. Decision-making in prenatal diagnosis. *In:* Carrera, Jose M.; Chervenak, Frank A.; Kurjak, Asim, eds. Controversies in Perinatal Medicine: Studies on the Fetus as a Patient. New York: Parthenon Pub. Group; 2003: 101-106. Subject: 15.2

Culbert, A.; Davis, D.J. Parental preferences for neonatal resuscitation research consent: a pilot study. *Journal of Medical Ethics* 2005 December; 31(12): 721-726. Subject: 18.5.2

Culver, Charles M.; Gert, Bernard. Competence. *In:* Radden, Jennifer, ed. The Philosophy of Psychiatry: A Companion. New York: Oxford University Press; 2004: 258-270. Subject: 8.3.1

Cunningham-Burley, Sarah; Boulton, Mary. The social context of the new genetics. *In:* Albrecht, Gary L.; Fitzpatrick, Ray; Scrimshaw, Susan C., eds. The Handbook of Social Studies in Health & Medicine. Thousand Oaks, CA: Sage; 2000: 173-187. Subject: 15.1

Cuomo, Peter. Regulation of biotechnology by executive orders: questions about constitutionality, legality and overall fairness to the American public. *Journal of Biolaw and Business* 2005; 8(2): 30-42. Subject: 18.6

Curfman, Gregory D.; Morrissey, Stephen; Drazen, Jeffrey M. Expression of concern: Bombardier et al., "Comparison of upper gastrointestinal toxicity of rofecoxib and naproxen in patients with rheumatoid arthritis," N Engl J Med 2000; 343: 1520-8 [editorial]. *New England Journal of Medicine* 2005 December 29; 353(26): 2813-2814. Subject: 1.3.9

Curie, Charles G. SAMHSA's commitment to eliminating the use of seclusion and restraint. *Psychiatric Services* 2005 September; 56(9): 1139-1140. Subject: 17.3

Curlin, Farr A.; Hall, Daniel E. Strangers or friends? A proposal for a new spirituality-in- medicine ethic [opinion]. *JGIM: Journal of General Internal Medicine* 2005 April; 20(4): 370-374. Subject: 8.1

Curlin, Farr A.; Roach, Chad J.; Gorawara-Bhat, Rita; Lantos, John D.; Chin, Marshall H. When patients choose faith over medicine. *Archives of Internal Medicine* 2005 January 10; 165(1): 88-91. Subject: 8.1

Curlin, Farr A.; Verhagen, Eduard; Sauer, Pieter J.J. Euthanasia in severely ill newborns [letter and reply]. *New England Journal of Medicine* 2005 June 2; 352(22): 2354-2355. Subject: 20.5.2

Currie, Peter M. Balancing privacy protections with efficient research: institutional review boards and the use of certificates of confidentiality. *IRB: Ethics and Human Research* 2005 September-October; 27(5): 7-12. Subject: 18.2

Curtin, Leah L.; Arnold, Lauren. A framework for analysis, Part I. *Nursing Administration Quarterly* 2005 April-June; 29(2): 183-187. Subject: 4.1.3

Curtis, J. Randall; Burt, Robert A. Why are critical care clinicians so powerfully distressed by family demands for futile care? [opinion]. *Journal of Critical Care* 2003 March; 18(1): 22-24. Subject: 20.5.1

Curtis, J.R.; Engelberg, R.A.; Nielsen, E.L.; Au, D.H.; Patrick, D.L. Patient-physician communication about end-of-life care for patients with severe COPD. *European Respiratory Journal* 2004 August; 24(2): 200-205. Subject: 20.4.1

Curtis, Laurie C.; Diamond, Ronald. Power and coercion in mental health practice. *In:* Blackwell, Barry, ed. Treatment compliance and the therapeutic alliance. Australia: Harwood Academic Publishers; 1997: 97-122. Subject: 17.7

Cushing, Simon. Against "humanism": speciesism, personhood, and preference. *Journal of Social Philosophy* 2003 Winter; 34(4): 556-571. Subject: 4.4

Cutas, Daniela-Ecaterina. Looking for the meaning of dignity in the Bioethics Convention and the Cloning Protocol. *Health Care Analysis: An International Journal of Health Care Philosophy and Policy* 2005 December; 13(4): 303-313. Subject: 2.1

Cutter, William. Terminal sedation: a Jewish perspective. *Update [Loma Linda University Center for Christian Bioethics]* 2002 September; 18(2): 4-6. Subject: 20.4.1

Cuttler, Leona; Whittaker, June L.; Kodish, Eric D. The overweight adolescent: clinical and ethical issues in intensive treatments for pediatric obesity. *Journal of Pediatrics* 2005 April; 146(4): 559-564. Subject: 9.5.7

Cyranoski, David. Consenting adults? Not necessarily . . . [news]. *Nature* 2005 May 12; 435(7039): 138-139. Subject: 18.3

Cyranoski, David. Japan sets rules for stem cell research [news]. *Nature Medicine* 2004 August; 10(8): 763. Subject: 18.5.4

Cyranoski, David. Japan's embryo experts beg for faster ethical reviews [news]. *Nature* 2005 November 17; 438(7066): 263. Subject: 18.5.4

Cyranoski, David. Japan's laws on recombinant DNA tie researchers' hands [news]. *Nature Medicine* 2004 June; 10(6): 557. Subject: 15.1

Cyranoski, David. Japanese call for more bite in animal rules [news]. *Nature* 2005 March 3; 434(7029): 6. Subject: 22.2

Cyranoski, David. Korean stem-cell crisis deepens [news]. *Nature* 2005 November 24; 438(7067): 405. Subject: 18.5.4

Cyranoski, David. Paper chase [news]. *Nature* 2005 October 6; 437(7060): 810-811. Subject: 19.5

Cyranoski, David. TV tests call into question cloner's stem-cell success [news]. *Nature* 2005 December 8; 438(7069): 718. Subject: 18.5.4

Cyranoski, David; Check, Erika. Clone star admits lies over eggs [news]. *Nature* 2005 December 1; 438(7068): 536-537. Subject: 18.5.4

Cyranoski, David; Check, Erika. Stem-cell brothers divide [news]. *Nature* 2005 November 17; 438(7066): 262-263. Subject: 18.5.4

Czerwinski, Alicia. Sex, politics, and religion: the clash between Poland and the European Union over abortion. *Denver Journal of International Law and Policy* 2004 Fall; 32(4): 653-674. Subject: 12.4.1

D

D'Souza, Lalitha. Sexual assault: the role of the examining doctor. *Issues in Medical Ethics* 1998 October-December; 6(4): 113-114. Subject: 9.5.5

da Lomba, Sylvie; Martin, Robyn. Public health powers in relation to infectious tuberculosis in England and France: a comparison of approaches. *Medical Law International* 2004; 6(2): 117-147. Subject: 9.1

Daar, Abdallah S.; Acharya, Tara; Filate, Isaac; Thorsteinsdottir, Halla; Singer, Peter. Beyond GM foods: genomics, biotechnology and global health equity. *In:* Thiele, F.; Ashcroft, R.E., eds. Bioethics in a Small World. Berlin: Springer; 2005: 33-44. Subject: 15.1

Daar, A.S. Non-heart-beating donation: ten evidence-based ethical recommendations. *Transplantation Proceedings* 2004 September; 36(7): 1885-1887. Subject: 19.5

Daar, A.S. Paid organ procurement: pragmatic and ethical viewpoints. *Transplantation Proceedings* 2004 September; 36(7): 1876-1877. Subject: 19.5

Daar, A.S.; Bhatt, A.; Court, E.; Singer, P.A. Stem cell research and transplantation: science leading ethics. *Transplantation Proceedings* 2004 October; 36(8): 2504-2506. Subject: 18.5.4

Daar, Judith F. Direct democracy and bioethical choices: voting life and death at the ballot box. *University of Michigan Journal of Law Reform* 1995 Summer; 28(4): 799-859. Subject: 20.5.1

Dabade, Gopal. Unhealthy drug donations. *Indian Journal of Medical Ethics* 2004 January-March; 1(1): 18. Subject: 9.7

Dabrock, Peter. "Suchet der Stadt Bestes" (Jer 29,7)—Transpartikularisierung als Aufgabe einer theologischen Bioethik—entwickelt im Gespräch mit der Differentialethik von Hans-Martin Sass. *In:* Baumann, Eva; Brink, Alexander; May, Arnd T.; Schröder; Peter; Schutzeichel, Corinna Iris, eds. Weltanschauliche Offenheit in der Bioethik. Berlin: Duncker & Humblot; 2004: 115-146. Subject: 2.1

Dada, Mahomed A.; Moorad, Ruweida. A review of a South African research ethics committee. *Issues in Medical Ethics* 2001 April-June; 9(2): 58-59. Subject: 18.2

Dada, M.A.; Dhai, A. South African medical ethics: Biko, Basson, Bezwoda . . . what's next? [letter]. *South African Medical Journal* 2001 January; 91(1): 10. Subject: 1.3.9

Dahl, Edgar. Babies by design: a response to Martin Johnson's moral case study on tissue typing [opinion]. *Reproductive BioMedicine Online [electronic]* 2004 December; 9(6): 597-598. Available: http://www.rbmonline.com/index.html [14 July 2005]. Subject: 15.2

Dahl, Edgar. Sex selection: laissez faire or family balancing? *Health Care Analysis: An International Journal of Health Care Philosophy and Policy* 2005 March; 13(1): 87-90. Subject: 14.3

Dahl, Edgar; Hinsch, K.D.; Brosig, B.; Beutel, M. Attitudes towards preconception sex selection: a representative survey from Germany. *Reproductive BioMedicine Online [electronic]* 2004 December; 9(6): 600-603. Available: http://www.rbmonline.com/index.html [14 July 2005]. Subject: 14.3

Dahlke, Marc H.; Popp, Felix C.; Eggert, Nadine; Hoy, Ludwig; Tanaka, Hideaki; Sasaki, Katsunori; Piso, Pompiliu; Schlitt, Hans J. Differences in attitude toward living and postmortal liver donation in the United States, Germany, and Japan. *Psychosomatics* 2005 January-February; 46(1): 58-64. Subject: 19.5

Dake, Amanda Christine. The application of "out-of-hospital" do not resuscitate order legislation to commercial airline travel. *Journal of Air Law and Commerce* 1997 November-December; 63(2): 443-473. Subject: 20.5.4

Dalby, Jan. Nurse participation in ethical decision making in the clinical setting. *AWHONN's Clinical Issues in Perinatal and Women's Health Nursing* 1993; 4(4): 606-610. Subject: 4.1.3

Dale, O.; Salo, Malti. The Helsinki Declaration, research guidelines and regulations: present and future editorial aspects [editorial]. *Acta Anaesthesiologica Scandinavica* 1996 August; 40(7): 771-772. Subject: 18.2

Daley, George Q.; Sandel, Michael J.; Moreno, Jonathan D. Stem cell research: science, ethics and policy. *Medical Ethics Newsletter [Lahey Clinic]* 2005 Winter; 12(1): 5-8. Subject: 18.5.4

Dallner, James E.; Manning, D. Scott. Death with dignity in Montana. *Montana Law Review* 2004 Winter; 65(1): 309-341. Subject: 20.7

Dallos, Rudi. Ethics and family therapy. *In:* Fairbairn, Susan; Fairbairn, Gavin, eds. Psychology, Ethics and Change. New York: Routledge & Kegan Paul; 1987: 136-160. Subject: 17.1

Dalpé, Robert; Bouchard, Louise; Houle, Anne-Julie; Bédard, Louis. Watching the race to find the breast cancer genes. *Science, Technology, and Human Values* 2003 Spring; 28(2): 187- 216. Subject: 15.3

Dalton, Rex. California prepares to roll out stem-cell funding [news]. *Nature* 2005 October 6; 437(7060): 800-801. Subject: 18.5.4

Dalton, Rex. Obesity expert owns up to million-dollar crime [news]. *Nature* 2005 March 24; 434(7032): 424. Subject: 1.3.9

Dalton, Rex; Check, Erika. Universities scramble to assess scope of falsified results [news]. *Nature* 2005 November 3; 438(7064): 7. Subject: 1.3.9

Daly, Patrick R. Point of view: who's on first? A reflection on euthanasia [opinion]. *Medicine and Health, Rhode Island* 1996 September; 79(9): 336-338. Subject: 20.5.1

Dalyan, Sener. Turkey. *Medical Ethics and Bioethics / Medicinska Etika & Bioetika* 2005; 11(Supplement): 22. Subject: 9.6

Dal-Ré, R.; Ortega, R.; Morejón, E. Multicentre trials review process by research ethics committees in Spain: where do they stand before implementing the new European regulation? *Journal of Medical Ethics* 2005 June; 31(6): 344-350. Subject: 18.2

Dal-Ré, Rafael; Morejón, Elena; Ortega, Rafael. Nature and extent of changes in the patient's information sheets of international multicentre clinical trials as requested by Spanish Research Ethics Committees. *Medicina Clinica* 2004 December 4; 123(20): 770-774. Subject: 18.2

Damm, Reinhard. Individualisierte Medizin und Patientenrechte. *In:* Honnefelder, Ludger; Mieth, Dietmar; Propping, Peter; Siep, Ludwig; Wiesemann, Claudia, eds. Das genetische Wissen und die Zukunft des Menschen. New York: De Gruyter; 2003: 361-368. Subject: 15.1

Damm, Reinhard. Prädiktive genetische Tests: Gesellschaftliche Folgen und rechtlicher Schutz der Persönlichkeit. *In:* Honnefelder, Ludger; Mieth, Dietmar; Propping, Peter; Siep, Ludwig; Wiesemann, Claudia, eds. Das genetische Wissen und die Zukunft des Menschen. New York: De Gruyter; 2003: 203-228. Subject: 15.3

Dancaster, J.T.; Dancaster, L.A. Confidentiality concerning HIV/AIDS status — the implications of the Appeal Court decision. *South African Medical Journal* 1995 March; 85(3): 141-144. Subject: 9.5.6

Danforth, William H.; Neaves, William B. Using words carefully [letter]. *Science* 2005 September 16; 309(5742): 1815-1816. Subject: 14.5

Daniels, K.; Blyth, E.; Crawshaw, M.; Curson, R. Short communication: previous semen donors and their views regarding the sharing of information with offspring. *Human Reproduction* 2005 June; 20(6): 1670-1675. Subject: 14.2

Daniels, Ken. The policy and practice of surrogacy in New Zealand. *In:* Cook, Rachel; Sclater, Shelley Day; Kaganas,

Felicity, eds. Surrogate Motherhood: International Perspectives. Portland, OR: Hart; 2003: 55-73. Subject: 14.2

Daniels, Ken. Recruiting gamete donors: response to Craft and Thornhill. *Reproductive BioMedicine Online [electronic]* 2005 April; 10(4): 430-431. Available: http://www.rbmonline.com/Article/1735 [30 September 2005]. Subject: 14.4

Daniels, Ken R.; Lewis, Gillian M.; Curson, Ruth. Information sharing in semen donation: the views of donors. *Social Science and Medicine* 1997 March; 44(5): 673-680. Subject: 14.6

Daniels, Norman. Fair process in patient selection for antiretroviral treatment in WHO's goal of 3 by 5. *Lancet* 2005 July 9-15; 366(9480): 169-171. Subject: 9.5.6

Daniels, Norman. How to Achieve Fair Distribution of ARTs in 3 by 5: Fair Process and Legitmacy in Patient Selection. Geneva, Switzerland: World Health Organization 2004 January 26-27; 41 p. [Online]. Available: http://www.who.int/ethics/en/background-daniels.pdf [8 March 2005]. Subject: 9.5.6

Daniels, Norman; Kennedy, Bruce; Kawachi, Ichiro. Health and inequality, or, why justice is good for our health. *In:* Anand, Sudhir; Peter, Fabienne; Sen, Amartya, eds. Public Health, Ethics, and Equity. New York: Oxford University Press; 2004: 63-91. Subject: 9.1

Daniels, Peter G. An Illinois Physician-Assisted Suicide Act: a merciful end to a terminally ill criminal tradition. *Loyola University of Chicago Law Journal* 1997 Summer; 28(4): 763-837. Subject: 20.7

Daniels, Stephen R. Should adolescents be paid to participate in research? [opinion]. *Journal of Pediatrics* 2005 April; 146(4): A1. Subject: 18.5.2

Darnovsky, Marcy. Human rights in a post-human future. *In:* Krimsky, Sheldon; Shorett, Peter, eds. Rights and Liberties in the Biotech Age: Why We Need a Genetic Bill of Rights. Lanham: Rowman and Littlefield Publishers; 2005: 209-215. Subject: 15.1

Darou, Wes G.; Hum, Andrew; Kurtness, Jacques. An investigation of the impact of psychosocial research on a native population. *Professional Psychology: Research and Practice* 1993 August; 24(3): 325-329. Subject: 18.6

Darr, Kurt. Going, going, . . . all but gone. *Hospital Topics* 2004 Winter; 82(1): 30-32. Subject: 4.1.1

Darr, Kurt. Terri Schindler Schiavo: an update. *Hospital Topics* 2004 Spring; 82(2): 28-31. Subject: 20.5.1

Das, Abhay K.; Mulley, Graham P. The value of an ethics history? *Journal of the Royal Society of Medicine* 2005 June; 98(6): 262-266. Subject: 20.5.1

Das, Abhijit. Ensuring quality of care in sterilisation services. *Indian Journal of Medical Ethics* 2004 July-September; 1(3): 79-80. Subject: 11.3

Das, Abhijit. The ethical implications of the targeted population programme proposed by the UPA. *Indian Journal of Medical Ethics* 2005 January-March; 2(1): 10- 11. Subject: 13.3

Das, Rajiv; Gostin, Lawrence O. Regulation of medical marijuana [letter and reply]. *JAMA: The Journal of the American Medical Association* 2005 December 28; 294(24): 3091-3092. Subject: 9.5.1

Dasti, Jerry L. Advocating a broader understanding of the necessity of sex- reassignment surgery under Medicaid. *New York University Law Review* 2002 December; 77(6): 1738-1775. Subject: 10

Dauer, Edward A. Ethical misfits: mediation and medical malpractice litigation. *In:* Sharpe, Virginia A., ed. Accountability: Patient Safety and Policy Reform. Washington, DC: Georgetown University Press; 2004: 185-201. Subject: 8.5

Davenport, Charles B. "The eugenics programme and progress in its achievement" in Eugenics, Twelve University Lectures, ed. Lucy James Wilson (1914), pp. 1-14. *In:* Ryan, Frank X., ed. Darwin's Impact: Social Evolution in America, 1880-1920. Volume 2. Race, Gender, and Supremacy. Bristol: Thoemmes; 2001: 150-157. Subject: 15.5

Davey, Claire; White, Victoria; Gattellari, Melina; Ward, Jeanette E. Reconciling population benefits and women's individual autonomy in mammographic screening: in-depth interviews to explore women's views about 'informed choice'. *Australian and New Zealand Journal of Public Health* 2005 February; 29(1): 69-77. Subject: 8.3.1

Davey, Monica. Illinois pharmacies ordered to provide birth control. *New York Times* 2005 April 2; p. A10. Subject: 4.1.1

Davey, Monica. Planned Parenthood sues over records request in Indiana. *New York Times* 2005 March 17; p. A27. Subject: 8.4

Davey, Monica; Belluck, Pam. Pharmacies balk on after-sex pill and widen fight; right of refusal cited; many states take up the issue, citing religious and moral concerns. *New York Times* 2005 April 19; p. A1, A16. Subject: 11.1

David, Rina Jimenez. Living with sin: the Catholic hierarchy and reproductive rights in the Philippines. *Conscience* 2003 Summer; 24(2): 18-21. Subject: 14.1

Davidovitch, Nadav. From a "humble humbug" to the "powerful placebo": the image of the placebo in the orthodox-alternative medicine debate. *In:* Roelcke, Volker; Maio, Giovanni, eds. Twentieth Century Ethics of Human Subjects Research: Historical Perspectives on Values, Practices, and Regulations. Stuttgart: Franz Steiner Verlag; 2004: 293-307. Subject: 4.1.1

Davidson, Graham; Garton, Alison F.; Joyce, Marie. Survey of ethics education in Australian university schools and departments of psychology. *Australian Psychologist* 2003 November; 38(3): 216-222. Subject: 7.2

Subject = NRCBL Primary Classification Number; See inside front cover

Davies, Bronwen R. Coercion or collaboration? Nurses doing research with people who have severe mental health problems. *Journal of Psychiatric and Mental Health Nursing* 2005 February; 12(1): 106-111. Subject: 18.5.6

Davies, Dawn E.; Kreicbergs, Ulrika; Valdimarsdóttir, Unnur; Steineck, Gunnar. Talking about death with dying children [letter and reply]. *New England Journal of Medicine* 2005 January 6; 352(1): 91-92. Subject: 20.3.3

Davies, Michael. Selective non-treatment of the newborn: in whose best interests? In whose judgment? *Northern Ireland Legal Quarterly* 1998 Spring; 49(1): 82-93. Subject: 20.5.2

Davin, Jim; Kaczor, Christopher. Would artificial wombs produce more harm than good? [letter and reply]. *National Catholic Bioethics Quarterly* 2005 Winter; 5(4): 657- 658. Subject: 14.2

Davis, Daniel H.J. Subjective estimates of cognitive impairment in older surgical patients: implications for giving informed consent [letter]. *Journal of the American Geriatrics Society* 2005 October; 53(10): 1842-1843. Subject: 9.5.2

Davis, Dena S. Genetic research and communal narratives. *Hastings Center Report* 2004 July-August; 34(4): 40-49. Subject: 15.1

Davis, Dena S. Tell me a story: using short fiction in teaching law and bioethics. *Journal of Legal Education* 1997 June; 47(2): 240-245. Subject: 2.3

Davis, John K. Life-extension and the Malthusian objection. *Journal of Medicine and Philosophy* 2005 February; 30(1): 27-44. Subject: 20.5.1

Davis, John K. Precedent autonomy and subsequent consent. *Ethical Theory and Moral Practice* 2004 June; 7(3): 267-291. Subject: 8.3.1

Davis, Kevin B. Privacy rights in personal information: HIPAA and the privacy gap between fundamental privacy rights and medical information. *John Marshall Journal of Computer and Information Law* 2001 Summer; 19(4): 535-555. Subject: 8.4

Davis, Lennard J. Life, death, and biocultural literacy. *Chronicle of Higher Education* 2006 January 6; 52(18): B9-B10. Subject: 20.1

Davis, Mardell; Johnston, Sarah R.; DiMicco, Wendy; Findlay, Margaret P.; Taylor, Judy A. The case for a student honor code and beyond. *Journal of Professional Nursing* 1996 January-February; 12(1): 24-30. Subject: 4.1.3

Davis, Matthew M. Varicella vaccine, cost-effectiveness analyses, and vaccination policy [editorial]. *JAMA: The Journal of the American Medical Association* 2005 August 17; 294(7): 845-846. Subject: 9.5.1

Davis, Michael. Comments on Baker's "Draft model aggregated code of ethics for bioethicists" [comment]. *American Journal of Bioethics* 2005 September-October; 5(5): 57-59. Subject: 6

Davis, N. Ann. Invisible disability. *Ethics: An International Journal of Social, Political, and Legal Philosophy* 2005 October; 116(1): 153-213. Subject: 4.2

Davis, Peggy Cooper; Gilligan, Carol. A woman decides: Justice O'Connor and due process rights of choice. *McGeorge Law Review* 2001; 32(3): 895-914. Subject: 10

Davis, Terry. Responsible conduct in research: recent policy developments in the area of research integrity. *Canadian Journal of Cardiovascular Nursing* 1996; 7(2): 21-24. Subject: 18.6

Dawe, Ursula; Verhoef, Marja J.; Page, Stacey A. Treatment refusal: the beliefs and experiences of Alberta nurses. *International Journal of Nursing Studies* 2002 January; 39(1): 71-77. Subject: 20.5.1

Dawson, A.; Spencer, S.A. Informing children and parents about research. *Archives of Disease in Childhood* 2005 March; 90(3): 233-235. Subject: 18.3

Dawson, A.J. The Ad Hoc Advisory Group's proposals for research ethics committees: a mixture of the timid, the revolutionary, and the bizarre [editorial]. *Journal of Medical Ethics* 2005 August; 31(8): 435-436. Subject: 18.2

Dawson, Angus. The determination of 'best interests' in relation to childhood vaccinations. *Bioethics* 2005 April; 19(2): 188-205. Subject: 9.7

Dawson, Angus. The determination of the best interests in relation to childhood immunisation. *Bioethics* 2005 February; 19(1): 72-89. Subject: 9.5.1

Dawson, Angus. Informed consent: bioethical ideal and empirical reality. *In:* Häyry, Matti; Takala, Tuija; Herissone-Kelly, Peter, eds. Bioethics and Social Reality. New York: Rodopi, 2005: 93-105. Subject: 8.3.1

Dawson, Angus. Therapeutic vaccines: a solution to the prevention problem? *Vaccine* 2005 March 18; 23(17-18): 2363-2366. Subject: 9.5.1

Dawson, Angus. What should we do about it? Implications of the empirical evidence in relation to comprehension and acceptability of randomisation. *In:* Holm, Søren; Jonas, Monique F., eds. Engaging the World: The Use of Empirical Research in Bioethics and the Regulation of Biotechnology. Washington, DC: IOS Press; 2004: 41-52. Subject: 18.3

Dawson, Angus J. An ethical argument in favour of routine hepatitis B vaccination in very low-incidence countries [opinion]. *Lancet Infectious Diseases* 2005 February; 5(2): 120-125. Subject: 9.5.1

Dawson, Ellen M. Confidentiality and computerized medical records. *NursingConnections* 1997 Spring; 10(1): 48-53. Subject: 8.4

Dawson, John; Foley, Mary; Peart, Nicola. Research ethics committees. *In:* Dawson, John; Peart, Nicola, eds.

The Law of Research: A Guide. Dunedin, NZ: University of Otago Press; 2003: 47-60. Subject: 18.2

de Beaufort, Inez. Patients in a persistent vegetative state — a Dutch perspective [opinion]. *New England Journal of Medicine* 2005 June 9; 352(23): 2373- 2375. Subject: 20.5.1

De Bona, M.; Canova, D.; Rumiati, R.; Russo, F.P.; Ermani, M.; Ancona, E.; Naccarato, R.; Burra, P. Understanding of and attitudes to xenotransplantation: a survey among Italian university students. *Xenotransplantation* 2004 March; 11(2): 133-140. Subject: 19.1

de Crespigny, L.; Chervenak, F.; Coquel, P.A.; Ville, Y.; McCullough, L. Practicing prenatal diagnosis within the law [editorial]. *Ultrasound in Obstetrics and Gynecology* 2004 October; 24(5): 489-494. Subject: 15.2

de Crespigny, Lachlan; Frcog, Franzcog; Cogu, Ddu. Australian abortion laws: do they pose a 'health hazard'? *O and G magazine* 2005 Autumn; 7(1): 52-54. Subject: 12.4.1

de Cruz, Peter. The terminally ill adult seeking assisted suicide abroad: the extent of the duty owed by a local authority. *Medical Law Review* 2005 Summer; 13(2): 257-267. Subject: 20.7

De Dijn, Herman. Care, communication and conversation. *Ethical Perspectives* 2005 September; 12(3): 357-370. Subject: 8.1

De Gendt, Cindy; Bilsen, Johan; Vander Stichele, Robert; Lambert, Margareta; Van Den Noortgate, Nele; Deliens, Luc. Do-not-resuscitate policy on acute geriatric wards in Flanders, Belgium. *Journal of the American Geriatrics Society* 2005 December; 53(12): 2221-2226. Subject: 20.5.1

De George, Richard T. Intellectual property and pharmaceutical drugs: an ethical analysis. *Business Ethics Quarterly* 2005 October; 15(4): 549-575. Subject: 9.7

de Grey, A.D.N.J. Life extension, human rights, and the rational refinement of repugnance. *Journal of Medical Ethics* 2005 November; 31(11): 659-663. Subject: 20.5.1

de Lacey, Sheryl. Parent identity and 'virtual' children: why patients discard rather than donate unused embryos. *Human Reproduction* 2005 June; 20(6): 1661-1669. Subject: 14.6

De Lepeleire, J.; Buntinx, F.; Aertgeerts, B. Disclosing the diagnosis of dementia: the performance of Flemish general practitioners. *International Psychogeriatrics* 2004 December; 16(4): 421-428. Subject: 8.2

de Melo-Martín, Inmaculada. Firing up the nature/nurture controversy: bioethics and genetic determinism. *Journal of Medical Ethics* 2005 September; 31(9): 526-530. Subject: 15.6

de Ortuzar, Maria Graciela. Towards a universal definition of "benefit-sharing.". *In:* Knoppers, Bartha Maria, ed.

Populations and Genetics: Legal and Socio-Ethical Perspectives. Boston: Martinus Nijhoff; 2003: 473-485. Subject: 15.1

de Raeve, Louise. Trust and trustworthiness in nurse-patient relationships. *Nursing Philosophy* 2002 July; 3(2): 152-162. Subject: 8.1

de Rosa, Francis M. The transfer of abandoned frozen embryos — identifying the object of the act. *National Catholic Bioethics Quarterly* 2005 Spring; 5(1): 59-62. Subject: 14.4

de Souza, Eustace J. Custody, ownership and confidentiality: there are many ethical concerns regarding human tissues. *Issues in Medical Ethics* 1999 January-March; 7(1): 19-20. Subject: 18.3

de Souza, Eustace J. Dying with dignity: a response. *Issues in Medical Ethics* 1999 October-December; 7(4): 127. Subject: 20.5.1

de Souza, Eustace J. The ethics of cloning [comment]. *Issues in Medical Ethics* 1998 July-September; 6(3): 90-91. Subject: 14.5

de Souza, Eustace J. The patient with AIDS — a response. *Indian Journal ofMedical Ethics* 1994 May-July; 1(4): 5. Subject: 9.5.6

de Souza, Eustace J. Surrogacy and human reproductive biology. *Issues in Medical Ethics* 1997 October-December; 5(4): 117-118. Subject: 14.2

de Thé, G.; Buonaguro, F.; Charpak, N.; Hutton, J.L.; Thorstensson, R.; Valdas, E.; Zetterström, R.; Franca Junior, I. Ethical issues in research on control of the HIV/AIDS epidemic: report from a workshop of the world federation of scientists, Erice, Sicily, Italy, 22-24 August 2003 [see correction in Acta Paediatrica 2004 October; 93(10): 1407]. *Acta Paediatrica* 2004 August; 93(8): 1125-1128. Subject: 18.5.9

De Ville, Kenneth. God, science, and history: the cultural origins of medical error. *In:* Sharpe, Virginia A., ed. Accountability: Patient Safety and Policy Reform. Washington, DC: Georgetown University Press; 2004: 143-158. Subject: 9.8

De Vise, Daniel. Years after giving marrow, the return gift of meeting: Alabama donor goes to Arundel (county) to see the young girl he saved. *Washington Post* 2005 July 11; p. B1, B7. Subject: 19.5

De Vries, Raymond. Framing neuroethics: a sociological assessment of the neuroethical imagination. *American Journal of Bioethics* 2005 March-April; 5(2): 25-27. Subject: 17.1

de Wachter, Maurice A.M. Ethical aspects of cryobiology: responsible applications in biomedicine and in clinical practice. *Cryobiology* 2004 April; 48(2): 205-213. Subject: 14.6

Subject = NRCBL Primary Classification Number; See inside front cover

de Wert, Guido. Preimplantation genetic diagnosis: the ethics of intermediate cases [opinion]. *Human Reproduction* 2005 December; 20(12): 3261-3266. Subject: 15.2

de Wolf, Virginia A.; Sieber, Joan E.; Steel, Philip M.; Zarate, Alvan O. Part I: what is the requirement for data sharing? *IRB: Ethics and Human Research* 2005 November-December; 27(6): 12-16. Subject: 1.3.9

Dean, Cornelia. Medical schools found to vary in their drug-testing standards. *New York Times* 2005 May 26; p. A24. Subject: 1.3.9

Dean, Cornelia. Mundane misdeeds skew finding, researchers say. *New York Times* 2005 June 14; p. F6. Subject: 1.3.9

Deane-Drummond, Celia. Aquinas, wisdom ethics and the new genetics. *In:* Deane-Drummond, Celia; Szerszynski, Bronislaw, eds. Re- ordering Nature: Theology, Society and the New Genetics. New York: T & T Clark; 2003: 293-311. Subject: 15.1

Deane-Drummond, Celia E. The ethics of biotechnology. *In her:* Ethics of Nature. Malden, MA: Blackwell Pub.; 2004: 86-110. Subject: 15.1

Deane-Drummond, Celia E. The ethics of cloning. *In her:* Ethics of Nature. Malden, MA: Blackwell Pub.; 2004: 111-135. Subject: 14.5

DeBaets, Amy Michelle. Patents, royalties, and publicly funded stem cell research. *Ethics and Medicine* 2005 Fall; 21(3): 188-190. Subject: 18.5.4

DeBaets, Amy Michelle. UNESCO bioethics declaration. *Ethics and Medicine* 2005 Fall; 21(3): 190-191. Subject: 2.1

Decker, Kevin. Habermas on human rights and cloning: a pragmatist response. *Essays in Philosophy* 2002 June; 3(2): 33 p. [Online]. Available: http://www.humboldt.edu/~essays/decker.html [14 September 2005]. Subject: 14.5

Deckers, Jan. Why current UK legislation on embryo research is immoral. How the argument from lack of qualities and the argument from potentiality have been applied and why they should be rejected. *Bioethics* 2005 June; 19(3): 251-271. Subject: 18.5.4

Decullier, Evelyne; Lhéritier, Véronique; Chapuis, François. Fate of biomedical research protocols and publication bias in France: retrospective cohort study. *BMJ: British Medical Journal* 2005 July 2; 331(7507): 19-22. Subject: 18.2

Decullier, Evelyne; Lhéritier, Véronique; Chapuis, François. The activity of French Research Ethics Committees and characteristics of biomedical research protocols involving humans: a retrospective cohort study. *BMC Medical Ethics [electronic].* 2005; 6(9); 10 p. Available: http://www.biomedcentral.com/bmcmedethics/ [24 November 2005]. Subject: 18.2

Dees, Richard H. Slippery slopes, wonder drugs, and cosmetic neurology: the neuroethics of enhancement [edito-rial]. *Neurology* 2004 September 28; 63(6): 951-952. Subject: 9.7

DeGrazia, David. Advance directives, dementia, and the someone else problem. *In his:* Human Identity and Bioethics. New York: Cambridge University Press; 2005: 159-202. Subject: 20.5.4

DeGrazia, David. Enhancement technologies and human identity. *Journal of Medicine and Philosophy* 2005 June; 30(3): 261-283. Subject: 4.5

DeGrazia, David. Enhancement technologies and self-creation. *In his:* Human Identity and Bioethics. New York: Cambridge University Press; 2005: 203-243. Subject: 4.5

DeGrazia, David. Identity, what we are, and the definition of death. *In his:* Human Identity and Bioethics. New York: Cambridge University Press; 2005: 115-158. Subject: 20.2.1

DeGrazia, David. Prenatal identity: genetic interventions, reproductive choices. *In his:* Human Identity and Bioethics. New York: Cambridge University Press; 2005: 244-294. Subject: 9.5.8

Dekkers, Wim. Medical philosophy and medical ethics [editorial]. *Medicine, Health Care and Philosophy: A European Journal* 2004; 7(3): 241-242. Subject: 4.1.2

Dekkers, Wim; Gordijn, Bert. The proper role of bioethics [editorial]. *Medicine, Health Care and Philosophy: A European Journal* 2005; 8(3): 271-272. Subject: 2.1

Dekkers, Wim; Hoffer, Cor; Wils, Jean-Pierre. Bodily integrity and male and female circumcision. *Medicine, Health Care and Philosophy: A European Journal* 2005; 8(2): 179-191. Subject: 4.4

Dekkers, Wim; Uerz, Inez; Wils, Jean-Pierre. Living well with end stage renal disease: patients' narratives interpreted from a virtue perspective. *Ethical Theory and Moral Practice* 2005 November; 8(5): 485-506. Subject: 19.3

Delatycki, M. Response to Spriggs: is conceiving a child to benefit another against the interest of the new child? *Journal of Medical Ethics* 2005 June; 31(6): 343. Subject: 15.2

DeLisa, Joel A.; Jain, Sudesh Sheela; Kirshblum, Steven. Medical ethics teaching in psychiatry residency training programs: a commentary. *American Journal of Physical Medicine and Rehabilitation* 1998 July-August; 77(4): 4 p. [Online]. Available: http://gateway.ut.ovid.com/gw1/ovidweb.cgi [29 September 2005]. Subject: 2.3

Delkeskamp-Hayes, Corinna. Between morality and repentance: recapturing "sin" for bioethics. *Christian Bioethics* 2005 August; 11(2): 93-132. Subject: 2.1

Delkeskamp-Hayes, Corinna; Zierenberg, Matthias. Gospel truth and societal consensus: recent bioethics statements by the Protestant church in Germany (EKD). *In:*

Peppin, John F.; Cherry, Mark J., eds. Religious Perspectives in Bioethics. New York: Taylor & Francis; 2004: 53-78. Subject: 2.1

Dell'Oro, Roberto. Contextualizando la discusion sobre clonacion: premisas ideologicas y asuntos olvidados / Contextualizing the discussion on cloning: ideological premises and forgotten topics. *Vida y Etica* 2003 December; 4(2): 53-65. Subject: 14.5

Dell'Oro, Roberto. The market ethos and the integrity of health care. *Journal of Contemporary Health Law and Policy* 2002 Fall; 18(3): 641-647. Subject: 9.3.1

Dellinger, Anne; Wall, Aimee. A brief review of North Carolina's law on dying. *North Carolina Medical Journal* 2004 July-August; 65(4): 221-225. Subject: 20.5.1

Delmonico, Francis L.; Harmon, William E. The use of a minor as a live kidney donor. *American Journal of Transplantation* 2002; 2: 333-336. Subject: 19.5

DeMarco, J.P. Principlism and moral dilemmas: a new principle. *Journal of Medical Ethics* 2005 February; 31(2): 101-105. Subject: 2.1

Demarquay, Geneviève; Derex, Laurent; Nighoghossian, Norbert; Adeleine, Patrice; Philippeau, Frédéric; Honnorat, Jérôme; Trouillas, Paul. Ethical issues of informed consent in acute stroke: analysis of the modalities of consent in 56 patients enrolled in urgent therapeutic trials. *Cerebrovascular Diseases* 2005; 19(2): 65-68. Subject: 8.3.3

Demetriou, Maria. Cyprus. *Medical Ethics and Bioethics / Medicinska Etika & Bioetika* 2005; 11(Supplement): 15. Subject: 9.6

Dempsey, Deborah. Donor, father or parent? Conceiving paternity in the Australian Family Court. *International Journal of Law, Policy and the Family* 2004 April; 18(1): 76-102. Subject: 14.2

den Exter, André. Access to health care in the Netherlands: the influence of (European) treaty law. *Journal of Law, Medicine and Ethics* 2005 Winter; 33(4): 698- 710. Subject: 9.2

Denholm, Justin. In that case. Response [case study]. *Journal of Bioethical Inquiry* 2005; 2(2): 112-113. Subject: 9.5.7

Denier, Yvonne. On personal responsibility and the human right to health care. *CQ: Cambridge Quarterly of Healthcare Ethics* 2005 Spring; 14(2): 224-234. Subject: 9.2

Denier, Yvonne. Public health, well-being and reciprocity. *Ethical Perspectives* 2005 March; 12(1): 41-66. Subject: 9.1

Denmark. Council of Ethics. Scandinavian recommendations: sperm donation [policy statement]. *Bulletin of Medical Ethics* 2003 September; (191): 8-9. Subject: 14.2

Dennis, Carina. Diet book attacked for its high-protein advice [news]. *Nature* 2005 December 22-29; 438(7071): 1060-1061. Subject: 1.3.9

Dennis, Carina. Korea launches network to share cloning information [news]. *Nature* 2005 October 20; 437(7062): 1077. Subject: 18.5.4

Dennis, Carina. Rugby team converts to give gene tests a try [news]. *Nature* 2005 March 17; 434(7031): 260. Subject: 15.3

Dennis, Carina; Check, Erika. 'Ethical' routes to stem cells highlight political divide [news]. *Nature* 2005 October 20; 437(7062): 1076-1077. Subject: 18.5.4

Dent, Nigel J.; Sweatman, W.J.F. Can non-regulators audit Independent Ethic Committees (IEC), and if so, how? *Quality Assurance* 2001-2002; 9(1): 43-54. Subject: 18.2

Deogaonkar, Milind. Day-to-day decision making as a physician in India. *Indian Journal of Medical Ethics* 2005 July-September; 2(3): 86-87. Subject: 9.1

Deosthali, Padma. Should case documentations be used for research? [case study]. *Indian Journal of Medical Ethics* 2005 October-December; 2(4): 129. Subject: 18.4

Derbyshire, Stuart W.G. The fetus does not feel pain [debate]. *Conscience* 2004-2005 Winter; 25(3): 32-35. Subject: 9.5.8

DeRenzo, Evan G. Conflict-of-interest policy at the National Institutes of Health: the pendulum swings wildly. *Kennedy Institute of Ethics Journal* 2005 June; 15(2): 199-210. Subject: 1.3.9

DeRenzo, Evan G.; Panzarella, Philip; Selinger, Steve; Schwartz, Jack. Emancipation, capacity, and the difference between law and ethics [case study and commentary]. *Journal of Clinical Ethics* 2005 Summer; 16(2): 144-150. Subject: 8.3.4

DeRenzo, Evan G.; Schwartz, Jack; Selinger, Stephen. Talking about dying: ethical obligations and Maryland state law. *Maryland Medicine* 2004 Summer; 5(3): 39-41. Subject: 20.3.1

Derivan, Albert T.; Leventhal, Bennett L.; March, John; Wolraich, Mark; Zito, Julie Magno. The ethical use of placebo in clinical trials involving children. *Journal of Child and Adolescent Psychopharmacology* 2004 Summer; 14(2): 169-174. Subject: 18.5.2

Derse, Arthur R. The seven-year itch. *American Journal of Bioethics* 2005 September-October; 5(5): 1- 5. Subject: 2.4

Derzko, Natalie M. In search of a compromised solution to the problem arising from patenting biomedical research tools. *Santa Clara Computer and High Technology Law Journal* 2004; 20(2): 347-410. Subject: 5.3

Deschamps, Jack-Yves; Roux, Françoise A.; Gouin, Edouard; Saï, Pierre. Reluctance of French patients with type 1 diabetes to undergo pig pancreatic islet xenotransplantation. *Xenotransplantation* 2005 May; 12(3): 175-180. Subject: 19.1

Deschênes, Mylène. Optimizing safety and benefits of genetic testing: a look at the Canadian policy. *In:* Brannigan, Michael C., ed. Cross-Cultural Biotechnology. Lanham: Rowman and Littlefield; 2004: 57-70. Subject: 15.3

Deschênes, Mylène; Sallée, Clémentine. Accountability in population biobanking: comparative approaches. *Journal of Law, Medicine and Ethics* 2005 Spring; 33(1): 40-53. Subject: 15.1

Deshmukh, Harsha. Cadaver transplantation: ground realities. *Issues in Medical Ethics* 2001 April-June; 9(2): 53. Subject: 19.5

Deshpande, Ohm; Reid, M. Carrington; Rao, Arun S. Attitudes of Asian-Indian Hindus toward end-of-life care. *Journal of the American Geriatrics Society* 2005 January; 53(1): 131-135. Subject: 20.4.1

Despoja, Natasha Stott. The Human Genome Project: how do we protect Australians? *Medical Journal of Australia* 2000 December 4-18; 173(11-12): 596-598. Subject: 15.10

Dessing, R.P. Ethical rationalism applied to pharmaceuticals. *In:* Salek, Sam; Edgar, Andrew, eds. Pharmaceutical Ethics. New York: Wiley; 2002: 27-43. Subject: 9.7

Desvarieux, Moïse; Landman, Roland; Liautaud, Bernard; Girard, Pierre-Marie. Antiretroviral therapy in resource-poor countries: illusions and realities. *American Journal of Public Health* 2005 July; 95(7): 1117-1122. Subject: 9.5.6

Deutsch, Erwin. Clinical studies in the intensive care unit: ethical and legal aspects. *Victoria University of Wellington Law Review* 1997 July; 27(2): 259-272. Subject: 18.5.1

Deutsch, Erwin. Research and use of stem cells. *Revista de Derecho y Genoma-Humano / Law and the Human Genome Review* 2004 July-December; (21): 51-65. Subject: 18.5.4

Deutsch, Erwin. Rights and obligations of the persons concerning their genetic data. *Revista de Derecho y Genoma Humano / Law and the Human Genome Review* 2005 January-June; (22): 75-84. Subject: 15.1

Devi, Sharmila. Research scandal forces Israel to tighten up supervision. *Lancet* 2005 June 4-10; 365(9475): 1915. Subject: 18.3

Devolder, K. Advance directives to protect embryos? [editorial]. *Journal of Medical Ethics* 2005 September; 31(9): 497-498. Subject: 18.5.4

Devolder, K. Creating and sacrificing embryos for stem cells. *Journal of Medical Ethics* 2005 June; 31(6): 366-370. Subject: 18.5.4

Devolder, Katrien. Human embryonic stem cell research: why the discarded-created- distinction cannot be based on

the potentiality argument. *Bioethics* 2005 April; 19(2): 167-186. Subject: 18.5.4

Devolder, Katrien. Preimplantation HLA typing: having children to save our loved ones. *Journal of Medical Ethics* 2005 October; 31(10): 582-586. Subject: 15.2

Dew, Kevin; Cumming, Jacqueline; McLeod, Deborah; Morgan, Sonya; McKinlay, Eileen; Dowell, Anthony; Love, Tom. Explicit rationing of elective services: implementing the New Zealand reforms. *Health Policy* 2005 September 28; 74(1): 1-12. Subject: 9.4

Dewan, Shaila. States taking a new look at end-of-life legislation; Schiavo case prompts flurry of activity. *New York Times* 2005 March 31; p. A14. Subject: 20.5.1

Dhai, A.; Moodley, J.; McQuoid-Mason, D.J.; Rodeck, C. Ethical and legal controversies in cloning for biomedical research — a South African perspective. *South African Medical Journal* 2004 November; 94(11): 906-909. Subject: 18.5.4

Dhai, Amaboo; Lavery, Jim. Beyond our borders: different laws, different languages. Universal ethics? [discussion]. *Protecting Human Subjects* 2005 Summer; (12): 15-17. Subject: 18.5.9

Dhai, Amaboo; Noble, Ray. Ethical issues in HIV. *Best Practice and Research: Clinical Obstetrics and Gynaecology* 2005 April; 19(2): 255-267. Subject: 9.5.6

Dhai, Ames. Module five: implementation of ethics review. *Developing World Bioethics* 2005 March; 5(1): 73-91. Subject: 18.2

Dhanda, Amita. The right to treatment of persons with psychosocial disabilities and the role of the courts. *International Journal of Law and Psychiatry* 2005 March-April; 28(2): 155-170. Subject: 17.5

Dhir, Aaron A. The maelstrom of civil commitment in Ontario: using examinations conducted during periods of unlawful detention to form the basis of subsequent involuntary detention under Ontario's Mental Health Act. *Health Law in Canada* 2003 November; 24(2): 9-18. Subject: 17.7

Di Pietro, M.L.; Giuli, A.; Spagnolo, A.G. Ethical implications of predictive DNA testing for hereditary breast cancer. *Annals of Oncology* 2004; 15(Supplement 1): I65-I70. Subject: 15.3

Diamond, Eugene F. Post-rape medications. *In:* McMahon, Kevin T., ed. Moral Issues in Catholic Health Care. Wynnewood, PA: Saint Charles Borromeo Seminary; 2004: 36-56. Subject: 12.3

Diamond, Eugene F. Stem cells and the culture wars. *Linacre Quarterly* 2005 August; 72(3): 240-245. Subject: 18.5.4

Diamond, Ian; Woodgate, Dawn. Genomics research in the UK — the social science agenda. *New Genetics and Society* 2005 August; 24(2): 239-252. Subject: 15.10

Diamond, Eugene F. Anencephaly and early delivery: can there ever be justification? *Ethics and Medics* 2003 October; 28(10): 2-3. Subject: 20.5.2

Dickens, B.M. Preimplantation genetic diagnosis and 'savior siblings'. *International Journal of Gynecology and Obstetrics* 2005 January; 88(1): 91-96. Subject: 15.2

Dickens, Bernard M. Conflicts between protecting and respecting women: the prohibition of sex-selected birth. *Humane Health Care International* 1997 Summer; 13(2): 14-15. Subject: 14.3

Dickens, Bernard M. Interactions of law and ethics affecting reproductive choice. *Medicine and Law: World Association for Medical Law* 2005 September; 24(3): 549-559. Subject: 12.3

Dickenson, Donna. Einwilligung, Kommodifizierung und Vorteilsausgleich in der Genforschung. *In:* Honnefelder, Ludger; Mieth, Dietmar; Propping, Peter; Siep, Ludwig; Wiesemann, Claudia, eds. Das genetische Wissen und die Zukunft des Menschen. New York: De Gruyter; 2003: 139-151. Subject: 15.1

Dickenson, Donna. The new French resistance: commodification rejected? *Medical Law International* 2005; 7(1): 41-63. Subject: 4.4

Dickersin, Kay; Goodman, Steven. The long and creative arm of the drug industry [letter]. *Lancet* 2005 February 19-25; 365(9460): 656. Subject: 9.7

Dickert, Neal; Kass, Nancy; Paasche-Orlow, Michael; Taylor, Holly. Excluding particular information from consent forms. *Accountability in Research* 2005 January-March; 12(1): 33-45. Subject: 18.3

Dickert, Neal; Sugarman, Jeremy. Ethical goals of community consultation in research. *American Journal of Public Health* 2005 July; 95(7): 1123-1127. Subject: 18.2

Dickey, Susan B.; Deatrick, Janet. Autonomy and decision making for health promotion in adolescence. *Pediatric Nursing* 2000 September-October; 26(5): 461-467. Subject: 9.5.7

Dickey, Susan B.; Kiefner, Jeanne; Beidler, Susan M. Consent and confidentiality issues among school-age children and adolescents. *Journal of School Nursing* 2002 June; 18(3): 179-186. Subject: 8.3.2

Dickinson, George E.; Field, David. Teaching end-of-life issues: current status in United Kingdom and United States medical schools. *American Journal of Hospice and Palliative Care* 2002 May-June; 19(3): 181-186. Subject: 7.2

Dickinson, Jan E. Late pregnancy termination within a legislated medical environment. *Australian and New Zealand Journal of Obstetrics and Gynaecology* 2004 August; 44(4): 337-341. Subject: 12.4.1

Dickson, Hugh G. Multicentre research: negotiating the ethics approval obstacle course [letter]. *Medical Journal of Australia* 2004 October 18; 181(8): 459-460. Subject: 18.2

DiDio, Arthur S. The right to refuse treatment during pregnancy: where maternal and fetal rights conflict. *Medical Trial Technique Quarterly* 1999; 45(3): 225-269. Subject: 8.3.4

Didion, Joan. The case of Theresa Schiavo. *New York Review* 2005 June 9; 52(10): 60-64, 69. Subject: 20.5.1

Diedrich, Lisa. AIDS and its treatments: two doctors' narratives of healing, desire, and belonging. *Journal of Medical Humanities* 2005 Winter; 26(4): 237-257. Subject: 9.5.6

Diedrich, Lisa. A bioethics of failure: antiheroic cancer narratives. *In:* Shildrick, Margrit; Mykitiuk, Roxanne, eds. Ethics of the Body: Postconventional Challenges. Cambridge, MA: MIT Press; 2005: 135-150. Subject: 4.2

Diekema, Douglas S. DNAR in the schools: watch your language! *American Journal of Bioethics* 2005 January-February; 5(1): 76-78. Subject: 20.5.2

Diekema, Douglas S. Payments for participation of children in research. *In:* Kodish, Eric, ed. Ethics and Research with Children: A Case-Based Approach. New York: Oxford University Press; 2005: 143-160. Subject: 18.5.2

Diekema, Douglas S. The preferential treatment of VIPs in the emergency department. *American Journal of Emergency Medicine* 1996 March; 14(2): 226-229. Subject: 9.5.1

Diethelm, Pascal A.; Rielle, Jean-Charles; McKee, Martin. The whole truth and nothing but the truth? The research that Philip Morris did not want you to see. *Lancet* 2005 July 2-8; 366(9479): 86-92. Subject: 9.5.9

Dignam, Paul. Ethics of community treatment orders [letter]. *Australian and New Zealand Journal of Psychiatry* 1998 December; 32(6): 890. Subject: 9.1

Dillen, Jeffrey S. DNA patentability — anything but obvious. *Wisconsin Law Review* 1997; 5: 1023-1046. Subject: 15.8

Diller, Lawrence. Fallout from the pharma scandals: the loss of doctors' credibility? *Hastings Center Report* 2005 May-June; 35(3): 28-29. Subject: 9.7

Dimond, Bridgit. Access to medical reports. *British Journal of Nursing* 2005 September 8-21; 14(16): 860-861. Subject: 8.4

Dimond, Bridgit. Access to records by persons other than the patient. *British Journal of Nursing* 2005 August 11-September 7; 14(15): 829-830. Subject: 8.4

Dimond, Bridgit. Consent to treatment records. *British Journal of Nursing* 2005 October 27-November 9; 14(19): 1024, 1026-1027. Subject: 8.3.1

Dimond, Bridgit. Data protection rights and preserving confidentiality. *British Journal of Nursing* 2005 September 22-October 12; 14(17): 936-937. Subject: 8.4

Subject = NRCBL Primary Classification Number; See inside front cover

Dimond, Bridgit. Law concerning organ transplants and dead donors in the UK. *British Journal of Nursing* 2005 January 13-26; 14(1): 47-48. Subject: 19.5

Dimond, Bridgit. The law regarding health records of the deceased in the UK. *British Journal of Nursing* 2005 April 14-27; 14(7): 391-392. Subject: 8.4

Dimond, Bridgit. Lawful disclosure of confidential information. *British Journal of Nursing* 2005 October 13-26; 14(18): 984- 985. Subject: 8.4

Dimond, Bridgit. The long-awaited Mental Capacity Bill has arrived [opinion]. *British Journal of Nursing* 2005 January 13-26; 14(1): 6. Subject: 8.3.3

Dimond, Bridgit. Removal, retention and storage of organs and tissue in the UK. *British Journal of Nursing* 2005 January 27-February 9; 14(2): 107-108. Subject: 19.5

Dimond, Bridgit. Rights to information access under the Data Protection Act. *British Journal of Nursing* 2005 July 28-August 10; 14(4): 774-776. Subject: 8.2

Ding, Lin; Landon, Bruce E.; Wilson, Ira B.; Wong, Mitchell D.; Shapiro, Martin F.; Cleary, Paul D. Predictors and consequences of negative physician attitudes toward HIV-infected injection drug users. *Archives of Internal Medicine* 2005 March 28; 165(6): 618-623. Subject: 9.5.6

Dinsdale, Henry. Professional responsibility and the protection of human subjects of research in Canada. *Health Law Review* 2005; 13(2-3): 80-85. Subject: 18.2

Dion, Sophie; Reizenstein, Peter. Ethical problems in clinical trials concerning minimal residual tumors. *Supplement to the Journal Medical Oncology and Tumor Pharmacotherapy* 1988; 1: 99-102. Subject: 18.2

DiPasquale, Tony; Gluck, John P. Psychologists, psychiatrists, and physician-assisted suicide: the relationship between underlying beliefs and professional behavior. *Professional Psychology: Research and Practice* 2001 October; 32(5): 501-506. Subject: 17.1

Diprose, Rosalyn. A "genethics" that makes sense: take two. *In:* Shildrick, Margrit; Mykitiuk, Roxanne, eds. Ethics of the Body: Postconventional Challenges. Cambridge, MA: MIT Press; 2005: 237- 258. Subject: 15.1

DiSilvestro, Russell. Human embryos in the original position? *Journal of Medicine and Philosophy* 2005 June; 30(3): 285-304. Subject: 4.4

Distelhorst, Michael. A business ethics approach to contractual good faith and fair dealing: briefly modeled in selected managed healthcare contexts. *Ohio Northern University Law Review* 2000; 26(1): 57-88. Subject: 9.3.2

Divan, Vivek. The Indian Medical Council Regulations 2002: non-application of mind and spirit. *Issues in Medical Ethics* 2002 October-December; 10(4): 83-84. Subject: 6

Dixon, Heather S. Pelvic exam prerequisite to hormonal contraceptives: unjustified infringement on constitutional rights, governmental coercion, and bad public policy. *Harvard Women's Law Journal* 2004 Spring; 27: 177-233. Subject: 11.1

Doaga, Octavian. Romania. *Medical Ethics and Bioethics / Medicinska Etika & Bioetika* 2005; 11(Supplement): 17-18. Subject: 9.6

Dobbs, David; Charo, R. Alta. The celestial fire of conscience [letter and reply]. *New England Journal of Medicine* 2005 September 22; 353(12): 1301-1302. Subject: 8.1

Dobson, Roger. Age discrimination denies elderly people a "dignified death" [news]. *BMJ: British Medical Journal* 2005 June 4; 330(7503): 1288. Subject: 20.4.1

Dobson, Roger. UK government responds to call for change in reproduction technology [news]. *BMJ: British Medical Journal* 2005 August 20-27; 331(7514): 421. Subject: 14.1

Dodd, Gena. Surrogacy and the law in Britain: users' perspectives. *In:* Cook, Rachel; Sclater, Shelley Day; Kaganas, Felicity, eds. Surrogate Motherhood: International Perspectives. Portland, OR: Hart; 2003: 113-120. Subject: 14.2

Dodds, S. Gender, ageing, and injustice: social and political contexts of bioethics. *Journal of Medical Ethics* 2005 May; 31(5): 295-298. Subject: 9.5.2

Doerflinger, Richard M. Experimentation on human subjects and stem cell research. *In:* McMahon, Kevin T., ed. Moral Issues in Catholic Health Care. Wynnewood, PA: Saint Charles Borromeo Seminary; 2004: 93-107. Subject: 18.1

Doerflinger, Richard M. Washington insider. Federal funding for embryonic stem cell researcj. *National Catholic Bioethics Quarterly* 2005 Autumn; 5(3): 455- 462. Subject: 18.5.4

Doerflinger, Richard M. Washington insider. The elections and Congress: a continued statement on embryo research? *National Catholic Bioethics Quarterly* 2005 Spring; 5(1): 25-33. Subject: 18.5.4

Dogan, Hanzade; Sahinoglu, Serap. Fetuses with neural tube defects: ethical approaches and the role of health care professionals in Turkish health care institutions. *Nursing Ethics* 2005 January; 12(1): 59-78. Subject: 9.5.8

Dolin, Gregory. A healer or an executioner? The proper role of a psychiatrist in a criminal justice system. *Journal of Law and Health* 2002-2003; 17(2): 169-216. Subject: 17.1

Dominguez, Roberto A.; Feaster, Daniel J.; Twiggs, Leo B.; Altman, Norman H. Searching for an efficient institutional review board review model: interrelationship of trainee-investigators, funding, and initial approval. *Journal of Laboratory and Clinical Medicine* 2005 February; 145(2): 65-71. Subject: 18.2

Dommergues, Marc; Cahen, Françoise; Garel, Micheline; Mahieu-Caputo, Dominique; Dumez, Yves.

Feticide during second- and third-trimester termination of pregnancy: opinions of health care professionals. *Fetal Diagnosis and Therapy* 2003 March-April; 18(2): 91-97. Subject: 12.5.2

Donat, Dennis C. Encouraging alternatives to seclusion, restraint, and reliance on PRN drugs in a public psychiatric hospital. *Psychiatric Services* 2005 September; 56(9): 1105-1108. Subject: 17.3

Donnelly, Mary. Non-consensual sterilisation of mentally disabled people: the law in Ireland. *Irish Jurist* 1997; 32: 297-322. Subject: 11.3

Donohoe, Martin. Increase in obstacles to abortion: the American perspective in 2004. *Journal of the American Medical Women's Association* 2005; 60(1): 16-25. Subject: 12.5.1

Donohoe, Martin. Urine trouble: practical, legal, and ethical issues surrounding mandated drug testing of physicians. *Journal of Clinical Ethics* 2005 Spring; 16(1): 85-96. Subject: 7.4

Donohue, Michaela. Maternal-fetal health: ethical issues. *AWHONN's Clinical Issues in Perinatal and Women's Health Nursing* 1993; 4(4): 561-569. Subject: 9.5.5

Doolan, Eddie; Brown, Joe. Lessons in death. *Nursing Standard* 2004 September 15-21; 19(1): 22-23. Subject: 20.7

Dorff, Elliot N. End-of-life: Jewish perspectives [opinion]. *Lancet* 2005 September 3-9; 366(9488): 862-865. Subject: 20.5.1

Dorfman, Howard L.; Reig, Linda Pissott. Avoiding legal and ethical pitfalls of industry-sponsored research: the co-existence of research, scholarship, and marketing in the pharmaceutical industry. *Food and Drug Law Journal* 2004; 59(4): 595-615. Subject: 5.3

Döring, Martin. A sequence of 'factishes': the media-metaphorical knowledge dynamics structuring the German press coverage of the human genome. *New Genetics and Society* 2005 December; 24(3): 317-336. Subject: 15.10

Döring, Ole. Searching for advances in biomedical ethics in China: recent trends. *China Analysis* 2003 October; (27); 14 p. [Online]. Available: http://www.chinapolitik. de/studien/china_analysis/no_27.pdf [31 August 2005]. Subject: 2.1

Döring, Ole. Was bedeutet "ethische Verständigung zwischen Kulturen"? Ein philosophischer Problemzugang am Beispiel der Auseinandersetzung mit der Forschung an menschlichen Embryonen in China. *In:* Baumann, Eva; Brink, Alexander; May, Arnd T.; Schröder; Peter; Schutzeichel, Corinna Iris, eds. Weltanschauliche Offenheit in der Bioethik. Berlin: Duncker & Humblot; 2004: 179-211. Subject: 21.7

Dormire, Sharon L. Ethical models: facilitating clinical practice. *AWHONN's Clinical Issues in Perinatal and*

Women's Health Nursing 1993; 4(4): 526-532. Subject: 4.1.3

Dorscheidt, Jozef H.H.M. Assessment procedures regarding end-of-life decisions in neonatology in the Netherlands. *Medicine and Law: World Association for Medical Law* 2005 December; 24(4): 803-829. Subject: 20.5.2

Dósa, Ágnes. New legislation on civil commitment in Hungary. *Medicine and Law: World Association for Medical Law* 1995; 14(7-8): 581-587. Subject: 17.7

Dossey, Larry. Privacy. *Alternative Therapies in Health and Medicine* 2003 May-June; 9(3): 12-16, 112-121. Subject: 8.4

Dostal, J.; Utrata, R.; Loyka, S.; Brezinova, J.; Svobodova, M.; Shenfield, F. Post-mortem sperm retrieval in new European Union countries: case report. *Human Reproduction* 2005 August; 20(8): 2359-2361. Subject: 14.6

Doubilet, Peter M.; Copel, Joshua A.; Benson, Carol B.; Bahado-Singh, Ray O.; Platt, Lawrence D. Choroid plexus cyst and echogenic intracardiac focus in women at low risk for chromosomal anomalies: the obligation to inform the mother. *Journal of Ultrasound in Medicine* 2004 July; 23(7): 883-885. Subject: 15.2

Doucet, Hubert. The concept of person in bioethics: impasse and beyond. *In:* Thomasma, David C.; Weisstud, David N.; Herve, Christian eds. Personhood and Health Care. Boston: Kluwer Academic Pub.; 2001: 121-128. Subject: 4.4

Doucet, Hubert. Imagining a neuroethics which would go further than genethics. *American Journal of Bioethics* 2005 March-April; 5(2): 29-31. Subject: 17.1

Doughton, Susan D. Response to professor Mark Hall. *Cumberland Law Review* 1997-1998; 28(2): 329-332. Subject: 9.4

Douglas, Claire A.; Lewis-Jones, Cathy. Cardiopulmonary resuscitation policies in northwest England hospices: a telephone survey. *International Journal of Palliative Nursing* 2004 December; 10(12): 588-591. Subject: 20.5.1

Douglas, Neil J.; Engleman, Heather M.; Faccenda, Jacqueline F.; McArdle, Nigel; Karlawish, Jason H.T.; Pack, Allan I. The science of designing ethical CPAP trials [letter and reply]. *American Journal of Respiratory and Critical Care Medicine* 2002 January 1; 165(1): 132-134. Subject: 18.2

Doukas, David John. "Family" in advance care planning: the family covenant in the wake of Terri Schiavo. *Journal of Law, Medicine and Ethics* 2005 Summer; 33(2): 372-374. Subject: 20.5.4

Doumbo, Ogobara K. It takes a village: medical research and ethics in Mali. *Science* 2005 February 4; 307(5710): 679-681. Subject: 1.3.9

Dowie, Jack. Why cost-effectiveness should trump (clinical) effectiveness: the ethical economics of the South West quadrant. *Health Economics* 2004 May; 13(5): 453-459. Subject: 9.3.1

Downie, Jocelyn. Voluntary euthanasia in Canada. *Health Law in Canada* 1993; 14: 13-30. Subject: 20.5.1

Downie, Jocelyn; Baird, Patricia; Thompson, Jon. Industry and the academy: conflicts of interest in contemporary health research. *Health Law Journal* 2002; 10: 103-122. Subject: 18.5.2

Downie, Jocelyn; Hadskis, Michael. Finding the right compass for issue-mapping in neuroimaging. *American Journal of Bioethics* 2005 March-April; 5(2): 27-29. Subject: 17.1

Downie, Jocelyn; McDonald, Fiona. Revisioning the oversight of research involving humans in Canada. *Health Law Journal* 2004; 12: 159-181. Subject: 18.2

Downie, Jocelyn; Thompson, Jon; Baird, Patricia; Dodds, Susan. The Olivieri case: lessons for Australasia. *Journal of Bioethical Inquiry* 2005; 2(2): 90-105. Subject: 18.2

Downing, Kimberly Kristin. A feminist is a person who answers "yes" to the question, "are women human?": an argument against the use of preimplantation genetic diagnosis for gender selection. *DePaul Journal of Health Care Law* 2005; 8(2): 431-460. Subject: 14.3

Dowty, Rachel. Clones and cloning. *In:* Restivo, Sal, ed. Science, Technology, and Society: An Encyclopedia. New York: Oxford University Press; 2005: 54-55. Subject: 14.5

Doyal, L. Informed consent: don't throw out the moral baby with the critical bath water [opinion]. *Quality and Safety in Health Care* 2004 December; 13(6): 414-415. Subject: 8.3.1

Doyal, Len; McLean, Sheila. Choosing children: intergenerational justice? (Supplement 1). *Reproductive BioMedicine Online [electronic]* 2005 March; 10: 119-124 Available: http://www.rbmonline.com/index.html [1 September 2005]. Subject: 14.1

Doyal, Len; Sheather, Julian. Mental health legislation should respect decision making capacity. *BMJ: British Medical Journal* 2005 December 17; 331(7530): 1467-1469. Subject: 17.1

Doyle, Peter. The ethical dilemmas of general practice. *Australian Family Physician* 1994 June; 23(6): 1028-1029, 1032. Subject: 7.1

Dracup, Kathleen; Bryan-Brown, Christopher W. Nurses and euthanasia: a tale of two studies [editorial]. *American Journal of Critical Care* 1996 July; 5(4): 249-252. Subject: 20.5.1

Drake, Stephen. Euthanasia is out of control in the Netherlands [opinion]. *Hastings Center Report* 2005 May-June; 35(3): inside back cover. Subject: 20.5.1

Draper, Elaine. The screening of America: the social and legal framework of employers' use of genetic information. *Berkeley Journal of Employment and Labor Law* 1999; 20(2): 286-324. Subject: 15.3

Drazen, Jeffrey M.; Wood, Alastair J.J. Trial registration report card [editorial]. *New England Journal of Medicine* 2005 December 29; 353(26): 2809-2811. Subject: 18.2

Dresser, Rebecca. Professionals, conformity, and conscience. *Hastings Center Report* 2005 November-December; 35(6): 9-10. Subject: 8.1

Dresser, Rebecca. Research ethics and maternal-fetal surgery. *In:* Kodish, Eric, ed. Ethics and Research with Children: A Case-Based Approach. New York: Oxford University Press; 2005: 223-240. Subject: 18.5.4

Dresser, Rebecca. Schiavo's legacy: the need for an objective standard. *Hastings Center Report* 2005 May-June; 35(3): 20-22. Subject: 20.5.1

Dresser, Rebecca. Stem cell research: the bigger picture. *Perspectives in Biology and Medicine* 2005 Spring; 48(2): 181-194. Subject: 18.5.4

Dresser, Rebecca; DeAngelis, Catherine D. Clinical trial registration and the ICMJE [letter and reply]. *JAMA: The Journal of the American Medical Association* 2005 January 12; 293(2): 157-158. Subject: 18.6

Dressing, Harald; Salize, Hans Joachim. Compulsory admission of mentally ill patients in European Union Member States. *Social Psychiatry and Psychiatric Epidemiology* 2004 October; 39(10): 797-803. Subject: 17.7

Drew, Melinda; Garrahan, Katherine. Whistleblower protection for nurses and other health care professionals. *Journal of Nursing Law* 2005 Summer; 10(2): 79-87. Subject: 7.3

Drgonec, Ján. The status of the foetus. *Medicine and Law: World Association for Medical Law* 1994; 13(3-4): 215-239. Subject: 4.4

Drociuk, Daniel; Gibson, J.; Hodge, J., Jr. Health information privacy and syndromic surveillance systems. *MMWR: Morbidity and Mortality Weekly Report* 2004 September 24; 53(Supplement): 221-225. Subject: 8.4

Drope, J.; Bialous, S.A.; Glantz, S.A. Tobacco industry efforts to present ventilation as an alternative to smoke-free environments in North America. *Tobacco Control* 2004 March; 13(Supplement 1): i41-i47. Subject: 9.5.9

Dubben, Hans-Hermann; Beck-Bornholdt, Hans-Peter. Systematic review of publication bias in studies on publication bias. *BMJ: British Medical Journal* 2005 August 20-27; 331(7514): 433-434. Subject: 1.3.7

Dubé-Baril, Cyndie. The personalized consent form: an optional, but useful tool! *Journal of the Canadian Dental Association* 2004 February; 70(2): 89-92. Subject: 8.3.1

Dubler, Nancy; Barnes, Mark. Has compliance eclipsed ethics? Should we expect serious ethical consideration or give up and admit that regulations are the only hope? [debate]. *Protecting Human Subjects* 2005 Summer; (12): 7-9. Subject: 18.6

Dubois, Michel Y.;Lipman, Arthur; Gitlin, Melvin C.; FeBornstein, Marcos; Passik, Steve. The case(from Dr. Edwards, University of Washington) :of "blind dosing" and detoxification: justifiable or ill conceived? [forum]. *Pain Medicine* 2001 September; 2(3): 234-237. Subject: 4.4

Duddington, John. The legal aspects of human cloning. *Catholic Medical Quarterly* 2000 August; 50(3); 10 p. [Online]. Available: http://www.catholicdoctors.org.uk/CMQ/Aug_2000/cloning_legal_aspe cts.htm [4 November 2005]. Subject: 14.5

Dudgeon, Matthew R.; Inhorn, Marcia C. Men's influences on women's reproductive health: medical anthropological perspectives. *Social Science and Medicine* 2004 October; 59(7): 1379-1395. Subject: 9.5.5

Dudley, Michael; Gale, Fran. Psychiatrists as a moral community? Psychiatry under the Nazis and its contemporary relevance. *Australian and New Zealand Journal of Psychiatry* 2002 October; 36(5): 585-594. Subject: 17.1

Dudley, Susan Hall. Medical treatment for Asian immigrant children — does mother know best? *Georgetown Law Journal* 2004 August; 92(6): 1287-1307. Subject: 9.5.7

Dudzinski, Denise M. "Amputate my arm please — I don't want it anymore". *Journal of Clinical Ethics* 2005 Fall; 16(3): 196-201. Subject: 9.6

Dudzinski, Denise M.; Sullivan, Mark. When agreeing with the patient is not enough: a schizophrenic woman requests pregnancy termination. *General Hospital Psychiatry* 2004 November-December; 26(6): 475-480. Subject: 8.3.3

Dugas, Robbie. Nursing and genetics: applying the American Nurses Association's Code of Ethics. *Journal of Professional Nursing* 2005 March-April; 21(2): 103- 113. Subject: 15.2

Duguet, Anne-Marie. Euthanasia and assistance to end of life legislation in France. *European Journal of Health Law* 2001 June; 8(2): 109-123. Subject: 20.5.1

Duncan, R.E.; Delatycki, M.B.; Collins, S.J.; Boyd, A.; Masters, C.L.; Savulescu, Julian. Ethical considerations in presymptomatic testing for variant CJD. *Journal of Medical Ethics* 2005 November; 31(11): 625-630. Subject: 9.1

Duncan, Rony E. Predictive genetic testing in young people: when is it appropriate? *Journal of Paediatrics and Child Health* 2004 November; 40(11): 593-595. Subject: 15.3

Duncan, Rony E.; Savulescu, Julian; Gillam, Lynn; Williamson, Robert; Delatycki, Martin B. An international survey of predictive genetic testing in children for adult onset conditions. *Genetics in Medicine* 2005 July-August; 7(6): 390-396. Subject: 15.3

Dunckley, Catherine; Foley, Mary; Hall, Geoff. Research with animals. *In:* Dawson, John; Peart, Nicola, eds. The Law of Research: A Guide. Dunedin, NZ: University of Otago Press; 2003: 155-174. Subject: 22.2

Dunn, Laura B.; Gordon, Nora E. Improving informed consent and enhancing recruitment for research by understanding economic behavior. *JAMA: The Journal of the American Medical Association* 2005 February 2; 293(5): 609-612. Subject: 18.3

Dunne, Tad. Group-level ethics in managed care. *Medical Group Management Journal* 1997 May-June; 44(3): 28, 30, 32-34, 36, 38-39. Subject: 9.3.2

Durfy, Sharon J.; Buchanan, Trisha E.; Burke, Wylie. Testing for inherited susceptibility to breast cancer: a survey of informed consent forms for BRCA1 and BRCA2 mutation testing. *American Journal of Medical Genetics* 1998 January 6; 75(1): 82-87. Subject: 8.3.1

Durosinmi, M.A.; Odebiyi, A.I.; Akinola, N.O.; Adediran, L.A.; Aken'Ova, Y.; Okunade, M.A.; Halim, N.K.; Onwukeme, K.E.; Olatunji, P.O.; Adegoroye, D.E. Acceptability of prenatal diagnosis of sickle cell anaemia by a sample of the Nigerian population. *African Journal of Medicine and Medical Sciences* 1997 March-June; 26(1-2): 55-58. Subject: 15.2

Dute, Joseph. ECHR 2004/9 Case of Glass v. The United Kingdom, 9 March 2004 no. 61827/00 (Fourth Section) [summary]. *European Journal of Health Law* 2004 June; 11(2): 216-220. Subject: 20.5.2

Dute, Joseph. ECHR 2004/16 Case of Vo v. France, 8 July 2004, no. 53924/00 (Grand Chamber) [summary]. *European Journal of Health Law* 2004 December; 11(4): 432-437. Subject: 4.4

Dute, Joseph. The Terri Schiavo case in a comparative perspective [editorial]. *European Journal of Health Law* 2005 December; 12(4): 317-319. Subject: 20.5.1

Dutra, Margarida Maria Dantas; Bonfim, T.A.S.; Pereira, I.S.; Figueiredo, I.C.; Dutra, A.M.D.; Lopes, A.A. Knowledge about transplantation and attitudes toward organ donation: a survey among medical students in Northeast Brazil. *Transplantation Proceedings* 2004 May; 36(4): 818-820. Subject: 7.2

DuVal, Gordon. Institutional conflicts of interest: protecting human subjects, scientific integrity, and institutional accountability. *Journal of Law, Medicine and Ethics* 2004 Winter; 32(4): 613- 625. Subject: 5.3

DuVal, Gordon; Gensler, Gary; Danis, Marion. Ethical dilemmas encountered by clinical researchers. *Journal of Clinical Ethics* 2005 Fall; 16(3): 267-276. Subject: 18.2

Subject = NRCBL Primary Classification Number; See inside front cover

Dvoskin, Joel A. Commentary: two sides to every story — the need for objectivity and evidence. *Journal of the American Academy of Psychiatry and the Law* 2005; 33(4): 482-483. Subject: 8.1

Dwyer, James. Global health and justice. *Bioethics* 2005 October; 19(5-6): 460-475. Subject: 4.2

Dwyer, Peter. Pharmacists and pharmaceutical manufacturers: some ethical considerations. *Medicine and Law: World Association for Medical Law* 2005 June; 24(2): 437-454. Subject: 9.7

Dyck, Arthur J. Justice and nurture: rescue and health care as rights and responsibilities. *In his:* Rethinking Rights and Responsiblities: The Moral Bonds of Community. Revised edition. Washington, DC: Georgetown University Press; 2005: 280-326. Subject: 9.2

Dyck, Arthur J. The moral bases of homicide law: the case against assisted suicide. *In his:* Rethinking Rights and Responsiblities: The Moral Bonds of Community. Revised edition. Washington, DC: Georgetown University Press; 2005: 241-279. Subject: 20.7

Dyens, Ollivier. Cloning: burning bright in the forest of the night. *Free Inquiry* 2002-2003 Winter; 23(1): 38-39. Subject: 14.5

Dyer, Clare. Court rules in favour of GMC's guidance on withholding treatment [news]. *BMJ: British Medical Journal* 2005 August 6; 331(7512): 309. Subject: 8.1

Dyer, Clare. Doctors who performed late abortion will not be prosecuted [news]. *BMJ: British Medical Journal* 2005 March 26; 330(7493): 688. Subject: 12.4.3

Dyer, Clare. GMC challenges court ruling on end of life decisions [news]. *BMJ: British Medical Journal* 2005 May 21; 330(7501): 1165. Subject: 20.5.1

Dyer, Clare. GP is disciplined for willingness to help friend commit suicide [news]. *BMJ: British Medical Journal* 2005 October 1; 331(7519): 717. Subject: 20.7

Dyer, Clare. Judge over-rules earlier decision on Charlotte Wyatt [news]. *BMJ: British Medical Journal* 2005 October 29; 331(7523): 985. Subject: 9.5.7

Dyer, Clare. Law lords give the go ahead for creation of "saviour siblings" [news]. *BMJ: British Medical Journal* 2005 May 7; 330(7499): 1041. Subject: 15.2

Dyer, Clare. Lords back bill to legalise assisted suicide [news]. *BMJ: British Medical Journal* 2005 November 19; 331(7526): 1160. Subject: 20.7

Dyer, Clare. Parents fail to overturn ruling not to resuscitate baby [news]. *BMJ: British Medical Journal* 2005 April 30; 330(7498): 985. Subject: 20.5.2

Dyer, Clare. Parents should have right to choose sex of child, say MPs [news]. *BMJ: British Medical Journal* 2005 April 2; 330(7494): 745. Subject: 14.3

Dyer, Clare. Woman fights for parents' right to know abortion advice to under 16s [news]. *BMJ: British Medical Journal* 2005 November 19; 331(7526): 1161. Subject: 12.4.2

Dyer, Clare. Woman seeks approval to use frozen embryos [news]. *BMJ: British Medical Journal* 2005 February 19; 330(7488): 380. Subject: 14.4

Dyer, Frederick N. Horatio Robinson Storer, M.D. and the physicians' crusade against abortion. *In:* Koterski, Joseph W., ed. Life and Learning IX: Proceedings of the Ninth University Faculty for Life Conference. Washington, DC: University Faculty for Life; 2000: 267-294. Subject: 12.1

Dyer, Owen. Alder Hey pathologist is struck off medical register [news]. *BMJ: British Medical Journal* 2005 June 25; 330(7506): 1464. Subject: 19.5

Dyer, Owen. Article removed after US complains it could help terrorists [news]. *BMJ: British Medical Journal* 2005 June 18; 330(7505): 1406. Subject: 21.1

Dyer, Owen. Fertility agency is to investigate single embryo transfer [news]. *BMJ: British Medical Journal* 2005 August 6; 331(7512): 308. Subject: 14.4

Dyer, Owen. Judges support doctors' decision to stop treating dying man [news]. *BMJ: British Medical Journal* 2005 September 10; 331(7516): 536. Subject: 20.5.1

Dyer, Owen. Parents of disabled baby lose appeal against court order [news]. *BMJ: British Medical Journal* 2005 September 3; 331(7515): 472. Subject: 20.5.1

Dyer, Sarah. Rationalising public participation in the health service: the case of research ethics committees. *Health and Place* 2004 December; 10(4): 339-348. Subject: 18.2

Dysart-Gale, Deborah. Communication models, professionalization, and the work of medical interpreters. *Health Communication* 2005; 17(1): 91-103. Subject: 8.1

Dziak, Kathleen; Anderson, Roger; Sevick, Mary Ann; Weisman, Carol S.; Levine, Douglas W.; Scholle, Sarah Hudson. Variations among institutional review board reviews in a multisite health services research study. *Health Services Research* 2005 February; 40(1): 279-290. Subject: 18.2

Dziewas, Rainer; Henningsen, Henning. Medicine, psychiatry and euthanasia: an argument against mandatory psychiatric review [letter]. *Australian and New Zealand Journal of Psychiatry* 2002 April; 36(2): 266. Subject: 20.5.1

E

Earl, Catherine E.; Penney, Pamela J. The significance of trust in the research consent process with African Americans. *Western Journal of Nursing Research* 2001 November; 23(7): 753-762. Subject: 18.3

Earnest, Frank IV; Swensen, Stephen J.; Zink, Frank E. Respecting patient autonomy: screening at CT and informed consent. *Radiology* 2003 March; 226(3): 633-634. Subject: 8.3.1

Easton, David. All in our genes? *Human Reproduction and Genetic Ethics: An International Journal* 2001; 7(1): 2. Subject: 14.5

Eaton, Lynn. Drug company chiefs accept the need for more openness [news]. *BMJ: British Medical Journal* 2005 January 22; 330(7484): 163. Subject: 9.7

Eberl, Jason T. Aquinas's account of human embryogenesis and recent interpretations. *Journal of Medicine and Philosophy* 2005 August; 30(4): 379-394. Subject: 4.4

Eberl, Jason T. Extraordinary care and the spiritual goal of life: a defense of the view of Kevin O'Rourke, O.P. *National Catholic Bioethics Quarterly* 2005 Autumn; 5(3): 491- 501. Subject: 20.5.1

Eberl, Jason T. A Thomistic understanding of human death. *Bioethics* 2005 February; 19(1): 29-48. Subject: 20.2.1

Eby, Maureen. Whose life is it anyway — the dying patient's or the nurse's? [editorial]. *Nursing Ethics* 2005 March; 12(2): 121-122. Subject: 20.7

Eccles, Jim. Ethical considerations in the care of older people. *Clinical Medicine* 2003 September-October; 3(5): 416-418. Subject: 9.5.2

Eckart, Wolfgang U. Medical experiments at the colonial periphery: the fight against sleeping sickness in German East Africa and Togo. *In:* Roelcke, Volker; Maio, Giovanni, eds. Twentieth Century Ethics of Human Subjects Research: Historical Perspectives on Values, Practices, and Regulations. Stuttgart: Franz Steiner Verlag; 2004: 65-82. Subject: 18.5.4

Eckenwiler, Lisa. Ethics and the underpinnings of policy in biodefense and emergency preparedness. *CQ: Cambridge Quarterly of Healthcare Ethics* 2005 Summer; 14(3): 306-315. Subject: 21.3

Eckles, Rachael E.; Meslin, Eric M.; Gaffney, Margaret; Helft, Paul R. Medical ethics education: where are we? Where should we be going? A review. *Academic Medicine* 2005 December; 80(12): 1143-1152. Subject: 2.3

Eckstein, Sue. Training for research ethics committees in the UK. *Issues in Medical Ethics* 2001 April-June; 9(2): 56-57. Subject: 18.2

Edelmann, Robert J. Psychological assessment in 'surrogate' motherhood relationships. *In:* Cook, Rachel; Sclater, Shelley Day; Kaganas, Felicity, eds. Surrogate Motherhood: International Perspectives. Portland, OR: Hart; 2003: 143-159. Subject: 14.2

Edelson, Paul J. Henry K. Beecher and Maurice Pappworth: honor in the development of the ethics of human experimentation. *In:* Roelcke, Volker; Maio, Giovanni, eds. Twentieth Century Ethics of Human Subjects Research: Historical Perspectives on Values, Prac-

tices, and Regulations. Stuttgart: Franz Steiner Verlag; 2004: 219-233. Subject: 18.1

Eder, Michelle. Testing drugs in developing countries: pediatric research ethics in an international context. *In:* Kodish, Eric, ed. Ethics and Research with Children: A Case-Based Approach. New York: Oxford University Press; 2005: 241- 261. Subject: 18.5.2

Edgar, Andrew. The expert patient: illness as practice. *Medicine, Health Care and Philosophy: A European Journal* 2005; 8(2): 165-171. Subject: 4.2

Edgar, Andrew. Health care and the Habermasian public sphere. *In:* Holm, Søren; Jonas, Monique F., eds. Engaging the World: The Use of Empirical Research in Bioethics and the Regulation of Biotechnology. Washington, DC: IOS Press; 2004: 8-17. Subject: 9.1

Edgar, Andrew. How effective are codes of nursing ethics? *In:* Tadd, Win, ed. Ethical and Professional Issues in Nursing: Perspectives from Europe. New York: Palgrave Macmillan; 2004: 155- 174. Subject: 6

Edgar, Andrew. Physician choice or patient choice: ethical dilemmas in science and politics. *In:* Salek, Sam; Edgar, Andrew, eds. Pharmaceutical Ethics. New York: Wiley; 2002: 97-109. Subject: 8.1

Edgar, Andrew. Principles of ethics focusing on the patient. *In:* Salek, Sam; Edgar, Andrew, eds. Pharmaceutical Ethics. New York: Wiley; 2002: 13-25. Subject: 8.1

Edge, J.M.; van Rensburg, E. Janse; Mostert, E. Ethico-legal aspects of the protocol for needlestick injuries. *South African Medical Journal* 2000 December; 90(12): 1182-1184. Subject: 9.5.6

Edgerton, Tracy J. Fundamental rights and physician-assisted suicide: protecting personal autonomy. *Journal of Gender, Race and Justice* 1997-1998; 1: 283-294. Subject: 20.7

Edwards, A.G.; Weale, A.R.; Morgan, J.D. Informed consent in renal transplantation. *Postgraduate Medical Journal* 2005 March; 81(953): 188-190. Subject: 8.3.1

Edwards, Adrian; Elwyn, Glyn. Involving patients in decision making and communicating risk: a longitudinal evaluation of doctors' attitudes and confidence during a randomized trial. *Journal of Evaluation in Clinical Practice* 2004 August; 10(3): 431-437. Subject: 18.3

Edwards, Brian E.; Gearhart, John D.; Wallach, Edward E. The human pluripotent stem cell: impact on medicine and society. *Fertility and Sterility* 2000 July; 74(1): 1-7. Subject: 18.5.4

Edwards, Miles J. Opioids and benzodiazepines appear paradoxically to delay inevitable death after ventilator withdrawal. *Journal of Palliative Care* 2005 Winter; 21(4): 299-302. Subject: 20.5.1

Edwards, R.G. British disciplinary or legal actions proliferate in IVF. *Reproductive BioMedicine Online [elec-*

tronic] 2001; 3(3): 263. Available: http://www.rbmonline. com/index.html [1 September 2005]. Subject: 7.1

Edwards, R.G. Cloning and embryo stem cells meet further but limited approvals. *Reproductive BioMedicine Online [electronic]* 2005 January; 10(1): 141. Available: http://www.rbmonline.com/index.html [17 February 2006]. Subject: 18.5.4

Edwards, Robert G. Ethics of PGD: thoughts on the consequences of typing HLA in embryos. *Reproductive BioMedicine Online [electronic]* 2004 August; 9(2): 222-224 Available: http://www.rbmonline.com/index. html [15 June 2005]. Subject: 15.2

Edwards, Sarah J.L. Research participation and the right to withdraw. *Bioethics* 2005 April; 19(2): 112-130. Subject: 18.3

Edwards, Steven. Human death. *Nursing Philosophy* 2005 April; 6(2): 148-149. Subject: 20.2.1

Edwards, Steven D.; Forbes, Kevin. Nursing practice and the definition of human death. *Nursing Inquiry* 2003 December; 10(4): 229-235. Subject: 20.2.1

Edwards, S.D.; McNamee, M.J. Ethical concerns regarding guidelines for the conduct of clinical research on children. *Journal of Medical Ethics* 2005 June; 31(6): 351-354. Subject: 18.5.2

Eedy, D.J.; Graham-Brown, R.A.C. Ethics and conflicts of interest in the BJD [editorial]. *British Journal of Dermatology* 2004 July; 151(1): 1-2. Subject: 1.3.7

Egan, Erin A. Bioterrorism defense education: prioritizing public health education. *American Journal of Bioethics* 2005 July-August; 5(4): 47-48. Subject: 21.3

Egan, Erin A. The role of ethics and ethics services in patient safety. *In:* Youngberg, Barbara J.; Hatlie, Martin J., eds. The Patient Safety Handbook. Sudbury, MA: Jones and Bartlett; 2004: 487-499. Subject: 9.6

Egan, Richard; Hurlbut, William B. The burden of proof [letter and reply]. *National Catholic Bioethics Quarterly* 2005 Spring; 5(1): 12- 13, 19-22. Subject: 18.5.4

Egan, Thomas M. Ethical issues in thoracic organ distribution for transplant. *American Journal of Transplantation* 2003 April; 3(4): 366-372. Subject: 19.6

Eggen, J.B. "The fallacy of eugenics" in Social Forces 5.1 (September 1926): 104-9. *In:* Ryan, Frank X., ed. Darwin's Impact: Social Evolution in America, 1880-1920. Volume 2. Race, Gender, and Supremacy. Bristol: Thoemmes; 2001: 171-177. Subject: 15.5

Eggenberger, Sandra K.; Nelms, Tommie P. Artificial hydration and nutrition in advanced Alzheimer's disease: facilitating family decision-making. *Journal of Clinical Nursing* 2004 September; 13(6): 661-667. Subject: 20.5.1

Eggertson, Laura. One-third of panel on breast implants declares conflict [news]. *CMAJ/JAMC: Canadian Medical Association Journal* 2005 August 2; 173(3): 241. Subject: 9.7

Eggertson, Laura. Physicians want transparency as Guidant lawsuits grow [news]. *CMAJ/JAMC: Canadian Medical Association Journal* 2005 October 11; 173(8): 855-856. Subject: 5.3

Eggertson, Laura; Murray, Sally. MPs call for removal of Health Canada's breast-implant panel members [news]. *CMAJ/JAMC: Canadian Medical Association Journal* 2005 November 8; 173(10): 1144. Subject: 5.3

Eggertson, Laura; Sibbald, Barbara. Privacy issues raised over Plan B: women asked for names, addresses, sexual history [news]. *CMAJ/JAMC: Canadian Medical Association Journal* 2005 December 6; 173(12): 1435-1436. Subject: 11.1

Egilman, David S. Suppression bias at the Journal of Occupational and Environmental Medicine. *International Journal of Occupational and Environmental Health* 2005 April-June; 11(2): 202-204. Subject: 7.3

Egilman, David; Fehnel, Corey; Bohme, Susanna Rankin. Exposing the "myth" of ABC, "anything but chrysotile": a critique of the Canadian asbestos mining industry and McGill University chrysotile studies. *American Journal of Industrial Medicine* 2003 November; 44(5): 540-557. Subject: 16.3

Ehman, Amy Jo. Saskatchewan MDs oppose new mandatory testing law [news]. *CMAJ/JAMC: Canadian Medical Association Journal* 2005 December 6; 173(12): 1437-1438. Subject: 9.5.6

Ehringhaus, Susan; Korn, David. U.S. Medical School Policies on Individual Financial Conflicts of Interest: Results of an AAMC Survey. Washington, DC: American Association of Medical Colleges [AAMC] 2004 September; 7 p. [Online]. Available: http://www.aamc.org/members/coitf/coiresults2003.pdf [2005 August 2]. Subject: 1.3.9

Ehrlich, J. Shoshanna. Journey through the courts: minors, abortion and the quest for reproductive fairness. *Yale Journal of Law and Feminism* 1998; 10(1): 1-27. Subject: 12.4.2

Eidelman, Arthur I. The living fetus—dilemmas in treatment at the edge of viability. *In:* Blazer, Shraga; Zimmer, Etan Z., eds. The Embryo: Scientific Discovery and Medical Ethics. New York: Karger; 2005: 351-370. Subject: 20.5.1

Eidelman, Leonid A.; Jakobson, Daniel J.; Worner, T.M.; Pizov, Reuven; Geber, Debora; Sprung, Charles L. End-of-life intensive care unit decisions, communication, and documentation: an evaluation of physician training. *Journal of Critical Care* 2003 March; 18(1): 11-16. Subject: 7.2

Eijk, Williams Jacobus. Proportionate and disproportionate treatment, exaggerated treatment and palliative care. *Dolentium Hominum* 2005; 20(1): 79-86. Subject: 20.5.1

Einav, Sharon; Rubinow, Alan; Avidan, Alexander; Brezis, Mayer. General medicine practitioners' attitudes towards "do not attempt resuscitation" orders. *Resuscitation* 2004 August; 62(2): 181-187. Subject: 20.5.1

Einsiedel, Edna F. Commentary: on the position paper of the Ethics Committee of the International Xenotransplantation Association. *Transplantation* 2004 October 27; 78(8): 1110-1111. Subject: 19.1

Eisen, Arri; Parker, Kathy P. A model for teaching research ethics. *Science and Engineering Ethics* 2004 October; 10(4): 693-704. Subject: 1.3.9

Eisenberg, Marla E.; Swain, Carolyne; Bearinger, Linda H.; Sieving, Renee E.; Resnick, Michael D. Parental notification laws for minors' access to contraception: what do parents say? *Archives of Pediatrics and Adolescent Medicine* 2005 February; 159(2): 120-125. Subject: 11.2

Eisenberg, Rebecca S. Genomics in the public domain: strategy and policy [opinion]. *Nature Reviews Genetics* 2000 October; 1(1): 70-74. Subject: 15.10

Eisenberg, Rebecca S. Patents, product exclusivity, and information dissemination: how law directs biopharmaceutical research and development. *Fordham Law Review* 2003 December; 72(3): 477-491. Subject: 15.8

Ekblad, Michele. The patient's right to refuse medical care: Michigan and federal law. *Journal of Medicine and Law* 2001 Fall; 6(1): 29-50. Subject: 8.3.4

Ekelin, Maria; Crang-Svalenius, Elizabeth. Midwives' attitudes to and knowledge about a newly introduced foetal screening method. *Scandinavian Journal of Caring Sciences* 2004 September; 18(3): 287-293. Subject: 15.2

Ekemo, Afton. Government support for embryonic stem cell research. *Journal of Biolaw and Business* 2005; 8(4): 66-67. Subject: 18.5.4

Ekouevi, Koumavi Didier; Becquet, Renaud; Viho, Ida; Bequet, Laurence; Dabis, François; Leroy, Valériane. Obtaining informed consent from HIV-infected pregnant women, Abidjan, Cote d'Ivoire [letter]. *AIDS* 2004 July 2; 18(10): 1486-1488. Subject: 18.5.1

Elbogen, Eric B.; Soriano, Catherine; Van Dorn, Richard; Swartz, Marvin S.; Swanson, Jeffrey W. Consumer views of representative payee use of disability funds to leverage treatment adherence. *Psychiatric Services* 2005 January; 56(1): 45-49. Subject: 17.7

Elcioglu, Omur; Unluoglu, Ilhami. Triage in terms of medicine and ethics. *Saudi Medical Journal* 2004 December; 25(12): 1815-1819. Subject: 9.4

Elder, Andrew T. Which benchmarks for age discrimination in acute coronary syndromes? *Age and Ageing* 2005 January; 34(1): 4-5. Subject: 9.5.2

Elger, B.; Mauron, A. A presumed-consent model for regulating informed consent of genetic research involving DNA banking. *In:* Knoppers, Bartha Maria, ed. Populations and Genetics: Legal and Socio-Ethical Perspectives. Boston: Martinus Nijhoff; 2003: 269-295. Subject: 15.1

Elger, Bernice S. Attitudes of future lawyers and psychologists to the use of genetic testing for criminal behavior. *CQ: Cambridge Quarterly of Healthcare Ethics* 2005 Summer; 14(3): 329-345. Subject: 15.6

Elger, Bernice S.; Harding, Timothy W. Avoidable breaches of confidentiality: a study among students of medicine and of law. *Medical Education* 2005 March; 39(3): 333-337. Subject: 8.4

Elger, Bernice S.; Harding, Timothy W. Compliance with the wishes of competent patients among future physicians and lawyers: is paternalism a predictable individual or group-specific trait? *Medical Teacher* 2004 August; 26(5): 458-462. Subject: 7.1

Elger, Bernice S.; Harding, Timothy W. Teaching changes attitudes to genetic testing for aggressive behaviour. *Medical Law International* 2004; 6(4): 277-295. Subject: 15.6

Elkeles, Barbara. The German debate on human experimentation between 1880 and 1914. *In:* Roelcke, Volker; Maio, Giovanni, eds. Twentieth Century Ethics of Human Subjects Research: Historical Perspectives on Values, Practices, and Regulations. Stuttgart: Franz Steiner Verlag; 2004: 19-33. Subject: 18.1

Elkin, Sandy. In that case. *Journal of Bioethical Inquiry* 2005; 2(3): 179. Subject: 9.5.1

Ellard, J. Euthanasia: over the Rubicon already? *Australian and New Zealand Journal of Medicine* 1998 February; 28(1): 57. Subject: 20.5.1

Elliott, Carl. Adventure! Comedy! Tragedy! Robots! How bioethicists learned to stop worrying and embrace their inner cyborgs. *Journal of Bioethical Inquiry* 2005; 2(1): 18-23. Subject: 5.1

Elliott, Carl. Caring about risks: are severely depressed patients competent to consent to research? *Archives of General Psychiatry* 1997 February; 54(2): 113-116. Subject: 8.3.3

Elliott, Carl. Enhancement technologies and identity ethics. *Society* 2004 July-August; 41(5): 25-31. Subject: 4.5

Elliott, Carl. Should journals publish industry-funded bioethics articles? [opinion]. *Lancet* 2005 July 30-August 5; 366(9483): 422-424. Subject: 2.1

Elliott, Carl. The soul of a new machine: bioethicists in the bureaucracy. *CQ: Cambridge Quarterly of Healthcare Ethics* 2005 Fall; 14(4): 379-384. Subject: 2.1

Elliott, Carl. To the editor [letter]. *American Journal of Bioethics [Online]* 2005 May-June; 5(3): W16. Subject: 1.3.7

Elliott, Kevin C. Developmental systems theory and human embryos: a response to Austriaco. *National Catholic*

Bioethics Quarterly 2005 Summer; 5(2): 249- 259. Subject: 4.4

Elliott, Michael K. Tales of parenthood from the crypt: the predicament of the posthumously conceived child. *Real Property, Probate and Trust Journal* 2004 Spring; 39(1): 47-69. Subject: 14.6

Ellis, Mark R.; Campbell, James D. Concordant spiritual orientations as a factor in physician- patient spiritual discussions: a qualitative study. *Journal of Religion and Health* 2005 Spring; 44(1): 39-53. Subject: 8.1

Ellis, Peter. Defining euthanasia [letter]. *Professional Nurse* 1997 May; 12(8): 600. Subject: 20.5.1

Éló, Gábor; Diószeghy, Csaba; Dobos, Márta; Andorka, Mátyás. Ethical considerations behind the limitation of cardiopulmonary resuscitation in Hungary — the role of education and training. *Resuscitation* 2005 January; 64(1): 71-77. Subject: 20.5.1

Elon, Menachem. Medicine, halacha, and law: the values of a Jewish and democratic state. *Jewish Medical Ethics and Halacha* 2005 August; 5(1): 4-21. Subject: 1.2

Elon, Menachem; Auerbach, Bernard; Chazin, Daniel D.; Sykes, Melvin J. Abortion. *In their:* Jewish Law (Mishpat Ivri): Cases and Materials. New York: M. Bender; 1999: 609-624. Subject: 12.3

Elon, Menachem; Auerbach, Bernard; Chazin, Daniel D.; Sykes, Melvin J. Artificial insemination. *In their:* Jewish Law (Mishpat Ivri): Cases and Materials. New York: M. Bender; 1999: 625-635. Subject: 14.2

Elon, Menachem; Auerbach, Bernard; Chazin, Daniel D.; Sykes, Melvin J. Euthanasia and the right to refuse treatment. *In their:* Jewish Law (Mishpat Ivri): Cases and Materials. New York: M. Bender; 1999: 637-696. Subject: 20.5.1

Elon, Menachem; Auerbach, Bernard; Chazin, Daniel D.; Sykes, Melvin J. Medical experimentation. *In their:* Jewish Law (Mishpat Ivri): Cases and Materials. New York: M. Bender; 1999: 737-741. Subject: 18.1

Elon, Menachem; Auerbach, Bernard; Chazin, Daniel D.; Sykes, Melvin J. Organ transplantation. *In their:* Jewish Law (Mishpat Ivri): Cases and Materials. New York: M. Bender; 1999: 697-731. Subject: 19.5

Elon, Menachem; Auerbach, Bernard; Chazin, Daniel D.; Sykes, Melvin J. Surrogate motherhood, in vitro fertilization, and genetic engineering. *In their:* Jewish Law (Mishpat Ivri): Cases and Materials. New York: M. Bender; 1999: 742-746. Subject: 14.2

Elphick, Heather L.; Gott, Merryn; Liddle, B. Jane; Stewart, Kevin; Spice, Claire. Where now with do not attempt resuscitation decisions? [letter and reply]. *Age and Ageing* 2004 January; 33(1): 86-87. Subject: 20.5.1

Elshtain, Jean Bethke. The body and the quest for control. *In:* Baillie, Harold W.; Casey, Timothy K., eds. Is Human Nature Obsolete? Genetics Bioengineering, and the Future of the Human Condition. Cambridge, MA: MIT Press; 2005: 155-175. Subject: 15.1

Elster, Nanette R.; Hoffman, Richard E.; Livengood, John R. Public health research and health information. *In:* Goodman, Richard A.; Rothstein, Mark A.; Hoffman, Richard E.; Lopez, Wilfredo; Matthews, Gene W., eds. Law in Public Health Practice. New York: Oxford University Press; 2003: 160-174. Subject: 18.1

Elwyn, Glyn; Seagrove, Anne; Thorne, Kym; Cheung, Wai Yee. Ethics and research governance in a multicentre study: add 150 days to your study protocol [letter]. *BMJ: British Medical Journal* 2005 April 9; 330(7495): 847. Subject: 18.2

Emanuel, Ezekiel J. Response to commentators on "Undue inducement: nonsense on stilts?" [letter]. *American Journal of Bioethics [Online]* 2005 September- October; 5(5): W8-W11. Subject: 18.3

Emanuel, Ezekiel J. Undue inducement: nonsense on stilts? *American Journal of Bioethics* 2005 September-October; 5(5): 9- 13. Subject: 18.3

Emanuel, Ezekiel J.; Currie, Xolani E.; Herman, Allen. Undue inducement in clinical research in developing countries: is it a worry? [opinion]. *Lancet* 2005 July 23-29; 366(9482): 336-340. Subject: 18.1

Emanuel, Ezekiel J.; Fuchs, Victory R. Health care vouchers — a proposal for universal coverage. *New England Journal of Medicine* 2005 March 24; 352(12): 1255-1260. Subject: 9.3.1

Emanuel, Ezekiel J.; Weijer, Charles. Protecting communities in research: from a new principle to rational protections. *In:* Childress, James F.; Meslin, Eric M.; Shapiro, Harold T., eds. Belmont Revisited: Ethical Principles for Research with Human Subjects. Washington, DC: Georgetown University Press; 2005: 165-183. Subject: 18.5.1

Emmett, Thomas H. Time to legalise assisted dying? No, thank you [letter]. *BMJ: British Medical Journal* 2005 October 8; 331(7520): 842. Subject: 20.5.1

Enck, Robert E. Advance directives: burden or benefit? [editorial]. *American Journal of Hospice and Palliative Care* 2003 September-October; 20(5): 329-330. Subject: 20.5.4

Endacott, R. Clinical research 2: legal and ethical issues in research. *Intensive and Critical Care Nursing* 2004 October; 20(5): 313-315. Subject: 18.2

Engelen, Bart; Vandevelde, Antoon. A defence of common sense: a reply to David Heyd's "The ethics of sex selection for non-medical reasons". *Ethical Perspectives* 2004; 11(1): 84-87. Subject: 14.3

Engelhardt, H. Tristram, Jr. The bioethics of care: widows, monastics, and a Christian presence in health care. *Christian Bioethics* 2005 April; 11(1): 1-10. Subject: 9.1

Engelhardt, H. Tristram, Jr. Health, disease, and persons: well-being in a post-modern world. *In:* Taboada, Paulina; Cuddeback, Kateryna Fedoryka; Donohue-White, Patricia, eds. Person, Society and Value: Towards a Personalist Concept of Health. Boston: Kluwer Academic Pub.; 2002: 147-163. Subject: 4.2

Engelhardt, H. Tristram, Jr. Orthodox Christian bioethics: medical morality in the mind of the fathers. *In:* Peppin, John F.; Cherry, Mark J., eds. Religious Perspectives in Bioethics. New York: Taylor & Francis; 2004: 21-30. Subject: 2.1

Engelhardt, H. Tristram, Jr. Sin and bioethics: why a liturgical anthropology is foundational. *Christian Bioethics* 2005 August; 11(2): 221-239. Subject: 2.1

Engelhardt, H. Tristram, Jr. What is Christian about Christian bioethics? Metaphysical, epistemological, and moral differences. *Christian Bioethics* 2005 December; 11(3): 241-253. Subject: 2.1

Engelhardt, H. Tristram, Jr.; Iltis, Ana Smith. End-of-life: the traditional Christian view. *Lancet* 2005 September 17-23; 366(9490): 1045-1049. Subject: 20.5.1

EngenderHealth. Law and policy. *In its: Contraceptive Sterilization: Global Issues and Trends. New York, NY: EngenderHealth; 2002: 87-106. Subject: 11.3*

English, Dan C. Moral obligations of patients: a clinical view. *Journal of Medicine and Philosophy* 2005 April; 30(2): 139-152. Subject: 8.1

English, Jane; Gensler, Henry J.; Marquis, Don; McInerney, Peter K.; Paske, Gerald H. Beyond the personhood argument. *In:* Pojman, Louis P.; Beckwith, Francis J., eds. The Abortion Controversy: A Reader. Boston: Jones and Bartlett; 1994: 293-369. Subject: 12.3

Enoch, S.; Shaaban, H.; Dunn; K.W. Informed consent should be obtained from patients to use products (skin substitutes) and dressings containing biological material. *Journal of Medical Ethics* 2005 January; 31(1): 2-6. Subject: 8.3.1

Ensenauer, Regina E.; Michels, Virginia V.; Reinke, Shanda S. Genetic testing: practical, ethical, and counseling considerations. *Mayo Clinic Proceedings* 2005 January; 80(1): 63-73. Subject: 15.3

Enzle, Michael E.; Schmaltz, Rodney. Ethics review of multi-centre clinical trials in Canada. *Health Law Review* 2005; 13(2-3): 51-57. Subject: 18.2

EPO [European Patent Office] Opposition Division. Patentability of test animals — the British Union for the abolition of vivisection et al. v. the President and Fellows of Harvard College — "Onco-Mouse". *International Review of Intellectual Property and Competition Law* 2004; 35(1): 72-78. Subject: 15.8

Epstein, Ernst. Are we consultants or peddlers? [letter]. *Archives of Dermatology* 1998 April; 134(4): 508-509. Subject: 4.1.1

Epstein, Julia. The pregnant imagination, fetal rights, and women's bodies: a historical inquiry. *Yale Journal of Law and Humanities* 1995 Winter; 7(1): 139-162. Subject: 9.5.5

Epstein, Richard A. Disparities and discrimination in health care coverage: a critique of the Institute of Medicine study. *Perspectives in Biology and Medicine* 2005 Winter; 48(1, Supplement): S26-S41. Subject: 9.5.4

Erard, Robert E. "A raw deal" reheated: reply to comments by Rogers, Fischer, and Smith and Evans. *Journal of Personality Assessment* 2004 February; 82(1): 44- 47. Subject: 17.1

Erard, Robert E. Release of test data under the 2002 Ethics Code and the HIPAA Privacy Rule: a raw deal or just a half-baked idea? *Journal of Personality Assessment* 2004 February; 82(1): 23- 30. Subject: 8.4

Erb, Christopher T.; Rich, Robert F.; Mariner, Wendy K.; Bloche, M. Gregg. The Supreme Court and managed-care liability [letter and replies]. *New England Journal of Medicine* 2005 January 13; 352(2): 201- 203. Subject: 9.3.2

Erickson, Jeanette Ives; Millar, Sally. Caring for patients while respecting their privacy: renewing our commitment. *Online Journal of Issues in Nursing [electronic]* 2005; 10(2); E1, 13 p. Available: http://www.nursingworld.org/ojin/ [15 June 2005]. Subject: 8.4

Erickson, Stephen A. On the Christian in Christian bioethics. *Christian Bioethics* 2005 December; 11(3): 269-279. Subject: 2.1

Eriksson, S.; Helgesson, Gert. Keep people informed or leave them alone? A suggested tool for identifying research participants who rightly want only limited information. *Journal of Medical Ethics* 2005 November; 31(11): 674-678. Subject: 18.3

Erlen, Judith A. Moral distress: a pervasive problem. *Orthopaedic Nursing* 2001 March-April; 20(2): 76-80. Subject: 8.1

Ernst, E. Informed consent: a potential dilemma for complementary medicine [opinion]. *Journal of Manipulative and Physiological Therapeutics* 2004 July-August; 27(6): 428-429. Subject: 4.1.1

Ersek, Mary. Assisted suicide: unraveling a complex issue. *Nursing* 2005 April; 35(4): 48-52. Subject: 20.7

Ervin, Naomi E.; Bell, Sue Ellen. Social justice issues related to uneven distribution of resources. *Journal of the New York State Nurses Association* 2004 Spring-Summer; 35(1): 8-13. Subject: 9.2

Estonia. Parliament. Human Genes Research Act [passed 2000 December 13]. Tallinn, Estonia: Riigi Teataja [State Gazette] I 2000, 104, 68.5, Legislation; 14 p. [Online]. Available: http://www.legaltext.ee/et/andmebaas/tekst.asp?dok=X50010&keel=en [22 July 2005]. Subject: 15.3

Subject = NRCBL Primary Classification Number; See inside front cover

Estonia. Parliament. Transplantation of Organs and Tissues Act [passed 30 January 2002; effective date: 4 March 2002]. Talinn, Estonia: Riigi Teataja [State Gazette] I 2002, 21, 118; 6 p. [Online]. Available: http://www.legaltext.ee/text/en/X60017K2.htm [11 July 2005]. Subject: 19.5

Ethics Committee of the American Medical Directors Association; Boult, Lisa; Dentler, Bruce; Volicer, Ladislav; Mead, Sharon; Evans, Jonathan M. Ethics and research in long-term care: a position statement from the American Medical Directors Association. *Journal of the American Medical Directors Association* 2003 May-June; 4(3): 171-174. Subject: 18.5.1

Ettorre, Elizabeth. The sociology of the new genetics: conceptualizing the links between reproduction, gender and bodies. *In:* Bunton, Robin; Petersen, Alan, eds. Genetic Governance: Health, Risk and Ethics in the Biotech Era. New York: Routledge; 2005: 107-120. Subject: 15.3

Etzioni, Amitai. DNA tests and databases in criminal justice: individual rights and the common good. *In:* Lazer, David, ed. DNA and the Criminal Justice System: The Technology of Justice. Cambridge, MA: MIT Press; 2004: 197-223. Subject: 15.1

Etzioni, Amos. Gene therapy — where do we go? [editorial]. *Israel Medical Association Journal* 2003 December; 5(12): 883-884. Subject: 15.4

European Commission; Matthiessen, Line; Lucaroni, Beatrice; Sachez, Elena. The Process of Addressing the Ethical Dimension of Animal Experimentation and Implementing the Principle of the Three Rs under the "Quality of Life" Programme. Brussells, Belgium: European Commission, 2002 July; 2 p. [Online]. Available: http://europa.eu.int/comm/research/biosociety/pdf/animal_experim.pdf [22 January 2004]. Subject: 22.2

European Commission. European Ethics Group for Science and New Technology. Les aspects ethiques des banques de sang de cordon ombilical: avis no 19 du 16 mars 2004 / Ethical aspects of banks of umbilical cord blood, advice no. 19 of 16 March 2004. *Journal International de Bioethique / International Journal of Bioethics* 2005 March-June; 16(1-2): 169-171. Subject: 19.4

European Commission. European Group on Ethics in Science and New Technologies. Ethical aspects of human stem cell research and use. *Human Reproduction and Genetic Ethics: An International Journal* 2001; 7(1): 7. Subject: 18.5.4

European Communities Confederation of Clinical Chemistry and Laboratory Medicine (EC4); Sanders, Gerard; Opp, Matthias; McMurray, Janet; Koeller, Ursula; Blaton, Vic; Lund, Erik; Harmoinen, Aimo; Zerah, Simone; Baum, Hannsjoerg; Rizos, Demetrios; Kenny, Desmond; Pazzagli, Mario; Hoffman, Hans; Reguengo, Henrique; Queraltó, Jose M.; Wallinder, Hans; Jansen, Rob; Hallworth, Michael;

Schuff-Werner, Peter. The European Register for Specialists in Clinical Chemistry and Laboratory Medicine: code of conduct. *Clinical Chemistry and Laboratory Medicine* 2004 May; 42(5): 563-565. Subject: 1.3.1

European Parliament; Council of the European Union. Directive 2001/20/EC of the European Parliament and of the Council of 4 April 2001 on the approximation of the laws, regulations and administrative provisions of the member states relating to the implementation of good clinical practice in the conduct of clinical trials on medicinal products for human use. *Medical Ethics and Bioethics / Medicinska Etika and Bioetika* 2002 Spring-Summer; 9(1-2): 12-19. Subject: 18.2

European Society for Human Reproduction and Embryology [ESHRE]. Task Force on Ethics and Law; Shenfield, F.; Pennings, G.; Cohen, J.; Devroey, P.; Tarlatzis, B. Taskforce 9: the application of preimplantation genetic diagnosis for human leukocyte antigen typing of embryos. *Human Reproduction* 2005 April; 20(4): 845-847. Subject: 14.4

European Society for Human Reproduction and Embryology [ESHRE]. Task Force on Ethics and Law; Shenfield, F.; Pennings, G.; Cohen, J.; Devroey, P.; de Wert, G.; Tarlatzis, B. ESHRE task force on ethics and law 10: surrogacy. *Human Reproduction* 2005 October; 20(10): 2705-2707. Subject: 14.2

Evans, Bronwynne C.; Bendel, Robert. Cognitive and ethical maturity in baccalaureate nursing students: did a class using Narrative Pedagogy make a difference? *Nursing Education Perspectives* 2004 July-August; 25(4): 188-195. Subject: 7.2

Evans, H.M. Reply to: Defining death: when physicians and families differ. *Journal of Medical Ethics* 2005 November; 31(11): 642-644. Subject: 20.2.1

Evans, H.M. Response to F.G. Miller and J.D. Moreno, "The state of research ethics: a tribute to John C. Fletcher". *Journal of Clinical Ethics* 2005 Winter; 16(4): 372-375. Subject: 18.3

Evans, John H. Bioethical consensus and the force of good ideas. *Hastings Center Report* 2005 May-June; 35(3): 3. Subject: 4.5

Evans, John H. Max Weber meets the Belmont Report: toward a sociological interpretation of principlism. *In:* Childress, James F.; Meslin, Eric M.; Shapiro, Harold T., eds. Belmont Revisited: Ethical Principles for Research with Human Subjects. Washington, DC: Georgetown University Press; 2005: 228-243. Subject: 2.1

Evans, Lesley A.M. "Right to die" — sensitivity and humility are needed when dealing with dying people [letter]. *BMJ: British Medical Journal* 2005 June 11; 330(7504): 1388. Subject: 20.4.1

Evans, M.D.R.; Kelley, Jonathan; Zanjani, Esmail D. The ethics of gene therapy and abortion: public opinion.

Fetal Diagnosis and Therapy 2005 May-June; 20(3): 223-234. Subject: 15.4

Evans, Roger W.; Kitzmann, Daniel J. The "arithmetic" of donor liver allocation. *Clinical Transplantation* 1996: 338-342. Subject: 19.6

Everett, Margaret. Response to Rich's letter regarding "the social life of genes: privacy, property and the new genetics" [letter]. *Social Science and Medicine* 2003 December; 57(12): 2473. Subject: 15.8

Everett, Margaret. The social life of genes: privacy, property and the new genetics. *Social Science and Medicine* 2003 January; 56(1): 53-65. Subject: 15.8

Evers, Kathinka. Neuroethics: a philosophical challenge. *American Journal of Bioethics* 2005 March-April; 5(2): 31-32. Subject: 17.1

F

Fabbro, Ronald. Stem cell research, cloning and Catholic moral theology. *Linacre Quarterly* 2005 November; 72(4): 294-306. Subject: 18.5.4

Faden, Ruth R.; Mastroianni, Anna C.; Kahn, Jeffrey P. Beyond Belmont: trust, openness, and the work of the Advisory Committee on Human Radiation Experiments. *In:* Childress, James F.; Meslin, Eric M.; Shapiro, Harold T., eds. Belmont Revisited: Ethical Principles for Research with Human Subjects. Washington, DC: Georgetown University Press; 2005: 41-54. Subject: 18.2

Faden, Ruth R.; Taylor, Holly A.; Seiler, Naomi K. Consent and compensation: a social compact for smallpox vaccine policy in the event of an attack. *Clinical Infectious Diseases* 2003; 36: 1547-1551. Subject: 9.1

Fahr, Uwe; Reiter-Theil, Stella; Rubin, Beatrix P. Ethik, Weltanschauung, Wissenschaft. Zur Kontroverse um die Stammzellforschung. *In:* Baumann, Eva; Brink, Alexander; May, Arnd T.; Schröder; Peter; Schutzeichel, Corinna Iris, eds. Weltanschauliche Offenheit in der Bioethik. Berlin: Duncker & Humblot; 2004: 233-256. Subject: 18.5.4

Fahrenwald, Nancy L.; Bassett, Susan D.; Tschetter, Lois; Carson, Paula P.; White, Lani; Winterboer, Venita J. Teaching core nursing values. *Journal of Professional Nursing* 2005 January-February; 21(1): 46-51. Subject: 4.1.3

Fairbairn, Gavin J. Brain transplants and the orthodox view of personhood. *In:* Fisher, Robert N.; Primozic, Daniel T.; Day, Peter A.; Thompson, Joel A., eds. Suffering, Death, and Identity. New York: Rodopi; 2002: 127-139. Subject: 4.4

Fairrow, A.M.; McCallum, T.J.; Messinger-Rapport, Barbara J. Preferences of older African-Americans for long-term tube feeding at the end of life. *Aging and Mental Health* 2004 November; 8(6): 530-534. Subject: 20.5.1

Fallberg, Lars; Mackenney, Stephen. Patient ombudsmen in seven European countries: an effective way to implement patients' rights? *European Journal of Health Law* 2003 December; 10(4): 343-357. Subject: 9.1

Fallon, L. Fleming, Jr. Ethics in the practice of occupational medicine. *Occupational Medicine* 2001 July-September; 16(3): 517-524. Subject: 16.3

Fallone, Sue. What is the responsibility of the nephrology nurse when the patient is chronically late? Nephrology nurses deserve respect [debate]. *Nephrology Nursing Journal* 2004 July-August; 31(4): 445-446. Subject: 8.1

Fangerau, H. Can artificial parthenogenesis sidestep ethical pitfalls in human therapeutic cloning? An historical perspective. *Journal of Medical Ethics* 2005 December; 31(12): 733-735. Subject: 14.5

Farah, Martha J. Neuroethics: the practical and the philosophical. *Trends in Cognitive Sciences* 2005 January; 9(1): 34-40. Subject: 17.1

Farberman, Rhea. A stain on medical ethics [letter]. *Lancet* 2005 August 27-September 2; 366(9487): 712. Subject: 21.4

Farberman, Rhea K. Terminal illness and hastened death requests: the important role of the mental health professional. *Professional Psychology: Research and Practice* 1997 December; 28(6): 544-547. Subject: 20.7

Farkas, Daniel H.; Goerl, Hans S.; Hyer, Randall N. Genetic privacy legislation: two views. *Molecular Diagnosis* 1997 March; 2(1): 83-87. Subject: 15.3

Farnalls, Martha. The use of limited critical care resources: an ethical dilemma. *Official Journal of the Canadian Association of Critical Care Nurses* 1997 Fall; 8(3): 23-26. Subject: 20.5.1

Farnell, Sheila M. Informed consent — east meets west — worlds apart? [opinion]. *Medical and Pediatric Oncology* 2002 March; 38(3): 201-202. Subject: 18.3

Farrell, Susan A. Reframing social justice, feminism and abortion. *Conscience* 2005 Spring; 26(1): 42-44. Subject: 12.3

Farrelly, Colin. Justice in the genetically transformed society. *Kennedy Institute of Ethics Journal* 2005 March; 15(1): 91-99. Subject: 15.1

Fasouliotis, Sozos J.; Schenker, Joseph G. Human umbilical cord blood banking and transplantation: a state of the art. *European Journal of Obstetrics, Gynecology and Reproductive Biology* 2000 May; 90(1): 13-25. Subject: 19.4

Fasouliotis, Sozos J.; Schenker, Joseph G. Maternal-fetal conflict. *European Journal of Obstetrics and Gynecology and Reproductive Biology* 2000 March; 89(1): 101-107. Subject: 9.5.5

Subject = NRCBL Primary Classification Number; See inside front cover

Faunce, Thomas. Coherence and healthcare whistle-blowing: a response to Parker. *Monash Bioethics Review* 2005 January; 24(1): 47-49. Subject: 7.3

Faunce, Thomas Alured. Collaborative research trials: a strategy for fostering mental health protections in developing nations. *International Journal of Law and Psychiatry* 2005 March- April; 28(2): 171-181. Subject: 17.1

Faunce, Thomas Alured. The UNESCO bioethics declaration `social responsibility' principle and cost-effectiveness price evaluations for essential medicines. *Monash Bioethics Review* 2005 July; 24(3): 10-19. Subject: 9.7

Faunce, T.A. Will international human rights subsume medical ethics? Intersections in the UNESCO universal bioethics declaration. *Journal of Medical Ethics* 2005 March; 31(3): 173-178. Subject: 21.1

Faunce, T.S.; Tomossy, G.F. The UK House of Commons report on the influence of the pharmaceutical industry: lessons for equitable access to medicines in Australia. *Monash Bioethics Review* 2005 April; 24(2): 38-42. Subject: 9.7

Fauriel, I.; Moutel, G.; Duchange, N.; Callies, I.; François, I.; Huriet, C.; Hervé, C. Improving protection for research subjects in France: analysis of regional ethics committees. *Regulatory Toxicology and Pharmacology* 2004 December; 40(3): 312-318. Subject: 18.2

Fauriel, Isabelle; Moutel, Grégoire; Moutard, Marie-Laure; Montuclard, Luc; Duchange, Nathalie; Callies, Ingrid; François, Irène; Cochat, Pierre; Hervé, Christian. Decisions concerning potentially life-sustaining treatments in paediatric nephrology: a multicentre study in French-speaking countries. *Nephrology, Dialysis, Transplantation* 2004 May; 19(5): 1252-1257. Subject: 20.5.2

Favor, Christi Dawn. Puzzling cases about killing and letting die. *Res Publica* 1996; 5(1): 18-21. Subject: 20.5.1

Fay, Allen. Ethical implications of charging for missed sessions. *Psychological Reports* 1995 December; 77(3, Part 2): 1251-1259. Subject: 17.2

Faye, David J. Bioprospecting, genetic patenting and indigenous populations: challenges under a restructured information commons. *Journal of World Intellectual Property* 2004 May; 7(3): 401-428. Subject: 15.8

Featherstone, Katie; Donovan, Jenny L. "Why don't they just tell me straight, why allocate it?" The struggle to make sense of participating in a randomised controlled trial. *Social Science and Medicine* 2002 September; 55(5): 709-719. Subject: 18.2

Feder, Ned. NIH must tell whole truth about conflicts of interest [letter]. *Nature* 2005 March 17; 434(7031): 271. Subject: 1.3.9

Feder, Ned. Public disclosure could deter conflicts of interest [letter]. *Nature* 2005 September 29; 437(7059): 620. Subject: 1.3.9

Feitshans, Ilise L. Legislating to preserve women's autonomy during pregnancy. *Medicine and Law: World Association for Medical Law* 1995; 14(5-6): 397-412. Subject: 15.2

Feldheim, Mary Ann. Health care policy evaluation: a conceptual model using medical ethics. *Journal of Health and Human Services Administration* 1998 Fall; 21(2): 181-198. Subject: 9.1

Feldman, Eric A. Blood justice: courts, conflict, and compensation in Japan, France, and the United States. *Law and Society Review* 2000; 34(3): 651-701. Subject: 19.4

Feldman, Tamara; Blass, Rachel. On the patient's right to tell [letter and reply]. *Journal of the American Psychoanalytic Association* 2004 Summer; 52(3): 903-907. Subject: 17.1

Fennig, Silvana; Secker, Aya; Levkovitz, Yechiel; Barak, Vered; Benyakar, Motty; Farina, Jorje; Roe, David; Treves, Ilan; Fennig, Shmuel. Are psychotherapists consistent in their ethical attitude to patient confidentiality? *Israel Journal of Psychiatry and Related Sciences* 2004; 41(2): 82-89. Subject: 17.2

Fentiman, Linda C. Patient advocacy and termination from managed care organizations. Do state laws protecting health care professional advocacy make any difference? *Nebraska Law Review* 2003; 82(2): 508-574. Subject: 9.3.2

Fenton, Elizabeth; Lomasky, Loren. Dispensing with liberty: conscientious refusal and the "morning-after pill". *Journal of Medicine and Philosophy* 2005 December; 30(6): 579- 592. Subject: 11.1

Fenton, Kathleen. Killing versus allowing to die: examining a critical moral difference. *Ethics and Medics* 2005 March; 30(3): 1-2. Subject: 20.5.1

Ferguson, Lindsay M. A moral emergency and a medical problem: negotiating the control of venereal disease — the Saskatchewan Venereal Disease Protection Act, 1946. *Saskatchewan Law Review* 2004; 67(1): 137-159. Subject: 9.5.1

Ferguson, Melissa E.; Ferguson, Ronald M. Rescuing Prometheus: a policy proposal to alleviate excess demand for liver transplantation. *Clinical Transplantation* 1997 February; 11(1): 49-55. Subject: 19.6

Fernandez, Holly K. Genetic privacy, abandonment, and DNA dragnets: is Fourth Amendment jurisprudence adequate? *Hastings Center Report* 2005 January-February; 35(1): 21-23. Subject: 15.1

Fernández, José V.; Greene, Michael F.; Drazen, Jeffrey M.; Wood, Alastair J.J. A sad day for science at the FDA [letter and reply]. *New England Journal of Medicine* 2005 December 15; 353(24): 2619-2621. Subject: 11.1

Fernandez, Richard; Gao, Connie; Genkin, William; Ghandi, Toral; Graham, Roseanna; Hou, Judy; Hsu,

Eugenia; Hwang, JungSun. Changing perspectives on dental advertising. *Journal of the American College of Dentists* 2005 Fall; 72(3): 24-26. Subject: 8.1

Fernández-Valdivia, A.; Ocón, P.; Osuna, E.; Luna, A. Placing medical information in the hands of the judiciary: medicolegal problems. *Medicine and Law: World Association for Medical Law* 1994; 13(3-4): 277-283. Subject: 8.4

Ferner, R.E. The influence of big pharma [editorial]. *BMJ: British Medical Journal* 2005 April 16; 330(7496): 855-856. Subject: 9.7

Fernie, G. Consent and the individual detained in custody. *Medicine and Law: World Association for Medical Law* 2005 September; 24(3): 515-523. Subject: 8.3.1

Ferrand, E.; Bachoud-Levi, A.-C.; Rodrigues, M.; Maggiore, S.; Brun-Buisson, C.; Lemaire, F. Decision-making capacity and surrogate designation in French ICU patients. *Intensive Care Medicine* 2001 August; 27(8): 1360-1364. Subject: 8.3.1

Ferreira, Lissett. Access to affordable HIV/AIDS drugs: the human rights obligations of multinational pharmaceutical corporations. *Fordham Law Review* 2002 December; 71(3): 1133-1179. Subject: 9.5.6

Festing, Simon; Patel, Tarah. The Ethics of Research Involving Animals: a review of the Nuffield Council on Bioethics Report from a research perspective. *ATLA: Alternatives to Laboratory Animals* 2005 December; 33(6): 654-658. Subject: 22.2

Feudtner, Chris. Control of suffering on the slippery slope of care. *Lancet* 2005 April 9-15; 365(9467): 1284-1286. Subject: 20.5.1

Fiddler, Morris; Pergament, Eugene. Medically-assisted procreation: a maturing technology or a premature fear? Response to Testart and Sele [opinion]. *Human Reproduction* 1996 April; 11(4): 708-709. Subject: 15.2

Fidler, David P. Mission impossible? International law and infectious diseases. *Temple International and Comparative Law Journal* 1996 Fall; 10(2): 493-502. Subject: 21.1

Field, Heather M. Increasing access to emergency contraceptive pills through state law enabled dependent pharmacist prescribers. *UCLA Women's Law Journal* 2000 Fall-Winter; 11(1): 141-253. Subject: 11.1

Field, Kelly. Biosafety committees come under scrutiny. *Chronicle of Higher Education* 2005 April 29; 51(34): A22-A23. Subject: 1.3.9

Field, Marilyn J.; Behrman, Richard E. Responsible research involving children. *Ambulatory Pediatrics* 2005 January-February; 5(1): 47-49. Subject: 18.5.2

Fielder, John. Following the money at NIH. *IEEE Engineering in Medicine and Biology Magazine* 2004 November-December; 23(6): 64-65, 76. Subject: 1.3.9

Fiesta, Janine. Informed consent: what health care professionals need to know, Part 1. *Nursing Management* 1999 June; 30(6): 8-9. Subject: 8.3.1

Fiesta, Janine. Informed consent: what health care professionals need to know, Part 2. *Nursing Management* 1999 July; 30(7): 6-7. Subject: 8.3.1

Fiester, Autumn. Creating Fido's twin: can pet cloning be ethically justified? *Hastings Center Report* 2005 July-August; 35(4): 34-39. Subject: 14.5

Fiester, Autumn. Ethical issues in animal cloning. *Perspectives in Biology and Medicine* 2005 Summer; 48(3): 328-343. Subject: 14.5

Fiester, Autumn. Reflections on Dolly: what can animal cloning tell us about the human cloning debate? *In:* McGee, Glenn; Caplan, Arthur, eds. The Human Cloning Debate. 4th edition. Berkeley, CA: Berkeley Hills Books; 2004: 107-125. Subject: 14.5

Finder, Stuart G. Moral experience and technicians of the heart: reflections on the practice of perfusionists. *Journal of Extra-Corporeal Technology* 2004 March; 36(1): 4-9. Subject: 4.1.1

Fine, Dionne Koller. Government as God: an update on federal intervention in the treatment of critically ill newborns. *New England Law Review* 2000; 34(2): 343-362. Subject: 20.5.2

Fine, Michael J.; Ibrahim, Said A.; Thomas, Stephen B. The role of race and genetics in health disparities research [editorial]. *American Journal of Public Health* 2005 December; 95(12): 2125-2128. Subject: 15.1

Fineschi, V.; Neri, M.; Turillazzi, E. The new Italian law on assisted reproduction technology (Law 40/2004). *Journal of Medical Ethics* 2005 September; 31(9): 536-539. Subject: 14.1

Finlay, Ilora. Euthanasia — what it is and what it is not. *Dolentium Hominum* 2005; 20(1): 46-50. Subject: 20.5.1

Finney, Phillip D. When consent information refers to risk and deception: implications for social research. *Journal of Social Behavior and Personality* 1987; 2(1): 37-48. Subject: 18.4

Fins, Joseph J. Baseball and bioethics. *CQ: Cambridge Quarterly of Healthcare Ethics* 2005 Fall; 14(4): 434-443. Subject: 2.1

Fins, Joseph J. Everyday disasters. *CQ: Cambridge Quarterly of Healthcare Ethics* 2005 Spring; 14(2): 207-213. Subject: 9.8

Fins, Joseph J. The Orwellian threat to emerging neurodiagnostic technologies. *American Journal of Bioethics* 2005 March-April; 5(2): 56-58. Subject: 17.1

Fins, Joseph J. The physician-patient relationship in managed care: a tale of two prescriptions. *Seminars in Medical Practice* 1998 August; 1(1): 22-26. Subject: 8.1

Fins, Joseph J. Rethinking disorders of consciousness: new research and its implications. *Hastings Center Report* 2005 March-April; 35(2): 22-24. Subject: 17.1

Fins, Joseph J.; Maltby, Barbara S.; Friedmann, Erika; Greene, Michele G.; Norris, Kaye; Adelman, Ronald; Byock, Ira. Contracts, covenants and advance care planning: an empirical study of the moral obligations of patient and proxy. *Journal of Pain and Symptom Management* 2005 January; 29(1): 55-68. Subject: 20.5.4

Fins, Joseph J.; Schiff, Nicholas D. The afterlife of Terri Schiavo. *Hastings Center Report* 2005 July-August; 35(4): 8. Subject: 20.5.1

Finucane, Thomas E. Choosing resuscitation late in life: problems with the paradigm [editorial]. *American Journal of Medicine* 1996 February; 100(2): 126-127. Subject: 20.5.1

Firth, Shirley. End-of-life: a Hindu view [opinion]. *Lancet* 2005 August 20-26; 366(9486): 682-686. Subject: 20.5.1

Fischbach, Gerald D.; Fischbach, Ruth L. Stem cells: science, policy, and ethics. *Journal of Clinical Investigation* 2004 November; 114(10): 1364-1370. Subject: 18.5.4

Fischbach, Ruth L.; Fischbach, Gerald D. The brain doesn't lie. *American Journal of Bioethics* 2005 March-April; 5(2): 54-55. Subject: 17.1

Fischman, Yael. Metaclinical issues in the treatment of psychopolitical trauma. *American Journal of Orthopsychiatry* 1998 January; 68(1): 27-38. Subject: 17.2

Fisher, Alfred L.; Hill, Renée. Ethical and legal issues in antiaging medicine. *Clinics in Geriatric Medicine* 2004 May; 20(2): 361-382. Subject: 9.5.2

Fisher, Celia B. Deception research involving children: ethical practices and paradoxes. *Ethics and Behavior* 2005; 15(3): 271-287. Subject: 18.2

Fisher, Celia B. Informed consent and clinical research involving children and adolescents: implications of the revised APA ethics code and HIPAA. *Journal of Clinical Child and Adolescent Psychology* 2004 December; 33(4): 832-839. Subject: 18.5.2

Fisher, Celia B.; Hoagwood, Kimberly; Boyce, Cheryl; Duster, Troy; Frank, Deborah A.; Grisso, Thomas; Levine, Robert J.; Macklin, Ruth; Spencer, Margaret Beale; Takanishi, Ruby; Trimble, Joseph E.; Zayas, Luis H. Research ethics for mental health science involving ethnic minority children and youths. *American Psychologist* 2002 December; 57(12): 1024-1040. Subject: 18.5.2

Fisher, Celia B.; Kornetsky, Susan Z. SACHRP recommendations for review of children's research requiring DHHS secretary's approval. *IRB: Ethics and Human Research* 2005 May-June; 27(3): 8-10. Subject: 18.2

Fisher, Eric S. Informed consent in Oklahoma: a search for reasonableness and predictability in the aftermath of Scott v. Bradford. *Oklahoma Law Review* 1996 Winter; 49(4): 651-675. Subject: 8.3.1

Fisher, Ian. Italian vote to ease fertility law fails for want of voters. *New York Times* 2005 June 14; p. A11. Subject: 14.4

Fisher, Ian; Povoleod, Elisabetta. In political step, Pope joins fray on fertility law. *New York Times* 2005 May 31; p. A1, A11. Subject: 14.1

Fisher, Jill A. Human subjects in medical experiments. *In:* Restivo, Sal, ed. Science, Technology, and Society: An Encyclopedia. New York: Oxford University Press; 2005: 195-201. Subject: 18.2

Fisher, Malcolm. Ethical issues in the intensive care unit. *Current Opinion in Critical Care* 2004 August; 10(4): 292-298. Subject: 20.5.1

Fitzgerald, Daniel W.; Wasunna, Angela. Away from exploitation and towards engagement: an ethical compass for medical researchers working in resource-poor countries. *Journal of Law, Medicine and Ethics* 2005 Fall; 33(3): 559-565. Subject: 18.2

Fitzgerald, Faith. An academic clinician's perspective on the care of the geriatric patient. *Health Care Analysis: An International Journal of Health Care Philosophy and Policy* 2005 June; 13(2): 95-100. Subject: 7.2

Fitzgerald, John; Hamilton, Margaret. The consequences of knowing: ethical and legal liabilities in illicit drug research. *Social Science and Medicine* 1996 December; 43(11): 1591-1600. Subject: 18.2

Fitzgerald, Paul. Sex, lies and training programs: the ethics of consensual sexual relationships between psychiatrists and trainee psychiatrists [letter]. *Australian and New Zealand Journal of Psychiatry* 1999 February; 33(1): 119-120. Subject: 7.2

Fitzgerald, R.D.; Fitzgerald, A.; Shaheen, F.A.M.; DuBois, J.M. Support for organ procurement: national, professional, and religious correlates among medical personnel in Austria and the Kingdom of Saudi Arabia. *Transplantation Proceedings* 2002 December; 34(8): 3042-3044. Subject: 19.5

Fitzgibbons, Richard P. The desire for a sex change: clinical observations and advice. *Ethics and Medics* 2005 October; 30(10): 1-2. Subject: 10

Fjellstrom, Roger. Respect for persons, respect for integrity. *Medicine, Health Care and Philosophy: A European Journal* 2005; 8(2): 231-242. Subject: 2.1

Flamigni, Carlo. Science and biotechnology: attempts of reconciliation. *Annals of the New York Academy of Sciences* 2004 December; 1034: 101-109. Subject: 14.1

Flanagan, Pádraig P. Banning partial-birth abortions: a few inches away from testing post-viability jurisprudence. *Seton Hall Legislative Journal* 1998; 23(1): 141-177. Subject: 12.4.1

Flanagin, Annette. Fraudulent publication [editorial]. *Orthopaedic Nursing* 1994 March-April; 13(2): 7. Subject: 1.3.7

Flannery, Michael T. First, do no harm: the use of covert video surveillance to detect Munchausen syndrome by proxy — an unethical means of "preventing" child abuse. *University of Michigan Journal of Law Reform* 1998 Fall; 32(1): 105-194. Subject: 9.5.7

Fleetwood, Janet; Novack, Dennis; Templeton, Bryce. Bringing medical ethics to life: an educational programme using standardised patients. *Medical Education* 2002 November; 36(11): 1100-1101. Subject: 7.2

Fleming, David A. Futility: revisiting a concept of shared moral judgment. *HEC (Healthcare Ethics Committee) Forum* 2005 December; 17(4): 260-275. Subject: 20.5.1

Fleming, David A. Making difficult choices at the end of life: a personal challenge for all participants. *Missouri Medicine* 2005 March-April; 102(2): 147-152. Subject: 20.4.1

Fleming, Jack. Hospital transfers into nursing homes: a potential charter remedy for unwilling transferees. *Journal of Law and Social Policy* 1985; 1: 50-76. Subject: 9.5.2

Fleming, Sheena. The pregnant woman's right to say no: a personal reflection [opinion]. *RCM Midwives* 2005 March; 8(3): 106-107. Subject: 8.3.4

Fletcher, James J. Virtues, moral decisions, and health care. *NursingConnections* 1999 Winter; 12(4): 26-32. Subject: 2.1

Fletcher, Joseph. New beginnings in life: a theologian's perspective. *In:* Hamilton, Michael P., ed. The New Genetics and the Future of Man. Grand Rapids, MI: William B. Eerdmans Publishing Co.; 1972: 78-89. Subject: 14.1

Fletcher, Ruth. "Pro-life" absolutes, feminist challenges: the fundamentalist narrative of Irish abortion law 1986-1992. *Osgoode Hall Law Journal* 1998 Spring; 36(1): 1-62. Subject: 12.4.2

Flood, Colleen M. Just medicare: the role of Canadian courts in determining health care rights and access. *Journal of Law, Medicine and Ethics* 2005 Winter; 33(4): 669-680. Subject: 9.2

Flood, Colleen M.; Gable, Lance; Gostin, Lawrence O. Legislating and litigating health care rights around the world. *Journal of Law, Medicine and Ethics* 2005 Winter; 33(4): 636- 640. Subject: 9.2

Flood, Patrick J. Mandatory viability testing and post-viability abortion restriction: the best way forward in the immediate future? *In:* Koterski, Joseph W., ed. Life and Learning XI: Proceedings of the Eleventh University Faculty for Life Conference. Washington, DC: University Faculty for Life; 2002: 111-130. Subject: 12.4.4

Florencio, Patrik S.; Wyatt, Brian M.; Barnes, Mark. Can informed consent be tailored for the critical care unit?

Health Law in Canada 2004 September; 25(1): 10-16. Subject: 8.3.1

Florida. Circuit Court. Pinellas County. Sixth Circuit. *Schiavo v. Bush* [Date of Decision: 5 May 2004] Order Granting Petitioner's Motion for Protective Order. Civil Case No. 03-008212-CI-20. Florida: Circuit Court 2004 May 5; 5 p. Subject: 20.5.3

Florida. Circuit Court. Pinellas County. Sixth Circuit. *Schiavo v. Bush* [Date of Decision: 5 May 2004] Order Granting Petitioner's Motion for Summary Judgment. Civil Case No. 03-008212-CI-20. Florida: Circuit Court 2004 May 5; 23 p. Subject: 20.5.3

Florida. Court of Appeal. In re Guardianship of Schiavo [Date of Decision: 2001 October 17]. *Southern Reporter,* 2d Series, 2001; 800: 640-647. Subject: 20.5.3

Florin, Dominique. 'Do not resuscitate' orders: the need for a policy. *Journal of the Royal College of Physicians of London* 1993 April; 27(2): 135-138. Subject: 20.5.1

Fluss, Sev S. The evolution of research ethics: the current international configuration. *Journal of Law, Medicine and Ethics* 2004 Winter; 32(4): 596- 603. Subject: 18.6

Flynn, Tom. Life: medicine, morals, and markets. Right . . . or commodity? *Free Inquiry* 2005 August-September; 25(5): 31-32. Subject: 20.3.1

Foëx, Bernard A. Is informed consent possible in acute myocardial infarction? [editorial]. *Heart* 2004 November; 90(11): 1237-1238. Subject: 8.3.1

Fohr, Susan Anderson. The double effect of pain medication: separating myth from reality. *Journal of Palliative Medicine* 1998 Winter; 1(4): 315-328. Subject: 20.4.1

Foley, Teresa. Dobson v. Dobson: tort liability for expectant mothers? *Saskatchewan Law Review* 1998; 61(1): 177-198. Subject: 4.4

Folland, Sherman. The quality of mercy: social health insurance in the charitable liberal state. *International Journal of Health Care Finance and Economics* 2005 March; 5(1): 23-46. Subject: 9.3.1

Fondacaro, Mark; Frogner, Bianca; Moos, Rudolf. Justice in health care decision-making: patients' appraisals of health care providers and health plan representatives. *Social Justice Research* 2005 March; 18(1): 63-81. Subject: 8.1

Fontanarosa, Phil B.; Flanagin, Annette; DeAngelis, Catherine D. Reporting conflicts of interest, financial aspects of research, and role of sponsors in funded studies [editorial]. *JAMA: The Journal of the American Medical Association* 2005 July 6; 294(1): 110-111. Subject: 1.3.9

Foran, John E. The human act and medical practice. *Linacre Quarterly* 2005 February; 72(1): 27-30. Subject: 2.1

Forbat, Liz; Henderson, Jeanette. "Stuck in the middle with you": the ethics and process of qualitative research with two people in an intimate relationship. *Qualitative Health Research* 2003 December; 13(10): 1453-1462. Subject: 18.2

Ford, Carol; English, Abigail; Sigman, Garry. Confidential health care for adolescents: position paper of the Society for Adolescent Medicine. *Journal of Adolescent Health* 2004 August; 35(2): 160-167. Subject: 8.4

Ford, Mary. The personhood paradox and the "right to die". *Medical Law Review* 2005 Spring; 13(1): 80-101. Subject: 4.4

Ford, Norman M. Cloning and embryo research in Australia: legalization of destructive embryo research. *Ethics and Medics* 2003 March; 28(3): 2-4. Subject: 14.5

Ford, Norman M. Early delivery of a fetus with anencephaly: the medical and moral aspects. *Ethics and Medics* 2003 July; 28(7): 1-4. Subject: 20.5.2

Ford, Norman M. Fetal surgery: the wisdom of Solomon. *Ethics and Medics* 2003 August; 28(8): 3-4. Subject: 9.5.8

Ford, Norman M. Newborns and organ donation: some guidelines for decision making. *Ethics and Medics* 2003 September; 28(9): 2-4. Subject: 19.5

Ford, Norman M. Thoughts on the papal address and MANH: reflections on post- coma unresponsiveness. *Ethics and Medics* 2005 February; 30(2): 3-4. Subject: 20.5.1

Ford, Paul J. Misjudging needs: a messy spiral of complexity. *Journal of Clinical Ethics* 2005 Fall; 16(3): 206-211. Subject: 9.6

Ford, Paul J.; Dudzinski, Denise M. Specters, traces, and regret in ethics consultation. *Journal of Clinical Ethics* 2005 Fall; 16(3): 193-195. Subject: 9.6

Ford, Paul J.; Fraser, Thomas G.; Davis, Mellar P.; Kodish, Eric. Anti-infective therapy at end of life: ethical decision-making in hospice-eligible patients. *Bioethics* 2005 August; 19(4): 379-392. Subject: 20.4.1

Ford, Paul J.; Kubu, Cynthia S. Caution in leaping from functional imaging to functional neurosurgery. *American Journal of Bioethics* 2005 March-April; 5(2): 23-25. Subject: 17.1

Ford, Paul J.; Nicoletti, Toni Ann. My organs, my choice. *American Journal of Bioethics* 2005 July-August; 5(4): 30-31. Subject: 19.5

Ford, Richard. The morality of biotech patents: differing legal obligations in Europe? *European Intellectual Property Review* 1997 June; 19(6): 315-318. Subject: 15.8

Forde, Catherine. Must we really make the case for abortion rights all over again? *Conscience* 2005 Spring; 26(1): 22-23. Subject: 12.4.2

Førde, R.; Vandvik, I.H. Clinical ethics, information, and communication: review of 31 cases from a clinical ethics committee. *Journal of Medical Ethics* 2005 February; 31(2): 73-77. Subject: 9.6

Foreman, David M. Detecting fabricated or induced illness in children: may now necessitate controversial surveillance tools [editorial]. *BMJ: British Medical Journal* 2005 October 29; 331(7523): 978- 979. Subject: 9.5.7

Forero, Juan. Push to loosen abortion laws in Latin America. *New York Times* 2005 December 3; p. A1, A6. Subject: 12.4.1

Forman, Lisa. Ensuring reasonable health: health rights, the judiciary, and South African HIV/AIDS policy. *Journal of Law, Medicine and Ethics* 2005 Winter; 33(4): 711-724. Subject: 9.2

Formiga, F.; Chivite, D.; Ortega, C.; Casas, S.; Ramón, J.M.; Pujol, R. End-of-life preferences in elderly patients admitted for heart failure. *Quarterly Journal of Medicine* 2004 December; 97(12): 803-808. Subject: 20.5.1

Forrester, Kim. Nursing ethics. *Medicine and Law: World Association for Medical Law* 2005 March; 24(1): 125-136. Subject: 4.1.3

Forsberg, Anna; Nilsson, Madeleine; Krantz, Marie; Olausson, Michael. The essence of living parental liver donation — donors' lived experiences of donation to their children. *Pediatric Transplantation* 2004 August; 8(4): 372-380. Subject: 19.5

Fortun, Mike. For an ethics of promising, or: a few kind words about James Watson. *New Genetics and Society* 2005 August; 24(2): 157-173. Subject: 2.1

Fost, Norman. Developing hospital policy: the University of Wisconsin experience. *In:* Youngner, Stuart J.; Anderson, Martha W.; Schapiro, Renie, eds. Transplanting Human Tissue: Ethics, Policy, and Practice. New York: Oxford University Press; 2004: 160-167. Subject: 19.5

Fost, Norman. Gather ye shibboleths while ye may [comment]. *American Journal of Bioethics* 2005 September-October; 5(5): 14-15. Subject: 18.3

Foster, Andrea L. New California law stiffens data-protection rules for research on human subjects [news]. *Chronicle of Higher Education* 2005 December 16; 52(17): 33. Subject: 18.2

Foster, Charles. What is man, that the judges are mindful of him?: lessons from the PVS cases. *Journal of Philosophy, Science and Law [electronic]* 2005 September 28; 5: 1-15. Available: http://www.psljournal.com/ [24 November 2005]. Subject: 20.5.1

Foster, Charles A. Time to legalise assisted dying? What autonomy really means [letter]. *BMJ: British Medical Journal* 2005 October 8; 331(7520): 841- 842. Subject: 20.5.1

Foster, Morris W.; Freeman, William L. Naming names in human genetic variation research. *Genome Research* 1998 August; 8(8): 755-757. Subject: 15.1

Foster, Morris W.; Sharp, Richard R. Genetic research with minority populations. *In:* Beech, Bettina; Goodman, Maurine, eds. Race & Research: Perspectives on Minority

Participation in Health Studies. Washington, DC: American Public Health Association; 2004: 113-123. Subject: 18.5.1

Foti, Mary Ellen; Bartels, Stephen J.; Merriman, Melanie P.; Fletcher, Kenneth E.; Van Citters, Aricca D. Medical advance care planning for persons with serious mental illness. *Psychiatric Services* 2005 May; 56(5): 576-584. Subject: 20.5.4

Foti, Mary Ellen; Bartels, Stephen J.; Van Citters, Aricca D.; Merriman, Melanie P.; Fletcher, Kenneth E. End-of-life treatment preferences of persons with serious mental illness. *Psychiatric Services* 2005 May; 56(5): 585-591. Subject: 20.5.1

Foulks, Edward F. Advocating for persons who are mentally ill: a history of mutual empowerment of patients and profession. *Administration and Policy in Mental Health* 2000 May; 27(5): 353-367. Subject: 17.1

Fournier, Veronique. The balance between beneficence and respect for patient autonomy in clinical medical ethics in France. *CQ: Cambridge Quarterly of Healthcare Ethics* 2005 Summer; 14(3): 281-286. Subject: 8.1

Fowler, Heather L. Misapplied ethical considerations: U.S. federal stem cell mandates lack global focus and market foresight. *Cornell International Law Journal* 2004; 36(3): 521-544. Subject: 18.5.4

Fox, Cynthia. Cloning laws, policies, and attitudes worldwide. *IEEE Engineering in Medicine and Biology Magazine* 2004 March-April; 23(2): 55-61. Subject: 18.5.4

Fox, Fiona. Come out and fight. *New Scientist* 2005 September 24-30; 187(2518): 22. Subject: 22.2

Fox, M.; Thomson, Michael. A covenant with the status quo? Male circumcision and the new BMA guidance to doctors. *Journal of Medical Ethics* 2005 August; 31(8): 463-469. Subject: 9.5.1

Fox, Mark D.; Allee, Margaret R. Values, policies, and the public trust [editorial]. *American Journal of Bioethics* 2005 July-August; 5(4): 1-3. Subject: 19.5

Fox, Renée C. Cultural competence and the culture of medicine [opinion]. *New England Journal of Medicine* 2005 September 29; 353(13): 1316-1319. Subject: 7.2

Fox, Renée C.; Swazey, Judith P. Examining American bioethics: its problems and prospects. *CQ: Cambridge Quarterly of Healthcare Ethics* 2005 Fall; 14(4): 361-373. Subject: 2.1

Frader, Joel E. Surveying euthanasia practices: methods and morality [editorial]. *Journal of Pediatrics* 2005 May; 146(5): 584-585. Subject: 20.5.2

Frader, Joel E. Withdrawing mechanical ventilation in children. *Critical Care Medicine* 2000 August; 28(8): 3119-3120. Subject: 20.5.2

Frampton, A. Reporting of gunshot wounds by doctors in emergency departments: a duty or a right? Some legal and ethical issues surrounding breaking patient confidentiality. *Emergency Medicine Journal* 2005 February; 22(2): 84-86. Subject: 8.4

France. National Consultative Ethics Committee. Congenital handicaps and prejudice: recommendation no. 68 of the National Consultative Ethics Committee May 29, 2001. *European Journal of Health Law* 2002 June; 9(2): 150-163. Subject: 2.4

Francione, Gary. One right for all [opinion]. *New Scientist* 2005 October 8-14; 188(2520): 24. Subject: 22.1

Francione, Gary L. You hypocrites! *New Scientist* 2005 June 4-10; 186(2502): 51-52. Subject: 22.1

Francis, C.M. Medical ethics in India: ancient and modern (I). *Issues in Medical Ethics* 1996 October-December; 4(4): 115-118. Subject: 2.1

Francis, Leslie P.; Battin, Margaret P.; Jacobson, Jay A.; Smith, Charles B.; Botkin, Jeffrey. How infectious diseases got left out — and what this omission might have meant for bioethics. *Bioethics* 2005 August; 19(4): 307-322. Subject: 9.5.1

Francis, Omar. The legal and ethical issues related to the control of HIV [opinion]. *West Indian Medical Journal* 2001 September; 50(3): 183-185. Subject: 9.5.6

Frank, Arthur W. Surgical body modification and altruistic individualism: a case for cyborg ethics and methods. *Qualitative Health Research* 2003 December; 13(10): 1407-1418. Subject: 4.4

Frank, Richard G.; Conti, Rena M.; Goldman, Howard H. Mental health policy and psychotropic drugs. *Milbank Quarterly* 2005; 83(2): 271-298. Subject: 17.4

Frankel, Mark S.; Somerville, Margaret A.; Atlas, Ronald M. Using ethics to fight bioterrorism [letter and reply]. *Science* 2005 August 12; 309(5737): 1012, 1014-1015, 1017. Subject: 21.3

Franklin, Julian H. Appendix 2: Biomedical testing and use of animals. *In her:* Animal Rights and Moral Philosophy. New York: Columbia University Press; 2005: 125-128. Subject: 22.2

Franklin, Sarah. What we know and what we don't about cloning and society. *New Genetics and Society* 1999; 18(1): 111-120. Subject: 14.5

Franzini, Luisa; Marks, Elena; Cromwell, Polly F.; Risser, Jan; McGill, Laurie; Markham, Christine; Selwyn, Beatrice; Shapiro, Carrie. Projected economic costs due to health consequences of teenagers' loss of confidentiality in obtaining reproductive health care services in Texas. *Archives of Pediatrics and Adolescent Medicine* 2004 December; 158(12): 1140-1146. Subject: 11.2

Frasca, Tim. Gaining ground: despite political and religious opposition, Latin American activists force advances in reproductive rights. *Conscience* 2003 Summer; 24(2): 22-24. Subject: 14.1

Fraser, John. Ethics of HIV testing in general practice without informed consent: a case series. *Journal of Medical Ethics* 2005 December; 31(12): 698-699. Subject: 9.5.6

Fraser, John J., Jr.; McAbee, Gary N. Dealing with the parent whose judgment is impaired by alcohol or drugs: legal and ethical considerations. *Pediatrics* 2004 September; 114(3): 869-873. Subject: 8.3.2

Frazzetto, Giovanni. Embryos, cells and God. *EMBO Reports* 2004 June; 5(6): 553-555. Subject: 14.5

Fredriksen, Ståle. Limits to doubt. *Theoretical Medicine and Bioethics* 2005; 26(5): 379-395. Subject: 4.1.2

Fredriksen, Ståle. Luck, risk, and blame. *Journal of Medicine and Philosophy* 2005 October; 30(5): 535- 553. Subject: 4.1.2

Freeden, Michael. Eugenics and progressive thought: a study in ideological affinity. *Historical Journal* 1979; 22(3): 645-671. Subject: 15.5

Freedman, Alfred M.; Halpern, Abraham L. A crisis in the ethical and moral behavior of psychiatrists [forum]. *Current Opinion in Psychiatry* 1998 January; 11(1); 3 p. [Online]. Available: http://gateway.ut.ovid.com/gw1/ovidweb.cgi [24 May 2005]. Subject: 20.6

Freedman, Alfred M.; Halpern, Abraham L. Response: a crisis in the ethical and moral behavior of psychiatrists [forum]. *Current Opinion in Psychiatry* 1998 January; 11(1); 4 p. [Online]. Available: http://gateway.ut.ovid.com/gw1/ovidweb.cgi [24 May 2005]. Subject: 20.6

Freedman, Barry I.; Wagenknecht, Lynne E.; Bowden, Donald W.; Vaccarino, Viola; Jha, Ashish K.; Epstein, Arnold M.; Orav, E. John. Trends in racial disparities in care [letter and reply]. *New England Journal of Medicine* 2005 November 10; 353(19): 2081-2085. Subject: 9.5.4

Freeland, Richard. Euthanasia and Islamic law. *Medico-Legal Journal* 1997; 65(4): 196-198. Subject: 20.5.1

Freeman, Robert A. Minimizing bias in industry-sponsored outcomes research. *Medical Interface* 1994 April; 7(4): 130-134. Subject: 9.8

French, Howard W. As girls "vanish", Chinese city battles tide of abortions. *New York Times* 2005 February 17; p. A3. Subject: 12.5.1

French, Kyle G. The elderly and the discriminatory use of genetic information. *Elder Law Journal* 1997 Spring; 5(1); 29 p. [Online]. Available: http://web.lexis-nexis.com/universe/printdoc [22 July 2005]. Subject: 15.3

Frewer, Andreas. Debates on human experimentation in Weimar and early Nazi Germany as reflected in the journal "Ethik" (1922-1938) and its context. *In:* Roelcke, Volker; Maio, Giovanni, eds. Twentieth Century Ethics of Human Subjects Research: Historical Perspectives on Values, Practices, and Regulations. Stuttgart: Franz Steiner Verlag; 2004: 137-150. Subject: 18.1

Frey, Christopher. Person oder empirisch verstandenes Faktum? Zum Bild vom Menschen in seinen Anfängen. *In:* Baumann, Eva; Brink, Alexander; May, Arnd T.; Schröder; Peter; Schutzeichel, Corinna Iris, eds. Weltanschauliche Offenheit in der Bioethik. Berlin: Duncker & Humblot; 2004: 147-161. Subject: 4.4

Frey, R.G. Animals. *In:* LaFollette, Hugh, ed. The Oxford Handbook of Practical Ethics. New York: Oxford University Press; 2003: 161-187. Subject: 22.2

Frey, R.G. Animals and their medical use. *In:* Cohen, Andrew I.; Wellman, Christopher Heath, eds. Contemporary Debates in Applied Ethics. Malden, MA: Blackwell Pub., 2005: 91-103. Subject: 22.2

Frey, R.G. Autonomy, diminished life, and the threshold for use. *In:* Taylor, James Stacey, ed. Personal Autonomy: New Essays on Personal Autonomy and Its Role in Contemporary Moral Philosophy. New York: Cambridge University Press; 2005: 330-346. Subject: 22.1

Frey, R.G. On the ethics of using animals for human benefit. *In:* Sherlock, Richard; Morrey, John D., eds. Ethical Issues in Biotechnology. Lanham: Rowman and Littlefield; 2002: 287-297. Subject: 22.2

Frey, R.G.; Thomas, D. Pain, vivisection, and the value of life. *Journal of Medical Ethics* 2005 April; 31(4): 202-204. Subject: 22.2

Frezza, Eldo Ermenegildo; Squillario, Denise M.; Smith, Thomas J. The ethical challenge and the futile treatment in the older population admitted to the intensive care unit. *American Journal of Medical Quality* 1998 Fall; 13(3): 121-126. Subject: 9.4

Fricker, P. Commentary: hypoxic air machines. *Journal of Medical Ethics* 2005 February; 31(2): 115. Subject: 9.5.1

Fried, Marlene Gerber. The economics of abortion access in the US: restrictions on government funding for abortion is the post-Roe battleground. *Conscience* 2005-2006 Winter; 26(4): 10-15. Subject: 12.5.1

Friedlaender, Michael M. A protocol for paid kidney donation in Israel. *IMAJ* 2003 September; 5: 611-614. Subject: 19.5

Friedlander, Henry. From "euthanasia" to the "final solution.". *In:* Bachrach, Susan, project director; Kuntz, Dieter, ed. Deadly Medicine: Creating the Master Race. Washington, DC: United States Holocaust Museum; 2004: 155-183. Subject: 21.4

Friedman, Joseph H. Ignorance is bliss? An ethical question [opinion]. *Medicine and Health, Rhode Island* 2004 May; 87(5): 126. Subject: 8.2

Friedman, Lee; Richter, Elihu D. Conflicts of interest and scientific integrity. *International Journal of Occupational and Environmental Health* 2005 April-June; 11(2): 205-206. Subject: 7.3

Friedman, Yaakov. Ethical issues in the critically ill patient. *Current Opinion in Critical Care* 2001 December; 7(6): 475-479. Subject: 20.5.1

Friedmann, Theodore. Lessons for the stem cell discourse from the gene therapy experience. *Perspectives in Biology and Medicine* 2005 Autumn; 48(4): 585-591. Subject: 18.5.4

Friedman-Ross, Lainie. The ethics of newborn screening diabetes research. *In:* Kodish, Eric, ed. Ethics and Research with Children: A Case-Based Approach. New York: Oxford University Press; 2005: 123- 142. Subject: 15.3

Friedrich, M.J. Neuroscience becomes image conscious as brain scans raise ethical issues. *JAMA: The Journal of the American Medical Association* 2005 August 17; 294(7): 781-783. Subject: 17.1

Frist, William H. Health care in the 21st century. *New England Journal of Medicine* 2005 January 20; 352(3): 267- 272. Subject: 9.3.1

Frith, Lucy. Ethical issues in community midwifery. *In:* Chadwick, Ruth; Levitt, Mairi, eds. Ethical Issues in Community Health Care. New York: Arnold; 1998: 115-124. Subject: 9.5.5

Frith, Lucy. HIV testing and informed consent. *Journal of Medical Ethics* 2005 December; 31(12): 699-700. Subject: 9.5.6

Frith, Michael. Asian nations approach cloning consensus [news]. *Nature Medicine* 2003 March; 9(3): 248. Subject: 14.5

Fritz, Mark. Last rights: how simple device set off a fight over elderly care; invented for younger patients, feeding tube now figures in end-of-life debate; a missed box on a living will. *Wall Street Journal* 2005 December 8; p. A1, A10. Subject: 20.5.1

Froom, Paul; Barak, M. An informed consent form for treatment with oral anticoagulants [letter]. *Journal of Thrombosis and Haemostasis* 2004 January; 2(1): 196-197. Subject: 8.3.1

Frueh, B. Christopher; Knapp, Rebecca G.; Cusack, Karen J.; Grubaugh, Anouk L.; Sauvageot, Julie A.; Cousins, Victoria C.; Yim, Eunsil; Robins, Cynthia S.; Monnier, Jeannine; Hiers, Thomas G. Patients' reports of traumatic or harmful experiences within the psychiatric setting. *Psychiatric Services* 2005 September; 56(9): 1123-1133. Subject: 17.1

Fry, C.L.; Ritter, A.; Baldwin, S.; Bowen, K.J.; Gardiner, P.; Holt, T.; Jenkinson, R.; Johnston, J. Paying research participants: a study of current practices in Australia. *Journal of Medical Ethics* 2005 September; 31(9): 542-547. Subject: 18.1

Fry, Frank. Certificates. *Australian Family Physician* 1994 June; 23(6): 1092-1093, 1095. Subject: 7.1

Fry, Sara T.; Veatch, Robert M. Abortion, contraception, and sterilization. *In their:* Case Studies in Nursing Ethics.

Third edition. Sudbury, MA: Jones and Bartlett Publishers; 2006: 227-245. Subject: 12.3

Fry, Sara T.; Veatch, Robert M. Benefiting the patient and others: the duty to produce good and avoid harm. *In their:* Case Studies in Nursing Ethics. Third edition. Sudbury, MA: Jones and Bartlett Publishers; 2006: 65-93. Subject: 4.1.3

Fry, Sara T.; Veatch, Robert M. Consent and the right to refuse treatment. *In their:* Case Studies in Nursing Ethics. Third edition. Sudbury, MA: Jones and Bartlett Publishers; 2006: 364-391. Subject: 8.3.1

Fry, Sara T.; Veatch, Robert M. Death and dying. *In their:* Case Studies in Nursing Ethics. Third edition. Sudbury, MA: Jones and Bartlett Publishers; 2006: 392-435. Subject: 20.5.1

Fry, Sara T.; Veatch, Robert M. Experimentation on human beings. *In their:* Case Studies in Nursing Ethics. Third edition. Sudbury, MA: Jones and Bartlett Publishers; 2006: 330-363. Subject: 18.1

Fry, Sara T.; Veatch, Robert M. Fidelity. *In their:* Case Studies in Nursing Ethics. Third edition. Sudbury, MA: Jones and Bartlett Publishers; 2006: 167-191. Subject: 8.1

Fry, Sara T.; Veatch, Robert M. Genetics, birth, and the biological revolution. *In their:* Case Studies in Nursing Ethics. Third edition. Sudbury, MA: Jones and Bartlett Publishers; 2006: 246-280. Subject: 14.1

Fry, Sara T.; Veatch, Robert M. HIV/AIDS care. *In their:* Case Studies in Nursing Ethics. Third edition. Sudbury, MA: Jones and Bartlett Publishers; 2006: 299-329. Subject: 9.5.6

Fry, Sara T.; Veatch, Robert M. Justice: the allocation of health resources. *In their:* Case Studies in Nursing Ethics. Third edition. Sudbury, MA: Jones and Bartlett Publishers; 2006: 94-118. Subject: 9.4

Fry, Sara T.; Veatch, Robert M. The principle of autonomy. *In their:* Case Studies in Nursing Ethics. Third edition. Sudbury, MA: Jones and Bartlett Publishers; 2006: 119-141. Subject: 8.1

Fry, Sara T.; Veatch, Robert M. Psychiatry and the control of human behavior. *In their:* Case Studies in Nursing Ethics. Third edition. Sudbury, MA: Jones and Bartlett Publishers; 2006: 281-298. Subject: 17.1

Fry, Sara T.; Veatch, Robert M. The sanctity of human life. *In their:* Case Studies in Nursing Ethics. Third edition. Sudbury, MA: Jones and Bartlett Publishers; 2006: 192-223. Subject: 20.5.1

Fry, Sara T.; Veatch, Robert M. Veracity. *In their:* Case Studies in Nursing Ethics. Third edition. Sudbury, MA: Jones and Bartlett Publishers; 2006: 142-166. Subject: 8.2

Frye, Carla B. Disclosing conflicts of interest involving clinicians who prepare therapeutic guidelines. *American Journal of Health System Pharmacy* 2005 February 15; 62(4): 361-362. Subject: 7.3

Fryer, Jonathan; Angelos, Peter. Is there a role for living donor intestine transplants? *Progress in Transplantation* 2004 December; 14(4): 321-329. Subject: 19.5

Fryer-Edwards, Kelly; Calogero, Carla. The challenge of the other. *American Journal of Bioethics* 2005 November-December; 5(6): 65-66. Subject: 2.1

Fuchs, Michael. Die Einschätzung des Kleinwuchses als Streitfall im Recht und die medizinethische Debatte um Therapie und Enhancement (Verbesserung). *In:* Jahrbuch für Wissenschaft und Ethik. Bd. 7. Berlin: Walter de Gruyter; 2002: 283-293. Subject: 9.5.1

Fugh-Berman, Adriane. The corporate coauthor [opinion]. *JGIM: Journal of General Internal Medicine* 2005 June; 20(6): 546-548. Subject: 1.3.7

Fukushima, Yoshimitsu; Sakurai, Akihiro. Comprehensive genetics clinic for familial tumors: proposal for a suitable system in Japan. *International Journal of Clinical Oncology* 2004 August; 9(4): 304-307. Subject: 15.3

Fukuyama, Francis. Human biomedicine and the problem of governance. *Perspectives in Biology and Medicine* 2005 Spring; 48(2): 195-200. Subject: 18.5.4

Fulford, K.W.M. Facts/values: ten principles of values-based medicine. *In:* Radden, Jennifer, ed. The Philosophy of Psychiatry: A Companion. New York: Oxford University Press; 2004: 205-234. Subject: 2.1

Fuller, R.; Dudley, N.; Blacktop, J. How informed is consent? Understanding of pictorial and verbal probability information by medical inpatients. *Postgraduate Medical Journal* 2002; 78: 543-544. Subject: 8.3.1

Fulton, Jane. Cooperative approaches to health-care rationing [editorial]. *Humane Health Care International* 1997 Summer; 13(2): 9-10. Subject: 9.4

Fung, John J.; Roberts, John P. The rationale for equitable liver allocation. *Clinical Transplantation* 1996: 325-332. Subject: 19.6

Funk, Laura M. Who wants to be involved? Decision-making preferences among residents of long-term care facilities. *Canadian Journal on Aging* 2004 Spring; 23(1): 47-58. Subject: 9.5.2

Funk, Nanette. Abortion counselling and the 1995 German abortion law. *Connecticut Journal of International Law* 1996 Fall; 12(1): 33-65. Subject: 12.5.3

Furedi, Ann. The case for second trimester abortion. *Conscience* 2004-2005 Winter; 25(3): 26-27. Subject: 12.4.2

Furst, Jessica. Modern eugenics. *Ivy Journal of Ethics* 2003; 3(1): 16-17. Subject: 15.5

Furton, Edward J. Catholic refusals of immunization: such actions are often unjustified. *Ethics and Medics* 2005 December; 30(12): 1-2. Subject: 9.5.7

Furton, Edward J. A critique of the five wishes: comments in the light of a papal statement. *Ethics and Medics* 2005 March; 30(3): 3-4. Subject: 20.5.1

Furton, Edward J. A defense of oocyte-assisted reprogramming. *National Catholic Bioethics Quarterly* 2005 Autumn; 5(3): 465- 468. Subject: 15.1

Furton, Edward J. On the death of Terri Schiavo. *Ethics and Medics* 2005 June; 30(6): 3-4. Subject: 20.5.1

Furton, Edward J.; Shannon, Thomas A.; Walter, James J.; Repenshek, Mark; Slosar, John Paul. Nutrition and hydration [letter and reply]. *Hastings Center Report* 2005 May-June; 35(3): 5-6. Subject: 20.5.1

Fuscaldo, Giuliana; Savulescu, Julian. Spare embryos: 3000 reasons to rethink the significance of genetic relatedness. *Reproductive BioMedicine Online [electronic]* 2005 February; 10(2): 164-168. Available: http://www.rbmonline.com/index.html [17 February 2006]. Subject: 14.4

G

Gaal, Peter; McKee, Martin. Fee-for-service or donation? Hungarian perspectives on informal payment for health care. *Social Science and Medicine* 2005 April; 60(7): 1445-1457. Subject: 9.3.1

Gabbay, Baback B.; Matsumura, Shinji; Etzioni, Shiri; Asch, Steven M; Rosenfeld, Kenneth E.; Shiojiri, Toshiaki; Balingit, Peter P.; Lorenz, Karl A. Negotiating end-of-life decision making: a comparison of Japanese and U.S. residents' approaches. *Academic Medicine* 2005 July; 80(7): 617-621. Subject: 20.5.1

Gacki-Smith, Jessica; Gordon, Elisa J. Residents' access to ethics consultations: knowledge, use, and perceptions. *Academic Medicine* 2005 February; 80(2): 168-175. Subject: 9.6

Gadd, Elaine. Ethics support in clinical practice in Europe — situation overview. *Medical Ethics and Bioethics / Medicinska Etika & Bioetika* 2005; 11(Supplement): 4-5. Subject: 9.6

Gagneux, Pascal; Moore, James J.; Varki, Ajit. The ethics of research on great apes. *Nature* 2005 September 1; 437(7055): 27-29. Subject: 22.2

Gajewska, Kalina; Schroeder, Michele; De Marre, Francoise; Vincent, Jean-Louis. Analysis of terminal events in 109 successive deaths in a Belgian intensive care unit. *Intensive Care Medicine* 2004 June; 30(6): 1224-1227. Subject: 20.5.1

Galbraith, Mhairi; McLachlan, Hugh V.; Swales, J. Kim. Commercial agencies and surrogate motherhood: a transaction cost approach. *Health Care Analysis: An International Journal of Health Care Philosophy and Policy* 2005 March; 13(1): 11-31. Subject: 14.2

Gale, Edwin A.M. Between two cultures: the expert clinician and the pharmaceutical industry. *Clinical Medicine* 2003 November-December; 3(6): 538-541. Subject: 7.3

Gallagher, Thomas H.; Levinson, Wendy. A prescription for protecting the doctor-patient relationship. *American*

Journal of Managed Care 2004 February; 10(2, Part 1): 61-68. Subject: 8.1

Gallagher, Thomas H.; Levinson, Wendy. Disclosing harmful medical errors to patients: a time for professional action. *Archives of Internal Medicine* 2005 September 12; 165(16): 1819-1824. Subject: 9.8

Galletly, Cherrie A. Crossing professional boundaries in medicine: the slippery slope to patient sexual exploitation. *Medical Journal of Australia* 2004 October 4; 181(7): 380-383. Subject: 7.4

Gallop, Ruth. Abuse of power in the nurse-client relationship. *Nursing Standard* 1998 June 3-9; 12(37): 43-47. Subject: 7.4

Galvão, Jane. Brazil and access to HIV/AIDS drugs: a question of human rights and public health. *American Journal of Public Health* 2005 July; 95(7): 1110-1116. Subject: 9.5.6

Gambino, Gabriella. Catholicism. *In:* Council of Europe Publishing, ed. Euthanasia. Volume I. Ethical and Human Aspects. Strasbourg: Council of Europe; Croton- on-Hudson, NY: Manhattan Publishing Co.; 2003: 135-140. Subject: 20.5.1

Gambino, Gabriella; Spagnolo, Antonio G. Ethical and juridical foundations of conscientious objection for health care workers. *Medical Ethics and Bioethics / Medicinska Etika and Bioetika* 2002 Spring-Summer; 9(1-2): 3-5. Subject: 8.1

Gamble, Denise. Potentialism and the value of an embryo. *Public Affairs Quarterly* 2005 October; 19(4): 265-299. Subject: 4.4

Gammelgaard, Anne. An empirical study of the informed consent process of a clinical trial. *In:* Holm, Søren; Jonas, Monique F., eds. Engaging the World: The Use of Empirical Research in Bioethics and the Regulation of Biotechnology. Washington, DC: IOS Press; 2004: 99-108. Subject: 18.3

Ganatra, Bela; Hirve, Siddhi. A community-based study on induced abortions. *Issues in Medical Ethics* 2001 January-March; 9(1): 7-8. Subject: 18.4

Ganchoff, Chris. Regenerating movements: embryonic stem cells and the politics of potentiality. *Sociology of Health and Illness* 2004 September; 26(6): 757-774. Subject: 5.1

Gandevia, S.C. Self-experimentation, ethics and efficacy. *Monash Bioethics Review* 2005 April; 24(2): 43-48. Subject: 18.5.1

Gandhi, Rupali. Research involving children: regulations, review boards and reform. *Journal of Health Care Law and Policy* 2005; 8(2): 264-330. Subject: 18.2

Gangoli, Geetanjali. Abortion: a fundamental right [letter]. *Issues in Medical Ethics* 2000 October-December; 8(4): 104. Subject: 12.1

Gangoli, Geetanjali. Reproduction, abortion and women's health. *Social Scientist* 1998 November-December; 26(11-12): 83-105. [Online]. Available: http://www.hsph.harvard.edu/Organizations/healthnet/SAsia/suchana/1299/h030.html [27 May 2005]. Subject: 13.3

Gann, Peter H. Informed consent for prostate-specific antigen testing [editorial]. *Urology* 2003 January; 61(1): 5-6. Subject: 8.3.1

Gannon, C. A request for hospice admission from hospital to withdraw ventilation. *Journal of Medical Ethics* 2005 July; 31(7): 383-384. Subject: 20.5.1

Ganten, Detlev. Selbstkontrolle und Vertrauen in die Wissenschaft. *In:* Maio, Giovanni; Just, Hanjörg, eds. Die Forschung an embryonalen Stammzellen in ethischer und rechtlicher Perspektive. Baden-Baden: Nomos Verlagsgesellschaft; 2003: 229-238. Subject: 18.5.4

Ganthaler, Heinrich. Experimentation on human embryos: the bioethical discussion in Europe with special attention to Austria and Germany. *In:* Brannigan, Michael C., ed. Cross-Cultural Biotechnology. Lanham: Rowman amd Littlefield; 2004: 71-79. Subject: 18.5.4

Ganzini, Linda; Back, Anthony. From the USA: understanding requests for physician-assisted death. *Palliative Medicine* 2003 March; 17(2): 113-114. Subject: 20.7

Ganzini, Linda; Prigerson, Holly. The other side of the slippery slope. *Hastings Center Report* 2004 July-August; 34(4): 3. Subject: 17.1

Garanis-Papadatos, Tina. Ethics committees in Greece. *Medical Ethics and Bioethics / Medicinska Etika & Bioetika* 2005; 11(Supplement): 16-17. Subject: 9.6

Garchar, Kimberly. The loyal patient at the end of life: a Roycean argument for assisted suicide. *CQ: Cambridge Quarterly of Healthcare Ethics* 2005 Spring; 14(2): 147-155. Subject: 20.7

Garcia, Laura L. Protecting persons. *In:* Tollefsen, Christopher, ed. John Paul II's Contribution to Catholic Bioethics. Norwell, MA: Springer; 2004: 93-105. Subject: 14.1

Garcia, V.D.; Garcia, C.D.; Keitel, E.; Santos, A.F.; Bianco, P.D.; Bittar, A.E.; Neumann, J.; Campos, H.H.; Pestana, J.O.M.; Abbud-Filho, M. Expanding criteria for the use of living donors: what are the limits? *Transplantation Proceedings* 2004 May; 36(4): 808-810. Subject: 19.5

Garel, M.; Seguret, S.; Kaminski, M.; Cuttini, M. Ethical decision-making for extremely preterm deliveries: results of a qualitative survey among obstetricians and midwives. *Journal of Maternal-Fetal and Neonatal Medicine* 2004 June; 15(6): 394-399. Subject: 20.3.2

Garfield, Christopher. Enabling responsibility: adolescent autonomy and the teen HIV crisis in the United States. *Journal of Medicine and Law* 2003 Fall-2004 Spring; 8(1-2): 87-100. Subject: 9.5.6

Subject = NRCBL Primary Classification Number; See inside front cover

Garity, Joan. Relationship of the ANA Code of Ethics to nurses' collaborative efforts. *Online Journal of Issues in Nursing [electronic]* 2005; 10(3); E9, 3 p. Available: http://www.nursingworld.org/ojin/ [23 November 2005]. Subject: 7.3

Garne, David; Watson, Megan; Chapman, Simon; Byrne, Fiona. Environmental tobacco smoke research published in the journal Indoor and Built Environment and associations with the tobacco industry. *Lancet* 2005 February 26-March 4; 365(9461): 804-809. Subject: 1.3.7

Garrard, E.; Wilkinson, S. Passive euthanasia. *Journal of Medical Ethics* 2005 February; 31(2): 64-68. Subject: 20.5.1

Garrard, Eve; Dawson, A. What is the role of the research ethics committee? Paternalism, inducements, and harm in research ethics. *Journal of Medical Ethics* 2005 July; 31(7): 419-423. Subject: 18.2

Garrard, Eve; Wilkinson, Stephen. Mind the gap: the use of empirical evidence in bioethics. *In:* Häyry, Matti; Takala, Tuija; Herissone-Kelly, Peter, eds. Bioethics and Social Reality. New York: Rodopi, 2005: 77-91. Subject: 2.1

Garrett, Lynnda. A response to Bilsen J.J.R., Vander Stichele R.H., Mortier F. and Deliens L. (2004), Involvement of nurses in physician-assisted dying [letter]. *Journal of Advanced Nursing* 2005 January; 49(1): 104. Subject: 20.5.1

Garrett, Robert E. Why philosophy matters. *Family Medicine* 2002 April; 34(4): 247-249. Subject: 4.1.2

Garrison, Marsha. Law making for baby making: an interpretive approach to the determination of legal parentage. *Harvard Law Review* 2000 February; 113(4): 835-923. Subject: 14.2

Garte, Seymour. The racial genetics paradox in biomedical research and public health [opinion]. *Public Health Reports* 2002 September-October; 117(5): 421-425. Subject: 15.11

Garwood-Gowers, Austen. Contemporary issues in the regulation of artificial reproduction and embryology in the UK. *Revista de Derecho y Genoma-Humano / Law and the Human Genome Review* 2004 July-December; (21): 67-101. Subject: 18.5.4

Gaskell, George; Einsiedel, Edna; Hallman, William; Priest, Susanna Hornig; Jackson, Jonathan; Olsthoorn, Johannus. Social values and the governance of science. *Science* 2005 December 23; 310(5756): 1908-1909. Subject: 5.3

Gasparini, Giulio; Boniello, Roberto; Longobardi, Gianluigi; Pelo, Sandro. Orthognathic surgery: an informed consent model. *Journal of Craniofacial Surgery* 2004 September; 15(5): 858-862. Subject: 8.3.1

Gast, Scott. Who defines "legitimate medical practice?" Lessons learned from the Controlled Substances Act, phy-

sician-assisted suicide, and Oregon v. Ashcroft. *Virginia Journal of Social Policy and the Law* 2002 Winter; 10(2): 261-291. Subject: 20.5.1

Gattellari, Melina; Ward, Jeanette E. Men's reactions to disclosed and undisclosed opportunistic PSA screening for prostate cancer. *Medical Journal of Australia* 2005 April 18; 182(8): 386-389. Subject: 8.3.1

Gatter, Robert. Faith, confidence, and health care: fostering trust in medicine through law. *Wake Forest Law Review* 2004 Summer; 39(2): 395-445. Subject: 9.1

Gatter, Robert. Walking the talk of trust in human subjects research: the challenge of regulating financial conflicts of interest. *Emory Law Journal* 2003 Winter; 52(1): 327-401. Subject: 18.2

Gaughan, Mary C. Legal review: the Patient Self-Determination Act — "Miranda" rights in health care. *Topics in Health Record Management* 1991 August; 12(1): 83-88. Subject: 20.5.4

Gauthier, Candace Cummins. The virtue of moral responsibility and the obligations of patients. *Journal of Medicine and Philosophy* 2005 April; 30(2): 153-166. Subject: 8.1

Gavey, Nicola; Braun, Virginia. Ethics and the publication of clinical case material. *Professional Psychology: Research and Practice* 1997 August; 28(4): 399-404. Subject: 1.3.7

Gawande, Atul. Naked [opinion]. *New England Journal of Medicine* 2005 August 18; 353(7): 645- 648. Subject: 9.5.5

Gaynor, Brian. A different dilemma every day. *Australian Family Physician* 1994 June; 23(6): 1038, 1040- 1041. Subject: 7.1

Gazzaniga, Michael S. The thoughtful distinction between embryo and human. *Chronicle of Higher Education* 2005 April 8; 51(31): B10-B12. Subject: 4.4

Gazzaniga, Michael S. What's on your mind? [opinion]. *New Scientist* 2005 June 11-17; 186(2503): 48-50. Subject: 17.1

Gearon, Christopher J.; Fields, Helen. Medicine's turf wars: specialists without M.D.'s are pushing for more medical power. Are they ready — and are you? *U.S. News and World Report* 2005 January 31-February 7; 138(4): 57-60, 62, 64. Subject: 7.3

Gebhardt, D.O.E. Off-label administration of drugs to healthy military personnel. Dubious ethics of preventive measures [opinion]. *Journal of Medical Ethics* 2005 May; 31(5): 268. Subject: 18.5.8

Gebhardt, D.O.E. The use of generic or patent medicines in the Netherlands [letter]. *Journal of Medical Ethics* 2005 July; 31(7): 409. Subject: 9.7

Gefenas, Eugenijus. Lithuania. *Medical Ethics and Bioethics / Medicinska Etika & Bioetika* 2005; 11(Supplement): 17. Subject: 9.6

Geiderman, Joel M. In defense of patient privacy [letter]. *Annals of Emergency Medicine* 2002 January; 39(1): 2 p. [Online]. Available: http://home.mdconsult.com/das/ article/body/51079232-2/jorg=journal&source=MI& sp=12 [5 October 2005]. Subject: 8.3.1

Geier, David; Geier, Mark. The true story of pertussis vaccination: a sordid legacy? *Journal of the History of Medicine and Allied Sciences* 2002 July; 57(3): 249-284. Subject: 9.7

Geller, Alisa L. Regulations limiting medical research in prisons remains necessary. *Journal of Biolaw and Business* 2005; 8(4): 72-73. Subject: 18.2

Geller, Gail. The ethics of predictive genetic testing in prevention trials involving adolescents. *In:* Kodish, Eric, ed. Ethics and Research with Children: A Case-Based Approach. New York: Oxford University Press; 2005: 194-220. Subject: 15.3

Geller, Gail; Bernhardt, Barbara A.; Gardner, Mary; Rodgers, Joann; Holtzman, Neil A. Scientists' and science writers' experiences reporting genetic discoveries: toward an ethic of trust in science journalism. *Genetics in Medicine* 2005 March; 7(3): 198-205. Subject: 15.1

Geller, Lisa N.; Alper, Joseph S.; Billings, Paul R.; Barash, Carol I.; Beckwith, Jonathan; Natowicz, Marvin R. Individual, family, and societal dimensions of genetic discrimination: a case study analysis. *Science and Engineering Ethics* 1996; 2(1): 71-88. Subject: 15.3

Geller, S.E.; Patel, A.; Niak, V.A.; Goudar, S.S.; Edlavitch, S.A.; Kodkany, B.S.; Derman, R.J. Conducting international collaborative research in developing nations. *International Journal of Gynecology and Obstetrics* 2004 December; 87(3): 267-271. Subject: 18.5.9

Gellerman, David M.; Suddath, Robert. Violent fantasy, dangerousness, and the duty to warn and protect. *Journal of the American Academy of Psychiatry and the Law* 2005; 33(4): 484-495. Subject: 8.4

Gemperli, Marcel P.; Stewart, Felicia H.; Phillips, Kathryn A.; Sakowski, Julie; Van Bebber, Stephanie; Bergthold, Linda. A qualitative study of insurers' coverage for mifepristone-induced abortion. *Managed Care Interface* 2005 March; 18(3): 26-30, 32. Subject: 9.7

Gene Therapy Advisory Committee [GTAC]; Committee on Safety of Medicines [CSM]. Recommendations of the Gene Therapy Advisory Committee / Committee on Safety of Medicines working party on retroviruses May 2005. *Human Gene Therapy* 2005 October; 16(10): 1237-1239. Subject: 15.4

Gennery, Brian. Academic clinical research in the new regulatory environment. *Clinical Medicine* 2005 January-February; 5(1): 39-41. Subject: 18.6

Gentry, Deborah B. Genetic technology and family conflict. *Mediation Quarterly* 2000 Fall; 18(1): 5-17. Subject: 15.1

George, R.J.D.; Finlay, I.G.; Jeffrey, David. Legalised euthanasia will violate the rights of vulnerable patients. *BMJ: British Medical Journal* 2005 September 24; 331(7518): 684-685. Subject: 20.5.1

George, Robert P.; Gómez-Lobo, Alfonso. The moral status of the human embryo. *Perspectives in Biology and Medicine* 2005 Spring; 48(2): 201-210. Subject: 4.4

George, Sabu M.; Dahiya, Ranbir S. Female foeticide in rural Haryana. Economic and Political Weekly 1998 August 8-14; 33(32); 18 p. [Online]. Available: http://www.hsph.harvard.edu/Organizations/healthnet/ SAsia/suchana/0628/george_dahiya.html [6 October 2005]. Subject: 14.3

George, Thomas. The case against kidney sales. *Issues in Medical Ethics* 2001 April-June; 9(2): 49-50. Subject: 19.5

George, Thomas. Should medical students resort to a strike? *Issues in Medical Ethics* 2000 April-June; 8(2): 59. Subject: 7.1

Georgia. Supreme Court. *Adams v. State* [Date of Decision: 4 May 1998]. *West's South Eastern Reporter*, 2d Series, 1998; 498: 268-274. Subject: 8.3.4

Gerald, Lynn B.; Sanderson, Bonnie; Fish, Larry; Li, Yufeng; Bittner, Vera; Brooks, Michael; Bailey, William C. Advance directives in cardiac and pulmonary rehabilitation patients. *Journal of Cardiopulmonary Rehabilitation* 2000 November-December; 20(6): 340-345. Subject: 20.5.4

Gerber, A.; Lauterbach, K.W. Evidence-based medicine: why do opponents and proponents use the same arguments? *Health Care Analysis: An International Journal of Health Care Philosophy and Policy* 2005 March; 13(1): 59-71. Subject: 9.8

Gericke, C.A.; Riesberg, A.; Busse, R. Ethical issues in funding orphan drug research and development. *Journal of Medical Ethics* 2005 March; 31(3): 164-168. Subject: 9.7

Germany. Bundestag. Study Commission on Ethics and Law in Modern Medicine. Interim Report on Living Wills: Short Version. Berlin, Germany: Secretariat of the Study Commission on the Law and Ethics of Modern Medicine, German Bundestag 2004 December; 12 p. [Online]. Available: http://www.bundestag.de/parlament/ kommissionen/archiv15/ethik_med/berichte_stellg/04_1 2_16_kurzfassung_zwischenbericht_patientenverfuegun gen_engl.pdf [29 November 2005]. Subject: 20.5.4

Gert, Heather J.; Steinberg, David. The characteristics of information and avoiding surprises [discussion]. *Medical Ethics Newsletter [Lahey Clinic]* 2003 Winter; 10(1): 6-7. Subject: 8.3.1

Gessert, Charles E. Daily decisions: even as new biotechnologies expand the horizons of bioethics, focus needs to be placed on the ethics of everyday practice. *Minnesota Medicine* 2004 June; 87(6): 30-31. Subject: 9.1

Subject = NRCBL Primary Classification Number; See inside front cover

Getz, Linn; Kirkengen, Anna Luise; Hetlevik, Irene; Romundstad, Solfrid; Sigurdsson, Johann A. Ethical dilemmas arising from implementation of the European guidelines on cardiovascular disease prevention in clinical practice: a descriptive epidemiological study. *Scandinavian Journal of Primary Health Care* 2004 December; 22(4): 202-208. Subject: 9.5.1

Gevers, J.K.M. Genetic databases and consent for use of medical records. *Community Genetics* 2005 January; 7(4): 173-175. Subject: 15.1

Gevers, J.K.M. Response of the law to developments in genetics. *Medicine and Law: World Association for Medical Law* 1995; 14(3-4): 199-206. Subject: 15.1

Gevers, Sjef. Advance directives in psychiatry. *European Journal of Health Law* 2002 March; 9(1): 19-29. Subject: 9.5.3

Gevers, Sjef. Terminal sedation: a legal approach. *European Journal of Health Law* 2003 December; 10(4): 359-367. Subject: 20.7

Gevers, Sjef. Withdrawing life support from patients in a persistent vegetative state: the law in the Netherlands. *European Journal of Health Law* 2005 December; 12(4): 347-355. Subject: 20.5.1

Gevers, Sjef; Janssen, Anke; Friele, Roland. Consent systems for post mortem organ donation in Europe. *European Journal of Health Law* 2004 June; 11(2): 175-186. Subject: 19.5

Ghali, R.P.; Woodside, J.L. Proposed Canadian legislation to regulate reproductive technologies and related research. *Reproductive BioMedicine Online [electronic]* 2003 January-February; 6(1): 114-116. Available: http://www.rbmonline.com/article/788 [1 September 2005]. Subject: 14.4

Giacino, Joseph; Whyte, John. The vegetative and minimally conscious states: current knowledge and remaining questions. *Journal of Head Trauma and Rehabilitation* 2005 January-February; 20(1): 30-50. Subject: 20.5.1

Giacomini, Mita. One of these things is not like the others: the idea of precedence in health technology assessment and coverage decisions. *Milbank Quarterly* 2005; 83(2): 193-223. Subject: 5.2

Giangrande, Paul L.F. Gene therapy for hemophilia? No [debate]. *Journal of Thrombosis and Haemostasis* 2004 August; 2(8): 1236-1237. Subject: 15.4

Giannini, Alberto; Pessina, Adriano; Tacchi, Enrico Maria. End-of-life decisions in intensive care units: attitudes of physicians in an Italian urban setting. *Intensive Care Medicine* 2003 September 11; 29: 1902-1910. Subject: 20.5.1

Gibbons, Robert D. Racial disparities in liver transplantation [editorial]. *Liver Transplantation* 2004 July; 10(7): 842-843. Subject: 19.1

Gibbons, Susan M.C.; Helgason, Hördur Helgi; Kaye, Jane; Nõmper, Ants; Wendel, Lotta. Lessons from European population genetic databases: comparing the law in Estonia, Iceland, Sweden and the United Kingdom. *European Journal of Health Law* 2005 June; 12(2): 103-133. Subject: 15.1

Gibson, Jennifer L.; Martin, Douglas K.; Singer, Peter A. Evidence, economics and ethics: resource allocation in health services organizations. *Healthcare Quarterly* 2005; 8(2): 50-59. Subject: 9.4

Gibson, Liza. Adverse reaction reports may be vulnerable to manipulation [news]. *BMJ: British Medical Journal* 2005 June 4; 330(7503): 1287. Subject: 9.7

Gibson, S. On judgment and judgmentalism: how counselling can make people better. *Journal of Medical Ethics* 2005 October; 31(10): 575-577. Subject: 17.1

Giesen, Dieter. Health care as a right: some practical implications. *Medicine and Law: World Association for Medical Law* 1994; 13(3-4): 285-296. Subject: 9.2

Gigli, G.L. Persistent vegetative state: let's not blow out the candle. *Neurological Science* 2002; 23: 251-254. Subject: 20.5.1

Gijsbers van Wijk, Cecile M.T.; van Vliet, Katja P.; Kolk, Annemarie M. Gender perspectives and quality of care: towards appropriate and adequate health care for women. *Social Science and Medicine* 1996 September; 43(5): 707-720. Subject: 9.5.5

Gilbert, David M. The future of human embryonic stem cell research: addressing ethical conflict with responsible scientific research. *Medical Science Monitor* 2004 May; 10(5): RA99-RA103. Subject: 18.5.4

Gilbert, James C.; Brigham, Lori; Batty, D. Scott, Jr.; Veatch, Robert M. The nondirected living donor program: a model for cooperative donation, recovery and allocation of living donor kidneys. *American Journal of Transplantation* 2005 January; 5(1): 167-174. Subject: 19.5

Gilbert, Lyn. In that case. Response [case study]. *Journal of Bioethical Inquiry* 2005; 2(1): 55. Subject: 9.5.1

Gilbert, Michele; Counsell, Colleen M.; Guin, Peggy; O'Neill, Rebecca; Briggs, Sandra. Determining the relationship between end-of-life decisions expressed in advance directives and resuscitation efforts during cardiopulmonary resuscitation. *Outcomes Management for Nursing Practice* 2001 April-June; 5(2): 87-92. Subject: 20.5.4

Gilbert, Sandra M. Writing/righting wrong. *In:* Sharpe, Virginia A., ed. Accountability: Patient Safety and Policy Reform. Washington, DC: Georgetown University Press; 2004: 27-41. Subject: 9.8

Gilbert, Tony. Involving people with learning disabilities in research: issues and possibilities. *Health and Social*

Care in the Community 2004 July; 12(4): 298-308. Subject: 18.5.1

Giles, Jim. Alertness drug arouses fears about 'lifestyle' misuse [news]. *Nature* 2005 August 25; 436(7054): 1076. Subject: 4.5

Giles, Jim. Industry money skews drug overviews [news]. *Nature* 2005 September 22; 437(7058): 458-459. Subject: 9.7

Giles, Jim. Journals lack explicit policies for separating eds from ads [news]. *Nature* 2005 March 31; 434(7033): 549. Subject: 1.3.7

Giles, Jim. Plans for research watchdog praised, but it may lack teeth [news]. *Nature* 2005 March 17; 434(7031): 263. Subject: 1.3.9

Giles, Jim. Researchers break the rules in frustration at review boards [news]. *Nature* 2005 November 10; 438(7065): 136-137. Subject: 18.2

Giles, Jim. Taking on the cheats. *Nature* 2005 May 19; 435(7040): 258-259. Subject: 1.3.9

Giles, Jim. UK panel urges animal researchers to go public [news]. *Nature* 2005 May 26; 435(7041): 392. Subject: 22.2

Giles, S. An antidote to the emerging two tier organ donation policy in Canada: the Public Cadaveric Organ Donation Program. *Journal of Medical Ethics* 2005 April; 31(4): 188-191. Subject: 19.5

Gill, Fiona; Kroese, B. Stenfert; Rose, J. General practitioners' attitudes to patients who have learning disabilities. *Psychological Medicine* 2002 November; 32(8): 1445-1455. Subject: 8.1

Gill, Robin. Response to: The human embryo in the Christian tradition. *Journal of Medical Ethics* 2005 December; 31(12): 713-714. Subject: 12.3

Gillam, Lynn; Little, J. Miles. Confidentiality. *Medical Journal of Australia* 2001 March 19; 174(6): 296-297. Subject: 8.4

Gillam, Lynn; Weedon, Kathryn. Medical research and involuntary mental health patients: implications of proposed changes to legislation in Victoria. *Monash Bioethics Review* 2005 October; 24(4): 45-49. Subject: 18.5.1

Gillett, G. The unwitting sacrifice problem. *Journal of Medical Ethics* 2005 June; 31(6): 327-332. Subject: 15.2

Gillett, Grant. Bioethics and cara sui. *Journal of Bioethical Inquiry* 2005; 2(1): 24-33. Subject: 2.1

Gillett, Grant. Brain death, vegetative state and the RUB: how does one arrive at the decision that a person's life is no longer worth living? *Issues in Medical Ethics* 1999 April-June; 7(2): 54-55. Subject: 20.2.1

Gillett, Grant. The ethical status of whistle-blowers. *Monash Bioethics Review* 2005 January; 24(1): 59-64. Subject: 7.3

Gillett, Grant. Euthanasia from the perspective of hospice care. *Medicine and Law: World Association for Medical Law* 1994; 13(3-4): 263-268. Subject: 20.4.1

Gilliotti, Catherine M. Medical disclosure and decision-making: excavating complexities of physician-patient information exchange. *In:* Thompson, Teresa L.; Dorsey, Alicia M.; Miller, Katherine I.; Parrott, Roxanne, eds. Handbook of Health Communication. Mahwah, NJ: Lawrence Erlbaum Associates; 2003: 163-181. Subject: 8.2

Gillon, John J., Jr. More subject and less human: the pain-filled journey of human subjects protection . . . and some differences in the United States and the European Union. *Medical Law International* 2005; 7(1): 65-89. Subject: 18.1

Gillon, Raanan. Toleration and healthcare ethics. *CQ: Cambridge Quarterly of Healthcare Ethics* 2005 Winter; 14(1): 100-106. Subject: 1.1

Gillott, John. 'Reprogenetics': hype, phobia and choice. *Conscience* 2003-2004 Winter; 24(4): 10-14. Subject: 14.1

Gilmer, Todd; Schneiderman, Lawrence J.; Teetzel, Holly; Blustein, Jeffrey; Briggs, Kathleen; Cohn, Felicia; Cranford, Ronald; Dugan, Daniel; Komatsu, Glen; Young, Ernlé. The costs of nonbeneficial treatment in the intensive care setting. *Health Affairs* 2005 July-August; 24(4): 961-971. Subject: 9.6

Gilson, Aaron M.; Maurer, Martha A.; Joranson, David E. State policy affecting pain management: recent improvements and the positive impact of regulatory health policies. *Health Policy* 2005 October; 74(2): 192-204. Subject: 9.1

Ginsberg, Brian. Tarasoff at thirty: victim's knowledge shrinks the psychotherapist's duty to warn and protect. *Journal of Contemporary Health Law and Policy* 2004 Winter; 21(1): 1-35. Subject: 8.4

Ginsberg, Karen M. FDA approved? A critique of the artificial insemination industry in the United States. *University of Michigan Journal of Law Reform* 1997 Summer; 30(4): 823-851. Subject: 14.2

Ginsburg, Shiphra; Kachan, Natasha; Lingard, Lorelei. Before the white coat: perceptions of professional lapses in the pre-clerkship. *Medical Education* 2005 January; 39(1): 12-19. Subject: 7.2

Giordano, Simona. Is the body a republic? *Journal of Medical Ethics* 2005 August; 31(8): 470-475. Subject: 19.5

Giordano, Simona. Respect for equality and the treatment of the elderly: declarations of human rights and age-based rationing. *CQ: Cambridge Quarterly of Healthcare Ethics* 2005 Winter; 14(1): 83-92. Subject: 1.1

Giordano, S. Risk and supervised exercise: the example of anorexia to illustrate a new ethical issue in the traditional

---

debates of medical ethics. *Journal of Medical Ethics* 2005 January; 31(1): 15-20. Subject: 9.5.1

Girbes, Armand R.J. Dying at the end of your life [editorial]. *Intensive Care Medicine* 2004 December; 30(12): 2143-2144. Subject: 20.3.2

Girod, Jennifer; Beckman, A.W. Just allocation and team loyalty: a new virtue ethic for emergency medicine. *Journal of Medical Ethics* 2005 October; 31(10): 567-570. Subject: 9.4

Girsberger, Martin A. Transparency measures under patent law regarding genetic resources and traditional knowledge: disclosure of source and evidence of prior informed consent and benefit-sharing. *Journal of World Intellectual Property* 2004 July; 7(4): 451-489. Subject: 15.8

Gisondi, Michael A.; Smith-Coggins, Rebecca; Harter, Phillip M.; Soltysik, Robert C.; Yarnold, Paul R. Assessment of resident professionalism using high-fidelity simulation of ethical dilemmas. *Academic Emergency Medicine* 2004 September; 11(9): 931-937. Subject: 4.1.2

Gittelman, David K. Euthanasia and physician-assisted suicide. *Southern Medical Journal* 1999 April; 92(4): 369-374. Subject: 20.5.1

Giuseppe, Bosio M.; De Senarclens, Jacques; Groen, J.J. Human experimentation — a world problem from the standpoint of spiritual leaders. *World Medical Journal* 1960 March; 8: 80-83. 96. Subject: 18.1; 1.2

Gladsjo, Julie Akiko; Breding, John; Sine, David; Wells, Robert; Kalemkiarian, Sharon; Oak, Joni; Vieira, Angela S.; Friedlander, Sheila Fallon. Termination of life support after severe child abuse: the role of a guardian ad litem. *Pediatrics* 2004 February; 113(2): e141-e145. Subject: 20.5.2

Glannon, Walter; Ross, Lainie Friedman. Motivation, risk, and benefit in living organ donation: a reply to Aaron Spital. *CQ: Cambridge Quarterly of Healthcare Ethics* 2005 Spring; 14(2): 191-194. Subject: 19.5

Glantz, Leonard H. Keeping genetic secrets. *Medical Ethics Newsletter [Lahey Clinic]* 2004 Winter; 11(1): 4, 11. Subject: 15.3

Glantz, Leonard; Grodin, Michael. Undue inducement [letter]. *Lancet* 2005 October 15-21; 366(9494): 1356-1357. Subject: 18.2

Glanville, Julie. Ethics of health care and research. *Journal of Health Services Research and Policy* 2004 July; 9(3): 189-190. Subject: 18.2

Glare, Paul A.; Tobin, Bernadette. End-of-life issues: case 2. *Medical Journal of Australia* 2002 January 21; 176(2): 80-81. Subject: 20.4.1

Glasa, Jozef. Activities of the Central Ethics Committee of the Ministry of Health of the Slovak Republic June 2002-May 2005. *Medical Ethics and Bioethics / Medicinska Etika & Bioetika* 2005 Spring-Summer; 12(1): 8-9. Subject: 2.4

Glasa, Jozef. Establishment and work of ethics committees in Central and Eastern European countries. *Medical Ethics and Bioethics / Medicinska Etika and Bioetika* 2002 Spring-Summer; 9(1-2): 9-12. Subject: 9.6

Glasa, Jozef. Perspectives of bioethics in the Central and East European context. *Medical Ethics and Bioethics / Medicinska Etika & Bioetika* 2003 Autumn-Winter; 10(3-4): 16. Subject: 2.1

Glasa, Jozef. Relationships between the central ("national") ethics committees and local ethics committees in the Slovak Republic. *Medical Ethics and Bioethics / Medicinska Etika & Bioetika* 2004 Autumn-Winter; 11(3-4): 9-10. Subject: 2.4

Glasa, Jozef. Slovak Republic. *Medical Ethics and Bioethics / Medicinska Etika & Bioetika* 2005; 11(Supplement): 20-21. Subject: 9.6

Glasa, Jozef. Training and dissemination of good practices for research ethics committees: standardization, harmonization and collaboration. *Medical Ethics and Bioethics / Medicinska Etika & Bioetika* 2005 Spring-Summer; 12(1): 7-8. Subject: 18.2

Glasa, Jozef; Glasová, Mária. Ethics committees and consensus in the post-totalitarian society. *Medical Ethics and Bioethics / Medicinska Etika & Bioetika* 2001 Spring-Summer; 8(1-2): 5-9. Subject: 9.6

Glaser, Bonnie E.; Bero, Lisa A. Attitudes of academic and clinical researchers toward financial ties in research: a systematic review. *Science and Engineering Ethics* 2005 October; 11(4): 553-573. Subject: 1.3.9

Glasgow, Richard. Forced medication of criminal defendants and the unintended consequences of Sell v. United States. *Journal of Contemporary Health Law and Policy* 2005 Summer; 21(2): 235-258. Subject: 8.3.4

Glasner, Peter. Banking on immortality? Exploring the stem cell supply chain from embryo to therapeutic application. *Current Sociology* 2005 March; 53(2): 355-366. Subject: 18.5.4

Glass, Kathleen Cranley; Waring, Duff. The physician/investigator's obligation to patients participating in research: the case of placebo controlled trials. *Journal of Law, Medicine and Ethics* 2005 Fall; 33(3): 575-585. Subject: 18.3

Glater, Jonathan D. In a surgery capital, a swirl of fraud charges. *New York Times* 2005 July 10; p. BU1, BU4. Subject: 7.4

Glauser, Jonathan. Rationing and the role of the emergency department as society's safety net. *Academic Emergency Medicine* 2001 November; 8(11): 1101-1106. Subject: 9.5.1

Glazer, James. The ethics of alternative medicine: an alternative standard? [editorial]. *Family Practice Management* 2005 April; 12(4): 13-14. Subject: 4.1.1

Glen, Sally. Dangerous and severe personality disorder: an ethical concept? *Nursing Philosophy* 2005 April; 6(2): 98-105. Subject: 17.1

Glenn, David. In South Korea, ethics questions prompt a stem-cell pioneer to resign a top post. *Chronicle of Higher Education* 2005 December 9; 52(16): 35. Subject: 18.5.4

Glenn, Linda MacDonald. Keeping an open mind: what legal safeguards are needed? *American Journal of Bioethics* 2005 March-April; 5(2): 60-61. Subject: 17.1

Glenn, Linda MacDonald. Lessons from other codes: is it the journey or the destination? [comment]. *American Journal of Bioethics* 2005 September-October; 5(5): 59-60. Subject: 6

Glover, Robert W. Reducing the use of seclusion and restraint: a NASMHPD priority. *Psychiatric Services* 2005 September; 56(9): 1141-1142. Subject: 17.3

Glover, Vivette. The fetus may feel pain from 20 weeks [debate]. *Conscience* 2004-2005 Winter; 25(3): 35-37. Subject: 9.5.8

Godard, Béatrice; Cardinal, Geneviève. Ethical implications in genetic counseling and family studies of the epilepsies. *Epilepsy and Behavior* 2004 October; 5(5): 621-626. Subject: 15.2

Godfrey, Kathryn. Assisted dying legislation must wait until after UK election [news]. *BMJ: British Medical Journal* 2005 April 9; 330(7495): 807. Subject: 20.5.1

Godkin, M.D.; Faith, K.; Upshur, R.E.G.; MacRae, S.K.; Tracy, C.S. Project examining effectiveness in clinical ethics (PEECE): Phase 1 — descriptive analysis of nine clinical ethics services. *Journal of Medical Ethics* 2005 September; 31(9): 505-512. Subject: 9.6

Godlovitch, Glenys; Mitchell, Ian; Doig, Christopher James. Discontinuing life support in comatose patients: an example from Canadian case law. *CMAJ/JAMC: Canadian Medical Association Journal* 2005 April 26; 172(9): 1172-1173. Subject: 20.5.1

Goedken, Jennifer. Pelvic examinations under anesthesia: an important teaching tool. *Journal of Health Care Law and Policy* 2005; 8(2): 232-239. Subject: 9.5.5

Goel, Ashish. Consent for intimate examinations [letter]. *Issues in Medical Ethics* 2003 October-December; 11(4): 134. Subject: 7.2

Goel, Ashish; Kalantri, S.P. When is enough enough? *Issues in Medical Ethics* 2003 January-March; 11(1): 21-22. Subject: 20.5.1

Goeltz, Roxanne. In memory of my brother, Mike. *In:* Sharpe, Virginia A., ed. Accountability: Patient Safety and Policy Reform. Washington, DC: Georgetown University Press; 2004: 49-57. Subject: 9.8

Gogorosi, Eleni. Untying the Gordian knot of creation: metaphors for the Human Genome Project in Greek newspapers. *New Genetics and Society* 2005 December; 24(3): 299-315. Subject: 15.10

Gökçora, Ismail Haluk. Ethics and animal use in biomedical research. *Advances in Experimental Medicine and Biology* 2004; 553: 359-371. Subject: 22.2

Gold, E. Richard; Adams, Wendy A. Reconciling private benefit and public risk in biotechnology: xenotransplantation as a case study in consent. *Health Law Journal* 2002; 10: 31-75. Subject: 18.3

Gold, F. The Manchester Siamese twins case — a French ethical analysis. *European Journal of Obstetrics and Gynecology, and Reproductive Biology* 2001 December 1; 99(2): 165-166. Subject: 20.5.2

Gold, Jennifer L. Watching the watchdogs: negligence liability, and research ethics boards. *Health Law Journal* 2003; 11: 153-176. Subject: 18.2

Gold, Jennifer L.; Dewa, Carolyn S. Institutional review boards and multisite studies in health services research: is there a better way? *Health Services Research* 2005 February; 40(1): 291-307. Subject: 18.2

Gold, Jennifer L.; Studdert, David M. Clinical trials registries: a reform that is past due. *Journal of Law, Medicine and Ethics* 2005 Winter; 33(4): 811- 820. Subject: 18.6

Gold, Michelle. Is honesty always the best policy? Ethical aspects of truth telling. *Internal Medicine Journal* 2004 September-October; 34(9-10): 578-580. Subject: 8.2

Gold, Steven A. When nobody's looking. *Journal of the American College of Dentists* 2005 Spring; 72(1): 32-33. Subject: 4.1.1

Goldberg, Alan M. Animals and alternatives: societal expectations and scientific need. *ATLA: Alternatives to Laboratory Animals* 2004 December; 32(6): 545-551. Subject: 22.2

Goldberg, Lisa Sara. Introductory engagement within the perinatal nursing relationship. *Nursing Ethics* 2005 July; 12(4): 401-413. Subject: 9.5.5

Goldberg, Steven. Cloning matters: how Lawrence v. Texas protects therapeutic research. *Yale Journal of Health Policy, Law, and Ethics* 2004 Summer; 4(2): 305-317. Subject: 14.5

Goldberg, Steven. Gene patents and the death of dualism. *South California Interdisciplinary Law Journal* 1996 Winter; 5(1): 25-40. Subject: 15.8

Goldblatt, David. Conflicting roles for the physician. *Medical Ethics Newsletter [Lahey Clinic]* 2003 Spring; 10(2): 3, 12. Subject: 8.3.3

Goldblatt, David. A messy necessary end: health care proxies need our support. *Neurology* 2001 January 23; 56(2): 148-152. Subject: 20.5.4

Goldenberg, Maya J. Evidence-based ethics? On evidence-based practice and the "empirical turn" from normative bioethics. *BMC Medical Ethics [electronic]* 2005;

6(11); 9 p. Available: http://www.biomedcentral.com/bmcmedethics/ [21 December 2005]. Subject: 2.1

Goldie, John G.S. The detrimental ethical shift towards cynicism: can medical educators help prevent it? [opinion]. *Medical Education* 2004 March; 38(3): 232-234. Subject: 7.2

Goldie, John; Schwartz, Lisa; McConnachie, Alex; Morrison, Jillian. The impact of three years' ethics teaching, in an integrated medical curriculum, on students' proposed behaviour on meeting ethical dilemmas. *Medical Education* 2002 May; 36(5): 489-497. Subject: 7.2

Goldie, J.; Schwartz, L.; Morrison, J. Whose information is it anyway? Informing a 12-year-old patient of her terminal prognosis. *Journal of Medical Ethics* 2005 July; 31(7): 427-434. Subject: 8.2

Golding, Martin P. Ethical issues in biological engineering. *UCLA Law Review* 1968 February; 15(2): 443-479. Subject: 15.5

Goldworth, Amnon. The challenge of DNAR orders in schools. *American Journal of Bioethics* 2005 January-February; 5(1): 71- 72. Subject: 20.5.2

Goldworth, Amnon. Disease, illness, and ethics. *CQ: Cambridge Quarterly of Healthcare Ethics* 2005 Summer; 14(3): 346-351. Subject: 4.2

Goldworth, Amnon; Robertson, John A. Neonatal care for premature infants [letter and reply]. *Hastings Center Report* 2005 January-February; 35(1): 6. Subject: 9.5.7

Golec, Lisa; Gibbins, Sharyn; Dunn, Michael S.; Hebert, Philip. Informed consent in the NICU setting: an ethically optimal model for research solicitation. *Journal of Perinatology* 2004 December; 24(12): 783-791. Subject: 18.5.2

Gollust, Sarah E.; Apse, Kira; Fuller, Barbara P.; Miller, Paul Steven; Biesecker, Barbara B. Community involvement in developing policies for genetic testing: assessing the interests and experiences of individuals affected by genetic conditions. *American Journal of Public Health* 2005 January; 95(1): 35-41. Subject: 15.3

Golmakani, Mohammad Mehdi; Niknam, Mohammad Hussein; Hedayat, Kamyar M. Transplantation ethics from the Islamic point of view. *Medical Science Monitor* 2005 April; 11(4): RA105-RA109. Subject: 19.1

Gomez, Paul A. Promises and pitfalls: an analysis of the shifting constitutional interests involved in the context of demanding a right to treatment in health care. *Albany Law Review* 2000; 64(1): 361-396. Subject: 8.3.4

Gómez-Lobo, Alfonso. On potentiality and respect for embryos: a reply to Mary Mahowald. *Theoretical Medicine and Bioethics* 2005; 26(2): 105-110. Subject: 4.4

Gonzalez-Arnal, Stella. Indigenous knowledge, patenting, and the biotechnology industry. *In:* Brannigan, Michael C., ed. Cross-Cultural Biotechnology. Lanham: Rowman and Littlefield; 2004: 139-151. Subject: 15.1

Good, Chris. Ethical problems of drug categorization for reimbursement. *In:* Salek, Sam; Edgar, Andrew, eds. Pharmaceutical Ethics. New York: Wiley; 2002: 179-190. Subject: 9.7

Goodkind, Daniel. Sex-selective abortion, reproductive rights, and the greater locus of gender discrimination in family formation: Cairo's unresolved questions. *PSC [Population Studies Center] Research Report Series* 1997 March; No. 97-383; 35 p. [Online]. Available: http://www.psc.lrs.umich.edu/pubs/papers/rr97-383.pdf [3 October 2005. Subject: 14.3

Goodman, Benny. Ms. B and legal competence: interprofessional collaboration and nurse autonomy. *Nursing in Critical Care* 2004 November-December; 9(6): 271-276. Subject: 8.3.4

Goodman, Kenneth W. Ethics, evidence, and public policy. *Perspectives in Biology and Medicine* 2005 Autumn; 48(4): 548-556. Subject: 9.8

Goodman, Martin D.; Tarnoff, Michael; Slotman, Gus J. Effect of advance directives on the management of elderly critically ill patients. *Critical Care Medicine* 1998 April; 26(4): 701-704. Subject: 20.5.4

Goodman, Neville W. Poor worth the sum of their parts. *British Journal of Hospital Medicine* 1994 January 19-February 1; 51(1- 2): 61. Subject: 19.3

Goodman, Neville W. Whose life is it anyway? *British Journal of Hospital Medicine* 1996 September 4-17; 56(5): 240. Subject: 14.1

Goodman, Timothy. Is there a right to health? *Journal of Medicine and Philosophy* 2005 December; 30(6): 643-662. Subject: 9.2

Goodnough, Abby. Behind life-and-death fight, a rift that began years ago. *New York Times* 2005 March 26; p. A1, A8. Subject: 20.5.1

Goodnough, Abby. Florida halts fight to bar girl's abortion: after resisting, Governor Bush says state will abide by ruling. *New York Times* 2005 May 4; p. A19. Subject: 12.4.1

Goodnough, Abby. Florida steps back into fight over feeding tube in woman. *New York Times* 2005 February 24; p. A14. Subject: 20.5.1

Goodnough, Abby. In Schiavo feeding-tube case, notoriety finds unlikely judge presiding. *New York Times* 2005 March 17; p. A18. Subject: 20.5.1

Goodnough, Abby. Judge delays feeding tube removal. *New York Times* 2005 February 23; p. A13. Subject: 20.5.1

Goodnough, Abby. Schiavo autopsy says brain, withered, was untreatable; Florida woman's collapse in 1990 is still a mystery. *New York Times* 2005 June 16; p. A1, A24. Subject: 20.5.4

Goodnough, Abby. Supreme court refuses to hear the Schiavo case; day of legal scrambling; governor rebuffed too — few options as parents return to U.S. court. *New York Times* 2005 March 25; p. A1, A14. Subject: 20.5.1

Goodnough, Abby. U.S. judge denies feeding-tube bid in Schiavo's case; parents quickly appeal; family cites urgency as woman enters 5th day without nutrition. *New York Times* 2005 March 23; p. A1, A14. Subject: 20.5.1

Goodnough, Abby. U.S. judge hears tense testimony in Schiavo's case; no quick ruling is made; he expresses doubts that a federal review will change outcome. *New York Times* 2005 March 22; p. A1, A14. Subject: 20.5.1

Goodnough, Abby; Hulse, Carl. Despite Congress, woman's feeding tube is removed: judge in Florida rejects effort by House. *New York Times* 2005 March 19; p. A1, A12. Subject: 20.5.1

Goodnough, Abby; Liptak, Adam. Court blocks bid; new Schiavo tack by governor Bush; appeal to supreme court; Florida judge agrees to hear new motions — neurologist in fray. *New York Times* 2005 March 24; p. A1, A20. Subject: 20.5.1

Goodnough, Abby; Yardley, William. Federal judge condemns intervention in Schiavo case. *New York Times* 2005 March 31; p. A14. Subject: 20.5.1

Goodrum, Linda A.; Hankins, Gary D.V.; Jermain, Donna; Chanaud, Cheryl M. Conference report: complex clinical, legal, and ethical issues of pregnant and postpartum women as subjects in clinical trials. *Journal of Women's Health* 2003 October; 12(9): 857-867. Subject: 18.2

Goodson, M.L.; Vernon, B.G. A study of public opinion on the use of tissue samples from living subjects for clinical research. *Journal of Clinical Pathology* 2004 February; 57(2): 135-138. Subject: 19.5

Goodwin, Guy. Conflict of interest is not just about advising pharmaceutical companies [editorial]. *Journal of Psychopharmacology* 2004 December; 18(4): 447-448. Subject: 7.3

Goodwin, Michele. Altruism's limits: law, capacity, and organ commodification. *Rutgers Law Review* 2004 Winter; 56(2): 305-407. Subject: 19.5

Goodwin, Peter A.; Schmidt, Terri A.; Zechnich, Andrew D. Death with dignity [letter and reply]. *Academic Emergency Medicine* 1997 September; 4(9): 926-928. Subject: 20.7

Goodwin, ZellaJane; Kiehl, Ermalynn M.; Peterson, Janice Z. King's theory as foundation for an advance directive decision-making model. *Nursing Science Quarterly* 2002 July; 15(3): 237-241. Subject: 20.5.4

Goold, Imogen. Should older and postmenopausal women have access to assisted reproductive technology? *Monash Bioethics Review* 2005 January; 24(1): 27-46. Subject: 14.1

Goold, Imogen. Surrogacy: is there a case for legal prohibition? *Journal of Law and Medicine* 2004 November; 12(2): 205-216. Subject: 14.2

Goold, Susan Dorr; Biddle, Andrea K.; Klipp, Glenn; Hall, Charles N.; Danis, Marion. Choosing healthplans all together: a deliberative exercise for allocating limited health care resources. *Journal of Health Politics, Policy and Law* 2005 August; 30(4): 563-602. Subject: 9.4

Gopalakrishnan, Somasundari; Pugh, R. Nicholas. Mandatory reporting of all sexually active under-13s: reporting is a public health imperative [letter]. *BMJ: British Medical Journal* 2005 November 5; 331(7524): 1083. Subject: 9.5.7

Gordijn, Bert. Nanoethics: from utopian dreams and apocalyptic nightmares towards a more balanced view. *Science and Engineering Ethics* 2005 October; 11(4): 521-533. Subject: 5.1

Gordijn, Bert; Dekkers, Wim. Autonomy, integrity and the human body [editorial]. *Medicine, Health Care and Philosophy: A European Journal* 2005; 8(2): 145-146. Subject: 4.4

Gordin, Vitaly. A lucrative routine, short on pain management. Outcome studies help ethics. *Pain Medicine* 2002 December; 3(4): 349-350. Subject: 4.4

Gordon, Alex. The Partial-Birth Abortion Ban Act of 2003. *Harvard Journal on Legislation* 2004 Summer; 41(2) 501-515. Subject: 12.4.2

Gordon, Elisa J. Make it so!: advocating for UNOS policy change. *American Journal of Bioethics* 2005 July-August; 5(4): 21-22. Subject: 19.6

Gordon, Elysa. Multiculturalism in medical decisionmaking: the notion of informed waiver. *Fordham Urban Law Journal* 1995-1996; 23(4): 1321-1362. Subject: 21.7

Gordon, Harvey L.; Washofsky, Mark. Jewish bioethics. *In:* Peppin, John F.; Cherry, Mark J., eds. Religious Perspectives in Bioethics. New York: Taylor & Francis; 2004: 131- 146. Subject: 2.1

Gordon, Susan M. Privacy standards for health information: the misnomer of administrative simplification. *Delaware Law Review* 2002; 5(1): 23-56. Subject: 8.4

Gordon-Ceresky, Daryl L. Artificial insemination: its effect on paternity and inheritance rights. *Connecticut Probate Law Journal* 1995; 9(2): 245-271. Subject: 14.2

Gore, D.M. Ethical, professional, and legal obligations in clinical practice: a series of discussion topics for postgraduate medical education. Topic 2: consent and legal competence. *Postgraduate Medical Journal* 2001 May; 77(907): 318-319. Subject: 8.3.3

Gore, D.M. Ethical, professional, and legal obligations in clinical practice: a series of discussion topics for postgraduate medical education. Topic 3: resuscitation decisions in adult patients. *Postgraduate Medical Journal* 2001 June; 77(908): 388-389. Subject: 20.5.1

Gore, D.M. Ethical, professional, and legal obligations in clinical practice: a series of discussion topics for postgraduate medical education. Topic 4: confidentiality. *Postgraduate Medical Journal* 2001 July; 77(909): 443-444. Subject: 8.4

Gormally, Luke. Marriage and the prophylactic use of condoms. *National Catholic Bioethics Quarterly* 2005 Winter; 5(4): 735- 749. Subject: 10

Gormally, Luke. Pope John Paul II's teaching on human dignity and its implications for bioethics. *In:* Tollefsen, Christopher, ed. John Paul II's Contribution to Catholic Bioethics. Norwell, MA: Springer; 2004: 7-33. Subject: 2.1

Gorman, Todd E.; Ahern, Stephane P.; Wiseman, Jeffrey; Skrobik, Yoanna. Residents' end-of-life decision making with adult hospitalized patients: a review of the literature. *Academic Medicine* 2005 July; 80(7): 622-633. Subject: 20.5.1

Gorman, Ulf. A theological approach to human cloning. *In:* Ostnor, Lars, ed. Bioethics and Cloning: Report from a Workshop Arranged by the Nordic Theological Network for Bioethics in Arhus, September 25-27, 1998. Oslo: Nordic Theological Network for Bioethics; 1998: 78-82. Subject: 14.5

Górski, Andrzej. The ethics of intellectual property rights in biomedicine and biotechnology: an introduction. *Science and Engineering Ethics* 2005 January; 11(1): 4-6. Subject: 5.3

Gory, Simona. Constructing the heterosexually inactive lesbian: assisted insemination in Queensland. *Australian Feminist Law Journal* 2002 June; 16: 75-94. Subject: 14.2

Gosfield, Alice G. The hidden costs of free lunches: fraud and abuse in physician-pharmaceutical arrangements. *Journal of Medical Practice Management* 2005 March-April; 20(5): 253-258. Subject: 9.7

Gosline, Anna. Will DNA profiling fuel prejudice? *New Scientist* 2005 April 9-15; 186(2494): 12-13. Subject: 15.1

Gostin, Lawrence O. The constitutional right to die: ethical considerations. *St. John's Journal of Legal Commentary* 1997 Summer; 12(3): 599-609. Subject: 20.7

Gostin, Lawrence O. Ethics, the Constitution, and the dying process: the case of Theresa Marie Schiavo. *JAMA: The Journal of the American Medical Association* 2005 May 18; 293(19): 2403-2407. Subject: 20.5.1

Gostin, Lawrence O. Fast and supersized: is the answer to diet by fiat? *Hastings Center Report* 2005 March-April; 35(2): 11-12. Subject: 9.1

Gostin, Lawrence O. Finding a space for the public's health in bioterrorism funding: a commentary. *American Journal of Bioethics* 2005 July-August; 5(4): 45-46. Subject: 21.3

Gostin, Lawrence O. The global reach of HIV/AIDS: science, politics, economics, and research. *Emory International Law Review* 2003 Spring; 17(1): 1-54. Subject: 9.5.6

Gostin, Lawrence O. Jacobson v Massachusetts at 100 years: police power and civil liberties in tension. *American Journal of Public Health* 2005 April; 95(4): 576-581. Subject: 9.1

Gostin, Lawrence O. Law and the public's health. *Issues in Science and Technology* 2005 Spring; 21(3): 71-77. Subject: 9.1

Gostin, Lawrence O. Medical marijuana, American federalism, and the Supreme Court. *JAMA: The Journal of the American Medical Association* 2005 August 17; 294(7): 842-844. Subject: 9.5.1

Gostin, Lawrence O. The negative Constitution: the duty to protect. *Hastings Center Report* 2005 September-October; 35(5): 10-11. Subject: 9.1

Gostin, Lawrence O. Pandemic influenza: public health preparedness for the next global health emergency. *Journal of Law, Medicine and Ethics* 2004 Winter; 32(4): 565-573. Subject: 9.1

Gostin, Lawrence O. The Supreme Court's influence on medicine and health: the Rehnquist Court, 1986-2005. *JAMA: The Journal of the American Medical Association* 2005 October 5; 294(13): 1685-1687. Subject: 2.1

Gostin, Lawrence O.; Hodge, James G.,Jr. Public health emergencies and legal reform: implications for public health policy and practice. *Public Health Reports* 2003 September-October; 118(3): 477-479. Subject: 9.1

Gostin, Lawrence O.; Lazarini, Zita; Flaherty, Kathleen M. Legislative survey of state confidentiality laws, with specific emphasis on HIV and immunization. Final Report presented to the U.S. Centers for Disease Control and Prevention [CDC], the Council of State and Territorial Epidemiologists and the Task force for Child Survival and Development Carter Presidential Center. Washington, DC: Epic Privacy Information Center 1997; 69 p. [Online]. Available: http://www.epic.org/privacy/medical/cdc_survey.html [30 November 2005]. Subject: 1.3.12

Gottenger, E.E.; Nagler, Harris M. The quagmire of postmortem sperm acquisition. *Journal of Andrology* 1999 July-August; 20(4): 458-462. Subject: 14.6

Gottweis, Herbert. Emerging forms of governance in genomics and post-genomics: structures, trends, perspectives. *In:* Bunton, Robin; Petersen, Alan, eds. Genetic Governance: Health, Risk and Ethics in the Biotech Era. New York: Routledge; 2005: 189-208. Subject: 15.1

Gottweis, Herbert. Governing genomics in the 21st century: between risk and uncertainty. *New Genetics and Society* 2005 August; 24(2): 175-193. Subject: 15.8

See SUBJECT HEADING KEY FOR SECTION II on inside back cover

Gottweis, Herbert. Regulating genomics in the 21st century: from logos to pathos? [opinion]. *Trends in Biotechnology* 2005 March; 23(3): 118-121. Subject: 15.1

Gottweis, Herbert. Transnationalizing recombinant-DNA regulation: between Asilomar, EMBO, the OECD, and the European Community. *Science as Culture* 2005 December; 14(4): 325-338. Subject: 15.1

Goyal, Venkat; Lokhandwala, Yash. Practising ethically in a high-tech specialty. *Issues in Medical Ethics* 1998 October-December; 6(4): 123-124. Subject: 9.3.1

Graber, Mark A.; Gjerde, Craig; Bergus, George; Ely, John. The use of unofficial "problem patient" files and interinstitutional information transfer in emergency medicine in Iowa. *American Journal of Emergency Medicine* 1995 September; 13(5): 509-511. Subject: 8.4

Graber, M.A.; Tansey, J.F. Autonomy, consent, and limiting healthcare costs. *Journal of Medical Ethics* 2005 July; 31(7): 424-426. Subject: 9.4

Grabowski, John S. Contraception, sterilization, abortion and the ethical and religious directives. *In:* McMahon, Kevin T., ed. Moral Issues in Catholic Health Care. Wynnewood, PA: Saint Charles Borromeo Seminary; 2004: 68-92. Subject: 4.4

Gräb-Schmidt, Elisabeth. Freedom in responsibility: on the relevance of "sin" as a hermeneutic guiding principle in bioethical decision making. *Christian Bioethics* 2005 August; 11(2): 147-165. Subject: 2.1

Grace, Mike. A cautionary tale [opinion]. *British Dental Journal* 2003 November 22; 195(10): 549. Subject: 1.3.7

Grace, Pamela J. Professional advocacy: widening the scope of accountability. *Nursing Philosophy* 2001 July; 2(2): 151-162. Subject: 9.1

Grace, Pamela J.; McLaughlin, Moriah. When consent isn't informed enough. *AJN: American Journal of Nursing* 2005 April; 105(4): 79, 81-84. Subject: 8.3.1

Grad, Frank P. New beginnings in life: a lawyer's response. *In:* Hamilton, Michael P., ed. The New Genetics and the Future of Man. Grand Rapids, MI: William B. Eerdmans Publishing Co.; 1972: 64-77. Subject: 14.1

Gradmann, Christoph. "It seemed about time to try one of those modern medicines": animal and human experimentation in the chemotherapy of sleeping sickness 1905-1908. *In:* Roelcke, Volker; Maio, Giovanni, eds. Twentieth Century Ethics of Human Subjects Research: Historical Perspectives on Values, Practices, and Regulations. Stuttgart: Franz Steiner Verlag; 2004: 83-97. Subject: 18.1

Grady, Christine. The challenge of assuring continued post-trial access to beneficial treatment. *Yale Journal of Health Policy, Law, and Ethics* 2005 Winter; 5(1): 425-435. Subject: 18.5.1

Grady, Denise. Study authors didn't report abortion ties. *New York Times* 2005 August 26; p. A15. Subject: 1.3.9

Grady, Denise. Study finds 29-week fetuses probably feel no pain and need no abortion anesthesia. *New York Times* 2005 August 24; p. A10. Subject: 12.1

Graham, Peter E.; Harel-Raviv, Mili. The law and ethics in relation to dentists treating HIV-positive patients: report on a recent U.S. Supreme Court case. *Journal of the Canadian Dental Association* 1999 January; 65(1): 27-30. Subject: 9.5.6

Graham-Rowe, Duncan. Privacy and prejudice: whose ID is it anyway? *New Scientist* 2005 September 17-23; 187(2517): 20-23. Subject: 8.4

Grant, A.M.; Altman, D.G.; Babiker, A.G.; Campbell, M.K.; Clemens, F.; Darbyshire, J.H.; Elbourne, D.R.; McLeer, S.K.; Parmar, M.K.B.; Pocock, S.J.; Spiegelhalter, D.J.; Sydes, M.R.; Walker, A.E.; Wallace, S.A. A proposed charter for clinical trial data monitoring committees: helping them to do their job well. *Lancet* 2005 February 19-25; 365(9460): 711-722. Subject: 18.2

Grant, Ellen C. A sad day for science at the FDA [letter and reply]. *New England Journal of Medicine* 2005 December 15; 353(24): 2619-2621. Subject: 11.1

Grant, Robert M.; Buchbinder, Susan; Cates, Willard, Jr.; Clarke, Edith; Coates, Thomas; Cohen, Myron S.; Delaney, Martin; Flores, Guiselly; Goicochea, Pedro; Gonsalves, Gregg; Harrington, Mark; Lama, Javier R.; MacQueen, Kathleen M.; Moore, John P.; Peterson, Leigh; Sanchez, Jorge; Thompson, Melanie; Wainberg, Mark A. Promote HIV chemoprophylaxis research, don't prevent it. *Science* 2005 September 30; 309(5744): 2170-2171. Subject: 9.5.6

Grass, Guido. Clinical trial registration. *New England Journal of Medicine* 2005 January 13; 352(2): 198. Subject: 18.6

Grau, Günter. "Unschuldige" Täter: Mediziner als Vollstrecker der nationalsozialistischen Homosexuellenpolitik. *In:* Jellonnek, Burkhard; Lautmann, Rüdiger, eds. Nationalsozialistischer Terror gegen Homosexuelle: verdrängt und ungesühnt. Paderborn: Schöningh; 2002: 209-235. Subject: 21.4

Graumann, Sigrid; Poltermann, Andreas. No end in sight to cloning debate. *Revista de Derecho y Genoma Humano / Law and the Human Genome Review* 2005 January-June; (22): 209-227. Subject: 14.5

Gray, John E.; O'Reilly, Richard L. Canadian compulsory community treatment laws: recent reforms. *International Journal of Law and Psychiatry* 2005 January-February; 28(1): 13-22. Subject: 17.1

Grayling, A.C. The power to choose. *New Scientist* 2005 April 9-15; 186(2494): 17. Subject: 14.3

Grayling, A.C. "Right to die": the moral basis of the right to die is the right to good quality life [editorial]. *BMJ: Brit-*

---

ish Medical Journal 2005 April 9; 330(7495): 799. Subject: 20.5.1

Grazi, Richard V. Assisted reproduction. *In:* Overcoming Infertility: A Guide for Jewish Couples. New Milford, Conn.: Toby, 2005: 311-364. Subject: 14.1

Grazi, Richard V.; Wolowelsky, Joel B. New ethical issues. *In:* Grazi, Richard V. Overcoming Infertility: A Guide for Jewish Couples. New Milford, Conn.: Toby, 2005: 409-424. Subject: 14.1

Grazier, Kyle L.; Mowbray, Carol T.; Holter, Mark C. Rationing psychosocial treatments in the United States. *International Journal of Law and Psychiatry* 2005 September- October; 28(5): 545-560. Subject: 17.1

Gready, Paul; de Gruchy, Jeanelle. District surgeons in apartheid South Africa: a case study of dual obligations. *Health and Human Rights: An International Journal* 2003; 7(1): 113-143. Subject: 8.1

Great Britain. Department of Health. Families and Post Mortems: A Code of Practice. London: Department of Health 2003 April 25; 44 p. Subject: 6

Great Britain. Department of Health; Medical Research Council [MRC]; Wellcome Trust; Interim Advisory Group on Ethics and Governance [IAG]. Setting standards: UK Biobank ethics and governance framework [EGF] [summary]. London: UKBiobank 2003 September 24; 4 p. [Online]. Available: http://www.ukbiobank.ac.uk/ethics/efg-summary.doc [8 August 2005]. Subject: 15.1

Great Britain. Department of Health; Medical Research Council [MRC]; Wellcome Trust; Interim Advisory Group on Ethics and Governance [IAG]. UK Biobank ethics and governance framework [EGF]: Version 1.0: for comment. London: UK Biobank 2003 September 24; 31 p. [Online]. Available: http://www.ukbiobank.ac.uk/ethics/efg.php [8 August2005]. Subject: 15.1

Great Britain. Department of Health; National Health Service. Central Office for Research Ethics Committees [COREC]; Welsh AssemblyGovernment. The Use of Human Organs and Tissue: An Interim Statement. London: Department of Health [31520], 2003 April; 19 p. Subject: 19.1

Great Britain. Department of Health; Wellcome Trust; Medical Research Council [MRC]; Scottish Executive; Interim Advisory Group on Ethics and Governance [IAG]. UK Biobank Ethics and Governance Framework [EGF]: Background Document. London: UK Biobank 2003 October 10; 21 p. [Online]. Available: http://www.ukbiobank.ac.uk/ethics/efg.php [8 August 2005]. Subject: 15.1

Great Britain. Department of Health; Welsh Assembly Government; Donaldson, Liam; Hall, Ruth. Proposals for new legislation on human organs and tissue: why we need new laws. London: Department of Health 2003 September; 8 p. [Online]. Available: http://www.dh.gov.uk/

assetRoot/04/07/02/97/04070297.pdf [25 July 2005]. Subject: 19.5

Great Britain. Department of Health. Secretary of State for Health. Government response to the report of the Joint Committee on the draft Mental Health Bill 2004. London: Department of Health 2005 July; 52 p. [Online]. Available: http://www.dh.gov.uk/assetRoot/04/11/52/68/04115268.pdf [14 September 2005]. Subject: 17.1

Great Britain. England. High Court of Justice. Family Division; Lloyd, Huw; Munby, James; Brown, Stephen P. Medical treatment — refusal of medical treatment — adult — refusal on religious grounds: re S. (refusal of medical treatment) [Date of Decision: 12 October 1992]. *New Law Journal* 1992 October 23; 142(6573): 1450-1451. Subject: 8.3.4

Great Britain. Human Genetics Commission. Profiling the newborn: a prospective gene technology? London: Human Genetics Commission 2005 March; 41 p. [Online]. Available: http://www.hgc.gov.uk/UploadDocs/Contents/Documents/Final%20Draft%20of%20Profiling%20Newborn%20Report%2003%2005.pdf [8 July 2005]. Subject: 15.3

Great Britain. Parliament. House of Commons. Human Tissue Act 2004 (Amendment) Bill. London: The Stationery Office, Ltd. 2005 January 12; 9 p. [Online]. Available: http://www.publications.parliament.uk/pa/cm200405/cmbills/032/200 5032.pdf [25 July 2005]. Subject: 19.5

Great Britain. Parliament. House of Commons. Committee on Science and Technology. Cloning of animals from adult cells (fifth report). *London: The Stationery Office* 1997 March 18; 23 p. Subject: 14.5

Greaves, Claire D.; Tindale, Wendy B. Implications of the UK NHS consent policy for nuclear medicine practice. *Nuclear Medicine Communications* 2005 February; 26(2): 167-174. Subject: 18.3

Greely, Henry T. Banning genetic discrimination [opinion]. *New England Journal of Medicine* 2005 September 1; 353(9): 865- 867. Subject: 15.1

Greely, Henry T. Iceland's plan for genomics research: facts and implications. *Jurimetrics* 2000 Winter; 40: 153-191. Subject: 15.10

Greely, Henry T. Premarket approval regulation for lie detections: an idea whose time may be coming. *American Journal of Bioethics* 2005 March-April; 5(2): 50-52. Subject: 17.1

Green, Carolyn; Schultz, Marina; Corea, Lynda; Dandekar, Ashwin. Perceived barriers to healthcare: a survey of clients of the County Board of Mental Retardation and Developmental Disabilities in Cuyahoga county. *Clinical Pediatrics* 2004 October; 43(8): 721-724. Subject: 9.5.3

Green, J.B.; Duncan, R.E.; Barnes, G.L.; Oberklaid, F. Putting the 'informed' into 'consent': a matter of plain language. *Journal of Paediatrics and Child Health* 2003 December; 39(9): 700-703. Subject: 18.3

Green, Jason. Refusal clauses and the Weldon amendment: inherently unconstitutional and a dangerous precedent. *Journal of Legal Medicine* 2005 September; 26(3): 401-415. Subject: 12.4.3

Green, Jennifer. Death with dignity: Rastafarianism. *Nursing Times* 1992 February 26; 88(9): 56-57. Subject: 20.4.1

Green, Jennifer. Death with dignity: the Mormon Church. *Nursing Times* 1992 February 5; 88(6): 44-45. Subject: 20.4.1

Green, Jennifer. Death with dignity: Zoroastrianism. *Nursing Times* 1992 February 12; 88(7): 44-45. Subject: 20.4.1

Green, Kelly. Physician-assisted suicide and euthanasia: safeguarding against the "slippery slope" — The Netherlands versus the United States. *Indiana International and Comparative Law Review* 2003; 13(2): 639-681. Subject: 20.7

Green, Ronald. Toward a full theory of moral status. *American Journal of Bioethics* 2005 November-December; 5(6): 44-46. Subject: 4.4

Green, Ronald M. Last word: imagining the future. *Kennedy Institute of Ethics Journal* 2005 March; 15(1): 101-106. Subject: 15.1

Green, Ronald M. Spy versus spy. *American Journal of Bioethics* 2005 March-April; 5(2): 53-54. Subject: 17.1

Green, Shane K.; Morin, Karine. Biodefense: spend, but spend wisely. *American Journal of Bioethics* 2005 July-August; 5(4): 50-52. Subject: 21.3

Green, Shane K.; Somerville, Margaret A.; Atlas, Ronald M. Using ethics to fight bioterrorism [letter and reply]. *Science* 2005 August 12; 309(5737): 1012, 1014-1015, 1017. Subject: 21.3

Greenberg, David; Mazar, Joseph; Brom, Danny; Barel, Yair Carlos. Involuntary outpatient commitment: a naturalistic study of its use and a consumer survey at one community mental health center in Israel. *Medicine and Law: World Association for Medical Law* 2005 March; 24(1): 95-110. Subject: 17.7

Greenberger, Marcia D.; Vogelstein, Rachel. Pharmacist refusals: a threat to women's health. *Science* 2005 June 10; 308(5728): 1557-1558. Subject: 9.7

Greene, Mark; Schill, Kathryn; Takahashi, Shoji; Bateman- House, Alison; Beauchamp, Tom; Bok, Hilary; Cheney, Dorothy; Coyle, Joseph; Deacon, Terrence; Dennett, Daniel; Donovan, Peter; Flanagan, Owen; Goldman, Steven; Greely, Henry; Martin, Lee; Miller, Earl; Mueller, Dawn; Siegel, Andrew; Solter, Davor; Gearhart, John; McKhann, Guy; Faden, Ruth. Moral issues of human-nonhuman primate neural grafting. *Science* 2005 July 15; 309(5733): 385-386. Subject: 22.2

Greene, Naomi; Platt, Lawrence D. Nonmedical use of ultrasound: greater harm than good? *Journal of Ultrasound in Medicine* 2005 January; 24(1): 123-125. Subject: 9.5.8

Greenfeld, Dorothy A.; Klock, Susan Caruso. Disclosure decisions among known and anonymous oocyte donation recipients. *Fertility and Sterility* 2004 June; 81(6): 1565-1571. Subject: 14.4

Greenhouse, Linda. Case reopens abortion issue for justices. *New York Times* 2005 November 29; p. A19. Subject: 12.4.1

Greenhouse, Linda. Court to tackle abortion again after 5 years; parent notification case; in considering technical issues, justices rejoin a fractious debate. *New York Times* 2005 May 24; p. A1, A17. Subject: 12.4.1

Greenhouse, Linda. Justices accept case weighing assisted suicide. *New York Times* 2005 February 23; p. A1, A14. Subject: 20.7

Greenhouse, Linda. Justices explores U.S. authority over states on assisted suicide. *New York Times* 2005 October 6; p. A1, A32. Subject: 20.7

Greenwald, Brian H. The real "toll" of A.G. Bell: lessons about genetics. *In:* Van Cleve, John Vickery, ed. Genetics, Disability, and Deafness. Washington, DC: Gallaudet University Press; 2004: 35-41. Subject: 15.5

Greenwell, Pamela. Germline gene therapy — changing future generations [opinion]. *International Journal of Biosciences and the Law* 1997; 1(3): 217-226. Subject: 15.4

Greenwood, Jason S. Congressional control of federal court jurisdiction: the case study of abortion. *South Carolina Law Review* 2003 Summer; 54(4): 1069-1112. Subject: 12.4.1

Greenwood, Jennifer; Holmes, Colin; Bidewell, John. Mission impossible? Developing best practice guidelines for institutional ethics committees (IECs) in Greater Sydney. *Collegian* 2001 January; 8(1): 8-13. Subject: 18.2

Gregory, Bernadette. Hunger striking prisoners: the doctors' dilemma [opinion]. *BMJ: British Medical Journal* 2005 October 15; 331(7521): 913. Subject: 21.5

Grenfell, Leigh. To strike or not to strike: is striking ethical, according to the code of ethics developed by NZNO? One nurse examines her own decision to strike. *Nursing New Zealand* 1994 March; 2(2): 16-18. Subject: 7.1

Greß, Stefan; Niebuhr, Dea; Rothgang, Heinz; Wasem, Jürgen. Criteria and procedures for determining benefit packages in health care. A comparative perspective. *Health Policy* 2005 July; 73(1): 78-91. Subject: 9.3.1

Grey, William. Design constraints for the post-human future. *Monash Bioethics Review* 2005 April; 24(2): 10-19. Subject: 15.4

Griener, Glenn. Electronic health records as a threat to privacy. *Health Law Review* 2005; 14(1): 14-17. Subject: 8.4

Griffin, Leslie. Watch out for whistleblowers. *Journal of Law, Medicine and Ethics* 2005 Spring; 33(1): 160- 162. Subject: 1.3.9

Griffith, Ezra E.H. Personal narrative and an African-American perspective on medical ethics. *Journal of the American Academy of Psychiatry and the Law* 2005; 33(3): 371-381. Subject: 7.1

Griffith, Lauren; Cook, Deborah; Hanna, Steven; Rocker, Graeme; Sjokvist, Peter; Dodek, Peter; Marshall, John; Levy, Mitchell; Varon, Joseph; Finfer, Simon; Jaeschke, Roman; Buckingham, Lisa; Guyatt, Gordon. Clinician discomfort with life support plans for mechanically ventilated patients. *Intensive Care Medicine* 2004 September; 30(9): 1783-1790. Subject: 20.5.1

Griffith, Richard. Childhood immunization: public health or parental choice? *British Journal of Community Nursing* 2004 September; 9(9): 379-382. Subject: 8.3.2

Griffith, Richard. Human rights and district nursing practice. *British Journal of Community Nursing* 2005 February; 10(2): 86-91. Subject: 21.1

Griffith, Richard. Living wills, duty of care and the right to treatment. *British Journal of Community Nursing* 2004 November; 9(11): 488-491. Subject: 20.5.4

Griggins, Cynthia. Dosing dilemmas: are you rich and white or poor and black? [comment]. *American Journal of Bioethics* 2005 May-June; 5(3): 55-57. Subject: 17.4

Grill, K.; Hansson, S.O. Epistemic paternalism in public health. *Journal of Medical Ethics* 2005 November; 31(11): 648-653. Subject: 9.1

Grimes, Richard M.; Helfgott, Andrew W.; Watson, Julie R.; Eriksen, Nancy L. For children's sake. New law mandates HIV testing of pregnant patients. *Texas Medicine* 1996 January; 92(1): 36-40. Subject: 9.5.6

Grimm, David. Is tobacco research turning over a new leaf? [news]. *Science* 2005 January 7; 307(5706): 36-37. Subject: 1.3.9

Grindon, Christina; Bhogal, Nirmala. The Fourth EC Report on the statistics of laboratory animal use: trends, recommendations and future prospects. *ATLA: Alternatives to Laboratory Animals* 2005 August; 33(4): 417-426. Subject: 22.2

Griniezakis, Makarios; Symeonides, Nathanael. Bioethics and Christian theology. *Journal of Religion and Health* 2005 Spring; 44(1): 7-11. Subject: 2.1

Grizzle, William; Grody, Wayne W.; Noll, Walter W.; Sobel, Mark E.; Stass, Sanford A.; Trainer, Thomas; Travers, Henry; Weedn, Victor; Woodruff, Kay. Recommended policies for uses of human tissue in research, education, and quality control. *Archives of Pathology and Laboratory Medicine* 1999 April; 123(4): 296-300. Subject: 15.1

Groenhout, Ruth. Reformed perspectives in bioethics. *In:* Peppin, John F.; Cherry, Mark J., eds. Religious Perspectives in Bioethics. New York: Taylor & Francis; 2004: 79-95. Subject: 2.1

Groenhout, Ruth; Hotz, Kendra; Joldersma, Clarence. Embodiment, nursing practice, and religious faith: a perspective from one tradition. *Journal of Religion and Health* 2005 Summer; 44(2): 147-160. Subject: 4.1.3

Groner, Jonathan. Lethal injection and the medicalization of capital punishment in the United States. *Health and Human Rights: An International Journal* 2002; 6(1): 65-79. Subject: 20.6

Groopman, Jerome. The pediatric gap: why have most medications never been properly tested on kids? *New Yorker* 2005 January 10; p. 32-37. Subject: 9.7

Groopman, Jerome E. A strategy for hope: a commentary on necessary collusion. *Journal of Clinical Oncology* 2005 May 1; 23(13): 3151-3152. Subject: 8.2

Gropelli, Theresa. A decision for Sam. *Journal of Gerontological Nursing* 2005 January; 31(1): 45-48. Subject: 8.3.3

Gross, M.L. Treating competent patients by force: the limits and lessons of Israel's Patient's Rights Act. *Journal of Medical Ethics* 2005 January; 31(1): 29-34. Subject: 8.3.4

Gross, Michael. Swiss back stem-cell studies [news]. *Current Biology* 2005 January 26; 15(2): R35. Subject: 18.5.4

Gross, Michael L. Dilemma over forced treatment [letter]. *Lancet* 2005 June 25-July 1; 365(9478): 2177. Subject: 8.3.4

Gross, Michael L. Physician-assisted draft evasion: civil disobedience, medicine, and war. *CQ: Cambridge Quarterly of Healthcare Ethics* 2005 Fall; 14(4): 444-454. Subject: 21.2

Gross, Michael; Latimer, Eric A.; Battista, Renaldo N.; Wright, Charles J.; Pelletier, L. Conrad; McMurtry, Robert Y. The ethical allocation of scarce resources in surgery: implants and cost [article and commentaries]. *Canadian Journal of Surgery* 1997 December; 40(6): 421-429. Subject: 9.4

Grout, Gwyn. Using negotiated consent in research and practice. *Nursing Older People* 2004 June; 16(4): 18-20. Subject: 18.3

Grove, Natalie; Brough, Mark; Canuto, Condy; Dobson, Annette. Aboriginal and Torres Strait Islander health research and the conduct of longitudinal studies: issues for debate. *Australian and New Zealand Journal of Public Health* 2003 December; 27(6): 637-641. Subject: 18.5.1

Grover, Anand; Dhaliwal, Mandeep; Dadwal, Sandeep. HIV bills, Maharashtra; Karnataka. *Issues in Medical Ethics* 2000 April-June; 8(2): 60-61. Subject: 9.5.6

Grover, Michael; Dharamshi, Farah; Goveia, Crystal. Deception by applicants to family practice residencies. *Family Medicine* 2001 June; 33(6): 441-446. Subject: 7.2

Grover, Sonja. Reification of psychiatric diagnoses as defamatory: implications for ethical clinical practice. *Ethical Human Psychology and Psychiatry* 2005 Spring; 7(1): 77-86. Subject: 4.3

Groves, Trish; Croot, Jan. Using pictures in the BMJ [editorial]. *BMJ: British Medical Journal* 2005 April 23; 330(7497): 916. Subject: 8.3.1

Grubb, Andrew. Euthanasia in England — a law lacking compassion? [editorial]. *European Journal of Health Law* 2001 June; 8(2): 89-93. Subject: 20.5.1

Gruber, Franz P.; Dewhurst, David G. Alternatives to animal experimentation in biomedical education. *ALTEX: Alternativen zu Tierexperimenten* 2004; 21 (Supplement 1): 33-48. Subject: 22.2

Grudzen, Corita R. One resident perspective: resident education and the pharmaceutical industry. *Annals of Emergency Medicine* 2005 January; 45(1): 27-31. Subject: 7.2

Grulich, Andrew E.; Kaldor, John M. Individual privacy and observational health research: violating an individual's privacy to benefit the health of others. *University of New South Wales Law Journal* 2001; 24(1): 298-305. Subject: 18.5.1

Grusky, Oscar; Roberts, Kathleen Johnston; Swanson, Aimee Noelle; Joniak, Elizabeth; Leich, Jennifer; McEvoy, Gwen; Murphy, Keith; Schilt, Kristen; Wilson, Valerie. Anonymous versus confidential HIV testing: client and provider decision making under uncertainty. *AIDS Patient Care and STDs* 2005 March; 19(3): 157-166. Subject: 9.5.6

Guarisco, Kristen K. Managing do-not-resuscitate orders in the perianesthesia period. *Journal of Perianesthesia Nursing* 2004 October; 19(5): 300-307. Subject: 20.5.1

Guedj, M.; Gibert, M.; Maudet, A.; Muñoz Sastre, M.T.; Mullet, E.; Sorum, P.C. The acceptability of ending a patient's life. *Journal of Medical Ethics* 2005 June; 31(6): 311-317. Subject: 20.5.1

Guenin, Louis M. A failed noncomplicity scheme. *Stem Cells and Development* 2004 October; 13(5): 456-459. Subject: 18.5.4

Guenin, Louis M. Stem cells, cloning, and regulation. *Mayo Clinic Proceedings* 2005 February; 80(2): 241-250. Subject: 14.5

Guenter, Dale; Kaczorowski, Janusz; Carroll, June; Sellors, John. Prenatal HIV tests: routine testing or informed choice? *Canadian Family Physician* 2003 October; 49: 1334-1340. Subject: 9.5.6

Guenther, Hilary. The development of the undue burden standard in Stenberg v. Carhart: will proposed RU-486 legislation survive? *Indiana Law Review* 2002; 35(3): 1021-1044. Subject: 12.4.2

Guerra Gonzalez, Jorge. Prevention of the xenogenic infection risk and the Spanish and German constitutions. *Revista de Derecho y Genoma Humano / Law and the Human Genome Review* 2004 January-June; (20): 123-146. Subject: 19.1

Guevara, Angie L. In re K.I.: an urgent need for a uniform system in the treatment of the critically ill infant — recognizing the sanctity of the life of the child. *University of San Francisco Law Review* 2001 Fall; 36(1): 237-260. Subject: 20.5.2

Guevin, Benedict M. Ordinary, extraordinary, and artificial means of care. *National Catholic Bioethics Quarterly* 2005 Autumn; 5(3): 471- 479. Subject: 20.4.1

Guevin, Benedict M. Sex reassignment surgery for transsexuals: an ethical conundrum? *National Catholic Bioethics Quarterly* 2005 Winter; 5(4): 719- 734. Subject: 10

Guevin, Benedict; Rhonheimer, Martin. On the use of condoms to prevent acquired immune deficiency syndrome [debate]. *National Catholic Bioethics Quarterly* 2005 Spring; 5(1): 37-48. Subject: 10

Guha, Amitava. A comparison of codes of pharmaceutical marketing practices. *Indian Journal of Medical Ethics* 2004 January-March; 1(1): 19- 21. Subject: 9.7

Guidotti, Tee L. Ethics and skeptics: what lies behind ethical codes in occupational health. *Journal of Occupational and Environmental Medicine* 2005 February; 47(2): 168-175. Subject: 16.3

Guigui, Albert. Judaism. *In:* Council of Europe Publishing, ed. Euthanasia. Volume I. Ethical and Human Aspects. Strasbourg: Council of Europe; Croton- on-Hudson, NY: Manhattan Publishing Co.; 2003: 145-147. Subject: 20.5.1

The Guild of Catholic Doctors; Jarmulowicz, Michael. The Guild of Catholic Doctors: comments to the chief medical officer's expert group on cloning. *Catholic Medical Quarterly* 2000 August; 50(3); 5 p. [Online]. Available: http://www.catholicdoctors.org.uk/submissions/cloning_expert_committee.htm [4 November 2005]. Subject: 14.5

Guillod, Olivier; Schmidt, Aline. Assisted suicide under Swiss law. *European Journal of Health Law* 2005 March; 12(1): 25-38. Subject: 20.7

Guinan, Patrick. The Christian origin of medical compassion. *National Catholic Bioethics Quarterly* 2005 Summer; 5(2): 243- 248. Subject: 4.1.2

Guinn, David E. Ethics and integrative medicine: moving beyond the biomedical model. *Alternative Therapies in Health and Medicine* 2001 November- December; 7(6): 68-72. Subject: 4.1.1

Subject = NRCBL Primary Classification Number; See inside front cover

Gulhati, C.M. Needed: closer scrutiny of clinical trials [editorial]. *Indian Journal of Medical Ethics* 2004 January-March; 1(1): 4-5. Subject: 18.1

Gulliford, Martin; Figueroa-Munoz, Jose; Morgan, Myfanwy,; Hughes, David; Gibson, Barry; Beech, Roger; Hudson, Meryl. What does 'access to health care' mean? [opinion]. *Journal of Health Services Research and Policy* 2002 July; 7(3): 186-188. Subject: 9.2

Gunderman, Richard B.; Hubbard, Mark Adam. The wages of healing: ethical issues in the compensation of physicians. *Medical Science Monitor* 2005 February; 11(2): SR5-SR10. Subject: 9.3.1

Gunderson, Martin. A Kantian view of suicide and end-of-life treatment. *Journal of Social Philosophy* 2004 Summer; 35(2): 277-287. Subject: 20.5.1

Gundle, Kenneth. Presumed consent: an international comparison and possibilities for change in the United States. *CQ: Cambridge Quarterly of Healthcare Ethics* 2005 Winter; 14(1): 113-118. Subject: 19.5

Gunn, John. Comments: a crisis in the ethical and moral behavior of psychiatrists [forum]. *Current Opinion in Psychiatry* 1998 January; 11(1); 2 p. [Online]. Available: http://gateway.ut.ovid.com/gw1/ovidweb.cgi [24 May 2005]. Subject: 20.6

Gunn, John; Hartmann, Lawrence; Pellegrino, Edmund D.; Bonnie, Richard J.; Bloche, M. Gregg; Appelbaum, Paul S.; Kastrup, Marianne; Okasha, Ahmed; Lopez-Ibor, Juan J. Comments: a crisis in the ethical and moral behavior of psychiatrists [forum]. *Current Opinion in Psychiatry* 1998 January; 11(1); 3 p. [Online]. Available: http://gateway.ut.ovid.com/gw1/ovidweb.cgi [24 May 2005]. Subject: 20.6

Gunning, Jennifer. Umbilical cord blood: banking and clinical application. *Revista de Derecho y Genoma Humano / Law and the Human Genome Review* 2004 January-June; (20): 217-226. Subject: 19.4

Gupta, Amit Sen. Intellectual capital as property. *Indian Journal of Medical Ethics* 2004 October-December; 1(4): 115-116. Subject: 9.5.6

Gupta, Amit Sen. Research on hire. *Issues in Medical Ethics* 2001 October-December; 9(4): 111-113. Subject: 18.5.9

Gupta, Mona. Evidence-based medicine: ethically obligatory or ethically suspect? *Evidence-Based Mental Health* 2004 November; 7(4): 96-97. Subject: 9.8

Gupte, M.D.; Sampath, D.K. Ethical issues considered in Tamil Nadu leprosy vaccine trial. *Issues in Medical Ethics* 2000 January-March; 8(1): 10-12. Subject: 18.2

Gurmankin, Andrea D.; Domchek, Susan; Stopfer, Jill; Fels, Christina; Armstrong, Katrina. Patients' resistance to risk information in genetic counseling for BRCA1/2. *Archives of Internal Medicine* 2005 March 14; 165(5): 523-529. Subject: 15.2

Gurwitz, David; Kimchi, Orit; Bonne-Tamir, Batsheva. The Israeli DNA and cell line collection: a human diversity repository. *In:* Knoppers, Bartha Maria, ed. Populations and Genetics: Legal and Socio-Ethical Perspectives. Boston: Martinus Nijhoff; 2003: 95-113. Subject: 15.1

Gustafson, Kathryn E.; McNamara, J. Regis. Confidentiality with minor clients: issues and guidelines for therapists. *Professional Psychology: Research and Practice* 1987 October; 18(5): 503-508. Subject: 8.4

Gutheil, Thomas G. Boundaries, blackmail, and double binds: a pattern observed in malpractice consultation. *Journal of the American Academy of Psychiatry and the Law* 2005; 33(4): 476-481. Subject: 8.1

Gutheil, Thomas G.; Simon, Robert I.; Hilliard, James T. "The wrong handle": flawed fixes of medicolegal problems in psychiatry and the law [editorial]. *Journal of the American Academy of Psychiatry and the Law* 2005; 33(4): 432-436. Subject: 17.7

Gutman, Virginia. Ethical reasoning and mental health services with deaf clients. *Journal of Deaf Studies and Deaf Education* 2005 Spring; 10(2): 171-183. Subject: 2.1

Guttmacher, Alan E.; Collins, Francis S. Realizing the promise of genomics in biomedical research. *JAMA: The Journal of the American Medical Association* 2005 September 21; 294(11): 1399-1402. Subject: 15.1

Guttman, Nurit. Ethics in health communication interventions. *In:* Thompson, Teresa L.; Dorsey, Alicia M.; Miller, Katherine I.; Parrott, Roxanne, eds. Handbook of Health Communication. Mahwah, NJ: Lawrence Erlbaum Associates; 2003: 651-679. Subject: 9.1

Guz, Abraham. Hering and Breuer revisited in humans: an invasive study before the days of ethics committees. *American Journal of Respiratory and Critical Care Medicine* 2001 October 1; 164(7): 1110-1111. Subject: 18.2

Gyrd-Hansen, Dorte. Investigating the social value of health changes. *Journal of Health Economics* 2004 November; 23(6): 1101-1116. Subject: 9.4

H

Haberfield, Les. Responding to "male circumcision: medical or ritual?". *Journal of Law and Medicine* 1997 May; 4(4): 379-385. Subject: 9.5.1

Habiba, M.; Jackson, C.; Akkad, A.; Kenyon, S.; Dixon-Woods, M. Women's accounts of consenting to surgery: is consent a quality problem? *Quality and Safety in Health Care* 2004; 13: 422-427. Subject: 9.5.5

Hack, Thomas F.; Chochinov, Harvey Max; Hassard, Thomas; Kristjanson, Linda J.; McClement, Susan; Harlos, Mike. Defining dignity in terminally ill cancer patients: a factor-analytic approach. *Psycho-Oncology* 2004 October; 13(10): 700-708. Subject: 20.4.1

Hack, Thomas F.; Degner, Lesley F.; Dyck, Dennis G. Relationship between preferences for decisional control and illness information among women with breast cancer: a quantitative and qualitative analysis. *Social Science and Medicine* 1994 July; 39(2): 279-289. Subject: 8.1

Hackett, Edward J.; Conz, David; Parker, John. Misconduct, scientific. *In:* Restivo, Sal, ed. Science, Technology, and Society: An Encyclopedia. New York: Oxford University Press; 2005: 338-343. Subject: 1.3.9

Hackleman, Tricia Jonas. Violation of an individual's right to die: the need for a wrongful living cause of action. *University of Cincinnati Law Review* 1996 Summer; 64(4): 1355-1381. Subject: 20.5.4

Hackler, Chris; Hester, D. Micah. Age and the allocation of organs for transplantation: a case study. *Health Care Analysis: An International Journal of Health Care Philosophy and Policy* 2005 June; 13(2): 129-136. Subject: 19.6

Haddad, Amy. Deciding for others. *RN* 2004 July; 67(7): 25-26, 28. Subject: 8.3.3

Haddad, Amy. End-of-life decisions: the family's role. *RN* 2004 January; 67(1): 25-26, 28. Subject: 20.3.3

Haddad, Amy. Ethics in action. A violent patient. *RN* 2004 May; 67(5): 21-23. Subject: 8.1

Haddad, Amy. Ethics in action. Durable power of attorney. *RN* 1999 September; 62(9): 25-26, 28. Subject: 8.3.3

Hadjistavropoulos, Thomas; Bieling, Peter J. When reviews attack: ethics, free speech, and the peer review process. *Canadian Psychology/Psychologie Canadienne* 2000 August; 41(3): 152-159. Subject: 1.3.7

Hadjistavropoulos, Thomas; Malloy, David Cruise. Making ethical choices: a comprehensive decision-making model for Canadian psychologists. *Canadian Psychology/Psychologie Canadienne* 2000 May; 41(2): 104-115. Subject: 17.1

Hadorn, David. The Chaoulli challenge: getting a grip on waiting lists [opinion]. *CMAJ/JAMC: Canadian Medical Association Journal* 2005 August 2; 173(3): 271-273. Subject: 9.3.2

Hadskis, Michael; Carver, Peter. The long arm of administrative law: applying administrative law principles to research ethics boards. *Health Law Review* 2005; 13(2-3): 19-32. Subject: 18.2

Hafemeister, Thomas L.; Robinson, Donna M. The views of the judiciary regarding life-sustaining medical treatment decisions. *Law and Psychology Review* 1994 Spring; 18: 189-246. Subject: 20.5.1

Hagelin, J. Use of live nonhuman primates in research in Asia. *Journal of Postgraduate Medicine* 2004 October-December; 50(4): 253-256. Subject: 22.2

Hagelin, Joakim. Public opinion surveys about xenotransplantation. *Xenotransplantation* 2004 November; 11(6): 551-558. Subject: 19.1

Hagelin, Joakim; Hau, Jann; Schapiro, Steven J.; Suleman, Mbaruk A.; Carlsson, Hans-Erik. Religious beliefs and opinions on clinical xenotransplantation — a survey of university students from Kenya, Sweden and Texas [reply]. *Clinical Transplantation* 2002 August; 16(4): 315. Subject: 19.1

Hagerty, Rebecca G.; Butow, Phyllis N.; Ellis, Peter M.; Lobb, Elizabeth A.; Pendlebury, Susan C.; Leighl, Natasha; MacLeod, Craig; Tattersall, Martin H.N. Communicating with realism and hope: incurable cancer patients' views on the disclosure of prognosis. *Journal of Clinical Oncology* 2005 February 20; 23(6): 1278-1288. Subject: 8.2

Hagger, Lynn; Woods, Simon; Barrow, Paul. Autonomy and audit — striking the balance. *Medical Law International* 2004; 6(2): 105-116. Subject: 8.4

Hagger, L.E.; Woods, S. Law and ethics support for health professionals: an alternative model. *Journal of Medical Ethics* 2005 February; 31(2): 111. Subject: 2.3

Haggerty, Lois A.; Hawkins, Joellen. Informed consent and the limits of confidentiality. *Western Journal of Nursing Research* 2000 June; 22(4): 508-514. Subject: 8.3.1

Hagstad, David. To give blood or not to give: should there be a question? *AJN: American Journal of Nursing* 2005 November; 105(11): 31. Subject: 19.4

Hahn, D.L.; Burge, P.S.; Lewis, S.A. Ethics of placebo controlled studies of inhaled steroids for COPD [letter and reply]. *Thorax* 2004 June; 59(6): 539-540. Subject: 18.3

Haigh, Carol; Jones, Neil A. An overview of the ethics of cyber-space research and the implication for nurse educators. *Nurse Education Today* 2005 January; 25(1): 3-8. Subject: 1.3.9

Hails, Rosie. Bioethics for technology? *Current Opinion in Biotechnology* 2004 June; 15(3): 250-253. Subject: 5.1

Haimes, Erica; Whong-Barr, Michael. Competing perspectives on reasons for participation and non- participation in the North Cumbria Community Genetics Project. *In:* Knoppers, Bartha Maria, ed. Populations and Genetics: Legal and Socio-Ethical Perspectives. Boston: Martinus Nijhoff; 2003: 199-216. Subject: 15.1

Haimes, Erica; Whong-Barr, Michael. Levels and styles of participation in genetic databases: a case study of the North Cumbria Community Genetics Project. *In:* Tutton, Richard; Corrigan, Oonagh, eds. Genetic Databases: Socio-ethical Issues in the Collection and Use of DNA. New York: Routledge; 2004: 57-77. Subject: 15.1

Haker, Hille. Genetische Diagnostik und die Entwicklung von Gentests: Reflexionen zur ethischen Urteilsbildung. *In:* Honnefelder, Ludger; Mieth, Dietmar; Propping, Peter; Siep, Ludwig; Wiesemann, Claudia, eds. Das genetische Wissen und die Zukunft des Menschen. New York: De Gruyter; 2003: 186-202. Subject: 15.3

Subject = NRCBL Primary Classification Number; See inside front cover

Haker, Hille. Harm as the price of liberty? Preimplantation diagnosis and reproductive freedom. *Ethical Perspectives* 2003; 10(3-4): 215-223. Subject: 15.2

Halem, Samantha Catherine. At what cost?: An argument against mandatory AZT treatment of HIV-positive pregnant women. *Harvard Civil Rights-Civil Liberties Law Review* 1997 Summer; 32(2): 492-528. Subject: 9.5.6

Halila, Ritva; Lötjönen, Salla. Children and medical research. *Medicine and Law: World Association for Medical Law* 2005 September; 24(3): 505-513. Subject: 18.3

Hall, Amy Laura. Ruth's resolve: what Jesus' great-grandmother may teach about bioethics and care. *Christian Bioethics* 2005 April; 11(1): 35-50. Subject: 9.1

Hall, Amy Laura. Welcome to ordinary? Marketing better boys [comment]. *American Journal of Bioethics* 2005 May-June; 5(3): 59-60. Subject: 17.4

Hall, Jacqulyn Kay. After Schiavo: next issue for nursing ethics. *JONA's Healthcare Law, Ethics, and Regulation* 2005 July- September; 7(3): 94-98. Subject: 20.5.1

Hall, Mark A. The importance of trust for ethics, law, and public policy. *CQ: Cambridge Quarterly of Healthcare Ethics* 2005 Spring; 14(2): 156-167. Subject: 8.1

Hall, Mark A. Managed care patient protection or provider protection? A qualitative assessment. *American Journal of Medicine* 2004 December 15; 117(12): 932-937. Subject: 9.3.2

Hall, Mark A.; Berenson, Robert A. The ethics of managed care: a dose of realism. *Cumberland Law Review* 1997-1998; 28(2): 287-314. Subject: 9.3.2

Hall, Mark A.; McEwen, Jean E.; Barton, James C.; Walker, Ann P.; Howe, Edmund G.; Reiss, Jacob A.; Power, Tara E.; Ellis, Shellie D.; Tucker, Diane C.; Harrison, Barbara W.; McLaren, Gordon D.; Ruggiero, Andrea; Thomson, Elizabeth J. Concerns in a primary care population about genetic discrimination by insurers. *Genetics in Medicine* 2005 May-June; 7(5): 311-316. Subject: 15.3

Hall, Mark A.; Trachtenberg, F.; Dugan, E. The impact on patient trust of legalising physician aid in dying. *Journal of Medical Ethics* 2005 December; 31(12): 693-697. Subject: 20.5.1

Hall, Mark A.; Zheng, Beiyao; Dugan, Elizabeth; Camacho, Fabian; Kidd, Kristin E.; Mishra, Aneil; Balkrishnan, Rajesh. Measuring patients' trust in their primary care providers. *Medical Care Research and Review* 2002 September; 59(3): 293-318. Subject: 8.1

Hall, Peter; Tornberg, David N. A stain on medical ethics [letters]. *Lancet* 2005 October 8-14; 366(9493): 1263-1264. Subject: 21.4

Hall, Stephen C. The physician's duty and role in communicating with family members regarding results of patients' genetic testing. *Journal of the Kentucky Medical Association* 2005 April; 103(4): 159-161. Subject: 15.2

Hall, Stephen S. The short of it: more short children are being given growth hormone in the hope that an extra inch will protect their supposedly fragile psyches. But research suggests that their height is a problem less for them than for us. *New York Times Magazine* 2005 October 16; p. 54-59. Subject: 4.5

Hall, Timothy. Abortion, the right to life, and dependence. *Social Theory and Practice* 2005 July; 31(3): 405-429. Subject: 12.3

Hall, Timothy. Life extension and creation: a reply to Silverstein and Boonin. *Journal of Social Philosophy* 2004 Winter; 35(4): 485-492. Subject: 12.3

Hall, Zach W. Mapping the future. *Cerebrum: The Dana Forum on Brain Science* 2002 Summer; 4(3): 72-76. Subject: 17.1

Halldenius, Lena. Dissecting "discrimination". *CQ: Cambridge Quarterly of Healthcare Ethics* 2005 Fall; 14(4): 455-463. Subject: 9.5.4

Hallgren, Anita; Kihlgren, Mona; Olsson, Pia. Ways of relating during childbirth: an ethical responsibility and challenge for midwives. *Nursing Ethics* 2005 November; 12(6): 606-621. Subject: 9.5.5

Halliday, Jane L.; Collins, Veronica R.; Aitken, Mary Ann; Richards, Martin P.M.; Olsson, Craig A. Genetics and public health — evolution, or revolution? *Journal of Epidemiology and Community Health* 2004 November; 58(11): 894-899. Subject: 15.1

Halliday, Samantha. A comparative approach to the regulation of human embryonic stem cell research in Europe. *Medical Law Review* 2004 Spring; 12(1): 40-69. Subject: 21.7

Halliday, Samantha; Steinberg, Deborah Lynn. The regulated gene: new legal dilemmas. *Medical Law Review* 2004 Spring; 12(1): 2-13. Subject: 15.1

Halloran, Liz. Of life and death: the Supreme Court opens its new term with arguments in a case whose implications could not be more profound. *U.S. News and World Report* 2005 October 10; 139(13): 31-33. Subject: 20.7

Hallström, Inger; Elander, Gunnel. Decision making in paediatric care: an overview with reference to nursing care. *Nursing Ethics* 2005 May; 12(3): 223-238. Subject: 8.3.2

Halpern, Scott D. HIV testing without consent in critically ill patients. *JAMA: The Journal of the American Medical Association* 2005 August 10; 294(6): 734-737. Subject: 9.5.6

Halpern, Scott D. Towards evidence based bioethics. *BMJ: British Medical Journal* 2005 October 15; 331(7521): 901- 903. Subject: 2.1

Halsted, Charles H. Responsibilities of authors [editorial]. *American Journal of Clinical Nutrition* 2002 January; 75(1): 1. Subject: 1.3.7

Ham, Chris; Coulter, Angela. Explicit and implicit rationing: taking responsibility and avoiding blame for health care choices. *Journal of Health Services Research and Policy* 2001 July; 6(3): 163-169. Subject: 9.4

Hamamy, Hanan A.; Dahoun, Sophie. Parental decisions following the prenatal diagnosis of sex chromosome abnormalities. *European Journal of Obstetrics and Gynecology and Reproductive Biology* 2004 September 10; 116(1): 58-62. Subject: 15.2

Hamann, Johannes; Cohen, Rudolf; Leucht, Stefan; Busch, Raymonde; Kissling, Werner. Do patients with schizophrenia wish to be involved in decisions about their medical treatment? *American Journal of Psychiatry* 2005 December; 162(12): 2382- 2384. Subject: 9.5.3

Hamaty, Daniel. Pain medicine's role in the restoration and reformation of medical ethics. *Pain Medicine* 2000 December; 1(4): 362-365. Subject: 4.4

Hamaty, Daniel. When it's hard to please everybody: etiquette serving ethics when you disagree with a colleague. Opinion #2: return to the sources: AMA guidelines. *Pain Medicine* 2001 March; 2(1): 83, 85. Subject: 4.4

Hambling, David. Maximum pain is aim of navy study. *New Scientist* 2005 March 5-11; 185(2489): 8. Subject: 1.3.9

Hamel, Ron. Rape and emergency contraception: a reply to Rev. Kevin McMahon. *Ethics and Medics* 2003 June; 28(6): 1-2. Subject: 11.1

Hamel, Ron; Panicola, Michael R. Low risks and moral certitude: response to Msgr. Mulligan. *Ethics and Medics* 2003 December; 28(12): 2-4. Subject: 11.1

Hamilton, Cindy W.; Mallia-Hughes, Marianne; Mitrany, Devora; Foote, MaryAnn; Fugh-Berman, Adriane. Comments on "the corporate author" [letter and reply]. *JGIM: Journal of General Internal Medicine* 2005 October; 20(10): 972-973. Subject: 1.3.7

Hamilton, David P. How Genentech, Novartis stifled a promising drug; biotech firm tried to pursue peanut allergy injection, but contract got in way; Zach avoids a "kiss of death". *Wall Street Journal* 2005 April 15; p. A1, A10. Subject: 9.7

Hamilton, N. Gregory; Hamilton, Catherine A. Competing paradigms of response to assisted suicide requests in Oregon. *American Journal of Psychiatry* 2005 June; 162(6): 1060-1065. Subject: 20.7

Hamilton, Rebekah J.; Bowers, Barbara J.; Williams, Janet K. Disclosing genetic test results to family members. *Journal of Nursing Scholarship* 2005; 37(1): 18-24. Subject: 15.3

Hammarstedt, Meta; Jacobsson, Lars; Wulff, Marianne; Lalos, Ann. Views of midwives and gynecologists on legal abortion — a population-based study. *Acta Obstetricia et Gynecologica Scandinavica* 2005 January; 84(1): 58-64. Subject: 12.5.2

Hammerschmidt, Dale E. Kibuka's umbilical cord. *Journal of Laboratory Clinical Medicine* 2005 March; 145(3): 163-164. Subject: 18.2

Hammerschmidt, Dale E.; Franklin, Michael. Secrecy in medical journals. *Minnesota Medicine* 2005 March; 88(3): 34-35. Subject: 1.3.9

Hammonds, Rachel; Ooms, Gorik. World Bank policies and the obligation of its members to respect, protect and fulfill the right to health. *Health and Human Rights: An International Journal* 2004; 8(1): 27-60. Subject: 21.1

Hamoda, Haitham; Critchley, Hilary O.D.; Paterson, Kate; Guthrie, Kate; Rodger, Mary; Penney, Gillian C. The acceptability of home medical abortion to women in UK settings. *BJOG: An International Journal of Obstetrics and Gynaecology* 2005 June; 112(6): 781-785. Subject: 12.5.2

Hampson, Lindsay A.; Emanuel, Ezekiel J. The prognosis for changes in end-of-life care after the Schiavo case. *Health Affairs* 2005 July-August; 24(4): 972-975. Subject: 20.5.1

Hampson, Lindsay A.; Emanuel, Ezekiel, J.; Topol, Eric J.; Blumenthal, David. Physicians advising investment firms [letter and reply]. *JAMA: The Journal of the American Medical Association* 2005 October 19; 294(15): 1897-1898. Subject: 7.3

Hampton, Sylvia. Should euthanasia be legalized? *British Journal of Nursing* 1993 April 22-May 12; 2(8): 429-431. Subject: 20.5.1

Hampton, Tracy. Anonymity of gamete donations debated [news]. *JAMA: The Journal of the American Medical Association* 2005 December 7; 294(21): 2681-2683. Subject: 14.2

Hampton, Tracy. Biomedical journals probe peer review [news]. *JAMA: The Journal of the American Medical Association* 2005 November 9; 294(18): 2287-2288. Subject: 1.3.7

Hampton, Tracy. Experts ponder pediatric research ethics. *JAMA: The Journal of the American Medical Association* 2005 November 2; 294(17): 2148, 2151. Subject: 18.5.2

Hampton, Tracy. NIH eases ethics rules on employees: consulting ban to remain [news]. *JAMA: The Journal of the American Medical Association* 2005 October 12; 294(14): 1749-1750. Subject: 1.3.9

Hampton, W.A. Legalising assistance with dying in South Africa [letter]. *South African Medical Journal* 2000 July; 90(7): 656-657. Subject: 20.7

Handelsman, Mitchell M.; Galvin, Michael D. Facilitating informed consent for outpatient psychotherapy: a suggested written format. *Professional Psychology: Research and Practice* 1988; 19(2): 223-225. Subject: 8.3.1

Handyside, Alan H. Commonsense as applied to eugenics: response to Testart and Sele [opinion]. *Human Reproduction* 1996 April; 11(4): 707. Subject: 15.2

Hanford, Jack T. A public religion and biomedical ethics. *Pastoral Psychology* 2000 January; 48(3): 191-195. Subject: 2.1

Hanft, Ruth S.; Spernak, Stephanie M. Social, ethical, and legal concerns: experimentation, rationing, and practice standards. *In their:* Technology in American Health Care: Policy Directions for Effective Evaluation and Management. Ann Arbor: The University of Michigan Press; 2004: 350-363, 387-431. Subject: 5.2

Hanna, N.J. Challenging medical decision-making: professional dominance, patient rights or collaborative autonomy? *Oxford Journal of Legal Studies* 1998 Spring; 18(1): 143-152. Subject: 8.1

Hansen, Lissi; Archbold, Patricia G.; Stewart, Barbara J. Role strain and ease in decision-making to withdraw or withhold life support for elderly relatives. *Journal of Nursing Scholarship* 2004; 36(3): 233-238. Subject: 20.5.1

Hanson, Stephen. Engelhardt and children: the failure of libertarian bioethics in pediatric interactions. *Kennedy Institute of Ethics Journal* 2005 June; 15(2): 179-198. Subject: 2.1

Hanson, Stephen. How should physicians decide to resuscitate a patient? [letter]. *American Family Physician* 2004 May 15; 69(10): 2322. Subject: 20.5.1

Hanson, Stephen. Teaching health care ethics: why we should teach nursing and medical students together. *Nursing Ethics* 2005 March; 12(2): 167-176. Subject: 2.3

Hanssen, Ingrid. From human ability to ethical principle: an intercultural perspective on autonomy. *Medicine, Health Care and Philosophy: A European Journal* 2004; 7(3): 269-279. Subject: 8.1

Hansson, Mats G. Building on relationships of trust in biobank research. *Journal of Medical Ethics* 2005 July; 31(7): 415-418. Subject: 15.1

Hansson, S.O. Extended antipaternalism. *Journal of Medical Ethics* 2005 February; 31(2): 97-100. Subject: 9.1

Hansson, S.O. Implant ethics. *Journal of Medical Ethics* 2005 September; 31(9): 519-525. Subject: 19.1

Hardart, George E.; Truog, Robert D. Practicing physicians and the role of family surrogate decision making. *Journal of Clinical Ethics* 2005 Winter; 16(4): 345-354. Subject: 8.1

Hardingham, Lorraine B. Integrity and moral residue: nurses as participants in a moral community. *Nursing Philosophy* 2004 July; 5(2): 127-134. Subject: 4.1.3

Hardwig, John. Families and futility: forestalling demands for futile treatment. *Journal of Clinical Ethics* 2005 Winter; 16(4): 335-344. Subject: 20.4.1

Hardy, J.R. Placebo-controlled trials in palliative care: the argument for. *Palliative Medicine* 1997 September; 11(5): 415-418. Subject: 18.3

Harish, Dasari; Sharma, B.R. Medical advances in transsexualism and the legal implications. *American Journal of Forensic Medicine and Pathology* 2003; 24(1): 100-105. Subject: 10

Harjai, Kishore J.; Nunez, Eduardo; Shah, Mehul; Newman, Jeff. Does racial bias exist in the medical management of heart failure? *Clinical Cardiology* 2002 October; 25(10): 479-483. Subject: 9.5.4

Harling, Christopher C.; Bloche, M. Gregg; Marks, Jonathan H. When doctors go to war [letter and reply]. *New England Journal of Medicine* 2005 April 7; 352(14): 1497- 1499. Subject: 2.1

Harmon, Amy. Hello, I'm your sister. Our father is donor 150. *New York Times* 2005 November 20; p. A1, A34. Subject: 14.6

Harmon, Amy. The problem with an almost-perfect genetic world. *New York Times* 2005 November 20; p. WK1, WK14. Subject: 15.3

Haroun, Ansar M.; Morris, Grant H. Weaving a tangled web: the deceptions of psychiatrists. *Journal of Contemporary Legal Issues* 1999; 10: 227-246. Subject: 8.2

Harper, C. Mark. Philosophy for physicians. *Journal of the Royal Society of Medicine* 2003 January; 96(1): 40-45. Subject: 4.1.2

Harper, Richard S. Adult refusal of medical treatment: non-consensual treatment. *In his:* Medical Treatment and the Law: The Protection of Adults and Minors in the Family Division. Bristol: Family Law; 1999: 55-67. Subject: 8.3.4

Harper, Richard S. Medical treatment and the mentally ill. *In his:* Medical Treatment and the Law: The Protection of Adults and Minors in the Family Division. Bristol: Family Law; 1999: 69-79. Subject: 17.1

Harper, Richard S. The withholding or withdrawal of life-sustaining treatment in relation to adults and minors. *In his:* Medical Treatment and the Law: The Protection of Adults and Minors in the Family Division. Bristol: Family Law; 1999: 33-54. Subject: 20.5.1

Harpes, Jean-Paul. The contemporary advocacy of euthanasia. *In:* Council of Europe Publishing, ed. Euthanasia. Volume I. Ethical and Human Aspects. Strasbourg: Council of Europe; Croton- on-Hudson, NY: Manhattan Publishing Co.; 2003: 27-36. Subject: 20.5.1

Harre, Rom. Rights to display: the masking of competence. *In:* Fairbairn, Susan; Fairbairn, Gavin, eds. Psychology, Ethics and Change. New York: Routledge & Kegan Paul; 1987: 58-73. Subject: 17.1

Harrington, Jennifer. Letter to the editor [letter]. *American Journal of Bioethics [Online]* 2005 March-April; 5(2): W2. Subject: 2.1

Harrington, Lindsay S. Life-term inmates' right to procreate via artificial insemination: why so much fuss over the contents of a plastic cup? *McGeorge Law Review* 2002; 33(3): 521-535. Subject: 14.2

Harris, Curtis E.; Orr, Robert D. The end of care [letter and reply]. *First Things* 2004 December; (148): 6-8. Subject: 20.7

Harris, D.G.; Linnane, S.J. Making do not attempt resuscitation decisions: do doctors follow the guidelines? *Hospital Medicine* 2005 January; 66(1): 43-45. Subject: 20.5.1

Harris, Gardiner. Agency scientists divided over ethics ban on consulting. *New York Times* 2005 February 2; p. A17. Subject: 1.3.9

Harris, Gardiner. Ban on federal scientists' consulting nears. *New York Times* 2005 February 1; p. A15. Subject: 1.3.9

Harris, Gardiner. Drug makers are still giving gifts to doctors, F.D.A. officials tell senators. *New York Times* 2005 March 4; p. A15. Subject: 9.7

Harris, Gardiner. Drugs, politics and the FDA: abortion issue hovers over morning-after pill. *New York Times* 2005 August 28; p. A1, A14. Subject: 5.3

Harris, Gardiner. FDA to weight at-home testing for AIDS virus. *New York Times* 2005 October 13; p. A1, A16. Subject: 9.5.6

Harris, Gardiner. Gene therapy is facing a crucial hearing. *New York Times* 2005 March 3; p. A16. Subject: 15.4

Harris, Gardiner. Health agency tightens rules governing federal scientists. *New York Times* 2005 August 26; p. A13. Subject: 1.3.9

Harris, Gerald J. The privacy rule and the ophthalmic plastic surgeon as author [editorial]. *Ophthalmic Plastic and Reconstructive Surgery* 2005 March; 21(2): 85-86. Subject: 18.2

Harris, John. The age-indifference principle and equality. *CQ: Cambridge Quarterly of Healthcare Ethics* 2005 Winter; 14(1): 93-99. Subject: 9.4

Harris, John. Ethical genetic research on human subjects. *Jurimetrics* 1999 Fall; 40: 77-91. Subject: 18.2

Harris, John. Four legs good, personhood better! *Res Publica* 1998; 4(1): 51-58. Subject: 4.4

Harris, John. It's not NICE to discriminate [editorial]. *Journal of Medical Ethics* 2005 July; 31(7): 373-375. Subject: 9.4

Harris, John. Nice and not so nice [editorial]. *Journal of Medical Ethics* 2005 December; 31(12): 685-688. Subject: 4.4

Harris, John. No sex selection please, we're British. *Journal of Medical Ethics* 2005 May; 31(5): 286-288. Subject: 14.3

Harris, John. Putting empirical studies in their place. *In:* Holm, Søren; Jonas, Monique F., eds. Engaging the World: The Use of Empirical Research in Bioethics and the Regulation of Biotechnology. Washington, DC: IOS Press; 2004: 18-27. Subject: 2.1

Harris, John. Scientific research is a moral duty. *Journal of Medical Ethics* 2005 April; 31(4): 242-248. Subject: 18.1

Harris, John. Sex selection and regulated hatred. *Journal of Medical Ethics* 2005 May; 31(5): 291-294. Subject: 14.3

Harris, John. The poverty of objections to human reproductive cloning. *In:* Cohen, Andrew I.; Wellman, Christopher Heath, eds. Contemporary Debates in Applied Ethics. Malden, MA: Blackwell Pub., 2005: 145-158. Subject: 14.5

Harris, John. The right to die lives! There is no personhood paradox [debate]. *Medical Law Review* 2005 Autumn; 13(3): 386-392. Subject: 20.5.1

Harris, John; Bortolotti, Lisa; Irving, Louise. An ethical framework for stem cell research in the European Union. *Health Care Analysis: An International Journal of Health Care Philosophy and Policy* 2005 September; 13(3): 157-162. Subject: 18.5.4

Harris, John; Holm, Søren. Abortion. *In:* LaFollette, Hugh, ed. The Oxford Handbook of Practical Ethics. New York: Oxford University Press; 2003: 112-135. Subject: 12.1

Harris, Marcelline R. Codes of ethics and scientific integrity: what relevance to outcomes activities? *Advanced Practical Nursing Quarterly* 1997 Winter; 3(3): 36-43. Subject: 4.1.3

Harris, Marion; Winship, Ingrid; Spriggs, Merle. Controversies and ethical issues in cancer-genetics clinics. *Lancet Oncology* 2005 May; 6(5): 301-310. Subject: 15.3

Harris, Richard Jackson; Jasper, John David; Shanteau, James; Smith, Stacy A. Organ donation consent decisions by the next of kin: an experimental simulation approach. *In:* Shanteau, James; Harris, Richard Jackson, eds. Organ Donation and Transplantation: Psychological and Behavioral Factors. Washington, DC: American Psychological Association, 1990: 13-24. Subject: 19.5

Harris, Tess; Cook, Derek G.; Victor, Christina; Beighton, Carole; DeWilde, Stephen; Carey, Iain. Linking questionnaires to primary care records: factors affecting consent in older people. *Journal of Epidemiology and Community Health* 2005 April; 59(4): 336-338. Subject: 8.3.1

Harris, Victoria. 22q11 deletion syndrome and forensic research: can we go there? *Journal of the American Academy of Psychiatry and the Law* 2005; 33(1): 106-111. Subject: 15.6

Subject = NRCBL Primary Classification Number; See inside front cover

Harrison, Helen; Robertson, John A. Neonatal care for premature infants [letter and reply]. *Hastings Center Report* 2005 January-February; 35(1): 5-6, 7. Subject: 9.5.7

Harrison, Ivor. Ethical promotion and advertising of medicines: where do we draw the line? *In:* Salek, Sam; Edgar, Andrew, eds. Pharmaceutical Ethics. New York: Wiley; 2002: 161-177. Subject: 9.7

Harrison, Stephen; Moran, Michael. Resources and rationing: managing supply and demand in health care. *In:* Albrecht, Gary L.; Fitzpatrick, Ray; Scrimshaw, Susan C., eds. The Handbook of Social Studies in Health & Medicine. Thousand Oaks, CA: Sage; 2000: 493-508. Subject: 9.4

Harris-Fain, Darren. Does it make sense to use fiction as a guide to bioethics? [letter]. *Chronicle of Higher Education* 2005 July 8; 51(44): B13. Subject: 2.1

Harry, Debra. Acts of self-determination and self-defense: indigenous peoples' responses to biocolonialism. *In:* Krimsky, Sheldon; Shorett, Peter, eds. Rights and Liberties in the Biotech Age: Why We Need a Genetic Bill of Rights. Lanham: Rowman and Littlefield Publishers; 2005: 87-97. Subject: 15.1

Hart, David B. The anti-theology of the body. *New Atlantis* 2005 Summer; 9: 65-73. Subject: 1.2

Hart, Sara Elizabeth. Hospital ethical climates and registered nurses' turnover intentions. *Journal of Nursing Scholarship* 2005; 37(2): 173-177. Subject: 4.1.3

Harth, S.C.; Thong, Y.H. Parental perceptions and attitudes about informed consent in clinical research involving children. *Social Science and Medicine* 1995 December; 41(12): 1647-1651. Subject: 18.3

Hartman, Rhonda Gay. Dying young: cues from the courts. *Archives of Pediatrics and Adolescent Medicine* 2004 July; 158(7): 615-619. Subject: 20.5.2

Hartman, Rhonda Gay. Face value: challenges of transplant technology. *American Journal of Law and Medicine* 2005; 31(1): 7-46. Subject: 4.4

Hartmann, Lawrence. Comments: a crisis in the ethical and moral behavior of psychiatrists [forum]. *Current Opinion in Psychiatry* 1998 January; 11(1); 2 p. [Online]. Available: http://gateway.ut.ovid.com/gw1/ovidweb.cgi [24 May 2005]. Subject: 20.6

Hartmann, Lynn C. The octogenarian's plan [opinion]. *JAMA: The Journal of the American Medical Association* 2005 January 5; 293(1): 15-16. Subject: 20.5.1

Hartshorne, Johan; Hasegawa, Thomas K., Jr. Overservicing in dental practice — ethical perspectives. *SADJ: Journal of the South African Dental Association* 2003 October; 58(9): 364-365, 367-369. Subject: 9.4

Harvard Medical School; Harvard School of Dental Medicine. Faculty Policies on Integrity in Science. Boston, MA: Harvard Medical School, 2000 October; 22 p. Subject: 1.3.9

Harvey, Olivia. Regulating stem-cell research and human cloning in an Australian context: an exercise in protecting the status of the human subject. *New Genetics and Society* 2005 August; 24(2): 125-135. Subject: 14.5

Hasegawa, Thomas K., Jr.; Matthews, Merrill; Wakefield, Charles W. Ethical dilemma #49: "extreme makeover: we want her to be a winner". *Texas Dental Journal* 2004 October; 121(10): 995-998. Subject: 8.1

Haslam, Darryl R.; Harris, Steven M. Informed consent documents of marriage and family therapists in private practice: a qualitative analysis. *American Journal of Family Therapy* 2004 July-September; 32(4): 359-374. Subject: 8.3.1

Haslett, Tracy. J.B. v. M.B.: the enforcement of disposition contracts and the competing interests of the right to procreate and the right not to procreate where donors of genetic material dispute the disposition of unused preembryos. *Temple Environmental Law and Technology Journal* 2002 Spring; 20(2): 195-217. Subject: 14.6

Hasman, Andreas; Holm, Søren. Accountability for reasonableness: opening the black box of process. *Health Care Analysis: An International Journal of Health Care Philosophy and Policy* 2005 December; 13(4): 261-273. Subject: 9.4

Hassan, Riaz. Social consequences of manufactured longevity. *Medical Journal of Australia* 2000 December 4-18; 173(11-12): 601-603. Subject: 9.1

Hassenfeld, Irwin N. Ethics and the role of the supervisor of psychotherapy. *Journal of Psychiatric Education* 1987; 11(2): 73-77. Subject: 7.2

Hassol, Andrea; Walker, James M.; Kidder, David; Rokita, Kim; Young, David; Pierdon, Steven; Deitz, Deborah; Kuck, Sarah; Ortiz, Eduardo. Patient experiences and attitudes about access to a patient electronic health care record and linked web messaging. *Journal of the American Medical Informatics Association* 2004 November-December; 11(6): 505-513. Subject: 8.4

Hathaway, Katherine A. Federal genetic nondiscrimination legislation: the new "right" and the race to protect DNA at the local, state, and federal level. *Catholic University Law Review* 2002 Autumn; 52(1): 133-177. Subject: 15.3

Hatton, Diane C.; Kaiser, Lisa. Methodological and ethical issues emerging from pilot testing an intervention with women in a transitional shelter. *Western Journal of Nursing Research* 2004 February; 26(1): 129-136. Subject: 18.5.3

Hattori, Toshiko. End-of-life care and advance directives in Japan. *Journal International de Bioéthique / International Journal of Bioethics* 2005 March-June; 16(1-2): 135-142, 198. Subject: 20.5.4

Hauerwas, Stanley. Should suffering be eliminated?: what the retarded have to teach us. *In:* Berkman, John;

Cartwright, Michael, eds. The Hauerwas Reader. Durham, NC: Duke University Press; 2001: 556-576. Subject: 4.3

Haug, Charlotte; Gøtzsche, Peter C.; Schroeder, Torben V. Registries and registration of clinical trials [editorial]. *New England Journal of Medicine* 2005 December 29; 353(26): 2811-2812. Subject: 18.2

Hauser, Stephen L. The shape of things to come [editorial]. *Neurology* 2004 September 28; 63(6): 948-950. Subject: 4.1.2

Haverkamp, Fritz; Rünger, Michaela. Medizinisch-psychosoziale Aspekte der ethischen Diskussion um den kindlichen Kleinwuchs und die Wachstumshormontherapie. *In:* Jahrbuch für Wissenschaft und Ethik. Bd. 7. Berlin: Walter de Gruyter; 2002: 295-310. Subject: 9.5.7

Havlir, Diane V.; Hammer, Scott M. Patents versus patients? Antiretroviral therapy in India [opinion]. *New England Journal of Medicine* 2005 August 25; 353(8): 749-751. Subject: 9.5.6

Hawkins, Anne Hunsaker. Epiphanic knowledge and medicine. *CQ: Cambridge Quarterly of Healthcare Ethics* 2005 Winter; 14(1): 40-46. Subject: 4.1.2

Hawkins, J.S. The ethics of Zelen consent [opinion]. *Journal of Thrombosis and Haemostasis* 2004 June; 2(6): 882-883. Subject: 18.3

Hawkins, Jennifer S.; Emanuel, Ezekiel J. Clarifying confusions about coercion. *Hastings Center Report* 2005 September-October; 35(5): 16-19. Subject: 18.2

Hawkins, Nikki Ayers; Ditto, Peter H.; Danks, Joseph H.; Smucker, William D. Micromanaging death: process preferences, values, and goals in end-of-life medical decision making. *Gerontologist* 2005 February; 45(1): 107-117. Subject: 20.5.4

Hayhurst, Matthew B. Parental notification of abortion and minors' rights under the Montana constitution. *Montana Law Review* 1997 Summer; 58(2): 565-598. Subject: 12.4.2

Häyry, Heta. AIDS, discimination and legal restrictions. *In her:* Individual Liberty and Medical Control. Brookfield, VT: Ashgate Pub., 1998: 82-91. Subject: 9.5.6

Häyry, Heta. Does democratic might make right in health care policy-making? *In her:* Individual Liberty and Medical Control. Brookfield, VT: Ashgate Pub., 1998: 92-102. Subject: 9.1

Häyry, Heta. Health education, the ideal observer and personal autonomy. *In her:* Individual Liberty and Medical Control. Brookfield, VT: Ashgate Pub., 1998: 57-66. Subject: 9.1

Häyry, Heta. Preventive medicine and the welfare of the population. *In her:* Individual Liberty and Medical Control. Brookfield, VT: Ashgate Pub., 1998: 67-81. Subject: 9.1

Häyry, Heta. Voluntary euthanasia and medical paternalism. *In her:* Individual Liberty and Medical Control. Brookfield, VT: Ashgate Pub., 1998: 28-39. Subject: 20.5.1

Häyry, Heta. Who is to live and who is to die? *In her:* Individual Liberty and Medical Control. Brookfield, VT: Ashgate Pub., 1998: 16-27. Subject: 20.5.1

Häyry, Heta. Wrongful medical authoritarianism. *In her:* Individual Liberty and Medical Control. Brookfield, VT: Ashgate Pub., 1998: 40-56. Subject: 8.1

Häyry, Matti. Can arguments address concerns? *Journal of Medical Ethics* 2005 October; 31(10): 598-600. Subject: 2.1

Häyry, Matti. A defense of ethical relativism. *CQ: Cambridge Quarterly of Healthcare Ethics* 2005 Winter, 14(1): 7-12. Subject: 1.1

Häyry, Matti. A defense of shallow listening. *Bioethics* 2005 October; 19(5-6): 565-567. Subject: 2.1

Häyry, Matti. Forget autonomy and give me freedom! *In:* Häyry, Matti; Takala, Tuija; Herissone-Kelly, Peter, eds. Bioethics and Social Reality. New York: Rodopi, 2005: 31-37. Subject: 9.5.1

Häyry, Matti. If you must make babies, then at least make the best babies you can? *Human Fertility* 2004 June; 7(2): 105-112. Subject: 14.1

Häyry, Matti. Precaution and solidarity. *CQ: Cambridge Quarterly of Healthcare Ethics* 2005 Spring; 14(2): 199-206. Subject: 2.1

Häyry, Matti. The rational cure for prereproductive stress syndrome revised. *Journal of Medical Ethics* 2005 October; 31(10): 606-607. Subject: 14.1

Häyry, Matti. The tension between self governance and absolute inner worth in Kant's moral philosophy. *Journal of Medical Ethics* 2005 November; 31(11): 645-647. Subject: 2.1

Häyry, Matti; Takala, Tuija. Cloning, naturalness and personhood. *In:* Thomasma, David C.; Weisstud, David N.; Herve, Christian eds. Personhood and Health Care. Boston: Kluwer Academic Pub., 2001: 281-298. Subject: 14.5

Häyry, Matti; Takala, Tuija. Human dignity, bioethics, and human rights. *Developing World Bioethics* 2005 September; 5(3): 225-233. Subject: 2.1

Hayward, Rodney A.; Kent, David M.; Vijan, Sandeep; Hofer, Timothy P. Reporting clinical trial results to inform providers, payers, and consumers. *Health Affairs* 2005 November-December; 24(6): 1571-1581. Subject: 18.2

Hazard, Gregory. Please, sir, I want some more: Congress' carrot-and-stick approach to pediatric testing leaves therapeutic orphans needing more protection. *Journal of Contemporary Health Law and Policy* 2004 Spring; 20(2): 467-508. Subject: 18.2

Hazelgrove, Jenny. British research ethics after the Second World War: the controversy at the British postgraduate medical school, Hammersmith Hospital. *In:* Roelcke, Volker; Maio, Giovanni, eds. Twentieth Century Ethics of Human Subjects Research: Historical Perspectives on Values, Practices, and Regulations. Stuttgart: Franz Steiner Verlag; 2004: 181-197. Subject: 18.1

Hazzard, William R. The conflict between biogerontology and antiaging medicine - - do geriatricians have a dog in this fight? [editorial]. *Journal of the American Geriatrics Society* 2005 August; 53(8): 1434-1435. Subject: 9.5.2

Heagle, Khristan A. Should there be another ewe? A critical analysis of the European Union cloning legislation. *Dickinson Journal of International Law* 1998 Fall; 17(1): 135- 158. Subject: 14.5

Healy, Bernadine. A medical-industrial complex. How about medical grand juries to oversee, analyze, and approve the experts' health guidelines? *U.S. News and World Report* 2005 January 24; 138(3): 54. Subject: 9.8

Healy, Bernadine. When life is on the line. *U.S. News and World Report* 2005 April 4; 138(12): 26. Subject: 20.5.1

Healy, David. Manufacturing consensus [opinion]. *Hastings Center Report* 2004 July-August; 34(4): inside back cover. Subject: 1.3.9

Heath, K.V.; Wood, E.; Bally, G.; Cornelisse, P.G.A.; Hogg, Robert S. Experience in treating persons with HIV/AIDS and the legalization of assisted suicide: the views of Canadian physicians. *AIDS Care* 1999 October; 11(5): 501-510. Subject: 20.7

Hechem, Maria I.; Gonorazky, Sergio. Looking for ways to avoid deception in the pursuit of science [letter]. *Archives of Internal Medicine* 2005 May 23; 165(10): 1199-1200. Subject: 18.2

Heckerling, Paul S. The ethics of single blind trials. *IRB: Ethics and Human Research* 2005 July-August; 27(4): 12-16. Subject: 18.2

Heenan, Andrew L.J. Research ethics [editorial]. *Professional Nurse* 1995 July; 10(10): 615. Subject: 18.2

Heffernan, Liz. Stenberg v Carhart: a divided US Supreme Court debates partial birth abortion. *Modern Law Review* 2001 July; 64(4): 618-627. Subject: 12.4.1

Heffner, John E.; Fahy, Bonnie; Hilling, Lana; Barbieri, Celia. Attitudes regarding advance directives among patients in pulmonary rehabilitation. *American Journal of Respiratory and Critical Care Medicine* 1996 December; 154(6 Part 1): 1735-1740. Subject: 20.5.4

Heilig, Steve; Blackburn, Elizabeth. Stem cell science and politics: a talk with Elizabeth Blackburn [interview]. *CQ: Cambridge Quarterly of Healthcare Ethics* 2005 Spring; 14(2): 214-217. Subject: 18.5.4

Heinemann, Richard A. Pushing the limits of informed consent: Johnson v. Kokemoor and physician-specific dis-

closure. *Wisconsin Law Review* 1997; 5: 1079-1121. Subject: 8.3.1

Heinrichs, Bert. What should we want to know about our future? A Kantian view on predictive genetic testing. *Medicine, Health Care and Philosophy: A European Journal* 2005; 8(1): 29-37. Subject: 15.3

Heinrichs, Bert. Zur Regelungsbedürftigkeit prädiktiver genetischer Tests und zur normativen Kraft des Gesundheitsbegriffs. *In:* Jahrbuch für Wissenschaft und Ethik. Bd. 7. Berlin: Walter de Gruyter; 2002: 197-215. Subject: 15.3

Heitman, Elizabeth; Anestidou, Lida; Olsen, Cara; Bulger, Ruth Ellen. Do researchers learn to overlook misbehavior? [opinion]. *Hastings Center Report* 2005 September-October; 35(5): inside back cover. Subject: 1.3.9

Heitman, Elizabeth; Bulger, Ruth Ellen. Assessing the educational literature in the responsible conduct of research for core content. *Accountability in Research* 2005 July-September; 12(3): 207- 224. Subject: 1.3.9

Heitman, Elizabeth; Wells, Alan L. Ethical issues and unethical conduct: race, racism, and the abuse of human subjects in research. *In:* Beech, Bettina; Goodman, Maurine, eds. Race & Research: Perspectives on Minority Participation in Health Studies. Washington, DC: American Public Health Association; 2004: 35-59. Subject: 18.5.1

Heitz, Ruth M. Recent developments in the doctrine of informed consent. *Wisconsin Medical Journal* 1999 September-October; 98(6): 56-57. Subject: 8.3.1

Hek, Gill. Ethical issues in community health care district nursing. *In:* Chadwick, Ruth; Levitt, Mairi, eds. Ethical Issues in Community Health Care. New York: Arnold; 1998: 125-134. Subject: 4.1.3

Helén, Ilpo. Risk management and ethics in high-tech antenatal care. *In:* Bunton, Robin; Petersen, Alan, eds. Genetic Governance: Health, Risk and Ethics in the Biotech Era. New York: Routledge; 2005: 47-63. Subject: 15.2

Helft, Paul R. Necessary collusion: prognostic communication with advanced cancer patients. *Journal of Clinical Oncology* 2005 May 1; 23(13): 3146-3150. Subject: 8.2

Helgesson, Gert. Children, longitudinal studies, and informed consent. *Medicine, Health Care and Philosophy: A European Journal* 2005; 8(3): 307-313. Subject: 18.5.2

Helgesson, Gert; Johnsson, Linus. The right to withdraw consent to research on biobank samples. *Medicine, Health Care and Philosophy: A European Journal* 2005; 8(3): 315-321. Subject: 15.1

Helgesson, Gert; Ludvigsson, J.; Gustafsson Stolt, U. How to handle informed consent in longitudinal studies when participants have a limited understanding of the study. *Journal of Medical Ethics* 2005 November; 31(11): 670-673. Subject: 18.3

See SUBJECT HEADING KEY FOR SECTION II on inside back cover

Heller, Jan C. Discussing the theological grounds of moral principles. *Health Care Ethics USA [electronic]* 2005; 13(2); 2 p. Available: http://www.slu.edu/centers/chce/hceusa/2_2005_1.html [19 September 2005]. Subject: 9.1

Hellsten, Iina. Dolly: scientific breakthrough or Frankenstein's monster? Journalistic and scientific metaphors of cloning. *Metaphor and Symbol* 2000; 15(4): 213-221. Subject: 14.5

Hellsten, Iina. From sequencing to annotating: extending the metaphor of the book of life from genetics to genomics. *New Genetics and Society* 2005 December; 24(3): 283-297. Subject: 15.10

Hellsten, Sirkku K. Bioethics in Tanzania: legal and ethical concerns in medical care and research in relation to the HIV/AIDS epidemic. *CQ: Cambridge Quarterly of Healthcare Ethics* 2005 Summer; 14(3): 256-267. Subject: 9.5.6

Henderson, Gail E.; Davis, Arlene M.; King, Nancy M.P.; Easter, Michele M.; Zimmer, Catherine R.; Rothschild, Barbra Bluestone; Wilfond, Benjamin S.; Nelson, Daniel K.; Churchill, Larry R. Uncertain benefit: investigators' views and communications in early phase gene transfer trials. *Molecular Therapy* 2004 August; 10(2): 225-231. Subject: 15.4

Henderson, Jeannette. The challenge of relationship boundaries in mental health. *Nursing Management* 2004 October; 11(6): 28-32. Subject: 17.1

Henderson, Mark. German doctors urged to shake off Nazi horrors [news]. *Times (London, Home section)* 2004 June 28; p. 4. Subject: 21.4

Henderson, R.; Keiding, N. Individual survival time prediction using statistical models. *Journal of Medical Ethics* 2005 December; 31(12): 703-706. Subject: 7.1

Hendricksen, Coenraad F.M. The ethics of Research Involving Animals: a review of the Nuffield Council on Bioethics Report from a three Rs perspective. *ATLA: Alternatives to Laboratory Animals* 2005 December; 33(6): 659-662. Subject: 22.2

Hendriks, Aart. Genetic discrimination: how to anticipate predictable problems? [editorial]. *European Journal of Health Law* 2002 June; 9(2): 87-92. Subject: 15.1

Heng, Boon Chin. Egg-sharing in return for subsidized fertility treatment: a possible solution for therapeutic cloning? [letter]. *Human Reproduction* 2005 November; 20(11): 3258. Subject: 14.4

Henig, Robin Marantz. Is this a solution? It may mollify some critics, but it's a stem cell shell game. *Washington Post* 2005 November 13; p. B2. Subject: 1.3.9

Henke, Donald E. A history of ordinary and extraordinary means. *National Catholic Bioethics Quarterly* 2005 Autumn; 5(3): 555-575. Subject: 20.5.1

Henry, David; Doran, Evan; Kerridge, Ian; Hill, Suzanne; McNeill, Paul M.; Day, Richard. Ties that bind: multiple relationships between clinical researchers and the pharmaceutical industry. *Archives of Internal Medicine* 2005 November 28; 165(21): 2493- 2496. Subject: 1.3.9

Hensl, Kursten B. Restored to health to be put to death: reconciling the legal and ethical dilemmas of medicating to execute in Singleton v. Norris. *Villanova Law Review* 2004; 49(2): 291-328. Subject: 17.8

Hensley, Scott; Martinez, Barbara. To sell their drugs, companies increasingly rely on doctors; for $750 and up, physicians tell peers about products; talks called educational; Dr. Pitts's busy speaking tour. *Wall Street Journal* 2005 July 15; p. A1, A2. Subject: 9.7

Hentoff, Nat. The legacy of Terri Schiavo: the disabled sound the alarm for the nonreligious. *Free Inquiry* 2005 August-September; 25(5): 33-35. Subject: 9.5.1

Herbert, Martha R. More than code: from genetic reductionism to complex biological systems. *In:* Bunton, Robin; Petersen, Alan, eds. Genetic Governance: Health, Risk and Ethics in the Biotech Era. New York: Routledge; 2005: 171-188. Subject: 15.1

Herdy, Wayne. Must the doctor tell? *Journal of Law and Medicine* 1996 February; 3(3): 270-282. Subject: 8.4

Herissone-Kelly, Peter. Bioethics, rights-based consequentialism, and social reality. *In:* Häyry, Matti; Takala, Tuija; Herissone-Kelly, Peter, eds. Bioethics and Social Reality. New York: Rodopi, 2005: 161-171. Subject: 2.1

Herissone-Kelly, Peter. The cloning debate in the United Kingdom: the academy meets the public. *CQ: Cambridge Quarterly of Healthcare Ethics* 2005 Summer; 14(3): 268-276. Subject: 14.5

Hermerén, Göran. Der Einfluss der Humangenomeprojekte auf unser Selbstverständnis. *In:* Honnefelder, Ludger; Mieth, Dietmar; Propping, Peter; Siep, Ludwig; Wiesemann, Claudia, eds. Das genetische Wissen und die Zukunft des Menschen. New York: De Gruyter; 2003: 57-77. Subject: 15.1

Hermerén, Göran. The debate about dignity. *In:* Council of Europe Publishing, ed. Euthanasia. Volume I. Ethical and Human Aspects. Strasbourg: Council of Europe; Croton-on-Hudson, NY: Manhattan Publishing Co.; 2003: 37-57. Subject: 20.5.1

Hermsen, Maaike; ten Have, Henk A.M.J. Decision-making in palliative care practice and the need for moral deliberation: a qualitative study. *Patient Education and Counseling* 2005 March; 56(3): 268-275. Subject: 20.5.1

Herranz, Jesús Conde. Palliative care: origins, precedents and the history of a Christian approach. *Dolentium Hominum* 2005; 20(1): 54-63. Subject: 20.4.1

Herring, Jonathan. Giving, selling and sharing bodies. *In:* Bainham, Andrew; Sclater, Shelley Day; Richards, Martin, eds. Body Lore and Laws. Portland, OR: Hart Pub.; 2002: 43-61. Subject: 19.5

Herring, Lynn W. The increasing role of constituencies of a federal public health agency: a case study on acquired immunodeficiency syndrome (AIDS). *International Journal of Public Administration* 1987; 10(3): 235-253. Subject: 9.5.6

Herron, William G. Revisiting fee policies. *Psychological Reports* 1996 June; 78(3, Part 1): 881-882. Subject: 9.3.1

Hershberger, Patricia. Recipients of oocyte donation: an integrative review. *Journal of Obstetric, Gynecologic, and Neonatal Nursing* 2004 September-October; 33(5): 610-621. Subject: 14.4

Hershenov, David. Do dead bodies pose a problem for biological approaches to personal identity? *Mind* 2005 January; 114(453): 31-59. Subject: 4.4

Hershenov, David B.; Koch, Rose J. How a hylomorphic metaphysics constrains the abortion debate. *National Catholic Bioethics Quarterly* 2005 Winter; 5(4): 751- 764. Subject: 12.3

Hershey, Nathan. The clinical investigator as target. *Controlled Clinical Trials* 1996 June; 17(3): 183-190. Subject: 18.1

Hertogh, Cees M.P.M.; The, B. Anne Mei; Miesen, Bere M.L.; Eefsting, Jan A. Truth telling and truthfulness in the care for patients with advanced dementia: an ethnographic study in Dutch nursing homes. *Social Science and Medicine* 2004 October; 59(8): 1685-1693. Subject: 8.2

Hervey, Tamara K. Buy baby: the European Union and regulation of human reproduction. *Oxford Journal of Legal Studies* 1998 Summer; 18(2): 207-233. Subject: 14.6

Hesketh, Therese; Lu, Li; Xing, Zhu Wei. The effect of China's one-child family policy after 25 years. *New England Journal of Medicine* 2005 September 15; 353(11): 1171-1176. Subject: 13.3

Hess, Joanne D. Gadow's relational narrative: an elaboration. *Nursing Philosophy* 2003 July; 4(2): 137-148. Subject: 4.1.3

Hester, D. Micah. Progressive dying: meaningful acts of euthanasia and assisted suicide. *Journal of Medical Humanities* 1998; 19(4): 279-298. Subject: 20.5.1

Heubel, Friedrich; Biller-Andorno, Nikola. The contribution of Kantian moral theory to contemporary medical ethics: a critical analysis. *Medicine, Health Care and Philosophy: A European Journal* 2005; 8(1): 5-18. Subject: 2.1

Hevia, Armando; Hobgood, Cherri. Medical error during residency: to tell or not to tell. *Annals of Emergency Medicine* 2003 October; 42(4): 565-570. Subject: 9.8

Hewson, Barbara. The law of abortion in Northern Ireland. *Public Law* 2004 Summer: 234-245. Subject: 12.4.1

Heyd, David. Male or female, we will create them: the ethics of sex selection for non-medical reasons. *Ethical Perspectives* 2003; 10(3-4): 204-214. Subject: 14.3

Heyland, Daren K.; Tranmer, Joan; O'Callaghan, C.J.; Gafni, Amiram. The seriously ill hospitalized patient: preferred role in end-of-life decision making? *Journal of Critical Care* 2003 March; 18(1): 3-10. Subject: 20.4.1

Heymann, S. Jody; Sell, Randall L. Mandatory public health programs: to what standards should they be held? *Health and Human Rights: An International Journal* 1999; 4(1): 193-203. Subject: 9.5.1

Heywood, Rob. Excessive risk disclosure: the effects of the law on medical practice. *Medical Law International* 2005; 7(2): 93-112. Subject: 8.3.1

Hicken, Bret L.; Foshee, Aimee; Tucker, Diane C. Perceptions and attitudes about HFE genotyping among college-age adults. *Journal of Genetic Counseling* 2005 December; 14(6): 465-472. Subject: 15.3

Hickey, Daniel P. The disutility of advance directives: we know the problems, but are there solutions? *Journal of Health Law* 2003 Summer; 36(3): 455-473. Subject: 20.5.4

Hickman, Susan E. Honoring resident autonomy in long-term care. Special considerations. *Journal of Psychosocial Nursing and Mental Health Services* 2004 January; 42(1): 12-16. Subject: 9.5.1

Hiday, Virginia Aldigé. Civil commitment: a review of empirical research. *Behavioral Sciences and the Law* 1988; 6(1): 15-43. Subject: 17.8

Higgins, Joan. Two sides of the fence. *Health Service Journal* 2004 October 7; 114(5926): 20-21. Subject: 8.4

Hijazi, Fadi; Holley, Jean L. Cardiopulmonary resuscitation and dialysis: outcome and patients' views. *Seminars in Dialysis* 2003 January-February; 16(1): 51-53. Subject: 20.5.1

Hildebrand, Adam J. On "vegetative" human beings. *Ethics and Medics* 2005 January; 30(1): 1-4. Subject: 20.5.1

Hildebrandt, Martin; Ludwig, W.-D. Clinical research and industrial sponsoring: avenues towards transparency and credibility. *Onkologie* 2003; 26(6): 529-534. Subject: 1.3.9

Hilhorst, Medard. 'Prosthetic fit': on personal identity and the value of bodily difference. *Medicine, Health Care and Philosophy: A European Journal* 2004; 7(3): 303-310. Subject: 4.2

Hilhorst, Medard T. Directed altruistic living organ donation: partial but not unfair. *Ethical Theory and Moral Practice* 2005 April; 8(1-2): 197-215. Subject: 19.3

Hilhorst, Medard T.; Kranenburg, Leonieke W.; Zuidema, Willij; Weimar, Willem; IJzermans, Jan N.M.; Passchier, Jan; Busschbach, Jan J.V. Altruistic living kidney donation challenges psychosocial research and policy: a response to previous articles. *Transplantation* 2005 June 15; 79(11): 1470-1474. Subject: 19.5

Hill, Daniel J. The morality of the separation of the conjoined Attard twins of Manchester. *Health Care Analysis: An International Journal of Health Care Philosophy and Policy* 2005 September; 13(3): 163-176. Subject: 20.5.2

Hill, David L.; Li, Man. What regulations for preimplantation genetic diagnosis? *Journal of Assisted Reproduction and Genetics* 2004 January; 21(1): 11-13. Subject: 15.2

Hill, J.; Foster, N.; Hughes, R.; Hay, E. Meeting the challenges of research governance [editorial]. *Rheumatology* 2005 May; 44(5): 571-572. Subject: 18.2

Hill, William Allen. PI and vet: potential conflict of interest? PI can't act as AV. *Lab Animal* 2004 October; 33(9): 22-23. Subject: 22.2

Hillbrand, Marc. Obstacles to research in forensic psychiatry [editorial]. *Journal of the American Academy of Psychiatry and the Law* 2005; 33(3): 295-298. Subject: 18.2

Hilliard, Bryan. Evaluating the dissent in State of Oregon v. Ashcroft: implications for the patient-physician relationship and the democratic process. *Journal of Law, Medicine and Ethics* 2005 Spring; 33(1): 142- 153. Subject: 20.7

Himma, K.E. A dualist analysis of abortion: personhood and the concept of self qua experiential subject. *Journal of Medical Ethics* 2005 January; 31(1): 48-55. Subject: 12.3

Hindmarsh, Richard. Genetic engineering regulation in Australia: an 'archaeology' of expertise and power. *Science as Culture* 2005 December; 14(4): 373-392. Subject: 15.1

Hindmarsh, Richard; Gottweis, Herbert. Recombinant regulation: the Asilomar legacy 30 years on [editorial]. *Science as Culture* 2005 December; 14(4): 299-307. Subject: 15.7

Hinds, Heather L. Pediatric obesity: ethical dilemmas in treatment and prevention. *Journal of Law, Medicine and Ethics* 2005 Fall; 33(3): 599-602. Subject: 9.5.7

Hinojosa, John Paul. The human genome, property of all: opportunities under the ALRC inquiry into gene patenting and human health. *Sydney Law Review* 2004 September; 26(3): 447-455. Subject: 15.8

Hinshaw, Stephen P. Objective assessment of covert antisocial behavior: predictive validity and ethical considerations. *Ethics and Behavior* 2005; 15(3): 259-269. Subject: 17.3

Hinshelwood, R.D. A psychoanalytic perspective on confidentiality: the divided mind in treatment. *In:* Koggel, Christine M.; Furlong, Allannah; Levin, Charles, eds. Confidential Relationships: Psychoanalytical, Ethical, and Legal Contexts. New York: Rodopi; 2003: 31-51. Subject: 8.4

Hintermair, Manfred; Albertini, John A. Ethics, deafness, and new medical technologies. *Journal of Deaf Studies and Deaf Education* 2005 Spring; 10(2): 184-192. Subject: 4.2

Hippen, Benjamin E. In defense of a regulated market in kidneys from living vendors. *Journal of Medicine and Philosophy* 2005 December; 30(6): 593- 626. Subject: 19.3

Hird, Crystal. A call for education [letter]. *Nursing Ethics* 2005 March; 12(2): 196-197. Subject: 8.2

Hiremath, Vijay. Law commission report proposes lethal injection for the death penalty. *Issues in Medical Ethics* 2003 July-September; 11(3): 93-94. Subject: 20.6

Hirsch, Joy. Raising consciousness [editorial]. *Journal of Clinical Investigation* 2005 May; 115(5): 1102- 1103. Subject: 20.5.1

Hirsch, Jules. A first brush with professional courtesy. *Annals of Internal Medicine* 2005 October 18; 143(8): 613. Subject: 7.3

Hirschfeld, Robert M.A.; Winslade, William; Krause, Todd L. Protecting subjects and fostering research: striking the proper balance [opinion]. *Archives of General Psychiatry* 1997 February; 54(2): 5 p. [Online]. Available: http://gateway.ut.ovid.com/gwl/ovidweb.cgi [6 October 2005]. Subject: 18.2

Hirshon, Jon Mark; Krugman, Scott D.; Witting, Michael D.; Furuno, Jon P.; Limcangco, M. Rhona; Perisse, Andre R.; Rasch, Elizabeth K. Variability in institutional review board assessment of minimal-risk research. *Academic Emergency Medicine* 2002 December; 9(12): 1417-1420. Subject: 18.2

Hirtle, Marie. The governance of research involving human participants in Canada. *Health Law Journal* 2003; 11: 137-152. Subject: 18.2

Hirtz, Deborah G.; Fitzsimmons, Lorraine G. Regulatory and ethical issues in the conduct of clinical research involving children. *Current Opinion in Pediatrics* 2002 December; 14(6): 669-675. Subject: 18.5.2

Hitchcock, James. The Schiavo case and the culture wars. *Human Life Review* 2005 Summer; 31(3): 50-60. Subject: 20.5.1

Hittinger, Russell. Private uses of lethal force: the case of assisted suicide. *Loyola Law Review* 1997 Summer; 43(2): 151-179. Subject: 20.7

Ho, Cynthia M. Patents, patients, and public policy: an incomplete intersection at 35 U.S.C. Section 287(c). *University of California Davis Law Review* 2000 Spring; 33(3): 601-675. Subject: 15.8

Ho, K.M.; Liang, J. Withholding and withdrawal of therapy in New Zealand intensive care units (ICUs): a survey of clinical directors. *Anaesthesia and Intensive Care* 2004 December; 32(6): 781-786. Subject: 20.5.1

Hobbins, Peter Graeme. Compromised ethical principles in randomised clinical trials of distant, intercessory prayer. *Journal of Bioethical Inquiry* 2005; 2(3): 142-152. Subject: 18.5.1

Hobgood, Cherri; Hevia, Armando. Disclosing medical error: a professional standard. *Seminars in Medical Practice* 2004; 7: 12-23. Subject: 9.8

Hobin, Terrence J. Abortion as liberty and right. *Human Life Review* 2005 Winter; 31(1): 67-78. Subject: 12.1

Hodder, Peter; Gallagher, Ann. Standard-setting. *In:* Chadwick, Ruth; Levitt, Mairi, eds. Ethical Issues in Community Health Care. New York: Arnold; 1998: 63-72. Subject: 9.8

Hodge, Belinda. Uncovering the ethic of care. *Nursing Praxis in New Zealand* 1993 July; 8(2): 13-22. Subject: 4.1.1

Hodge, James G., Jr. An enhanced approach to distinguishing public health practice and human subjects research. *Journal of Law, Medicine and Ethics* 2005 Spring; 33(1): 125- 141. Subject: 18.2

Hodge, James G., Jr.; Gostin, Kieran G. Challenging themes in American health information privacy and the public's health: historical and modern assessments. *Journal of Law, Medicine and Ethics* 2004 Winter; 32(4): 670-679. Subject: 8.4

Hodge, James G., Jr.; Parini, Michael J. Perinatal HIV transmission: a children's human rights perspective. *Children's Legal Rights Journal* 1998 Spring; 18(2): 6-19. Subject: 9.5.6

Hodgson, Jan; Spriggs, Merle. A practical account of autonomy: why genetic counseling is especially well suited to the facilitation of informed autonomous decision making. *Journal of Genetic Counseling* 2005 April; 14(2): 89-97. Subject: 15.2

Hoehn, K.S.; Wernovsky, G.; Rychik, J.; Gaynor, J.W.; Spray, T.L.; Feudtner, C.; Nelson, R.M. What factors are important to parents making decisions about neonatal research? *Archives of Disease in Childhood. Fetal and Neonatal Edition* 2005 May; 90(3): F267-F269. Subject: 18.5.2

Hoehner, Paul J. "Altered nuclear transfer": probing the nature of being human. *National Catholic Bioethics Quarterly* 2005 Summer; 5(2): 261- 269. Subject: 4.4

Hoeyer, Klaus. Ambiguous gifts: public anxiety, informed consent and biobanks. *In:* Tutton, Richard; Corrigan, Oonagh, eds. Genetic Databases: Socio-ethical Issues in the Collection and Use of DNA. New York: Routledge; 2004: 97-116. Subject: 18.3

Hoeyer, Klaus. The role of ethics in commercial genetic research: notes on the notion of commodification. *Medical Anthropology* 2005 January-March; 24(1): 45-70. Subject: 15.1

Hoeyer, Klaus; Olofsson, Bert-Ove; Mjörndal, Tom; Lynöe, Niels. The ethics of research using biobanks. *Archives of Internal Medicine* 2005 January 10; 165(1): 97-100. Subject: 15.1

Hoffman, David N. The medical malpractice insurance crisis, again. *Hastings Center Report* 2005 March-April; 35(2): 15-19. Subject: 8.5

Hoffman, Jan. Awash in information, patients face a lonely, uncertain road. *New York Times* 2005 August 14; p. A1, A18, A19. Subject: 8.3.1

Hoffman, Jan. Doctors' delicate balance in keeping hope alive. *New York Times* 2005 December 24; p. A1, A14. Subject: 20.4.1

Hoffman, Jascha. New York City foster home accused of unethical AIDS drug trials [news]. *Nature Medicine* 2005 January; 11(1): 5. Subject: 9.5.6

Hoffman, Sarah Z. HIV/AIDS in Cuba: a model for care or an ethical dilemma? *African Health Sciences* 2004 December; 4(3): 208-209. Subject: 9.5.6

Hoffman, Sharona. AIDS caps, contraceptive coverage, and the law: an analysis of the federal anti-discrimination statutes' applicability to health insurance. *Cardozo Law Review* 2002 March; 23(4): 1315-1362. Subject: 9.3.1

Hoffman, Sharona. Beneficial and unusual punishment: an argument in support of prisoner participation in clinical trials. *Indiana Law Review* 2000; 33(2): 475-515. Subject: 18.5.5

Hoffman, Sharona. Continued concern: human subject protection, the institutional review board, and continuing review. *Tennessee Law Review* 2001 Summer; 68(4): 725-770. Subject: 18.2

Hoffman, Sharona; Morriss, Andrew P. Birth after death: perpetuities and the new reproductive technologies. *Georgia Law Review* 2004 Winter; 38(2): 575-631. Subject: 14.6

Hoffmann, Diane E.; Rothenberg, Karen H. When should judges admit or compel genetic tests? *Science* 2005 October 14; 310(5746): 241-242. Subject: 15.3

Hoffmann, Diane E.; Schwartz, Jack; DeRenzo, Evan G. Regulating research with decisionally impaired individuals: are we making progress? *DePaul Journal of Health Care Law* 2000 Spring-Summer; 3(3-4): 547-608. Subject: 18.3

Hoffmann, Diane E.; Tarzian, Anita J. Dying in America — an examination of policies that deter adequate end-of-life care in nursing homes. *Journal of Law, Medicine and Ethics* 2005 Summer; 33(2): 294- 309. Subject: 20.4.1

Hoffmaster, Barry. 'Real' ethics for 'real' boys: context and narrative in bioethics [comment]. *American Journal of Bioethics* 2005 May-June; 5(3): 50-51. Subject: 17.4

Hoffmeister, Thaddeus A. The growing importance of advance medical directives. *Military Law Review* 2003 Fall; 177: 110-132. Subject: 20.5.4

Höfling, Wolfram. Die Forschung an embryonalen Stammzellen in verfassungsrechtlicher Perspektive. *In:* Maio, Giovanni; Just, Hanjörg, eds. Die Forschung an embryonalen Stammzellen in ethischer und rechtlicher Perspektive. Baden-Baden: Nomos Verlagsgesellschaft; 2003: 141-155. Subject: 18.5.4

Hofman, Nila Ginger. Toward critical research ethics: transforming ethical conduct in qualitative health care research. *Health Care for Women International* 2004 August; 25(7): 647-662. Subject: 18.4

Hofmann, B.; Håheim, L.L.; Søreide, J.A. Ethics of palliative surgery in patients with cancer. *British Journal of Surgery* 2005 July; 92(7): 802-809. Subject: 20.4.1

Hofmann, Bjørn. Simplified models of the relationship between health and disease. *Theoretical Medicine and Bioethics* 2005; 26(5): 355-377. Subject: 4.2

Hofmann, Bjørn. Toward a procedure for integrating moral issues in health technology assessment. *International Journal of Technology Assessment in Health Care* 2005 Summer; 21(3): 312-318. Subject: 5.2

Hofmeyer, Timothy G. Everybody's got something to hide except me and my patented monkey: patentability of cloned organisms. *John Marshall Journal of Computer and Information Law* 1998 Summer; 16(4): 971-995. Subject: 15.8

Hogan, Walter; Bucciarelli, Elizabeth Retzel. Ethical treatment of animals. *Choice* 2005 December; 43(4): 595-600, 602-609. Subject: 22.1

Hogben, Susan; Boddington, Paula. Policy recommendations for carrier testing and predictive testing in childhood: a distinction that makes a real difference. *Journal of Genetic Counseling* 2005 August; 14(4): 271-281. Subject: 15.3

Högberg, Torbjörn; Magnusson, Annabella; Lützén, Kim. To be a nurse or a neighbour? A moral concern for psychiatric nurses living next door to individuals with a mental illness. *Nursing Ethics* 2005 September; 12(5): 468-478. Subject: 17.1

Hogle, Linda F. Medical technologies. *In:* Restivo, Sal, ed. Science, Technology, and Society: An Encyclopedia. New York: Oxford University Press; 2005: 311-318. Subject: 5.1

Hogstel, Mildred O.; Curry, Linda C.; Walker, Charles A.; Burns, Paulette G. Ethics committees in long-term care facilities. *Geriatric Nursing* 2004 November-December; 25(6): 364-369. Subject: 9.6

Hohl, M.K. Restrictive ART laws sense or non sense? *Journal of Assisted Reproduction and Genetics* 2004 January; 21(1): 1. Subject: 14.1

Hohmann, Elizabeth; Woodson, Jonathan. "Inefficient, arbitrary, inconsistent": a frank look at how some investigators view IRBs and a few suggestions for improvement [discussion]. *Protecting Human Subjects* 2005 Summer; (12): 12-14. Subject: 18.2

Holden, Constance. California's bold $3 billion initiative hits the ground running [news]. *Science* 2005 January 14; 307(5707): 195. Subject: 18.5.4

Holden, Constance. Korean cloner admits lying about oocyte donations [news]. *Science* 2005 December 2; 310(5753): 1402-1403. Subject: 1.3.9

Holden, Constance. Pellegrino to succeed Kass on U.S. panel [news]. *Science* 2005 September 16; 309(5742): 1800. Subject: 2.4

Holden, Constance. Restiveness grows at NIH over Bush research restrictions [news]. *Science* 2005 April 15; 308(5720): 334-335. Subject: 18.5.4

Holden, Constance. Withdrawn parasite paper stirs criticism of Cell [news]. *Science* 2005 October 7; 310(5745): 34. Subject: 1.3.7

Holdstock, Douglas; Gross, Michael. Wartime medical ethics [letter and reply]. *Hastings Center Report* 2005 May-June; 35(3): 6-7. Subject: 21.2

Holland, Paul; Mlyniec, Wallace J. Whatever happened to the right to treatment?: the modern quest for a historical promise. *Temple Law Review* 1995 Winter; 68(4): 1791-1835. Subject: 9.5.7

Holley, Mark T.; Morrissey, Thomas K.; Seabera, David C.; Afessa, Bekele; Wears, Robert L. Ethical dilemmas in a randomized trial of asthma treatment: can Bayesian statistical analysis explain the results? *Academic Emergency Medicine* 2001 December; 8(12): 1128-1135. Subject: 9.5.1

Holliman, Richard. Media coverage of cloning: a study of media content, production and reception. *Public Understanding of Science* 2004 April; 13(2): 107-130. Subject: 14.5

Hollingsworth, Leslie Doty. Ethical considerations of prenatal sex selection. *Health and Social Work* 2005 May; 30(2): 126-134. Subject: 14.3

Hollon, Matthew F. Direct-to-consumer advertising: a haphazard approach to health promotion [editorial]. *JAMA: The Journal of the American Medical Association* 2005 April 27; 293(16): 2030-2033. Subject: 9.7

Holm, Søren. Bioethics down under — medical ethics engages with political philosophy [editorial]. *Journal of Medical Ethics* 2005 January; 31(1): 1. Subject: 2.1

Holm, Søren. The blastocyst transfer method cannot rescue human embryonic stem cell research. *American Jour-*

nal of Bioethics 2005 November-December; 5(6): 20-21. Subject: 18.5.4

Holm, Søren. Justifying patient self-management — evidence based medicine or the primacy of the first person perspective. *Medicine, Health Care and Philosophy: A European Journal* 2005; 8(2): 159-164. Subject: 4.2

Holm, Søren. Laissez faire sex selection — a response to Edgar Dahl. *Health Care Analysis: An International Journal of Health Care Philosophy and Policy* 2005 March; 13(1): 91-93. Subject: 14.3

Holm, Søren. The phenomenological ethics of K.E. Løgstrup — a resource for health care ethics and philosophy? *Nursing Philosophy* 2001 April; 2(1): 26-33. Subject: 2.1

Holm, Søren. Religion and bioethics. *Medical Ethics and Bioethics / Medicinska Etika & Bioetika* 2004 Spring-Summer; 11(1-2): 2-4. Subject: 2.1

Holm, Søren. What empirical bioethics can learn from empirical business ethics. *In:* Häyry, Matti; Takala, Tuija; Herissone-Kelly, Peter, eds. Bioethics and Social Reality. New York: Rodopi, 2005: 107-111. Subject: 2.1

Holm, Søren; Irving, Louise. Empirical research in bioethics: report for the European Commission. *In:* Holm, Søren; Jonas, Monique F., eds. Engaging the World: The Use of Empirical Research in Bioethics and the Regulation of Biotechnology. Washington, DC: IOS Press; 2004: 131-155. Subject: 2.1

Holman, Molly A.; Munzer, Stephen R. Intellectual property rights in genes and gene fragments: a registration solution for expressed sequence tags. *Iowa Law Review* 2000 March; 85(3): 735-848. Subject: 15.8

Holmes, Bob. Alive! *New Scientist* 2005 February 12-18; 185(2486): 28-33. Subject: 15.1

Holt, Ed. Roma women reveal that forced sterilisation remains. *Lancet* 2005 March 12-18; 365(9463): 927-928. Subject: 11.3

Holt, Janet; Long, Tony. Moral guidance, moral philosophy, and moral issues in practice. *Nurse Education Today* 1999 April; 19(3): 246-249. Subject: 7.2

Holt, Jim. Euthanasia for babies? Dutch doctors have proposed a procedure for infant mercy killing. Is this humane or barbaric? *New York Times Magazine* 2005 July 10; p. 11,12,14. Subject: 20.5.2

Honeyman, Alasdair; Cox, Benita; Fisher, Brian. Potential impacts of patient access to their electronic care records. *Informatics in Primary Care* 2005; 13(1): 55-60. Subject: 8.2

Hongladarom, Tongchan. Ethical decision-making and its teaching. *Journal of the Medical Association of Thailand* 1998 August; 81(8): 647-651. Subject: 9.4

Honnefelder, Ludger. Bioethik und Menschenbild. *In:* Jahrbuch für Wissenschaft und Ethik. Bd. 7. Berlin: Walter de Gruyter; 2002: 33-52. Subject: 2.1

Hoop, Jinger G. Hidden ethical dilemmas in psychiatric residency training: the psychiatry resident as dual agent. *Academic Psychiatry* 2004 Fall; 28(3): 183-189. Subject: 7.2

Hope, Donald. The hand as emblem of human identity: a solution to the abortion controversy based on science and reason. *University of Toledo Law Review* 2001 Winter; 32(2): 205-228. Subject: 4.4

Hope, Tony; Frith, Peggy; Craze, Janet; Mussai, Francis; Chadha-Gupta, Ambika; Noble, Douglas. Developing guidelines for medical students about the examination of patients under 18 years old. *BMJ: British Medical Journal* 2005 December 10; 331(7529): 1384-1386. Subject: 7.2

Horizons; Population Council; IMPACT; Family Health International; Schenk, Katie; Williamson, Jan. Ethical approaches to gathering information from children and adolescents in international settings: guidelines and resources. Washington, DC: Population Council 2005 August; 78 p. [Online]. Available: http//www.popcouncil.org/pdfs/horizons/childrenethics.pdf [23 January 2006]. Subject: 18.5.2

Horner, J. Stuart. Ethics and public health. *In:* Chadwick, Ruth; Levitt, Mairi, eds. Ethical Issues in Community Health Care. New York: Arnold; 1998: 34-50. Subject: 9.1

Horner, Sharon D. Ethics and genetics: implications for CNS practice. *Clinical Nurse Specialist* 2004 September-October; 18(5): 228-231. Subject: 15.3

Horrobin, S. Report on the 10th congress of the International Association of Biomedical Gerontology, the bioethicist's view. *Experimental Gerontology* 2004 March; 39(3): 285-287. Subject: 4.5

Horton, Richard. A dismal and dangerous verdict against Roy Meadow. *Lancet* 2005 July 23-29; 366(9482): 277-278. Subject: 7.4

Horton, Richard. Expression of concern: Indo-Mediterranean diet heart study. *Lancet* 2005 July 30-August 5; 366(9483): 354-356. Subject: 18.2

Horton, Richard. In defence of Roy Meadow [opinion]. *Lancet* 2005 July 2-8; 366(9479): 3-5. Subject: 17.4

Horttor, Bretton J. A survey of living will and advanced health care directives. *North Dakota Law Review* 1998; 74(2): 233-293. Subject: 20.5.4

Horwitz, Jill R. Why we need the independent sector: the behavior, law, and ethics of not-for-profit hospitals. *UCLA Law Review* 2003 August; 50(6): 1345-1411. Subject: 9.3.1

Hoskins, Sylvia Anne. Nurses and national socialism — a moral dilemma: one historical example of a route to euthanasia. *Nursing Ethics* 2005 January; 12(1): 79-91. Subject: 21.4

Hougham, Gavin W. Waste not, want not: cognitive impairment should not preclude research participation.

American Journal of Bioethics 2005 January-February; 5(1): 36- 37. Subject: 18.2

Houston, R.A. Rights and wrongs in the confinement of the mentally incapable in eighteenth-century Scotland. *Continuity and Change* 2003 December; 18(3): 373-394. Subject: 17.7

Houts, Renate M.; Smucker, William D.; Jacobson, Jill A.; Ditto, Peter H.; Danks, Joseph H. Predicting elderly outpatients' life-sustaining treatment preferences over time: the majority rules. *Medical Decision Making* 2002 January-February; 22(1): 39-52. Subject: 20.5.1

Howard, David H. Dynamic analysis of liver allocation policies. *Medical Decision Making* 2001; 21: 257-266. Subject: 19.6

Howard, David H. Hope versus efficiency in organ allocation. *Transplantation* 2001 September 27; 72(6): 1169-1173. Subject: 19.6

Howard, Joseph. The moral status of the human embryo according to Peter Singer: individuality, humanity, and personhood. *Linacre Quarterly* 2005 August; 72(3): 212-228. Subject: 4.4

Howarth, G.R. A plea for a bioethics elite? [letter]. *South African Medical Journal* 2002 May; 92(5): 323. Subject: 2.3

Howe, Edmund G. Commentary on "psychiatric advance directives: an alternative to coercive treatment": lessons from advance directives for PADs. *Psychiatry* 2000 Summer; 63(2): 173-177. Subject: 20.5.4

Howe, Edmund G. Shame, slap jack, and familes [sic; families] that should lie. *Journal of Clinical Ethics* 2005 Winter; 16(4): 279-291. Subject: 20.4.1

Howe, Edmund G. When should ethics consultants risk giving their personal views? *Journal of Clinical Ethics* 2005 Fall; 16(3): 183-192. Subject: 9.6

Howe, Edmund G. Why are they boxing us in like this? *Journal of Clinical Ethics* 2005 Summer; 16(2): 99-107. Subject: 8.3.4

Howlader, Mohammad H.; Dhanji, Al-Rehan; Uppal, Rakesh; Magee, Patrick; Wood, Alan J.; Anyanwu, Ani C. Patients' views of the consent process for adult cardiac surgery: questionnaire survey. *Scandinavian Cardiovascular Journal* 2004 December; 38(6): 363-368. Subject: 8.3.1

Howland, John. Questions about palliative sedation: an act of mercy or of mercy killing? *Ethics and Medics* 2005 August; 30(8): 1-2. Subject: 20.4.1

Howland, John S. A family physician grapples with vaccine ethics. *Linacre Quarterly* 2005 August; 72(3): 260-266. Subject: 9.7

Høyer, Klaus. Conflicting notions of personhood in genetic research. *Anthropology Today* 2002 October; 18(5): 9-13. Subject: 15.1

Hrabak, Maja; Vujaklija, Ana; Vodopivec, Ivana; Hren, Darko; Marušic, Matko; Marušic, Ana. Academic misconduct among medical students in a post-communist country. *Medical Education* 2004 March; 38(3): 276-285. Subject: 7.2

Hsieh, Alice. A nation's genes for a cure to cancer: evolving ethical, social and legal issues regarding population genetic databases. *Columbia Journal of Law and Social Problems* 2004 Spring; 37(3): 359-411. Subject: 15.1

Hsin-Chen Hsin, Dena; Macer, Darryl. Contrasting expectations of biotechnology for medical care in Taiwan between seniors and medical students. *Revista de Derecho y Genoma Humano / Law and the Human Genome Review* 2004 January-June; (20): 195-216. Subject: 20.3.1

Hu, W.; Kerridge, I; Kemp, A. Risk, rationality, and regret: responding to the uncertainty of childhood food anaphylaxis. *Medical Humanities* 2005 June; 31(1): 12-16. Subject: 9.5.7

Hu, Xiangen; Graesser, Arthur C. Human use regulatory affairs advisor (HURAA): learning about research ethics with intelligent learning modules. *Behavior Research Methods, Instruments, and Computers* 2004 May; 36(2): 241-249. Subject: 2.3

Huang, M-C; Lee, C-K; Lin, S-J; Lu, I-C. Parental consent for newborn screening in southern Taiwan. *Journal of Medical Ethics* 2005 November; 31(11): 621-624. Subject: 8.3.2

Huarte, Joachim; Suarez, Antoine; Hurlbut, William B. An unanswered question [letter and reply]. *National Catholic Bioethics Quarterly* 2005 Spring; 5(1): 9, 19-22. Subject: 18.5.4

Hubbard, Dorothy. An ethical framework for operating room infection control. *Seminars in Perioperative Nursing* 1994 April; 3(2): 88-92. Subject: 9.5.1

Hubbard, Julie A. Eliciting and measuring children's anger in the context of their peer interactions: ethical considerations and practical guidelines. *Ethics and Behavior* 2005; 15(3): 247-258. Subject: 17.3

Hubbard, Ruth. Procreative autonomy versus eugenic and economic interests of the state. *In:* Krimsky, Sheldon; Shorett, Peter, eds. Rights and Liberties in the Biotech Age: Why We Need a Genetic Bill of Rights. Lanham: Rowman and Littlefield Publishers; 2005: 141-145. Subject: 15.5

Hubbard, Ruth. Rights for fetuses and embryos? *In:* Krimsky, Sheldon; Shorett, Peter, eds. Rights and Liberties in the Biotech Age: Why We Need a Genetic Bill of Rights. Lanham: Rowman and Littlefield Publishers; 2005: 216-218. Subject: 15.1

Huddle, Thomas S. Teaching professionalism: is medical morality a competency? [opinion]. *Academic Medicine* 2005 October; 80(10): 885-891. Subject: 4.1.2

Subject = NRCBL Primary Classification Number; See inside front cover

Hudson, Kathy. Something old and something new. *Hastings Center Report* 2004 July-August; 34(4): 14-15. Subject: 14.1

Hudson, Kathy. The vagaries of government regulation [response]. *Conscience* 2003-2004 Winter; 24(4): 18. Subject: 14.1

Hudson, Michelle; Bhogal, Nirmala; Balls, Michael. The use of non-human primates in regulatory toxicology: comments submitted by FRAME to the home office. *ATLA: Alternatives to Laboratory Animals* 2005 October; 33(5): 529-538. Subject: 22.2

Hufford, David J. Authority, knowledge, and substituted judgment. *Alternative Therapies in Health and Medicine* 1996 November; 2(6): 92-94. Subject: 8.3.1

Hughes, David; Griffiths, Lesley. "Ruling in" and "ruling out": two approaches to the micro-rationing of health care. *Social Science and Medicine* 1997 March; 44(5): 589-599. Subject: 9.4

Hughes, James. Beyond "real boys" and back to parental obligations [comment]. *American Journal of Bioethics* 2005 May-June; 5(3): 61-62. Subject: 9.7

Hughes, James E. Eugenic sterilization in the United States: a comparative summary of statutes and review of court decisions. *Washington, DC: United States Government Printing Office, Supplement No. 162 to the Public Health Reports,* 1940; 45 p. Subject: 11.3

Hughes, Jonathan. Palliative care and the QALY problem. *Health Care Analysis: An International Journal of Health Care Philosophy and Policy* 2005 December; 13(4): 289-301. Subject: 20.4.1

Hughes, Nic; Clark, David. "A thoughtful and experienced physician": William Munk and the care of the dying in late Victorian England. *Journal of Palliative Medicine* 2004 October; 7(5): 703-710. Subject: 20.4.1

Hughes, Richard A. The death of children by faith-based medical neglect. *Journal of Law and Religion* 2004-2005; 20(1): 247-265. Subject: 8.3.4

Huhn, Wilson. Three legal frameworks for regulating genetic technology. *Journal of Contemporary Health Law and Policy* 2002 Winter; 19(1): 1-36. Subject: 18.6

Hui, Pui Wah; Lam, Yung Hang; Chen, Min; Tang, Mary Hoi Yin; Yeung, William Shu Biu; Ng, Ernest Hung Yu; Ho, Pak Chung. Attitude of at-risk subjects towards preimplantation genetic diagnosis of (alpha)- and (beta)-thalassaemias in Hong Kong. *Prenatal Diagnosis* 2002 June; 22(6): 508-511. Subject: 15.2

Hull, Richard T. The case for physician-assisted suicide. *Free Inquiry* 2003 Spring; 23(2): 35-36. Subject: 20.7

Hulse, Carl. Despite Congress, woman's feeding tube is removed: the medical turns political. *New York Times* 2005 March 19; p. A1, A12. Subject: 20.5.1

Hulse, Carl; Kirkpatrick, David D. Even death does not quiet harsh political fight. *New York Times* 2005 April 1; p. A1. A16. Subject: 20.5.1

Hulse, Carl; Kirkpatrick, David D. Moving quickly, Senate approves Schiavo measure; allows review by judge; Bush rushes to capital to sign bill in clash over feeding tube case. *New York Times* 2005 March 21; p. A1, A14. Subject: 20.5.1

Human Fertilisation and Embryology Authority [HFEA] (United Kingdom). Choices and Boundaries. Should people be able to select embryos free from an inherited suceptibility to cancer? London: Human Fertilisation and Embryology Authority 2005 November; 15 p. [Online]. Available: http://www.hfea.gov.uk/AboutHFEA/HFEAPolicy/Choicesandboundaries/Choices_Boundaries.pdf [7 February 2006]. Subject: 15.2

Human Fertilisation and Embryology Authority [HFEA] (United Kingdom). Sex Selection: Choice and Responsibility in Human Reproduction Consultation Document. London: Human Fertilisation and Embryology Authority 2002 October; 37 p. Subject: 14.3

Human Fertilisation and Embryology Authority [HFEA] (United Kingdom). Sex Selection - Policy and Regulatory Review: A Report on the Key Findings from a Qualitative Research Study. London: Human Fertilisation and Embryology Authority [HFEA], [CPR825] 2002 October; 38 p. [Online]. Available: http://www.hfea.gov.uk/AboutHFEA/Consultations/Appendix E - Qualitative Research Findings report of research conducted by Counterpoint (UK) Ltd.pdf [6 October 2004]. Subject: 14.3

Human Fertilisation and Embryology Authority [HFEA] (United Kingdom). Sex Selection — Public Consultation. Research Study Conducted for Human Fertilisation and Embryology Authority. London: Human Fertilisation and Embryology Authority [HFEA] 2003 January; 70 p. [Online]. Available: http://www.hfea.gov.uk/AboutHFEA/Consultations/Appendix F - Quantitative Research Findings report of research conducted by Market and Opinion Research International (MORI).pdf [6 October 2004]. Subject: 14.3

Human Genetics Alert [HGA]. The case against sex selection. *Human Reproduction and Genetic Ethics: An International Journal* 2005; 11(1): 3-5. Subject: 14.3

Humphreys, Melanie; Smallwood, Andrew. An exploration of the ethical dimensions pertinent to gaining consent for thrombolysis. *Nursing in Critical Care* 2004 November-December; 9(6): 264-270. Subject: 8.3.1

Humphreys, Sally. Patient autonomy: legal and ethical issues in the post-anaesthetic care unit. *British Journal of Perioperative Nursing* 2005 January; 15(1): 35-38, 40-41, 43. Subject: 8.3.1

Humphries, S.E.; Galton, D.; Nicholls, P. Genetic testing for familial hypercholesterolaemia: practical and ethical issues. *QJM: Monthly Journal of the Association of Physicians* 1997 March; 90(3): 169-181. Subject: 15.3

Hundert, Edward M. Ethical issues in the practice of psychiatry. *In:* Nicholi, Armand M., ed. The Harvard Guide to Psychiatry. 3rd ed. Cambridge, MA: Belknap Press of Harvard University; 1999: 744-751. Subject: 17.1

Hunt, John. Abortion and the Nuremberg prosecutors: a deeper analysis. *In:* Koterski, Joseph W., ed. Life and Learning VII: Proceedings of the Seventh University Faculty for Life Conference. Washington, DC: University Faculty for Life; 1998: 198-209. Subject: 12.3

Hunt, John. Out of respect for life: Nazi abortion policy in the eastern occupied territories. *In:* Koterski, Joseph W., ed. Life and Learning IX: Proceedings of the Ninth University Faculty for Life Conference. Washington, DC: University Faculty for Life; 2000: 295-304. Subject: 12.5.1

Hunt, Linda M.; de Voogd, Katherine B. Clinical myths of the cultural "other": implications for Latino patient care. *Academic Medicine* 2005 October; 80(10): 918-924. Subject: 21.7

Hunt, Linda M.; de Voogd, Katherine B.; Castañeda, Heide. The routine and the traumatic in prenatal genetic diagnosis: does clinical information inform patient decision-making? *Patient Education and Counseling* 2005 March; 56(3): 302-312. Subject: 15.2

Hunt, Paul. The UN special rapporteur on the right to health: key objectives, themes, and interventions. *Health and Human Rights: An International Journal* 2003; 7(1): 1-27. Subject: 9.2

Hunt, William E. The right to die in Montana: the Montana Uniform Rights of the Terminally Ill Act. *Montana Law Review* 1993 Summer; 54(2): 339-356. Subject: 20.5.4

Hunter, Alasdair G.W.; Sharpe, Neil; Mullen, Michelle; Meschino, Wendy S. Ethical, legal, and practical concerns about recontacting patients to inform them of new information: the case in medical genetics. *American Journal of Medical Genetics* 2001; 103: 265-276. Subject: 15.3

Hunter, Katherine. A new direction on DNA? *Criminal Law Review* 1998 July: 478-480. Subject: 15.1

Hurlbut, William B. Altered nuclear transfer as a morally acceptable means for the procurement of human embryonic stem cells. *National Catholic Bioethics Quarterly* 2005 Spring; 5(1): 145- 151. Subject: 18.5.4

Hurlbut, William B. Altered nuclear transfer as a morally acceptable means for the procurement of human embryonic stem cells. *Perspectives in Biology and Medicine* 2005 Spring; 48(2): 211-228. Subject: 18.5.4

Hurlbut, William B. Patenting humans: clones, chimeras, and biological artifacts. *Science and Engineering Ethics* 2005 January; 11(1): 21-29. Subject: 5.3

Hurlbut, William B.; Melton, Douglas A.; Daley, George Q.; Jennings, Charles G. Altered nuclear transfer [letter and reply]. *New England Journal of Medicine* 2005 March 17; 352(11): 1153- 1154. Subject: 18.5.4

Hurst, Samia A.; Mauron, Alex. Selective contracting of Swiss physicians: ethical issues and open questions. *Swiss Medical Weekly* 2004 October 30; 134(43-44): 632-639. Subject: 9.3.2

Hurst, S.A.; Hull, S.C.; DuVal, G.; Danis, M. How physicians face ethical difficulties: a qualitative analysis. *Journal of Medical Ethics* 2005 January; 31(1): 7-14. Subject: 7.1

Hurwitz, Andrew D. Jon O. Newman and the abortion decisions: a remarkable first year. *New York Law School Law Review* 2002-2003; 46(1 and 2): 231-247. Subject: 12.4.2

Hurwitz, Joshua M.; Batzer, Frances R. Posthumous sperm procurement: demand and concerns [editorial]. *Obstetrical and Gynecological Survey* 2004 December; 59(12): 806-808. Subject: 14.6

Huss, Matthew T.; Zeiss, Robert A. You have the right not to have a hearing: an evaluation of the impact of fully advising civilly committed patients on their rights. *International Journal of Law and Psychiatry* 2005 July- August; 28(4): 334-341. Subject: 17.7

Husted, Gladys L.; Husted, James H. The bioethical standards: the analysis of dilemmas through the analysis of persons. *Advanced Practice Nursing Quarterly* 1995 Fall; 1(2): 69-76. Subject: 2.1

Husted, Gladys L.; Husted, James H. Is a return to a caring perspective desirable? *Advanced Practice Nursing Quarterly* 1997 Summer; 3(1): 14-17. Subject: 4.1.3

Husted, Gladys L.; Husted, James H. A modest proposal concerning policies. *Advanced Practical Nursing Quarterly* 1997 Winter; 3(3): 17- 19. Subject: 4.1.1

Husted, Gladys L.; Husted, James H. Strength of character through the ethics of nursing. *Advanced Practice Nursing Quarterly* 1998 Spring; 3(4): 23-25. Subject: 2.1

Huston, Janis L.; Brox, Georg A. Professional ethics at the bottom line. *Health Care Manager* 2004 July-September; 23(3): 267-272. Subject: 7.3

Hutton, John. Hutton announces strengthened code of practice covering recruitment of overseas healthcare staff. London: Department of Health 2004 December 8; 2 p. [Online]. Available: http://www.dh.gov.uk/PublicationsAndStatistics/PressReleases/PressReleasesNotices/fs/en?CONTENT_ID=4097747&chk=GiuK6D [5 July 2005]. Subject: 21.6

Huxtable, Richard. Get out of jail free? The doctrine of double effect in English law. *Palliative Medicine* 2004; 18(1): 62-68. Subject: 20.5.1

Huxtable, Richard. Re M (medical treatment: consent): time to remove the 'flak jacket'? *Child and Family Law Quarterly* 2000; 12(1): 83-88. Subject: 8.3.2

Subject = NRCBL Primary Classification Number; See inside front cover

Huxtable, Richard; Woodley, Julie. Gaining face or losing face? Framing the debate on face transplants. *Bioethics* 2005 October; 19(5-6): 505-522. Subject: 19.1

Hwang, Jessica P.; Smith, Martin L.; Flamm, Anne L. Challenges in outpatient end-of-life care: wishes to avoid resuscitation. *Journal of Clinical Oncology* 2004 November 15; 22(22): 4643-4645. Subject: 20.5.1

Hyatt, Stephanie. A shared history of shame: Sweden's four-decade policy of forced sterilization and the eugenics movement in the United States. *Indiana International and Comparative Law Review* 1998; 8(2): 475-503. Subject: 11.3

Hyder, Adnan A.; Dawson, Liza. Defining standard of care in the developing world: the intersection of international research ethics and health systems analysis. *Developing World Bioethics* 2005 May; 5(2): 142-152. Subject: 18.5.9

Hyler, Steven E.; Gangure, Dinu P. Legal and ethical challenges in telepsychiatry. *Journal of Psychiatric Practice* 2004 July; 10(4): 272-276. Subject: 1.3.12

I

Ibata, Brent. Institutional review and clinical research — proactive IRBs and risk reduction. *Medical Trial Technique Quarterly* 2002; 48(3): 253-270. Subject: 18.2

Ibrahim, Hythum; Newman, Michael. Ultrasound soft markers of chromosomal abnormalities; an ethical dilemma for obstetricians. *Human Reproduction and Genetic Ethics: An International Journal* 2005; 11(2): 25-27. Subject: 15.2

Ibrahim, Talal; Ong, Shong Meng; Taylor, Grahame John Saint Clair. The new consent form: is it any better? *Annals of the Royal College of Surgeons of England* 2004 May; 86(3): 206-209. Subject: 8.3.1

Iceland. Supreme Court. Icelandic. Decision of the Supreme Court on the protection of privacy with regard to the processing of Health Sector Databases. *Revista de Derecho y Genoma-Humano / Law and the Human Genome Review* 2004 July-December; (21): 127-138. Subject: 15.10

Ida, Ryuichi. Ethical and legal aspects of biotechnology. *In:* Brannigan, Michael C., ed. Cross-Cultural Biotechnology. Lanham: Rowman and Littlefield; 2004: 25-35. Subject: 15.1

Idänpään-Heikkilä, Juhana E. US exceptionalism and research ethics [letter]. *Lancet* 2005 May 7-13; 365(9471): 1617. Subject: 18.2

Iglehart, John K. The emergence of physician-owned specialty hospitals. *New England Journal of Medicine* 2005 January 6; 352(1): 78-84. Subject: 9.3.1

Ijichi, Shinji; Ijichi, Naomi. The scientific establishment of a new therapeutic intervention for developmental conditions: practical and ethical principles. *Child's Nervous System* 2003 November; 19(10-11): 711-715. Subject: 18.5.2

Ikemoto, Lisa C. The fuzzy logic of race and gender in the mismeasure of Asian American women's health needs. *University of Cincinnati Law Review* 1997 Spring; 65(3): 799-824. Subject: 9.5.4

Ilencíková, Denisa. Clinical genetics: views of ethical and legislative conclusions in the Slovak Republic. *Human Reproduction and Genetic Ethics: An International Journal* 2005; 11(2): 49-54. Subject: 15.1

Ilkilic, Ilhan. Der moralische Status des Embryos im Islam und die wertplurale Gesellschaft. *In:* Baumann, Eva; Brink, Alexander; May, Arnd T.; Schröder; Peter; Schutzeichel, Corinna Iris, eds. Weltanschauliche Offenheit in der Bioethik. Berlin: Duncker & Humblot; 2004: 163-176. Subject: 4.4

Illes, Judy. Neuroethics in a new era of neuroimaging [editorial]. *AJRN: American Journal of Neuroradiology* 2003 October; 24(9): 1739-1741. Subject: 17.1

Illes, Judy; Blakemore, Colin; Gazzaniga, Michael S.; Kotulak, Ron; Mobley, William. Brain science and public discourse. *Cerebrum: The Dana Forum on Brain Science* 2002 Summer; 4(3): 68-70. Subject: 17.1

Illes, Judy; Kirschen, Matthew P.; Karetsky, Kim; Kelly, Megan; Saha, Arnold; Desmond, John E.; Raffin, Thomas A.; Glover, Gary H.; Atlas, Scott W. Discovery and disclosure of incidental findings in neuroimaging research. *Journal of Magnetic Resonance Imaging* 2004 November; 20(5): 743-747. Subject: 18.1

Illes, Judy; Racine, E. Neuroethics: dialogue on a continuum from tradition to innovation [letter]. *American Journal of Bioethics [Online]* 2005 March-April; 5(2): W3-W4. Subject: 17.1

Illes, Judy; Racine, Eric. Imaging or imagining? A neuroethics challenge informed by genetics. *American Journal of Bioethics* 2005 March-April; 5(2): 5-18. Subject: 17.1

Illes, Judy; Raffin, Thomas A. No child left without a brain scan? Toward a pediatric neuroethics. *Cerebrum: The Dana Forum on Brain Science* 2005 Summer; 7(3): 33-46. Subject: 17.1

Illingworth, R. Fraud and other misconduct in biomedical research [editorial]. *British Journal of Neurosurgery* 2004 August; 18(4): 325-327. Subject: 1.3.9

Illinois. Laws. An act concerning family law [effective: 29 July 1999]. Illinois General Assembly, Public Act 093-1095; 3 p. [Online]. Available: http://www.ilga.gov/legislation/publicacts/93/093-1095.htm [8 September 2005]. Subject: 14.2

Iltis, Ana Smith. Bioethics consultation in the private sector. *HEC (Healthcare Ethics Committee) Forum* 2005 June; 17(2): 87- 93. Subject: 9.6

Iltis, Ana Smith. Professional promises and limits on the scope of practice. *HEC (Healthcare Ethics Committee) Forum* 2005 September; 17(3): 196-209. Subject: 8.1

Iltis, Ana Smith. Stopping trials early for commercial reasons: the risk-benefit relationship as a moral compass. *Journal of Medical Ethics* 2005 July; 31(7): 410-414. Subject: 18.2

Iltis, Ana Smith. Third-party payers and the costs of biomedical research. *Kennedy Institute of Ethics Journal* 2005 June; 15(2): 135-160. Subject: 18.1

Iltis, Ana Smith. Timing invitations to participate in clinical research: preliminary versus informed consent. *Journal of Medicine and Philosophy* 2005 February; 30(1): 89-106. Subject: 18.3

Iltis, Ana Smith. Values based decision making: organizational mission and integrity. *HEC (Healthcare Ethics Committee) Forum* 2005 March; 17(1): 6-17. Subject: 9.1

Iltis, Ana Smith; Rasmussen, Lisa M. Patient ethics and responsibilities. *Journal of Medicine and Philosophy* 2005 April; 30(2): 131-137. Subject: 8.1

IMANA Ethics Committee [Islamic Medical Association of North America]; Athar, Shahid; Fadel, Hossam E.; Ahmed, Wahaj D.; Haque, Malika; Nagamia, Hussain F.; Hathout, Hassan; Amine, Abdul R.C.; Khan, Faroque A.; Shanawani, Hasan. Islamic medical ethics: the IMANA perspective. Illinois: Islamic Medical Association of North America 2005 May 15; 12 p. [Online]. Available: http://data.memberclicks.com/site/imana/IMANAEthicsPaperPartl.pdf [20 September 2005]. Subject: 2.1

Imrényi, Tibor. Sin and bioethics. *Christian Bioethics* 2005 August; 11(2): 133-145. Subject: 2.1

Imwinkelried, Edward J. Expert testimony by ethicists: what should be the norm? *Journal of Law, Medicine and Ethics* 2005 Summer; 33(2): 198-221. Subject: 2.1

Indian Council of Medical Research [ICMR]. AIDS: Indian Council of Medical Research (ICMR) Guidelines. *Medical Ethics: Journal of Forum for Medical Ethics Society* 1995 April-June; 3(2): 35. Subject: 9.5.6

Ingelfinger, Julie R. Risks and benefits to the living donor [opinion]. *New England Journal of Medicine* 2005 August 4; 353(5): 447-449. Subject: 19.5

Ingham, Kim M.; Schmitt, Gina. Novel IACUC outreach effort to facilitate animal protocol submission and review. *Contemporary Topics in Laboratory Animal Science* 2005 March; 44(2): 72-74. Subject: 22.2

Inhorn, Marcia C. Privacy, privatization, and the politics of patronage: ethnographic challenges to penetrating the secret world of Middle Eastern, hospital-based in vitro fertilization. *Social Science and Medicine* 2004 November; 59(10): 2095-2108. Subject: 14.4

Inions, Noela J. Substitute decision-makers in privacy legislation that affects health information in Alberta. *Health Law Review* 2005; 14(1): 26-41. Subject: 8.4

Inman, Mason. Divided committee urges less restriction on embryo research [news]. *Science* 2005 April 1; 308(5718): 30. Subject: 18.5.4

Institut Borja de Bioetica. Hacia una posible despenalizacion de la eutanasia: declaracion del Institut Borja de Bioetica (URL) / Toward a possible decriminalization of euthanasia: statement of the Institut Borja de Bioetica. *Bioetica & Debat* 2005; 11(39): 1, 3-7. Subject: 20.5.1

Institute of Medicine (United States) [IOM]. Committee on Establishing a National Cord Blood Stem Cell Bank Program. Ethical and legal issues. *In its: Cord Blood: Establishing a National Hematopoietic Stem Cell Bank Program. Washington, DC: National Academies Press; 2005: 106-119. Subject: 19.4*

International Association of Cancer Registries. Guidelines on confidentiality for population-based cancer registration. *Asian Pacific Journal of Cancer Prevention* 2005 January-March; 6(1): 87-103. Subject: 18.2

International Association of Catholic Bioethicists. Consensus statement on dignity in illness, disability, and dying; and a response to the UNESCO Universal Draft Declaration on Bioethics and Human Rights. *National Catholic Bioethics Quarterly* 2005 Winter; 5(4): 767-781. Subject: 2.4

International Committee of Medical Journal Editors; De Angelis, Catherine; Drazen, Jeffrey M.; Frizelle, Frank A.; Haug, Charlotte; Joey, John; Horton, Richard; Kotzin, Sheldon; Laine, Christine; Marušic, Ana; Overbeke, John P.M.; Schroeder, Torben V.; Sox, Harold C.; Van Der Weyden, Martin B. Is This Clinical Trial Fully Registered?: A Statement from the International Committee of Medical Journal Editors. Philadelphia, PA: The Committee, 2005 May; 7 p. [Online]. Available: http://www.icmje.org/clin_trialup.htm [1 July 2005]. Subject: 18.6

International Federation of Associations of Catholic Physicians [FIAMC]. Statement on euthanasia in children. *Medical Ethics and Bioethics / Medicinska Etika & Bioetika* 2004 Autumn-Winter; 11(3-4): 22. Subject: 20.5.2

International Federation of Gynecology and Obstetrics [FIGO]; Society of Obstetricians and Gynaecologists of Canada [SOGC]. International joint policy statement: FIGO professional and ethical responsibilities concerning sexual and reproductive rights / Responsabilites professionnelles et ethiques de la FIGO en ce qui a trait aux droits sexuels et genesiques [policy statement]. *Journal of Obstetrics and Gynaecology Canada* 2004 December; 26(12): 1097-1099, 1105-1107. Subject: 9.5.5

Subject = NRCBL Primary Classification Number; See inside front cover

International Federation of Gynecology and Obstetrics [FIGO]. Committee for the Ethical Aspects of Human Reproduction and Women's Health; Schenker, J.G.; Cain, J.M. International medical ethics: the FIGO Committee for the Ethical Aspects of Human Reproduction and Women's Health. *International Journal of Gynecology and Obstetrics* 2004 August; 86(2): 267-275. Subject: 14.1

International Federation of Gynecology and Obstetrics [FIGO]. Committee for Women's Sexual and Reproductive Rights; Shaw, D. History of the FIGO Committee for Women's Sexual and Reproductive Rights. *International Journal of Gynecology and Obstetrics* 2004 August; 86(2): 294-316. Subject: 9.5.5

International Xenotransplantation Association [IXA]. Ethics Committee.; Sykes, Megan; d'Apice, Anthony; Sandrin, Mauro. Position paper of the Ethics Committee of the International Xenotransplantation Association. *Transplantation* 2004 October 27; 78(8): 1101-1107. Subject: 19.1

Ioirysh, A.I.; Krasovskii, O.A. Legal aspects of genetic engineering. *Russian Politics and Law* 1998 July-August; 36(4): 77-83. Subject: 15.1

Ionescu, Carmiola. Donor charged in Romania's first organ trafficking trial. *Lancet* 2005 June 4-10; 365(9475): 1918. Subject: 19.5

Ip, Mary; Gilligan, Timothy; Koenig, Barbara; Raffin, Thomas A. Ethical decision-making in critical care in Hong Kong. *Critical Care Medicine* 1998 March; 26(3): 447-451. Subject: 21.7

Ip, Po-Keung. Developing medical ethics in China's reform era. *Developing World Bioethics* 2005 May; 5(2): 176-187. Subject: 2.1

Irvine, R. Mediating telemedicine: ethics at a distance. *Internal Medicine Journal* 2005 January; 35(1): 56-58. Subject: 1.3.12

Irvine, Rob; McPhee, John; Kerridge, Ian H. The challenge of cultural and ethical pluralism to medical practice. *Medical Journal of Australia* 2002 February 18; 176(4): 174-175. Subject: 21.7

Irvine, Robert; Kerridge, I.; McPhee, J. Towards a dialogical ethics of interprofessionalism. *Journal of Postgraduate Medicine* 2004 October-December; 50(4): 278-280. Subject: 7.3

Irvine, W. Nigel. An ill-conceived conception? *Medical Law International* 2004; 6(3): 231-249. Subject: 14.4

Irving, Louise. The problem of intangibles. *In:* Häyry, Matti; Takala, Tuija; Herissone-Kelly, Peter, eds. Bioethics and Social Reality. New York: Rodopi, 2005: 67-76. Subject: 19.5

Irving, Louise; Hallowell, Nina. Can there be moral experts? *In:* Holm, Søren; Jonas, Monique F., eds. Engaging the World: The Use of Empirical Research in Bioethics and the Regulation of Biotechnology. Washington, DC: IOS Press; 2004: 28-37. Subject: 2.1

Isaac, K. Abortion legislation in Eritrea: an overview of law and practice. *Medicine and Law: World Association for Medical Law* 2005 March; 24(1): 137-161. Subject: 12.4.1

Isasi, Rosario M.; Annas, George J. Arbitrage, bioethics, and cloning: the ABCs of gestating a United Nations Cloning Convention. *Case Western Reserve Journal of International Law* 2003 Fall; 35(3): 397-414. Subject: 14.5

Isasi, Rosario M.; Knoppers, Bartha Maria; Singer, Peter A.; Daar, Abdallah S. Legal and ethical approaches to stem cell and cloning research: a comparative analysis of policies in Latin America, Asia, and Africa. *Journal of Law, Medicine and Ethics* 2004 Winter; 32(4): 626-640. Subject: 18.5.4

Iserson, Kenneth V. Teaching without harming the living: performing minimally invasive procedures on the newly dead. *Journal of Health Care Law and Policy* 2005; 8(2): 216-231. Subject: 20.3.1

Ishak, April; Miller, Robert T. Schiavo under the law [letter and reply]. *First Things* 2005 October; (156): 5, 6-8. Subject: 20.5.1

Islamic Organization for Medical Sciences [IOMS]; Al-Abd, Osama Muhammad. Islamic law rulings on certain medical questions: the arguments and the supporting evidence. Cairo, Egypt: Islamic Organization for Medical Sciences 2004 April 10; 37 p. [Online]. Available: http://www.islamset.com/ioms/Code2004/Islamic_vision2.html [5 August 2005]. Subject: 2.1

Israni, Ajay K.; Halpern, Scott D.; Zink, Sheldon; Sidhwani, Sonal A.; Caplan, Arthur. Incentive models to increase living kidney donation: encouraging without coercing [opinion]. *American Journal of Transplantation* 2005 January; 5(1): 15-20. Subject: 19.5

Issa, Amalia M. Ethical perspectives on pharmacogenomic profiling in the drug development process. *Nature Reviews Drug Discovery* 2002 April; 1(4): 300-308. Subject: 15.1

J

Jacelon, Cynthia S. Older adults and autonomy in acute care: increasing patients' independence and control during hospitalization. *Journal of Gerontological Nursing* 2004 November; 30(11): 29-36. Subject: 9.5.2

Jackson, Emily. Abortion, autonomy and prenatal diagnosis. *Social and Legal Studies* 2000 December; 9(4): 467-494. Subject: 12.5.1

Jacobi, John V. Prison health, public health: obligations and opportunities. *American Journal of Law and Medicine* 2005; 31(4): 447-478. Subject: 9.2

Jacobs, Alice K.; Smith, Sidney C., Jr.; Popp, Richard L.; Joscalzo, Joseph. Ethics and professionalism: can there be consensus? An editorial comment on the report of the ACCF/AHA consensus conference on professionalism and ethics. *Circulation* 2004 October 19; 110(16): 2278-2279. Subject: 4.1.2

Jacobs, Barbara Bennett. Respect for human dignity in nursing: philosophical and practical perspectives. *Canadian Journal of Nursing Research* 2000 September; 32(2): 15-33. Subject: 4.1.3

Jacobs, Frans. Reasonable partiality in professional ethics: the moral division of labour. *Ethical Theory and Moral Practice* 2005 April; 8(1-2): 141-154. Subject: 1.3.1

Jacobson, Jennifer. MIT fires biology professor who admitted faking data [news]. *Chronicle of Higher Education* 2005 November 11; 52(12): 13. Subject: 1.3.9

Jacobson, Joy. When providing care is amoral issue: is nurses' first priority protecting the patient or their own moral convictions? *AJN: American Journal of Nursing* 2005 October; 105(10): 27- 28. Subject: 4.1.3

Jacobson, Peter D. Health law 2005: an agenda. *Journal of Law, Medicine and Ethics* 2005 Winter; 33(4): 725- 738. Subject: 9.2

Jacobson, Peter D.; Bloche, M. Gregg. Improving relations between attorneys and physicians. *JAMA: The Journal of the American Medical Association* 2005 October 26; 294(16): 2083-2085. Subject: 7.3

Jacobson, Peter Lars; Mann, J. Douglas. The valid informed consent-treatment contract in chronic non-cancer pain: its role in reducing barriers to effective pain management. *Comprehensive Therapy* 2004 Summer; 30(2): 101-104. Subject: 8.3.1

Jaeger, Suzanne M. Ethical reasoning and the embodied, socially situated subject. *Theoretical Medicine and Bioethics* 2005; 26(1): 55-72. Subject: 9.6

Jaeger, Suzanne M. Teaching health care ethics: the importance of moral sensitivity for moral reasoning. *Nursing Philosophy* 2001 July; 2(2): 131-142. Subject: 2.3

Jafarey, Aamir M. The bioethics group of the Aga Khan University, Karachi. *Issues in Medical Ethics* 2002 January-March; 10(1): 163-164. Subject: 2.4

Jafarey, A.M.; Farooqui, A. Informed consent in the Pakistani milieu: the physician's perspective. *Journal of Medical Ethics* 2005 February; 31(2): 93-96. Subject: 8.3.1

Jairath, Nalini; Ulrich, Connie M.; Ley, Cathaleen. Ethical considerations in the recruitment of research subjects from hospitalized, cardiovascular patient populations. *Journal of Cardiovascular Nursing* 2005 January-February; 20(1): 56-61. Subject: 18.3

Jakobson, Daniel J.; Eidelman, Leonid A.; Worner, T.M.; Oppenheim, Arieh Eden; Pizov, Reuven; Sprung, Charles L. Evaluation of changes in forgoing life-sustaining treatment in Israeli ICU patients. *Chest* 2004 December; 126(6): 1969-1973. Subject: 20.5.1

Jalgaonkar, Mangesh. Consumer Protection Act — an introspection by a general practitioner. *Medical Ethics: Journal of Forum for Medical Ethics Society* 1994 November-December; 2(2): 12-13. Subject: 9.1

Jallinoja, Piia. Ethics of clinical genetics: the spirit of the profession and trials of suitability from 1970 to 2000. *In:* Bunton, Robin; Petersen, Alan, eds. Genetic Governance: Health, Risk and Ethics in the Biotech Era. New York: Routledge; 2005: 31-45. Subject: 15.2

Jalsevac, Paul. The inherent racism of population control. *LifeSiteNews.com* 2004: i-iv, 1-54 [Online]. Available: http://www.lifesite.net/waronfamily/Population_control/Inherentra cism.pdf [28 July 2005]. Subject: 13.3

James, Chris; Carrin, Guy; Savedoff, William; Hanvoravongchai, Piya. Clarifying efficiency-equity tradeoffs through explicit criteria, with a focus on developing countries. *Health Care Analysis: An International Journal of Health Care Philosophy and Policy* 2005 March; 13(1): 33-51. Subject: 9.4

Jameton, Andrew. Dilemmas of moral distress: moral responsibility and nursing practice. *AWHONN's Clinical Issues in Perinatal and Women's Health Nursing* 1993; 4(4): 542-551. Subject: 4.1.3

Jameton, Andrew. Sustainable bioethics: extending care to an aging planet. *Bulletin of Science, Technology and Society* 1999 August; 19(4): 314-322. Subject: 2.1

Jamieson, Denise J.; O'Sullivan, Mary Jo; Maupin, Robert; Cohen, Mardge; Webber, Mayris P.; Nesheim, Steven; Lampe, Margaret; Garcia, Patricia; Lindsay, Michael; Bulterys, Marc. The challenges of informed consent for rapid HIV testing in labor. *Journal of Women's Health* 2003 October; 12(9): 889-895. Subject: 8.3.1

Jamison, John E. Spirituality and medical ethics. *American Journal of Hospice and Palliative Care* 1995 May-June; 12(3): 41-45. Subject: 2.1

Janger, Edward J. Genetic information, privacy and insolvency. *Journal of Law, Medicine and Ethics* 2005 Spring; 33(1): 79-88. Subject: 15.1

Janoff, Abby F. Rights of the pregnant child vs. rights of the unborn under the Convention on the Rights of the Child. *Boston University International Law Journal* 2004 Spring; 22(1): 163-188. Subject: 12.4.2

Jansen, Brigitte E.S.; Paslack, Rainer. Social risks and social perception of animal cloning. *Revista de Derecho y Genoma Humano / Law and the Human Genome Review* 2003 July-December; (19): 231-236. Subject: 22.2

Jansen, Brigitte; Simon, Juergen. Some ethical and legal issues in Germany involving informed consent and patenting. *Science and Engineering Ethics* 2005 January; 11(1): 93-96. Subject: 8.3.1

Jansen, L.A. HIV exceptionalism, CD4+ cell testing, and conscientious subversion. *Journal of Medical Ethics* 2005 June; 31(6): 322-326. Subject: 9.5.6

Jansen, Lynn A. A closer look at the bad deal trial: beyond clinical equipoise. *Hastings Center Report* 2005 September-October; 35(5): 29-36. Subject: 18.2

Jansen, Lynn A. Local IRBs, multicenter trials, and the ethics of internal amendments. *IRB: Ethics and Human Research* 2005 July-August; 27(4): 7-11. Subject: 18.2

Jansen-van der Weide, Marijke C.; Onwuteaka-Philipsen, Bregje D.; van der Wal, Gerrit. Granted, undecided, withdrawn, and refused requests for euthanasia and physician-assisted suicide. *Archives of Internal Medicine* 2005 August 8-22; 165(15): 1698- 1704. Subject: 20.5.1

Janssen, Anke; Gevers, Sjef. Explicit or presumed consent and organ donation post-mortem: does it matter? *Medicine and Law: World Association for Medical Law* 2005 September; 24(3): 575-583. Subject: 19.5

Jasanoff, Sheila. In the democracies of DNA: ontological uncertainty and political order in three states. *New Genetics and Society* 2005 August; 24(2): 139-155. Subject: 21.1

Jasper, J.D.; Nickerson, Carol A.E.; Ubel, Peter A.; Asch, David A. Altruism, incentives, and organ donation: attitudes of the transplant community. *Medical Care* 2004 April; 42(4): 378-386. Subject: 19.5

Javitt, Gail H. Old legacies and new paradigms: confusing "research" and "treatment" and its consequences in responding to emergent health threats. *Journal of Health Care Law and Policy* 2005; 8(1): 38-70. Subject: 18.3

Jayakrishnan, T.; Jeeja, M.C. Human organ sale: the Kerala story. *Issues in Medical Ethics* 2003 July-September; 11(3): 81-82. Subject: 19.3

Jayaraman, K.S. Indian regulations fail to monitor growing stem-cell use in clinics [news]. *Nature* 2005 March 17; 434(7031): 259. Subject: 18.5.4

Jayasinghe, K.S.A.; De Silva, D.; Mendis, N.; Lie, R.K. Ethics of resource allocation in developing countries: the case of Sri Lanka. *Social Science and Medicine* 1998 November; 47(10): 1619-1625. Subject: 9.4

Jecker, Nancy S. Health care reform: what history doesn't teach. *Theoretical Medicine and Bioethics* 2005; 26(4): 277-305. Subject: 9.3.1

Jeena, P.M.; McNally, L.M.; Stobie, M.; Coovadia, H.M.; Adhikari, M.A.; Petros, A.J. Challenges in the provision of ICU services to HIV infected children in resource poor settings: a South African case study. *Journal of Medical Ethics* 2005 April; 31(4): 226-230. Subject: 9.5.6

Jeffers, Brenda Recchia. Continuing education in research ethics for the clinical nurse. *Journal of Continuing Education in Nursing* 2002 November- December; 33(6): 265-269, 284-285. Subject: 1.3.9

Jeffers, Brenda Recchia; Whittemore, Robin. Research environments that promote integrity. *Nursing Research* 2005 January-February; 54(1): 63-70. Subject: 1.3.9

Jeffery, A.; Snaith, R.; Voss, L. Ethical dilemmas: feeding back results to members of a longitudinal cohort study. *Journal of Medical Ethics* 2005 March; 31(3): 153. Subject: 18.5.2

Jefford, Michael; Savulescu, Julian; Thomson, Jacqui; Schofield, Penelope; Mileshkin, Linda; Agalianos, Emilia; Zalcberg, John. Medical paternalism and expensive unsubsidised drugs. *BMJ: British Medical Journal* 2005 November 5; 331(7524): 1075- 1077. Subject: 9.7

Jeffrey, David I. Time to legalise assisted dying? Response from the Association for Palliative Medicine [letter]. *BMJ: British Medical Journal* 2005 October 8; 331(7520): 841. Subject: 20.7

Jenkins, Bill; Jones, Camara; Blumenthal, Daniel S. Public health ethics and community-based research: lessons from the Tuskegee Syphilis Study. *In:* Blumenthal, D.S.; Diclemente, R.J., eds. Community- Based Health Research: Issues and Methods. New York: Springer Publishing Company, 2004: 47-62. Subject: 18.5.1

Jenkins, G.; Merz, J.F.; Sankar, P. A qualitative study of women's views on medical confidentiality. *Journal of Medical Ethics* 2005 September; 31(9): 499-504. Subject: 8.4

Jenkins, Gwynne L.; Sugarman, Jeremy. The importance of cultural considerations in the promotion of ethical research with human biologic material. *Journal of Laboratory Clinical Medicine* 2005 March; 145(3): 118-124. Subject: 18.2

Jennings, Bruce; Heitman, Elizabeth. Genetics and genetic technology in social context. *In:* Smith, David H.; Cohen, Cynthia B., eds. A Christian Response to the New Genetics: Religious, Ethical, and Social Issues. Lanham, MD: Rowman & Littlefield Publishers; 2003: 131-146. Subject: 15.3

Jennings, Elaine Marie. And some grow mad, and all grow bad: prisoners constitutional right to receive psychiatric treatment. *New England Journal on Criminal and Civil Confinement* 1985 Winter; 11(1): 160-185. Subject: 17.8

Jennings, John C. Forum on ethics. Small babies and hard decisions. *Texas Medicine* 1998 August; 94(8): 24-25. Subject: 20.5.2

Jenny-Avital, Elizabeth R.; Blumenthal, David. Doctors and drug companies [letter and reply]. *New England Journal of Medicine* 2005 February 17; 352(7): 733- 734. Subject: 9.7

Jensen, Arthur R. The ethical issues. *In his:* Genetics and Education. New York: Harper & Row, Publishers; 1972: 327-332. Subject: 15.6

Jensen, Kyle; Murray, Fiona. Intellectual property landscape of the human genome. *Science* 2005 October 14; 310(5746): 239-240. Subject: 15.8

Jensen, Uffe Juul. Evidence, effectiveness and ethics: Cochrane's legacy. *In:* Kristiansen, Ivar Sonbo; Mooney, Gavin, eds. Evidence- Based Medicine: In its Place. New York: Routledge; 2004: 20-32. Subject: 9.8

Jenson, Larry E. Why our ethics curricula do work. *Journal of Dental Education* 2005 February; 69(2): 225-228. Subject: 7.2

Jenson, Robert W. Reading the body. *New Atlantis* 2005 Summer; 9: 73-82. Subject: 1.2

Jepson, R.G.; Hewison, J.; Thompson, A.G.H.; Weller, D. How should we measure informed choice? The case of cancer screening. *Journal of Medical Ethics* 2005 April; 31(4): 192-196. Subject: 9.1

Jerrold, Laurance. Right to refuse treatment. *American Journal of Orthodontics and Dentofacial Orthopedics* 2005 April; 127(4): 520-522. Subject: 8.1

Jesani, Amar. Banning pre-natal sex determination: the scope and the limits of the Maharashtra legislation. *In:* Lingam, Lakshmi, ed. Understanding Women's Health Issues: A Reader 1998; 6 p. [Online]. Available: http://www.hsph.harvard.edu/Organizations/healthnet/SAsia/suchana/0804/rh345.html [7 October 2005]. Subject: 14.3

Jesani, Amar. Calls for advertising and market reforms in health care [debate]. *Issues in Medical Ethics* 2001 January-March; 9(1): 19. Subject: 9.3.1

Jesani, Amar. Ethics, rights and strike of health workers [editorial]. *Issues in Medical Ethics* 1998 July-September; 6(3): 73, 103. Subject: 4.1.3

Jesani, Amar. Medicalisation of 'legal' killing: doctors' participation in the death penalty [editorial]. *Indian Journal of Medical Ethics* 2004 October-December; 1(4): 104-105. Subject: 20.6

Jesani, Amar; Kalantri, S.P.; Thomas, George; Srinivasan, Sandhya. Government-funded anti-retroviral therapy for HIV/AIDS: new ethical challenges [editorial]. *Indian Journal of Medical Ethics* 2004 July-September; 1(3): 70-71. Subject: 9.5.6

Jesani, Amar; Pilgaokar, Anil. Patient's autonomy: throwing it to the winds? *Medical Ethics: Journal of Forum for Medical Ethics Society* 1993 August-October; 1(1): 6-7. Subject: 1.1

Jesilow, Paul. The effects of fraud on the evaluation of health care. *Health Care Analysis: An International Journal of Health Care Philosophy and Policy* 2005 September; 13(3): 239-245. Subject: 9.3.1

Jesus, John E.; Higgs, Elizabeth S. International research ethics: progress, but not perfection. *Trends in Molecular Medicine* 2002 February; 8(2): 93-95. Subject: 18.5.9

Jewell, Sarah. Elderly patients' participation in discharge decision making: 1. *British Journal of Nursing* 1996 August 8-September 11; 5(15): 914-916, 929-932. Subject: 9.5.2

Jezuit, Deborah L. Suffering of critical care nurses with end-of-life decisions. *Medsurg Nursing* 2000 June; 9(3): 145-152. Subject: 20.5.1

Jha, Ashish K.; Fisher, Elliott S.; Li, Zhonghe; Orav, E. John; Epstein, Arnold M. Racial trends in the use of major procedures among the elderly. *New England Journal of Medicine* 2005 August 18; 353(7): 683- 691. Subject: 9.5.4

Jindal, Surinder. Privatisation of health care: new ethical dilemmas. *Issues in Medical Ethics* 1998 July-September; 6(3): 85-86. Subject: 9.3.1

Jindal, S.K. Issues in the care of the dying. *Indian Journal of Medical Ethics* 2005 July-September; 2(3): 79-80. Subject: 20.5.1

Jing-Bao, Nie. Cultural values embodying universal norms: a critique of a popular assumption about cultures and human rights. *Developing World Bioethics* 2005 September; 5(3): 251-257. Subject: 2.1

Jintarkanon, Seree; Nakapiew, Supatra; Tienudom, Nimit; Suwannawong, Paisan; Wilson, David. Unethical clinical trials in Thailand: a community reponse [letter]. *Lancet* 2005 May 7-13; 365(9471): 1617-1618. Subject: 18.2

Joffe, C.E.; Weitz, T.A.; Stacey, C.L. Uneasy allies: pro-choice physicians, feminist health activists and the struggle for abortion rights. *Sociology of Health and Illness* 2004 September; 26(6): 775-796. Subject: 12.5.1

Joffe, Steven; Simon, Christian. Informed consent from the doctor? [case study]. *Hastings Center Report* 2004 July-August; 34(4): 12-13. Subject: 18.3

Johannes, Laura. Double standard: for some transplant patients, diseased hearts are lifesavers. Surgeons enlist elderly, sick to receive inferior organs; the new ethical issues; facing a risk of hepatitis C. *Wall Street Journal* 2005 April 14; p. A1,A8. Subject: 19.6

Johansen, Carol K.; Harris, David E. Teaching the ethics of biology. *American Biology Teacher* 2000 May; 62(5): 352-358. Subject: 2.3

John Paul II, Pope. Address of John Paul II to the participants at the International Congress on "Life-sustaining Treatments and the Vegetative State: Scientific Advances and Ethical Dilemmas". *Dolentium Hominum* 2004; 19(2): 20-22. Subject: 20.5.1

John Paul II, Pope. Address of John Paul II to the 18th International Congress of the Transplantation Society. *Medical Ethics and Bioethics / Medicinska Etika & Bioetika* 2001 Spring-Summer; 8(1-2): 12-14. Subject: 19.5

John Paul II, Pope. Euthanasia must be avoided. *Dolentium Hominum* 2005; 20(1): 7-8. Subject: 20.5.1

John Paul II, Pope. Imperative of "signs of clinical death" for organ transplants: message to the Pontifical Academy of Sciences. *Issues in Law and Medicine* 2005 Spring; 20(3): 261-263. Subject: 20.2.1

Subject = NRCBL Primary Classification Number; See inside front cover

John Paul II, Pope. Life-sustaining treatments and vegetative state: scientific advances and ethical dilemmas. *Issues in Law and Medicine* 2004 Fall; 20(2): 167-170. Subject: 20.5.1

John Paul II, Pope. To the participants in the 19th International Conference of the Pontifical Council for Pastoral Health Care. *National Catholic Bioethics Quarterly* 2005 Spring; 5(1): 153- 155. Subject: 9.1

John, George. Caring for a patient in a vegetative state. *Issues in Medical Ethics* 2001 July-September; 9(3): 77-78. Subject: 20.5.1

John, T. Jacob. Polio eradication and ethical issues. *Indian Journal of Medical Ethics* 2005 October-December; 2(4): 117-118. Subject: 9.5.1

Johns, Kimberly A. Reproductive rights of women: construction and reality in international and United States law. *Cardozo Women's Law Journal* 1998; 5(1): 1-32. Subject: 9.5.5

Johnson, Alissa. Stem cell research. *NCSL Legisbrief* 2005 March; 13(15): 1-2. Subject: 18.5.4

Johnson, Andrew. How not to argue for abortion rights: fighting for choice is not enough. *Free Inquiry* 2005 February-March; 25(2): 38-41. Subject: 12.3

Johnson, Eric J.; Goldstein, Daniel G. Defaults and donation decisions. *Transplantation* 2004 December 27; 78(12): 1713-1716. Subject: 19.5

Johnson, Ian S. Assisted dying for the terminally ill [letter]. *Lancet* 2005 October 22-28; 366(9495): 1433-1434. Subject: 20.4.1

Johnson, Jonas T. Conflicts of interest in medical publishing [editorial]. *Laryngoscope* 2004 October; 114(10): 1685. Subject: 1.3.7

Johnson, Kimberly S.; Elbert-Avila, Katja I.; Tulsky, James A. The influence of spiritual beliefs and practices on the treatment preferences of African Americans: a review of the literature. *Journal of the American Geriatrics Society* 2005 April; 53(4): 711-719. Subject: 20.5.1

Johnson, Louise. The legal implications of abuse of the unborn foetus. *Medicine and Law: World Association for Medical Law* 1994; 13(1-2): 19-27. Subject: 9.5.5

Johnson, Martin. Notes on the tension between privacy and surveillance in nursing. *Online Journal of Issues in Nursing [electronic]* 2005; 10(2); E3, 13 p. Available: http://www.nursingworld.org/ojin/ [15 June 2005]. Subject: 8.4

Johnson, Martin H. A moral case study for discussion: designer babies and tissue typing. *Reproductive BioMedicine Online [electronic]* 2004 October; 9(4): 372. Available: http://www.rbmonline.com [29 June 2005]. Subject: 15.2

Johnson, Martin H. Surrogacy and the Human Fertilisation and Embryology Act. *In:* Cook, Rachel; Sclater, Shelley Day; Kaganas, Felicity, eds. Surrogate Motherhood: International Perspectives. Portland, OR: Hart; 2003: 93-97. Subject: 14.2

Johnson, Sandra. Legal issues in the use of controlled substances in pain management. *Medical Ethics Newsletter [Lahey Clinic]* 2005 Winter; 12(1): 4, 12. Subject: 9.5.9

Johnson, Sandra H. The social, professional, and legal framework for the problem of pain management in emergency medicine. *Journal of Law, Medicine and Ethics* 2005 Winter; 33(4): 741- 760. Subject: 4.4

Johnson, Summer; Kass, Nancy E.; Natowicz, Marvin. Disclosure of personal medical information: differences among parents and affected adults for genetic and nongenetic conditions. *Genetic Testing* 2005 Fall; 9(3): 269-280. Subject: 15.3

Johnson, Timothy R.B.; Harris, Lisa H.; Dalton, Vanessa K.; Howell, Joel D. Language matters: legislation, medical practice, and the classification of abortion procedures. *Obstetrics and Gynecology* 2005 January; 105(1): 201-204. Subject: 12.4.1

Johnson-Greene, D. Informed consent in clinical neuropsychology practice: official statement of the National Academy of Neuropsychology. *Archives of Clinical Neuropsychology* 2005 May; 20(3): 335-340. Subject: 8.3.1

Johnston, Carolyn; Kaye, Jane. Does the UK biobank have a legal obligation to feedback individual findings to participants? *Medical Law Review* 2004 Autumn; 12(3): 239-267. Subject: 15.10

Johnston, Josephine. Stem cell protocols: the NAS guidelines are a useful start. *Hastings Center Report* 2005 November-December; 35(6): 16-17. Subject: 18.5.4

Johnston, Josephine; Elliott, Carl. Healthy limb amputation: ethical and legal aspects. *Clinical Medicine* 2002 September-October; 2(5): 431-435. Subject: 17.1

Johnstone, Julie. Ethics, identity, and new social movements in mental health services. *Res Publica* 2005; 14(2): 6-10. Subject: 17.1

Johnstone, Megan-Jane; Kanitsaki, Olga. Processes for disciplining nurses for unprofessional conduct of a serious nature: a critique. *Journal of Advanced Nursing* 2005 May; 50(4): 363-371. Subject: 7.4

Joly, Y.; Knoppers, Bartha Maria; Nguyen, M.T. Stored tissue samples: through the confidentiality maze. *Pharmacogenomics Journal* 2005; 5(1): 2-5. Subject: 15.1

Jonas, Monique. Choosing between claims: allocating parental responsibility in surrogacy disputes. *In:* Häyry, Matti; Takala, Tuija; Herissone-Kelly, Peter, eds. Bioethics and Social Reality. New York: Rodopi, 2005: 39-51. Subject: 14.2

Jones, D. Gareth. Making human life captive to biomedical technology: Christianity and the demise of human values. *Update [Loma Linda University Center for Christian Bioethics]* 1995 December; 11(4); 18 p. Subject: 5.1

Jones, D.A. The human embryo in the Christian tradition: a reconsideration. *Journal of Medical Ethics* 2005 December; 31(12): 710-713. Subject: 18.5.4

Jones, James W. Ethics of rapid surgical technological advancement. *Annals of Thoracic Surgery* 2000; 69: 676-677. Subject: 5.3

Jones, James W. Surgical databases: ethics in evolution. *Annals of Thoracic Surgery* 2002; 74: 983-985. Subject: 18.2

Jones, James W.; McCullough, Laurence B. Abdominal aortic aneurysm in death row inmate. *Journal of Vascular Surgery* 2002 March; 35(3): 621-622. Subject: 9.5.1

Jones, James W.; McCullough, Laurence B. Disclosure of intraoperative events. *Surgery* 2002 September; 133(4): 531-532. Subject: 9.8

Jones, James W.; McCullough, Laurence B. Futility and surgical intervention. *Journal of Vascular Surgery* 2002 June; 35(6): 1305. Subject: 8.1

Jones, James W.; McCullough, Laurence B. When does conventional surgical therapy become research? *Journal of Vascular Surgery* 2002 August; 35(8): 423-424. Subject: 18.3

Jones, James W.; McCullough, Laurence B.; Crigger, Nancy A.; Richman, Bruce W. The ethics of administrative credentialing. *Journal of Vascular Surgery* 2005 April; 41(4): 729-731. Subject: 7.1

Jones, James W.; McCullough, Laurence B.; Richman, Bruce W. Damned if you do and damned if you don't: medical ethics and a second career. *Journal of Vascular Surgery* 2005 March; 41(3): 556-558. Subject: 20.6

Jones, James W.; McCullough, Laurence B.; Richman, Bruce W. Ethical nuances of combining romance with medical practice. *Journal of Vascular Surgery* 2005 January; 41(1): 174-175. Subject: 7.4

Jones, James W.; McCullough, Laurence B.; Richman, Bruce W. The ethics of odd ideas, good science, and academic freedom. *Journal of Vascular Surgery* 2005 June; 41(6): 1074-1076. Subject: 1.3.9

Jones, James W.; McCullough, Laurence B.; Richman, Bruce W. Ethics of refusal to treat patients as a social statement. *Journal of Vascular Surgery* 2004 November; 40(5): 1057-1059. Subject: 8.1

Jones, James W.; McCullough, Laurence B.; Richman, Bruce W. The ethics of sham surgery in research. *Journal of Vascular Surgery* 2003 February; 37(2): 482-483. Subject: 18.2

Jones, James W.; McCullough, Laurence B.; Richman, Bruce W. Ethics of the new economic credentialing: conflicted leadership roles. *Journal of Vascular Surgery* 2005 February; 41(2): 366-368. Subject: 7.1

Jones, James W.; McCullough, Laurence B.; Richman, Bruce W. Family-surgeon disagreements over interventions. *Journal of Vascular Surgery* 2004 October; 40(4): 831-832. Subject: 20.5.1

Jones, James W.; McCullough, Laurence B.; Richman, Bruce W. The military physician's ethical response to evidence of torture. *Surgery* 2004 November; 136(5): 1090-1093. Subject: 21.4

Jones, James W.; McCullough, Laurence B.; Richman, Bruce W. A surgeon's obligations to a Jehovah's Witness child. *Surgery* 2003 January; 133(1): 110-111. Subject: 8.3.4

Jones, James W.; McCullough, Laurence B.; Richman, Bruce W. Truth-telling about terminal diseases. *Surgery* 2005 March; 137(3): 380-382. Subject: 8.2

Jones, James W.; McCullough, Laurence B.; Richman, Bruce W. What to tell patients harmed by other physicians. *Journal of Vascular Surgery* 2003 October; 38(4): 866-867. Subject: 9.8

Jones, James W.; Richman, Bruce W.; McCullough, Laurence B. HIV-infected surgeon: professional responsibility and self interest. *Journal of Vascular Surgery* 2003 April; 37(4): 914-915. Subject: 9.5.6

Jones, Jeffrey S.; Johnson, Ken; McNinch, Michael. Age as a risk factor for inadequate emergency department analgesia. *American Journal of Emergency Medicine* 1996 March; 14(2): 157-160. Subject: 9.5.2

Jones, Jeffrey S.; White, Lynn J.; Pool, Linda C.; Dougherty, James M. Structure and practice of institutional review boards in the United States. *Academic Emergency Medicine* 1996 August; 3(8): 804-809. Subject: 18.2

Jones, Kenneth D., Jr. Extreme makeovers. *Journal of the American Dental Association* 2005 March; 136(3): 395-396. Subject: 8.1

Jones, Kenneth D., Jr. Is it ethical to offer financial incentives to staff who convince patients to consent to treatment? *Journal of the American Dental Association* 2004 November; 135(11): 1619. Subject: 9.3.1

Jones, Melinda. Can international law improve mental health? Some thoughts on the proposed convention on the rights of people with disabilities. *International Journal of Law and Psychiatry* 2005 March- April; 28(2): 183-205. Subject: 9.5.3

Jones, Nancy L.; Cheshire, William P., Jr. Can artificial techniques supply morally neutral human embryos for research? Part I. Creating novel categories of human embryos. *Ethics and Medicine* 2005 Spring; 21(1): 29-40. Subject: 18.5.4

Jones, Owen D. Sex selection: regulating technology enabling the predetermination of a child's gender. *Harvard Journal of Law and Technology* 1992 Fall; 6(1): 1-62. Subject: 14.3

Subject = NRCBL Primary Classification Number; See inside front cover

Jones, Rachel K.; Boonstra, Heather. Confidential reproductive health services for minors: the potential impact of mandated parental involvement for contraception. *Perspectives on Sexual and Reproductive Health* 2004 September-October; 36(5): 182-191. Subject: 11.2

Jones, Rachel K.; Purcell, Alison; Singh, Susheela; Finer, Lawrence B. Adolescents' reports of parental knowledge of adolescents' use of sexual health services and their reactions to mandated parental notification for prescription contraception. *JAMA: The Journal of the American Medical Association* 2005 January 19; 293(3): 340-348. Subject: 11.2

Jones, Richard P.O.; Prasad, V.; Kuruvatti, J.; Tahir, N.; Whitaker, P.; Dawson, A.S.J.; Harrison, M.A.; Williams, R. Remuneration for blood donation and attitudes towards blood donation and receipt in Leeds. *Transfusion Medicine* 2003 June; 13(3): 131-140. Subject: 19.4

Jones, R.B.; Hedley, A.J.; Allison, S.P.; Tattersall, R.B. Censoring of patient-held records by doctors. *Journal of the Royal College of General Practitioners* 1988 March; 38(308): 117-118. Subject: 8.2

Jones, Shirley L.; Fallon, Lee A. Reproductive options for individuals at risk for transmission of a genetic disorder. *JOGNN: Journal of Obstetric, Gynecologic and Neonatal Nursing* 2002 March-April; 31(2): 193-199. Subject: 15.3

Jonsen, Albert R. Abortion. *In his:* Bioethics Beyond the Headlines: Who Lives? Who Dies? Who Decides? Lanham, MD: Rowman and Littlefield; 2005: 77-84. Subject: 12.3

Jonsen, Albert R. Animal ethics. *In his:* Bioethics Beyond the Headlines: Who Lives? Who Dies? Who Decides? Lanham, MD: Rowman and Littlefield; 2005: 160-166. Subject: 22.2

Jonsen, Albert R. Assisted reproduction. *In his:* Bioethics Beyond the Headlines: Who Lives? Who Dies? Who Decides? Lanham, MD: Rowman and Littlefield; 2005: 67-76. Subject: 14.1

Jonsen, Albert R. Autonomy of the patient. *In his:* Bioethics Beyond the Headlines: Who Lives? Who Dies? Who Decides? Lanham, MD: Rowman and Littlefield; 2005: 40-47. Subject: 8.3.1

Jonsen, Albert R. Bioethics and the health care system. *In his:* Bioethics Beyond the Headlines: Who Lives? Who Dies? Who Decides? Lanham, MD: Rowman and Littlefield; 2005: 141-153. Subject: 9.4

Jonsen, Albert R. Cloning and stem cell research. *In his:* Bioethics Beyond the Headlines: Who Lives? Who Dies? Who Decides? Lanham, MD: Rowman and Littlefield; 2005: 127-138. Subject: 18.5.4

Jonsen, Albert R. Cultural bioethics. *In his:* Bioethics Beyond the Headlines: Who Lives? Who Dies? Who Decides? Lanham, MD: Rowman and Littlefield; 2005: 154-159. Subject: 2.1

Jonsen, Albert R. Defining death. *In his:* Bioethics Beyond the Headlines: Who Lives? Who Dies? Who Decides? Lanham, MD: Rowman and Littlefield; 2005: 26-34. Subject: 20.2.1

Jonsen, Albert R. Environmental ethics. *In his:* Bioethics Beyond the Headlines: Who Lives? Who Dies? Who Decides? Lanham, MD: Rowman and Littlefield Pub.; 2005: 167-176. Subject: 15.1

Jonsen, Albert R. Euthanasia. *In his:* Bioethics Beyond the Headlines: Who Lives? Who Dies? Who Decides? Lanham, MD: Rowman and Littlefield; 2005: 48-58. Subject: 20.5.1

Jonsen, Albert R. Forgoing life support: the quality of life. *In his:* Bioethics Beyond the Headlines: Who Lives? Who Dies? Who Decides? Lanham, MD: Rowman and Littlefield; 2005: 35-39. Subject: 20.5.1

Jonsen, Albert R. Genetics. *In his:* Bioethics Beyond the Headlines: Who Lives? Who Dies? Who Decides? Lanham, MD: Rowman and Littlefield; 2005: 96-113. Subject: 15.1

Jonsen, Albert R. Neuroscience. *In his:* Bioethics Beyond the Headlines: Who Lives? Who Dies? Who Decides? Lanham, MD: Rowman and Littlefield; 2005: 114-126. Subject: 17.1

Jonsen, Albert R. On the origins and future of the Belmont Report. *In:* Childress, James F.; Meslin, Eric M.; Shapiro, Harold T., eds. Belmont Revisited: Ethical Principles for Research with Human Subjects. Washington, DC: Georgetown University Press; 2005: 3-11. Subject: 18.2

Jonsen, Albert R. Organ transplantation. *In his:* Bioethics Beyond the Headlines: Who Lives? Who Dies? Who Decides? Lanham, MD: Rowman and Littlefield; 2005: 59-66. Subject: 19.1

Jonsen, Albert R. Research with humans: experimentation, autonomy, and benefits to others. *In his:* Bioethics Beyond the Headlines: Who Lives? Who Dies? Who Decides? Lanham, MD: Rowman and Littlefield; 2005: 86-95. Subject: 18.2

Jonsen, Albert R. What it means to "map" the field of neuroethics. *Cerebrum: The Dana Forum on Brain Science* 2002 Summer; 4(3): 71-72. Subject: 17.1

Jonsen, Albert R.; Churchland, Patricia S.; Damasio, Antonio R.; Moreno, Jonathan; Schaffner, Kenneth F.; Mobley, William. Brain science and the self. *Cerebrum: The Dana Forum on Brain Science* 2002 Summer; 4(3): 56-58. Subject: 17.1

Jordan, Caren B.; Belar, Cynthia D.; Williams, R. Stan. Anonymous oocyte donation: a follow-up analysis of donors' experiences. *Journal of Psychosomatic Obstetrics and Gynecology* 2004 June; 25(2): 145-151. Subject: 14.4

Jordan, Karen A. Financial conflicts of interest in human subjects research: proposals for a more effective regulatory scheme. *Washington and Lee Law Review* 2003 Winter; 60(1): 15-109. Subject: 18.2

Jordens, Christopher; Anderson, Lynley. Should we be concerned about direct-to-consumer advertising of prescription drugs? [editorial]. *Journal of Bioethical Inquiry* 2005; 2(2): 61-62. Subject: 9.7

Jormsri, Pantip. Moral conflict and collaborative mode as moral conflict resolution in health care. *Nursing and Health Sciences* 2004 September; 6(3): 217-221. Subject: 7.3

Jormsri, Pantip; Kunaviktikul, Wipada; Ketefian, Shaké; Chaowalit, Aranya. Moral competence in nursing practice. *Nursing Ethics* 2005 November; 12(6): 582-594. Subject: 4.1.3

Joseph, Jay. The 1942 'euthanasia' debate in the American Journal of Psychiatry. *History of Psychiatry* 2005 June; 16(2): 171-179. Subject: 20.5.1

Joseph, Sarah. Pharmaceutical corporations and access to drugs: the "fourth wave" of corporate human rights scrutiny. *Human Rights Quarterly* 2003 May; 25(2): 425-452. Subject: 9.7

Jost, Timothy Stoltzfus. The role of the courts in health care rationing: the German model. *Journal of Contemporary Health Law and Policy* 2002 Fall; 18(3): 613-617. Subject: 9.4

Jotkowitz, Alan B.; Clarfield, A. Mark; Glick, Shimon. The care of patients with dementia: a modern Jewish ethical perspective. *Journal of the American Geriatrics Society* 2005 May; 53(5): 881-884. Subject: 17.1

Jotkowitz, Alan B.; Porath, Avi; Glick, Shimon. The professionalism movement. *IMAJ: Israel Medical Association Journal* 2004 November; 6(11): 661-664. Subject: 1.3.1

Jotkowitz, A.B.; Glick, S. The physician charter on medical professionalism: a Jewish ethical perspective. *Journal of Medical Ethics* 2005 July; 31(7): 404-405. Subject: 4.1.2

Jotterand, Fabrice. The Hippocratic oath and contemporary medicine: dialectic between past ideals and present reality? *Journal of Medicine and Philosophy* 2005 February; 30(1): 107- 128. Subject: 6

Juengst, Eric T. Anti-aging research and the limits of medicine. *In:* Post, Stephen G.; Binstock, Robert H., eds. The Fountain of Youth: Cultural, Scientific, and Ethical Perspectives on a Biomedical Goal. New York: Oxford University Press; 2004: 321-339. Subject: 9.5.2

Juengst, Eric T. Community engagement in genetic research: the "slow code" of research ethics? *In:* Knoppers, Bartha Maria, ed. Populations and Genetics: Legal and Socio-Ethical Perspectives. Boston: Martinus Nijhoff; 2003: 181-197. Subject: 15.1

Junghans, Cornelia; Feder, Gene; Hemingway, Harry; Timmis, Adam; Jones, Melvyn. Recruiting patients to medical research: double blind randomised trial of "opt-in" versus "opt-out" strategies. *BMJ: British Medical Journal* 2005 October 22; 331(7522): 940- 942. Subject: 18.3

Jurevic, Amy M. When technology and health care collide: issues with electronic medical records and electronic mail. *UMKC Law Review* 1998 Summer; 66(4): 809-836. Subject: 8.4

Jurgus, Maryann; Welsh, Thomas J. PI and vet: potential conflict of interest? Definite potential for conflict of interest. *Lab Animal* 2004 October; 33(9): 22. Subject: 22.2

Justo, Luis. Trust, understanding and utopia in the research setting. *American Journal of Bioethics* 2005 January-February; 5(1): 56- 58. Subject: 18.2

Justus, Kelly. Oral aversion: a case and discussion. *Pediatric Nursing* 1998 September-October; 24(5): 474, 478. Subject: 8.3.4

K

Kabra, S.G. Abortion in India: not a right but a state-sponsored programme [letter]. *Issues in Medical Ethics* 2000 July-September; 8(3): 70. Subject: 12.1

Kabra, S.G. Gender disparity: need to look beyond 'female foeticide'. *Issues in Medical Ethics* 2002 April-June; 10(2): 24. Subject: 15.2

Kabra, S.G. Unsafe abortions and experimental excesses. *Issues in Medical Ethics* 2003 July-September; 11(3): 79-80. Subject: 12.1

Kaczor, Christopher. Could artificial wombs end the abortion debate? *National Catholic Bioethics Quarterly* 2005 Summer; 5(2): 283- 301. Subject: 19.1

Kaebnick, Gregory E. Rethinking the ethics of research. *Hastings Center Report* 2005 September-October; 35(5): 2. Subject: 18.2

Kahn, Jeffrey P. To the editor [letter]. *American Journal of Bioethics [Online]* 2005 May-June; 5(3): W13. Subject: 1.3.7

Kahn, Jeffrey P.; Mastroianni, Anna C. The ethics and policy issues in creating a stem cell donor: a case study in reproductive genetics. *In:* Brannigan, Michael C., ed. Cross-Cultural Biotechnology. Lanham: Rowman and Littlefield; 2004: 43-55. Subject: 15.2

Kahn, Jonathan. BiDil: false promises: faulty statistics and reasoning have lead [sic; led] to the first "racial medicine". *GeneWatch* 2005 November-December; 18(6): 6-9, 18. Subject: 15.11

Kahn, Jonathan D.; Bhopal, Raj; Rahemtulla, Taslin. Pharmacogenetics and ethnically targeted therapies: racial drugs need to be put in context; authors' reply [letter and reply]. *BMJ: British Medical Journal* 2005 June 25; 330(7506): 1508- 1509. Subject: 15.1

Kaiser, Jocelyn. An earlier look at baby's genes [news]. *Science* 2005 September 2; 309(5740): 1476-1478. Subject: 15.2

Kaiser, Jocelyn. Final NIH rules ease stock limits [news]. *Science* 2005 September 2; 309(5740): 1469. Subject: 1.3.9

Kaiser, Jocelyn. Forty-four researchers broke NIH consulting rules [news]. *Science* 2005 July 22; 309(5734): 546. Subject: 1.3.9

Kaiser, Jocelyn. House would foil human pesticide studies [news]. *Science* 2005 May 27; 308(5726): 1234. Subject: 18.6

Kaiser, Jocelyn. NIH chief clamps down on consulting and stock ownership [news]. *Science* 2005 February 11; 307(5711): 824-825. Subject: 1.3.9

Kaiser, Jocelyn. NIH rules make some pack, others plead [news]. *Science* 2005 March 18; 307(5716): 1703. Subject: 1.3.9

Kaiser, Jocelyn. NIH scientists raise fuss about scope of new rules [news]. *Science* 2005 March 4; 307(5714): 1390. Subject: 1.3.9

Kaiser, Jocelyn. NIH wants public access to papers 'as soon as possible' [news]. *Science* 2005 February 11; 307(5711): 825, 827. Subject: 5.3

Kaiser, Jocelyn. Panel urges limits on X-SCID trials [news]. *Science* 2005 March 11; 307(5715): 1544-1545. Subject: 15.4

Kaiser, Jocelyn. Resurrected influenza virus yields secrets of deadly 1918 pandemic [news]. *Science* 2005 October 7; 310(5745): 28-29. Subject: 15.1

Kaiser, Jocelyn. Scientists, societies blast NIH ethics rules [news]. *Science* 2005 April 8; 308(5719): 175, 177. Subject: 5.3

Kalantri, S.P. Ethics of drug trials in India [letter]. *National Medical Journal of India* 2002 May-June; 15(3): 179. Subject: 18.3

Kalantri, S.P. Informed consent in public hospitals. *Issues in Medical Ethics* 2000 October-December; 8(4): 116-117. Subject: 8.3.1

Kalb, Claudia. Ethics, eggs and embryos: thanks to medical advances, scientists are looking for a few good women to donate their oocytes to stem-cell research. *Newsweek* 2005 June 20; 145(25): 52-53. Subject: 14.4

Kalbian, Aline H. Narrative ARTifice and women's agency. *Bioethics* 2005 April; 19(2): 93-111. Subject: 14.1

Kaldis, Byron. Could the ethics of institutionalized health care be anything but Kantian? Collecting building blocks for a unifying metaethics. *Medicine, Health Care and Philosophy: A European Journal* 2005; 8(1): 39-52. Subject: 9.1

Kaldjian, Lauris C.; Weir, Robert F.; Duffy, Thomas P. A clinician's approach to clinical ethical reasoning. *JGIM:*

Journal of General Internal Medicine 2005 March; 20(3): 306-311. Subject: 8.1

Kaldjian, Lauris C.; Wu, Barry J.; Kirkpatrick, James N.; Thomas-Geevarghese, Asha; Vaughan-Sarrazin, Mary. Medical house officers' attitudes toward vigorous analgesia, terminal sedation, and physician-assisted suicide. *American Journal of Hospice and Palliative Medicine* 2004 September-October; 21(5): 381-387. Subject: 20.3.2

Kalekin-Fishman, Devorah. The impact of globalization on the determination and management of ethical choices in the health arena. *Social Science and Medicine* 1996 September; 43(5): 809-822. Subject: 21.7

Kalis, Annemarie; Schermer, Maartje H.N.; van Delden, Johannes J.M. Ideals regarding a good life for nursing home residents with dementia: views of professional caregivers. *Nursing Ethics* 2005 January; 12(1): 30-42. Subject: 17.1

Kalkut, Gary; Dubler, Nancy Neveloff. The line between life and death [opinion]. *New York Times* 2005 May 10; p. A17. Subject: 20.5.1

Kalra, Jawahar; Massey, K. Lorne; Mulla, Amith. Disclosure of medical error: policies and practice. *Journal of the Royal Society of Medicine* 2005 July; 98(7): 307-309. Subject: 9.8

Kalso, Eija. Opioids for persistent non-cancer pain [editorial]. *BMJ: British Medical Journal* 2005 January 22; 330(7484): 156- 157. Subject: 9.7

Kaminsky, Carmen. Kann man bio- und medizinethische Probleme lösen? *In:* Baumann, Eva; Brink, Alexander; May, Arnd T.; Schröder; Peter; Schutzeichel, Corinna Iris, eds. Weltanschauliche Offenheit in der Bioethik. Berlin: Duncker & Humblot; 2004: 81-93. Subject: 2.1

Kamm, Frances M. Deciding whom to help, health-adjusted life years and disabilities. *In:* Anand, Sudhir; Peter, Fabienne; Sen, Amartya, eds. Public Health, Ethics, and Equity. New York: Oxford University Press; 2004: 225-242. Subject: 9.4

Kamm, Frances M. Is there a problem with enhancement? [comment]. *American Journal of Bioethics* 2005 May-June; 5(3): 5-14. Subject: 15.1

Kamm, F.M. Moral status and personal identity: clones, embryos, and future generations. *Social Philosophy and Policy* 2005 Summer; 22(2): 283-307. Subject: 4.4

Kampits, Peter. Offene Ethik angesichts des Lebensendes. *In:* Baumann, Eva; Brink, Alexander; May, Arnd T.; Schröder; Peter; Schutzeichel, Corinna Iris, eds. Weltanschauliche Offenheit in der Bioethik. Berlin: Duncker & Humblot; 2004: 95-112. Subject: 20.5.1

Kamtekar, Rachna. Why life-saving drugs should be public goods. *Indian Journal of Medical Ethics* 2004 July-September; 1(3): 77-78. Subject: 9.7

Kane, Kanoelani M. Driving into the sunset: a proposal for mandatory reporting to the DMV by physicians treating unsafe elderly drivers. *University of Hawaii Law Review* 2002 Winter; 25(1): 59-83. Subject: 8.4

Kansas. Laws. Prevention of Assisted Suicide Act [effective 1 July 1998]. Kansas Statutes Annotated, Sections 60-4401 through 60-4407; 7 p. [Online]. Available: http://www.kslegislature.org/legsrv-statutes/getStatute.do [22 September 2005]. Subject: 20.7

Kansu, E.; Ruacan, S. Research ethics and scientific misconduct in biomedical research. *Acta Neurochirurgica* 2002; 83(supplement): 11-15. Subject: 1.3.9

Kapadia, Farhad; Singh, Manoj; Divatia, Jigeeshu; Vaidyanathan, Priya; Udwadia, Farokh E.; Raisinghaney, Sumit J.; Limaye, Harshad S.; Karnad, Dilip R. Limitation and withdrawal of intensive therapy at the end of life: practices in intensive care units in Mumbai, India. *Critical Care Medicine* 2005 June; 33(6): 1272-1275. Subject: 20.5.1

Kaplow, Roberta. Use of nursing resources and comfort of cancer patients with and without do-not-resuscitate orders in the intensive care unit. *American Journal of Critical Care* 2000 March; 9(2): 87-95. Subject: 20.5.1

Kaplowitz, Stan A.; Campo, Shelly; Chiu, Wai Tat. Cancer patients' desires for communication of prognosis information. *Health Communication* 2002; 14(2): 221-241. Subject: 8.1

Kapp, Marshall B. 'Ageism' and right to die litigation. *Medicine and Law: World Association for Medical Law* 1994; 13(1-2): 69-77. Subject: 20.5.1

Kapp, Marshall B. Decision making for vulnerable populations in the nursing home. *In:* Katz, Paul B.; Mezey, Mathy D.; Kapp, Marshall B., eds. Vulnerable Populations in the Long Term Care Continuum. New York, NY: Springer Pub. Co.; 2004:. Subject: 9.5.1

Kappauf, Herbert W.; Bolletino, Ruth Cohn. More on a new medical ethics: do we really need a new ethical model in medicine? [letter and reply]. *Advances in Mind-Body Medicine* 1998 Spring; 14(2); 8 p. [Online]. Available: http://weblinks3.epnet.com/citation.asp?tb=1&_ua=bo+B%5F+shn+1+db+aphjnh+bt+TD [23 September 2005]. Subject: 2.1

Kaptchuk, Ted J.; Miller, Franklin G. What is the best and most ethical model for the relationship between mainstream and alternative medicine: opposition, integration, or pluralism? *Academic Medicine* 2005 March; 80(3): 286-290. Subject: 4.1.1

Karel, Michele J.; Powell, Jean; Cantor, Michael D. Using a values discussion guide to facilitate communication in advance care planning. *Patient Education and Counseling* 2004 October; 55(1): 22-31. Subject: 20.5.4

Karkal, Malini. Sex selection and the population policy: the medical profession's responsibilities. *Issues in Medical Ethics* 2002 April-June; 10(2): 25. Subject: 14.3

Karkal, Malini. Surrogacy from a feminist perspective. *Issues in Medical Ethics* 1997 October-December; 5(4): 115-116. Subject: 14.2

Kärkkäinen, Oili; Bondas, Terese; Eriksson, Katie. Documentation of individualized patient care: a qualitative metasynthesis. *Nursing Ethics* 2005 March; 12(2): 123-132. Subject: 8.1

Karlawish, Jason; Whitehouse, Peter; McShane, Rupert H. Silence science: the problem of not reporting negative trials [editorial]. *Alzheimer Disease and Associated Disorders* 2004 October-December; 18(4): 180-182. Subject: 1.3.9

Karmakar, Santosh J. Dilemmas in the management of neural tube defects. *Issues in Medical Ethics* 2000 April-June; 8(2): 43-44. Subject: 9.5.7

Karmarkar, Santosh J. Learning 'on' patients: medical education cannot be at the patient's expense. *Issues in Medical Ethics* 1999 January-March; 7(1): 23-24. Subject: 7.2

Karnad, Dilip. A competent patient can decide. *Issues in Medical Ethics* 2001 January-March; 9(1): 27-28. Subject: 20.5.1

Karpin, Isabel. Genetics and the legal conception of self. *In:* Shildrick, Margrit; Mykitiuk, Roxanne, eds. Ethics of the Body: Postconventional Challenges. Cambridge, MA: MIT Press; 2005: 195- 216. Subject: 15.1

Karpowicz, Phillip; Cohen, Cynthia B.; van der Kooy, Derek. Developing human-nonhuman chimeras in human stem cell research: ethical issues and boundaries. *Kennedy Institute of Ethics Journal* 2005 June; 15(2): 107-134. Subject: 15.1

Karpowicz, Phillip; Cohen, Cynthia B.; van der Kooy, Derek. It is ethical to transplant human stem cells into non-human embryos. *Nature Medicine* 2004 April; 10(4): 331-335. Subject: 15.1

Karseth, Berit. Curriculum changes and moral issues in nursing education. *Nurse Education Today* 2004 November; 24(8): 638-643. Subject: 7.2

Kasher, Asa. At the edge of viability: philosophical, moral and ethical aspects and proposals. *In:* Blazer, Shraga; Zimmer, Etan Z., eds. The Embryo: Scientific Discovery and Medical Ethics. New York: Karger; 2005: 371-400. Subject: 20.5.1

Kasher, Asa. Professional ethics and collective professional autonomy: a conceptual analysis. *Ethical Perspectives* 2005 March; 12(1): 67-97. Subject: 1.3.1

Kasper, Judith D.; Giovannini, Terence A.; Hoffman, Catherine. Gaining and losing health insurance: strengthening the evidence for effects on access to care and health

---

outcomes. *Medical Care Research and Review* 2000 September; 57(3): 298-318. Subject: 9.3.1

Kass, Leon R. Lingering longer: who will care? [opinion]. *Washington Post* 2005 September 25; p. A23. Subject: 9.5.2

Kass, Leon R. New beginnings in life. *In:* Hamilton, Michael P., ed. The New Genetics and the Future of Man. Grand Rapids, MI: William B. Eerdmans Publishing Co.; 1972: 15-63. Subject: 14.4

Kass, Leon R. Reflections on public bioethics: a view from the trenches. *Kennedy Institute of Ethics Journal* 2005 September; 15(3): 221-250. Subject: 2.4

Kass, Leon R. Triumph or tragedy? The moral meaning of genetic technology. *American Journal of Jurisprudence* 2000; 45: 1-16. Subject: 15.1

Kass, Leon R. A way forward on stem cells [opinion]. *Washington Post* 2005 July 12; p. A21. Subject: 18.5.4

Kass, Nancy E.; Hull, Sara Chandros; Natowicz, Marvin R.; Faden, Ruth R.; Plantinga, Laura; Gostin, Lawrence O.; Slutsman, Julia. Medical privacy and the disclosure of personal medical information: the beliefs and experiences of those with genetic and other clinical conditions. *American Journal of Medical Genetics* 2004 July 30; 128A(3): 261-270. Subject: 8.4

Kass, Nancy E.; Maman, Suzanne; Atkinson, Joan. Motivations, understanding, and voluntariness in international randomized trials. *IRB: Ethics and Human Research* 2005 November-December; 27(6): 1-8. Subject: 18.3

Kassim, Puteri Nemie Jahn. Organ transplantation in Malaysia: a need for a comprehensive legal regime. *Medicine and Law: World Association for Medical Law* 2005 March; 24(1): 173-189. Subject: 19.5

Kassirer, Jerome P. Physicians' financial ties with the pharmaceutical industry: a critical element of a formidable marketing network. *In:* Moore, Don A.; Cain, Daylian M.; Loewenstein, George; Bazerman, Max H., eds. Conflicts of Interest: Challenges and Solutions in Business, Law, Medicine, and Public Policy. New York: Cambridge University Press; 2005: 133-141. Subject: 9.7

Kastrup, Marianne. Comments: a crisis in the ethical and moral behavior of psychiatrists [forum]. *Current Opinion in Psychiatry* 1998 January; 11(1); 2 p. [Online]. Available: http://gateway.ut.ovid.com/gw1/ovidweb.cgi [24 May 2005]. Subject: 20.6

Katerberg, Robert J. Institutional review boards, research on children, and informed consent of parents: walking the tightrope between encouraging vital experimentation and protecting subjects' rights. *Journal of College and University Law* 1998 Winter; 24(3): 545-579. Subject: 18.2

Katner, David R. Confidentiality and juvenile mental health records in dependency proceedings. *William and Mary Bill of Rights Journal* 2004 February; 12(2): 511-576. Subject: 8.4

Katumba-Lunyenya, J.; Joss, V.; Latham, P.; Abbatuan, C.; Hurley, P.; Isaacs, D.; Pollard, A.J.; Elias-Jones, A.C.; Larcher, V. Pulmonary tuberculosis and extreme prematurity [case study]. *Archives of Disease in Childhood. Fetal and Neonatal Edition* 2005 March; 90(2): F178-F183. Subject: 9.5.7

Katz, Jay. Experimentation with captive subjects. *In his:* Experimentation with Human Beings: The Authority of the Investigator, Subject, Professions, and State in the Human Experimentation Process. New York: Russell Sage Foundation; 1972: 1013-1052. Subject: 18.5.5

Katz, Jay. Experimentation with dying subjects. *In his:* Experimentation with Human Beings: The Authority of the Investigator, Subject, Professions, and State in the Human Experimentation Process. New York: Russell Sage Foundation; 1972: 1053-1108. Subject: 18.5.7

Katz, Jay. Experimentation with human beings. *In his:* Experimentation with Human Beings: The Authority of the Investigator, Subject, Professions, and State in the Human Experimentation Process. New York: Russell Sage Foundation; 1972: 283-321. Subject: 1.3.9

Katz, Jay. Experimenting with uncomprehending subjects. *In his:* Experimentation with Human Beings: The Authority of the Investigator, Subject, Professions, and State in the Human Experimentation Process. New York: Russell Sage Foundation; 1972: 955-1011. Subject: 18.5.2

Katz, Jay. The Jewish chronic disease hospital case. *In his:* Experimentation with Human Beings: The Authority of the Investigator, Subject, Professions, and State in the Human Experimentation Process. New York: Russell Sage Foundation; 1972: 9-65. Subject: 1.3.9

Katz, Jay. What are the functions of informed consent? *In his:* Experimentation with Human Beings: The Authority of the Investigator, Subject, Professions, and State in the Human Experimentation Process. New York: Russell Sage Foundation; 1972: 523-608. Subject: 18.3

Katz, Jay. What consequences to society should affect the authority of the investigator? *In his:* Experimentation with Human Beings: The Authority of the Investigator, Subject, Professions, and State in the Human Experimentation Process. New York: Russell Sage Foundation; 1972: 435-520. Subject: 18.1

Katz, Jay. What consequences to subjects should affect the authority of the investigator? *In his:* Experimentation with Human Beings: The Authority of the Investigator, Subject, Professions, and State in the Human Experimentation Process. New York: Russell Sage Foundation; 1972: 323-434. Subject: 18.1

Katz, Jay. What limitations are inherent in informed consent? *In his:* Experimentation with Human Beings: The Authority of the Investigator, Subject, Professions, and

State in the Human Experimentation Process. New York: Russell Sage Foundation; 1972: 609-673. Subject: 18.3

Katz, Jay. What limitations should be imposed on informed consent? *In his:* Experimentation with Human Beings: The Authority of the Investigator, Subject, Professions, and State in the Human Experimentation Process. New York: Russell Sage Foundation; 1972: 675-724. Subject: 18.3

Katz, Robert A. Who should capture the value of donated tissue? *Medical Ethics Newsletter [Lahey Clinic]* 2005 Fall; 12(3): 4, 9. Subject: 19.5

Kaufman, K.R. Modafinil in sports: ethical considerations. *British Journal of Sports Medicine* 2005 April; 39(4): 241-244. Subject: 9.7

Kaufman, Sharon R.; Shim, Janet K.; Russ, Ann J. Revisiting the biomedicalization of aging: clinical trends and ethical challenges. *Gerontologist* 2004 December; 44(6): 731-738. Subject: 9.5.2

Kaur, Manmeet. Female foeticide: a sociological perspective. *Journal of Family Welfare* 1993 March; 39(1); 4 p. [Online]. Available: http://www.hsph.harvard.edu/ Organizations/healthnet/SAsia/suchana /0326/kaur.html [7 October 2005]. Subject: 20.5.2

Kavanaugh, A. Ethical and practical issues in conducting clinical trials in psoriasis and psoriatic arthritis. *Annals of the Rheumatic Diseases* 2005 March; 64(Supplement 2): ii46-ii48. Subject: 18.1

Kavanaugh, John F. Brainism: 'we are not our brains; we are embodied persons'. *America* 2005 August 15-22; 193(4): 8. Subject: 4.4

Kavanaugh, John F. Leftover embryos: 'this is not junk science'. *America* 2005 June 20-27; 192(21): 8. Subject: 18.5.4

Kaveny, M. Cathleen. The order of widows: what the early church can teach us about older women and health care. *Christian Bioethics* 2005 April; 11(1): 11-34. Subject: 9.1

Kawakami, Satoru; Arai, Gaku; Ueda, Keiji; Murai, Yoshiro; Yokomichi, Hiroshi; Aoshima, Masao; Takagi, Kentaro. Physician's attitudes towards disclosure of cancer diagnosis to elderly patients: a report from Tokyo, Japan. *Archives of Gerontology and Geriatrics* 2001; 33: 29-36. Subject: 9.5.2

Kaye, D.H.; Smith, Michael E. DNA databases for law enforcement: the coverage question and the case for a population-wide database. *In:* Lazer, David, ed. DNA and the Criminal Justice System: The Technology of Justice. Cambridge, MA: MIT Press; 2004: 247-284. Subject: 15.1

Kaye, Jane. Abandoning informed consent: the case of genetic research in population collections. *In:* Tutton, Richard; Corrigan, Oonagh, eds. Genetic Databases: Socio-ethical Issues in the Collection and Use of DNA. New York: Routledge; 2004: 117-138. Subject: 18.3

Kayser, Bengt; Mauron, Alexandre; Miah, Andy. Legalisation of performance-enhancing drugs [opinion]. *Lancet* 2005 December; 366(Medicine and Sport): S21. Subject: 9.7

Kean, Brian. The risk society and attention deficit hyperactivity disorder (ADHD): a critical social research analysis concerning the development and social impact of the ADHD diagnosis. *Ethical Human Psychology and Psychiatry* 2005 Summer; 7(2): 131-142. Subject: 17.3

Keane, Helen. Addiction and the bioethics of difference. *In:* Shildrick, Margrit; Mykitiuk, Roxanne, eds. Ethics of the Body: Postconventional Challenges. Cambridge, MA: MIT Press; 2005: 91- 112. Subject: 9.5.9

Keefer, Christopher M. Bridging the gap between life insurer and consumer in the genetic testing era: the RF proposal. *Indiana Law Journal* 1999 Autumn; 74(4): 1375-1395. Subject: 15.2

Keehan, Carol. Catholic health care's community benefit role. *Origins* 2005 June 16; 35(5): 75-79. Subject: 9.1

Keeling, Sharon L. Duty to warn of genetic harm in breach of patient confidentiality. *Journal of Law and Medicine* 2004 November; 12(2): 235-253. Subject: 15.2

Keenan, James F. Developments in bioethics from the perspective of HIV/AIDS. *CQ: Cambridge Quarterly of Healthcare Ethics* 2005 Fall; 14(4): 416-423. Subject: 2.1

Kegley, J. A new framework for facilitating decisions on death and dying. *Medicine and Law: World Association for Medical Law* 2005 June; 24(2): 403-410. Subject: 20.3.1

Kegley, Jacquelyn Ann K. Challenges to informed consent. *EMBO Reports* 2004 September; 5(9): 832-836. Subject: 8.3.1

Keim, Twila. Physicians for professional sports teams: health care under the pressure of economic and commercial interests. *Seton Hall Journal of Sports Law* 1999 February; 97(4): 196-225. Subject: 7.3

Keith-Spiegel, Patricia; Koocher, Gerald P. The IRB paradox: could the protectors also encourage deceit? *Ethics and Behavior* 2005; 15(4): 339-349. Subject: 18.2

Keizer, Garret. Life everlasting: the religious right and the right to die. *Harper's Magazine* 2005 February; 310(1857): 53-61. Subject: 20.7

Kelleher, Finnuala. The pharmaceutical industry's responsibility for protecting human subjects of clinical trials in developing nations. *Columbia Journal of Law and Social Problems* 2004 Fall; 38(1): 67-106. Subject: 18.5.9

Kellen, Joyce C.; Oberle, Kathleen; Girard, Francine; Falkenberg, Loren. Exploring ethical perspectives of nurses and nurse managers. *Canadian Journal of Nursing Leadership* 2004 March; 17(1): 78-87. Subject: 4.1.3

Kelley, Maureen. Limits on patient responsibility. *Journal of Medicine and Philosophy* 2005 April; 30(2): 189-206. Subject: 8.3.4

Subject = NRCBL Primary Classification Number; See inside front cover

Kellicott, William E. "The sources and aims of the science of eugenics" in The Social Direction of Human Evolution (1911), pp.3-45. *In:* Ryan, Frank X., ed. Darwin's Impact: Social Evolution in America, 1880-1920. Volume 2. Race, Gender, and Supremacy. Bristol: Thoemmes; 2001: 132-149. Subject: 15.5

Kelly, Bernard. The matter of informed consent: a case history. *Australian Family Physician* 1994 June; 23(6): 1047-1049, 1052-1053. Subject: 8.3.1

Kelly, Brendan D.; McLoughlin, Declan M. Euthanasia, assisted suicide and psychiatry: a Pandora's box [editorial]. *British Journal of Psychiatry* 2002 October; 181: 278-279. Subject: 20.5.1

Kelly, David F. Allocating health care resources. *In his:* Contemporary Catholic Health Care Ethics. Washington, DC: Georgetown University Press; 2004: 270-282. Subject: 9.4

Kelly, David F. Embryonic stem cells and the beginning of personhood. *In his:* Contemporary Catholic Health Care Ethics. Washington, DC: Georgetown University Press; 2004: 245-254. Subject: 18.5.4

Kelly, David F. Ethics committees. *In his:* Contemporary Catholic Health Care Ethics. Washington, DC: Georgetown University Press; 2004: 229-244. Subject: 9.6

Kelly, David F. Forgoing treatment, pillar one: ordinary and extraordinary means. *In his:* Contemporary Catholic Health Care Ethics. Washington, DC: Georgetown University Press; 2004: 127-133. Subject: 20.5.1

Kelly, David F. Forgoing treatment, pillar three: advance directives. *In his:* Contemporary Catholic Health Care Ethics. Washington, DC: Georgetown University Press; 2004: 170-182. Subject: 20.5.4

Kelly, David F. Forgoing treatment, pillar three: decisions by competent patients. *In his:* Contemporary Catholic Health Care Ethics. Washington, DC: Georgetown University Press; 2004: 143-152. Subject: 8.3.4

Kelly, David F. Forgoing treatment, pillar three: decisions for incompetent patients. *In his:* Contemporary Catholic Health Care Ethics. Washington, DC: Georgetown University Press; 2004: 153-169. Subject: 20.5.1

Kelly, David F. Forgoing treatment, pillar two: killing and allowing to die. *In his:* Contemporary Catholic Health Care Ethics. Washington, DC: Georgetown University Press; 2004: 134-142. Subject: 20.5.1

Kelly, David F. Genetic engineering. *In his:* Contemporary Catholic Health Care Ethics. Washington, DC: Georgetown University Press; 2004: 260-268. Subject: 15.1

Kelly, David F. Hydration and nutrition. *In his:* Contemporary Catholic Health Care Ethics. Washington, DC: Georgetown University Press; 2004: 183-195. Subject: 20.5.1

Kelly, David F. Medical futility. *In his:* Contemporary Catholic Health Care Ethics. Washington, DC: Georgetown University Press; 2004: 206-218. Subject: 20.5.1

Kelly, David F. Pain and pain management. *In his:* Contemporary Catholic Health Care Ethics. Washington, DC: Georgetown University Press; 2004: 220-228. Subject: 4.4

Kelly, David F. Physician-assisted suicide and euthanasia. *In his:* Contemporary Catholic Health Care Ethics. Washington, DC: Georgetown University Press; 2004: 196-205. Subject: 20.5.1

Kelly, David F. The use and misuse of the allocation argument. *In his:* Contemporary Catholic Health Care Ethics. Washington, DC: Georgetown University Press; 2004: 286-296. Subject: 9.4

Kelly, Gillian D.; Blunt, Cornelia; Moore, Philip A.; Lewis, Margo. Consent for regional anaesthesia in the United Kingdom: what is material risk? *International Journal of Obstetric Anesthesia* 2004 April; 13(2): 71-74. Subject: 8.3.1

Kelly, Linda. Reproductive liberty under the threat of care: deputizing private agents and deconstructing state action. *Michigan Journal of Gender and Law* 1998-1999; 5(1): 81-111. Subject: 12.4.2

Kelly, Lorraine. In vitro fertilisation: the science and the ethics in the 21st century. *Human Reproduction and Genetic Ethics: An International Journal* 2001; 7(1): 15-20. Subject: 14.4

Kelly, P. Adam; Johnson, Michael L. Just-in-time IRB review: capitalizing on scientific merit review to improve human subjects research compliance. *IRB: Ethics and Human Research* 2005 March-April; 27(2): 6-10. Subject: 18.2

Kelly, Susan E. Bioethics and rural health: theorizing place, space, subjects. *Social Science and Medicine* 2003 June; 56(11): 2277-2288. Subject: 2.1

Kelly, Susan E. 'New' genetics meets the old underclass: findings from a study of genetic outreach services in rural Kentucky. *In:* Bunton, Robin; Petersen, Alan, eds. Genetic Governance: Health, Risk and Ethics in the Biotech Era. New York: Routledge; 2005: 137-151. Subject: 15.1

Kelly, Susan E. Public bioethics and publics: consensus, boundaries, and participation in biomedical science policy. *Science, Technology, and Human Values* 2003 Summer; 28(3): 339- 364. Subject: 2.4

Kelly, Victoria J. The effects of financial incentives on health care decisions. *Medical Trial Technique Quarterly* 2000; 46(4): 195-210. Subject: 9.3.2

Kemdal, Anna Blom; Montgomery, Henry. Explaining own and others' behavior in a controversial issue: animal experimentation. *Journal of Social Psychology* 2001 December; 141(6): 693-713. Subject: 22.2

Kemp, Thomas. The stem cell debate: a Veblenian perspective. *Journal of Economic Issues* 2004 June; 38(2): 421-428. Subject: 15.1

Kempers, Roger D. Ethical issues in biomedical publications. *Fertility and Sterility* 2002 May; 77(5): 883-888. Subject: 1.3.7

Kendrick, Kevin. Accountability in practice: professional codes and accountable practice. *Professional Nurse* 1995 April; 10(7): supplement 1-4. Subject: 4.1.3

Kennedy, Donald. Better never than late [editorial]. *Science* 2005 October 14; 310(5746): 195. Subject: 21.3

Kennedy, Donald. Neuroimaging: revolutionary research tool or a post-modern phrenology? *American Journal of Bioethics* 2005 March-April; 5(2): 19. Subject: 17.1

Kennedy, Donald; Mobley, William. Are there things we'd rather not know? *Cerebrum: The Dana Forum on Brain Science* 2002 Summer; 4(3): 67-68. Subject: 17.1

Kennedy, Patrick J. Why we must end insurance discrimination against mental health care. *Harvard Journal on Legislation* 2004 Summer; 41(2): 363-375. Subject: 9.3.1

Kennedy, Sheila Suess. The muffled voice of the child: American health care and children's rights. *Journal of Medicine and Law* 2001 Fall; 6(1): 51-64. Subject: 8.3.2

Kennedy, Wendy. Beneficence and autonomy in nursing: a moral dilemma. *British Journal of Perioperative Nursing* 2004 November; 14(11): 500-506. Subject: 8.3.4

Kennett, Jeanette; Matthews, Steve. Seeing the self: the moral goals of service provision in the mental health sector. *Res Publica* 2005; 14(2): 1-5. Subject: 17.1

Kennicott, Philip. The seduction of science to perfect an imperfect race. *International Journal of Health Services* 2005; 35(2): 399- 404. Subject: 15.5

Kenny, Michael G. Racial science in social context: John R. Baker on eugenics, race, and the public role of the scientist. *Isis* 2004 September; 95(3): 394-419. Subject: 15.5

Kenny, Nuala; Giacomini, Mita. Wanted: a new ethics field for health policy analysis. *Health Care Analysis: An International Journal of Health Care Philosophy and Policy* 2005 December; 13(4): 247-260. Subject: 2.1

Kenny, Robert Wade. A cycle of terms implicit in the idea of medicine: Karen Ann Quinlan as a rhetorical icon and the transvaluation of the ethics of euthanasia. *Health Communication* 2005; 17(1): 17-39. Subject: 20.5.1

Kent, Gerry. Shared understandings for informed consent: the relevance of psychological research on the provision of information. *Social Science and Medicine* 1996 November; 43(10): 1517-1523. Subject: 18.3

Keogh, Louise A.; Southey, Melissa C.; Maskiell, Judi; Young, Mary-Anne; Gaff, Clara L.; Kirk, Judy; Tucker, Katherine M.; Rosenthal, Doreen; McCredie, Margaret R.E.; Giles, Graham G.; Hopper, John L. Uptake of offer to receive genetic information about BRCA1 and BRCA2 mutations in an Australian population-based study. *Cancer Epidemiology, Biomarkers and Prevention* 2004 December; 13(12): 2258-2263. Subject: 15.3

Keough, William J. All in the family: a child welfare perspective on human reproductive cloning. *Health Law Journal* 2003; 11: 71-87. Subject: 14.5

Keown, Damien. Buddhism and bioethics. *In:* Peppin, John F.; Cherry, Mark J., eds. Religious Perspectives in Bioethics. New York: Taylor & Francis; 2004: 173- 188. Subject: 2.1

Keown, Damien. End of life: the Buddhist view [opinion]. *Lancet* 2005 September 10-16; 366(9489): 952-955. Subject: 20.5.1

Keown, John. Dehydrating bodies: the Bland case, the Winterton bill and the importance of intention in evaluating end-of-life decision-making. *In:* Bainham, Andrew; Sclater, Shelley Day; Richards, Martin, eds. Body Lore and Laws. Portland, OR: Hart Pub.; 2002: 249-264. Subject: 20.5.1

Keown, John. A futile defence of Bland: a reply to Andrew McGee [debate]. *Medical Law Review* 2005 Autumn; 13(3): 393-402. Subject: 20.5.1

Keown, John. Medical murder by omission? The law and ethics of withholding and withdrawing treatment and tube feeding. *Clinical Medicine* 2003 September-October; 3(5): 460-463. Subject: 20.5.1

Keown, John. No charter for assisted suicide. *Cambridge Law Journal* 1994 July; 53(2): 234-236. Subject: 20.5.1

Keown, Rebecca. In that case. Response [case study]. *Journal of Bioethical Inquiry* 2005; 2(1): 56. Subject: 16.3

Keppel, Kenneth G.; Pearcy, Jeffrey N.; Weissman, Joel S.; Vaccarino, Viola; Jha, Ashish K.; Epstein, Arnold M.; Orav, E. John. Trends in racial disparities in care [letter and reply]. *New England Journal of Medicine* 2005 November 10; 353(19): 2082-2085. Subject: 9.5.4

Kerekes, Robert J. My child . . . but not my heir: technology, the law, and post-mortem conception. *Real Property, Probate and Trust Journal* 1996 Summer; 31(2): 213-249. Subject: 14.6

Kerian, Christine L. Surrogacy: a last resort alternative for infertile women or a commodification of women's bodies and children? *Wisconsin Women's Law Journal* 1997 Spring; 12(1): 113-166. Subject: 14.2

Kerkhof, Ad J.F.M. End-of-Life decisions in The Netherlands, 1990-2001 [editorial]. *Crisis* 2004; 25(3): 97-98. Subject: 20.5.1

Kero, A.; Högberg, U.; Jacobsson, L.; Lalos, A. Legal abortion: a painful necessity. *Social Science and Medicine* 2001 December; 53(11): 1481-1490. Subject: 12.5.2

Kero, A.; Lalos, Ann. Reactions and reflections in men, 4 and 12 months post-abortion. *Journal of Psychosomatic* *and Obstetric Gynaecology* 2004 June; 25(2): 135-143. Subject: 12.5.2

Kerr, Susan M.; McIntosh, Jean B. Disclosure of disability: exploring the perspective of parents. *Midwifery* 1998 December; 14(4): 225-232. Subject: 9.5.7

Kerridge, I.H.; Pearson, S.; Rolfe, I.E. Determining the function of a hospital clinical ethics committee: making ethics work. *Journal of Quality in Clinical Practice* 1998 June; 18(2): 117-124. Subject: 9.6

Kerridge, Ian; Gilroy, Nicole. In that case [case study]. *Journal of Bioethical Inquiry* 2005; 2(1): 51. Subject: 9.5.1

Kerridge, Ian H.; Savulescu, Julian; Komesaroff, Paul A. Is there a future for clinical ethics services in Australia? *Medical Journal of Australia* 2001 August 20; 175(4): 211-213. Subject: 9.6

Kerrison, S.; Pollock, A.M. The reform of UK research ethics committees: throwing the baby out with the bath water? *Journal of Medical Ethics* 2005 August; 31(8): 487-489. Subject: 18.2

Kerruish, N.J.; Robertson, S.P. Newborn screening: new developments, new dilemmas. *Journal of Medical Ethics* 2005 July; 31(7): 393-398. Subject: 9.5.7

Kersh, Rogan; Morone, James A. Obesity, courts, and the new politics of public health. *Journal of Health Politics, Policy and Law* 2005 October; 30(5): 839-868. Subject: 9.1

Kerstein, Samuel J. Extra embryos. *Maryland Medicine* 2003 Summer; 4(3): 31-33. Subject: 18.5.4

Keshavarz, Reza; Merchant, Roland C.; McGreal, John. Emergency contraception provision: a survey of emergency department practitioners. *Academic Emergency Medicine* 2002 January; 9(1): 69-74. Subject: 9.5.1

Keshavjee, Salmaan. Medicine and money: the ethical transformation of medical practice. *Medical Education* 2004 March; 38(3): 271-275. Subject: 9.3.1

Kesselheim, Aaron S.; Avorn, Jerry. University-based science and biotechnology products: defining the boundaries of intellectual property. *JAMA: The Journal of the American Medical Association* 2005 February 16; 293(7): 850-854. Subject: 5.3

Kettner, Matthias. Überlegungen zu einer integrierten Theorie von Ethik- Kommissionen und Ethik-Komitees. *In:* Jahrbuch für Wissenschaft und Ethik. Bd. 7. Berlin: Walter de Gruyter; 2002: 53-71. Subject: 2.4

Keulartz, Jozef; Schermer, Maartje; Korthals, Michiel; Swierstra, Tsjalling. Ethics in technological culture: a programmatic proposal for a pragmatist approach. *Science, Technology, and Human Values* 2004 Winter; 29(1): 3-29. Subject: 5.3

Kevles, Daniel J. International eugenics. *In:* Bachrach, Susan, project director; Kuntz, Dieter, ed. Deadly Medi-cine: Creating the Master Race. Washington, DC: United States Holocaust Museum; 2004: 41-59. Subject: 15.5

Keyes, W. Noel. The choice of participation by physicians in capital punishment. *Whittier Law Review* 2001 Spring; 22(3): 809-840. Subject: 20.6

Khajawi, Fei. Personal autonomy when deciding on medical treatment: placental and umbilical cord blood stem cell transplantation. *Medical Trial Technique Quarterly* 2002; 48(4): 347-373. Subject: 9.2

Khalil, Omar; Govinarajan, Rangaswamy; Safar, Mazin; Hutchins, Laura; Mehta, Paulette; DeAngelis, Catherine D. Clinical trial registration and the ICMJE [letter and reply]. *JAMA: The Journal of the American Medical Association* 2005 January 12; 293(2): 157-158. Subject: 18.6

Khanijou, Siddharth. Multifetal pregnancy reduction in assisted reproductive technologies: a license to kill? *DePaul Journal of Health Care Law* 2005; 8(2): 403-430. Subject: 14.4

Khanlou, N.; Peter, E. Participatory action research: considerations for ethical review. *Social Science and Medicine* 2005 May; 60(10): 2333-2340. Subject: 18.1

Kharaboyan, Linda; Avard, Denise; Knoppers, Bartha Maria. Storing newborn blood spots: modern controversies. *Journal of Law, Medicine and Ethics* 2004 Winter; 32(4): 741- 748. Subject: 15.2

Khoshnood, Babak; De Vigan, Catherine; Vodovar, Véronique; Goujard, Janine; Lhomme, Anne; Bonnet, Damien; Goffinet, François. Trends in prenatal diagnosis, pregnancy termination, and perinatal mortality of newborns with congenital heart disease in France, 1983-2000: a population-based evaluation. *Pediatrics* 2005 January; 115(1): 95-101. Subject: 15.2

Kian, Catherine Tay Swee; Leng, Tien Sim. The Singapore approach to human stem cell research, therapeutic and reproductive cloning. *Bioethics* 2005 June; 19(3): 290-303. Subject: 18.5.4

Kiel, Helen. Pharmacist misconduct: the pitfalls of practice. *Journal of Law and Medicine* 2005 February; 12(3): 348-353. Subject: 9.7

Kielstein, Rita. Differenzierte Selbstbestimmung bei der Organspende—ethische und rechtliche Konsequenzen einer empirischen Umfrage. *In:* Baumann, Eva; Brink, Alexander; May, Arnd T.; Schröder; Peter; Schutzeichel, Corinna Iris, eds. Weltanschauliche Offenheit in der Bioethik. Berlin: Duncker & Humblot; 2004: 271-290. Subject: 19.5

Kier, Frederick J.; Molinari, Victor. Do-it-yourself testing for mental illness: ethical issues, concerns, and recommendations. *Professional Psychology: Research and Practice* 2004 June; 35(3): 261-267. Subject: 17.1

Kiessling, Ann A. Eggs alone — human parthenotes: an ethical source of stem cells for therapies? *Nature* 2005 March 10; 434(7030): 145. Subject: 18.5.4

Kietinun, Somboon; Gupte, M.D.; Sengupta, Amit. A clinical trial in a developing country: many questions, few answers [case study and commentaries]. *Issues in Medical Ethics* 2003 July-September; 11(3): 89-90. Subject: 18.5.9

Kikuchi, June F. 2002 CNA Code of Ethics: some recommendations. *Canadian Journal of Nursing Leadership* 2004 July; 17(3): 28-38. Subject: 6

Killen, Jack; Grady, Christine; Folkers, Gregory K.; Fauci, Anthony S. Ethics of clinical research in the developing world [opinion]. *Nature Reviews Immunology* 2002 March; 2(3): 210-215. Subject: 18.5.9

Kilpatrick, Shelley Dean; Weaver, Andrew J.; McCullough, Michael E.; Puchalski, Christina; Larson, David B.; Hays, Judith C.; Farran, Carol J.; Flannelly, Kevin J. A review of spiritual and religious measures in nursing research journals: 1995-1999. *Journal of Religion and Health* 2005 Spring; 44(1): 55-66. Subject: 4.1.3

Kilpi, Jukka. On corporate ethical responsibility, stakeholder value, and strict liability in biotechnology. *In:* Häyry, Matti; Takala, Tuija; Herissone-Kelly, Peter, eds. Bioethics and Social Reality. New York: Rodopi, 2005: 113-125. Subject: 15.7

Kim, Eunjung. Protection of child human subjects. *Journal of Wound, Ostomy, and Continence Nursing* 2004 July-August; 31(4): 161-167. Subject: 18.5.2

Kim, Jim Yong; Gilks, Charlie. Scaling up treatment — why we can't wait [editorial]. *New England Journal of Medicine* 2005 December 1; 353(22): 2392-2394. Subject: 9.5.6

Kim, Scott Y.H. Commentary: financial conflicts of interest and the identity of academic medicine. *In:* Moore, Don A.; Cain, Daylian M.; Loewenstein, George; Bazerman, Max H., eds. Conflicts of Interest: Challenges and Solutions in Business, Law, Medicine, and Public Policy. New York: Cambridge University Press; 2005: 181-186. Subject: 7.3

Kim, Scott Y.H. The dilemma of hidden ethical dilemmas. *Academic Psychiatry* 2004 Fall; 28(3): 168-169. Subject: 2.3

Kim, Scott Y.H.; Karlawish, Jason H.T. Ethics and politics of research involving subjects with impaired decision-making abilities [editorial]. *Neurology* 2003 December 23; 61(12): 1645-1646. Subject: 18.5.6

Kim, Su Hyun; Kjervik, Diane. Deferred decision making: patients' reliance on family and physicians for CPR decisions in critical care. *Nursing Ethics* 2005 September; 12(5): 493-506. Subject: 20.5.1

Kim, Yong-Soon; Park, Jee-Won; You, Mi-Ae; Seo, Ye-Suk; Han, Sung-Suk. Sensitivity to ethical issues confronted by Korean hospital staff nurses. *Nursing Ethics* 2005 November; 12(6): 595-605. Subject: 4.1.3

Kimbel, Anne Sullivan. Pregnant drug abusers are treated like criminals or not treated at all: a third option proposed. *Journal of Contemporary Health Law and Policy* 2004 Winter; 21(1): 36-66. Subject: 9.5.5

Kimberly, Michael B.; Forte, Amanda L.; Carroll, Jean M.; Feudtner, Chris. A response to selected commentaries on "pediatric do-not- attempt-resuscitation orders and public schools: a national assessment of policies and laws" [letter]. *American Journal of Bioethics [Online]* 2005 January-February; 5(1): W19-W21. Subject: 20.5.2

Kimberly, Michael B.; Forte, Amanda L.; Carroll, Jean M.; Feudtner, Chris. Pediatric do-not-attempt-resuscitation orders and public schools: a national assessment of policies and laws. *American Journal of Bioethics* 2005 January-February; 5(1): 59- 65. Subject: 20.5.2

Kimmelman, Jonathan. Medical research, risk, and bystanders. *IRB: Ethics and Human Research* 2005 July-August; 27(4): 1-6. Subject: 18.2

Kimmelman, Jonathan. Recent developments in gene transfer: risk and ethics. *BMJ: British Medical Journal* 2005 January 8; 330(7482): 79-82. Subject: 15.4

Kimmelman, Jonathan; Levenstadt, Aaron. Elements of style: consent form language and the therapeutic misconception in phase 1 gene transfer trials. *Human Gene Therapy* 2005 April; 16(4): 502-508. Subject: 15.4

Kimmelman, J.; Palmour, N. Therapeutic optimism in the consent forms of phase 1 gene transfer trials: an empirical analysis. *Journal of Medical Ethics* 2005 April; 31(4): 209-214. Subject: 18.3

Kimsma, Gerrit K.; van Leeuwen, Evert. The human body as field of conflict between discourses. *Theoretical Medicine and Bioethics* 2005; 26(6): 559-574. Subject: 9.5.6

Kimsma, Gerrit K.; van Leeuwen, Evert. Shifts in the direction of Dutch bioethics: forward or backward? *CQ: Cambridge Quarterly of Healthcare Ethics* 2005 Summer; 14(3): 292-297. Subject: 9.3.1

Kimsma, Gerrit; Obstein, Keith L.; Chambers, Tod. A response to Shalowitz and Emanuel. *Journal of Clinical Ethics* 2005 Summer; 16(2): 176-178. Subject: 20.5.1

Kind, Terry; Silber, Tomas Jose. Ethical issues in pediatric e-health. *Clinical Pediatrics* 2004 September; 43(7): 593-599. Subject: 1.3.12

Kindell, Kathryn. Prescription for fairness: health insurance reimbursement for Viagra and contraceptives. *Tulsa Law Journal* 2000 Winter; 35(2): 399-419. Subject: 9.3.1

Kindregan, Charles P., Jr.; McBrien, Maureen. Embryo donation: unresolved legal issues in the transfer of surplus cryopreserved embryos. *Villanova Law Review* 2004; 49(1): 169-206. Subject: 14.6

King, Cheryl Slagle. Managed care: is it moral? [interview]. *Advanced Practice Nursing Quarterly* 1995 Winter; 1(3): 7-11. Subject: 9.3.2

Subject = NRCBL Primary Classification Number; See inside front cover

King, Jennifer. Informed consent: does practice match conviction? *Journal of the American College of Dentists* 2005 Spring; 72(1): 27-31. Subject: 8.3.1

King, Jonathan; Stabinsky, Doreen. Life patents undermine the exchange of technology and scientific ideas. *In:* Krimsky, Sheldon; Shorett, Peter, eds. Rights and Liberties in the Biotech Age: Why We Need a Genetic Bill of Rights. Lanham: Rowman and Littlefield Publishers; 2005: 49-54. Subject: 15.8

King, Kevin M. A proposal for the effective international regulation of biomedical research involving human subjects. *Stanford Journal of International Law* 1998 Winter; 34(1): 163-206. Subject: 18.3

King, Milandria. Cold shoulder treatment: the disposition of frozen embryos post-divorce. *Thurgood Marshall Law Review* 1999 Fall-2000 Spring; 25(1-2): 99-137. Subject: 14.6

King, Nancy M.P.; Churchill, Larry R. Ethical principles guiding research on child and adolescent subjects. *Journal of Interpersonal Violence* 2000 July; 15(7): 710-724. Subject: 18.5.2

King, Nancy M.P.; Henderson, Gail E.; Churchill, Larry R.; Davis, Arlene M.; Hull, Sara Chandros; Nelson, Daniel K.; Parham- Vetter, P. Christy; Rothschild, Barbra Bluestone; Easter, Michele M.; Wilfond, Benjamin S. Consent forms and the therapeutic misconception: the example of gene transfer research. *IRB: Ethics and Human Research* 2005 January-February; 27(1): 1-8. Subject: 18.3

King, Nicholas B. The ethics of biodefense. *Bioethics* 2005 August; 19(4): 432-446. Subject: 21.3

King, Patricia A. Justice beyond Belmont. *In:* Childress, James F.; Meslin, Eric M.; Shapiro, Harold T., eds. Belmont Revisited: Ethical Principles for Research with Human Subjects. Washington, DC: Georgetown University Press; 2005: 136-147. Subject: 18.2

King, William D. Examining African Americans' mistrust of the health care system: expanding the research question. Commentary on "Race and trust in the health care system". *Public Health Reports* 2003 July-August; 118(3): 366-367. Subject: 9.5.4

Kingdon, David; Jones, Roland; Lönnqvist, Jouko. Protecting the human rights of people with mental disorder: new recommendations emerging from the Council of Europe [editorial]. *British Journal of Psychiatry* 2004 October; 185: 277-279. Subject: 17.1

Kingsland, James. Colour-coded cures. *New Scientist* 2005 June 11-17; 186(2503): 42-47. Subject: 15.1

Kinlaw, Kathy. Ethical issues in palliative care. *Seminars in Oncology Nursing* 2005 February; 21(1): 63-68. Subject: 20.5.1

Kinney, Anita Yeomans; Choi, Yeon-Ah; DeVellis, Brenda; Millikan, Robert; Kobetz, Erin; Sandler, Rob-

ert S. Attitudes toward genetic testing in patients with colorectal cancer. *Cancer Practice* 2000 July-August; 8(4): 178-186. Subject: 15.3

Kinney, Eleanor D. The international human right to health: what does this mean for our nation and world? *Indiana Law Review* 2001; 34(4): 1457-1475. Subject: 9.2

Kinsella, Elizabeth Anne. Constructions of self: ethical overtones in surprising locations. *Medical Humanities* 2005 December; 31(2): 67-71. Subject: 4.1.1

Kintisch, Eli. Anticloning forces launch second-term offensive [news]. *Science* 2005 March 18; 307(5716): 1702-1703. Subject: 14.5

Kintisch, Eli. Researcher faces prison for fraud in NIH grant applications and papers. *Science* 2005 March 25; 307(5717): 1851. Subject: 1.3.9

Kinzbrunner, Barry M. Jewish medical ethics and end-of-life care. *Journal of Palliative Medicine* 2004 August; 7(4): 558-573. Subject: 20.5.1

Kipnis, Kenneth. The elements of code development [comment]. *American Journal of Bioethics* 2005 September-October; 5(5): 48-50. Subject: 6

Kipnis, Kenneth. Ethics expertise in civil litigation. *Journal of Law, Medicine and Ethics* 2005 Summer; 33(2): 274- 278. Subject: 2.1

Kipnis, Kenneth. Vulnerability in research subjects: an analytical approach. *In:* Thomasma, David C.; Weisstub, David N., eds. The Variables of Moral Capacity. Boston: Kluwer Academic Publishers; 2004: 217- 231. Subject: 18.5.1

Kipnis, Kenneth; Gerhard, Anita. Some ethical principles for adult critical care. *In:* Thomasma, David C.; Weisstub, David N., eds. The Variables of Moral Capacity. Boston: Kluwer Academic Publishers; 2004: 151- 157. Subject: 9.5.1

Kirby, Michael. The Human Genome Project in the dock. *Medical Journal of Australia* 2000 December 4-18; 173(11-12): 599-600. Subject: 15.10

Kirby, Michael. The right to health fifty years on: still skeptical? *Health and Human Rights: An International Journal* 1999; 4(1): 7-25. Subject: 9.2

Kirchhof, Paul. Ethik und Recht als Maßstabe fur medizinisches und biotechnologisches Handeln. *In:* Jahrbuch für Wissenschaft und Ethik. Bd. 7. Berlin: Walter de Gruyter; 2002: 5-21. Subject: 14.1

Kirigia, Joses M.; Wambebe, Charles; Baba-Moussa, Amido. Status of national research bioethics committees in the WHO African region. *BMC Medical Ethics [electronic]* 2005; 6(10); 7 p. Available: http://www.biomedcentral.com/bmcmedethics/ [24 November 2005]. Subject: 18.2

Kirk, Dwayne D.; Robert, Jason Scott. Assessing commercial feasibility: a practical and ethical prerequisite for human clinical testing. *Accountability in Research* 2005 October-December; 12(4): 281- 297. Subject: 18.2

Kirk, Linda. Dialysis decisions: should everyone be dialyzed? *Nephrology Nursing Journal* 2005 January-February; 32(1): 96. Subject: 8.3.3

Kirk, Lynne M.; Blank, Linda L. Professional behavior — a learner's permit for licensure [editorial]. *New England Journal of Medicine* 2005 December 22; 353(25): 2709-2711. Subject: 7.2

Kirkevold, Øyvind; Engedal, Knut. Concealment of drugs in food and beverages in nursing homes: cross sectional study. *BMJ: British Medical Journal* 2005 January 1; 330(7481): 20-22. Subject: 9.5.2

Kirkevold, Øyvind; Engedal, Knut. Prevalence of patients subjected to constraint in Norwegian nursing homes. *Scandinavian Journal of Caring Sciences* 2004 September; 18(3): 281-286. Subject: 17.3

Kirkman, Maggie. Egg and embryo donation and the meaning of motherhood. *Women and Health* 2003; 38(2): 1-18. Subject: 14.4

Kirkpatrick, David D.; Stolberg, Sheryl Gay. How family's cause reached the halls of congress; network of Christians rallied to case of Florida woman. *New York Times* 2005 March 22; p. A1, A18. Subject: 20.5.1

Kirsh, Nurit. Genetic research on Israel's populations: two opposite tendencies. *In:* Roelcke, Volker; Maio, Giovanni, eds. Twentieth Century Ethics of Human Subjects Research: Historical Perspectives on Values, Practices, and Regulations. Stuttgart: Franz Steiner Verlag; 2004: 309-317. Subject: 15.1

Kirtane, Jyotsna. Ethics in intersex disorders. *Issues in Medical Ethics* 2000 April-June; 8(2): 47-48. Subject: 10

Kishore, R.R. Human organs, scarcities, and sale: morality revisited. *Journal of Medical Ethics* 2005 June; 31(6): 362-365. Subject: 19.5

Kissane, David W. The contribution of demoralization to end of life decisionmaking. *Hastings Center Report* 2004 July-August; 34(4): 21-31. Subject: 20.5.1

Kissell, Judith Lee. The procedural morphing of the person: from self to property. *In:* Thomasma, David C.; Weisstub, David N.; Herve, Christian eds. Personhood and Health Care. Boston: Kluwer Academic Pub.; 2001: 191-202. Subject: 4.4

Kissell, Judith Lee. "Suspended animation," my mother's wife and cultural discernment: considerations for genetic research among immigrants. *Theoretical Medicine and Bioethics* 2005; 26(6): 515-528. Subject: 15.1

Kissling, Frances. Is there life after Roe? How to think about the fetus. *Conscience* 2004-2005 Winter; 25(3): 10-18. Subject: 12.3

Kittay, Eva Feder. At the margins of moral personhood. *Ethics: An International Journal of Social, Political, and*

Legal Philosophy 2005 October; 116(1): 100-131. Subject: 4.4

Klaiman, M.H. Whose brain is it anyway? The comparative law of post-mortem organ retention. *Journal of Legal Medicine* 2005 December; 26(4): 475-490. Subject: 19.5

Klanica, Kaley. Conflicts of interest in medical research: how much conflict should exceed legal boundaries? *Journal of Biolaw and Business* 2005; 8(3): 37-45. Subject: 1.3.9

Klein, Dora W. Involuntary treatment of the mentally ill: autonomy is asking the wrong question. *Specialty Law Digest: Health Care Law* 2004 August; (304): 9-40. Subject: 17.7

Klein, Jonathan D.; McNulty, Molly; Flatau, Claudia N. Adolescents' access to care: teenagers' self-reported use of services and perceived access to confidential care. *Archives of Pediatric and Adolescent Medicine* 1998 July; 152(7): 676-682. Subject: 9.5.7

Klein, Michael C. Quick fix culture: the cesarean-section-on-demand debate [editorial]. *Birth* 2004 September; 31(3): 161-164. Subject: 9.5.5

Klein, Robert. The next big thing [opinion]. *New Scientist* 2005 August 6-12; 187(2511): 19. Subject: 18.5.4

Kleinman, Arthur. Ethics and experience: an anthropological approach to health equity. *In:* Anand, Sudhir; Peter, Fabienne; Sen, Amartya, eds. Public Health, Ethics, and Equity. New York: Oxford University Press; 2004: 269-282. Subject: 9.2

Klepatsky, Arlene; Mahlmeister, Laura. Consent and informed consent in perinatal and neonatal settings. *Journal of Perinatal and Neonatal Nursing* 1997 June; 11(1): 34-51. Subject: 8.3.1

Klinck, Elsabé. Health databases: basic legal and ethical principles. *South African Medical Journal* 2001 August; 91(8): 642. Subject: 8.4

Kline, Robert L. Give me liberty and give me death: assisted suicide as a fundamental liberty interest. *Boston University Public Interest Law Journal* 1997 Winter; 6(2): 527- 550. Subject: 20.7

Klinkenberg, Marianne; Willems, Dick L.; Onwuteaka-Philipsen, Bregje D.; Deeg, Dorly J.H.; van der Wal, Gerrit. Preferences in end-of-life care of older persons: after-death interviews with proxy respondents. *Social Science and Medicine* 2004 December; 59(12): 2467-2477. Subject: 20.3.1

Klitzman, Robert. The importance of social, cultural, and economic contexts, and empirical research in examining "undue inducement" [comment]. *American Journal of Bioethics* 2005 September-October; 5(5): 19-21. Subject: 18.3

Klitzman, Robert; Siragusa, Joseph. Contexts, anyone? The need for contextualization in the debate about the moral status of embryos. *American Journal of Bioethics* 2005 November-December; 5(6): 56-58. Subject: 4.4

Kluge, Eike-Henner W. Informed consent to the secondary use of EHRs: informatic rights and their limitations. *Medinfo* 2004; 11(Part 1): 635-638. Subject: 8.3.1

Klugman, Craig M. As advisors, nondirectional consultation is best [comment]. *American Journal of Bioethics* 2005 September-October; 5(5): 56-57. Subject: 2.1

Kmietowicz, Zosia. Plan aims to end discrimination in mental health services [news]. *BMJ: British Medical Journal* 2005 January 15; 330(7483): 113. Subject: 17.1

Knight, Elizabeth Dawes; Runyan, Desmond K.; Dubowitz, Howard; Brandford, Carol; Kotch, Jonathan; Litrownik, Alan; Hunter, Wanda. Methodological and ethical challenges associated with child self-report of maltreatment: solutions implemented by the LongSCAN Consortium. *Journal of Interpersonal Violence* 2000 July; 15(7): 760-775. Subject: 18.5.2

Knoll, Andrew M. The reawakening of complementary and alternative medicine at the turn of the twenty-first century: filling the void in conventional biomedicine. *Journal of Contemporary Health Law and Policy* 2004 Spring; 20(2): 329-366. Subject: 4.1.1

Knoll, Greg; Cockfield, Sandra; Blydt-Hansen, Tom; Baran, Dana; Kiberd, Bryce; Landsberg, David; Rush, David; Cole, Edward. Canadian Society of Transplantation consensus guidelines on eligibility for kidney transplantation. *CMAJ/JAMC: Canadian Medical Association Journal* 2005 November 8; 173(10): 1181-1184. Subject: 19.3

Knoppers, Bartha Maria. Biobanking: international norms. *Journal of Law, Medicine and Ethics* 2005 Spring; 33(1): 7-14. Subject: 15.1

Knoppers, Bartha Maria. Consent revisited: points to consider. *Health Law Review* 2005; 13(2-3): 33-38. Subject: 18.3

Knoppers, Bartha Maria. Duty to recontact: a legal harbinger? [editorial]. *American Journal of Medical Genetics* 2001 November 1; 103(4): 277. Subject: 15.3

Knoppers, Bartha Maria. Genetic information and the family: are we our brother's keeper? *Trends in Biotechnology* 2002 February; 20(2): 85-86. Subject: 15.1

Knoppers, Bartha Maria. Neuroethics, new ethics? *American Journal of Bioethics* 2005 March-April; 5(2): 33. Subject: 17.1

Knoppers, Bartha Maria. Of biotechnology and man [opinion]. *Community Genetics* 2005 January; 7(4): 176-181. Subject: 15.1

Knoppers, Bartha Maria. Of genomics and public health: building public "goods"? *CMAJ/JAMC: Canadian Medical Association Journal* 2005 November 8; 173(10): 1185-1186. Subject: 15.1

Knoppers, Bartha Maria; Chadwick, Ruth. Human genetic research: emerging trends in ethics [opinion]. *Nature Reviews Genetics* 2005 January; 6(1): 75-79. Subject: 15.1

Knoppers, Bartha Maria; Isasi, Rosario M. Regulatory approaches to reproductive genetic testing [opinion]. *Human Reproduction* 2004 December; 19(12): 2695-2701. Subject: 15.3

Koay, Pei P. An Icelandic (ad-)venture: new research? new subjects? new ethics? *In:* Roelcke, Volker; Maio, Giovanni, eds. Twentieth Century Ethics of Human Subjects Research: Historical Perspectives on Values, Practices, and Regulations. Stuttgart: Franz Steiner Verlag; 2004: 335-348. Subject: 15.1

Koch, Hans-Georg. Vom Embryonenschutzgesetz zum Stammzellgesetz: Überlegungen zum Status des Embryos in vitro aus rechtlicher und rechtsvergleichender Sicht. *In:* Maio, Giovanni; Just, Hanjörg, eds. Die Forschung an embryonalen Stammzellen in ethischer und rechtlicher Perspektive. Baden-Baden: Nomos Verlagsgesellschaft; 2003: 97-118. Subject: 18.5.4

Koch, Lene. The meaning of eugenics: reflections on the government of genetic knowledge in the past and the present. *Science in Context* 2004 September; 17(3): 315-331. Subject: 15.5

Koch, Lene; Svendsen, Mette Nordahl. Providing solutions — defining problems: the imperative of disease prevention in genetic counselling. *Social Science and Medicine* 2005 February; 60(4): 823-832. Subject: 15.3

Koch, T. The challenge of Terri Schiavo: lessons for bioethics. *Journal of Medical Ethics* 2005 July; 31(7): 376-378. Subject: 20.5.1

Kocieniewski, David. New Jersey med school board faces ethics charges. *New York Times* 2005 September 23; p. B1, B7. Subject: 7.2

Kocis, Keith C. Pediatric cardiac extracorporeal membrane oxygenation: supporting life or prolonging death? *Critical Care Medicine* 2000 February; 28(2): 594-595. Subject: 20.5.2

Kodish, Eric D. Testing children for cancer genes: the rule of earliest onset. *Journal of Pediatrics* 1999 September; 135(3): 390-395. Subject: 15.2

Kodner, Ira J. Surgeons' ethics? You bet! [editorial]. *Surgery* 2002 May; 131(5): 581-582. Subject: 4.1.2

Koenig, Barbara A.; Greely, Henry; Schacter, Daniel L.; Winslade, William J.; Mobley, William. Brain science and social policy. *Cerebrum: The Dana Forum on Brain Science* 2002 Summer; 4(3): 59-62. Subject: 17.1

Koerber, Anne; Botto, Ronald W.; Pendleton, Darryl D.; Albazzaz, Michael B.; Doshi, Siddhi J.; Rinando, Victoria A. Enhancing ethical behavior: views of students, administrators, and faculty. *Journal of Dental Education* 2005 February; 69(2): 213-224. Subject: 7.2

Koggel, Christine M. Confidentiality in the liberal tradition: a relational critique. *In:* Koggel, Christine M.; Furlong, Allannah; Levin, Charles, eds. Confidential Relationships: Psychoanalytical, Ethical, and Legal Contexts. New York: Rodopi; 2003: 113-131. Subject: 8.4

Kohane, Isaac S.; Altman, Russ B. Health-information altruists — a potentially critical resource. *New England Journal of Medicine* 2005 November 10; 353(19): 2074-2077. Subject: 15.1

Kohm, Lynne Marie. Sex selection abortion and the boomerang effect of a woman's right to choose: a paradox of the skeptics. *William and Mary Journal of Women and the Law* 1997 Winter; 4(1): 91-128. Subject: 14.3

Kohrs, Brendon. Bioterrorism defense: are state mandated compulsory vaccination programs an infringement upon a citizen's constitutional rights? *Journal of Law and Health* 2002-2003; 17(2): 241-270. Subject: 8.3.4

Kol, Shahar; Itskovitz-Eldor, Joseph. Society's contribution to assisted reproductive technology abuse [letter]. *Human Reproduction* 2005 August; 20(8): 2362. Subject: 14.6

Kolata, Gina. Beating hurdles, scientists clone a dog for a first; feat for South Koreans; success with afghan pup is called "dry run" for debate on humans. *New York Times* 2005 August 4; p. A1, A10. Subject: 14.5

Kolata, Gina. Clone scandal: "a tragic turn" for science. *New York Times* 2005 December 16; p. A6. Subject: 1.3.9

Kolata, Gina. Koreans report ease in cloning for stem cells; work on human embryos; researchers say goal is better medicine, not reproduction. *New York Times* 2005 May 20; p. A1, A22. Subject: 14.5

Kolata, Gina. Panel to advise tests on babies for 29 diseases. *New York Times* 2005 February 21; p. A1, A14. Subject: 15.3

Kolata, Gina. When the doctor is in, but you wish he wasn't. *New York Times* 2005 November 30; p. A1, A28. Subject: 8.1

Kolber, Adam J. A matter of priority: transplanting organs preferentially to registered donors. *Rutgers Law Review* 2003 Spring; 55(3): 671-740. Subject: 19.5

Kolenc, Antony Barone. Easing abortion's pain: the new fight to help the unborn. *America* 2005 September 26; 193(8): 18-21. Subject: 12.4.4

Kolker, Emily S.; Timmermans, Stefan. Medical values and ethics. *In:* Restivo, Sal, ed. Science, Technology, and Society: An Encyclopedia. New York: Oxford University Press; 2005: 318-323. Subject: 2.1

Kollef, Marin H.; Ward, Suzanne. The influence of access to a private attending physician on the withdrawal of life-sustaining therapies in the intensive care unit. *Critical Care Medicine* 1999 October; 27(10): 2125-2132. Subject: 20.5.1

Kolodner, Deborah E. Advance medical directives after Cruzan [opinion]. *Medsurg Nursing* 1992 September; 1(1): 56-59. Subject: 20.5.4

Komesaroff, Paul A. Clinical research in the emergency setting: the role of ethics committees. *Medical Journal of Australia* 2001 December 3-17; 175(11-12): 630-631. Subject: 18.2

Komesaroff, Paul A. Use of complementary medicines: scientific and ethical issues [editorial]. *Medical Journal of Australia* 1998 August 17; 169(4): 180-181. Subject: 4.1.1

Komesaroff, Paul A.; Cohen, Alex. The growth of ethics in medicine over the past 50 years. *Medical Journal of Australia* 2001 January 1; 174(1): 41-44. Subject: 2.1

Komesaroff, Paul A.; Kerridge, Ian H. Ethical issues concerning the relationships between medical practitioners and the pharmaceutical industry. *Medical Journal of Australia* 2002 February 4; 176(3): 118-121. Subject: 7.1

Komesaroff, P.A. Misconduct in medical research: ethics and democracy [editorial]. *Internal Medicine Journal* 2003 April; 33(4): 137-139. Subject: 1.3.9

Kondo, Kazuya. The organ transplant law of Japan — the past, the present, and the future. *Journal International de Bioethique / International Journal of Bioethics* 2005 March-June; 16(1-2): 91-102, 195. Subject: 19.5

Kondro, Wayne. Animal rules keep grad students out of the lab [news]. *Science* 2005 December 2; 310(5753): 1405. Subject: 22.2

Kondro, Wayne. Debate over online recruitment of organ donors. *CMAJ/JAMC: Canadian Medical Association Journal* 2005 January 18; 172(2): 165-166. Subject: 19.5

Kong, Wing May. The regulation of gene therapy research competent adult patients, today and tomorrow: implications of EU directive 2001/20/EC. *Medical Law Review* 2004 Summer; 12(2): 164-180. Subject: 15.4

Kong, W.M. Legitimate requests and indecent proposals: matters of justice in the ethical assessment of phase I trials involving competent patients. *Journal of Medical Ethics* 2005 April; 31(4): 205-208. Subject: 18.1

Koniaris, Leonidas G.; Zimmers, Teresa A.; Lubarsky, David A.; Sheldon, Jonathan P. Inadequate anaesthesia in lethal injection for execution. *Lancet* 2005 April 16-22; 365(9468): 1412-1414. Subject: 20.6

Konrad, Monica. From secrets of life to the life of secrets: tracing genetic knowledge as genealogical ethics in biomedical Britain. *Journal of the Royal Anthropological Institute* 2003 June; 9(2): 339-358. Subject: 15.1

Koocher, Gerald P. Behavioral research with children: the fenfluramine challenge. *In:* Kodish, Eric, ed. Ethics and Research with Children: A Case-Based Approach. New York: Oxford University Press; 2005: 179- 193. Subject: 18.4

Kopala, Beverly. The influence of pressure on nurses' moral capacity. *In:* Thomasma, David C.; Weisstub, David N., eds. The Variables of Moral Capacity. Boston: Kluwer Academic Publishers; 2004: 159- 171. Subject: 4.1.3

Kopelman, Loretta M. Are the 21-year-old Baby Doe rules misunderstood or mistaken? *Pediatrics* 2005 March; 115(3): 797-802. Subject: 20.5.2

Kopelman, Loretta M. The incompatibility of the United Nation's goals and conventionalist ethical relativism. *Developing World Bioethics* 2005 September; 5(3): 234-243. Subject: 2.1

Kopelman, Loretta M. Rejecting the Baby Doe Rules and defending a "negative" analysis of the best interests standard. *Journal of Medicine and Philosophy* 2005 August; 30(4): 331-352. Subject: 20.5.2

Kopelman, Loretta M. What conditions justify risky nontherapeutic or "no benefit" pediatric studies: a sliding scale analysis. *Journal of Law, Medicine and Ethics* 2004 Winter; 32(4): 749- 758. Subject: 18.2

Kopinski, Nicole E. Human-nonhuman chimeras: a regulatory proposal on the blurring of species lines. *Boston College Law Review* 2004 May; 45(3): 619-666. Subject: 15.1

Koppelman-White, Elysa. On the nature and purpose of public discourse. *American Journal of Bioethics* 2005 November-December; 5(6): 48-51. Subject: 4.4

Korcz, Keith Allen. Two moral strategies regarding abortion. *Journal of Social Philosophy* 2002 Winter; 33(4): 581-605. Subject: 12.3

Koren, Gideon; Selby, Peter; Kapur, Bhushan. Is a fetus a non-consenting patient? *Canadian Family Physician* 2004 September; 50: 1219-1221. Subject: 9.5.8

Korenman, Stanley G. Research in children: assessing risks and benefits. *Pediatric Research* 2004 August; 56(2): 165-166. Subject: 18.5.2

Korland, Lee. Sex discrimination or a hard pill for employers to swallow: examining the denial of contraceptive benefits in the wake of Erickson v. Bartell Drug Co. *Case Western Reserve Law Review* 2002; 53(2): 531-567. Subject: 11.1

Kornblut, Anne E. A next step: making rules to die by. Legislation. *New York Times* 2005 April 1; p. A18. Subject: 20.5.1

Korr, Wynne S.; Encandela, John A.; Brieland, Donald. Independence or autonomy: which is the goal? *International Journal of Law and Psychiatry* 2005 May-June; 28(3): 290-299. Subject: 17.1

Korthals, Michiel. Neither golden nugget nor Frankenstein. The need to re-embed food biotechnologies in sociocultural contexts. *In:* Thiele, F.; Ashcroft, R.E., eds. Bioethics in a Small World. Berlin: Springer; 2005: 23-31. Subject: 15.1

Körtner, Ulrich. The challenge of genetic engineering to medical anthropology and ethics. *Human Reproduction and Genetic Ethics: An International Journal* 2001; 7(1): 21-24. Subject: 15.1

Körtner, Ulrich H.J. Forschung an embryonalen Stammzellen—Zur Diskussion und Gesetzeslage in Österreich. *In:* Maio, Giovanni; Just, Hanjörg, eds. Die Forschung an embryonalen Stammzellen in ethischer und rechtlicher Perspektive. Baden-Baden: Nomos Verlagsgesellschaft; 2003: 124-140. Subject: 18.5.4

Koski, Cheryl A. The Human Genome Project: an examination of its challenge to the technological imperative. *New Genetics and Society* 2005 December; 24(3): 265-281. Subject: 15.10

Koski, Greg. Changing the paradigm: new directions in federal oversight of human research. *Journal of Pediatric Gastroenterology and Nutrition* 2003 November-December; 37 (Supplement 1): S2-S6. Subject: 18.6

Koski, Greg; Aungst, Jessica; Kupersmith, Joel; Getz, Kenneth; Rimoin, David. Cooperative research ethics review boards: a win-win solution? *IRB: Ethics and Human Research* 2005 May-June; 27(3): 1-7. Subject: 18.2

Kosner, Katka. Gypsy women launch claim following sterilisation [news]. *BMJ: British Medical Journal* 2005 February 5; 330(7486): 275. Subject: 11.3

Kosseim, Patricia. The landscape of rules governing access to personal information for health research: a view from afar. *Health Law Journal* 2003; 11: 199-215. Subject: 8.4

Kostka, Ulrike. Die Reproduktionsmedizin im Kontext der Stammzellforschung. *In:* Maio, Giovanni; Just, Hanjörg, eds. Die Forschung an embryonalen Stammzellen in ethischer und rechtlicher Perspektive. Baden-Baden: Nomos Verlagsgesellschaft; 2003: 32-41. Subject: 18.5.4

Kotalik, Jaro. Preparing for an influenza pandemic: ethical issues. *Bioethics* 2005 August; 19(4): 422-431. Subject: 9.1

Kotch, Jonathan B. Ethical issues in longitudinal child maltreatment research. *Journal of Interpersonal Violence* 2000 July; 15(7): 696-709. Subject: 18.5.2

Kothari, Manu; Mehta, Lopa. The cloning bandwagon: current discussion on the ethical consequences of genetic research is misplaced [opinion]. *Issues in Medical Ethics* 1998 January; 6(1): 17-19. Subject: 15.1

Kothari, Manu; Mehta, Lopa. Trust her inner voice. *Issues in Medical Ethics* 2001 January-March; 9(1): 27. Subject: 20.5.1

Kothari, M.L.; Mehta, L.A.; Kothari, V.M. The ethics of evidence-based therapy. *Issues in Medical Ethics* 1999 January-March; 7(1): 16-18. Subject: 9.8

Kottkamp, Nathan A. Finding clarity in a Gray opinion: a critique of Pennsylvania's informed consent doctrine. *Uni-*

versity of Pittsburgh Law Review 1999 Fall; 61(1): 241-285. Subject: 8.3.1

Kottow, Michael H. Between caring and curing. *Nursing Philosophy* 2001 April; 2(1): 53-61. Subject: 4.1.1

Kottow, Michael H. Vulnerability: what kind of principle is it? *Medicine, Health Care and Philosophy: A European Journal* 2004; 7(3): 281-287. Subject: 2.1

Kotval, Jeroo. Genetic privacy in the health care system. *In:* Krimsky, Sheldon; Shorett, Peter, eds. Rights and Liberties in the Biotech Age: Why We Need a Genetic Bill of Rights. Lanham: Rowman and Littlefield Publishers; 2005: 153-158. Subject: 15.1

Kouchner, Bernard. End-of-life reflections. *In:* Council of Europe Publishing, ed. Euthanasia. Volume I. Ethical and Human Aspects. Strasbourg: Council of Europe; Croton- on-Hudson, NY: Manhattan Publishing Co.; 2003: 97-107. Subject: 20.5.1

Kovach, Kimberlee K. Neonatology life and death decisions: can mediation help? *Capital University Law Review* 2000; 28(2): 251-292. Subject: 20.5.1

Kovacs, Gabor T.; Breheny, Sue A.; Dear, Melinda J. Embryo donation at an Australian university in-vitro fertilisation clinic: issues and outcomes. *Medical Journal of Australia* 2003 February 3; 178(3): 127-129. Subject: 14.4

Kovacs, Gabor T.; Morgan, Gary; Wood, E. Carl; Forbes, Catherine; Howlett, Donna. Community attitudes to assisted reproductive technology: a 20-year trend. *Medical Journal of Australia* 2003 November 17; 179(10): 536-538. Subject: 14.4

Kovitz, Jodi. Property in potential human life? Predicting a Canadian approach. *Health Law in Canada* 2003 August; 24(1): 1-8. Subject: 4.4

Kowalik, Monika. A brief study about the dignity of man. *Annales Universitatis Marie Curie-Sklodowska. Sectio D: Medicina* 2003; 58(2): 459-461. Subject: 4.4

Kozlowski, L.T. First, tell the truth: a dialogue on human rights, deception, and the use of smokeless tobacco as a substitute for cigarettes. *Tobacco Control* 2003 March; 12(1): 34-36. Subject: 9.5.9

Kraco, K. Body bequest programs in Minnesota. *Minnesota Medicine* 2004 June; 87(6): 8-9. Subject: 19.1

Kralik, Debbie; Warren, Jim; Price, Kay; Koch, Tina; Pignone, Gino. The ethics of research using electronic mail discussion groups. *Journal of Advanced Nursing* 2005 December; 52(5): 537-545. Subject: 18.4

Krall, Ronald; Rockhold, Frank; Rennie, Drummond. Trial registration: ignored to irresistible [letter and reply]. *JAMA: The Journal of the American Medical Association* 2005 January 12; 293(2): 158. Subject: 18.6

Kramer, Matthew H. Do animals and dead people have legal rights? *Canadian Journal of Law and Jurisprudence* 2001 January; 14(1): 29-54. Subject: 4.4

Kramer, Peter D. Real impairments, real treatments [comment]. *American Journal of Bioethics* 2005 May-June; 5(3): 62-63. Subject: 17.4

Krane, Vikki. Conversing about ethics [editorial]. *Sport Psychologist* 2003 December; 17(4): 387-390. Subject: 1.3.7

Krause, Joan H. The brief life of the gag clause: why anti-gag clause legislation isn't enough. *Tennessee Law Review* 1999 Fall; 67(1): 1-44. Subject: 9.3.2

Krause, Joan H.; Saver, Richard S. Ethics in the practice of health law. *Journal of Law, Medicine and Ethics* 2004 Winter; 32(4): 766- 769. Subject: 7.3

Krautkramer, Christian J. Beyond creativity: ADHD drug therapy as a moral damper on a child's future success [comment]. *American Journal of Bioethics* 2005 May-June; 5(3): 52-53. Subject: 17.4

Krautkramer, Christian J. Pediatric resuscitation: questioning DNAR legitimacy and offering an alternative decision-making model. *American Journal of Bioethics* 2005 January-February; 5(1): 86- 88. Subject: 20.5.2

Kravitz, Richard L.; Epstein, Ronald M.; Feldman, Mitchell D.; Franz, Carol E.; Azari, Rahman; Wilkes, Michael S.; Hinton, Ladson; Franks, Peter. Influence of patients' requests for direct-to-consumer advertised antidepressants: a randomized controlled trial. *JAMA: The Journal of the American Medical Association* 2005 April 27; 293(16): 1995-2002. Subject: 9.7

Kremer, Thomas G.; Gesten, Ellis L. Confidentiality limits of managed care and clients' willingness to self-disclose. *Professional Psychology: Research and Practice* 1998 December; 29(6): 553-558. Subject: 9.3.2

Krentz, Christopher. Frankenstein, *Gattaca*, and the quest for perfection. *In:* Van Cleve, John Vickery, ed. Genetics, Disability, and Deafness. Washington, DC: Gallaudet University Press; 2004: 189- 201. Subject: 15.1

Kreutzberg, Georg W. The rules of good science [opinion]. *EMBO Reports* 2004 April; 5(4): 330-332. Subject: 1.3.9

Kriari-Catranis, Ismini. Genetic data and confidentiality, the Estonian experiment. *Revista de Derecho y Genoma Humano / Law and the Human Genome Review* 2003 July-December; (19): 147-157. Subject: 15.10

Krieg, Randall G. A social contract for deinstitutionalization. *Journal of Social Philosophy* 2003 Fall; 34(3): 475-486. Subject: 17.7

Krimsky, Sheldon. China's gene therapy drug: do Shenzen SiBiono Gen-Tech's claims hold up? *GeneWatch* 2005 November-December; 18(6): 10-13. Subject: 15.4

Krimsky, Sheldon. From Asilomar to industrial biotechnology: risks, reductionism and regulation. *Science as Culture* 2005 December; 14(4): 309-323. Subject: 15.7

Krimsky, Sheldon; Shorett, Peter. The genetic bill of rights: advancing a rights platform in biotechnology. *GeneWatch* 2005 January-February; 18(1): 12-14, 18. Subject: 15.1

Krisberg, Kim. Court decision on medical marijuana use worries patient advocates. *Nation's Health* 2005 August; 35(6): 1, 14. Subject: 9.7

Krisberg, Kim. Law takes effect — refusal clause seen as threat to reproductive health, gag on information. *Nation's Health* 2005 February; 35(1): 1, 10. Subject: 12.4.1

Krishnan, Suneeta. Dynamic relationships in community-based research [comment]. *Indian Journal of Medical Ethics* 2005 January-March; 2(1): 25. Subject: 18.5.1

Krishnasamy, Meinir. Nursing, mortality, and emotions: Phase I and phase II clinical trials and patients with cancer. *Cancer Nursing* 1999 August; 22(4): 15 p. [Online]. Available: http://gateway.ut.ovid.com/gw1/ovidweb.cgi [3 November 2005]. Subject: 4.1.3

Kristan, Ivan. Constitutional aspects of the right to health care in Slovenia. *Medicine and Law: World Association for Medical Law* 1995; 14(3-4): 239-244. Subject: 9.2

Krones, Tanja; Schlüter, Elmar; Manolopoulos, Konstantin; Bock, Karin; Tinneberg, Hans-Rudolf; Koch, Manuela C.; Lindner, Martin; Hoffmann, Georg F.; Mayatepek, Ertan; Huels, Gerd; Neuwohner, Elke; El Ansari, Susan; Wissner, Thomas; Richter, Gerd. Public, expert and patients' opinions on preimplantation genetic diagnosis (PGD) in Germany. *Reproductive BioMedicine Online [electronic]* 2005 January; 10(1): 116-123. Available: http://www.rbmonline.com/index. html [17 February 2006]. Subject: 15.2

Krongard, Mara Lynn. A population at risk: civil commitment of substance abusers after Kansas v. Hendricks. *California Law Review* 2002 January; 90(1): 111-163. Subject: 17.7

Krosnick, Arthur; Costante, Patricia A.; Hirsch, Paul J.; Gutmann, Amy. Biomedical ethics in a democratic society. A conversation with Amy Gutmann, PhD [interview]. *New Jersey Medicine* 2003 October; 100(10): 14-20. Subject: 2.1

Krugman, Paul. Drugs, devices and doctors [opinion]. *New York Times* 2005 December 16; p. A41. Subject: 9.7

Krugman, Saul. Experiments at the Willowbrook State School [letter]. *Lancet* 1971 May 8; 1(7706): 966-967. Subject: 18.5.2

Kruip, Stephan. Prädiktive genetische Tests—Eine Stellungnahme aus der Patientenperspektive. *In:* Honnefelder, Ludger; Mieth, Dietmar; Propping, Peter; Siep, Ludwig; Wiesemann, Claudia, eds. Das genetische Wissen und die Zukunft des Menschen. New York: De Gruyter; 2003: 229-234. Subject: 15.3

Krulwich, Andrew S.; McDonald, Bruce L. Evolving constitutional privacy doctrines affecting healthcare enter-

prises. *Food and Drug Law Journal* 2000; 55(4): 491-516. Subject: 8.4

Kryworuk, Peter W.; Nickle, Susan E. Mandatory physician reporting of drivers with medical conditions: legal considerations. *Canadian Journal of Cardiology* 2004 November; 20(13): 1324-1328. Subject: 8.4

Kucher, Nils; Tapson, Victor F.; Quiroz, Rene; Mir, Samy S.; Morrison, Ruth B.; McKenzie, David; Goldhaber, Samuel Z. Gender differences in the administration of prophylaxis to prevent deep venous thrombosis. *Thrombosis and Haemostasis* 2005 February; 93(2): 284-288. Subject: 9.5.5

Kuczewski, Mark; Fiedler, Irma. Ethical issues in rehabilitation: conceptualizing the next generation of challenges [opinion]. *American Journal of Physical Medicine and Rehabilitation* 2001 November; 80(11): 848-851. Subject: 9.5.1

Kuehn, Bridget M. Advances aim to ease stem cell concerns [news]. *JAMA: The Journal of the American Medical Association* 2005 November 23-20; 294(20): 2557-2558. Subject: 18.5.4

Kuehn, Bridget M. Genetic information: how much can patients handle? *JAMA: The Journal of the American Medical Association* 2005 July 20; 294(3): 295-296. Subject: 15.1

Kuehn, Bridget M. Pharmaceutical industry funding for residencies sparks controversy. *JAMA: The Journal of the American Medical Association* 2005 April 6; 293(13): 1572, 1579-1580. Subject: 9.7

Kuflik, Arthur. Liberalism, legal moralism and moral disagreement. *Journal of Applied Philosophy* 2005; 22(2): 185-198. Subject: 2.1

Kukla, Rebecca. Conscientious autonomy: displacing decisions in health care. *Hastings Center Report* 2005 March-April; 35(2): 34-44. Subject: 8.3.1

Kulik, Ellen Gottmann. The gift of tissue: a donor mom's perspective. *In:* Youngner, Stuart J.; Anderson, Martha W.; Schapiro, Renie, eds. Transplanting Human Tissue: Ethics, Policy, and Practice. New York: Oxford University Press; 2004: 91-98. Subject: 19.5

Kulkarni, Sanjeev. Sex determination tests in India: a survey report. *Reprinted from: Radical Journal of Health* 1986; 1(3); 4 p. [Online]. Available: http://www.hsph. harvard.edu/Organizations/healthnet/SAsia/suchana /9999sexdetermination2.html [7 October 2005]. Subject: 14.3

Kuller, Lewis H.; Vaccarino, Viola; Jha, Ashish K.; Epstein, Arnold M.; Orav, E. John. Trends in racial disparities in care [letter and reply]. *New England Journal of Medicine* 2005 November 10; 353(19): 2081, 2083-2085. Subject: 9.5.4

Kulvichit, Kittisak; Kulwichit, Wanla; Lumbiganon, Pisake. Clinical trial registration. *New England Journal of Medicine* 2005 January 13; 352(2): 198-199. Subject: 18.6

Kumar, T.C. Anand. Proposed legislation for assisted reproduction technology clinics in India. *Reproductive BioMedicine Online [electronic]* 2002 November-December; 5(3): 351. Available: http://www.rbmonline.com/article/778 [1 September 2005]. Subject: 14.4

Kunin, Joshua. Brain death: revisiting the rabbinic opinions in light of current medical knowledge. *Tradition* 2004 Winter; 38(4): 48-62. Subject: 20.2.1

Kunin, Joshua. Caring for the terminally ill: halachic approaches to withholding and withdrawing of therapy. *Jewish Medical Ethics and Halacha* 2005 August; 5(1): 22-28. Subject: 20.5.1

Kunin, J.D. The search for organs: halachic perspectives on altruistic giving and the selling of organs. *Journal of Medical Ethics* 2005 May; 31(5): 269-272. Subject: 19.5

Kuntsmann, Erdmute; Maas, Ines; Epplen, Jörg T. Nicht-direktive Beratung im Rahmen prädiktiver Diagnostik bei genetischen Risiken für Kinder? *In:* Baumann, Eva; Brink, Alexander; May, Arnd T.; Schröder; Peter; Schutzeichel, Corinna Iris, eds. Weltanschauliche Offenheit in der Bioethik. Berlin: Duncker & Humblot; 2004: 259-270. Subject: 15.2

Kuramochi, Takeshi. Applications for human rights relief and the recommendations of the Japan Federation of bar associations. *Journal International de Bioethique / International Journal of Bioethics* 2005 March-June; 16(1-2): 103-116, 195-196. Subject: 19.5

Kuramochi, Takeshi. Reconsidering the dead donor rule. *Journal International de Bioethique / International Journal of Bioethics* 2005 March-June; 16(1-2): 117-122, 196-197. Subject: 20.2.1

Kurjak, Asim; Tripalo, Ana. The facts and doubts about beginning of the human life and personality. *Bosnian Journal of Basic Medical Sciences* 2004 February; 4(1): 5-14. Subject: 4.4

Kurtz, Sheldon F. The law of informed consent: from "doctor is right" to "patient has rights". *Syracuse Law Review* 2000; 50(4): 1243-1260. Subject: 8.3.1

Kurzrock, Razelle; Benjamin, Robert S. Risks and benefits of phase 1 oncology trials, revisited [editorial]. *New England Journal of Medicine* 2005 March 3; 352(9): 930-932. Subject: 18.2

Kurzweil, Ray. Human 2.0. *New Scientist* 2005 September 24-30; 187(2518): 32-37. Subject: 5.2

Kuther, Tara L. Medical decision-making and minors: issues of consent and assent. *Adolescence* 2003 Summer; 38(150): 343-358. Subject: 8.3.2

Kutlesa, Nicole J. Creating a sustainable immunization system in Canada — the case for a vaccine-related injury

compensation scheme. *Health Law Journal* 2004; 12: 201-242. Subject: 9.7

Kutty, V. Raman. Ethics in public health practice. *Issues in Medical Ethics* 2000 October-December; 8(4): 111-112. Subject: 9.1

Kvalsvig, A.J.; Unsworth, D.J. Ethics approvals and quagmires [letter]. *Clinical Medicine* 2002 November-December; 2(6): 599. Subject: 18.2

Kvist, Hans-Olof. Cloning of human beings? Theological perspectives. *In:* Ostnor, Lars, ed. Bioethics and Cloning: Report from a Workshop Arranged by the Nordic Theological Network for Bioethics in Arhus, September 25-27, 1998. Oslo: Nordic Theological Network for Bioethics; 1998: 83-88. Subject: 14.5

Kwan, Eva. Organ donation: Alabama uses common law to uphold healthcare providers' duty to secure consent from next of kin — George H. Lanier Memorial Hospital v. Andrews. *Journal of Law, Medicine and Ethics* 2005 Fall; 33(3): 620-622. Subject: 19.5

Kwok, L.S. The White Bull effect: abusive coauthorship and publication parasitism. *Journal of Medical Ethics* 2005 September; 31(9): 554-556. Subject: 1.3.9

Kyambi, J.M. Issues involved in pre-operative consent [editorial]. *East African Medical Journal* 2004 July; 81(7): 329-330. Subject: 8.3.1

Kyriazi, Harold. The ethics of organ selling: a libertarian perspective. *Issues in Medical Ethics* 2001 April-June; 9(2): 44-46. Subject: 19.5

L

Laabs, Carolyn A. Moral problems and distress among nurse practitioners in primary care. *Journal of the American Academy of Nurse Practitioners* 2005 February; 17(2): 76-84. Subject: 4.1.3

Laakkonen, Marja-Liisa; Pitkala, Kaisu H.; Strandberg, Timo E.; Tilvis, Reijo S. Physical and cognitive functioning and resuscitation preferences of aged patients [letter]. *Journal of the American Geriatrics Society* 2005 January; 53(1): 168-170. Subject: 20.5.1

Laberge, Claude. Why another statement from the RMGA? *In:* Knoppers, Bartha Maria, ed. Populations and Genetics: Legal and Socio-Ethical Perspectives. Boston: Martinus Nijhoff; 2003: 641-648. Subject: 15.1

Labonte, Ronald. Global right to health campaign launched [news]. *BMJ: British Medical Journal* 2005 July 30; 331(7511): 252. Subject: 9.2

Lacasse, Jeffrey R. Consumer advertising of psychiatric medications biases the public against nonpharmacological treatment [editorial]. *Ethical Human Psychology and Psychiatry* 2005 Fall-Winter; 7(3): 175-179. Subject: 17.4

Lacey, Linda J. "O wind, remind him that I have no child": infertility and feminist jurisprudence. *Michigan*

Journal of Gender and Law 1998-1999; 5(1): 163-203. Subject: 14.2

Ladikas, Miltos; Schroeder, Doris. Too early for global ethics? *CQ: Cambridge Quarterly of Healthcare Ethics* 2005 Fall; 14(4): 404-415. Subject: 2.1

Lagay, Faith. Humanitas and the human genome: a guiding principle for decision making. *Free Inquiry* 2002-2003 Winter; 23(1): 34-37. Subject: 15.10

Lagitch, Kellie E. Mandatory HIV testing: an Orwellian proposition. *St. John's Law Review* 1998 Winter; 72(1): 103-139. Subject: 9.5.6

Lahn, Michael; Friedman, Benjamin; Bijur, Polly; Haughey, Marianne; Gallagher, E.J. Advance directives in skilled nursing facility residents transferred to emergency departments. *Academic Emergency Medicine* 2001 December; 8(12): 1158-1162. Subject: 20.5.4

Laine, Christine; Mulrow, Cynthia D. Exorcising ghosts and unwelcome guests [editorial]. *Annals of Internal Medicine* 2005 October 18; 143(8): 611-612. Subject: 1.3.7

Laing, Jacqueline A.; Oderberg, David S. Artificial reproduction, the 'welfare principle' and the common good. *Medical Law Review* 2005 Autumn; 13(3): 328-356. Subject: 4.4

Lakhani, Mayur K. Time to legalise assisted dying? RCGP is not neutral: it opposes a change in legislation [letter]. *BMJ: British Medical Journal* 2005 October 8; 331(7520): 841. Subject: 20.5.1

Lal, Meena. The role of the federal government in assisted reproductive technologies. *Santa Clara Computer and High Technology Law Journal* 1997; 13(2): 517-543. Subject: 14.4

Lally, Matthew C.; Freeman, Scott A. The struggle to maintain neutrality in the treatment of a patient with pedophilia. *Ethics and Behavior* 2005; 15(2): 182-190. Subject: 17.1

Lamb, Gregory M. A mix of mice and men [news]. *Christian Science Monitor* 2005 March 17: 13, 15. Subject: 15.1

Lamb, H. Richard. Commentary: on research and forensic patients' capacity. *Journal of the American Academy of Psychiatry and the Law* 2005; 33(3): 308-309. Subject: 18.3

Lamberg, Jennifer L.; Person, Carmel J.; Kiely, Dan K.; Mitchell, Susan L. Decisions to hospitalize nursing home residents dying with advanced dementia. *Journal of the American Geriatrics Society* 2005 August; 53(8): 1396-1401. Subject: 20.5.1

Lambert, Laura A.; Blumenthal, David. Doctors and drug companies [letter and reply]. *New England Journal of Medicine* 2005 February 17; 352(7): 733-734. Subject: 9.7

Lammers, Stephen E. Deep disagreement, respect, and the role of women: some room for development. *American*

Journal of Bioethics 2005 November-December; 5(6): 63-64. Subject: 4.4

Lammers, Stephen E. What wasn't discussed. *Christian Century* 2005 April 19; 122(8): 11. Subject: 20.5.1

LaMonica, Jay. Compulsory sterilization, euthanasia, and propaganda: the Nazi experience. *In:* Koterski, Joseph W., ed. Life and Learning VII: Proceedings of the Seventh University Faculty for Life Conference. Washington, DC: University Faculty for Life; 1998: 187-197. Subject: 21.4

Land, Spencer; Ross, Lawrence S. Posthumous reproduction: current and future status. *Urologic Clinics of North America* 2002 November; 29(4): 863-871. Subject: 14.6

Landau, Ruth. The promise of post-menopausal pregnancy (PMP). *Social Work in Health Care* 2004; 40(1): 53-69. Subject: 14.4

Landman, Willem A.; Henley, Lesley D. Legalising advance directives in South Africa [editorial]. *South African Medical Journal* 2000 August; 90(8): 785-787. Subject: 20.5.4

Landman, Willem; Schüklenk, Udo. UNESCO 'declares' universals on bioethics and human rights — many unexpected universal truths unearthed by UN body. *Developing World Bioethics* 2005 September; 5(3): iii-vi. Subject: 2.1

Landon, Melissa R. Ethics and policy perspectives on personalized medicine in the post-genomic era. *Journal of Biolaw and Business* 2005; 8(3): 28-36. Subject: 15.1

Landow, Laurence; Truog, Robert D. Financial disclosure is needed at the lectern, as well as in print [letter and reply]. *Critical Care Medicine* 1998 December; 26(12): 2093-2094. Subject: 7.1

Landro, Laura. Teaching doctors to be nicer; new accreditation rules spur medical schools to beef up interpersonal-skills training. *Wall Street Journal* 2005 September 28; p. D1, D4. Subject: 7.2

Landry, Donald W.; Zucker, Howard A. Embryonic death and the creation of human embryonic stem cells. *Journal of Clinical Investigation* 2004 November; 114(9): 1184-1186. Subject: 18.5.4

Lane, Alan; Westbrook, Andrew; Grady, Deirdre; O'Connor, Rory; Counihan, Timothy J.; Marsh, Brian; Laffey, John G. Maternal brain death: medical, ethical and legal issues. *Intensive Care Medicine* 2004 July; 30(7): 1484-1486. Subject: 20.2.1

Lane, Melissa. Ethical issues in surrogacy arrangements. *In:* Cook, Rachel; Sclater, Shelley Day; Kaganas, Felicity, eds. Surrogate Motherhood: International Perspectives. Portland, OR: Hart; 2003: 121-139. Subject: 14.2

Langat, Simon K. Reuse of samples: ethical issues encountered by two institutional ethics review committees in Kenya. *Bioethics* 2005 October; 19(5-6): 537-549. Subject: 19.5

Langerman, Alex; Angelos, Peter; Johnston, Chad. Opinions and use of advance directives by physicians at a tertiary care hospital. *Quality Management in Health Care* 2000 Spring; 8(3): 14-18. Subject: 20.5.4

Lannon, Andrew P. Let him die with dignity or hope for a cure: the consequences of modern medicine. *Journal of Contemporary Health Law and Policy* 2002 Winter; 19(1): 279-307. Subject: 20.5.2

Lantos, John. Ethics class. *Hastings Center Report* 2005 May-June; 35(3): 9. Subject: 2.3

Lantos, John D. Commentary on "A draft model aggregated code for bioethicists" [comment]. *American Journal of Bioethics* 2005 September-October; 5(5): 45-46. Subject: 2.1

Lantz, Elizabeth Johnson. Life-or-death decisions and informed consent: communication key to hospital informed consent policies. *QRC Advisor* 1999 April; 15(6): 8-12. Subject: 8.3.1

Lantz, Göran. War, nursing and morality. *Nursing Ethics* 2005 March; 12(2): 193-195. Subject: 21.2

Lanzerath, Dirk. Bioethics in Germany: debates and infrastructure. *Annali dell'Istituto Superiore di Sanita* 2004; 40(3): 287-296. Subject: 2.1

Lanzerath, Dirk. Enhancement: Form der Vervollkommnung des Menschen durch Medikalisierung der Lebenswelt?—Ein Werkstattbericht. *In:* Jahrbuch für Wissenschaft und Ethik. Bd. 7. Berlin: Walter de Gruyter; 2002: 319-336. Subject: 4.5

Lanzerath, Dirk. Der Vorstoß in die molekulare Dimension des Menschen— Möglichkeiten und Grenzen. *In:* Honnefelder, Ludger; Mieth, Dietmar; Propping, Peter; Siep, Ludwig; Wiesemann, Claudia, eds. Das genetische Wissen und die Zukunft des Menschen. New York: De Gruyter; 2003: 120-135. Subject: 15.1

Lapin, Eve. Public comment. *Human Gene Therapy* 2003 May 20; 14(8): 845-846. Subject: 15.4

LaPlante, Pierre. Purity of standards: at what price? *Indian Journal of Medical Ethics* 2004 October-December; 1(4): 124. Subject: 18.5.9

Larcher, Vic. Consent, competence, and confidentiality. *BMJ: British Medical Journal* 2005 February 12; 330(7487): 353- 356. Subject: 8.3.2

Lareau, Alyssa Connell. Who decides? Genital-normalizing surgery on intersexed infants. *Georgetown Law Journal* 2003 November; 92(1): 129-151. Subject: 8.3.2

Larijani, Bagher; Zahedi, F. Islamic perspective on human cloning and stem cell research. *Transplantation Proceedings* 2004 December; 36(10): 3188-3189. Subject: 14.5

Larkin, Gregory L.; Marco, Catherine A. Ethics seminars: beyond authorship requirements — ethical considerations in writing letters of recommendation. *Academic Emergency Medicine* 2001 January; 8(1): 70-73. Subject: 7.3

Larkins, Richard G.; Kerridge, Ian H.; Myser, Catherine; Mitchell, Kenneth R.; Hamblin, Julie. Guidelines for no-CPR orders [letter and reply]. *Medical Journal of Australia* 1994 December 5-19; 161(11-12): 724-725. Subject: 20.5.1

LaRosa, Judith H. Reflections: guidelines for the inclusion of women and minorities in clinical studies. *In:* Beech, Bettina; Goodman, Maurine, eds. Race & Research: Perspectives on Minority Participation in Health Studies. Washington, DC: American Public Health Association; 2004: 143-161. Subject: 18.2

Larriviere, Dan. Duty hours vs professional ethics: ACGME rules create conflicts. *Neurology* 2004 July 13; 63(1): E4-E5. Subject: 4.1.2

Larson, David; Winslow, Gerald; Corselli, Johanna; Whitney, Elvonne; Orr, Robert; Brock, Brian. Adventism and assisted procreation: excerpts from a panel discussion at LLU. *Update [Loma Linda University Center for Christian Bioethics]* 1996 February; 12(1): 14 p. Subject: 14.1

Larson, Edward J. Prescription for death: a second opinion. *DePaul Law Review* 1995 Winter; 44(2): 461-482. Subject: 20.7

Larson, Elaine; Bratts, Tiffany; Zwanziger, Jack; Stone, Patricia. A survey of IRB process in 68 U.S. hospitals. *Journal of Nursing Scholarship* 2004; 36(3): 260-264. Subject: 18.2

Larson, Eric B.; Yao, Xin. Clinical empathy as emotional labor in the patient-physician relationship. *JAMA: The Journal of the American Medical Association* 2005 March 2; 293(9): 1100-1106. Subject: 8.1

Larsson-Kronberg, Marianne; Öjehagen, Agneta; Berglund, Mats. Experiences of coercion during investigation and treatment. *International Journal of Law and Psychiatry* 2005 November- December; 28(6): 613-621. Subject: 9.5.9

LaRusse, Susan; Roberts, J. Scott; Marteau, Theresa M.; Katzen, Heather; Linnenbringer, Erin L.; Barber, Melissa; Whitehouse, Peter; Quaid, Kimberly; Brown, Tamsen; Green, Robert C.; Relkin, Norman R. Genetic susceptibility testing versus family history-based risk assessment: impact on perceived risk of Alzheimer disease. *Genetics in Medicine* 2005 January; 7(1): 48-53. Subject: 15.3

Lashwood, Alison. Preimplantation genetic diagnosis to prevent genetic disorders in children. *British Journal of Nursing* 2005 January 27-February 9; 14(2): 64-70. Subject: 15.2

Latessa, Robyn; Ray, Lisa. Should you treat yourself, family or friends? *Family Practice Management* 2005 March; 12(3): 41-44. Subject: 7.1

Subject = NRCBL Primary Classification Number; See inside front cover

Latham, Stephen R. Expert bioethics testimony. *Journal of Law, Medicine and Ethics* 2005 Summer; 33(2): 242-247. Subject: 2.1

Latham, Stephen R. The (low) life of ethics codes [comment]. *American Journal of Bioethics* 2005 September-October; 5(5): 46-48. Subject: 6

Latkovic, Mark S. The morality of tube feeding PVS patients. *National Catholic Bioethics Quarterly* 2005 Autumn; 5(3): 503- 513. Subject: 20.5.1

Lau, Yvonne. Is banning direct to consumer advertising of prescription medicine justified paternalism? *Journal of Bioethical Inquiry* 2005; 2(2): 69-74. Subject: 9.7

Laufer, Suzie. The regulation of medical/scientific research practices involving experimentation on human beings. *Law in Context* 1990; 8(1): 78-105. Subject: 18.2

Laughlin, Catherine. U.S. Supreme Court hears oral arguments in Ashcroft v. Raich background. *Journal of Law, Medicine and Ethics* 2005 Summer; 33(2): 396- 399. Subject: 20.4.1

Launer, John. All doctors are liars. *QJM: An International Journal of Medicine* 2003 January; 96(1): 85-86. Subject: 4.1.2

Laurie, Graeme. Physician assisted suicide in Europe: some lessons and trends [editorial]. *European Journal of Health Law* 2005 March; 12(1): 5-9. Subject: 20.7

Lauritzen, Paul. Stem cells, biotechnology, and human rights: implications for a posthuman future. *Hastings Center Report* 2005 March-April; 35(2): 25-33. Subject: 18.5.4

Lavelle, Sylvain. Science, technology and ethics: from critical perspective to dialectical perspective. *Ethical Theory and Moral Practice* 2005 June; 8(3): 217-238. Subject: 1.3.9

Lavery, James V. Putting international research ethics guidelines to work for the benefit of developing countries. *Yale Journal of Health Policy, Law, and Ethics* 2004 Summer; 4(2): 319-336. Subject: 18.2

Lavery, James V.; McDonald, Michael; Meslin, Eric M. Research ethics across the 49th parallel: the potential value of pilot testing "equivalent protections" in Canadian research institutions. *Health Law Review* 2005; 13(2-3): 86-96. Subject: 18.2

Lavery, Stuart. Preimplantation genetic diagnosis and the welfare of the child. *Human Fertility* 2004 December; 7(4): 295-300. Subject: 15.2

Lavi, Shai. Euthanasia and the changing ethics of the deathbed. *Theoretical Inquiries in Law* 2003 July; 4(2): 729-761. Subject: 20.1

Lavrijsen, Jan; van den Bosch, Hans; Koopmans, Raymond; van Weel, Chris; Froeling, Paul. Events and decision-making in the long-term care of Dutch nursing home patients in a vegetative state. *Brain Injury* 2005 January; 19(1): 67-75. Subject: 20.5.1

Lawhorne, Larry; VandeKieft, Gregg; Fleck, Leonard M. A daughter's duty. *Journal of the American Board of Family Practice* 2005 January-February; 18(1): 57-62. Subject: 9.5.2

Lawless, Sonia; Kippax, Susan; Crawford, June. Dirty, diseased and undeserving: the positioning of HIV positive women. *Social Science and Medicine* 1996 November; 43(9): 1371-1377. Subject: 9.5.6

Lazar, R. Up for grabs — authors are a dime a dozen: the problem of multiple authors [opinion]. *Acta Paediatrica* 2004 May; 93(5): 589-591. Subject: 1.3.7

Lazarus, Arthur. The moral obligations of physician executives. *Physician Executive* 2004 November-December; 30(6): 40-43. Subject: 4.1.2

Lazzarini, Ivelisse. Neuroethics: the new millennium view. *In:* Purtilo, Ruth B.; Jensen, Gail M.; Brasic Royeen, Charlotte, eds. Educating for Moral Action: A Sourcebook in Health and Rehabilitation Ethics. Philadelphia: F.A. Davis; 2005: 145-157. Subject: 17.1

Le Conte, Philippe; Baron, Denis; Trewick, David; Touzé, Marie Dominique; Longo, Céline; Vial, Irshaad; Yatim, Danielle; Potel, Gille. Withholding and withdrawing life-support therapy in an emergency department: prospective survey. *Intensive Care Medicine* 2004 December; 30(12): 2216-2221. Subject: 20.5.1

Le Melle, Stephanie M.; Entelis, Charles. Heart transplant in a young man with schizophrenia. *American Journal of Psychiatry* 2005 March; 162(3): 453-457. Subject: 19.2

Le Morvan, Pierre; Stock, B. Medical learning curves and the Kantian ideal. *Journal of Medical Ethics* 2005 September; 31(9): 513-518. Subject: 7.2

Leach, Joan. Perspectives on medicine and society. *In:* Restivo, Sal, ed. Science, Technology, and Society: An Encyclopedia. New York: Oxford University Press; 2005: 379-387. Subject: 7.1

Leadbeatter, Stephen; Williams, Dillwyn; Cross, Simon; Start, Roger; Cotton, Dennis; Slater, David. Human tissue research: is legislation needed? [letters and reply]. *British Journal of Hospital Medicine* 1994 February 2-15; 51(3): 132-133. Subject: 18.3

Learman, Lee A.; Drey, Eleanor A.; Gates, Elena A.; Kang, Mi-Suk; Washington, A. Eugene; Kuppermann, Miriam; Nelson, Anita; Powers, Thomas; Schwartz, Martin; Smith, Wendy; Burgoine, Gary. Abortion attitudes of pregnant women in prenatal care. *American Journal of Obstetrics and Gynecology* 2005 June; 192(6): 1939-1947. Subject: 12.5.2

Leather, Suzi. Human cloning — what should we really be frightened of? [editorial]. *Clinical Medicine* 2004 July-August; 4(4): 299-301. Subject: 14.5

Leavitt, Frank J. Neonates must sometimes be allowed to die, but err in favour of life [letter]. *BMJ: British Medical Journal* 2005 September 24; 331(7518): 695-696. Subject: 20.5.2

Leavitt, F.J.; Peleg, R.; Peleg, A. Informal medicine: ethical analysis. *Journal of Medical Ethics* 2005 December; 31(12): 689-692. Subject: 8.1

Leavitt, Mairi. 'Just because we can do something doesn't mean we should': young people's responses to biotechnology. *In:* Deane-Drummond, Celia; Szerszynski, Bronislaw, eds. Re- ordering Nature: Theology, Society and the New Genetics. New York: T & T Clark; 2003: 186-201. Subject: 15.1

Leavitt, Wilder J. Regulating human gene therapy: legislative overreaction to human subject protection failures. *Administrative Law Review* 2001 Winter; 53(1): 315-341. Subject: 15.4

Lebacqz, Karen. The ethics of ethical advising: confessions of an ethical advisor. Santa Clara, CA: Markkula Center for Applied Ethics, Santa Clara University 2003 May 14; 9 p. [Online]. Available: http://www.scu.edu/ethics/practicing/events/lecture/2003/ethicala dvice.html [15 June 2005]. Subject: 9.6

Lebacqz, Karen. We sure are older but are we wiser? *In:* Childress, James F.; Meslin, Eric M.; Shapiro, Harold T., eds. Belmont Revisited: Ethical Principles for Research with Human Subjects. Washington, DC: Georgetown University Press; 2005: 99-110. Subject: 2.1

Lebeer, Guy. Clinical ethics support services in Europe. *Medical Ethics and Bioethics / Medicinska Etika & Bioetika* 2005; 11(Supplement): 8-11. Subject: 9.6

LeBlang, Theodore R. Informed consent and disclosure in the physician-patient relationship: expanding obligations for physicians in the United States. *Medicine and Law: World Association for Medical Law* 1995; 14(5-6): 429-444. Subject: 8.3.1

Lebner, Ashley. Genetic "mysteries" and international adoption: the cultural impact of biomedical technologies on the adoptive family experience. *Family Relations* 2000 October; 49(4): 371-377. Subject: 14.1

Lebovits, Allen. The ethical implications of racial disparities in pain: are some of us more equal? [editorial]. *Pain Medicine* 2005 January-February; 6(1): 3-4. Subject: 9.5.4

Leclerc, S.; Herrera, C.D. Sport medicine and the ethics of boxing. *British Journal of Sports Medicine* 1999 December; 33(6): 426- 429. Subject: 9.5.1

Lecompte, D. The paradoxical increase in involuntary admissions after the revision of the Civil Commitment Law in Belgium. *Medicine and Law: World Association for Medical Law* 1995; 14(1-2): 53-57. Subject: 17.7

LeCraw, Linda L.; Roble, Daniel T. Physicians on the board: competitive conflicts of interest. *Trustee* 2005 January; 58(1): 27-28. Subject: 7.3

Lederer, Susan E. Research without borders: the origins of the Declaration of Helsinki. *In:* Roelcke, Volker; Maio, Giovanni, eds. Twentieth Century Ethics of Human Subjects Research: Historical Perspectives on Values, Practices, and Regulations. Stuttgart: Franz Steiner Verlag; 2004: 199-217. Subject: 18.2

Ledger, Sylvia Dianne. The duty of nurses to meet patients' spiritual and/or religious needs. *British Journal of Nursing* 2005 February 24-March 9; 14(4): 220-225. Subject: 7.1

Lee, Ellie. Debating late abortion: time to tell the truth [opinion]. *Journal of Family Planning and Reproductive Health Care* 2005 January; 31(1): 7, 9. Subject: 12.4.1

Lee, Ellie. Tensions in the regulation of abortion in Britain. *Journal of Law and Society* 2003 December; 30(4): 532-553. Subject: 12.5.3

Lee, Felicia R. Driven by costs, fertility clients head overseas. *New York Times* 2005 January 25; p. A1, A14. Subject: 14.4

Lee, Matthew; Charo, R. Alta. The celestial fire of conscience [letter and reply]. *New England Journal of Medicine* 2005 September 22; 353(12): 1301-1302. Subject: 8.1

Lee, Patrick; George, Robert P. The wrong of abortion. *In:* Cohen, Andrew I.; Wellman, Christopher Heath, eds. Contemporary Debates in Applied Ethics. Malden, MA: Blackwell Pub., 2005: 13-26. Subject: 12.3

Lee, Philip R.; Conant, Marcus; Heilig, Steve. Participation of health care personnel in torture and interrogation [letter]. *New England Journal of Medicine* 2005 October 13; 353(15): 1634-1635. Subject: 21.4

Lee, Robert C.; Kmet, Leanne; Cook, Linda S.; Lorenzetti, Diane; Godlovitch, Glenys; Einsiedel, Edna. Risk assessment for inherited susceptibility to cancer: a review of the psychosocial and ethical dimensions. *Genetic Testing* 2005 Spring; 9(1): 66-79. Subject: 15.3

Lee, Sandra Soo-Jin. Racializing drug design: implications of pharmacogenomics for health disparities. *American Journal of Public Health* 2005 December; 95(12): 2133- 2138. Subject: 15.1

Lee, Simon J. Craddock. The risks of race in addressing health disparities [opinion]. *Hastings Center Report* 2005 July-August; 35(4): inside back cover. Subject: 9.5.4

Lee, Susan J.; Ralston, Henry J. Peter; Drey, Eleanor A.; Partridge, John Colin; Rosen, Mark A. Fetal pain — a systematic multidisciplinary review of the evidence. *JAMA: The Journal of the American Medical Association* 2005 August 24-31; 294(8): 947-954. Subject: 9.5.8

Lee, Won-Hee; Pope, Marion; Han, Sung-Suk; Yang, Soon-Ok. Korean nurses' perceptions of ethical problems: toward a new code of ethics for nursing. *Nursing and Health Sciences* 2000 December; 2(4): 217-224. Subject: 4.1.3

Subject = NRCBL Primary Classification Number; See inside front cover

Leeder, Stephen R. Ethics and public health. *Internal Medicine Journal* 2004 July; 34(7): 435-439. Subject: 9.1

Leenen, H.J.J. The development of euthanasia in the Netherlands. *European Journal of Health Law* 2001 June; 8(2): 125-133. Subject: 20.5.1

Lefebvre, Carol A.; Lang, Brien R. The Journal of Prosthetic Dentistry publication standards of ethical conduct. *Journal of Prosthetic Dentistry* 2005 April; 93(4): 311-314. Subject: 1.3.7

Leflar, Robert B. Informed consent and patients' rights in Japan. *Houston Law Review* 1996 Spring; 33(1): 1-112. Subject: 8.3.1

Leggett, Andrew. Origins and development of the injunction prohibiting sexual relationships with patients. *Australian and New Zealand Journal of Psychiatry* 1995 December; 29(4): 586-590. Subject: 8.1

Leggon, Cheryl. Tuskegee project, the. *In:* Restivo, Sal, ed. Science, Technology, and Society: An Encyclopedia. New York: Oxford University Press; 2005: 646-648. Subject: 18.5.1

LeGros, Nancy; Pinkall, Jason D. The new JCAHO patient safety standards and the disclosure of unanticipated outcomes. *Journal of Health Law* 2002 Spring; 35(2): 189-210. Subject: 8.2

Lehmann, Lisa Soleymani; Puopolo, Ann Louise; Shaykevich, Shimon; Brennan, Troyen A. Iatrogenic events resulting in intensive care admission: frequency, cause, and disclosure to patients and institutions. *American Journal of Medicine* 2005 April; 118(4): 409-413. Subject: 9.8

Lehman-Wilzig, Sam N. Political ill-health coverage: professional-ethical questions regarding news reporting of leaders' ailments. *Journal of Health Communication* 2003 January-February; 8(1): 59-77. Subject: 1.3.7

Lehoux, Pascale; Denis, Jean-Louis; Tailliez, Stéphanie; Hivon, Myriam. Dissemination of health technology assessments: identifying the visions guiding an evolving policy innovation in Canada. *Journal of Health Politics, Policy and Law* 2005 August; 30(4): 603-641. Subject: 5.2

Leib, Jennifer R.; Gollust, Sarah E.; Hull, Sara Chandros; Wilfond, Benjamin S. Carrier screening panels for Ashkenazi Jews: is more better? *Genetics in Medicine* 2005 March; 7(3): 185-190. Subject: 15.3

Leichtentritt, Ronit D.; Rettig, Kathryn D.; Miles, Steven H. Holocaust survivors' perspectives on the euthanasia debate. *Social Science and Medicine* 1999; 48: 185-196. Subject: 20.5.1

Leidig, Michael. Dignitas is investigated for helping healthy woman to die [news]. *BMJ: British Medical Journal* 2005 November 19; 331(7526): 1160. Subject: 20.7

Leigh, Greg; Marschark, Marc. Ethics and deafness: a matter of perspective? [editorial]. *Journal of Deaf Studies and Deaf Education* 2005 Spring; 10(2): 109-110. Subject: 5.1

Leino-Kilpi, Helena. Editorial comment. *Nursing Ethics* 2005 January; 12(1): 3-4. Subject: 4.1.3

Leisinger, Klaus M. The corporate social responsibility of the pharmaceutical industry: idealism without illusion and realism without resignation. *Business Ethics Quarterly* 2005 October; 15(4): 577-594. Subject: 9.7

Lekovic, Gregory P. Genetic diagnosis and intellectual property rights: a proposal to amend "the Physician Immunity Statute". *Yale Journal of Health Policy, Law, and Ethics* 2004 Summer; 4(2): 275-304. Subject: 15.8

Leland, John. Did Descartes doom Terri Schiavo? [opinion]. *New York Times* 2005 March 27; Sec 4, p. 1, 3. Subject: 4.4

Leland, John. Under din of abortion debate, an experience shared quietly. *New York Times* 2005 September 18; p. A1, A28. Subject: 12.5.1

Lemaire, François J.P. A law for end of life care in France? [news]. *Intensive Care Medicine* 2004 November; 30(11): 2120. Subject: 20.5.1

Lemke, Thomas. From eugenics to the government of genetic risks. *In:* Bunton, Robin; Petersen, Alan, eds. Genetic Governance: Health, Risk and Ethics in the Biotech Era. New York: Routledge; 2005: 95-105. Subject: 15.3

Lemmens, Trudo. Federal regulation of REB review of clinical trials: a modest but easy step towards an accountable REB review structure in Canada. *Health Law Review* 2005; 13(2-3): 39-50. Subject: 18.2

Lemmens, Trudo. Leopards in the temple: restoring scientific integrity to the commercialized research scene. *Journal of Law, Medicine and Ethics* 2004 Winter; 32(4): 641- 657. Subject: 18.2

Lemmens, Trudo; Dickens, Bernard. Canadian law on euthanasia: contrasts and comparisons. *European Journal of Health Law* 2001 June; 8(2): 135-155. Subject: 20.5.1

Lemmens, Trudo; Sprumont, Dominique; Nys, Herman; Singh, Jerome; Glass, Kathleen Cranley. CIOMS' placebo rule and the promotion of negligent medical practice. *European Journal of Health Law* 2004 June; 11(2): 153-174. Subject: 18.3

Leng, Chee Heng. Genomics and health: ethical, legal and social implications for developing countries. *Issues in Medical Ethics* 2002 January-March; 10(1): 146-149. Subject: 15.1

Lenhardt, Erin. Why so glum? Toward a fair balance of competitive interests in direct-to-consumer advertising and the well-being of the mentally ill consumers it targets. *Health Matrix: Journal of Law-Medicine* 2005 Winter; 15(1): 165-204. Subject: 9.7

Lennerling, Annette; Nyberg, Gudrun. Written information for potential living kidney donors. *Transplant In-*

ternational 2004 September; 17(8): 449-452. Subject: 19.5

Lenow, Jeffrey L. Fetal interests. *In:* American College of Legal Medicine Textbook Committee, Sanbar, S. Sandy; Firestone, Marvin H.; Buckner, Fillmore; Gibofsky, Allan; LeBlang, Theodore R.; Snyder, Jack W.; Wecht, Cyril H.; Zaremski, Miles J. Legal Medicine. 6th ed. St. Louis: Mosby; 2004: 264-270. Subject: 9.5.8

Lenzen, Wolfgang. Therapeutic versus genuine cloning: what are the real moral issues? *Ethical Perspectives* 2003; 10(3-4): 176-184. Subject: 14.5

Lenzer, Jeanne. American Medical Association rejects proposal to ban consumer adverts for prescription medicines [news]. *BMJ: British Medical Journal* 2005 July 2; 331(7507): 7. Subject: 9.7

Lenzer, Jeanne. Doctors refuse space to group fighting drug company influence [news]. *BMJ: British Medical Journal* 2005 September 24; 331(7518): 653. Subject: 9.7

Lenzer, Jeanne. US teenager's parents sue school over depression screening test [news]. *BMJ: British Medical Journal* 2005 October 1; 331(7519): 714. Subject: 18.5.2

Leo, John. End of the Affair. *U.S. News and World Report* 2005 April 11; 138(13): 46. Subject: 20.5.1

Leonard, Colm; Mohindra, Vibha; Ruoss, Stephen; Doyle, Ramona L.; Raffin, Thomas A. European life-support questionnaire. *Critical Care Medicine* 1999 August; 27(8): 1686-1687. Subject: 20.5.1

Leonard, Thomas C. "More merciful and not less effective": eugenics and American economics in the Progressive Era. *History of Political Economy* 2003; 35(4): 687-712. Subject: 15.5

Leong, Gregory B. Sell v. U.S.: involuntary treatment case or catalyst for change? [editorial]. *Journal of the American Academy of Psychiatry and the Law* 2005; 33(3): 292-294. Subject: 17.7

Lepicard, Etienne. The construction of human experimentation ethics: Catholic voices in context. *In:* Roelcke, Volker; Maio, Giovanni, eds. Twentieth Century Ethics of Human Subjects Research: Historical Perspectives on Values, Practices, and Regulations. Stuttgart: Franz Steiner Verlag; 2004: 35-49. Subject: 18.1

Lépine, Suzanne; Smolla, Nicole. Ethical issues concerning participants in community surveys of child and adolescent mental disorders. *Canadian Journal of Psychiatry* 2000 February; 45(1): 48-54. Subject: 18.5.2

Lerman, Caryn; Shields, Alexandra E. Genetic testing for cancer susceptibility: the promise and the pitfalls [opinion]. *Nature Reviews Cancer* 2004 March; 4(3): 235-241. Subject: 15.3

Lerner, Barron H. From careless consumptives to recalcitrant patients: the historical construction of noncompliance. *Social Science and Medicine* 1997 November; 45(9): 1423-1431. Subject: 8.3.4

Lerner, Barron H. Last-ditch medical therapy — revisiting lobotomy [opinion]. *New England Journal of Medicine* 2005 July 14; 353(2): 119-121. Subject: 17.6

Lerner, Barron H. Playing God with birth defects in the nursery. *New York Times* 2005 June 14; p.F5. Subject: 20.5.2

Lertsithichai, Panuwat. Medical research ethics in Thailand: what should be the most appropriate approach? An analysis based on western ethical principles. *Journal of the Medical Association of Thailand* 2004 October; 87(10): 1253-1261. Subject: 18.1

Lertsithichai, Panuwat. Waiver of consent in clinical observational research. *Journal of the Medical Association of Thailand* 2005 February; 88(2): 275-281. Subject: 18.3

Leshner, Alan I. It's time to go public with neuroethics [editorial]. *American Journal of Bioethics* 2005 March-April; 5(2): 1-2. Subject: 17.1

Lesser, Harry. The case of back-street abortion. *In:* Häyry, Matti; Takala, Tuija; Herissone-Kelly, Peter, eds. Bioethics and Social Reality. New York: Rodopi, 2005: 7-15. Subject: 12.4.1

Lesser, Harry. Priorities in the use of research into ageing. *Health Care Analysis: An International Journal of Health Care Philosophy and Policy* 2005 March; 13(1): 53-58. Subject: 9.5.2

Letellier, Philippe. History and definition of a word. *In:* Council of Europe Publishing, ed. Euthanasia. Volume I. Ethical and Human Aspects. Strasbourg: Council of Europe; Croton- on-Hudson, NY: Manhattan Publishing Co.; 2003: 13-24. Subject: 20.5.1

Leuck, Jared C. Roe v. Wade and its Supreme Court progeny. *Journal of Contemporary Legal Issues* 2004; 14(1): 209-227. Subject: 12.4.1

Leung, Tse Ngong; Ching Chau, Macy Mo; Chang, Joseph Jeremy; Leung, Tak Yeung; Fung, Tak Yuen; Lau, Tze Kin. Attitudes towards termination of pregnancy among Hong Kong Chinese women attending prenatal diagnosis counselling clinic. *Prenatal Diagnosis* 2004 July; 24(7): 546-551. Subject: 15.2

Leute, Kirsten. Patenting and licensing of university-based genetic inventions — a view from experience at Stanford University's Office of Technology Licensing. *Community Genetics* 2005 October; 8(4): 217-222. Subject: 15.8

Levee, Ellen M. IACUC replacement parts: what are the requirements? No authority. *Lab Animal* 2004 November; 33(10): 16-17. Subject: 9.6

Levene, Malcolm. Is intensive care for very immature babies justified? [opinion]. *Acta Paediatrica* 2004 February; 93(2): 149-152. Subject: 20.5.2

Levetown, Marcia. Ensuring that difficult decisions are honored — even in school settings. *American Journal of*

Bioethics 2005 January-February; 5(1): 78- 81. Subject: 20.5.2

Levi, Benjamin H. Ethical conflicts between residents and attending physicians. *Clinical Pediatrics* 2002 November-December; 41(9): 659-667. Subject: 7.3

Levin, Phillip D.; Sprung, Charles L. Are ethics consultations worthwhile? *Critical Care Medicine* 2000 December; 28(12): 3942-3944. Subject: 9.6

Levine, Carol. Acceptance, avoidance, and ambiguity: conflicting social values about childhood disability. *Kennedy Institute of Ethics Journal* 2005 December; 15(4): 371- 383. Subject: 9.5.7

Levine, Carol. She died the same way she lived: planning well in advance. *New York Times* 2005 December 6; p. F5. Subject: 20.5.4

Levine, David Z.; Kielstein, Rita; Sass, Hans-Martin; Wesson, Donald E.; Oberbauer, Rainer; Kurtzman, Neil A.; Aufricht, Christoph; Muehlbacher, Ferdinand; Laski, Melvin; Mannhalter, Christine; Hörl, Walter; Druml, Christiane; Jones, Brent. Genetics in kidney disease: how much do we want to know? *American Journal of Kidney Diseases* 2002 March; 39(3): 637-652. Subject: 15.3

Levine, Robert J. International codes of research ethics: current controversies and the future. *Indiana Law Review* 2002; 35(2): 557-567. Subject: 18.2

Levine, Robert J. The National Commission's ethical principles with special attention to beneficence. *In:* Childress, James F.; Meslin, Eric M.; Shapiro, Harold T., eds. Belmont Revisited: Ethical Principles for Research with Human Subjects. Washington, DC: Georgetown University Press; 2005: 126-135. Subject: 18.2

Levine, Robert J. Reflections on 'rethinking research ethics' [editorial]. *American Journal of Bioethics* 2005 January-February; 5(1): 1-3. Subject: 18.2

Levine, Robert J.; Lebacqz, Karen. Some ethical considerations in clinical trials. *Clinical Pharmacology and Therapeutics* 1979 May; 25(5 Part 2): 728-741. Subject: 18.2

Levinson, Wendy; Kao, Audiey; Kuby, Alma M.; Thisted, Ronald A. The effect of physician disclosure of financial incentives on trust. *Archives of Internal Medicine* 2005 March 28; 165(6): 625-630. Subject: 9.3.2

Levinson, Wendy; Kao, Audiey; Kuby, Alma; Thisted, Ronald A. Not all patients want to participate in decision making: a national study of public preferences. *JGIM: Journal of General Internal Medicine* 2005 June; 20(6): 531-535. Subject: 8.1

Levin-Epstein, Michael. Time to decipher legislation's DNA. *Managed Care* 2005 April; 14(4): 29-30. Subject: 15.3

Levitt, Mairi; Häyry, Matti. Overcritical, overfriendly? A dialogue between a sociologist and a philosopher on ge-

netic technology and its applications. *Medicine, Health Care and Philosophy: A European Journal* 2005; 8(3): 377-383. Subject: 15.1

Levitt, Mairi; Weiner, Kate; Goodacre, John. Stimulating public debate on the ethical and social issues raised by the new genetics. *In:* Holm, Søren; Jonas, Monique F., eds. Engaging the World: The Use of Empirical Research in Bioethics and the Regulation of Biotechnology. Washington, DC: IOS Press; 2004: 109-118. Subject: 15.1

Levkovitz, Alon. A halachic approach to transgender. *CCAR Journal: A Reform Jewish Quarterly* 2005 Fall; 52(4): 84- 93. Subject: 10

Levy, Cari R.; Fish, Ronald; Kramer, Andrew. Do-not-resuscitate and do-not-hospitalize directives of persons admitted to skilled nursing facilities under the Medicare benefit. *Journal of the American Geriatrics Society* 2005 December; 53(12): 2060-2068. Subject: 20.5.1

Levy, Christopher J. Conflict of duty: capital punishment regulations and AMA medical ethics. *Journal of Legal Medicine* 2005 June; 26(2): 261-274. Subject: 20.6

Levy, Joe S. Medical ethics. *Allergy and Asthma Proceedings* 2003 July-August; 24(4): 295-297. Subject: 8.1

Levy, Michael H.; Cohen, Seth D. Sedation for the relief of refractory symptoms in the imminently dying: a fine intentional line. *Seminars in Oncology* 2005 April; 32(2): 237-246. Subject: 20.4.1

Levy, Michael H.; Reyes, Hernán; Coninx, Rudi. Overwhelming consumption in prisons: human rights and tuberculosis control. *Health and Human Rights: An International Journal* 1999; 4(1): 167-191. Subject: 9.5.1

Levy, Neil. Let life shape personality, not genetics [response]. *Conscience* 2003-2004 Winter; 24(4): 15-16. Subject: 14.1

Levy, Neil; Lotz, Mianna. Reproductive cloning and a (kind of) genetic fallacy. *Bioethics* 2005 June; 19(3): 232-250. Subject: 14.5

Levy, Sharon. Asserting the right to life — a challenge to medical guidance on withdrawing treatment. *Medicine and Law: World Association for Medical Law* 2005 March; 24(1): 11-20. Subject: 9.2

Levy, Stuart B.; Star, Larry; Kupferberg, Eric D.; Roselin, Joel. The misuse of antibiotics [forum]. *Medical Ethics Newsletter [Lahey Clinic]* 2004 Winter; 11(1): 5-8. Subject: 9.7

Lewenson, Sandra B.; Truglio-Londrigan, Marie; Singleton, Joanne. Practice what you teach: a case study of ethical conduct in the academic setting. *Journal of Professional Nursing* 2005 March-April; 21(2): 89-96. Subject: 7.2

Lewin, Simon; Meyer, Ilan H. Torture and ill-treatment based on sexual identity: the roles and responsibilities of health professionals and their institutions. *Health and Hu-*

man Rights: An International Journal 2002; 6(1): 161-176. Subject: 21.4

Lewis, Graham. Tissue collection and the pharamceutical industry: investigating corporate biobanks. *In:* Tutton, Richard; Corrigan, Oonagh, eds. Genetic Databases: Socio-ethical Issues in the Collection and Use of DNA. New York: Routledge; 2004: 181-202. Subject: 15.1

Lewis, Karen J.; Shimabukuro, Jon O. Abortion law development: a brief overview. Congressional Research Service 2001 January 2; 20 p. [Online]. Available: http://www.law.maryland.edu/marshall/crsreports/crsdocuments/95- 724_A.pdf [31 August 2005]. Subject: 12.4.4

Lewis, Neil A. Guantanamo tour focuses on medical ethics. *New York Times* 2005 November 13; p. A34. Subject: 21.4

Lewis, Neil A. Head of hospital at Guantanamo faces complaint. *New York Times* 2005 July 15; p. A13. Subject: 21.4

Lewis, Neil A. Interrogators cite doctors' aid at Guantanamo; ethics questions raised; Pentagon says personnel are advisers who do not treat patients. *New York Times* 2005 June 24; p. A1, A19. Subject: 21.4

Lewis, Neil A. Psychologists warned on role in detentions. *New York Times* 2005 July 6; p. A14. Subject: 21.4

Lewis, Oliver. Protecting the rights of people with mental disabilities: the European Convention on Human Rights. *European Journal of Health Law* 2002 December; 9(4): 293-320. Subject: 9.5.3

Lewis, Penney. The necessary implications of wrongful life claims: lessons from France. *European Journal of Health Law* 2005 June; 12(2): 135-152. Subject: 4.4

Lewis, Rodney S.; Wilson, Roger D.; Biegler, Paul; Stewart, Cameron; Savulescu, Julian; Skene, Loane. Determining the validity of advance directives [letter and reply]. *Medical Journal of Australia* 2000 September 18; 173(6): 335-336. Subject: 20.5.4

Lewontin, Richard C. The fallacy of racial medicine: confusions about human races. *GeneWatch* 2005 July-August; 18(4): 5-7, 17. Subject: 15.1

Lexchin, Joel R. Implications of pharmaceutical industry funding on clinical research [opinion]. *Annals of Pharmacotherapy* 2005 January; 39(1): 194-197. Subject: 9.7

Lexchin, Joel; Cassels, Alan. Does the C in CME stand for "continuing" or "commercial"? [letter]. *CMAJ/JAMC: Canadian Medical Association Journal* 2005 January 18; 172(2): 160-162. Subject: 9.7

Li, Lewyn; Somerville, Margaret A.; Atlas, Ronald M. Using ethics to fight bioterrorism [letter and reply]. *Science* 2005 August 12; 309(5737): 1012, 1014-1015, 1017. Subject: 21.3

Li, L.J.; Lu, G.X. How medical ethical principles are applied in treatment with artificial insemination by donors (AID) in Hunan, China: effective practice at the Reproductive and Genetic Hospital of CITIC-Xiangya. *Journal of Medical Ethics* 2005 June; 31(6): 333-337. Subject: 14.2

Li, Nicole. Out of the armchair: a bioethics student's search for practical knowledge in Kenya. *Journal of Bioethical Inquiry* 2004; 1(1): 20-26. Subject: 18.5.1

Liang, Angela. The argument against a physician's duty to warn for genetic diseases: the conflicts created by Safer v. Estate of Pack. *Journal of Health Care Law and Policy* 1998; 1(2): 437-453. Subject: 8.4

Liang, Bryan A. Error disclosure for quality improvement: authenticating a team of patients and providers to promote patient safety. *In:* Sharpe, Virginia A., ed. Accountability: Patient Safety and Policy Reform. Washington, DC: Georgetown University Press; 2004: 59-82. Subject: 9.8

Liao, S. Matthew. Are 'ex ante' enhancements always permissible? [comment]. *American Journal of Bioethics* 2005 May-June; 5(3): 23-25. Subject: 15.1

Liao, S. Matthew. The ethics of using genetic engineering for sex selection. *Journal of Medical Ethics* 2005 February; 31(2): 116-118. Subject: 15.1

Liao, S. Matthew. Rescuing human embryonic stem cell research: the blastocyst transfer method. *American Journal of Bioethics* 2005 November-December; 5(6): 8- 16. Subject: 18.5.4

Liao, S. Matthew. Response to commentators on "Rescuing human embryonic stem cell research: the blastocyst transfer method". *American Journal of Bioethics [Online]* 2005 November- December; 5(6): W10-W13. Subject: 18.5.4

Liaschenko, Joan. Death: can Monty Python do what philosophers can not? [editorial]. *Nursing Philosophy* 2005 July; 6(3): 159-60. Subject: 20.5.1

Licht, Eugene. Paging Dr. Death. *Ivy Journal of Ethics; 3(1): 18*-20. Subject: 20.7

Lichtman, Joan. Access to medical care. *In:* American College of Legal Medicine Textbook Committee, Sanbar, S. Sandy; Firestone, Marvin H.; Buckner, Fillmore; Gibofsky, Allan; LeBlang, Theodore R.; Snyder, Jack W.; Wecht, Cyril H.; Zaremski, Miles J. Legal Medicine. 6th ed. St. Louis: Mosby; 2004: 230-237. Subject: 9.1

Liddell, Kathleen; Hall, Alison. Beyond Bristol and Alder Hey: the future regulation of human tissue. *Medical Law Review* 2005 Summer; 13(2): 170-223. Subject: 19.5

Liddy, Maryellen. The "new body snatchers": analyzing the effect of presumed consent organ donation laws on privacy, autonomy, and liberty. *Fordham Urban Law Journal* 2001 February; 28(3): 815-853. Subject: 19.5

Lidge, Ernest F., III. An employer's exclusion of coverage for contraceptive drugs is not per se sex discrimination.

Temple Law Review 2003 Fall; 76(3): 533-577. Subject: 11.1

Lieberson, Alan D. Commentary: advance medical directives — 1998: a medical view. *Quinnipiac Probate Law Journal* 1998; 12(3): 305-338. Subject: 20.5.4

Liebman, Jerome. Some legal, social, and ethical issues related to the genetic testing revolution, as exemplified in the Long QT Syndrome. *Journal of Electrocardiology* 2001; 34 (Supplement): 183-188. Subject: 15.3

Liebman, Monte Harris. Democracy and abortion. *Linacre Quarterly* 2005 November; 72(4): 331-337. Subject: 12.3

Liégeois, A.; Van Audenhove, C. Ethical dilemmas in community mental health care. *Journal of Medical Ethics* 2005 August; 31(8): 452-456. Subject: 17.1

Lievrouw, Leah A. Biotechnology, intellectual property, and the prospects for scientific communication. *In:* Braman, Sandra, ed. Biotechnology and Communication: The Meta-Technologies of Information. Mahwah, NJ: Lawrence Erlbaum Associates; 2004: 145-172. Subject: 15.8

Light, Sarah E. Rejecting the logic of confinement: care relationships and the mentally disabled under tort law. *Yale Law Journal* 1999 November; 109(2): 381-416. Subject: 9.5.3

Lightfoot, Lance. The ethical health lawyer: incompetent decisionmakers and withdrawal of life-sustaining treatment: a case study. *Journal of Law, Medicine and Ethics* 2005 Winter; 33(4): 851- 856. Subject: 20.5.2

Lilani, Anjali. Ethical issues and policy analysis for genetic testing: Huntington's disease as a paradigm for diseases with a late onset. *Human Reproduction and Genetic Ethics: An International Journal* 2005; 11(2): 28-34. Subject: 15.2

Lilja, John; Larsson, Sam; Hamilton, David; Bauer, Mia. Ethical values in the treatment of depression and anxiety. *In:* Salek, Sam; Edgar, Andrew, eds. Pharmaceutical Ethics. New York: Wiley; 2002: 137-160. Subject: 17.4

Lim, Meng-Kin. Hostile use of the life sciences [opinion]. *New England Journal of Medicine* 2005 November 24; 353(21): 2214-2215. Subject: 21.3

Limoges, Roger J. Prescriptions denied: pharmacy refusal clauses have become the latest battleground in the provision of safe and legal medical services. *Conscience* 2005 Autumn; 26(3): 36-38. Subject: 11.1

Lin, Chii-Dean; Lui, Kung-Jong; Zelen, Marvin. Randomized consent designs for clinical trials: an update [letter and reply]. *Statistics in Medicine* 2002 September 15; 21(17): 2601-2605. Subject: 18.2

Lin, Laura. International stem cell use and regulation in research. *Journal of Biolaw and Business* 2005; 8(1): 47-48. Subject: 14.5

Lin, Olivia. Rehabilitating bioethics: recontextualizing in vitro fertilization outside contractual autonomy. *Duke Law Journal* 2004 November; 54(2): 485-511. Subject: 14.6

Linane, Marianne; Miller, Robert T. Schiavo under the law [letter and reply]. *First Things* 2005 October; (156): 5, 6-8. Subject: 20.5.1

Linck, Jeanette C. Confidentiality, professionalism, ethics and the student. *Journal of AHIMA* 1993 December; 64(12): 67-68. Subject: 7.2

Lind, Rebecca Ann. Evaluating research misconduct policies at major research universities: a pilot study. *Accountability in Research* 2005 July-September; 12(3): 241- 262. Subject: 1.3.9

Lindegger, G.; Slack, C.; Vardas, E. HIV vaccine trials in South Africa — some ethical considerations. *South African Medical Journal* 2000 August; 90(8): 769-770, 772. Subject: 18.5.1

Lindemann, Hilde. On the mend: Alzheimer's and family caregiving. *Journal of Clinical Ethics* 2005 Winter; 16(4): 314-320. Subject: 20.4.1

Lindemann, Hilde; Callahan, Daniel. Before he wakes [case study and commentary]. *Hastings Center Report* 2005 July-August; 35(4): 15-16. Subject: 20.5.1

Lindemann, Hilde; Kukla, Rebecca. Conscientious autonomy: what patients do vs. what is done to them [letter and reply]. *Hastings Center Report* 2005 September-October; 35(5): 4, 6-7. Subject: 8.3.1

Lindley, Richard. Psychotherapy as essential care. *In:* Fairbairn, Susan; Fairbairn, Gavin, eds. Psychology, Ethics and Change. New York: Routledge & Kegan Paul; 1987: 212- 230. Subject: 17.2

Lindsay, Ronald A. Enhancements and justice: problems in determining the requirements of justice in a genetically transformed society. *Kennedy Institute of Ethics Journal* 2005 March; 15(1): 3-38. Subject: 15.1

Lindsay, Ronald A. Slaves, embryos, and nonhuman animals: moral status and the limitations of common morality theory. *Kennedy Institute of Ethics Journal* 2005 December; 15(4): 323- 346. Subject: 4.4

Linker, Beth. The business of ethics: gender, medicine, and the professional codification of the American Physiotherapy Association, 1918-1935. *Journal of the History of Medicine and Allied Sciences* 2005 July; 60(3): 320-354. Subject: 4.1.1

Linnard-Palmer, Luanne; Kools, Susan. Parents' refusal of medical treatment based on religious and/or cultural beliefs: the law, ethical principles, and clinical implications. *Journal of Pediatric Nursing* 2004 October; 19(5): 351-356. Subject: 8.3.4

Linnard-Palmer, Luanne; Kools, Susan. Parents' refusal of medical treatment for cultural or religious beliefs: an ethnographic study of health care professionals' experiences. *Journal of Pediatric Oncology Nursing* 2005 January-February; 22(1): 48-57. Subject: 8.3.4

Liokis, Michelle Garriga; Herbert, Paul B. Involuntary medications not allowed to restore competence to stand trial. *Journal of the American Academy of Psychiatry and the Law* 2005; 33(4): 554-555. Subject: 17.4

Lipman, Arthur G. Pain and the pharmacist: opinion #3: communication is key. *Pain Medicine* 2003 June; 4(2): 190-194. Subject: 9.7

Lipman, Timothy O. Ethics and gastrointestinal artificial feeding. *Current Gastroenterology Reports* 2004 August; 6(4): 314-319. Subject: 20.5.1

Lippman, Abby; Newman, Stuart A.; Testa, Giuseppe; Harris, John. The ethics of deriving gametes from ES cells [letter and reply]. *Science* 2005 January 28; 307(5709): 515, 517. Subject: 18.5.4

Liptak, Adam. On death row, a battle over the fatal cocktail: critics say executions amount to torture. *New York Times* 2004 September 16; p A16. Subject: 20.6

Liptak, Adam. On moral grounds, some judges are opting out of abortion cases. *New York Times* 2005 September 4; p. A21. Subject: 12.4.1

Lipworth, Wendy. Generating a taxonomy of regulatory responses to emerging issues in biomedicine. *Journal of Bioethical Inquiry* 2005; 2(3): 130-141. Subject: 5.3

Liska, Adam J. The morality of problem selection in proteomics [opinion]. *Proteomics* 2004 July; 4(7): 1929-1931. Subject: 15.1

List, Justin M. Histories of mistrust and protectionism: disadvantaged minority groups and human-subject research policies. *American Journal of Bioethics* 2005 January-February; 5(1): 53- 56. Subject: 18.2

Lister, Sam; Charter, David. BMA drops its opposition to doctor-assisted suicide. *Times (London)* 2005 July 1; p. 11. Subject: 20.7

Lithuania. Seimas. Law on the Ethics of Biomedical Research. No. VIII-1679. Vilnius: Seimas of the Republic of Lithuania 2000 May 11; 10 p. [Online]. Available: http://www3.lrs.lt/c-bin/eng/preps2?Condition1=148740&Condition2= [11 July 2005]. Subject: 1.3.9

Littell, Amanda. Can a constitutional right to health guarantee universal health care coverage or improved health outcomes?: a survey of selected states. *Connecticut Law Review* 2002 Fall; 35(1): 289-318. Subject: 9.2

Little, M. Understanding medical ethics. *Central African Journal of Medicine* 2000 March; 46(3): 69-76. Subject: 2.1

Little, Margaret Olivia. Abortion, intimacy, and the duty to gestate. *Ethical Theory and Moral Practice* 1999; 2: 295-312. Subject: 12.4.2

Little, Margaret Olivia. The moral permissibility of abortion. *In:* Cohen, Andrew I.; Wellman, Christopher Heath,

eds. Contemporary Debates in Applied Ethics. Malden, MA: Blackwell Pub., 2005: 27-39. Subject: 12.3

Little, Margaret O.; Moczynski, Walter V.; Richardson, Paul G.; Joffe, Steven. Dana-Farber Cancer Institute ethics rounds: life-threatening illness and the desire to adopt. *Kennedy Institute of Ethics Journal* 2005 December; 15(4): 385- 393. Subject: 14.1

Little, Traci R. Protecting the right to live: international comparison of physician-assisted suicide systems. *Indiana International and Comparative Law Review* 1997; 7(2): 433-465. Subject: 20.7

Litton, Paul. ADHD, values, and the self [comment]. *American Journal of Bioethics* 2005 May-June; 5(3): 65-67. Subject: 17.4

Litton, Paul; Miller, Franklin G. A normative justification for distinguishing the ethics of clinical research from the ethics of medical care. *Journal of Law, Medicine and Ethics* 2005 Fall; 33(3): 566-574. Subject: 18.2

Liu, A. Legal recognition of advance refusal needed. *Hong Kong Medical Journal* 2005 April; 11(2): 133-134. Subject: 20.5.4

LiVolsi, Virginia A. Use of human tissue blocks for research [editorial]. *American Journal of Clinical Pathology* 1996 March; 105(3): 260-261. Subject: 18.2

Lizza, John P. Defining death: a biological or cultural matter? *In:* Fisher, Robert N.; Primozic, Daniel T.; Day, Peter A.; Thompson, Joel A., eds. Suffering, Death, and Identity. New York: Rodopi; 2002: 155-166. Subject: 4.4

Lizza, John P. Potentiality, irreversibility, and death. *Journal of Medicine and Philosophy* 2005 February; 30(1): 45-64. Subject: 20.2.1

Llewelyn, Sue. Ethical issues in psychology for women. *In:* Fairbairn, Susan; Fairbairn, Gavin, eds. Psychology, Ethics and Change. New York: Routledge & Kegan Paul; 1987: 115- 135. Subject: 17.2

Lloyd, Stanley J.; Whitney, Harvey. Publishing ethics: duplication indiscretion [editorial]. *Annals of Pharmacotherapy* 2003 January; 37(1): 147. Subject: 1.3.7

Lloyd-Puryear, Michele A.; Kyler, Penny; Weissman, Gloria. The engagement of consumers in genetic education: lessons learned. *In:* Knoppers, Bartha Maria, ed. Populations and Genetics: Legal and Socio-Ethical Perspectives. Boston: Martinus Nijhoff; 2003: 217-230. Subject: 15.1

Lo, Bernard; Albert, Marilyn S.; Hyman, Steven; Parens, Erik; Wolpe, Paul Root. Ethics and the practice of brain science. *Cerebrum: The Dana Forum on Brain Science* 2002 Summer; 4(3): 64-66. Subject: 17.1

Lo, Bernard; Dornbrand, Laurie; Dubler, Nancy N. HIPAA and patient care: the role for professional judgment. *JAMA: The Journal of the American Medical Association* 2005 April 13; 293(14): 1766-1771. Subject: 8.4

Lo, Bernard; Katz, Mitchell H. Clinical decision making during public health emergencies: ethical considerations. *Annals of Internal Medicine* 2005 October 4; 143(7): 493-498. Subject: 9.1

Lo, Bernard; Rubenfeld, Gordon. Palliative sedation in dying patients: "we turn to it when everything else hasn't worked". *JAMA: The Journal of the American Medical Association* 2005 October 12; 294(14): 1810-1816. Subject: 20.4.1

LoBiondo, Anthony R. Patient autonomy and biomedical research: judicial compromise in Moore v. Regents of the University of California. *Albany Law Journal of Science and Technology* 1991; 1: 277-305. Subject: 18.3

Lock, Stephen. Fraud and misconduct in medical research. *Medico-Legal Journal* 1996; 64(Part 4): 139-152. Subject: 18.1

Lock, Stephen. Fraud in medical research. *Issues in Medical Ethics* 1997 October-December; 5(4): 112-114. Subject: 1.3.9

Loder, Elizabeth; Goldstein, R.; Biondi, D. Placebo effects in oral triptan trials: the scientific and ethical rationale for continued use of placebo controls. *Cephalalgia* 2005 February; 25(2): 124-131. Subject: 18.3

Loew, Caroline J.; Fontanarosa, Phil B.; DeAngelis, Catherine D. Conflict of interest and independent data analysis in industry-funded studies [letter and reply]. *JAMA: The Journal of the American Medical Association* 2005 November 23-20; 294(20): 2575, 2576-2577. Subject: 1.3.9

Loewy, Erich H. Age discrimination at its best: should chronological age be a prime factor in medical decision making? *Health Care Analysis: An International Journal of Health Care Philosophy and Policy* 2005 June; 13(2): 101-117. Subject: 9.4

Loewy, Erich H. In defense of paternalism. *Theoretical Medicine and Bioethics* 2005; 26(6): 445-468. Subject: 9.1

Loewy, Erich H.; Loewy, Roberta Springer. Use and abuse of bioethics: integrity and professional standing. *Health Care Analysis: An International Journal of Health Care Philosophy and Policy* 2005 March; 13(1): 73-86. Subject: 2.1

Loewy, Roberta Springer. Ageisms. *Health Care Analysis: An International Journal of Health Care Philosophy and Policy* 2005 June; 13(2): 147-156. Subject: 9.4

Loff, Bebe; Black, Jim. Principles for public health action on infectious diseases. *Issues in Medical Ethics* 2003 October-December; 11(4): 113-115. Subject: 9.1

Loff, Bebe; Black, Jim. Research ethics committees: what is their contribution? [opinion]. *Medical Journal of Australia* 2004 October 18; 181(8): 440-441. Subject: 18.2

Loff, Bebe; Hofman, Karen; Muthuswamy, Vasantha. The Global Forum for Bioethics in Research: report of a meeting. *Issues in Medical Ethics* 2001 April-June; 9(2): 63-64. Subject: 2.1

Loff, Bebe; Jenkins, Carol; Ditmore, Melissa; Overs, Cheryl; Barbero, Rosanna. Unethical clinical trials in Thailand: a community response [letter]. *Lancet* 2005 May 7-13; 365(9471): 1618-1619. Subject: 18.2

Lofft, Annette L. Informed consent for endoscopy. *Gastrointestinal Endoscopy Clinics of North America* 1995 April; 5(2): 457-470. Subject: 8.3.1

Löfman, Päivi; Pelkonen, Marjaana; Pietilä, Anna-Maija. Ethical issues in participatory action research. *Scandinavian Journal of Caring Sciences* 2004 September; 18(3): 333-340. Subject: 18.1

Löfstedt, Petra; Shusheng, Luo; Johansson, Annika. Abortion patterns and reported sex ratios at birth in rural Yunnan, China. *Reproductive Health Matters* 2004 November; 12(24): 86-95. Subject: 14.3

Loftis, J. Robert. Germ-line enhancement of humans and nonhumans. *Kennedy Institute of Ethics Journal* 2005 March; 15(1): 57-76. Subject: 15.1

Lohmann, Georg. On the relation between moral, legal and evaluative justifications of pre-implantation genetic diagnosis (PGD). *Ethical Perspectives* 2003; 10(3-4): 196-203. Subject: 15.2

Lohr, Steve. IBM to put genetic data of workers off limits. *New York Times* 2005 October 10; p. C1, C4. Subject: 15.3

Lomanno, Matthew P. Politics and protecting human life: "private" versus "public" actions. *Ethics and Medics* 2003 October; 28(10): 1-2. Subject: 4.4

Lomas, Jonathan. Reluctant rationers: public input to health care priorities. *Journal of Health Services Research Policy* 1997 April; 2(2): 103-111. Subject: 9.4

Lombardo, Paul A. Phantom tumors and hysterical women: revising our view of the Schloendorff case. *Journal of Law, Medicine and Ethics* 2005 Winter; 33(4): 791-801. Subject: 8.3.1

London, Alex John. Does research ethics rest on a mistake? The common good, reasonable risk and social justice. *American Journal of Bioethics* 2005 January-February; 5(1): 37- 39. Subject: 18.2

London, Alex John. Justice and the human development approach to international research. *Hastings Center Report* 2005 January-February; 35(1): 24-37. Subject: 18.5.9

London, Alex John. Undue inducements and reasonable risks: will the dismal science lead to dismal research ethics? [comment]. *American Journal of Bioethics* 2005 September-October; 5(5): 29-32. Subject: 18.3

London, Leslie. Dual loyalties and HIV policy in South Africa — a challenge to the institutions of our professions [editorial]. *South African Medical Journal* 2002 November; 92(11): 882-883. Subject: 7.3

London, Leslie. Dual loyalties and the ethical and human rights obligations of occupational health professionals. *American Journal of Industrial Medicine* 2005 April; 47(4): 322-332. Subject: 16.3

London, Leslie. Health and human rights: what can ten years of democracy in South Africa tell us? *Health and Human Rights: An International Journal* 2004; 8(1): 1-25. Subject: 21.1

London, Leslie; Baldwin-Ragaven, Laurel; Bloche, M. Gregg; Marks, Jonathan H. When doctors go to war [letter and reply]. *New England Journal of Medicine* 2005 April 7; 352(14): 1497- 1499. Subject: 2.1

London, Leslie; Benjamin, Paul; Bass, David H. HIV testing and the Employment Equity Act — putting an end to the confusion [opinion]. *South African Medical Journal* 2002 March; 92(3): 199-201. Subject: 9.5.6

London, Leslie; Rangaka, Thabo; Ratamane, Solly; Orr, Wendy; Holland, Erroll; McCarthy, Greg; van Heerden, Judith; Wadee, Shabbir; Daniels, Letticia; Bruning, Axel; Dada, Mahomed; Baqwa, Zanele; Ramlakan, Vijay. Medical complicity in torture — healing the past [editorial]. *South African Medical Journal* 1996 September; 86(9): 1069-1070. Subject: 21.4

Longley, Clifford. Is the fetus a person? [opinion]. *Conscience* 2004 Summer-Autumn; 25(2): 45. Subject: 4.4

Longtin, Robert. Canadian province seeks control of its genes [news]. *Journal of the National Cancer Institute* 2004 November 3; 96(21): 1567-1569. Subject: 15.1

Loomis, C. Keanin. A battle over birth "control": legal and legislative employer prescription contraception benefit mandates. *William and Mary Bill of Rights Journal* 2002 December; 11(1): 463-494. Subject: 11.1

López, José. How sociology can save bioethics . . . maybe. *Sociology of Health and Illness* 2004 November; 26(7): 875-896. Subject: 2.1

Lorence, Daniel P. Confidentiality measures in mental health delivery settings: report of US health information managers. *Journal of Behavioral Health Services and Research* 2004 April-June; 31(2): 199-207. Subject: 17.1

Lott, J.P. Direct organ solicitation deserves reconsideration [letter]. *Journal of Medical Ethics* 2005 September; 31(9): 558. Subject: 9.5

Lott, Jason P. Module three: vulnerable/special participant populations. *Developing World Bioethics* 2005 March; 5(1): 30-54. Subject: 18.5.1

Lougheed, Tim. New US guidelines for research on human embryos [news]. *CMAJ/JAMC: Canadian Medical Association Journal* 2005 June 21; 172(13): 1672. Subject: 18.5.4

Loughlin, Kelly. Spectacle and secrecy: press coverage of conjoined twins in 1950s Britain. *Medical History* 2005 April; 49(2): 197-212. Subject: 9.5.7

Loughlin, Kevin R. Illness and secrecy on the Supreme Court [letter]. *New England Journal of Medicine* 2005 March 31; 352(13): 1387- 1388. Subject: 8.4

Loughlin, Michael. Camouflage is still no defence — another plea for a straight answer to the question 'what is bioethics?'. *Journal of Evaluation in Clinical Practice* 2004 February; 10(1): 75-83. Subject: 2.1

Loughrey, Joan. Public bodies and private medical records: the Health and Social Care (Community Health and Standards) Act 2003. *Medical Law International* 2004; 6(4): 317-337. Subject: 8.4

Louhiala, Pekka. But who can say what's right and wrong? Medicine as a moral enterprise. *In:* Evans, Martyn; Louhiala, Pekka; Puustinen, Raimo, eds. Philosophy for Medicine: Applications in a Clinical Context. San Francisco: Radcliffe Medical Press; 2004: 135-142. Subject: 2.1

Louw, André. Doctors advised not to disclose illnesses on sick certificates without patients' signed consent [letter]. *South African Medical Journal* 2002 November; 92(11): 840. Subject: 8.4

Lovat, Terence J. The implications of bioethics for teachers and teacher researchers. *British Educational Research Journal* 1994; 20(2): 187-196. Subject: 2.1

Lovejoy, Wendy. Ending the genetic discrimination barrier: regaining confidence in preconception, prenatal, and neonatal genetic testing. *Southern California Law Review* 2001 March; 74(3): 873-911. Subject: 15.3

Lovering, Robert P. Does a normal foetus really have a future of value? A reply to Marquis. *Bioethics* 2005 April; 19(2): 131-145. Subject: 12.4.2

Lowe, Julia; Kerridge, I. Implementation of guidelines for no-CPR orders by a general medicine unit in a teaching hospital. *Australian and New Zealand Journal of Medicine* 1997 August; 27(4): 379-383. Subject: 20.5.1

Lowe, LaShunda R. An inside look at partial birth abortion. *Thurgood Marshall Law Review* 1998-1999; 24: 327-357. Subject: 12.4.2

Lowenstein, Jerome K. The weight of shared lives: truth telling and family caregiving. *In:* Levine, Carol; Murray, Thomas H., eds. The Cultures of Caregiving: Conflict and Common Ground among Families, Health Professionals, and Policy Makers. Baltimore: Johns Hopkins University Press; 2004: 47-53. Subject: 8.2

Lowrey, Kerri McGowan. Legal and ethical issues in cancer genetics nursing. *Seminars in Oncology Nursing* 2004 August; 20(3): 203-208. Subject: 15.3

Lucas, Peter. Perspectivism in risk management. *In:* Häyry, Matti; Takala, Tuija; Herissone-Kelly, Peter, eds. Bioethics and Social Reality. New York: Rodopi, 2005: 127-135. Subject: 9.3.1

Luce, John M. New standards for patient rights and medical competence. *Critical Care Medicine* 2000 August; 28(8): 3114-3115. Subject: 8.3.4

Luce, John M. Physician variability in limiting life-sustaining treatment. *Critical Care Medicine* 1999 October; 27(10): 2291-2292. Subject: 20.5.1

Luce, John M. Research ethics and consent in the intensive care unit. *Current Opinion in Critical Care* 2003 December; 9(6): 540-544. Subject: 18.3

Luce, John M.; Alpers, Ann. Legal aspects of withholding and withdrawing life support from critically ill patients in the United States and providing palliative care to them. *American Journal of Respiratory and Critical Care Medicine* 2000 December; 162(6): 2029-2032. Subject: 20.5.1

Luce, John M.; Rubenfeld, Gordon D. Can health care costs be reduced by limiting intensive care at the end of life? *American Journal of Respiratory and Critical Care Medicine* 2002 March 15; 165(6): 750-754. Subject: 20.4.1

Lucke, Jayne C.; Hall, Wayne. Who wants to live forever? [opinion]. *EMBO Reports* 2005 February; 6(2): 98-102. Subject: 20.5.1

Luckhaupt, Sara E.; Yi, Michael, S.; Mueller, Caroline V.; Mrus, Joseph M.; Peterman, Amy H.; Puchalski, Christina M.; Tsevat, Joel. Beliefs of primary care residents regarding spirituality and religion in clinical encounters with patients: a study at a Midwestern U.S. teaching institution. *Academic Medicine* 2005 June; 80(6): 560-570. Subject: 8.1

Ludlam, Christopher A.; Pasi, K.J.; Bolton-Maggs, P.; Collins, P.W.; Cumming, A.M.; Dolan, G.; Fryer, A.; Harrington, C.; Hill, F.G.H.; Peake, I.R.; Perry, D.J.; Skirton, H.; Smith, M. A framework for genetic service provision for haemophilia and other inherited bleeding disorders. *Haemophilia* 2005 March; 11(2): 145-163. Subject: 15.3

Ludwig, M. Martin Johnson's moral case study: a reply [opinion]. *Reproductive BioMedicine Online [electronic]* 2004 December; 9(6): 598-599. Available: http://www.rbmonline.com/index.html [14 July 2005]. Subject: 15.2

Lugosi, Charles I. Respecting human life in 21st century America: a moral perspective to extend civil rights to the unborn from creation to natural death. *Issues in Law and Medicine* 2005 Spring; 20(3): 211-258. Subject: 4.4

Lugosi, Charles I. Respecting human life in 21st century America: a moral perspective to extend civil rights to the unborn from creation to natural death. *St. Louis University Law Journal* 2004 Winter; 48(2): 425-474. Subject: 12.3

Lumley, Judith. Conscience, regulation and scientific misconduct. *Res Publica* 1994; 3(1): 1-3. Subject: 1.3.9

Luna, Florencia. Poverty and inequality: challenges for the IAB: IAB presidential address. *Bioethics* 2005 October; 19(5-6): 451-459. Subject: 2.1

Lupton, Deborah. Feminisms and medicine. *In her:* Medicine as Culture: Illness, Disease and the Body in Western Societies. Second ed. Thousand Oaks, CA: Sage Publications; 2003: 142-172. Subject: 10

Lupton, Deborah. Power relations and the medical encounter. *In her:* Medicine as Culture: Illness, Disease and the Body in Western Societies. Second ed. Thousand Oaks, CA: Sage Publications; 2003: 113-141. Subject: 10

Lupton, M.L. Is the foetal alcohol syndrome child protected by South African law? *Medicine and Law: World Association for Medical Law* 1994; 13(1-2): 79-94. Subject: 9.5.5

Lupton, Martin G.F.; Williams, David J. The ethics of research on pregnant women: is maternal consent sufficient? [opinion]. *BJOG: An International Journal of Obstetrics and Gynaecology* 2004 December; 111(12): 1307-1312. Subject: 18.5.3

Lurie, Nicole. Health disparities — less talk, more action [editorial]. *New England Journal of Medicine* 2005 August 18; 353(7): 727- 729. Subject: 9.8

Lurie, Peter; Greco, Dirceu B. US exceptionalism comes to research ethics. *Lancet* 2005 March 26-April 1; 365(9465): 1117-1119. Subject: 18.2

Lurie, Peter; Wolfe, Sidney M. Should research ethics change at the border? [letter]. *Medical Journal of Australia* 1999 August 2; 171(3): 167-168. Subject: 18.3

Lustig, Andrew. John Paul II on the good of life. *In:* Tollefsen, Christopher, ed. John Paul II's Contribution to Catholic Bioethics. Norwell, MA: Springer; 2004: 131-150. Subject: 2.1

Lustig, B. Andrew. Challenging "common-sense" assumptions in bioethics. *Journal of Medicine and Philosophy* 2005 August; 30(4): 325-329. Subject: 2.1

Lustig, B. Andrew. Introduction: text, tradition, authority, and method in religious bioethics. *In:* Peppin, John F.; Cherry, Mark J., eds. Religious Perspectives in Bioethics. New York: Taylor & Francis; 2004: ix- xiii. Subject: 2.1

Luu, Arlene D. The impact of the HIPAA Privacy Rule on research participation. *Journal of Biolaw and Business* 2005; 8(4): 68-69. Subject: 18.2

Lycett, Emma; Daniels, Ken; Curson, Ruth; Golombok, Susan. Offspring created as a result of donor insemination: a study of family relationships, child adjustment, and disclosure. *Fertility and Sterility* 2004 July; 82(1): 172-179. Subject: 14.2

Lycett, E.; Daniels, K.; Curson, R.; Golombok, S. School-aged children of donor insemination: a study of parents' disclosure patterns. *Human Reproduction* 2005 March; 20(3): 810-819. Subject: 14.2

Lyles, Alan. Must an interest be a conflict? [editorial]. *Clinical Therapeutics* 2005 March; 27(3): 344-345. Subject: 9.7

Lynch, Maureen. Palliative sedation. *Clinical Journal of Oncology Nursing* 2003 November-December; 7(6): 653-657, 667. Subject: 20.4.1

Lynch, Patrick M. Protection of confidentiality and privacy in family studies. *Progress in Clinical and Biological Research* 1983; 115: 181- 198. Subject: 8.4

Lyng, Kristin; Syse, Aslak; Børdahl, Per E. Can cesarean section be performed without the woman's consent? *Acta Obstetricia et Gynecologica Scandinavica* 2005 January; 84(1): 39-42. Subject: 8.3.4

Lynn, Joanne. End-of-life options [letter]. *Health Affairs* 2005 September-October; 24(5): 1377-1378. Subject: 20.4.1

Lynn, Joanne; Berger, Jeffrey T. Deactivating implantable cardioverter defibrillators [letter and reply]. *Annals of Internal Medicine* 2005 November 1; 143(9): 690-691. Subject: 20.5.1

Lynöe, N.; Hoeyer, K. Quantitative aspects of informed consent: considering the dose response curve when estimating quantity of information. *Journal of Medical Ethics* 2005 December; 31(12): 736-738. Subject: 18.3

Lynöe, Niels; Mattsson, Bengt. Doctor for patients or doctor for society? Comparative study of GPs' and psychiatrists' assessments of clinical practice. *Scandinavian Journal of Primary Health Care* 2004 December; 22(4): 228-232. Subject: 4.1.2

Lynöe, Niels; Näsström, Birgit; Sandlund, Mikael. Study of the quality of information given to patients participating in a clinical trial regarding chronic hemodialysis. *Scandinavian Journal of Urology and Nephrology* 2004; 38(6): 517-520. Subject: 18.3

Lynöe, Niels; Sandlund, Mikael; Jacobsson, Lars; Nordberg, Gunnar; Jin, Taiyi. Informed consent in China: quality of information provided to participants in a research project. *Scandinavian Journal of Public Health* 2004; 32(6): 472-475. Subject: 18.3

Lyon, Maureen E.; McCabe, Mary Ann; Patel, Kantilal M.; D'Angelo, Lawrence J. What do adolescents want? An exploratory study regarding end-of-life decision-making. *Journal of Adolescent Health* 2004 December; 35(6): 529.e1- 529.e6 [Online]. Available: http://jahonline.org/issues [22 July 2005]. Subject: 20.3.1

Lysaught, M. Therese. Practicing the order of widows: a new call for an old vocation. *Christian Bioethics* 2005 April; 11(1): 51-68. Subject: 9.1

Lyttle, C. Paul. Elderly consumers' and community nurses' experience of bereavement visiting: navigating, networking and negotiating with a local research ethics committee. *Managing Clinical Nursing* 1998 June; 2(2): 41-44. Subject: 18.5.7

M

Maas, Meridean L.; Kelley, Lisa S.; Park, Myonghwa; Specht, Janet P. Issues in conducting research in nursing homes. *Western Journal of Nursing Research* 2002 June; 24(4): 373-389. Subject: 18.5.7

Maas, Susan. Thoughtful Trekkie: medical practice, faith, philosophy, and a bit of sci-fi inform the thinking of Mayo Clinic hematologist and ethicist C. Christopher Hook. *Minnesota Medicine* 2004 June; 87(6): 18-22. Subject: 2.1

Macauley, Domhnall. Fair, honest, ethical, and last [editorial]. *British Journal of Sports Medicine* 1999 October; 33(5): 293-294. Subject: 9.1

Macauley, Robert. The Hippocratic underground: civil disobedience and health care reform. *Hastings Center Report* 2005 January-February; 35(1): 38-45. Subject: 9.3.1

Maccoon, Kathryn. To what extent should a colleague be unnecessarily exposed to risks for the sake of protecting patient privacy: an ethical dilemma. *Health Law in Canada* 2005 November; 26(2): 13-16. Subject: 8.4

Macdonald, Alastair J.D.; Roberts, Alice; Carpenter, Iain. De facto imprisonment and covert medication use in general nursing homes for older people in South East England. *Aging Clinical and Experimental Research* 2004 August; 16(4): 326-330. Subject: 9.5.2

MacDonald, Chris. Corporate ethics in the life sciences: can bioethics help? Should it? *HEC (Healthcare Ethics Committee) Forum* 2005 June; 17(2): 122- 134. Subject: 9.6

MacDonald, Chris. Patents and benefit-sharing as a challenge for corporate ethics. *In:* Knoppers, Bartha Maria, ed. Populations and Genetics: Legal and Socio-Ethical Perspectives. Boston: Martinus Nijhoff; 2003: 505-523. Subject: 15.1

Macer, Darryl. Do the ethical duties of donor, and administrators, depend on whether the database is public or private? *In:* Knoppers, Bartha Maria, ed. Populations and Genetics: Legal and Socio-Ethical Perspectives. Boston: Martinus Nijhoff; 2003: 311-321. Subject: 15.1

Macer, Darryl. End-of-life care in Japan. *In:* Blank, Robert H.; Merrick, Janna C., eds. End-of-Life Decision Making: A Cross-National Study. Cambridge, MA: MIT Press; 2005: 109-129. Subject: 20.4.1

Macer, Darryl. Ethical, legal and social issues of genetically modifying insect vectors for public health. *Insect Biochemistry and Molecular Biology* 2005 July; 35(7): 649-660. Subject: 15.1

Machado, Calixto. Consciousness as a definition of death: its appeal and complexity. *Clinical Electroencephalography* 1999 October; 30(4): 156-164. Subject: 20.2.1

Machado, Nora; Burns, Tom R. The new genetics: a social science and humanities research agenda. *Canadian Journal of Sociology/Cahiers Canadiens de Sociologie* 2000 Autumn; 25(4): 495-506. Subject: 15.1

Subject = NRCBL Primary Classification Number; See inside front cover

Macintyre, Sally. The Black Report and beyond: what are the issues? *Social Science and Medicine* 1997 March; 44(6): 723-745. Subject: 9.1

MacIver, Jane; Ross, Heather J. Withdrawal of ventricular assist device support. *Journal of Palliative Care* 2005 Autumn; 21(3): 151-156. Subject: 20.5.1

Mack, George S. Revolt in Bethesda [news]. *Nature Medicine* 2005 September; 11(9): 914-915. Subject: 1.3.9

Mackay, Michael J. A time to die: is there something wrong with the way CPR is presently practised? [opinion]. *Medical Journal of Australia* 2004 December 6-20; 181(11-12): 667-668. Subject: 20.5.1

Mackenbach, Johan P. On the survival of the altruistic trait in medicine: is there a link with the placebo effect? [opinion]. *Journal of Clinical Epidemiology* 2005 May; 58(5): 433-435. Subject: 4.1.2

Mackenzie, R.A. Ethical considerations in epilepsy management. *Medicine and Law: World Association for Medical Law* 2004; 23(4): 781-789. Subject: 8.3.1

Mackenzie, Robin. Reprogenetics and pharmacogenetics: in whose best interests? *Medicine and Law: World Association for Medical Law* 2005 June; 24(2): 343-354. Subject: 18.6

Mackey, Denise; Kjerulf, Maria. The ethics of organ donation: examining consent policies and donor criteria. *University of Toronto Medical Journal* 2000 December; 78(1): 51-54. Subject: 19.5

Mackie, Phil; Sim, Fiona. Publishing ethics and public health [editorial]. *Public Health* 2005 April; 119(4): 223-224. Subject: 1.3.7

Mackler, Aaron L. Jewish perspectives on embryo and stem cell research. *In:* Peppin, John F.; Cherry, Mark J., eds. Religious Perspectives in Bioethics. New York: Taylor & Francis; 2004: 147- 152. Subject: 18.5.4

Macklin, Ruth. Ethics and Equity in Access to HIV Treatment — 3 by 5 Initiative. Geneva, Switzerland: World Health Organization 2004 January 26-27; 18 p. [Online]. Available: http://www.who.int/ethics/en/background-macklin.pdf [8 March 2005]. Subject: 9.5.6

Macklin, Ruth. Some questionable premises about research ethics. *American Journal of Bioethics* 2005 January-February; 5(1): 29- 31. Subject: 18.2

Macklin, Ruth. Yet another guideline? The UNESCO draft declaration. *Developing World Bioethics* 2005 September; 5(3): 244-250. Subject: 2.1

MacLaren, Robert E.; Ali, Robin R.; Thrasher, Adrian J. Risks of gene therapy should be weighed against lack of alternatives for many diseases [letter]. *BMJ: British Medical Journal* 2005 April 2; 330(7494): 791. Subject: 15.4

Maclean, Alasdair. Giving the reasonable patient a voice: information disclosure and the relevance of empirical evidence. *Medical Law International* 2005; 7(1): 1-40. Subject: 8.3.1

Maclean, Mavis. Letting go: parents, professionals and the law in the retention of human material after post mortem. *In:* Bainham, Andrew; Sclater, Shelley Day; Richards, Martin, eds. Body Lore and Laws. Portland, OR: Hart Pub.; 2002: 79-89. Subject: 19.5

Maclin, Tracey. Is obtaining an arrestee's DNA a valid special needs search under the Fourth Amendment? What should (and will) the Supreme Court do? *Journal of Law, Medicine and Ethics* 2005 Spring; 33(1): 102- 124. Subject: 15.1

MacRae, S.; Chidwick, P.; Berry, S.; Secker, B.; Hébert, P.; Zlotnik Shaul, R.; Faith, K.; Singer, P.A. Clinical bioethics integration, sustainability, and accountability: the Hub and Spokes Strategy. *Journal of Medical Ethics* 2005 May; 31(5): 256-261. Subject: 9.6

MacReady, Norra. Criticism of US fetal pain study escalates [news]. *BMJ: British Medical Journal* 2005 September 10; 331(7516): 532. Subject: 4.4

Maddocks, Ian. 'Good palliative care' orders. *Palliative Medicine* 1993; 7(1): 35-37. Subject: 20.4.1

Madhiwalla, Neha. Experiences in health research with women. *Issues in Medical Ethics* 2001 January-March; 9(1): 12-14. Subject: 18.5.3

Madhiwalla, Neha. National meeting on ethical guidelines for social science research. *Issues in Medical Ethics* 2000 October-December; 8(4): 131. Subject: 18.4

Madhiwalla, Neha. Sex selection: ethics in the context of development. *Issues in Medical Ethics* 2001 October-December; 9(4): 125-126. Subject: 14.3

Madoyan, Igor. Armenia. *Medical Ethics and Bioethics / Medicinska Etika & Bioetika* 2005; 11(Supplement): 14. Subject: 9.6

Maekawa, Fumi; Macer, Darryl. Bioethics of teaching about reproductive technology and prenatal diagnosis choices in Japan. *Journal International de Bioethique / International Journal of Bioethics* 2005 March-June; 16(1-2): 53-67, 192. Subject: 2.3

Magid, Julie Manning. Contraception and contractions: a divergent decade following Johnson controls. *American Business Law Journal* 2003 Fall; 41(1); 26 p. [Online]. Available: http://web.lexis-nexis.com/universe/printdoc [3 June 2005]. Subject: 10

Magill, Gerard. Ethical perspectives on life sciences research after mapping the human genome. *Medical Ethics and Bioethics / Medicinska Etika & Bioetika* 2001 Spring-Summer; 8(1-2): 3-5. Subject: 15.10

Magnus, David; Cho, Mildred K. Issues in oocyte donation for stem cell research. *Science* 2005 June 17; 308(5729): 1747-1748. Subject: 18.5.4

Magnusson, Roger S. The changing legal and conceptual shape of health care privacy. *Journal of Law, Medicine and Ethics* 2004 Winter; 32(4): 680- 691. Subject: 8.4

Magnusson, Roger S. The recognition of proprietary rights in human tissue in common law jurisdictions. *Melbourne University Law Review* 1992 June; 18: 601-629. Subject: 4.4

Magotra, Ratna. Sponsorships for medical specialists. *Issues in Medical Ethics* 1997 October-December; 5(4): 122-125. Subject: 7.2

Magotra, Ratna; Dastur, F.D. Iatrogenic complications: what are doctors' and hospitals' responsibilities? [case study and commentary]. *Issues in Medical Ethics* 2001 July-September; 9(3): 95-96. Subject: 9.8

Mahawar, Kamal Kumar. End-of-life issues [letter]. *Lancet* 2005 November 26-December 2; 366(9500): 1848. Subject: 20.5.1

Maher, Daniel P. Managed care and undividing loyalties. *Journal of Contemporary Health Law and Policy* 2002 Fall; 18(3): 703-709. Subject: 9.3.2

Mahon, Margaret M.; Deatrick, Janet A.; McKnight, Heather J.; Mohr, Wanda K. Discontinuing treatment in children with chronic, critical illnesses. *Nurse Practitioner Forum* 2000 March; 11(1): 6-14. Subject: 20.5.2

Mahowald, Mary B. Another view of potentiality and human embryos. *Theoretical Medicine and Bioethics* 2005; 26(2): 111-113. Subject: 4.4

Mahowald, Mary B. The President's Council on Bioethics, 2002-2004: an overview. *Perspectives in Biology and Medicine* 2005 Spring; 48(2): 159-171. Subject: 2.4

Maifeld, Michelle; Hahn, Sandra; Titler, Marita G.; Mullen, Meredithe. Decision making regarding multifetal reduction. *JOGNN: Journal of Obstetric, Gynecologic and Neonatal Nursing* 2003 May-June; 32(3): 357-369. Subject: 12.1

Maio, Giovanni. Medical ethics and human experimentation in France after 1945. *In:* Roelcke, Volker; Maio, Giovanni, eds. Twentieth Century Ethics of Human Subjects Research: Historical Perspectives on Values, Practices, and Regulations. Stuttgart: Franz Steiner Verlag; 2004: 235-252. Subject: 18.1

Maio, Giovanni. Zur Begründung der Schutzwürdigkeit des Embryos e contrario. *In:* Maio, Giovanni; Just, Hanjörg, eds. Die Forschung an embryonalen Stammzellen in ethischer und rechtlicher Perspektive. Baden-Baden: Nomos Verlagsgesellschaft; 2003: 168-177. Subject: 4.4

Maithel, Shishir Kumar. Iatrogenic error and truth telling: a comparison of the United States and India. *Issues in Medical Ethics* 1998 October-December; 6(4): 125-127. Subject: 8.2

Major, Ken. Latinos and electroconvulsive therapy: implications for treatment, research, and reform in Texas and beyond. *Ethical Human Psychology and Psychiatry* 2005 Summer; 7(2): 159-166. Subject: 17.5

Majors, M. Jason. Constitutional law — clarity or confusion? The constitutionality of a Nebraska statute prohibiting partial-birth abortion procedures. Stenberg v. Carhart, 120 S.Ct. 2597 (2000). *Wyoming Law Review* 2001; 1(1): 231-261. Subject: 12.4.3

Majumder, Mary Anderlik. Cyberbanks and other virtual research repositories. *Journal of Law, Medicine and Ethics* 2005 Spring; 33(1): 31-39. Subject: 15.1

Majumder, Mary Anderlik. Respecting difference and moving beyond regulation: tasks for U.S. bioethics commissions in the twenty-first century. *Kennedy Institute of Ethics Journal* 2005 September; 15(3): 289-303. Subject: 2.4

Majumder, Mary Anderlik. The roles of ethicists in managed care litigation. *Journal of Law, Medicine and Ethics* 2005 Summer; 33(2): 264- 273. Subject: 2.1

Majumder, Mary Anderlik. Uncharitable care? *Hastings Center Report* 2004 July-August; 34(4): 7. Subject: 9.3.1

Majumder, Mary Anderlik; Brakman, Sarah-Vaughan. The politics of embryo transfer [discussion]. *Medical Ethics Newsletter [Lahey Clinic]* 2005 Fall; 12(3): 10- 11. Subject: 14.4

Malavige, G.N. Doctors, drug companies and medical ethics: a Sri Lankan perspective. *Indian Journal of Medical Ethics* 2004 January-March; 1(1): 26. Subject: 9.7

Malby, Steven. Human dignity and human reproductive cloning. *Health and Human Rights: An International Journal* 2002; 6(1): 103-135. Subject: 14.5

Malcolm, David. The Everett Magnus Oration: euthanasia and the law: crossing the rubicon? *Australian and New Zealand Journal of Medicine* 1998 February; 28(1): 46-54. Subject: 20.5.1

Malcolm, Helen A. Does privacy matter? Former patients discuss their perceptions of privacy in shared hospital rooms. *Nursing Ethics* 2005 March; 12(2): 156-166. Subject: 8.4

Malfroy, Moira; Llewelyn, C.A.; Johnson, T.; Williamson, L.M. Using patient-identifiable data for epidemiological research. *Transfusion Medicine* 2004 August; 14(4): 275-279. Subject: 18.2

Malin, Bradley A. An evaluation of the current state of genomic data privacy protection technology and a roadmap for the future. *Journal of the American Medical Informatics Association* 2005 January-February; 12(1): 28-34. Subject: 15.1

Malina, Debra. Compliance, caricature, and culturally aware care [opinion]. *New England Journal of Medicine* 2005 September 29; 353(13): 1317-1318. Subject: 21.7

Malinowski, Michael J. Technology transfer in biobanking: credits, debits, and population health futures. *Journal of Law, Medicine and Ethics* 2005 Spring; 33(1): 54-69. Subject: 15.1

Mallia, Pierre; ten Have, Henk A.M.J. Applying theological developments to bioethical issues such as genetic screening. *Ethics and Medicine* 2005 Summer; 21(2): 95-107. Subject: 15.3

Mallia, Pierre; ten Have, Henk A.M.J. Pragmatic approaches to genetic screening. *Medicine, Health Care and Philosophy: A European Journal* 2005; 8(1): 69-77. Subject: 15.3

Mallia, Pierre; Williams, Anne. The use of emergency hormonal contraception in cases of rape - - revisiting the Catholic position. *Human Reproduction and Genetic Ethics: An International Journal* 2005; 11(2): 35-42. Subject: 11.1

Malone, Kevin M.; Hinman, Alan R. Vaccination mandates: the public health imperative and individual rights. *In:* Goodman, Richard A.; Rothstein, Mark A.; Hoffman, Richard E.; Lopez, Wilfredo; Matthews, Gene W., eds. Law in Public Health Practice. New York: Oxford University Press; 2003: 262-284. Subject: 9.7

Maloney, Dennis M. Agency proposes major expansion of its regulations for human subjects. *Human Research Report* 2005 October; 20(10): 1-2. Subject: 18.6

Maloney, Dennis M. Both accused researchers and whistle-blowers stay anonymous when no misconduct is found. *Human Research Report* 2005 July; 20(7): 8. Subject: 1.3.9

Maloney, Dennis M. Complaint alleges "coercion" and "undue influence" in IRB- approved consent form. *Human Research Report* 2005 September; 20(9): 8. Subject: 18.3

Maloney, Dennis M. Complaint alleges many deficiencies in IRB-approved informed consent form. *Human Research Report* 2005 October; 20(10): 8. Subject: 18.3

Maloney, Dennis M. Complaint alleges that informed consent procedures were used after experiment began. *Human Research Report* 2005 November; 20(11): 8. Subject: 18.3

Maloney, Dennis M. Congressmen say military should have the right to informed consent. *Human Research Report* 2005 March; 20(3): 9. Subject: 18.3

Maloney, Dennis M. Creation of new national committee on bioethics. *Human Research Report* 2002 January; 17(1): 4. Subject: 2.4

Maloney, Dennis M. Critics claim even babies could be exposed to pesticides in research. *Human Research Report* 2005 August; 20(8): 1-2. Subject: 18.1

Maloney, Dennis M. Death of research subject leads to lawsuit. *Human Research Report* 2002 January; 17(1): 8. Subject: 18.2

Maloney, Dennis M. Ethical requirements would apply to stem cell research. *Human Research Report* 2002 January; 17(1): 9. Subject: 14.5

Maloney, Dennis M. Federal case is settled over death of research subject. *Human Research Report* 2005 April; 20(4): 1-2. Subject: 15.4

Maloney, Dennis M. Final rule on additional protections for women. *Human Research Report* 2002 January; 17(1): 3. Subject: 18.2

Maloney, Dennis M. Former human subjects sue over their allegations of inadequate informed consent. *Human Research Report* 2005 August; 20(8): 8. Subject: 18.3

Maloney, Dennis M. Institutional review boards (IRBs) and working with adverse event reports. *Human Research Report* 2005 December; 20(12): 1-3. Subject: 18.2

Maloney, Dennis M. Institutional review boards must conduct safety review. *Human Research Report* 2005 February; 20(2): 3. Subject: 18.2

Maloney, Dennis M. IRB opts for "user friendly" letter rather than an informed consent form. *Human Research Report* 2005 January; 20(1): 6-7. Subject: 18.3

Maloney, Dennis M. IRBs and human embryonic stem cell experimentation. *Human Research Report* 2002 January; 17(1): 5. Subject: 18.2

Maloney, Dennis M. IRBs and the new rule on research with children. *Human Research Report* 2002 January; 17(1): 4. Subject: 18.2

Maloney, Dennis M. IRBs, human subjects, and reporting adverse events. *Human Research Report* 2005 November; 20(11): 3. Subject: 18.2

Maloney, Dennis M. More flexibility on reporting to federal agencies about injuries to research subjects. *Human Research Report* 2002 January; 17(1): 1-2. Subject: 18.2

Maloney, Dennis M. New federal guidance adds duties for institutional review boards (IRBs). *Human Research Report* 2005 November; 20(11): 1-2. Subject: 18.2

Maloney, Dennis M. New guidance on reviews by central institutional review boards (IRBs). *Human Research Report* 2005 May; 20(5): 1-2. Subject: 18.2

Maloney, Dennis M. New guidance on when and how to report human research problems. *Human Research Report* 2005 July; 20(7): 1-2. Subject: 18.6

Maloney, Dennis M. New human subject protection regulations are being delayed. *Human Research Report* 2005 January; 20(1): 1-2. Subject: 18.2

Maloney, Dennis M. Plaintiffs claim that research subject was too drowsy to give informed consent. *Human Research Report* 2005 December; 20(12): 8. Subject: 18.3

Maloney, Dennis M. Privacy of researchers versus public's right to know their names. *Human Research Report* 2005 May; 20(5): 8. Subject: 1.3.9

Maloney, Dennis M. Protecting against financial conflict of interest at the NIH. *Human Research Report* 2005 January; 20(1): 3. Subject: 1.3.9

Maloney, Dennis M. Protection of human subjects and coded private information. *Human Research Report* 2005 February; 20(2): 1-2. Subject: 18.2

Maloney, Dennis M. Research subject complains about how she was treated by an institutional review board (IRB) [case study]. *Human Research Report* 2005 December; 20(12): 7. Subject: 18.2

Maloney, Dennis M. Researcher said his colleague should have revealed possible conflicts of interest. *Human Research Report* 2005 January; 20(1): 8. Subject: 1.3.9

Maloney, Dennis M. Researcher wins the battle but loses the war. *Human Research Report* 2005 April; 20(4): 8. Subject: 1.3.9

Maloney, Dennis M. University denies that it failed to comply with special rule for subjects who are prisoners [case study]. *Human Research Report* 2002 January; 17(1): 6-7. Subject: 18.2

Maloney, Dennis M. University ordered to halt human research [case study]. *Human Research Report* 2005 April; 20(4): 6-7. Subject: 18.2

Maloney, Dennis M. University says research subjects' family members are not research subjects too. *Human Research Report* 2005 February; 20(2): 6-7. Subject: 18.3

Maloney, Dennis M. University uses "implied informed consent". *Human Research Report* 2005 March; 20(3): 6-7. Subject: 18.3

Malpani, Aniruddha. Doctors should be allowed to advertise [debate]. *Issues in Medical Ethics* 2001 January-March; 9(1): 16-17. Subject: 8.1

Malterud, Kirsti. Humiliation instead of care? [opinion]. *Lancet* 2005 September 3-9; 366(9488): 785-786. Subject: 8.1

Mamdani, Bashir. He's ethical but has bad taste . . . *Issues in Medical Ethics* 2003 January-March; 11(1): 24. Subject: 8.1

Mamdani, Bashir. The Helsinki Declaration, 2000, and ethics of human research in developing countries. *Indian Journal of Medical Ethics* 2004 July-September; 1(3): 94-95. Subject: 18.2

Mamdani, Bashir. In support of sex selection. *Indian Journal of Medical Ethics* 2005 January-March; 2(1): 26-27. Subject: 14.3

Mamdani, Bashir. The Terry Schiavo case: possible implications for India. *Indian Journal of Medical Ethics* 2005 July-September; 2(3): 97-98. Subject: 20.5.1

Mamdani, Bashir; Mamdani, Meenal. Colonialism of clinical trials: discerning the positive spin offs [summary]. *Indian Journal of Medical Ethics* 2005 October-December; 2(4): 132-133. Subject: 18.5.9

Mamdani, Bashir; Mamdani, Meenal. Ethics of professional advertising [debate]. *Issues in Medical Ethics* 2001 January-March; 9(1): 18. Subject: 8.1

Mamdani, Bashir; Mamdani, Meenal. Export of managed care: Europe, Latin America and implications for India. *Issues in Medical Ethics* 2002 April-June; 10(2): 17-19. Subject: 9.3.2

Mamdani, Meenal. Case studies for medical ethics. *Issues in Medical Ethics* 2000 April-June; 8(2): 65. Subject: 20.5.1

Mamdani, Meenal B.; Mamdani, Bashir. Commercial support for continuing medical education. *Issues in Medical Ethics* 1997 April-June; 5(2): 43-45. Subject: 7.2

Mamdani, Meenal; Mamdani, Bashir. Follow-up: should the elderly woman have been put on a ventilator against her wishes? *Issues in Medical Ethics* 2001 January-March; 9(1): 27. Subject: 20.1

Mamdani, Meenal; Mamdani, Bashir; Pandya, Sunil K. Informed consent for brain surgery [case study]. *Issues in Medical Ethics* 2000 January-March; 8(1): 29. Subject: 8.3.1

Mamo, Laura. Biomedicalizing kinship: sperm banks and the creation of affinity-ties. *Science as Culture* 2005 September; 14(3): 237-264. Subject: 14.2

Manaloto, Renato B.; Alvarez, Allen Andrew A.; Alvarez, Mary Ann V. Analysis of some Filipino perspectives on ethical issues in multi-country collaborative research: a case of deep listening. *Bioethics* 2005 October; 19(5-6): 550-564. Subject: 18.2

Manaouil, C.; Chatelain, D.; Montpellier, D.; Graser, M.; Jardé, O. New French legislation governing organ removals for therapeutic and scientific purposes. *Medicine and Law: World Association for Medical Law* 2005 September; 24(3): 585-603. Subject: 19.5

Manaouil, Cécile; Graser, Marie; Chatelain, Denis; Jardé, Olivier. The examination of genetic characteristics since the adoption of the French law on bioethics. *Medicine and Law: World Association for Medical Law* 2005 December; 24(4): 783-789. Subject: 2.1

Manasco, Penelope K. Ethical and legal aspects of applied genomic technologies: practical solutions. *Current Molecular Medicine* 2005 February; 5(1): 23-28. Subject: 18.2

Manasse, Henri R., Jr. Conscientious objection and the pharmacist. *Science* 2005 June 10; 308(5728): 1558-1559. Subject: 9.7

Manasse, Henri R., Jr.; Cantor, Julie; Baum, Ken. Pharmacists and emergency contraception [letter and reply]. *New England Journal of Medicine* 2005 March 3; 352(9): 943-944. Subject: 11.1

Manavi, Kaveh; Welsby, Philip D. HIV testing: should no longer be accorded any special status [editorial]. *BMJ:*

British Medical Journal 2005 March 5; 330(7490): 492-493. Subject: 9.5.6

Mandavilli, Apoorva. Scientists seek simple remedies to cloning conundrums [news]. *Nature Medicine* 2005 May; 11(5): 459. Subject: 18.5.4

Mandavilli, Apoorva. Screen savers [news]. *Nature Medicine* 2005 October; 11(10): 1020-1021. Subject: 15.3

Mandavilli, Apoorva. Woo-Suk Hwang. *Nature Medicine* 2005 May; 11(5): 464. Subject: 18.5.4

Mandel, Gregory N. Gaps, inexperience, inconsistencies, and overlaps: crisis in the regulation of genetically modified plants and animals. *William and Mary Law Review* 2004 April; 45(5): 2167-2259. Subject: 15.1

Mandl, Kenneth D.; Feit, Shlomit; Larson, Cecilia; Kohane, Isaac S. Newborn screening program practices in the United States: notification, research and consent. *Pediatrics* 2002 February; 109(2): 269-273. Subject: 15.3

Mandler, George. Psychologists and the National Socialist access to power. *History of Psychology* 2002 May; 5(2): 190-200. Subject: 21.4

Mandry, Tilo. Legal implications of pharmacogenomics regarding drug trials, drug labeling, and genetic testing for drug prescription: an international approach. *Food and Drug Law Journal* 2004; 59(4): 519-535. Subject: 15.1

Mangal, Rambarran. Consent to medical treatment. *West Indian Law Journal* 1999 May and October; 24(2): 83-91. Subject: 8.3.1

Manias, Elizabeth. Australian nurses' experiences and attitudes in the "do not resuscitate" decision. *Research in Nursing and Health* 1998 October; 21(5): 429-441. Subject: 20.5.1

Manilla, Peter; Rebello, Tessio; Afable, Cathleen; Lu, Xiaobin; Slepushkin, Vladimir; Humeau, Laurent M.; Schonely, Kathy; Ni, Yajin; Binder, Gwendolyn K.; Levine, Bruce L.; MacGregor, Rob-Roy; June, Carl H.; Dropulic, Boro. Regulatory considerations for novel gene therapy products: a review of the process leading to the first clinical lentiviral vector. *Human Gene Therapy* 2005 January; 16(1): 17-25. Subject: 15.4

Mann, Charles C. A new skirmish in the Yanomamo wars [news]. *Science* 2005 July 8; 309(5732): 227, 229. Subject: 18.5.9

Mann, H. Controversial choice of a control intervention in a trial of ventilator therapy in ARDS: standard of care arguments in a randomised controlled trial. *Journal of Medical Ethics* 2005 September; 31(9): 548-553. Subject: 18.2

Mann, Jim. The Indo-Mediterranean diet revisited. *Lancet* 2005 July 30-August 5; 366(9483): 353-354. Subject: 18.2

Mannikko, Nancy Farm; Ness, Bryan D. Gene therapy: ethical and economic issues. *In:* Ness, Bryan D., ed. Ency-

clopedia of Genetics. Revised edition. Volume I. Pasadena, Calif.: Salem Press; 2004: 309-313. Subject: 15.4

Mannikko, Nancy Farm; Ness, Bryan D. Insurance. *In:* Ness, Bryan D., ed. Encyclopedia of Genetics. Revised edition. Volume II. Pasadena, Calif.: Salem Press; 2004: 471-474. Subject: 15.3

Manning, Donal. Proxy consent in neonatal care — goal-directed or procedure- specific? *Health Care Analysis: An International Journal of Health Care Philosophy and Policy* 2005 March; 13(1): 1-9. Subject: 8.3.2

Manning, Georgina. Care ethics in pediatric critical care nursing. *Update [Loma Linda University Center for Christian Bioethics]* 2002 March; 17(3): 8-11. Subject: 4.1.3

Manning, Joanna. Informed consent to medical treatment: the common law and New Zealand's Code of Patient's Rights. *Medical Law Review* 2004 Summer; 12(2): 181-216. Subject: 8.3.1

Manning, Joanna; Paterson, Ron. "Prioritization": rationing health care in New Zealand. *Journal of Law, Medicine and Ethics* 2005 Winter; 33(4): 681- 697. Subject: 9.4

Manning, Paula J. Baby needs a new set of rules: using adoption doctrine to regulate embryo donation. *Georgetown Journal of Gender and the Law* 2004 Spring; 5(2): 677-721. Subject: 14.6

Mansell, Diana; Hibberd, Judith. 'We picked the wrong one to sterilise': the role of nursing in the eugenics movement in Alberta, 1920-1940. *International History of Nursing Journal* 1998 Summer; 3(4): 4-11. Subject: 15.5

Mansfield, Peter R. Banning all drug promotion is the best option pending major reforms. *Journal of Bioethical Inquiry* 2005; 2(2): 75-81. Subject: 9.7

Mansfield, Peter R.; Mintzes, Barbara; Richards, Dee; Toop, Les. Direct to consumer advertising [editorial]. *BMJ: British Medical Journal* 2005 January 1; 330(7481): 5. Subject: 9.7

Manship, Greg. Hope and the ethics of disclosure for terminally ill cancer patients. *Health Care Ethics USA [electronic]* 2005; 13(3); E4, 3 p. Available: http://www.slu.edu/centers/chce/hceusa/3_2005_index.html [21 February 2006]. Subject: 8.2

Manson, Neil C. How not to think about genetic information [opinion]. *Hastings Center Report* 2005 July-August; 35(4): 3. Subject: 15.1

Mantz, Allison. Do not resuscitate decision-making: Ohio's do not resuscitate law should be amended to include a mature minor's right to initiate a DNR order. *Journal of Law and Health* 2002-2003; 17(2): 359-384. Subject: 20.5.2

Manzelli, Antonio; Fisichella, P. Marco; Bonfrate, Giuseppe; Gaspari, Achille Lucio. When living related organ donation does not entail a healthy organ: moral implications for both the donor and the recipient [opinion].

Archives of Surgery 2004 November; 139(11): 1259. Subject: 19.5

Marcelletti, Carlo. Bioethics and medicine. *Medicine and Law: World Association for Medical Law* 1995; 14(1-2): 9-12. Subject: 20.5.2

Marcellus, Lenora. The ethics of relation: public health nurses and child protection clients. *Journal of Advanced Nursing* 2005 August; 51(4): 414-420. Subject: 8.1

Marcin, Raymond B. "Posterity" in the preamble and a positivist pro-life position. *American Journal of Jurisprudence* 1993; 38: 273-295. Subject: 12.1

Marckmann, Georg. Access to essential drugs: the ethical challenge of allocating obligations. *In:* Thiele, F.; Ashcroft, R.E., eds. Bioethics in a Small World. Berlin: Springer; 2005: 111-119. Subject: 9.7

Marckmann, Georg. Ending or extending life-sustaining treatment: ethics of the decisions. *In:* Council of Europe Publishing, ed. Euthanasia. Volume I. Ethical and Human Aspects. Strasbourg: Council of Europe; Croton- on-Hudson, NY: Manhattan Publishing Co.; 2003: 83-96. Subject: 20.5.1

Marco, Catherine A. Ethics seminars: teaching professionalism to "problem" residents. *Academic Emergency Medicine* 2002 October; 9(10): 1001-1006. Subject: 7.2

Marco, Catherine A.; Schears, Raquel M. Prehospital resuscitation practices: a survey of prehospital providers. *Journal of Emergency Medicine* 2003 January; 24(1): 101-106. Subject: 20.5.1

Marcum, James A. Biomechanical and phenomenological models of the body, the meaning of illness and quality of care. *Medicine, Health Care and Philosophy: A European Journal* 2004; 7(3): 311-320. Subject: 4.2

Marcus, Amy Dockser. A brother's survey touches a nerve in abortion fight; mothers were asked how they found out their babies had Down syndrome; teaching his sister to read. *Wall Street Journal* 2005 October 3; p. A1, A8. Subject: 9.5.3

Marcus, E-L.; Wasserstein Fassberg, C.; Namestnik, J.; Guedj, D.; Caine, Y. Strict vegan, low-calorie diet administered by care-giving daughter to elderly mother — is this elder abuse? *Medicine and Law: World Association for Medical Law* 2005 June; 24(2): 279-296. Subject: 8.3.3

Marczyk, Geoffrey R.; Wertheimer, Ellen. The bitter pill of empiricism: health maintenance organizations, informed consent and the reasonable psychotherapist standard of care. *Villanova Law Review* 2001; 46(1): 33-93. Subject: 8.3.1

Mareiniss, Darren P. A comparison of Cruzan and Schiavo: the burden of proof, due process, and autonomy in the persistently vegetative patient. *Journal of Legal Medicine* 2005 June; 26(2): 233-259. Subject: 20.5.1

Margalith, Ilana; Musgrave, Catherine F.; Goldschmidt, Lydia. Physician-assisted dying: are education and religious beliefs related to nursing students' attitudes? *Journal of Nursing Education* 2003 February; 42(2): 91-96. Subject: 20.7

Margolin, Gayla; Chien, Deborah; Duman, Sarah E.; Fauchier, Angele; Gordis, Elana B.; Oliver, Pamella H.; Ramos, Michelle C.; Vickerman, Katrina A. Ethical issues in couple and family research. *Journal of Family Psychology* 2005 March; 19(1): 157-167. Subject: 18.2

Mariner, Joanne. Latin America's abortion battles. *Conscience* 2005 Autumn; 26(3): 10-14. Subject: 12.4.2

Mariner, Wendy K.; Annas, George J.; Glantz, Leonard H. Jacobson v Massachusetts: it's not your great-great- grandfather's public health law. *American Journal of Public Health* 2005 April; 95(4): 581-590. Subject: 9.1

Markie, Peter J. Respect for people and animals. *Journal of Value Inquiry* 2004; 38(1): 33-47. Subject: 22.1

Markin, Karen M. Playing it safe with research risk: if you fail to follow the rules, you could conduct an entire project and be forbidden to publish the results. *Chronicle of Higher Education* 2005 August 12; 51(49): C1, C4. Subject: 18.2

Markman, Maurie. Ethical conflict in providing informed consent for clinical trials: a problematic example from the gynecologic cancer research community. *Oncologist* 2004; 9(1): 3-7. Subject: 18.3

Markman, Maurie. Genetic discrimination arising from cancer risk assessments: a societal dilemma. *Cleveland Clinic Journal of Medicine* 2004 January; 71(1): 12, 15-18. Subject: 15.3

Markovits, Daniel. Quarantines and distributive justice. *Journal of Law, Medicine and Ethics* 2005 Summer; 33(2): 323- 344. Subject: 9.7

Marks, Jonathan. New information, enduring questions: race, genetics, and medicine in the 21st century. *GeneWatch* 2005 July-August; 18(4): 11-16. Subject: 15.11

Marks, Jonathan H. Doctors of interrogation. *Hastings Center Report* 2005 July-August; 35(4): 17-22. Subject: 21.4

Marks, Stephen P. Human rights assumptions of restrictive and permissive approaches to human reproductive cloning. *Health and Human Rights: An International Journal* 2002; 6(1): 81-100. Subject: 14.5

Markwell, Hazel. End-of-life: a Catholic view [opinion]. *Lancet* 2005 September 24-30; 366(9491): 1132-1135. Subject: 20.5.1

Marques, M.B. Pharmaceutical patents and benefit-sharing: evolution of drug accessibility in Brazil since the 1980's. *In:* Knoppers, Bartha Maria, ed. Populations and

Genetics: Legal and Socio-Ethical Perspectives. Boston: Martinus Nijhoff; 2003: 525-542. Subject: 15.1

Marquis, D. Savulescu's objections to the future of value argument. *Journal of Medical Ethics* 2005 February; 31(2): 119-122. Subject: 12.3

Marquis, Don. How not to argue that embryos lack full moral status. *American Journal of Bioethics* 2005 November-December; 5(6): 54-56. Subject: 4.4

Marquis, Don. Stem cell research: the failure of bioethics. *Free Inquiry* 2002-2003 Winter; 23(1): 40-44. Subject: 18.5.4

Marris, Emma. NIH ethics rules come off probation [news]. *Nature* 2005 September 1; 437(7055): 9. Subject: 1.3.9

Marris, Emma. Unchecked by government, genetic tests sell hope and hype [news]. *Nature Medicine* 2005 June; 11(6): 584. Subject: 15.3

Marris, Emma; Simonite, Tom. Animal-rights militancy exported to US and Europe [news]. *Nature* 2005 December 8; 438(7069): 717. Subject: 22.2

Marsh, Andrea K. Sacrificing patients for profits: physician incentives to limit care and ERISA fiduciary duty. *Washington University Law Quarterly* 1999 Winter; 77(4): 1323-1342. Subject: 9.3.2

Marshall, Eliot. BRCA2 claim faces new challenge [news]. *Science* 2005 June 24; 308(5730): 1851. Subject: 15.8

Marshall, Eliot. Flawed statistics in murder trial may cost expert his medical license [news]. *Science* 2005 July 22; 309(5734): 543. Subject: 7.4

Marshall, Patricia A. Human rights, cultural pluralism, and international health research. *Theoretical Medicine and Bioethics* 2005; 26(6): 529-557. Subject: 18.5.9

Marston, Cicely; Meltzer, Howard; Majeed, Azeem. Impact on contraceptive practice of making emergency hormonal contraception available over the counter in Great Britain: repeated cross sectional surveys. *BMJ: British Medical Journal* 2005 July 30; 331(7511): 271-273. Subject: 11.1

Martens, W. Harmful and unethical pressure on psychiatrists as a consequence of governments' policies [letter]. *Medicine and Law: World Association for Medical Law* 2005 December; 24(4): 853-854. Subject: 17.1

Martin, Adrienne M.; Peerzada, Jehanna. The expressive meaning of enhancement [comment]. *American Journal of Bioethics* 2005 May-June; 5(3): 25-27. Subject: 4.5

Martin, Jennifer. Coercive abortions and criminalizing the birth of children: some thoughts on the impact on women of State v. Oakley. *Western New England Law Review* 2004; 26(1): 67-80. Subject: 12.4.2

Martin, John. Collaboration in cardiovascular stem-cell research [opinion]. *Lancet* 2005 June 18-24; 365(9477): 2070-2071. Subject: 18.5.4

Martin, Jonathan; Lloyd, Margaret; Singh, Surinder. Professional attitudes: can they be taught and assessed in medical education? *Clinical Medicine* 2002 May-June; 2(3): 217-223. Subject: 7.2

Martin, J.; Guillod, O. The doctor's duty to maintain confidentiality ("medical secret") in Switzerland: what attitude should the practitioner adopt when authorities or outside people ask for information about a patient? *European Journal of Health Law* 2001 June; 8(2): 163-172. Subject: 8.4

Martin, Linda; Baker, Bud; Fairall, Deborah; Florell, Kenn; Foster, Alice; Gilbert, Karen; O'Donoghue, John. A code of ethics for the medical dosimetrist — the American Association of Medical Dosimetrists experience. *Medical Dosimetry* 1997 Winter; 22(4): 339-340. Subject: 6

Martin, Linda; Baker, Bud; Fairall, Deborah; Florell, Kenn; Foster, Alice; Gilbert, Karen; O'Donoghue, John. A code of ethics for the medical dosimetrist — the American Association of Medical Dosimetrists experience. *Medical Dosimetry* 1998 Summer; 23(2): 131-132. Subject: 6

Martin, Molly; Lantos, John. Bioethics meets the barrios: community-based research involving children. *In:* Kodish, Eric, ed. Ethics and Research with Children: A Case-Based Approach. New York: Oxford University Press; 2005: 63- 76. Subject: 18.5.2

Martin, Robyn. Undue inducement in clinical research. *Lancet* 2005 July 23-29; 366(9482): 275-276. Subject: 18.1

Martínez, Jaime Vidal. The regulation of assisted reproduction in Spanish law. The ruling of the Spanish Constitutional Court of 17 June 1999. *European Journal of Health Law* 2002 June; 9(2): 121-137. Subject: 14.4

Martinez, Lee Anne. Eugenics. *In:* Ness, Bryan D., ed. Encyclopedia of Genetics. Revised edition. Volume I. Pasadena, Calif.: Salem Press; 2004: 259-264. Subject: 15.5

Martinez, Richard; Candilis, Philip J. Commentary: toward a unified theory of personal and professional ethics. *Journal of the American Academy of Psychiatry and the Law* 2005; 33(3): 382-385. Subject: 7.1

Martinson, Brian C.; Anderson, Melissa S.; de Vries, Raymond. Scientists behaving badly. *Nature* 2005 June 9; 435(7043): 737-738. Subject: 1.3.9

Martyn, Susan R.; Reagan, James E.; Minogue, Brendan; Dippel, Debra L.; Schimer, Maria R.; Taraszewski, Robert. Redrafting Ohio's advance directive laws. *Akron Law Review* 1992 Fall; 26(2): 229-292. Subject: 20.5.4

Maruyama, Eiji. Japanese law of informed consent. *Kobe University Law Review* 1991; 25: 39-43. Subject: 8.3.1

Marušic, Ana. Author misconduct: editors as educators of research integrity [opinion]. *Medical Education* 2005 January; 39(1): 7-8. Subject: 1.3.7

Marušic, Ana. Commentary: ethics in health care and research in European transition countries: reality and future prospects. *BMJ: British Medical Journal* 2005 July 23; 331(7510): 230. Subject: 7.2

Marwick, Charles. US academy calls for new bodies to oversee stem cell research [news]. *BMJ: British Medical Journal* 2005 April 30; 330(7498): 982. Subject: 18.5.4

Maryland. Court of Appeals. Kassama v. Magat [Date of Decision: 2002 February 5]. *Atlantic Reporter*, 2d Series, 2002; 792: 1102-1124. Subject: 15.2

Maryland. Court of Special Appeals. Kassama v. Magat [Date of Decision: 2001 February 28]. *Atlantic Reporter*, 2d Series, 2001; 767: 348-369. Subject: 15.2

Maschke, Karen. Patients, patents, profits. *Hastings Center Report* 2005 July-August; 35(4): inside front cover. Subject: 9.7

Maschke, Karen J. Reconciling protection with scientific progress. *Hastings Center Report* 2005 September-October; 35(5): 3. Subject: 18.2

Masek, Theodore D. CEJA reverses its stance on using anencephalic neonates as live organ donors. *Update [Loma Linda University Center for Christian Bioethics]* 1996 July; 12(2); 4 p. Subject: 20.5.2

Mason, J.K. Wrongful life: the problem of causation. *Medical Law International* 2004; 6(2): 149-161. Subject: 15.2

Mason, Michael. A new face. *New York Times* 2005 July 26; p. F1, F6. Subject: 19.1

Mason, Michael; Altman, Lawrence K. Ethical concerns on face transplant grow; American scientists raise medical and psychological issues. *New York Times* 2005 December 6; p. A12. Subject: 19.1

Massachusetts. Supreme Judicial Court. Culliton v. Beth Israel Deaconess Medical Center [Date of Decision: 2001 October 12]. *West's North Eastern Reporter*, 2d Series, 2001; 756: 1133- 1141. Subject: 14.2

Masserman, Dean E. Preimplanation genetic testing: undivine intervention? *Journal of Assisted Reproductive Law* 1997; 3 p. [Online]. Available: http://www.vgme.com/pgd.htm [21 July 2005]. Subject: 15.2

Massin, Benoit. The "science of race.". *In:* Bachrach, Susan, project director; Kuntz, Dieter, ed. Deadly Medicine: Creating the Master Race. Washington, DC: United States Holocaust Museum; 2004: 89-125. Subject: 15.5

Master, Zubin. Can we really bypass the moral debate for embryo research? *American Journal of Bioethics* 2005 November-December; 5(6): 27-28. Subject: 18.5.4

Matas, Arthur J. The case for living kidney sales: rationale, objections and concerns. *American Journal of Transplantation* 2004 December; 4(12): 2007-2017. Subject: 19.5

Matas, Arthur J.; Sutherland, David E.R. The importance of innovative efforts to increase organ donation [editorial]. *JAMA: The Journal of the American Medical Association* 2005 October 5; 294(13): 1691-1693. Subject: 19.5

Mathai, Saramma T. Making abortion safer. *Journal of Family Welfare* 1997 June; 43(2); 9 p. [Online]. Available: http://www.hsph.harvard.edu/Organizations/healthnet/SAsia/suchana/0617/mathai.html [7 October 2005]. Subject: 12.1

Mathes, Michele. Ethical decision making and nursing. *MEDSURG Nursing* 2004 December; 13(6): 429-431. Subject: 4.1.3

Mathews, Anna Wilde. Detective work: reading fine print, insurers question studies of drugs; Kaiser's veteran sleuth scours medical-journal articles and sees marketing spin; doctors fear loss of choices. *Wall Street Journal* 2005 August 24; p. A1, A6. Subject: 9.7

Mathews, Anna Wilde. An FDA reviewer battles the drug his boss approved: private letter gets Dr. Misbin pulled from diabetes case but he pursues it anyway; "I get to count the bodies". *Wall Street Journal* 2005 October 26; p. A1, A13. Subject: 9.7

Mathews, Anna Wilde. Ghost story: at medical journals, writers paid by industry play big role; articles appear under name of academic researchers, but they often get help; J & J receives a positive "spin". *Wall Street Journal* 2005 December 13; p. A1, A8. Subject: 1.3.7

Mathews, Anna Wilde. Worrisome ailment in medicine: misleading journal articles; editors demand more data to ensure full disclosure of drug risks, trial gaps; Sarbanes-Oxley for professors. *Wall Street Journal* 2005 May 10; p. A1, A9. Subject: 1.3.7

Mathews, Anna Wilde; Wonacott, Peter. Playing detective: at medical journal, editor finds truth hard to track down; termite-eaten data plague Dr. Smith's 12-year probe of an Indian researcher; pestering a busy statistician. *Wall Street Journal* 2005 December 27; p. A1, A2. Subject: 1.3.9

Mathews, Catherine; Guttmacher, Sally J.; Flisher, Alan J.; Mtshizana, Yolisa; Hani, Andiswa; Zwarenstein, Merrick. Written parental consent in school-based HIV/AIDS prevention research. *American Journal of Public Health* 2005 July; 95(7): 1266-1269. Subject: 8.3.2

Mathie, William. Justice, rhetoric and law: reflections on Latimer v. The Queen. *In:* Koterski, Joseph W., ed. Life and Learning XI: Proceedings of the Eleventh University Faculty for Life Conference. Washington, DC: University Faculty for Life; 2002: 46-62. Subject: 20.5.1

Mathiharan, K. The fundamental right to health care. *Issues in Medical Ethics* 2003 October-December; 11(4): 123. Subject: 9.2

Mathiharan, K. The medical profession and human rights. *Issues in Medical Ethics* 1998 October-December; 6(4): 117-118. Subject: 21.4

Mathiharan, K. Some legal and ethical implications for the medical profession. *Issues in Medical Ethics* 2002 October-December; 10(4): 79-82. Subject: 9.5.6

Mati, Jona. Albania. *Medical Ethics and Bioethics / Medicinska Etika & Bioetika* 2005; 11(Supplement): 14. Subject: 9.6

Matloff, Ellen T.; Shappell, Heather; Brierley, Karina; Bernhardt, Barbara A.; McKinnon, Wendy; Peshkin, Beth N. What would you do? Specialists' perspectives on cancer genetic testing, prophylactic surgery, and insurance discrimination. *Journal of Clinical Oncology* 2000 June; 18(12); 17 p. [Online]. Available: http://gateway.ut.ovid.com/gw2/ovidweb.cgi [21 July 2005]. Subject: 15.3

Matorras, Roberto; Pennings, Guido. Reproductive exile versus reproductive tourism [letter and reply]. *Human Reproduction* 2005 December; 20(12): 3571-3572. Subject: 14.1

Matschinger, Herbert; Angermeyer, Matthias C. The public's preferences concerning the allocation of financial resources to health care: results from a representative population survey in Germany. *European Psychiatry* 2004 December; 19(8): 478-482. Subject: 9.4

Matsui, K.; Kita, Y.; Ueshima, H. Informed consent, participation in, and withdrawal from a population based cohort study involving genetic analysis. *Journal of Medical Ethics* 2005 July; 31(7): 385-392. Subject: 15.1

Matsuura, Koïchiro. Address on the occasion of the opening of the International Congress of Bioethics 2005. Geneva, Switzerland: UNESCO 2005 March 26; 5 p. [Online]. Available: http://unesdoc.unesco.org/images/0013/001390/139o41e.pdf [6 April 2005]. Subject: 2.4

Matta, Christina. Ambiguous bodies and deviant sexualities: hermaphrodites, homosexuality, and surgery in the United States, 1850-1904. *Perspectives in Biology and Medicine* 2005 Winter; 48(1): 74-83. Subject: 9.5.1

Mattern, R.; Schueler, F.; Kallieris, D. Traumatology of the traffic accident — dead people for the safety in traffic. *Forensic Science International* 2004 September 10; 144(2-3): 193-200. Subject: 18.5.1

Matthews, Robert. No way to treat a patient: tens of thousands of people have been subjected to unnecessary drug trials. *New Scientist* 2005 July 9-15; 187(2507): 19. Subject: 18.2

Matthews, Robert. A risk we have to swallow: can we ever be sure that medicines are safe before they hit the market? [opinion]. *New Scientist* 2005 March 5-11; 185(2489): 23. Subject: 9.7

Maugh, Thomas H., II. Ethics violations by medical staff at Abu Ghraib alleged [news]. *Los Angeles Times* 2004 August 20; p. A8. Subject: 21.4

Mauleon, Annika Larsson; Palo-Bengtsson, Liisa; Ekman, Sirkka- Liisa. Anaesthesia care of older patients as experienced by nurse anaesthetists. *Nursing Ethics* 2005 May; 12(3): 263-272. Subject: 9.5.2

Maundrell, Richard; Kotalik, Jaro. The ethics of age discrimination and cost-benefit accounting. *Issues in Medical Ethics* 1999 October-December; 7(4): 118-120. Subject: 9.5.2

Mavroforou, Anna; Giannoukas, Athanasios D.; Mavrophoros, Dimitrios; Michalodimitrakis, Emmanuel. Confidentiality governing surgical research practice. *World Journal of Surgery* 2005 February; 29(2): 122-123. Subject: 18.2

Mavroforou, Anna; Koumantakis, Evgenios; Michalodimitrakis, Emmanuel. Adolescence and abortion in Greece: women's profile and perceptions. *Journal of Pediatric and Adolescent Gynecology* 2004 October; 17(5): 321-326. Subject: 12.5.2

Mavroforou, Anna; Michalodimitrakis, Emmanuel. Euthanasia in Greece, Hippocrates' birthplace. *European Journal of Health Law* 2001 June; 8(2): 157-162. Subject: 20.5.1

Mavroforou, Anna; Michalodimitrakis, Emmanuel. Moral arguments on the use of ovarian tissue from aborted foetuses in infertility treatment. *Human Reproduction and Genetic Ethics: An International Journal* 2005; 11(1): 6-11. Subject: 18.5.4

Mavroforou, A.; Giannoukas, A.D.; Gaines, P.; Michalodimitrakis, E.; Beard, J.D. Ethical dilemmas regarding treatment when recruitment ends in randomized trials [editorial]. *European Journal of Vascular and Endovascular Surgery* 2004 December; 28(6): 571-572. Subject: 18.2

Maxwell, David J.; Kaye, Karen I. Multicentre research: negotiating the ethics approval obstacle course [letter]. *Medical Journal of Australia* 2004 October 18; 181(8): 460. Subject: 18.2

Maxwell, Lesley-Ann. Purposeful dehydration in a terminally ill cancer patient. *British Journal of Nursing* 2005 November 24-December 7; 14(21): 1117-1119. Subject: 20.5.1

May, Christopher. Justifying enclosure? Intellectual property and meta- technologies. *In:* Braman, Sandra, ed. Biotechnology and Communication: The Meta-Technologies of Information. Mahwah, NJ: Lawrence Erlbaum Associates; 2004: 119-143. Subject: 15.8

May, Simon Cabulea. Principled compromise and the abortion controversy. *Philosophy and Public Affairs* 2005 Fall; 33(4): 317-348. Subject: 12.3

May, Thomas. The concept of autonomy in bioethics: an unwarranted fall from grace. *In:* Taylor, James Stacey, ed. Personal Autonomy: New Essays on Personal Autonomy and Its Role in Contemporary Moral Philosophy. New York: Cambridge University Press; 2005: 299-309. Subject: 2.1

May, Thomas. Funding agendas: has bioterror defense been over-prioritized? *American Journal of Bioethics* 2005 July-August; 5(4): 34-44. Subject: 21.3

May, Thomas. Public communication, risk perception, and the viability of preventive vaccination against communicable diseases. *Bioethics* 2005 August; 19(4): 407-421. Subject: 9.5.1

May, Thomas; Craig, J.M.; May, Carol; Tomkowiak, John. Quality of life, justice, and the demands of hospital-based nursing. *Public Affairs Quarterly* 2005 July; 19(3): 213-225. Subject: 4.1.3

May, William E. John Paul II's encyclical *Veritatis Splendor* and bioethics. *In:* Tollefsen, Christopher, ed. John Paul II's Contribution to Catholic Bioethics. Norwell, MA: Springer; 2004: 35-50. Subject: 2.1

May, William E. On "rescuing" frozen embryos — why the decision to do so is moral. *National Catholic Bioethics Quarterly* 2005 Spring; 5(1): 51-57. Subject: 14.4

May, William E.; Repenshek, Mark; Slosar, John Paul. Nutrition and hydration [letter and reply]. *Hastings Center Report* 2005 May-June; 35(3): 4-6. Subject: 20.5.1

May, William F. The President's Council on Bioethics: my take on some of its deliberations. *Perspectives in Biology and Medicine* 2005 Spring; 48(2): 229-240. Subject: 2.4

Mayberry, Margaret K.; Mayberry, John F. Consent with understanding: a movement towards informed decisions. *Clinical Medicine* 2002 November-December; 2(6): 523-526. Subject: 8.3.1

Mayeda, Mayumi; Takase, Kozo. Need for enforcement of ethicolegal education — an analysis of the survey of postgraduate clinical trainees. *BMC Medical Ethics [electronic]* 2005; 6(8); 12 p. Available: http://www.biomedcentral.com/bmcmedethics/ [6 September 2005]. Subject: 7.2

Maynard, Douglas W. On predicating a diagnosis as an attribute of a person. *Discourse Studies* 2004 February; 6(1): 53-76. Subject: 8.2

Mayor, Susan. Clinicians need better access to ethics advice, report says [news]. *BMJ: British Medical Journal* 2005 June 11; 330(7504): 1345. Subject: 9.6

Mayor, Susan. Drug companies agree to make clinical trial results public [news]. *BMJ: British Medical Journal* 2005 January 15; 330(7483): 109. Subject: 18.2

Mayor, Susan. UK insurers postpone using predictive genetic testing until 2011 [news]. *BMJ: British Medical Journal* 2005 March 19; 330(7492): 617. Subject: 15.3

Mayor, Susan. UK team hopes to create a human embryo from three donors [news]. *BMJ: British Medical Journal* 2005 September 17; 331(7517): 591. Subject: 18.5.4

Mayor, Susan. UN committee approves declaration on human cloning [news]. *BMJ: British Medical Journal* 2005 March 5; 330(7490): 496. Subject: 14.5

Mayrhofer-Reinhartshuber, David; Fitzgerald, Robert. Financial incentives for cadaveric organ donation. *Annals of Transplantation* 2004; 9(1): 25-27. Subject: 19.5

Mazzoni, Cosimo Marco. Real protection for the embryo. *Revista de Derecho y Genoma Humano / Law and the Human Genome Review* 2005 January-June; (22): 115-132. Subject: 4.4

McAdam, Catherine; Barton, Anna; Bull, Patricia; Rai, Gurcharan. An audit of nurses' views on DNR decisions in 1989 and 2003. *British Journal of Nursing* 2005 November 10-23; 14(20): 1061-1062, 1064-1065. Subject: 20.5.1

McAlpine, Heather; Lockerbie, Linda; Ramsay, Deyanne; Beaman, Sue. Evaluating a web-based graduate level nursing ethics course: thumbs up or thumbs down? *Journal of Continuing Education in Nursing* 2002 January-February; 33(1): 12-18. Subject: 1.3.12

McArdle, John. Legal protection for rats, mice, and birds: long overdue and the right thing to do [opinion]. *Comparative Medicine* 2001 June; 51(3): 203-204. Subject: 22.2

McAuley, William J.; Travis, Shirley S. Advance care planning among residents in long-term care. *American Journal of Hospice and Palliative Care* 2003 September-October; 20(5): 353-359. Subject: 20.5.4

McCabe, Alison R. A precarious balancing act — the role of the FDA as protector of public health and industry wealth. *Suffolk University Law Review* 2003; 36(3): 787-819. Subject: 9.7

McCabe, Christopher; Claxton, Karl; Tsuchiya, Aki. Orphan drugs and the NHS: should we value rarity? *BMJ: British Medical Journal* 2005 October 29; 331(7523): 1016- 1019. Subject: 9.7

McCabe, Helen. Financial incentives, cross-purposes, and moral motivation in health care provision. *Monash Bioethics Review* 2005 July; 24(3): 20-35. Subject: 9.3.2

McCallum, Hamish; Hocking, Barbara Ann. Reflecting on ethical and legal issues in wildlife disease. *Bioethics* 2005 August; 19(4): 336-347. Subject: 9.1

McCarthy, Michael J. After horrific burn, a wife's choice: is treatment wise? Artificial skin for Ted Fink meant pain and risks; a 7-month coma; I really didn't want to look. *Wall Street Journal* 2005 April 29; p. A1, A12. Subject: 20.5.1

McCarthy, Michelle. Interviewing people with learning disabilities about sensitive topics: a discussion of ethical issues. *British Journal of Learning Disabilities* 1998 Winter; 26(4): 140-145. Subject: 18.5.6

Subject = NRCBL Primary Classification Number; See inside front cover

McCartney, James J. Values based decision making in healthcare. *HEC (Healthcare Ethics Committee) Forum* 2005 March; 17(1): 1-5. Subject: 9.1

McCauley, Jeanne; Jenckes, Mollie W.; Tarpley, Margaret J.; Koenig, Harold G.; Yanek, Lisa R.; Becker, Diane M. Spiritual beliefs and barriers among managed care practitioners. *Journal of Religion and Health* 2005 Summer; 44(2): 137-146. Subject: 8.1

McClure, Andy. Psychiatric ethics and forensic assessments [letter]. *Australian and New Zealand Journal of Psychiatry* 1999 October; 33(5): 770. Subject: 17.1

McConnaha, Scott. Blessed are the pluripotent: New Testament guidance for the embryonic stem cell debate. *National Catholic Bioethics Quarterly* 2005 Winter; 5(4): 707- 715. Subject: 18.5.4

McCord, Gary; Gilchrist, Valerie J.; Grossman, Steven D.; King, Bridget D.; McCormick, Kenelm F.; Oprandi, Allison M.; Schrop, Susan Labuda; Selius, Brian A.; Smucker, William D.; Weldy, David L.; Amorn, Melissa; Carter, Melissa A.; Deak, Andrew J.; Hefzy, Hebah; Srivastava, Mohit. Discussing spirituality with patients: a rational and ethical approach. *Annals of Family Medicine* 2004 July-August; 2(4): 356-361. Subject: 8.1

McCormack, Brendan. The person of the voice: narrative identities in informed consent. *Nursing Philosophy* 2002 July; 3(2): 114-119. Subject: 8.3.3

McCrummen, Stephanie. Brain-dead mother is taken off life support; healthy premature baby is likely to avoid cancer. *Washington Post* 2005 August 4; p. A1, A4. Subject: 20.5.1

McCrummen, Stephanie. Brain-dead Virginia woman gives birth; baby appears healthy after 3-month ordeal. *Washington Post* 2005 August 3; p. A1, A8. Subject: 20.5.1

McCrummen, Stephanie. Inside stricken mother, a race between life and death; cancer that felled woman now threatens fetus. *Washington Post* 2005 June 17; p. A1, A13. Subject: 20.5.1

McCrummen, Stephanie. Weary father left to count the days: doctors hope technology can sustain fetus. *Washington Post* 2005 June 27; p. B1, B4. Subject: 20.5.1

McCullagh, Peter. A perspective of disability. *In his:* Conscious in a Vegetative State? A Critique of the PVS Concept. Boston: Kluwer Academic; 2004: 175-192. Subject: 9.5.1

McCullagh, Peter. Authoritative statements. *In his:* Conscious in a Vegetative State? A Critique of the PVS Concept. Boston: Kluwer Academic; 2004: 43-57. Subject: 20.5.1

McCullagh, Peter. History and context of the persistent vegetative state. *In his:* Conscious in a Vegetative State? A Critique of the PVS Concept. Boston: Kluwer Academic; 2004: 1-28. Subject: 20.5.1

McCullagh, Peter. Positive management or an exercise in futility? *In his:* Conscious in a Vegetative State? A Critique of the PVS Concept. Boston: Kluwer Academic; 2004: 193-216. Subject: 9.5.1

McCullagh, Peter. Some economic considerations. *In his:* Conscious in a Vegetative State? A Critique of the PVS Concept. Boston: Kluwer Academic; 2004: 261-281. Subject: 9.4

McCullagh, Peter. Vegetative states in court. *In his:* Conscious in a Vegetative State? A Critique of the PVS Concept. Boston: Kluwer Academic; 2004: 282-314. Subject: 20.5.1

McCullagh, Peter. Withdrawal of hydration and nutrition from patients in vegetative states. *In his:* Conscious in a Vegetative State? A Critique of the PVS Concept. Boston: Kluwer Academic; 2004: 233-260. Subject: 20.5.1

McCullough, Laurence B. The critical turn in clinical ethics and its continuous enhancement. *Journal of Medicine and Philosophy* 2005 February; 30(1): 1-8. Subject: 2.1

McCullough, Laurence B.; Coverdale, John H.; Chervenak, Frank A. Argument-based medical ethics: a formal tool for critically appraising the normative medical ethics literature. *American Journal of Obstetrics and Gynecology* 2004 October; 191(4): 1097-1102. Subject: 2.1

McDermott, Barbara E.; Gerbasi, Joan B.; Quanbeck, Cameron; Scott, Charles L. Capacity for forensic patients to consent to research: the use of the MacCAT-CR. *Journal of the American Academy of Psychiatry and the Law* 2005; 33(3): 299-307. Subject: 18.3

McDermott, Margaret. Attempting to "correct some of the misimpressions": a review of the President's Council on Bioethics website. *Journal of Law, Medicine and Ethics* 2005 Fall; 33(3): 608-610. Subject: 2.4

McDonagh, Sean. Genetic engineering is not the answer. *America* 2005 May 2; 192(15): 8-10. Subject: 15.1

McDougall, Rosalind. Best interests, dementia, and end of life decision-making: the case of Mrs S [case study]. *Monash Bioethics Review* 2005 July; 24(3): 36-46. Subject: 20.5.1

McDougall, R. Acting parentally: an argument against sex selection. *Journal of Medical Ethics* 2005 October; 31(10): 601-605. Subject: 14.3

McEachern, Terrence P. The inducement of meaningful work: a response to Anderson and Weijer. *Theoretical Medicine and Bioethics* 2005; 26(5): 427-430. Subject: 18.2

McGee, Andrew. Finding a way through the ethical and legal maze: withdrawal of medical treatment and euthanasia. *Medical Law Review* 2005 Autumn; 13(3): 357-385. Subject: 20.5.1

McGee, Ellen M. Using personal narratives to encourage organ donation. *American Journal of Bioethics* 2005 July-August; 5(4): 19-20. Subject: 19.5

McGee, Glenn. Dying for food. *American Journal of Bioethics [Online]* 2005 March-April; 5(2): W1. Subject: 9.5.5

McGee, Glenn; Patrizio, Pasquale; Kuhn, Vanessa; Robertson- Kraft, Claire. The ethics of stem cell therapy. *In:* Patrizio, Pasquale; Tucker, Michael J.; Guelman, Vanessa, eds. A Color Atlas for Human Assisted Reproduction: Laboratory and Clinical Insights. Philadelphia: Lippincott Williams & Wilkins; 2003: 297-309. Subject: 18.5.4

McGee, Glenn; Patrizio, Pasquale; Kuhn, Vanessa; Robertson- Kraft, Claire. The ethics of stem cell therapy. *In:* McGee, Glenn; Caplan, Arthur, eds. The Human Cloning Debate. 4th edition. Berkeley, CA: Berkeley Hills Books; 2004: 37- 56. Subject: 18.5.4

McGee, Glenn; Wilmut, Ian. A model for regulating cloning. *In:* McGee, Glenn; Caplan, Arthur, eds. The Human Cloning Debate. 4th edition. Berkeley, CA: Berkeley Hills Books; 2004: 221- 232. Subject: 14.5

McGill, Joff; Wood-Harper, Janice. Informing education policy on MMR [letter and reply]. *Nursing Ethics* 2005 September; 12(5): 537-539. Subject: 9.5.1

McGough, Laura J.; Reynolds, Steven J.; Quinn, Thomas C.; Zenilman, Jonathan M. Which patients first? Setting priorities for antiretroviral therapy where resources are limited. *American Journal of Public Health* 2005 July; 95(7): 1173-1180. Subject: 9.4

McGovern, Theresa M. Mandatory HIV testing and treating of child-bearing women: an unnatural, illegal, and unsound approach. *Columbia Human Rights Law Review* 1997 Spring; 28(3): 469-499. Subject: 9.5.6

McGregor, Joan. Culture clashes in bioethics. *In her:* War and Border Crossings: Ethics When Cultures Clash. Lanham, MD: Rowman & Littlefield; 2005: 225-237. Subject: 2.1

McGregor, Joan. 'Undue inducement' as coercive offers [comment]. *American Journal of Bioethics* 2005 September-October; 5(5): 24-25. Subject: 18.3

McGregor, Maurice; Chen, Jun. Should the implantable cardiac defibrillator be used for primary prevention of sudden death? A review of the issues relevant to hospital decision making [opinion]. *Canadian Journal of Cardiology* 2004 October; 20(12): 1199-1204. Subject: 9.3.1

McGrew, Lydia; Miller, Robert T. Schiavo under the law [letter and reply]. *First Things* 2005 October; (156): 5-8. Subject: 20.5.1

McGuire, Amy L.; Majumder, Mary A.; Cheney, J. Richard. The ethics of lawyer-ethicists. *Journal of Law, Medicine and Ethics* 2005 Fall; 33(3): 603-607. Subject: 9.6

McGuire, Amy L.; McCullough, Laurence B. Respect as an organizing normative category for research ethics. *American Journal of Bioethics [Online]* 2005 January-February; 5(1): W1-W2. Subject: 18.2

McGuire, Amy L.; McCullough, Laurence B.; Weller, Susan C.; Whitney, Simon N. Missed expectations? Physicians' views of patients' participation in medical decision-making. *Medical Care* 2005 May; 43(5): 466-470. Subject: 8.1

McHale, J.V. Law and clinical research — from rights to regulation? An English perspective. *Journal of Law, Medicine and Ethics* 2004 Winter; 32(4): 718- 730. Subject: 18.6

McHale, J.V. Regulating genetic databases: some legal and ethical issues. *Medical Law Review* 2004 Spring; 12(1): 70-96. Subject: 15.10

McHenry, Leemon. On the origin of great ideas: science in the age of big pharma. *Hastings Center Report* 2005 November-December; 35(6): 17-19. Subject: 9.7

McHugh, Paul. Annihilating Terri Schiavo. *Human Life Review* 2005 Summer; 31(3): 67-77. Subject: 20.5.1

McInroy, Ally. Blood transfusion and Jehovah's Witnesses: the legal and ethical issues. *British Journal of Nursing* 2005 March 10-23; 14(5): 270-274. Subject: 8.3.4

McIntosh, Tania. "An abortionist city": maternal mortality, abortion, and birth control in Sheffield, 1920-1940. *Medical History* 2000 January; 44(1): 75-96. Subject: 12.5.2

McKane, Maureen; Tolson, Debbie. Research, ethics and the data protection legislation. *Nursing Standard* 2000 February 2-8; 14(20): 36-41. Subject: 18.5.1

McKay, Daniel L. Patent law and human genome research at the crossroads: the need for Congressional action. *Santa Clara Computer and High Technology Law Journal* 1994; 10(2): 465-498. Subject: 15.8

McKechnie, Ron. The moral context of therapy. *In:* Fairbairn, Susan; Fairbairn, Gavin, eds. Psychology, Ethics and Change. New York: Routledge & Kegan Paul; 1987: 161- 172. Subject: 17.1

McKee, Martin; Raine, Rosalind. Choosing health? First choose your philosophy [opinion]. *Lancet* 2005 January 29-February 4; 365(9457): 369-371. Subject: 4.2

McKenna, Jeffrey W.; Pechacek, Terry F.; Stroup, Donna F. Health communication ethics and CDC quality-control guidelines for information. *Public Health Reports* 2003 May-June; 118(3): 193-196. Subject: 1.3.7

McKenney, Elizabeth; Parker, Bridgette. Legal and ethical issues related to nonheart beating organ donation. *AORN: Association of Operating Room Nurses Journal* 2003 May; 77(5): 973-976. Subject: 19.5

Subject = NRCBL Primary Classification Number; See inside front cover

McKenzie, David. Church, state, and physician-assisted suicide. *Journal of Church and State* 2004 Autumn; 46(4): 787-809. Subject: 20.7

McKinney, Patricia A.; Jones, Samantha; Parslow, Roger; Davey, Nicola; Darowski, Mark; Chaudhry, Bill; Stack, Charles; Parry, Gareth; Draper, Elizabeth S. A feasibility study of signed consent for the collection of patient identifiable information for a national paediatric clinical audit database. *BMJ: British Medical Journal* 2005 April 16; 330(7496): 877-879. Subject: 8.3.2

McKneally, Martin F.; Daar, Abdallah S. Introducing new technologies: protecting subjects of surgical innovation and research. *World Journal of Surgery* 2003; 27: 930-935. Subject: 5.1

McKoy, June M.; Karsjens, Kari L.; Wynia, Matthew; MacDonald-Glenn, Linda. Is ethics for sale? . . . Juggling law and ethics in managed care. *DePaul Journal of Health Care Law* 2005 Spring; 8(3): 559-613. Subject: 9.3.2

McLachlan, H.V. Justice and the NHS: a comment on Culyer. *Journal of Medical Ethics* 2005 July; 31(7): 379-382. Subject: 9.1

McLachlan, Hugh V. Drunks, pedestrians and hospitals in Britain and the U.S.A. *In his:* Social Justice, Human Rights and Public Policy. Glasgow, Scotland: Humming Earth; 2005: 79-86. Subject: 9.1

McLachlan, Hugh V. Health, health care, justice and rights. *In his:* Social Justice, Human Rights and Public Policy. Glasgow, Scotland: Humming Earth; 2005: 57-64. Subject: 9.2

McLachlan, Hugh V. Justice, health and inequality. *In his:* Social Justice, Human Rights and Public Policy. Glasgow, Scotland: Humming Earth; 2005: 65-78. Subject: 9.1

McLachlan, Hugh V. Surrogate motherhood: beyond the Warnock and Brazier reports. *Human Reproduction and Genetic Ethics: An International Journal* 2005; 11(1): 12-23. Subject: 14.2

McLachlan, Hugh V. Unique persons and the replicable gene-sets of their reproducible bodies: a defence of human cloning. *Human Reproduction and Genetic Ethics: An International Journal* 2005; 11(2): 43-48. Subject: 14.5

McLachlan, Hugh V.; Swales, J.K. Exploitation and commercial surrogate motherhood. *Human Reproduction and Genetic Ethics: An International Journal* 2001; 7(1): 8-14. Subject: 14.2

McLean, Margaret R. Xenotransplantation: weighting individual benefit and risks to the public. Santa Clara, CA: Markkula Center for Applied Ethics, Santa Clara University 2004 February; 3 p. [Online]. Available: http://www.scu.edu/ethics/publications/ethicalperspectives/xenotr ansplant.html [15 June 2005]. Subject: 19.1

McLean, Sheila A.M. Regulating research and experimentation: a view from the UK. *Journal of Law, Medicine and Ethics* 2004 Winter; 32(4): 604- 612. Subject: 18.2

McLean, Sheila A.M. Sex selection: intergenerational justice or injustice? *Medicine and Law: World Association for Medical Law* 2005 December; 24(4): 761-773. Subject: 14.3

McLeod, Carolyn. "Embryo autonomy?" What about the autonomy of infertility patients. *American Journal of Bioethics* 2005 November-December; 5(6): 25-26. Subject: 4.4

McLeod, Carolyn; Kukla, Rebecca. Conscientious autonomy: what patients do vs. what is done to them [letter and reply]. *Hastings Center Report* 2005 September-October; 35(5): 5, 6-7. Subject: 8.3.1

McLochlin, Deborah L. Whose genetic information is it anyway? A legal analysis of the effects that mapping the human genome will have on privacy rights and genetic discrimination. *John Marshall Journal of Computer and Information Law* 2001 Summer; 19(4): 609-646. Subject: 15.10

McMahan, Jeff. Causing disabled people to exist and causing people to be disabled. *Ethics: An International Journal of Social, Political, and Legal Philosophy* 2005 October; 116(1): 77-99. Subject: 15.3

McMahan, Jeff. Preventing the existence of people with disabilities. *In:* Wasserman, David; Bickenbach, Jerome; Wachbroit, Robert, eds. Quality of Life and Human Difference: Genetic Testing, Health Care, and Disability. New York: Cambridge University Press; 2005: 142-171. Subject: 15.3

McMahon, Kevin T. Nutrition and hydration: should they be considered medical therapy? *Linacre Quarterly* 2005 August; 72(3): 229-239. Subject: 20.5.1

McMahon, Kevin T. Why fear ovulation testing? A response to Ron Hamel. *Ethics and Medics* 2003 June; 28(6): 3-4. Subject: 11.1

McMillan, Gigi. What do researchers say? What do subjects hear? Not what they would like to hear. What do subjects need? More information. *Protecting Human Subjects* 2005 Summer; (12): 10-11. Subject: 18.3

McMillan, John. Commentary: doing what's best and best interests. *BMJ: British Medical Journal* 2005 May 7; 330(7499): 1069. Subject: 8.3.1

McMillan, John; Sheehan, Mark. Commentary: ethical review and ethical behaviour. *BMJ: British Medical Journal* 2005 February 26; 330(7489): 473. Subject: 18.2

McMurdo, Marion E.T.; Witham, Miles D.; Gillespie, Neil D. Including older people in clinical research [editorial]. *BMJ: British Medical Journal* 2005 November 5; 331(7524): 1036- 1037. Subject: 18.5.7

McMurray, Terry. The changing face of research ethics [editorial]. *Ulster Medical Journal* 2002 November; 71(2): 98-100. Subject: 18.2

McNally, Stephen J.; Harrison, E.M.; Wigmore, S.J. Ethical considerations in the application of preconditioning to solid organ transplantation. *Journal of Medical Ethics* 2005 November; 31(11): 631-634. Subject: 19.5

McNay, Laura A.; Tavel, Jorge A.; Oseekey, Karen; McDermott, Cathy M.; Mollerup, David; Bebchuk, Judith D. Regulatory approvals in a large multinational clinical trial: the ESPRIT experience. *Controlled Clinical Trials* 2002 February; 23(1): 59-66. Subject: 18.2

McNeil, Donald G., Jr. Review cites ethical lapses by scientists. *New York Times* 2005 July 15; p. A15. Subject: 1.3.9

McNeill, Paul M. Should research ethics change at the border? [editorial]. *Medical Journal of Australia* 1998 November 16; 169(10): 509-510. Subject: 18.3

McNulty, Patrick J.; Stanwood, Francis M.; Gallas, Sherrie M.; Zavodny, Madeline. Parental consent for minors to receive contraceptives [letter and reply]. *American Journal of Public Health* 2005 February; 95(2): 191-192. Subject: 11.2

McPhee, John; Stewart, Cameron. Recent developments. *Journal of Bioethical Inquiry* 2004; 1(1): 43-48. Subject: 2.1

McPhee, John; Stewart, Cameron. Recent developments in law. *Journal of Bioethical Inquiry* 2005; 2(1): 4-9. Subject: 20.5.1

McPhee, John; Stewart, Cameron. Recent developments in law. *Journal of Bioethical Inquiry* 2005; 2(2): 63-68. Subject: 2.1

McPhee, John; Stewart, Cameron. Recent developments in law. *Journal of Bioethical Inquiry* 2005; 2(3): 122-129. Subject: 9.5.6

McPherson, Jean. In that case. Response [case study]. *Journal of Bioethical Inquiry* 2005; 2(2): 114-115. Subject: 9.5.7

McQuay, H.J.; Moore, R.A. Placebo. *Postgraduate Medical Journal* 2005 March; 81(953): 155-160. Subject: 18.3

McQueen, Matthew J. Ethical and legal issues in the procurement, storage and use of DNA. *Clinical Chemistry and Laboratory Medicine* 1998 August; 36(8): 545-549. Subject: 15.1

McQuoid-Mason, David. Parental refusal of blood transfusions for minor children solely on religious grounds — the doctor's dilemma resolved. *South African Medical Journal* 2005 January; 95(1): 29-30. Subject: 8.3.4

McRae, Andrew D.; Weijer, Charles. Waiver of consent for emergency research [letter]. *Annals of Emergency Medicine* 2004 September; 44(3): 278-279. Subject: 18.3

McSherry, Bernadette. Ethical issues in HealthConnect's shared electronic health record system. *Journal of Law and Medicine* 2004 August; 12(1): 60-68. Subject: 8.4

McSorley, Stephen J. It's not just theologians who are morally troubled [letter]. *Nature* 2005 January 27; 433(7024): 355. Subject: 1.3.9

McSweeny, A. John. Regarding ethics in forensic neuropsychological consultation: a comment on Guilmette and Hagan. *Clinical Neuropsychologist* 1997 August; 11(3): 291-293. Subject: 7.3

McTighe, Maggie; Hanley, Greg. IACUC replacement parts: what are the requirements? Inappropriate actions. *Lab Animal* 2004 November; 33(10): 17. Subject: 22.2

Meacham, Katharine R.; Croom, Jo Ann T. Tricksters, The Plague, and mirrors: biotechnology, bioterrorism, and justice. *In:* Brannigan, Michael C., ed. Cross-Cultural Biotechnology. Lanham: Rowman and Littlefield; 2004: 177-191. Subject: 21.3

Mead, Rebecca. Eggs for sale. *New Yorker* 1999 August 9: 56-65. Subject: 14.4

Meadowcroft, John. Health care markets, prices, and coordination: the epistemic explanation of government failure and the UK National Health Service. *HEC (Healthcare Ethics Committee) Forum* 2005 September; 17(3): 159-177. Subject: 9.3.1

Means, Cyril C., Jr. The phoenix of abortional freedom: is a penumbral or Ninth-Amendment right about to arise from the nineteenth-century legislative ashes of a fourteenth-century common-law liberty? *New York Law Forum* 1971; 17(2): 335-410. Subject: 12.4.1

Medical Council of India. The Indian Medical Council (professional conduct, etiquette and ethics) regulations, 2002. *Issues in Medical Ethics* 2002 July-September; 10(3): 66-70. Subject: 6

Medical Professionalism Project; Brennan, Troy; Blank, Linda; Cohen, Jordan; Kimball, Harry; Smelser, Neil; Copeland, Robert; Lavizzo-Mourey, Risa; McDonald, Walter; Brenning, Gunilla; Davidson, Christopher; Jaeger, Philippe; Malliani, Alberto; Muller, Hein; Sareni, Daniel; Sutorius, Eugene; Cruess, Richard; Cruess, Sylvia; Merino, Jaime. Medical professionalism in the new millennium: a physicians' charter. *Clinical Medicine* 2002 March-April; 2(2): 116-118. Subject: 4.1.2

Medicines Australia. In that case. Response [case study]. *Journal of Bioethical Inquiry* 2005; 2(3): 181-182. Subject: 9.5.1

Meehan, Mary. Tiptoeing around Roe. *Human Life Review* 2005 Fall; 31(4): 44-64. Subject: 12.4.4

Meehan, Michael J. The constitutionality of physician-assisted suicide: the cases and issues before the US Supreme Court. *Cleveland Clinic Journal of Medicine* 1997 January; 64(1): 13-15. Subject: 20.7

Meeks, Suzanne. Age bias in the diagnostic decision-making behavior of clinicians. *Professional Psychology: Research and Practice* 1990 August; 21(4): 279-284. Subject: 9.5.2

Mehendale, Sanjay. Ethical considerations in AIDS vaccine trials. *Issues in Medical Ethics* 2000 January-March; 8(1): 13-15. Subject: 18.2

Mehlman, Maxwell J. Genetic enhancement: plan now to act later. *Kennedy Institute of Ethics Journal* 2005 March; 15(1): 77-82. Subject: 15.1

Mehra, Preeti. Of human guinea pigs. Illustrated Weekly of India 1992 May 2-8; 5 p. [Online]. Available: http://www.hsph.harvard.edu/Organizations/healthnet/SAsia/suchana /0400/h011.html [6 October 2005]. Subject: 18.5.3

Mehta, Lopa. Ethical basis for charging medical fees. *Issues in Medical Ethics* 2000 April-June; 8(2): 49-50. Subject: 9.3.1

Meier, Barry. A choice for the heart: it's easier to get data on a car than on a medical device. *New York Times* 2005 June 23; p. C1, C19. Subject: 9.7

Meier, Barry. Dispute puts a medical journal under fire. *New York Times* 2005 January 17; p. C1, C5. Subject: 1.3.9

Meier, Barry. Drug industry plans release of more data about studies. *New York Times* 2005 January 7; p. C4. Subject: 9.7

Meier, Barry. Faulty heart devices force some scary decisions; patients weigh risks of replacing unit through surgery. *New York Times* 2005 June 20; p. A1, A12. Subject: 9.7

Meier, Barry. FDA had report of short circuit in heart devices; confidentiality at issue; policies of regulator may keep data on problems away from doctors. *New York Times* 2005 September 12; p. A1, A18. Subject: 5.3

Meier, Barry. Implant program for heart device was a sales spur. *New York Times* 2005 September 27; p. A1, C4. Subject: 9.7

Meier, Barry. Implants with flaws: disclosure and delay. *New York Times* 2005 June 14; p. C1, C3. Subject: 9.7

Meier, Barry. Maker of heart device kept flaw from doctors. *New York Times* 2005 May 24; p. A1, C3. Subject: 9.7

Meilaender, Gilbert. Living life's end. *First Things* 2005 May; (153): 17-21. Subject: 20.5.1

Meininger, Herman P. Autonomy and professional responsibility in care for persons with intellectual disabilities. *Nursing Philosophy* 2001 October; 2(3): 240-250. Subject: 9.5.3

Meininger, Herman P. Narrative ethics in nursing for persons with intellectual disabilities. *Nursing Philosophy* 2005 April; 6(2): 106-118. Subject: 9.5.3

Meir, Asher. Ethics at the doctor's office. *In his:* The Jewish Ethicist: Everyday Ethics for Business and Life. Jersey City, NJ: KTAV; 2005: 125-144. Subject: 4.1.2

Meisel, Alan. Quality of life and end-of-life decisionmaking. *Quality of Life Research* 2003; 12(Supplement 1): 91-94. Subject: 20.5.1

Meisel, Alan. Thwarting assisted suicide threatens palliative care. *Medical Ethics Newsletter [Lahey Clinic]* 2003 Winter; 10(1): 4, 8. Subject: 20.7

Meister, U.; Finck, C.; Stöbel-Richter, Y.; Schmutzer, G.; Brähler, E. Knowledge and attitudes towards preimplantation genetic diagnosis in Germany. *Human Reproduction* 2005 January; 20(1): 231-238. Subject: 15.2

Mela, Mansfield. Folie a trois in a multilevel security forensic treatment center: forensic and ethics-related implications. *Journal of the American Academy of Psychiatry and the Law* 2005; 33(3): 310-316. Subject: 17.7

Meland, Eivind. Research ethics — revisited [editorial]. *Scandinavian Journal of Primary Health Care* 2003 September; 21(3): 129-131. Subject: 1.3.9

Melchoir, Jill A. The quiet battle for the heart of liberty — a victory for the cautious: Washington v. Glucksberg, 117 S. Ct. 2258 (1997). *University of Cincinnati Law Review* 1998 Summer; 66(4): 1359- 1386. Subject: 20.7

Melia, Kath M. Ethical issues and the importance of consensus for the intensive care team. *Social Science and Medicine* 2001 September; 53(6): 707-719. Subject: 20.5.1

Mello, Michelle M.; Brennan, Troyen A. Legal concerns and the influenza vaccine shortage [opinion]. *JAMA: The Journal of the American Medical Association* 2005 October 12; 294(14): 1817-1820. Subject: 9.7

Mello, Michelle M.; Clarridge, Brian R.; Studdert, David M. Academic medical centers' standards for clinical-trial agreements with industry. *New England Journal of Medicine* 2005 May 26; 352(21): 2202- 2210. Subject: 5.3

Mello, Michelle M.; Clarridge, Brian R.; Studdert, David M. Researchers' views of the acceptability of restrictive provisions in clinical trial agreements with industry sponsors. *Accountability in Research* 2005 July-September; 12(3): 163- 191. Subject: 1.3.9

Melnick, Alan; Kaplowitz, Lisa; Lopez, Wilfredo; Murphy, Anne M.; Bernheim, Ruth Gaare. Public health ethics in action: flu vaccine and drug allocation strategies. *Journal of Law, Medicine and Ethics* 2005 Winter; 33(4, Supplement): 102-105. Subject: 9.4

Melson, Ashley R. Bioterrorism, biodefense, and biotechnology in the military: a comparative analysis of legal and ethical issues in the research, development, and use of biotechnological products on American and British soldiers. *Albany Law Journal of Science and Technology* 2004;

14(2): 497-534 [Online]. Available: http://heinonline.org [3 May 2006]. Subject: 18.5.8

Melton, Gary B. Mental health and social justice: a vision for the 21st century. *American Journal of Orthopsychiatry* 2003 July; 73(3): 245-247. Subject: 17.1

Melton, Pamela Rogers. Reviews in medical ethics: an open access electronic journal comes to bioethics: a review of BMC Biomedical Ethics. *Journal of Law, Medicine and Ethics* 2004 Winter; 32(4): 770- 772. Subject: 2.3

Meltzer, Bari; Rothman, Barbara Katz. Bioengineering. *In:* Restivo, Sal, ed. Science, Technology, and Society: An Encyclopedia. New York: Oxford University Press; 2005: 23-28. Subject: 14.2

Melville, Craig. Discrimination and health inequalities experienced by disabled people. *Medical Education* 2005 February; 39(2): 124-126. Subject: 9.5.1

Melvin, Louise. Reproductive issues and learning disability: different perspectives of professionals and parents. *Journal of Family Planning and Reproductive Health Care* 2004 October; 30(4): 263-264. Subject: 9.5.3

Menikoff, Jerry. Full disclosure: telling patients when not being a research subject is a good choice. *Perspectives in Biology and Medicine* 2005 Winter; 48(1, Supplement): S139-S149. Subject: 18.3

Menkin, Elizabeth. Artificial nutrition and the public guardian. *Journal of Palliative Medicine* 2004 October; 7(5): 723-726. Subject: 20.5.1

Mennemeyer, Stephen T. Response to professor Mark Hall. *Cumberland Law Review* 1997-1998; 28(2): 321-323. Subject: 9.3.2

Menzel, Paul T. Determining the value of life: discrimination, advance directives, and the right to die with dignity. *Free Inquiry* 2005 August-September; 25(5): 39-41. Subject: 9.5.1

Merali, Zara; Singer, Peter A.; Boulyjenkov, Victor; Daar, Abdallah S. The ELSI genetics regulatory resource kit: a tool for policymakers in developing countries. *Journal of Law, Medicine and Ethics* 2004 Winter; 32(4): 692- 700. Subject: 15.1

Meran, Johannes Gobertus. Consent and equipoise, the crucial ethical issues in randomised clinical trials. *Onkologie* 2003; 26(6): 524-528. Subject: 18.3

Mercurio, Bryan C. TRIPS, patents, and access to life-saving drugs in the developing world. *Marquette Intellectual Property Law Review* 2004 Summer; 8(2): 211-253. Subject: 5.3

Meredith, Barbara. Data protection and freedom of information: the law is only a catalyst for changing the culture in the NHS [editorial]. *BMJ: British Medical Journal* 2005 March 5; 330(7490): 490-491. Subject: 8.2

Merges, Robert P. Intellectual property in higher life forms: the patent system and controversial technologies.

Maryland Law Review 1988 Summer; 47(4): 1051-1075. Subject: 15.8

Merianos, Angela; Peiris, Malik. International Health Regulations (2005) [opinion]. *Lancet* 2005 October 8-14; 366(9493): 1249-1251. Subject: 9.1

Merideth, Philip. Medical ethics: charting a new course [editorial]. *Journal of the Mississippi State Medical Association* 2004 September; 45(9): 275. Subject: 4.1.2

Merrick, Janna C. Death and dying: the American experience. *In:* Blank, Robert H.; Merrick, Janna C., eds. End-of-Life Decision Making: A Cross-National Study. Cambridge, MA: MIT Press; 2005: 219-241. Subject: 20.5.1

Merrill, Matthew M. The sheep heard 'round the world: legislation vs. self- regulation of human cloning. *Kansas Journal of Law and Public Policy* 1997-1998; 7(3): 169-188. Subject: 14.5

Merrills, Jon. The basis of ethics. *In:* Salek, Sam; Edgar, Andrew, eds. Pharmaceutical Ethics. New York: Wiley; 2002: 1-12. Subject: 9.7

Merritt, Maria. Moral conflict in clinical trials. *Ethics: An International Journal of Social, Political, and Legal Philosophy* 2005 January; 115(2): 306-330. Subject: 18.1

Merz, Jon F. On the intersection of privacy, consent, commerce and genetics research. *In:* Knoppers, Bartha Maria, ed. Populations and Genetics: Legal and Socio-Ethical Perspectives. Boston: Martinus Nijhoff; 2003: 257-268. Subject: 15.1

Merz, Jon F.; Cho, Mildred K. What are gene patents and why are people worried about them? *Community Genetics* 2005 October; 8(4): 203-208. Subject: 15.8

Mesich-Brant, Jennifer L.; Grossback, Lawrence J. Assisting altruism: evaluating legally binding consent in organ donation policy. *Journal of Health Politics, Policy and Law* 2005 August; 30(4): 687-717. Subject: 8.3.1

Meslin, Eric. Of clones, stem cells, and children: issues and challenges in human research ethics. *In:* Actes du Colloque International AMADE-UNESCO sur Bioethique et Droits de L'enfant (Monaco, 28-30 Avril 2000)/Proceedings of the International Symposium AMADE-UNESCO on Bioethics and the Rights of the Child (Monaco, 28-30 April 2000). Paris: UNESCO, Division des Sciences Humaines, de la Philosophie et de L'ethique des Sciences et des Technologies; 2001: 87-104. Subject: 14.5

Meslin, Eric M.; Quaid, Kimberly A. Ethical issues in the collection, storage, and research use of human biological materials. *Journal of Laboratory and Clinical Medicine* 2004 November; 144(5): 229-234. Subject: 19.5

Meslin, Eric M.; Sidle, John E.; Wools-Kaloustian, Kara; Were, Edwin; Salmon, Karen; Chuani, Christine. International research ethics: a needs assessment of research ethics capacity at Moi University and Indiana

---

University. Volume I: Final report. Indianapolis, IN; Eldoret, Kenya: Indiana University Center for Bioethics 2005 June; 31 p. [Online]. Available: http://www. bioethics.iu.edu/moi_vol1.pdf [4 January 2006]. Subject: 18.6

Mester, Roberto; Pinals, Debra. Comparing aspects of mental health legislation of Israel and Massachusetts. *Israel Journal of Psychiatry and Related Sciences* 2004; 41(2): 133-139. Subject: 17.7

Meulenbergs, T.; Vermylen, J.; Schotsmans, P.T. The current state of clinical ethics and healthcare ethics committees in Belgium. *Journal of Medical Ethics* 2005 June; 31(6): 318-321. Subject: 9.6

Meyer, Charles R. Slippery concepts for a slippery slope [review of Life, Liberty, and the Defense of Dignity: The Challenge for Bioethics, by Leon R. Kass]. *Minnesota Medicine* 2004 June; 87(6): 46. Subject: 2.1

Meyer, David D. Lochner redeemed: family privacy after Troxel and Carhart. *UCLA Law Review* 2001 June; 48(5): 1125-1190. Subject: 12.4.2

Meyer, John R. The brave new world of embryonic stem cell research: utilitarian consequentialism and faulty moral reasoning. *Linacre Quarterly* 2005 November; 72(4): 319-330. Subject: 18.5.4

Meyer, Lukas H. Reproductive rights [editorial]. *Ethical Perspectives* 2003; 10(3-4): 173-175. Subject: 14.1

Meyers, Christopher. Codifying but not professionalizing bioethics [comment]. *American Journal of Bioethics* 2005 September-October; 5(5): 68-69. Subject: 6

Meyers, Derek H.; Komesaroff, Paul A. Whose ethics? [letter and reply]. *Medical Journal of Australia* 2001 May 21; 174(10): 546-547. Subject: 18.2

Meyers, Judy L.; Moore, Crystal; McGrory, Alice; Sparr, Jennifer; Ahern, Melissa. Physician orders for life-sustaining treatment form: honoring end-of-life directives for nursing home residents. *Journal of Gerontological Nursing* 2004 September; 30(9): 37-46. Subject: 20.5.4

Miah, Andy. Bioethics, sport and the genetically enhanced athlete. *Medical Ethics and Bioethics / Medicinska Etika & Bioetika* 2002 Autumn-Winter; 9(3-4): 2-6. Subject: 15.1

Miah, Andy. Doping and the child: an ethical policy for the vulnerable. *Lancet* 2005 September 10-16; 366(9489): 874-876. Subject: 9.5.7

Miah, Andy. The engineered athlete: human rights in the genetic revolution. *Culture, Sport, Society* 2000 Autumn; 3(3): 25-40. Subject: 15.4

Michael, Mike; Brown, Nik. Scientific citizenships: self-representations of xenotransplantation's publics. *Science as Culture* 2005 March; 14(1): 39-57. Subject: 19.1

Michael, Steve. Animal personhood — a threat to research? *Physiologist* 2004 December; 47(6): 447, 449-450. Subject: 22.1

Michara, Brian L.; Weisstub, David N. Ethical and legal issues in suicide research. *International Journal of Law and Psychiatry* 2005 January- February; 28(1): 23-41. Subject: 18.5.6

Michie, Colin. Xenotransplantation, endogenous pig retroviruses and the precautionary principle [opinion]. *Trends in Molecular Medicine* 2001 February; 7(2): 62-63. Subject: 19.1

Michie, Susan; Allanson, Abi; Armstrong, David; Weinman, John; Bobrow, Martin; Marteau, Theresa M. Objectives of genetic counselling: differing views of purchasers, providers and users. *Journal of Public Health Medicine* 1998; 20(4): 404-408. Subject: 15.2

Michie, Susan; Dormandy, Elizabeth; Marteau, Theresa M. Informed choice: understanding knowledge in the context of screening uptake. *Patient Education and Counseling* 2003 July; 50(3): 247-253. Subject: 15.2

Micklos, David; Carlson, Elof. Engineering American society: the lesson of eugenics [opinion]. *Nature Reviews Genetics* 2000 November; 1(2): 153-158. Subject: 15.5

Middleton, Anna. Deaf and hearing adults' attitudes toward genetic testing for deafness. *In:* Van Cleve, John Vickery, ed. Genetics, Disability, and Deafness. Washington, DC: Gallaudet University Press; 2004: 127- 147. Subject: 15.2

Middleton, Carl; Biegert, Mary Elise. Planning for the age of genetics: a Denver-based system makes ethical, theological, and practical decisions about genetic medicine. *Health Progress* 2005 January-February; 86(1): 35-40, 60. Subject: 15.1

Miech, Ralph P. A proposed novel treatment for rape victims. *National Catholic Bioethics Quarterly* 2005 Winter; 5(4): 687- 695. Subject: 9.5.5

Miech, Ralph; Schwarz, Stephen D.; Latimer, James S. The supposed conflict between religion and science. *National Catholic Bioethics Quarterly* 2005 Autumn; 5(3): 450- 451. Subject: 18.5.4

Mielke, J. Teaching medical ethics. *Central African Journal of Medicine* 2000 March; 46(3): 79-81. Subject: 2.3

Miesfeldt, Susan; Jones, Susan M.; Cohn, Wendy; Lippert, Marguerite; Haden, Kathleen; Turner, Beverely L.; Martin-Fries, Tracee; Clark, Stephanie M. Men's attitudes regarding genetic testing for hereditary prostate cancer risk. *Urology* 2000 January; 55(1): 46-50. Subject: 15.3

Mifflin, Pauline. 'Personhood' and the right to life. *Practising Midwife* 2004 September; 7(8): 25-26. Subject: 4.4

Mihanovic, Mate; Restek-Petrovic, Branka; Babic, Goran; Sain, Ivica; Telarovic, Sinisa; Zilic-Dzeba, Jadranka. Involuntary hospitalizations in the psychiatric hospital "Jankomir" before and following the alterations and amendments made to ZZODS. *Collegium Antropologicum* 2004 June; 28(1): 385-391. Subject: 17.7

Milani, Adam A. Better off dead than disabled?: should courts recognize a "wrongful living" cause of action when doctors fail to honor patients' advance directives? *Washington and Lee Law Review* 1997; 54(1): 149-228. Subject: 20.7

Milani-Comparetti, Marco. Bioethical considerations on cloning and twinning. *Acta Geneticae Medicae et Gemellologicae (Roma)* 1997; 46(3): 135-137. Subject: 14.5

Millard, Peter. Euthanasia: is there a time to die? *Medico-Legal Journal* 1997; 65(4): 173-192. Subject: 20.5.1

Millard, Peter H. Ethical decisions at the end of life. *Journal of the Royal College Physicians of London* 1999 July-August; 33(4): 365-367. Subject: 20.5.1

Miller, Alfred E. Social ethics and organizational structures influencing the allocation of health care in Germany and the United States. *Journal of Contemporary Health Law and Policy* 2002 Fall; 18(3): 649-661. Subject: 9.4

Miller, A. Ethical issues in MS clinical trials. *Multiple Sclerosis* 2005 February; 11(1): 97-98. Subject: 18.3

Miller, Colin. A death by any other name: the federal government's inconsistent treatment of drugs used in lethal injections and physician-assisted suicide. *Journal of Law and Health* 2002-2003; 17(2): 217-240. Subject: 20.7

Miller, Franklin G. Does research ethics rest on a mistake? *American Journal of Bioethics* 2005 January-February; 5(1): 34- 36. Subject: 18.2

Miller, Franklin G. The case for a code of ethics for bioethicists: some reasons for skepticism [comment]. *American Journal of Bioethics* 2005 September-October; 5(5): 50-52. Subject: 6

Miller, Franklin G.; Brody, Howard. Enhancement technologies and professional integrity [comment]. *American Journal of Bioethics* 2005 May-June; 5(3): 15-17. Subject: 4.5

Miller, Franklin G.; Brody, Howard. Professional integrity in industry-sponsored clinical trials [opinion]. *Academic Medicine* 2005 October; 80(10): 899-904. Subject: 1.3.9

Miller, Franklin G.; Kaptchuk, Ted J. Sham procedures and the ethics of clinical trials. *Journal of the Royal Society of Medicine* 2004 December; 97(12): 576-578. Subject: 18.3

Miller, Franklin G.; Moreno, Jonathan D. Informed consent and the ethics of clinical research: reply to commentaries. *Journal of Clinical Ethics* 2005 Winter; 16(4): 376-379. Subject: 18.3

Miller, Franklin G.; Moreno, Jonathan D. The state of research ethics: a tribute to John C. Fletcher. *Journal of Clinical Ethics* 2005 Winter; 16(4): 355-364. Subject: 18.3

Miller, Franklin G.; Wendler, David; Kravitz, Richard L.; Franks, Peter; Epstein, Ronald M.; Feldman, Mitchell D.; Franz, Carol E. Direct-to-consumer advertising and physician prescribing [letter and reply]. *JAMA: The Journal of the American Medical Association* 2005 August 10; 294(6): 678-679. Subject: 18.3

Miller, Gary D.; Key, Charles M. Health Care Decisions Act — problems with consents, surrogacy, and end-of-life choices addressed by the new Tennessee Health Care Decisions Act. *Tennessee Medicine* 2004 October; 97(10): 448-451. Subject: 20.5.4

Miller, Henry. Cat and mouse in regulating genetic 'enhancement' [opinion]. *Nature Biotechnology* 2005 February; 23(2): 171-172. Subject: 15.4

Miller, Jennifer. Physician-patient confidentiality and familial access to genetic information. *Health Law Journal* 1994; 2: 141-158. Subject: 15.3

Miller, Jessica P. A code of ethics for bioethicists: prospects and problems [comment]. *American Journal of Bioethics* 2005 September-October; 5(5): 66-68. Subject: 6

Miller, Kevin E. Ending renal dialysis: ethical issues in refusing life- sustaining treatment. *In:* Koterski, Joseph W., ed. Life and Learning IX: Proceedings of the Ninth University Faculty for Life Conference. Washington, DC: University Faculty for Life; 2000: 59-78. Subject: 8.3.4

Miller, Lois L.; Harvath, Theresa A.; Ganzini, Linda; Goy, Elizabeth R.; Delorit, Molly A.; Jackson, Ann. Attitudes and experiences of Oregon hospice nurses and social workers regarding assisted suicide. *Palliative Medicine* 2004 December; 18(8): 685-691. Subject: 20.7

Miller, Mark; Robertson, John A. Neonatal care for premature infants [letter and reply]. *Hastings Center Report* 2005 January-February; 35(1): 4, 7. Subject: 9.5.7

Miller, Matthew J.; Horstmann, Elizabeth; Emanuel, Ezekiel J.; Grady, Christine; Kurzrock, Razelle; Benjamin, Robert S. Phase 1 clinical trials in oncology [letter and replies]. *New England Journal of Medicine* 2005 June 9; 352(23): 2452- 2453. Subject: 18.3

Miller, Monica K. Refusal to undergo a cesarean section: a woman's right or a criminal act? *Health Matrix: Journal of Law-Medicine* 2005 Summer; 15(2): 383-400. Subject: 9.5.5

Miller, Pamela J. Care at the end of life: Oregon's Death with Dignity Act. *Continuum* 1998 September-October; 18(5): 7-13. Subject: 20.7

Miller, Paul Steven. Analyzing genetic discrimination in the workplace. *In:* Krimsky, Sheldon; Shorett, Peter, eds. Rights and Liberties in the Biotech Age: Why We Need a Genetic Bill of Rights. Lanham: Rowman and Littlefield Publishers; 2005: 173-177. Subject: 15.3

Miller, Robert G.; Munsat, Theodore L.; Swash, Michael; Brooks, Benjamin R. Consensus guidelines for the design and implementation of clinical trials in ALS. *Journal of Neurological Sciences* 1999 October 31; 169(1-2): 2-12. Subject: 18.2

Miller, Robert T. The legal death of Terri Schiavo. *First Things* 2005 May; (153): 14-16. Subject: 20.5.1

Miller, Victoria A.; Nelson, Robert M. Moving beyond the consent document in research on informed consent [editorial]. *Archives of Pediatric and Adolescent Medicine* 2005 April; 159(4): 396-397. Subject: 18.3

Miller, William R. Motivational interviewing: III. On the ethics of motivational intervention. *Behavioral and Cognitive Psychotherapy* 1994; 22: 111-123. Subject: 17.2

Miller, William R. The ethics of motivational interviewing revisited. *Behavioural and Cognitive Psychotherapy* 1995; 23: 345-348. Subject: 17.2

Millett, Christopher; Parker, M. Informed decision making for cancer screening — not all of the ethical issues have been considered [editorial]. *Cytopathology* 2003 February; 14(1): 3-4. Subject: 15.3

Millette, Brenda E. Client advocacy and the moral orientation of nurses. *Western Journal of Nursing Research* 1993 October; 15(5): 607-618. Subject: 4.1.3

Milliken, Jan. One palliative care nurse's view of euthanasia: a social movement reflective of a self-serving generation. *International Journal of Palliative Nursing* 2004 June; 10(6): 308-311. Subject: 20.5.1

Mills, Ann E.; Spencer, Edward M. Values based decision making: a tool for achieving the goals of healthcare. *HEC (Healthcare Ethics Committee) Forum* 2005 March; 17(1): 18- 32. Subject: 9.1

Mills, Ann E.; Tereskerz, Patricia; Davis, Walt. Is evaluating ethics consultation on the basis of cost a good idea? *CQ: Cambridge Quarterly of Healthcare Ethics* 2005 Winter; 14(1): 57-64. Subject: 9.6

Mills, Claudia. Are there morally problematic reasons for having children? *Philosophy and Public Policy Quarterly* 2005 Fall; 25(4): 2-9. Subject: 14.1

Mills, Edward J.; Singh, Sonal; Singh, Jerome A.; Orbinski, James J.; Warren, Mitchell; Upshur, Ross E. Designing research in vulnerable populations: lessons from HIV prevention trials that stopped early. *BMJ: British Medical Journal* 2005 December 10; 331(7529): 1403-1406. Subject: 18.5.9

Mills, John W. HIV confidentiality law has serious flaws [editorial]. *Pennsylvania Medicine* 2000 May; 103(5): 6. Subject: 9.5.6

Millson, David S. Are consenters representative of a target population? [letter]. *BMJ: British Medical Journal* 2005 November 5; 331(7524): 1082- 1083. Subject: 18.3

Milner, Karen K.; Collins, Elizabeth E.; Connors, Geoffrey R.; Petty, Elizabeth M. Attitudes of young adults to prenatal screening and genetic correction for human attributes and psychiatric conditions. *American Journal of Medical Genetics* 1998 March 5; 76(2): 111-119. Subject: 15.2

Milton, Constance L. Ethics content in nursing education: pondering with the possible. *Nursing Science Quarterly* 2004 October; 17(4): 308-311. Subject: 4.1.3

Milton, Constance L. The ethics of respect in nursing. *Nursing Science Quarterly* 2005 January; 18(1): 20-23. Subject: 4.4

Milton, Constance L. Scholarship in nursing: ethics of a practice doctorate. *Nursing Science Quarterly* 2005 April; 18(2): 113-116. Subject: 4.1.3

Minicucci, Daryl Sharp; Schmitt, Madeline H.; Dombeck, Mary T.; Williams, Geoffrey C. Actualizing Gadow's moral framework for nursing through research. *Nursing Philosophy* 2003 July; 4(2): 92-103. Subject: 4.1.3

Minkoff, Howard; Paltrow, Lynn M. Melissa Rowland and the rights of pregnant women [opinion]. *Obstetrics and Gynecology* 2004 December; 104(6): 1234-1236. Subject: 9.5.5

Minnes, Patricia M. Ethical issues in supervision. *Canadian Psychology/Psychologie Canadienne* 1987 August; 28(3): 285-290. Subject: 17.2

Minnesota Medical Association [MMA]; University of Minnesota Extension Service. The Minnesota Health Care Directive: A Suggested Form, Suggestions for Completing. Minneapolis, MN: The Association [MMA], 1998 August; various pagings. Subject: 20.5.4

Mino, Jean-Christophe; Lert, France. Beyond the biomedical model: palliative care and its holistic model. *HEC (Healthcare Ethics Committee) Forum* 2005 September; 17(3): 227-236. Subject: 20.4.1

Minwalla, Sherizaan. A modest proposal to amend the Patent Code 35 U.S.C. Section 287(c) to allow health care providers to examine their patients' DNA. *Southern Illinois University Law Journal* 2002 Spring; 26(3): 471-504. Subject: 15.8

Minwalla, Sherizaan. The high price of silence: requiring ERISA regulated managed care organizations to disclose financial incentives used to limit medical care. *Journal of Medicine and Law* 2001 Fall; 6(1): 1-28. Subject: 9.3.2

Miola, José. Medical law and medical ethics — complementary or corrosive? *Medical Law International* 2004; 6(3): 251-274. Subject: 2.1

Mirza, Ayoub; Kad, Rishi; Ellison, Neil M. Cardiopulmonary resuscitation is not addressed in the admitting medical records for the majority of patients who undergo CPR in the hospital. *American Journal of Hospice and Palliative Care* 2005 January-February; 22(1): 20-25. Subject: 20.5.1

Mirza, Bushra. Islamic perspectives on biotechnology. *In:* Brannigan, Michael C., ed. Cross-Cultural Biotechnology. Lanham: Rowman and Littlefield; 2004: 105-114. Subject: 15.1

Mirza, Sohail K. Accountability of the accused: facing public perceptions about financial conflicts of interest in spine surgery [editorial]. *Spine Journal* 2004 September-October; 4(5): 491-494. Subject: 9.3.1

Misak, Cheryl. ICU psychosis and patient autonomy: some thoughts from the inside. *Journal of Medicine and Philosophy* 2005 August; 30(4): 411-430. Subject: 17.1

Miser, William F. Educational research — to IRB, or not to IRB? *Family Medicine* 2005 March; 37(3): 168-173. Subject: 18.2

Mishkin, Douglas B.; Povar, Gail. The District of Columbia amends its Health-Care Decisions Act: bioethics committees in the arena of public policy. *Journal of Clinical Ethics* 2005 Winter; 16(4): 292-298. Subject: 9.6

Misrahi, James J.; Matthews, Gene W.; Hoffman, Richard E. Legal authorities for interventions during public health emergencies. *In:* Goodman, Richard A.; Rothstein, Mark A.; Hoffman, Richard E.; Lopez, Wilfredo; Matthews, Gene W., eds. Law in Public Health Practice. New York: Oxford University Press; 2003: 195-210. Subject: 9.1

Mississippi. Supreme Court. *66 Federal Credit Union v. Tucker* [Date of Decision: 21 August 2003]. *West's Southern Reporter*, 2d Series, 2003; 853: 104-122. Subject: 4.4

Mistry, D.; Kelly, G. Consent for tonsillectomy. *Clinical Otolaryngology and Allied Sciences* 2004 August; 29(4): 362-368. Subject: 8.3.1

Mitchell, C. Ben. The return of eugenics [editorial]. *Ethics and Medicine* 2005 Summer; 21(2): 67. Subject: 15.1

Mitchell, C. Ben. Southern Baptists and bioethics. *In:* Peppin, John F.; Cherry, Mark J., eds. Religious Perspectives in Bioethics. New York: Taylor & Francis; 2004: 97-108. Subject: 2.1

Mitchell, C. Ben. The wisdom of Costa Rica [editorial]. *Ethics and Medicine* 2005 Spring; 21(1): 3-4. Subject: 14.5

Mitchell, David R. Ethical and legal issues in providing medical treatment for seriously ill handicapped persons. *Australia and New Zealand Journal of Developmental Disabilities* 1985; 10(4): 245-256. Subject: 9.5.3

Mitchell, David; Snyder, Sharon. The eugenic Atlantic: race, disability, and the making of an international eugenic science, 1800-1945. *Disability and Society* 2003 December; 18(7): 843-864. Subject: 15.5

Mitchell, John. Who knows best? *Medico-Legal Journal* 2005; 73(Part 1): 34-38. Subject: 8.3.2

Mitchell, Kay; Owens, Glynn. End of life decision-making by New Zealand general practitioners: a national survey. *New Zealand Medical Journal* 2004 June 18; 117(1196); 11 p. Subject: 20.5.1

Mitchell, Peter. Europe dithers over stem cell patents [news]. *Nature Medicine* 2003 February; 9(2): 154. Subject: 15.8

Mitchell, Peter. UK to regulate 'serious' genetic tests [news]. *Nature Medicine* 2003 March; 9(3): 250. Subject: 15.3

Mitka, Mike. Scenarios for stem cell creation debated: panel members spar over ethical and scientific issues. *JAMA: The Journal of the American Medical Association* 2005 June 22-29; 293(24): 2990-2991. Subject: 18.5.4

Mittra, I. Mishandling misconduct: the breast cancer trials scandal [editorial]. *National Medical Journal of India* 1994 November-December; 7(6): 255-257. Subject: 18.2

Mixon, Don. Deception, self-deception and self-determination. *In:* Fairbairn, Susan; Fairbairn, Gavin, eds. Psychology, Ethics and Change. New York: Routledge & Kegan Paul; 1987: 44-57. Subject: 17.1

Miya, Pamela A.; Megel, Mary E. Confidentiality and electronic medical records. *Medsurg Nursing* 1997 August; 6(4): 222-224, 212. Subject: 8.4

Miyasaka, Michio. Resourcifying human bodies — Kant and bioethics. *Medicine, Health Care and Philosophy: A European Journal* 2005; 8(1): 19-27. Subject: 19.5

Miyata, Hioraki; Takahashi, M.; Saito, T.; Tachimori, H.; Kai, I. Disclosure preferences regarding cancer diagnosis and prognosis: to tell or not to tell? *Journal of Medical Ethics* 2005 August; 31(8): 447-451. Subject: 8.2

Miyazaki, Satoru; Tateno, Yoshio. DNA data bank of Japan as an indispensable public database. *In:* Knoppers, Bartha Maria, ed. Populations and Genetics: Legal and Socio-Ethical Perspectives. Boston: Martinus Nijhoff; 2003: 115-121. Subject: 15.1

Mize, Selene. Non-disclosing and deceptive research design. *In:* Dawson, John; Peart, Nicola, eds. The Law of Research: A Guide. Dunedin, NZ: University of Otago Press; 2003: 253-267. Subject: 18.4

Mize, Selene; Dawson, John; Peart, Nicola. Privacy and access to information. *In:* Dawson, John; Peart, Nicola, eds. The Law of Research: A Guide. Dunedin, NZ: University of Otago Press; 2003: 81-104. Subject: 8.4

Mizukami, Akiyasu; Peterson, C. Matthew; Huang, Ivan; Cook, Christopher; Boyack, Lisa M.; Emery, Benjamin R.; Carrell, Douglas T. The acceptability of posthumous human ovarian tissue donation in Utah. *Human Reproduction* 2005 December; 20(12): 3560-3565. Subject: 19.5

Moayery, Sheedeh. National HIV reporting: what's in a name? *Virginia Journal of Social Policy and the Law* 2001 Winter; 8(2): 439-473. Subject: 9.5.6

Moazam, Farhat; Jafarey, Aamir M. Pakistan and biomedical ethics: report from a Muslim country. *CQ: Cambridge Quarterly of Healthcare Ethics* 2005 Summer; 14(3): 249-255. Subject: 2.1

Moffit, Robert E. The economic and ethical dimensions of health policy. *Journal of Contemporary Health Law and Policy* 2002 Fall; 18(3): 663-672. Subject: 9.1

Mojon-Azzi, Stefania M.; Mojon, Daniel S. Scientific misconduct: from salami slicing to data fabrication [editorial]. *Ophthalmologica* 2004 January-February; 218(1): 1-3. Subject: 1.3.9

Mokotedi, S.; Modiba, M.C.M.; Ndlovu, S.R. Attitudes of black South Africans to living related kidney transplantation. *Transplantation Proceedings* 2004 September; 36(7): 1896-1897. Subject: 19.5

Moldow, Gay; Bartels, Dianne; Brunnquell, Don; Cranford, Ron. Why address medical futility now? *Minnesota Medicine* 2004 June; 87(6): 38-44. Subject: 20.5.1

Møldrup, Claus. Medical technology assessment of the ethical, social, and legal implications of pharmacogenomics: a research proposal for an Internet citizen jury. *International Journal of Technology Assessment in Health Care* 2002 Summer; 18(3): 728-732. Subject: 15.1

Molenberghs, Geert; Imrey, Peter; Drake, Christiana; Fontanarosa, Phil B.; DeAngelis, Catherine D. Conflict of interest and independent data analysis in industry-funded studies [letter and reply]. *JAMA: The Journal of the American Medical Association* 2005 November 23-20; 294(20): 2575-2577. Subject: 1.3.9

Moler, Frank W. Resuscitation research and the final rule: is there an impasse? [opinion]. *Pediatrics* 2004 September; 114(3): 859-861. Subject: 18.2

Molin, Ronald; Palmer, Sally. Consent and participation: ethical issues in the treatment of children in out-of-home care. *American Journal of Orthopsychiatry* 2005 January; 75(1): 152-157. Subject: 8.3.2

Molinari, Patrick A. Trends in health legislation and human rights. *Medicine and Law: World Association for Medical Law* 1995; 14(7-8): 589-599. Subject: 9.2

Molmenti, Ernesto P.; Dunn, Geoffrey P. Transplantation and palliative care: the convergence of two seemingly opposite realities. *Surgical Clinics of North America* 2005 April; 85(2): 373-382. Subject: 20.4.1

Molyneux, C.S.; Peshu, N.; Marsh, K. Understanding of informed consent in a low-income setting: three case studies from the Kenyan Coast. *Social Science and Medicine* 2004 December; 59(12): 2547-2559. Subject: 18.3

Molzahn, Anita E.; Starzomski, Rosalie; McDonald, Michael; O'Loughlin, Chloe. Chinese Canadian beliefs toward organ donation. *Qualitative Health Research* 2005 January; 15(1): 82-98. Subject: 19.5

Monahan, John; Redlich, Allison D.; Swanson, Jeffrey; Robbins, Pamela Clark; Appelbaum, Paul S.; Petrila, John; Steadman, Henry J.; Swartz, Marvin; Angell, Beth; McNiel, Dale E. Use of leverage to improve adherence to psychiatric treatment in the community. *Psychiatric Services* 2005 January; 56(1): 37-44. Subject: 17.7

Monastersky, Richard. Cell divisions. *Chronicle of Higher Education* 2006 January 6; 52(18): A26-A28. Subject: 18.5.4

Mongan, James J.; Lee, Thomas H. Do we really want broad access to health care? *New England Journal of Medicine* 2005 March 24; 352(12): 1260-1263. Subject: 9.2

Moniz, Helena. Privacy and intra-family communication of genetic information. *Revista de Derecho y Genoma-Humano / Law and the Human Genome Review* 2004 July-December; (21): 103-124. Subject: 15.1

Montello, Martha. Novel perspectives on bioethics. *Chronicle of Higher Education* 2005 May 13; 51(36): B6-B8. Subject: 2.1

Montgomery, Kathryn. How not to philosophize with a hammer: a reply to Spike. *In:* Thomasma, David C.; Weisstub, David N., eds. The Variables of Moral Capacity. Boston: Kluwer Academic Publishers; 2004: 121-127. Subject: 2.1

Montori, Victor M.; Devereaux, P.J.; Adhikari, Neill K.J.; Burns, Karen E.A.; Eggert, Christoph H.; Briel, Matthias; Lacchetti, Christina; Leung, Teresa W.; Darling, Elizabeth; Bryant, Dianne M.; Bucher, Heiner C.; Schünemann, Holger J.; Meade, Maureen O.; Cook, Deborah J.; Erwin, Patricia J.; Sood, Amit; Sood, Richa; Lo, Benjamin; Thompson, Carly A.; Zhou, Qi; Mills, Edward; Guyatt, Gordon H. Randomized trials stopped early for benefit: a systematic review. *JAMA: The Journal of the American Medical Association* 2005 November 2; 294(17): 2203-2209. Subject: 18.2

Moodley, K.; Pather, M.; Myer, L. Informed consent and participant perceptions of influenza vaccine trials in South Africa. *Journal of Medical Ethics* 2005 December; 31(12): 727-732. Subject: 18.3

Moodley, Keymanthri. Physician-assisted suicide — an oxymoron? [letter]. *South African Medical Journal* 2000 July; 90(7): 657. Subject: 20.7

Mooney, Gavin. Evidence-based medicine: objectives and values. *In:* Kristiansen, Ivar Sonbo; Mooney, Gavin, eds. Evidence-Based Medicine: In its Place. New York: Routledge; 2004: 62-72. Subject: 9.8

Mooney, Gavin; Jan, Stephen; Wiseman, Virginia. Staking a claim for claims: a case study of resource allocation in Australian Aboriginal health care. *Social Science and Medicine* 2002 June; 54(11): 1657-1667. Subject: 9.4

Moore, Dale L. Recurrent issues in the review of medical research on human subjects. *Albany Law Journal of Science and Technology* 1991; 1: 1-33. Subject: 8.2

Moore, Debra L. Don't rush to judgment on "Dolly": human cloning and its individual procreative liberty implications. *UMKC Law Review* 1997 Winter; 66(2): 425-449. Subject: 14.5

Moore, Linda Weaver; Rieg, Linda S. The ethics of using cybernetics and cyborg technologies: what every rehabilitation nurse should know. *Rehabilitation Nursing* 2005 March-April; 30(2): 40-43. Subject: 5.1

Moore, Zella E. Ethical dilemmas in sport psychology: discussion and recommendations for practice. *Professional Psychology: Research and Practice* 2003 December; 34(6): 601-610. Subject: 17.1

Moores, Donald F. Genetic engineering and our brave new world [editorial]. *American Annals of the Deaf* 1998 July; 143(3): 223-224. Subject: 15.4

Moraczewski, Albert S. Stem cells: answers to three questions. *Ethics and Medics* 2003 March; 28(3): 1-2. Subject: 18.5.4

Morag, Rumm M.; DeSouza, Sylvie; Steen, Petter A.; Salem, Ashraf; Harris, Mark; Ohnstad, Oyvind; Fosen, Jan T.; Brenner, Barry E. Performing procedures on the newly deceased for teaching purposes: what if we were to ask? *Archives of Internal Medicine* 2005 January 10; 165(1): 82-96. Subject: 8.3.3

Morain, William D. Primum non nocere [editorial]. *Annals of Plastic Surgery* 2004 November; 53(5): 513-514. Subject: 4.1.2

Morelli, Mariano G. La peligrosa pendiente que convierte los delitos en derechos / The dangerous slope that changes crimes into rights: juridical protection of the embryo 30 years after Roe v. Wade. *Vida y Etica* 2003 December; 4(2): 67-96. Subject: 12.4.2

Moreno, Jonathan D. The end of the great bioethics compromise. *Hastings Center Report* 2005 January-February; 35(1): 14-15. Subject: 2.2

Moreno, Jonathan D. In the wake of Katrina: has "bioethics" failed? *American Journal of Bioethics [Online]* 2005 September- October; 5(3): W18-W19. Subject: 2.1

Moreno, Jonathan D. Neuroethics: an agenda for neuroscience and society. *Nature Reviews Neuroscience* 2003 February; 4(2): 149-153. Subject: 17.1

Moreno, Jonathan D.; Gross, Michael. Wartime medical ethics [letter and reply]. *Hastings Center Report* 2005 May-June; 35(3): 7. Subject: 21.2

Moreno, Jonathan David. Dual use and the "moral taint" problem. *American Journal of Bioethics* 2005 March-April; 5(2): 52-53. Subject: 17.1

Morgan, Alan. Informed consent: finding a path toward prudent policy. *Pacing and Clinical Electrophysiology* 1997 March; 20(3, Part 1): 730-731. Subject: 18.3

Morgan, Derek. Enigma variations: surrogacy, rights and procreative tourism. *In:* Cook, Rachel; Sclater, Shelley Day; Kaganas, Felicity, eds. Surrogate Motherhood: Inter-

national Perspectives. Portland, OR: Hart; 2003: 75-92. Subject: 14.2

Morgan, Derek. Science, medicine and ethical change. *In:* Bainham, Andrew; Sclater, Shelley Day; Richards, Martin, eds. Body Lore and Laws. Portland, OR: Hart Pub.; 2002: 329-342. Subject: 14.5

Morgan, Derek; Bernat, Erwin. The reproductive waltz: the Austrian Act on Procreative Medicine 1992. *Journal of Social Welfare and Family Law* 1992; 5: 420-426. Subject: 14.4

Morgan, Derek; Veitch, Kenneth. Being Ms B: B, autonomy and the nature of legal regulation. *Sydney Law Review* 2004 March; 26(1): 107-130. Subject: 20.5.1

Morgan, John M.; Marco, J.; Stockx, L.; Zannad, F. Educational governance for the regulation of industry sponsored continuing medical education in interventional and device based therapies [editorial]. *Heart* 2005 June; 91(6): 710-712. Subject: 7.1

Morgan, Rebecca C.; Sutherland, D. Dixon. Last rights? Confronting physician-assisted suicide in law and society: legal liturgies on physician-assisted suicide. *Stetson Law Review* 1996 Winter; 26(2): 481-528. Subject: 20.7

Morgenstern, Leon. Proactive bioethics screening: a prelude to bioethics consultation. *Journal of Clinical Ethics* 2005 Summer; 16(2): 151-155. Subject: 9.6

Morin, Karine. Code of ethics for bioethicists: medicine's lessons worth heeding [comment]. *American Journal of Bioethics* 2005 September-October; 5(5): 60-62. Subject: 6

Morley, C.J.; Lau, R.; Davis, P.G.; Morse, C. What do parents think about enrolling their premature babies in several research studies? *Archives of Disease in Childhood. Fetal and Neonatal Edition* 2005 May; 90(3): F225-F228. Subject: 18.5.2

Morreim, E. Haavi. Another kind of end-run: status upgrade. *American Journal of Bioethics* 2005 July-August; 5(4): 11-12. Subject: 19.6

Morreim, E. Haavi. The clinical investigator as fiduciary: discarding a misguided idea. *Journal of Law, Medicine and Ethics* 2005 Fall; 33(3): 586-598. Subject: 8.1

Morreim, E. Haavi. Clinical trials litigation: practical realities as seen from the trenches. *Accountability in Research* 2005 January-March; 12(1): 47-67. Subject: 18.1

Morreim, E. Haavi. Medical errors: pinning the blame versus blaming the system. *In:* Sharpe, Virginia A., ed. Accountability: Patient Safety and Policy Reform. Washington, DC: Georgetown University Press; 2004: 213-232. Subject: 9.8

Morreim, E. Haavi. Research versus innovation: real differences. *American Journal of Bioethics* 2005 January-February; 5(1): 42- 43. Subject: 18.2

Morreim, E. Haavi; Macauley, Robert. Civil disobedience: the devil is in the details [letter and reply]. *Hastings*

Center Report 2005 July-August; 35(4): 4, 5-6. Subject: 9.3.1

Morris, Amelia D.; Zaritsky, Arno L.; LeFever, Gretchen. Evaluation of ethical conflicts associated with randomized, controlled trials in critically ill children. *Critical Care Medicine* 2000 April; 28(4): 1152-1156. Subject: 18.2

Morris, Caroline. Technology and the legal discourse of fetal autonomy. *UCLA Women's Law Journal* 1997 Fall-Winter; 8(1): 47-97. Subject: 4.4

Morris, Marilyn C.; Nadkarni, Vinay M.; Ward, Frances R.; Nelson, Robert M. Exception from informed consent for pediatric resuscitation research: community consultation for a trial of brain cooling after in-hospital cardiac arrest. *Pediatrics* 2004 September; 114(3): 776-781. Subject: 18.3

Morris, Peter J.; Monaco, Anthony P. Ethical issues and xenotransplantation. *Transplantation* 2004 October 27; 78(8): 1099-1100. Subject: 19.1

Morrison, Doug. A holistic approach to clinical and research decision- making: lessons from the UK organ-retention scandals. *Medical Law Review* 2005 Spring; 13(1):45-79. Subject: 19.5

Morrison, Joanne; MacKenzie, I.Z. Cesarean section on demand. *Seminars in Perinatology* 2003 February; 27(1): 20-33. Subject: 9.5.5

Morrison, Laura J.; Sinclair, Christian T.; Goldstein, Nathan E.; Lampert, Rachel; Krumholz, Harlan M. Next-of-kin responses and do-not-resuscitate implications for implantable cardioverter defibrillators [letter and reply]. *Annals of Internal Medicine* 2005 April 19; 142(8): 676-677. Subject: 20.5.1

Morrison, Patrick J. Insurance, unfair discrimination, and genetic testing. *Lancet* 2005 September 10-16; 366(9489): 877-880. Subject: 15.3

Morrison, R. Sean; Chichin, Eileen; Carter, John; Burack, Orah; Lantz, Melinda; Meier, Diane E. The effect of a social work intervention to enhance advance care planning documentation in the nursing home. *Journal of the American Geriatrics Society* 2005 February; 53(2): 290-294. Subject: 20.5.4

Morscher, Edgar. Why is it morally wrong to clone a human being? How to evaluate arguments of biopolitics, biomorality, and bioethics. *In:* Thiele, F.; Ashcroft, R.E., eds. Bioethics in a Small World. Berlin: Springer; 2005: 121-128. Subject: 14.5

Morse, Janice M. Ethical issues in institutional research [editorial]. *Qualitative Health Research* 2005 April; 15(4): 435-437. Subject: 18.2

Morse, Janice M. The paid/unpaid work of participants [editorial]. *Qualitative Health Research* 2005 July; 15(6): 727-728. Subject: 18.2

Morton, John. In support of the consent process for organ donation from deceased persons. *New Zealand Medical Journal* 2004 September 10; 117(1201); 3 p. Subject: 19.5

Morton, Newton E. Genetic aspects of population policy. *Clinical Genetics* 1999 August; 56(2): 105-109. Subject: 15.2

Morton, Oliver. Biology's new forbidden fruit [opinion]. *New York Times* 2005 February 11; p. A25. Subject: 15.7

Moser, David J.; Reese, Rebecca L.; Schultz, Susan K.; Benjamin, Michelle L.; Arndt, Stephan; Fleming, Frank W.; Andreasen, Nancy C. Informed consent in medication-free schizophrenia research. *American Journal of Psychiatry* 2005 June; 162(6): 1209-1211. Subject: 18.3

Mosher, Paul W. Psychotherapist-patient privilege: the history and significance of the United States Supreme Court's decision in the case of Jaffee v. Redmond. *In:* Koggel, Christine M.; Furlong, Allannah; Levin, Charles, eds. Confidential Relationships: Psychoanalytical, Ethical, and Legal Contexts. New York: Rodopi; 2003: 177-206. Subject: 8.4

Mosimann, François. Procurement of organs from executed prisoners [letter]. *Lancet* 2005 March 5-11; 365(9462): 843-844. Subject: 19.5

Moskop, John C.; Marco, Catherine A.; Larkin, Gregory Luke; Geiderman, Joel M.; Derse, Arthur R. From Hippocrates to HIPAA: privacy and confidentiality in emergency medicine — Part I: conceptual, moral, and legal foundations. *Annals of Emergency Medicine* 2005 January; 45(1): 53-59. Subject: 8.4

Moskop, John C.; Marco, Catherine A.; Larkin, Gregory Luke; Geiderman, Joel M.; Derse, Arthur R. From Hippocrates to HIPAA: privacy and confidentiality in emergency medicine — Part II: challenges in the emergency department. *Annals of Emergency Medicine* 2005 January; 45(1): 60-67. Subject: 8.4

Mossialos, Elias; Thomson, Sarah; Ter Linden, Annemarie. Information technology law and health systems in the European Union. *International Journal of Technology Assessment in Health Care* 2004 Fall; 20(4): 498-508. Subject: 1.3.12

Mosteller, Timothy. Aristotle and headless clones. *Theoretical Medicine and Bioethics* 2005; 26(4): 339-350. Subject: 14.5

Motluk, Alison. Tracing dad online [news]. *New Scientist* 2005 November 5-11; 188(2524): 6-7. Subject: 14.2

Motluk, Alison. Which IVF test is best for baby? [news]. *New Scientist* 2005 October 29-November 4; 188(2523): 10. Subject: 15.2

Motta, Elizabeth D. The ethics of heparin administration to the potential non- heart-beating organ donor. *Journal of Professional Nursing* 2005 March-April; 21(2): 97- 102. Subject: 19.5

Mouchawar, Judy; Hensley-Alford, Sharon; Laurion, Suzanne; Ellis, Jennifer; Kulchak-Rahm, Alanna; Finucane, Melissa L.; Meenan, Richard; Axell, Lisen; Pollack, Rebecca; Ritzwoller, Debra. Impact of direct-to-consumer advertising for hereditary breast cancer testing on genetic services at a managed care organization: a naturally-occurring experiment. *Genetics in Medicine* 2005 March; 7(3): 191-197. Subject: 15.3

Mouradian, Wendy E. Who decides? Patients, parents, or gatekeepers: pediatric decisions in the craniofacial setting. *Cleft Palate-Craniofacial Journal* 1995 November; 32(6): 510-514. Subject: 9.5.7

Mowat, David. Ethical, legal and social issues surrounding the Human Genome Project. *Internal Medicine Journal* 2002 March; 32(3): 89-90. Subject: 15.10

Mowery, Grace-Marie. A patient's right of privacy in computerized pharmacy records. *University of Cincinnati Law Review* 1998 Winter; 66(2): 697-746. Subject: 9.7

Moyer, Anne; Finney, John W. Rating methodological quality: toward improved assessment and investigation. *Accountability in Research* 2005 October-December; 12(4): 299- 313. Subject: 1.3.9

Moynihan, Ray. The marketing of a disease: female sexual dysfunction. *BMJ: British Medical Journal* 2005 January 22; 330(7484): 192- 194. Subject: 9.7

Mpendawatu, Jean-Marie Musivi. Bioethics in UNESCO. *Dolentium Hominum* 2004; 19(2): 48-50. Subject: 2.4

Mudur, Ganapati. India plans to audit clinical trials [news]. *BMJ: British Medical Journal* 2005 November 5; 331(7524): 1044. Subject: 18.6

Mueller, Eric; Mondragón, Delfi. Ethical implications of type I, type II error in patient competency assessment. *Nebraska Medical Journal* 1996 November; 81(11): 356-358. Subject: 8.3.3

Mueller, Paul S.; Hook, C. Christopher; Fleming, Kevin C. Ethical issues in geriatrics: a guide for clinicians. *Mayo Clinic Proceedings* 2004 April; 79(4): 554-562. Subject: 9.5.2

Muggia, Franco M.; Horstmann, Elizabeth; Emanuel, Ezekiel J.; Grady, Christine; Kurzrock, Razelle; Benjamin, Robert S. Phase 1 clinical trials in oncology [letter and replies]. *New England Journal of Medicine* 2005 June 9; 352(23): 2451- 2453. Subject: 18.3

Mühlhauser, Ingrid. Understanding breast cancer screening: should the intellectually non-disabled make decisions for the intellectually disabled? [editorial]. *Sozial- und Praventivmedizin* 2004; 49(6): 359-360. Subject: 9.5.3

Mulay, Shree. Quinacrine non-surgical sterilisation: troubling questions. *Issues in Medical Ethics* 2000 July-September; 8(3): 87-88. Subject: 11.3

Mulherkar, Rita. Biotechnology and medicine: ethical concerns. *Issues in Medical Ethics* 1997 October-December; 5(4): 110-111. Subject: 15.4

Mulholland, Daniel. Unanticipated consequences of unanticipated outcomes disclosures. *Journal of Health Law* 2002 Spring; 35(2): 211-226. Subject: 8.2

Mullally, Siobhán. Debating reproductive rights in Ireland. *Human Rights Quarterly* 2005; 27: 78-104. Subject: 12.5.1

Mullan, Fitzhugh. The metrics of the physician brain drain. *New England Journal of Medicine* 2005 October 27; 353(17): 1810-1818. Subject: 21.6

Mullaney, Patrick J. John Paul II and America's laws on life. *Human Life Review* 2005 Summer; 31(3): 78-86. Subject: 12.3

Müller, Carola. The status of the extracorporeal embryo in German law (Part 1). *Revista de Derecho y Genoma Humano / Law and the Human Genome Review* 2005 January-June; (22): 133-151. Subject: 4.4

Muller, David. Do NOT resuscitate: a well-orchestrated plan for death ends on a brutal note. *Health Affairs* 2005 September-October; 24(5): 1317-1322. Subject: 20.5.1

Muller, Herman J. Means and aims in human genetic betterment. *In:* Sonneborn, T.M., ed. The Control of Human Heredity and Evolution. New York: The Macmillan Company; 1965: 100-122. Subject: 15.5

Müller-Busch, H.C.; Oduncu, F.S.; Woskanjan, S.; Klaschik, E. Attitudes on euthanasia, physician-assisted suicide and terminal sedation — a survey of the members of the German Association for Palliative Medicine. *Medicine, Health Care and Philosophy: A European Journal* 2004; 7(3): 333-339. Subject: 20.3.2

Müller-Hill, Benno. Reflections of a German scientist. *In:* Bachrach, Susan, project director; Kuntz, Dieter, ed. Deadly Medicine: Creating the Master Race. Washington, DC: United States Holocaust Museum; 2004: 185-199. Subject: 15.5

Mulligan, Ea; Paterson, Moira. Patients rarely detect breaches of confidence. *Australian Health Review* 2003; 26(3): 73-78. Subject: 8.4

Mulligan, James J. Caring for the unconscious. *Ethics and Medics* 2005 July; 30(7): 2-4. Subject: 20.5.1

Mulligan, James J. Catholic identity and the rationale for the ethical and religiouss directives. *In:* McMahon, Kevin T., ed. Moral Issues in Catholic Health Care. Wynnewood, PA: Saint Charles Borromeo Seminary; 2004: 19-35. Subject: 2.1

Mulligan, James J. Peace of conscience for rape victims: ovulation testing and emergency contraception. *Ethics and Medics* 2003 December; 28(12): 1-2. Subject: 11.1

Mullin, Amy. The ethical significance of pregnancy. *In her:* Reconceiving Pregnancy and Childcare: Ethics, Ex-

---

perience, and Reproductive Labor. New York: Cambridge University Press; 2005: 72-105. Subject: 14.1

Mullin, Amy. What about birth? *In her:* Reconceiving Pregnancy and Childcare: Ethics, Experience, and Reproductive Labor. New York: Cambridge University Press; 2005: 106-118. Subject: 14.1

Mulvenna, Beverley. Pre-implantation genetic diagnosis, tissue typing and beyond: the legal implications of the Hashmi case. *Medical Law International* 2004; 6(2): 163-182. Subject: 15.2

Munby, James; Francis, Robert; Taylor, Michael R.; Lester, Anthony; Saini, Pushbinder. Medical treatment — withdrawal of treatment — patient in persistent vegetative state: Airedale National Health Service Trust v. Bland [Date of Decision: 9 December 1992]. *New Law Journal* 1992 December 18; 142(6581): 1755-1758. Subject: 20.5.1

Munhall, Patricia L. Ethical juxtapositions in nursing research. *Topics in Clinical Nursing* 1982 April; 4(1): 66-73. Subject: 1.3.9

Munné, Santiago; Cohen, Jacques. The status of preimplantation genetic diagnosis in Japan: a criticism [opinion]. *Reproductive BioMedicine Online [electronic]* 2004 September; 9(3): 258-259. Available: http://www.rbmonline.com/index.html [14 July 2005]. Subject: 15.2

Muntarbhorn, Vitit. Child rights and use of the child's body. *In:* Actes du Colloque International AMADE-UNESCO sur Bioethique et Droits de L'enfant (Monaco, 28-30 Avril 2000)/Proceedings of the International Symposium AMADE-UNESCO on Bioethics and the Rights of the Child (Monaco, 28-30 April 2000). Paris: UNESCO, Division des Sciences Humaines, de la Philosophie et de L'ethique des Sciences et des Technologies; 2001: 123-139. Subject: 18.5.2

Munthe, Christian. Selected champions: making winners in the age of genetic technology. *In:* Tannsjo, Torbjorn; Tamburrini, Claudio, eds. Values in Sport: Elitism, Nationalism, Gender Equality, and the Scientific Manufacture of Winners. New York: E & FN Spon; 2000: 217-231. Subject: 15.1

Muraskas, Jonathan. A small life in detail [opinion]. *Journal of Perinatology* 2005 January; 25(1): 72-73. Subject: 20.3.1

Murphy, Dean E. Court rules U.S. need not pay for abortion of doomed fetus. *New York Times* 2005 August 19; p. A16. Subject: 12.4.1

Murphy, Dermot M.; Pritchard, Jon; Verhagen, Eduard; Sauer, Pieter J.J. Euthanasia in severely ill newborns [letter and reply]. *New England Journal of Medicine* 2005 June 2; 352(22): 2353-2355. Subject: 20.4.2

Murphy, Leslie C. Mandatory health insurance coverage for cancer clinical trials. *McGeorge Law Review* 2001; 33(2): 314-322. Subject: 9.3.1

Murphy, Peter. Are patients' decisions to refuse treatment binding on health care professionals? *Bioethics* 2005 June; 19(3): 189-201. Subject: 8.3.4

Murphy, Timothy E. Bioethics: past, present, and future [letter]. *Hastings Center Report* 2005 November-December; 35(6): 7. Subject: 6

Murphy, Timothy F. Does it make sense to use fiction as a guide to bioethics? [letter]. *Chronicle of Higher Education* 2005 July 8; 51(44): B13. Subject: 2.1

Murphy, Timothy F. Ethical justifications for moratoriums on vanguard scientific research. *American Journal of Bioethics* 2005 November-December; 5(6): 51-52. Subject: 18.5.4

Murphy, Timothy F. Gay and lesbian exceptions to the heterosexual rule. *American Journal of Bioethics* 2005 July-August; 5(4): 18. Subject: 19.5

Murphy, Timothy F. Physicians, medical ethics, and capital punishment. *Journal of Clinical Ethics* 2005 Summer; 16(2): 160-169. Subject: 20.6

Murphy, Timothy F.; White, Gladys B. Dead sperm donors or world hunger: are bioethicists studying the right stuff? [opinion]. *Hastings Center Report* 2005 March-April; 35(2): inside back cover. Subject: 14.1

Murray, Elizabeth; Lo, Bernard; Pollack, Lance; Donelan, Karen. Direct-to-consumer advertising: physicians' views of its effects on quality of care and the doctor-patient relationship. *Journal of the American Board of Family Practice* 2003 November-December; 16(6): 513-524. Subject: 9.7

Murray, Thomas H. Will new ways of creating stem cells dodge the objections? *Hastings Center Report* 2005 January-February; 35(1): 8-9. Subject: 18.5.4

Murthy, Laxmi. 'Foeticide' is problematic terminology [letter]. *Issues in Medical Ethics* 2002 January-March; 10(1): 138. Subject: 12.4.2

Musschenga, Albert W. Empirical ethics, context-sensitivity, and contextualism. *Journal of Medicine and Philosophy* 2005 October; 30(5): 467-490. Subject: 2.1

Muthappan, Palaniappan; Forster, Heidi; Wendler, David. Research advance directives: protection or obstacle? *American Journal of Psychiatry* 2005 December; 162(12): 2389-2391. Subject: 18.5.6

Muthuswamy, Vasantha. Ethical issues in HIV/AIDS research. *Indian Journal of Medical Research* 2005 April; 121(4): 601-610. Subject: 9.5.6

Muula, Adamson S. What should HIV/AIDS be called in Malawi? *Nursing Ethics* 2005 March; 12(2): 187-192. Subject: 9.5.6

Muula, Adamson S.; Mfutso-Bengo, Joseph M. When is public decision disclosure of HIV seropositivity acceptable? *Nursing Ethics* 2005 May; 12(3): 288-295. Subject: 9.5.6

Mwase, Isaac M.T. Genetic enhancement and the fate of the worse off. *Kennedy Institute of Ethics Journal* 2005 March; 15(1): 83-89. Subject: 15.1

Mwase, Isaac M.T.; London, Alex John. Justice in research [letter and reply]. *Hastings Center Report* 2005 July-August; 35(4): 7. Subject: 18.5.9

Myers, John. End-of-life decisions: ethical principles. *Origins* 2005 September 22; 35(15): 248-253. Subject: 20.5.1

Myers, Nancy A; London, Andrew S. Health care, access to. *In:* Restivo, Sal, ed. Science, Technology, and Society: An Encyclopedia. New York: Oxford University Press; 2005: 183-188. Subject: 9.2

Myers, Richard S. Physician-assisted suicide and euthanasia: a current legal perspective. *In:* Koterski, Joseph W., ed. Life and Learning XI: Proceedings of the Eleventh University Faculty for Life Conference. Washington, DC: University Faculty for Life; 2002: 3-27. Subject: 20.7

Myerson, Abraham. Sterilization. *In his:* Speaking of Man. New York: Alfred A. Knopf; 1958: 164- 190. Subject: 11.3

Myhrvold, Trine. The exclusion of the other: challenges to the ethics of closeness. *Nursing Philosophy* 2003 April; 4(1): 33-43. Subject: 8.1

Mykitiuk, Roxanne. Beyond conception: legal determinations of filiation in the context of assisted reproductive technologies. *Osgoode Hall Law Journal* 2001 Winter; 39(4): 771-815. Subject: 14.1

Mystakidou, Kyriaki; Parpa, Efi; Tsilika, Eleni; Katsouda, Emmanuela; Vlahos, Lambros. The evolution of euthanasia and its perceptions in Greek culture and civilization. *Perspectives in Biology and Medicine* 2005 Winter; 48(1): 95- 104. Subject: 20.5.1

Mytton, O. Should doctors talk to relatives without a competent patient's consent? [opinion]. *Journal of Medical Ethics* 2005 May; 31(5): 266. Subject: 8.1

N

Nadav, Daniel S. The "death dance of Lubeck": Julius Moses and the German guidelines for human experimentation, 1930. *In:* Roelcke, Volker; Maio, Giovanni, eds. Twentieth Century Ethics of Human Subjects Research: Historical Perspectives on Values, Practices, and Regulations. Stuttgart: Franz Steiner Verlag; 2004: 129-135. Subject: 18.6

Nadel, Mark S.; Nadel, Carolina A. Using reciprocity to motivate organ donations. *Yale Journal of Health Policy, Law, and Ethics* 2005 Winter; 5(1): 293-325. Subject: 19.5

Nadelson, Carol C. Ethics and women's health. *In:* Stotland, Nada L.; Stewart, Donna E., eds. Psychological Aspects of Women's Health Care: The Interface Between Psychiatry and Obstetrics and Gynecology. Washington,

DC: American Psychiatric Press; 2001: 571-584. Subject: 9.5.5

Nadolski, Heidi. Budgeting and rationing in the German health care system. *Journal of Contemporary Health Law and Policy* 2002 Fall; 18(3): 697-702. Subject: 9.4

Nadoolman, Wolffe; Charo, R. Alta. The celestial fire of conscience [letter and reply]. *New England Journal of Medicine* 2005 September 22; 353(12): 1301-1302. Subject: 8.1

Nagashima, Takashi. Freedom of scientific research and human dignity: Japanese discussions following wartime human experimentation and implications for today's debates on medical ethics. *In:* Roelcke, Volker; Maio, Giovanni, eds. Twentieth Century Ethics of Human Subjects Research: Historical Perspectives on Values, Practices, and Regulations. Stuttgart: Franz Steiner Verlag; 2004: 261-273. Subject: 18.1

Nagl, Sylvia. Biomedicine and moral agency in a complex world. *In:* Shildrick, Margrit; Mykitiuk, Roxanne, eds. Ethics of the Body: Postconventional Challenges. Cambridge, MA: MIT Press; 2005: 155- 174. Subject: 1.3.9

Nagral, Sanjay. Ethics of organ transplantation. *Medical Ethics: Journal of Forum for Medical Ethics Society* 1995 April-June; 3(2): 19-22. Subject: 19.5

Nagral, Sanjay. The kidney trade again [editorial]. *Indian Journal of Medical Ethics* 2004 April-June; 1(2): 36-37. Subject: 19.3

Nagral, Sanjay. Organ transplantation: ethical issues and the Indian scenario. *Issues in Medical Ethics* 2001 April-June; 9(2): 41-43. Subject: 19.1

Nagral, Sanjay. SARS: infectious diseases, public health and medical ethics [editorial]. *Issues in Medical Ethics* 2003 July-September; 11(3): 70-71. Subject: 9.1

Nagral, Sanjay. Sponsored medical education? [editorial]. *Issues in Medical Ethics* 1998 January; 6(1): 3. Subject: 9.3.1

Nagral, Sanjay. Wanted: ethical 'role models'! *Medical Ethics: Journal of Forum for Medical Ethics Society* 1994 November-December; 2(2): 8-9. Subject: 2.1

Nair, K. Rajasekharan. Clinical tales in neurology: a vegetative existence. *Issues in Medical Ethics* 2002 July-September; 10(3): 55-57. Subject: 20.5.1

Nair, V. Mohanan; Martin, Douglas K. Concerns about ethical review of health research in India. *Indian Journal of Medical Ethics* 2004 October-December; 1(4): 119-120. Subject: 18.2

NARAL Pro-Choice America Foundation. Fetal tissue research: moving beyond anti-choice politics. Washington, DC: NARAL Pro-Choice America, 2004 January 1; 14 p. [Online]. Available: http://www.naral.org/facts/loader.cfm?url=commonspot/security/getfile.cfm&PageID=8080 [24 May 2005]. Subject: 18.5.4

Subject = NRCBL Primary Classification Number; See inside front cover

NARAL Pro-Choice America Foundation. Mandatory parental consent and notice laws burden the freedom to choose. Washington, DC: NARAL Pro-Choice America 2003 January 20; 9 p. [Online]. Available: http://www.naral.org/facts/loader.cfm?url=commonspot/ security/getfile.cfm&PageID=2058 [27 May 2005]. Subject: 12.4.2

NARAL Pro-Choice America Foundation. Refusal Clauses: Dangerous for Women's Health. Washington, DC: The Foundation 2005 January 1; 9 p. [Online]. Available: http://www.naral.org/facts/loader.cfm?url=/ commonspot/security/getfile.cfm&PageID=16140 [24 May 2005]. Subject: 12.4.3

NARAL Pro-Choice America Foundation. State Refusal Clauses for Abortion. Washington, DC: The Foundation 2004 January 1; 12 p. [Online]. Available: http://www.naral.org/facts/loader.cfm?url=/commonspot/ security/ge tfile.cfm&PageID=7839 [26 May 2005]. Subject: 12.4.3

Narbekovas, Andrius; Meilius, Kazimieras. Letting die and mercy killing. *Medical Ethics and Bioethics / Medicinska Etika & Bioetika* 2003 Autumn-Winter; 10(3-4): 2-7. Subject: 20.5.1

Narbekovas, Andrius; Meilius, Kazimieras. Why is the ethics of euthanasia wrong? *Medical Ethics and Bioethics / Medicinska Etika & Bioetika* 2004 Autumn-Winter; 11(3-4): 2-6. Subject: 20.5.1

Narins, Craig R.; Dozier, Ann M.; Ling, Frederick S.; Zareba, Wojciech. The influence of public reporting of outcome data on medical decision making by physicians. *Archives of Internal Medicine* 2005 January 10; 165(1): 83-87. Subject: 9.8

Nash, Donald J. Miscegnation and antimiscegnation laws. *In:* Ness, Bryan D., ed. Encyclopedia of Genetics. Revised edition. Volume II. Pasadena, Calif.: Salem Press; 2004: 501-503. Subject: 15.5

Nash, Donald J. Sterilization laws. *In:* Ness, Bryan D., ed. Encyclopedia of Genetics. Revised edition. Volume II. Pasadena, Calif.: Salem Press; 2004: 715-717. Subject: 11.3

Nash, Michael J.; Cohen, Hannah. Management of Jehovah's Witness patients with haematological problems. *Blood Reviews* 2004 September; 18(3): 211-217. Subject: 8.3.4

Nasraway, Stanley A. Unilateral withdrawal of life-sustaining therapy: is it time? Are we ready? *Critical Care Medicine* 2001 January; 29(1): 215-217. Subject: 20.5.1

Nataraj, Shyamala. Ethical considerations in research on preventing mother-to- child HIV transmission. *Monash Bioethics Review* 2005 October; 24(4): 28-39. Subject: 18.5.3

Nathanson, Vivienne. Why we need a new Hippocratic Oath [opinion]. *Medical Education* 2003 December; 37(12): 1123-1124. Subject: 4.1.2

National Aged Care Forum. Code of Conduct and Ethical Practice Working Group; Fleming, John; Leaper, John; Hardy, Ian; Moait, Sandra; Heinrich, June; Rimmer, Sheila; Valadian, Bernie; Lyttle, Mary; Ramadge, Joanne. Code of ethics and guide to ethical conduct for residential aged care. Canberra: Commonwealth Department of Health and Aged Care 2001: i-vi, 1-22 [Online] Available: http://www.seniors.gov.au/ Internet/wcms/Publishing.nsf/Content/ag eing_workforce -codetext.html/$files/code.pdf [5 August 2005]. Subject: 9.5.2

National Health and Medical Research Council [NHMRC] (Australia). Ethical considerations relating to health care resource allocation decisions. Canberra, ACT: The Council 1993; 7 p. [Online]. Available: http://www7.health.gov.au/nhmrc/publications/pdf/ e24.pdf [31 March 2005]. Subject: 9.4

National Health and Medical Research Council [NHMRC] (Australia). NHMRC statement on human experimentation and supplementary notes (No. 5). Canberra, ACT: The Council 1992; 3 p. [Online]. Available: http://www7.health.gov.au/nhmrc/issues/humanexp/ supp5.htm [31 March 2005]. Subject: 18.5.4

National Health and Medical Research Council [NHMRC] (Australia). Policy on the care and use of non-human primates for scientific purposes — to be read in conjunction with The Australian Code of Practice for the Care and Use of Animals for Scientific Purposes. Canberra, ACT: The Council 2003; 22 p. [Online]. Available: http://www7.health.gov.au/nhmrc/research/awc/ nonhum2.pdf [31 March 2005]. Subject: 22.2

National Health and Medical Research Council [NHMRC] (Australia). Recommendations for the donation of cadaveric organs and tissues for transplantation. Canberra, ACT: The Council [NHMRC], 1996; 33 p. Subject: 19.5

National Health and Medical Research Council [NHMRC] (Australia). Report of the 1999 Workshops on the National Statement on Ethical Conduct in Research Involving Humans. Canberra, ACT: The Council 2000; 46 p. [Online]. Available: http://www7.health.gov.au/nhmrc/ publications/pdf/e40.pdf [31 March 2005]. Subject: 18.2

National Health and Medical Research Council [NHMRC] (Australia); Royal Australasian College of Surgeons. NHMRC guidelines on the use of animals for training surgeons and demonstrating new surgical equipment and techniques. Canberra, ACT: The Council 1997 September; 4 p. [Online]. Available: http://www7.health. gov.au/nhmrc/research/awc/surgeon.pdf [31 March 2005]. Subject: 22.2

National Institutes of Health [NIH] (United States). Questions and answers for employees: supplemental standards of ethical conduct and financial disclosure requirements. Bethesda, MD: National Institutes of Health 2005 February 1; 6 p. [Online]. Available: http://www.nih.gov/about/ethics/020105COI_QandA.htm [2 February 2005]. Subject: 1.3.9

National Institutes of Health [NIH] (United States). Summary of NIH-Specific Amendments to Conflict of Interest Ethics Regulations. Bethesda, MD: National Institutes of Health 2005 August 25; 2 p. [Online]. Available: http://www.nih.gov/about/ethics/summary_amendments_08252005.htm [12 September 2005]. Subject: 1.3.9

National Institutes of Health [NIH] (United States). Department of Health and Human Services. Policy on enhancing public access to archived publications resulting from NIH-funded research [policy statement]. *Federal Register* 2005 February 9; 70(26): 6891-6900 [Online]. Available: http://a257.g.akamaitein.net/7/257/2422/01jan20051800/edocket [14 September 2005]. Subject: 5.3

National Institutes of Health [NIH] (United States). Office of Biotechnology Activities. Points to consider in the design and submission of protocols for the transfer of recombinant DNA molecules into one or more human research participants. Appendix M. Bethesda, MD: National Institutes of Health. Office of Biotechnology Activities 2002; 15 p. [Online]. Available: http://www4.od.nih.gov/oba/rac/guidelines_02/Appendix_M.htm#_Appendix_M-I._Requirements [25 July 2005]. Subject: 18.2

National Institutes of Health [NIH] (United States). Recombinant DNA Advisory Committee [RAC]. Informed Consent Working Group. NIH Guidance on informed consent for gene transfer research. Bethesda, MD: National Institutes of Health. Office of Biotechnology Activities 2004 February; 39 p. [Online]. Available: http://www4.od.nih.gov/oba/rac/ic/pdfs/temp_pdf.pdf [25 July 2005]. Subject: 15.4

National Physician Orders for Life-Sustaining Treatment [POLST]. Paradigm Task Force. The National POLST Paradigm Initiative. Portland, Oregon: Center for Ethics in Health Care; 6 p. [Online]. Available: http://www.ohsu.edu/ethics/polst/docs/POLST_nppi.pdf [25 January 2006]. Subject: 20.5.4

Natour, Ahmad; Bakri, Baha'eddin; Rispler-Chaim, Vardit. An Islamic perspective. *In:* Blazer, Shraga; Zimmer, Etan Z., eds. The Embryo: Scientific Discovery and Medical Ethics. New York: Karger; 2005: 53-73. Subject: 4.4

Natowicz, Marvin. Newborn screening — setting evidence-based policy for protection [opinion]. *New England Journal of Medicine* 2005 September 1; 353(9): 867- 870. Subject: 9.1

Navarro-Michel, Monica. Advance directives: the Spanish perspective. *Medical Law Review* 2005 Summer; 13(2): 137-169. Subject: 20.5.4

Neal, Joseph M. Author misconduct — a continuing saga [editorial]. *Regional Anesthesia and Pain Medicine* 2004 March-April; 29(2): 90-91. Subject: 7.4

Nedelcu, R.; Blazer, K.R.; Schwerin, B.U.; Gambol, P.; Mantha, P.; Uman, G.C.; Weitzel, J.N. Genetic discrimination: the clinician perspective. *Clinical Genetics* 2004 October; 66(4): 311-317. Subject: 15.1

Nedelsky, Jennifer. Property in potential life? A relational approach to choosing legal categories. *Canadian Journal of Law and Jurisprudence* 1993; 6(2): 343- 365. Subject: 14.1

Needell, Mervin H.; Kenyon, John S. Ethical evaluation of "retainer fee" medical practice. *Journal of Clinical Ethics* 2005 Spring; 16(1): 72-84. Subject: 9.3.1

Needham, Charles W. Pride, shame, and the oath. *Connecticut Medicine* 2005 February; 69(2): 113-114. Subject: 4.1.2

Negrier, Claude. Gene therapy for hemophilia? Yes [debate]. *Journal of Thrombosis and Haemostasis* 2004 August; 2(8): 1234- 1235. Subject: 15.4

Negus, Jennie; Viney, Kerri; Bothamley, Graham. The ethics of legally detaining a patient who has tuberculosis. *Nursing Times* 2004 September 7-13; 100(36): 52-53, 55. Subject: 9.5.1

Neher, Jon O. A measure of success. *Hastings Center Report* 2005 March-April; 35(2): 9-10. Subject: 20.5.1

Neill, Sarah J. Research with children: a critical review of the guidelines. *Journal of Child Health Care* 2005 March; 9(1): 46-58. Subject: 18.5.2

Neilsen, K.; Glantz, S.A. A tobacco industry study of airline cabin air quality: dropping inconvenient findings. *Tobacco Control* 2004 March; 13(Supplement 1): i20-i29. Subject: 9.5.9

Neitzke, Gerald; Fehr, Folkert. Teachers' responsibility: a Socratic dialogue about teaching medical ethics [opinion]. *Medical Teacher* 2003 January; 25(1): 92-93. Subject: 2.3

Nekhlyudov, Larissa; Li, Rong; Fletcher, Suzanne W. Information and involvement preferences of women in their 40s before their first screening mammogram. *Archives of Internal Medicine* 2005 June 27; 165(12): 1370-1374. Subject: 9.5.5

Nelson, Deborah; Wright, M.; Walsh, I.; Moody, K.; Beveridge, L. The use of consent-to-treatment forms at the state hospital: an audit in 1996 and 2000. *Medicine, Science, and the Law* 2003 April; 43(2): 132-135. Subject: 8.3.1

Subject = NRCBL Primary Classification Number; See inside front cover

Nelson, Erin L. Informed consent in the (mis)information age. *Journal of Obstetrics and Gynaecology Canada* 2004 January; 26(1): 43-48. Subject: 8.3.1

Nelson, James Lindemann. The baroness's committee and the president's council: ambition and alienation in public bioethics. *Kennedy Institute of Ethics Journal* 2005 September; 15(3): 251-267. Subject: 2.4

Nelson, James Lindemann. Families and bioethics: old problems, new themes. *Journal of Clinical Ethics* 2005 Winter; 16(4): 299-302. Subject: 8.1

Nelson, James Lindemann. Trust and transplants. *American Journal of Bioethics* 2005 July-August; 5(4): 26-28. Subject: 19.5

Nelson, Janet R. Bioethics and the marginalization of mental illness. *Journal of the Society of Christian Ethics* 2003 Fall-Winter; 23(2): 179-197. Subject: 17.1

Nelson, John C.; Bloche, M. Gregg; Marks, Jonathan H. When doctors go to war [letter and reply]. *New England Journal of Medicine* 2005 April 7; 352(14): 1497- 1499. Subject: 2.1

Nelson, Laura. Biosafety law brings stem-cell research to Brazil [news]. *Nature* 2005 March 10; 434(7030): 128. Subject: 18.5.4

Nelson, Lawrence J. Is there any indication for ethics evidence? An argument for the admissibility of some expert bioethics testimony. *Journal of Law, Medicine and Ethics* 2005 Summer; 33(2): 248- 263. Subject: 2.1

Nelson, Lawrence J. Persistent indeterminate state: reflections on the Wendland case. *Issues in Ethics* 2003 Winter; 14(1): 14-17. Subject: 20.5.1

Nelson, Lawrence J. The Wendland case: on families and fantasies. *Medical Ethics Newsletter [Lahey Clinic]* 2003 Spring; 10(2): 8, 12. Subject: 20.5.4

Nelson, Lawrence J.; Meyer, Michael J. Confronting deep moral disagreement: the President's Council on Bioethics, moral status, and human embryos. *American Journal of Bioethics* 2005 November-December; 5(6): 33-42. Subject: 4.4

Nelson, Lawrence J.; Meyer, Michael J. Response to commentators on "Confronting deep moral disagreement: the President's Council on Bioethics, moral status, and human embryos". *American Journal of Bioethics [Online]* 2005 November- December; 5(6): W14-W16. Subject: 4.4

Nelson, Leonard J., III. Markets and managed care ethics. *Cumberland Law Review* 1997-1998; 28(2): 325-328. Subject: 9.3.2

Nelson, Robert M. Justice, lead, and environmental research involving children. *In:* Kodish, Eric, ed. Ethics and Research with Children: A Case-Based Approach. New York: Oxford University Press; 2005: 161- 178. Subject: 18.5.2

Nelson, Thomas. Is the human zygote a person? *Linacre Quarterly* 2005 November; 72(4): 281-293. Subject: 4.4

Neresini, Federico. And man descended from the sheep: the public debate on cloning in the Italian press. *Public Understanding of Science* 2000; 9: 359-382. Subject: 14.5

Nerlich, Brigitte; Clarke, David D.; Dingwall, Robert. Fictions, fantasies, and fears: the literary foundations of the cloning debate. *Journal of Literary Semantics* 2001; 30: 37-52. Subject: 14.5

Nerlich, Brigitte; Dingwall, Robert; Clarke, David D. The book of life: how the completion of the Human Genome Project was revealed to the public. *Health: An Interdisciplinary Journal for the Social Study of Health, Illness and Medicine* 2002; 6(4): 445-469. Subject: 15.10

Nespolon, Harry M.; Kuhse, Helga; Clark, Malcolm; Woollard, Keith V. Medical end-of-life decisions and legislation [opinion]. *Medical Journal of Australia* 1997 September 1; 167(5): 282-283. Subject: 20.5.1

Ness, Bryan D. Genetic testing: ethical and economic issues. *In his : Ness, Bryan D., ed. Encyclopedia of Genetics. Revised edition. Volume I. Pasadena, Calif.: Salem Press; 2004: 364-366. Subject: 15.3*

Nessa, John. Autonomy and dialogue: about the patient-doctor relationship. *In:* Thomasma, David C.; Weisstud, David N.; Herve, Christian eds. Personhood and Health Care. Boston: Kluwer Academic Pub.; 2001: 355-362. Subject: 8.1

Neter, Efrat; Wolowelsky, Yael; Borochowitz, Zvi U. Attitudes of Israeli Muslims at risk of genetic disorders towards pregnancy termination. *Community Genetics* 2005 May; 8(2): 88-93. Subject: 15.1

Netherlands. Laws. Review procedures for the termination of life on request and assisted suicide and amendment of the Criminal Code and the Burial and Cremation Act (Termination of Life on Request and Assisted Suicide (Review Procedures) Act). *European Journal of Health Law* 2001 June; 8(2): 183-191. Subject: 20.7

Neufeld, Renata. The realities of implementing health information legislation: the Manitoba experience, 1997-2004. *Health Law Review* 2005; 14(1): 47-50. Subject: 8.4

Neumann, Joyce L. Ethical issues confronting oncology nurses. *Nursing Clinics of North America* 2001 December; 36(4): 827- 841. Subject: 4.1.3

Neumann, Peter J.; Rosen, Allison B.; Weinstein, Milton C. Medicare and cost-effectiveness analysis. *New England Journal of Medicine* 2005 October 3; 353(14): 1516- 1522. Subject: 9.3.1

Nevada. Laws. An act relating to genetic information; providing that it is an unlawful employment practice for an employer, a labor organization or an employment agency to discriminate against a person based on genetic information; and providing other matters properly relating thereto [approved: 9 July 1999]. Nevada. Senate Bill No. 16, 1999 Statutes of Nevada, Chapter 551; 3 p. Subject: 15.3

Nevins, Daniel S. Dead or alive? Halakhah and brain death. *Conservative Judaism* 2005 Winter; 57(2): 3-29. Subject: 20.2.1

New Jersey. Superior Court. Appellate Division. *J.B. v. M.B.* [Date of Decision: 1 June 2000]. *Atlantic Reporter*, 2d Series, 2000; 751: 613-620. Subject: 14.6

New Jersey. Supreme Court. *J.B. v. M.B.* [Date of Decision: 2001 August 14]. *West's Atlantic Reporter*, 2d Series, 2001; 783: 707-720. Subject: 14.6

New York (State). Civil Court. Kings County. *Itskov v. New York Fertility Institute* [Date of Decision: 29 July 2004]. *West's New York Supplement*, 2d Series, 2004; 782: 584-589. Subject: 14.2

New York (State). Senate; Marchi, John. Cloning of a human being. New York: New York SB 2877, 1997 February 26; 4 p. Subject: 14.5

Newdick, Christopher. Accountability for rationing — theory into practice. *Journal of Law, Medicine and Ethics* 2005 Winter; 33(4): 660- 668. Subject: 9.4

Newell, Christopher. In that case. Response [case study]. *Journal of Bioethical Inquiry* 2005; 2(2): 113. Subject: 9.5.7

Newhart, Allison B. The intersection of law and medicine: the case for providing federal funding for embryonic stem cell research. *Villanova Law Review* 2004; 49(2): 329-361. Subject: 18.5.4

Newman, Alison W.; Wright, Seth W.; Wrenn, Keith D.; Bernard, Aline. Should physicians have facial piercings? *JGIM: Journal of General Internal Medicine* 2005 March; 20(3): 213-218. Subject: 7.1

Newman, Maria. Gov. Bush's role is ended in feeding tube dispute. *New York Times* 2005 January 25; p. A21. Subject: 20.5.1

Newman, Robert G. US exceptionalism and research ethics [letter]. *Lancet* 2005 May 7-13; 365(9471): 1617. Subject: 18.2

Newman, Stuart A. The perils of human developmental modification. *In:* Krimsky, Sheldon; Shorett, Peter, eds. Rights and Liberties in the Biotech Age: Why We Need a Genetic Bill of Rights. Lanham: Rowman and Littlefield Publishers; 2005: 203-208. Subject: 15.1

Newnham, Helen. Should nurses act legally or ethically? *Contemporary Nurse* 1998 March; 7(1): 42-47. Subject: 20.5.1

Newson, A.J.; Smajdor, A.C. Artificial gametes: new paths to parenthood? *Journal of Medical Ethics* 2005 March; 31(3): 184-186. Subject: 14.1

Newson, Ainsley J.; Ashcroft, Richard E. Whither authenticity? [comment]. *American Journal of Bioethics* 2005 May-June; 5(3): 53-55. Subject: 2.1

Ng, Mary Ann Chen; Takeda, Chika; Watanabe, Tomoyuki; Macer, Darryl. Attitudes of the public and scientists to biotechnology in Japan at the start of 2000. *Eubios Journal of Asian and International Bioethics* 2000 July; 10(4): 106-113. Subject: 5.3

Ngah, Anisah Che. Organ transplantation in Malaysia: a socio-legal study. *Formosan Journal of Medical Humanities* 2005 September; 6(1-2): 39-48. Subject: 19.1

Ngahooro, Jennifer; Gillett, Grant. Over my dead body: the ethics of organ donation in New Zealand. *New Zealand Medical Journal* 2004 September 10; 117(1201); 6 p. Subject: 19.5

Ngai, Stephanie; Gold, Jennifer L.; Gill, Sudeep S.; Rochon, Paula A. Haunted manuscripts: ghost authorship in the medical literature. *Accountability in Research* 2005 April-June; 12(2): 103-114. Subject: 1.3.7

Nguyen, Tuong-Nam; Silver, David; Arthurs, Bryan. Consent to cataract surgery performed by residents. *Canadian Journal of Ophthalmology* 2005 February; 40(1): 34-37. Subject: 8.3.1

Ngwafor, Ephraim N. Childlessness in Cameroon: artificially assisted fertility or the customary law solution. *Medicine and Law: World Association for Medical Law* 1994; 13(3-4): 297-306. Subject: 14.2

Ngwena, Charles. An appraisal of abortion laws in Southern Africa from a reproductive health rights perspective. *Journal of Law, Medicine and Ethics* 2004 Winter; 32(4): 708- 717. Subject: 12.4.1

Nibert, Ainslie T. Teaching clinical ethics using a case study family presence during cardiopulmonary resuscitation. *Critical Care Nurse* 2005 February; 25(1): 38-44. Subject: 20.5.1

Nichols, Polly S.; Winslow, Gerald. Transparent truthfulness. *General Dentistry* 2005 January-February; 53(1): 15-16. Subject: 8.2

Nicol, Dianne. Balancing innovation and access to healthcare through the patent system — an Australian perspective. *Community Genetics* 2005 October; 8(4): 228-234. Subject: 15.8

Nicol, Dianne. Cross-cultural issues in balancing patent rights and consumer access to biotechnological and pharmaceutical inventions. *In:* Brannigan, Michael C., ed. Cross-Cultural Biotechnology. Lanham: Rowman and Littlefield; 2004: 155-164. Subject: 9.7

Nicolai, Katherine M.; Scott, Norman A. Provision of confidentiality information and its relation to child abuse reporting. *Professional Psychology: Research and Practice* 1994 May; 25(2): 154-160. Subject: 17.1

Nie, Jing-Bao. The West's dismissal of the Khabarovsk Trial as `Communist propaganda': ideology, evidence and international bioethics. *Journal of Bioethical Inquiry* 2004; 1(1): 32-42. Subject: 18.5.8

Subject = NRCBL Primary Classification Number; See inside front cover

Nieburg, Phillip; Bernheim, Ruth Gaare; Bonnie, Richard J. Ethics and the practice of public health. *In:* Goodman, Richard A.; Rothstein, Mark A.; Hoffman, Richard E.; Lopez, Wilfredo; Matthews, Gene W., eds. Law in Public Health Practice. New York: Oxford University Press; 2003: 43-62. Subject: 9.1

Ninth General Assembly of the Pontifical Academy of Life. Concluding communique on the "ethics of biomedical research for a Christian vision" (26 February 2003). *Linacre Quarterly* 2005 February; 72(1): 74-78. Subject: 1.3.9

Nishimura, Takahiro. The present state and problems of "The Code of Medical Ethics" in Japan. *Journal International de Bioethique / International Journal of Bioethics* 2005 March-June; 16(1-2): 41-50, 191. Subject: 6

Nisker, Jeffrey A. Ethical issues of "case" reports: what can we learn from case studies? [editorial]. *Journal of Obstetrics and Gynaecology Canada* 2004 January; 26(1): 7-13. Subject: 8.3.1

Nisker, Jeffrey; White, Angela. The CMA Code of Ethics and the donation of fresh embryos for stem cell research. *CMAJ/JAMC: Canadian Medical Association Journal* 2005 September 13; 173(6): 621-622. Subject: 18.5.4

Niven, Elizabeth. Mortality, morality and the media [editorial]. *Nursing Ethics* 2005 September; 12(5): 429-430. Subject: 20.5.1

Noah, Barbara A. Racial disparities in the delivery of health care. *San Diego Law Review* 1998 Winter; 35(1): 135-178. Subject: 9.5.4

Noah, Lars. The coming pharmacogenomics revolution: tailoring drugs to fit patients' genetic profiles. *Jurimetrics* 2002 Fall; 43(1): 1-28. Subject: 15.1

Noble-Allgire, Alice M. Switched at the fertility clinic: determining maternal rights when a child is born from stolen or misdelivered genetic material. *Missouri Law Review* 1999 Summer; 64(3): 517-594. Subject: 14.4

Nolan, Laurence C. Posthumous conception: a private or public matter? *Brigham Young University Journal of Public Law* 1997; 11(1): 1-32. Subject: 14.6

Nolan, Marie T.; Walton-Moss, Benita; Taylor, Laura; Dane, Kathryn. Living kidney donor decision making: state of the science and directions for future research. *Progress in Transplantation* 2004 September; 14(3): 201-209. Subject: 19.3

Nomura, Hideki; Nakayama, Takeo. The Japanese healthcare system [editorial]. *BMJ: British Medical Journal* 2005 September 24; 331(7518): 648-649. Subject: 9.3.1

Norcross, William A.; Ganiats, Theodore G. Illness and secrecy on the Supreme Court [letter]. *New England Journal of Medicine* 2005 March 31; 352(13): 1388. Subject: 7.4

Nord, Erik. The use of cost-value analysis to judge patients' right to treatment. *Medicine and Law: World Association for Medical Law* 1995; 14(7-8): 553-558. Subject: 9.2

Nord, Erik. Values for health states in QALYs and DALYs: desirability versus well-being and worth. *In:* Wasserman, David; Bickenbach, Jerome; Wachbroit, Robert, eds. Quality of Life and Human Difference: Genetic Testing, Health Care, and Disability. New York: Cambridge University Press; 2005: 125-141. Subject: 4.4

Norheim, Ole Frithjof. Rights to specialized health care in Norway: a normative perspective. *Journal of Law, Medicine and Ethics* 2005 Winter; 33(4): 641-649. Subject: 9.2

Norko, Michael A. Comment: compassion at the core of forensic ethics. *Journal of the American Academy of Psychiatry and the Law* 2005; 33(3): 386-389. Subject: 7.1

Norman, Douglas J. Allocation of livers for liver transplantation: ethics and politics. *Clinics in Liver Disease* 1997 August; 1(2): 281-286, viii. Subject: 19.6

Normile, Dennis. Tokyo professor asked to redo experiments [news]. *Science* 2005 September 23; 309(5743): 1973. Subject: 1.3.9

Normile, Dennis; Vogel, Gretchen. Korean university will investigate cloning paper [news]. *Science* 2005 December 16; 310(5755): 1748-1749. Subject: 1.3.9

Normile, Dennis; Vogel, Gretchen; Holden, Constance. Cloning researcher says work is flawed but claims results stand [news]. *Science* 2005 December 23; 310(5756): 1886-1887. Subject: 14.5

Noroian, Paul. Ethical issues in surreptitious prescribing [letter]. *Psychiatric Services* 2005 August; 56(8): 1023. Subject: 17.4

Norris, Pauline. In that case. Response. *Journal of Bioethical Inquiry* 2005; 2(3): 179-180. Subject: 9.5.1

Norris, Wendi M.; Nielsen, Elizabeth L.; Engelberg, Ruth A.; Curtis, J. Randall. Treatment preferences for resuscitation and critical care among homeless persons. *Chest* 2005 June; 127(6): 2180-2187. Subject: 20.5.1

Norsigian, Judy. Egg donation dangers: additional demand for eggs leads to additional risks. *GeneWatch* 2005 September-October; 18(5): 6-8, 16. Subject: 14.4

North Carolina Medical Society. Ethical and Judicial Affairs Committee. Guiding the decisions of physicians and families in end-of-life care: the case of long-term feeding tube placement. *North Carolina Medical Journal* 2004 July-August; 65(4): 242-245. Subject: 20.5.1

Northup, Patrick Grant; Berg, Carl Lansing. Living donor liver transplantation: the historical and cultural basis of policy decisions and ongoing ethical questions. *Health Policy* 2005 May; 72(2): 175-185. Subject: 19.5

Nortvedt, Per. Needs, closeness and responsibilities. An inquiry into some rival moral considerations in nursing care. *Nursing Philosophy* 2001 July; 2(2): 112-121. Subject: 8.1

Nortvedt, Per; Kvarstein, Gunnvald; Jønland, Ingvild. Sedation of patients in intensive care medicine and nursing: ethical issues. *Nursing Ethics* 2005 September; 12(5): 522-536. Subject: 9.7

Nosé, Yukihiko. Institutional review board approval for clinical application of new medical devices rather than government agency [editorial]. *Artificial Organs* 2004 December; 28(12): 1057-1058. Subject: 18.2

Notzer, Netta; Abramovitch, Henry; Dado-Harari, Roni; Abramovitz, Ruth; Rudnick, Abraham. Medical students' ethical, legal and cross-cultural experiences during their clinical studies. *Israel Medical Association Journal* 2005 January; 7(1): 58-61. Subject: 7.2

Novak, Kris. New Stanford institute sparks cloning quarrel [news]. *Nature Medicine* 2003 February; 9(2): 156-157. Subject: 14.5

Novak, Kris. US scientific panels Bush-whacked [news]. *Nature Medicine* 2003 February; 9(2): 153. Subject: 5.3

Nowell, David; Spruill, Jean. If it's not absolutely confidential, will information be disclosed? *Professional Psychology: Research and Practice* 1993 August; 24(3): 367-369. Subject: 8.4

Noys, Benjamin. Bioethics and death. *In his:* The Culture of Death. New York: Berg; 2005: 77-99. Subject: 2.1

Nuffield Council on Bioethics. The Ethics of Prolonging Life in Fetuses and the Newborn: Consultation Paper. London: Nuffield Council on Bioethics 2005; 40 p. [Online]. Available: http://www.nuffieldbioethics.org/fileLibrary/ pdf/NCOB_prolong_lif e-consult_paper.pdf [25 May 2005]. Subject: 20.5.2

Nuffield Council on Bioethics. Experts give go-ahead for human stem cell research but safeguards are needed. *Human Reproduction and Genetic Ethics: An International Journal* 2001; 7(1): 1. Subject: 18.5.4

Nundy, Samiran; Gulhati, Chandra M. A new colonialism? — conducting clinical trials in India [opinion]. *New England Journal of Medicine* 2005 April 21; 352(16): 1633- 1636. Subject: 18.5.9

Nunn, Amy; Miller, Kate; Alpert, Hilary; Ellertson, Charlotte. Contraceptive emergency: Catholic hospitals overwhelmingly refuse to provide EC. *Conscience* 2003 Summer; 24(2): 38-41. Subject: 11.1

Nunnally, Allen C.; Webster, Christopher J.; Brown, Scott A.; Cohen, Gary A. Genetic patent protection in the pharmaceutical and biotechnology industries. *Community Genetics* 2005 October; 8(4): 209-216. Subject: 15.8

Nurmi, Suvielise. Discussion concerning cloning in *Die Zeit*: an introduction. *In:* Ostnor, Lars, ed. Bioethics and Cloning: Report from a Workshop Arranged by the Nordic Theological Network for Bioethics in Arhus, September

25-27, 1998. Oslo: Nordic Theological Network for Bioethics; 1998: 56-64. Subject: 14.5

Nurock, Shirley. Commentary: patients may be less risk averse than committees. *BMJ: British Medical Journal* 2005 February 26; 330(7489): 471- 472. Subject: 9.6

Nyapadi, T.J. What are ethics (more particularly medical ethics)? *Central African Journal of Medicine* 2000 March; 46(3): 76-79. Subject: 2.1

Nyman, D.J.; Sprung, C.L. End-of-life decision making in the intensive care unit. *Intensive Care Medicine* 2000 October; 26(10): 1414-1420. Subject: 20.5.1

Nys, Herman. Emerging legislation in Europe on the legal status of advance directives and medical decision-making with respect to an incompetent patient ('living wills'). *European Journal of Health Law* 1997; (4): 61-70. Subject: 20.5.4

Nys, Herman. Physician assisted suicide in Belgian law. *European Journal of Health Law* 2005 March; 12(1): 39-41. Subject: 20.7

O

O'Boyle, Donna. Informed consent: danger is ahead when staff don't know what they don't know [letter]. *BMJ: British Medical Journal* 2005 November 5; 331(7524): 1082. Subject: 8.3.1

O'Brien, Dan. Borderline viability resuscitation cases. *Medical Ethics and Bioethics / Medicinska Etika & Bioetika* 2002 Autumn-Winter; 9(3-4): 6-10. Subject: 20.5.2

O'Brien, Dennis. No to abortion: posture, not policy. *America* 2005 May 30; 192(19): 7-9. Subject: 12.3

O'Brien, Eoin. Human rights and the making of a good doctor. *In:* Cahill, Kevin M., ed. Traditions, Values, and Humanitarian Action. New York: Fordham University Press and The Center for International Health and Cooperation; 2003: 136-152. Subject: 7.2

O'Brien, Kylie. Commentary on C Zaslawski and S Davis, 'The ethics of complementary and alternative medicine research'. *Monash Bioethics Review* 2005 July; 24(3): 62-66. Subject: 18.2

O'Brien, Tony. What is palliative care? *In:* Council of Europe Publishing, ed. Euthanasia. Volume I. Ethical and Human Aspects. Strasbourg: Council of Europe; Croton-on-Hudson, NY: Manhattan Publishing Co.; 2003: 73-82. Subject: 20.4.1

O'Connell, James J. Raging against the night: dying homeless and alone. *Journal of Clinical Ethics* 2005 Fall; 16(3): 262-266. Subject: 9.5.10

O'Connell, Karen. The devouring: genetics, abjection, and the limits of law. *In:* Shildrick, Margrit; Mykitiuk, Roxanne, eds. Ethics of the Body: Postconventional Challenges. Cambridge, MA: MIT Press; 2005: 217- 234. Subject: 15.1

O'Connell, Maria J.; Stein, Catherine H. Psychiatric advance directives: perspectives of community stakeholders. *Administration and Policy in Mental Health* 2005 January; 32(3): 241-265. Subject: 20.5.4

O'Connor, Michael J. Bearing true faith and allegiance? Allowing recovery for soldiers under fire in military experiments that violate the Nuremberg Code. *Suffolk Transnational Law Review* 2002 Summer; 25(3): 649-686. Subject: 18.5.8

O'Connor, Nancy K. Physician-assisted suicide and 'moral neutrality' [letter]. *American Family Physician* 1998 February 1; 57(3): 427-429, 433. Subject: 20.7

O'Connor, Tom; Kelly, Billy. Bridging the gap: a study of general nurses' perceptions of patient advocacy in Ireland. *Nursing Ethics* 2005 September; 12(5): 453-467. Subject: 8.1

O'Donnell, Máire; Entwistle, Vikki. Consumer involvement in decisions about what health-related research is funded. *Health Policy* 2004 December; 70(3): 281-290. Subject: 1.3.9

O'Dowd, Adrian. Joffe will amend role for doctors in new bill on assisted dying [news]. *BMJ: British Medical Journal* 2005 October 15; 331(7521): 863. Subject: 20.7

O'Flynn, Norma; Britten, Nicky. Use of chaperones in general practice: GPs try to balance doctors' and patients' needs [letter]. *BMJ: British Medical Journal* 2005 April 9; 330(7495): 846. Subject: 8.1

O'Flynn, Norma; Rymer, Janice. Consent for teaching: the experience of women attending a gynaecology clinic. *Medical Education* 2003 December; 37(12): 1109-1114. Subject: 7.2

O'Keefe, Mary E.; Crawford, Kate. End-of-life care: legal and ethical considerations. *Seminars in Oncology Nursing* 2002 May; 18(2): 143-148. Subject: 20.5.1

O'Leary, Ian P. AIDS: the attitudes and experience of final year European dental students. *Journal of the Irish Dental Association* 2005 Spring; 51(1): 19-22. Subject: 9.5.6

O'Lonergan, Theresa. Creative solutions: research subject advocates: increase in reports of human subject protection deficiencies brings scrutiny as well as more efforts at education and support. *Protecting Human Subjects* 2003 Spring; (8): 10-11. Subject: 18.2

O'Neill, Onora. Informed consent and public health. *Philosophical Transactions of the Royal Society of London. Series B, Biological Sciences* 2004 July 29; 359(1447): 1133-1136. Subject: 8.3.1

O'Rourke, Kevin D. The Catholic tradition on forgoing life support. *National Catholic Bioethics Quarterly* 2005 Autumn; 5(3): 537-553. Subject: 20.5.1

Oakley, Godfrey P., Jr.; Verhagen, Eduard; Sauer, Pieter J.J. Euthanasia in severely ill newborns [letter and reply]. *New England Journal of Medicine* 2005 June 2; 352(22): 2354-2355. Subject: 20.5.2

Oakley, Justin; Cocking, Dean. Consequentialism, complacency, and slippery slope arguments. *Theoretical Medicine and Bioethics* 2005; 26(3): 227-239. Subject: 2.1

Obasi, Annissa R. Protecting our vital organs: the case for fetal homicide laws in Texas. *Texas Wesleyan Law Review* 1998 Spring; 4(2): 207-230. Subject: 4.4

Obinata, Naomi. Genetic screening and insurance: too valuable an underwriting tool to be banned from the system. *Santa Clara Computer and High Technology Law Journal* 1992; 8(1): 145-167. Subject: 15.3

Obyerodhyambo, Oby. Keeping medical research ethical [letter]. *Science* 2005 July 8; 309(5732): 246. Subject: 18.5.9

Oderberg, David S. Abortion. *In his:* Applied Ethics: A Non-Consequentialist Approach. Malden, MA: Blackwell Publishers; 2000: 1-47. Subject: 12.3

Oderberg, David S. Euthanasia. *In his:* Applied Ethics: A Non-Consequentialist Approach. Malden, MA: Blackwell Publishers; 2000: 48-96. Subject: 20.5.1

Oderberg, David S. Human embryonic stem cell research: what's wrong with it? *Human Life Review* 2005 Fall; 31(4): 21-33. Subject: 18.5.4

Oetjen, Dawn; Rotarius, Timothy. Incorporating ethics into your comprehensive organizational plan. *Health Care Manager* 2005 January-March; 24(1): 61-67. Subject: 9.1

Ofri, Danielle. They sent me here [opinion]. *New England Journal of Medicine* 2005 April 28; 352(17): 1746-1748. Subject: 8.2

Ogundiran, Temidayo O. Enhancing the African bioethics initiative. *BMC Medical Education [electronic]* 2004 October 15; 4(1); 6 p. [Online]. Available: http://www.biomedcentral.com/1472-6920/4/21 [14 July 2005]. Subject: 2.1

Oguz, N.Y.; Miles, S.H. The physician and prison hunger strikes: reflecting on the experience in Turkey. *Journal of Medical Ethics* 2005 March; 31(3): 169-172. Subject: 21.5

Øhrstrom, Peter; Albretsen, Jørgen; Holm, Søren. The use of computer simulation and artificial intelligence in the study of ethical components of medical decision-making. *In:* Holm, Søren; Jonas, Monique F., eds. Engaging the World: The Use of Empirical Research in Bioethics and the Regulation of Biotechnology. Washington, DC: IOS Press; 2004: 119-128. Subject: 9.4

Ojha, Rohit P.; Thertulien, Raymond. Health care policy issues as a result of the genetic revolution: implications for public health. *American Journal of Public Health* 2005 March; 95(3): 385-388. Subject: 15.3

Ojikutu, Bisola O.; Stone, Valerie E. Women, inequality, and the burden of HIV [opinion]. *New England Journal of Medicine* 2005 February 17; 352(7): 649-652. Subject: 9.5.6

Okasha, Ahmed. Comments: a crisis in the ethical and moral behavior of psychiatrists [forum]. *Current Opinion in Psychiatry* 1998 January; 11(1); 2 p. [Online]. Available: http://gateway.ut.ovid.com/gw1/ovidweb.cgi [24 May 2005]. Subject: 20.6

Okie, Susan. Glimpses of Guantanamo — medical ethics and the war on terror [opinion]. *New England Journal of Medicine* 2005 December 15; 353(24): 2529-2534. Subject: 9.5.1

Okie, Susan. Medical marijuana and the Supreme Court [opinion]. *New England Journal of Medicine* 2005 August 18; 353(7): 648- 651. Subject: 9.5.9

Okie, Susan. An offshore haven for human embryonic stem-cell research? [opinion]. *New England Journal of Medicine* 2005 October 20; 353(16): 1645-1649. Subject: 18.5.4

Okie, Susan. Physician-assisted suicide — Oregon and beyond [opinion]. *New England Journal of Medicine* 2005 April 21; 352(16): 1627- 1630. Subject: 20.7

Okie, Susan. Stem-cell research — signposts and road-blocks [opinion]. *New England Journal of Medicine* 2005 July 7; 353(1): 1-5. Subject: 18.5.4

Okifuji, Akiko. Opinion #1. Confidentiality: a delicate balance [case study]. *Pain Medicine* 2002 June; 3(2): 169. Subject: 8.4

Okonofua, Friday E.; Shittu, S.O.; Oronsaye, F.; Ogunsakin, D.; Ogbomwan, S.; Zayyan, M. Attitudes and practices of private medical providers towards family planning and abortion services in Nigeria. *Acta Obstetricia Gynecologica Scandinavica* 2005 March; 84(3): 270-280. Subject: 12.5.2

Oldani, Michael J. Pharma PR or medical education? [letter]. *Hastings Center Report* 2005 March-April; 35(2): 5-7. Subject: 9.7

Olde Rikkert, Marcel G.M.; Lauque, S.; Frölich, L.; Vellas, B.; Dekkers, W. The practice of obtaining approval from medical research ethics committees: a comparison within 12 European countries for a descriptive study on acetylcholinesterase inhibitors in Alzheimer's dementia. *European Journal of Neurology* 2005 March; 12(3): 212-217. Subject: 18.2

Olds, R. Scott. Informed-consent issues with adolescent health behavior research. *American Journal of Health Behavior* 2003 November-December; 27(Supplement 3): S248-S263. Subject: 18.5.2

Oleson, Kimberly A. Role of the industry sponsor: protection of human subjects in early device-application studies. *Journal of Laboratory and Clinical Medicine* 2005 January; 145(1): 17-20. Subject: 18.2

Olick, Robert S. Carcinogenic plumes and aerophobia: ethical tensions in the public smoking debate. *Journal of Public Health Management and Practice* 2004 November-December; 10(6): 569-570. Subject: 9.5.9

Olive, Kenneth E. Physician religious beliefs and the physician-patient relationship: a study of devout physicians. *Southern Medical Journal* 1995 December; 88(12): 1249-1255. Subject: 8.1

Oliver, A.; Evans, J.G. The paradox of promoting choice in a collectivist system [editorial]. *Journal of Medical Ethics* 2005 April; 31(4): 187. Subject: 9.1

Oliver, J. Eric; Lee, Taeku. Public opinion and the politics of obesity in America. *Journal of Health Politics, Policy and Law* 2005 October; 30(5): 923-954. Subject: 9.1

Oliver, Leah. Abortion laws in the states. *NCSL Legisbrief* 2004 October; 12(38): 1-2. Subject: 12.4.1

Oliver, S.; Dezateux, C.; Kavanagh, J.; Lempert, T.; Stewart, R. Disclosing to parents newborn carrier status identified by routine blood spot screening. *Cochrane Library* 2004; (4): 14 p. [Online]. Available: http://www.mrw.interscience.wiley.com/cochrane/clsysrev/articles/CD003859/frame.html [19 July 2005]. Subject: 15.3

Oliver, Samuel L.; Baumrucker, Steven J.; Rousseau, Paul; Stolick, Matt; Morris, Gerald M.; Ufema, Joy. Case study: death or damnation — refusing life-prolonging therapy on religious grounds. *American Journal of Hospice and Palliative Medicine* 2004 November-December; 21(6): 469-473. Subject: 8.3.4

Olivier, S. Informed consent and transcultural research [editorial]. *South African Medical Journal* 1995 October; 85(10): 984-985. Subject: 8.3.1

Olsen, Jørn; Mulvad, Gert; Pedersen, Mille Søvndah; Christiansen, Thue; Sørensen, Paul Henrik. An ethics committee for medical research in Greenland: history and challenges. *International Journal of Circumpolar Health* 2004; 63(Supplement 2): 144-146. Subject: 18.2

Olson, Steve. Brain scans raise privacy concerns. *Science* 2005 March 11; 307(5715): 1548-1550. Subject: 17.1

Olthuis, Gert; Dekkers, Wim. Quality of life considered as well-being: views from philosophy and palliative care practice. *Theoretical Medicine and Bioethics* 2005; 26(4): 307-337. Subject: 4.4

Olusanya, B.O.; Luxon, L.M.; Wirz, S.L. Infant hearing screening: route to informed choice. *Archives of Disease in Childhood* 2004 November; 89(11): 1039-1040. Subject: 8.3.2

Omer, Adzivic. Serbia and Montenegro. *Medical Ethics and Bioethics / Medicinska Etika & Bioetika* 2005; 11(Supplement): 19. Subject: 9.6

Onder, Robert F., Jr. Practical and moral caveats on heterologous embryo transfer. *National Catholic Bioethics Quarterly* 2005 Spring; 5(1): 75-94. Subject: 14.4

Ong, Burton T. Patenting the biological bounty: re-examining the status of organic inventions as patentable subject matter. *Marquette Intellectual Property Law Review* 2004 Winter; 8(1): 1-62. Subject: 15.8

Onotai, L.O.; Nwaorgu, O.G.B.; Okoye, B.C.C. Ethical issues in HIV/AIDS infections. *Nigerian Journal of Medicine* 2004 July-September; 13(3): 282-285. Subject: 9.5.6

Onwuteaka-Philipsen, Bregje D.; van der Heide, Agnes; Muller, Martien T.; Rurup, Mette; Rietjens, Judith A.C.; Georges, Jean- Jacques; Vrakking, Astrid M.; Cuperus-Bosma, Jacqueline M.; van der Wal, Gerrit; van der Maas, Paul J. Dutch experience of monitoring euthanasia. *BMJ: British Medical Journal* 2005 September 24; 331(7518): 691-693. Subject: 20.5.1

Opacich, Karin J. Moral tensions and obligations of occupational therapy practitioners providing home care. *American Journal of Occupational Therapy* 1997 June; 51(6): 430-435. Subject: 4.1.1

Oppenheim, Arieh; Sprung, Charles L. Cross-cultural ethical decision-making in critical care. *Critical Care Medicine* 1998 March; 26(3): 423-424. Subject: 9.5.1

Oppenheim, Daniel; Brugières, Laurence; Corradini, Nadège; Vivant, Florence; Hartmann, Olivier. An ethics dilemma: when parents and doctors disagree on the best treatment for the child. *Bulletin du Cancer* 2004 September; 91(9): 735-738. Subject: 9.5.7

Oregon Department of Human Services. Office of Disease Prevention and Epidemiology. Fifth Annual Report on Oregon's Death with Dignity Act. Portland, Oregon: Oregon Department of Human Services 2003 March 6; 21 p. [Online]. Available: http://www.oregon.gov/DHS/ph/pas/docs/year5.pdf [5 October 2005]. Subject: 20.7

Oregon Department of Human Services. Office of Disease Prevention and Epidemiology. Seventh Annual Report on Oregon's Death with Dignity Act. Portland, Oregon: Oregon Department of Human Services, 2005 March 10; 25 p. [Online]. Available: http://www.oregon.gov/DHS/ph/pas/docs/year7.pdf [2005 October 5]. Subject: 20.7

Orellana, Claudia. Mexico reverses ban on stem cell research [news]. *Nature Medicine* 2004 July; 10(7): 656. Subject: 18.5.4

Orentlicher, David. Making research a requirement of treatment: why we should sometimes let doctors pressure patients to participate in research. *Hastings Center Report* 2005 September-October; 35(5): 20-28. Subject: 18.3

Orentlicher, David; Callahan, Christoper M. Feeding tubes, slippery slopes, and physician-assisted suicide. *Journal of Legal Medicine* 2004 December; 25(4): 389-409. Subject: 20.7

Oreopoulos, D.G. Should we let them die? *In:* Parsons, Frank M.; Ogg, Chisholm S., eds. Renal Failure — Who Cares? Boston: MTP Press; 1983: 65-73. Subject: 19.3

Orfali, Kristina; Anderson-Shaw, Lisa. When medical cure is not an unmitigated good. *Perspectives in Biology and Medicine* 2005 Spring; 48(2): 282-292. Subject: 19.1

Orlans, F. Barbara. Case studies of ethical dilemmas. *Laboratory Animal Science* 1987 January; 37: 59-64. Subject: 22.2

Orlans, F. Barbara. Scientists' attitudes toward animal care and use committees. *Laboratory Animal Science* 1987 January; 37: 162-166. Subject: 22.2

Orme, Daniel R.; Doerman, Alan L. Ethical dilemmas and U.S. Air Force clinical psychologists: a survey. *Professional Psychology: Research and Practice* 2001 June; 32(3): 305-311. Subject: 17.1

Ornish, Steven A. Psychiatry and police interrogations [letter]. *AAPL (American Academy of Psychiatry and the Law) Newsletter* 2005 September; 30(3): 26. Subject: 1.3.1

Orr, Robert D. Clinical ethics consultation. *Update [Loma Linda University Center for Christian Bioethics]* 1999 December; 15(4); 4 p. Subject: 20.5.4

Orr, Robert D. The Hippocratic Oath: is it still relevant? *Update [Loma Linda University Center for Christian Bioethics]* 1998 March; 14(1); 5 p. Subject: 6

Orr, Robert D. Just put me to sleep . . . please! Ethical issues in palliative and "terminal" sedation. *Update [Loma Linda University Center for Christian Bioethics]* 2002 September; 18(2): 1-4, 8. Subject: 20.4.1

Orr, Robert D. When it's hard to please everybody: etiquette serving ethics when you disagree with a colleague. Opinion #3: professional autonomy. *Pain Medicine* 2001 March; 2(1): 83, 85-86. Subject: 7.3

Orr, Robert D. Who does the ethics consultation serve? *Medical Ethics Newsletter [Lahey Clinic]* 2004 Winter; 11(1): 10-11. Subject: 9.6

Orr, Robert D.; Cranston, Robert; Beals, Daniel. Ethics and medicine: clinical ethics dilemmas [case study and commentary]. *Ethics and Medicine* 2005 Summer; 21(2): 89-93. Subject: 8.3.4

Orr, Wendy. Abortion reform — imperative or outrageous? [editorial]. *South African Medical Journal* 1995 March; 85(3): 139-140. Subject: 12.1

Osime, O.C.; Okojie, O.; Osadolor, F.; Mohammed, S. Current practices and medico-legal aspects of pre-operative consent. *East African Medical Journal* 2004 July; 81(7): 331-335. Subject: 8.3.1

Ossa, Diego F.; Towse, Adrian. Genetic screening, health care and the insurance industry. Should genetic information be made available to insurers? *European Journal of Health Economics* 2004 June; 5(2): 116-121. Subject: 15.3

Otlowski, Margaret. Exploring the concept of genetic discrimination. *Journal of Bioethical Inquiry* 2005; 2(3): 165-176. Subject: 15.1

Otsubo, Sumiko. Between two worlds: Yamanouchi Shigeo and eugenics in early twentieth-century Japan. *Annals of Science* 2005 April; 62(2): 205-231. Subject: 15.5

Otte, Jean-Bernard; Janssen, Magda; Rosati, Maria-Rita; Gonze, Dominique. Parental experience with living-related donor liver transplantation [editorial]. *Pediatric Transplantation* 2004 August; 8(4): 317-321. Subject: 19.5

Otto, Mary. Drugs tested on HIV-positive foster children; Hill investigates ethical questions raised by 1990s trials in Maryland, elsewhere. *Washington Post* 2005 May 19; p. B1, B4. Subject: 18.5.2

Ouellette, Alicia R. When vitalism is dead wrong: the discrimination against and torture of incompetent patients by compulsory life-sustaining treatment. *Indiana Law Journal* 2004 Winter; 79(1): 1-55. Subject: 20.5.1

Ouellette, Alicia; Caplan, Arthur; Carroll, Kelly; Fossett, James W.; Bjarnadottir, Dyrleif; Shickle, Darren; McGee, Glenn. Lessons across the pond: assisted reproductive technology in the United Kingdom and the United States. *American Journal of Law and Medicine* 2005; 31(4): 419-446. Subject: 14.4

Ouimet, Marie-Andrée; Dendukuri, Nandini; Dion, Dominique; Belzile, Eric; Élie, Michel. Disclosure of Alzheimer's disease: senior citizens' opinions. *Canadian Family Physician* 2004 December; 50: 1671-1677. Subject: 8.2

Overall, Christine. Longevity, identity, and moral character: a feminist approach. *In:* Post, Stephen G.; Binstock, Robert H., eds. The Fountain of Youth: Cultural, Scientific, and Ethical Perspectives on a Biomedical Goal. New York: Oxford University Press; 2004: 286-303. Subject: 9.5.2

Overby, Philip. The moral education of doctors. *New Atlantis* 2005 Fall; 10: 17-26. Subject: 7.2

Owens, Glynn. Radical behaviourism and the ethics of clinical psychology. *In:* Fairbairn, Susan; Fairbairn, Gavin, eds. Psychology, Ethics and Change. New York: Routledge & Kegan Paul; 1987: 91- 114. Subject: 17.3

Owens, Nancy G. Human subjects — are they protected? *Plastic Surgical Nursing* 1999 Winter; 19(4): 212-217. Subject: 18.2

Ozdag, Nurten. Public awareness and acceptance of tissue and organ donation. *EDTNA/ERCA Journal* 2004 October-December; 30(4): 188-195. Subject: 19.5

P

Paalman, Mark H. Stem cells and cloning: the fuss, revisited [editorial]. *Anatomical Record* 2001 June 15; 265(3): 121-122. Subject: 18.5.1

Paasche-Orlow, Michael K.; Brancati, Frederick L. Assessment of medical school institutional review board policies regarding compensation of subjects for research-related injury. *American Journal of Medicine* 2005 February; 118(2): 175-180. Subject: 18.2

Paasche-Orlow, Michael K.; Jacob, Dan M.; Powell, Joshua N. Notices of privacy practices: a survey of the Health Insurance Portability and Accountability Act of 1996 documents presented to patients at US hospitals. *Medical Care* 2005 June; 43(6): 558-564. Subject: 8.4

Paaso, Ilpo. Current challenges to the principles of medical law and their new interpretation. *Medicine and Law: World Association for Medical Law* 1995; 14(7-8): 611-621. Subject: 2.1

Pace, Christine A.; Emanuel, Ezekiel J. The ethics of research in developing countries: assessing voluntariness [opinion]. *Lancet* 2005 January 1-7; 365(9453): 11-12. Subject: 18.5.9

Pace, Christine; Emanuel, Ezekiel J.; Chuenyam, Theshinee; Duncombe, Chris; Bebchuk, Judith D.; Wendler, David; Tavel, Jorge A.; McNay, Laura A.; Phanuphak, Praphan; Forster, Heidi P.; Grady, Christine. The quality of informed consent in a clinical research study in Thailand. *IRB: Ethics and Human Research* 2005 January-February; 27(1): 9-17. Subject: 18.3

Pace, Christine; Talisuna, Ambrose; Wendler, David; Maiso, Faustin; Wabwire-Mangen, Fred; Bakyaita, Nathan; Okiria, Edith; Garrett-Mayer, Elizabeth S.; Emanuel, Ezekiel; Grady, Christine. Quality of parental consent in Ugandan malaria study. *American Journal of Public Health* 2005 July; 95(7): 1184-1189. Subject: 8.3.2

Pachman, Tracey S. Disputes over frozen preembryos and the "right not to be a parent". *Columbia Journal of Gender and Law* 2003; 12(1): 128-153. Subject: 14.6

Pacholczyk, Tadeusz. Ethical considerations in oocyte assisted reprogramming. *National Catholic Bioethics Quarterly* 2005 Autumn; 5(3): 446- 447. Subject: 15.1

Pacholczyk, Tadeusz; Hurlbut, William B. The substantive issues raised by altered nuclear transfer [letter and reply]. *National Catholic Bioethics Quarterly* 2005 Spring; 5(1): 17- 19, 19-22. Subject: 18.5.4

Page, Alice K. Ethical issues in international biomedical research: an overview. *Journal of Health Law* 2004 Fall; 37(4): 629-665. Subject: 18.5.9

Page-Shafer, Kimberly; Saphonn, Vonthanak; Sun, Ly Penh; Vun, Mean Chhi; Cooper, David A.; Kaldor, John M. HIV prevention research in a resource-limited setting: the experience of planning a trial in Cambodia [opinion]. *Lancet* 2005 October 22-28; 366(9495): 1499-1503. Subject: 18.2

Pai, Sanjay A. The medical profession and human rights [editorial]. *Issues in Medical Ethics* 1998 October-December; 6(4): 107. Subject: 21.1

Pai, Sanjay A. Publication ethics policies for medical journals. *Indian Journal of Medical Ethics* 2004 July-September; 1(3): 93. Subject: 1.3.7

Subject = NRCBL Primary Classification Number; See inside front cover

Paine, Shirley J.; Moore, Patrick K.; Hill, David L. Ethical dilemmas in reproductive medicine. *Whittier Law Review* 1996 Fall; 18(1): 51-66. Subject: 14.4

Palermo, George B. Forensic mental health experts in the court — an ethical dilemma [editorial]. *International Journal of Offender Therapy and Comparative Criminology* 2003 April; 47(2): 122-125. Subject: 7.3

Paley, John. Virtues of autonomy: the Kantian ethics of care. *Nursing Philosophy* 2002 July; 3(2): 133-143. Subject: 4.1.1

Palmer, Kim. Doing the right thing: hospital ethics committees help clinicians, families, and facilities wrestle with tough questions. *Minnesota Medicine* 2004 June; 87(6): 26-29. Subject: 9.6

Palmer, Larry I. Should liability play a role in social control of biobanks? *Journal of Law, Medicine and Ethics* 2005 Spring; 33(1): 70-78. Subject: 15.1

Palmer, Nigel; Rogers, Wendy A. Whistle-blowing in the medical curriculum: a response to Faunce. *Monash Bioethics Review* 2005 January; 24(1): 50-58. Subject: 7.3

Palmour, Nicole. A survey of the variability of DNA banks worldwide. *In:* Knoppers, Bartha Maria, ed. Populations and Genetics: Legal and Socio-Ethical Perspectives. Boston: Martinus Nijhoff; 2003: 123-140. Subject: 15.1

Pampilly, Varghese Sebastian. Cadavers for anatomical dissection. *Indian Journal of Medical Ethics* 2005 January-March; 2(1): 16- 17. Subject: 19.5

Pan, Philip P. China terse about action on abuses of one-child policy. *Washington Post* 2005 September 20; p. A17. Subject: 13.3

Pancevski, Bojan. Swiss hospital investigates heart transplant "experiment". *Lancet* 2005 August 20-26; 366(9486): 624. Subject: 19.2

Pandya, S.K. Ethical aspects of clinical trials in gene therapy. *Issues in Medical Ethics* 2000 October-December; 8(4): 122-124. Subject: 15.4

Pandya, Sunil. Dying with dignity: a round-table discussion. *Issues in Medical Ethics* 1999 July-September; 7(3): 99. Subject: 20.5.1

Pandya, Sunil K. Advertising remains unethical even in the digital age [debate]. *Issues in Medical Ethics* 2001 January-March; 9(1): 15. Subject: 8.1

Pandya, Sunil K. Bioethics in Asia. *Issues in Medical Ethics* 1999 January-March; 7(1): 27-28. Subject: 2.1

Pandya, Sunil K. Brain death and our transplant law. *Issues in Medical Ethics* 2001 April-June; 9(2): 51-52. Subject: 20.2.1

Pandya, Sunil K. Doctor-patient relationship. *Medical Ethics: Journal of Forum for Medical Ethics Society* 1995 April-June; 3(2): 23-24. Subject: 8.1

Pandya, Sunil K. End-of-life decision making in India. *In:* Blank, Robert H.; Merrick, Janna C., eds. End-of-Life Decision Making: A Cross-National Study. Cambridge, MA: MIT Press; 2005: 79-96. Subject: 20.4.1

Pandya, Sunil K. Impact of life-prolonging technologies on end-of-life care in India [editorial]. *Indian Journal of Medical Ethics* 2005 July-September; 2(3): 76-77. Subject: 20.5.1

Pandya, Sunil K. The patient with AIDS. *Medical Ethics: Journal of Forum for Medical Ethics Society* 1994 February-April; 1(3): 1-3. Subject: 9.5.6

Pandya, Sunil K. Patients testing positive for HIV — ethical dilemmas in India. *Issues in Medical Ethics* 1997 April-June; 5(2): 49-55. Subject: 9.5.6

Pandya, Sunil K. Taking a second look: some opinions on the second opinion [discussion]. *Issues in Medical Ethics* 1998 January; 6(1): 9-16. Subject: 7.3

Pandya, Sunil K. An unusual forum for a discussion on medical ethics [letter]. *National Medical Journal of India* 1999 March-April; 12(2): 79-81. Subject: 18.5.3

Panetta, Joe; Wetherell, John; Mehok, Michelle. California Stem Cell Research and Cures Act — what to expect from stem cell research? *Journal of Biolaw and Business* 2005; 8(4): 3-12. Subject: 18.5.4

Pang, Samantha M.C.; Tse, Chun-yan.; Chan, Kin-sang; Chung, Betty P.M.; Leung, Amanda K.A.; Leung, Edward M.F.; Ko, Stanley K.K. An empirical analysis of the decision-making of limiting life-sustaining treatment for patients with advanced chronic obstructive pulmonary disease in Hong Kong, China. *Journal of Critical Care* 2004 September; 19(3): 135-144. Subject: 20.5.1

Panicek, David M.; Schwartz, Lawrence H.; Dershaw, D. David; Ercolani, Matthew C.; Castellino, Ronald A. Misrepresentation of publications by applicants for radiology fellowships: is it a problem? *AJR: American Journal of Roentgenology* 1998 March; 170(3): 577-581. Subject: 4.1.2

Panush, Richard S. Why I no longer accept pens (or other "gifts") from industry (and why you shouldn't either) [editorial]. *Journal of Rheumatology* 2004 August; 31(8): 1478-1482. Subject: 9.7

Panzini, Gianluca; Lorenzini, Rodolfo Nello. Animal experimentation in Italy. Legislation and the authorisation of research protocols. *Annali dell Istituto Superiore di Sanita* 2004; 40(2): 205-210. Subject: 22.2

Papachristou, Christina; Walter, Marc; Dietrich, Kerstin; Danzer, Gerhard; Klupp, Jochen; Klapp, Burghard F.; Frommer, Jörg. Motivation for living-donor liver transplantation from the donor's perspective: an in-depth qualitative research study. *Transplantation* 2004 November 27; 78(10): 1506-1514. Subject: 19.5

Papadimos, Thomas J.; Papadimos, Alexa T. The student and the ovum: the lack of autonomy and informed consent in trading genes for tuition. *Reproductive Biology and Endocrinology [electronic]* 2004 July 12; 2(1): 56; 6

p. Available: http://www.rbej.com/content/2/1/56 [21 March 2005]. Subject: 14.2

Papageorgiou, Alexia; King, Michael; Janmohamed, Anis; Davidson, Oliver; Dawson, John. Advance directives for patients compulsorily admitted to hospital with serious mental illness. Randomised controlled trial. *British Journal of Psychiatry* 2002 December; 181(6): 513-519. Subject: 20.5.4

Papanikitas, Andrew N. Is it historically possible for a consensus to be reached on the subject of euthanasia, voluntary or otherwise? *Catholic Medical Quarterly* 2000 February; 50(1); 12 p. [Online]. Available: http://www.catholicdoctors.org.uk/CMQ/Feb_2000/censensus_on_eutha nasia.htm [4 November 2005]. Subject: 20.5.1

Papdakis, Maxine A.; Teherani, Arianne; Banach, Mary A.; Knettler, Timothy R.; Rattner, Susan L.; Stern, David T.; Veloski, J. Jon; Hodgson, Carol S. Disciplinary action by medical boards and prior behavior in medical school. *New England Journal of Medicine* 2005 December 22; 353(25): 2673-2682. Subject: 7.4

Paradis, Emily K. Feminist and community psychology ethics in research with homeless women. *American Journal of Community Psychology* 2000 December; 28(6): 839-858. Subject: 17.1

Paradise, Jordan; Andrews, Lori; Holbrook, Timothy. Patents on human genes: an analysis of scope and claims. *Science* 2005 March 11; 307(5715): 1566-1567. Subject: 15.8

Parens, Erik. Authenticity and ambivalence: toward understanding the enhancement debate. *Hastings Center Report* 2005 May-June; 35(3): 34-41. Subject: 4.5

Parfett, Julianne. Canada's DNA databank: public safety and private costs. *Manitoba Law Journal* 2002; 29(1): 33-79. Subject: 15.1

Parfitt, Tom. Russian scientists voice concern over "stem-cell cosmetics". *Lancet* 2005 April 2-8; 365(9466): 1219-1220. Subject: 18.5.4

Parikh, Ketan. The right to refuse treatment. *Issues in Medical Ethics* 2003 July-September; 11(3): 75-76. Subject: 9.5.6

Parikh, Michelle. Burning the candle at both ends, and there is nothing left for proof: the Americans with Disabilities Act's disservice to persons with mental illness. *Cornell Law Review* 2004 March; 89(3): 721-762. Subject: 4.3

Paris, J.J.; Elias-Jones, A.C. "Do we murder Mary to save Jodie?" An ethical analysis of the separation of the Manchester conjoined twins [opinion]. *Postgraduate Medical Journal* 2001 September; 77(911): 593-598. Subject: 20.5.2

Paris, J.J.; Schreiber, M.D.; Elias-Jones, Alun. Resuscitation of the preterm infant against parental wishes. *Archives of Disease in Childhood. Fetal and Neonatal Edition* 2005 May; 90(3): F208-F210. Subject: 20.5.2

Paris, John J.; Webster, Gregory. Back to the future: overcoming reluctance to honor in-school DNAR orders. *American Journal of Bioethics* 2005 January-February; 5(1): 67-69. Subject: 20.5.2

Park, Elyse R.; Betancourt, Joseph R.; Kim, Minah K.; Maina, Angela W.; Blumenthal, David; Weissman, Joel S. Mixed messages: residents' experiences learning cross-cultural care. *Academic Medicine* 2005 September; 80(9): 874-880. Subject: 21.7

Park, Jong-Hyun; Park, Joong-Won; Koo, Young-Mo; Kim, Jang Han. Relay kidney transplantation in Korea — legal, ethical and medical aspects. *Legal Medicine* 2004 July; 6(3): 178-181. Subject: 19.5

Park, Julie. In that case. Response [case study]. *Journal of Bioethical Inquiry* 2005; 2(2): 111-112. Subject: 9.5.7

Park, Shellie K. Severing the bond of life: when conflicts of interest fail to recognize the value of two lives. *University of Hawai'i Law Review* 2002 Winter; 25(1): 157-198. Subject: 8.3.2

Parker, Damon B.; James, Michael; Barrett, Robert J. The practical logic of reasonableness: an ethnographic reconnaissance of a research ethics committee. *Monash Bioethics Review* 2005 October; 24(4): 7-27. Subject: 18.2

Parker, Frederick R., Jr.; Rubin, Harvey W.; Winslade, William J. Life insurance, living benefits, and physician-assisted death. *Behavioral Sciences and the Law* 2004; 22(5): 615-626. Subject: 20.7

Parker, Judith M.; Gibbs, Martin. Truth, virtue and beauty: midwifery and philosophy. *Nursing Inquiry* 1998 September; 5(3): 146-153. Subject: 9.5.5

Parker, Lisa M. What's wrong with the dead body? Use of the human cadaver in medical education [opinion]. *Medical Journal of Australia* 2002 January 21; 176(2): 74-76. Subject: 7.2

Parker, M. False dichotomies: EBM, clinical freedom, and the art of medicine. *Medical Humanities* 2005 June; 31(1): 23-30. Subject: 9.8

Parker, Malcolm. End games: euthanasia under interminable scrutiny. *Bioethics* 2005 October; 19(5-6): 523-536. Subject: 20.5.1

Parker, Malcolm. Medicine, psychiatry and euthanasia: an argument against mandatory psychiatric review. *Australian and New Zealand Journal of Psychiatry* 2000 April; 34(2): 318-324. Subject: 20.5.1

Parker, Malcolm H. Posthumous conception and the need for consent [letter]. *Medical Journal of Australia* 1999 May 3; 170(9): 452-453. Subject: 14.1

Parkinson, Lynne; Rainbird, Katherine; Kerridge, Ian; Carter, Gregory; Cavenagh, John; McPhee, John; Ravenscroft, Peter. Cancer patients' attitudes towards euthanasia and physician-assisted suicide: the influence of question wording and patients' own definitions on re-

---

Subject = NRCBL Primary Classification Number; See inside front cover

sponses. *Journal of Bioethical Inquiry* 2005; 2(2): 82-89. Subject: 20.5.1

Parmar, H.R. Doctor-doctor ethics [letter]. *Issues in Medical Ethics* 1998 January; 6(1): 2. Subject: 2.1

Parmet, Wendy E. Informed consent and public health: are they compatible when it comes to vaccines? *Journal of Health Care Law and Policy* 2005; 8(1): 71-110. Subject: 8.3.1

Parmet, Wendy E.; Goodman, Richard A.; Farber, Amy. Individual rights versus the public's health — 100 years after Jacobson v. Massachusetts [opinion]. *New England Journal of Medicine* 2005 February 17; 352(7): 652-654. Subject: 9.1

Parmet, Wendy E.; Scott, Charity; Hodge, James G., Jr.; Nahmias, David E.; DeMaria, Alfred, Jr.; Rees, Clifford M.; Goodman, Richard A. Plenary program: Jacobson v. Massachusetts. *Journal of Law, Medicine and Ethics* 2005 Winter; 33(4, Supplement): 24-27. Subject: 9.7

Parnis, Deborah; Du Mont, Janice; Gombay, Brydon. Cooperation or co-optation?: assessing the methodological benefits and barriers involved in conducting qualitative research through medical institutional settings. *Qualitative Health Research* 2005 May; 15(5): 686-697. Subject: 18.2

Parry, Bronwyn. From the corporeal to the informational: exploring the scope of benefit sharing agreements and their applicability to sequence databases. *In:* Thiele, F.; Ashcroft, R.E., eds. Bioethics in a Small World. Berlin: Springer; 2005: 73-91. Subject: 15.1

Parsa, Michael; Walsh, Matthew J. Ethics seminars: HIV testing, consent, and physician responsibilities. *Academic Emergency Medicine* 2001 December; 8(12): 1197-1199. Subject: 9.5.6

Parsi, Kayhan. Bioethics consultation in the private sector: what is an appropriate model. *HEC (Healthcare Ethics Committee) Forum* 2005 June; 17(2): 135- 145. Subject: 9.6

Parthasarathy, Shobita. The patent is political: the consequences of patenting the BRCA genes in Britain. *Community Genetics* 2005 October; 8(4): 235-242. Subject: 15.8

Partridge, Ann H.; Wong, Julia S.; Knudsen, Katherine; Gelman, Rebecca; Sampson, Ebonie; Gadd, Michele; Bishop, Karyn L.; Harris, Jay R.; Winer, Eric P. Offering participants results of a clinical trial: sharing results of a negative study. *Lancet* 2005 March 12-18; 365(9463): 963-964. Subject: 18.2

Partridge, Christina T.; Turiaso, Jennifer. Widows, women, and the bioethics of care. *Christian Bioethics* 2005 April; 11(1): 77-92. Subject: 9.1

Partridge, Robert A.; Virk, Alam; Sayah, Assaad; Antosia, Robert. Field experience with prehospital advance directives. *Annals of Emergency Medicine* 1998 No-

vember; 32(5); 6 p. [Online]. Available: http://home. mdconsult.com/das/article/body/50990752-3/jorg= journal&source=MI7sp=10 [3 October 2005]. Subject: 20.5.4

PARYAY. Hysterectomy in the mentally handicapped: an abridged version of the statement issued by PARYAY. *Medical Ethics: Journal of Forum for Medical Ethics Society* 1994 August-October; 2(1): 6-7. Subject: 11.3

Pascal, Chris B. Scientific misconduct and research integrity for the bench scientist. *Proceedings of the Society for Experimental Biology and Medicine* 2000 September; 224(4): 220-230. Subject: 1.3.9

Pasetti, Carlo. The teaching of bioethics to the health care team: the neurologist's role. *Medicine and Law: World Association for Medical Law* 1995; 14(1-2): 87-91. Subject: 2.1

Pask, Elizabeth J. Nursing responsibility and conditions of practice: are we justified in holding nurses responsible for their behaviour in situations of patient care? *Nursing Philosophy* 2001 April; 2(1): 42-52. Subject: 8.1

Pasman, H. Roeline W.; Onwuteaka-Philipsen, Bregje D.; Ooms, Marcel E.; van Wigcheren, Petra T.; van der Wal, Gerrit; Ribbe, Miel W. Forgoing artificial nutrition and hydration in nursing home patients with dementia: patients, decision making, and participants. *Alzheimer Disease and Associated Disorders* 2004 July-September; 18(3): 154-162. Subject: 20.5.1

Patel, Angira; Wilke, Hans J., II.; Mingay, David; Ellis, John E. Patient attitudes toward granting consent to participate in perioperative randomized clinical trials. *Journal of Clinical Anesthesia* 2004 September; 16(6): 426-434. Subject: 18.3

Patel, Kant. Euthanasia and physician-assisted suicide policy in the Netherlands and Oregon: a comparative analysis. *Journal of Health and Social Policy* 2004; 19(1): 37-55. Subject: 20.5.1

Patel, Kant; Rushefsky, Mark E. The politics of genetics and public health. *In their:* The Politics of Public Health in the United States. Armonk, NY: M.E. Sharpe; 2005: 176-209. Subject: 15.1; 9.1

Paterson, I.C.M. The concept of intellectual property and its implications for oncology [opinion]. *Clinical Oncology* 1993; 5(4): 234-236. Subject: 5.3

Paterson, Moira. HealthConnect and privacy: a policy conundrum. *Journal of Law and Medicine* 2004 August; 12(1): 80-90. Subject: 8.4

Pathare, Soumitra. Beyond ECT: priorities in mental health care in India. *Issues in Medical Ethics* 2003 January-March; 11(1): 11-12. Subject: 17.1

Patil, Rajan. Discussion on transplant ethics. *Issues in Medical Ethics* 2002 July-September; 10(3): 62. Subject: 19.5

Patil, Rajan R. Research in a tribal community [case study]. *Indian Journal of Medical Ethics* 2004 October-December; 1(4): 122-123. Subject: 18.5.9

Patmas, Michael A.; Topol, Eric J.; Blumenthal, David. Physicians advising investment firms [letter and reply]. *JAMA: The Journal of the American Medical Association* 2005 October 19; 294(15): 1897-1898. Subject: 7.3

Patrawala, Zeenat. The Down syndrome abortion dilemma. *Ivy Journal of Ethics* 2003; 3(1): 24-27. Subject: 15.2

Patrizio, Pasquale; Butts, Samantha; Caplan, Arthur. Ovarian tissue preservation and future fertility: emerging technologies and ethical considerations. *Journal of the National Cancer Institute Monographs* 2005; (34): 107-110. Subject: 14.6

Patterson, Annette R.; Robinson, Linda D.; Naftalis, Elizabeth Z.; Haley, Barbara B.; Tomlinson, Gail E. Custodianship of genetic information: clinical challenges and professional responsibility. *Journal of Clinical Oncology* 2005 March 20; 23(9): 2100-2104. Subject: 15.3

Patterson, Laura. Communication and termination: whose choice? *Journal of Family Planning and Reproductive Health Care* 2005 January; 31(1): 75-76. Subject: 12.5.3

Pattinson, Shaun D. Some problems challenging the UK's Human Fertilisation and Embryology Authority. *Medicine and Law: World Association for Medical Law* 2005 June; 24(2): 391-401. Subject: 14.5

Paul, Diane B. Genetic engineering and eugenics: the uses of history. *In:* Baillie, Harold W.; Casey, Timothy K., eds. Is Human Nature Obsolete? Genetics Bioengineering, and the Future of the Human Condition. Cambridge, MA: MIT Press; 2005: 123-151. Subject: 15.1

Paul, Yash. Polio eradication programme: some ethical issues. *Indian Journal of Medical Ethics* 2005 October-December; 2(4): 115-116. Subject: 9.5.1

Paul, Yash; Dawson, Angus. Some ethical issues arising from polio eradication programmes in India. *Bioethics* 2005 August; 19(4): 393-406. Subject: 9.5.1

Paulsen, Michael Stokes. Abrogating stare decisis by statute: may Congress remove the precedential effect of Roe and Casey? *Yale Law Journal* 2001; 109(7): 1535-1602. Subject: 12.4.1

Paulsen, Michael Stokes. Looking for a model answer: may Congress prohibit sex-selective abortions? *Constitutional Commentary* 2000; 17(2): 165-169. Subject: 12.1

Pauly, Mark V. What if technology never stops improving? Medicare's future under continuous cost increases. *Washington and Lee Law Review* 2003 Fall; 60(4): 1233-1250. Subject: 9.5.2

Pavelic, Krešimir. Arguments for human therapeutic cloning. *Bosnian Journal of Basic Medical Sciences* 2004 February 4(1): 15-18. Subject: 14.5

Pawlik, Timothy M.; Curley, Steven A. Ethical issues in surgical palliative care: am I killing the patient by "letting him go"? *Surgical Clinics of North America* 2005 April; 85(2): 273-286. Subject: 20.5.1

Paxson, Heather. Abortion/anti-abortion conflict. *In:* Restivo, Sal, ed. Science, Technology, and Society: An Encyclopedia. New York: Oxford University Press; 2005: 1-2. Subject: 12.4.1

Payne, Jan. Informed consent: reconsideration of its structure and role in medicine. *In:* Salek, Sam; Edgar, Andrew, eds. Pharmaceutical Ethics. New York: Wiley; 2002: 61-69. Subject: 8.3.1

Payne, S.A.; Langley-Evans, A.; Hillier, R. Perceptions of a 'good' death: a comparative study of the views of hospice staff and patients. *Palliative Medicine* 1996 October; 10(4): 307-312. Subject: 20.4.1

Paz, David A.; Dunn, Laura B.; Gordon, Nora E. Economic behavior and informed consent [letter and reply]. *JAMA: The Journal of the American Medical Association* 2005 May 4; 293(17): 2092. Subject: 18.3

Peach, Lucinda. Religious lawmakers on moral identity and abortion law. *In her:* Legislating Morality: Pluralism and Religious Identity in Lawmaking. New York: Oxford University Press; 2002: 63-94. Subject: 12.3

Peacocke, Arthur. Relating genetics to theology on the map of scientific knowledge. *In:* Deane-Drummond, Celia; Szerszynski, Bronislaw, eds. Re- ordering Nature: Theology, Society and the New Genetics. New York: T & T Clark; 2003: 122-137. Subject: 15.1

Pear, Robert. New attention for 2002 law on survivors of abortions. *New York Times* 2005 April 23; p. A10. Subject: 12.4.2

Pearlman, Robert A.; Hsu, Clarissa; Starks, Helene; Back, Anthony L.; Gordon, Judith R.; Bharucha, Ashok J.; Koenig, Barbara A.; Battin, Margaret P. Motivations for physician-assisted suicide: patient and family voices. *Journal of General Internal Medicine* 2005 March; 20(3): 234- 239. Subject: 20.7

Pearson, Yvette E. What's blood got to do with it? It's time to say goodbye to directed cadaveric donation. *American Journal of Bioethics* 2005 July-August; 5(4): 31-33. Subject: 19.5

Peart, Nicola; Adams, Jane; Dunckley, Catherine. Research on human tissue. *In:* Dawson, John; Peart, Nicola, eds. The Law of Research: A Guide. Dunedin, NZ: University of Otago Press; 2003: 211-230. Subject: 18.1

Peart, Nicola; Dawson, John; Ferguson, Judy; Foley, Mary; Dunckley, Catherine. Liability for misconduct in research. *In:* Dawson, John; Peart, Nicola, eds. The Law of Research: A Guide. Dunedin, NZ: University of Otago Press; 2003: 323-344. Subject: 1.3.9

Peart, Nicola; Foley, Mary; Henaghan, Mark. Children as research participants. *In:* Dawson, John; Peart, Nicola, eds. The Law of Research: A Guide. Dunedin, NZ: University of Otago Press; 2003: 269-284. Subject: 18.5.2

Peart, Nicola; McCrimmon, Fiona; Dawson, John. Clinical trials. *In:* Dawson, John; Peart, Nicola, eds. The Law of Research: A Guide. Dunedin, NZ: University of Otago Press; 2003: 175-195. Subject: 18.2

Peckitt, Michael G. Time to legalise assisted dying? BMA should take an active role, whatever that may be [letter]. *BMJ: British Medical Journal* 2005 October 8; 331(7520): 841. Subject: 20.5.1

Pedersen, Kjeld Moller. Randomised controlled trials in drug policies: can the best be the enemy of the good? *In:* Kristiansen, Ivar Sonbo; Mooney, Gavin, eds. Evidence-Based Medicine: In its Place. New York: Routledge; 2004: 124-140. Subject: 9.8

Peduzzi-Nelson, Jean D. Criticism of the Hurlbut ANT proposal. *National Catholic Bioethics Quarterly* 2005 Summer; 5(2): 226. Subject: 18.5.4

Peel, Michael. Human rights and medical ethics. *Journal of the Royal Society of Medicine* 2005 April; 98(4): 171-173. Subject: 21.1

Peerzada, Jehanna M.; Richardson, Douglas K.; Burns, Jeffrey P. Delivery room decision-making at the threshold of viability. *Journal of Pediatrics* 2004 October; 145(4): 492-498. Subject: 20.5.2

Pegoraro, Renzo. The challenges for clinical ethics education in Europe. *Medical Ethics and Bioethics / Medicinska Etika & Bioetika* 2005; 11(Supplement): 11-13. Subject: 2.3

Pegoraro, Renzo. Dialogue with David C. Thomasma and Renzo Pegoraro. *Theoretical Medicine and Bioethics* 2005; 26(6): 575-589. Subject: 2.1

Pekmezaris, Renée; Breuer, Lorraine; Zaballero, Arturo; Wolf-Klein, Gisele; Jadoon, Erum; D'Olimpio, James T.; Guzik, Howard; Foley, Cornelius J.; Weiner, Joseph; Chan, Susanna. Predictors of site of death of end-of-life patients: the importance of specificity in advance directives. *Journal of Palliative Medicine* 2004 February; 7(1): 9-17. Subject: 20.4.1

Pelias, Mary Z. Genetic testing: who decides, who informs? [opinion]. *Children's Legal Rights Journal* 1998 Spring; 18(2): 43-46. Subject: 15.3

Pellegrino, Edmund D. Balancing science, ethics and politics: stem cell research, a paradigm case. *Journal of Contemporary Health Law and Policy* 2002 Fall; 18(3): 591-611. Subject: 18.5.4

Pellegrino, Edmund D. Comments: a crisis in the ethical and moral behavior of psychiatrists [forum]. *Current Opinion in Psychiatry* 1998 January; 11(1); 4 p. [Online]. Available: http://gateway.ut.ovid.com/gw1/ovidweb.cgi [24 May 2005]. Subject: 20.6

Pellegrino, Edmund D. Futility in medical decisions: the word and the concept. *HEC (Healthcare Ethics Commit-*

tee) Forum 2005 December; 17(4): 308-318. Subject: 20.5.1

Pellegrino, Edmund D. The present and future importance of Catholic health care in the United States. *In:* McMahon, Kevin T., ed. Moral Issues in Catholic Health Care. Wynnewood, PA: Saint Charles Borromeo Seminary; 2004: 1-18. Subject: 9.1

Pellegrino, Edmund D. Prevention of medical error: where professional and organizational ethics meet. *In:* Sharpe, Virginia A., ed. Accountability: Patient Safety and Policy Reform. Washington, DC: Georgetown University Press; 2004: 83-98. Subject: 9.8

Pellegrino, Edmund D. Some things ought never be done: moral absolutes in clinical ethics. *Theoretical Medicine and Bioethics* 2005; 26(6): 469-486. Subject: 8.1

Peltier, Bruce N. White coat principles. *Journal of the American College of Dentists* 2004 Winter; 71(4): 53-56. Subject: 4.1.1

Pembrey, Marcus E. In the light of preimplantation genetic diagnosis: some ethical issues in medical genetics revisited [opinion]. *European Journal of Human Genetics* 1998 January; 6(1): 4-11. Subject: 15.2

Penas, Cheri D.; Barkley, Thomas W., Jr. Ethical theory and principles of decision making for the acute care nurse practitioner. *Nurse Practitioner Forum* 2001 September; 12(3): 161-165. Subject: 4.1.3

Pence, Gregory E. Classic cases about death and dying. *In his:* Classic Cases in Medical Ethics: Accounts of Cases That Have Shaped Medical Ethics, with Philosophical, Legal, and Historical Backgrounds. Fourth edition. Boston, MA: McGraw- Hill; 2004: 27-120. Subject: 20.5.1

Pence, Gregory E. Classic cases about individual rights and the public good. *In his:* Classic Cases in Medical Ethics: Accounts of Cases That Have Shaped Medical Ethics, with Philosophical, Legal, and Historical Backgrounds. Fourth edition. Boston, MA: McGraw- Hill; 2004: 367-470. Subject: 9.3.1

Pence, Gregory E. Classic cases about research and experimental treatments. *In his:* Classic Cases in Medical Ethics: Accounts of Cases That Have Shaped Medical Ethics, with Philosophical, Legal, and Historical Backgrounds. Fourth edition. Boston, MA: McGraw- Hill; 2004: 245-365. Subject: 18.1

Pence, Gregory E. Classic cases about the beginning of life. *In his:* Classic Cases in Medical Ethics: Accounts of Cases That Have Shaped Medical Ethics, with Philosophical, Legal, and Historical Backgrounds. Fourth edition. Boston, MA: McGraw- Hill; 2004: 121-243. Subject: 12.4.1

Pence, Gregory E. Moral reasoning and ethical theories in medical ethics. *In his:* Classic Cases in Medical Ethics: Accounts of Cases That Have Shaped Medical Ethics, with Philosophical, Legal, and Historical Backgrounds. Fourth edition. Boston, MA: McGraw- Hill; 2004: 1-25. Subject: 2.1

Pennachio, Dorothy L. Caring for your Muslim patients: stereotypes and misunderstandings affect the care of patients from the Middle East and other parts of the Islamic world. *Medical Economics* 2005 May 6; 82(9): 46-50. Subject: 8.1

Penney, Darby; McGee, Glenn. Chemical trust: oxytocin oxymoron? [editorial]. *American Journal of Bioethics* 2005 May-June; 5(3): 1-2. Subject: 18.4

Pennings, G. Demanding pure motives for donation: the moral acceptability of blood donations by haemochromatosis patients. *Journal of Medical Ethics* 2005 February; 31(2): 69-72. Subject: 19.4

Pennings, G. Philosophical and ethical considerations regarding assisted reproductive technologies. *In:* Gerris, Jan; Olivennes, Francois; De Sutter, Petra, eds. Assisted Reproductive Technologies: Quality and Safety. Boca Raton: Taylor & Francis; 2004: 267-276. Subject: 14.1

Pennings, Guido. Gamete donation in a system of need-adjusted reciprocity [opinion]. *Human Reproduction* 2005 November; 20(11): 2990-2993. Subject: 19.5

Pennings, Guido. Legal harmonization and reproductive tourism in Europe [opinion]. *Human Reproduction* 2004 December; 19(12): 2689-2694. Subject: 14.1

Pennsylvania. Court of Common Pleas. Erie County. *J.F. v. D.B.* [Date of Decision: 2 April 2004]. *Pennsylvania District and County Reports*, 4th Series, 2004; 66: 1-33. Subject: 14.2

Penticuff, Joy Hinson; Walden, Marlene. Influence of practice environment and nurse characteristics on perinatal nurses' responses to ethical dilemmas. *Nursing Research* 2000 March-April; 49(2): 64-72. Subject: 4.1.3

Pentz, Rebecca D.; Cohen, Cynthia B.; Wicclair, Mark; DeVita, Michael A.; Flamm, Anne Lederman; Youngner, Stuart J.; Hamric, Ann B.; McCabe, Mary S.; Glover, Jacqueline J.; Kittiko, Winona J.; Kinlaw, Kathy; Keller, James; Asch, Adrienne; Kavanagh, John J.; Arap, Wadih. Ethics guidelines for research with the recently dead. *Nature Medicine* 2005 November; 11(11): 1145-1149. Subject: 18.2

Pentz, Rebecca D.; Peterson, Susan K.; Watts, Beatty; Vernon, Sally W.; Lynch, Patrick M.; Koehly, Laura M.; Gritz, Ellen R. Hereditary nonpolyposis colorectal cancer family members' perceptions about the duty to inform and health professionals' role in disseminating genetic information. *Genetic Testing* 2005 Fall; 9(3): 261-268. Subject: 15.3

People's Republic of China. Eighth National People's Congress. Standing Committee. Law of the People's Republic of China on maternal and infant health care [effective 1 June 1995]. People's Republic of China: Standing Committee of the Eighth National People's Congress 1994

October 27; 6 p. [Online]. Available: http://isinolaw.com/isinolaw/english/detail.jsp?iscatalog=0&statutes_id=131686&ski [22 September 2005]. Subject: 9.5.5

Peota, Carmen. Expertly stated. *Minnesota Medicine* 2005 June; 88(6): 12-14. Subject: 7.3

Peraud, Peter J.; Kulstad, Erik B. Another resident perspective: resident education and the pharmaceutical industry. *Annals of Emergency Medicine* 2005 January; 45(1): 32-36. Subject: 7.2

Pereira, Shiranee; Tettamanti, Massimo. Ahimsa and alternatives — the concept of the 4th R. The CPCSEA in India. *ALTEX: Alternativen zu Tierexperimenten* 2005; 22(1): 3-6. Subject: 22.1

Peretti-Watel, P.; Bendiane, M.K.; Moatti, J.P. Attitudes toward palliative care, conceptions of euthanasia and opinions about its legalization among French physicians. *Social Science and Medicine* 2005 April; 60(8): 1781-1793. Subject: 20.5.1

Peretti-Watel, P.; Bendiane, M.K.; Obadia, Y.; Lapiana, J.M.; Galinier, A.; Pegliasco, H.; Favre, R.; Moatti, J.P. Disclosure of prognosis to terminally ill patients: attitudes and practices among French physicians. *Journal of Palliative Medicine* 2005 April; 8(2): 280-290. Subject: 8.2

Pérez-Cárceles, M.D.; Pereñiguez, J.E.; Osuan, E.; Luna, A. Balancing confidentiality and the information provided to families of patients in primary care. *Journal of Medical Ethics* 2005 September; 31(9): 531-535. Subject: 8.4

Perkins, Henry S.; Shepherd, Krysten J.; Cortez, Josie D.; Hazuda, Helen P. Exploring chronically ill seniors' attitudes about discussing death and postmortem medical procedures. *Journal of the American Geriatrics Society* 2005 May; 53(5): 895-900. Subject: 9.5.2

Perkoff, Gerald T. The boundaries of medicine. *Journal of Chronic Diseases* 1985; 38(3): 271-278. Subject: 4.1.2

Perlin, Michael L. "May you stay forever young": Robert Sadoff and the history of Mental Disability Law. *Journal of the American Academy of Psychiatry and the Law* 2005; 33(2): 236-244. Subject: 17.7

Perlis, Roy H.; Perlis, Clifford S.; Wu, Yelena; Hwang, Cindy; Joseph, Megan; Nierenberg, Andrew A. Industry sponsorship and financial conflict of interest in the reporting of clinical trials in psychiatry. *American Journal of Psychiatry* 2005 October; 162(10): 1957- 1960. Subject: 18.2

Perlman, David. Bioethics in industry settings: one situation where a code for bioethicists would help [comment]. *American Journal of Bioethics* 2005 September-October; 5(5): 62-64. Subject: 6

Perls, Thomas T.; Reisman, Neal R.; Olshansky, S. Jay. Provision or distribution of growth hormone for "antiaging": clinical and legal issues. *JAMA: The Journal*

---

of the American Medical Association 2005 October 26; 294(16): 2086-2090. Subject: 9.7

Perman, Ben; Somerville, Margaret A.; Atlas, Ronald M. Using ethics to fight bioterrorism [letter and reply]. *Science* 2005 August 12; 309(5737): 1013, 1014-1015, 1017. Subject: 21.3

Perneger, Thomas V. Why we need ethical oversight of quality improvement projects [editorial]. *International Journal for Quality in Health Care* 2004 October; 16(5): 343-344. Subject: 9.6

Perneger, Thomas V.; Martin, Diane P.; Bovier, Patrick A. Physicians' attitudes toward health care rationing. *Medical Decision Making* 2002 January-February; 22(1): 65-70. Subject: 7.1

Peron, A.L.; Rodrigues, A.B.; Leite, D.A.; Lopes, J.L.; Ceschim, P.C.; Alter, R.; Roza, B.A.; Pestana, J.O.; Schirmer, J. Organ donation and transplantation in Brazil: university students' awareness and opinions. *Transplantation Proceedings* 2004 May; 36(4): 811-813. Subject: 19.5

Perring, Christian. Expanding the repertoire of bioethics: what next? [comment]. *American Journal of Bioethics* 2005 May-June; 5(3): 63-65. Subject: 17.4

Perry, Constance K. Personhood and relational persons. *In:* Thomasma, David C.; Weisstud, David N.; Herve, Christian eds. Personhood and Health Care. Boston: Kluwer Academic Pub.; 2001: 333-345. Subject: 9.5.5

Perry, Daniel. Someone's knocking on the laboratory door [opinion]. *Rejuvenation Research* 2004 Spring; 7(1): 49-52. Subject: 9.5.2

Perry, Joshua E.; Churchill, Larry R.; Kirshner, Howard S. The Terri Schiavo case: legal, ethical, and medical perspectives. *Annals of Internal Medicine* 2005 November 15; 143(10): 744-748. Subject: 20.5.1

Perry, Michael J. Religion, politics, and abortion. *University of Detroit Mercy Law Review* 2001 Fall; 79(1): 1-37. Subject: 12.3

Perry, Ronen; Adar, Yehuda. Wrongful abortion: a wrong in search of a remedy. *Yale Journal of Health Policy, Law, and Ethics* 2005 Summer; 5(2): 507-586. Subject: 12.4.2

Persing, John A. Craniofacial surgery and the ethics of decision-making. *Cleft Palate-Craniofacial Journal* 1995 November; 32(6): 504-506. Subject: 9.4

Pesonen, Lorie M. Genetic screening: an employer's tool to differentiate or to discriminate? *Journal of Contemporary Health Law and Policy* 2002 Winter; 19(1): 187-223. Subject: 15.3

Pessini, Leo. Ethical questions related to end-of-life decisions: the Brazilian reality. *In:* Blank, Robert H.; Merrick, Janna C., eds. End-of-Life Decision Making: A Cross-National Study. Cambridge, MA: MIT Press; 2005: 13-31. Subject: 20.5.1

Peter, Elizabeth. Commentary: who will define the values? [opinion]. *Canadian Journal of Nursing Leadership* 2004 July; 17(3): 39-40. Subject: 6

Peter, Fabienne. Health equity and social justice. *In:* Anand, Sudhir; Peter, Fabienne; Sen, Amartya, eds. Public Health, Ethics, and Equity. New York: Oxford University Press; 2004: 93-106. Subject: 9.1

Peterman, J.F.; Desbiens, N.A. Should physicians be allowed to use alcohol while on call? *Journal of Medical Ethics* 2005 January; 31(1): 21-26. Subject: 9.5.9

Peternelj-Taylor, Cindy A. Conceptualizing nursing research with offenders: another look at vulnerability. *International Journal of Law and Psychiatry* 2005 July-August; 28(4): 348-359. Subject: 18.5.5

Peters, Catherine; Kantaris, Xenya; Barnes, Jacqueline; Sutcliffe, Alastair. Parental attitudes toward disclosure of the mode of conception to their child conceived by in vitro fertilization. *Fertility and Sterility* 2005 April; 83(4): 914-919. Subject: 8.2

Petersen, Alan; Anderson, Alison; Allan, Stuart. Science fiction/science fact: medical genetics in news stories. *New Genetics and Society* 2005 December; 24(3): 337-353. Subject: 15.7

Petersen, Andrea. Negotiating the terms of your death: medical advances give patients more control over how and when they die. *Wall Street Journal* 2005 May 10; p. D1, D3. Subject: 20.5.4

Petersen, Andrea. A new approach for the sickest babies: some hospice programs begin accepting infants; managing pain in the NICU. *Wall Street Journal* 2005 July 26; p. D1, D4. Subject: 20.5.2

Petersen, Kerry; Baker, H.W.G.; Pitts, Marian; Thorpe, Rachel. Assisted reproductive technologies: professional and legal restrictions in Australian clinics. *Journal of Law and Medicine* 2005 February; 12(3): 373-385. Subject: 14.1

Peterson, Dymphna Rees. The ethics of research into schizophrenia prevention: a carer's perspective. *Australian and New Zealand Journal of Psychiatry* 2000 November; 34 (supplement): S201-S203. Subject: 18.3

Peterson, M.M. Assisted reproductive technologies and equity of access issues. *Journal of Medical Ethics* 2005 May; 31(5): 280-285. Subject: 14.1

Peterson, T.S. Just diagnosis? Preimplantation genetic diagnosis and injustices to disabled people. *Journal of Medical Ethics* 2005 April; 31(4): 231-234. Subject: 15.2

Petit, François; Paraskevas, Antonis; Minns, Alicia B.; Lee, W.P. Andrew; Lantieri, Laurent A. Face transplantation: where do we stand? *Plastic and Reconstructive Surgery* 2004 April 15; 113(5): 1429-1433. Subject: 19.1

Petratos, Pythagoras. Does the private finance initiative promote innovation in health care? The case of the British

National Health Service. *Journal of Medicine and Philosophy* 2005 December; 30(6): 627- 642. Subject: 9.3.1

Phadke, Anant. Doctors do not have the right to refuse treatment to HIV- positive patients. *Issues in Medical Ethics* 2003 July-September; 11(3): 77-78. Subject: 9.5.6

Pham, Hien; Spigner, Clarence. Knowledge and opinions about organ donation and transplantation among Vietnamese Americans in Seattle, Washington: a pilot study. *Clinical Transplantation* 2004 December; 18(6): 707-715. Subject: 19.5

Phaosavasdi, Sukhit; Thamkhantho, Manopchai; Uerpairojkit, Boonchai; Pruksapong, Chumask; Kanjanapitak, Aurchart. Searching for medical ethics in Dharma conversation. *Journal of the Medical Association of Thailand* 2005 March; 88(3): 440-441. Subject: 2.1

Phatak, Arun. The pharmaceutical industry and the medical profession. *Issues in Medical Ethics* 1998 October-December; 6(4): 131-132. Subject: 9.7

Phillips, Michael. Coping with unsuspected findings in volunteers [letter]. *Nature* 2005 March 3; 434(7029): 17. Subject: 18.3

Phillips, Robert T.M. Expanding the role of the forensic consultant. *AAPL Newsletter (American Acaedemy of Psychiatry and the Law Newsletter)* 2005 January; 30(1): 4-5. Subject: 1.3.1

Philpott, Sean. Eggs, lies and compromise [editorial]. *American Journal of Bioethics* 2005 November-December; 5(6): 1- 3. Subject: 18.5.4

Piattelli, Abramo Alberto. Inter-religious dialogue: palliative care in the other great religions: Judaism. *Dolentium Hominum* 2005; 20(1): 87-88. Subject: 20.4.1

Piccoli, G.B.; Putaggio, S.; Soragna, G.; Mezza, E.; Burdese, M.; Bergamo, D.; Longo, P.; Rinaldi, D.; Bermond, F.; Gai, M.; Motta, D.; Novaresio, C.; Jeantet, A.; Segoloni, G.P. Kidney vending: opinions of the medical school students on this controversial issue. *Transplantation Proceedings* 2004 April; 36(3): 446-447. Subject: 19.5

Piccoli, G.B.; Soragna, G.; Putaggio, S.; Burdese, M.; Bergamo, D.; Mezza, E.; Gai, M.; Motta, D.; Rossetti, M.; Malfi, B.; Anania, P.; Marchetti, P.; Vistoli, F.; Barsotti, M.; Bianchi, A.M.; Longo, P.; Rinaldi, D.; Giacchino, F.; Jeantet, A.; Boggi, U.; Segoloni, G.P. To give or to receive? Opinions of teenagers on kidney donation. *Transplantation Proceedings* 2004 April; 36(3): 448-449. Subject: 19.5

Piccoli, G.B.; Soragna, G.; Putaggio, S.; Burdese, M.; Longo, P.; Rinaldi, D.; Bergamo, D.; Mezza, E.; Consiglio, V.; Novaresio, C.; Gai, M.; Motta, D.; Malfi, B.; Giacchino, F.; Jeantet, A.; Segoloni, G.P. How many organs should one patient receive? The ethics of transplantation in the medical school. *Transplantation Proceedings* 2004 April; 36(3): 444-445. Subject: 19.6

Piccoli, Giorgina Barbara; Soragna, G.; Mezza, E.; Putaggio, S.; Garelli, G.; Bermond, F.; Burdese, M.; Jeantet, A.; Vercellone, F.; Segoloni, G.P.; Piccoli, G. Ethics of transplantation in the medical school: a pilot study. *International Journal of Artificial Organs* 2004 November; 27(11): 1003-1004. Subject: 7.2

Piccoli, Giuseppe; Segoloni, Giuseppe Paolo; Soragna, Giorgio; Mezza, Elisabetta; Burdese, Manuel; Tognarelli, Giuliana; Putaggio, Stefania; Bergamo, Daniela; Consiglio, Valentina; Vespertino, Elisa; Bonetto, Antonella; Jeantet, Alberto; Piccoli, Giorgina Barbara. Teenagers' point of view on living donor kidney transplantation: Cinderella or princess? *Journal of Nephrology* 2004 November-December; 17(Supplement 8): S47-S54. Subject: 19.5

Pickard, John D.; Gillard, Jonathan H. Guidelines reduce the risk of brain-scan shock: responsibility for research is separate from a centre's duty of care to MRI volunteers [letter]. *Nature* 2005 May 5; 435(7038): 17. Subject: 18.1

Pickens, Donald K. Sterilization: the search for purity in mind and body. *In his:* Eugenics and the Progressives. Nashville: Vanderbilt University Press; 1968: 86-101. Subject: 15.5

Piercy, Hilary; Hargate, Maria. Social research on the under-16s: a consideration of the issues from a UK perspective. *Journal of Child Health Care* 2004 December; 8(4): 253-263. Subject: 18.5.2

Pignatelli, B.; Maisonneuve, Hervé; Chapuis, F. Authorship ignorance: views of researchers in French clinical settings. *Journal of Medical Ethics* 2005 October; 31(10): 578-581. Subject: 1.3.9

Pijnenburg, Martien A.M.; Gordijn, Bert. Identity and moral responsibility on healthcare organizations. *Theoretical Medicine and Bioethics* 2005; 26(2): 141-160. Subject: 9.1

Pike, Jeff H.; McLean, Deirdre. Ethical concerns in isolating patients with methicillin-resistant staphylococcus aureus on the rehabilitation ward: a case report. *Archives of Physical Medicine and Rehabilitation* 2002 July; 83(7): 1028-1030. Subject: 2.1

Pilgaokar, Anil. The doctor, the patient and the relative [case study]. *Issues in Medical Ethics* 2000 October-December; 8(4): 129-130. Subject: 8.1

Pilon, Susan. Protecting psychiatric patients in research [comment]. *Indian Journal of Medical Ethics* 2005 April-June; 2(2): 59. Subject: 18.3

Pilotto, Franco; Badon, Pierluigi. Informed consent: between ethics and law. *Dolentium Hominum* 2002; 17(3): 29-34. Subject: 8.3.1

Pilpel, Dina; Leavitt, Frank J.; Elizur-Leiberman, Esther. Ethical and cross cultural questions concerning pediatric clinical trials. *Controlled Clinical Trials* 1996 June; 17(3): 201-208. Subject: 18.2

Pincock, Stephen. Gene doping. *Lancet* 2005 December; 366(Medicine and Sport): S18-S19. Subject: 15.1

Pingle, Suhas. Medical ethics in paediatric practice: a GP's viewpoint. *Issues in Medical Ethics* 2000 April-June; 8(2): 46. Subject: 4.1.2

Pintos, Guillermo Diaz. The medical interpretation of pain and the concept of a person. *In:* Thomasma, David C.; Weisstub, David N.; Herve, Christian eds. Personhood and Health Care. Boston: Kluwer Academic Pub.; 2001: 363-371. Subject: 4.4

Piotrowicz, Michael S.; Leahy, William J. Assisted suicide and terminating life support: the state of the law. *Medsurg Nursing* 1996 October; 5(5): 367-369, 379. Subject: 20.7

Pisal, Hemlata; Bandewar, Sunita. Research with transgendered people [case study]. *Indian Journal of Medical Ethics* 2005 January-March; 2(1): 22- 23. Subject: 18.5.1

Pishchita, A. The practice of applying compulsory treatment to mentally disturbed people: a view from Russia. *Medicine and Law: World Association for Medical Law* 2005 December; 24(4): 717-725. Subject: 8.3.4

Pitetti, Raymond D. Do no harm — but first, do not hurt [opinion]. *CMAJ/JAMC: Canadian Medical Association Journal* 2005 June 21; 172(13): 1699. Subject: 9.5.1

Pitkin, Roy M. Ethical and quasi-ethical issues in medical editing and publishing [editorial]. *Croatian Medical Journal* 1998 June; 39(2): 95-101. Subject: 1.3.7

Pittenger, David J. Preserving the ethical propriety of statistical devices. *Journal of Psychology* 2002 March; 136(2): 117-124. Subject: 18.4

Pittman, Phillip R.; Norris, Sarah L.; Coonan, Kevin M.; McKee, Kelly T., Jr. An assessment of health status among medical research volunteers who served in the Project Whitecoat program at Fort Detrick, Maryland. *Military Medicine* 2005 March; 170(3): 183-187. Subject: 18.5.8

Plachot, Michelle; Cohen, Jean. Regulations for preimplantation genetic diagnosis in France. *Journal of Assisted Reproduction and Genetics* 2004 January; 21(1): 5-6. Subject: 15.2

Plantak, Zdravko. Universal access to health care and religious basis of human rights. *Update [Loma Linda University Center for Christian Bioethics]* 2005 June; 20(2): 1-12. Subject: 9.4

Pleat, Jonathon M.; Dunkin, Chris S.J.; Davies, Charlotte; Adams, Titus. Breast augmentation should be on the NHS: a discussion of the ethics of rationing [letter]. *Annals of the Royal College of Surgeons in England* 2003 March; 85(2): 145-146. Subject: 9.4

Pleterski-Riegler, Dusica. Slovenia. *Medical Ethics and Bioethics / Medicinska Etika & Bioetika* 2005; 11(Supplement): 20. Subject: 9.6

Plomer, Aurora. Embryonic stem cell research: human dignity and the right to life. *In her:* The Law and Ethics of Medical Research: International Bioethics and Human Rights. Portland, OR: Cavendish; 2005: 67-92. Subject: 18.5.4

Plomer, Aurora. Non-therapeutic research: domestic remedies and convention rights. *In her:* The Law and Ethics of Medical Research: International Bioethics and Human Rights. Portland, OR: Cavendish; 2005: 43-65. Subject: 18.3

Plomer, Aurora. Research in developing countries: new ethics and new threats to human rights. *In her:* The Law and Ethics of Medical Research: International Bioethics and Human Rights. Portland, OR: Cavendish; 2005: 113-135. Subject: 18.5.9

Plomer, Aurora. The rights of the dead: research on human tissue and body parts after Bristol and Alder Hey. *In her:* The Law and Ethics of Medical Research: International Bioethics and Human Rights. Portland, OR: Cavendish; 2005: 93-112. Subject: 19.5

Plotnikoff, Gregory A. From informed consent to informed coercion? [opinion]. *Minnesota Medicine* 2005 October; 88(10): 34-35. Subject: 8.3.1

Plourde, Simonne. A key term in ethics: the person and his dignity. *In:* Thomasma, David C.; Weisstub, David N.; Herve, Christian eds. Personhood and Health Care. Boston: Kluwer Academic Pub.; 2001: 137-148. Subject: 4.4

Plunkett, Lance R. Informed consent — more and more important in optometric practice. *Optometry* 2004 November; 75(11): 723-725. Subject: 8.3.1

Pochard, Frédéric; Abroug, Fekri. End-of-life decisions in ICU and cultural specificities [editorial]. *Intensive Care Medicine* 2005 April; 31(4): 506-507. Subject: 20.5.1

Pochard, Frédéric; Azoulay, Elie; Chevret, Sylvie; Lemaire, François; Hubert, Philippe; Canoui, Pierre; Grassin, Marc; Zittoun, Robert; le Gall, Jean-Roger; Dhainaut, Jean François; Schlemmer, Benoît. Symptoms of anxiety and depression in family members of intensive care unit patients: ethical hypothesis regarding decision-making capacity. *Critical Care Medicine* 2001 October; 29(10): 1893-1897. Subject: 20.5.1

Pocock, Stuart J. When (not) to stop a clinical trial for benefit [editorial]. *JAMA: The Journal of the American Medical Association* 2005 November 2; 294(17): 2228-2230. Subject: 18.2

Poe, Amy. Cancer prevention or drug promotion? Journalists mishandle the tamoxifen story. *International Journal of Health Services* 1999; 29(3): 657- 661. Subject: 9.7

Pogash, Carol. A California murder case raises troubling issues. *New York Times* 2005 September 18; p. A14. Subject: 7.4

Pogge, Thomas W. Relational conceptions of justice: responsibilities for health outcomes. *In:* Anand, Sudhir; Peter, Fabienne; Sen, Amartya, eds. Public Health, Ethics, and Equity. New York: Oxford University Press; 2004: 135-161. Subject: 9.1

Pojman, Louis P.; Beckwith, Francis J. Breaking through the stereotypes. *In their:* Pojman, Louis P.; Beckwith, Francis J., eds. The Abortion Controversy: A Reader. Boston: Jones and Bartlett; 1994: 1-11. Subject: 12.5.2

Pojman, Louis P.; Beckwith, Francis J. The major Supreme Court decisions. *In their:* Pojman, Louis P.; Beckwith, Francis J., eds. The Abortion Controversy: A Reader. Boston: Jones and Bartlett; 1994: 13-83. Subject: 12.4.1

Pojman, Louis P.; Beckwith, Francis J.; Horan, Dennis J.; Balch, Thomas J.; MacKinnon, Catharine; Ginsburg, Ruth Bader. Evaluations of Roe v. Wade. *In:* Pojman, Louis P.; Beckwith, Francis J., eds. The Abortion Controversy: A Reader. Boston: Jones and Bartlett; 1994: 85-128. Subject: 12.4.2

Pojman, Louis P.; Beckwith, Francis J.; Markowitz, Sally; Whitbeck, Caroline; Wolf-Devine, Celia; Warren, Mary Anne. Feminist arguments on abortion. *In:* Pojman, Louis P.; Beckwith, Francis J., eds. The Abortion Controversy: A Reader. Boston: Jones and Bartlett; 1994: 371-444. Subject: 12.3

Pojman, Louis P.; Beckwith, Francis J.; Nathanson, Bernard; Davis, Susan E. Abortion and militancy. *In:* Pojman, Louis P.; Beckwith, Francis J., eds. The Abortion Controversy: A Reader. Boston: Jones and Bartlett; 1994: 445-461. Subject: 12.3

Pojman, Louis P.; Beckwith, Francis J.; Noonan, John T.; Tooley, Michael; Devine, Philip; Schwarz, Stephen; Gillespie, Norman C.; Summer, L.W. Personhood arguments on abortion. *In:* Pojman, Louis P.; Beckwith, Francis J., eds. The Abortion Controversy: A Reader. Boston: Jones and Bartlett; 1994: 177-292. Subject: 12.3

Pojman, Louis P.; Beckwith, Francis J.; Thompson, Judith Jarvis; Tribe, Laurence. Arguments from a woman's right to her body. *In:* Pojman, Louis P.; Beckwith, Francis J., eds. The Abortion Controversy: A Reader. Boston: Jones and Bartlett; 1994: 129-175. Subject: 12.3

Poland, Susan Cartier. Bioethics, biolaw, and western legal heritage. *Kennedy Institute of Ethics Journal* 2005 June; 15(2): 211-218. Subject: 2.1

Polis, Chelsea; Schaffer, Kate; Harrison, Teresa. Accessibility of emergency contraception in California's Catholic hospitals. *Women's Health Issues* 2005 July-August; 15(4): 174-178. Subject: 11.1

Pollack, Andrew. Justices expand rights to experiment with patented drugs. *New York Times* 2005 June 14; p. C1, C8. Subject: 9.7

Pollack, Andrew. Medical researcher moves to sever ties to companies. *New York Times* 2005 January 25; p. C4. Subject: 1.3.9

Pollack, Andrew. Moving stem cells front and center: researcher makes paralyzed rats walk and asks, why not people? *New York Times* 2005 February 23; p. C1, C10. Subject: 18.5.4

Pollack, Andrew. Patients in test won't get drug, Amgen decides. *New York Times* 2005 February 12; p. C1, C2. Subject: 9.7

Pollack, Simeon. A new approach to advance directives. *Critical Care Medicine* 2000 September; 28(9): 3146-3148. Subject: 20.5.4

Pollack, Simeon; Phillips, Russell S. Near end-of-life care preferences [letter and reply]. *American Journal of Medicine* 1996 December; 101(6): 663. Subject: 20.5.1

Pollitt, Rodney J. Compliance with science: consent or coercion in newborn screening [editorial]. *European Journal of Pediatrics* 2004 December; 163(12): 757-758. Subject: 8.3.4

Pols, Jeannette. Enacting appreciations: beyond the patient perspective. *Health Care Analysis: An International Journal of Health Care Philosophy and Policy* 2005 September; 13(3): 203-221. Subject: 18.5.6

Polzer, Jessica. Choice as responsibility: genetic testing as citizenship through familial oblation and the management of risk. *In:* Bunton, Robin; Petersen, Alan, eds. Genetic Governance: Health, Risk and Ethics in the Biotech Era. New York: Routledge; 2005: 79-92. Subject: 15.3

Pomerantz, A.M.; Pettibone, J.C. The influence of client characteristics on psychologists' ethical beliefs: an empirical investigation. *Journal of Clinical Psychology* 2005 April; 61(4): 517-528. Subject: 17.2

Pomerantz, Andrew M. Increasingly informed consent: discussing distinct aspects of psychotherapy at different points in time. *Ethics and Behavior* 2005; 15(4): 351-360. Subject: 8.3.1

Pomerantz, Anita; Rintel, E. Sean. Practices for reporting and responding to test results during medical consultations: enacting the roles of paternalism and independent expertise. *Discourse Studies* 2004 February; 6(1): 9-26. Subject: 8.1

Pontifical Academy for Life. Ethics and biomedical research. *Medical Ethics and Bioethics / Medicinska Etika & Bioetika* 2003 Spring-Summer; 10(1-2): 13-14. Subject: 18.1

Pontifical Academy for Life. Respect for the dignity of the dying person ethical observations on euthanasia. *Medical Ethics and Bioethics / Medicinska Etika & Bioetika* 2001 Spring-Summer; 8(1-2): 10-12. Subject: 20.5.1

Pope, Thaddeus Mason. Counting the dragon's teeth and claws: the definition of hard paternalism. *Georgia State University Law Review* 2004 Spring; 20(3): 659- 722. Subject: 9.1

Popov, Hristo. Psychotherapy ethics with violence victims. *Medicine and Law: World Association for Medical Law* 2005 March; 24(1): 81-93. Subject: 17.2

Popp, Richard L. Conflict of interest for the physician-inventor using a device in human subjects [editorial]. *American Heart Journal* 2005 January; 149(1): 1-3. Subject: 9.7

Portenoy, Russell; Lupu, Dale. Misconceptions about hospice [letter]. *Health Affairs* 2005 November-December; 24(6): 1686. Subject: 20.4.1

Porter, John D.H.; Ogden, Jessica A. Public health, ethics, and tuberculosis: is DOTs a breakthrough or inappropriate strategy in the Indian context? *Issues in Medical Ethics* 1999 July-September; 7(3): 79-84. Subject: 9.1

Porter, Theresa; Johnson, Punporn; Warren, Nancy A. Bioethical issues concerning death: death, dying, and end-of-life rights. *Critical Care Nursing Quarterly* 2005 January-March; 28(1): 85-92. Subject: 20.5.1

Post, May Mon. Human cloning: new hope, new implications, new challenges. *Temple International and Comparative Law Journal* 2001 Spring; 15(1): 171-193. Subject: 14.5

Post, Stephen G. Decelerated aging: should I drink from the fountain of youth? *In:* Post, Stephen G.; Binstock, Robert H., eds. The Fountain of Youth: Cultural, Scientific, and Ethical Perspectives on a Biomedical Goal. New York: Oxford University Press; 2004: 72-93. Subject: 9.5.2

Post, Stephen G. Dementia care ethics. *In:* Weisstub, David N.; Thomasma, David C.; Gauthier, Serge; Tomossy, George F., eds. Aging: Caring for Our Elders. Boston: Kluwer Academic; 2001: 177-190. Subject: 9.5.2

Postovsky, Sergey; Levenzon, Anna; Ofir, Ruth; Ben Arush, Myriam Weyl. "Do not resuscitate" orders among children with solid tumors at the end of life. *Pediatric Hematology and Oncology* 2004 October-November; 21(7): 661-668. Subject: 20.5.2

Pothier, David D. Many patients may not understand consent forms [letter]. *BMJ: British Medical Journal* 2005 May 14; 330(7500): 1151. Subject: 8.3.1

Potter, C. Ann. Will the "right to die" become a license to kill? The growth of euthanasia in America. *Journal of Legislation* 1993; 19(1): 31-62. Subject: 20.5.1

Potter, Nancy. Liberatory psychiatry and an ethics of the in-between. *In:* Shildrick, Margrit; Mykitiuk, Roxanne, eds. Ethics of the Body: Postconventional Challenges. Cambridge, MA: MIT Press; 2005: 113- 133. Subject: 17.1

Potts, M.; Evans, D.W. Does it matter that organ donors are not dead? Ethical and policy implications. *Journal of Medical Ethics* 2005 July; 31(7): 406-409. Subject: 19.5

Potts, Malcolm. A retreat from reason? The Catholic church and scientific progress. *Conscience* 2003 Spring; 24(1): 16-19. Subject: 14.1

Poutanen, Seppo. The first genetic screening in Finland: its execution, evaluation and some possible implications for liberal government. *In:* Bunton, Robin; Petersen, Alan, eds. Genetic Governance: Health, Risk and Ethics in the Biotech Era. New York: Routledge; 2005: 65-78. Subject: 15.3

Powell, Tia. Voice: cognitive impairment and medical decision making. *Journal of Clinical Ethics* 2005 Winter; 16(4): 303-313. Subject: 20.4.1

Powell, Tia P.; Oz, Mehmet C. Discontinuing the LVAD: ethical considerations [editorial]. *Annals of Thoracic Surgery* 1997 May; 63(5): 1223-1224. Subject: 20.5.1

Powers, Bethel Ann. Ethnographic analysis of everyday ethics in the care of nursing home residents with dementia: a taxonomy. *Nursing Research* 2001 November-December; 50(6): 332-339. Subject: 7.1

Powers, Bethel Ann. Everyday ethics in assisted living facilities: a framework for assessing resident-focused issues. *Journal of Gerontological Nursing* 2005 January; 31(1): 31-37. Subject: 9.5.2

Powers, John H.; Cooper, Charles K.; Lin, Daphne; Ross, David B. Sample size and the ethics of non-inferiority trials [letter]. *Lancet* 2005 July 2-8; 366(9479): 24-25. Subject: 18.2

Powers, Madison. Bioethics as politics: the limits of moral expertise. *Kennedy Institute of Ethics Journal* 2005 September; 15(3): 305-322. Subject: 2.1

Powhida, Alexander. Forced organ donation: the presumed consent to organ donation laws of the various states and the United States Constitution. *Albany Law Journal of Science and Technology* 1999; 9(2): 349-374. Subject: 19.5

Pradella, Geoffrey M. Substituting a judgment of best interests: dignity and the application of objective principles to PVS cases in the U.K. *European Journal of Health Law* 2005 December; 12(4): 335-345. Subject: 20.5.1

Prainsack, Barbara; Firestine, Ofer. Genetically modified survival: red and green biotechnology in Israel. *Science as Culture* 2005 December; 14(4): 355-372. Subject: 5.3

Prasad, M. Veera. Response: living donor liver transplantation [comment]. *Indian Journal of Medical Ethics* 2005 July-September; 2(3): 91-93. Subject: 19.5

Praskwiecz, Beth H. Assisted suicide: right or wrong? *Plastic Surgical Nursing* 2000 Spring; 20(1): 37-40. Subject: 20.7

Pratt, David A. Too many physicians: physician-assisted suicide after Glucksberg/Quill. *Albany Law Journal of Science and Technology* 1999; 9(2): 161-234. Subject: 20.7

Prendergast, Thomas J. Advance care planning: pitfalls, progress, promise. *Critical Care Medicine* 2001 February; 29(2, Supplement): N34-N39. Subject: 20.5.4

Prendergast, Thomas J.; Luce, John M. Increasing incidence of withholding and withdrawal of life support from the critically ill. *American Journal of Respiratory and Critical Care Medicine* 1997 January; 155(1): 15-20. Subject: 20.5.1

Prentice, Ross. Invited commentary: ethics and sample size — another view. *American Journal of Epidemiology* 2005 January 15; 161(2): 111-112. Subject: 18.2

President's Council on Bioethics (United States). The moral retrieval of ES cells: a new and promising proposal. *Ethics and Medics* 2005 July; 30(7): 1-2. Subject: 18.5.4

Pressel, David M. Nuremberg and Tuskegee: lessons for contemporary American medicine. *Journal of the National Medical Association* 2003 December; 95(12): 1216-1225. Subject: 2.2

Preston, Deborah Bray; Forti, Esther M.; Kassab, Cathy; Koch, Patricia Barthalow. Personal and social determinants of rural nurses' willingness to care for persons with AIDS. *Research in Nursing and Health* 2000 February; 23(1): 67-78. Subject: 9.5.6

Pretzlaff, Robert K. Should age be a deciding factor in ethical decision-making? *Health Care Analysis: An International Journal of Health Care Philosophy and Policy* 2005 June; 13(2): 119-128. Subject: 8.3.2

Preziosi, Paolo. Science, pharmacoeconomics and ethics in drug R&D: a sustainable future scenario? [opinion]. *Nature Reviews Drug Discovery* 2004 June; 3(6): 521-526. Subject: 9.7

Priaulx, Nicolette. Health, disability and parental interests: adopting a contextual approach in the reproductive torts. *European Journal of Health Law* 2005 September; 12(3): 213- 243. Subject: 4.4

Priaulx, Nicolette. Joy to the world! A (healthy) child is born! Reconceptualizing 'harm' in wrongful conception. *Social and Legal Studies* 2004; 13(1): 5-26. Subject: 11.4

Priaulx, Nicolette M. Conceptualising harm in the case of the 'unwanted' child. *European Journal of Health Law* 2002 December; 9(4): 337-359. Subject: 11.4

Price, Alan R.; Hallum, Jules V. The Office of Scientific Integrity investigations: the importance of data analysis. *Accountability in Research* 1992; 2(2): 133-137. Subject: 1.3.9

Price, Bob. Demonstrating respect for patient dignity. *Nursing Standard* 2004 December 1-7; 19(12): 45-52. Subject: 4.4

Price, Donald D. New facts and improved ethical guidelines for placebo analgesia [editorial]. *Journal of Pain* 2005 April; 6(4): 213-214. Subject: 18.3

Price, Linnie. Research ethics committees and conflicts of interest. *Bulletin of Medical Ethics* 2003 September; (191): 13-16. Subject: 18.2

Price-Hoskins, Pam. The right thing — for the right reason. *Journal of Christian Nursing* 2004 Fall; 21(4): 6-13. Subject: 4.1.3

Priest, Susanna Hornig; Eyck, Toby Ten. Transborder information, local resistance, and the spiral of silence: biotechnology and public opinion in the United States. *In:* Braman, Sandra, ed. Biotechnology and Communication: The Meta-Technologies of Information. Mahwah, NJ: Lawrence Erlbaum Associates; 2004: 175-194. Subject: 5.1

Prior, Pauline M. Dangerous lunacy: the misuse of mental health law in nineteenth-century Ireland. *Journal of Forensic Psychiatry and Psychology* 2003 December; 14(3): 525-541. Subject: 4.3

Pritt, Stacy; Nostrant, J.Fred; Smith, Barbara. PI and vet: potential conflict of interest? PI can't go it alone. *Lab Animal* 2004 October; 33(9): 21-22. Subject: 1.3.9

Priya, Ritu. Qualitative research in public health: perspectives and ethics. *Issues in Medical Ethics* 2000 October-December; 8(4): 113-115. Subject: 1.3.9

Proctor, S.E. School nurses and ethical dilemmas: are schools short on ethics? [editorial]. *Journal of School Nursing* 1998 April; 14(2): 3. Subject: 4.1.3

Pronchik, David J.; Melanson, Scott W.; Sexton, Joseph. Practicing emergency procedures on recently deceased patients [letter]. *Prehospital and Disaster Medicine* 1996 April-June; 11(2): 121-122. Subject: 7.2

Prothro, Gwendolyn. RU 486 examined: impact of a new technology on an old controversy. *University of Michigan Journal of Law Reform* 1997 Summer; 30(4): 715-741. Subject: 12.1

Prottas, Jeffrey. Ethics of allocation: lessons from organ procurement history. *In:* Youngner, Stuart J.; Anderson, Martha W.; Schapiro, Renie, eds. Transplanting Human Tissue: Ethics, Policy, and Practice. New York: Oxford University Press; 2004: 120-136. Subject: 19.6

Provoost, Veerle; Cools, Filip; Mortier, Freddy; Bilsen, Johan; Ramet, José; Vandenplas, Yvan; Deliens, Luc. Medical end-of-life decisions in neonates and infants in Flanders. *Lancet* 2005 April 9-15; 365(9467): 1315-1320. Subject: 20.5.2

Prusak, Bernard G. Rethinking "liberal eugenics": reflections and questions on Habermas on bioethics. *Hastings Center Report* 2005 November-December; 35(6): 31-42. Subject: 15.5

Public Access Defibrillation [PAD] Trial Investigators ; Mosesso, Vincent N., Jr.; Brown, Lawrence H.; Greene, H. Leon; Schmidt, Terri A.; Aufderheide, Tom P.; Sayre, Michael R.; Stephens, Shannon W.; Travers, Andrew; Craven, Richard A.; Weisfeldt, Myron L.

Conducting research using the emergency exception from informed consent: the Public Access Defibrillation (PAD) Trial experience. *Resuscitation* 2004 April; 61(1): 29-36. Subject: 18.3

Puchalski, Christina M.; Dorff, Elliot; Hendi, Yahya. Spirituality, religion, and healing in palliative care. *Clinics in Geriatric Medicine* 2004 November; 20(4): 689-714, vi-vii. Subject: 20.4.1

Pujari, Sanjay. Antiretrovirals in India [opinion]. *Issues in Medical Ethics* 1998 January; 6(1): 24-25. Subject: 9.5.6

Pullman, Daryl. Ethics first aid: reframing the role of "principlism" in clinical ethics education and practice. *Journal of Clinical Ethics* 2005 Fall; 16(3): 223-229. Subject: 2.1

Pullman, Daryl. Research governance, bio-politics and political will: recent lessons from Newfoundland and Labrador. *Health Law Review* 2005; 13(2-3): 75-79. Subject: 18.2

Pullman, Daryl; Latus, Andrew. Reconciling social justice and economic opportunism: regulating the Newfoundland genome. *In:* Knoppers, Bartha Maria, ed. Populations and Genetics: Legal and Socio-Ethical Perspectives. Boston: Martinus Nijhoff; 2003: 543-564. Subject: 15.1

Purdy, Laura. Like a motherless child: fetal eggs and families. *Journal of Clinical Ethics* 2005 Winter; 16(4): 329-334. Subject: 14.2

Purtilo, Ruth B. Managed care: challenges facing interdisciplinary health care teams. *Update [Loma Linda University Center for Christian Bioethics]* 1995 October; 11(3); 8 p. Subject: 9.3.2

Putnam, Andrew. Do I have to resuscitate this patient against her wishes? *American Family Physician* 2003 May 1; 67(9): 2025-2028. Subject: 20.5.1

Putnam, Andrew T. Pain management and palliative care. *In:* McMahon, Kevin T., ed. Moral Issues in Catholic Health Care. Wynnewood, PA: Saint Charles Borromeo Seminary; 2004: 139- 152. Subject: 20.4.1

Putnam, Jonathan D. Costs and benefits of genomics patents. *American Journal of Pharmacogenomics* 2004; 4(5): 277-292. Subject: 15.8

Putsch, Robert W.; Pololi, Linda. Distributive justice in American healthcare: institutions, power, and the equitable care of patients. *American Journal of Managed Care* 2004 September; 10(Special Issue): SP45-SP53. Subject: 9.2

Pyper, Cecilia; Amery, Justin; Watson, Marion; Crook, Claire. Access to electronic health records in primary care — a survey of patients' views. *Medical Science Monitor* 2004 November; 10(11): SR17-SR22. Subject: 1.3.12

Q

Quammen, David. Clone your troubles away: dreaming of the frontiers of animal husbandry. *Harper's Magazine* 2005 February; 310(1857): 33-43. Subject: 14.5

Quick, John J. Genetic discrimination and the need for federal legislation. *Journal of Biolaw and Business* 2005; 8(1): 22-26. Subject: 15.3

Quill, Timothy E. The million dollar question. *New England Journal of Medicine* 2005 April 21; 352(16): 1632. Subject: 20.5.1

Quill, Timothy E. Terri Schiavo — a tragedy compounded [opinion]. *New England Journal of Medicine* 2005 April 21; 352(16): 1630- 1631, 1633. Subject: 20.5.1

Quilligan, Edward J. Conflict of interest [editorial]. *American Journal of Obstetrics and Gynecology* 2004 October; 191(4): 1057-1058. Subject: 1.3.9

Quinlan, Megan. Forcible medication and personal autonomy: the case of Charles Thomas Sell. *Boston University Law Review* 2004 February; 84(1): 275-299. Subject: 17.4

Quintavalle, Josephine; Hurlbut, William B. The many perils that lie ahead [letter and reply]. *National Catholic Bioethics Quarterly* 2005 Spring; 5(1): 16- 17, 19-22. Subject: 18.5.4

R

Raab, Edward L. The parameters of informed consent. *Transactions of the American Ophthalmological Society* 2004; 102: 225-232. Subject: 8.3.1

Raabe, Hans-Christian. Mandatory reporting of all sexually active under-13s: confidential sexual health services to young people: part of the solution or part of the problem? [letter]. *BMJ: British Medical Journal* 2005 November 5; 331(7524): 1083. Subject: 9.5.7

Rabino, Isaac. Genetic testing and its implications: human genetics researchers grapple with ethical issues. *Science, Technology, and Human Values* 2003 Summer; 28(3): 365- 402. Subject: 15.2

Rabinow, Paul. Life sciences: discontents and consolations. *In:* Baillie, Harold W.; Casey, Timothy K., eds. Is Human Nature Obsolete? Genetics Bioengineering, and the Future of the Human Condition. Cambridge, MA: MIT Press; 2005: 99-121. Subject: 15.1

Rademakers, J.; Koster, E.; Jansen-van Hees, A.C.V.; Willems, F. Medical abortion as an alternative to vacuum aspiration: first experiences with the 'abortion pill' in The Netherlands. *European Journal of Contraception and Reproductive Health Care* 2001 December; 6(4): 185-191. Subject: 12.5.2

Radick, Gregory. Discovering and patenting human genes. *In:* Bainham, Andrew; Sclater, Shelley Day; Richards, Martin, eds. Body Lore and Laws. Portland, OR: Hart Pub.; 2002: 63-78. Subject: 15.8

Radstone, S.J.J. Practising on the poor? Healthcare workers' beliefs about the role of medical students during their elective. *Journal of Medical Ethics* 2005 February; 31(2): 109-110. Subject: 7.2

Rady, Mohamed Y.; Johnson, Daniel J. Admission to intensive care unit at the end-of-life: is it an informed decision? *Palliative Medicine* 2004 December; 18(8): 705-711. Subject: 20.4.1

Ragni, G.; Allegra, A.; Anserini, P.; Causio, F.; Ferraretti, A.P.; Greco, E.; Palermo, R.; Somigliana, E. The 2004 Italian legislation regulating assisted reproduction technology: a multicentre survey on the results of IVF cycles. *Human Reproduction* 2005 August; 20(8): 2224-2228. Subject: 14.4

Ragone, Helena. The gift of life: surrogate motherhood, gamete donation and constructions of altruism. *In:* Cook, Rachel; Sclater, Shelley Day; Kaganas, Felicity, eds. Surrogate Motherhood: International Perspectives. Portland, OR: Hart; 2003: 209-226. Subject: 14.2

Ragone, Helena; Willis, Sharla K. Reproduction and assisted reproductive technologies. *In:* Albrecht, Gary L.; Fitzpatrick, Ray; Scrimshaw, Susan C., eds. The Handbook of Social Studies in Health & Medicine. Thousand Oaks, CA: Sage; 2000: 308-322. Subject: 14.1

Rahdert, George K.; Lapertosa, Max. Brief of amici curiae Not Dead Yet et al., Jeb Bush v. Michael Schiavo. *Issues in Law and Medicine* 2004 Fall; 20(2): 171-181. Subject: 20.5.1

Rahemtulla, Taslin; Bhopal, Raj. Pharmacogenetics and ethnically targeted therapies: the new drug BiDil marks the return of biology to the debate about race and ethnicity [editorial]. *BMJ: British Medical Journal* 2005 May 7; 330(7499): 1036-1037. Subject: 15.1

Rahman, Mahbubur; Morita, Satoshi; Fukui, Tsuguya; Sakamoto, Junichi. Physicians' reasons for not entering their patients in a randomized controlled trial in Japan. *Tohoku Journal of Experimental Medicine* 2004 June; 203(2): 105-109. Subject: 18.2

Rahman, Masoor-Ur; Arabi, Yaseen; Adhami, Naeem A.; Parker, Barbara; Al-Shimemeri, Abdullah. The practice of do-not-resuscitate orders in the Kingdom of Saudi Arabia. The experience of a tertiary care center. *Saudi Medical Journal* 2004 September; 25(9): 1278-1279. Subject: 20.5.1

Rai, Arti K. The information revolution reaches pharmaceuticals: balancing innovation incentives, cost, and access in the post-genomics era. *University of Illinois Law Review* 2001; 2001(1): 173-210. Subject: 15.10

Rai, Saritha. Drug companies cut costs with foreign clinical trials. *New York Times* 2005 February 24; p. C4. Subject: 18.5.9

Raines, Deborah A. Ethical reflection and resolution. *AWHONN's Clinical Issues in Perinatal and Women's Health Nursing* 1993; 4(4): 641-647. Subject: 4.1.3

Raines, Deborah A. Values: a guiding force. *AWHONN's Clinical Issues in Perinatal and Women's Health Nursing* 1993; 4(4): 533-541. Subject: 4.4

Raj, Kirath. The presidents' mental health. *American Journal of Law and Medicine* 2005; 31(4): 509-524. Subject: 17.1

Raja, Asad Jamil. The revised Helsinki Declaration: is it enough? *Issues in Medical Ethics* 2001 October-December; 9(4): 114-116. Subject: 18.2

Rajput, Vijay. Addressing the organ shortage: presumed consent and xenotransplants. *Issues in Medical Ethics* 2001 April-June; 9(2): 54-55. Subject: 19.5

Rajput, Vijay; Golden, William E.; Doherty, Robert B. Position paper: ethics manual [letter and reply]. *Annals of Internal Medicine* 2005 October 18; 143(8): 618. Subject: 2.1

Ralstin-Lewis, D. Marie. The continuing struggle against genocide: indigenous women's reproductive rights. *Wicazo SA Review* 2005 Spring; 20(1): 71-95. Subject: 11.3

Ramadge, Joanne. Regulating ethics [editorial]. *Collegian* 2001 January; 8(1): 5. Subject: 9.5.2

Ramakrishna, Jayashree. Rapport building and blurring identity [comment]. *Indian Journal of Medical Ethics* 2005 April-June; 2(2): 57. Subject: 18.5.6

Ramakrishna, Jayashree. Values and obligations in qualitative research. *Issues in Medical Ethics* 2001 January-March; 9(1): 5-6. Subject: 18.1

Ramellini, Pietro. Some critical comments on oocyte-assisted reprogramming [letter]. *National Catholic Bioethics Quarterly* 2005 Winter; 5(4): 658- 660. Subject: 15.4

Ramesh, H. Live operative workshops: ethical issues [letter]. *National Medical Journal of India* 2004; 17(4): 224. Subject: 7.2

Ramfelt, Ethel; Lützén, Kim. Patients with cancer: their approaches to participation in treatment plan decisions. *Nursing Ethics* 2005 March; 12(2): 143-155. Subject: 8.1

Ramsey, Gloria. Nurses, medical errors, and the culture of blame. *Hastings Center Report* 2005 March-April; 35(2): 20-21. Subject: 9.8

Ramsey, Paul. Genetic therapy: a theologian's response. *In:* Hamilton, Michael P., ed. The New Genetics and the Future of Man. Grand Rapids, MI: William B. Eerdmans Publishing Co.; 1972: 157-175. Subject: 15.4

Rance, Susanna; Salinas, Silvia. Ethical mapping: a methodological proposal. *Issues in Medical Ethics* 2001 July-September; 9(3): 86-87. Subject: 18.2

Rand, Cynthia S.; Sevick, Mary Ann. Ethics in adherence promotion and monitoring. *Controlled Clinical Trials* 2000 October; 21(5 Supplement): 241S-247S. Subject: 2.1

Randal, Asha Emsley. The personal, interpersonal, and political issues of egg donation. *Journal of Obstetrics and Gynaecology Canada* 2004 December; 26(12): 1087-1090. Subject: 14.4

Rane, Wishwas; Deodhar, N.S. The ethics of public health: how can equity, social justice and human rights be incorporated into public health programmes? *Issues in Medical Ethics* 1998 October-December; 6(4): 119-120. Subject: 9.1

Ranganathan, M.; Raghuraman, G. Ethical considerations in obtaining consent under anaesthesia [letter]. *Anaesthesia* 2003 December; 58(12): 1250-1251. Subject: 8.3.2

Rankin, Mark J. Contemporary Australian abortion law: the description of a crime and the negation of a woman's right to abortion. *Monash University Law Review* 2001; 27(2): 229-252. Subject: 12.4.1

Rannamae, Andres. Estonian Genome Project—large scale health status description and DNA collection. *In:* Knoppers, Bartha Maria, ed. Populations and Genetics: Legal and Socio-Ethical Perspectives. Boston: Martinus Nijhoff; 2003: 17-36. Subject: 15.1

Rao, Kamini A. Infertility treatment is a human right [case study]. *Indian Journal of Medical Ethics* 2005 October-December; 2(4): 128. Subject: 14.1

Rao, Mohan. Female foeticide: where do we go? *Issues in Medical Ethics* 2001 October-December; 9(4): 123-124. Subject: 12.4.2

Rao, Mohan. Neo-eugenics: the quinacrine sterilisation of women in India. *Women's Link* 1997 July-September; 3(3): 12-15. [Online]. Available: http://www.hsph.harvard.edu/ Organizations/healthnet/SAsia/suchana/0200/h024.html [27 May 2005]. Subject: 11.3

Rao, Mohan. Quinacrine sterilisation trials: a scientific scandal? *Reprinted from: Economic and Political Weekly* 1998 March 28; 33(13); 7 p. [Online]. Available: http://www.hsph.harvard.edu/Organizations/ healthnet/SAsia/suchana/9999/quinacrine.html [7 October 2005]. Subject: 11.3

Rao, Mohan. Quinacrine sterilisations banned. Health for Millions 1998 May-June; 2 p. [Online]. Available: http://www.hsph.harvard.edu/Organizations/healthnet/ SAsia/suchana/0719/rh189.html [7 October 2005]. Subject: 11.3

Rao, Mohan. Supreme Court judgement on sterilisations [editorial]. *Indian Journal of Medical Ethics* 2005 April-June; 2(2): 40-41. Subject: 11.3

Rao, Neomi. A backdoor to policy making: the use of philosophers by the Supreme Court. *University of Chicago Law Review* 1998 Fall; 65(4): 1371-1401. Subject: 20.7

Rao, Radhika. Property, privacy, and the human body. *Boston University Law Review* 2000 April; 80(2): 359-460. Subject: 4.4

Rao, Radhika. Surrogacy law in the United States: the outcome of ambivalence. *In:* Cook, Rachel; Sclater, Shelley Day; Kaganas, Felicity, eds. Surrogate Motherhood: International Perspectives. Portland, OR: Hart; 2003: 23-34. Subject: 14.2

Rappaport, Aaron J. Beyond personhood and autonomy: moral theory and the premises of privacy. *Utah Law Review* 2001; 2001(2): 441-507. Subject: 4.4

Rappert, Brian. Responsibility in the life sciences: assessing the role of professional codes. *Biosecurity and Bioterrorism: Biodefense Strategy, Practice, and Science* 2004; 2(3): 164-174. Subject: 6

Rasch, Vibeke; Muhammad, Hamed; Urassa, Ernest; Bergström, Staffan. The problem of illegally induced abortion: results from a hospital-based study conducted at district level in Dar es Salaam. *Tropical Medicine and International Health* 2000 July; 5(7): 495-502. Subject: 12.1

Rasmussen, Colin. Canada's Assisted Human Reproductive Act: is it scientific censorship, or a reasoned approach to the regulation of rapidly emerging reproductive technologies? *Saskatchewan Law Review* 2004; 67(1): 97-135. Subject: 18.5.4

Rasmussen, Lisa M. The ethics and aesthetics of for-profit bioethics consultation. *HEC (Healthcare Ethics Committee) Forum* 2005 June; 17(2): 94-121. Subject: 9.6

Rasmussen, Nicolas. The drug industry and clinical research in interwar America: three types of physician collaborator. *Bulletin of the History of Medicine* 2005 Spring; 79(1): 50-80. Subject: 9.7

Rassin, Michal; Lowenthal, Miri; Silner, Dina. Fear, ambivalence, and liminality: key concepts in refusal to donate an organ after brain death. *JONA's Healthcare Law, Ethics, and Regulation* 2005 July- September; 7(3): 79-85. Subject: 19.5

Rastogi, Anil Kumar. End-of-life issues neglected in India. *Indian Journal of Medical Ethics* 2005 July-September; 2(3): 83-84. Subject: 20.5.1

Ratcliff, Kathryn Strother. Contraception and abortion. *In her:* Women and Health: Power, Technology, Inequality, and Conflict in a Gendered World. Boston, MA: Allyn and Bacon; 2002: 191-209. Subject: 11.1

Ratcliff, Kathryn Strother. Fetal quality control. *In her:* Women and Health: Power, Technology, Inequality, and Conflict in a Gendered World. Boston, MA: Allyn and Bacon; 2002: 245-260. Subject: 15.2

Ratcliff, Kathryn Strother. Technology-assisted contraception. *In her:* Women and Health: Power, Technology, Inequality, and Conflict in a Gendered World. Boston, MA: Allyn and Bacon; 2002: 228-244. Subject: 11.1

Rath, Johannes; Jank, Bernhard; Somerville, Margaret A.; Atlas, Ronald M. Using ethics to fight bioterrorism [letter and reply]. *Science* 2005 August 12; 309(5737): 1012-1013, 1014-1015, 1017. Subject: 21.3

Ratner, Edward; Bartels, Dianne; Song, John. A perspective on homelessness, ethics, and medical care. *Minnesota Medicine* 2004 June; 87(6): 50-52. Subject: 20.4.1

Raval, Nischol K.; Andrade, Chittaranjan. Unmodified ECT vs modified ECT [letter and reply]. *Issues in Medical Ethics* 2003 July-September; 11(3): 100-101. Subject: 17.5

Ravelingien, A.; Braeckman, J. To the core of porcine matter: evaluating arguments against producing transgenic pigs. *Xenotransplantation* 2004 July; 11(4): 371-375. Subject: 15.1

Ravelingien, An. Use of pigs for xenotransplantation: the speciesism by proxy syndrome. *Xenotransplantation* 2005 May; 12(3): 235-239. Subject: 22.2

Ravelingien, An. The world is my patient: a discussion of Martine Rothblatt's Your Life or Mine: how geoethics can resolve the conflict between public and private interests in xenotransplantation [opinion]. *Xenotransplantation* 2005 March; 12(2): 88-90. Subject: 19.1

Ravelingien, An; Braeckman, Johan. The patients' perspective: comments on 'Reluctance of French patients with type 1 diabetes to undergo pig pancreatic islet xenotransplantation' [opinion]. *Xenotransplantation* 2005 May; 12(3): 173-174. Subject: 19.1

Ravelingien, An; Krom, André. Earning points for moral behavior: organ allocation based on reciprocity. *International Journal of Applied Philosophy* 2005 Spring; 19(1): 73-83. Subject: 19.6

Ravenstein, Christian. Discontinuation of life supporting measures in Germany. *European Journal of Health Law* 2002 December; 9(4): 321-335. Subject: 20.5.1

Ravindra, R.P. The campaign against sex determination tests. *In:* Datar, Chhaya, ed. The Struggle Against Violence. Calcutta: Shree Pub. 1993; 27 p. [Online]. Available: http://www.hsph.harvard.edu/Organizations/healthnet/SAsia/suchana/0400b/h060.html [7 October 2005]. Subject: 14.3

Ravindra, R.P. Ethics in human medical research: views of a non-medical person. *Medical Ethics: Journal of Forum for Medical Ethics Society* 1994 May-July; 1(4): 6-7. Subject: 18.1

Ravindra, R.P. Myths about sex determination tests. *Facts Against Myths* 1995 June; 2(3): 1-6. [Online]. Available: http://www.hsph.harvard.edu/Organizations/healthnet/Sasia/suchana/0500/h003.html [27 May 2005]. Subject: 14.3

Ravindra, R.P. New reproductive technologies and the Indian woman. *In:* Shankar, Jogan, ed. Social Problems and Welfare in India. Delhi: Ashish Publ. 1992; 14 p. [On-line]. Available: http://www.hsph.harvard.edu/Organizations/healthnet/SAsia/suchana/0400b/h022.html [3 October 2005]. Subject: 14.1

Ravindran, G.D. The physician and the pharmaceutical industry: both must keep the patient's interests at heart. *Issues in Medical Ethics* 1999 January-March; 7(1): 21-22. Subject: 9.7

Ravindran, G.D.; Kalam, T.; Lewin, S.; Pais, P. Teaching medical ethics: a model. *Issues in Medical Ethics* 1998 July-September; 6(3): 83-84. Subject: 2.3

Ravindran, T.K. Sundari; Ramanathan, Mala; Alex, Shiney C. A community-based study on induced abortions: some unanswered questions [letter]. *Issues in Medical Ethics* 2001 April-June; 9(2): 36-37. Subject: 18.4

Ravitsky, Vardit. Timers on ventilators. *BMJ: British Medical Journal* 2005 February 19; 330(7488): 415- 417. Subject: 20.5.1

Ravitsky, Vardit; Wendler, David. Dissolving the dilemma over forced treatment. *Lancet* 2005 April 30-May 6; 365(9470): 1525-1526. Subject: 8.3.4

Rawbone, Roger G. Future impact of genetic screening in occupational and environmental medicine. *Occupational and Environmental Medicine* 1999 November; 56: 721-724. Subject: 15.3

Rawle, Frances C. UK DNA sample collections for research. *In:* Knoppers, Bartha Maria, ed. Populations and Genetics: Legal and Socio-Ethical Perspectives. Boston: Martinus Nijhoff; 2003: 3-15. Subject: 15.1

Rawlinson, Mary C.; Donchin, Anne. The quest for universality: reflections on the universal draft declaration on bioethics and human rights. *Developing World Bioethics* 2005 September; 5(3): 258-266. Subject: 2.1

Ray, Pierre F.; Munnich, Arnold; Nisand, Israël; Frydman, René; Vekemans, Michel; Viville, Stéphane. Is preimplantation genetic diagnosis for 'social sexing' desirable in today's and tomorrow's society? [letter]. *Human Reproduction* 2003 February; 18(2): 463-464. Subject: 15.2

Raz, Aviad. "Important to test, important to support": attitudes toward disability rights and prenatal diagnosis among leaders of support groups for genetic disorders in Israel. *Social Science and Medicine* 2004 November; 59(9): 1857-1866. Subject: 15.2

Raz, Aviad E. Disability rights, prenatal diagnosis and eugenics: a cross- cultural view. *Journal of Genetic Counseling* 2005 June; 14(3): 183-187. Subject: 15.2

Raza, Mohsin; Hedayat, K.M. Some sociocultural aspects of cadaver organ donation: recent rulings from Iran. *Transplantation Proceedings* 2004 December; 36(10): 2888-2890. Subject: 19.5

Ready, Tinker. Cornell University scientists face charges of fraud [news]. *Nature Medicine* 2005 August; 11(8): 810. Subject: 1.3.9

Subject = NRCBL Primary Classification Number; See inside front cover

Ready, Tinker. Courts crack down on drug marketing strategies [news]. *Nature Medicine* 2004 July; 10(7): 655. Subject: 9.7

Ready, Tinker. Private donors breathe new life into US stem cell research [news]. *Nature Medicine* 2004 April; 10(4): 320. Subject: 18.5.4

Ready, Tinker. Scientists irked by ethicists' alternatives for embryo research [news]. *Nature Medicine* 2005 February; 11(2): 108. Subject: 18.5.4

Reagan, Leslie J. Crossing the border for abortions: California activists, Mexican clinics, and the creation of a feminist health agency in the 1960s. *Feminist Studies* 2000 Summer; 26(2): 323-348. Subject: 12.4.1

Reardon, David C. Abortion decisions and the duty to screen: clinical, ethical, and legal implications of predictive risk factors of post-abortion maladjustment. *Journal of Contemporary Health Law and Policy* 2003 Winter; 20(1): 33-114. Subject: 12.5.3

Reardon, David C.; Strahan, Thomas W.; Thorp, John M., Jr.; Shuping, Martha W. Deaths associated with abortion compared to childbirth — a review of new and old data and the medical and legal implications. *Journal of Contemporary Health Law and Policy* 2004 Spring; 20(2): 279-327. Subject: 12.4.3

Recupero, Patricia R. E-mail and the psychiatrist-patient relationship. *Journal of the American Academy of Psychiatry and the Law* 2005; 33(4): 465-475. Subject: 1.3.12

Rediger, Bryon B. Living in a world with HIV: balancing privacy, privilege and the right to know between patients and health care professionals. *Hamline Journal of Public Law and Policy* 2000; 21(2): 443-487. Subject: 9.5.6

Redman, Barbara K. The ethics of self-management preparation for chronic illness. *Nursing Ethics* 2005 July; 12(4): 360-369. Subject: 9.5.1

Redman, Barbara K.; Caplan, Arthur L. Off with their heads: the need to criminalize some forms of scientific misconduct. *Journal of Law, Medicine and Ethics* 2005 Summer; 33(2): 345- 348. Subject: 1.3.9

Redman, Barbara K.; Merz, Jon F. Evaluating the oversight of scientific misconduct. *Accountability in Research* 2005 July-September; 12(3): 157- 162. Subject: 5.3

Redman, Paul C., II; Redman, Lauren Fielder. Seeking a better solution for the disposition of frozen embryos: is embryo adoption the answer? *Tulsa Law Journal* 2000 Spring-Summer; 35(3-4): 583-598. Subject: 14.6

Regalado, Antonio. Senators mull new ways to make stem cells. *Wall Street Journal* 2005 July 20; p. B1, B4. Subject: 18.5.4

Regalado, Antonio. Stem-cell rift shows difficulty obtaining eggs. *Wall Street Journal* 2005 November 14; p. B1, B3. Subject: 14.6

Regalado, Antonio; Dumcius, Gintautas. Stem-cell labs to get guidance on ethics issues. *Wall Street Journal* 2005 April 26; p. B1, B7. Subject: 18.5.4

Regan, Tom. Empty cages: animal rights and vivisection. *In:* Cohen, Andrew I.; Wellman, Christopher Heath, eds. Contemporary Debates in Applied Ethics. Malden, MA: Blackwell Pub., 2005: 77-90. Subject: 22.2

Regenberg, Alan C.; Mathews, Debra J.H. Resisting the tide of professionalization: valuing diversity in bioethics [comment]. *American Journal of Bioethics* 2005 September-October; 5(5): 44-45. Subject: 2.1

Regidor, Enrique. The use of personal data from medical records and biological materials: ethical perspectives and the basis for legal restrictions in health research. *Social Science and Medicine* 2004 November; 59(9): 1975-1984. Subject: 18.3

Rehm, Jürgen; Fischer, Benedikt; Hayden [sic, Haydon], Emma; Room, Robin. Abstinence ideology and somatic treatment for addicts — ethical considerations [editorial]. *Addiction Research and Theory* 2003 October; 11(5): 287-293. Subject: 9.5.9

Reich, Eugenie Samuel. Cloning crisis goes from bad to worse [news]. *New Scientist* 2005 December 24-2006 January 6; 188(2531-2532): 4. Subject: 14.5

Reichman, Edward. Don't pull the plug on brain death just yet. *Tradition* 2004 Winter; 38(4): 63-69. Subject: 20.2.1

Reichman, Edward. Why is this gene different from all other genes? The Jewish approach to biotechnology. *In:* Brannigan, Michael C., ed. Cross-Cultural Biotechnology. Lanham: Rowman and Littlefield; 2004: 93-104. Subject: 15.1

Reicin, Cheryl; McMahon, Eileen. Stem cell research in Canada: business opportunities for U.S. companies. *Journal of Biolaw and Business* 2005; 8(1): 61-64. Subject: 18.5.4

Reid, Lynette. Diminishing returns? Risk and the duty to care in the SARS epidemic. *Bioethics* 2005 August; 19(4): 348-361. Subject: 8.1

Reid, Lynette. Nice work if you can get it [comment]. *American Journal of Bioethics* 2005 September-October; 5(5): 27-29. Subject: 18.3

Reid, Lynette; Baylis, Françoise. Brains, genes, and the making of the self. *American Journal of Bioethics* 2005 March-April; 5(2): 21-23. Subject: 17.1

Reidenberg, Marcus M. Decreasing publication bias [opinion]. *Clinical Pharmacology and Therapeutics* 1998 January; 63(1): 1-3. Subject: 1.3.9

Reigle, Juanita. The ethics of physical restraints in critical care. *AACN Clinical Issues* 1996 November; 7(4): 585-591. Subject: 17.3

Reilly, Elizabeth A. The rhetoric of disrespect: uncovering the faulty premises infecting reproductive rights. *American University Journal of Gender, Social Policy, and the Law* 1996 Fall; 5(1): 147-205. Subject: 12.4.2

Reilly, Phil. Legal and public policy issues in DNA forensics [opinion]. *Nature Reviews Genetics* 2001 April; 2(4): 313-317. Subject: 15.1

Rein, Andrea J.; Harshman, Dana L.; Frick, Trisha; Phillips, Jean M.; Lewis, Shirley; Nolan, Marie T. Advance directive decision making among medical inpatients. *Journal of Professional Nursing* 1996 January-February; 12(1): 39-46. Subject: 20.5.4

Rein, Diane C. Icelandic genetic database. *In:* Ness, Bryan D., ed. Encyclopedia of Genetics. Revised edition. Volume II. Pasadena, Calif.: Salem Press; 2004: 447-449. Subject: 15.1

Reinders, Hans S. The ethics of behavior modification. *Ethics and Intellectual Disability Newsletter* 2003 Spring; 7(2): 1-3. Subject: 17.3

Reiser, Stanley Joel. Research compensation and the monetarization of medicine. *JAMA: The Journal of the American Medical Association* 2005 February 2; 293(5): 613-614. Subject: 18.3

Reisman, Anna B. Indiscretions. *Hastings Center Report* 2005 September-October; 35(5): 8-9. Subject: 8.4

Reisner, Avram Israel; Parens, Erik. Genetics and complexity [letter and reply]. *Hastings Center Report* 2004 July-August; 34(4): 4-5. Subject: 15.1

Reiss, Michael J. Is it right to move genes between species? A theological perspective. *In:* Deane-Drummond, Celia; Szerszynski, Bronislaw, eds. Re- ordering Nature: Theology, Society and the New Genetics. New York: T & T Clark; 2003: 138-150. Subject: 15.1

Reitsma, Angelique M.; Moreno, Jonathan D. Ethics of innovative surgery: US surgeons' definitions, knowledge, and attitudes. *Journal of the American College of Surgeons* 2005 January; 200(1): 103-110. Subject: 18.2

Rempusheski, Veronica F.; Hurley, Ann C. Advance directives and dementia. *Journal of Gerontological Nursing* 2000 October; 26(10): 27-34. Subject: 20.5.4

Renke, Wayne. The constitutionality of mandatory reporting of gunshot wounds legislation. *Health Law Review* 2005; 14(1): 3-8. Subject: 8.4

Rentetzi, Maria. The women radium dial painters as experimental subjects (1920- 1990), or: what counts as human experimentation? *In:* Roelcke, Volker; Maio, Giovanni, eds. Twentieth Century Ethics of Human Subjects Research: Historical Perspectives on Values, Practices, and Regulations. Stuttgart: Franz Steiner Verlag; 2004: 275-291. Subject: 18.5.3

Rentetzi, Maria. The women radium dial painters as experimental subjects (1920-1990) or what counts as human experimentation. *NTM* 2004; 12(4): 233-248. Subject: 18.5.3

Rentmeester, Christy A. Pharma PR or medical education? [letter]. *Hastings Center Report* 2005 March-April; 35(2): 6-7. Subject: 9.7

Repenshek, Mark; Belde, David. Honoring experience in moral discourse. *Health Care Ethics USA [electronic]* 2005; 13(1); 3 p. Available: http://www.slu.edu/centers/chce/hceusa/1_2005_2.html [19 September 2005]. Subject: 2.3

Resnicow, Ken; Braithwaite, Ronald L. Cultural sensitivity in public health. *In:* Braithwaite, Ronald L.; Taylor, Sandra E., eds. Health Issues in the Black Community. 2nd ed. San Francisco: Jossey-Bass; 2001: 516-542. Subject: 9.5.4

Resnik, D.B. Eliminating the daily life risks standard from the definition of minimal risk. *Journal of Medical Ethics* 2005 January; 31(1): 35-38. Subject: 18.2

Resnik, David B. Conflicts of interest at the NIH: no easy solution. *Hastings Center Report* 2005 January-February; 35(1): 18-20. Subject: 1.3.9

Resnik, David B. Genetic engineering and social justice: a Rawlsian approach. *Social Theory Practice* 1997 Fall; 23(3): 427-448. Subject: 15.1

Resnik, David B. The patient's duty to adhere to prescribed treatment: an ethical analysis. *Journal of Medicine and Philosophy* 2005 April; 30(2): 167-188. Subject: 8.3.4

Resnik, David B. Using electronic discussion boards to teach responsible conduct of research. *Science and Engineering Ethics* 2005 October; 11(4): 617-630. Subject: 2.3

Resnik, David B.; Zeldin, Darryl C.; Sharp, Richard R. Research on environmental health interventions: ethical problems and solutions. *Accountability in Research* 2005 April-June; 12(2): 69-101. Subject: 18.6

Restum, Zulficar Gregory. Public health implications of substandard correctional health care. *American Journal of Public Health* 2005 October; 95(10): 1689- 1691. Subject: 9.5.1

Retsas, Spyros. Treatment at random: the ultimate science or the betrayal of Hippocrates? *Journal of Clinical Oncology* 2004 December 15; 22(24): 5005-5008. Subject: 18.2

Reusser, Ruth. Nationale Modelle zur Regelung des Gebrauchs der Gendiagnostik. Schweiz: Die schweizerische Rechtsordnung—Ein Beispiel für Regelungsansätze in Etappen. *In:* Honnefelder, Ludger; Mieth, Dietmar; Propping, Peter; Siep, Ludwig; Wiesemann, Claudia, eds. Das genetische Wissen und die Zukunft des Menschen. New York: De Gruyter; 2003: 237-243. Subject: 15.3

Reuter, Lars. Pandora's box? Theological perspectives on cloning. *In:* Ostnor, Lars, ed. Bioethics and Cloning: Report from a Workshop Arranged by the Nordic Theological Network for Bioethics in Arhus, September 25-27, 1998.

Subject = NRCBL Primary Classification Number; See inside front cover

Oslo: Nordic Theological Network for Bioethics; 1998: 73-77. Subject: 14.5

Reuter, Lars. The saving power of biotechnology: on public perceptions of a field of technology. *Ethical Perspectives* 2005 March; 12(1): 3-16. Subject: 5.1

Reveiz, Ludovic; Cardona, Andres Felipe; Ospina, Edgar Guillermo. Clinical trial registration. *New England Journal of Medicine* 2005 January 13; 352(2): 198. Subject: 18.6

Revel, Michel. Are genes our destiny?: Implications and ethical limitations of genetic determination in medicine and behavioral sciences. *In:* Blazer, Shraga; Zimmer, Etan Z., eds. The Embryo: Scientific Discovery and Medical Ethics. New York: Karger; 2005: 143-165. Subject: 15.1

Revel, Michel. Ethical issues of human embryo cloning technologies for stem cell research. *In:* Blazer, Shraga; Zimmer, Etan Z., eds. The Embryo: Scientific Discovery and Medical Ethics. New York: Karger; 2005: 107-119. Subject: 14.5

Reverby, Susan M. Rethinking the Tuskegee Syphilis Study: Nurse Rivers, silence and the meaning of treatment. *Nursing History Review* 1999; 7: 3-28. Subject: 18.5.1

Reymond, M.A.; Steinert, R.; Escourrou, J.; Fourtanier, G. Ethical, legal and economic issues raised by the use of human tissue in postgenomic research. *Digestive Diseases* 2002; 20: 257-265. Subject: 15.1

Reynolds, Carson; Picard, Rosalind. Ethical evaluation of displays that adapt to affect. *Cyberpsychology and Behavior* 2004 December; 7(6): 662-666. Subject: 4.3

Reynolds, Gretchen. Will any organ do? Transplant surgeons are increasingly using organs from drug users, the obese and the very ill. But with little known for certain about the consequences, doctors are confronting complex medical and ethical questions. *New York Times Magazine* 2005 July 10; p. 36-41. Subject: 19.5

Reynolds, P. Preston; Kamei, Robert K.; Sundquist, Janet; Khanna, Niharika; Palmer, Elissa J.; Palmer, Trish. Using the PRACTICE mnemonic to apply cultural competency to genetics in medical education and patient care. *Academic Medicine* 2005 December; 80(12): 1107-1113. Subject: 15.3

Rhodes, Rosamond. Justice in medicine and public health. *CQ: Cambridge Quarterly of Healthcare Ethics* 2005 Winter; 14(1): 13-26. Subject: 9.4

Rhodes, Rosamond. Response to commentators on "Rethinking Research Ethics" [letter]. *American Journal of Bioethics [Online]* 2005 January-February; 5(1): W15-W18. Subject: 18.2

Rhodes, Rosamond. Rethinking research ethics. *American Journal of Bioethics* 2005 January-February; 5(1): 7-28. Subject: 18.2

Rhodes, Rosamond; Holzman, Ian. Surrogate decision making: a case for boundaries. *In:* Thomasma, David C.;

Weisstub, David N., eds. The Variables of Moral Capacity. Boston: Kluwer Academic Publishers; 2004: 173- 185. Subject: 8.3.3

Rice, Berkeley. Publishing physician profiles: what's fair? *Medical Economics* 2004 December 17; 81(24): 16-19. Subject: 7.4

Rich, Ben A. Introduction: bioethics in court. *Journal of Law, Medicine and Ethics* 2005 Summer; 33(2): 194- 197. Subject: 2.1

Rich, Ben A. Medical custom and medical ethics: rethinking the standard of care. *CQ: Cambridge Quarterly of Healthcare Ethics* 2005 Winter; 14(1): 27-39. Subject: 9.8

Rich, Ben A. Oregon versus Ashcroft: pain relief, physician-assisted suicide, and the Controlled Substances Act. *Pain Medicine* 2002 December; 3(4): 353-360. Subject: 4.4

Rich, Ben A. The politics of pain: rhetoric or reform? *DePaul Journal of Health Care Law* 2005 Spring; 8(3): 519-558. Subject: 4.4

Rich, Ben A. The process of dying. *In:* American College of Legal Medicine Textbook Committee, Sanbar, S. Sandy; Firestone, Marvin H.; Buckner, Fillmore; Gibofsky, Allan; LeBlang, Theodore R.; Snyder, Jack W.; Wecht, Cyril H.; Zaremski, Miles J. Legal Medicine. 6th ed. St. Louis: Mosby; 2004: 308-314. Subject: 20.5.1

Rich, Leigh. Letter response to Margaret Everett (2003) "the social life of genes: privacy, property and the new genetics" Social Science and Medicine, 56:1 [letter]. *Social Science and Medicine* 2003 December; 57(12): 2471-2472. Subject: 15.8

Rich, Robert F. Health policy, health insurance and the social contract. *Comparative Labor Law and Policy Journal* 2000 Winter; 21(2): 397-421. Subject: 9.2

Richard, Shawn A.; Rawal, Shail; Martin, Douglas K. An ethical framework for cardiac report cards: a qualitative study. *BMC Medical Ethics [electronic]* 2005; 6(3); 7 p. Available: http://www.biomedcentral.com/bmcmedethics/[17 May 2005]. Subject: 9.8

Richards, Amy. What is abortion? *Conscience* 2005-2006 Winter; 26(4): 35-37. Subject: 12.5.2

Richards, David. Male circumcision: medical or ritual? *Journal of Law and Medicine* 1996 May; 3(4): 371-376. Subject: 9.5.1

Richards, Edward P.; Burris, Scott; McNelis, Richard P.; Hargan, Eric. Quarantine laws and public health realities. *Journal of Law, Medicine and Ethics* 2005 Winter; 33(4, Supplement): 69-72. Subject: 9.1

Richards, Janet Radcliffe. Organs for sale. *Issues in Medical Ethics* 2001 April-June; 9(2): 47-48. Subject: 19.5

Richards, Martin. Attitudes to genetic research and uses of genetic information support: concerns and genetic discrimination. *In:* Knoppers, Bartha Maria, ed. Populations and Genetics: Legal and Socio-Ethical Perspectives. Boston: Martinus Nijhoff; 2003: 567-578. Subject: 15.1

Richards, Martin. Future bodies: some history and future prospects for human genetic selection. *In:* Bainham, Andrew; Sclater, Shelley Day; Richards, Martin, eds. Body Lore and Laws. Portland, OR: Hart Pub.; 2002: 289-307. Subject: 15.5

Richardson, Eileen H.; Turner, Bryan S. Bodies as property: from slavery to DNA maps. *In:* Bainham, Andrew; Sclater, Shelley Day; Richards, Martin, eds. Body Lore and Laws. Portland, OR: Hart Pub.; 2002: 29-42. Subject: 4.4

Richardson, G. The European convention and mental health law in England and Wales: moving beyond process? *International Journal of Law and Psychiatry* 2005 March-April; 28(2): 127-139. Subject: 17.1

Richardson, Henry S. Specifying, balancing, and interpreting bioethical principles. *In:* Childress, James F.; Meslin, Eric M.; Shapiro, Harold T., eds. Belmont Revisited: Ethical Principles for Research with Human Subjects. Washington, DC: Georgetown University Press; 2005: 205-227. Subject: 2.1

Richardson, Lynne D.; Hwang, Ula. Access to care: a review of the emergency medicine literature. *Academic Emergency Medicine* 2001 November; 8(11): 1030-1036. Subject: 9.2

Richardt, Nicole. A comparative analysis of the embryological research debate in Great Britain and Germany. *Social Politics* 2003 Spring; 10(1): 86-128. Subject: 18.5.4

Richarson, Genevra. The banking of embryonic stem cells: the legal and ethical framework in the UK. *Revista de Derecho y Genoma Humano / Law and the Human Genome Review* 2004 January-June; (20): 147-160. Subject: 18.5.4

Rickert, Kevin G. Alternative medicine and the duty to employ ordinary means. *National Catholic Bioethics Quarterly* 2005 Autumn; 5(3): 481- 489. Subject: 4.1.1

Ricoeur, Paul. The just and medical ethics. *In:* Thomasma, David C.; Weisstub, David N.; Herve, Christian eds. Personhood and Health Care. Boston: Kluwer Academic Pub.; 2001: 115-120. Subject: 2.1

Rier, David A. Publication visibility of sensitive public health data: when scientists bury their results. *Science and Engineering Ethics* 2004 October; 10(4): 597-613. Subject: 1.3.7

Ries, Nola M. The uncertain state of the law regarding health care and section 15 of the Charter. *Health Law Journal* 2003; 11: 217-239. Subject: 9.4

Ries, Nola M.; Moysa, Geoff. Legal protections of electronic health records: issues of consent and security. *Health Law Review* 2005; 14(1): 18-25. Subject: 8.4

Riestra, Sergio Gallego; Jarreta, Begoña Martinez; Fonseca, Rafael Hinojal; Caro, Javier Sanchez. Medicolegal problems arising from AIDS and health care personnel with special reference to Spanish law. *Medicine and Law: World Association for Medical Law* 1994; 13(3-4): 241-249. Subject: 9.5.6

Rieth, Katherine A. How do we withhold or withdraw life-sustaining therapy? *Nursing Management* 1999 October; 30(10): 20-25, M139. Subject: 20.5.1

Rifkin, Jeremy. Why I oppose human cloning. *In:* Cohen, Andrew I.; Wellman, Christopher Heath, eds. Contemporary Debates in Applied Ethics. Malden, MA: Blackwell Pub., 2005: 141-144. Subject: 14.5

Riley, Joan M.; Fry, Sara T. Nurses report widespread ethical conflicts. *Reflections on Nursing Leadership* 2000; 26(2): 35-36, 45. Subject: 8.1

Rinaldi, Andrea. A new code for life. *EMBO Reports* 2004 April; 5(4): 336-339. Subject: 15.1

Ringel, Eileen W. The morality of cosmetic surgery for aging. *Archives of Dermatology* 1998 April; 134(4): 427-431. Subject: 9.5.1

Ring-Cassidy, Elizabeth. Multifetal pregnancy reduction (MFPR): the psychology of desperation and the ethics of justification. *In:* Koterski, Joseph W., ed. Life and Learning IX: Proceedings of the Ninth University Faculty for Life Conference. Washington, DC: University Faculty for Life; 2000: 331-346. Subject: 12.1

Ritvo, Roger A.; Ohlsen, Joel D.; Holland, Thomas P. Exercising ethical leadership: conflicts of interest. *Trustee* 2004 October; 57(9): 27-30. Subject: 9.1

Rivera, Roberto; Borasky, David; Rice, Robert; Carayon, Florence. Many worlds, one ethic: design and development of a global research ethics training curriculum. *Developing World Bioethics* 2005 May; 5(2): 169-175. Subject: 18.1

Rivett, Andrew G. "Right to die" — no man (or woman) is an island [letter]. *BMJ: British Medical Journal* 2005 June 11; 330(7504): 1388- 1389. Subject: 20.5.1

Rizzo, Robert F. Genetic testing and therapy: a pathway to progress and/or profit? *International Journal of Social Economics* 1999; 26(1-3); 18 p. [Online]. Available: http://proquest.umi.com/pqdlink?did=116352591&sid=9&Fmt=3&clientl d=5604&RQT=309&VName=PQD [21 July 2005]. Subject: 15.3

Roach, Lynne. Patents and property in the biotechnology sector: some clarifications. *King's College Law Journal* 2002; 13(1): 101-109. Subject: 5.3

Robb, Anja; Etchells, Edward; Cusimano, Michael D.; Cohen, Robert; Singer, Peter A.; McKneally, Martin. A randomized trial of teaching bioethics to surgical residents. *American Journal of Surgery* 2005 April; 189(4): 453-457. Subject: 2.3

Robert, Jason Scott. Human dispossession and human enhancement [comment]. *American Journal of Bioethics* 2005 May-June; 5(3): 27-29. Subject: 4.5

Robert, Jason Scott; Baylis, Françoise. Stem cell politics: the NAS prohibition pack more bark than bite. *Hastings Center Report* 2005 November-December; 35(6): 15-16. Subject: 18.5.4

Roberts, Christy D.; Stough, Laura M.; Parrish, Linda H. The role of genetic counseling in the elective termination of pregnancies involving fetuses with disabilities. *Journal of Special Education* 2002 Spring; 36(1): 48-55. Subject: 15.2

Roberts, James A.; Brown, Douglas; Elkins, Thomas; Larson, David B. Factors influencing views of patients with gynecologic cancer about end-of-life decisions. *American Journal of Obstetrics and Gynecology* 1997 January; 176 (1, Part 1): 166-172. Subject: 20.5.1

Roberts, Laura Weiss. Evidence-based ethics and informed consent in mental illness research [opinion]. *Archives of General Psychiatry* 2000 June; 57(6): 5 p. [Online]. Available: http://gateway.ut.ovid.come/gw1/ovidweb.cgi [6 October 2005]. Subject: 18.5.1

Roberts, Laura Weiss. Mental illness and informed consent: seeking an empirically derived understanding of voluntarism. *Current Opinion in Psychiatry* 2003 September; 16(5): 543-545. Subject: 8.3.3

Roberts, Laura Weiss; Dunn, Laura B. Ethical considerations in caring for women with substance use disorders. *Obstetrics and Gynecology Clinics of North America* 2003 September; 30(3): 559-582. Subject: 9.5.5

Roberts, Laura Weiss; Geppert, Cynthia M.A.; Brody, Janet L. A framework for considering the ethical aspects of psychiatric research protocols. *Comprehensive Psychiatry* 2001 September-October; 42(5): 351-363. Subject: 18.2

Roberts, Laura Weiss; Geppert, Cynthia M.A.; Warner, Teddy D.; Hammond, Katherine A. Green; Rogers, Melinda; Smrcka, Julienne; Roberts, Brian B. Perspectives on use and protection of genetic information in work settings: results of a preliminary study. *Social Science and Medicine* 2005 April; 60(8): 1855-1858. Subject: 15.1

Roberts, Laura Weiss; Hammond, Katherine A. Green; Warner, Teddy D.; Lewis, Rae. Influence of ethical safeguards on research participation: comparison of perspectives of people with schizophrenia and psychiatrists. *American Journal of Psychiatry* 2004 December; 161(12): 2309-2311. Subject: 18.5.6

Roberts, Laura Weiss; Warner, Teddy D.; Geppert, Cynthia M.A.; Rodgers, Melinda; Hammond, Katherine A. Green. Employees' perspectives on ethically important aspects of genetic research participation: a pilot study. *Comprehensive Psychiatry* 2005; 46: 27-33. Subject: 15.1

Roberts, Laura Weiss; Warner, Teddy D.; Hammond, Katherine A. Green. Coexisting commitments to ethics and human research: a preliminary study of the perspectives of 83 medical students. *American Journal of Bioethics [Online]* 2005 November- December; 5(6): W1-W7. Subject: 18.1

Roberts, Laura Weiss; Warner, Teddy D.; Hammond, Katherine A. Green; Brody, Janet L.; Kaminsky, Alexis; Roberts, Brian B. Teaching medical students to discern ethical problems in human clinical research studies. *Academic Medicine* 2005 October; 80(10): 925-930. Subject: 18.1

Roberts, Laura W.; Warner, Teddy D.; Hammond, Katherine Green. Ethical challenges of mental health clinicians in rural and frontier areas [letter]. *Psychiatric Services* 2005 March; 56(3): 358-359. Subject: 17.1

Roberts, Lynne M.; Bowyer, Lucy; Homer, Caroline S.; Brown, Mark A. Multicentre research: negotiating the ethics approval obstacle course [letter]. *Medical Journal of Australia* 2004 February 2; 180(3): 139. Subject: 18.2

Roberts, M. Psychiatric ethics; a critical introduction for mental health nurses. *Journal of Psychiatric and Mental Health Nursing* 2004 October; 11(5): 583-588. Subject: 17.1

Roberts, Robin S. Early closure of the Watterberg trial. *Pediatrics* 2004 December; 114(6): 1670-1671. Subject: 18.2

Robertson, Christopher. Organ advertising: desperate patients solicit volunteers. *Journal of Law, Medicine and Ethics* 2005 Spring; 33(1): 170- 174. Subject: 19.5

Robertson, Christopher. Recent developments in the law and ethics of embryonic research: can science resolve the ethical problems it creates? *Journal of Law, Medicine and Ethics* 2005 Summer; 33(2): 384- 388. Subject: 18.5.4

Robertson, Christopher. Who is really hurt anyway? The problem of soliciting designated organ donations. *American Journal of Bioethics* 2005 July-August; 5(4): 16-17. Subject: 19.5

Robertson, John A. Assisted reproduction in Germany and the United States: an essay in comparative law and bioethics. Bepress Legal Repository, Paper 226 2004: 1-47 [Online] Available: http://law.bepress.com/cgi/viewcontent/cgi?article=1552&content=expresso [31 August 2005]. Subject: 14.2

Robertson, John A. Blastocyst transfer (sic) is no solution. *American Journal of Bioethics* 2005 November-December; 5(6): 18-20. Subject: 18.5.4

Robertson, John A. Cancer and fertility: ethical and legal challenges. *Journal of the National Cancer Institute Monograph* 2005; (34): 104-106. Subject: 14.6

Robertson, John A. Ethical and legal issues in genetic biobanking. *In:* Knoppers, Bartha Maria, ed. Populations and Genetics: Legal and Socio-Ethical Perspectives. Boston: Martinus Nijhoff; 2003: 297-309. Subject: 15.1

Robertson, John A. Extreme prematurity and parental rights after Baby Doe. *Hastings Center Report* 2004 July-August; 34(4): 32-39. Subject: 20.5.2

Robertson, John A. Human embryonic stem cell research: ethical and legal issues. *Nature Reviews Genetics* 2001 January; 2: 74-78. Subject: 18.5.4

Robertson, John A. Is preimplantation genetic diagnosis for 'social sexing' desirable in today's and tomorrow's society? View of the ASRM ethics committee [letter]. *Human Reproduction* 2003 February; 18(2): 464. Subject: 15.2

Robertson, John A. Special respect redux. *American Journal of Bioethics* 2005 November-December; 5(6): 46-48. Subject: 4.4

Robertson, R.G. Rumours: constructive or corrosive. *Journal of Medical Ethics* 2005 September; 31(9): 540-541. Subject: 7.3

Robins, Cynthia S.; Sauvageot, Julie A.; Cusack, Karen J.; Suffoletta-Maierle, Samantha; Frueh, B. Christopher. Consumers' perceptions of negative experiences and "sanctuary harm" in psychiatric settings. *Psychiatric Services* 2005 September; 56(9): 1134-1138. Subject: 17.1

Robley, Lois R. The benefits of serving on a hospital ethics committee: a faculty perspective. *Nurse Educator* 2005 May-June; 30(3): 123-126. Subject: 9.6

Roche, James B. After Bragdon v. Abbott: why legislation is still needed to mandate infertility insurance. *Boston University Public Interest Law Journal* 2002 Spring- Summer; 11(2-3): 215- 228. Subject: 9.2

Rocklinsberg, Helena. Theocentrism or a re-dressed anthropocentrism? A response to Professor Schroten's lecture. *In:* Ostnor, Lars, ed. Bioethics and Cloning: Report from a Workshop Arranged by the Nordic Theological Network for Bioethics in Arhus, September 25-27, 1998. Oslo: Nordic Theological Network for Bioethics; 1998: 45-50. Subject: 14.5

Roden, Gregory J. Prenatal tort law and the personhood of the unborn child: a separate legal existence. *St. Thomas Law Review* 2003 Fall; 16(1): 207-286. Subject: 4.4

Rodotà, Stefano. Body transformations [opinion]. *Revista de Derecho y Genoma-Humano / Law and the Human Genome Review* 2004 July-December; (21): 29-47. Subject: 4.4

Rodrigues, Praveen B.E. Dermatology and ethics: some case studies. *Issues in Medical Ethics* 2000 October-December; 8(4): 118. Subject: 9.5.1

Rodriguez del Pozo, Pablo; Fins, Joseph J. Death, dying and informatics: misrepresenting religion on MedLine. *BMC Medical Ethics [electronic]* 2005 July 1; 6(6); 5 p. Available: http://www.biomedcentral.com/content/pdf/1472-6939-6-6.pdf [1 February 2006]. Subject: 20.5.1

Rodríguez del Pozo, Pablo; Fins, Joseph J. The globalization of education in medical ethics and humanities: evolving pedagogy at Weill Cornell Medical College in Qatar. *Academic Medicine* 2005 February; 80(2): 135-140. Subject: 2.3

Roehr, Bob. FDA seeks to ease burden on trial review boards [news]. *BMJ: British Medical Journal* 2005 April 2; 330(7494): 748. Subject: 18.2

Roelcke, Volker. Human subjects research during the National Socialist era, 1933-1945: programs, practices, and motivations. *In:* Roelcke, Volker; Maio, Giovanni, eds. Twentieth Century Ethics of Human Subjects Research: Historical Perspectives on Values, Practices, and Regulations. Stuttgart: Franz Steiner Verlag; 2004: 151-166. Subject: 18.1

Roen, Katrina. Intersex embodiment: when health care means maintaining binary sexes [editorial]. *Sexual Health* 2004; 1(3): 127-130. Subject: 10

Roen, Katrina. Queer kids: toward ethical clinical interactions with intersex people. *In:* Shildrick, Margrit; Mykitiuk, Roxanne, eds. Ethics of the Body: Postconventional Challenges. Cambridge, MA: MIT Press; 2005: 259- 278. Subject: 10

Roetz, Heiner. Muss der kulturelle Pluralismus einen substantiellen ethischen Konsens verhindern? Zur Bioethik im Zeitalter der Globalisierung. *In:* Baumann, Eva; Brink, Alexander; May, Arnd T.; Schröder; Peter; Schutzeichel, Corinna Iris, eds. Weltanschauliche Offenheit in der Bioethik. Berlin: Duncker & Humblot; 2004: 213-231. Subject: 21.7

Rogers, Anne; Day, Jenny; Randall, Fiona; Bentall, Richard P. Patients' understanding and participation in a trial designed to improve the management of anti-psychotic medication: a qualitative study. *Social Psychiatry and Psychiatric Epidemiology* 2003 December; 38(12): 720-727. Subject: 18.2

Rogers, Bonnie. Research with protected populations — vulnerable participants. *AAOHN Journal* 2005 April; 53(4): 156-157. Subject: 18.5.1

Rogers, Jonathan. Necessity, private defence and the killing of Mary. *Criminal Law Review* 2001 July: 515-526. Subject: 20.5.2

Rogers, Wendy A.; Mansfield, Peter R.; Braunack-Mayer, Annette J.; Jureidini, Jon N. The ethics of pharmaceutical industry relationships with medical students. *Medical Journal of Australia* 2004 April 19; 180: 411-414. Subject: 7.2

Rogers, W.A. Ethical issues in public health: a qualitative study of public health practice in Scotland. *Journal of Epidemiology and Community Health* 2004; 58: 446-450. Subject: 9.1

Subject = NRCBL Primary Classification Number; See inside front cover

Rogers-Hayden, Tee. Asilomar's legacy in Aotearoa New Zealand. *Science as Culture* 2005 December; 14(4): 393-410. Subject: 15.1

Rohlf, Vanessa; Bennett, Pauleen. Perpetration-induced traumatic stress in persons who euthanize nonhuman animals in surgeries, animal shelters, and laboratories. *Society and Animals: Journal of Human-Animal Studies* 2005; 13(3): 201-219. Subject: 22.1

Roig-Franiza, Manuel. Court lets right-to-die ruling stand: parents at odds with husband over removing Fla. woman's feeding tube. *Washington Post* 2005 January 25; p. A7. Subject: 20.5.1

Roig-Franzia, Manuel; Connolly, Ceci. La. investigates allegations of euthanasia at hospital; autopsies sought on 45 in post-Katrina inquiry. *Washington Post* 2005 October 15; p. A3. Subject: 20.5.1

Rollin, Bernard E. Keeping up with the cloneses — issues in human cloning. *Journal of Ethics* 1999; 3(1): 51-71. Subject: 14.5

Rollin, Bernard E. Reasonable partiality and animal ethics. *Ethical Theory and Moral Practice* 2005 April; 8(1-2): 105-121. Subject: 22.1

Rollin, Bernard E. Telos, value, and genetic engineering. *In:* Baillie, Harold W.; Casey, Timothy K., eds. Is Human Nature Obsolete? Genetics Bioengineering, and the Future of the Human Condition. Cambridge, MA: MIT Press; 2005: 317-336. Subject: 15.1

Rollin, B.E.; Universities Federation for Animal Welfare [UFAW]; Fund for the Replacement of Animals in Medical Experiments [FRAME]; Seriously Ill for Medical Research [SIMR]; Research Defence Society [RDS]. Defending the use of animals to research human disease [letters]. *Molecular Medicine Today* 1995 October; 1(7): 308-309. Subject: 22.1

Rolph, Sheena. Ethical dilemmas in historical research with people with learning difficulties. *British Journal of Learning Disabilities* 1998 Winter; 26(4): 135-139. Subject: 9.5.3

Romano, Gaetano. Stem cell transplantation therapy: controversy over ethical issues and clinical relevance. *Drug News and Perspectives* 2004 December; 17(10): 637-645. Subject: 18.5.4

Romans, Sarah; Dawson, John; Mullen, Richard; Gibbs, Anita. How mental health clinicians view community treatment orders: a national New Zealand survey. *Australian and New Zealand Journal of Psychiatry* 2004 October; 38(10): 836-841. Subject: 17.7

Romero, Linda J.; Garry, Philip J.; Schuyler, Mark; Bennahum, David A.; Qualls, Clifford; Ballinger, Lori; Kelly, Velma; Schmitt, Cheryl; Skipper, Betty; Ortiz, Irene E.; Rhyne, Robert L. Emotional responses to APO E genotype disclosure for Alzheimer disease. *Journal of*

Genetic Counseling 2005 April; 14(2): 141-150. Subject: 15.2

Ronco, Claudio. The morality of medicine. *International Journal of Artificial Organs* 2004 August; 27(8): 647-648. Subject: 4.1.2

Rørbye, Christina; Nørgaard, Mogens; Nilas, Lisbeth. Medical versus surgical abortion: comparing satisfaction and potential confounders in a partly randomized study. *Human Reproduction* 2005 March; 20(3): 834-838. Subject: 12.5.2

Rosato, Jennifer L. The children of ART (assisted reproductive technology): should the law protect them from harm? *Utah Law Review* 2004; 2004(1): 57-110. Subject: 14.1

Roscam Abbing, Henriette D.C. A Council of Europe protocol on transplantation of organs and tissues of human origin. *European Journal of Health Law* 2002 March; 9(1): 63-76. Subject: 19.5

Roscam Abbing, Henriette D.C. Constitutional treaty of the European Union, health and human rights. An appraisal [editorial]. *European Journal of Health Law* 2004 December; 11(4): 337-345. Subject: 9.1

Roscam Abbing, Henriette D.C. Neonatal screening, new technologies, old and new legal concerns [editorial]. *European Journal of Health Law* 2004 June; 11(2): 129-137. Subject: 15.3

Roscoe, Lori A.; Malphurs, Julie E.; Dragovic, L.J.; Cohen, Donna. Antecedents of euthanasia and suicide among older women. *JAMWA: Journal of the American Medical Women's Association* 2003 Winter; 58(1): 44-48. Subject: 20.7

Rose, Abigail L.; Peters, Nikki; Shea, Judy A.; Armstrong, Katrina. Attitudes and misconceptions about predictive genetic testing for cancer risk. *Community Genetics* 2005 August; 8(3): 145-151. Subject: 15.3

Rose, Andre P. Reproductive misconception: why cloning is not just another assisted reproductive technology. *Duke Law Journal* 1999 March; 48(5): 1133-1156. Subject: 14.5

Rose, Darrell E. The ethics of cochlear implants in young children [letter]. *American Journal of Otology* 1994 November; 15(6): 813-814. Subject: 9.5.7

Rose, Diana S.; Wykes, Til H.; Bindman, Jonathan P.; Fleischmann, Pete S. Information, consent and perceived coercion: patients' perspectives on electroconvulsive therapy. *British Journal of Psychiatry* 2005 January; 186: 54-59. Subject: 17.5

Rose, Julia Hannum; O'Toole, Elizabeth E.; Dawson, Neal V.; Lawrence, Renee; Gurley, Diana; Thomas, Charles; Hamel, Mary Beth; Cohen, Harvey J. Perspectives, preferences, care practices, and outcomes among older and middle-aged patients with late-stage cancer. *Journal of Clinical Oncology* 2004 December 15; 22(24): 4907-4917. Subject: 20.3.1

Rose, Mat. A practitioner's response to the Final Report of the Select Special Health Information Act Review Committee. *Health Law Review* 2005; 14(1): 12-13. Subject: 8.4

Roselin, Joel M.; Koski. Pharma PR or medical education? [letter]. *Hastings Center Report* 2005 March-April; 35(2): 5-6. Subject: 9.7

Rosen, Ami; Wallenstein, Sylvan; McGovern, Margaret M. Attitudes of pediatric residents toward ethical issues associated with genetic testing in children. *Pediatrics* 2002 August; 110(2): 360-363. Subject: 15.3

Rosén, Elisabeth. Genetic information and genetic discrimination how medical records vitiate legal protection: a comparative analysis of international legislation and policies. *Scandinavian Journal of Public Health* 1999 September; 27(3): 166-172. Subject: 15.1

Rosen, Sydney; Sanne, Ian; Collier, Alizanne; Simon, Jonathon L. Hard choices: rationing antiretroviral therapy for HIV/AIDS in Africa. *Lancet* 2005 January 22-28; 365(9456): 354-356. Subject: 9.5.6

Rosenau, Pauline Vaillancourt; Roemer, Ruth. Ethical issues in public health and health services. *In:* Andersen, Ronald M.; Rice, Thomas H.; Kominski, Gerald F., eds. Changing the U.S. Health Care System: Key Issues in Health Services, Policy, and Management. 2nd ed. San Francisco: Jossey- Bass; 2001: 503-535. Subject: 9.1

Rosenbaum, Julie R.; Bravata, Dawn M.; Concato, John; Brass, Lawrence M.; Kim, Nancy; Fried, Terri R. Informed consent for thrombolytic therapy for patients with acute ischemic stroke treated in routine clinical practice. *Stroke* 2004 September; 35(9): e353-e355. Subject: 8.3.1

Rosenberg, Kenneth D.; DeMunter, Jodi K.; Liu, Jihong. Emergency contraception in emergency departments in Oregon, 2003. *American Journal of Public Health* 2005 August; 95(8): 1453- 1457. Subject: 11.1

Rosengarten, Marsha. The measure of HIV as a matter of bioethics. *In:* Shildrick, Margrit; Mykitiuk, Roxanne, eds. Ethics of the Body: Postconventional Challenges. Cambridge, MA: MIT Press; 2005: 71-90. Subject: 9.5.6

Rosenman, Stephen. Mental health law: an idea whose time has passed. *Australia and New Zealand Journal of Psychiatry* 1994 December; 28(4): 560-565. Subject: 4.3

Rosenthal, Elisabeth. A most personal test for the Church's rules; what is a natural death? *New York Times* 2005 March 27; p. WK5. Subject: 20.4.1

Rosenthal, Elisabeth. Under a microscope: high-profile cases bring new scrutiny to science's superstars. *New York Times* 2005 December 24; p. A6. Subject: 1.3.9

Rosenthal, M. Sara; Pierce, Heather Hanson. Inherited medullary thyroid cancer and the duty to warn: revisiting Pate v. Threlkel in light of HIPAA. *Thyroid* 2005 February; 15(2): 140-145. Subject: 15.3

Roses, Allen D. Genetic testing for Alzheimer disease: practical and ethical issues. *Archives of Neurology* 1997 October; 54(10): 1226-1229. Subject: 15.3

Rosik, Christopher H. Motivational, ethical, and epistemological foundations in the treatment of unwanted homoerotic attraction. *Journal of Marital and Family Therapy* 2003 January; 29(1): 13-28. Subject: 10

Rosin, A.J.; van Dijk, Y. Subtle ethical dilemmas in geriatric management and clinical research. *Journal of Medical Ethics* 2005 June; 31(6): 355-359. Subject: 9.5.2

Rosner, David; Markowitz, Gerald. The states and the war against bioterrorism: reactions to the federal smallpox campaign and the Model State Emergency Health Powers Act. *In:* Kleinman, Daniel Lee; Kinchy, Abby J.; Handelsman, J. eds. Controversies in Science and Technology: From Maize to Menopause. Madison, Wis.: University of Wisconsin Press; 2005: 297-310. Subject: 21.3

Rosner, Fred. Allocation or misallocation of limited medical resources [editorial]. *Cancer Investigation* 2004; 22(5): 810-812. Subject: 9.4

Rosner, Fred. Assisted reproduction: a Jewish perspective. *Mount Sinai Journal of Medicine* 2001 May; 68(3): 219-223. Subject: 14.2

Rosner, Fred. Informing the patient about a fatal disease: from paternalism to autonomy — the Jewish view. *Cancer Investigation* 2004; 22(6): 949-953. Subject: 8.2

Rosner, Fred. An observant Jewish physician working in a secular ethical society: ethical dilemmas. *Israel Medical Association Journal* 2005 January; 7(1): 53-57. Subject: 2.1

Rosner, Fred. Research and training on the newly dead [letter]. *Archives of Pathology and Laboratory Medicine* 1997 October; 121(10): 1029. Subject: 7.2

Ross, Heather M.; Berger, Jeffrey T. Deactivating implantable cardioverter defibrillators [letter and reply]. *Annals of Internal Medicine* 2005 November 1; 143(9): 690-691. Subject: 20.5.1

Ross, Julie A. Genetics and childhood cancer. Commentary on: inherited cancer in children: practical/ethical problems and challenges. *European Journal of Cancer* 2004 November; 40(16): 2471-2472. Subject: 15.2

Ross, Lainie Friedman. Children as research subjects: a proposal to revise the current federal regulations using a moral framework. *Stanford Law and Policy Review* 1997 Winter; 8(1): 159-176. Subject: 18.5.2

Ross, Lainie Friedman. Lessons to be learned from the 407 process. *Health Matrix: Journal of Law-Medicine* 2005 Summer; 15(2): 401-421. Subject: 18.2

Ross, Lainie Friedman; Zenios, Stefanos. Practical and ethical challenges to paired exchange programs [editorial]. *American Journal of Transplantation* 2004 October; 4(10): 1553-1554. Subject: 19.5

Subject = NRCBL Primary Classification Number; See inside front cover

Ross, Patricia A. Sorting out the concept disorder. *Theoretical Medicine and Bioethics* 2005; 26(2): 115-140. Subject: 4.3

Rothblatt, Martine. Of pigs and men: issues of speciesism and chimerism. *In her:* Your Life or Mine: How Geoethics Can Resolve the Conflict Between Public and Private Interests in Xenotransplantation. Burlington, VT: Ashgate; 2004: 71-95. Subject: 19.1

Rothblatt, Martine. The right to life: society's obligation to provide health care and xenotransplantation. *In her:* Your Life or Mine: How Geoethics Can Resolve the Conflict Between Public and Private Interests in Xenotransplantation. Burlington, VT: Ashgate; 2004: 97-116. Subject: 19.1

Rothfield, Philipa. Attending to difference: phenomenology and bioethics. *In:* Shildrick, Margrit; Mykitiuk, Roxanne, eds. Ethics of the Body: Postconventional Challenges. Cambridge, MA: MIT Press; 2005: 29-48. Subject: 2.1

Rothman, Barbara Katz. What if I just say "a pox on both your houses"? [response]. *Conscience* 2003-2004 Winter; 24(4): 14-15. Subject: 14.1

Rothman, David J. Other people's bodies: human experimentation on the fiftieth anniversary of the Nuremberg Code. *In:* Longo, Lawrence D., ed. Our Lords, The Sick: McGovern Lectures on the History of Medicine and Medical Humanism. Malabar, Fla.: Krieger Pub. Co.; 2004: 125-144. Subject: 18.1

Rothman, Kenneth J.; Evans, Stephen. Extra scrutiny for industry funded trials: JAMA's demand for an additional hurdle is unfair — and absurd [editorial]. *BMJ: British Medical Journal* 2005 December 10; 331(7529): 1350-1351. Subject: 18.2

Rothschild, Alan. Oregon: does physician-assisted suicide work? *Journal of Law and Medicine* 2004 November; 12(2): 217-225. Subject: 20.7

Rothschild, Barbra B.; King, Nancy M.P.; Horstmann, Elizabeth; Emanuel, Ezekiel J.; Grady, Christine; Kurzrock, Razelle; Benjamin, Robert S. Phase 1 clinical trials in oncology [letter and replies]. *New England Journal of Medicine* 2005 June 9; 352(23): 2451- 2453. Subject: 18.3

Rothschild, Joan. Bioethics discourse and reproductive practice. *In her:* The Dream of the Perfect Child. Bloomington, IN: Indiana University Press; 2005: 157-187. Subject: 15.1

Rothstein, David A. Practice of medicine? [letter]. *AAPL (American Academy of Psychiatry and the Law) Newsletter* 2005 September; 30(3): 28-29. Subject: 1.3.1

Rothstein, Mark A. Ethical guidelines for medical research on workers. *Journal of Occupational and Environmental Medicine* 2000 December; 42(12): 1166-1171. Subject: 18.5.1

Rothstein, Mark A. Expanding the ethical analysis of biobanks. *Journal of Law, Medicine and Ethics* 2005 Spring; 33(1): 89-101. Subject: 15.1

Rothstein, Mark A. Genetic exceptionalism and legislative pragmatism. *Hastings Center Report* 2005 July-August; 35(4): 27-33. Subject: 15.1

Rothstein, Mark A. Genetic justice [opinion]. *New England Journal of Medicine* 2005 June 30; 352(26): 2667-2668. Subject: 15.1

Rothstein, Mark A. Genetic testing: employability, insurability, and health reform. *Journal of the National Cancer Institute Monographs* 1995; (17): 87-90. Subject: 15.3

Rothstein, Mark A. Research privacy under HIPAA and the common rule. *Journal of Law, Medicine and Ethics* 2005 Spring; 33(1): 154- 159. Subject: 8.4

Rothwell, Peter M. External validity of randomised controlled trials: "to whom do the results of this trial apply?". *Lancet* 2005 January 1-7; 365(9453): 82-93. Subject: 18.2

Rougé, Daniel; Telmon, Norbert; Albarède, Jean-Louis; Arbus, Louis. Questions raised by artificial prolongation of life of the aged patient. *Medicine and Law: World Association for Medical Law* 1994; 13(3-4): 269-275. Subject: 20.5.1

Rougé-Maillart, C.; Jousset, J.; Gaches, T.; Gaudin, A.; Penneau, M. Patients refusing medical attention: the case of Jehovah's Witnesses in France. *Medicine and Law: World Association for Medical Law* 2004; 23(4): 715-723. Subject: 8.3.4

Rough, Bonnie J. His genes hold gifts. Mine carry risk. *New York Times* 2005 January 30; p.ST7. Subject: 15.2

Roupie, E.; Santin, A.; Boulme, R.; Wartel, J.S.; Lepage, E.; Lemaire, F.; Lejonc, J.L.; Montagne, O. Patients' preferences concerning medical information and surrogacy: results of a prospective study in a French emergency department. *Intensive Care Medicine* 2000 January; 26(1): 52-56. Subject: 8.3.3

Rowan, Andrew N. The use of animals in experimentation: an examination of the 'technical' arguments used to criticize the practice. *In:* Garner, Robert, ed. Animal Rights: The Changing Debate. New York: New York University Press; 1996: 104-122. Subject: 22.1

Rowan, Andrew N.; Loew, Franklin M. Animal research: a review of developments, 1950-2000. *In:* Salem, Deborah J.; Rowan, Andrew N., eds. The State of the Animals 2001. Washington, DC: Humane Society Press; 2001: 111-120. Subject: 22.2

Rowe, Michael. Doctors' responses to medical errors. *Critical Reviews in Oncology/Hematology* 2004 December; 52(3): 147-163. Subject: 9.8

Roy, Nobhojit. Medical ethics: funding the discourse. *Issues in Medical Ethics* 2002 April-June; 10(2): 20-21. Subject: 1.3.7

Roy, Nobhojit. Who rules the great Indian drug bazaar? [editorial]. *Indian Journal of Medical Ethics* 2004 January-March; 1(1): 2-3. Subject: 9.7

Roy, R.; Aladangady, N.; Costeloe, K.; Larcher, V. Decision making and modes of death in a tertiary neonatal unit. *Archives of Disease in Childhood. Fetal and Neonatal Edition* 2004 November; 89(6): F527-F530. Subject: 20.5.2

Royal College of Physicians of London (United Kingdom). Doctors in society: medical professionalism in a changing world; report of a working party of the Royal College of Physicians of London. London: Royal College of Physicians of London 2005 December; 65 p. [Online]. Available: http://www.rcplondon.ac.uk/pubs/books/docinsoc/docinsoc.pdf [6 March 2006]. Subject: 2.1

Royal College of Psychiatrists. Ethics Sub-Committee. Psychiatry and the death penalty: revised statement from the Ethics Sub-Committee. *Psychiatric Bulletin* 2003; 27(10): 396-397. Subject: 20.6

Roychowdhury, Debasish; Meropol, Neal J.; Weinfurt, Kevin P.; Schulman, Kevin A. Phase I trials: physician and patient perceptions [letter and reply]. *Journal of Clinical Oncology* 2003 December 15; 21(24): 4658-4660. Subject: 18.2

Rubenfeld, Gordon D.; Curtis, J. Randall. Beyond ethical dilemmas: improving the quality of end-of-life care in the intensive care unit. *Critical Care* 2003 February; 7(1): 11-13. Subject: 20.4.1

Rubenfeld, Gordon D.; Curtis, J. Randall. End-of-life care in the intensive care unit: a research agenda. *Critical Care Medicine* 2001 October; 29(10): 2001-2006. Subject: 20.4.1

Rubens, Arthur J.; Wimberley, Edward T. Contrasting the American College of Healthcare Executives' code of ethics with undergraduate health administration students' values and ethical decision choices. *Hospital Topics* 2004 Summer; 82(3): 10-17. Subject: 7.2

Rubenstein, Leonard; Pross, Christian; Davidoff, Frank; Iacopino, Vincent. Coercive US interrogation policies: a challenge to medical ethics. *JAMA: The Journal of the American Medical Association* 2005 September 28; 294(12): 1544-1549. Subject: 21.4

Rubin, Eugene H. The complexities of individual financial conflicts of interest. *Neuropsychopharmacology* 2005 January; 30(1): 1-6. Subject: 1.3.9

Rubinow, Alan. The physician and the dying patient: a question of control? [opinion]. *Israel Medical Association Journal* 2005 January; 7(1): 3-4. Subject: 20.3.1

Rudolph, William C. Social issues in perinatal screening for sickle cell anemia. *Urban Health* 1983 August; 12(8): 32-34. Subject: 15.2

Ruethling, Gretchen. Illinois pharmacist sues over contraceptive rule. *New York Times* 2005 June 10; p. A18. Subject: 4.1.1

Runkel, Thomas. Kleinwuchs und medizinethische Beurteilung. Expose eines Forschungsprojekts. *In:* Jahrbuch für Wissenschaft und Ethik. Bd. 7. Berlin: Walter de Gruyter; 2002: 311-318. Subject: 9.5.7

Runyan, Desmond K. The ethical, legal, and methodological implications of directly asking children about abuse. *Journal of Interpersonal Violence* 2000 July; 15(7): 675-681. Subject: 18.5.2

Ruroede, Kathleen. Attitudes of risk management professionals toward disclosure of medical mistakes. *Risk: Health, Safety and Environment* 2001 Spring; 12(1 and 2): 67-90. Subject: 9.8

Rurup, Mette L.; Onwuteaka-Philipsen, Bregje D.; Jansen-van der Weide, Marijke; van der Wal, Gerrit. When being 'tired of living' plays an important role in a request for euthanasia or physician-assisted suicide: patient characteristics and the physician's decision. *Health Policy* 2005 October; 74(2): 157-166. Subject: 20.7

Rurup, Mette L.; Onwuteaka-Philipsen, Bregje D.; van der Heide, Agnes; van der Wal, Gerrit; van der Maas, Paul J. Physicians' experiences with demented patients with advance euthanasia directives in the Netherlands. *Journal of the American Geriatrics Society* 2005 July; 53(7): 1138-1144. Subject: 20.5.4

Rusche, Brigitte. The 3Rs and animal welfare — conflict or the way forward? *ALTEX: Alternativen zu Tierexperimenten* 2003; 20(Supplement 1): 63-76. Subject: 22.2

Ruschioni, Sherry L. Confidentiality of mental health records in federal courts: the path blazed by Sabree v. United Brotherhood of Carpenters and Joinders of America, Local No. 33. *New England Law Review* 2004 Summer; 38(4): 923-937. Subject: 8.4

Ruse, Cathy Cleaver. Partial-birth abortion on trial. *Human Life Review* 2005 Spring; 31(2): 87-104. Subject: 12.4.1

Rushforth, Kay; McKinney, Patricia A. Issues of patient consent: a study of paediatric high- dependency care. *British Journal of Nursing* 2005 May 12-25; 14(9): 519-523. Subject: 8.3.2

Rushton, Cindy Hylton. Creating an ethical practice environment: a focus on advocacy. *Critical Care Nursing Clinics of North America* 1995 June; 7(2): 387-397. Subject: 4.1.3

Russell, F.M.; Carapetis, J.R.; Liddle, H.; Edwards, T.; Ruff, T.A.; Devitt, J. A pilot study of the quality of informed consent materials for Aboriginal participants in clinical trials. *Journal of Medical Ethics* 2005 August; 31(8): 490-494. Subject: 18.3

Russell, W.M.S. A comment from a humane experimental technique perspective on the Nuffield Council on Bioethics Report on The Ethics of Research Involving Animals. *ATLA: Alternatives to Laboratory Animals* 2005 December; 33(6): 650-653. Subject: 22.2

Rutkow, Lainie. Dying to live: the effect of the Patient Self-Determination Act on hospice care. *New York University Journal of Legislation and Public Policy* 2004; 7(2): 393-435. Subject: 20.4.1

Rutsohn, Phil; Ibrahim, Nabil. An analysis of provider attitudes toward end-of-life decision-making. *American Journal of Hospice and Palliative Care* 2003 September-October; 20(5): 371-378. Subject: 20.5.4

Ryan, Ann E. Protecting the rights of pediatric research subjects in the International Conference on Harmonisation of Technical Requirements for Registration of Pharmaceuticals for Human Use. *Fordham International Law Journal* 2000 March; 23(3): 848-934. Subject: 18.5.2

Ryan, Catherine J.; Santucci, Mary Ann; Gattuso, Michele C.; Czurylo, Kathy; O'Brien, Jim; Stark, Barbara. Perceptions about advance directives by nurses in a community hospital. *Clinical Nurse Specialist* 2001 November; 15(6): 246-252. Subject: 20.5.4

Ryan, Christopher James. Velcro on the slippery slope: the role of psychiatry in active voluntary euthanasia. *Australian and New Zealand Journal of Psychiatry* 1995 December; 29: 580-585. Subject: 20.5.1

Ryan, Christopher James; Anderson, Josephine. Sleeping with the past: the ethics of post-termination patient-therapist sexual contact [opinion]. *Australian and New Zealand Journal of Psychiatry* 1996 April; 30(2): 171-178. Subject: 7.1

Ryan, Christopher James; Furlong, Mark; Leggatt, Margaret. Comment on reconciling the patient's right to confidentiality and the family's need to know [letter and reply]. *Australian and New Zealand Journal of Psychiatry* 1997 June; 31(3): 429-431. Subject: 8.4

Ryan, Joseph G. The chapel and the operating room: the struggle of Roman Catholic clergy, physicians, and believers with the dilemmas of obstetric surgery, 1800-1900. *Bulletin of the History of Medicine* 2002 Autumn; 76(3): 461- 494. Subject: 9.5.5

Ryan, Michael P. Introduction: ethical responsibilities regarding drugs, patents, and health. *Business Ethics Quarterly* 2005 October; 15(4): 543-547. Subject: 9.7

Ryan, Patrick J. Unnatural selection: intelligence testing, eugenics, and American political cultures. *Journal of Social History* 1997 Spring; 30(3): 669-685. Subject: 15.5

Ryan, Peter F. The value of life and its bearing on three issues of medical ethics. *In:* Koterski, Joseph W., ed. Life and Learning IX: Proceedings of the Ninth University Faculty for Life Conference. Washington, DC: University Faculty for Life; 2000: 41-57. Subject: 4.4

S

Saal, Howard M. Neonatal intensive care as a locus for ethical decisions. *Cleft Palate-Craniofacial Journal* 1995 November; 32(6): 500-503. Subject: 20.5.2

Sabik, Lindsay; Pace, Christine A.; Forster-Gertner, Heidi P.; Wendler, David; Bebchuk, Judith D.; Tavel, Jorge A.; McNay, Laura A.; Killen, Jack; Emanuel, Ezekiel J.; Grady, Christine. Informed consent: practices and views of investigators in a multinational clinical trial. *IRB: Ethics and Human Research* 2005 September-October; 27(5): 13-18. Subject: 18.3

Sabini, John; Monterosso, John. Judgments of the fairness of using performance enhancing drugs. *Ethics and Behavior* 2005; 15(1): 81-94. Subject: 17.4

Sachdev, Perminder; Sachdev, Jagdeep. Sixty years of psychosurgery: its present status and its future. *Australian and New Zealand Journal of Psychiatry* 1997 August; 31(4): 457-464. Subject: 17.6

Sachedina, Abdulaziz. End-of-life: the Islamic view [opinion]. *Lancet* 2005 August 27-September 2; 366(9487): 774-779. Subject: 20.5.1

Sachedina, Abdulaziz. Islamic bioethics. *In:* Peppin, John F.; Cherry, Mark J., eds. Religious Perspectives in Bioethics. New York: Taylor & Francis; 2004: 153- 171. Subject: 2.1

Sackett, David L. Participants in research: neither guinea pigs nor sacrificial lambs, but pointers to better health care [editorial]. *BMJ: British Medical Journal* 2005 May 21; 330(7501): 1164. Subject: 9.8

Sadan, Batami; Chajek-Shaul, Tova. Attitudes and practices of patients and physicians towards patient autonomy: a survey conducted prior to the enactment of the Patients' Rights Bill in Israel. *Eubios Journal of Asian and International Bioethics* 2000 July; 10(4): 119-125. Subject: 8.3.1

Sadasivam, Bharati. The rights framework in reproductive health advocacy — a reappraisal. *Hastings Women's Law Journal* 1997 Fall; 8(2): 313-350. Subject: 9.5.5

Sadler, Troy D. Moral sensitivity and its contribution to the resolution of socio-scientific issues. *Journal of Moral Education* 2004 September; 33(3): 339-358. Subject: 5.3

Safire, William. Our new Promethean gift. *Cerebrum: The Dana Forum on Brain Science* 2002 Summer; 4(3): 54-55. Subject: 17.1

Sage, William M. Reputation, malpractice liability, and medical error. *In:* Sharpe, Virginia A., ed. Accountability: Patient Safety and Policy Reform. Washington, DC: Georgetown University Press; 2004: 159-183. Subject: 9.8

Saginur, Madelaine; Kharaboyan, Linda; Knoppers, Bartha Maria. Umbilical cord blood stem cells: issues with private and public banks. *Health Law Journal* 2004; 12: 17-34. Subject: 19.4

Sagoff, Mark. Extracorporeal embryos and three conceptions of the human. *American Journal of Bioethics* 2005 November-December; 5(6): 52-54. Subject: 18.5.4

Sagoff, Mark. Nature and human nature. *In:* Baillie, Harold W.; Casey, Timothy K., eds. Is Human Nature Obsolete? Genetics Bioengineering, and the Future of the Human Condition. Cambridge, MA: MIT Press; 2005: 67-98. Subject: 15.1

Sagoff, Mark. Patented genes: an ethical appraisal. *Issues in Science and Technology* 1998 Spring; 14(3): 37-41. Subject: 15.8

Saguy, Abigail C.; Riley, Kevin W. Weighing both sides: morality, mortality, and framing contests over obesity. *Journal of Health Politics, Policy and Law* 2005 October; 30(5): 869-921. Subject: 9.1

Saha, Shelley. Challenges in research in tribal communities. *Indian Journal of Medical Ethics* 2004 October-December; 1(4): 125. Subject: 18.5.9

Sahay, Seema; Mehendale, Sanjay. Addressing ethical concerns in the Indian HIV vaccine trials. *Indian Journal of Medical Ethics* 2004 October-December; 1(4): 109-112. Subject: 9.5.6

Saheli Women's Health Centre. Research on anti-fertility vaccines: serious concerns for women's health. *Issues in Medical Ethics* 2000 April-June; 8(2): 51-52. Subject: 18.5.3

Saheli Women's Resource Centre. ICMR draft ethical guidelines: a critique. *Issues in Medical Ethics* 2000 January-March; 8(1): 20-21. Subject: 18.2

Sahm, S.; Will, R.; Hommel, G. Attitudes towards and barriers to writing advance directives amongst cancer patients, healthy controls, and medical staff. *Journal of Medical Ethics* 2005 August; 31(8): 437-440. Subject: 20.5.4

Sahm, S.; Will, R.; Hommel, G. Would they follow what has been laid down? Cancer patients' and healthy controls' views on adherence to advance directives compared to medical staff. *Medicine, Health Care and Philosophy: A European Journal* 2005; 8(3): 297-305. Subject: 20.5.4

Saint Raymond, Agnès; Brasseur, Daniel. Development of medicines for children in Europe: ethical implications. *Paediatric Respiratory Reviews* 2005 March; 6(1): 45-51. Subject: 18.5.2

Saito, Masahiko. Decision-making in social and medical services for patients with dementia in Japan. *In:* Weisstub, David N.; Thomasma, David C.; Gauthier, Serge; Tomossy, George F., eds. Aging: Caring for Our Elders. Boston: Kluwer Academic; 2001: 191-202. Subject: 9.5.3

Sajoo, Amyn B. Taking ethics seriously: adab to zygotes. *In his:* Muslim Ethics: Emerging Vistas. New York: I.B. Tauris Publishers; 2004: 1-24. Subject: 2.1

Sakamoto, Hyakudai. Globalization of bioethics as an intercultural social tuning technology. *Journal Interna-tional de Bioethique / International Journal of Bioethics* 2005 March-June; 16(1-2): 17-27, 189-190. Subject: 21.7

Saks, Samuel J. Call 911: psychiatry and the new Emergency Medical Treatment and Active Labor Act (EMTALA) regulations. *Journal of Psychiatry and Law* 2004 Winter; 32(4): 483-512. Subject: 17.1

Salacz, Michael E.; Weissman, David E. Controlled sedation for refractory suffering: Part I. *Journal of Palliative Medicine* 2005 February; 8(1): 136-137. Subject: 20.4.1

Salazar, Juan C. Pediatric clinical trial experience: government, child, parent and physician's perspective. *Pediatric Infectious Disease Journal* 2003 December; 22(12): 1124-1127. Subject: 18.5.2

Salbu, Steven R. AIDS and the blood supply: an analysis of law, regulation, and public policy. *Washington University Law Quarterly* 1996 Winter; 74(4): 913-980. Subject: 19.4

Saldeen, Pia; Sundström, Per. Would legislation imposing single embryo transfer be a feasible way to reduce the rate of multiple pregnancies after IVF treatment? *Human Reproduction* 2005 January; 20(1): 4-8. Subject: 14.4

Salek, Sam. Holistic approach in choice of pharmaceutical agents: ethical responsibilities. *In:* Salek, Sam; Edgar, Andrew, eds. Pharmaceutical Ethics. New York: Wiley; 2002: 123-135. Subject: 9.7

Salkovskis, Paul M.; Dennis, Ruth; Wroe, Abigail L. An experimental study of influences on the perceived likelihood of seeking genetic testing: "nondirectiveness" may be misleading. *Journal of Psychosomatic Research* 1999 November; 47(5): 439- 447. Subject: 15.3

Salladay, Susan A. Clinician-assisted suicide: merciful release or unlawful death? *Journal of Christian Nursing* 2004 Fall; 21(4): 14-17. Subject: 20.7

Salmeron, Betty Jo. Autonomy and contraception [letter]. *IRB: Ethics and Human Research* 2005 September-October; 27(5): 20. Subject: 18.5.3

Salmon, Daniel A.; Moulton, Lawrence H.; Omer, Saad B.; deHart, M. Patricia; Stokley, Shannon; Halsey, Neal A. Factors associated with refusal of childhood vaccines among parents of school-aged children: a case-control study. *Archives of Pediatric and Adolescent Medicine* 2005 May; 159(5): 470-476. Subject: 8.3.4

Salmond, Susan W.; David, Estrella. Attitudes toward advance directives and advance directive completion rates. *Orthopaedic Nursing* 2005 March-April; 24(2): 117-129. Subject: 20.5.4

Saltzman, Carl; Beach, Thomas E.; Whitman, Andrew K. Managing obligations: right of privacy and release of clinical records. *Journal of Healthcare Risk Management* 2003 Summer; 23(3): 27-32. Subject: 8.4

Salvatierra, Oscar, Jr. Transplant physicians bear full responsibility for the consequences of kidney donation by a minor [editorial]. *American Journal of Transplantation* 2002 April; 2(4): 297- 298. Subject: 19.5

Samanta, Ash; Samanta, Jo. End of life decisions: clinical decisions are increasingly shaped by legal judgments [editorial]. *BMJ: British Medical Journal* 2005 December 3; 331(7528): 1284- 1285. Subject: 20.5.1

Samanta, Ash; Samanta, Jo; Price, David. Who owns my body — thee or me? The human tissue story continues. *Clinical Medicine* 2004 July-August; 4(4): 327-331. Subject: 18.1

Samuels, Sheldon W. Occupational medicine and its moral discontents [editorial]. *Journal of Occupational and Environmental Medicine* 2003 December; 45(12): 1226-1233. Subject: 16.3

Sanal, Aslihan. "Robin Hood" of techno-Turkey or organ trafficking in the state of ethical beings. *Culture, Medicine and Psychiatry* 2004 September; 28(3): 281-309. Subject: 19.5

Sanbar, S. Sandy; Annas, George J.; Grodin, Michael A.; Wecht, Cyril H. Legal medicine: historical roots and current status. *In:* Sanbar, S. Sandy; Firestone, Marvin H.; Buckner, Fillmore; Gibofsky, Allan; LeBlang, Theodore R.; Snyder, Jack W.; Wecht, Cyril H.; Zaremski, Miles J. Legal Medicine. 6th ed. St. Louis: Mosby; 2004: 3-23. Subject: 2.3

Sanbar, S. Sandy; Selkin, Stuart G. Physician-assisted suicide. *In:* American College of Legal Medicine Textbook Committee, Sanbar, S. Sandy; Firestone, Marvin H.; Buckner, Fillmore; Gibofsky, Allan; LeBlang, Theodore R.; Snyder, Jack W.; Wecht, Cyril H.; Zaremski, Miles J. Legal Medicine. 6th ed. St. Louis: Mosby; 2004: 315-320. Subject: 20.7

Sanders, Stacy J.; Kittay, Eva Feder. Shouldering the burden of care [case study]. *Hastings Center Report* 2005 September-October; 35(5): 14-15. Subject: 9.5.2

Sanders, Tom; Skevington, Suzanne. Participation as an expression of patient uncertainty: an exploration of bowel cancer consultations. *Psycho-Oncology* 2004 October; 13(10): 675-688. Subject: 8.3.1

Sanderson, Simon; Zimmern, Ron; Kroese, Mark; Higgins, Julian; Patch, Christine; Emery, Jon. How can the evaluation of genetic tests be enhanced? Lessons learned from the ACCE framework and evaluating genetic tests in the United Kingdom. *Genetics in Medicine* 2005 September; 7(7): 495-500. Subject: 15.3

Sandman, Lars. On the autonomy turf. Assessing the value of autonomy to patients. *Medicine, Health Care and Philosophy: A European Journal* 2004; 7(3): 261-268. Subject: 8.1

Sandman, Lars. Should people die a natural death? *Health Care Analysis: An International Journal of Health Care Philosophy and Policy* 2005 December; 13(4): 275-287. Subject: 20.5.1

Sandman, Lars. What's the use of human dignity within palliative care? *Nursing Philosophy* 2002 July; 3(2): 177-181. Subject: 20.4.1

Sandor, Judit. Personal identification and genetic fingerprinting: "secrets or lies.". *In:* Actes du Colloque International AMADE-UNESCO sur Bioethique et Droits de L'enfant (Monaco, 28-30 Avril 2000) = Proceedings of the International Symposium AMADE-UNESCO on Bioethics and the Rights of the Child (Monaco, 28-30 April 2000). Paris: UNESCO, Division des Sciences Humaines, de la Philosophie et de L'ethique des Sciences et des Technologies; 2001: 69-79. Subject: 15.3

Sang-Hun, Choe; Wade, Nicholas. Korean cloning scientist quits over report he faked research; backers of stem cell work fear larger setback. *New York Times* 2005 December 24; p. A1, A6. Subject: 1.3.9

Sankar, Pamela. Communication and miscommunication in informed consent to research. *Medical Anthropology Quarterly* 2004 December; 18(4): 429-446. Subject: 18.3

Sankar, Pamela; Kahn, Jonathan. BiDil: race medicine or race marketing? *Health Affairs* 2005 July-December; 24(Supplement 3): W5-455- W5-463. Subject: 15.11

Sanner, Margareta A. A Swedish survey of young people's views on organ donation and transplantation. *Transplant International* 2002 December; 15(12): 641-648. Subject: 19.5

Sanson-Fisher, Rob; Turnbull, Deborah. 'To do or not do?': ethical problems for behavioural medicine. *In:* Fairbairn, Susan; Fairbairn, Gavin, eds. Psychology, Ethics and Change. New York: Routledge & Kegan Paul; 1987: 191- 211. Subject: 9.1

Santelli, John; Geller, Gail; Chen, Donna T.; Speers, Marjorie A.; Botkin, Jeffrey B.; Laswell, Stacy. Recruitment of pregnant, minor adolescents and minor adolescents at risk of pregnancy into longitudinal, observational research: the case of the National Children's Study. *In:* Kodish, Eric, ed. Ethics and Research with Children: A Case-Based Approach. New York: Oxford University Press; 2005: 100- 119. Subject: 18.5.3

Santen, Sally A.; Hemphill, Robin R.; Spanier, Cindy M.; Fletcher, Nicholas D. 'Sorry, it's my first time!' Will patients consent to medical students learning procedures? *Medical Education* 2005 April; 39(4): 365-369. Subject: 7.2

Santora, Marc. Cardiologists say rankings affect surgical decisions. *New York Times* 2005 January 11; p. B3. Subject: 7.1

Santora, Marc; Carey, Benedict. Depressed? New York screens for people at risk. *New York Times* 2005 April 13; p. A1, A16. Subject: 17.1

Sardinia, Lisa M. Stem cells. *In:* Ness, Bryan D., ed. Encyclopedia of Genetics. Revised edition. Volume II. Pasadena, Calif.: Salem Press; 2004: 710-715. Subject: 18.5.4

See SUBJECT HEADING KEY FOR SECTION II on inside back cover

Sarkin, Jeremy. Patriarchy and discrimination in apartheid South Africa's abortion law. *Buffalo Human Rights Law Review* 1998; 4: 141-184. Subject: 12.4.1

Sarson-Lawrence, M.; Alt, C.; Mok, M.T.; Dodds, M.; Rosenthal, M.A. Trust and confidence: towards mutual acceptance of ethics committee approval of multicentre studies. *Internal Medicine Journal* 2004 November; 34(11): 598-603. Subject: 18.2

Sarteschi, L.M. Jehovah's witnesses, blood transfusions and transplantations. *Transplantation Proceedings* 2004 April; 36(3): 499-501. Subject: 19.1

Sass, Hans-Martin. Narrative approaches in patient information and communication. *Formosan Journal of Medical Humanities* 2005 September; 6(1-2): 15-29. Subject: 8.2

Sataloff, Robert T. Correcting the medical literature: ethics and policy [editorial]. *Ear, Nose and Throat Journal* 2005 February; 84(2): 65-66. Subject: 1.3.9

Satchwill, Allison A. Asymptomatic HIV and the Americans with Disabilities Act: Runnebaum v. Nationsbank of Maryland, N.A. *University Of Cincinnati Law Review* 1998 Summer; 66(4): 1387-1410. Subject: 9.5.6

Satel, Sally; Klick, Jonathan. The Institute of Medicine report: too quick to diagnose bias. *Perspectives in Biology and Medicine* 2005 Winter; 48(1, Supplement): S15-S25. Subject: 9.5.4

Satin, David J. More realism about informed consent. *Journal of Laboratory and Clinical Medicine* 2005 June; 145(6): 292-294. Subject: 18.3

Sato, Hajime; Akabayashi, Akira; Kai, Ichiro. Public appraisal of government efforts and participation intent in medico-ethical policymaking in Japan: a large scale national survey concerning brain death and organ transplant. *BMC Medical Ethics [electronic]* 2005; 6; E1, 12 p. Available: http://www.biomedcentral.com/1472-6939/6/1 [18 February 2005]. Subject: 20.2.1

Sattar, S. Pirzada; Ahmed, Mohammed Shakeel; Madison, James; Olsen, Denise R.; Bhatia, Subhash C.; Ellahi, Shahid; Majeed, Farhan; Ramaswamy, Sriram; Petty, Frederick; Wilson, Daniel R. Patient and physician attitudes to using medications with religiously forbidden ingredients. *Annals of Pharmacotherapy* 2004 November; 38(11): 1830-1835. Subject: 9.7

Sauer, Mark V. Gender selection: pressure from patients and industry should not alter our adherence to ethical guidelines. *American Journal of Obstetrics and Gynecology* 2004 November; 191(5): 1543-1545. Subject: 14.3

Saul, Stephanie. FDA approves a heart drug for African-Americans. *New York Times* 2005 June 24; p. C2. Subject: 9.7

Saul, Stephanie. FDA panel approves heart remedy for blacks. *New York Times* 2005 June 17; p. C4. Subject: 9.5.4

Saul, Stephanie. Maker of heart drug intended for blacks bases price on patients' wealth. *New York Times* 2005 July 8; p. C3. Subject: 9.5.4

Saul, Stephanie. Selling dreams and drugs; some diet doctors test the boundaries of accepted practices. *New York Times* 2005 September 22; p. G1, G9. Subject: 9.5.1

Saul, Stephanie. US to review drug intended for one race. *New York Times* 2005 June 13; p. A1, A15. Subject: 9.5.4

Saul, Stephanie; Anderson, Jenny. Doctors' links with investors raise concerns. *New York Times* 2005 August 17; p. A1, C6. Subject: 1.3.9

Saunders, Cicely. Care of the dying- 1: the problem of euthanasia. *Nursing Times* 1976 July 1; 72(26): 1003-1005. Subject: 20.5.1

Saunders, John; Wainwright, Paul. Risk, Helsinki 2000 and the use of placebo in medical research. *Clinical Medicine* 2003 September-October; 3(5): 435-439. Subject: 18.3

Saunders, William L. Washington insider. The Terri Schiavo case. *National Catholic Bioethics Quarterly* 2005 Summer; 5(2): 229- 239. Subject: 2.4

Saunders, William L., Jr. Embryology: inconvenient facts [opinion]. *First Things* 2004 December; (148): 13-15. Subject: 18.5.4

Savage, Teresa A. DNAR in schools: questions and concerns. *American Journal of Bioethics* 2005 January-February; 5(1): 72- 74. Subject: 20.5.2

Savell, Kristin. Human rights in the age of technology: can law rein in the medical juggernaut? *Sydney Law Review* 2001 September; 23(3): 423-460. Subject: 20.5.1

Savell, Kristin. Sex and the sacred: sterilization and bodily integrity in English and Canadian law. *McGill Law Journal* 2004 October; 49(4): 1093-1141. Subject: 11.3

Saver, Richard S. Squandering the gain: gainsharing and the continuing dilemma of physician financial incentives. *Northwestern University Law Review* 2003 Fall; 98(1): 145-238. Subject: 9.3.1

Saver, Richard S. What IRBs could learn from corporate boards. *IRB: Ethics and Human Research* 2005 September-October; 27(5): 1-6. Subject: 18.2

Savitz, Martin H.; Rivlin, Michael M.; Fleetwood, Janet; Caputo, Zach; Perry, Constance. Ethical differences between socialized and HMO systems. *Mount Sinai Journal of Medicine* 2004 November; 71(6): 392-400. Subject: 9.3.2

Savulescu, Julian. Reproductive technology, efficiency and equality. *Medical Journal of Australia* 1999 December 6-20; 171(11-12): 668-670. Subject: 14.1

Savulescu, Julian. Should all patients who attempt suicide be treated? *Monash Bioethics Review* 1995 October; 14(4): 33-40. Subject: 8.3.4

Savulescu, Julian; Skene, Loane. Who has the right to access medical information from a deceased person? Ethical and legal perspectives. *Journal of Law and Medicine* 2000 August; 8(1): 81-88. Subject: 8.4

Savulescu, Julian; Viens, A.M. What makes the best medical ethics journal? A North American perspective. *Journal of Medical Ethics* 2005 October; 31(10): 591-597. Subject: 1.3.7

Sawa, Russell J. Foundations of interdisciplinarity: a Lonergan perspective. *Medicine, Health Care and Philosophy: A European Journal* 2005; 8(1): 53-61. Subject: 7.3

Sayers, Gwen M.; Nesbitt, Tim. Ageism in the NHS and the Human Rights Act 1998: an ethical and legal enquiry. *European Journal of Health Law* 2002 March; 9(1): 5-18. Subject: 9.5.2

Sayers, G.M.; Bethell, H.W.L. Pacing extremely old patients: who decides — the doctor, the patient, or the relatives? *Heart* 2004 February 1; 90(2): 134-135. Subject: 8.1

Scaldo, Stacy A. The Born-Alive Infants Protection Act: baby steps toward the recognition of life after birth. *Nova Law Review* 2002 Winter; 26(2): 485-510. Subject: 4.4

Scalise, Daniele Maria; Bognolo, Giulio. The new pope and medical ethics — can Benedict XVI strike a balance between Catholic doctrines and health? [editorial]. *BMJ: British Medical Journal* 2005 June 4; 330(7503): 1281-1282. Subject: 2.1

Schaap, Tamar. Confidentiality in counseling for X-linked conditions. *Clinical Genetics* 1995 March; 47(3): 155-157. Subject: 15.2

Schachman, Howard K. On scientific freedom and responsibility. *Biophysical Chemistry* 2003; 100(1-3): 615-625. Subject: 1.3.9

Schachter, Leora; Emanuel, Ezekiel J.; Emanuel, Linda J. Talking about death, dying, and bereavement with terminally ill patients and their caregivers [letter and reply]. *Archives of Internal Medicine* 2005 June 27; 165(12): 1437. Subject: 20.4.1

Schadick, Kevin. Bioethics consultants: corporate reliance on a new field of consultation. *Health Matrix: Journal of Law-Medicine* 2005 Summer; 15(2): 433-458. Subject: 18.2

Schäfer, Christof; Nelson, Kristin; Herbst, Manfred. Waiting for radiotherapy: a national call for ethical discourse on waiting lists in radiotherapy: findings from a preliminary survey. *Strahlentherapie und Onkologie* 2005 January; 181(1): 9-19. Subject: 9.4

Schaffer, Marjorie A.; Juárez, Maureen. An ethical analysis of student-faculty interactions. *Nurse Educator* 1993 May-June; 18(3): 25-28. Subject: 7.2

Schans, Bette A. Radiologic technologists and ethical reasoning. *Radiologic Technology* 2004 March-April; 75(4): 263-271. Subject: 2.3

Schatz, Gerald S. Are the rationale and regulatory system for protecting human subjects of biomedical and behavioral research obsolete and unworkable, or ethically important but inconvenient and inadequately enforced? *Journal of Contemporary Health Law and Policy* 2003 Winter; 20(1): 1-31. Subject: 18.2

Schatz, Gerald S. Health records privacy and confidentiality: pending questions. *Journal of Contemporary Health Law and Policy* 2002 Fall; 18(3): 685-691. Subject: 8.4

Schears, Raquel M.; Marco, Catherine A.; Iserson, Kenneth V. "Do not attempt resuscitation" (DNAR) in the out-of-hospital setting. *Annals of Emergency Medicine* 2004 July; 44(1): 68-70. Subject: 20.5.4

Schecter, Alissa. Choosing balance: congressional powers and the Partial-Birth Abortion Ban Act of 2003. *Fordham Law Review* 2005 March; 73(4): 1987-2026. Subject: 12.4.1

Scheib, J.E.; Riordan, M.; Rubin, S. Adolescents with open-identity sperm donors: reports from 12-17 year olds. *Human Reproduction* 2005 January; 20(1): 239-252. Subject: 14.2

Scheid, Teresa L. Stigma as a barrier to employment: mental disability and the Americans with Disabilities Act. *International Journal of Law and Psychiatry* 2005 November- December; 28(6): 670-690. Subject: 9.5.3

Schellings, Ron; Kessels, Alfons G.; ter Riet, Gerben; Kleijnen, Jos; Leffers, Pieter; Knottnerus, J. André; Sturmans, Ferd. Members of research ethics committees accepted a modification of the randomized consent design. *Journal of Clinical Epidemiology* 2005 June; 58(6): 589-594. Subject: 18.3

Schenker, Joseph. Legitimising surrogacy in Israel: religious perspectives. *In:* Cook, Rachel; Sclater, Shelley Day; Kaganas, Felicity, eds. Surrogate Motherhood: International Perspectives. Portland, OR: Hart; 2003: 243-260. Subject: 14.2

Schenker, Joseph G.; Laufer, Neri; Navot, Daniel; Margalioth, Ehud J.; Yarkoni, Shaul; Rabinowitz, Ron; Voss, Ruth. In vitro fertilization and embryo transfer — legal and religious aspects in Israel, patient selection, and a modified technique for oocyte collection. *Israel Journal of Medical Sciences* 1983 March; 19(3): 218- 224. Subject: 14.4

Scherer, David G.; Brody, Janet L.; Annett, Robert D.; Hetter, Jeanne; Roberts, Laura Weiss; Cofrin, Keely M.W. Financial compensation to adolescents for participation in biomedical research: adolescent and parent perspectives in seven studies. *Journal of Pediatrics* 2005 April; 146(4): 552-558. Subject: 18.5.2

Scherer, Robert Craig. Mandatory genetic dogtags and the Fourth Amendment: the need for a new post-Skinner test. *Georgetown Law Journal* 1997 June; 85(6): 2007-2038. Subject: 15.1

Scheurich, Neil. Spirituality, medicine, and the possibility of wisdom [editorial]. *JGIM: Journal of General Internal Medicine* 2005 April; 20(4): 379-380. Subject: 8.1

Schick, Ari. Neuro exceptionalism? *American Journal of Bioethics* 2005 March-April; 5(2): 36-38. Subject: 17.1

Schiermeier, Quirin. German tobacco papers reveal lump sums for health experts [news]. *Nature* 2005 June 16; 435(7044): 866. Subject: 1.3.9

Schiermeier, Quirin. Political deadlock leaves scientists frustrated [news]. *Nature* 2005 September 29; 437(7059): 603. Subject: 15.1

Schiffer, David. The limits of scientific research [debate]. *Neurological Sciences* 2005 February; 25(6): 351-354. Subject: 5.1

Schiller, Charity. Stem cell research and conditional federal funding: do state laws allowing more extensive research pose a problem for federalism? *Pepperdine Law Review* 2004 May; 31(4): 1017-1054. Subject: 18.5.4

Schlafly, Andrew L. Brief of amicus curiae Eagle Forum Education and Legal Defense Fund in support of petitioner. *Issues in Law and Medicine* 2005 Fall; 21(2): 147-158. Subject: 12.4.2

Schlegel, Rainer. German health care — towards universal access: an overview of the principles of access and benefits. *Journal of Contemporary Health Law and Policy* 2002 Fall; 18(3): 673-683. Subject: 9.3.1

Schlenzka, Hans J. The role of health personnel in the protection of prisoners against torture and inhuman treatment. *Acta Medicinae Legalis et Sociales* 1980; 30(1): 19-24. Subject: 21.4

Schlessinger, Shirley; Crook, Errol D.; Black, Ruth; Barber, Henry. Case studies in ethics from the G.V. "Sonny" Montgomery VA Medical Center and the University of Mississippi Medical Center: ethical issues in transplantation: living related donation in the setting of severe neurological damage without brain death. *American Journal of the Medical Sciences* 2002 October; 324(4): 232-236. Subject: 19.5

Schmidt, Kurt W. ". . . As we forgive those who trespass against us . . .": theological reflections on sin and guilt in the hospital environment. *Christian Bioethics* 2005 August; 11(2): 201-219. Subject: 2.1

Schmidt, Terri A. The legacy of the Tuskegee syphilis experiments for emergency exception from informed consent. *Annals of Emergency Medicine* 2003 January; 41(1): 79-81. Subject: 18.3

Schmidt, Ulla. Cloning of human beings? Theological perspectives. *In:* Ostnor, Lars, ed. Bioethics and Cloning: Report from a Workshop Arranged by the Nordic Theological Network for Bioethics in Arhus, September 25-27, 1998. Oslo: Nordic Theological Network for Bioethics; 1998: 65-72. Subject: 14.5

Schmidt, Volker H. Rationing health care in the welfare state: three policies. *Journal of Health and Social Policy* 2004; 19(1): 57-76. Subject: 9.4

Schmidt, Volker H.; Lim, Chee Han. Organ transplantation in Singapore: history, problems, and policies. *Social Science and Medicine* 2004 November; 59(10): 2173-2182. Subject: 19.6

Schmidt, Winsor C., Jr. Critique of the American Psychiatric Association's guidelines for state legislation on civil commitment of the mentally ill. *New England Journal on Criminal and Civil Confinement* 1985 Winter; 11(1): 11-43. Subject: 17.7

Schmittlein, David C.; Morrison, Donald G. A live baby or your money back: the marketing of in vitro fertilization procedures. *Management Science* 2003 December; 49(12): 1617-1635. Subject: 14.4

Schmitz, Michael L.; Taylor, Bonnie J.; Anand, Kanwaljeet J.S. End-of-life decisions in the neonatal intensive care unit: medical infanticide or palliative terminal care? *Critical Care Medicine* 2000 July; 28(7): 2668-2671. Subject: 20.5.2

Schneider, Benjamin; Schüklenk, Udo. Module six: special issues. *Developing World Bioethics* 2005 March; 5(1): 92-108. Subject: 1.3.9

Schneider, Carl E. A government of limited powers. *Hastings Center Report* 2005 July-August; 35(4): 11-12. Subject: 9.5.1

Schneider, Carl E. Hard cases and the politics of righteousness. *Hastings Center Report* 2005 May-June; 35(3): 24-27. Subject: 20.5.1

Schneider, Carl E. Liability for life. *Hastings Center Report* 2004 July-August; 34(4): 10-11. Subject: 20.5.4

Schneider, Carl E. Reaching disclosure. *Hastings Center Report* 2005 January-February; 35(1): 12-13. Subject: 2.1

Schneider, Carl E. Some realism about informed consent [editorial]. *Journal of Laboratory and Clinical Medicine* 2005 June; 145(6): 289-291. Subject: 18.3

Schneider, Gregory W.; Snell, Laura. C.A.R.E.: an approach for teaching ethics in medicine. *Social Science and Medicine* 2000 November 16; 51(10): 1563-1567. Subject: 7.2

Schneider, Keith. Repro madness. *New Age Journal* 1986 January; 3: 34-39, 72-74. Subject: 14.1

Schneiderman, Lawrence; Gilmer, Todd. Ethics and futility [letter]. *Health Affairs* 2005 September-October; 24(5): 1376-1377. Subject: 20.5.1

Schneiderman, Lawrence J. The perils of hope [opinion]. *CQ: Cambridge Quarterly of Healthcare Ethics* 2005 Spring; 14(2): 235-239. Subject: 20.5.1

Schneiderman, Lawrence J.; Gilmer, Todd; Teetzel, Holly D. Ethics consultations in the intensive care setting

---

[letter]. *Critical Care Medicine* 2002 February; 30(2): 489. Subject: 9.6

Schoen, Johanna. I knew that it was a serious crime: negotiating abortion before Roe v. Wade. *In her:* Choice and Coercion: Birth Control, Sterilization and Abortion in Public Health and Welfare. Chapel Hill: University of North Carolina Press; 2005: 139-196. Subject: 12.5.1

Schoen, Johanna. Nothing is removed except the possibility of parenthood: women and the politics of sterilization. *In her:* Choice and Coercion: Birth Control, Sterilization and Abortion in Public Health and Welfare. Chapel Hill: University of North Carolina Press; 2005: 75-138. Subject: 11.3

Schoenholtz, Jack C. Psychiatry and police interrogations [letter]. *AAPL (American Academy of Psychiatry and the Law) Newsletter* 2005 September; 30(3): 26-27. Subject: 1.3.1

Schommer, Jon C. Direct-to-consumer advertising for prescription drugs. *Minnesota Medicine* 2005 March; 88(3): 32-33, 45. Subject: 9.7

Schonfeld, Toby L.; Brown, Joseph S.; Gordon, Bruce G. Subject protection and the risk-benefit relationship [comment]. *American Journal of Bioethics* 2005 September-October; 5(5): 22-23. Subject: 18.3

Schonfeld, Toby L.; Gordon, Bruce G. Contraception in research: a policy suggestion. *IRB: Ethics and Human Research* 2005 March-April; 27(2): 15-20. Subject: 18.5.3

Schoub, Barry D. The ethics of immunisation [editorial]. *South African Medical Journal* 2002 January; 92(1): 47. Subject: 9.5.1

Schouten, Barbara C.; Hoogstraten, Johan; Eijkman, Michiel A.J. Dutch dentists' views of informed consent: a replication study. *Patient Education and Counseling* 2004 February; 52(2): 165-168. Subject: 8.3.1

Schouten, Ronald. The psychotherapist-patient privilege. *Harvard Review of Psychiatry* 1998 May-June; 6(1): 44-48. Subject: 8.4

Schrecker, Ted. Benefit-sharing in the new genomic marketplace: expanding the ethical frame of reference. *In:* Knoppers, Bartha Maria, ed. Populations and Genetics: Legal and Socio-Ethical Perspectives. Boston: Martinus Nijhoff; 2003:. Subject: 15.1

Schreiber, Hans-Ludwig. The legal situation regarding assisted reproduction in Germany. *Reproductive BioMedicine Online [electronic]* 2003 January-February; 6(1): 8-12. Available: http://www.rbmonline.com/article/729 [1 September 2005]. Subject: 14.2

Schroeder, Doris. Human rights and their role in global bioethics. *CQ: Cambridge Quarterly of Healthcare Ethics* 2005 Spring; 14(2): 221-223. Subject: 2.1

Schroeder, Doris. Suicide, self-sacrifice, and the duty to die. *In:* Häyry, Matti; Takala, Tuija; Herissone-Kelly, Pe-

ter, eds. Bioethics and Social Reality. New York: Rodopi, 2005: 17-29. Subject: 20.7

Schroeder, Doris; Ladikas, Miltos; Schuklenk, Udo; Diáz, Carolina Lasén; Kleinsmidt, Anita; Alvarez-Castillo, Fatima; Feinholz, Dafna. Sharing the benefits of genetic research: will the World Trade Organization act to stop the exploitation of biodiversity? [editorial]. *BMJ: British Medical Journal* 2005 December 10; 331(7529): 1351-1352. Subject: 15.1

Schroeter, Kathryn. Expanded practice: the nurse as bioethics consultant. *Seminars in Perioperative Nursing* 2000 April; 9(2): 65-70. Subject: 9.6

Schroeter, Kathryn. Perioperative nurses' involvement on nursing ethics committees. *AORN Journal* 1996 October; 64(4): 588-589, 592-596. Subject: 9.6

Schroeter, Kathryn. A study of proactive ethics consultation for critically and terminally ill patients with extended lengths of stay. *AORN Journal* 2000 April; 71(4): 902, 904. Subject: 9.6

Schroten, Egbert. A theological-ethics perspective on cloning. *In:* Ostnor, Lars, ed. Bioethics and Cloning: Report from a Workshop Arranged by the Nordic Theological Network for Bioethics in Arhus, September 25-27, 1998. Oslo: Nordic Theological Network for Bioethics; 1998: 35-44. Subject: 14.5

Schuchman, John S. Deafness and eugenics in the Nazi era. *In:* Van Cleve, John Vickery, ed. Genetics, Disability, and Deafness. Washington, DC: Gallaudet University Press; 2004: 72-78. Subject: 15.5

Schudt, Karl. What is chosen in the act of embryo adoption? *National Catholic Bioethics Quarterly* 2005 Spring; 5(1): 63-71. Subject: 14.4

Schuh, Lori A.; Burdette, David E. Initiation of an effective neurology resident ethics curriculum. *Neurology* 2004 May 25; 62(10): 1897-1898. Subject: 7.2

Schüklenk, Udo. Ethics and AIDS vaccine trials: a response [letter]. *Issues in Medical Ethics* 2000 April-June; 8(2): 37. Subject: 18.2

Schüklenk, Udo. Helsinki Declaration revisions. *Issues in Medical Ethics* 2001 January-March; 9(1): 29. Subject: 18.2

Schüklenk, Udo. International research ethics guidelines under threat: a full-scale attack on the CIOMS Guidelines and the Declaration of Helsinki is currently underway. *Issues in Medical Ethics* 1999 July-September; 7(3): 97-98. Subject: 18.2

Schüklenk, Udo. Module one: introduction to research ethics. *Developing World Bioethics* 2005 March; 5(1): 1-13. Subject: 18.1

Schüklenk, Udo; Gallagher, Jim. Status, careers and influence in bioethics [comment]. *American Journal of Bioethics* 2005 September-October; 5(5): 64-66. Subject: 6

Schüklenk, Udo; Lott, Jason. Ethics, politics and embryo stem cell research in South Africa. *South African Medical Journal* 2002 October; 92(10): 782, 784-786. Subject: 18.5.4

Schüklenk, Udo; Lott, Jason P. Bioethics and (public) policy advice. *In:* Thiele, F.; Ashcroft, R.E., eds. Bioethics in a Small World. Berlin: Springer; 2005: 129-138. Subject: 2.4

Schulenberg, Stefan E.; Yutrzenka, Barbara A. Ethical issues in the use of computerized assessment. *Computers in Human Behavior* 2004 July; 20(4): 477-490. Subject: 1.3.12

Schultz, Robert C. Ethical principles and theories. *AWHONN's Clinical Issues in Perinatal and Women's Health Nursing* 1993; 4(4): 517-525. Subject: 1.1

Schultz-Grant, Lois D.; Young-Cureton, Virginia; Kataoka-Yahiro, Merle. Advance directives and do not resuscitate orders: nurses' knowledge and the level of practice in school settings. *Journal of School Nursing* 1998 April; 14(2): 4, 6-10, 12-13. Subject: 20.5.4

Schuppli, Catherine A.; Fraser, David. The interpretation and application of the three Rs by animal ethics committee members. *ATLA: Alternatives to Laboratory Animals* 2005 October; 33(5): 487-500. Subject: 22.2

Schuppli, Catherine A.; McDonald, Michael. Contrasting modes of governance for the protection of humans and animals in Canada: lessons for reform. *Health Law Review* 2005; 13(2-3): 97-106. Subject: 22.2

Schuster, Mark A.; Collins, Rebecca; Cunningham, William E.; Morton, Sally C.; Zierler, Sally; Wong, Myra; Tu, Wenli; Kanouse, David E. Perceived discrimination in clinical care in a nationally representative sample of HIV-infected adults receiving health care. *JGIM: Journal of General Internal Medicine* 2005 September; 20(9): 807-813. Subject: 9.5.6

Schuz, Rhona. Surrogacy in Israel: an analysis of the law in practice. *In:* Cook, Rachel; Sclater, Shelley Day; Kaganas, Felicity, eds. Surrogate Motherhood: International Perspectives. Portland, OR: Hart; 2003: 35-53. Subject: 14.2

Schwab, Abe. The biases of bioterror funding. *American Journal of Bioethics* 2005 July-August; 5(4): 54-56. Subject: 21.3

Schwab, Abraham P. Would you know an undue inducement if you saw one? [letter]. *American Journal of Bioethics [Online]* 2005 September- October; 5(5): W17. Subject: 18.3

Schwappach, David L.B.; Koeck, Christian M. Preferences for disclosure: the case of bedside rationing. *Social Science and Medicine* 2004 November; 59(9): 1891-1897. Subject: 9.4

Schwappach, David L.B.; Koeck, Christian M. What makes an error unacceptable? A factorial survey on the dis-

closure of medical errors. *International Journal for Quality in Health Care* 2004 August; 16(4): 317-326. Subject: 9.8

Schwartz, John. Experts say ending feeding can lead to a gentle death. *New York Times* 2005 March 20; p. A29. Subject: 20.5.1

Schwartz, John. For the end of life, hospital pairs ethics and medicine: a team effort to resolve family bedside conflicts. *New York Times* 2005 July 4; p. B1, B5. Subject: 9.6

Schwartz, John. Neither "starvation" nor the suffering it connotes applies to Schiavo, doctors say; the medical situation. *New York Times* 2005 March 25; p. A14. Subject: 20.5.1

Schwartz, John. New openness in deciding when and how to die. *New York Times* 2005 March 21; p. A1, A14. Subject: 20.5.4

Schwartz, John; Estrin, James. In Vermont, a bid to legalize physician-assisted suicide. *New York Times* 2005 March 30; p. A12. Subject: 20.7

Schwartz, John; Estrin, James. Many seeking one final say on end of life. *New York Times* 2005 June 17; p. A1, A22. Subject: 20.5.4

Schwartz, John; Grady, Denise. A diagnosis with a dose of religion; the bioethicist. *New York Times* 2005 March 24; p. A20. Subject: 20.5.1

Schwartz, Kevin O. Uninformed consent: the undisclosed risk rooted in our current informed consent framework. *Medical Trial Technique Quarterly* 2002; 48(3): 311-347. Subject: 8.3.1

Schwartz, Lita Linzer. Surrogacy arrangements in the USA: what relationships do they spawn? *In:* Cook, Rachel; Sclater, Shelley Day; Kaganas, Felicity, eds. Surrogate Motherhood: International Perspectives. Portland, OR: Hart; 2003: 161-178. Subject: 14.2

Schwartz, Marlene B.; Chambliss, Heather O'Neal; Brownell, Kelly D.; Blair, Steven N.; Billington, Charles. Weight bias among health professionals specializing in obesity. *Obesity Research* 2003 September; 11(9): 1033-1039. Subject: 8.1

Schwartz, Michael Alan. Practical reasons for lifting bans on physician-assisted suicide. *St. John's Journal of Legal Commentary* 1997 Summer; 12(3): 626-633. Subject: 20.7

Schwartz, Peter H. Defending the distinction between treatment and enhancement [comment]. *American Journal of Bioethics* 2005 May-June; 5(3): 17-19. Subject: 4.5

Schwarz, Eleanor Bimla; Luetkemeyer, Anne; Foster, Diana Greene; Weitz, Tracy A.; Lindes, Deborah; Stewart, Felicia H. Willing and able? Provision of medication for abortion by future internists. *Women's Health Issues* 2005 January-February; 15(1): 39-44. Subject: 12.1

Subject = NRCBL Primary Classification Number; See inside front cover

Schwarz, Judith Kennedy. Revisiting New York State's proposed surrogate decision-making legislation. *Journal of the New York State Nurses Association* 1995 September; 26(3): 18-23. Subject: 8.3.3

Schweikardt, Christoph. "You gained honor for your profession as a Brown nurse" : the career of a Nationalist Socialist nurse mirrored by her letters home. *Nursing History Review* 2004; 12: 121-138. Subject: 21.4

Scoccia, Danny. Slippery-slope objections to legalizing physician assisted suicide and voluntary euthanasia. *Public Affairs Quarterly* 2005 April; 19(2): 143-161. Subject: 20.7

Scofield, Giles. Motion(less) in limine. *Journal of Law, Medicine and Ethics* 2005 Winter; 33(4): 821- 833. Subject: 9.6

Scolding, Neil. Stem-cell therapy: hope and hype [opinion]. *Lancet* 2005 June 18-24; 365(9477): 2073-2075. Subject: 18.5.4

Scopelliti, Joseph; Judd, Fiona; Grigg, Margaret; Hodgins, Gene; Fraser, Cait; Hulbert, Carol; Endacott, Ruth; Wood, Anita. Dual relationships in mental health practice: issues for clinicians in rural settings. *Australian and New Zealand Journal of Psychiatry* 2004 November-December; 38(11-12): 953-959. Subject: 8.1

Scott, Andrea K. Gender discrimination in the medical community. *Update [Loma Linda University Center for Christian Bioethics]* 1995 July; 11(2): 12 p. Subject: 9.5.4

Scott, Debbie A.; Valery, Patricia C.; Boyle, Frances M.; Bain, Christopher J. Does research into sensitive areas do harm? Experiences of research participation after a child's diagnosis with Ewing's sarcoma. *Medical Journal of Australia* 2002 November 4; 177(9): 507-510. Subject: 18.5.1

Scott, Elizabeth S.; Reppucci, N. Dickon; Woolard, Jennifer L. Evaluating adolescent decision making in legal contexts. *Law and Human Behavior* 1995 June; 19(3): 221-244. Subject: 8.3.2

Scott, Janny; Kaufman, Leslie. Belated charge ignites furor over AIDS drug trial. *New York Times* 2005 July 17; p. A1, A10. Subject: 18.5.2

Scott, Jennifer A.; Campos-Outcalt, Doug. Non-consented IUD placement reported by Mexican immigrants: a caution for caregivers in the US? *Journal of Family Practice* 2005 March; 54(3): 263-264. Subject: 8.3.1

Scott, Larry D. Ethical issues in genetic testing. *American Journal of Gastroenterology* 2004 October; 99(10): 1871-1873. Subject: 15.3

Scott, Larry D. The PEG "consult". *American Journal of Gastroenterology* 2005 April; 100(4): 740-743. Subject: 20.5.1

Scott, Mark L.; Whelan, Anna; Dewdney, John; Zwi, Anthony B. "Brain drain" or ethical recruitment? Solving health workforce shortages with professionals from developing countries. *Medical Journal of Australia* 2004 February 16; 180(4): 174-176. Subject: 21.6

Scott, Peter. Nature, technology and the rule of God: (en)countering the disgracing of nature. *In:* Deane-Drummond, Celia; Szerszynski, Bronislaw, eds. Re- ordering Nature: Theology, Society and the New Genetics. New York: T & T Clark; 2003: 275-292. Subject: 15.1

Scott, P. Anne. Emotion, moral perception, and nursing practice. *Nursing Philosophy* 2000 October; 1(2): 123-133. Subject: 4.1.3

Scott, Rosamund. The English fetus and the right to life. *European Journal of Health Law* 2004 December; 11(4): 347-364. Subject: 4.4

Scott, Rosamund. Prenatal screening, autonomy and reasons: the relationship between the law of abortion and wrongful birth. *Medical Law Review* 2003 Autumn; 11(3): 265-325. Subject: 15.2

Scott, Rosamund. Prenatal testing, reproductive autonomy, and disability interests. *CQ: Cambridge Quarterly of Healthcare Ethics* 2005 Winter; 14(1): 65-82. Subject: 15.1

Scott, Rosamund. The uncertain scope of reproductive autonomy in preimplantation genetic diagnosis and selective abortion. *Medical Law Review* 2005 Autumn; 13(3): 291-327. Subject: 15.2

Scuder, Amanda C. The inapplicability of parental involvement laws to the distribution of mifepristone (RU-486) to minors. *American University Journal of Gender, Social Policy, and the Law* 2002; 10(3): 711-741. Subject: 12.4.2

Scully, Jackie Leach. Admitting all variations? Postmodernism and genetic normality. *In:* Shildrick, Margrit; Mykitiuk, Roxanne, eds. Ethics of the Body: Postconventional Challenges. Cambridge, MA: MIT Press; 2005: 49-68. Subject: 4.2

Scully, Jackie Leach. What is a disease? Disease, disability and their definitions [opinion]. *EMBO Reports* 2004 July; 5(7): 650-653. Subject: 4.2

Scully, Jackie Leach; Rippberger, Christine; Rehmann-Sutter, Christoph. Additional ethical issues in genetic medicine perceived by the potential patients. *In:* Knoppers, Bartha Maria, ed. Populations and Genetics: Legal and Socio-Ethical Perspectives. Boston: Martinus Nijhoff; 2003: 623-638. Subject: 15.1

Scully, Judith A.M. Maternal mortality, population control, and the war in women's wombs: a bioethical analysis of quinacrine sterilizations. *Wisconsin International Law Journal* 2000-2001; 19(2): 103-151. Subject: 9.5.5

Scully-Hill, Anne. Consent, frozen embryos, procreative choice and the ideal family. *Cambridge Law Journal* 2004 March; 63(1): 47-49. Subject: 14.6

Seabrook, Robert; Collins, Ben. The duty of care of the occupational physician in assessing job applicants. *Occupational Medicine* 1999 April; 49(3): 189-192. Subject: 16.3

Seale, Clive; Kirk, Debbie; Tobin, Martin; Burton, Paul; Grundy, Richard; Pritchard-Jones, Kathy; Dixon-Woods, Mary. Effect of media portrayals of removal of children's tissue on UK tumour bank. *BMJ: British Medical Journal* 2005 August 13; 331(7513): 401-403. Subject: 19.5

Seaman, Rachel M.H. The ethics and economics of consuming Canadian drugs. *Journal of the Oklahoma State Medical Association* 2005 January; 98(1): 22-26. Subject: 9.7

Seamark, Clare; Blake, Sue. Concerning women: questionnaire survey of consultations, embarrassment, and views on confidentiality in general practice among women in their teens, thirties and fifties. *Journal of Family Planning and Reproductive Health Care* 2005 January; 31(1): 31-33. Subject: 9.5.5

Sears, Jeanne M. Context is key for voluntary and informed consent. *American Journal of Bioethics* 2005 January-February; 5(1): 47- 48. Subject: 18.3

Seay, Gary. Euthanasia and physicians' moral duties. *Journal of Medicine and Philosophy* 2005 October; 30(5): 517- 533. Subject: 20.5.1

Sebastian, J. Jayakiran. A theological perspective on the withdrawal of care. *Issues in Medical Ethics* 2001 July-September; 9(3): 79-81. Subject: 20.5.1

Seedat, Soraya; Pienaar, Willem P.; Williams, David; Stein, Daniel J. Ethics of research on survivors of trauma. *Current Psychiatry Reports* 2004 August; 6(4): 262-267. Subject: 18.5.1

Seel, Klaus-M. Zum Umgang mit Information, Tests und Diagnostik im Bereich der Humangenetik. Wie müsste eine Regelung aussehen, die auch in Zukunft Bestand haben soll? *In:* Jahrbuch für Wissenschaft und Ethik. Bd. 7. Berlin: Walter de Gruyter; 2002: 217-242. Subject: 15.3

Seelmann, Kurt. Menschenwürde und Embryonen. *In:* Maio, Giovanni; Just, Hanjörg, eds. Die Forschung an embryonalen Stammzellen in ethischer und rechtlicher Perspektive. Baden-Baden: Nomos Verlagsgesellschaft; 2003: 156-167. Subject: 4.4

Seeman, Mary V. Psychiatry in the Nazi era. *Canadian Journal of Psychiatry/Revue Canadienne de Psychiatrie* 2005 March; 50(4): 218-225. Subject: 21.4

Segal, Thalia. A lucrative routine, short on pain management. Good ethical decision is akin to good medical decision. *Pain Medicine* 2002 December; 3(4): 349-350. Subject: 4.4

Segest, Erling. The legal position with regard to informed consent in Denmark. *Medicine and Law: World Associa-* *tion for Medical Law* 1995; 14(3-4): 245-254. Subject: 8.3.1

Segev, Re'em. Well-being and fairness in the distribution of scarce health resource. *Journal of Medicine and Philosophy* 2005 June; 30(3): 231-260. Subject: 9.4

Segre, Marco. Ethics and the management of terminally ill children [editorial]. *Revista do Hospital das Clinicas* 2004 January; 59(1): 1-2. Subject: 20.4.2

Seibold, Carmel. Qualitative research from a feminist perspective in the postmodern era: methodological, ethical and reflexive concerns. *Nursing Inquiry* 2000 September; 7(3): 147-155. Subject: 18.2

Seidel, Asher. Facing immortality. *International Journal of Applied Philosophy* 2005 Spring; 19(1): 85-104. Subject: 20.5.1

Seif, Rony. Sex selection by preimplantation genetic diagnosis: should it be carried out for social reasons? [letter]. *Human Reproduction* 2003 February; 18(2): 461-462. Subject: 15.2

Selemogo, Mpho. An unequal activism for an unequal epidemic? *Developing World Bioethics* 2005 May; 5(2): 153-168. Subject: 9.5.6

Selemogo, Mpho. The future of AIDS and the ethics of seclusion in the face of an impending danger. *Indian Journal of Medical Ethics* 2005 January-March; 2(1): 14- 15. Subject: 9.5.6

Selgelid, Michael J. Democratic defense spending in an age of bioterrorism. *American Journal of Bioethics* 2005 July-August; 5(4): 49-50. Subject: 21.3

Selgelid, Michael J. Ethics and infectious disease. *Bioethics* 2005 June; 19(3): 272-289. Subject: 5.1

Selgelid, Michael J. In that case. Response [case study]. *Journal of Bioethical Inquiry* 2005; 2(1): 52. Subject: 9.5.1

Selgelid, Michael J. Module four: standards of care and clinical trials. *Developing World Bioethics* 2005 March; 5(1): 55-72. Subject: 18.6

Selgelid, Michael J. Universal norms and conflicting values. *Developing World Bioethics* 2005 September; 5(3): 267-273. Subject: 2.1

Sellman, Derek. Towards an understanding of nursing as a response to human vulnerability. *Nursing Philosophy* 2005 January; 6(1): 2-10. Subject: 9.5.1

Sells, Robert. Incentives for organ donation: some ethical issues. *Annals of Transplantation* 2004; 9(1): 23-24. Subject: 19.5

Semensohn, Jaime. Roe vs. Casey. *Ivy Journal of Ethics* 2003; 3(1): 6-9. Subject: 12.4.2

Sen, Amartya. Population policy: authoritarianism versus cooperation. *Social Change* 1994 September-December; 24(3-4); 17 p. [Online]. Available: http://www.hsph. harvard.edu/Organizations/healthnet/SAsia/suchana/ 9999/rh080.html [7 October 2005]. Subject: 13.3

Subject = NRCBL Primary Classification Number; See inside front cover

Sen, Amartya. Why health equity? *In:* Anand, Sudhir; Peter, Fabienne; Sen, Amartya, eds. Public Health, Ethics, and Equity. New York: Oxford University Press; 2004: 21-33. Subject: 9.1

Seng, Kang Phee. Cloning humans? Some moral considerations. *In:* Qiu, Ren-Zong, ed. Bioethics: Asian Perspectives: A Quest for Moral Diversity. Boston: Kluwer Academic Publishers; 2004: 115- 127. Subject: 14.5

Senior, Kathryn. Defending the use of animals to research human disease [opinion]. *Molecular Medicine Today* 1995 August; 1(5): 220-225. Subject: 22.1

Senior, Victoria; Marteau, Theresa M.; Peters, Timothy J. Will genetic testing for predisposition for disease result in fatalism? A qualitative study of parents responses to neonatal screening for familial hypercholesterolaemia. *Social Science and Medicine* 1999 June; 48(12): 1857-1860. Subject: 15.3

Sequist, Thomas D.; Narva, Andrew S.; Stiles, Sharon K.; Karp, Shelley K.; Cass, Alan; Ayanian, John Z. Access to renal transplantation among American Indians and Hispanics. *American Journal of Kidney Diseases* 2004 August; 44(2): 344-352. Subject: 19.6

Sera, Jean M. Surrogacy and prostitution: a comparative analysis. *American University Journal of Gender and the Law* 1997 Spring; 5(2): 315-342. Subject: 14.2

Sermon, Karen. Sex selection by preimplantation genetic diagnosis: should it be carried out for social reasons? A personal view [letter]. *Human Reproduction* 2003 February; 18(2): 462-463. Subject: 15.2

Serour, G.I.; Dickens, B.M. Ethics in medical information and advertising. *International Journal of Gynaecology and Obstetrics* 2004 May; 85(2): 195-200. Subject: 1.3.9

Sessa, A. When dialysis becomes worse than death [editorial]. *Nephrology, Dialysis, Transplantation* 1995; 10(7): 1128-1130. Subject: 20.5.1

Seto, Belinda. History of medical ethics and perspectives on disparities in minority recruitment and involvement in health research. *American Journal of the Medical Sciences* 2001 November; 322(5): 246-250. Subject: 2.2

Setoyama, Koichi. Privacy of genetic information. *Osaka University Law Review* 2005 February; 52: 75-105. Subject: 15.3

Severijnen, René; Hulstijn-Dirkmaat, Ineke; Gordijn, Bert; Bakker, Leo; Bongaerts, Ger. Acute loss of the small bowel in a school-age boy. Difficult choices: to sustain life or to stop treatment? *European Journal of Pediatrics* 2003 November; 162(11): 794-798. Subject: 20.5.2

Sevick, Mary Ann; Nativio, Donna G.; McConnell, Terrance. Genetic testing of children for late onset disease. *CQ: Cambridge Quarterly of Healthcare Ethics* 2005 Winter; 14(1): 47-56. Subject: 9.5.7

Sewell, Adrian C.; Gebhardt, Boris; Herwig, Jürgen; Rauterberg, Ernst W. Acceptance of extended newborn

screening: the problem of parental non-compliance. *European Journal of Pediatrics* 2004 December; 163(12): 755-756. Subject: 8.3.4

Seyfer, Tara L. Medical and ethical concerns over IVF: potential harms and available options. *Ethics and Medics* 2003 August; 28(8): 1-3. Subject: 14.4

Sgreccia, Elio. The embryo: a sign of contradiction. *Medical Ethics and Bioethics / Medicinska Etika & Bioetika* 2001 Autumn-Winter; 8(3-4): 13. Subject: 4.4

Shabanowitz, Robert. The disposer's dilemma. *American Journal of Bioethics* 2005 November-December; 5(6): 60-61. Subject: 4.4

Shafran, Yigal; Kupietzky, Ari. General anesthesia or conscious sedation with restraint: treating the young child from a Jewish ethical perspective. *Jewish Medical Ethics and Halacha* 2005 August; 5(1): 29-39. Subject: 9.5.7

Shah, Ghanshyam. Doctors and the plague. *Issues in Medical Ethics* 1996 October-December; 4(4): 119-121. Subject: 9.1

Shah, Mamta K. Inconsistencies in the legal status of an unborn child: recognition of a fetus as potential life. *Hofstra Law Review* 2001; 29(3): 931-969. Subject: 4.4

Shah, Sapan S. Medical decision-making in non-life threatening situations for minor children. *Medical Trial Technique Quarterly* 2003; 49(3): 189-216. Subject: 8.3.2

Shah, Sonia. Globalizing clinical research. *Nation* 2002 July 1: 23-24, 26-28. Subject: 18.5.9

Shaheen, Faissal A.M.; Al-Jondeby, Mohammad; Kurpad, Ramprasad; Al-Khader, Abdullah A. Social and cultural issues in organ transplantation in Islamic countries. *Annals of Transplantation* 2004; 9(2): 11-13. Subject: 19.5

Shakespeare, Tom. The social context of individual choice. *In:* Wasserman, David; Bickenbach, Jerome; Wachbroit, Robert, eds. Quality of Life and Human Difference: Genetic Testing, Health Care, and Disability. New York: Cambridge University Press; 2005: 217-236. Subject: 15.3

Shalev, Carmel. Access to essential drugs, human rights and global justice. *In:* Thiele, F.; Ashcroft, R.E., eds. Bioethics in a Small World. Berlin: Springer; 2005: 93-109. Subject: 9.7

Shalev, Carmel. Human cloning and human rights: a commentary. *Health and Human Rights: An International Journal* 2002; 6(1): 137-151. Subject: 14.5

Shalev, Carmel; Chinitz, David. Joe Public v. the general public: the role of the courts in Israeli health care policy. *Journal of Law, Medicine and Ethics* 2005 Winter; 33(4): 650- 659. Subject: 9.2

Shalowitz, David I.; Miller, Franklin G. Disclosing individual results of clinical research: implications of respect for participants. *JAMA: The Journal of the American Med-*

ical Association 2005 August 10; 294(6): 737-740. Subject: 18.1

Shalowitz, David I.; Wolf, Michael S. Shared decision-making and the lower literate patient. *Journal of Law, Medicine and Ethics* 2004 Winter; 32(4): 759- 764. Subject: 8.3.1

Shand, Hope. New enclosures: why civil society and governments should look beyond life patents. *In:* Krimsky, Sheldon; Shorett, Peter, eds. Rights and Liberties in the Biotech Age: Why We Need a Genetic Bill of Rights. Lanham: Rowman and Littlefield Publishers; 2005: 40-48. Subject: 15.8

Shanley, Mary Lyndon. Collaboration and commodification in assisted procreation: reflections on an open market and anonymous donation in human sperm and eggs. *Law and Society Review* 2002; 36(2): 257-283. Subject: 14.2

Shanmugan, Geetha. Miracle grow for children. *Ivy Journal of Ethics* 2003; 3(1): 10-13. Subject: 9.7

Shannon, Sarah E.; Verkerk, Marian. Enhancing reflection [letter and reply]. *Hastings Center Report* 2005 July-August; 35(4): 6-7. Subject: 7.2

Shannon, Thomas. The genetic fallacy: perfect genes do not eliminate schmucks [response]. *Conscience* 2003-2004 Winter; 24(4): 16-17. Subject: 14.1

Shannon, Thomas A. Human nature in a post-human genome project world. *In:* Baillie, Harold W.; Casey, Timothy K., eds. Is Human Nature Obsolete? Genetics Bioengineering, and the Future of the Human Condition. Cambridge, MA: MIT Press; 2005: 269-316. Subject: 15.1

Shannon, Thomas A. The legacy of the Schiavo case: the atmosphere around end-of- life decisions has changed. *America* 2005 June 6-13; 192(20): 17-19. Subject: 20.5.1

Shannon, Thomas A. The moral status of the early human embryo: is a via media possible? *American Journal of Bioethics* 2005 November-December; 5(6): 43-44. Subject: 4.4

Shannon, Thomas A.; Walter, James J. Implications of the papal allocution on feeding tubes. *Hastings Center Report* 2004 July-August; 34(4): 18-20. Subject: 20.5.1

Shannon, Thomas A.; Walter, James J.; Repenshek, Mark; Slosar, John Paul. Nutrition and hydration [letter and reply]. *Hastings Center Report* 2005 May-June; 35(3): 4-6. Subject: 20.5.1

Shapira, Amos. 'Wrongful life' lawsuits for faulty genetic counselling: legal, ethical and policy aspects. *In:* Blazer, Shraga; Zimmer, Etan Z., eds. The Embryo: Scientific Discovery and Medical Ethics. New York: Karger; 2005: 340-350. Subject: 15.2

Shapiro, Carla. Organ transplantation in infants and children — necessity or choice: the case of K'aila Paulette. *Pediatric Nursing* 2005 March-April; 31(2): 121-122. Subject: 19.5

Shapiro, Harold T.; Meslin, Eric M. Relating to history: the influence of the National Commission and its Belmont Report on the National Bioethics Advisory Commission. *In:* Childress, James F.; Meslin, Eric M.; Shapiro, Harold T., eds. Belmont Revisited: Ethical Principles for Research with Human Subjects. Washington, DC: Georgetown University Press; 2005: 55-76. Subject: 18.2

Shapiro, Jane D.; Bowles, Kathleen. Nurses' and consumers' understanding of and comfort with the Patient Self-determination Act. *Journal of Nursing Administration* 2002 October; 32(10): 503- 508. Subject: 20.5.4

Shapiro, K.; Benatar, S.R. HIV prevention research and global inequality: steps towards improved standards of care. *Journal of Medical Ethics* 2005 January; 31(1): 39-47. Subject: 9.5.6

Shapiro, Michael H. The identity of identity: moral and legal aspects of technological self-transformation. *Social Philosophy and Policy* 2005 Summer; 22(2): 308-373. Subject: 15.1

Sharav, Vera Hassner. Screening for mental illness: the merger of eugenics and the drug industry. *Ethical Human Psychology and Psychiatry* 2005 Summer; 7(2): 111-124. Subject: 15.5

Sharma, B.R. Cloning controversies: an overview of the science, ethics and politics. *Medicine, Science, and the Law* 2005 January; 45(1): 17-26. Subject: 14.5

Sharma, B.R. The end of life decisions — should physicians aid their patients in dying? *Journal of Clinical Forensic Medicine* 2004 June; 11(3): 133-140. Subject: 20.7

Sharma, B.R. Ethical and practical principles underlying the end of life decisions. *American Journal of Forensic Medicine and Pathology* 2004 September; 25(3): 216-219. Subject: 20.5.1

Sharma, B.R. Research on human embryos: issues, politics and solutions. *Medicine Science and the Law* 2004 January; 44(1): 41-46. Subject: 18.5.4

Sharma, Shridhar. Human rights of mental patients in India: a global perspective. *Current Opinion in Psychiatry* 2003 September; 16(5): 547-551. Subject: 21.1

Sharp, Helen M. Ethical decision-making in interdisciplinary team care. *Cleft Palate-Craniofacial Journal* 1995 November; 32(6): 495-499. Subject: 4.1.2

Sharp, Phillip A. 1918 flu and responsible science [editorial]. *Science* 2005 October 7; 310(5745): 17. Subject: 15.1

Sharp, Richard R.; Foster, Morris W. Community involvement in the ethical review of genetic research: lessons from American Indian and Alaska Native populations. *Environmental Justice* 2002 April; 110(supplement 2): 145-148. Subject: 18.2

Sharp, Richard R.; Yarborough, Mark. Additional thoughts on rethinking research ethics. *American Journal of Bioethics* 2005 January-February; 5(1): 40- 42. Subject: 18.2

Subject = NRCBL Primary Classification Number; See inside front cover

Sharp, S. Michael. Consent documents for oncology trials: does anybody read these things? *American Journal of Clinical Oncology* 2004 December; 27(6): 570-575. Subject: 18.3

Sharp, S. Michael; Pentz, Rebecca D. Issues, both ethical and practical, in the development and conduct of chemoprevention trials. *Current Problems in Cancer* 2004 July-August; 28(4): 186-200. Subject: 18.2

Sharpe, Virginia A. Privacy and security for electronic health records [opinion]. *Hastings Center Report* 2005 November-December; 35(6): inside back cover. Subject: 8.4

Sharzer, Leonard A. Tradition, obligation, and healthcare. *Sh'ma* 2005 October; 36(624): 5-6. Subject: 9.2

Shaul, Randi Zlotnik; Birenbaum, Shelley; Evans, Megan. Legal liabilities in research: early lessons from North America. *BMC Medical Ethics [electronic].* 2005; 6(4); 4 p. Available: http://www.biomedcentral.com/bmcmedethics/ [6 September 2005]. Subject: 18.2

Shavit, Natalie; Bucky, Steven; Danielian, Jack. Sexual contact between psychologists and their former therapy patients: psychoanalytic perspectives and professional implications. *American Journal of Psychoanalysis* 2004 September; 64(3): 229-251. Subject: 7.4

Shaw, Alexander S.J. Do we really know the law about students and patient consent? [opinion]. *BMJ: British Medical Journal* 2005 September 3; 331(7515): 522. Subject: 8.3.1

Shaw, Dorothy. Understanding the relevance of sexual and reproductive rights to professional responsibilities / Comprehension de la pertinence des droits sexuels et genesiques en matiere de responsabilites professionnelles. *Journal of Obstetrics and Gynaecology Canada* 2004 December; 26(12): 1095-1096, 1103-1104. Subject: 9.5.5

Sheehan, Katherine C. The hand that rocks the cradle. *University of Toledo Law Review* 2001 Winter; 32(2): 229-247. Subject: 4.4

Sheehan, Mark. Healthcare and (a kind of) virtue ethics. *In:* Häyry, Matti; Takala, Tuija; Herissone-Kelly, Peter, eds. Bioethics and Social Reality. New York: Rodopi, 2005: 149-160. Subject: 2.1

Sheikh, Asim A. The Data Protection (Amendment) Act, 2003: the Data Protection Directive and its implications for medical research in Ireland. *European Journal of Health Law* 2005 December; 12(4): 357-372. Subject: 18.2

Sheikh, Asim A. Genetic research and human biological samples: some legal and ethical considerations. *Medicine and Law: World Association for Medical Law* 2004; 23(4): 897-912. Subject: 18.3

Sheldon, Sally. Saviour siblings and the discretionary power of the HFEA: Quintavalle (on behalf of Comment on Reproductive Ethics) v. Human Fertilisation and Embryology Authority. *Medical Law Review* 2005 Autumn; 13(3): 403-411. Subject: 15.3

Sheldon, Sally; Wilkinson, Stephen. Hashmi and Whitaker: an unjustifiable and misguided distinction? *Medical Law Review* 2004 Summer; 12(2): 137-163. Subject: 15.3

Sheldon, Tony. Dutch approve euthanasia for a patient with Alzheimer's disease [news]. *BMJ: British Medical Journal* 2005 May 7; 330(7499): 1041. Subject: 20.7

Sheldon, Tony. Dutch doctors adopt guidelines on mercy killing of newborns [news]. *BMJ: British Medical Journal* 2005 July 16; 331(7509): 126. Subject: 20.5.2

Sheldon, Tony. Dutch doctors are given guidance on sedation [news]. *BMJ: British Medical Journal* 2005 December 17; 331(7530): 1422. Subject: 20.4.1

Sheldon, Tony. Dutch murder case leads to talks with attorney general [news]. *BMJ: British Medical Journal* 2005 September 3; 331(7515): 473. Subject: 20.5.1

Sheldon, Tony. Dutch Supreme Court backs damages for child for having been born [news]. *BMJ: British Medical Journal* 2005 April 2; 330(7494): 747. Subject: 15.2

Sheldon, Tony. The Netherlands regulates ending the lives of severely ill neonates [news]. *BMJ: British Medical Journal* 2005 December 10; 331(7529): 1357. Subject: 20.5.2

Sheldon, Tony; Verhagen, Eduard. Killing or caring? *BMJ: British Medical Journal* 2005 March 12; 330(7491): 560. Subject: 20.5.2

Shell-Duncan, Bettina. The medicalization of female "circumcision": harm reduction or promotion of a dangerous practice? *Social Science and Medicine* 2001 April; 52(7): 1013-1028. Subject: 9.5.5

Shenfield, Françoise. Semantics and ethics of human embryonic stem-cell research [opinion]. *Lancet* 2005 June 18-24; 365(9477): 2071-2073. Subject: 18.5.4

Shenfield, Françoise. To know or not to know the identity of gametes donors? The UK and European legal context. *Journal of Assisted Reproduction and Genetics* 2004 April; 21(4): 95-96. Subject: 14.1

Shenolikar, Rahul A.; Balkrishnan, Rajesh; Hall, Mark A. How patient-physician encounters in critical medical situations affect trust: results of a national survey. *BMC Health Services Research [electronic]* 2004 September 7; 4: 24-29. Available: http://www.biomedcentral.com/ [8 September 2005]. Subject: 8.1

Sheon, Amy R.; Wagner, Lois; McElrath, M. Juliana; Keefer, Michael C.; Zimmerman, Eric; Israel, Heidi; Berger, David; Fast, Patricia. Preventing discrimination against volunteers in prophylactic HIV vaccine trials: lessons from a phase II trial. *Journal of Acquired Immune Deficiency Syndromes and Human Retrovirology* 1998 December 15; 19(5): 519-526. Subject: 9.5.6

Shephard, Roy J. Ethics in exercise science research. *Sports Medicine* 2002; 32(3): 169-183. Subject: 18.2

Sheremeta, Lorraine; Gold, E. Richard; Caulfield, Timothy. Harmonizing commercialisation and gene patent policy with other social goals. *In:* Knoppers, Bartha Maria, ed. Populations and Genetics: Legal and Socio-Ethical Perspectives. Boston: Martinus Nijhoff; 2003: 423-452. Subject: 15.1

Sheremeta, Lorraine; Knoppers, Bartha Maria. Beyond the rhetoric: population genetics and benefit-sharing. *Health Law Journal* 2003; 11: 89-117. Subject: 15.10

Sherman, Frederick T. Nutrition in advanced dementia — tube-feeding or hand-feeding until death? [editorial]. *Geriatrics* 2003 November; 58(11): 10, 12. Subject: 20.4.1

Sherman, Heather B.; McGaghie, William C.; Unti, Sharon M.; Thomas, John X. Teaching pediatrics residents how to obtain informed consent. *Academic Medicine* 2005 October; 80(10, Supplement): S10-S13. Subject: 8.3.3

Shermer, Michael. Only God can do that? Cloning and genetic engineering test the moral limits of science. *Skeptic* 1999; 7(2): 58-63. Subject: 14.5

Sherwin, Susan. Belmont revisited through a feminist lens. *In:* Childress, James F.; Meslin, Eric M.; Shapiro, Harold T., eds. Belmont Revisited: Ethical Principles for Research with Human Subjects. Washington, DC: Georgetown University Press; 2005: 148-164. Subject: 18.2

Sheth, Arun. Informed consent — a view from the trenches [letter]. *Indian Journal of Medical Ethics* 2004 January-March; 1(1): 33. Subject: 8.3.1

Shewchuk, Tara Rayne. The uncertain 'best interests' of neonates: decision making in the neonatal intensive care unit. *Medicine and Law: World Association for Medical Law* 1995; 14(5-6): 331-358. Subject: 20.5.2

Shi, Leiyu. Vulnerable populations and health insurance. *Medical Care Research and Review* 2000 March; 57(1): 110-134. Subject: 9.3.1

Shickle, Darren. Rationing of health care: why do acute hospital services have higher priority? *In:* Chadwick, Ruth; Levitt, Mairi, eds. Ethical Issues in Community Health Care. New York: Arnold; 1998: 51-62. Subject: 9.4

Shickle, Darren; Hapgood, Rhydian; Carlisle, Jane; Shackley, Phil; Morgan, Ann; McCabe, Chris. Public attitudes to participating in UK BioBank: a DNA bank, lifestyle and morbidity database on 500,000 members of the UK public aged 45-69. *In:* Knoppers, Bartha Maria, ed. Populations and Genetics: Legal and Socio-Ethical Perspectives. Boston: Martinus Nijhoff; 2003:. Subject: 15.1

Shields, Alexandra E.; Fortun, Michael; Hammonds, Evelynn M.; King, Patricia A.; Lerman, Caryn; Rapp, Rayna; Sullivan, Patrick F. The use of race variables in genetic studies of complex traits and the goal of reducing health disparities: a transdisciplinary perspective. *American Psychologist* 2005 January; 60(1): 77-103. Subject: 15.11

Shields, Alexandra E.; Lerman, Caryn; Sullivan, Patrick F. Translating emerging research on the genetics of smoking into clinical practice: ethical and social considerations. *Nicotine and Tobacco Research* 2004 August; 6(4): 675-688. Subject: 15.6

Shields, Linda. Report on: Complicity and Compassion: the First International Conference on Nursing and Midwifery in the Third Reich, 10-11 June 2004, Limerick, Republic of Ireland. *Nursing Ethics* 2005 January; 12(1): 106-107. Subject: 21.4

Shildrick, Margrit. Beyond the body of bioethics: challenging the conventions. *In:* Shildrick, Margrit; Mykitiuk, Roxanne, eds. Ethics of the Body: Postconventional Challenges. Cambridge, MA: MIT Press; 2005: 1-26. Subject: 2.1

Shimoda, Motomu. "Death with dignity" in the Japanese context. *Journal International de Bioethique / International Journal of Bioethics* 2005 March-June; 16(1-2): 125-134, 197. Subject: 20.5.1

Shin, Michael S. Redressing wounds: finding a legal framework to remedy racial disparities in medical care. *California Law Review* 2002 December; 90(6): 2047-2100. Subject: 9.5.4

Shinn, Carolynne. The right to the highest attainable standard of health: public health's opportunity to reframe a human rights debate in the United States. *Health and Human Rights: An International Journal* 1999; 4(1): 115-133. Subject: 9.2

Shiraz, B.; Shamim, M. Shahzad; Shamim, M. Shahid; Ahmed, Asif. Medical ethics in surgical wards: knowledge, attitude and practice of surgical team members in Karachi. *Indian Journal of Medical Ethics* 2005 July-September; 2(3): 94-96. Subject: 2.3

Shirey, Maria R. Ethical climate in nursing practice: the leader's role. *JONA's Healthcare Law, Ethics, and Regulation* 2005 April-June; 7(2): 59-67. Subject: 4.1.3

Shkiryak-Nyzhnyk, Zoreslava. Ukraine. *Medical Ethics and Bioethics / Medicinska Etika & Bioetika* 2005; 11(Supplement): 22-23. Subject: 9.6

Shoemaker, David W. Embryos, souls, and the fourth dimension. *Social Theory and Practice* 2005 January; 31(1): 51-75. Subject: 18.5.4

Shoham-Vardi, I.; Weiner, N.; Weitzman, D.; Levcovich, A. Termination of pregnancy: attitudes and behavior of women in a traditional society. *Prenatal Diagnosis* 2004 November; 24(11): 869-875. Subject: 12.5.2

Short, Bradford William. The healing philosopher: John Locke's medical ethics. *Issues in Law and Medicine* 2004 Fall; 20(2): 103-154. Subject: 2.2

Subject = NRCBL Primary Classification Number; See inside front cover

Short, Bradford William. More history "lite" in modern American bioethics. *Issues in Law and Medicine* 2005 Summer; 21(1): 3-34. Subject: 2.1

Shrank, William H.; Kutner, Jean S.; Richardson, Terri; Mularski, Richard A.; Fischer, Stacy; Kagawa-Singer, Marjorie. Focus group findings about the influence of culture on communication preferences in end-of-life care. *JGIM: Journal of General Internal Medicine* 2005 August; 20(8): 703-709. Subject: 20.4.1

Shreeve, Jamie. I, chimera. *New Scientist* 2005 June 25-July 1; 186(2505): 39-43. Subject: 15.1

Shreeve, Jamie. The other stem-cell debate: to test the potential curative powers of human embryonic stem cells, biologists want to inject them into lab animals. Creating such chimeras makes perfect sense, to a point: a sheep with a human liver? O.K. A mouse brain made up of human cells? Maybe. But a chimp that sobs? *New York Times Magazine* 2005 April 10; p. 42-47. Subject: 15.1

Shrotri, D.S. Role of ethics committees in medical research. *Indian Journal of Medical Ethics* 2004 October-December; 1(4): 121. Subject: 18.2

Shuchman, Miriam. Stalled US plan for Plan B [news]. *CMAJ/JAMC: Canadian Medical Association Journal* 2005 December 6; 173(12): 1437. Subject: 11.1

Shultz, Marjorie M. Abortion and maternal-fetal conflict: broadening our concerns. *Southern California Review of Law and Women's Studies* 1992; 1: 79-98. Subject: 12.4.2

Shuman, Daniel W.; Greenberg, Stuart; Heilbrun, Kirk; Foote, William E. Special perspective: an immodest proposal: should treating mental health professionals be barred from testifying about their patients? *Behavioral Sciences and the Law* 1998 Autumn; 16(4): 509-523. Subject: 17.2

Shuster, Evelyne. My clone, myself, my daughter, my sister: echoes of *Le Petit Prince. In:* Actes du Colloque International AMADE-UNESCO sur Bioethique et Droits de L'enfant (Monaco, 28-30 Avril 2000)/Proceedings of the International Symposium AMADE-UNESCO on Bioethics and the Rights of the Child (Monaco, 28-30 April 2000). Paris: UNESCO, Division des Sciences Humaines, de la Philosophie et de L'ethique des Sciences et des Technologies; 2001: 37-46. Subject: 14.5

Sibbald, Barbara. Nonprescription status for emergency contraception [news]. *CMAJ/JAMC: Canadian Medical Association Journal* 2005 March 29; 172(7): 861-862. Subject: 11.1

Sibbald, Bonnie. COPE guidelines on good publication practice: an author's view [editorial]. *Health and Social Care in the Community* 2000 November; 8(6): 355-361. Subject: 6

Sidley, Pat. South African doctors arrested in kidney sale scandal [news]. *BMJ: British Medical Journal* 2005 September 3; 331(7515): 473. Subject: 19.3

Sieber, William J.; Kaplan, Robert M. Informed adherence: the need for shared medical decision making. *Controlled Clinical Trials* 2000 October; 21(5 Supplement): 233S-240S. Subject: 9.1

Siebert, Charles. What does an aging chimp do when his working days are done? A journey into the realm - and the issue - of primate retirement sanctuaries. *New York Times Magazine* 2005 July 24; p. 28-35, 61-63. Subject: 22.2

Sieck, William A. In vitro fertilization and the right to procreate: the right to no. *University of Pennsylvania Law Review* 1998 December; 147(2): 435-485. Subject: 14.4

Siegal, Gil; Bonnie, Richard J. Reflections on fairness in UNOS allocation policies. *American Journal of Bioethics* 2005 July-August; 5(4): 28-29. Subject: 19.6

Siegel, David M.; Grudzinskas, Albert J.; Pinals, Debra A. Old law meets new medicine: revisiting involuntary psychotropic medication of the criminal defendant. *Wisconsin Law Review* 2001; 2: 307-380. Subject: 17.4

Siegel, Marc. What doctors fear most. *Hastings Center Report* 2005 November-December; 35(6): 8. Subject: 4.2

Siegel, Shana. Can we learn anything from the tragedy that is the Schiavo case? *Health Care Law Monthly* 2004 November: 3-8. Subject: 20.5.1

Siegel-Itzkovich, Judy. Israeli doctors want to stop European patent for genetic test [news]. *BMJ: British Medical Journal* 2005 July 2; 331(7507): 8. Subject: 15.8

Siegel-Itzkovich, Judy. Israelis turn to timer device to facilitate passive euthanasia [news]. *BMJ: British Medical Journal* 2005 December 10; 331(7529): 1357. Subject: 20.5.1

Siegfried, Nandi; Clarke, Mike; Volmink, Jimmy. Randomised controlled trials in Africa of HIV and AIDS: descriptive study and spatial distribution. *BMJ: British Medical Journal* 2005 October 1; 331(7519): 742- 746. Subject: 18.5.1

Siegler, Jessica; Siegler, Mark; Cronin, David C., II. Recipient death during a live donor liver transplantation: who gets the "orphan" graft? *Transplantation* 2004 November 15; 78(9): 1241-1244. Subject: 19.6

Siep, Ludwig. Konsens und Dissens in Recht und Ethik. *In:* Jahrbuch für Wissenschaft und Ethik. Bd. 7. Berlin: Walter de Gruyter; 2002: 23-31. Subject: 2.1

Siep, Ludwig. Kriterien und Argumenttypen im Streit um die Embryonenforschung in Europa. *In:* Jahrbuch für Wissenschaft und Ethik. Bd. 7. Berlin: Walter de Gruyter; 2002: 179-195. Subject: 18.5.4

Siep, Ludwig. Wissen—Vorbeugen—Verändern: Über die ethischen Probleme beim gegenwärtigen Stand des Genomprojekts. *In:* Honnefelder, Ludger; Mieth, Dietmar; Propping, Peter; Siep, Ludwig; Wiesemann, Claudia, eds. Das genetische Wissen und die Zukunft des Menschen. New York: De Gruyter; 2003: 78-86. Subject: 15.1

Sierles, Frederick S.; Brodkey, Amy C.; Cleary, Lynn M.; McCurdy, Frederick A.; Mintz, Matthew; Frank, Julia; Lynn, D. Joanne; Chao, Jason; Morgenstern, Bruce Z.; Shore, William; Woodard, John L. Medical students' exposure to and attitudes about drug company interactions: a national survey. *JAMA: The Journal of the American Medical Association* 2005 September 7; 294(9): 1034-1042. Subject: 7.3

Sievernich, Michael. The significance of the concept of sin for bioethics. *Christian Bioethics* 2005 August; 11(2): 189-199. Subject: 2.1

Silberfeld, Michel. Vulnerable persons. *In:* Thomasma, David C.; Weisstub, David N.; Herve, Christian eds. Personhood and Health Care. Boston: Kluwer Academic Pub.; 2001: 299-316. Subject: 8.3.3

Silberfeld, Michel. Vulnerable persons: measuring moral capacity. *In:* Thomasma, David C.; Weisstub, David N., eds. The Variables of Moral Capacity. Boston: Kluwer Academic Publishers; 2004: 203- 215. Subject: 8.3.3; 4.3

Silberfeld, Michel; Finstad, Mary; Stephens, Derek. Agreement between professions on ethical decisions: an empirical demonstration. *Medicine and Law: World Association for Medical Law* 1995; 14(3-4): 191-197. Subject: 8.3.3

Silbert, M. The patient-physician relationship [letter]. *South African Medical Journal* 2001 August; 91(8): 616-617. Subject: 8.1

Silva, Mary Cipriano; Lewis, Carolyn K. Ethics, policy, and allocation of scarce resources in nursing service administration: a pilot study. *NursingConnections* 1991 Summer; 4(2): 44-52. Subject: 9.4

Silveira, Maria J.; Feudtner, Chris; McNutt, Robert A. Shared medical decision making. *JAMA: The Journal of the American Medical Association* 2005 March 2; 293(9): 1058-1059. Subject: 8.1

Silver, Ken. Corporate influence on chemical exposure levels. *Science for the People* 1989 January-February; 21(1): 24-25. Subject: 1.3.9

Silver, Michael G. Eugenics and compulsory sterilization laws: providing redress for the victims of a shameful era in United States history. *George Washington Law Review* 2004 April; 72(4): 862-892. Subject: 15.5

Silver, Stephen Aaron. Beyond Jaffee v. Redmond: should the federal courts recognize a right to physician-patient confidentiality? *Ohio State Law Journal* 1998; 58(5): 1809-1866. Subject: 8.4

Silverman, Henry J.; Druml, Christiane; Lemaire, Francois; Nelson, Robert. The European Union Directive and the protection of incapacitated subjects in research: an ethical analysis. *Intensive Care Medicine* 2004 September; 30(9): 1723-1729. Subject: 18.5.6

Silverman, Henry J.; Luce, John M.; Lanken, Paul N.; Morris, Alan H.; Harabin, Andrea L.; Oldmixon, Cathryn F.; Thompson, B. Taylor; Bernard, Gordon R. Recommendations for informed consent forms for critical care clinical trials. *Critical Care Medicine* 2005 April; 33(4): 867-882. Subject: 18.3

Silverman, Henry J.; Luce, John M.; Schwartz, Jack. Protecting subjects with decisional impairment in research: the need for a multifaceted approach. *American Journal of Respiratory and Critical Care Medicine* 2004 January 1; 169(1): 10-14. Subject: 18.5.6

Silverman, Jerald. IACUC replacement parts: what are the requirements? *Lab Animal* 2004 November; 33(10): 16. Subject: 9.6

Silverman, Jerald. PI and vet: potential conflict of interest? *Lab Animal* 2004 October; 33(9): 21. Subject: 1.3.9

Silverman, Paul H.; Parens, Erik. Genetics and complexity [letter and reply]. *Hastings Center Report* 2004 July-August; 34(4): 4-5. Subject: 15.1

Silverman, William A.; Robertson, John A. Neonatal care for premature infants [letter and reply]. *Hastings Center Report* 2005 January-February; 35(1): 6, 7. Subject: 9.5.7

Silvers, Anita. Going to school to die: equal treatment for well and ill children. *American Journal of Bioethics* 2005 January-February; 5(1): 69- 71. Subject: 20.5.2

Silvers, Anita. Predicting genetic disability while commodifying health. *In:* Wasserman, David; Bickenbach, Jerome; Wachbroit, Robert, eds. Quality of Life and Human Difference: Genetic Testing, Health Care, and Disability. New York: Cambridge University Press; 2005: 43-66. Subject: 4.2

Silvers, Anita; Francis, Leslie Pickering. Justice through trust: disability and the "outlier problem" in social contract theory. *Ethics: An International Journal of Social, Political, and Legal Philosophy* 2005 October; 116(1): 40-76. Subject: 9.5.1

Silvers, Anita; Lauritzen, Paul. Our posthuman future: discussing the consequences of biotechnological advances [letter and reply]. *Hastings Center Report* 2005 November-December; 35(6): 4-5, 6-7. Subject: 18.5.4

Silverstein, Harry S. Creation and abortion: a reply to Hall. *Journal of Social Philosophy* 2004 Winter; 35(4): 493-505. Subject: 12.3

Simek, Jiri. Human experimentation in the Czech Republic during the last decades. *In:* Roelcke, Volker; Maio, Giovanni, eds. Twentieth Century Ethics of Human Subjects Research: Historical Perspectives on Values, Practices, and Regulations. Stuttgart: Franz Steiner Verlag; 2004: 253-259. Subject: 18.1

Simeoni, Umberto; Vendemmia, Mariella; Rizzotti, Alina; Gamerre, Marc. Ethical dilemmas in extreme prematurity: recent answers; more questions. *European Journal of Obstetrics and Gynecology and Reproductive*

Biology 2004 November 15; 117(Supplement 1): S33-S36. Subject: 20.5.2

Simha, S.N. Issues faced by a hospice. *Indian Journal of Medical Ethics* 2005 July-September; 2(3): 85. Subject: 20.4.1

Siminoff, Laura A.; Burant, Christopher; Youngner, Stuart J. Death and organ procurement: public beliefs and attitudes. *Social Science and Medicine* 2004 December; 59(11): 2325-2334. Subject: 19.5

Simmerling, Mary; Schwegler, Brian. Beginning anew: same principles, different direction for research ethics. *American Journal of Bioethics* 2005 January-February; 5(1): 44- 46. Subject: 18.2

Simmons, Peter; Orrell, Martin. State funded continuing care for the elderly mentally ill: a legal and ethical solution? [editorial]. *International Journal of Geriatric Psychiatry* 2001 October; 16(10): 931-934. Subject: 9.5.2

Simon, Alfred. End-of-life decision making in Germany. *In:* Blank, Robert H.; Merrick, Janna C., eds. End-of-Life Decision Making: A Cross-National Study. Cambridge, MA: MIT Press; 2005: 61-78. Subject: 20.5.1

Simon, Christian M.; Kodish, Eric D. "Step into my zapatos, doc": understanding and reducing communication disparities in the multicultural informed consent setting. *Perspectives in Biology and Medicine* 2005 Winter; 48(1, Supplement): S123-S138. Subject: 18.3

Simon, Christian M.; Siminoff, Laura A.; Kodish, Eric D.; Burant, Christopher. Comparison of the informed consent process for randomized clinical trials in pediatric and adult oncology. *Journal of Clinical Oncology* 2004 July 1; 22(13): 2708-2717. Subject: 18.3

Simon, Laurence. Psychotherapy as civics: the patient and therapist as citizens. *Ethical Human Psychology and Psychiatry* 2005 Spring; 7(1): 57- 64. Subject: 17.2

Simoncelli, Tania; Steinhardt, Barry. California's proposition 69: a dangerous precedent for criminal DNA databases. *Journal of Law, Medicine and Ethics* 2005 Summer; 33(2): 279- 293. Subject: 15.1

Simonite, Tom; Giles, Jim. UK animal labs still under siege [news]. *Nature* 2005 December 8; 438(7069): 716. Subject: 22.2

Simonstein, F. A rational cure for prereproductive stress syndrome — a perspective from Israel: a rejoinder to Häyry, Bennet, Holm, and Aksoy. *Journal of Medical Ethics* 2005 September; 31(9): 557. Subject: 14.1

Simonstein, Frida. Genetic screening and reproductive choice: is making a child to save another unethical? *Medicine and Law: World Association for Medical Law* 2005 December; 24(4): 775-781. Subject: 15.3

Simonstein, Frida F. Germ-line engineering and late-onset diseases: the ethics of self-evolution [opinion]. *IMAJ: Israel Medical Association Journal* 2004 November; 6(11): 652-657. Subject: 15.4

Simpson, Bob. Response to Athula Sumathipala and Sisira Siribaddana, "Revisiting 'Freely Given Informed Consent' in Relation to the Developing World: the Role of an Ombudsman" (AJOB 4:3). *American Journal of Bioethics [Online]* 2005 January-February; 5(1): W24-W26. Subject: 18.3

Simpson, Bob; Dissanayake, V.H.W.; Jayasekara, R.W. Contemplating choice: attitudes towards intervening in human reproduction in Sri Lanka. *New Genetics and Society* 2005 April; 24(1): 99-117. Subject: 15.2

Simpson, Christopher S.; Hoffmaster, Barry; Mitchell, L. Brent; Klein, George J. Mandatory physician reporting of drivers with cardiac disease: ethical and practical considerations. *Canadian Journal of Cardiology* 2004 November; 20(13): 1329-1334. Subject: 8.4

Simpson, Christy; Kirby, Jeffrey; Davies, Maura. Building a culture of ethics: the Capital Health Ethics Support model. *Healthcare Management Forum* 2004 Autumn; 17(3): 14-17. Subject: 9.1

Simpson, Roy L. e-Ethics: new dilemmas emerge alongside new technologies. *Nursing Administration Quarterly* 2005 April-May; 29(2): 179-182. Subject: 4.1.3

Sims, Mary. On-line physician-patient care: the future of electronic medicine. *Ethics and Medics* 2005 February; 30(2): 1-3. Subject: 8.1

Sinderbrand, Rebecca. A shameful little secret: North Carolina confronts its history of forced sterilization. Some women were sterilized for being seen as lazy or promiscuous. *Newsweek* 2005 March 28; 145(13): 33. Subject: 15.5

Singapore. Bioethics Advisory Committee. Ethical, legal and social issues in genetic testing and genetics research: a consultation paper. Singapore: The Bioethics Advisory Committee 2005 April 5; 55 p. [Online] Available: http://www.bioethics-singapore.org/resources/pdfg/GT%20CP%20Final.pdf [14 April 2005]. Subject: 15.3

Singer, Emily. Race-based heart drug might stall search for better markers [news]. *Nature Medicine* 2005 August; 11(8): 812. Subject: 15.11

Singer, Merrill; Huertas, Elsa; Scott, Glenn. Am I my brother's keeper?: a case study of the responsibilities of research. *Human Organization* 2000 Winter; 59(4): 389-400. Subject: 18.5.1

Singer, Peter. Law reform, or DIY suicide [editorial]. *Free Inquiry* 2005 February-March; 25(2): 19-20. Subject: 20.7

Singer, Peter. Making our own decisions about death: competency should be paramount. *Free Inquiry* 2005 August-September; 25(5): 36-38. Subject: 20.5.1

Singh, Ilina. Will the "real boy" please behave: dosing dilemmas for parents of boys with ADHD. *American Journal of Bioethics* 2005 May-June; 5(3): 34-47. Subject: 17.4

Singh, Jaideep; Lantos, John; Meadow, William. End-of-life after birth: death and dying in a neonatal intensive care unit. *Pediatrics* 2004 December; 114(6): 1620-1626. Subject: 20.5.2

Singh, P.; Kumar, A.; Sharma, R.K. Factors influencing refusal by relatives of brain-dead patients to give consent for organ donation: experience at a transplant centre. *Journal of the Indian Medical Association* 2004 November; 102(11): 630, 632, 643. Subject: 19.5

Singh, S. Kumar. Responsibilities in the post genome era: are we prepared? *Issues in Medical Ethics* 2002 January-March; 10(1): 150-151. Subject: 15.1

Singhal, Nalini; Oberle, Kathleen; Darwish, Amy; Burgess, Ellen. Attitudes of health-care providers towards research with newborn babies. *Journal of Perinatology* 2004 December; 24(12): 775-782. Subject: 18.5.2

Singleton, Peter D. Informed consent: talking with patients, not at them [letter]. *BMJ: British Medical Journal* 2005 November 5; 331(7524): 1082. Subject: 8.3.1

Sinsky, Christine. Unreimbursed services in primary care [letter]. *Archives of Internal Medicine* 2005 March 28; 165(6): 702-703. Subject: 20.5.4

Sinton, Jennifer. Rights discourse and mandatory HIV testing of pregnant women and newborns. *Journal of Law and Policy* 1997; 6(1): 187-245. Subject: 9.5.5

Siotia, A.K.; Chaudhuri, A.; Muzulu, S.I.; Harling, D.; Muthusamy, R. Postoperative hypoxia in a woman with Down's syndrome: case outcome. *BMJ: British Medical Journal* 2005 May 7; 330(7499): 1068. Subject: 8.3.1

Širinskiene, Agne; Juškevicius, Jonas; Naberkovas, Andrius. Confidentiality and duty to warn the third parties in HIV/AIDS context. *Medical Ethics and Bioethics / Medicinska Etika & Bioetika* 2005 Spring-Summer; 12(1): 2-7. Subject: 9.5.6

Sivarajah, Neeraja. Neuroregenerative gene therapy: the implications for informed consent laws. *Health Law in Canada* 2005 November; 26(2): 19-28. Subject: 18.3

Sjögren, Berit; Uddenberg, Nils. Attitudes towards disabled persons and the possible effects of prenatal diagnosis. An interview study among 53 women participating in prenatal diagnosis and 20 of their husbands. *Journal of Psychosomatic Obstetrics and Gynaecology* 1987; 6: 187-196. Subject: 15.2

Skeel, Joy D.; Williams, Kristi S. Helping staff help a "hateful" patient: the case of TJ. *Journal of Clinical Ethics* 2005 Fall; 16(3): 202-205. Subject: 9.5.3

Skeen, Andrew. Living wills and advance directives in South African law. *Medicine and Law: World Association for Medical Law* 2004; 23(4): 937-943. Subject: 20.5.4

Skegg, P.D.G. Consent and information disclosure. *In:* Dawson, John; Peart, Nicola, eds. The Law of Research: A Guide. Dunedin, NZ: University of Otago Press; 2003: 233-251. Subject: 18.3

Skene, L. Terminally ill infants, parents and the courts. *Medicine and Law: World Association for Medical Law* 2005 December; 24(4): 663-671. Subject: 20.5.2

Skene, Loane. Courts as communicators: can doctors learn from judges' decisions? *Journal of Bioethical Inquiry* 2004; 1(1): 49-56. Subject: 2.1

Skene, Loane. Disputes about the withdrawal of treatment: the role of the courts. *Journal of Law, Medicine and Ethics* 2004 Winter; 32(4): 701- 707. Subject: 20.5.1

Skorecki, Karl L., et al. The unborn child: scientific discovery, medical and ethical dilemmas. *In:* Blazer, Shraga; Zimmer, Etan Z., eds. The Embryo: Scientific Discovery and Medical Ethics. New York: Karger; 2005: 120-142. Subject: 18.5.4

Skov, Suzanne E. Stenberg v. Carhart: the abortion debate goes technical. *Journal of Contemporary Legal Issues* 2004; 14(1): 235-241. Subject: 12.4.3

Slabbert, Magda; Oosthuizen, Hennie. Commercialization of human organs for transplantation: a view from South Africa. *Medicine and Law: World Association for Medical Law* 2005 March; 24(1): 191-201. Subject: 19.5

Slabbert, Melodie Nöthling. Parental access to minors' health records in the South African health care context: concerns and recommendations. *Medicine and Law: World Association for Medical Law* 2005 December; 24(4): 743-759. Subject: 8.4

Slack, Catherine; Kruger, Mariana. The South African Medical Research Council's Guidelines on Ethics for Medical Research — implications for HIV-preventive vaccine trials with children. *South African Medical Journal* 2005 April; 95(4): 269-271. Subject: 9.5.6

Slaughter, Bill. Animal use in biomedicine: an annotated bibliography of Buddhist and related perspectives. *Journal of Buddhist Ethics [electronic]* 2002; 9: 149-158. Available: http://jbe.gold.ac.uk/9/current9.html [16 May 2003]. Subject: 22.2

Sleeboom, Margaret. The Harvard case of Xu Xiping: exploitation of the people, scientific advance, or genetic theft? *New Genetics and Society* 2005 April; 24(1): 57-78. Subject: 15.10

Slingsby, Brian Taylor. The nature of relative subjectivity: a reflexive mode of thought. *Journal of Medicine and Philosophy* 2005 February; 30(1): 9-25. Subject: 8.2

Slosar, John Paul. Discontinuing implantable cardiac devices and the ERDs. *Health Care Ethics USA [electronic]* 2005; 13(2); 3 p. Available: http://www.slu.edu/centers/chce/hceusa/2_2005_2.html [19 September 2005]. Subject: 20.5.1

Slosar, John Paul. Ethical issues in genetic testing. *Health Care Ethics USA [electronic]* 2005; 13(3); E2, 3 p. Available: http://www.slu.edu/centers/chce/hceusa/3_2005_index.html [21 February 2006]. Subject: 15.3

Subject = NRCBL Primary Classification Number; See inside front cover

Slovak Association of Research Based Pharmaceutical Companies in Slovakia [SAFS]; Association of Producers of Generic Drugs [GENAS]; Association of Distributors of Drugs [ADL]. Ethical code of the pharmaceutical industry in Slovakia. *Medical Ethics and Bioethics / Medicinska Etika & Bioetika* 2004 Autumn-Winter; 11(3-4): 11-22. Subject: 6

Slovak Republic. Ministry of Health. Central Ethics Committee. Statut: centralnej etickej komisie ministerstva zdravotnictva Slovenskej Republiky / Statute: Central Ethics Committee Ministry of Health of the Slovak Republic. *Medical Ethics and Bioethics / Medicinska Etika & Bioetika* 2004 Spring-Summer; 11(1-2): 7-13. Subject: 2.4

Slovenko, Ralph. Civil commitment [opinion]. *Medicine and Law* 1982; 1: 217-226. Subject: 17.7

Slovenko, Ralph. The evolution of standards for experimental treatment or research. *Journal of Psychiatry and Law* 2005 Spring; 33(1): 129-174. Subject: 18.2

Slowther, Anne-Marie. Current ethical dilemmas in clinical practice in Europe. *Medical Ethics and Bioethics / Medicinska Etika & Bioetika* 2005; 11(Supplement): 5-8. Subject: 9.6

Slutsman, Julia; Kass, Nancy; McGready, John; Wynia, Matthew. Health information, the HIPAA privacy rule, and health care: what do physicians think? *Health Affairs* 2005 May-June; 24(3): 832-842. Subject: 8.4

Small, Bruce H.; Fisher, Mark W. Measuring biotechnology employees' ethical attitudes towards a controversial transgenic cattle project: the Ethical Valence Matrix. *Journal of Agricultural and Environmental Ethics* 2005; 18(5): 495-508. Subject: 22.3

Smith, Alexander McCall. Nationale Modelle zur Regelung des Gebrauchs der Gendiagnostik. Großbritannien: Tests und Screening zur Gewinnung persönlicher genetischer Informationen: Die britische Erfahrung. *In:* Honnefelder, Ludger; Mieth, Dietmar; Propping, Peter; Siep, Ludwig; Wiesemann, Claudia, eds. Das genetische Wissen und die Zukunft des Menschen. New York: De Gruyter; 2003: 275-285. Subject: 15.3

Smith, Carole. Understanding trust and confidence: two paradigms and their significance for health and social care. *Journal of Applied Philosophy* 2005; 22(3): 299-316. Subject: 8.1

Smith, Cedric M. Origin and uses of primum non nocere — above all, do no harm! [opinion]. *Journal of Clinical Pharmacology* 2005 April; 45(4): 371-377. Subject: 2.2

Smith, Craig S. Abuse of electroshock found in Turkish mental hospitals. *New York Times* 2005 September 29; p. A3. Subject: 17.5

Smith, Craig S. As a face transplant heals, flurries of questions arise; doctors differ on ethics and patient's mental state. *New York Times* 2005 December 14; p A1, A14. Subject: 19.1

Smith, Craig S. Dire wounds, a new face, a glimpse in a mirror: doctors describe and defend transplant for Frenchwoman. *New York Times* 2005 December 3; p. A1, A8. Subject: 19.1

Smith, Craig S. France lets terminally ill refuse care, but still bans euthanasia. *New York Times* 2005 April 14; p. A13. Subject: 20.5.1

Smith, David Barton. The politics of racial disparities: desegregating the hospitals in Jackson, Mississippi. *Milbank Quarterly* 2005; 83(2): 247-269. Subject: 9.5.4

Smith, David H.; Sedgwick, Timothy. Theological perspectives. *In:* Smith, David H.; Cohen, Cynthia B., eds. A Christian Response to the New Genetics: Religious, Ethical, and Social Issues. Lanham, MD: Rowman & Littlefield Publishers; 2003: 1-13. Subject: 15.1

Smith, G. Ethics and research in anaesthesia [letter]. *Anaesthesia* 1998 September; 53(9): 930. Subject: 1.3.7

Smith, George P., II. Human rights and bioethics: formulating a universal right to health, health care or health protection? *Vanderbilt Journal of Transnational Law* 2005 November; 38(5): 1295-1321. Subject: 9.2

Smith, George P., II. Law, medicine, and religion: towards a dialogue and a partnership in biomedical technology and decision making. *Journal of Contemporary Health Law and Policy* 2005 Summer; 21(2): 169-203. Subject: 2.1

Smith, George P., II. Of Panjandrums, Pooh Bahs, Parvenus, and Prophets: Law, Religion, and Medical Sciences. Sydney, Australia: Macquarie University, Division of Law, 2005; 92 p. Subject: 2.1

Smith, George P., II. The promise of abundant life: patenting a magnificent obsession. *Utah Journal of Contemporary Law* 1982; 8: 85-96. Subject: 15.8

Smith, Hazel; Smith, Richard. Time to legalise assisted dying? Doctors cannot simultaneously be patient centred and reject assisted suicide [letter]. *BMJ: British Medical Journal* 2005 October 8; 331(7520): 842- 843. Subject: 20.7

Smith, J. David. The Bell Curve and Carrie Buck: eugenics revisited. *Mental Retardation* 1995 February; 33(1): 60-61. Subject: 11.3

Smith, Jane; Godlee, Fiona. Investigating allegations of scientific misconduct: journals can do only so much; institutions need to be willing to investigate [editorial]. *BMJ: British Medical Journal* 2005 July 30; 331(7511): 245-246. Subject: 1.3.9

Smith, Jennifer A. Terminating the provider-patient relationship. *Nurse Practitioner* 2005 May; 30(5): 58-60. Subject: 8.1

Smith, Katharine V. Ethical issues related to health care: the older adult's perspective. *Journal of Gerontological Nursing* 2005 February; 31(2): 32-39. Subject: 2.1

Smith, M.; Doyle, F.; McGee, H.M.; De La Harpe, D. Ethical approval for national studies in Ireland: an illustration of current challenges. *Irish Journal of Medical Science* 2004 April-June; 173(2): 72-74. Subject: 18.2

Smith, Mable H. Legal obligations to human immunodeficiency virus-seropositive patients and health care providers. *Journal of Professional Nursing* 1995 May-June; 11(3): 183-191. Subject: 9.5.6

Smith, Pam; Lorentzon, Maria. Is emotional labour ethical? *Nursing Ethics* 2005 November; 12(6): 638-642. Subject: 4.1.3

Smith, Richard. Investigating the previous studies of a fraudulent author. *BMJ: British Medical Journal* 2005 July 30; 331(7511): 288-291. Subject: 1.3.9

Smith, Richard D.; Richardson, Jeff. Can we estimate the 'social' value of a QALY? Four core issues to resolve. *Health Policy* 2005 September 28; 74(1): 77-84. Subject: 4.4

Smith, Stephen W. Evidence for the practical slippery slope in the debate on physician-assisted suicide and euthanasia. *Medical Law Review* 2005 Spring; 13(1): 17-44. Subject: 20.7

Smith, Stephen W. Fallacies of the logical slippery slope in the debate on physician-assisted suicide and euthanasia. *Medical Law Review* 2005 Summer; 13(2): 224-243. Subject: 20.7

Smith, Stephen W. The killing of severely disabled newborns: the spectre behind the legalisation of physician-assisted suicide and euthanasia. *Medicine and Law: World Association for Medical Law* 2005 December; 24(4): 791-802. Subject: 20.5.2

Smith, Wesley J. Why secular humanism is wrong about assisted suicide. *Free Inquiry* 2003 Spring; 23(2): 31-32. Subject: 20.7

Smith, Wilbur L. Re: misrepresentation of publications by applicants for radiology fellowships. *AJR: American Journal of Roentgenology* 1998 March; 170(3): 582-583. Subject: 4.1.2

Smolin, David M. Fourteenth Amendment unenumerated rights jurisprudence: an essay in response to Stenberg v. Carhart. *Harvard Journal of Law and Public Policy* 2001; 24(3): 815-839. Subject: 12.4.2

Smylie, Janet; Tonelli, Marcello; Hemmelgarn, Brenda; Yeates, Karen; Gill, John; Wenman, Wanda M.; Joffres, Michel R.; Tataryn, Ivanna V.; Cass, Alan. The ethics of research involving Canada's Aboriginal populations [letters and replies]. *CMAJ/JAMC: Canadian Medical Association Journal* 2005 April 12; 172(8): 977-979. Subject: 18.5.9

Snead, O. Carter. The pedagogical significance of the Bush stem cell policy: a window into bioethical regulation in the United States. *Yale Journal of Health Policy, Law, and Ethics* 2005 Winter; 5(1): 491-504. Subject: 18.5.4

Sneiderman, Barney; Deutscher, Raymond. Dr. Nancy Morrison and her dying patient: a case of medical necessity. *Health Law Journal* 2002; 10: 1-30. Subject: 20.7

Snell, Gregory I.; Levvey, B.J.; Williams, T.J. Non-heart beating organ donation. *Internal Medicine Journal* 2004 August; 34(8): 501-503. Subject: 19.5

Snelling, Paul C.; Lipscomb, Martin. Academic freedom, analysis, and the Code of Professional Conduct. *Nurse Education Today* 2004 November; 24(8): 615-621. Subject: 7.2

Snow, Rachel C. Female genital cutting: distinguishing the rights from the health agenda [editorial]. *Tropical Medicine and International Health* 2001 February; 6(2): 89-91. Subject: 9.5.5

Snyder, David. A dispute over brain donations: families allege improper consent in lawsuits against Bethesda institute. *Washington Post* 2005 June 30; p. B1, B5. Subject: 19.5

Society for Academic Emergency Medicine [SAEM]. Board of Directors; Schmidt, Terri A.; Abbott, Jean T.; Geiderman, Joel M.; Hughes, Jason A.; Johnson, Catherine X.; McClure, Katie B.; McKay, Mary P.; Razzak, Junaid A.; Salo, David; Schears, Raquel M.; Solomon, Robert C. Ethics seminars: the ethical debate on practicing procedures on the newly dead. *Academic Emergency Medicine* 2004 September; 11(9): 962-966. Subject: 7.2

Society for Academic Emergency Medicine [SAEM]. Ethics Committee; Marco, Catherine A. The Society for Academic Emergency Medicine position on informed consent for emergency medicine research. *Academic Emergency Medicine* 2004 October; 11(10): 1090-1091. Subject: 18.3

Society for Academic Emergency Medicine [SAEM]. Ethics Committee; Schmidt, Terri A.; Salo, David; Hughes, Jason A.; Abbott, Jean T.; Geiderman, Joel M.; Johnson, Catherine X.; McClure, Katie B.; McKay, Mary Pat; Razzak, Junaid A.; Schears, Raquel M.; Solomon, Robert C. Confronting the ethical challenges to informed consent in emergency medicine research. *Academic Emergency Medicine* 2004 October; 11(10): 1082-1089. Subject: 18.3

Society of Obstetricians and Gynaecologists of Canada [SOGC]; International Women's Health Programme Committee. Conflict of interest [policy statement]. *JOGC: Journal of Obstetrics and Gynaecology Canada* 2003 December; 25(12): 1044-1045. Subject: 7.3

Sodeke, Stephen. Protecting vulnerable populations: Tuskegee's National Center for Bioethics in Research and Health Care is helping to pioneer participatory methods. *Protecting Human Subjects* 2003 Fall; (9): 8-9. Subject: 18.5.1

Sohler, Nancy L.; Bromet, Evelyn J.; Lavelle, Janet; Craig, Thomas J.; Mojtabai, Ramin. Are there racial dif-

---

ferences in the way patients with psychotic disorders are treated at their first hospitalization? *Psychological Medicine* 2004 May; 34(4): 705-718. Subject: 9.5.4

Soin, A.S. Ethical dilemmas in living donor liver transplantation [editorial]. *Issues in Medical Ethics* 2003 October-December; 11(4): 104-105. Subject: 19.5

Sokol, Daniel K. Calling a spade a spade [opinion]. *BMJ: British Medical Journal* 2005 September 3; 331(7515): 523. Subject: 8.2

Sokol, Daniel K. Commentary on ethics of HIV testing in general practice without informed consent: a case series [commentary]. *Journal of Medical Ethics* 2005 December; 31(12): 701-702. Subject: 9.5.6

Sokol, Daniel K. Meeting the ethical needs of doctors [editorial]. *BMJ: British Medical Journal* 2005 April 2; 330(7494): 741-742. Subject: 9.6

Solbakk, Jan Helge. Use and abuse of empirical knowledge in contemporary bioethics: a critical analysis of empirical arguments employed in the controversy surrounding stem cell research. *In:* Holm, Søren; Jonas, Monique F., eds. Engaging the World: The Use of Empirical Research in Bioethics and the Regulation of Biotechnology. Washington, DC: IOS Press; 2004: 53-60. Subject: 18.5.4

Soler-González, J.; Ruiz, M.C. Patients' written consent when photographed could suffice for journals [letter]. *BMJ: British Medical Journal* 2005 June 25; 330(7506): 1509. Subject: 8.3.1

Solomon, Daniel H.; Avorn, Jerry. Coxibs, science, and the public trust [editorial]. *Archives of Internal Medicine* 2005 January 24; 165(2): 158-160. Subject: 9.7

Solomon, David. Christian bioethics, secular bioethics, and the claim to cultural authority. *Christian Bioethics* 2005 December; 11(3): 349-359. Subject: 2.1

Solomon, Mildred Z. Realizing bioethics' goals in practice: ten ways "is" can help "ought". *Hastings Center Report* 2005 July-August; 35(4): 40-47. Subject: 2.1

Soloway, Richard A. The 'perfect contraceptive': eugenics and birth control research in Britain and America in the interwar years. *Journal of Contemporary History* 1995 October; 30(4): 637-664. Subject: 15.5

Solter, Davor. Politically correct human embryonic stem cells? [opinion]. *New England Journal of Medicine* 2005 December 1; 353(22): 2321-2323. Subject: 18.5.4

Solyom, Antal E. Improving the health of the public requires changes in medical education. *Academic Medicine* 2005 December; 80(12): 1089-1093. Subject: 9.1

Solyom, Antal E.; Moreno, Jonathan D. Protection of children and adolescents in psychiatric research: an unfinished business. *HEC (Healthcare Ethics Committee) Forum* 2005 September; 17(3): 210-226. Subject: 18.5.2

Somer, Eli; Nachmani, Irit. Constructions of therapist-client sex: a comparative analysis of retrospective vic-

tim reports. *Sexual Abuse* 2005 January; 17(1): 47-62. Subject: 17.2

Somer, Eli; Saadon, Meir. Therapist-client sex: clients' retrospective reports. *Professional Psychology: Research and Practice* 1999 October; 30(5): 504-509. Subject: 7.4

Somerville, Margaret. Commentary: social-ethical values issues in the political public square: principles vs. packages. *Journal of Law, Medicine and Ethics* 2004 Winter; 32(4): 731- 740. Subject: 2.1

Somerville, Margaret. The case against euthanasia and physician-assisted suicide. *Free Inquiry* 2003 Spring; 23(2): 33-34. Subject: 20.7

Somerville, Margaret A. Towards taming the tiger: reflections on prothanasia: personal fulfillment and readiness to die [comment]. *Humane Health Care International* 1997 Summer; 13(2): 38-40. Subject: 20.3.1

Somerville, Margaret A.; Atlas, Ronald M. Ethics: a weapon to counter bioterrorism. *Science* 2005 March 25; 307(5717): 1881-1882. Subject: 21.3

Sommerville, Ann. Changes in BMA policy on assisted dying. *BMJ: British Medical Journal* 2005 September 24; 331(7518): 686-688. Subject: 20.5.1

Sommerville, Ann. Recommendations concerning human rights for the medical profession. *Issues in Medical Ethics* 2003 January-March; 11(1): 19-20. Subject: 21.1

Sommerville, Ann; Reyes, Hernan; Peel, Michael. Doctors and torture. *In:* Peel, Michael; Iacopino, Vincent, eds. The Medical Documentation of Torture. San Francisco: Greenwich Medical Media; 2002: 63-76. Subject: 21.4

Song, John; Ratner, Edward R.; Bartels, Dianne M. Dying while homeless: is it a concern when life itself is such a struggle? *Journal of Clinical Ethics* 2005 Fall; 16(3): 251-261. Subject: 9.5.10

Song, Robert. Christian bioethics and the church's political worship. *Christian Bioethics* 2005 December; 11(3): 333-348. Subject: 2.1

Sonnenblick, Moshe; Gratch, Lena; Reveh, David; Steinberg, Abraham; Yinnon, Amos M. Epidemiology of decision on life-sustaining treatment in the general internal medicine division. *Harefuah* 2003 October; 142(10): 650-653, 720. Subject: 20.5.1

Sontag, David N. Are clinical ethics consultants in danger? An analysis of the potential legal liability of individual clinical ethicists. *University of Pennsylvania Law Review* 2002 December; 151(2): 667-705. Subject: 9.6

Sontag, Deborah. Abuses endangered veterans in cancer drug experiments. *New York Times* 2005 February 6; p. A1, A28. Subject: 18.5.8

Soon, Judith A.; Levine, Marc; Osmond, Brenda L.; Ensom, Mary H.H.; Fielding, David W. Effects of making emergency contraception available without a physician's prescription: a population-based study.

CMAJ/JAMC: Canadian Medical Association Journal 2005 March 29; 172(7): 878-883. Subject: 11.1

Soo-Jin Lee, Sandra; Koenig, Barbara A. Racial profiling of DNA samples: will it affect scientific knowledge about human genetic variation? *In:* Knoppers, Bartha Maria, ed. Populations and Genetics: Legal and Socio-Ethical Perspectives. Boston: Martinus Nijhoff; 2003: 231-244. Subject: 15.11

Soragna, G.; Carrano, R.; Putaggio, S.; Bergamo, D.; Burdese, M.; Mezza, E.; Motta, D.; Gai, M.; Bermond, F.; Jeantet, A.; Stefoni, S.; Federico, S.; Segoloni, G.P.; Piccoli, G.B. Opinions on renal transplantation and organ donation in high school students in two large northern (Torino) and southern (Napoli) Italian cities. *Transplantation Proceedings* 2004 April; 36(3): 428-430. Subject: 19.5

Sørlie, Venke; Kihlgren, Annica; Kihlgren, Mona. Meeting ethical challenges in acute nursing care as narrated by registered nurses. *Nursing Ethics* 2005 March; 12(2): 133-142. Subject: 8.1

Sorrell, Jeanne Merkle; Silva, Mary Cipriano. Unethical behaviors of student nurses: implications for nursing education and practice. *NursingConnections* 1991 Fall; 4(3): 25-28. Subject: 4.1.3

Sosis, Mitchel B.; McCartney, Colin J.L.; Brull, Richard; Chan, Vincent; Chung, Frances. Proper consent for clinical anesthesia research may be difficult to obtain on the day of surgery [letter and reply]. *Anesthesia and Analgesia* 2004 October; 99(4): 1272. Subject: 8.3.1

Sousa, Mário; Barros, Alberto. A moral case study for discussion: designer babies and tissue typing [opinion]. *Reproductive BioMedicine Online [electronic]* 2004 December; 9(6): 596-597. Available: http://www.rbmonline.com/index.html [14 July 2005]. Subject: 15.2

South Africa. Parliament. National Health Bill: As amended by the Portfolia Committee on Health (National Assembly) [B 32B-2003]. Pretoria, South Africa: Parliament 2003; 46 p. [Online]. Available: http://www.polity.org.za/pdf/NationalHealthB32B.pdf [9 August 2005]. Subject: 9.1

Sovacool, Benjamin K. Using criminalization and due process to reduce scientific misconduct. *American Journal of Bioethics [Online]* 2005 September- October; 5(5): W1-W7. Subject: 1.3.9

Spack, Norman. Transgenderism. *Medical Ethics Newsletter [Lahey Clinic]* 2005 Fall; 12(3): 1- 2, 12. Subject: 10

Spahn, Elizabeth; Andrade, Barbara. Mis-conceptions: the moment of conception in religion, science, and law. *University of San Francisco Law Review* 1998 Winter; 32(2): 261-333. Subject: 4.4

Spar, Debora. Reproductive tourism and the regulatory map [opinion]. *New England Journal of Medicine* 2005 February 10; 352(6): 531- 533. Subject: 14.1

Spear, Hila J. On ethical peer review and publication: the importance of professional conduct and communication. *Nurse Author and Editor* 2004 Fall; 14(4): 1-3. Subject: 1.3.7

Speck, Peter. Research and ethical scrutiny: an editor's dilemma? [editorial]. *Palliative Medicine* 2001 March 1; 15(2): 89-90. Subject: 18.2

Spectar, J.M. Patent necessity: intellectual property dilemmas in the biotech domain and treatment equity for developing countries. *Houston Journal of International Law* 2002; 24(2): 227-278. Subject: 9.5.6

Speers, Marjorie A. Making human research safe: why we cannot afford to fail. *Science and Engineering Ethics* 2005 January; 11(1): 53-59. Subject: 18.2

Spektorowski, Alberto. The eugenic temptation in socialism: Sweden, Germany, and the Soviet Union. *Comparative Studies in Society and History* 2004 January; 46(1): 84-106. Subject: 15.5

Spence, Des. The age of entitlement [opinion]. *BMJ: British Medical Journal* 2005 November 26; 331(7527): 1279. Subject: 9.7

Spencer, A.; Eggar, R.; Anderson, D. Whose consent is it anyway? [letter]. *British Journal of Psychiatry* 2001 February; 178; 3 p. [Online]. Available: http://bjp.rcpsych.org/cgi/content/full/178/2/177.a [28 October 2005]. Subject: 9.5.2

Sperling, Daniel. Do pregnant women have (living) will? *Journal of Health Care Law and Policy* 2005; 8(2): 331-342. Subject: 20.5.4

Spiegel, W.; Colella, T.; Lupton, P. Private or intimate relations between doctor and patient: is zero tolerance warranted? *Journal of Medical Ethics* 2005 January; 31(1): 27-28. Subject: 8.1

Spielman, Bethany. Professional independence and corporate employment in bioethics. *HEC (Healthcare Ethics Committee) Forum* 2005 June; 17(2): 146- 156. Subject: 9.6

Spielman, Bethany J. Bioethics testimony: untangling the strands and testing their reliability. *Journal of Law, Medicine and Ethics* 2005 Summer; 33(2): 222- 233. Subject: 2.1

Spielman, Bethany J. Non-family directed donation: the perils of policy-making. *American Journal of Bioethics* 2005 July-August; 5(4): 24-26. Subject: 19.5

Spier, Raymond. Observations on a meeting on the ethics of intellectual property rights and patents. *Science and Engineering Ethics* 2005 January; 11(1): 151-158. Subject: 15.8

Spier, R.E. Therapeutic vaccines. A pandoric prospect. *Advances in Experimental Medicine and Biology* 1996; 397: 183-189. Subject: 9.7

Spigt, M.G.; Knipschild, P.G.; van Schayck, C.P.; Knottnerus, J.A. The validity and ethics of giving placebo in a randomized nonpharmacologic trial was evaluated. *Journal of Clinical Epidemiology* 2005 April; 58(4): 350-356. Subject: 18.3

Spike, Jeffrey. A hearty critique of Baker's proposed code for bioethicists [comment]. *American Journal of Bioethics* 2005 September-October; 5(5): 54-55. Subject: 6

Spike, Jeffrey. How not to philosophize with a hammer: reply to Montgomery. *In:* Thomasma, David C.; Weisstub, David N., eds. The Variables of Moral Capacity. Boston: Kluwer Academic Publishers; 2004: 129- 135. Subject: 2.1

Spike, Jeffrey. Personhood and a paradox about capacity. *In:* Thomasma, David C.; Weisstub, David C.; Herve, Christian eds. Personhood and Health Care. Boston: Kluwer Academic Pub.; 2001: 243-251. Subject: 8.3.4

Spike, Jeffrey. Putting the "ethics" into "research ethics". *American Journal of Bioethics* 2005 January-February; 5(1): 51- 53. Subject: 18.2

Spike, Jeffrey. The sound of chains: a tragedy. *Journal of Clinical Ethics* 2005 Fall; 16(3): 212-217. Subject: 20.4.2

Spindelman, Marc S. Some initial thoughts on sexuality and gay men with AIDS in relation to physician-assisted suicide. *Georgetown Journal of Gender and the Law* 2000 Fall; 2(1): 91-105. Subject: 9.5.6

Spink, J.; Geddes, D. Gene therapy progress and prospects: bringing gene therapy into medical practice: the evolution of international ethics and the regulatory environment. *Gene Therapy* 2004 November; 11(22): 1611-1616. Subject: 15.4

Spinney, Laura. Last rights: if someone wants help to end their life, should the law stand in their way. *New Scientist* 2005 April 23-29; 186(2496): 46-49. Subject: 20.5.1

Spital, Aaron. Conscription of cadaveric organs for transplantation: a stimulating idea whose time has not yet come. *CQ: Cambridge Quarterly of Healthcare Ethics* 2005 Winter; 14(1): 107-112. Subject: 19.5

Spital, Aaron. Reply to Glannon and Ross: may parent to child organ donation be altruistic? *CQ: Cambridge Quarterly of Healthcare Ethics* 2005 Spring; 14(2): 195-198. Subject: 19.5

Spital, Aaron. Should people who commit themselves to organ donation be granted preferred status to receive organ transplants? *Clinical Transplantation* 2005 April; 19(2): 269-272. Subject: 19.5

Splawinski, Jacek. Patents and ethics: is it possible to be balanced? *Science and Engineering Ethics* 2005 January; 11(1): 71-74. Subject: 5.3

Sponholz, Gerlinde; Baitsch, Helmut. Der Bochumer Arbeitsbogen zur medizinethischen Praxis und die Kluft zwischen Wissen und Handeln. *In:* Baumann, Eva; Brink, Alexander; May, Arnd T.; Schröder; Peter; Schutzeichel, Corinna Iris, eds. Weltanschauliche Offenheit in der Bioethik. Berlin: Duncker & Humblot; 2004: 291-303. Subject: 2.1

Sporle, Andrew; Koea, Jonathan. Maori responsiveness in health and medical research: key issues for researchers (Part 1). *New Zealand Medical Journal* 2004 August 6; 117(1199): 10 p. Subject: 18.2

Sporle, Andrew; Koea, Jonathan. Maori responsiveness in health and medical research: clarifying the roles of the researcher and the institution (Part 2). *New Zealand Medical Journal* 2004 August 6; 117(1199); 7 p. Subject: 18.2

Spranger, Tade Matthias. Patent protection for stem cell procedures under the law of the European Union. *Medical Ethics and Bioethics / Medicinska Etika & Bioetika* 2003 Spring-Summer; 10(1-2): 4-8. Subject: 15.7

Spriggs, M. Hypoxic air machines: performance enhancement through effective training — or cheating? *Journal of Medical Ethics* 2005 February; 31(2): 112-113. Subject: 9.5.1

Spriggs, M. Is conceiving a child to benefit another against the interests of the new child? *Journal of Medical Ethics* 2005 June; 31(6): 341-342. Subject: 15.2

Spring, Julia C. Singleton's story: choosing between psychosis and execution. *Hastings Center Report* 2005 May-June; 35(3): 30-33. Subject: 20.6

Springen, Karen. The ultimate transplant: surgeons are ready to offer burn victims entire faces from donors, but there are risks. *Newsweek* 2005 December 12; 146(24): 60-61. Subject: 19.1

Sprumont, Dominique; Gytis, Andrulionis. The importance of national laws in the implementation of European legislation of biomedical research. *European Journal of Health Law* 2005 September; 12(3): 245- 267. Subject: 18.2

Spurgeon, Brad. Surgeons pleased with patient's progress after face transplant [news]. *BMJ: British Medical Journal* 2005 December 10; 331(7529): 1359. Subject: 19.1

Sque, Magi; Payne, Sheila A. Dissonant loss: the experiences of donor relatives. *Social Science and Medicine* 1996 November; 43(9): 1359-1370. Subject: 19.5

Squier, Susan. Coda: the pluripotent discourse of stem cells: liminality, reflexivity, and literature. *In her:* Liminal Lives: Imaging the Human at the Frontiers of Biomedicine. Durham: Duke University Press; 2004: 253-280. Subject: 2.1

Squier, Susan. The cultured cell: life and death at strangeways. *In her:* Liminal Lives: Imaging the Human at the Frontiers of Biomedicine. Durham: Duke University Press; 2004: 58-88. Subject: 1.3.9

Squier, Susan. Giant babies: graphing growth in the early twentieth century. *In her:* Liminal Lives: Imaging the Human at the Frontiers of Biomedicine. Durham: Duke University Press; 2004: 112-145. Subject: 5.1

Squier, Susan. The hybrid embryo and xenogenic desire. *In her:* Liminal Lives: Imaging the Human at the Frontiers of Biomedicine. Durham: Duke University Press; 2004: 89-111. Subject: 15.1

Squier, Susan. Incubabies and rejuvenates: the traffic between technologies of reproduction and age extension. *In her:* Liminal Lives: Imaging the Human at the Frontiers of Biomedicine. Durham: Duke University Press; 2004: 146-167. Subject: 4.5

Squier, Susan. Liminal performances of aging: from replacement to regeneration. *In her:* Liminal Lives: Imaging the Human at the Frontiers of Biomedicine. Durham: Duke University Press; 2004: 214-252. Subject: 5.1

Squier, Susan. Transplant medicine and transformative narrative. *In her:* Liminal Lives: Imaging the Human at the Frontiers of Biomedicine. Durham: Duke University Press; 2004: 168-213. Subject: 19.1

Squier, Susan; Waldby, Catherine; Lauritzen, Paul. Our posthuman future: discussing the consequences of biotechnological advances [letter and reply]. *Hastings Center Report* 2005 November-December; 35(6): 4, 6-7. Subject: 18.5.4

Srebnik, Debra S.; Rutherford, Lindsay T.; Peto, Tracy; Russo, Joan; Zick, Ellen; Jaffe, Craig; Holtzheimer, Paul. The content and clinical utility of psychiatric advance directives. *Psychiatric Services* 2005 May; 56(5): 592-598. Subject: 17.1

Sreenivasan, Gopal. Informed consent and the therapeutic misconception: clarifying the challenge. *Journal of Clinical Ethics* 2005 Winter; 16(4): 369-371. Subject: 18.3

Srinivas, A.V. Living donor liver transplantation. *Indian Journal of Medical Ethics* 2005 July-September; 2(3): 89-90. Subject: 19.5

Srinivasan, Sandhya. After the floods: health services' responsibilities in a crisis [editorial]. *Indian Journal of Medical Ethics* 2005 October-December; 2(4): 108-109. Subject: 9.1

Srinivasan, Sandhya. Physician, do no harm [opinion]. *Issues in Medical Ethics* 1998 January; 6(1): 22-23. Subject: 9.5.6

Srinivasan, Sandhya. Research on public health interventions in poor countries. *Issues in Medical Ethics* 2001 October-December; 9(4): 118-119. Subject: 18.5.9

Srinivasan, Sandhya. Surrogacy comes out of the closet. *Sunday Times of India* 1997 July 6; 3 p. [Online]. Available: http://www.hsph.harvard.edu/Organizations/healthnet/SAsia/suchana/0400/h012.html [3 October 2005]. Subject: 14.2

Srinivasan, Sandhya; Pai, Sanjay A. Research: history repeats itself [editorial]. *Issues in Medical Ethics* 2001 October-December; 9(4): 108. Subject: 18.2

Sriram, Sujata. Data can be used with safeguards [case study]. *Indian Journal of Medical Ethics* 2005 October-December; 2(4): 130. Subject: 18.4

Stadtländer, Christian T.K.-H.; Dickens, Bernard. Challenges and opportunities for ethics in public health [letter and reply]. *American Journal of Public Health* 2005 December; 95(12): 2122. Subject: 9.1

Stähelin, Hannes; Bondolfi, Alberto; Fischer, Johannes; Gerber, Andreas U.; Kesselring, Annemarie; Kind, Christian; Klauser, Cornelia; Ritz, Rudolf; Salathé, Michelle; de Stoutz, Noëmi; Stratenwerth, Günter; Vallotton, Michel; Zulian, Gilbert. Treatment and care of patients with chronic severe brain damage. *Swiss Medical Weekly* 2004 April 17; 134(15-16): 225-229. Subject: 20.5.1

Stahnisch, Frank W. Historical and philosophical perspectives on experimental practice in medicine and the life sciences. *Theoretical Medicine and Bioethics* 2005; 26(5): 397-425. Subject: 4.1.2

Stair, Thomas O.; Reed, Caitlin R.; Radeos, Michael S.; Koski, Greg; Camargo, Carlos A. Variation in institutional review board responses to a standard protocol for a multicenter clinical trial. *Academic Emergency Medicine* 2001 June; 8(6): 636-641. Subject: 18.2

Standish, Dominic. Italy: fertile ground for reform. *Conscience* 2005 Spring; 26(1): 24-26. Subject: 14.1

Stanford, Joseph B. Mormon bioethics [letter]. *First Things* 2005 October; (156): 8. Subject: 4.4

Stanley, Lauren. Storm clouds gathering: while the number of mergers wanes, the threats from the Catholic hierarchy to reproductive health care continue. *Conscience* 2004-2005 Winter; 25(3): 40-41. Subject: 14.1

Stanton, Catherine; Harris, John. The moral status of the embryo post-Dolly. *Journal of Medical Ethics* 2005 April; 31(4): 221-225. Subject: 4.4

Stark, Andrew. Why are (some) conflicts of interest in medicine so uniquely vexing? *In:* Moore, Don A.; Cain, Daylian M.; Loewenstein, George; Bazerman, Max H., eds. Conflicts of Interest: Challenges and Solutions in Business, Law, Medicine, and Public Policy. New York: Cambridge University Press; 2005: 152-180. Subject: 7.3

Stark, Judith; Thape, Janice. Decision making in neonatal intensive care: a collaboration of parents, physicians, and nurses. *AWHONN's Clinical Issues in Perinatal and Women's Health Nursing* 1993; 4(4): 589-595. Subject: 20.4.2

Stassen, Glen H. Supporting parents. *Christian Century* 2005 February 22; 122(4): 10-11. Subject: 9.5.10

Statman, Daniel. The right to parenthood: an argument for a narrow interpretation. *Ethical Perspectives* 2003; 10(3-4): 224-235. Subject: 14.1

Stavropoulos, Alexandre M. Orthodox Church. *In:* Council of Europe Publishing, ed. Euthanasia. Volume I.

Subject = NRCBL Primary Classification Number; See inside front cover

Ethical and Human Aspects. Strasbourg: Council of Europe; Croton- on-Hudson, NY: Manhattan Publishing Co.; 2003: 149-151. Subject: 20.5.1

Stead, Martine; Eadie, D.; Gordon, D.; Angus, K. "Hello, hello — it's English I speak!": a qualitative exploration of patients' understanding of the science of clinical trials. *Journal of Medical Ethics* 2005 November; 31(11): 664-669. Subject: 18.3

Stebbing, Justin; Bower, Mark. Lessons for HIV from Tuskegee. *Journal of HIV Therapy* 2004 September; 9(3): 50-52. Subject: 9.5.6

Steckmann, Ulrich. Patientenautonomie und Paternalismus in der Medizinethik. *In:* Jahrbuch für Wissenschaft und Ethik. Bd. 7. Berlin: Walter de Gruyter; 2002: 73-100. Subject: 8.1

Steer, Philip. The bioethics of preterm labour. *BJOG: An International Journal of Obstetrics and Gynaecology* 2005 March; 112(Supplement 1): 109-112. Subject: 8.3.1

Steers, William D. Academic urologists and their relationships with industry [editorial]. *Journal of Urology* 2005 March; 173(3): 677-678. Subject: 9.7

Stehney, Michael. Legacy of the American eugenics movement: implications for primary care. *Primary Care: Clinics in Office Practice* 2004 September; 31(3): 525-541, ix. Subject: 15.5

Stein, C. Michael. Publishing work sponsored by the tobacco industry. *Clinical Pharmacology and Therapeutics* 2004 December; 76(6): 517-518. Subject: 1.3.7

Stein, Rob. Found on the web, with DNA: a boy's father. *Washington Post* 2005 November 13; p. A9. Subject: 15.3

Stein, Rob. Pharmacists' rights at front of new debate; because of beliefs, some refuse to fill birth control prescriptions. *Washington Post* 2005 March 28; p. A1, A10. Subject: 7.1

Steinberg, Alan M.; Pynoos, Robert S.; Goenjian, Armen K.; Sossanabadi, Haleh; Sherr, Larissa. Are researchers bound by child abuse reporting laws? *Child Abuse and Neglect* 1999 August; 23(8): 771-777. Subject: 9.5.7

Steinberg, Avraham. Jewish perspectives. *In:* Blazer, Shraga; Zimmer, Etan Z., eds. The Embryo: Scientific Discovery and Medical Ethics. New York: Karger; 2005: 21-39. Subject: 4.4

Steinberg, David. Exchanging kidneys: how much unfairness is justified by an extra kidney and who decides? [editorial]. *American Journal of Kidney Diseases* 2004 December; 44(6): 1115-1120. Subject: 19.5

Steinberg, David. Response to "Special section on children as organ donors": a critique. *CQ: Cambridge Quarterly of Healthcare Ethics* 2005 Summer; 14(3): 301-305. Subject: 19.5

Steinberg, Jesse R. Response to Fritz Allhoff, "Telomeres and the Ethics of Human Cloning" (AJOB 4:2). *American Journal of Bioethics [Online]* 2005 January-February; 5(1): W27-W28. Subject: 14.5

Steinberg, Karen K. Ethical challenges at the beginning of the millennium. *Statistics in Medicine* 2001 May 15; 20(9-10): 1415-1419. Subject: 15.3

Steinberg, Karen L.; Levine, Murray; Doueck, Howard J. Effects of legally mandated child-abuse reports on the therapeutic relationship: a survey of psychotherapists. *American Journal of Orthopsychiatry* 1997 January; 67(1): 112-122. Subject: 17.2

Steinbock, B. The case for physician assisted suicide: not (yet) proven. *Journal of Medical Ethics* 2005 April; 31(4): 235-241. Subject: 9.7

Steinbock, Bonnie. Alternative sources of stem cells. *Hastings Center Report* 2005 July-August; 35(4): 24-26. Subject: 18.5.4

Steinbrook, Robert. Biomedical research and biosecurity [opinion]. *New England Journal of Medicine* 2005 November 24; 353(21): 2212-2214. Subject: 21.3

Steinbrook, Robert. Commercial support and continuing medical education [opinion]. *New England Journal of Medicine* 2005 February 10; 352(6): 534- 535. Subject: 7.2

Steinbrook, Robert. Financial conflicts of interest and the Food and Drug Administration's advisory committees [opinion]. *New England Journal of Medicine* 2005 July 14; 353(2): 116-118. Subject: 9.7

Steinbrook, Robert. Gag clauses in clinical-trial agreements [opinion]. *New England Journal of Medicine* 2005 May 26; 352(21): 2160- 2162. Subject: 18.6

Steinbrook, Robert. Public access to NIH-funded research [opinion]. *New England Journal of Medicine* 2005 April 28; 352(17): 1739- 1741. Subject: 18.2

Steinbrook, Robert. Public solicitation of organ donors [opinion]. *New England Journal of Medicine* 2005 August 4; 353(5): 441-444. Subject: 19.5

Steinbrook, Robert. Standards of ethics at the National Institutes of Health [opinion]. *New England Journal of Medicine* 2005 March 31; 352(13): 1290- 1292. Subject: 1.3.9

Steinbrook, Robert. Wall street and clinical trials [opinion]. *New England Journal of Medicine* 2005 September 15; 353(11): 1091-1093. Subject: 1.3.9

Steinbruner, John; Okutani, Stacy. The protective oversight of biotechnology. *Biosecurity and Bioterrorism* 2004; 2(4): 273-280. Subject: 5.1

Steineck, Christian. Japanese discussions on the concept of "person" and its function in bioethics. *Journal International de Bioethique / International Journal of Bioethics* 2005 March-June; 16(1-2): 29-40, 190. Subject: 4.4

Steinhardt, Barry. Privacy and forensic DNA data banks. *In:* Lazer, David, ed. DNA and the Criminal Justice System: The Technology of Justice. Cambridge, MA: MIT Press; 2004: 173-196. Subject: 15.1

Steinman, Michael A.; Shlipak, Michael G.; McPhee, Stephen J. Of principles and pens: attitudes and practices of medicine housestaff toward pharmaceutical industry promotions. *American Journal of Medicine* 2001 May; 110(7): 551-557. Subject: 9.7

Steinvorth, Ulrich. Über den Anfang des menschlichen Individuums. *In:* Jahrbuch für Wissenschaft und Ethik. Bd. 7. Berlin: Walter de Gruyter; 2002: 165-178. Subject: 4.4

Stempsey, William E. The philosophy of medicine: development of a discipline. *Medicine, Health Care and Philosophy: A European Journal* 2004; 7(3): 243-251. Subject: 4.1.2

Steneck, Nicholas H. The role of professional societies in promoting integrity in research. *American Journal of Health Behavior* 2003 November-December; 27(Supplement 3): S239-S247. Subject: 1.3.9

Stenson, B.; McIntosh, N. Some ethical considerations in the neonatal care area. *European Journal of Pediatrics* 1999 December; 158(Supplement 1): S13-S17. Subject: 9.5.7

Stephens, Kevin U., Sr. Reproductive capacity: what does the embryo get? *Southern University Law Review* 1997 Spring; 24(2): 263-291. Subject: 14.1

Stephens, Martin L.; Goldberg, Alan M.; Rowan, Andrew N. The first forty years of the alternatives approach: refining, reducing, and replacing the use of laboratory animals. *In:* Salem, Deborah J.; Rowan, Andrew N., eds. The State of the Animals 2001. Washington, DC: Humane Society Press; 2001: 121-135. Subject: 22.2

Stephenson, Lucinda. The changing nature of death — what you need to know about OOH DNRs. *Iowa Medicine* 2004 July-August; 94(4): 24-26. Subject: 20.5.1

Sterba, James P. Abortion and euthanasia. *In his:* Sterba, James P., ed. Morality in Practice. 7th edition. Belmont, CA: Wasworth/Thompson Learning; 2004: 121-189. Subject: 12.3

Sterba, James P. Genetic engineering. *In his:* Sterba, James P., ed.: Morality in Practice. 7th edition. Belmont, CA: Wasworth/Thompson Learning; 2004: 191-212. Subject: 14.5

Sterckx, Sigrid. Can drug patents be morally justified? *Science and Engineering Ethics* 2005 January; 11(1): 81-92. Subject: 5.3

Sterckx, Sigrid. Some ethically problematic aspects of the proposal for a directive on the legal protection of biotechnological inventions [opinion]. *EIPR: European Intellectual Property Review* 1998 April; 20(4): 123-128. Subject: 5.3

Stern, Alexandra Minna. Sterilized in the name of public health: race, immigration, and reproductive control in modern California. *American Journal of Public Health* 2005 July; 95(7): 1128-1138. Subject: 11.3

Stevens, Lesley; Cook, Deborah; Guyatt, Gordon; Griffith, Lauren; Walter, Steven; McMullin, Joseph. Education, ethics, and end-of-life decisions in the intensive care unit. *Critical Care Medicine* 2002 February; 30(2): 290-296. Subject: 20.5.1

Stevens, Patricia E.; Pletsch, Pamela K. Ethical issues of informed consent: mothers' experiences enrolling their children in bone marrow transplantation research. *Cancer Nursing* 2002 April; 25(2): 81-87. Subject: 8.3.2

Stevens, Tony; Wilson, Roger. Patients' interests: paramount in randomised trials [letter]. *BMJ: British Medical Journal* 2005 January 1; 330(7481): 44-45. Subject: 18.1

Stevenson, Fiona; Scambler, Graham. The relationship between medicine and the public: the challenge of concordance. *Health (London)* 2005 January; 9(1): 5-21. Subject: 8.1

Steward, Caroline. What is the responsibility of the nephrology nurse when the patient is chronically late? Nephrology nurses must follow the Nightingale Pledge. *Nephrology Nursing Journal* 2004 July-August; 31(4): 445-446. Subject: 8.1

Steward, Melissa. Electronic medical records: privacy, confidentiality, liability. *Journal of Legal Medicine* 2005 December; 26(4): 491-506. Subject: 8.4

Stewart, Cameron; Lynch, Andrew. Undue influence, consent and medical treatment. *Journal of the Royal Society of Medicine* 2003 December; 96(12): 598-601. Subject: 8.3.4

Stewart, Charles L. Making decisions about neonatal life support: respecting the views of all concerned requires co-ordinated communication among all parties. *Healthcare Executive* 2005 March-April; 20(2): 42-43. Subject: 20.5.2

Stewart, Douglas O.; DeMarco, Joseph P. An economic theory of patient decision-making. *Journal of Bioethical Inquiry* 2005; 2(3): 153-164. Subject: 8.3.1

Stewart, Kevin; Bowker, Lesley. Advance directives and living wills. *Postgraduate Medical Journal* 1998 March; 74(869): 151-156. Subject: 20.5.4

Stiffman, Arlene Rubin; Brown, Eddie; Striley, Catherine Woodstock; Ostmann, Emily; Chowa, Gina. Cultural and ethical issues concerning research on American Indian youth. *Ethics and Behavior* 2005; 15(1): 1-14. Subject: 18.5.2

Stirrat, G.M.; Gill, R. Autonomy in medical ethics after O'Neill. *Journal of Medical Ethics* 2005 March; 31(3): 127-130. Subject: 8.3.1

Stith, Richard. Death by hunger and thirst. *Ethics and Medics* 2005 June; 30(6): 1-2. Subject: 20.5.1

Subject = NRCBL Primary Classification Number; See inside front cover

Stocking, Carol B.; Hougham, Gavin W.; Baron, Aliza R.; Sachs, Greg A. Are the rules for research with subjects with dementia changing?: views from the field. *Neurology* 2003 December 23; 61(12): 1649-1651. Subject: 18.5.7

Stokstad, Erik. EPA draft rules for human subjects draw fire [news]. *Science* 2005 July 8; 309(5732): 232. Subject: 18.5.1

Stolberg, Sheryl Gay. A collision of disparate forces may be reshaping American law; the Schiavo case: looking ahead and looking back. *New York Times* 2005 April 1; p. A18. Subject: 20.5.1

Stolberg, Sheryl Gay. House approves a stem cell bill opposed by Bush; margin is not veto-proof; bipartisan senate support may set up showdown over federal funds. *New York Times* 2005 May 25; p. A1, A22. Subject: 18.5.4

Stolberg, Sheryl Gay. Lawmakers ready to again debate end-of-life issues. *New York Times* 2005 March 28; p. A1, A14. Subject: 20.5.1

Stolk, Elly A.; Pickee, Stefan J.; Ament, André H.J.A.; Busschbach, Jan J.V. Equity in health care prioritisation: an empirical inquiry into social value. *Health Policy* 2005 November; 74(3): 343-355. Subject: 4.4

Stollmeyer, Alice. The politics of care: dementia and accounting versus caring for mortification. *Journal of Clinical Ethics* 2005 Summer; 16(2): 116-126. Subject: 20.4.1

Stolt, Ulrica Gustafsson; Liss, Per-Erik; Ludvigsson, Johnny. Nurses' views of longitudinal genetic screening of and research on children. *British Journal of Nursing* 2005 January 27-February 9; 14(2): 71-77. Subject: 15.3

Stone, Alan A. Psychiatry and the law. *In:* Nicholi, Armand M., ed. The Harvard Guide to Psychiatry. 3rd ed. Cambridge, MA: Belknap Press of Harvard University; 1999: 798-823. Subject: 17.1

Stone, A.J., III. Consti-tortion: tort law as an end-run around abortion rights after Planned Parenthood v. Casey [112 S.Ct 2791 (1992)]. *American University Journal of Gender, Social Policy and the Law* 2000; 8(2): 471-515. Subject: 12.4.2

Stone, Donald H. The benefits of voluntary inpatient psychiatric hospitalization: myth or reality? *Boston University Public Interest Law Journal* 1999 Fall; 9(1): 25-52. Subject: 17.7

Stone, Lesley; Gostin, Lawrence O.; Hodge, James G. The Model State Emergency Health Powers Act: a tool for public health preparedness. *In:* Kleinman, Daniel Lee; Kinchy, Abby J.; Handelsman, eds. Controversies in Science and Technology: From Maize to Menopause. Madison, Wis.: University of Wisconsin Press; 2005: 283-296. Subject: 21.3

Stone, T. Howard; Horton, Heather H.; Pestronk, Robert M. Considerations for special populations. *In:* Goodman, Richard A.; Rothstein, Mark A.; Hoffman, Richard E.; Lopez, Wilfredo; Matthews, Gene W., eds. Law in Public Health Practice. New York: Oxford University Press; 2003: 211-241. Subject: 9.1

Stoneking, Carole Bailey. Receiving communion: euthanasia, suicide, and letting die. *In:* Hauerwas, Stanley; Wells, Samuel eds. The Blackwell Companion to Christian Ethics. Oxford, UK: Blackwell Publishers Ltd.; 2004: 375-387. Subject: 20.5.1

Storrow, Richard F.; Martinez, Sandra. "Special weight" for best-interests minors in the new era of parental autonomy. *Wisconsin Law Review* 2003; (5): 789-841. Subject: 12.4.2

Stossel, Thomas P. Regulating academic-industrial research relationships — solving problems or stifling progress? *New England Journal of Medicine* 2005 September 8; 353(10): 1060-1065. Subject: 5.3

Stotland, Nada L. Induced abortion in the United States. *In:* Stotland, Nada L.; Stewart, Donna E., eds. Psychological Aspects of Women's Health Care: The Interface Between Psychiatry and Obstetrics and Gynecology. Washington, DC: American Psychiatric Press; 2001: 219-239. Subject: 12.1

Strachan, Heather. Ethics. *Research and Theory for Nursing Practice* 2004 Summer-Fall; 18(2-3): 123-126. Subject: 4.1.3

Strahan, Thomas W. The natural law philosophy of Lon L. Fuller in contrast to Roe v. Wade and its progeny. *In:* Koterski, Joseph W., ed. Life and Learning XI: Proceedings of the Eleventh University Faculty for Life Conference. Washington, DC: University Faculty for Life; 2002: 85-97. Subject: 12.4.4

Strasberg-Cohen, Tova. The status of the embryo under Israeli law. *In:* Blazer, Shraga; Zimmer, Etan Z., eds. The Embryo: Scientific Discovery and Medical Ethics. New York: Karger; 2005: 329-339. Subject: 4.4

Strasburger, Larry H.; Jorgenson, Linda; Sutherland, Pamela. The prevention of psychotherapist sexual misconduct: avoiding the slippery slope. *American Journal of Psychotherapy* 1992 October; 46(4): 544-555. Subject: 17.2

Strathern, Marilyn. Still giving nature a helping hand? Surrogacy: a debate about technology and society. *In:* Cook, Rachel; Sclater, Shelley Day; Kaganas, Felicity, eds. Surrogate Motherhood: International Perspectives. Portland, OR: Hart; 2003: 281-296. Subject: 14.2

Straus, Joseph. Patents on biomaterial—a new colonialism or a means for technology transfer and benefit-sharing? *In:* Thiele, F.; Ashcroft, R.E., eds. Bioethics in a Small World. Berlin: Springer; 2005: 45-72. Subject: 15.8

Street, Annette F.; Love, Anthony. Dimensions of privacy in palliative care: views of health professionals. *Social Science and Medicine* 2005 April; 60(8): 1795-1804. Subject: 20.4.1

Streiffer, Robert. At the edge of humanity: human stem cells, chimeras, and moral status. *Kennedy Institute of Ethics Journal* 2005 December; 15(4): 347- 370. Subject: 4.4

Stringer, Mark D. Informed consent and choice in cholecystectomy. *Pediatric Surgery International* 2004 October; 20(10): 741-743. Subject: 8.3.1

Strode, Ann; Grant, Catherine; Slack, Catherine; Mushariwa, Muriel. How well does South Africa's National Health Act regulate research involving children? *South African Medical Journal* 2005 April; 95(4): 265-268. Subject: 18.6

Stromberg, Daniel; Tortoriello, Tia; Adame, Tracine; Morris, Marilyn C. Waiver of prospective consent for pediatric resuscitation research [letters and reply]. *Pediatrics* 2005 March; 115(3): 828-829. Subject: 18.5.2

Strong, C. Reproductive cloning combined with genetic modification. *Journal of Medical Ethics* 2005 November; 31(11): 654-658. Subject: 14.5

Strong, Carson. Harming by conceiving: a review of misconceptions and a new analysis. *Journal of Medicine and Philosophy* 2005 October; 30(5): 491- 516. Subject: 14.1

Strong, Carson. Lost in translation: religious arguments made secular [comment]. *American Journal of Bioethics* 2005 May-June; 5(3): 29-31. Subject: 15.1

Strong, Carson. Obtaining stem cells: moving from Scylla toward Charybdis. *American Journal of Bioethics* 2005 November-December; 5(6): 21-23. Subject: 18.5.4

Strong, Louise C.; Marteau, Theresa. Evaluating children and adolescents for heritable cancer risk. *Journal of the National Cancer Institute Monographs* 1995; (17): 111-113. Subject: 15.3

Struhkamp, Rita M. Patient autonomy: a view from the kitchen. *Medicine, Health Care and Philosophy: A European Journal* 2005; 8(1): 105-114. Subject: 9.1

Stuck, Jamalynne; McElroy, Dough. Genetic counseling. *In:* Ness, Bryan D., ed. Encyclopedia of Genetics. Revised edition. Volume I. Pasadena, Calif.: Salem Press; 2004: 321-326. Subject: 15.2

Studdert, David M. On selling "no-fault.". *In:* Sharpe, Virginia A., ed. Accountability: Patient Safety and Policy Reform. Washington, DC: Georgetown University Press; 2004: 203-212. Subject: 8.5

Stuhrmann, Manfred; Hoy, Ludwig; Nippert, Irmgard; Schmidtke, Jörg. Genotype-based screening for hereditary Hemochromatosis: II. Attitudes toward genetic testing and psychosocial impact — a report from a German pilot study. *Genetic Testing* 2005 Fall; 9(3): 242-254. Subject: 15.3

Sturgis, Patrick; Cooper, Helen; Fife-Schaw, Chris. Attitudes to biotechnology: estimating the opinions of a better-informed public. *New Genetics and Society* 2005 April; 24(1): 31-56. Subject: 15.4

Sturm, Bonnie A. Ethics and care: an ethnographic study of psychiatric community health nursing practice. *Archives of Psychiatric Nursing* 2004 June; 18(3): 106-115. Subject: 4.1.3

St. Amand, Paul C. Genetic engineering: risks. *In:* Ness, Bryan D., ed. Encyclopedia of Genetics. Revised edition. Volume I. Pasadena, Calif.: Salem Press; 2004: 347-350. Subject: 15.7

St. John, Justin C.; Alderson, Jon. Stem-cell banking: the size of the task [opinion]. *Lancet* 2005 December 10-16; 366(9502): 1991-1992. Subject: 18.5.4

St. Mary, Edward W. Legal and ethical dilemmas in drug management for team physicians and athletic trainers. *Southern Medical Journal* 1998 May; 91(5): 421-424. Subject: 9.5.9

Su, Baoqi; Macer, Darryl R.J. A sense of autonomy is preserved under Chinese reproductive policies. *New Genetics and Society* 2005 April; 24(1): 15-29. Subject: 13.3

Sudzina, Michael R. Industry support for dental education. *Journal of the American College of Dentists* 2005 Summer; 72(2): 12-14. Subject: 4.1.1

Sugarman, Jeremy. Should the gold rule? Assessing "equivalent protections" for research participants across international borders. *Hastings Center Report* 2005 September-October; 35(5): 12-13. Subject: 18.5.9

Sugarman, Jeremy; Getz, Kenneth; Speckman, Jeanne L.; Byrne, Margaret M.; Gerson, Jason; Emanuel, Ezekiel J. The cost of institutional review boards in academic medical centers [letter]. *New England Journal of Medicine* 2005 April 28; 352(17): 1825- 1827. Subject: 18.2

Sugunasiri, S.H.J. The Buddhist view concerning the dead body. *Transplantation Proceedings* 1990 June; 22(3): 947-949. Subject: 4.4

Sullivan, Danny. State-sanctioned intervention on behalf of the fetus. *Journal of Law and Medicine* 2000 August; 8(1): 44-55. Subject: 9.5.5

Sullivan, Dennis. Euthanasia versus letting die: Christian decision-making in terminal patients. *Ethics and Medicine* 2005 Summer; 21(2): 109-118. Subject: 20.5.1

Sullivan, Dennis J.; Hansen-Flaschen, John. Termination of life support after major trauma. *Surgical Clinics of North America* 2000 June; 80(3): 1055-1066. Subject: 20.5.1

Sullivan, Ellen E. Issues of informed consent in the geriatric population. *Journal of Perianesthesia Nursing* 2004 December; 19(6): 430-432. Subject: 8.3.3

Sullivan, Lucy. Embryo experimentation and the murder prohibition: a casuistic examination of the utilitarian and pro-life positions on the moral status of the embryo. *Medicine and Law: World Association for Medical Law* 1995; 14(5-6): 369-386. Subject: 18.5.4

Subject = NRCBL Primary Classification Number; See inside front cover

Sullivan, Mark. Ethical principles in pain management. *Pain Medicine* 2000 September; 1(3): 274-279. Subject: 4.4

Sullivan, Mark; Ferrell, Betty. Ethical challenges in the management of chronic nonmalignant pain: negotiating through the cloud of doubt. *Journal of Pain* 2005 January; 6(1): 2-9. Subject: 4.4

Sullivan, Mark; Paice, Judith A.; Benedetti, Fabrizio. Placebos and treatment of pain [case study and commentary]. *Pain Medicine* 2004 September; 5(3): 325-328. Subject: 8.2

Sullivan, MaryCarroll. Ethical considerations in managed care: a commentary. *UMKC Law Review* 1998 Summer; 66(4): 757-762. Subject: 9.3.2

Sullivan, Timothy M. Ethics and the physician-industry relationship [opinion]. *Annals of Vascular Surgery* 2004 May; 18(3): 263-264. Subject: 9.7

Sullivan-Marx, Eileen M.; Strumpf, Neville E. Restraint-free care for acutely ill patients in the hospital. *AACN Clinical Issues* 1996 November; 7(4): 572-578. Subject: 17.3

Sulmasy, Daniel P. "Diseases and natural kinds". *Theoretical Medicine and Bioethics* 2005; 26(6): 487-513. Subject: 4.1.2

Sulmasy, Daniel P. Duty to warn about hereditary disease risks [letter]. *JAMA: The Journal of the American Medical Association* 2005 February 9; 293(6): 676. Subject: 15.2

Sulmasy, Daniel P. Terri Schiavo and the Roman Catholic tradition of forgoing extraordinary means of care. *Journal of Law, Medicine and Ethics* 2005 Summer; 33(2): 359-362. Subject: 20.4.1

Sulmasy, Daniel P.; Ferris, Robert E.; Ury, Wayne A. Confidence and knowledge of medical ethics among interns entering residency in different specialties. *Journal of Clinical Ethics* 2005 Fall; 16(3): 230-235. Subject: 7.2

Sulston, John. Society and human genome [opinion]. *Revista de Derecho y Genoma Humano / Law and the Human Genome Review* 2004 January-June; (20): 25-33. Subject: 15.10

Sumathipala, Athula; Siribaddana, Sisira. Research and clinical ethics after the tsunami: Sri Lanka [opinion]. *Lancet* 2005 October 22-28; 366(9495): 1418-1420. Subject: 18.2

Sundram, Clarence J.; Stavis, Paul F. Obtaining informed consent for treatment of mentally incompetent patients: a decade under New York's innovative approach. *International Journal of Law and Psychiatry* 1999 March-April; 22(2): 107-123. Subject: 8.3.3

Supe, Avinash. Ethical considerations in medical photography. *Issues in Medical Ethics* 2003 July-September; 11(3): 83-84. Subject: 1.3.7

Supe, Avinash N.; Kumar, Nishant; Ramakanthan, Ravi; D'Souza, Ravi; Ashtekar, Shyam. Medical ethics and medical education: some thoughts [discussion]. *Issues in Medical Ethics* 1998 July-September; 6(3): 79-82. Subject: 2.3

Surbone, Antonella. Complexity and the future of the patient-doctor relationship [editorial]. *Critical Reviews in Oncology/Hematology* 2004 December; 52(3): 143-145. Subject: 9.8

Surbone, Antonella; Ritossa, Claudio; Spagnolo, Antonio G. Evolution of truth-telling attitudes and practices in Italy. *Critical Reviews in Oncology/Hematology* 2004 December; 52(3): 165-172. Subject: 8.2

Surbone, A. Genetic medicine: the balance between science and morality. *Annals of Oncology* 2004; 15(Supplement 1): I60-I64. Subject: 15.1

Surman, Owen S.; Fukunishi, Isao; Allen, Terre; Hertl, Martin. Live organ donation: social context, clinical encounter, and the psychology of communication. *Psychosomatics* 2005 January-February; 46(1): 1-6. Subject: 19.5

Susanne, Charles; Casado, María; Buxo, María Jesús. What challenges offers nanotechnology to bioethics? [opinion]. *Revista de Derecho y Genoma Humano / Law and the Human Genome Review* 2005 January-June; (22): 27-45. Subject: 4.4

Suter, Sonia M. Disentangling privacy from property: toward a deeper understanding of genetic privacy. *George Washington Law Review* 2004 April; 72(4): 737-814. Subject: 15.8

Sutton, Victoria. A multidisciplinary approach to an ethic of biodefense and bioterrorism. *Journal of Law, Medicine and Ethics* 2005 Summer; 33(2): 310-322. Subject: 2.1

Suziedelis, Ann. Requests for inappropriate treatment: can a doctor "just say 'no'"? *Health Care Ethics USA* [electronic] 2005; 13(1); 2 p. Available: http://www.slu.edu/centers/chce/hceusa/1_2005_3.html [19 September 2005]. Subject: 8.1

Suziedelis, Ann K. Conjoined twins: the ambiguity of double effect reasoning. *Medical Ethics and Bioethics / Medicinska Etika & Bioetika* 2001 Autumn-Winter; 8(3-4): 3-5. Subject: 20.5.2

Swartz, Omar. Access to AIDS medicine: ethical considerations. *Indian Journal of Medical Ethics* 2004 July-September; 1(3): 75-76. Subject: 9.5.6

Sweeney, Harry A.; Elliott, Carl. Pharma PR or medical education? [letter and reply]. *Hastings Center Report* 2005 March-April; 35(2): 4-5. Subject: 9.7

Swift, Patricia. Ethical considerations in research from a cancer nurse's perspective. *Professional Nurse* 2002 November; 18(3): 171-175. Subject: 18.5.1

Swiss Academy of Medical Sciences. Medical-ethical principles on xenotransplantation. *Swiss Medical Weekly* 2001 June 30; 131(25-26): 388-394. Subject: 19.1

Switzer, David. All medical physicists entering the field should have a specific course on research and practice ethics in their educational background. *Medical Physics* 2003 December; 30(12): 3049-3050. Subject: 1.3.9

Syme, Rodney R.A.; Zalcberg, John R.; Buchanan, John D. The euthanasia controversy. Decision-making in extreme circumstances [letter and reply]. *Medical Journal of Australia* 1996 March 4; 164(5): 317-318. Subject: 20.5.1

Syrett, K. Deference or deliberation: rethinking the judicial role in the allocation of healthcare resources. *Medicine and Law: World Association for Medical Law* 2005 June; 24(2): 309-322. Subject: 9.4

Syrett, Keith. "Child B": reasons, rationing and the right to life. *Personal Injury Law and Medical Review* 1995 Summer; 2(2): 156-170. Subject: 9.4

Syrett, Keith. Impotence or importance? Judicial review in an era of explicit NHS rationing. *Modern Law Review* 2004 March; 67(2): 289-304. Subject: 14.1

Szalavitz, Maia. Give us the drugs. *New Scientist* 2005 January 29-February 4; 185(2484): 19. Subject: 9.5.1

Szasz, T. "Idiots, infants, and the insane": mental illness and legal incompetence. *Journal of Medical Ethics* 2005 February; 31(2): 78-81. Subject: 4.3

Szasz, Thomas. Protecting patients against psychiatric intervention [opinion]. *Society* 2004 March-April; 41(3): 7-9. Subject: 17.8

Szatmari, Peter. Response to Dr Gupta. *Evidence-Based Mental Health* 2004 November; 7(4): 97-98. Subject: 9.8

T

Tabak, N. Doctors' policy on explaining the implementation of novel experimental treatment to cancer patients. *Medicine and Law: World Association for Medical Law* 1994; 13(3-4): 331-355. Subject: 18.3

Tagliabue, John. Discovery of stored fetuses and stillborns roils France. *New York Times* 2005 August 4; p. A10. Subject: 8.3.2

Tai, Michael Cheng-tek. The contextualized Asian principles of medical ethics. *Synthesis Philosophica* 2002 February; 34: 351-360. Subject: 2.1

Tai, Michael Cheng-tek. The death of a little girl exposes an ethical hole [editorial]. *Formosan Journal of Medical Humanities* 2005 September; 6(1-2): 1-2. Subject: 4.1.2

Tait, Alan R.; Voepel-Lewis, Terri; Malviya, Shobha; Philipson, Sandra J. Improving the readability and processability of a pediatric informed consent document: effects on parents' understanding. *Archives of Pediatric and Adolescent Medicine* 2005 April; 159(4): 347-352. Subject: 18.3

Taitz, J.; Weekers, J.E.M.; Mosca, D.T. The last resort: exploring the use of DNA testing for family reunification. *Health and Human Rights: An International Journal* 2002; 6(1): 21-32. Subject: 15.1

Tak, Peter. Recent developments concerning euthanasia in the Netherlands. *Tilburg Foreign Law Review* 1999; 8(1): 43-80. Subject: 20.5.1

Takala, Tuija. Demagogues, firefighters, and window dressers: who are we and what should we be? *CQ: Cambridge Quarterly of Healthcare Ethics* 2005 Fall; 14(4): 385-388. Subject: 2.1

Takala, Tuija. Genetic knowledge and our conception of ourselves as persons. *In:* Thomasma, David C.; Weisstub, David N.; Herve, Christian eds. Personhood and Health Care. Boston: Kluwer Academic Pub.; 2001: 91-97. Subject: 15.3

Takala, Tuija. The many wrongs of human reproductive cloning. *In:* Häyry, Matti; Takala, Tuija; Herissone-Kelly, Peter, eds. Bioethics and Social Reality. New York: Rodopi, 2005: 53-66. Subject: 14.5

Takala, Tuija. Who should decide and why? The futility of philosophy, sociology and law in institutionalised bioethics, and the unwarrantability of ethics committees. *In:* Holm, Søren; Jonas, Monique F., eds. Engaging the World: The Use of Empirical Research in Bioethics and the Regulation of Biotechnology. Washington, DC: IOS Press; 2004: 69-75. Subject: 2.4

Takasugi, Miyuki; Iwamoto, Eriko; Akashi-Tanaka, Sadako; Kinoshita, Takayuki; Fukutomi, Takashi; Kubouchi, Kohichi. General aspects and specific issues of informed consent on breast cancer treatments. *Breast Cancer* 2005 January; 12(1): 39-44. Subject: 8.3.1

Takayesu, James Kimo; Hutson, H. Range. Communicating life-threatening diagnoses to patients in the emergency department. *Annals of Emergency Medicine* 2004 June; 43(6): 749-755. Subject: 8.2

Takeshita, Naoki; Kubo, Harumi. Regulating preimplantation genetic diagnosis — how to control PGD. *Journal of Assisted Reproduction and Genetics* 2004 January; 21(1): 19-25. Subject: 15.2

Talcott, James A. What patients should be told before agreeing to a blood test that could change their lives [editorial]. *Urology* 2003 January; 61(1): 7-9. Subject: 8.3.1

Talesh, Shauhin A. Breaking the learned helplessness of patients: why MCOs should be required to disclose financial incentives. *Law and Psychology Review* 2002 Spring; 26(1): 49-95. Subject: 9.3.2

Talib, Norchaya. Dilemmas surrounding passive euthanasia — a Malaysian perspective. *Medicine and Law: World Association for Medical Law* 2005 September; 24(3): 605-613. Subject: 20.5.1

Tallacchini, Mariachiara. Rhetoric of anonymity and property rights in human biological materials (HBMs). *Revista de Derecho y Genoma Humano / Law and the Human Genome Review* 2005 January-June; (22): 153-175. Subject: 4.4

Tallis, Raymond; Saunders, John. The Assisted Dying for the Terminally Ill Bill, 2004. *Clinical Medicine* 2004 November-December; 4(6): 534-540. Subject: 20.7

Talukder, Md Humayun Kabir; Chowdhury, Fatima Parveen; Shuvra Muhammad Mizanur Rashid. Teachers' views of WHO teaching guidelines on health ethics for undergraduate medical education in Bangladesh. *Indian Journal of Medical Ethics* 2005 April-June; 2(2): 54. Subject: 7.2

Talvik, Tiina. Estonia. *Medical Ethics and Bioethics / Medicinska Etika & Bioetika* 2005; 11(Supplement): 15-16. Subject: 9.6

Tamakoshi, Akiko. Informed consent in epidemiologic research before the implementation of ethical guidelines. *Journal of Epidemiology* 2004 November; 14(6): 177-181. Subject: 18.2

Tamburrini, C. Commentary: hypoxic air machines. *Journal of Medical Ethics* 2005 February; 31(2): 114. Subject: 9.5.1

Tanaka, Masahiro. Buddhism and palliative care in Japan. *Dolentium Hominum* 2005; 20(1): 94-96. Subject: 20.4.1

Tanaka, Yutaka. Major psychological factors affecting acceptance of gene-recombination technology. *Risk Analysis* 2004 December; 24(6): 1575-1583. Subject: 15.7

Tandon, P.N. Bioethics: an emerging discipline [editorial]. *Indian Journal of Medical Research* 2005 January; 121(1): 1-4. Subject: 2.1

Tanne, Janice Hopkins. American Medical Association fights pharmacists who won't dispense contraceptives [news]. *BMJ: British Medical Journal* 2005 July 2; 331(7507): 11. Subject: 11.1

Tanne, Janice Hopkins. Emergency contraception is under attack by US pharmacists [news]. *BMJ: British Medical Journal* 2005 April 30; 330(7498): 983. Subject: 11.1

Tanne, Janice Hopkins. FDA ducks decision on emergency contraceptive [news]. *BMJ: British Medical Journal* 2005 September 17; 331(7517): 596. Subject: 11.1

Tanne, Janice Hopkins. FDA official resigns over emergency contraception decision [news]. *BMJ: British Medical Journal* 2005 September 10; 331(7516): 532. Subject: 11.1

Tanne, Janice Hopkins. Royalty payments to staff researchers cause new NIH troubles [news]. *BMJ: British Medical Journal* 2005 January 22; 330(7484): 162. Subject: 1.3.9

Tanne, Janice Hopkins. US National Institutes of Health issue new ethics guidelines [news]. *BMJ: British Medical Journal* 2005 September 3; 331(7515): 472. Subject: 5.3

Tanne, Janice Hopkins. US Senate leader gives support to expanded stem cell research [news]. *BMJ: British Medical Journal* 2005 August 6; 331(7512): 307. Subject: 18.5.4

Tännsjö, Torbjörn. Commentary: hypoxic air machines. *Journal of Medical Ethics* 2005 February; 31(2): 113. Subject: 9.5.1

Tännsjö, Torbjörn. Moral dimensions. *BMJ: British Medical Journal* 2005 September 24; 331(7518): 689-691. Subject: 20.5.1

Tanvetyanon, Tawee; Kreicbergs, Ulrika; Valdimarsdóttir, Unnur; Steineck, Gunnar. Talking about death with dying children [letter and reply]. *New England Journal of Medicine* 2005 January 6; 352(1): 91-92. Subject: 20.3.3

Tao, J.L.P.W.; Engelhardt, H.T., Jr. Towards a "One Country Two Systems" medical ethics for the regulation of practice promotion: Hong Kong as a case study. *Hong Kong Medical Journal* 2004 December; 10(6): 435-437. Subject: 2.1

Tardy, B.; Venet, C.; Zeni, F.; Berthet, O.; Viallon, A.; Lemaire, F.; Bertrand, J.C. Death of terminally ill patients on a stretcher in the emergency department: a French specialty? *Intensive Care Medicine* 2002 November; 28(11): 1625-1628. Subject: 20.4.1

Tarnow-Mordi, William O. "Right to die" — . . . but context of limited resources can be encountered in developed countries too [letter]. *BMJ: British Medical Journal* 2005 June 11; 330(7504): 1389. Subject: 20.5.2

Tarrant, Stella. Western Australia's persistent enforcement of an invalid law: Section 23(c) of the Human Reproductive Technology Act 1991 (WA). *Journal of Law and Medicine* 2000 August; 8(1): 92-111. Subject: 14.4

Tarzian, Anita J.; Neal, Maggie T.; O'Neil, J. Anne. Attitudes, experiences, and beliefs affecting end-of-life decision-making among homeless individuals. *Journal of Palliative Medicine* 2005 February; 8(1): 36-48. Subject: 20.4.1

Tassy, Sebastien; Gorincour, Guillaume; Le Coz, Pierre. Emotions stimulate ethical debate but must not seize it: the example of end-of-life decision-making process [letter]. *Journal of the American Geriatrics Society* 2005 December; 53(12): 2231. Subject: 20.5.1

Tassy, Sebastien; Gorincour, Guillaume; Le Coz, Pierre. Prenatal research: a very sensitive field [letter]. *Lancet* 2005 October 1-7; 366(9492): 1162. Subject: 18.5.4

Tatara, Kozo. Prescribing and dispensing in Japan: conflict of interest? *Clinical Medicine* 2003 November-December; 3(6): 555. Subject: 7.3

Tate, Sarah K.; Goldstein, David B. Will tomorrow's medicines work for everyone? [opinion]. *Nature Genetics* 2004 November; 36(11, Supplement): S34-S42. Subject: 15.1

Tatelbaum, Mark F. Practice resource: checklist of federal and state privacy issues. *Journal of Health Law* 2002 Spring; 35(2): 283-290. Subject: 8.4

Tauber, Alfred I. A philosophical approach to rationing. *Medical Journal of Australia* 2003 May 5; 178(9): 454-456. Subject: 9.4

Tauer, Carol A. Obstetrics and pediatrics: the second article in a series about the significance of genetic science for Catholic health care — an ethical view. *Health Progress* 2005 July-August; 86(4): 13-18. Subject: 15.1

Tauer, Carol A. When pregnant patients refuse interventions. *AWHONN's Clinical Issues in Perinatal and Women's Health Nursing* 1993; 4(4): 596-605. Subject: 9.5.5

Taupitz, Jochen. Nationale Modelle zur Regelung des Gebrauchs der Gendiagnostik. Deutschland: Wie regeln wir den Gebrauch der Gendiagnostik? *In:* Honnefelder, Ludger; Mieth, Dietmar; Propping, Peter; Siep, Ludwig; Wiesemann, Claudia, eds. Das genetische Wissen und die Zukunft des Menschen. New York: De Gruyter; 2003: 244-274. Subject: 15.3

Taupitz, Jochen; Brewe, Manuela. Der Status des Embryos im Rechtsvergleich. *In:* Maio, Giovanni; Just, Hanjörg, eds. Die Forschung an embryonalen Stammzellen in ethischer und rechtlicher Perspektive. Baden-Baden: Nomos Verlagsgesellschaft; 2003: 85-96. Subject: 18.5.4

Taussig, Karen-Sue. Bovine abominations: genetic culture and politics in the Netherlands. *Cultural Anthropology* 2004 August; 19(3): 305-336. Subject: 22.2

Taussig, Karen-Sue. Genetics and genetic engineering. *In:* Restivo, Sal, ed. Science, Technology, and Society: An Encyclopedia. New York: Oxford University Press; 2005: 156-162. Subject: 15.1

Tavcar, Rok; Dernovsek, Mojca Z.; Grubic, Virginija Novak. Use of coercive measures in a psychiatric intensive care unit in Slovenia [letter]. *Psychiatric Services* 2005 April; 56(4): 491-492. Subject: 17.7

Taylor, Bettina; Burns, Derrick. Can medical scheme reform lead to fairer distribution of limited resources? A funding perspective. *South African Medical Journal* 2005 March; 95(3): 175-179. Subject: 9.4

Taylor, Brigit R.; McCann, Robert M. Controlled sedation for physical and existential suffering? *Journal of Palliative Medicine* 2005 February; 8(1): 144-147. Subject: 20.5.1

Taylor, Carol. Dilemas en el tratamiento al inicio de la vida / Dilemmas in beginning-of-life treatment. *Vida y Etica* 2003 December; 4(2): 45-52. Subject: 9.5.7

Taylor, Craig J.; Bolton, Eleanor M.; Pocock, Susan; Sharples, Linda D.; Pedersen, Roger A.; Bradley, J. Andrew. Banking on human embryonic stem cells: estimating the number of donor cell lines needed for HLA matching. *Lancet* 2005 December 10-16; 366(9502): 2019-2025. Subject: 18.5.4

Taylor, Elizabeth Johnston; Mamier, Iris. Spiritual care nursing: what cancer patients and family caregivers want. *Journal of Advanced Nursing* 2005 February; 49(3): 260-267. Subject: 9.5.1

Taylor, Eric. To the editor [letter]. *American Journal of Bioethics [Online]* 2005 May-June; 5(3): W17. Subject: 17.4

Taylor, G.J.; Wainwright, P. Open label extension studies: research or marketing? *BMJ: British Medical Journal* 2005 September 10; 331(7516): 572-574. Subject: 18.2

Taylor, Graham P.; Pennings, Guido. Ethics of assisted reproduction for HIV concordant couples [letter and reply]. *Human Reproduction* 2005 May; 20(5): 1430-1431. Subject: 14.1

Taylor, J. Blinkered objections to bioethics: a response to Benatar. *Journal of Medical Ethics* 2005 March; 31(3): 179-180. Subject: 19.5

Taylor, James Stacey. Autonomy and informed consent on the Navajo Reservation. *Journal of Social Philosophy* 2004 Winter; 35(4): 506-516. Subject: 20.5.4

Taylor, James Stacey. Why not a kidney market? An obvious solution to the organ shortage. *Free Inquiry* 2005 August-September; 25(5): 42-43. Subject: 19.3

Taylor, Jennifer R. Mixing the gene pool and the labor pool: protecting workers from genetic discrimination in employment. *Temple Environmental Law and Technology Journal* 2001 Fall; 20(1): 51-72. Subject: 15.3

Taylor, M.J. Problems of practice and principle if centring law reform on the concept of genetic discrimination. *European Journal of Health Law* 2004 December; 11(4): 365-380. Subject: 15.1

Taylor, Patrick L. The gap between law and ethics in human embryonic stem cell research: overcoming the effect of U.S. federal policy on research advances and public benefit. *Science and Engineering Ethics* 2005 October; 11(4): 589-616. Subject: 18.5.4

Taylor, Robert M. Is terminal sedation really euthanasia? *Medical Ethics Newsletter [Lahey Clinic]* 2003 Winter; 10(1): 3, 8. Subject: 20.4.1

Taylor, Rodney J.; Chiu, Alexander G.; Palmer, James N.; Schofield, Kim; O'Malley, Bert W., Jr.; Wolf, Jeffrey S. Informed consent in sinus surgery: link between demographics and patient desires. *Laryngoscope* 2005 May; 115(5): 826-831. Subject: 8.3.1

Taylor, Rosie; Giles, Jim. Cash interests taint drug advice [news]. *Nature* 2005 October 20; 437(7062): 1070-1071. Subject: 9.7

Taylor, Sandra. Gender differences in attitudes among those at risk for Huntington's disease. *Genetic Testing* 2005 Summer; 9(2): 152-157. Subject: 15.3

Taylor, Sandy. A case study of genetic discrimination: social work and advocacy within a new context. *Australian Social Work* 1998 December; 51(4): 51-57. Subject: 15.1

te Braake, Trees A.M. Does a fetus have a right to life? The case of Vo v. France. *European Journal of Health Law* 2004 December; 11(4): 381-389. Subject: 4.4

te Braake, Trees A.M. The Dutch 2002 Embryos Act and the Convention on Human Rights and Biomedicine: some issues. *European Journal of Health Law* 2004 June; 11(2): 139-151. Subject: 18.4

Telman, D.A. Jeremy. Abortion and women's legal personhood in Germany: a contribution to the feminist theory of the state. *New York University Review of Law and Social Change* 1998; 24(1): 91-148. Subject: 12.4.2

Teman, Elly. 'Knowing' the surrogate body in Israel. *In:* Cook, Rachel; Sclater, Shelley Day; Kaganas, Felicity, eds. Surrogate Motherhood: International Perspectives. Portland, OR: Hart; 2003: 261-279. Subject: 14.2

Teman, Elly. The medicalization of "nature" in the "artificial body": surrogate motherhood in Israel. *Medical Anthropology Quarterly* 2003 March; 17(1): 78-98. Subject: 14.2

Templeton, Alan R. When does life begin?: An evolutionary genetic answer to a central ethical question. *In:* Blazer, Shraga; Zimmer, Etan Z., eds. The Embryo: Scientific Discovery and Medical Ethics. New York: Karger; 2005: 1-20. Subject: 15.1

ten Have, Henk A.M.J. End-of-life decision making in the Netherlands. *In:* Blank, Robert H.; Merrick, Janna C., eds. End-of-Life Decision Making: A Cross-National Study. Cambridge, MA: MIT Press; 2005: 147-168. Subject: 20.5.1

ten Have, Henk A.M.J. Horror regulationum. *Hastings Center Report* 2004 July-August; 34(4): 16-17. Subject: 14.1

ten Have, Henk A.M.J.; Borovecki, Ana; Oreškovic, Stjepan. Master programme "Health, human rights and ethics": a curriculum development experience at Andrija Stampar School of Public Health, medical school, University of Zagreb. *Medicine, Health Care and Philosophy: A European Journal* 2005; 8(3): 371-376. Subject: 2.3

ter Heerdt, J. Ethics and medical liability: a minefield for physicians? *Acta Clinica Belgica* 2002 June-July; 57(3): 117-125. Subject: 8.5

ter Meulen, Ruud H.J. Towards a social concept of the person. *In:* Thomasma, David C.; Weisstub, David N.; Herve, Christian eds. Personhood and Health Care. Boston: Kluwer Academic Pub.; 2001: 129-135. Subject: 4.4

Tereskerz, Patricia M.; Moreno, Jonathan. Ten steps to developing a national agenda to address financial conflicts of interest in industry sponsored clinical research. *Accountability in Research* 2005 April-June; 12(2): 139-155. Subject: 1.3.9

Terry, Louise M.; Campbell, Anne. Protecting the interests of the child bone marrow donor. *Medicine and Law: World Association for Medical Law* 2004; 23(4): 805-819. Subject: 19.5

Terry, Nicholas P. Prescriptions sans frontieres (or how I stopped worrying about Viagra on the web but grew concerned about the future of health care delivery. *Yale Journal of Health Policy, Law, and Ethics* 2004 Summer; 4(2): 183-272. Subject: 9.7

Terry, Patrick F. PXE International: harnessing intellectual property law for benefit-sharing. *In:* Knoppers, Bartha Maria, ed. Populations and Genetics: Legal and Socio-Ethical Perspectives. Boston: Martinus Nijhoff; 2003: 377-393. Subject: 15.8

Tervo, Raymond C.; Palmer, Glen; Redinius, Pat. Health professional student attitudes towards people with disability. *Clinical Rehabilitation* 2004 December; 18(8): 908-915. Subject: 7.2

Testa, Giuseppe; Harris, John. Ethics and synthetic gametes. *Bioethics* 2005 April; 19(2): 146-166. Subject: 14.5

Testart, Jacques; Sele, Bernard. Towards an efficient medical eugenics: is the desirable always the feasible? *Human Reproduction* 1995 December; 10(12): 3086-3090. Subject: 15.5

Tettamanti, Massimo; Tralamazza, Sara; Berati, Marina; Molteni, Max; Gamba, Natascia. Human research tissue banks: the ATRA Project for establishing a human research tissue bank in Switzerland. *ATLA: Alternatives to Laboratory Animals* 2005 February; 33(1): 29-36. Subject: 19.5

Texas Partnership for End-of-Life Care [TxPEC]. Directive to Physicians and Family or Surrogates (Living Will). Austin, TX: Texas Department of State Health Services undated; 4 p. [Online]. Available: http://www.txpec.org/docs/DirtoPhysFamilySurrogates.doc [25 May 2005]. Subject: 20.5.4

Texas Partnership for End-Of-Life Care [TxPEC]. Medical Power of Attorney. Austin, TX: Texas Partnership for End-Of-Life Care undated; 6 p. [Online]. Available: http://www.txpec.org/docs/MedicalPowerofAttorney.doc [25 May 2005]. Subject: 20.5.4

Thabane, Lehana; Childs, Aaron; Lafontaine, Amanda. Determining the level of statistician participation on Canadian-based research ethics boards. *IRB: Ethics and Human Research* 2005 March-April; 27(2): 11-14. Subject: 18.2

Tharien, A.K. Human values in genetics and embryo experiments. *Issues in Medical Ethics* 1997 April-June; 5(2): 46-47. Subject: 15.10

Tharyan, Prathap. Audits of electroconvulsive therapy [letter]. *Issues in Medical Ethics* 2003 July-September; 11(3): 99-100. Subject: 17.5

Thawani, Vijay. The doctor-doctor relationship: professional criticism. *Issues in Medical Ethics* 2000 July-September; 8(3): 82-83. Subject: 7.3

Thawani, Vijay. Drug samples are meant for advertising [opinion]. *Issues in Medical Ethics* 2001 July-September; 9(3): 91. Subject: 9.7

Then, Shih-Ning. Stem cell technologies: regulation, patents and problems. *Journal of Law and Medicine* 2004 November; 12(2): 188-204. Subject: 18.5.4

Thomas, C. The use and control of heel prick blood samples. *Medicine and Law: World Association for Medical Law* 2005 June; 24(2): 259-277. Subject: 18.3

Thomas, Carol. Doctors for Life abortion on demand survey [letter]. *South African Medical Journal* 1996 December; 86(12): 1561-1562. Subject: 1.3.7

Thomas, D. Laboratory animals and the art of empathy. *Journal of Medical Ethics* 2005 April; 31(4): 197-202. Subject: 22.2

Thomas, David. The Ethics of Research Involving Animals: a review of the Nuffield Council on Bioethics Report from an antivivisectionist perspective. *ATLA: Alternatives to Laboratory Animals* 2005 December; 33(6): 663-667. Subject: 22.2

Thomas, David L. Bioethics and corrections: an experiment in bioethics in the Florida Department of Corrections. *Corrections Today* 2003 October; 4 p. [Online]. Available: http://www.aca.org/publications/ctarchivespdf/october03/thomas.pd f [25 May 2005]. Subject: 2.4

Thomas, George. Practicing medicine in India: some ethical dilemmas. *Indian Journal of Medical Ethics* 2005 July-September; 2(3): 88. Subject: 9.1

Thomas, James C. Skills for the ethical practice of public health. *Journal of Public Health Management and Practice* 2005 May-June; 11(3): 260-261. Subject: 6

Thomas, James C. Teaching ethics in schools of public health. *Public Health Reports* 2003 May-June; 118(3): 279-286. Subject: 7.2

Thomas, James C.; Irwin, Debra E.; Zuiker, Erin Shaugnessy; Millikan, Robert C. Genomics and the public health code of ethics. *American Journal of Public Health* 2005 December; 95(12): 2139-2143. Subject: 15.1

Thomas, James; Williams, A. Susan. Women and abortion in 1930s Britain: a survey and its data. *Social History of Medicine* 1998 August; 11(2): 283-309. Subject: 12.5.2

Thomas, Joe. Essential AIDS medications in India. *Issues in Medical Ethics* 2000 April-June; 8(2): 62. Subject: 9.5.6

Thomas, Joe. HIV and confidentiality in India. *Issues in Medical Ethics* 1998 July-September; 6(3): 87. Subject: 9.5.6

Thomas, Joe. Unmet ethical concerns of the proposed preventive HIV vaccine trials in India. *Indian Journal of Medical Ethics* 2004 July-September; 1(3): 87-88. Subject: 9.5.6

Thomas, Karen A. Safety: when infants and parents are research subjects. *Journal of Perinatal and Neonatal Nursing* 2005 January-March; 19(1): 52-58. Subject: 18.5.2

Thomas, Sandy. Paradoxes and political problems: the U.S. approach to ART as seen from the UK. *Hastings Center Report* 2004 July-August; 34(4): 15-16. Subject: 14.1

Thomas, Sandy M. Society and ethics — the genetics of disease. *Current Opinion in Genetics and Development* 2004 June; 14(3): 287-291. Subject: 15.1

Thombs, J.; Borthwick, N.J.; Hungerford, J.L.; Cree, I.A. Recruiting donors for autopsy based cancer research. *Journal of Medical Ethics* 2005 June; 31(6): 360-361. Subject: 18.5.7

Thompson, Dennis F. Conflicts of interest in medicine. *In his:* Restoring Responsibility: Essays on Ethics in Government, Business, and Healthcare. New York: Cambridge University Press; 2005: 290-299. Subject: 1.3.9

Thompson, Dennis F. Hospital ethics. *In his:* Restoring Responsibility: Essays on Ethics in Government, Business, and Healthcare. New York: Cambridge University Press; 2005: 278-289. Subject: 9.1

Thompson, Ian M. Informed consent for prostate cancer screening — a call for equity in medical interventions [editorial]. *Urology* 2003 January; 61(1): 15-16. Subject: 8.3.1

Thompson, Richard E. Misbehaving physicians and professional ethics. *Physician Executive* 2004 September-October; 30(5): 32-34. Subject: 7.4

Thomson, Alan B.R. Perhaps the time has come [editorial]. *Canadian Journal of Gastroenterology* 2003 October; 17(10): 613-615. Subject: 7.3

Thomson, Colin. Medical research and participants with disabilities. *Monash Bioethics Review* 2005 October; 24(4): 56-63. Subject: 18.3

Thomson, Judith. Legal and ethical problems of human cloning. *Journal of Law and Medicine* 2000 August; 8(1): 31-43. Subject: 14.5

Thorne, Sally E.; Robinson, Carol A. Reciprocal trust in health care relationships. *Journal of Advanced Nursing* 1988 November; 13(6): 782-789. Subject: 8.1

Thorp, John M., Jr.; Hartmann, Katherine E.; Shadigan, Elizabeth. Long-term physical and psychological health consequences of induced abortion: a review of the evidence. *Linacre Quarterly* 2005 February; 72(1): 44-69. Subject: 12.5.2

Subject = NRCBL Primary Classification Number; See inside front cover

Thorsteinsdottir, Halla; Daar, Abdallah S.; Smith, Richard D.; Singer, Peter A. Do patents encourage or inhibit genomics as a global public good? *In:* Knoppers, Bartha Maria, ed. Populations and Genetics: Legal and Socio-Ethical Perspectives. Boston: Martinus Nijhoff, 2003: 487-504. Subject: 15.8

Thurston, George D. Mandating the release of health research data: issues and implications. *Tulane Environmental Law Journal* 1998 Summer; 11(2): 331-354. Subject: 18.6

Thurston, Wilfreda E.; MacKean, Gail; Vollman, Ardene; Casebeer, Ann; Weber, Myron; Maloff, Bretta; Bader, Judy. Public participation in regional health policy: a theoretical framework. *Health Policy* 2005 September 8; 73(3): 237-252. Subject: 9.1

Tierney, William M.; Gerrity, Martha S. Scientific discourse, corporate ghostwriting, journal policy, and public trust [editorial]. *JGIM: Journal of General Internal Medicine* 2005 June; 20(6): 550-551. Subject: 1.3.7

Tilden, Samuel J. Ethical and legal aspects of using an identical twin as a skin transplant donor for a severely burned minor. *American Journal of Law and Medicine* 2005; 31(1): 87-116. Subject: 8.3.2

Tilden, Virginia P.; Tolle, Susan W.; Nelson, Christine A.; Fields, Jonathan. Family decision-making to withdraw life-sustaining treatments from hospitalized patients. *Nursing Research* 2001 March-April; 50(2): 105-115. Subject: 20.5.1

Tillett, Jackie. Should elective cesarean birth be an accepted option for women? *Journal of Perinatal and Neonatal Nursing* 2005 January-March; 19(1): 4-6. Subject: 9.5.5

Tilton, Susan Hanley. Right to privacy and confidentiality of medical records. *Occupational Medicine* 1996 January-March; 11(1): 17-29. Subject: 8.4

Tindall, Gillian. Mixed blessings: ethical issues in assisted conception. *Journal of the Royal Society of Medicine* 2003 January; 96(1): 34-35. Subject: 14.1

Tipene-Matua, Bevan; Dawson, John. The Treaty of Waitangi and research. *In:* Dawson, John; Peart, Nicola, eds. The Law of Research: A Guide. Dunedin, NZ: University of Otago Press; 2003: 61-79. Subject: 18.2

Tischauser, Leslie V.; Ness, Bryan D. Patents on life-forms. *In:* Ness, Bryan D., ed. Encyclopedia of Genetics. Revised edition. Volume II. Pasadena, Calif.: Salem Press; 2004: 594-596. Subject: 15.8

Tischenko, Pavel. Russian Federation. *Medical Ethics and Bioethics / Medicinska Etika & Bioetika* 2005; 11(Supplement): 18-19. Subject: 9.6

Tobin, Bernadette. Australian consequentialism: an Australian critique. *Theoretical Medicine and Bioethics* 2005; 26(3): 165-173. Subject: 2.1

Tobin, J. The challenges and ethical dilemmas of a military medical officer serving with a peacekeeping operation in regard to the medical care of the local population. *Journal of Medical Ethics* 2005 October; 31(10): 571-574. Subject: 21.2

Toiviainen, Leila. Can practical nursing ethics be taught? [editorial]. *Nursing Ethics* 2005 July; 12(4): 335-336. Subject: 4.1.3

Toldson, Ivory Lee; Toldson, Ivory Achebe. Biomedical ethics: an African-centered psychological perspective. *Journal of Black Psychology* 2001 November; 27(4): 401-423. Subject: 9.5.4

Tolich, Martin; Baldwin, Kate Mary. Informing consent in New Zealand research: researchers' conflict of interest and patient vulnerability. *New Zealand Medical Journal* 2005 February 25; 118(1210); 8 p. Subject: 18.3

Tolich, Martin; Baldwin, Kate Mary. Unequal protection for patient rights: the divide between university and health ethics committees. *Journal of Bioethical Inquiry* 2005; 2(1): 34-40. Subject: 8.1

Tollefsen, Christopher; Boyle, Joseph. Roman Catholic bioethics. *In:* Peppin, John F.; Cherry, Mark J., eds. Religious Perspectives in Bioethics. New York: Taylor & Francis; 2004: 1-20. Subject: 2.1

Tolloczko, Tadeusz. Surgical patents and patients — the ethical dilemmas. *Science and Engineering Ethics* 2005 January; 11(1): 61-69. Subject: 5.3

Tolson, Jay. Wrestling with the final call: when it comes to end-of-life decisions, taking an ethical path isn't always easy. *U.S. News and World Report* 2005 April 4; 138(12): 22-23. Subject: 20.5.1

Tonelli, Mark R. Waking the dying: must we always attempt to involve critically ill patients in end-of-life decisions? *Chest* 2005 February; 127(2): 637-642. Subject: 20.5.1

Toner, Robin; Hulse, Carl. Congress ready to approve bill in Schiavo case: look to federal courts; family's battle is forcing the public to confront end-of-life issues. *New York Times* 2005 March 20; p. A1, A19. Subject: 20.5.1

Toner, Robin; Liptak, Adam. In new court, Roe may stand, so foes look to limit its scope. *New York Times* 2005 July 10; p. A1, A16. Subject: 12.4.1

Tong, Elisa K.; England, Lucinda; Glantz, Stanton A. Changing conclusions on secondhand smoke in a sudden infant death syndrome review funded by the tobacco industry. *Pediatrics* 2005 March; 115(3): e356-e366. Subject: 1.3.9

Tonti-Filippini, Nicholas. Some refusals of medical treatment which changed the law of Victoria. *Medical Journal of Australia* 1992 August 17; 157(4): 277-279. Subject: 20.5.1

Tooley, Michael. In defense of voluntary active euthanasia and assisted suicide. *In:* Cohen, Andrew I.; Wellman,

Christopher Heath, eds. Contemporary Debates in Applied Ethics. Malden, MA: Blackwell Pub., 2005: 161-178. Subject: 20.5.1

Toombs, S.K. 'Is she experiencing any pain?': disability and the physician-patient relationship. *Internal Medicine Journal* 2004 November; 34(11): 645-647. Subject: 8.1

Töpfer, F.; Wiesing, U. The medical theory of Richard Koch I: theory of science and ethics. *Medicine, Health Care and Philosophy: A European Journal* 2005; 8(2): 207-219. Subject: 4.1.2

Topol, Eric J. Nesiritide — not verified [opinion]. *New England Journal of Medicine* 2005 July 14; 353(2): 113-116. Subject: 9.7

Topol, Eric J.; Blumenthal, David. Physicians and the investment industry. *JAMA: The Journal of the American Medical Association* 2005 June 1; 293(21): 2654-2657. Subject: 7.3

Torda, Adrienne. In that case. Response [case study]. *Journal of Bioethical Inquiry* 2005; 2(1): 54-55. Subject: 16.3

Torjuul, Kirsti; Nordam, Ann; Sørlie, Venke. Action ethical dilemmas in surgery: an interview study of practicing surgeons. *BMC Medical Ethics [electronic]* 2005; 6(7); 9 p. Available: http://www.biomedcentral.com/bmcmedethics/. Subject: 2.1

Torpy, Janet M. Randomized controlled trials. *JAMA: The Journal of the American Medical Association* 2005 November 2; 294(17): 2262. Subject: 18.3

Torreão, Lara de Araújo; Pereira, Crésio Romeu; Troster, Eduardo. Ethical aspects in the management of the terminally ill patient in the pediatric intensive care unit. *Revista do Hospital das Clinicas* 2004 January; 59(1): 3-9. Subject: 20.4.2

Torzilli, Paolo. Reconciling the sanctity of human life, the Declaration of Independence and the Constitution. *Catholic Lawyer* 2000-2001; 40(2): 197-226. Subject: 12.4.1

Touitou, Yvan; Portaluppi, Francesco; Smolensky, Michael H.; Rensing, Ludger. Ethical principles and standards for the conduct of human and animal biological rhythm research. *Chronobiology International* 2004 January; 21(1): 161-170. Subject: 18.2

Toumbourou, John W.; Evans-Whipp, Tracy; Clements, Jackie; McMorris, Barbara J.; Mathers, Megan; Catalano, Richard F. Ethical guidelines for the payment of research participants should be clarified: reflections from cross-national research. *Australian and New Zealand Journal of Public Health* 2004; 28(6): 584-585. Subject: 18.2

Tovino, Stacey A. Currents in contemporary ethics: the confidentiality and privacy implications of functional magnetic resonance imaging. *Journal of Law, Medicine and Ethics* 2005 Winter; 33(4): 844-850. Subject: 8.4

Tovino, Stacey A. The use and disclosure of protected health information for research under the HIPAA privacy rule: unrealized patient autonomy and burdensome government regulation. *South Dakota Law Review* 2004; 49(3): 447-502. Subject: 8.4

Towers, Anna; MacDonald, Neil; Wallace, Ellen. Ethical issues in palliative care: views of patients, families, and nonphysician staff. *Canadian Family Physician* 2003 December; 49: 1626-1631. Subject: 20.4.1

Trachtman, Howard. Does Uncle Sam really want you?: a response to "Rethinking Research Ethics" by Rosamond Rhodes (AJOB 5:1). *American Journal of Bioethics [Online]* 2005 January-February; 5(1): W22-W23. Subject: 18.2

Trachtman, Howard. Is the middle ground vanishing? *American Journal of Bioethics* 2005 November-December; 5(6): 68-70. Subject: 4.4

Trachtman, Howard. A man is a man is a man [comment]. *American Journal of Bioethics* 2005 May-June; 5(3): 31-33. Subject: 4.5

Tracy, Paul E.; Morgan, Vincent. Big brother and his science kit: DNA databases for 21st century crime control? *Journal of Criminal Law and Criminology* 2000 Winter; 90(2): 635-690. Subject: 15.1

Trahan, Jennifer. Constitutional law: parental denial of a child's medical treatment for religious reasons. *Annual Survey of American Law* 1989; 1989(1): 307-341. Subject: 8.3.2

Tranberg, H.A.; Rous, B.A.; Rashbass, J. Legal and ethical issues in the use of anonymous images in pathology teaching and research. *Histopathology* 2003 February; 42(2): 104-109. Subject: 8.3.1

Trapp, Mark. Created equal: how the Declaration of Independence recognizes and guarantees the right to life for the unborn. *Pepperdine Law Review* 2001; 28(4): 819-847. Subject: 4.4

Travis, Sara; Mason, Jill; Mallett, Jane; Laverty, Diane. Guidelines in respect of advance directives: the position in England. *International Journal of Palliative Nursing* 2001 October; 7(10): 493-500. Subject: 20.5.4

Treloar, Susan; Taylor, Sandra; Otlowski, Margaret; Barlow-Stewart, Kristine; Stranger, Mark; Chenoweth, Kellie. Methodological considerations in the study of genetic discrimination. *Community Genetics* 2005 January; 7(4): 161-168. Subject: 15.1

Trent, Ronald J.A. Oversight and monitoring of clinical research with gene therapy in Australia [editorial]. *Medical Journal of Australia* 2005 May 2; 182(9): 441-442. Subject: 15.4

Treschan, Tanja A.; Scheck, Thomas; Kober, Alexander; Fleischmann, Edith; Birkenberg, Beatrice; Petschnigg, Brigitte; Akça, Ozan; Lackner, Franz X.; Jandl-Jager, Elisabeth; Sessler, Daniel I. The influence of protocol pain and risk on patients' willingness to consent for clinical studies: a randomized trial. *Anesthesia and Analgesia* 2003 February; 96(2): 498-506. Subject: 18.5.1

Trevizan, Maria Auxiliadora; Mendes, Isabel Amélia Costa; Lourenço, Maria Regina; de Godoy, Simone; Rodriguez, Eliana Llapa. Spirituality: the basis for nurses' ethics. *Medicine and Law: World Association for Medical Law* 2004; 23(4): 791-796. Subject: 4.1.3

Trew, Andrew. Regulating life and death: the modification and commodification of nature. *University of Toledo Law Review* 1998 Winter; 29(2): 271-326. Subject: 5.3

Triggle, David J. Everybody must get cloned: ideological objections do not hold up. *Free Inquiry* 2002-2003 Winter; 23(1): 32-33. Subject: 14.5

Trivedi, Amal N.; Zaslavsky, Alan M.; Schneider, Eric C.; Ayanian, John Z. Trends in the quality of care and racial disparities in Medicare managed care. *New England Journal of Medicine* 2005 August 18; 353(7): 692- 700. Subject: 9.8

Trivedi, Amar D. Rethinking adolescent assent: a triangular approach [comment]. *American Journal of Bioethics* 2005 September-October; 5(5): 75-76. Subject: 18.5.2

Trotter, Griffin. Bioethics, Christian charity and the view from no place. *Christian Bioethics* 2005 December; 11(3): 317-331. Subject: 2.1

Trotter, Griffin. Of lotteries lost and partnerships forged: the perils and promises of patient ethics [editorial]. *CQ: Cambridge Quarterly of Healthcare Ethics* 2005 Spring; 14(2): 131-139. Subject: 8.1

Trotter, Griffin. What jurisdiction? Whose justice? A response to Eckenwiler. *CQ: Cambridge Quarterly of Healthcare Ethics* 2005 Summer; 14(3): 316-321. Subject: 21.3

Trounson, Alan O. Cloning: potential benefits for human medicine [editorial]. *Medical Journal of Australia* 1997 December 1-15; 167(11-12): 568-569. Subject: 14.5

Trower, Peter. On the ethical basis of 'scientific' behaviour therapy. *In:* Fairbairn, Susan; Fairbairn, Gavin, eds. Psychology, Ethics and Change. New York: Routledge & Kegan Paul; 1987: 74-90. Subject: 17.3

Trujillo, Alfonso López. Clonacion: perdida de la paternidad y negacion de la familia / Cloning: loss of paternity and negation of the family. *Vida y Etica* 2003 December; 4(2): 119-139. Subject: 14.5

Trump, Eric F. Identity crisis. *Hastings Center Report* 2004 July-August; 34(4): 2. Subject: 15.1

Truog, Robert D. Are organs personal property or a societal resource? *American Journal of Bioethics* 2005 July-August; 5(4): 14-16. Subject: 19.6

Truog, Robert D. The ethics of organ donation by living donors [opinion]. *New England Journal of Medicine* 2005 August 4; 353(5): 444-446. Subject: 19.5

Truog, Robert D. Informed consent: an end or a means? A response to Miller and Moreno. *Journal of Clinical Ethics* 2005 Winter; 16(4): 365-368. Subject: 18.3

Truog, Robert D. Organ donation without brain death? *Hastings Center Report* 2005 November-December; 35(6): 3. Subject: 19.5

Truog, Robert D.; Cochrane, Thomas I. Refusal of hydration and nutrition: irrelevance of the "artificial" vs "natural" distinction. *Archives of Internal Medicine* 2005 December 12-26; 165(22): 2574-2576. Subject: 20.5.1

Truog, Robert D.; Lowney, Jeremiah; Hanto, Douglas; Caplan, Arthur; Brock, Dan. Soliciting organs on the Internet [forum]. *Medical Ethics Newsletter [Lahey Clinic]* 2005 Fall; 12(3): 5-8. Subject: 19.5

Truog, Robert D.; Waisel, David B.; Burns, Jeffrey P. Do-not-resuscitate orders in the surgical setting [opinion]. *Lancet* 2005 February 26-March 4; 365(9461): 733-735. Subject: 20.5.1

Tsafrir, Avi; Shufaro, Yoel; Simon, Alex; Laufer, Neri. Preimplantation genetic diagnosis. *In:* Blazer, Shraga; Zimmer, Etan Z., eds. The Embryo: Scientific Discovery and Medical Ethics. New York: Karger; 2005: 166-201. Subject: 15.2

Tsai, D.F.-C. The bioethical principles and Confucius' moral philosophy. *Journal of Medical Ethics* 2005 March; 31(3): 159-163. Subject: 2.1

Tsai, D.F.-C. Human embryonic stem cell research debates: a Confucian argument. *Journal of Medical Ethics* 2005 November; 31(11): 635-640. Subject: 18.5.4

Tucker, Kathryn L. The chicken and the egg: the pursuit of choice for a human hastened-death as a catalyst for improved end-of-life care; improved end-of-life care as a precondition for legalization of assisted dying. *New York University Annual Survey of American Law* 2004; 60(2): 355-378. Subject: 20.4.1

Tuech, J.J.; Pessaux, P.; Moutel, G.; Thoma, V.; Schraub, S.; Herve, C. Methodological quality and reporting of ethical requirements in phase III cancer trials. *Journal of Medical Ethics* 2005 May; 31(5): 251-255. Subject: 18.2

Tully, Paul. Dollywood is not just a theme park in Tennessee anymore: unwarranted prohibitory human cloning legislation and policy guidelines for a regulatory approach to cloning. *John Marshall Law Review* 1998 Summer; 31(4): 1385-1422. Subject: 14.5

Tulsky, James A. Beyond advance directives: importance of communication skills at the end of life. *JAMA: The Journal of the American Medical Association* 2005 July 20; 294(3): 359-365. Subject: 20.5.4

Tuohimäki, C.; Kaltiala-Heino, R.; Korkeila, J.; Tuori, T.; Lehtinen, V.; Joukamaa, M. The use of harmful to others-criterion for involuntary treatment in Finland. *Eu-*

ropean Journal of Health Law 2003 June; 10(2): 183-199. Subject: 17.7

Tuorto, Scott; Chan, Mei-Ki; Adusumilli, Prasad S. Drug companies, doctors and disclosures [letter]. *National Medical Journal of India* 2004 July-August; 17(4): 215-216. Subject: 9.7

Tur, Richard H.S. The doctor's defense. *Mount Sinai Journal of Medicine* 2002 October; 69(5): 317-328. Subject: 20.5.1

Tur, Richard H.S. Legislative technique and human rights: the sad case of assisted suicide. *Criminal Law Review* 2003 January: 3-12. Subject: 20.7

Turkoski, Beatrice B. When a child's treatment decisions conflict with the parents'. *Home Healthcare Nurse* 2005 February; 23(2): 123-126. Subject: 8.3.2

Turkoski, Beatrice B. When patients won't share the prognosis with family. *Home Healthcare Nurse* 2004 August; 22(8): 566-568. Subject: 8.4

Turner, Dwayne C. Safer laws?: problematic civil/criminal liability and curbing New York's HIV/AIDS epidemic. *Quinnipac Health Law Journal* 2003; 6(2): 173-192. Subject: 9.5.6

Turner, Leigh. Bioethics, social class, and the sociological imagination. *CQ: Cambridge Quarterly of Healthcare Ethics* 2005 Fall; 14(4): 374-378. Subject: 2.1

Turner, Leigh. Biotechnology, bioethics and anti-aging interventions [opinion]. *Trends in Biotechnology* 2004 May; 22(5): 219-221. Subject: 4.5

Turner, Leigh. From the local to the global: bioethics and the concept of culture. *Journal of Medicine and Philosophy* 2005 June; 30(3): 305-320. Subject: 2.1

Turney, Lyn. The incidental discovery of nonpaternity through genetic carrier screening: an exploration of lay attitudes. *Qualitative Health Research* 2005 May; 15(5): 620-634. Subject: 15.3

Turnpenny, Lee. Embryo's moral status is unaffected by alteration [letter]. *Nature* 2005 September 1; 437(7055): 26. Subject: 18.5.4

Turone, Fabio. Italians fail to overturn restrictive reproduction law [news]. *BMJ: British Medical Journal* 2005 June 18; 330(7505): 1405. Subject: 14.1

Tutton, Richard. Person, property and gift: exploring languages of tissue donation to biomedical research. *In:* Tutton, Richard; Corrigan, Oonagh, eds. Genetic Databases: Socio-ethical Issues in the Collection and Use of DNA. New York: Routledge; 2004: 19-38. Subject: 19.5

Tutton, Richard; Kaye, Jane; Hoeyer, Klaus. Governing UK Biobank: the importance of ensuring public trust [opinion]. *Trends in Biotechnology* 2004 June; 22(6): 284-285. Subject: 15.1

Twine, Richard. Constructing critical bioethics by deconstructing culture/nature dualism. *Medicine, Health*

Care and Philosophy: A European Journal 2005; 8(3): 285-295. Subject: 2.1

Twisselmann, Birte. Time to legalise assisted suicide? Summary of responses [letter]. *BMJ: British Medical Journal* 2005 October 8; 331(7520): 843. Subject: 20.5.1

Twomey, John G., Jr. The ethics of clinical research with children with HIV infection. *Virginia Nurse* 1989 Summer; 57(3): 38-40, 42-43. Subject: 18.5.2

Tylim, Isaac. Ethical notes on disrupted frames and violated boundaries. *Psychoanalytic Psychology* 2004 Fall; 21(4): 609-613. Subject: 17.2

Tynan, Anne. Time to legalise assisted dying? Recruiting more vulnerable doctors may be the answer [letter]. *BMJ: British Medical Journal* 2005 October 8; 331(7520): 842. Subject: 20.5.1

Tyreman, Stephen. An expert in what?: the need to clarify meaning and expectations in "The Expert Patient". *Medicine, Health Care and Philosophy: A European Journal* 2005; 8(2): 153-157. Subject: 4.2

Tyreman, Stephen. The expert patient: outline of UK government paper. *Medicine, Health Care and Philosophy: A European Journal* 2005; 8(2): 149-151. Subject: 4.2

U

Ubel, P.A.; Loewenstein, G. The role of decision analysis in informed consent: choosing between intuition and systematicity. *Social Science and Medicine* 1997; 44(5): 647-656. Subject: 8.3.1

Ubel, Peter A. Commentary: how did we get into this mess? *In:* Moore, Don A.; Cain, Daylian M.; Loewenstein, George; Bazerman, Max H., eds. Conflicts of Interest: Challenges and Solutions in Business, Law, Medicine, and Public Policy. New York: Cambridge University Press; 2005: 142-151. Subject: 9.7

Udwadia, F.E. Ethical problems in medical education. *Issues in Medical Ethics* 1997 April-June; 5(2): 37-39. Subject: 7.2

Ulmer, Jeffrey B.; Liu, Margaret A. Ethical issues for vaccines and immunization [opinion]. *Nature Reviews Immunology* 2002 April; 2(4): 291-296. Subject: 9.7

Ulrich, Connie M.; Soeken, Karen L. A path analytic model of ethical conflict in practice and autonomy in a sample of nurse practitioners. *Nursing Ethics* 2005 May; 12(3): 305-316. Subject: 4.1.3

Ulrich, Connie M.; Wallen, Gwenyth R.; Feister, Autumn; Grady, Christine. Respondent burden in clinical research: when are we asking too much of subjects? [case study]. *IRB: Ethics and Human Research* 2005 July-August; 27(4): 17-20. Subject: 18.5.1

Ulrich, Connie M.; Wallen, Gwenyth R.; Grady, Christine. Research vulnerability and patient advocacy: balance-seeking perspectives for the clinical nurse scientist?

[editorial]. *Nursing Research* 2002 March-April; 51(2): 71. Subject: 18.2

Underwood, Marion K. Observing anger and aggression among preadolescent girls and boys: ethical dilemmas and practical solutions. *Ethics and Behavior* 2005; 15(3): 235-245. Subject: 17.3

Undis, David J. LifeSharers: increasing organ supply through directed donation. *American Journal of Bioethics* 2005 July-August; 5(4): 22-24. Subject: 19.5

United Kingdom Xenotransplantation Interim Regulatory Authority [UKXIRA]. Guidance on Making Proposals to Conduct Xenotransplantation on Human Subjects. London: The Authority 1998; 14 p., 9 p. annexes [Online]. Available: http://www.advisorybodies.doh.gov. uk/pub/docs/doh/ukxirag.pdf; http://www. advisorybodies.doh.gov.uk/pub/docs/doh/ukxiraa.pdf [15 April 2005]. Subject: 19.1

United Kingdom. Department of Health. Report of the ad hoc advisory group on the operation of NHS research ethics committees. London: Department of Health 2005; 26 p. [Online]. Available: http://www.dh.gov.uk/ assetRoot/04/11/24/17/04112417.pdf [7 March 2006]. Subject: 18.2

United Kingdom. Law Commission. Mental Incapacity Bill (draft). *Bulletin of Medical Ethics* 2003 October; (192): 22-24. Subject: 4.3

United Kingdom. Royal College of Physicians of London[RCP]. Working Party. Ethics in practice: background and recommendations for enhanced support. London: Royal College of Physicians 2005 June; 8 p. [Online]. Available: http://www.rcplondon.ac.uk/pubs/ books/ethics/ethicsinpractice.pdf [6 March 2006]. Subject: 2.1

United Nations Educational, Scientific and Cultural Organization [UNESCO]. Universal Declaration on Bioethics and Human Rights. Paris, France: UNESCO 2005 October 19; 9 p. [Online]. Available: http://portal. unesco.org/shs/en/file_download.php/46133e1f4691e4c 6e57566763d474a4dBioethicsDeclaration_EN.pdf [3 January 2006]. Subject: 21.1

United Nations Educational, Scientific and Cultural Organization [UNESCO]. Reflections on the UNESCO draft declaration on bioethics and human rights: universal draft declaration on bioethics and human rights. *Developing World Bioethics* 2005 September; 5(3): 197-209. Subject: 2.1

United Nations Educational, Scientific and Cultural Organization [UNESCO]. Division of Ethics of Science and Technology; ten Have, Henk A.M.J. Establishing Bioethics Committees: Guide No. 1. Paris, France: UNESCO 2005; 72 p. [(Online]. Available: http:// portal.unesco.org/shs/en/ev.php-URL_ID=7771& URL_DO=DO_TOPIC&URL_SECTION=201.html [5 July 2005]. Subject: 9.6

United Nations Educational, Scientific and Cultural Organization [UNESCO]. Division of Ethics of Science and Technology. Explanatory memorandum on the elaboration of the preliminary draft declaration on universal norms on bioethics. Paris, France: UNESCO 2005 February 21; 18 p. [Online] Available: http://portal. unesco.org/shs/en/file_download.php/d3b7e79dd46a023 o46ff9392ofb6oc35EXplanMemorandum_en.pdf [6 April 2005]. Subject: 2.1

United Nations Educational, Scientific and Cultural Organization [UNESCO]. Division of Ethics of Science and Technology. International Bioethics Committee. Preliminary Draft Declaration on Universal Norms on Bioethics. Paris, France: UNESCO 2005 February 9; 9 p. [Online]. Available: http://portal.unesco.org/shs/en/ file_download.php/10d16a8d802Caebf882673 e444395ofdPreliminary_Draft_EN.pdf [6 April 2005]. Subject: 2.1

United Nations General Assembly. United Nations declaration on human cloning. *National Catholic Bioethics Quarterly* 2005 Summer; 5(2): 357- 358. Subject: 14.5

United Nations High Commissioner for Human Rights [UNHCHR]. Expert Group on Human Rights and Biotechnology. Expert group on human rights and biotechnology convened by the UN high commissioner for human rights: conclusions on human reproductive cloning. *Health and Human Rights: An International Journal* 2002; 6(1): 153-159. Subject: 14.5

United Nations. Office of the High Commissioner for Human Rights [OHCHR]; Joint United Nations Programme on HIV/AIDS [UNAIDS]. HIV/AIDS and Human Rights International Guidelines. Revised Guideline 6: Access to Prevention, Treatment, Care and Support. New York: United Nations, Revised reprint 2003 March; 25 p. [Online]. Available: http://www.unaids.org/html/ pub/Publications/IRC-pub02/JC905-Guideline6_en_ pdf.pdf [4 August 2005]. Subject: 9.5.6

United States. Congress. United States Leadership Against HIV/AIDS, Tuberculosis, and Malaria Act of 2003. [approved: 2003 May 27]. United States: Public Law 108-025 [HR 1298], 117 Stat. 2003 May 27: 711-750 [Online]. Available: http://frwebgate.access.gpo.gov/cgi- bin/ getdoc/cgi?dbname=108_cong_public_laws& docid=f:publ025.108.pdf [22 February 2006]. Subject: 9.5.6

United States. Congress. House. Highly Essential Lifesaving Pharmaceuticals for Africa Act. H.R. 2700 [introduced: 4 August 1999]. United States House of Representatives, 106th Congress; 4 p. [Online]. Available: http://thomas.loc.gov/cgi-bin/query/C?c106:./temp/~c10 6ydmtuA [9 September 2005]. Subject: 18.5.9

United States. Congress. Senate. Pain Relief Promotion Act of 1999. S. 1272 [introduced 23 June 1999]. United States Senate, 106th Congress; 4 p. [Online]. Available:

---

http://thomas.loc.gov/cgi-bin/query/C?c106:./temp/~106 FcIhSs [22 September 2005]. Subject: 20.4.1

United States. Department of Agriculture. Office of Inspector General, Western Region. Audit report: APHIS animal care program inspection and enforcement activities. Washington, DC: United States Department of Agriculture. Office of Inspector General Western Region 2005 September; 60 p. [Online]. Available: http://www.usda.gov/oig/webdocs/33002-03- SF.pdf [10 November 2005]. Subject: 22.2

United States. Department of Health and Human Services [DHHS]. Public Health Service policies on research misconduct; final rule. *Federal Register* 2005 May 17; 70(94): 28370-28400 [Online]. Available:http://a257.g.akamaitech.net/7/257/2422/01jan20051800/edocket.access.gpo.gov/2005/pdf/05-9643.pdf [23 May 2005]. Subject: 1.3.9

United States. Department of Health and Human Services [DHHS]. Supplemental standards of ethical conduct and financial disclosure requirements for employees of the Department of Health and Human Services [interim final rule with request for comments]. *Federal Register* 2005 February 3; 70(22): 5543-5565. Subject: 1.3.9

United States. Department of Health and Human Services [DHHS]. Supplemental Standards of Ethical Conduct and Financial Disclosure Requirements for Employees of the Department of Health and Human Services [Final Action]. 5 CFR Parts 5501 and 5502. *Federal Register* 2005 August 31; 70(168): 51559-51574. Subject: 1.3.9

United States. Department of Health and Human Services. Equivalent Protections Working Group. Report of the Equivalent Protections Working Group, Department of Health and Human Services. Washington, DC: Department of Health and Human Services 2003 July 17; 21 p., 4 p. appendix [Online]. Available: http://hhs.gov.ohrp/international/EPWGReport2003.pdf; http://hhs.gov/ohrp/international/EPWGFramework.pdf [2 December 2005]. Subject: 18.2

United States. Department of Health and Human Services. Office for Human Research Protections [OHRP]. OHRP Guidance on the Involvement of Prisoners in Research. Washington, DC: Department of Health and Human Services 2003 May 23; 8 p. [Online]. Available: http://www.hhs.gov/ohrp/humansubjects/guidance/prisoner.pdf [18 April 2005]. Subject: 18.5.5

United States. Department of Labor; Department of Health and Human Services; Equal Employment Opportunity Commission; Department of Justice. Genetic information in the workplace. *Labor Law Journal* 1998 February; 49(2): 867-876. Subject: 15.1

United States. District Court. Central District of California. *Kevorkian v. Arnett* [Date of Decision: 11 September 1996]. *West's Federal Supplement* 1996; 939: 725-732. Subject: 20.5.3

United States. District Court. Eastern District of Michigan. *Kevorkian v. Thompson* [Date of Decision: 6 January 1997]. *Federal Supplement* 1997; 947: 1152-1179. Subject: 20.5.3

United States. District Court. Eastern District of Virginia. *United States v. Jacobson* [Date of Decision: 9 January 1992]. *Federal Supplement* 1992; 785: 563-569. Subject: 14.2

United States. District Court. Pennsylvania. Eastern District. Settlement Agreement (with James M. Wilson, M.D., Ph.D.). Philadelphia, PA: United States Attorney's Office 2005; 21 p. [Online]. Available: http://www.usdoj.gov/usao/pae/News/Pr/2005/feb/Wilson5.settlement.pdf [29 August 2005]. Subject: 15.4

United States. District Court. Pennsylvania. Eastern District. Settlement Agreement (with Mark L. Batshaw, M.D. and Children's National Medical Center [CNMC]). Philadelphia, PA: United States Attorney's Office 2005; 26 p. [Online]. Available: http://www.usdoj.gov/usao/pae/News/Pr/2005/feb/batshawsettlement draft 1-23-05.pdf [29 August 2005]. Subject: 15.4

United States. District Court. Pennsylvania. Eastern District. Settlement Agreement (with Steven E. Raper, M.D.). Philadelphia, PA: United States Attorney's Office 2005; 19 p. [Online]. Available: http://www.usdoj.gov/usao/pae/News/Pr/2005/feb/raper.settlement.pdf [29 August 2005]. Subject: 15.4

United States. District Court. Pennsylvania. Eastern District. Settlement Agreement (with the Trustees of the University of Pennsylvania). Philadelphia, PA: United States Attorney's Office 2005; 11 p. [Online]. Available: http://www.usdoj.gov/usao/pae/News/Pr/2005/feb/IHGT settlement 5.pdf [29 August 2005]. Subject: 15.4

United States. District Court. Pennsylvania. Eastern District. U.S. settles case of gene therapy study that ended with teen's death [press release]. *Philadelphia, PA: United States Attorney's Office* 2005 February 9; 4 p. [Online]. Available: http://www.usdoj.gov/usao/pae/News/Pr/2005/feb/UofPSettlement%20release.html [21 July 2005]. Subject: 15.4

United States. Food and Drug Administration. Protection of human subjects; informed consent; final rules. *Federal Register* 1996 October 2; 61(192): 51498-51531 [Online] Available: http://frwebgate.access.gpo.gov/cgi-bin/multidb.cgi [12 December 2005]. Subject: 18.3

United States. Food and Drug Administration [FDA]; Good Clinical Practice Program, Office of the Commissioner [OC]; Center for Drug Evaluation and Research [CDER]; Center for Biologics Evaluation and Research [CBER]; Office of Regulatory Affairs [ORA]. Guidance for industry. Using a centralized IRB review process in multicenter clinical trials. Draft guidance.

Rockville, MD: Food and Drug Administration 2005 March; 10 p. [Online]. Available: http://www.fda/gov/cder/guidance/OC273dft.pdf [20 July 2005]. Subject: 18.2

United States. Government Accountability Office [GAO]. Food and Drug Administration: Decision Process to Deny Initial Application for Over-the-Counter Marketing of the Emergency Contraceptive Drug Plan B Was Unusual. Washington, DC: GAO, 2005 November; 57 p. Subject: 11.1

United States. National Conference of Commissioners on Uniform State Laws. Uniform Health Care Decisions Act. [approved by the American Bar Association, Kansas City, Missouri, February 7, 1994]. Charleston, South Carolina: Annual Conference, National Conference of Commissioners on Uniform State Laws 1993 July 30-August 6; 36 p. [Online]. Available: http://www.law.upenn.edu/bll/ulc/fnact99/1990s/uhcda93.pdf [25 January 2006]. Subject: 9.4

University of California San Francisco [UCSF] Mount Zion Hospital; University of California San Francisco Mount Zion Cancer Center. Planning for your future: a gift of love. An approach to life and death with dignity: a guide to help you make decisions on advance directives and organize your life. San Francisco, CA: University of California, 1996; 31 p. Subject: 20.5.4

University of Toronto Joint Centre for Bioethics. Clinical Ethics Group; Breslin, Jonathan M.; MacRae, Susan K.; Bell, Jennifer; Singer, Peter A. Top 10 health care ethics challenges facing the public: views of Toronto bioethicists. *BMC Medical Ethics [electronic]* 2005 June 26; 6(5); 10 p. Available: http://www.biomedcentral.com/content/pdf/1472-6939-6-5.pdf [1 February 2006]. Subject: 2.1

University of Toronto Joint Centre for Bioethics. Pandemic Influenza Working Group; Upshur, Ross E.G.; Faith, Karen; Gibson, Jennifer L.; Thompson, Alison K.; Tracy, C. Shawn; Wilson, Kumanan; Singer, Peter A. Stand on Guard for Thee: Ethical considerations in preparedness planning for pandemic influenza. Toronto: University of Toronto Joint Centre for Bioethics 2005 November; 29 p. [Online]. Available: http://www.utoronto.ca/jcb/home/documents/pandemic.pdf [4 January 2006]. Subject: 9.1

Upadya, Anupama; Muralidharan, Visvanathan; Thorevska, Natalya; Amoateng-Adjepong, Yaw; Manthous, Constantine A. Patient, physician, and family member understanding of living wills. *American Journal of Respiratory and Critical Care Medicine* 2002 December 1; 166(11): 1430-1435. Subject: 20.5.4

Upton, Hugh. Ethical theories and practical problems. *Nursing Philosophy* 2003 July; 4(2): 170-172. Subject: 2.1

Uranga, Amelia Martín; Arribas, Concepción Martín; Jaeger, Cécile; Posadas, Manuel. Outstanding ethical-legal issues on biobanks. An overview on the regulations of the Member States of the EuroBiobank project. *Revista de Derecho y Genoma Humano / Law and the Human Genome Review* 2005 January-June; (22): 103-114. Subject: 15.10

Urbiztondo, Ned. The economic efficiency behind genetic "discrimination". *Ivy Journal of Ethics* 2003; 3(1): 4-6. Subject: 15.3

Üstün, Cagatay. Medical ethics at Ege University Faculty of Medicine [letter]. *Nursing Ethics* 2005 March; 12(2): 198-199. Subject: 2.1

Üstün, Cagatay; Ceber, Esin. Ethical issues for cancer screenings: five countries — four types of cancer. *Preventive Medicine* 2004 August; 39(2): 223-229. Subject: 9.1

Uttley, Lois. An inconceivable argument: does a law ensuring equal access to prescription drugs mean that the Catholic hierarchy will become morally complicit in "immoral acts"? *Conscience* 2005 Summer; 26(2): 39-40. Subject: 11.1

Uvey, Dogan; Gokce, Ayse Nur; Basagaoglu, Ibrahim. Euthanasia: the concept and the situation in Turkey. *Medical Ethics and Bioethics / Medicinska Etika & Bioetika* 2004 Autumn-Winter; 11(3-4): 7-8. Subject: 20.5.1

V

Vaccarino, Viola; Rathore, Saif S.; Wenger, Nanette K.; Frederick, Paul D.; Abramson, Jerome L.; Barron, Hal V.; Manhapra, Ajay; Mallik, Susmita; Krumholz, Harlan M. Sex and racial differences in the management of acute myocardial infarction, 1994 through 2002. *New England Journal of Medicine* 2005 August 18; 353(7): 671- 682. Subject: 9.5.4

Vaidya, Ashok. Ethics in the clinical practice of integral medicine: there are many ethical, legal and technical problems resulting from 'mixopathy'. *Issues in Medical Ethics* 1999 January-March; 7(1): 9-10. Subject: 4.1.1

Vainiomäki, Maija; Helve, Otto; Vuorenkoski, Lauri. A national survey on the effect of pharmaceutical promotion on medical students. *Medical Teacher* 2004 November; 26(7): 630-634. Subject: 9.7

Valapour, Maryam. Ethics of organ distribution in lung transplantation. *Minnesota Medicine* 2004 June; 87(6): 36-37. Subject: 19.6

Valdez-Martinez; Edith; Trumbull, Bernardo; Garduño-Espinosa, Juan; Porter, John David Henley. Understanding the structure and practices of research ethics committees through research and audit: a study from Mexico. *Health Policy* 2005 September 28; 74(1): 56-68. Subject: 18.2

Valerio, Carlos J. The legal situation concerning notification of sexual partners of HIV/AIDS patients in Costa Rica: problems in contact tracing. *Medicine and Law: World Association for Medical Law* 2004; 23(4): 925-936. Subject: 8.4

See SUBJECT HEADING KEY FOR SECTION II on inside back cover

Välimäki, Maritta; Leino-Kilpi, Helena; Grönroos, Matti; Dassen, Theo; Gasull, Maria; Lemonidou, Chryssoula; Scott, P. Anne; Arndt, Marianne Benedicta. Self-determination in surgical patients in five European countries. *Journal of Nursing Scholarship* 2004; 36(4): 305-311. Subject: 8.1

Vallance, James H.; Ahmed, Mehra; Dhillon, Baljean. Cataract surgery and consent: recall, anxiety, and attitude toward trainee surgeons preoperatively and postoperatively. *Journal of Cataract and Refractive Surgery* 2004 July; 30(7): 1479-1483. Subject: 8.3.1

Vallance, Patrick. Developing an open relationship with the drug industry [opinion]. *Lancet* 2005 September 24-30; 366(9491): 1062-1064. Subject: 9.7

van Bogaert, Louis-Jacques. The right to procreate — freedom and necessity [opinion]. *South African Medical Journal* 2005 January; 95(1): 32-34. Subject: 14.1

Van Court, Rebecca L. Uterine fibroids and women's right to choose: hysterectomies and informed consent. *Journal of Legal Medicine* 2005 December; 26(4): 507-521. Subject: 9.5.5

Van Damme, Karel; Vineis, Paolo; Sorsa, Marja; Casteleyn, Ludwine. Ethical issues in genetic screening and genetic monitoring of employees. *Annals of the New York Academy of Sciences* 1997 December 26; 837: 554-565. Subject: 16.3

van den Berg, Matthijs; Timmermans, Danielle R.M.; ten Kate, Leo P.; van Vugt, John M.G.; van der Wal, Gerrit. Are pregnant women making informed choices about prenatal screening? *Genetics in Medicine* 2005 May-June; 7(5): 332-338. Subject: 15.2

van den Hoven, Mariëtte A.; Verweij, Marcel F. Should we promote influenza vaccination of health care workers in nursing homes? Some ethical arguments in favour of immunization. *Age and Ageing* 2003 September; 32(5): 487-489. Subject: 16.3

van der Heide, Agnes; Vrakking, Astrid; van Delden, Hans; Looman, Caspar; van der Maas, Paul. Medical and nonmedical determinants of decision making about potentially life-prolonging interventions. *Medical Decision Making* 2004 September-October; 24(5): 518-524. Subject: 20.3.2

Van Der Weyden, Martin B. Managing allegations of scientific misconduct and fraud: lessons from the "Hall affair" [editorial]. *Medical Journal of Australia* 2004 February 16; 180(4): 149-151. Subject: 1.3.9

Van Der Weyden, Martin B. Multicentre research: negotiating the ethics approval obstacle course [letter]. *Medical Journal of Australia* 2004 October 18; 181(8): 460-461. Subject: 18.2

Van Detta, Jeffrey A. Constitutionalizing Roe, Casey and Carhart: a legislative due-process anti-discrimination principle that gives constitutional content to the "undue bur-

den" standard of review applied to abortion control legislation. *Southern California Review of Law and Women's Studies* 2001 Spring; 10(2): 211-292. Subject: 12.4.1

Van Detta, Jeffrey A. "Typhoid Mary" meets the ADA: a case study of the "direct threat" standard under the Americans with Disabilities Act. *Harvard Journal of Law and Public Policy* 1999 Summer; 22(3): 849-958. Subject: 9.1

Van Dijck, José. Cloning humans, cloning literature: genetics and the imagination deficit. *New Genetics and Society* 1999; 18(1): 9-22. Subject: 14.5

van Gorp, Wilfred G.; Tranel, Daniel. Editorial statement: disclosure of funding sources and financial interests by authors. *Journal of Clinical and Experimental Neuropsychology* 2004 May; 26(3): 306. Subject: 1.3.9

Van Hollen, Cecilia. Invoking vali: painful technologies of modern birth in south India. *Medical Anthropology Quarterly* 2003 March; 17(1): 49-77. Subject: 9.5.5

Van Hoof, Thomas J.; Taggart, W. Blake. Mental retardation and decision making: balancing autonomy and protection. *Connecticut Medicine* 1998 August; 62(8): 455-460. Subject: 9.5.3

van Hooft, Stan. Kuhse on caring. *Nursing Inquiry* 1999 June; 6(2): 112-122. Subject: 4.1.3

Van Houtven, Courtney Harold; Voils, Corrine I.; Oddone, Eugene Z.; Weinfurt, Kevin P.; Friedman, Joëlle Y.; Schulman, Kevin A.; Bosworth, Hayden B. Perceived discrimination and reported delay of pharmacy prescriptions and medical tests. *JGIM: Journal of General Internal Medicine* 2005 July; 20(7): 578-583. Subject: 9.5.4

Van Hoyweghen, Ine; Horstman, Klasien; Schepers, Rita. 'Genetics is not the issue': insurers on genetics and life insurance. *New Genetics and Society* 2005 April; 24(1): 79-98. Subject: 15.1

van Kammen, Jessika. Informed consent in clinical trials. *Issues in Medical Ethics* 2000 July-September; 8(3): 84-86. Subject: 18.3

van Kleffens, T.; van Leeuwen, E. Physicians' evaluations of patients' decisions to refuse oncological treatment. *Journal of Medical Ethics* 2005 March; 31(3): 131-136. Subject: 8.3.4

van Leeuwen, Anna F.; Voogt, Elsbeth; Visser, Adriaan; van der Rijt, Carin C.D.; van der Heide, Agnes. Considerations of healthcare professionals in medical decision-making about treatment for clinical end-stage cancer patients. *Journal of Pain and Symptom Management* 2004 October; 28(4): 351-355. Subject: 20.5.1

van Leeuwen, Evert. On the origin, use and destination of human embryos. *European Journal of Endocrinology* 2004 November; 151 (Supplement 3): U13-U16. Subject: 4.4

Van Leeuwen, Evert; Vellinga, Astrid. Knowing well or living well: is competence relevant to moral experience

---

Subject = NRCBL Primary Classification Number; See inside front cover

and capacity in clinical decision-making? *In:* Thomasma, David C.; Weisstub, David N., eds. The Variables of Moral Capacity. Boston: Kluwer Academic Publishers; 2004: 187- 202. Subject: 8.3.3

van Niekerk, Anton. Commercial surrogacy and the commodification of children: an ethical perspective. *Medicine and Law: World Association for Medical Law* 1995; 14(3-4): 163-170. Subject: 14.2

Van Overwalle, Geertrui. Bio-patents, law and ethics. Critical analysis of the EU Biotechnology Directive. *Revista de Derecho y Genoma Humano / Law and the Human Genome Review* 2003 July-December; (19): 187-203. Subject: 15.8

Van Parijs, Philippe. Just health care in a pluri-national country. *In:* Anand, Sudhir; Peter, Fabienne; Sen, Amartya, eds. Public Health, Ethics, and Equity. New York: Oxford University Press; 2004: 163-180. Subject: 9.4

van Rooyen, D.; Elfick, M.; Strümpher, J. Registered nurses' experience of the withdrawal of treatment from the critically ill patient in an intensive care unit. *Curationis* 2005 February; 28(1): 42-51. Subject: 20.5.1

van Straaten, Justine. The minor's limited right to confidential health care and the inverse of confidentiality: a parent's decision not to disclose illness status to a minor child. *Children's Legal Rights Journal* 2000 Spring; 20(1): 46-54. Subject: 9.5.7

Van Vlierberghe, H.; Colle, I.; Troisi, R.; de Hemptinne, B.; De Vos, M. Liver transplantation and mental retardation. *Acta Gastro-Enterologica Belgica* 2002 April-June; 65(2): 131-132. Subject: 19.1

van Willigenburg, Theo. Protecting autonomy as authenticity using Ulysses contracts. *Journal of Medicine and Philosophy* 2005 August; 30(4): 395-409. Subject: 17.1

VanCannon, Kayla. Fathering a child from the grave: what are the inheritance rights of children born through new technology after the death of a parent? *Drake Law Review* 2004 Winter; 52(2): 331-362. Subject: 14.6

VandeBerg, John L.; Zola, Stuart M. A unique biomedical resource at risk. *Nature* 2005 September 1; 437(7055): 30-32. Subject: 22.2

VanderPlaat, Madine; Teles, Nair. Mainstreaming social justice: human rights and public health. *Canadian Journal of Public Health / Revue Canadienne de Sante Publique* 2005 January-February; 96(1): 34-36. Subject: 9.1

Vanderpool, Harold Y. A quartet of criticisms [comment]. *American Journal of Bioethics* 2005 September-October; 5(5): 16-19. Subject: 18.3

Vandervert, Larry R. The inheritance of the core self in human clones. *Free Inquiry* 2005 December-2006 January; 26(1): 37-39. Subject: 14.5

VanderWalde, Ari. Undue inducement: the only objection to payment? [comment]. *American Journal of*

Bioethics 2005 September-October; 5(5): 25-27. Subject: 18.3

Vanfraussen, Katrien; Ponjaert-Kristoffersen, I.; Brewaeys, A. What does it mean for youngsters to grow up in a lesbian family created by means of donor insemination? *Journal of Reproductive and Infant Psychology* 2002 November; 20(4): 237-252. Subject: 14.2

Vanfraussen, K.; Ponjaert-Kristoffersen, I.; Brewaeys, A. Why do children want to know more about the donor? The experience of youngsters raised in lesbian families. *Journal of Psychosomatic Obstetrics and Gynecology* 2003 March; 24(1): 31-38. Subject: 19.5

VanGeest, Jonathan B.; Wynia, Matthew K.; Cummins, Deborah S.; Wilson, Ira B. Measuring deception: test-retest reliability of physicians' self-reported manipulation of reimbursement rules for patients. *Medical Care Research and Review* 2002 June; 59(2): 184-196. Subject: 9.4

Vanguri, Swathi Sri; Rajput, Vijay. Patents and biotechnology. *Issues in Medical Ethics* 2002 January-March; 10(1): 152-153. Subject: 15.8

Vanitzian, Donie; Kopkin, Andrew H. 'In the name of the people' — a Faustian paradox: the betrayal by physicians, lawyers, judges, academics and ethicists of the sovereign people's ultimate civil liberty. *University of West Los Angeles Law Review* 1997; 28: 81-247. Subject: 20.3.1

Varatharajan, D. Provision of health care by the government. *Indian Journal of Medical Ethics* 2004 October-December; 1(4): 117-118. Subject: 9.3.1

Varatharajan, D. Taking biotechnology to the patient: at what cost? *Issues in Medical Ethics* 2003 April-June; 11(2): 54-55. Subject: 9.3.1

Vardy, Peter. The correction of human physical defects. *In his:* Being Human: Fulfilling Genetic and Spiritual Potential. London: Darton, Longman and Todd; 2003: 47-62. Subject: 15.4

Vardy, Peter. The physical enhancement of humanity. *In his:* Being Human: Fulfilling Genetic and Spiritual Potential. London: Darton, Longman and Todd; 2003: 63-74. Subject: 15.1

Vardy, Peter. A test case—the challenge of genetic engineering. *In his:* Being Human: Fulfilling Genetic and Spiritual Potential. London: Darton, Longman and Todd; 2003: 19-25. Subject: 15.1

Varekamp, I. Ulysses directives in the Netherlands: opinions of psychiatrists and clients. *Health Policy* 2004 December; 70(3): 291-301. Subject: 17.1

Varelius, Jukka. Health and autonomy. *Medicine, Health Care and Philosophy: A European Journal* 2005; 8(2): 221-230. Subject: 4.2

Varma, Anjali; Appelbaum, Paul S. Advance directives for persons with serious mental illness [letter and reply].

Psychiatric Services 2005 July; 56(7): 874-875. Subject: 17.1

Varnhagen, Connie K.; Gushta, Matthew; Daniels, Jason; Peters, Tara C.; Parmar, Neil; Law, Danielle; Hirsch, Rachel; Takach, Bonnie Sadler; Johnson, Tom. How informed is online informed consent? *Ethics and Behavior* 2005; 15(1): 37-48. Subject: 18.3

Vaughn, Michael S. Penal harm medicine: state tort remedies for delaying and denying health care to prisoners. *Crime, Law, and Social Change* 1999; 31(4): 273-302. Subject: 9.2

Vayena, Effy; Rowe, Patrick J.; Peterson, Herbert B. Assisted reproductive technology in developing countries: why should we care? *Fertility and Sterility* 2002 July; 78(1): 13-15. Subject: 14.1

Veatch, Robert M. Common morality and human finitude: a foundation for bioethics. *In:* Baumann, Eva; Brink, Alexander; May, Arnd T.; Schröder; Peter; Schutzeichel, Corinna Iris, eds. Weltanschauliche Offenheit in der Bioethik. Berlin: Duncker & Humblot; 2004: 37-50. Subject: 2.1

Veatch, Robert M. The death of whole-brain death: the plague of the disaggregators, somaticists, and mentalists. *Journal of Medicine and Philosophy* 2005 August; 30(4): 353-378. Subject: 20.2.1

Veatch, Robert M. Organs on the Internet [letter]. *Hastings Center Report* 2005 May-June; 35(3): 6. Subject: 19.1

Veatch, Robert M. Ranking, balancing, or simultaneity: resolving conflicts among the Belmont principles. *In:* Childress, James F.; Meslin, Eric M.; Shapiro, Harold T., eds. Belmont Revisited: Ethical Principles for Research with Human Subjects. Washington, DC: Georgetown University Press; 2005: 184-204. Subject: 18.2

Veatch, Robert M. Terri Schiavo, Son Hudson, and 'nonbeneficial' medical treatments. *Health Affairs* 2005 July-August; 24(4): 976-979. Subject: 20.5.1

Veatch, Robert M. Tissue issues: the ethical dilemmas of collecting human tissues for research. *Formosan Journal of Medical Humanities* 2005 September; 6(1-2): 3-13. Subject: 19.5

Veatch, Robert M. The total artificial heart: is paying for it immoral and stopping it murder? *Medical Ethics Newsletter [Lahey Clinic]* 2004 Winter; 11(1): 1-2, 12. Subject: 20.5.1

Veatch, Robert M. Transplants and mental disability: the meaning of discrimination. *Ethics and Intellectual Disability Newsletter* 2001 Summer; 6(1): 1-5. Subject: 9.5.3

Veatch, Robert M. Withholding nutrition on the conscious mentally disabled patient: a review and commentary. *Ethics and Intellectual Disability Newsletter* 2002 Fall; 7(1): 5-7. Subject: 9.5.3

Vedantam, Shankar; Weiss, Rick. Medical, ethical questions largely decided, experts say. *Washington Post* 2005 March 22; p. A6. Subject: 20.5.1

Vélez G., Juan R. Death of John Paul II and the basic human care for the sick and the dying. *Ethics and Medicine* 2005 Fall; 21(3): 167-177. Subject: 20.5.1

Vélez G., Juan R. Immediate animation: Thomistic principles applied to Norman Ford's objections. *Ethics and Medicine* 2005 Spring; 21(1): 11-28. Subject: 4.4

Veljkovic, Veljko; Prljic, Jelena; Veljkovic, Tatjana. Safety and ethical consideration of AIDS vaccine. *International Reviews of Immunology* 2004 September-December; 23(5-6): 465-486. Subject: 9.5.6

Vellinga, A.; Smit, J.H.; Van Leeuwen, E.; Van Tilburg, W.; Jonker, C. Competence to consent to treatment of geriatric patients: judgements of physicians, family members and the vignette method. *International Journal of Geriatric Psychiatry* 2004 July; 19(7): 645-654. Subject: 8.3.3

Venne, Vickie L.; Botkin, Jeffrey R.; Buys, Saundra S. Professional opportunities and responsibilities in the provision of genetic information to children relinquished for adoption. *American Journal of Medical Genetics* 2003 May 15; 119A(1): 41-46. Subject: 15.2

Vercellone, Paolo. Children's rights and artificial procreation. *Medicine and Law: World Association for Medical Law* 1995; 14(1-2): 13-22. Subject: 14.4

Verhagen, Eduard; Sauer, Pieter J.J. The Groningen protocol — euthanasia in severely ill newborns [opinion]. *New England Journal of Medicine* 2005 March 10; 352(10): 959- 962. Subject: 20.5.2

Verhey, Allen. Necessary decisions. *Christian Century* 2005 April 19; 122(8): 9-10. Subject: 20.5.1

Verhey, Allen. What makes Christian bioethics Christian? Bible, story, and communal discernment. *Christian Bioethics* 2005 December; 11(3): 297-315. Subject: 2.1

Vermeulen, Eric. Dealing with doubt: making decisions in a neonatal ward in the Netherlands. *Social Science and Medicine* 2004 November; 59(10): 2071-2085. Subject: 20.5.2

Vermij, Peter. Scientists charged with choosing publication over public health [news]. *Nature Medicine* 2005 May; 11(5): 461. Subject: 13.9

Verpeet, Ellen; Dierckx de Casterle, Bernadette; Van der Arend, Arie; Gastmans, Chris A.E. Nurses' views on ethical codes: a focus group study. *Journal of Advanced Nursing* 2005 July; 51(2): 188-195. Subject: 6

Verweij, M.F.; van den Hoven, M.A. Influenza vaccination in Dutch nursing homes: is tacit consent morally justified? *Medicine, Health Care and Philosophy: A European Journal* 2005; 8(1): 89-95. Subject: 8.3.1

Verweij, Marcel. Obligatory precautions against infection. *Bioethics* 2005 August; 19(4): 323-335. Subject: 9.1

Subject = NRCBL Primary Classification Number; See inside front cover

Veterans Health Administration. National Ethics Committee; Fox, Ellen; Tulsky, James A. Recommendations for the ethical conduct of quality improvement. *Journal of Clinical Ethics* 2005 Spring; 16(1): 61-71. Subject: 9.8

Vetsch, G.; Uehlinger, D.E.; Zenklusen, Regula M. Zürcher. DNR orders at a tertiary care hospital — are they appropriate? *Swiss Medical Weekly* 2002 April 20; 132(15-16): 190-196. Subject: 20.5.1

Veysman, Boris. Full code: a young physician is confounded by — then learns from — a dying patient's decisions. *Health Affairs* 2005 September-October; 24(5): 1311-1316. Subject: 20.5.1

Vick, Katherine. Judge declares pre-embryo is human. *Journal of Biolaw and Business* 2005; 8(3): 52-53. Subject: 4.4

Victoroff, Michael S. We don't serve your kind! *Managed Care* 2004 August; 13(8): 14, 16. Subject: 8.1

Viens, Adrian M.; Bibbee, Jeffrey R. Legal frameworks for addressing the well-being of terminally ill children. *American Journal of Bioethics* 2005 January-February; 5(1): 74- 76. Subject: 20.5.2

Vijayashankara, Nanjegowda. "Right to die" — situation is different in developing countries . . . [letter]. *BMJ: British Medical Journal* 2005 June 11; 330(7504): 1389. Subject: 9.4

Vince, Gaia. Rewriting your past: drugs that rid people of terrifying memories could be a lifeline for many. *New Scientist* 2005 December 3-9; 188(2528): 32-35. Subject: 4.5

Vinten, Gerald. Whistleblowing in the health-related professions. *Issues in Medical Ethics* 1996 October-December; 4(4): 108-111. Subject: 7.3

Vis, Theodorus A.M.; Onwuteaka-Philipsen, Bregje D.; Muller, Martien T.; van der Wal, Gerrit. Euthanasia and old age [letter and reply]. *Age and Ageing* 1999 July; 28(4): 414. Subject: 20.5.1

Visser, H.K.A. Experimental malaria in human volunteers: ethical aspects [editorial]. *Netherlands Journal of Medicine* 2005 February; 63(2): 41-42. Subject: 18.1

Vist, Gunn Elisabeth; Hagen, Kåre Birger; Devereaux, P.J.; Bryant, Dianne; Kristoffersen, Doris Tove; Oxman, Andrew David. Systematic review to determine whether participation in a trial influences outcome. *BMJ: British Medical Journal* 2005 May 21; 330(7501): 1175-1179. Subject: 9.8

Viswanath, Kalpana; Kirbat, Preeti. Genealogy of a controversy: development of an anti-fertility vaccine. *Economic and Political Weekly* 2000 February 19-26; 34(8 and 9); 15 p. [Online]. Available: http://www.hsph.harvard.edu/Organizations/healthnet/SAsia/suchana /0500/h071.html [7 October 2005]. Subject: 18.5.3

Vitello, Stanley J. On the value of a life with mental retardation: Keene v. Brigham and Women's Hospital, Inc. *Eth-ics and Intellectual Disability Newsletter* 2002 Fall; 7(1): 1-3. Subject: 9.5.3

Voelker, Rebecca. The business of baby pictures — controversy brews over "keepsake" fetal ultrasounds. *JAMA: The Journal of the American Medical Association* 2005 January 5; 293(1): 25-27. Subject: 15.2

Vogel, Gretchen. Abstentions scuttle drive to liberalize Italy's embryo laws [news]. *Science* 2005 June 17; 308(5729): 1722. Subject: 18.5.4

Vogel, Gretchen. Collaborators split over ethics allegations [news]. *Science* 2005 November 19; 310(5751): 1100. Subject: 7.4

Vogel, Gretchen. Deriving 'controversy-free' ES cells is controversial [news]. *Science* 2005 October 21; 310(5747): 416-417. Subject: 18.5.4

Vogel, Gretchen. Embryo-free techniques gain momentum [news]. *Science* 2005 July 8; 309(5732): 240-241. Subject: 18.5.4

Vogel, Gretchen. Korean team speeds up creation of cloned human stem cells [news]. *Science* 2005 May 20; 308(5725): 1096-1097. Subject: 18.5.4

Vogel, Gretchen. Landmark paper has an image problem [news]. *Science* 2005 December 9; 310(5754): 1595. Subject: 1.3.9

Vogel, Gretchen. U.S. public supports stem cell research [news]. *Science* 2005 October 21; 310(5747): 416. Subject: 18.5.4

Volker, Deborah L. Assisted dying and end-of-life symptom management. *Cancer Nursing* 2003 October; 26(5): 392-399. Subject: 20.7

Vollmann, Jochen; Bauer, A.; Danker-Hopfe, H.; Helmchen, H. Competence of mentally ill patients: a comparative empirical study. *Psychological Medicine* 2003 November; 33(8): 1463-1471. Subject: 4.3

von Bubnoff, Andreas. The 1918 flu virus is resurrected [news]. *Nature* 2005 October 6; 437(7060): 794-795. Subject: 15.1

von Bubnoff, Andreas. Spanish flu papers put spotlight on 'dual use' decisions [news]. *Nature Medicine* 2005 November; 11(11): 1130. Subject: 1.3.7

von Cranach, Michael. Menschenversuche in den bayerischen Heil- und Pflegeanstalten. *In:* von Cranach, Michael; Siemen, Hans-Ludwig, eds. Psychiatrie im Nationalsozialismus: die Bayerischen Heil- und Pflegeanstalten zwischen 1933 und 1945. München: Oldenbourg; 1999: 405-411. Subject: 18.5.6

von Gruenigen, Vivian E.; Daly, Barbara J. Futility: clinical decisions at the end-of-life in women with ovarian cancer. *Gynecologic Oncology* 2005 May; 97(2): 638-644. Subject: 20.5.1

von Zielbauer, Paul. As health care in jails goes private, 10 days can be a death sentence. *New York Times* 2005 February 27; p. A1, A32. Subject: 9.5.1

von Zielbauer, Paul. Missed signals in New York jails open way to season of suicides. *New York Times* 2005 February 28; p. A1, B6, B7. Subject: 9.5.1

von Zielbauer, Paul. A spotty record of health care for children in city detention. *New York Times* 2005 March 1; p. A1, B9. Subject: 9.5.1

Vonk, Machteld. One, two or three parents? Lesbian co-mothers and a known donor with 'family life' under Dutch law. *International Journal of Law, Policy and the Family* 2004 April; 18(1): 103-117. Subject: 14.2

Voogt, Elsbeth; van der Heide, Agnes; Rietjens, Judith A.C.; van Leeuwen, Anna F.; Visser, Adriaan P.; van der Rijt, Carin C.D.; van der Maas, Paul J. Attitudes of patients with incurable cancer toward medical treatment in the last phase of life. *Journal of Clinical Oncology* 2005 March 20; 23(9): 2012-2019. Subject: 20.4.1

Vrakking, Astrid M.; van der Heide, Agnes; Looman, Caspar W.N.; van Delden, Johannes J.M.; Onwuteaka-Philipsen, Bregje D.; van der Maas, Paul J.; van der Wal, Gerrit. Physicians' willingness to grant requests for assistance in dying for children: a study of hypothetical cases. *Journal of Pediatrics* 2005 May; 146(5): 611-617. Subject: 20.5.2

Vrakking, Astrid M.; van der Heide, Agnes; Onwuteaka- Philipsen, Bregje D.; Keij-Deerenberg, Ingeborg M.; van der Maas, Paul J.; van der Wal, Gerrit. Medical end-of-life decisions made for neonates and infants in the Netherlands, 1995-2001. *Lancet* 2005 April 9-15; 365(9467): 1329-1331. Subject: 20.5.2

Vrakking, Astrid M.; van der Heide, Agnes; van Delden, Johannes J.M.; Looman, Caspar W.N.; Visser, Michelle H.; van der Maas, Paul J. Medical decision-making for seriously ill non-elderly and elderly patients. *Health Policy* 2005 December; 75(1): 40-48. Subject: 20.5.1

Vrhovac, Bozidar. Croatia. *Medical Ethics and Bioethics / Medicinska Etika & Bioetika* 2005; 11(Supplement): 14-15. Subject: 9.6

Vuckovich, Paula K.; Artinian, Barbara M. Justifying coercion. *Nursing Ethics* 2005 July; 12(4): 370-380. Subject: 17.7

Vukadinovich, David M. Minors' rights to consent to treatment: navigating the complexity of state laws. *Journal of Health Law* 2004 Fall; 37(4): 667-691. Subject: 8.3.2

Vulchev, Anntim; Roberts, John P.; Stock, Peter G. Ethical issues in split versus whole liver transplantation. *American Journal of Transplantation* 2004 November; 4(11): 1737-1740. Subject: 19.6

W

Wachbroit, Robert. Assessing quality of life: clinical versus health policy uses. *In:* Wasserman, David; Bickenbach, Jerome; Wachbroit, Robert, eds. Quality of Life and Human Difference: Genetic Testing, Health Care, and Disability. New York: Cambridge University Press; 2005: 27-42. Subject: 4.4

Wachbroit, Robert; Wasserman, David. Reproductive technology. *In:* LaFollette, Hugh, ed. The Oxford Handbook of Practical Ethics. New York: Oxford University Press; 2003: 136-160. Subject: 14.1

Wachbroit, Robert; Wasserman, David. Research participation: are we subject to a duty? *American Journal of Bioethics* 2005 January-February; 5(1): 48- 49. Subject: 18.2

Wade, Derick T. Ethics, audit, and research: all shades of grey. *BMJ: British Medical Journal* 2005 February 26; 330(7489): 468- 471. Subject: 18.2

Wade, Nicholas. Bioethics panel suggests stem cell alternatives. *New York Times* 2005 May 13; p. A21. Subject: 2.4

Wade, Nicholas. Chimeras on the horizon, but don't expect centaurs. *New York Times* 2005 May 3; p. F1, F8. Subject: 15.1

Wade, Nicholas. Clone scientist relied on peers and Korean pride. *New York Times* 2005 December 25; p. A1, A8. Subject: 1.3.9

Wade, Nicholas. Ethicists offer advice for testing human brain cells in primates. *New York Times* 2005 July 15; p. A12. Subject: 22.2

Wade, Nicholas. Genetic catalog may aid search for roots of disease. *New York Times* 2005 October 27; p. A20. Subject: 15.11

Wade, Nicholas. Korean researchers to help others clone cells for study. *New York Times* 2005 October 19; p. A14. Subject: 14.5

Wade, Nicholas. Korean scientist said to admit fabrication in a cloning study. *New York Times* 2005 December 16; p. A1, A6. Subject: 1.3.9

Wade, Nicholas. Scientists draft rules on ethics for stem cells; academy cites lack of guidelines by U.S. *New York Times* 2005 April 27; p. A1, A16. Subject: 18.5.4

Wade, Nicholas. Stem cell test tried on mice saves embryo; technique could shift debate on humans. *New York Times* 2005 October 17; p. A1, A16. Subject: 22.2

Wadman, Meredith. Drug targeting: is race enough? [news]. *Nature* 2005 June 23; 435(7045): 1008-1009. Subject: 15.1

Wadman, Meredith. Licensing fees slow advance of stem cells. *Nature* 2005 May 19; 435(7040): 272-273. Subject: 18.5.4

Subject = NRCBL Primary Classification Number; See inside front cover

Wadman, Meredith. Medicare compels heart patients to enlist in follow-up research [news]. *Nature* 2005 January 27; 433(7024): 341. Subject: 18.3

Wadman, Meredith. NIH workers see red over revised rules for conflicts of interest [news]. *Nature* 2005 March 3; 434(7029): 3-4. Subject: 1.3.9

Wadman, Meredith. US Senate votes to ban pesticide tests on humans [news]. *Nature Medicine* 2005 August; 11(8): 811. Subject: 18.6

Wadman, Meredith. US set to endorse human pesticide testing. *Nature* 2005 September 1; 437(7055): 24-25. Subject: 18.2

Wagena, Edwin J. The scandal of unfair behaviour of senior faculty. *Journal of Medical Ethics* 2005 May; 31(5): 308. Subject: 1.3.9

Wagena, Edwin J.; Knipschild, P. Do drug firms hoodwink medical journals? Or is something wrong with the contribution and integrity of declared authors? *Journal of Medical Ethics* 2005 May; 31(5): 307. Subject: 1.3.7

Wager, Elizabeth; Jacobs, Adam. Response to "The Corporate Coauthor" [letter]. *JGIM: Journal of General Internal Medicine* 2005 July; 20(7): 672. Subject: 1.3.7

Waggoner, Jeffrey R.; McNutt, Robert A. Shared medical decision making [letter and reply]. *JAMA: The Journal of the American Medical Association* 2005 March 2; 293(9): 1058-1059. Subject: 8.1

Waghela, Jagruti; George, Jameela. Euthanasia: a worldwide dilemma. *Indian Journal of Medical Ethics* 2004 July-September; 1(3): 92. Subject: 20.5.1

Wagle, Rinata K.; Ede, Kekoa; Craig, Jana; Bottum, Kathleen. An ethical dilemma: when the family wants the withdrawal of care. *Journal of Psychiatric Practice* 2004 September; 10(5): 334-336. Subject: 20.5.1

Wagner, Lynn. Providing comfort to dying residents. *Provider* 1999 May; 25(5): 52-54, 57-58, 63-65. Subject: 20.4.1

Wagner, Richard M. Ethical review of research involving human subjects: when and why is IRB review necessary? *Muscle and Nerve* 2003 July; 28: 27-39. Subject: 18.2

Wagner, William Joseph. Constitutional values and the ethics of health care: a comparison of the United States and Germany. *Journal of Contemporary Health Law and Policy* 2002 Fall; 18(3): 619-632. Subject: 9.1

Waikar, Aparna; Davar, Bhargavi; Karhadkar, Chandra; Bansode, Darshana; Dandekar, Deepra; Kakade, Seema; Wayal, Sonali; Kulkarni, Yogita. ECT without anaesthesia is unethical. *Issues in Medical Ethics* 2003 April-June; 11(2): 41-43. Subject: 17.5

Wainwright, Paul. Persistent vegetative state: ethical issues for nursing. *Nursing Standard* 1996 November 20; 11(9): 39-44. Subject: 20.5.1

Waisel, David B. Moral permissibility as a guide for decision making about conjoined twins [editorial]. *Anesthesia and Analgesia* 2005 July; 101(1): 41-43. Subject: 20.5.2

Waisel, David B.; Truog, Robert D. How an anesthesiologist can use the ethics consultation service. *Anesthesiology* 1997 November; 87(5): 1231-1238. Subject: 9.6

Waisel, David B.; Truog, Robert D. Informed consent. *Anesthesiology* 1997 October; 87(4): 968-978. Subject: 8.3.1

Waisel, David B.; Truog, Robert D. An introduction to ethics. *Anesthesiology* 1997 August; 87(2): 411-417. Subject: 2.1

Waite, Michelle. Altering the future. *Ivy Journal of Ethics; 3(1):* 20-23. Subject: 15.4

Waldby, Catherine. Literature Review and Annotated Bibliography: Social and Ethical Aspects of Sex Selection. London: Human Fertilisation and Embryology Authority [HFEA] undated; 18 p. [Online]. Available: http://www.hfea.gov.uk/AboutHFEA/Consultations/AppendixD - Social and Ethical Literature Review.pdf [6 October 2004]. Subject: 14.3

Walden, Marlene; Sala, D. Jean. Controversies in the resuscitation of infants of borderline viability. *AWHONN's Clinical Issues in Perinatal and Women's Health Nursing* 1993; 4(4): 570-577. Subject: 20.5.2

Waldinger, Robert J. Boundary crossings and boundary violations: thoughts on navigating a slippery slope. *Harvard Review of Psychiatry* 1994 November-December; 2(4): 225-227. Subject: 7.4

Waldman, Ellen. The parent trap: uncovering the myth of "coerced parenthood" in frozen embryo disputes. *American University Law Review* 2004 June; 53(5): 1021-1062. Subject: 14.6

Waldschmidt, Anne. Who is normal? Who is deviant?: "normality" and "risk" in genetic diagnostics and counseling. *In:* Tremain, Shelley, ed. Foucault and the Government of Disability. Ann Arbor: University of Michigan Press; 2005: 191-207. Subject: 15.2

Wales, Steven D. The Stark Law: boon or boondoggle? An analysis of the prohibition on physician self-referrals. *Law and Psychology Review* 2003 Spring; 27: 1-28. Subject: 7.3

Walfish, Steven; Sharp, Sean P. Readability level of HIPAA notices of privacy practices used by physical rehabilitation centers. *Journal of Clinical Ethics* 2005 Summer; 16(2): 156-159. Subject: 8.4

Walker, Gay; de Valois, Beverley; Davies, Raten; Young, Teresa; Maher, Jane. Opinions of research participants about study paperwork [review]. *Bulletin of Medical Ethics* 2005 February; (205): 21-24. Subject: 18.2

Walker, Kristen. 1950s family values vs human rights: in vitro fertilisation, donor insemination and sexuality in Victoria. *Public Law Review* 2000 December; 11(4): 292-307. Subject: 14.1

Walker, Roger. Can we afford the medicines we need: an ethical dilemma? *In:* Salek, Sam; Edgar, Andrew, eds. Pharmaceutical Ethics. New York: Wiley; 2002: 91-95. Subject: 9.7

Wallace, Helen M. The misleading marketing of genetic tests: will the genome become the source of diagnostic miracles or potential scams? *GeneWatch* 2005 March-April; 18(2): 3-5. Subject: 15.3

Wallace, Susannah Kish; Martin, Charles G.; Shaw, Andrew D.; Price, Kristen J. Influence of an advance directive on the initiation of life support technology in critically ill cancer patients. *Critical Care Medicine* 2001 December; 29(12): 2294-2298. Subject: 20.5.4

Wallbank, Julie. The role of rights and utility in instituting a child's right to know her genetic history. *Social and Legal Studies* 2004 June 1; 13(2): 245-264. Subject: 15.11

Wallbank, Julie. "Throwing baby out with the bath water": some reflections on the evolution of reproductive technology. *Res Publica* 1999; 5(1): 47-67. Subject: 14.4

Waller, Bruce N. Responsibility and health. *CQ: Cambridge Quarterly of Healthcare Ethics* 2005 Spring; 14(2): 177-188. Subject: 9.1

Wallsten, Tuula; Kjellin, Lars. Involuntarily and voluntarily admitted patients' experiences of psychiatric admission and treatment — a comparison before and after changed legislation in Sweden. *European Psychiatry* 2004 December; 19(8): 464-468. Subject: 17.7

Wallwork, Ernest. Failed community representation: does the process inhibit full IRB participation by community representatives? *Protecting Human Subjects* 2003 Fall; (9): 4, 14. Subject: 18.2

Walmsley, Jan. Research ethics [editorial]. *British Journal of Learning Disabilities* 1998 Winter; 26(4): 126-127. Subject: 18.5.6

Walpole, Ian R.; Dawkins, Hugh J.S.; Sinden, Peter D.; O'Leary, Peter C. Human gene patents: the possible impacts on genetic services healthcare [opinion]. *Medical Journal of Australia* 2003 August 18; 179(4): 203-205. Subject: 15.8

Walsh, John P.; Cho, Charlene; Cohen, Wesley M. View from the bench: patents and material transfers. *Science* 2005 September 23; 309(5743): 2002-2003. Subject: 5.3

Walsh, K. The winner takes it all [opinion]. *Journal of Medical Ethics* 2005 May; 31(5): 267. Subject: 9.7

Walsh, Michael K.; McNeil, John J.; Breen, Kerry J. Improving the governance of health research. *Medical Journal of Australia* 2005 May 2; 182(9): 468-471. Subject: 18.2

Walter, Fiona M.; Emery, Jon D.; Rogers, Margaret; Britten, Nicky. Women's views of optimal risk communication and decision making in general practice consultations about the menopause and hormone replacement therapy. *Patient Education and Counseling* 2004 May; 53(2): 121-128. Subject: 8.1

Walter, Garry; Bloch, Sidney. Publishing ethics in psychiatry. *Australian and New Zealand Journal of Psychiatry* 2001 February; 35(1): 28-35. Subject: 17.1

Walter, James. Why did Jesse die? *Update [Loma Linda University Center for Christian Bioethics]* 2001 November; 17(2): 4 p. Subject: 15.4

Walter, James J. Terminal sedation: a Catholic perspective. *Update [Loma Linda University Center for Christian Bioethics]* 2002 September; 18(2): 6-8. Subject: 20.4.1

Walter, Nicholas; Schillinger, Dean. Front-line bureaucracies and the moral mechanics of US health care [editorial]. *Medical Care* 2004 April; 42(4): 303-305. Subject: 9.4

Walters, Jim. AMA council's ethics overwhelmed by public sentiment. *Update [Loma Linda University Center for Christian Bioethics]* 1996 July; 12(2): 4 p. Subject: 20.5.2

Walters, LeRoy. Genforschung und Gesellschaft: Erwartungen, Ziele und Grenzen. *In:* Honnefelder, Ludger; Mieth, Dietmar; Propping, Peter; Siep, Ludwig; Wiesemann, Claudia, eds. Das genetische Wissen und die Zukunft des Menschen. New York: De Gruyter; 2003: 152-166. Subject: 15.4

Walters, LeRoy. Human genetic intervention: past, present, and future. *In:* Baillie, Harold W.; Casey, Timothy K., eds. Is Human Nature Obsolete? Genetics Bioengineering, and the Future of the Human Condition. Cambridge, MA: MIT Press; 2005: 367-384. Subject: 15.4

Walters, Stacey R. Life-sustaining medical decisions involving children: father knows best. *Thomas M. Cooley Law Review* 1998; 15(1): 115-154. Subject: 20.5.2

Wang, Shing-Yaw; Chen, Chung-Hey; Chen, Yong-Shing; Huang, Huei-Lin. The attitude toward truth telling of cancer in Taiwan. *Journal of Psychosomatic Research* 2004 July; 57(1): 53-58. Subject: 8.2

Wang, Xin Shelley; Di, Li Jun; Reyes-Gibby, Cielito C.; Guo, Hong; Liu, Shu Jun; Cleeland, Charles S. End-of-life care in urban areas of China: a survey of 60 oncology clinicians. *Journal of Pain and Symptom Management* 2004 February; 27(2): 125-132. Subject: 20.4.1

Wann, Samuel. Conflicts of interest, integrity, and public respect: challenges to the professional standing of modern cardiologists [opinion]. *American Heart Hospital Journal* 2003 Summer; 1(3): 236-239. Subject: 4.1.2

Ward Platt, M.P. Participation in multiple neonatal research studies [opinion]. *Archives of Disease in Child-*

hood. Fetal and Neonatal Edition 2005 May; 90(3): F191. Subject: 18.5.2

Ward, Linda. Whose right to choose?: the new genetics, prenatal testing and people living with learning difficulties. *In:* Bunton, Robin; Petersen, Alan, eds. Genetic Governance: Health, Risk and Ethics in the Biotech Era. New York: Routledge; 2005: 121-135. Subject: 15.2

Wareham, Pauline; McCallin, Antoinette; Diesfeld, Kate. Advance directives: the New Zealand context. *Nursing Ethics* 2005 July; 12(4): 349-359. Subject: 20.5.4

Warlow, Charles. Over-regulation of clinical research: a threat to public health. *Clinical Medicine* 2005 January-February; 5(1): 33-38. Subject: 18.6

Warren-Jones, Amanda. Patenting DNA: a lot of controversy over a little intangibility. *Medical Law Review* 2004 Spring; 12(1): 97-124. Subject: 15.8

Washington, Harriet A. Born for evil? Stereotyping the karyotype: a case history in the genetics of aggressiveness. *In:* Roelcke, Volker; Maio, Giovanni, eds. Twentieth Century Ethics of Human Subjects Research: Historical Perspectives on Values, Practices, and Regulations. Stuttgart: Franz Steiner Verlag; 2004: 319-333. Subject: 15.6

Wasnick, John D. Virtue, ethics, and anesthesia [letter]. *Anesthesiology* 1998 August; 89(2): 537. Subject: 4.1.2

Wasserman, David. The nonidentity problem, disability, and the role morality of prospective parents. *Ethics: An International Journal of Social, Political, and Legal Philosophy* 2005 October; 116(1): 132-152. Subject: 4.4

Wasserman, David. What qualifies as a live embryo? *American Journal of Bioethics* 2005 November-December; 5(6): 23-25. Subject: 4.4

Wasserman, Jason; Clair, Jeffrey Michael; Ritchey, Ferris J. A scale to assess attitudes toward euthanasia. *Omega: Journal of Death and Dying* 2005; 51(3): 229-237. Subject: 20.5.1

Wasunna, Angela. End-of-life decision making in Kenya. *In:* Blank, Robert H.; Merrick, Janna C., eds. End-of-Life Decision Making: A Cross-National Study. Cambridge, MA: MIT Press; 2005: 131-146. Subject: 20.4.1

Wasunna, Angela. Researchers abroad. *Hastings Center Report* 2005 January-February; 35(1): 3. Subject: 18.5.9

Wasunna, Angela; Murray, Thomas. Professional responsibilities in medical research. *In:* Restivo, Sal, ed. Science, Technology, and Society: An Encyclopedia. New York: Oxford University Press; 2005: 407-414. Subject: 1.3.9

Watchirs, Helen. Human rights audit of mental health legislation — results of an Australian pilot. *International Journal of Law and Psychiatry* 2005 March- April; 28(2): 99-125. Subject: 17.1

Waters, Brent. Freedom in responsibility: a response. *Christian Bioethics* 2005 August; 11(2): 167-173. Subject: 2.1

Waters, Brent. What is Christian about Christian bioethics? *Christian Bioethics* 2005 December; 11(3): 281-295. Subject: 2.1

Watson, Donald C., Jr.; Robicsek, Francis; Sade, Robert M. Are thoracic surgeons ethically obligated to serve as expert witnesses for the plaintiff? [debate]. *Annals of Thoracic Surgery* 2004 October; 78(4): 1137-1141. Subject: 8.5

Watson, M.; Foster, C.; Eeles, R.; Eccles, D.; Ashley, S.; Davidson, R.; Mackay, J.; Morrison, P.J.; Hopwood, P.; Evans, D.G.R. Psychosocial impact of breast/ovarian (BRCA1/2) cancer-predictive genetic testing in a UK multi-centre clinical cohort. *British Journal of Cancer* 2004 November 15; 91(10): 1787-1794. Subject: 15.3

Watson, Peter Y.; Khandelwal, Akshay K.; Musial, Joseph L.; Buckley, John D. Brief report: resident and faculty perceptions of conflict of interest in medical education. *JGIM: Journal of General Internal Medicine* 2005 April; 20(4): 357-359. Subject: 7.2

Watson, Sidney D. Race, ethnicity and hospital care: the need for racial and ethnic data [opinion]. *Journal of Health and Hospital Law* 1997 June; 30(2): 125-132. Subject: 9.5.4

Watt, Helen. Ethical aspects of use of fetal/embryonic cells in treatment and research. *Zentralblatt fur Neurochirurgie* 2005 May; 66(2): 75-78. Subject: 18.5.4

Watt, Helen. Ethical problems in assisted conception. *In:* McMahon, Kevin T., ed. Moral Issues in Catholic Health Care. Wynnewood, PA: Saint Charles Borromeo Seminary; 2004: 57-67. Subject: 14.4

Watts, Jonathan. Chinese officials accused of forcing abortions in Shandong. *Lancet* 2005 October 8-14; 366(9493): 1253. Subject: 13.3

Waxman, Henry A. The lessons of Vioxx — drug safety and sales. *New England Journal of Medicine* 2005 June 23; 352(25): 2576- 2578. Subject: 9.7

Waxman, Judy; Laser, Rachel; Cantor, Julie; Baum, Ken. Pharmacists and emergency contraception [letter and reply]. *New England Journal of Medicine* 2005 March 3; 352(9): 942-944. Subject: 11.1

Weasel, Lisa H.; Jensen, Eric. Language and values in the human cloning debate: a web-based survey of scientists and Christian fundamentalist pastors. *New Genetics and Society* 2005 April; 24(1): 1-14. Subject: 14.5

Weaver, Jane. Court-ordered caesarean sections. *In:* Bainham, Andrew; Sclater, Shelley Day; Richards, Martin, eds. Body Lore and Laws. Portland, OR: Hart Pub.; 2002: 229-247. Subject: 9.5.5

Weaver, Lara A.; Andrutis, Karl. IACUC replacement parts: what are the requirements? Bad choices. *Lab Animal* 2004 November; 33(10): 17-18. Subject: 22.2

Webb, Jane; Siotia, A.K. Commentary: patient's perspective. *BMJ: British Medical Journal* 2005 May 7; 330(7499): 1069. Subject: 8.3.1

Webby, Terri. Dealing with ethical challenges in practice. *Nursing New Zealand* 2004 March; 10(2): 26-27. Subject: 9.5.7

Weber, Leonard J. Integrated ethics for the clinical systems manager. *Clinical Laboratory Management Review* 1998 September-October; 12(5): 384-388. Subject: 9.6

Weber, Leonard J.; Bissell, Michael G. Reporting lab results directly to the patient. *Clinical Leadership and Management Review* 2004 September-October; 18(5): 291-292. Subject: 8.1

Weber, Susan M. Court affirms relatives' right to shut off life support. *Pennsylvania Medicine* 1996 June; 99(6): 24-25. Subject: 20.5.1

Webster, Andrew. Social science and a post-genomic future: alternative readings of genomic agency. *New Genetics and Society* 2005 August; 24(2): 227-238. Subject: 15.10

Wecht, Cyril H. Research and experimentation. *In:* American College of Legal Medicine Textbook Committee, Sanbar, S. Sandy; Firestone, Marvin H.; Buckner, Fillmore; Gibofsky, Allan; LeBlang, Theodore R.; Snyder, Jack W.; Wecht, Cyril H.; Zaremski, Miles J. Legal Medicine. 6th ed. St. Louis: Mosby; 2004: 238-255. Subject: 18.1

Wechter, David. Response to Catherine Althaus on heterologous embryo transfer. *National Catholic Bioethics Quarterly* 2005 Summer; 5(2): 225. Subject: 14.4

Wechter, David; Althaus, Catherine. Response to Catherine Althaus on heterologous embryo transfer [article and commentary]. *National Catholic Bioethics Quarterly* 2005 Autumn; 5(3): 451- 452. Subject: 14.4

Weddle, Melissa; Kokotailo, Patricia. Adolescent substance abuse: confidentiality and consent. *Pediatric Clinics of North America* 2002 April; 49(2): 301-315. Subject: 9.5.7

Weed, James L.; Raber, James M. Balancing animal research with animal well-being: establishment of goals and harmonization of approaches. *ILAR Journal* 2005; 46(2): 118-128. Subject: 22.2

Weed, Matthew. Discourse on embryo science and human cloning in the United States and Great Britain: 1984-2002. *Journal of Law, Medicine and Ethics* 2005 Winter; 33(4): 802- 810. Subject: 18.5.4

Weijer, Charles. A death in the family: reflections on the Terri Schiavo case [opinion]. *CMAJ/JAMC: Canadian Medical Association Journal* 2005 April 26; 172(9): 1197-1198. Subject: 20.5.1

Weijer, Charles. Is clinical research and ethics a zero-sum game? *Critical Care Medicine* 2005 April; 33(4): 912-913. Subject: 18.2

Weijer, Charles. Meaningful work as due inducement. *Theoretical Medicine and Bioethics* 2005; 26(5): 431-435. Subject: 18.2

Weijer, Charles; Miller, Paul B. When are research risks reasonable in relation to anticipated benefits? *Nature Medicine* 2004 June; 10(6): 570-573. Subject: 18.3

Weiman, Darryl S. Genes and the law. *In:* Ellis, C.N., ed. Inherited Cancer Syndromes: Current Clinical Management. New York: Springer-Verlag; 2004: 83-90. Subject: 15.1

Weinberg, Susan R. A maternal duty to protect fetal health? *Indiana Law Journal* 1983; 58(3): 531-546. Subject: 9.5.8

Weindling, Paul. "No mere murder trial": the discourse on human experiments at the Nuremberg medical trial. *In:* Roelcke, Volker; Maio, Giovanni, eds. Twentieth Century Ethics of Human Subjects Research: Historical Perspectives on Values, Practices, and Regulations. Stuttgart: Franz Steiner Verlag; 2004: 167-180. Subject: 18.1

Weindling, Paul. International eugenics: Swedish sterilization in context. *Scandinavian Journal of History* 1991 June 1; 24(2): 179-197. Subject: 15.5

Weiner, Saul J.; Laporte, Margaret; Abrams, Richard I.; Moswin, Arthur; Warnecke, Richard. Rationing access to care to the medically uninsured: the role of bureaucratic front-line discretion at large healthcare institutions. *Medical Care* 2004 April; 42(4): 306-312. Subject: 9.4

Weinrib, Lorraine Eisenstat. The body and the body politic: assisted suicide under the Canadian Charter of Rights and Freedoms. *McGill Law Journal* 1994; 39(3): 618-643. Subject: 20.5.1

Weinstein, Brent. The state's constitutional power to regulate abortion. *Journal of Contemporary Legal Issues* 2004; 14(1): 229-234. Subject: 12.4.3

Weisbaum, Karen M.; Slaughter, Pamela M.; Collins, Paulette K. A voluntary privacy standard for health services and policy research: legal, ethical and social policy issues in the Canadian context. *Health Law Review* 2005; 14(1): 42-46. Subject: 8.4

Weise, Kathryn. Finding our way. *Hastings Center Report* 2004 July-August; 34(4): 8-9. Subject: 20.5.2

Weise, Kathryn L. The spectrum of our obligations: DNR in public schools [case studies]. *American Journal of Bioethics* 2005 January-February; 5(1): 81- 83. Subject: 20.5.2

Weisfeld, Alix; Perlman, Robert L. Disparities and discrimination in health care: an introduction. *Perspectives in Biology and Medicine* 2005 Winter; 48(1, Supplement): S1-S9. Subject: 9.5.4

Weiss, Barry D.; Smith, Mindy A.; Magill, Michael K. Journal policy statement — IRB approval for educational research [policy statement]. *Family Medicine* 2005 March; 37(3): 219-220. Subject: 18.2

Weiss, Rick. British to clone human embryos for stem cells. *Washington Post* 2005 February 9; p. A2. Subject: 18.5.4

Weiss, Rick. Lab animal violations decried: activists urge NIH to sanction university for repeat offense. *Washington Post* 2005 December 2; p. A21. Subject: 22.2

Weiss, Rick. Many scientists admit to misconduct: degrees of deception vary in poll; researchers say findings could hurt the field. *Washington Post* 2005 June 9; p. A3. Subject: 1.3.9

Weiss, Rick. Medical studies and the average American kid. *Washington Post* 2005 August 22; p. A5. Subject: 18.5.2

Weiss, Rick. NIH clears most researchers in conflict-of-interest probe. *Washington Post* 2005 February 23; p. A1, A4. Subject: 1.3.9

Weiss, Rick. NIH will restrict outside income: tighter rules address concerns about conflicts of interest. *Washington Post* 2005 February 2; p. A1, A7. Subject: 1.3.9

Weiss, Rick. U.S. denies patent for a too-human hybrid: scientist sought legal precedent to keep others from profiting from similar "inventions". *Washington Post* 2005 February 13; p. A3. Subject: 15.8

Weiss, Rick. U.S. researchers reach deal in '99 gene therapy case. *Washington Post* 2005 February 10; p. A3. Subject: 15.4

Weiss, Sheila Faith. German eugenics, 1890-1933. *In:* Bachrach, Susan, project director; Kuntz, Dieter, ed. Deadly Medicine: Creating the Master Race. Washington, DC: United States Holocaust Museum; 2004: 15-39. Subject: 15.5

Weissman, Irving. Stem cell research: paths to cancer therapies and regenerative medicine. *JAMA: The Journal of the American Medical Association* 2005 September 21; 294(11): 1359-1366. Subject: 18.5.1

Weissman, Joel S. The trouble with uncompensated hospital care [opinion]. *New England Journal of Medicine* 2005 March 24; 352(12): 1171- 1173. Subject: 9.3.1

Weissman, Joel S.; Annas, Catherine L.; Epstein, Arnold M.; Schneider, Eric C.; Clarridge, Brian; Kirle, Leslie; Gatsonis, Constantine; Feibelmann, Sandra; Ridley, Nancy. Error reporting and disclosure systems: views from hospital leaders. *JAMA: The Journal of the American Medical Association* 2005 March 16; 293(11): 1359-1366. Subject: 9.8

Weissman, Joel S.; Betancourt, Joseph; Campbell, Eric G.; Park, Elyse R.; Kim, Minah; Clarridge, Brian; Blumenthal, David; Lee, Karen C.; Maina, Angela W. Resident physicians' preparedness to provide cross-cultural care. *JAMA: The Journal of the American Medical Association* 2005 September 7; 294(9): 1058-1067. Subject: 7.2

Weisstub, David N.; Thomasma, David C. Human dignity, vulnerability, personhood. *In:* Thomasma, David C.; Weisstub, David N.; Herve, Christian eds. Personhood and Health Care. Boston: Kluwer Academic Pub.; 2001: 317-332. Subject: 4.4

Weisstub, David N.; Thomasma, David C. Moral capacity: the tension between professional nurture and universal nature. *In their:* Thomasma, David C.; Weisstub, David N., eds. The Variables of Moral Capacity. Boston: Kluwer Academic Publishers; 2004: 139- 149. Subject: 1.3.1

Welch, Lisa C.; Teno, Joan M.; Mor, Vincent. End-of-life care in black and white: race matters for medical care of dying patients and their families. *Journal of the American Geriatrics Society* 2005 July; 53(7): 1145-1153. Subject: 20.4.1

Welchman, Jennifer. Xenografting, species loyalty, and human solidarity. *Journal of Social Philosophy* 2003 Summer; 34(2): 244-255. Subject: 19.1

Welchman, Jennifer; Griener, Glenn G. Patient advocacy and professional associations: individual and collective responsibilities. *Nursing Ethics* 2005 May; 12(3): 296-304. Subject: 8.1

Weldon, Sue. 'Public consent' or 'scientific citizenship'?: what counts as public participation in population-based DNA collection? *In:* Tutton, Richard; Corrigan, Oonagh, eds. Genetic Databases: Socio-ethical Issues in the Collection and Use of DNA. New York: Routledge; 2004: 161-180. Subject: 18.3

Welie, Jos V.M. When medical treatment is no longer in order: toward a new interpretation of the ordinary-extraordinary distinction. *National Catholic Bioethics Quarterly* 2005 Autumn; 5(3): 517- 536. Subject: 20.4.1

Welie, Sander P.K.; Dute, Joseph; Nys, Herman; van Wijman, Frans C.B. Patient incompetence and substitute decision-making: an analysis of the role of the health care professional in Dutch law. *Health Policy* 2005 July; 73(1): 21-40. Subject: 8.3.3

Welin, Stellan. Reproductive ectogenesis: the third era of human reproduction and some moral consequences. *Science and Engineering Ethics* 2004 October; 10(4): 615-626. Subject: 14.1

Welkenhuysen, M.; Evers-Kiebooms, G.; Van den Berghe, H. Attitudes toward predictive testing for Alzheimer's disease in a student population. *Psychiatric Genetics* 1997; 7: 121-126. Subject: 15.3

Wells, Michael. Policy on ethics and patient consent [editorial]. *Histopathology* 2003 February; 42(2): 103. Subject: 1.3.7

Wells, Robert J.; Gross, Michael. Wartime medical ethics [letter and reply]. *Hastings Center Report* 2005 May-June; 35(3): 7. Subject: 21.2

Wendler, David. Protecting subjects who cannot give consent. *Hastings Center Report* 2005 September-October; 35(5): 37-43. Subject: 18.2

Wendler, David; Belsky, Leah; Thompson, Kimberly M.; Emanuel, Ezekiel J. Qualifying the federal minimal risk standard: implications for pediatric research without a prospect of direct benefit. *JAMA: The Journal of the American Medical Association* 2005 August 17; 294(7): 826-832. Subject: 18.5.2

Wendler, David; Pace, Christine; Talisuna, Ambrose O.; Maiso, Faustine; Grady, Christine; Emanuel, Ezekiel. Research on stored biological samples: the views of Ugandans. *IRB: Ethics and Human Research* 2005 March-April; 27(2): 1-5. Subject: 15.1

Wenger, Neil S.; Carmel, Sara. Physicians' religiosity and end-of-life care attitudes and behaviors. *Mount Sinai Journal of Medicine* 2004 October; 71(5): 335-343. Subject: 20.3.2

Wenz, Peter. Engineering genetic injustice. *Bioethics* 2005 February; 19(1): 1-11. Subject: 15.1

Werhane, Patricia H.; Gorman, Michael. Intellectual property rights, moral imagination, and access to life-enhancing drugs. *Business Ethics Quarterly* 2005 October; 15(4): 595-613. Subject: 9.7

Werkö, Lars. Informed consent in routine healthcare. *Scandinavian Cardiovascular Journal* 2004 December; 38(6): 323-324. Subject: 8.3.1

Werner, Rachel M.; Asch, David A. The unintended consequences of publicly reporting quality information. *JAMA: The Journal of the American Medical Association* 2005 March 9; 293(10): 1239-1244. Subject: 9.8

Werth, James L., Jr. Incorporating end-of-life issues into psychology courses. *Teaching of Psychology* 2002 Spring; 29(2): 106-111. Subject: 20.5.1

Werth, James L., Jr. The relationships among clinical depression, suicide, and other actions that may hasten death. *Behavioral Sciences and the Law* 2004; 22(5): 627-649. Subject: 20.7

Wertheimer, Alan. Exploitation and commercial surrogacy. *Denver University Law Review* 1997; 74(4): 1215-1229. Subject: 14.2

Wertz, Dorothy. "Genetic discrimination" in an international context. *In:* Knoppers, Bartha Maria, ed. Populations and Genetics: Legal and Socio-Ethical Perspectives. Boston: Martinus Nijhoff; 2003: 603-622. Subject: 15.3

Wertz, Dorothy C. Archived specimens: ethics concerns. *Acta Tropica* 2001 January 15; 78(Supplement): S77-S84. Subject: 18.1

Wertz, Dorothy C. Biomedical research: genetic testing and confidentiality. *World and I* 1990 September; 543-555. Subject: 15.3

Wertz, Dorothy C. Embryo and stem cell research: views from the USA. *Journal of Commercial Biotechnology* 2002; 8(3): 200-208. Subject: 18.5.4

Wertz, Dorothy C. Ethical issues in the application of knowledge from molecular genetics to mental disorders. *In:* Bulyzhenkov, V.; Christen, Y.; Prilipko, L., eds. Genetic Approaches in the Prevention of Mental Disorders. New York: Springer-Verlag; 1990: 92-106. Subject: 15.2

Wertz, Dorothy C. International perspectives on privacy and access to genetic information. *Microbial and Comparative Genomics* 1997; 2(1): 53-61. Subject: 15.1

Wertz, Dorothy C.; Fletcher, John C. Ethical and social issues in prenatal sex selection: a survey of geneticists in 37 nations. *Social Science and Medicine* 1998 January; 46(2): 255-273. Subject: 14.3

Wertz, Dorothy C.; Knoppers, Bartha Maria. Serious genetic disorders: can or should they be defined? *American Journal of Medical Genetics* 2002; 108: 29-35. Subject: 15.2

Westberg, Katarina; Duchek, Miloš; Sandlund, Mikael; Lynöe, Niels. Informed consent for clinical education: randomized study of two different strategies at a urology surgery. *Scandinavian Journal of Urology and Nephrology* 2004; 38(6): 490-494. Subject: 8.3.1

Wettstein, Robert M. Ethical practice [letter]. *AAPL (American Academy of Psychiatry and the Law) Newsletter* 2005 September; 30(3): 29-30. Subject: 1.3.1

Wexler, Barbara. Cloning. *In her:* Genetics and Genetic Engineering. Detroit, MI: Gale Group; 2004: 101-114. Subject: 14.5

Wexler, Barbara. Ethical issues and public opinion. *In her:* Genetics and Genetic Engineering. Detroit, MI: Gale Group; 2004: 133-141. Subject: 15.1

Wexler, Barbara. Genetic testing. *In her:* Genetics and Genetic Engineering. Detroit, MI: Gale Group; 2004: 71-83. Subject: 15.3

Weyrauch, Samantha. Decision making for incompetent patients: who decides and by what standards? *Tulsa Law Journal* 2000 Spring-Summer; 35(3-4): 765-789. Subject: 8.3

Weyrauch, Samantha. The fetus and the drug addicted mother: whose rights should prevail? *Journal of Medicine and Law* 2001 Spring; 5(2): 95-120. Subject: 9.5.5

Whalen, Jeanne. Valued lives: Britain stirs outcry by weighing benefits of drugs versus price; government arm finds pills for Alzheimer's too costly, angering patients, Pfizer; Ms. Dennis, 80, joins the protest. *Wall Street Journal* 2005 November 22; p. A1, A11. Subject: 9.7

Subject = NRCBL Primary Classification Number; See inside front cover

Wharton, Barbara. Ethical issues in the publication of clinical material. *Journal of Analytical Psychology* 2005 February; 50(1): 83-89. Subject: 1.3.7

Wharton, Mary Ann. Enhancing professional accountability: inquiry into the work of a professional ethics committee. *In:* Purtilo, Ruth B.; Jensen, Gail M.; Brasic Royeen, Charlotte, eds. Educating for Moral Action: A Sourcebook in Health and Rehabilitation Ethics. Philadelphia: F.A. Davis; 2005: 131-143. Subject: 9.6

Wheat, Kay. Progress of the prudent patient: consent after Chester v Afshar [editorial]. *Anaesthesia* 2005 March; 60(3): 217-219. Subject: 8.3.1

Wheeler, R. Children's rights: a surgeon's view. *Archives of Disease in Childhood* 2005 February; 90(2): 174-175. Subject: 9.5.7

Wheeler, Sondra. Contemporary ethics from an ambiguous past. *Christian Bioethics* 2005 April; 11(1): 69-76. Subject: 9.1

Wheeler, Sondra. Making babies? Genetic engineering and the character of parenthood [opinion]. *Sojourners* 1999 May-June; 28(3): 14. Subject: 15.1

Whitcomb, David J. Genetic discrimination. Individual protection legislation stalls in Congress. *AWHONN Lifelines* 2004 October-November; 8(5): 414-416. Subject: 15.1

White, Angela; MacDonald, Chris. Deep disagreement and Rawlsian "public reasons". *American Journal of Bioethics* 2005 November-December; 5(6): 62-63. Subject: 2.4

White, Ben; Willmott, Lindy. The edge of palliative care: certainty, but at what price? *Flinders Journal of Law Reform* 2004 July; 7(2): 225-242. Subject: 20.4.1

White, Bruce David; Singer, Peter A.; Siegler, Mark. Continuing problems with patient self-determination. *American College of Medical Quality* 1993 Winter; 8(4): 187-193. Subject: 20.5.4

White, Caroline. Suspected research fraud: difficulties of getting at the truth. *BMJ: British Medical Journal* 2005 July 30; 331(7511): 281-288. Subject: 1.3.9

White, Caroline. UK agency to combat research misconduct [news]. *BMJ: British Medical Journal* 2005 March 19; 330(7492): 616. Subject: 1.3.9

White, Deena. Consumer and community participation: a reassessment of process, impact, and value. *In:* Albrecht, Gary L.; Fitzpatrick, Ray; Scrimshaw, Susan C., eds. The Handbook of Social Studies in Health & Medicine. Thousand Oaks, CA: Sage; 2000: 465-480. Subject: 9.1

White, Gladys. Nurses at the helm: implementing DNAR orders in the public school setting. *American Journal of Bioethics* 2005 January-February; 5(1): 83- 85. Subject: 20.5.2

White, Gladys B. Splitting the self: the not-so-subtle consequences of medicating boys for ADHD [comment]. *American Journal of Bioethics* 2005 May-June; 5(3): 57-59. Subject: 17.4

White, Katherine. Stem cells 201: an overview of the ethics of stem cell research. *Topics in Stroke Rehabilitation* 2005 Winter; 12(1): 83-88. Subject: 18.5.4

White, Mary T. The many facets of genetic testing. *In:* Smith, David H.; Cohen, Cynthia B., eds. A Christian Response to the New Genetics: Religious, Ethical, and Social Issues. Lanham, MD: Rowman & Littlefield Publishers; 2003: 27-52. Subject: 15.3

White, Paul S. The experimental animal in Victorian Britain. *In:* Daston, Lorraine; Mitman, Gregg, eds. Thinking with Animals: New Perspectives on Anthropomorphism. New York: Columbia University Press; 2005: 59-81. Subject: 22.2

White, Robert M. Misrepresentations of the Tuskegee Study of Untreated Syphilis. *Journal of the National Medical Association* 2005 April; 97(4): 564-581. Subject: 18.5.1

White, Robert M.; Schmidt, Terri. The Tuskegee Syphilis Study and informed consent [letter and reply]. *Annals of Emergency Medicine* 2003 September; 42(3): 430-431. Subject: 18.5.1

Whitehouse, Peter J.; Juengst, Eric T. Antiaging medicine and mild cognitive impairment: practice and policy issues for geriatrics. *Journal of the American Geriatrics Society* 2005 August; 53(8): 1417-1422. Subject: 9.5.2

Whitford, Ben. Who gets the organs? Experts say transplant medicine has a race problem. *Newsweek* 2005 November 28; 146(22): 49. Subject: 19.6

Whittaker, Rosemary. Re-framing the representation of women in advertisements for hormone replacement therapy. *Nursing Inquiry* 1998 June; 5(2): 77-86. Subject: 10

Whittington, Dale. Ethical issues with contingent valuation surveys in developing countries: a note on informed consent and other concerns. *Environmental and Resource Economics* 2004 August; 28(4): 507-515. Subject: 18.5.9

Wicks, Elizabeth; Wyldes, Michael; Kilby, Mark. Late termination of pregnancy for fetal abnormality: medical and legal perspectives. *Medical Law Review* 2004 Autumn; 12(3): 285-305. Subject: 12.4.3

Widdershoven, Guy A.M.; Widdershoven-Heerding, Ineke. Understanding dementia: a hermeneutic perspective. *In:* Fulford, Bill; Morris, Katherine; Sadler, John Z.; Stanghellini, Giovanni, eds. Nature and Narrative: An Introduction to the New Philosophy of Psychiatry. New York: Oxford University Press; 2003: 103-111. Subject: 9.5.2

Widom, Cathy Spatz; Czaja, Sally J. Reactions to research participation in vulnerable subgroups. *Accountabil-*

ity in Research 2005 April-June; 12(2): 115-138. Subject: 18.4

Wieand, Samuel; Murphy, Kate. A commentary on treatment at random: the ultimate science or the betrayal of Hippocrates? *Journal of Clinical Oncology* 2004 December 15; 22(24): 5009- 5011. Subject: 18.2

Wiedemann, Peter M.; Simon, Judith; Schicktanz, Silke; Tannert, Christof. The future of stem-cell research in Germany: a Delphi study [opinion]. *EMBO Reports* 2004 October; 5(10): 927-931. Subject: 18.5.4

Wiener, Martin J. The health of prisoners and the two faces of Benthamism. *Clio Medica* 1995; 34: 44-58. Subject: 2.2

Wiener, Richard L.; Eton, David; Gibbons, Vincent P.; Goldner, Jesse A.; Johnson, Sandra H. Research report: a preliminary analysis of medical futility decisionmaking: law and professional attitudes. *Behavioral Sciences and the Law* 1998 Autumn; 16(4): 497-508. Subject: 20.3.2

Wientjes, Linda. An ethical dilemma: who should know and who should tell. *Pediatric Nursing* 1998 May-June; 24(3): 249-250. Subject: 8.4

Wiesel, Elie. Without conscience [opinion]. *New England Journal of Medicine* 2005 April 14; 352(15): 1511- 1513. Subject: 21.4

Wiesing, Urban. Gendiagnostik und Gesundheitsversorgung. *In:* Honnefelder, Ludger; Mieth, Dietmar; Propping, Peter; Siep, Ludwig; Wiesemann, Claudia, eds. Das genetische Wissen und die Zukunft des Menschen. New York: De Gruyter; 2003: 369-374. Subject: 15.3

Wig, N.N. Ethical issues in psychiatry. *Indian Journal of Medical Ethics* 2004 July-September; 1(3): 83-84. Subject: 17.1

Wigder, Herbert N.; Propp, Douglas; Leslie, Kim. Patients' perception of the physician-patient relationship [letter]. *American Journal of Emergency Medicine* 2003 November; 21(7): 607. Subject: 8.1

Wiggins, Osborne P.; Sadler, John Z. A window into Richard M. Zaner's clinical ethics. *Theoretical Medicine and Bioethics* 2005; 26(1): 1-6. Subject: 2.1

Wiggins, Osborne P.; Schwartz, Michael A. Richard Zaner's phenomenology of the clinical encounter. *Theoretical Medicine and Bioethics* 2005; 26(1): 73-87. Subject: 2.1

Wijdicks, Eelco F.M.; Rabinstein, Alejandro A. Absolutely no hope? Some ambiguity of futility of care in devastating acute stroke. *Critical Care Medicine* 2004 November; 32(11): 2332-2342. Subject: 20.5.1

Wijnberg, Bart. Consent of children and minors. *In:* Actes du Colloque International AMADE-UNESCO sur Bioethique et Droits de L'enfant (Monaco, 28-30 Avril 2000)/Proceedings of the International Symposium AMADE-UNESCO on Bioethics and the Rights of the Child (Monaco, 28-30 April 2000). Paris: UNESCO, Division des Sciences Humaines, de la Philosophie et de L'ethique des Sciences et des Technologies; 2001: 105-110. Subject: 8.3.2

Wikler, Daniel. Personal and social responsibility for health. *In:* Anand, Sudhir; Peter, Fabienne; Sen, Amartya, eds. Public Health, Ethics, and Equity. New York: Oxford University Press; 2004: 109-134. Subject: 9.1

Wikler, Daniel; Cash, Richard. Ethical issues in global public health. *In:* Beaglehole, Robert, ed. Global Public Health: A New Era. New York: Oxford University Press; 2003: 226-242. Subject: 9.1

Wilborn, S. Elizabeth. The right to refuse medical treatment: where there is a right, there ought to be a remedy. *Northern Kentucky Law Review* 1998 Summer; 25(4): 649-673. Subject: 8.3.4

Wilcoxon, Kimberly D. Statutory remedies for judicial torts: the need for wrongful birth legislation. *University of Cincinnati Law Review* 2001 Spring; 69(3): 1023-1053. Subject: 8.5

Wilde, Marshall L. Bioethical and legal implications of pediatric gastric bypass. *Willamette Law Review* 2004 Summer; 40(3): 575-625. Subject: 9.5.7

Wildes, Kevin Wm. Patients: the Rosetta Stone in the crisis of medicine. *CQ: Cambridge Quarterly of Healthcare Ethics* 2005 Spring; 14(2): 168-176. Subject: 8.1

Wilfond, Benjamin; Candotti, Fabio. When eligibility criteria clash with personal treatment choice: a dilemma of clinical research. *In:* Kodish, Eric, ed. Ethics and Research with Children: A Case-Based Approach. New York: Oxford University Press; 2005: 310- 322. Subject: 18.5.2

Wilfond, Benjamin S.; Ravitsky, Vardit. On the proliferation of bioethics sub-disciplines: do we really need "genethics" and "neuroethics"? *American Journal of Bioethics* 2005 March-April; 5(2): 20-21. Subject: 17.1

Wilgoren, Jodi. Clinics' bid to withhold abortion files is criticized. *New York Times* 2005 March 4; p. A15. Subject: 12.4.1

Wilgoren, Jodi. Kansas prosecutor demands files on late-term abortion patients. *New York Times* 2005 February 25; p. A1, A19. Subject: 12.4.1

Wilkes, Lesley. Ethics on the floor. *Collegian* 2003 April; 10(2): 34-39. Subject: 18.2

Wilkinson, Dominic J.C. Selling organs and souls: should the state prohibit `demeaning' practices? *Journal of Bioethical Inquiry* 2004; 1(1): 27-31. Subject: 19.5

Wilkinson, Martin. Payments to research subjects. *Monash Bioethics Review* 2005 January; 24(1): 70-74. Subject: 18.2

Wilkinson, T.M. Individual and family consent to organ and tissue donation: is the current position coherent? *Journal of Medical Ethics* 2005 October; 31(10): 587-590. Subject: 19.5

Subject = NRCBL Primary Classification Number; See inside front cover

Wilks, Michael. A stain on medical ethics [opinion]. *Lancet* 2005 August 6-12; 366(9484): 429-431. Subject: 21.4

Will, Janet C. A dilemma within the family: commentary on who should know and who should tell [opinion]. *Pediatric Nursing* 1998 May-June; 24(3): 251-253. Subject: 8.4

Willard, Laura A. California makes unprecedented commitment to fund stem cell research. *Journal of Biolaw and Business* 2005; 8(2): 47-48. Subject: 18.5.4

Willcox, Breckinridge L. Fraud in scientific research: the prosecutor's approach. *Accountability in Research* 1992; 2(2): 139-151. Subject: 1.3.9

Willems, D.L.; Hak, A.; Visser, F.; Van der Wal, G. Thoughts of patients with advanced heart failure on dying. *Palliative Medicine* 2004 September; 18(6): 564-572. Subject: 20.3.1

Williams, Anne. A response to: the use of emergency hormonal contraception in cases of rape — revisiting the Catholic position. *Human Reproduction and Genetic Ethics: An International Journal* 2005; 11(2): 40-42. Subject: 11.1

Williams, Anne M.H. Time to legalise assisted dying? Do we make decisions by our feelings or the truth? [letter]. *BMJ: British Medical Journal* 2005 October 8; 331(7520): 842. Subject: 20.7

Williams, Clare. Framing the fetus in medical work: rituals and practices. *Social Science and Medicine* 2005 May; 60(9): 2085-2095. Subject: 4.4

Williams, David R.; Collins, Chiquita. Reparations: a viable strategy to address the enigma of African American health. *American Behavioral Scientist* 2004 March; 47(7): 977-1000. Subject: 9.5.4

Williams, Garrath. Human gene banks. *Medical Ethics Newsletter [Lahey Clinic]* 2005 Winter; 12(1): 1-2. Subject: 15.1

Williams, John R. The ethics activities of the World Medical Association. *Science and Engineering Ethics* 2005 January; 11(1): 7-12. Subject: 2.4

Williams, John R. International medical ethics [opinion]. *World Hospitals and Health Services* 2005; 41(1): 47-48. Subject: 2.1

Williams, John R. UNESCO's proposed declaration on bioethics and human rights — a bland compromise. *Developing World Bioethics* 2005 September; 5(3): 210-215. Subject: 2.1

Williams, Kevin W. Managing physician financial conflicts of interest in clinical trials conducted in the private practice setting. *Food and Drug Law Journal* 2004; 59(1): 45-77. Subject: 7.3

Williams, Melanie. An ethics ensemble: abortion, Thomson, Finnis and the case of the violin-player. *Ratio Juris* 2004 September; 17(3): 381-397. Subject: 12.1

Williams, Michael A.; Haywood, Carlton, Jr. Critical care research on patients with advance directives or do-not-resuscitate status: ethical challenges for clinician-investigators. *Critical Care Medicine* 2003 March; 31(3, Supplement): S167-S171. Subject: 18.5.1

Williams, Rowan; Murphy-O'Connor, Cormac. From the right to die to the duty to die? *Dolentium Hominum* 2004; 19(3): 47-49. Subject: 20.5.1

Williams, Thomas D. The least of my brethren: the ethics of heterologous embryo transfer. *Human Life Review* 2005 Summer; 31(3): 87-98. Subject: 14.4

Williams, Tricia. Paternalism and autonomy in dentistry. *Update [Loma Linda University Center for Christian Bioethics]* 2002 March; 17(3): 2-7. Subject: 8.1

Williamson, Charlotte. Withholding policies from patients restricts their autonomy. *BMJ: British Medical Journal* 2005 November 5; 331(7524): 1078-1080. Subject: 9.1

Williamson, Emma; Goodenough, Trudy; Kent, Julie; Ashcroft, Richard. Children's participation in genetic epidemiology: consent and control. *In:* Tutton, Richard; Corrigan, Oonagh, eds. Genetic Databases: Socio-ethical Issues in the Collection and Use of DNA. New York: Routledge; 2004: 139-160. Subject: 18.5.2

Williamson, Shanti. Sex(ist) selection? *Medical Law International* 2004; 6(3): 185-206. Subject: 14.3

Williams-Jones, Bryn. Knowledge commons or economic engine — what's a university for? [editorial]. *Journal of Medical Ethics* 2005 May; 31(5): 249-250. Subject: 1.3.9

Williams-Jones, Bryn; Corrigan, Oonagh P. Rhetoric and hype: where's the 'ethics' in pharmacogenomics? *American Journal of Pharmacogenomics* 2003; 3(6): 375-383. Subject: 15.1

Willis, Evan. Public health and the 'new genetics': balancing individual and collective outcomes. *In:* Bunton, Robin; Petersen, Alan, eds. Genetic Governance: Health, Risk and Ethics in the Biotech Era. New York: Routledge; 2005: 155-169. Subject: 15.3

Willis, Evan. Public health, private genes: the social context of genetic biotechnologies. *Critical Public Health* 1998 June; 8(2): 131-139. Subject: 15.1

Willis, Mark. Not this pig: dignity, imagination, and informed consent. *In:* Van Cleve, John Vickery, ed. Genetics, Disability, and Deafness. Washington, DC: Gallaudet University Press; 2004: 174-185. Subject: 15.1

Willison, Donald J. Trends in collection, use and disclosure of personal information in contemporary health research: challenges for research governance. *Health Law Review* 2005; 13(2-3): 107-113. Subject: 8.4

Willmott, Lindy. Surrogacy: ill-conceived rights. *Journal of Law and Medicine* 2002 November; 10(2): 198-220. Subject: 14.2

See SUBJECT HEADING KEY FOR SECTION II on inside back cover

Wills, David J. A survey of nurses attitudes to AIDS related issues. *New Zealand Nursing Forum* 1990 November-December; 18(4): 7-9. Subject: 9.5.6

Wills, Nathan J. A tripartite threat to medical records privacy: technology, HIPAA's privacy rule and the USA Patriot Act. *Journal of Law and Health* 2002-2003; 17(2): 271-296. Subject: 8.4

Wilmshurst, Peter. Fraud in research. *Clinical Medicine* 2002 March-April; 2(2): 159-160. Subject: 1.3.9

Wilmut, Ian; West, Michael D.; Lanza, Robert P.; Gearhart, John D.; Smith, Austin; Colman, Alan; Trounson, Alan O.; Campbell, Keith H. Human embryonic stem cells [letter]. *Science* 2005 December 23; 310(5756): 1903. Subject: 18.5.4

Wilson, Clare. Miracle weed: cannabis can be a lifeline, and a fortunate few will soon get it on prescription. *New Scientist* 2005 February 5-11; 185(2485): 38-41. Subject: 9.5.1

Wilson, Donna M. Highlighting the role of policy in nursing practice through a comparison of "DNR" policy influences and "no CPR" decision influences. *Nursing Outlook* 1996 November-December; 44(6): 272-279. Subject: 20.5.1

Wilson, Elisabeth; Grumbach, Kevin; Huebner, Jeffrey; Agrawal, Jaya; Bindman, Andrew B. Medical student, physician, and public perceptions of health care disparities. *Family Medicine* 2004 November-December; 36(10): 715-721. Subject: 9.2

Wilson, Hamish J. In that case. Response [case study]. *Journal of Bioethical Inquiry* 2005; 2(3): 180-181. Subject: 9.5.1

Wilson, Jane. To know or not to know? Genetic ignorance, autonomy and paternalism. *Bioethics* 2005 October; 19(5-6): 492-504. Subject: 15.1

Wilson, John T.; Kearns, G.; Springer, M.A. Role of the research-subject locator (RSL) in the performance of a pediatric drug trial. *Journal of Clinical Pharmacology* 2003 November; 43(11): 1196-1202. Subject: 18.2

Wilson, Mark. Vulnerable subjects and Canadian research governance. *IRB: Ethics and Human Research* 2005 November-December; 27(6): 9-11. Subject: 18.2

Wilson, Phil. Jehovah's Witness children: when religion and the law collide. *Paediatric Nursing* 2005 April; 17(3): 34-37. Subject: 8.3.4

Wilson, Robin Fretwell. Autonomy suspended: using female patients to teach intimate exams without their knowledge or consent. *Journal of Health Care Law and Policy* 2005; 8(2): 240-263. Subject: 8.3.1

Wilson, Robin Fretwell. Unauthorized practice: teaching pelvic examination on women under anesthesia [opinion]. *JAMWA: Journal of the American Medical Women's Association* 2003 Fall; 58(4): 217-220. Subject: 8.3.1

Wilson, Sarah. Identity, genealogy, and the social family: the case of donor insemination. *International Journal of Law, Policy, and the Family* 1997; 11(2): 270-297. Subject: 14.2

Winch, Sarah. Ethics, government and sexual health: insights from Foucault. *Nursing Ethics* 2005 March; 12(2): 177-186. Subject: 4.1.3

Wingfield, Joy; Bissell, Paul; Anderson, Claire. The scope of pharmacy ethics — an evaluation of the international research literature, 1990-2002. *Social Science and Medicine* 2004 June; 58(12): 2383-2396. Subject: 9.7

Winkelmann, Bernhard R.; Prickett, Katie. Pharmacogenomics, genetic testing and ethnic variability: tackling the ethical questions [interview]. *Pharmacogenomics* 2003 September; 4(5): 531-535. Subject: 15.1

Winkler, Eva C. The ethics of policy writing: how should hospitals deal with moral disagreement about controversial medical practices? *Journal of Medical Ethics* 2005 October; 31(10): 559-566. Subject: 9.1

Winkler, Eva C.; Gruen, Russell L. First principles: substantive ethics for healthcare organizations. *Journal of Healthcare Management* 2005 March-April; 50(2): 109-119. Subject: 9.1

Winner, Langdon. Resistance is futile: the posthuman condition and its advocates. *In:* Baillie, Harold W.; Casey, Timothy K., eds. Is Human Nature Obsolete? Genetics Bioengineering, and the Future of the Human Condition. Cambridge, MA: MIT Press; 2005: 385-411. Subject: 15.1

Winship, Ingrid; Marbrook, John. Ethical considerations relating to research in human genetics. *Auckland City, New Zealand: Health Research Council of New Zealand,* 1998 December: 1-12. Subject: 18.2

Winslade, William J.; Tovino, Stacey A. Research with brain-injured subjects. *Journal of Head Trauma Rehabilitation* 2004 November-December; 19(6): 513-515. Subject: 18.5.6

Winslow, Gerald R. Christian theology and the Hippocratic Oath. *Update [Loma Linda University Center for Christian Bioethics]* 1998 March; 14(1): 6 p. Subject: 6

Winston, Carole A.; Leshner, Paula; Kramer, Jennifer; Allen, Gillian. Overcoming barriers to access and utilization of hospice and palliative care services in African-American communities. *Omega: Journal of Death and Dying* 2004-2005; 50(2): 151-163. Subject: 20.4.1

Winzelberg, Gary S.; Hanson, Laura C.; Tulsky, James A. Beyond autonomy: diversifying end-of-life decision-making approaches to serve patients and families. *Journal of the American Geriatrics Society* 2005 June; 53(6): 1046-1050. Subject: 20.5.1

Wirshing, Donna A.; Sergi, Mark J.; Mintz, Jim. A videotape intervention to enhance the informed consent process for medical and psychiatric treatment research.

American Journal of Psychiatry 2005 January; 162(1): 186-188. Subject: 18.5.6

Wirtz, Veronika; Cribb, Alan; Barber, Nick. Reimbursement decisions in health policy — extending our understanding of the elements of decision-making. *Health Policy* 2005 September 8; 73(3): 330-338. Subject: 9.4

Wise, M.E. Jan. Understanding, not wisdom, needed for capacity [letter]. *BMJ: British Medical Journal* 2005 July 30; 331(7511): 294. Subject: 8.3.2

Wisser, Josef. Der menschliche Embryo vor der Implantation—Gedanken aus der vorgeburtlichen Medizin. *In:* Maio, Giovanni; Just, Hanjörg, eds. Die Forschung an embryonalen Stammzellen in ethischer und rechtlicher Perspektive. Baden-Baden: Nomos Verlagsgesellschaft; 2003: 42-51. Subject: 4.4

Wissow, Larry. Does the journal need a special policy for ethical aspects of research in professional education? [editorial]. *Patient Education and Counseling* 2005 January; 56(1): 1-2. Subject: 18.5.1

Witek, Rafal. Ethics and patentability in biotechnology. *Science and Engineering Ethics* 2005 January; 11(1): 105-111. Subject: 15.8

Witte, Courtney. Cord blood storage: property and liability issues. *Journal of Legal Medicine* 2005 June; 26(2): 275-292. Subject: 19.4

Wivel, Ashley. Abortion policy and politics on the Lane Committee of Enquiry, 1971-1974. *Social History of Medicine* 1998 April; 11(1): 109-135. Subject: 12.4.1

Wlasienko, Pawel. Ethical and legal aspects in teaching students of medicine. *Science and Engineering Ethics* 2005 January; 11(1): 75-80. Subject: 7.3

Wocial, Lucia D.; Robertson, John A. Neonatal care for premature infants [letter and reply]. *Hastings Center Report* 2005 January-February; 35(1): 6-7. Subject: 9.5.7

Wogalter, Michael S.; Howe, Julie E.; Sifuentes, Alla H.; Luginbuhl, James. On the adequacy of legal documents: factors that influence informed consent. *Ergonomics* 1999; 42(4): 593-613. Subject: 18.3

Wolbring, Gregor. The animal farm philosophy of genetic discrimination. *Revista de Derecho y Genoma-Humano / Law and the Human Genome Review* 2004 July-December; (21): 165-184. Subject: 15.1

Wolbring, Gregor. Disability rights and genetic discrimination. *In:* Krimsky, Sheldon; Shorett, Peter, eds. Rights and Liberties in the Biotech Age: Why We Need a Genetic Bill of Rights. Lanham: Rowman and Littlefield Publishers; 2005: 178-182. Subject: 15.3

Wolbring, Gregor. A disability rights approach to eugenics. *In:* Krimsky, Sheldon; Shorett, Peter, eds. Rights and Liberties in the Biotech Age: Why We Need a Genetic Bill of Rights. Lanham: Rowman and Littlefield Publishers; 2005: 146-150. Subject: 15.5

Wolf, Jeffrey S.; Chiu, Alexander G.; Palmer, James N.; O'Malley, Bert W., Jr.; Schofield, Kimberly; Taylor, Rodney J. Informed consent in endoscopic sinus surgery: the patient perspective. *Laryngoscope* 2005 March; 115(3): 492-494. Subject: 8.3.1

Wolf, Susan M. Assessing physician compliance with the rules for euthanasia and assisted suicide [editorial]. *Archives of Internal Medicine* 2005 August 8-22; 165(15): 1677- 1679. Subject: 20.5.1

Wolf, Susan M. Death and dying in America: Schiavo's implications [opinion]. *Minnesota Medicine* 2005 June; 88(6): 34-35. Subject: 20.5.1

Wolf, Susan M.; Kahn, Jeffrey P. Bioethics matures: the field faces the future. *Hastings Center Report* 2005 July-August; 35(4): 22-24. Subject: 2.3

Wolfberg, Jennifer. Two kinds of statistics, the kind you look up and the kind you make up: a critical analysis of comparative provider statistics and the doctrine of informed consent. *Pepperdine Law Review* 2002; 29(3): 585-608. Subject: 8.3.1

Wolfson, Adam. Killing off the dying? *Public Interest* 1998 Spring; 131: 50-70. Subject: 20.7

Wolfson, Jay. Erring on the side of Theresa Schiavo: reflections of the special guardian ad litem. *Hastings Center Report* 2005 May-June; 35(3): 16-19. Subject: 20.5.1

Wollin, David A.; Avanzato, Joseph. Informed consent: a primer for health care practitioners [opinion]. *Medicine and Health, Rhode Island* 1996 April; 79(4): 155-157. Subject: 8.3.1

Wolowelsky, Joel B.; Grazi, Richard V. Future directions. *In:* Grazi, Richard V. Overcoming Infertility: A Guide for Jewish Couples. New Milford, Conn.: Toby, 2005: 425-440. Subject: 14.1

Wolpe, Paul Root. Ethics and social policy in research on the neuroscience of human sexuality [opinion]. *Nature Neuroscience* 2004 October; 7(10): 1031-1033. Subject: 18.4

Wolpe, Paul Root; Foster, Kenneth R.; Langleben, Daniel D. Emerging neurotechnologies for lie-detection: promises and perils. *American Journal of Bioethics* 2005 March-April; 5(2): 39-49. Subject: 17.1

Wolpe, Paul Root; Foster, Kenneth R.; Langleben, Daniel D. Response to commentators on "Emerging Neurotechnologies for Lie-Detection: Promises and Perils?" [letter]. *American Journal of Bioethics [Online]* 2005 March-April; 5(2): W5. Subject: 17.1

Wolpe, Paul Root; Robinson, Walter M. Bioethics in space (dialogue). *Medical Ethics Newsletter [Lahey Clinic]* 2005 Winter; 12(1): 10-11. Subject: 2.1

Wong, J.G.W.S.; Poon, Y.; Hui, E.C. "I can put the medicine in his soup, doctor!" [case study]. *Journal of Medical Ethics* 2005 May; 31(5): 262-265. Subject: 17.4

Wood, Alastair J.J.; Drazen, Jeffrey M.; Greene, Michael F. A sad day for science at the FDA [opinion]. *New England Journal of Medicine* 2005 September 22; 353(12): 1197-1199. Subject: 11.1

Wood, Christopher P.J.; Blackburn, Simon C. Informed consent: is frightening patients really in their best interests? [letter]. *BMJ: British Medical Journal* 2005 November 5; 331(7524): 1082. Subject: 8.3.1

Wood, John. The challenge of individual rights: mental health review tribunals [editorial]. *British Journal of Psychiatry* 1995 April; 166(4): 417-420. Subject: 9.2

Wood, Susan F. Women's health and the FDA [opinion]. *New England Journal of Medicine* 2005 October 20; 353(16): 1650-1651. Subject: 11.1

Woodhouse, S.P.; Wilkinson, T.J.; Watson, D.R.; Sainsbury, R.; Kidd, J.E.; Lowe, J.; Kerridge, I. Implementation of guidelines for no-CPR orders [letters and reply]. *Australian and New Zealand Journal of Medicine* 1998 February; 28(1): 67-68. Subject: 20.5.1

Woods, Martin. Nursing ethics education: are we really delivering the good(s)? *Nursing Ethics* 2005 January; 12(1): 5-18. Subject: 4.1.3

Woods, Simon. Moral progress. *In:* Häyry, Matti; Takala, Tuija; Herissone-Kelly, Peter, eds. Bioethics and Social Reality. New York: Rodopi, 2005: 137-148. Subject: 8.1

Woods, Simon. Persons and personal identity. *Nursing Philosophy* 2000 October; 1(2): 169-172. Subject: 4.4

Woods, Simon. Respect for persons, autonomy and palliative care. *Medicine, Health Care and Philosophy: A European Journal* 2005; 8(2): 243-253. Subject: 20.5.1

Woodsong, Cynthia; Karim, Quarraisha Abdool. A model designed to enhance informed consent: experiences from the HIV Prevention Trials Network. *American Journal of Public Health* 2005 March; 95(3): 412-419. Subject: 8.3.1

Woodward, Bryan J.; Norton, W.J.; Neuberg, R.W. Case report: grandmother, mother and another — an intergenerational surrogacy using anonymous donated embryos. *Reproductive BioMedicine Online [electronic]* 2004 September; 9(3): 260-263. Available: http://www.rbmonline.com/index.html [14 July 2005]. Subject: 14.2

Wood-Harper, Janice. Informing education policy on MMR: balancing individual freedoms and collective responsibilities for the promotion of public health. *Nursing Ethics* 2005 January; 12(1): 43-58. Subject: 9.5.1

Woogara, Jay. International Centre for Nursing Ethics summer school: teaching ethics to healthcare students, 21-23 July 2004, European Institute of Health and Medical sciences, University of Surrey, Guildford, UK. *Nursing Ethics* 2005 January; 12(1): 108-109. Subject: 2.3

Woogara, Jay. Patients' privacy of the person and human rights. *Nursing Ethics* 2005 May; 12(3): 273-287. Subject: 8.4

Woogara, Jay. Patients' rights to privacy and dignity in the NHS. *Nursing Standard* 2005 January 12-18; 19(18): 33-37. Subject: 8.4

Woolf, Steven H.; Chan, Evelyn C.Y.; Harris, Russell; Sheridan, Stacey L.; Braddock, Clarence H., III; Kaplan, Robert M.; Krist, Alex; O'Connor, Annette M.; Tunis, Sean. Promoting informed choice: transforming health care to dispense knowledge for decision making. *Annals of Internal Medicine* 2005 August 16; 143(4): 293-300. Subject: 8.3.1

Woolhead, Gillian; Calnan, Michael; Dieppe, Paul; Tadd, Win. Dignity in older age: what do older people in the United Kingdom think? *Age and Ageing* 2004; 33(2): 165-170. Subject: 4.4

Working Group of Intensive Care in the Delivery Room of Extremely Premature Newborns; Verlato, Giovanna; Gobber, Daniela; Drago, Donatella; Chiandetti, Lino; Drigo, Paola. Guidelines for resuscitation in the delivery room of extremely preterm infants. *Journal of Child Neurology* 2004 January; 19(1): 31-34. Subject: 20.5.2

World Association of Medical Editors [WAME]. Ghost writing initiated by commercial companies. *JGIM: Journal of General Internal Medicine* 2005 June; 20(6): 549. Subject: 1.3.7

World Federation of Catholic Medical Associations [FIAMC]. Considerations of the scientific and ethical problems related to vegetative state. *Medical Ethics and Bioethics / Medicinska Etika & Bioetika* 2004 Spring-Summer; 11(1-2): 20-21. Subject: 20.5.1

World Health Organization [WHO]. Ethical choices in long-term care: what does justice require? Geneva, Switzerland: World Health Organization 2002; 90 p. [Online]. Available: http://wholibdoc.who.int/publications/2002/9291562285.pdf [7 November 2005]. Subject: 9.5.1

World Health Organization [WHO]; Joint United Nations Programme on HIV/AIDS [UNAIDS]. Consultation on Ethics and Equitable Access to Treatment and Care for HIV/AIDS. Summary of Issues and Discussion. Geneva, Switzerland: World Health Organization 2004; 29 p. [Online]. Available: http://www.who.int/ethics/en/equity_art_meeting_report_e.pdf [4 March 2004]. Subject: 9.5.6

World Health Organization [WHO]. Joint United Nations Programme on HIV/AIDS [UNAIDS]. Consultation on ethics and equitable access to treatment and care for HIV/AIDS. Geneva, Switzerland: World Health Organization 2004; 29 p. [Online]. Available: http://www.who.int/hiv/pub/advocacy/en/ethicsmeetingreport_e.pdf [27 May 2005]. Subject: 9.5.6

Subject = NRCBL Primary Classification Number; See inside front cover

Worth, Allison. Ethical issues in the discharge of patients from hospital to community care. *In:* Chadwick, Ruth; Levitt, Mairi, eds. Ethical Issues in Community Health Care. New York: Arnold; 1998: 135-145. Subject: 9.1

Wright, James R., Jr. Public consultation on xenotransplantation. *Transplantation* 2004 October 27; 78(8): 1112-1113. Subject: 19.1

Wright, Jessica. Medically necessary organ transplants for prisoners: who is responsible for payment? *Boston College Law Review* 1998 September; 39(5): 1251-1292. Subject: 19.6

Wright, Linda; Faith, Karen; Richardson, Robert; Grant, David. Ethical guidelines for the evaluation of living organ donors. *Canadian Journal of Surgery* 2004 December; 47(6): 408-413. Subject: 19.5

Wright, Linda; Ross, Kelley; Daar, Abdallah S. The roles of a bioethicist on an organ transplantation service. *American Journal of Transplantation* 2005 April; 5(4 Part 1): 821-826. Subject: 2.1

Wright, Scott M.; Carrese, Joseph A. Which values do attending physicians try to pass on to house officers? *Medical Education* 2001 October; 35(10): 941-945. Subject: 7.3

Wright, Stephen. Speak up for life. *Nursing Standard* 2004 September 15-21; 19(1): 22-23. Subject: 20.7

Wu, Albert W. Is there an obligation to disclose near-misses in medical care? *In:* Sharpe, Virginia A., ed. Accountability: Patient Safety and Policy Reform. Washington, DC: Georgetown University Press; 2004: 135-142. Subject: 9.8

Wu, Annie O. Surpassing the material: the human rights implications of informed consent in bioprospecting cells derived from indigenous people groups. *Washington University Law Quarterly* 2000 Fall; 78(3): 979-1003. Subject: 15.10

Wuerl, Donald. Pastoral letter on human, embryonic stem cell research. *Origins* 2005 April 7; 34(42): 674-676. Subject: 18.5.4

Wueste, Daniel E. A philosophical yet user-friendly framework for ethical decision making in critical care nursing. *Dimensions of Critical Care Nursing* 2005 March-April; 24(2): 70-79. Subject: 2.1

Wyke, Alexandra. Inherited wealth. *Economist* 1988 April 30; 307: 3-18. Subject: 15.1

Wynia, Matthew K. Consequentialism and harsh interrogations. *American Journal of Bioethics* 2005 January-February; 5(1): 4-6. Subject: 21.4

Wynia, Matthew K. Judging public health research: epistemology, public health and the law. *American Journal of Bioethics* 2005 November-December; 5(6): 4-7. Subject: 1.3.9

Wynia, Matthew K. Oversimplifications I: physicians don't do public health. *American Journal of Bioethics* 2005 July-August; 5(4): 4-5. Subject: 9.1

Wynia, Matthew K. Oversimplifications II: public health ethics ignores individual rights. *American Journal of Bioethics* 2005 September-October; 5(5): 6-8. Subject: 9.1

Wynia, Matthew K. Public health principlism: the precautionary principle and beyond. *American Journal of Bioethics* 2005 May-June; 5(3): 3-4. Subject: 9.1

Wynia, Matthew K. Science, faith and AIDS: the battle over harm reduction. *American Journal of Bioethics* 2005 March-April; 5(2): 3-4. Subject: 9.5.6

Wynia, Matthew K.; Macauley, Robert. Civil disobedience: the devil is in the details [letter and reply]. *Hastings Center Report* 2005 July-August; 35(4): 4-6. Subject: 4.1.2

Wynn, Francine. Nursing and the concept of life: towards an ethics of testimony. *Nursing Philosophy* 2002 July; 3(2): 120-132. Subject: 20.5.2

Wynn, Francine; Peter, Elizabeth. Nurses and quarantine: reflections upon the SARS crisis in Toronto [editorial]. *Nursing Inquiry* 2003 December; 10(4): 207-208. Subject: 8.1

Wynne, Brian. Interpreting public concerns about GMOs—questions of meaning. *In:* Deane-Drummond, Celia; Szerszynski, Bronislaw, eds. Re- ordering Nature: Theology, Society and the New Genetics. New York: T & T Clark; 2003: 221-248. Subject: 15.1

Wyszynski, Diego F.; Perandones, Claudia; Bennun, Ricardo D. Attitudes toward prenatal diagnosis, termination of pregnancy, and reproduction by parents of children with nonsyndromic oral clefts in Argentina. *Prenatal Diagnosis* 2003 September; 23(9): 722-727. Subject: 15.2

X

Xenakis, Stephen N. From the medics, unhealthy silence. *Washington Post* 2005 February 6; p. B4. Subject: 21.4

Xu, Yu; Zhang, Jianhui. One size doesn't fit all: ethics of international nurse recruitment from the conceptual framework of stakeholder interests. *Nursing Ethics* 2005 November; 12(6): 571-581. Subject: 21.6

Y

Yaguchi, Arino; Truog, Robert D.; Curtis, J. Randall; Luce, John M.; Levy, Mitchell M.; Mélot, Christian; Vincent, Jean-Louis. International differences in end-of-life attitudes in the intensive care unit. *Archives of Internal Medicine* 2005 September 26; 165(17): 1970-1975. Subject: 20.5.1

Yamin, Alicia Ely. Challenges and possibilities for innovative praxis in health and human rights: reflections from Peru. *Health and Human Rights: An International Journal* 2002; 6(1): 35-62. Subject: 9.2

Yamin, Alicia Ely. Not just a tragedy: access to medications as a right under international law. *Boston University International Law Journal* 2003 Fall; 21(2): 325-371. Subject: 9.7

Yamin, Alicia Ely. Promising but elusive engagements: combining human rights and public health to promote women's well-being. *Health and Human Rights: An International Journal* 2004; 8(1): 63-92. Subject: 9.1

Yamin, Alicia Ely. The right to health under international law and its relevance to the United States. *American Journal of Public Health* 2005 July; 95(7): 1156-1161. Subject: 9.2

Yang, Anthony D.; Bentrem, David J.; Pappas, Sam G.; Amundsen, Elizabeth; Ward, James E.; Ujiki, Michael B.; Angelos, Peter. Advance directive use among patients undergoing high-risk operations. *American Journal of Surgery* 2004 July; 188(1): 98-101. Subject: 20.5.4

Yang, Che-Ming; Chung, Chun-Chih; Lu, Meei-Shiow; Lin, Chiou-Fen; Chen, Jiun-Shyan. Ethical attitudes on human cloning among professionals in Taiwan and the policy implications for regulation. *Issues in Law and Medicine* 2005 Summer; 21(1): 35-44. Subject: 14.5

Yang, Huanming. Advances in science and progress of humanity: a global perspective on DNA sampling. *In:* Knoppers, Bartha Maria, ed. Populations and Genetics: Legal and Socio-Ethical Perspectives. Boston: Martinus Nijhoff; 2003: 395-404. Subject: 15.1

Yap, H.Y.; Joynt, G.M.; Gomersall, C.D. Ethical attitudes of intensive care physicians in Hong Kong: questionnaire survey. *Hong Kong Medical Journal* 2004 August; 10(4): 244-250. Subject: 20.3.2

Yarborough, Mark. Deciding for others at the end of life: storytelling and moral agency. *Journal of Clinical Ethics* 2005 Summer; 16(2): 127-143. Subject: 20.4.1

Yardley, William. For role in suicide, a friend to the end is now facing jail. *New York Times* 2005 March 4; p. A1, B7. Subject: 20.7

Yates, Ferdinand D., Jr. Clinical ethics case consultation [case study]. *Ethics and Medicine* 2005 Fall; 21(3): 163-165. Subject: 20.5.4

Yavarone, Mark. Is bioethics "pastorally relevant?". *Ethics and Medics* 2003 September; 28(9): 1-2. Subject: 2.1

Yazigi, Alexandre; Riachi, Moussa; Dabbar, Georges. Withholding and withdrawal of life-sustaining treatment in a Lebanese intensive care unit: a prospective observational study. *Intensive Care Medicine* 2005 April; 31(4): 562-567. Subject: 20.5.1

Yealy, Donald M.; Paris, Paul M.; Vukmir, Rade B.; Kim, David T. Prehospital IRBs and consent . . . [letter and reply]. *Annals of Emergency Medicine* 1994 October; 24(4): 759-760. Subject: 18.2

Yearby, Ruqaiijah. Good enough to use for research, but not good enough to benefit from the results of that research: are the clinical HIV vaccine trials in Africa unjust? *DePaul Law Review* 2004 Spring; 53(3): 1127-1154. Subject: 18.5.9

Yentis, S.M. The use of patients for learning and maintaining practical skills. *Journal of the Royal Society of Medicine* 2005 July; 98(7): 299-302. Subject: 7.2

Yeo, Michael; Brook, Andrew. The moral framework of confidentiality and the electronic panopticon. *In:* Koggel, Christine M.; Furlong, Allannah; Levin, Charles, eds. Confidential Relationships: Psychoanalytical, Ethical, and Legal Contexts. New York: Rodopi; 2003: 85-112. Subject: 8.4

Yesley, Michael. What's in a name? Bioethics — and human rights — at UNESCO. *Hastings Center Report* 2005 March-April; 35(2): 8. Subject: 2.1

Yeun, Eun-Ja; Kwon, Young-Mi; Kim, Hung-Kyu. A Q-methodological study on nursing students' attitudes toward nursing ethics. *Journal of Korean Academy of Nursing* 2004 December; 34(8): 1434-1442. Subject: 2.1

Yeung, Patrick, Jr. When does human life begin? [opinion]. *Ethics and Medicine* 2005 Summer; 21(2): 69-71. Subject: 4.4

Yidong, Gong. China science foundation takes action against 60 grantees [news]. *Science* 2005 September 16; 309(5742): 1798-1799. Subject: 1.3.9

Yin, Xiuyun; Li, Benfu; Cong, Yali. Should this 96-year-old woman be allowed to die? *Medical Ethics Newsletter [Lahey Clinic]* 2005 Winter; 12(1): 3, 12. Subject: 20.5.1

Yip, Kam-shing. Political dominance of mental health services in the People's Republic of China [opinion]. *Administration and Policy in Mental Health* 2004 July; 31(6): 495-502. Subject: 17.1

Yiting, Li; Döring, Ole; Fang, Liu; Baoqi, Su. End-of-life care in China: a view from Beijing. *In:* Blank, Robert H.; Merrick, Janna C., eds. End-of-Life Decision Making: A Cross-National Study. Cambridge, MA: MIT Press; 2005: 33-59. Subject: 20.4.1

Yoo, Kristin. Self-prescribing medication: regulating prescription drug sales on the Internet. *John Marshall Journal of Computer and Information Law* 2001 Fall; 20(1): 57-89. Subject: 9.7

Young, Amanda J.; Ofori-Boateng, Terri; Rodriguez, Keri L.; Plowman, Judith L. Meaning and agency in discussing end-of-life care: a study of elderly veterans' values and interpretations. *Qualitative Health Research* 2003 October; 13(8): 1039-1062. Subject: 20.5.4

Young, Chari J. Telemedicine: patient privacy rights of electronic medical records. *UMKC Law Review* 1998 Summer; 66(4): 921-937. Subject: 8.4

Subject = NRCBL Primary Classification Number; See inside front cover

Young, Charles; Horton, Richard. Putting clinical trials into context [opinion]. *Lancet* 2005 July 9-15; 366(9480): 107-108. Subject: 18.1

Young, Diony. Will exercising informed consent stop "unfortunate experiments"? [editorial]. *Birth* 2005 March; 32(1): 1-3. Subject: 18.3

Young, Emma. Laws fail to stop India's organ trade [news]. *New Scientist* 2005 October 22-28; 188(2522): 20. Subject: 19.5

Young, Ernlé W.D. Ethical issues at the end of life. *Stanford Law and Policy Review* 1998 Spring; 9(2): 267-288. Subject: 20.5.1

Young, Hilary Hughes. Assisted suicide and physician liability. *Review of Litigation* 1992; 11(3): 623-656. Subject: 20.7

Young, Janine; Flores, Glenn; Berman, Stephen. Providing life-saving health care to undocumented children: controversies and ethical issues. *Pediatrics* 2004 November; 114(5): 1316-1320. Subject: 9.5.10

Young, John L. Comment: refusing to give up on forensic research. *Journal of the American Academy of Psychiatry and the Law* 2005; 33(3): 368-370. Subject: 18.5.6

Young, Katherine K. Health. *In:* Schweiker, William, ed. The Blackwell Companion to Religious Ethics. Malden, MA: Blackwell Pub.; 2005: 519-526. Subject: 4.2

Young, Robert. Should voluntary euthanasia be legally permitted? *Res Publica* 1996; 5(1): 1-7. Subject: 20.5.1

Young, Simon N.; Joffe, Russell T. Ethical conduct of journal editors [editorial]. *Journal of Psychiatry and Neuroscience* 2004 September; 29(5): 334-336. Subject: 1.3.7

Youngner, Stuart J. Informed consent. *In:* Youngner, Stuart J.; Anderson, Martha W.; Schapiro, Renie, eds. Transplanting Human Tissue: Ethics, Policy, and Practice. New York: Oxford University Press; 2004: 168-185. Subject: 19.5

Youngner, Stuart J. School DNAR in the real world. *American Journal of Bioethics* 2005 January-February; 5(1): 66-67. Subject: 20.5.2

Yudin, Boris. Human experimentation in Russia/the Soviet Union in the first half of the 20th century. *In:* Roelcke, Volker; Maio, Giovanni, eds. Twentieth Century Ethics of Human Subjects Research: Historical Perspectives on Values, Practices, and Regulations. Stuttgart: Franz Steiner Verlag; 2004: 99-110. Subject: 18.1

Yun, Young Ho; Lee, Chang Geol; Kim, Si-young; Lee, Sang-wook; Heo, Dae Seog; Kim, Jun Suk; Lee, Keun Seok; Hong, Young Seon; Lee, Jung Suk; You, Chang Hoon. The attitudes of cancer patients and their families toward the disclosure of terminal illness. *Journal of Clinical Oncology* 2004 January 15; 22(2): 307-314. Subject: 8.2

Z

Zachry, Woodie M.; Ginsburg, Diane B. Patient autonomy and the regulation of direct-to-consumer advertising. *Clinical Therapeutics* 2001 December; 23(12): 2024-2037. Subject: 9.7

Zaner, Richard M. "But how can we choose?". *Journal of Clinical Ethics* 2005 Fall; 16(3): 218-222. Subject: 9.5.5

Zaner, Richard M. Reflections on the appointment of Edmund Pellegrino to the President's Council on Bioethics. *American Journal of Bioethics [Online]* 2005 September- October; 5(5): W25-W26. Subject: 2.4

Zaner, Richard M. Visions and re-visions: life and the accident of birth. *In:* Baillie, Harold W.; Casey, Timothy K., eds. Is Human Nature Obsolete? Genetics Bioengineering, and the Future of the Human Condition. Cambridge, MA: MIT Press; 2005: 177-207. Subject: 15.1

Zaner, Richard M. A work in progress. *Theoretical Medicine and Bioethics* 2005; 26(1): 89-104. Subject: 2.1

Zaner, Richard M.; Beauchamp, Tom L. Reflections on the appointment of Dr. Edmund Pellegrino to the President's Council on Bioethics. *American Journal of Bioethics [Online]* 2005 November- December; 5(6): W8-W9. Subject: 2.4

Zanotti, Barbara J.; Becker, Rick A. Marching to the beat of a different drummer: is military law and mental health out-of-step after Jaffee v. Redmond? *Air Force Law Review* 1997; 41: 1-82. Subject: 17.2

Zaslawski, Chris; Davis, Susanna. The ethics of complementary and alternative medicine research: a case study of traditional Chinese medicine at the University of Technology, Sydney. *Monash Bioethics Review* 2005 July; 24(3): 52-60. Subject: 18.2

Zatz, Mayana. When science is not enough: fighting genetic disease in Brazil. *Science* 2005 April 1; 308(5718): 55-57. Subject: 15.2

Zayas, Luis H.; Torres, Luis R.; Malcolm, Joan; DesRosiers, Fabiana S. Clinicians' definitions of ethnically sensitive therapy. *Professional Psychology: Research and Practice* 1996 February; 27(1): 78-82. Subject: 17.1

Zenkich, Sabina. X marks the spot while Casey strikes out: two controversial abortion decisions. *Golden Gate University Law Review* 1993 Summer; 23(3): 1001- 1040. Subject: 12.4.1

Zerhouni, Elias. Memorandum (regarding new NIH ethics regulations). Bethesda, MD: National Institutes of Health 2005 February 1; 2 p. [Online]. Available: http://www.nih.gov/about/ethics/020105COImemo.pdf [2 February 2005]. Subject: 1.3.9

Zermansky, Arnold G. Including care home residents in clinical research is fraught [letter]. *BMJ: British Medical Journal* 2005 November 26; 331(7527): 1271-1272. Subject: 18.5.7

See SUBJECT HEADING KEY FOR SECTION II on inside back cover

Zernike, Kate. The difference between steroids and Ritalin is . . . . *New York Times* 2005 March 20; p. WK3. Subject: 9.7

Zetterström, Rolf. Decisions on therapeutic intervention in neonatal intensive care [editorial]. *Acta Paediatrica* 2004 February; 93(2): 148. Subject: 20.5.2

Zhang, Heather Xiaoquan; Locke, Catherine. Interpreting reproductive rights: institutional responses to the agenda in the 1990s. *Public Administration and Development* 2004 February; 24(1): 41-50. Subject: 14.1

Ziaja, Jacek; Cierpka, Lech; Król, Robert; Szczepanski, Marek S.; Tyrybon, Malgorzata; Sekta, Sylwia. Transplantation procedures in social awareness opinion poll of Silesian Province citizens on living donor organ transplantation. *Annals of Transplantation* 2003; 8(4): 43-45. Subject: 19.5

Zick, Cathleen D.; Mathews, Charles J.; Roberts, J. Scott; Cook-Deegan, Robert; Pokorski, Robert J.; Green, Robert C. Genetic testing for Alzheimer's disease and its impact on insurance purchasing behavior. *Health Affairs* 2005 March-April; 24(2): 483-490. Subject: 15.3

Ziegler, Stephen J. Physician-assisted suicide and criminal prosecution: are physicians at risk? *Journal of Law, Medicine and Ethics* 2005 Summer; 33(2): 349-358. Subject: 20.7

Zientek, David M. The Texas Advance Directives Act of 1999: an exercise in futility? *HEC (Healthcare Ethics Committee) Forum* 2005 December; 17(4): 245-259. Subject: 20.5.4

Zigmond, A.; Holland, A.J. Unethical mental health law; history repeats itself. *Journal of Mental Health Law* 2000 February: 50-57. Subject: 4.3

Zimmer, Franz-Josef; Sethmann, Svenja. The immoral gene: does it really exist? *Science and Engineering Ethics* 2005 January; 11(1): 97-104. Subject: 15.8

Zimmerli, Walter Ch. Natur als technische Kultur: Veränderung der Ethik durch Gentechnik. *In:* Baumann, Eva; Brink, Alexander; May, Arnd T.; Schröder; Peter; Schutzeichel, Corinna Iris, eds. Weltanschauliche Offenheit in der Bioethik. Berlin: Duncker & Humblot; 2004: 65-80. Subject: 5.1

Zimmerman, Rachel; Tomsho, Robert. Medical editor turns activist on drug trials. *Wall Street Journal* 2005 May 26; p. B1, B5. Subject: 1.3.9

Zimmerman, Richard Kent. Ethical analyses of vaccines grown in human cell strains derived from abortion: arguments and Internet search. *Vaccine* 2004 October 22; 22(31-32): 4238-4244. Subject: 9.7

Zimmerman, Susan V. Translating ethics into law: duties of care in health research involving humans. *Health Law Review* 2005; 13(2-3): 13-18. Subject: 18.2

Zinberg, Joel M.; Mariner, Wendy K.; Bloche, M. Gregg. The Supreme Court and managed-care liability [letter and replies]. *New England Journal of Medicine* 2005 January 13; 352(2): 201-203. Subject: 9.3.2

Zingmond, David S.; Wenger, Neil S. Regional and institutional variation in the initiation of early do-not-resuscitate orders. *Archives of Internal Medicine* 2005 August 8-22; 165(15): 1705-1712. Subject: 20.5.1

Zink, Sheldon; Wertlieb, Stacey. Response to commentators on "Examining the potential exploitation of UNOS policies" [letter]. *American Journal of Bioethics [Online]* 2005 September-October; 5(5): W15-W16. Subject: 19.6

Zink, Sheldon; Wertlieb, Stacey; Catalano, John; Marwin, Victor. Examining the potential exploitation of UNOS policies. *American Journal of Bioethics* 2005 July-August; 5(4): 6-10. Subject: 19.6

Zinser, Jason. The public's role in science policy. *American Journal of Bioethics* 2005 November-December; 5(6): 58-59. Subject: 4.4

Zion, Deborah. Caring for detained asylum seekers, human rights and bioethics [editorial]. *Australian and New Zealand Journal of Public Health* 2004 December; 28(6): 510-512. Subject: 21.1

Zion, Deborah. Community without communitarianism: HIV/AIDS research, prevention and treatment in Australia and the developing world. *Monash Bioethics Review* 2005 April; 24(2): 20-31. Subject: 9.5.6

Zion, Deborah. Does autonomy require freedom? The importance of options in international HIV/AIDS research. *Health Care Analysis: An International Journal of Health Care Philosophy and Policy* 2005 September; 13(3): 189-202. Subject: 9.5.6

Zipkin, Daniella A.; Steinman, Michael A. Interactions between pharmaceutical representatives and doctors in training: a thematic review. *JGIM: Journal of General Internal Medicine* 2005 August; 20(8): 777-786. Subject: 9.7

Zlotnik Shaul, Randi; Reid, Lynette; Essue, Beverley; Gibson, Julie; Marzinotto, Velma; Daneman, Denis. Dissemination to research subjects: operationalizing investigator accountability. *Accountability in Research* 2005 January-March; 12(1): 1-16. Subject: 18.2

Zoloth-Dorfman, Laurie. Standing at the gate: managed care and daily ethical choices. *Managed Care Medicine* 1994 November-December; 1: 26-27, 31-33, 37-38. Subject: 9.3.2

Zonana, Howard. AAPL's new ethics guidelines. *AAPL (American Academy of Psychiatry and the Law) Newsletter* 2005 September; 30(3): 5, 9. Subject: 2.4

Zonana, Howard. Physicians should not be agents of the police [opinion]. *Psychiatric Services* 2005 August; 56(8): 1021. Subject: 8.4

Zubatov, Alex. Does it make sense to use fiction as a guide to bioethics? [letter]. *Chronicle of Higher Education* 2005 July 8; 51(44): B13. Subject: 2.1

Zupancic, Karel; Meden, Helena; Tomazevic, Tomaz; Žnidaršic, Viktorija. The future law on infertility treatment and on biomedically assisted procreation in Slovenia. *Journal of Assisted Reproduction and Genetics* 2000 October; 17(9): 496-497. Subject: 14.1

Zupp, Jacqueline. Concern at animal research should not be dismissed [letter]. *Nature* 2005 October 20; 437(7062): 1089. Subject: 22.2

Zwanziger, Lee L. Biology, ethics, and public policy: deliberations at an unstable intersection [opinion]. *Anatomical Record. Part B, New Anatomist* 2003 December; 275(1): 185-189. Subject: 2.1

Zwillich, Todd. Financial ethics pit NIH scientists against government. *Lancet* 2005 August 13-19; 366(9485): 537-538. Subject: 1.3.9

Zwillich, Todd. Guidelines set ethical bar for US stem cell research. *Lancet* 2005 May 7-13; 365(9471): 1612. Subject: 18.5.4

Zwillich, Todd. US pharmacies vow to withhold emergency contraception. *Lancet* 2005 May 14-20; 365(9472): 1677-1678. Subject: 11.1

Anonymous

Abortion drugs must become WHO essential medicines [editorial]. *Lancet* 2005 May 28-June 3; 365(9474): 1826. Subject: 12.1

Abortion: facing facts [opinion]. *Christian Century* 2005 February 22; 122(4): 5. Subject: 12.3

Additional protocol to the convention for the protection of human rights and dignity of the human being with regard to the application of biology and medicine, on biomedical research. *Revista de Derecho y Genoma-Humano / Law and the Human Genome Review* 2004 July-December; (21): 201-214. Subject: 18.2

Adventist guidelines on assisted procreation. *Update [Loma Linda University Center for Christian Bioethics]* 1996 February; 12(1); 3 p. Subject: 14.1

Agency under siege: conflicts-of-interest at the US National Institutes of Health justify the agency's ethics crackdown [editorial]. *Nature* 2005 July 21; 436(7049): 304. Subject: 1.3.9

Anonymity vanishes for sperm donors [editorial]. *New Scientist* 2005 November 5-11; 188(2524): 3. Subject: 14.2

Appendix B: Bill of rights for donor families. *In:* Youngner, Stuart J.; Anderson, Martha W.; Schapiro, Renie, eds. Transplanting Human Tissue: Ethics, Policy, and Practice. New York: Oxford University Press; 2004: 199-202. Subject: 19.5

Appendix C: informed consent policy for tissue donation. *In:* Youngner, Stuart J.; Anderson, Martha W.; Schapiro, Renie, eds. Transplanting Human Tissue: Ethics, Policy, and Practice. New York: Oxford University Press; 2004: 203. Subject: 19.5

'Are you Jewish?' [news]. *New Scientist* 2005 July 9-15; 187(2507): 7. Subject: 15.3

Assessing the viability of a substantive due process right to in vitro fertilization. *Harvard Law Review* 2005 June; 118(8): 2792-2813. Subject: 14.4

Assisted dying elsewhere in Europe [news]. *Bulletin of Medical Ethics* 2003 October; (192): 5-6. Subject: 20.7

Bad medicine [editorial]. *Nature Medicine* 2005 March; 11(3): 235. Subject: 1.3.9

Ban on import of embryos in Israel [news]. *European Journal of Obstetrics, Gynecology, and Reproductive Biology* 2001 November; 99(1): 1. Subject: 14.4

Beyond the yuck factor: revulsion isn't reason enough to close the door on controversial research [editorial]. *New Scientist* 2005 June 25-July 1; 186(2505): 5. Subject: 15.1

Bioethics. *In:* Concise Routledge Encyclopedia of Philosophy. New York: Routledge; 2000: 89. Subject: 2.1

Breach of trust: events in South Korea have highlighted a deep-seated problem [editorial]. *New Scientist* 2005 December 24-2006 January 6; 188(2531-2532): 3. Subject: 1.3.9

Britain grants "Dolly" scientist cloning license. *New York Times* 2005 February 9; p. A6. Subject: 14.5

The case for confidentiality. *Southern Africa HIV/AIDS Action* 2002 April-June; (52): 6. Subject: 9.5.6

Clamp down on copycats: plagiarism is on the rise, thanks to the Internet. Universities and journals need to take action [editorial]. *Nature* 2005 November 3; 438(7064): 2. Subject: 1.3.7

Clearing the myths of time: Tuskegee revisited. *Lancet Infectious Diseases* 2005 March; 5(3): 127. Subject: 18.5.1

Clinical practice guidelines and conflict of interest [editorial]. *CMAJ/JAMC: Canadian Medical Association Journal* 2005 November 22; 173(11): 1297. Subject: 9.7

Cloning around [editorial]. *Nature Cell Biology* 2004 December; 6(12): 1145. Subject: 14.5

'Code' called contrary to pt.'s advance directives. *Nursing Law's Regan Report* 2005 January; 45(8): 1. Subject: 20.5.4

Code of ethics for emergency physicians [policy statement]. *Annals of Emergency Medicine* 2004 May; 43(5): 686-694. Subject: 6

Code of ethics of nurses: making enlightened decisions about overtime. *Perspective Infirmiere* 2004 September-October; 2(1, Supplement): 7. Subject: 9.4

Compulsory community treatment of mentally disordered patients. *Medical Law Review* 2003 Autumn; 11(3): 381-384. Subject: 17.7

Constraint and coercion in psychiatry [news]. *Bulletin of Medical Ethics* 2003 September; (191): 4-5. Subject: 17.7

Consultation on Human Fertilisation and Embryology Act. *Bulletin of Medical Ethics* 2005 August-September; (210): 10-13. Subject: 18.5.4

Court can make parental decisions [news]. *Bulletin of Medical Ethics* 2003 November; (193): 4. Subject: 8.3.2

Death no longer a bar to fatherhood [news]. *Bulletin of Medical Ethics* 2003 September; (191): 5. Subject: 14.4

Declaracion de las Naciones Unidas sobre la Clonacion Humana / United Nations Declaration on Human Cloning. *Revista de Derecho y Genoma Humano / Law and the Human Genome Review* 2005 January-June; (22): 231-234. Subject: 14.5

Disclosure and performance: expecting more, and better [editorial]. *CMAJ/JAMC: Canadian Medical Association Journal* 2005 August 30: 173(5): 457. Subject: 9.8

Disputes between parents, immunisation and the welfare of the child. *Medical Law Review* 2003 Autumn; 11(3): 377-380. Subject: 9.7

Divided loyalties: trust in science is being eroded. How can we restore it? [editorial]. *New Scientist* 2005 February 26-March 4; 185(2488): 3. Subject: 1.3.9

Doctors and detention [editorial]. *Washington Post* 2005 July 13; p. A20. Subject: 21.4

Doctors with ties to device makers [editorial]. *New York Times* 2005 September 24; p. A14. Subject: 9.7

Does mother know best? *Hospital Law Newsletter* 1999 May; 16(7): 1-4. Subject: 9.5.6

Don't keep your distance: investigations that involve human subjects always require a close relationship between the researchers and those being studied [editorial]. *Nature* 2005 September 22; 437(7058): 451. Subject: 18.5.1

Don't mention the syndrome. *New Scientist* 2005 October 22-28; 188(2522): 6. Subject: 21.4

Editors' statement on considerations of biodefence and biosecurity [editorial]. *Nature Medicine* 2003 March; 9(3): 240. Subject: 21.3

Emergency contraception moves behind the counter [editorial]. *CMAJ/JAMC: Canadian Medical Association Journal* 2005 March 29; 172(7): 845. Subject: 11.1

Emergency contraception: prudes and prejudice [editorial]. *Lancet* 2005 July 2-8; 366(9479): 2. Subject: 11.1

Ethics committee gets it wrong [news]. *Bulletin of Medical Ethics* 2003 November; (193): 6. Subject: 18.2

Ethics, molecular biology, and sports medicine [editorial]. *British Journal of Sports Medicine* 2001 June; 35(3): 142-143. Subject: 9.5.1

The ethics of research involving animals. *ATLA: Alternatives to Laboratory Animals* 2005 August; 33(4): 324-325. Subject: 22.2

EU clinical trials directive: 0% inspiration, 100% perspiration? *Lancet Neurology* 2004 June; 3(6): 321. Subject: 18.2

The European Constitution establishing a core of human rights as applied to the fields of medicine and biology / La Constitucion Europea, un nucleo de los derechos humanos de la medicina y la biologia [editorial]. *Revista de Derecho y Genoma-Humano / Law and the Human Genome Review* 2004 July-December; (21): 15-26. Subject: 8.3.1

EUROSTEM. An ethical framework for stem cell research. *Revista de Derecho y Genoma Humano / Law and the Human Genome Review* 2005 January-June; (22): 235-248. Subject: 18.5.4

Euthanasia and assisted dying [news]. *Bulletin of Medical Ethics* 2003 October; (192): 3-4. Subject: 20.7

Every little helps [editorial]. *Nature* 2005 October 20; 437(7062): 1065. Subject: 18.5.4

Exit strategies [editorial]. *New Scientist* 2005 April 23-29; 186(2496): 5. Subject: 20.5.1

The first facial transplant [editorial]. *Lancet* 2005 December 10-16; 366(9502): 1984. Subject: 19.1

Flu vaccine shortage creates ethical issues, safety challenges. *Healthcare Benchmarks and Quality Improvement* 2004 December; 11(12): 133-136. Subject: 9.7

A fragile gift: sharing and saving life through embryo adoption. *Today's Christian Doctor* 2005 Fall; 36(3): 28-30. Subject: 14.4

French mother helps son to die [news]. *Bulletin of Medical Ethics* 2003 October; (192): 4-5. Subject: 20.7

Gene patent fight [news]. *New Scientist* 2005 June 25-July 1; 186(2505): 7. Subject: 15.3

Genetics and ethics. *In:* Concise Routledge Encyclopedia of Philosophy. New York: Routledge; 2000: 309. Subject: 15.1

Genomics and economics [editorial]. *CMAJ/JAMC: Canadian Medical Association Journal* 2005 August 16; 173(4): 329. Subject: 9.3.1

Getting a grip on genetic testing [editorial]. *Nature Medicine* 2003 February; 9(2): 147. Subject: 15.3

A gift to pharma? [editorial]. *Nature Medicine* 2005 July; 11(7): 693. Subject: 21.3

Health and Social Care (Community Health and Standards) Bill. *Bulletin of Medical Ethics* 2003 October; (192): 2. Subject: 8.2

How volunteering for an MRI scan changed my life: discovering a serious problem not only causes shock but can have financial implications [letter]. *Nature* 2005 March 3; 434(7029): 17. Subject: 18.3

HR 810: Stem Cell Research Enhancement Act. *GeneWatch* 2005 September-October; 18(5): 13. Subject: 18.5.4

Subject = NRCBL Primary Classification Number; See inside front cover

In vitro embryos and DNA profiling: far from clear legal reform / Los embriones in vitro y los perfiles de ADN: reformas legales con tonos en gris [editorial]. *Revista de Derecho y Genoma Humano / Law and the Human Genome Review* 2003 July-December; (19): 15-27. Subject: 14.6

Infant born to dying mother dies as result of infection. *New York Times* 2005 September 13; p. A18. Subject: 9.5.7

Insider trading versus medical professionalism [editorial]. *Lancet* 2005 September 3-9; 366(9488): 781. Subject: 1.3.9

Laying the foundations for a transcultural biotechnology law / Las bases para un derecho de la biotecnologia transcultural [editorial]. *Revista de Derecho y Genoma Humano / Law and the Human Genome Review* 2004 January-June; (20): 15-22. Subject: 21.7

A less toxic solution: industry should get behind a European partnership that will explore alternatives to animal testing [editorial]. *Nature* 2005 November 10; 438(7065): 129-130. Subject: 22.2

Lives of the embryo [opinion]. *Christian Century* 2005 June 28; 122(13): 5. Subject: 18.5.4

Living wills. *Bulletin of Medical Ethics* 2003 November; (193): 2. Subject: 20.5.4

Making babies: will a new UK law stop people donating eggs and sperm? [editorial]. *New Scientist* 2005 March 12-18; 185(2490): 3. Subject: 14.2

Making health care a moral issue [news]. *Christian Century* 2005 February 22; 122(4): 18-19. Subject: 9.3.1

Manipulating a journal article [editorial]. *New York Times* 2005 December 11; p. WK11. Subject: 1.3.7

Medical collusion in the death penalty: an American atrocity [editorial]. *Lancet* 2005 April 16-22; 365(9468): 1361. Subject: 20.6

Medical ethics. *In:* Concise Routledge Encyclopedia of Philosophy. New York: Routledge; 2000: 551-552. Subject: 2.1

Medical ethics — as prescribed by Caraka, Susruta, and other ancient Indian physicians. *Medical Ethics: Journal of Forum for Medical Ethics Society* 1995 January-March; 3(1): CI-CIV. Subject: 2.1

Medical ethics — general principles. *Medical Ethics: Journal of Forum for Medical Ethics Society* 1995 April-June; 3(2): CV-CVIII. Subject: 2.1

Method may yield pluripotent stem cells without killing embryos: statement of thirty-five scientists and ethicists. *Origins* 2005 July 7; 35(8): 126-128. Subject: 18.5.4

Missed opportunity to ban reproductive cloning [editorial]. *Nature Cell Biology* 2005 April; 7(4): 323. Subject: 18.6

Moralists at the pharmacy [editorial]. *New York Times* 2005 April 3; p. WK12. Subject: 9.7

Navajo nation IRB: a unique human research review board has three primary concerns: protecting its community, its people, and its heritage. *Protecting Human Subjects* 2003 Spring; (8): 1-2. Subject: 18.2

New ethics rules at NIH. *Journal of Investigative Medicine* 2004 May; 52(4): 233. Subject: 1.3.9

Newborn screening grows up [editorial]. *Nature Medicine* 2005 October; 11(10): 1013. Subject: 18.5.2

The next abortion decision [editorial]. *New York Times* 2005 November 30; p. A34. Subject: 12.4.1

NIH announces aweeping ethics reform [press release]. *Bethesda, MD: National Institutes of Health* 2005 February 1; 2 p. [Online]. Available: http://www.nih.gov/news/pr/feb2005/od-01.htm [1 February 20051]. Subject: 1.3.9

No place for conflict of interest [editorial]. *Lancet* 2005 May 14-20; 365(9472): 1664. Subject: 9.7

No such thing as a non-lethal weapon [editorial]. *New Scientist* 2005 March 5-11; 185(2489): 3. Subject: 1.3.9

No use of stored embryos without consent [news]. *Bulletin of Medical Ethics* 2003 September; (191): 5-6. Subject: 14.6

Not black and white: BiDil my work best for African Americans — but do we know why? [editorial]. *New Scientist* 2005 June 11-17; 186(2503): 3. Subject: 15.1

Not so fast: anyone thinking of collaborations with emerging biomedical powers should test the ethical waters before jumping in [editorial]. *Nature* 2005 February 10; 433(7026): 557. Subject: 18.6

Nursing ethics. *In:* Concise Routledge Encyclopedia of Philosophy. New York: Routledge; 2000: 638. Subject: 4.1.3

On the shoulders of fraudsters [editorial]. *New Scientist* 2005 March 19-25; 185(2491): 5. Subject: 1.3.9

One bad apple: people will never trust science so long as researchers make up results [editorial]. *New Scientist* 2005 November 5-11; 188(2524): 3. Subject: 1.3.9

Open sesame [editorial]. *Nature Biotechnology* 2005 June; 23(6): 633. Subject: 1.3.9

Out in the open [editorial]. *Nature Biotechnology* 2005 February; 23(2): 153. Subject: 18.2

Patenting the poor. *Lancet Oncology* 2005 April; 6(4): 191. Subject: 9.7

Patient choice in clinical trials [editorial]. *Lancet* 2005 June 11-17; 365(9476): 1984. Subject: 18.5.1

The perils of public debate [editorial]. *Nature Neuroscience* 2005 May; 8(5): 535. Subject: 5.1

Physicians and advocacy [editorial]. *CMAJ/JAMC: Canadian Medical Association Journal* 2005 May 24; 172(11): 1413. Subject: 7.3

See SUBJECT HEADING KEY FOR SECTION II on inside back cover

Playing the name game: stem-cell biologists should not try to change the definition of the word 'embryo' [editorial]. *Nature* 2005 July 7; 436(7047): 2. Subject: 18.5.4

Professional values. London: British Medical Association 2005 November; 12 p. [Online]. Available: http://www.bma.org/ap.nsf/AttachmentsByTitle/PDFprofval/$FILE/professional.pdf [6 March 2006]. Subject: 2.1

Prozac papers. *New Scientist* 2005 January 8-14; 185(2481): 4. Subject: 9.7

Regulating preimplantation genetic diagnosis: the pathologization problem. *Harvard Law Review* 2005 June; 118(8): 2770-2791. Subject: 15.2

Removing the uterus from mentally handicapped women: some ethical considerations. *Medical Ethics: Journal of the Forum for Medical Ethics Society* 1994 February-April; 1(3): 10. Subject: 11.3

Reproduction and ethics. *In:* Concise Routledge Encyclopedia of Philosophy. New York: Routledge; 2000: 766-767. Subject: 14.1

Research with adults who lack capacity. *Bulletin of Medical Ethics* 2005 February; (205): 8-11. Subject: 18.5.6

The right of a treatment proxy to challenge a decision to administer diamorphine to a patient. *Medical Law Review* 2004 Autumn; 12(3): 317-322. Subject: 20.5.2

The right to die [editorial]. *New York Times* 2005 October 5; p. A26. Subject: 20.7

The right to require life-prolonging treatment: R (Burke) v. General Medical Council (Defendant) and Disability Rights Commission (Interested Party) and The Official Solicitor (Intervener). *Medical Law Review* 2004 Autumn; 12(3): 306-316. Subject: 20.5.1

Rules of engagement: biologists may soon have little option but to sign up to codes of conduct [editorial]. *Nature* 2005 July 7; 436(7047): 2. Subject: 1.3.9

The sacred and the secular: the life and death of Terri Schiavo [editorial]. *CMAJ/JAMC: Canadian Medical Association Journal* 2005 April 26; 172(9): 1149. Subject: 20.5.1

Seclusion of psychiatric patients. *Medical Law Review* 2003 Autumn; 11(3): 384-393. Subject: 9.5.3

The sounds of silence [editorial]. *Nature Medicine* 2004 July; 10(7): 653. Subject: 9.7

South Korea's cloning crisis [editorial]. *New York Times* 2005 December 4; p. WK11. Subject: 14.5

Spain's constitutional court and assisted reproduction techniques [editorial]. *Law and the Human Genome Review* 1999 July-December; 11: 15-17. Subject: 14.1

A state of ignorance: severe brain damage attracts little research attention, yet science could help inform the decisions of doctors and families [editorial]. *Nature* 2005 March 31; 434(7033): 545. Subject: 20.5.1

Stem cell debacle [editorial]. *New Scientist* 2005 December 3-9; 188(2528): 3. Subject: 18.5.4

Stem-cell lines [editorial]. *Wall Street Journal* 2005 May 26; p. A12. Subject: 18.5.4

Stem-cell probe needed [editorial]. *Nature* 2005 December 1; 438(7068): 532. Subject: 18.5.4

Still not deterred: universities should back researchers determined to stand up for animal research in the face of terrorism. *Nature* 2005 September 1; 437(7055): 1-2. Subject: 22.2

'Stutterers' sue over research study [news]. *Bulletin of Medical Ethics* 2003 September; (191): 3-4. Subject: 18.4

Suggested guidelines for hysterectomy in mentally handicapped women. *Medical Ethics: Journal of the Forum for Medical Ethics Society* 1994 May-July; 1(4): 1-3. Subject: 11.3

The Supreme Court judgment dated May 4, 2001 in the PNDT Act, 1994. *Issues in Medical Ethics* 2001 July-September; 9(3): 97-98. Subject: 20.5.2

Sydney fertility clinics ban sex-selection [news brief]. *Monash Bioethics Review* 2005 April; 24(2): 3. Subject: 14.3

Taking a hard line on conflicts [editorial]. *Nature* 2005 February 10; 433(7026): 557. Subject: 1.3.9

Terri Schiavo [editorial]. *Bioetica & Debat* 2005; 11(39): 2. Subject: 20.5.1

Texas judge orders treatment for a 13-year-old with cancer. *New York Times* 2005 September 10; p. A15. Subject: 8.3.2

That little ball of cells: what we do with embryos depends on what we think they are [editorial]. *New Scientist* 2005 August 20-26; 187(2513): 5. Subject: 15.2

Theresa Marie Schiavo [editorial]. *New York Times* 2005 April 1; p. A24. Subject: 20.5.1

The Theresa Schiavo case [news]. *Mental and Physical Disability Law Reporter* 2005 March- April; 29(2): 154-156. Subject: 20.5.1

Too strict at NIH [editorial]. *Washington Post* 2005 February 23; p. A18. Subject: 1.3.9

The trials of tenofovir trials [editorial]. *Lancet* 2005 March 26-April 1; 365(9465): 1111. Subject: 18.2

A troubling but necessary debate [editorial]. *Lancet* 2005 October 15-21; 366(9494): 1332. Subject: 20.7

Turkey's disabled [editorial]. *New York Times* 2005 September 30; A28. Subject: 17.5

Turn of the tide [editorial]. *Nature Medicine* 2004 April; 10(4): 317. Subject: 18.5.4

Unapproved tests on a chip [editorial]. *Nature* 2005 December 8; 438(7069): 711. Subject: 15.2

An unhealthy practice [editorial]. *Nature* 2005 October 20; 437(7062): 1065-1066. Subject: 9.7

Subject = NRCBL Primary Classification Number; See inside front cover

The United Nations Declaration on Human Cloning [editorial]. *Revista de Derecho y Genoma Humano / Law and the Human Genome Review* 2005 January-June; (22): 15-18. Subject: 14.5

Vast abuses cited at National Health Institutes. *New York Times* 2005 April 12; p. A18. Subject: 1.3.9

What information must be disclosed and by whom? *Hospital Law Newsletter* 1999 January; 16(3): 1-4. Subject: 8.3.1

What Schiavo taught [editorial]. *New Republic* 2005 April 11; 232(13): 7. Subject: 20.5.1

When the patient changed her mind. *Hospital Law Newsletter* 1999 March; 16(5): 1-3. Subject: 8.3.1

Why should clinical trials be registered? [editorial]. *CMAJ/JAMC: Canadian Medical Association Journal* 2005 June 21; 172(13): 1653. Subject: 18.6

Will consumerism lead to better health? [editorial]. *Lancet* 2005 July 30-August 5; 366(9483): 343. Subject: 8.1

Will the regulator please stand up [editorial]. *Nature* 2005 November 17; 438(7066): 257. Subject: 18.5.4

SECTION III:
MONOGRAPHS

SUBJECT ENTRIES

Section III: Monographs Contents*

1 Ethics
    1.1 Philosophical Ethics 737
    1.2 Religious Ethics 738
    1.3 Applied and Professional Ethics
        1.3.1 General 739
        1.3.2 Business 740
        1.3.3 Education 740
        1.3.5 Government/Criminal Justice 740
        1.3.6 International Affairs 741
        1.3.7 Journalism/Mass Media 741
        1.3.8 Law 741
        1.3.9 Scientific Research 741
        1.3.10 Social Work 741
        1.3.12 Information Technology 742

2 Bioethics
    2.1 General 742
    2.2 History of Health Ethics 745
    2.3 Education/Programs 745

3 Philosophy of Biology
    3.1 General 745
    3.2 Evolution and Creation 745

4 Philosophy of Medicine and Health
    4.1 Philosophy of Medicine, Nursing and Other Health Professions
        4.1.1 General 746
        4.1.2 Philosophy of Medicine 746
        4.1.3 Philosophy of Nursing 746
    4.2 Concept of Health 747
    4.3 Concept of Mental Health 747
    4.4 Quality/Value of Life/Personhood 747

Only those classes with entries in this volume appear on this Contents list.

5 Science/Technology and Society

5.1 General 748
5.2 Technology Assessment 748
5.3 Social Control of Science/Technology 748

7 Sociology of Health Care

7.1 General 749
7.2 Education for Health Care Professionals 750
7.3 Professional-Professional Relationship 750
7.4 Professional Misconduct 750

8 Patient Relationships

8.1 General 750
8.3 Informed Consent
    8.3.1 General 751
    8.3.3 Third Party Consent/Incompetents 751
8.4 Confidentiality 751
8.5 Malpractice 751

9 Health Care

9.1 General 751
9.2 Right to Health Care 752
9.3 Health Care Economics
    9.3.1 General 752
    9.3.2 Managed Care 753
9.4 Allocation of Health Care Resources 753
9.5 Health Care for Specific Diseases or Groups
    9.5.1 Health Care for General 753
    9.5.2 Health Care for the Aged 754
    9.5.3 Health Care for Mentally Disabled Persons 754
    9.5.4 Health Care for Minorities 755
    9.5.5 Health Care for Women 755
    9.5.6 Health Care for HIV Infection and AIDS 756
    9.5.7 Health Care for Minors 756
    9.5.8 Health Care for Embryos and Fetuses 757
    9.5.9 Health Care for Substance Abusers/Users of Controlled Substances . . 757
9.7 Drugs and Pharmaceutical Industry 757
9.8 Quality of Health Care 758

10 Sexuality/Gender

10 General 758

11 Contraception

11.1 General 759

12 Abortion

12.1 General 759

12.3 Moral and Religious Aspects 759
12.4 Legal Aspects
    12.4.1 General 759
    12.4.2 Interests of Woman/Fetus/Father 760
12.5 Social Aspects
    12.5.2 Abortion: Demographic Surveys 760

13 Population
13.1 General 760
13.2 Population Growth 760

14 Reproduction/Reproductive Technologies
14.1 General 760
14.2 Artificial Insemination and Surrogacy 761
14.4 In Vitro Fertilization and Embryo Transfer 761
14.5 Cloning 761

15 Genetics, Molecular Biology and Microbiology
15.1 General 762
15.2 Genetic Counseling/Prenatal Diagnosis 764
15.3 Genetic Screening/Testing 764
15.5 Eugenics 765
15.6 Behavioral Genetics 766
15.7 Biohazards of Genetic Research 766
15.8 Genetic Patents 766
15.10 Genome Mapping 766
15.11 Genetics and Human Ancestry 767

16 Environmental Quality
16.1 General 767
16.2 Nuclear Power/Radiation 768
16.3 Occupational Health 768

17 The Neurosciences and Mental Health Therapies
17.1 General 768
17.2 Psychotherapy 769
17.3 Behavior Modification 769
17.4 Psychopharmacology 770
17.5 Electrical Stimulation of the Brain 770
17.6 Psychosurgery 770
17.7 Involuntary Civil Commitment 770

18 Human Experimentation
18.1 General 770
18.2 Policy Guidelines/Institutional Review Boards 770
18.3 Informed Consent 771
18.4 Behavioral Research 771

18.5 Research on Special Populations
    18.5.1 General 771
    18.5.2 Research on Newborns or Minors 771
    18.5.3 Research on Women 771
    18.5.4 Research on Embryos or Fetuses 771
    18.5.5 Research on Prisoners. 772
    18.6 Social Control of Human Experimentation 772

19 Artificial and Transplanted Organs/Tissues
    19.1 Artificial and Transplanted Organs or Tissues (General). 772
    19.2 Artificial and Transplanted Hearts 772
    19.3 Artificial and Transplanted Kidneys 772
    19.4 Blood Transfusion 772
    19.5 Donation/Procurement of Organs/Tissues 773
    19.6 Allocation of Organs/Tissues 773

20 Death and Dying
    20.1 General 773
    20.3 Attitudes Toward Death
        20.3.1 General 773
    20.4 Care of the Dying Patient
        20.4.1 General 773
    20.5 Prolongation of Life and Euthanasia
        20.5.1 General 774
        20.5.4 Living Wills/Advance Directives 775
    20.6 Capital Punishment 775
    20.7 Suicide/Assisted Suicide 775

21 International/Political Dimensions of Biology and Medicine
    21.1 General 775
    21.2 War 776
    21.3 Chemical and Biological Weapons 776
    21.4 Torture and Genocide. 777
    21.7 Cultural Pluralism. 778

22 Animal Welfare
    22.1 General 778
    22.2 Animal Experimentation 779
    22.3 Animal Production 779

New Publications from the Kennedy Institute of Ethics. 779

Title Index 783

National Reference Center for Bioethics Literature Classification Scheme:
                                      Inside Front Cover

SECTION III: MONOGRAPHS
SUBJECT ENTRIES

1.1 PHILOSOPHICAL ETHICS

Becker, Lawrence C. and Becker, Charlotte B., eds. A HISTORY OF WESTERN ETHICS. New York: Routledge, 2003. 208 p. ISBN 0-415-96825-9. (Second edition.) [BJ71 .H56 2003] (1.1)

Benjamin, Martin. PHILOSOPHY & THIS ACTUAL WORLD: AN INTRODUCTION TO PRACTICAL PHILOSOPHICAL INQUIRY. Lanham, MD: Rowman & Littlefield, 2003. 223 p. ISBN 0-7425-1399-8. [B72 .B45 2003] (1.1; 1.2; 1.3.5; 4.4; 20.2.1; 20.5.1; 20.7)

Bergo, Bettina. LEVINAS BETWEEN ETHICS & POLITICS: FOR THE BEAUTY THAT ADORNS THE EARTH. Pittsburgh, PA: Duquesne University Press, 2003, c1999. 309 p. ISBN 0-8207-0334-6. (Phaenomenologica series; No. 152. Originally published: Kluwer Academic, Dordrecht/Boston, 1999. Gift of Max M. and Marjorie B. Kampelman.) [B2430 .L484 B46 2003] (1.1; 1.2; 1.3.5)

Bunge, Mario. PHILOSOPHICAL DICTIONARY. Amherst, NY: Prometheus Books, 2003. 315 p. ISBN 1-59102-037-9. (Enlarged edition.) [B791 .B765 2003] (1.1; Reference)

Byron, Michael, ed. SATISFICING AND MAXIMIZING: MORAL THEORISTS ON PRACTICAL REASON. Cambridge/New York: Cambridge University Press, 2004. 245 p. ISBN 0-521-01005-5. [BJ1419 .S28 2004] (1.1)

Casebeer, William D. NATURAL ETHICAL FACTS: EVOLUTION, CONNECTIONISM, AND MORAL COGNITION. Cambridge, MA: MIT Press, 2003. 214 p. ISBN 0-262-03310-0. [BJ1311 .C37 2003] (1.1)

CONCISE ROUTLEDGE ENCYCLOPEDIA OF PHILOSOPHY. London/New York: Routledge, 2000. 1030 p. ISBN 0-415-22364-4. [B51 .C58 2000] (1.1; 1.2; 1.3.1; Reference)

Cyberspace and Privacy: A New Legal Paradigm? STANFORD LAW REVIEW 2000 May; 52(5): 987-1572. (ISSN 0038-9765.) (1.1; 1.3.8; 1.3.12)

Fleischacker, Samuel. A SHORT HISTORY OF DISTRIBUTIVE JUSTICE. Cambridge, MA: Harvard University Press,

2004. 190 p. ISBN 0-674-01340-9. [HB523 .F58 2004] (1.1; 1.3.2; 1.3.5)

Fuller, Michael. MAKING SENSE OF MACINTYRE. Aldershot, Hants/Brookfield, VT: Ashgate, 1998. 149 p. ISBN 1-84014-173-5. (Avebury Series in Philosophy.) [B1647 .M124 F85 1998] (1.1; 1.3.1; 1.3.5)

Gert, Bernard. COMMON MORALITY: DECIDING WHAT TO DO. Oxford/New York: Oxford University Press, 2004. 179 p. ISBN 0-19-517371-6. [BJ1012 .G445 2004] (1.1)

Gert, Bernard. MORALITY: ITS NATURE AND JUSTIFICATION. New York: Oxford University Press, 2005. 438 p. ISBN 0-19-517690-1. (Revised edition. Gift of the publisher.) [BJ1012 .G45 2005] (1.1; 1.3.1)

Giebel, Heidi Marie. INTENTIONS IN ACTION: CONTEMPORARY INTERPRETATIONS OF THE PRINCIPLE OF DOUBLE EFFECT. Ann Arbor, MI: ProQuest Information and Learning/UMI, 2003. 226 p. (Publication No. AAT-3080954. Dissertation, (Ph.D.)— University of Notre Dame, 2003.) (1.1)

Johnson, Peter. MORAL PHILOSOPHERS AND THE NOVEL: A STUDY OF WINCH, NUSSBAUM AND RORTY. New York: Palgrave Macmillan, 2004. 203 p. ISBN 1-4039-3365-0. [PN3347 .J596 2004] (1.1; Fiction)

Kekes, John. THE ROOTS OF EVIL. Ithaca, NY: Cornell University Press, 2005. 261 p. ISBN 0-8014-4368-7. [BJ1401 .K435 2005] (1.1)

Oakley, Justin and Cocking, Dean. VIRTUE ETHICS AND PROFESSIONAL ROLES. Cambridge/New York: Cambridge University Press, 2001. 188 p. ISBN 0-521-79305-X. [BJ1725 .O18 2001] (1.1; 1.3.1; 4.1.2)

Oderberg, David S. MORAL THEORY: A NON-CONSEQUENTIALIST APPROACH. Malden, MA: Blackwell Publishers, 2000. 197 p. ISBN 0-631-21903-X. (Companion volume to: *Applied Ethics: A Non-Consequentialist Approach*.) [BJ1012 .O34 2000] (1.1; 4.4)

O'Manique, John. THE ORIGINS OF JUSTICE: THE EVOLUTION OF MORALITY, HUMAN RIGHTS, AND LAW. Philadelphia: University of Pennsylvania Press, 2003. 206 p. ISBN

0-8122-3706-4. (Pennsylvania Studies in Human Rights series.) [JC578 .O43 2003] (1.1; 15.9; 21.1)

Singer, Peter and Singer, Renata, eds. THE MORAL OF THE STORY: AN ANTHOLOGY OF ETHICS THROUGH LITERATURE. Malden, MA: Blackwell, 2005. 621 p. ISBN 1-4051-0584-4. [PN6071 .E74 M67 2005] (1.1; Fiction)

Sterba, James p. THE TRIUMPH OF PRACTICE OVER THEORY IN ETHICS. New York: Oxford University Press, 2005. 206 p. ISBN 0-19-513285-8. (Gift of the publisher.) [BJ71 .S69 2005] (1.1; 10; 21.2)

Symposium: Rawls and the Law. FORDHAM LAW REVIEW 2004 April; 72(5): 1381-2175. (ISSN 0015-704X.) (1.1; 1.2; 1.3.8; 9.5.4; 9.5.7; 10; 21.1)

Taylor, James Stacey, ed. PERSONAL AUTONOMY: NEW ESSAYS ON PERSONAL AUTONOMY AND ITS ROLE IN CONTEMPORARY MORAL PHILOSOPHY. New York: Cambridge University Press, 2005. 350 p. ISBN 0-521-83796-0. (Gift of the publisher.) [BJ324 .A88 P47 2005] (1.1; 2.2; 4.4; 10; 22.1)

Thomasma, David C. and Weisstub, David N., eds. THE VARIABLES OF MORAL CAPACITY. Dordrecht/Boston: Kluwer Academic, 2004. 332 p. ISBN 1-4020-2551-3. (International Library of Ethics, Law, and New Medicine series; Vol. 21.) [BJ1012 .V37 2004] (1.1; 1.3.1; 1.3.5; 4.1.3; 4.3; 4.4; 8.3.3; 9.5.1; 9.5.9; 17.1; 18.5.1)

Uslaner, Eric M. THE MORAL FOUNDATIONS OF TRUST. Cambridge/New York: Cambridge University Press, 2002. 298 p. ISBN 0-512-01103-5. (1.1; 1.3.1)

Walker, Margaret Urban. MORAL CONTEXTS. Lanham, MD: Rowman & Littlefield, 2003. 229 p. ISBN 0-7425-1379-3. (Feminist Constructions series.) [BJ1395 .W34 2003] (1.1; 10)

Walker, Vanessa Siddle and Snarey, John R., eds. RACE-ING MORAL FORMATION: AFRICAN AMERICAN PERSPECTIVES ON CARE AND JUSTICE. New York: Teachers College Press, 2004. 194 p. ISBN 0-8077-4449-2. (Foreword by Carol Gilligan and Janie Ward. "Teachers College, Columbia University.") [E185.86 .R244 2004] (1.1; 1.3.1; 1.3.3; 10)

Wilson, Catherine. MORAL ANIMALS: IDEALS AND CONSTRAINTS IN MORAL THEORY. Oxford: Clarendon Press/New York: Oxford University Press, 2004. 316 p. ISBN 0-19-926767-7. [BJ1031 .W55 2004] (1.1)

1.2 RELIGIOUS ETHICS

Aarons, Victoria. WHAT HAPPENED TO ABRAHAM? REINVENTING THE COVENANT IN AMERICAN JEWISH FICTION. Newark: University of Delaware; Distributed by: Associated University Presses, 2005. 181 p. ISBN 0-87413-901-5. (Gift of Max M. and Marjorie B. Kampelman.) [PS647 .J4 A15 2005] (1.2; Fiction)

Agnon, S.Y. A GUEST FOR THE NIGHT: A NOVEL. Madison: University of Wisconsin Press, [2004?]. 485 p. ISBN 0-299-20644-0. (Library of World Fiction series. Transla-

tion from the Hebrew by Misha Louvish of: *Oreah natah la-lun*; Schocken Books, New York, 1968. Gift of Max M. and Marjorie B. Kampelman.) [PJ5053 .A4 O713 2004] (1.2; Fiction)

Berlin, Adele and Brettler, Marc Zvi, eds. THE JEWISH STUDY BIBLE. Oxford/New York: Oxford University Press, 2004. 2181 p. ISBN 0-19-529751-2. (TANAKH translation. Gift of Max M. and Marjorie B. Kampelman.) [BS895 .J4 2004] (1.2; Reference)

Biale, David, ed. CULTURES OF THE JEWS: A NEW HISTORY. New York: Schocken Books, 2002. 1196 p. ISBN 0-8052-4131-0. (Gift of Max M. and Marjorie B. Kampelman.) [DS102.95 .C85 2002] (1.2; 21.7)

Bukhari, Muhammad ibn Ismail. MORAL TEACHINGS OF ISLAM: PROPHETIC TRADITIONS FROM AL-ADAB AL-MUFRAD. Walnut Creek, CA: Alta Mira Press, 2003. 132 p. ISBN 0-7591-0417-4. (Sacred Literature Series. Translation from the Arabic with introduction by Abdul Ali Hamid. Published in co-operation with the International Sacred Literature Trust.) [BP135 .A124 U75 2003] (1.2; 1.3.1; 9.1)

Curran, Charles E. and Griffin, Leslie, eds. THE CATHOLIC CHURCH, MORALITY AND POLITICS. New York: Paulist Press, 2001. 384 p. ISBN 0-8091-4040-3. (Readings in Moral Theology series; No. 12.) [BX1406.3 .C38 2001] (1.2; 1.3.1; 1.3.2; 1.3.5; 4.4; 10; 12.3; 20.5.1; 20.6)

Feiner, Shmuel. THE JEWISH ENLIGHTENMENT. Philadelphia: University of Pennsylvania Press, 2002. 440 p. ISBN 0-8122-3755-2. (Jewish Culture and Contexts series. Gift of Max M. and Marjorie B. Kampelman.) [DS113 .F4413 2004] (1.2)

Fine, Lawrence. PHYSICIAN OF THE SOUL, HEALER OF THE COSMOS: ISAAC LURIA AND HIS KABBALISTIC FELLOWSHIP. Stanford, CA: Stanford University Press, 2003. 480 p. ISBN 0-8047-4826-8. (Stanford Studies in Jewish History and Culture series. Gift of Max M. and Marjorie B. Kampelman.) [BM525 .L835 F56 2003] (1.2)

Fountain, Daniel E. GOD, MEDICINE & MIRACLES: THE SPIRITUAL FACTOR IN HEALING. Colorado Springs, CO: Shaw/WaterBrooks Press, 1999. 265 p. ISBN 0-87788-321-1. ("A Shaw Book.") (1.2; 9.1)

Friedmann, Daniel. TO KILL AND TAKE POSSESSION: LAW, MORALITY, AND SOCIETY IN BIBLICAL STORIES. Peabody, MA: Hendrickson Publishers, 2002. 327 p. ISBN 1-56563-641-4. (Translation from the Hebrew of: *Ha-ratsahta ve-gam yarashta*; Dvir Publishing House, Tel Aviv, 2000. Gift of Max M. and Marjorie B. Kampelman.) [BS680 .E84 F7513 2002] (1.2; 10; 14.1; 14.2; 20.1)

Goldberg, Harvey E. JEWISH PASSAGES: CYCLES OF JEWISH LIFE. Berkeley: University of California Press, 2003. 379 p. ISBN 0-520-20693-2. (Gift of Max M. and Marjorie B. Kampelman.) [BM700 .G613 2003] (1.2)

Green, Arthur. A GUIDE TO THE ZOHAR. Stanford, CA: Stanford University Press, 2004. 191 p. ISBN 0-8047-4908-6.

(Gift of Max M. and Marjorie B. Kampelman.) [BM525 .A59 G73 2004] (1.2)

Hahn, Barbara. THE JEWESS PALLAS ATHENA: THIS TOO A THEORY OF MODERNITY. Princeton, NJ: Princeton University Press, 2005. 233 p. ISBN 0-691-11614-8. (Translation from the German by James McFarland of: *Die Jüdin Pallas Athene: Auch eine Theorie der Moderne*; Berlin Verlag, Berlin, 2002. Gift of Max M. and Marjorie B. Kampelman.) [PT74 .H34 2005] (1.2)

Hauerwas, Stanley. THE HAUERWAS READER. Durham, NC: Duke University Press, 2001. 729 p. ISBN 0-8223-2691-4. (Edited by John Berkman and Michael Cartwright.) [BJ1251 .H326 2001] (1.2; 4.4; 10; 12.3; 20.5.1; 20.7)

Heschel, Abraham Joshua. HEAVENLY TORAH AS RE-FRACTED THROUGH THE GENERATIONS. New York: Continuum, 2005. 814 p. ISBN 0-8264-0802-8. (Translation from the Hebrew by Gordon Tucker and Leonard Levin. Gift of Max M. and Marjorie B. Kampelman.) [BM504.3 .H4713 2005] (1.2)

Idel, Moshe. ABSORBING PERFECTIONS: KABBALAH AND INTERPRETATION. New Haven, CT: Yale University Press, 2002. 668 p. ISBN 0-300-08379-3. (Foreword by Harold Bloom. Gift of Max M. and Marjorie B. Kampelman.) [BM526 .I295 2002] (1.2)

King, Winston L. IN THE HOPE OF NIBBANA: THE ETHICS OF THERAVADA BUDDHISM. Seattle, WA: Pariyatti Press, 2001. 309 p. ISBN 1-928706-08-8. (Second edition. Originally published by: Open Court, 1964. Publisher's address: PO Box 15926, zip 98115.) [BQ4263 .K56 2001] (1.2; 1.3.1; 22.1)

Krell, Marc A. INTERSECTING PATHWAYS: MODERN JEWISH THEOLOGIANS IN CONVERSATION WITH CHRISTIANITY. New York: Oxford University Press, 2003. 200 p. ISBN 0-19-515935-7. (American Academy of Religion Cultural Criticism Series. Gift of Max M. and Marjorie B. Kampelman.) [BM535 .K74 2003] (1.2)

Linas, Eli, ed. OHR YISRAEL: THE CLASSIC WRITINGS OF RAV YISRAEL SALANTER AND HIS DISCIPLE RAV YITZCHAK BLAZER. Southfield, MI: Targum Press; Distributed by: Nanuet, NY: Feldheim, 2004. 605 p. ISBN 1-56871-302-9. (Translation from the Hebrew by Zvi Miller. Gift of Max M. and Marjorie B. Kampelman.) [BJ1287 .S253 O713 2004] (1.2)

Magness, Jodi. THE ARCHAEOLOGY OF QUMRAN AND THE DEAD SEA SCROLLS. Grand Rapids, MI: William B. Eerdmans, 2002. 238 p. ISBN 0-8028-2687-3. (Studies in the Dead Sea Scrolls and Related Literature series. Gift of Max M. and Marjorie B. Kampelman.) [BM175 .Q6 M34 2002] (1.2)

Meir, Asher. THE JEWISH ETHICIST: EVERYDAY ETHICS FOR BUSINESS AND LIFE. New York: Ktav in association with Business Ethics Center of Jerusalem, 2005. 295 p. ISBN 0-88125-809-1. (Gift of Max M. and Marjorie B.

Kampelman.) [BJ1285 .M44 2005] (1.2; 1.3.1; 1.3.2; 1.3.12)

Mittleman, Alan, ed. RELIGION AS A PUBLIC GOOD: JEWS AND OTHER AMERICANS ON RELIGION IN THE PUBLIC SQUARE. Lanham, MD: Rowman & Littlefield, 2003. 336 p. ISBN 0-7425-3124-4. (Gift of Max M. and Marjorie B. Kampelman.) [BM205 .R42 2003] (1.2; 1.3.5)

Sacks, Jonathan. DIGNITY OF DIFFERENCE: HOW TO AVOID THE CLASH OF CIVILIZATIONS. London/New York: Continuum, c2002, 2003. 216 p. ISBN 0-8264-6850-0. [BL410 .S33 2003] (1.2; 1.3.2; 1.3.5; 21.1)

Sajoo, Amyn B. MUSLIM ETHICS: EMERGING VISTAS. London/New York: I.B. Pauris Publishers in association with The Institute of Ismaili Studies, 2004. 164 p. ISBN 1-85043-550-2. (Publisher's address: 6 Salem Road, London W2 4BU [or] 175 Fifth Avenue, New York 10010.) [BJ1291 .S29 2004] (1.2; 1.3.5; 2.1; 21.1)

Sarna, Jonathan D. AMERICAN JUDAISM: A HISTORY. New Haven, CT: Yale University Press, 2004. 490 p. ISBN 0-300-10197-X. (Gift of Max M. and Marjorie B. Kampelman.) [BM205 .S26 2004] (1.2)

Schweiker, William, ed. THE BLACKWELL COMPANION TO RELIGIOUS ETHICS. Malden, MA: Blackwell Publishers, 2005. 613 p. ISBN 0-631-21634-0. (Blackwell Companions to Religion series. Gift of the publisher.) [BJ1188 .B57 2005] (1.2; 1.1; 1.3.1; 16.1; 21.1; 21.2; Reference)

Soloveitchik, Joseph B. COMMUNITY, COVENANT, AND COMMITMENT: SELECTED LETTERS AND COMMUNICATIONS. New York: The Toras HoRav Foundation; Distributed by: Ktav, 2005. 352 p. ISBN 0-88125-872-5. (MeOtzar HoRav Series; Vol. 4. Edited by Nathaniel Helfgot. Gift of Max M. and Marjorie B. Kampelman.) [BM205 .S65 2005] (1.2)

van Huyssteen, J. Wentzel. THE SHAPING OF RATIONALITY: TOWARD INTERDISCIPLINARITY IN THEOLOGY AND SCI-ENCE. Grand Rapids, MI: William B. Eerdmans, 1999. 303 p. ISBN 0-8028-3868-5. [BL240.2 .V315 1999] (1.2; 5.1; 21.7)

Wallace, B. Alan, ed. BUDDHISM & SCIENCE: BREAKING NEW GROUND. New York: Columbia University Press, 2003. 444 p. ISBN 0-231-12335-3. (Columbia Series in Science and Religion.) [BQ4570 .S3 B836 2003] (1.2; 4.4; 5.1; 17.1)

Wiesel, Elie. WISE MEN AND THEIR TALES: PORTRAITS OF BIBLICAL TALMUDIC, AND HASIDIC MASTERS. New York: Schocken Books, 2003. 337 p. ISBN 0-8052-1120-9. (Gift of Max M. and Marjorie B. Kampelman.) [BS571 .W5485 2003] (1.2; Biography)

1.3.1 APPLIED AND PROFESSIONAL ETHICS (GENERAL)

Baines, Barry K. ETHICAL WILLS: PUTTING YOUR VALUES ON PAPER. Cambridge, MA: Perseus, 2002. 133 p. ISBN

0-7382-0611-3. (" A Life Institute Book.") [BJ1286 .W6 B35 2002] (1.3.1; 1.1)

Borofsky, Robert. YANOMAMI: THE FIERCE CONTROVERSY AND WHAT WE CAN LEARN FROM IT. Berkeley: University of California Press, 2005. 372 p. ISBN 0-520-24404-4. (California Series in Public Anthropology; Vol. 12. Gift of the publisher.) [F2520.1 .Y3 B67 2005] (1.3.1; 15.9)

Feezell, Randolph. SPORT, PLAY, AND ETHICAL REFLECTION. Urbana: University of Illinois Press, 2004. 173 p. ISBN 0-252-02955-0. [GV706.3 .F44 2004] (1.3.1)

Moore, Don A.; Cain, Daylian M.; Loewenstein, George; Bazerman, Max H., eds. CONFLICTS OF INTEREST: CHALLENGES AND SOLUTIONS IN BUSINESS, LAW, MEDICINE, AND PUBLIC POLICY. Cambridge/New York: Cambridge University Press, 2005. 300 p. ISBN 0-521-84439-8. (Gift of the publisher.) [HF5387 .C6614 2005] (1.3.1; 1.1; 1.3.2; 1.3.5; 1.3.8; 2.1; 7.3; 9.7; LE)

O'Neill, Onora. A QUESTION OF TRUST. Cambridge/New York: Cambridge University Press, 2002. 100 p. ISBN 0-521-52996-4. (Reith Lectures series; 2002.) [HM1106 .O54 2002] (1.3.1; 1.3.5)

Satris, Stephen, ed. TAKING SIDES: CLASHING VIEWS ON MORAL ISSUES. New York: Dushkin/ McGraw-Hill, 2006. 357 p. ISBN 0-07-312950-X. (10th edition. Gift of the publisher.) [BJ1012 .T24 2006] (1.3.1; 1.1; 1.2; 1.3.5; 8.1; 9.3.1; 9.7; 10; 12.3; 14.5; 19.5; 20.5.1; 20.7; 22.1)

Smith, David Livingstone. WHY WE LIE: THE EVOLUTIONARY ROOTS OF DECEPTION AND THE UNCONSCIOUS MIND. New York: St. Martin's Press, 2004. 238 p. ISBN 0-312-31039-0. (Gift of the publisher.) [BF637 .D42 S65 2004] (1.3.1; 8.2; 8.4; 15.9; 17.1; 18.4)

Stoczkowski, Wiktor. EXPLAINING HUMAN ORIGINS: MYTH, IMAGINATION AND CONJECTURE. Cambridge/New York: Cambridge University Press, 2002. 234 p. ISBN 0-521-65730-X. [GN281 .S85813 2002] (1.3.1; 3.1)

1.3.2 APPLIED AND PROFESSIONAL ETHICS: BUSINESS

Blank, Rebecca M. and McGurn, William. IS THE MARKET MORAL? A DIALOGUE ON RELIGION, ECONOMICS, AND JUSTICE. Washington, DC: Brookings Institution Press, 2004. 151 p. ISBN 0-8157-1021-6. (Pew Forum Dialogues on Religion and Public Life series.) [BR115 .E3 B58 2004] (1.3.2; 1.2)

McLemore, Clinton W. STREET-SMART ETHICS: SUCCEEDING IN BUSINESS WITHOUT SELLING YOUR SOUL. Louisville, KY: Westminster John Knox Press, 2003. 186 p. ISBN 0-664-22628-0. [HF5387 .M432 2003] (1.3.2; 1.2; 1.3.1)

Parsons, Patricia J.; Institute of Public Relations (Great Britain). ETHICS IN PUBLIC RELATIONS: A GUIDE TO BEST PRACTICE. London/Sterling VA: Kogan Page, 2004. 187 p. ISBN 0-7494-4276-X. [HD59 .P3548 2004] (1.3.2; 1.3.1; 1.3.7; 10)

Special Issue on Business Ethics. AMERICAN BUSINESS LAW JOURNAL 2001 Winter; 38(2): 209-440. (ISSN 0002-7766.) (1.3.2; 1.1; 1.3.8)

1.3.3 APPLIED AND PROFESSIONAL ETHICS: EDUCATION

Binder, Amy J. CONTENTIOUS CURRICULA: AFROCENTRISM AND CREATIONISM IN AMERICAN PUBLIC SCHOOLS. Princeton, NJ: Princeton University Press, 2002. 307 p. ISBN 0-691-09180-3. (Princeton Studies in Cultural Sociology series.) [LB1570 .B52 2002] (1.3.3; 3.2; 21.7)

Halstead, J. Mark and Taylor, Monica J., eds. VALUES EDUCATION AND EDUCATION IN VALUES. London/New York: RoutledgeFalmer, 1996. 215 p. ISBN 0-7507-0510-8. (1.3.3; 1.1; 1.3.1; 1.3.5; 16.1)

Keith-Spiegel, Patricia; Whitley, Bernard E.; Balogh, Deborah Ware; Perkins, David V.; and Wittig, Arno F. THE ETHICS OF TEACHING: A CASEBOOK. Mahwah, NJ: Lawrence Erlbaum Associates, 2002. 273 p. ISBN 0-8058-4063-X. (Second edition.) [LB1779 .E76 2002] (1.3.3)

Macfarlane, Bruce. TEACHING WITH INTEGRITY: THE ETHICS OF HIGHER EDUCATION PRACTICE. London/New York: RoutledgeFalmer, 2004. 184 p. ISBN 0-415-33509-4. [LB1779 .M32 2004] (1.3.3)

McSherry, Corynne. WHO OWNS ACADEMIC WORK? BATTLING FOR CONTROL OF INTELLECTUAL PROPERTY. Cambridge, MA: Harvard University Press, 2001. 275 p. ISBN 0-674-00629-1. (1.3.3; 1.3.7; 1.3.9; 5.3)

Washburn, Jennifer. UNIVERSITY, INC.: THE CORPORATE CORRUPTION OF HIGHER EDUCATION. New York: Basic Books, 2005. 326 p. ISBN 0-465-09051-6. [LC1085.2 .W37 2005] (1.3.3; 1.3.2; 5.3; 9.7)

1.3.5 APPLIED AND PROFESSIONAL ETHICS: GOVERNMENT/CRIMINAL JUSTICE

Aly, Götz and Heim, Susanne. ARCHITECTS OF ANNIHILATION: AUSCHWITZ AND THE LOGIC OF DESTRUCTION. Princeton, NJ: Princeton University Press, 2002. 378 p. ISBN 0-691-08938-8. (Translation from the German by A.G. Blunden of: *Vordenker der Vernichtung.* Gift of Max M. and Marjorie B. Kampelman.) [D804.3 .A4613 2002] (1.3.5; 13.3; 15.5; 21.4)

Berkhoff, Karel C. HARVEST OF DESPAIR: LIFE AND DEATH IN UKRAINE UNDER NAZI RULE. Cambridge, MA: Belknap Press of Harvard University Press, 2004. 463 p. ISBN 0-674-01313-1. (Gift of Max M. and Marjorie B. Kampelman.) [DK508.833 .B47 2004] (1.3.5; 1.2; 21.4)

Brustein, William I. ROOTS OF HATE: ANTI-SEMITISM IN EUROPE BEFORE THE HOLOCAUST. New York: Cambridge University Press, 2003. 384 p. ISBN 0-521-77478-0. (Gift of Max M. and Marjorie B. Kampelman.) [DS146 .E8 B78 2003] (1.3.5; 15.5; 21.1)

Georgetown University. Woodstock Theological Center. THE ETHICS OF LOBBYING: ORGANIZED INTERESTS, POLITICAL POWER, AND THE COMMON GOOD. Washington, DC: Georgetown University Press, 2002. 97 p. ISBN 0-87840-905-X. ("Ethics in Public Policy Program.") (1.3.5)

Hitler, Adolf. MEIN KAMPF. Boston: Houghton Mifflin, 2001, 1943. 694 p. ISBN 0-395-92503-7. (Translation from the German by: Ralph Manheim. Introduction by: Abrahman Foxman. "A Mariner Book." Originally published: Houghton Mifflin, Boston, 1943.) (1.3.5)

Koonz, Claudia. THE NAZI CONSCIENCE. Cambridge, MA: Belknap Press of Harvard University Press, 2003. 362 p. ISBN 0-674-01172-4. (Gift of Max M. and Marjorie B. Kampelman.) [DD256.5 .K6185 2003] (1.3.5; 17.1; 21.4)

McLachlan, Hugh V. SOCIAL JUSTICE, HUMAN RIGHTS AND PUBLIC POLICY. Glasgow [Scotland]: Humming Earth, 2005. 179 p. ISBN 1-84622-003-3. [HN385.5 .M35 2005] (1.3.5; 1.1; 1.3.1; 1.3.2; 9.2; 21.1)

1.3.6 APPLIED AND PROFESSIONAL ETHICS: INTERNATIONAL AFFAIRS

French, Peter A. and Short, Jason A., eds. WAR AND BORDER CROSSINGS: ETHICS WHEN CULTURES CLASH. Lanham, MD: Rowman & Littlefield, 2005. 307 p. ISBN 0-7425-4386-2. ("Chiefly papers from a conference held in February 2003, sponsored by Peter A. French and Jason A. Short." Gift of the publisher.) [JZ1306 .W37 2005] (1.3.6; 1.2; 1.3.7; 2.1; 9.5.9; 16.1; 21.2; 21.7)

Lozowick, Yaacov. RIGHT TO EXIST: A MORAL DEFENSE OF ISRAEL'S WARS. New York: Doubleday, 2003. 326 p. ISBN 0-385-50905-7. (Gift of Max M. and Marjorie B. Kampelman.) [DS119.7 .L69 2003] (1.3.6; 1.3.5; 21.2)

1.3.7 APPLIED AND PROFESSIONAL ETHICS: JOURNALISM/MASS MEDIA

Harrabin, Roger; Coote, Anna; and Allen, Jessica. HEALTH IN THE NEWS: RISK, REPORTING AND MEDIA INFLUENCE. London: King's Fund, 2003. 47 p. ISBN 1-85717-480-1. (September 2003. Discussion paper. Publisher's address: 11-13 Cavendish Square, postal code W1G 0AN; fax: 020-7307-2801; Web: kingsfund.org.uk/publications.) (1.3.7; 5.2; 5.3; 7.1; 9.1)

1.3.8 APPLIED AND PROFESSIONAL ETHICS: LAW

Faigman, David L. LABORATORY OF JUSTICE: THE SUPREME COURT'S 200-YEAR STRUGGLE TO INTEGRATE SCIENCE AND THE LAW. New York: Times Books, 2004. 417 p. ISBN 0-8050-7274-8. [KF8748 .F27 2004] (1.3.8; 1.2; 1.3.5; 12.4.1; 15.1; 15.5)

Patterson, Richard North. PROTECT AND DEFEND: A NOVEL. New York: Ballantine Books, 2001. 591 p. ISBN 0-345-40479-3. ("On a cold day in January, President-elect Kerry Kilcannon takes the oath of office—and within days makes his first, most important move: appointing a new chief justice of the Supreme Court. Kilconnon's choice is a female judge with a brilliant record. And a secret. While the Senate spars over Caroline Master's nomination, an inflammatory abortion rights case is making its way toward the judge—and will explode into the headlines. Suddenly, the most divisive issue in America turns the president's nomination into all-out war. And from Judge Masters to a conservative, war-hero senator facing a crisis of conscience and a fifteen-year-old girl battling for her future, no one will be safe.") [PS3566 .A8242 P76 2001] (1.3.8; 1.3.5; 12.3; 12.4.2; Fiction)

1.3.9 APPLIED AND PROFESSIONAL ETHICS: SCIENTIFIC RESEARCH

BIOMEDICAL RESEARCH. Strasbourg: Council of Europe Publishing, 2004. 205 p. ISBN 92-871-5462-7. (Ethical Eye series. Also available in French as: *Regard éthique: La recherche biomédicale*; ISBN 92-871-5461-9. Distributed in the U.S. and Canada by: Manhattan Publishing Company, 468 Albany Post Road, Croton-on-Hudson, NY 10520; tel: 888-686-7066; Web: http://www.manhattanpublishing.com. Gift of the distributor.) [R854 .E85 B56 2004] (1.3.9; 1.3.12; 5.3; 8.4; 18.2; 18.3; 18.5.3; LE)

Buchanan, Elizabeth A., ed. READINGS IN VIRTUAL RESEARCH ETHICS: ISSUES AND CONTROVERSIES. Hershey, PA: Information Science Publishing, 2004. 362 p. ISBN 1-59140-289-1. [ZA4228 .R43 2004] (1.3.9; 1.1; 1.3.12; 7.1; 18.2; 18.3; 18.4; 21.7)

Judson, Horace Freeland. THE GREAT BETRAYAL: FRAUD IN SCIENCE. Orlando, FL: Harcourt Brace, 2004. 463 p. ISBN 0-15-100877-9. (Gift of the publisher.) [Q175.37 .J84 2004] (1.3.9; 1.3.7; 1.3.12; 5.3)

Shuchman, Miriam. THE DRUG TRIAL: NANCY OLIVIERI AND THE SCIENCE SCANDAL THAT ROCKED THE HOSPITAL FOR SICK CHILDREN. Toronto: Random House of Canada, 2005. 451 p. ISBN 0-679-31084-3. (Gift of the publisher.) [RS100.5 .S58 2005] (1.3.9; 9.7; 18.2; 18.5.2)

1.3.10 APPLIED AND PROFESSIONAL ETHICS: SOCIAL WORK

Congress, Elaine P. SOCIAL WORK VALUES AND ETHICS: IDENTIFYING AND RESOLVING PROFESSIONAL DILEMMAS. Belmont, CA: Wadsworth/Thomson Learning, 1999. 197 p. ISBN 0-8304-1492-4. [HV10.5 .C64 1999] (1.3.10; 1.1; 6; 7.1; 7.3; 9.5.2; 9.5.6; 9.5.7; 17.1)

Reamer, Frederic G. SOCIAL WORK VALUES AND ETHICS. New York: Columbia University Press, 1999. 247 p. ISBN 0-231-11391-9. (Second edition. Foundations of Social Work Knowledge Series.) [HV10.5 .R427 1999] (1.3.10; 1.1; 6; 7.4; 8.4; 9.4)

1.3.12 APPLIED AND PROFESSIONAL ETHICS: INFORMATION TECHNOLOGY

Heller, James S. THE LIBRARIAN'S COPYRIGHT COMPANION. Buffalo, NY: William S. Hein, 2004. 257 p. ISBN 0-8377-3300-6. [KF2995 .H45 2004] (1.3.12; Reference)

Moore, Adam D., ed. INFORMATION ETHICS: PRIVACY, PROPERTY, AND POWER. Seattle: University of Washington Press, 2005. 455 p. ISBN 0-295-98489-9. (Gift of the publisher.) [JC585 .I59 2005] (1.3.12; 1.1; 1.3.7; 5.3; 10; 15.8)

Quigley, Marian, ed. INFORMATION SECURITY AND ETHICS: SOCIAL AND ORGANIZATIONAL ISSUES. Hershey, PA: IRM Press, 2005. 317 p. ISBN 1-59140-233-6. (Gift of the publisher.) [T14.5 .I55 2005] (1.3.12; 5.3)

2.1 BIOETHICS (GENERAL)

Acosta Sariego, José R., ed. BIOÉTICA PARA LA SUSTENTABILIDAD. La Habana, Cuba: Publicaciones Acuario, Centro Félix Varela, 2002. 742 p. ISBN 959-7071-21-5. (Gift of Edmund D. Pellegrino.) [QH332 .B5268 2002] (2.1; 2.2)

Annas, George J. THE RIGHTS OF PATIENTS: THE AUTHORITATIVE ACLU GUIDE TO THE RIGHTS OF PATIENTS. New York: New York University Press, 2004. 387 p. ISBN 0-8093-2515-2. (Third edition. An American Civil Liberties Union Handbook series.) [KF3823 .A96 2004] (2.1; 4.4; 8.3.1; 8.4; 8.5; 9.1; 9.5.1; 14.1; 18.1; 19.1; 20.4.1; 20.7)

Anselm, Reiner and Körtner, Ulrich H.J., eds. STREITFALL BIOMEDIZIN: URTEILSFINDUNG IN CHRISTLICHER VERANTWORTUNG. Göttingen: Vandenhoeck & Ruprecht, 2003. 216 p. ISBN 3-525-58168-8. (Gift of LeRoy Walters.) [R725.56 .S77 2003] (2.1; 1.2)

Ashcroft, Richard; Lucassen, Anneke; Parker, Michael; Verkerk, Marian; and Widdershoven, Guy, eds. CASE ANALYSIS IN CLINICAL ETHICS. Cambridge/New York: Cambridge University Press, 2005. 246 p. ISBN 0-521-54315-0. (Gift of the publisher.) [R724 .C356 2005] (2.1; 1.1; 8.1; 10; 15.3)

Baumann, Eva; Brink, Alexander; May, Arnd T.; Schröder, Peter; and Schutzeichel, Corinna Iris, eds. WELTANSCHAULICHE OFFENHEIT IN DER BIOETHIK. Berlin: Duncker & Humblot, 2004. 311 p. ISBN 3-428-11602-X. (Erfahrung und Denken series; Bd. 94. ISSN 0425-1806. Gift of Hans-Martin Sass.) [QH332 .W45 2004] (2.1; 1.1; 1.2; 15.2; 18.5.4; 19.5; 20.1; 21.7)

Baylis, Françoise; Downie, Jocelyn; Hoffmaster, Barry; and Sherwin, Susan, eds. HEALTH CARE ETHICS IN CANADA. Toronto: Nelson/Thomson, 2004. 518 p. ISBN 0-17-641553-X. (Second edition.) [R724 .H346 2004] (2.1)

Beam, Thomas E. and Sparacino, Linette R., eds.; United States. Department of the Army. Office of the Surgeon

General [and] Walter Reed Army Medical Center. Borden Institute; [and] Uniformed Services University of the Health Sciences. MILITARY MEDICAL ETHICS. Washington, DC: TMM Publications, Borden Institute, Walter Reed Army Medical Center, 2003. 2 volumes, boxed set. [868 p.]. (Textbooks of Military Medicine series. Section editors: Edmund D. Pellegrino, Anthony E. Hartle, and Edmund G. Howe. Available on the Web at: http://www.bordeninstitute.army.mil/ethicsbook_files/Ethics. Gift of the Borden Institute.) [RC971 .M638 2003] (2.1; 1.2; 1.3.5; 4.1.2; 4.1.3; 9.5.1; 18.2; 18.5.1; 18.5.5; 21.1; 21.2)

Berglund, Catherine. ETHICS FOR HEALTH CARE. South Melbourne, Victoria/New York: Oxford University Press, 2004. 222 p. ISBN 0-19-551730-X. (Second edition.) [R724 .B43 2004] (2.1; 6; 8.1)

Choi, Kyungsuk. MORAL REASONING AND JUSTIFICATION IN MEDICAL ETHICS. Ann Arbor, MI: ProQuest Information and Learning/UMI, 2004. 214 p. (Publication No. AAT-3100402. Dissertation, (Ph.D.)—Michigan State University, 2004.) (2.1; 1.1; 8.3.4; 20.5.1; 21.7)

Devine, Richard J. GOOD CARE, PAINFUL CHOICES: MEDICAL ETHICS FOR ORDINARY PEOPLE. Mahwah, NJ: Paulist Press, 2004. 270 p. ISBN 0-8091-4273-2. (Third edition.) [R724 .D485 2004] (2.1; 1.2)

Döring, Ole. CHINAS BIOETHIK VERSTEHEN: ERGEBNISSE, ANALYSEN UND ÜBERLEGUNGEN AUS EINEM FORSCHUNGSPROJEKT ZUR KULTURELL AUFGEKLÄRTEN BIOETHIK. Hamburg: Abera, 2004. 334 p. ISBN 3-934376-58-4. (Originally presented as the author's thesis (Doctoral—Bochum) under the title: *Systematische Aspekte medizinischer Ethik in kulturübergreifenden Kontexten. . .*) (2.1; 2.2)

Egendorf, Laura K., ed. MEDICAL ETHICS. Detroit: Thomson Gale/Farmington Hills, MI: Greenhaven Press, 2005. 190 p. ISBN 0-7377-2213-4. (Current Controversies series. Gift of the publisher.) [R724 .M29273 2005] (2.1; 9.4; 14.1; 15.1; 19.1)

Eich, Thomas and Reifeld, Helmut, eds. BIOETHIK IM CHRISTLICH-ISLAMISCHEN DIALOG. Bornheim: Konrad-Adenauer-Stiftung e.V., 2004. 126 p. ISBN 3-937731-35-0. (2.1; 1.2; 14.5; 15.1; 18.5.4)

Flancbaum, Louis. "...AND YOU SHALL LIVE BY THEM": CONTEMPORARY JEWISH APPROACHES TO MEDICAL ETHICS. Pittsburgh, PA: Mirkov Publications, 2001. 404 p. ISBN 0-9648508-4-2. (Publisher's address: PO Box 81971, zip 15217. Gift of Max M. and Marjorie B. Kampelman.) [BM538 .H43 F55 2001] (2.1; 1.2)

Frey, Christofer. KONFLIKTFELDER DES LEBENS: THEOLOGISCHE STUDIEN ZUR BIOETHIK. Göttingen: Vandenhoeck & Ruprecht, 1998. 236 p. ISBN 3-525-58128-9. (Edited by Peter Dabrock and Wolfgang Maaser.) [R725.56 .F745 1998] (2.1; 1.1; 1.2; 10; 15.1; 19.1; LE)

Furrow, Barry R.; Greaney, Thomas L.; Johnson, Sandra H.; Jost, Timothy Stolzfus; and Schwartz, Robert L. BIOETHICS: HEALTH CARE LAW AND ETHICS. St. Paul, MN: Thomson/West, 2004. 505 p. ISBN 0-314-15406-X. (Fifth edition. American Casebook Series.) [KF3821 .A7 B56 2004] (2.1; LE)

Furton, Edward James and Mitchell, Louise A., eds.; National Catholic Bioethics Center. WALK AS CHILDREN OF LIGHT: THE CHALLENGE OF COOPERATION IN A PLURALISTIC SOCIETY. Boston: National Catholic Bioethics Center, 2003. 276 p. ISBN 0-935372-46-6. (Nineteenth Workshop for Bishops of the United States and Canada, held in Dallas, TX in 2003. Publisher's address: 159 Washington Street, zip 02135.) [R725.56 .W67 2003] (2.1; 1.2; 1.3.5; 4.4; 10; 12.1; 20.5.1; 20.7; 21.3; 21.7)

Gordijn, Bert and ten Have, Henk, eds. MEDIZINETHIK UND KULTUR: GRENZEN MEDIZINISCHEN HANDELNS IN DEUTSCHLAND UND DEN NIEDERLANDEN. Stuttgart: FrommannHolzboog, 2000. 507 p. ISBN 3-7728-2028-X. (Medizin und Philosophie series; Bd. 5.) [R724 .M335 2000] (2.1; 4.4; 20.5.1; 20.7; 21.7)

Häyry, Matti; Takala, Tuija; and Herissone-Kelly, Peter, eds. BIOETHICS AND SOCIAL REALITY. Amsterdam/New York: Rodopi, 2005. 180 p. ISBN 90-420-1655-8. (Value Inquiry Book Series; Vol. 165. Gift of the publisher.) [QH332 .B496 2005] (2.1; 1.1; 1.3.2; 8.3.1; 12.4.1; 14.2; 14.5; 15.1; 20.5.1; 20.7)

Hope, Tony. MEDICAL ETHICS: A VERY SHORT INTRODUCTION. Oxford/New York: Oxford University Press, 2004. 152 p. ISBN 0-19-280282-8. (Very Short Introductions series; Vol. 114.) [R724 .H625 2004] (2.1)

Jagielo, Ted and Guinan, Patrick, eds. CATHOLIC MEDICAL ETHICS: CORE READINGS. [Chicago] : Catholic Physicians' Guild of Chicago, 2000, c1999. 269 p. ISBN 1-58500-801-X. ("This book is a compilation of articles taken from the *Linacre Quarterly*, a publication of the Catholic Medical Association, which includes the Chicago Catholic Physician's Guild." Distributed by: 1st Books Library, 2511 West 3rd Street, Suite 1, Bloomington, IN 47404.) [R725.56 .C365 2000] (2.1; 1.2; 2.3; 4.1.2; 4.4; 9.7; 11.1; 12.3; 12.5.1; 15.4; 15.5; 18.5.4; 20.5.1; 21.4)

Jonsen, Albert R. BIOETHICS BEYOND THE HEADLINES: WHO LIVES? WHO DIES? WHO DECIDES? Lanham, MD: Rowman & Littlefield, 2005. 209 p. ISBN 0-7425-4524-5. (Gift of the publisher.) [R724 .J655 2005] (2.1; 2.2; 2.3)

Jussim, Daniel. MEDICAL ETHICS: MORAL AND LEGAL CONFLICTS IN HEALTH CARE. New York: Julian Messner, 1991. 124 p. ISBN 0-671-70015-4. (Issues for the 90s series. Juvenile literature.) [R724 .J86 1990] (2.1; POP)

Kautzky, Rudolf. EUTHANASIE UND GOTTESFRAGE: MEDIZINISCHE TEXTE UND THEOLOGISCHE PROVOKATIONEN. Stuttgart: Radius, 2004. 357 p. ISBN 3-87173-281-8. (Collection of texts previously published. Edited and with an introduction by Siegfried Scharrer.) (2.1; 1.2; 4.4; 20.5.1)

Koterski, Joseph W., ed. LIFE AND LEARNING VI: PROCEEDINGS OF THE SIXTH UNIVERSITY FACULTY FOR LIFE CONFERENCE JUNE 1996 AT GEORGETOWN UNIVERSITY. Washington, DC: University Faculty for Life, 1997. 342 p. ISBN 1-886387-04-4. [HQ767.15 .U55a 1996] (2.1; 1.2; 1.3.5; 1.3.7; 4.4; 7.1; 9.1; 10; 11.1; 12.1; 12.3; 13.1; 20.5.1; 20.5.2; 20.7; 21.1)

Koterski, Joseph W., ed. LIFE AND LEARNING VII: PROCEEDINGS OF THE SEVENTH UNIVERSITY FACULTY FOR LIFE CONFERENCE, JUNE 1997 AT LOYOLA COLLEGE. Washington, DC: University Faculty for Life, 1998. 248 p. ISBN 1-886387-05-2. [HQ767.15 .U55a 1997] (2.1; 1.1; 1.2; 1.3.5; 4.4; 7.1; 8.1; 9.7; 11.3; 12.3; 12.5.2; 13.2; 20.5.1; 20.7)

Koterski, Joseph W., ed. LIFE AND LEARNING IX: PROCEEDINGS OF THE NINTH UNIVERSITY FACULTY FOR LIFE CONFERENCE, JUNE 1999 AT TRINITY INTERNATIONAL UNIVERSITY, DEERFIELD, ILL. Washington, DC: University Faculty for Life, 2000. 404 p. ISBN 1-886387-07-9. [HQ767.15 .U55a 1999] (2.1; 1.1; 1.2; 1.3.5; 4.4; 7.1; 11.1; 12.3; 12.4.2; 14.4; 14.5; 20.5.1; 20.5.2; 20.6; 21.1)

Koterski, Joseph W., ed. LIFE AND LEARNING XI: PROCEEDINGS OF THE ELEVENTH UNIVERSITY FACULTY FOR LIFE CONFERENCE, JUNE 2001 AT ST. JOSEPH'S UNIVERSITY, WASHINGTON, D.C. Washington, DC: University Faculty for Life, 2002. 270 p. (ISSN 1097-0878.) [HQ767.15 .U55a 2001] (2.1; 1.2; 4.4; 7.1;8.1; 9.7; 12.4.1; 12.4.2; 18.5.3; 20.5.1; 20.7)

Leies, John A.; McCarthy, Donald G.; and Bayer, Edward J. HANDBOOK ON CRITICAL LIFE ISSUES. Boston: National Catholic Bioethics Center, 2004. 254 p. ISBN 0-935372-47-4. (Third edition. Edited by Louise A. Mitchell. Publisher's address: 159 Washington Street, zip 02135; tel.: 215-877-2660.) [R724 .H23 2004] (2.1; 1.2; 4.4; 12.3; 12.4.1; 14.1; 18.5.4; 19.1; 20.2.1; 20.5.1; 20.7; LE)

Lemaire, Jacques and Susanne, Charles, eds. BIOÉTHIQUE: JUSQU'OÙ PEUT-ON ALLER? Bruxelles: Editions de l'université de Bruxelles, 1996. 83 p. (Pensée et les hommes, New Series; No. 31. ISSN 0774-2754.) (2.1; 2.4; 4.4; 7.1; 10; 14.1; 17.1; 18.2)

Ling, John R. RESPONDING TO THE CULTURE OF DEATH: A PRIMER OF BIOETHICAL ISSUES. Epsom, [England]: DayOne, 2001. 128 p. ISBN 1-903087-26-0. (Publisher's address: 3 Epsom Business Park, Kiln Lane, Epsom, Surrey, postal code KT17 1JF.) [QH332 .L56 2001] (2.1; 1.2; 4.4; 12.3)

Malherbe, Jean-François. COMPROMIS, DILEMMES ET PARADOXES EN ÉTHIQUE CLINIQUE. [Saint-Laurent, Québec]: Artel -Fides, 1999. 210 p. ISBN 2-87374-049-3 [Artel]; ISBN 2-7621-2121-3 [Fides]. (Catalyses series.) (2.1; 4.1.2; 9.3.1; 9.6)

Matulic, Tonci. BIOETIKA. Zagreb: Glas Koncila, 2001. 539 p. ISBN 953-6258-19-6. (Biblioteka Tertium Millennium series; Knj. 1. Text in Croatian. Gift of the author.) (2.1; 1.1; 1.2)

Miller, Frances H. RIGHTS AND RESOURCES. Aldershot, Hants/Burlington, VT: Ashgate, 2002. 597 p. ISBN 0-7546-2156-1. (International Library of Medicine, Ethics and the Law series.) [K3601 .R54 2003] (2.1; 1.1; 4.4; 4.5; 8.3.1; 9.4; 15.1; 18.1)

Moreno, Jonathan D. IS THERE AN ETHICIST IN THE HOUSE? ON THE CUTTING EDGE OF BIOETHICS. Bloomington: Indiana University Press, 2005. 274 p. ISBN 0-253-34635-5. (Bioethics and the Humanities series. Gift of the publisher.) [R724 .M833 2005] (2.1; 6; 7.2; 9.6; 17.1; 18.2; 18.3; 20.5.1)

Oderberg, David S. APPLIED ETHICS: A NON-CONSEQUENTIALIST APPROACH. Malden, MA: Blackwell Publishers, 2000. 248 p. ISBN 0-631-21905-6. (Companion volume to: *Moral Theory: A Non-Consequentialist Approach*.) [BJ1031 .O34 2000] (2.1; 1.1; 4.4; 10; 12.3; 20.5.1; 20.6; 21.2; 22.1)

Pessini, Leo and Barchifontaine, Christian de Paul de. PROBLEMAS ATUAIS DE BIOÉTICA. São Paulo: Editora do Centro Universitário São Camilo [and] Edições Loyola, 2005. 579 p. ISBN 85-15-00321-X. (Seventh edition, revised and enlarged. Gift of the authors.) (2.1; 4.4; 6; Reference)

Pozgar, George D. LEGAL AND ETHICAL ISSUES FOR HEALTH PROFESSIONALS. Sudbury, MA: Jones and Bartlett, 2005. 378 p. ISBN 0-7637-2633-8. (Gift of the publisher.) [KF3821 .P68 2005] (2.1; 8.1; 9.1; LE)

Purtilo, Ruth B. ETHICAL DIMENSIONS IN THE HEALTH PROFESSIONS. Philadelphia: Elsevier Saunders, 2005. 346 p. ISBN 0-7216-0243-6. (Fourth edition. Gift of the publisher.) [R724 .P82 2005] (2.1; 1.1; 2.3)

Purtilo, Ruth B.; Jensen, Gail M.; and Royeen, Charlotte Brasic. EDUCATING FOR MORAL ACTION: A SOURCEBOOK IN HEALTH AND REHABILITATION ETHICS. Philadelphia: F.A. Davis, 2005. 318 p. ISBN 0-8036-1261-3. (Gift of the publisher.) [R724 .E325 2005] (2.1; 1.1; 1.2; 2.3; 4.1.1; 5.1; 6; 7.2; 8.1; 9.6; 9.8; 16.3; 17.1; 18.2; 21.7)

Rich, Ben A. STRANGE BEDFELLOWS: HOW MEDICAL JURISPRUDENCE HAS INFLUENCED MEDICAL ETHICS AND MEDICAL PRACTICE. New York: Kluwer Academic, 2001. 196 p. ISBN 0-306-46665-1. (2.1; 1.1; 2.2; 4.4; 8.1; 8.3.1; 8.4; 12.4.1; 20.2.1; 20.5.1; 20.5.4; 20.7)

Romanucci-Ross, Lola and Tancredi, Laurence R. WHEN LAW AND MEDICINE MEET: A CULTURAL VIEW. Dordrecht/Boston: Kluwer Academic, 2004. 189 p. ISBN 1-4020-2756-7. (International Library of Ethics, Law, and the New Medicine series; Vol. 24.) [RA1053 .R66 2004] (2.1; 1.3.5; 4.3; 5.1; 5.3; 7.1; 10; 15.1; 17.1)

Russo, Giovanni, ed. ENCICLOPEDIA DI BIOETICA E SESSUOLOGIA. Leumann (Torino), Italy: Elledici; [Gorle], (Bergamo): Velar; [Roma]: CIC Edizioni Internazionali, 2004. 1849 p. ISBN 88-01-03023-1. (Gift of the publisher.) (2.1; 10; Reference)

Russo, Giovanni. FORMARSI ALLA BIOETICA E AL VALORE DELLA VITA: LINEE GUIDA PER L'INSEGNAMENTO DELLA RELIGIONE CATTOLICA LA CATECHESI, LA PARROCCHIA, L'ANIMAZIONE DI QUARTIERE. Messina [Italy]: Coop. S. Tom., 1996. 127 p. ISBN 88-86212-09-7. (Gift of the author.) (2.1)

Sgreccia, Elio. MANUALE DI BIOETICA, VOLUME I: FONDAMENTI ED ETICA BIOMEDICA. Milano: Vita e Pensiero, 1994. 734 p. ISBN 88-343-6919-X. (Second edition. Trattati e manuali series. Gift of Warren Reich.) [R724 .S453 1994 v.1] (2.1; 4.1.2)

Shildrick, Margrit and Mykitiuk, Roxanne, eds. ETHICS OF THE BODY: POSTCONVENTIONAL CHALLENGES. Cambridge, MA: MIT Press, 2005. 288 p. ISBN 0-262-19523-2. (Basic Bioethics series. Gift of the publisher.) [QH332 .E736 2005] (2.1; 4.4; 10; 15.1)

Snyder, Lois and Leffler, Cathy, eds.; American College of Physicians. Ethics and Human Rights Committee. ETHICS MANUAL. Philadelphia: American College of Physicians, 2005. 66 p. ISBN 1-930513-65-8. (Fifth edition. Product No. 330351010. Reprinted from: *Annals of Internal Medicine* 2005; 142: 561-583. Publisher's address: 190 N. Independence Mall West, zip 19106-1572. Gift of the publisher.) (2.1; 6)

Stepke, Fernando Lolas and Corbinos, Lorenzo Agar, eds.; World Health Organization [and] Pan American Health Organization. INTERFACES BETWEEN BIOETHICS AND THE EMPIRICAL SOCIAL SCIENCES. Buenos Aires, Argentina: World Health Organization, 2002. 110 p. ISBN 956-7938-02-4. (Regional Program on Bioethics series; 2002. "Contains the documents elaborated by the members of the International Bioethics Advisory Committee of PAHO, that was established in the official meeting held on October 2-3, 2001 in Buenos Aires, Argentina." Gift of LeRoy Walters.) (2.1; 9.4; 9.7; 9.8; 15.1; 18.3; 18.4)

Thiele, F. and Ashcroft, R.E., eds. BIOETHICS IN A SMALL WORLD. Berlin: Springer-Verlag, 2005. 138 p. ISBN 3-540-23595-7. (Wissenschaftsethik und Technikfolgenbeurteilung series; Bd. 24. Papers presented at the conference "Bioethics in a Small World" held 10-12 April 2003 as part of the Europäische Akademie's programme for international interdisciplinary exchange. Gift of the publisher.) [QH332 .B498 2005] (2.1; 1.1; 1.3.11; 1.3.12; 2.4; 5.3; 9.4; 9.7; 14.5; 15.1; 15.8; 21.1; 21.7)

Tollefsen, Christopher, ed. JOHN PAUL II'S CONTRIBUTION TO CATHOLIC BIOETHICS. Dordrecht: Springer, 2004. 186 p. ISBN 1-4020-3129-7. (Philosophy and Medicine series; Vol. 84. Catholic Studies in Bioethics series; Vol. 3.) [R725.56 .J64 2004] (2.1; 1.2; 1.3.1; 4.4; 8.1; 10; 14.1)

Vollmann, Jochen, ed. MEDIZIN UND ETHIK: AKTUELLE ETHISCHE PROBLEME IN THERAPIE UND FORSCHUNG: RINGVORLESUNG DER FRIEDRICH-ALEXANDER-UNIVERSITÄT ERLANGEN-NÜRNBERG. Erlangen: Universitätsbund Erlangen, 2003. 182 p. ISBN 3-930357-61-5. (Erlanger Forschungen: Sonderreihe series; No. 11. ISSN 0940- 4694.) (2.1; 14.4; 15.2; 18.5.2; 18.5.4; 20.5.1)

Numbers in ( ) = NRCBL Classification Numbers

Voyer, Gilles. QU'EST QUE L'ÉTHIQUE CLINIQUE? ESSAI PHILOSOPHIQUE SUR L'ÉTHIQUE CLINIQUE CONÇUE COMME RÉACTUALISATION DE L'ÉTHIQUE ARISTOTÉLICIENNE. [Namur, Belgique]: Artel [and] [Saint-Laurent, Québec]: Fides, 1996. 179 p. ISBN 2-87374-031-0 [Artel]; ISBN 2-7621-1915-4 [Fides]. (Catalyses series. Originally published as the author's thesis (master's)—Université de Sherbrooke, 1995.) (2.1; 1.1)

Walters, LeRoy; Kahn, Tamar Joy; and Goldstein, Doris Mueller, eds. BIBLIOGRAPHY OF BIOETHICS, VOLUME 31. Washington, DC: Kennedy Institute of Ethics, Georgetown University, 2005. 701 p. ISBN 1-883913-12-8. [Z6675 .E8 W34 v.31] (2.1; Reference)

Wong, John B. ETHICS TODAY: FOR MINISTERS AND HEALTHCARE PROFESSIONALS: PROBLEMS AND SOME PRACTICAL ANSWERS. Riverside, CA: Loma Linda University Press, 2003. 308 p. ISBN 1-59410-003-9. (Publisher's address: 24951 Stewart Street, PO Drawer P, zip 92354; tel.: 909-558-4552.) [R724 .W588 2003] (2.1; 1.2; 10; 15.1; 16.1)

2.2 BIOETHICS: HISTORY OF HEALTH ETHICS

Bergdolt, Klaus. DAS GEWISSEN DER MEDIZIN: ÄRZTLICHE MORAL VON DER ANTIKE BIS HEUTE. München: C.H. Beck, 2004. 376 p. ISBN 3-406-52192-4. [R724 .B424 2004] (2.2; 1.1; 1.2; 2.1; 21.1)

Schomerus, Georg. EIN IDEAL UND SEIN NUTZEN: ÄRZTLICHE ETHIK IN ENGLAND UND DEUTSCHLAND 1902-1933. Frankfurt am Main/New York: Peter Lang, 2001. 211 p. ISBN 3-631-38131-X. (Medizingeschichte im Kontext series; Bd. 8. ISSN 1437-3122. Originally presented as the author's thesis (doctoral)—Freiburg im Breisgau, 2001.) (2.2; 1.3.5; 2.3; 4.1.2; 6; 7.1; 7.2; 8.1; 9.1; 15.5; 20.5.1; 22.2)

Veatch, Robert M. DISRUPTED DIALOGUE: MEDICAL ETHICS AND THE COLLAPSE OF PHYSICIAN-HUMANIST COMMUNICATION (1770-1980). Oxford/New York: Oxford University Press, 2005. 317 p. ISBN 0-19-516976-X. [R724 .V414 2005] (2.2; 1.2; 6; 7.1; 7.2; 7.3)

2.3 BIOETHICS: EDUCATION/PROGRAMS

Ahronheim, Judith C.; Moreno, Jonathan D.; and Zuckerman, Connie. ETHICS IN CLINICAL PRACTICE. Sudbury, MA: Jones and Bartlett, 2005. 508 p. ISBN 0-7637-2945-0. (Second edition. Originally published: Aspen Publishers, 2000. Gift of the publisher.) [R724 .A33 2005] (2.3; 2.1)

Snyder, Lois. ETHICAL CHOICES: CASE STUDIES FOR MEDICAL PRACTICE. Philadelphia: American College of Physicians, 2005. 188 p. ISBN 1-930513-57-7. (Second edition. Gift of the publisher.) [R724 .E784 2005] (2.3; 2.1)

Sokol, Daniel K. and Bergson, Gillian. MEDICAL ETHICS AND LAW: SURVIVING ON THE WARDS AND PASSING EXAMS.

London: Trauma Publishing, 2005. 293 p. ISBN 0-9547657-1-0. (Trauma Medical School Survival Guide Series.) (2.3; 1.1; 7.2; 8.1; 8.3.1; 8.3.4; 8.4; 9.2; 9.4; 9.5.7; 14.1; 15.1; 17.1; 20.5.1)

Wilcockson, Michael. ISSUES OF LIFE AND DEATH. London: Hodder & Stoughton Educational, 1999. 138 p. ISBN 0-340-72488-9. (Access to Philosophy Series.) (2.3; 4.4; 12.1; 16.2; 20.5.1; 20.6; 20.7; 21.2)

3.1 PHILOSOPHY OF BIOLOGY (GENERAL)

Amundson, Ronald. THE CHANGING ROLE OF THE EMBRYO IN EVOLUTIONARY THOUGHT: ROOTS OF EVO-DEVO. Cambridge/New York: Cambridge University Press, 2005. 280 p. ISBN 0-521-80699-2. (Cambridge Studies in Philosophy and Biology series. Gift of the publisher.) [QH360.5 .A48 2005] (3.1; 5.1)

Ceccarelli, Leah. SHAPING SCIENCE WITH RHETORIC: THE CASES OF DOBZHANSKY, SCHRÖDINGER, AND WILSON. Chicago: University of Chicago Press, 2001. 204 p. ISBN 0-226-09907-5. [QH303.6 .C433 2001] (3.1; 5.1; 5.3; 15.1; 15.9)

Martensen, Robert L. THE BRAIN TAKES SHAPE: AN EARLY HISTORY. Oxford/New York: Oxford University Press, 2004. 247 p. ISBN 0-19-515172-0. (The book represents circa 17th century social, scientific, and philosophical history of mind-body views.) [R723 .M336 2004] (3.1; 4.1.2; 4.4; 7.1; 17.1)

Wright, John p. and Potter, Paul, eds. PSYCHE AND SOMA: PHYSICIANS AND METAPHYSICIANS ON THE MIND-BODY PROBLEM FROM ANTIQUITY TO ENLIGHTENMENT. Oxford: Clarendon Press/New York: Oxford University Press, 2000. 298 p. ISBN 0-19-925674-8. [BD450 .P75 2000] (3.1; 1.1; 1.2; 4.4)

3.2 EVOLUTION AND CREATION

Clayton, Philip and Schloss, Jeffrey, eds. EVOLUTION AND ETHICS: HUMAN MORALITY IN BIOLOGICAL AND RELIGIOUS PERSPECTIVE. Grand Rapids, MI: William B. Eerdmans, 2004. 339 p. ISBN 0-8028-2695-4. [BJ1311 .E95 2004] (3.2; 1.1; 1.2; 3.1)

Darwin, Charles [and] Wilson, Edward O., ed. FROM SO SIMPLE A BEGINNING: THE FOUR GREAT BOOKS OF CHARLES DARWIN. New York: Norton, 2006. 1706 p. ISBN 0-393-06134-5. (3.2)

Dawkins, Richard. THE ANCESTOR'S TALE: A PILGRIMAGE TO THE DAWN OF EVOLUTION. New York: Houghton Mifflin, 2004. 673 p. ISBN 0-618-61916-X. (3.2)

Dembski, William A. and Ruse, Michael, eds. DEBATING DESIGN: FROM DARWIN TO DNA. Cambridge/New York: Cambridge University Press, 2004. 405 p. ISBN 0-521-82949-6. [QH360.5 .D42 2004] (3.2; 1.2; 15.1)

Regal, Brian. HUMAN EVOLUTION: A GUIDE TO THE DEBATES. Santa Barbara, CA: ABC-CLIO, 2004. 357 p. ISBN 1-85109-418-0. (Controversies in Science series.) [GN281 .R412313 2004] (3.2)

Ruse, Michael. THE EVOLUTION-CREATION STRUGGLE. Cambridge: Harvard University Press, 2005. 327 p. ISBN 0-674-01687-4. (Gift of the publisher.) [BT712 .R68 2005] (3.2; 1.2; 13.1; 15.1)

Scott, Eugenie C. EVOLUTION VS. CREATIONISM: AN INTRODUCTION. Berkeley: University of California Press, 2005, c2004. 272 p. ISBN 0-520-24650-0. (Originally published: Greenwood Press, Westport, CT, 2004. Gift of the publisher.) [QH367 .S395 2005] (3.2; 1.2)

Wirzba, Norman. THE PARADISE OF GOD: RENEWING RELIGION IN AN ECOLOGICAL AGE. New York: Oxford University Press, 2003. 240 p. ISBN 0-19-515716-8. (3.2; 1.2; 16.1)

Witham, Larry A. WHERE DARWIN MEETS THE BIBLE: CREATIONISTS AND EVOLUTIONISTS IN AMERICA. Oxford/New York: Oxford University Press, 2002. 330 p. ISBN 0-19-515045-7. (3.2; 1.2)

4.1.1 PHILOSOPHY OF MEDICINE, NURSING, & OTHER HEALTH PROFESSIONS

Global Perspectives on Complementary and Alternative Medicine. ANNALS OF THE AMERICAN ACADEMY OF POLITICAL AND SOCIAL SCIENCE 2002 September; 583: 6-232. (ISSN 0002-7162.) (4.1.1; 1.2; 7.1; 8.1; 9.5.1; 21.1)

Hugman, Richard. NEW APPROACHES IN ETHICS FOR THE CARING PROFESSIONS. New York: Palgrave/Macmillan, 2005. 190 p. ISBN 1-4039-1471-0. (Gift of the publisher.) [HV10.5 .H84 2005] (4.1.1; 1.1.; 1.3.1; 1.3.10; 4.1.3; 10)

Institute of Medicine (United States). Committee on the Use of Complementary and Alternative Medicine by the American Public. COMPLEMENTARY AND ALTERNATIVE MEDICINE IN THE UNITED STATES. Washington, DC: National Academies Press, 2005. 337 p. ISBN 0-309-09270-1. (Also available on the Web at: http://www.nap.edu.) [R733 .I5633 2004] (4.1.1; 5.2; 7.2)

Kunow, Marianna Appel. MAYA MEDICINE: TRADITIONAL HEALING IN YUCATAN. Albuquerque: University of New Mexico Press, 2003. 152 p. ISBN 0-8263-2864-4. [F1435.3 .M4 K86 2003] (4.1.1; 1.2; 4.2)

Kuriyama, Shigehisa. THE EXPRESSIVENESS OF THE BODY AND THE DIVERGENCE OF GREEK AND CHINESE MEDICINE. New York: Zone Books, 1999. 340 p. ISBN 0-942299-88-4. [R723 .K87 1999] (4.1.1; 4.4)

Murcott, Toby. THE WHOLE STORY: ALTERNATIVE MEDICINE ON TRIAL? New York: Macmillan, 2005. 173 p. ISBN 1-4039-4500-4. (Gift of the publisher.) [R733 .M87 2005] (4.1.1; 9.7; 15.1; 18.3)

Ruggie, Mary. MARGINAL TO MAINSTREAM: ALTERNATIVE MEDICINE IN AMERICA. Cambridge/New York: Cambridge University Press, 2004. 232 p. ISBN 0-521-54222-7. [R733 .R84 2004] (4.1.1; 7.1)

Stone, Julie. AN ETHICAL FRAMEWORK FOR COMPLEMENTARY AND ALTERNATIVE THERAPISTS. London/New York: Routledge, 2002. 285 p. ISBN 0-415-27900-3. [R733 .S865 2002] (4.1.1; 2.1; 6)

White, Peter, ed. BIOPSYCHOSOCIAL MEDICINE: AN INTEGRATED APPROACH TO UNDERSTANDING ILLNESS. Oxford/New York: Oxford University Press, 2005. 242 p. ISBN 0-19-853034-X. [R733 .B565 2005] (4.1.1; 7.1; 17.1)

4.1.2 PHILOSOPHY OF MEDICINE

Bevins, Michael B. THE PRACTICE OF MEDICINE. Ann Arbor, MI: ProQuest/UMI], 2004. 253 p. (Publication No. AAT-3113418. Dissertation, (Ph.D.)— University of Texas Graduate School of Biomedical Science at Galveston, 2004.) (4.1.2)

Evans, Martyn; Louhiala, Pekka; and Puustinen, Raimo, eds. PHILOSOPHY FOR MEDICINE: APPLICATIONS IN A CLINICAL CONTEXT. Oxford/San Francisco: Radcliffe Medical Press, 2004. 157 p. ISBN 1-85775-943-5. [R723 .P4445 2004] (4.1.2; 7.1; 21.7)

Seifert, Josef. THE PHILOSOPHICAL DISEASES OF MEDICINE AND THEIR CURE: PHILOSOPHY AND ETHICS OF MEDICINE, VOLUME 1: FOUNDATIONS. Dordrecht/Norwell, MA: Springer, 2004. 399 p. ISBN 1-4020-2870-9. (Philosophy and Medicine series; Vol. 82.) [R723 .S454 2004 v.1] (4.1.2; 1.1; 2.1; 4.4)

4.1.3 PHILOSOPHY OF NURSING

Burnard, Philip; Chapman, Christine M.; and Smallman, Susan. PROFESSIONAL AND ETHICAL ISSUES IN NURSING. Edinburgh/New York: Baillière Tindall, 2004. 153 p. ISBN 0-7020-2685-9. (Third edition. Gift of the publisher.) [RT85 .B87 2004] (4.1.3; 6; 8.1; 8.3.1; 8.4; 9.8; 21.7)

Butts, Janie B. and Rich, Karen L. NURSING ETHICS: ACROSS THE CURRICULUM INTO PRACTICE. Sudbury, MA: Jones and Bartlett, 2005. 277 p. ISBN 0-7637-4735-1. (Gift of the publisher.) [RT85 .B78 2005] (4.1.3; 1.1; 6; 7.3; 8.1; 8.4; 9.5.1; 9.5.2; 9.5.7; 14.1; 17.1; 19.1; 20.1)

Doornbos, Mary Molewyk; Groenhout, Ruth E.; Hotz, Kendra G.; et al. TRANSFORMING CARE: A CHRISTIAN VISION OF NURSING PRACTICE. Grand Rapids, MI: William B. Eerdmans, 2005. 211 p. ISBN 0-8028-2874-4. (Gift of the publisher.) [BT732 .D66 2005] (4.1.3; 1.2; 9.1; 17.1)

Fry, Sara T. and Veatch, Robert M. CASE STUDIES IN NURSING ETHICS. Sudbury, MA: Jones and Bartlett Publishers, 2006. 460 p. ISBN 0-7637-3037-8. (Third edition. Gift of the publisher.) [RT85 .V4 2006] (4.1.3; 2.1; 2.3)

Numbers in ( ) = NRCBL Classification Numbers

Keatings, Margaret and Smith, O'Neil B. ETHICAL & LEGAL ISSUES IN CANADIAN NURSING. Toronto: W.B. Saunders Canada, 2000. 358 p. ISBN 0-9205-1336-0. (Second edition.) (4.1.3; 2.1; 6; 8.1)

McHale, Jean V. and Tingle, John. LAW AND NURSING. Edinburgh/New York: Butterworth-Heinemann, 2001. 282 p. ISBN 0-7506-4806-6. (Second edition.) (4.1.3; 7.4; 8.1; 8.3.1; 8.3.2; 8.3.3; 8.4; 14.1; 19.1; 20.5.1)

Tadd, Win, ed. ETHICAL AND PROFESSIONAL ISSUES IN NURSING: PERSPECTIVES FROM EUROPE. Basingstoke, Hampshire, UK: Palgrave, 2004. 197 p. ISBN 0-333-74993-6. [RT10 .E84 2004] (4.1.3; 6; 7.3; 8.1; 9.1; 21.1)

Taylor, Carol; Lillis, Carol; and LeMone, Priscilla. FUNDAMENTALS OF NURSING: THE ART AND SCIENCE OF NURSING CARE. Philadelphia: Lippincott Williams & Wilkins, 2005. 1555 p. ISBN 0-7817-4480-6. (Fifth edition. Gift of the publisher.) [RT41 .T396 2005] (4.1.3; 8.1; Reference)

Watson, Jean. CARING SCIENCE AS SACRED SCIENCE. Philadelphia: F.A. Davis, 2005. 242 p. ISBN 0-8036-1169-2. (Gift of the publisher.) [RT84.5 .W366 2005] (4.1.3; 1.1; 8.1)

4.2 CONCEPT OF HEALTH

Sargent, Michael G. BIOMEDICINE AND THE HUMAN CONDITION: CHALLENGES, RISKS, AND REWARDS. New York: Cambridge University Press, 2004. 350 p. ISBN 0-521-83366-3. (Gift of the publisher.) [R723 .S223 2004] (4.2; 2.1; 4.1.2; 15.1)

Taboada, Paulina; Cuddeback, Kateryna Fedoryka; and Donohue-White, Patricia, eds. PERSON, SOCIETY, AND VALUE: TOWARDS A PERSONALIST CONCEPT OF HEALTH. Dordrecht/Boston: Kluwer Academic, 2002. 259 p. ISBN 1-4020-0503-2. (Philosophy and Medicine series; Vol. 72.) [R723 .P386 2002] (4.2; 1.1; 1.2; 4.1.2; 4.4)

4.3 CONCEPT OF MENTAL HEALTH

Cooper, Rachel. CLASSIFYING MADNESS: A PHILOSOPHICAL EXAMINATION OF THE DIAGNOSTIC AND STATISTICAL MANUAL OF MENTAL DISORDERS. Dordrecht/New York: Springer, 2005. 172 p. ISBN 1-4020-3344-3. (Philosophy and Medicine series; Vol. 86. Revised thesis (Ph.D.)—Cambridge University, 2002.) [RC455.2 .C4 C67 2005] (4.3; 5.3; 17.1)

Monahan, John; et al. RETHINKING RISK ASSESSMENT: THE MACARTHUR STUDY OF MENTAL DISORDER AND VIOLENCE. New York: Oxford University Press, 2001. 197 p. ISBN 0-19-513882-1. (4.3; 7.1; 9.1; 17.1; 17.7)

Nicholi, Armand M., ed. THE HARVARD GUIDE TO PSYCHIATRY. Cambridge, MA: Belknap Press of Harvard University Press, 1999. 856 p. ISBN 0-674-37570-X. (Third edition. Revised edition of: *The New Harvard Guide to Psychiatry*, 1988.) [RC454 .N47 1999] (4.3; 7.1; 8.1; 9.3.2; 9.5.2; 9.5.3; 9.5.7; 9.5.9; 10; 13.1; 17.2; 17.3; 17.4; 17.5; 20.1; 21.7; LE)

Sadler, John Z. VALUES AND PSYCHIATRIC DIAGNOSIS. New York: Oxford University Press, 2005. 540 p. ISBN 0-19-852637-7. (International Perspectives in Philosophy and Psychiatry series. Gift of the publisher.) [RC437.5 .S32 2005] (4.3; 1.1; 4.1.2; 5.1; 10; 15.6; 17.1; 21.1)

Tengland, Per-Anders. MENTAL HEALTH: A PHILOSOPHICAL ANALYSIS. Dordrecht/Boston: Kluwer Academic, 2001. 182 p. ISBN 1-4020-0179-7. (International Library of Ethics, Law, and the New Medicine series; No. 9.) [RC437.5 .T455 2001] (4.3; 1.1; 17.1)

4.4 QUALITY/VALUE OF LIFE/PERSONHOOD

DeGrazia, David. HUMAN IDENTITY AND BIOETHICS. New York: Cambridge University Press, 2005. 300 p. ISBN 0-521-53268-X. (Gift of the publisher.) [BD236 .D44 2005] (4.4; 2.1; 4.5; 15.1; 20.2.1; 20.5.4)

Hamington, Maurice. EMBODIED CARE: JANE ADDAMS, MAURICE MERLEAU-PONTY, AND FEMINIST ETHICS. Urbana: University of Illinois Press, 2004. 181 p. ISBN 0-252-02928-3. [BJ1475 .H37 2004] (4.4; 10)

Jones, David Albert. THE SOUL OF THE EMBRYO: AN ENQUIRY INTO THE STATUS OF THE HUMAN EMBRYO IN THE CHRISTIAN TRADITION. London/New York: Continuum, 2004. 266 p. ISBN 0-8264-6296-0. (Gift of the publisher.) [QM611 .J65 2004] (4.4; 1.2; 12.3; 12.4.2; 14.1; 20.5.2)

Lindman, Janet Moore and Tarter, Michele Lise, eds. A CENTRE OF WONDERS: THE BODY IN EARLY AMERICA. Ithaca, NY: Cornell University Press, 2001. 283 p. ISBN 0-8014-8739-0. [GT497 .U6 C46 2001] (4.4; 7.1)

Pitts, Victoria L. IN THE FLESH: THE CULTURAL POLITICS OF BODY MODIFICATION. New York: Palgrave Macmillan, 2003. 239 p. ISBN 0-312-29311-9. [GN419.15 .P57 2003] (4.4; 5.1; 9.5.1; 10)

Scheper-Hughes, Nancy and Wacquant, Loïc, eds. COMMODIFYING BODIES. London/Thousand Oaks, CA: Sage, 2002. 199 p. ISBN 0-7619-4034-0. (Published in association with Theory, Culture & Society, Nottingham Trent University. Originally published as: *Body & Society* 2001; 7(2-3).) [QH332 .C6525 2002] (4.4; 1.3.2; 9.3.1; 10; 14.2; 15.5; 19.5; 20.3.1; 21.1)

Serlin, David. REPLACEABLE YOU: ENGINEERING THE BODY IN POSTWAR AMERICA. Chicago: University of Chicago Press, 2004. 244 p. ISBN 0-226-74884-7. [R856 .S457 2004] (4.4; 5.1; 9.5.1; 10)

Smith, Christian. MORAL, BELIEVING ANIMALS: HUMAN PERSONHOOD AND CULTURE. Oxford/New York: Oxford University Press, 2003. 164 p. ISBN 0-19-516202-1. [BD450 .S555 2003] (4.4; 1.1; 1.2; 15.9; 21.7)

Thomasma, David C.; Weisstub, David N.; and Hervé, Christian, eds. PERSONHOOD AND HEALTH CARE. Dordrecht/Boston: Kluwer Academic, 2001. 449 p. ISBN 1-4020-0098-7. (International Library of Ethics, Law, and the New Medicine series; No. 7.) [R724 .T536 2001] (4.4; 1.1; 1.2; 2.1; 7.1; 8.1; 14.5; 15.1; 17.1; 20.5.4)

Welton, Donn, ed. THE BODY: CLASSIC AND CONTEMPORARY READINGS. Malden, MA: Blackwell, 1999. 375 p. ISBN 0-631-21185-3. (Blackwell Readings in Continental Philosophy series; Vol. 1.) [B105 .B64 B64 1999] (4.4; 10; 15.1)

5.1 SCIENCE, TECHNOLOGY AND SOCIETY (GENERAL)

Asimov, Isaac. I, ROBOT. New York: Bantam Books, 2004, 1950. 272 p. 0-553-29438-5. (Doubleday Science Fiction series. Juvenile literature.) (5.1; 4.4; Fiction)

Barbour, Ian G. WHEN SCIENCE MEETS RELIGION. [San Francisco]: HarperSanFrancisco, 2000. 205 p. ISBN 0-06-060381-X. [BL240.2 .B375 2000] (5.1; 1.2; 3.2; 15.6; 17.1)

Drayton, Richard. NATURE'S GOVERNMENT: SCIENCE, IMPERIAL BRITAIN, AND THE 'IMPROVEMENT' OF THE WORLD. New Haven, CT: Yale University Press, 2000. 346 p. ISBN 0-300-05976-0. [DA470 .D73 2000] (5.1; 1.3.5; 21.1)

European Commission. European Group on Ethics in Science and New Technologies. THE ETHICAL ASPECTS OF ICT IMPLANTS IN THE HUMAN BODY: PROCEEDINGS OF THE ROUNDTABLE DEBATE, AMSTERDAM, 21 DECEMBER 2004. Luxembourg: Office for Official Publications of the European Communities, 2005. 81 p. ISBN 92-894-9035-7. ("Opinion No. 20 on this issue has now been adopted by the EGE and was presented to the President of the European Commission on 16 March 2005." The full Opinion and the associated press release are available at: http://europa.eu.int/comm/european_group_ethics. Gift of the publisher.) [RA418.5 .M4 E84 2005] (5.1; 4.4; 7.1)

Fara, Patricia. PANDORA'S BREECHES: WOMEN, SCIENCE AND POWER IN THE ENLIGHTENMENT. London: Pimlico, 2004. 274 p. ISBN 1-8441-3082-7. [Q130 .F37 2004] (5.1; 5.3)

Golan, Tal. LAWS OF MEN AND LAWS OF NATURE: THE HISTORY OF SCIENTIFIC EXPERT TESTIMONY IN ENGLAND AND AMERICA. Cambridge, MA: Harvard University Press, 2004. 325 p. ISBN 0-674-01286-0. [KD7521 .G65 2004] (5.1; 1.3.5; 7.1)

Haack, Susan. DEFENDING SCIENCE—WITHIN REASON: BETWEEN SCIENTISM AND CYNICISM. Amherst, NY: Prometheus Books, 2003. 411 p. ISBN 1-59102-117-0. [Q172.5 .C74 H33 2003] (5.1; 1.2; 1.3.5; 5.2)

Lovelock, James. HOMAGE TO GAIA: THE LIFE OF AN INDEPENDENT SCIENTIST. Oxford/New York: Oxford University Press, 2000. 428 p. ISBN 0-19-860429-7. [Q143 .L88 A3 2001] (5.1; 16.1; Biography)

Perkowitz, Sidney. DIGITAL PEOPLE: FROM BIONIC HUMANS TO ANDROIDS. Washington, DC: Joseph Henry Press, 2004. 238 p. ISBN 0-309-09619-7. [TJ211 .P44 2004] (5.1; 4.4)

Restivo, Sal, ed. SCIENCE, TECHNOLOGY, AND SOCIETY: AN ENCYCLOPEDIA. New York: Oxford University Press, 2005. 701 p. ISBN 0-19-514193-8. (Gift of the publisher.) [HM846 .S43 2005] (5.1; 1.3.9; 2.1; 5.3; 15.1; 21.1; Reference)

Roco, Mihail C. and Montemagno, Carlo D., eds. THE CO-EVOLUTION OF HUMAN POTENTIAL AND CONVERGING TECHNOLOGIES. New York: New York Academy of Sciences, 2004. 259 p. ISBN 1-57331-501-X. (Annals of the New York Academy of Sciences series; Vol. 1013. ISSN 0077-8923. Gift of the publisher.) [TP248.14 .C64 2004] (5.1; 1.3.12; 4.5; 17.1)

Stenmark, Mikael. HOW TO RELATE SCIENCE AND RELIGION: A MULTIDIMENSIONAL MODEL. Grand Rapids, MI: William B. Eerdmans, 2004. 287 p. ISBN 0-8028-2823-X. [BL240.3 .S744 2004] (5.1; 1.2; 3.2)

Thomson, Keith. BEFORE DARWIN: RECONCILING GOD AND NATURE. New Haven, CT: Yale University Press, 2005. 314 p. ISBN 0-300-10793-5. [BL245 .T56 2005] (5.1; 1.2)

Thomson, Keith. THE WATCH ON THE HEATH: SCIENCE AND RELIGION BEFORE DARWIN. London: HarperCollins, 2005. 314 p. ISBN 0-00-713313-8. [BL245 .T462 2005] (5.1; 1.2)

Warwick, Kevin. I, CYBORG. Urbana: University of Illinois Press, c2002, 2004. 311 p. ISBN 0-252-07215-4. (5.1; 1.3.12; 4.4; 18.1; Biography)

5.2 TECHNOLOGY ASSESSMENT

Garreau, Joel. RADICAL EVOLUTION: THE PROMISE AND PERIL OF ENHANCING OUR MINDS, OUR BODIES—AND WHAT IT MEANS TO BE HUMAN. New York: Doubleday, 2005. 384 p. ISBN 0-385-50965-0. (Gift of the publisher.) [T174.5 .G35 2005] (5.2; 1.2; 5.1; 15.1)

Mazur, Allan. TRUE WARNINGS AND FALSE ALARMS: EVALUTING FEARS ABOUT THE HEALTH RISKS OF TECHNOLOGY, 1948-1971. Washington, DC: Resources for the Future, 2004. 191 p. ISBN 1-891853-56-2. (Publisher's address: 1616 P Street, NW, zip 20036-1400.) [RA427.3 .M39 2004] (5.2; 7.1)

5.3 SOCIAL CONTROL OF SCIENCE/TECHNOLOGY

Bailey, Ronald. LIBERATION BIOLOGY: THE SCIENTIFIC AND MORAL CASE FOR THE BIOTECH REVOLUTION. Amherst, MA: Prometheus Books, 2005. 332 p. ISBN 1-59102-227-4. (Gift of the publisher.) [TP248.23 .B35 2005] (5.3; 1.3.11; 4.5; 9.7; 14.1; 14.5; 15.1; 18.5.4; 19.1; 21.1)

Cohen, Alan B. and Hanft, Ruth S. TECHNOLOGY IN AMERICAN HEALTH CARE: POLICY DIRECTIONS FOR EFFECTIVE EVALUATION AND MANAGEMENT. Ann Arbor: University of Michigan Press, 2004. 460 p. ISBN 0-472-11326-7. (Gift of the publisher.) [R855.5 .U6 C64 2004] (5.3; 5.2; 9.1; 9.3.1; 9.4; 9.8; 18.1; LE)

Numbers in ( ) = NRCBL Classification Numbers

Freeman, Michael and Reece, Helen, eds. SCIENCE IN COURT. Brookfield, VT: Ashgate/Dartmouth, 1998. 206 p. ISBN 1-84014-039-9. (Issues in Law and Society series. "*Science in Court* is one of two volumes to result from a very successful colloquium on 'Law and Science' held in the Faculty of Laws at University College, London on 30 June and 1 July 1997.") [K2283 .S39 1998] (5.3; 1.1; 9.5.5; 10; 15.1; 15.7; 16.1; 17.1)

Jasanoff, Sheila. DESIGNS ON NATURE: SCIENCE AND DEMOCRACY IN EUROPE AND THE UNITED STATES. Princeton, NJ: Princeton University Press, 2005. 374 p. ISBN 0-691-11811-6. [Q127 .E8 J37 2005] (5.3; 1.3.5; 15.1; 21.1)

Koertge, Noretta, ed. SCIENTIFIC VALUES AND CIVIC VIRTUES. Oxford/New York: Oxford University Press, 2005. 245 p. ISBN 0-19-517224-8. (Gift of the publisher.) [JA80 .S37 2005] (5.3; 1.2; 1.3.3; 1.3.5; 3.2)

National Research Council (United States). Committee on Intellectual Property Rights in the Knowledge-Based Economy. A PATENT SYSTEM FOR THE 21ST CENTURY. Washington, DC: National Academies Press, 2004. 171 p. ISBN 0-309-08910-7. (Also available on the Web at: http://www.nap. edu.) [T211 .P384 2004] (5.3; 15.8)

Taverne, Dick. THE MARCH OF UNREASON: SCIENCE, DEMOCRACY, AND THE NEW FUNDAMENTALISM. New York: Oxford University Press, 2005. 310 p. ISBN 0-19-280485-5. (Gift of the publisher.) [Q175.5 .T38 2005] (5.3; 1.3.11; 15.1; 16.1)

Vicente, Kim. THE HUMAN FACTOR: REVOLUTIONIZING THE WAY PEOPLE LIVE WITH TECHNOLOGY. New York: Routledge, 2004. 352 p. ISBN 0-415-97064-4. [T14.5 .V52 2004] (5.3; 7.1)

7.1 SOCIOLOGY OF HEALTH CARE (GENERAL)

Adler, Robert E. MEDICAL FIRSTS: FROM HIPPOCRATES TO THE HUMAN GENOME. New York: John Wiley & Sons, 2004. 232 p. ISBN 0-471-40175-7. [R133 .A43 2004] (7.1; 1.3.11; 9.1; 9.7; 11.1; 14.4; 15.1; 19.1; 22.3; Biography)

Albrecht, Gary L.; Fitzpatrick, Ray; and Scrimshaw, Susan C., eds. THE HANDBOOK OF SOCIAL STUDIES IN HEALTH AND MEDICINE. London/Thousand Oaks, CA: Sage, 2003, c2000. 545 p. ISBN 0-7619-5617-4. [RA418 .H36 2000] (7.1; 4.2; 4.4; 9.3.1; 9.4; 14.1; 15.1; 21.1; 21.7)

Emery, Alan E.H. and Emery, Marcia O.H. MEDICINE AND ART. London: Royal Society of Medicine Press in association with the Royal College of Physicians, 2003. 112 p. ISBN 1-85315-501-2. (Foreword by Sir John Hanson.) [N8223 .E46 2003] (7.1)

Faunce, Thomas Alured. PILGRIMS IN MEDICINE: CONSCIENCE, LEGALISM AND HUMAN RIGHTS: AN ALLEGORY OF MEDICAL HUMANITIES, FOUNDATIONAL VIRTUES, ETHICAL PRINCIPLES, LAW AND HUMAN RIGHTS IN MEDICAL PERSONAL AND PROFESSIONAL DEVELOPMENT. Leiden: Brill, 2005. 651 p. ISBN 90-04-13962-1. [R702 .F38 2005] (7.1; 1.1; 2.1; 6; 8.1; 8.3.1; 8.4; 9.3.1; 9.3.2; 9.4; 12.3; 15.5; 19.5; 20.5.1; 21.1; 21.4; LE)

Fenster, Julie M. MAVERICKS, MIRACLES, AND MEDICINE: THE PIONEERS WHO RISKED THEIR LIVES TO BRING MEDICINE INTO THE MODERN AGE. New York: Carroll & Graff, 2003. 304 p. ISBN 0-7867-1236-8. (The companion to The History Channel® series *Mavericks, Miracles, and Medicine.*) [R134.5 .F46 2003] (7.1; 9.1; 9.7; 14.5; 19.1; 22.2)

Gordon, Suzanne. NURSING AGAINST THE ODDS: HOW HEALTH CARE COST CUTTING, MEDIA STEREOTYPES, AND MEDICAL HUBRIS UNDERMINE NURSES AND PATIENT CARE. Ithaca, NY: ILR Press/Cornell University Press, 2005. 489 p. ISBN 0-8014-3976-0. (The Culture and Politics of Health Care Work series. Gift of the publisher.) (7.1; 1.3.7; 4.1.3; 7.3; 8.1; 9.3.2; 21.1)

Gwyn, Richard. COMMUNICATING HEALTH AND ILLNESS. London/Thousand Oaks, CA: Sage, 2002. 182 p. ISBN 0-7619-6475-4. [R118 .G86 2002] (7.1; 1.3.7; 8.1)

Haggard, Howard W. FROM MEDICINE MAN TO DOCTOR: THE STORY OF THE SCIENCE OF HEALING. Mineola, NY: Dover Publications, 2004. 405 p. ISBN 0-486-43541-5. ("This Dover edition, first published in 2004, is an unabridged republication of the work originally published in 1929 by Harper & Brothers Publishers, New York and London, under the title: *Devils, Drugs, and Doctors: The Story of the Science of Healing from Medicine-Man to Doctor.*") [R131 .H198 2004] (7.1)

Marmot, Michael. THE STATUS SYNDROME: HOW SOCIAL STANDING AFFECTS OUR HEALTH AND LONGEVITY. New York: Times Books, 2004. 319 p. ISBN 0-8050-7370-1. (Originally published in the United Kingdom in 2004 under the title: *Status Syndrome*, Bloomsbury Publishing, London; ISBN 0-7475-7049-3. Distributed in Canada by: H.B. Fenn and Company.) [RA418.5 .S63 M37 2004] (7.1; 9.5.1; 9.5.2; 9.5.7; 16.3)

Mohr, James C. PLAGUE AND FIRE: BATTLING BLACK DEATH AND THE 1900 BURNING OF HONOLULU'S CHINATOWN. New York: Oxford University Press, 2005. 235 p. ISBN 0-19-516231-5. (7.1; 9.1; 9.5.1)

Moore, Wendy. THE KNIFE-MAN: THE EXTRAORDINARY LIFE AND TIMES OF JOHN HUNTER, FATHER OF MODERN SURGERY. New York: Broadway Books, 2005. 341 p. ISBN 0-7679-1652-2. (Gift of the publisher.) [RD27.35 .H86 M66 2005] (7.1; Biography)

Moote, A. Lloyd and Moote, Dorothy C. THE GREAT PLAGUE: THE STORY OF LONDON'S MOST DEADLY YEAR. Baltimore, MD: Johns Hopkins University Press, 2004. 357 p. ISBN 0-8018-7783-0. [RC178 .G72 L665 2004] (7.1; 9.1; 9.3.1; 9.5.1)

Nutton, Vivian. ANCIENT MEDICINE. London/New York: Routledge, 2004. 486 p. ISBN 0-415-36848-0. (Sciences of Antiquity series.) [R135 .N88 2004] (7.1; 1.2; 4.1.2; 6; 21.1)

Porter, Roy. QUACKS: FAKERS & CHARLATANS IN MEDICINE. Stroud, Gloucestershire: Tempus, 2003. 383 p. ISBN 0-7524-2590-0. (7.1; 8.5; 10)

Posen, Solomon. THE DOCTOR IN LITERATURE: SATISFACTION OR RESENTMENT? Oxford/Seattle, WA: Radcliffe Publishing, 2005. 298 p. ISBN 1-85775-609-6. (Foreword by Edward J. Huth. Gift of the publisher.) [PN6071 .P45 D58 2005] (7.1; 8.1)

Reynolds, Richard; Stone, John; Nixon, Lois LaCivita; and Wear, Delese, eds. ON DOCTORING: STORIES, POEMS, ESSAYS. New York: Simon & Schuster, 2001. 414 p. ISBN 0-7432-0153-1. (Third edition, revised and expanded.) [PN6071 .P45 O5 2001] (7.1)

Ruggiero, Kristin. MODERNITY IN THE FLESH: MEDICINE, LAW, AND SOCIETY IN TURN-OF-THE-CENTURY ARGENTINA. Stanford, CA: Stanford University Press, 2004. 244 p. ISBN 0-8047-4871-3. [HV6885 .B8 R84 2004] (7.1; 1.3.5; 4.4; 9.1; LE)

Senn, Stephen. DICING WITH DEATH: CHANCE, RISK AND HEALTH. Cambridge/New York: Cambridge University Press, 2003. 251 p. ISBN 0-521-54023-2. [RA407 .S46 2003] (7.1; 4.1.2; Biography)

Stripling, Mahala Yates. BIOETHICS AND MEDICAL ISSUES IN LITERATURE. Westport, CT: Greenwood Press, 2005. 224 p. ISBN 0-313-32040-3. (Exploring Social Issues through Literature series. ISSN 1551-0263. Gift of the publisher.) [PN56 .M38 S76 2005] (7.1; 2.1; Fiction)

Tregaskis, Claire. CONSTRUCTIONS OF DISABILITY: RESEARCHING THE INTERFACE BETWEEN DISABLED AND NON-DISABLED PEOPLE. London/New York: Routledge, 2004. 164 p. ISBN 0-415-32183-2. [HV1559 .G7 T74 2004] (7.1; 4.2; 9.5.1)

Whyte, Susan Reynolds; Geest, Sjaack van der; and Hardon, Anita. SOCIAL LIVES OF MEDICINES. Cambridge/New York: Cambridge University Press, 2002. 200 p. ISBN 0-521-80469-8. (Cambridge Studies in Medical Anthropology series.) [RS153 .W496 2002] (7.1; 9.1; 9.7)

Wilkinson, Richard G. THE IMPACT OF INEQUALITY: HOW TO MAKE SICK SOCIETIES HEALTHIER. New York: New Press, 2005. 355 p. ISBN 1-56584-925-6. [RA418 .W448 2005] (7.1; 9.1; 9.5.10; 10; 17.1)

7.2 EDUCATION FOR HEALTH CARE PROFESSIONALS

Institute of Medicine (United States). Committee on Behavioral and Social Sciences in Medical School Curricula. IMPROVING MEDICAL EDUCATION: ENHANCING THE BEHAVIORAL AND SOCIAL SCIENCE CONTENT OF MEDICAL SCHOOL CURRICULA. Washington, DC: National Academies Press, 2005. 147 p. ISBN 0-309-09142-X. (Edited by Patricia A. Cuff and Neal A. Vanselow. Also available on the Web at: http://www.nap.edu.) [R745 .I47 2004] (7.2; 7.1; 17.1)

Special Section: Ethical Challenges in Public Health Education Research and Practice. HEALTH EDUCATION AND BEHAVIOR 2002 February; 29(1): 5-72. (ISSN 1090-1981.) (7.2; 6; 8.3.1; 8.4; 9.1; 9.5.9; 15.1; 18.1; 18.5.6; 20.5.1)

7.3 PROFESSIONAL-PROFESSIONAL RELATIONSHIP

Conflicts of Interest in Clinical Research: Legal and Ethical Issues. WIDENER LAW SYMPOSIUM JOURNAL 2001; 8(1): 1-152. (7.3; 1.3.9; 5.3; 8.1; 18.2; 18.3; 18.6; 21.1)

7.4 PROFESSIONAL MISCONDUCT

Stahl, Michael J. and Foreman, Stephen M. ETHICAL PERSPECTIVES: SEXUAL BOUNDARY ISSUES AND THE CHIROPRACTIC PARADIGM. Philadelphia: Lippincott Williams & Wilkins, 2005. 126 p. ISBN 0-7817-5541-7. [RZ236.5 .S86 2005] (7.4; 4.1.1; 7.1; 8.1; 10)

Stern, David Thomas, ed. MEASURING MEDICAL PROFESSIONALISM. Oxford/New York: Oxford University Press, 2006. 311 p. ISBN 0-19-517226-4. (Gift of the publisher.) [R837 .A2 M43 2006] (7.4; 4.1.2; 7.2; 9.8)

8.1 PATIENT RELATIONSHIPS (GENERAL)

Cox, Ken. DOCTOR & PATIENT: EXPLORING CLINICAL THINKING. Sydney: University of New South Wales Press, 1999. 304 p. ISBN 0-86840-505-1. (Publisher's address: University of New South Wales, Sydney 2052 Australia; Web: http://www.unswpress.com.au.) [R727.3 .C685 1999] (8.1; 7.1)

Degnin, Francis Dominic. COMPASSION AND MEDICINE: POSTMODERN ETHICS AND THE PHYSICIAN-PATIENT RELATIONSHIP. Ann Arbor, MI: ProQuest Information and Learning/UMI, 2001. 213 p. (Publication No. AAT-3005302. Dissertation, (Ph.D.)—Vanderbilt University, 2001.) (8.1; 1.3.5; 4.1.1; 4.4; 7.1; 9.1; 9.3.2)

Kavanagh, Kathryn Hopkins and Krowlden, Virginia, eds. MANY VOICES: TOWARD CARING CULTURE IN HEALTHCARE AND HEALING. Madison: University of Wisconsin Press, 2004. 312 p. ISBN 0-299-19764-6. (Interpretive Studies in Healthcare and the Human Sciences series; Vol. 3.) [RT86 .M367 2004] (8.1; 4.1.3; 21.7)

Macdonald, Elisabeth, ed. DIFFICULT CONVERSATIONS IN MEDICINE. Oxford/New York: Oxford University Press, 2004. 231 p. ISBN 0-19-852774-8. [R118 .D53 2004] (8.1; 8.2; 9.5.7; 17.1; 20.4.1; 21.7)

McCabe, Matthew Scott. ETHICAL CARING AND THE PHYSICIAN-PATIENT RELATIONSHIP: A DUAL DEFENSE OF A VIRTUE ETHICS OF CARE. Ann Arbor, MI: ProQuest/UMI, 2001. 184 p. (Publication No. AAT-3035852. Dissertation, (Ph.D.)—University of Maryland, College Park, 2001.) (8.1; 1.1; 8.2; 8.4)

Morrison, Blake. AND WHEN DID YOU LAST SEE YOUR FATHER? New York: Picador USA, 1995. 219 p. ISBN

Numbers in ( ) = NRCBL Classification Numbers

0-312-13023-6. (First published in Great Britain by Granta Books, 1993; ISBN 1-86207-093-8.) [PR6063 .O7938 Z463 1995] (8.1; Biography)

O'Mathúna, Dónal p.; Hensley, Samuel D.; Adam, Mary B.; Kilner, John F.; Orr, Robert D.; and Stewart, Gary p. BASIC QUESTIONS ON HEALTHCARE: WHAT SHOULD GOOD CARE INCLUDE? Grand Rapids, MI: Kregel, 2004. 111 p. ISBN 0-8254-3081-X. (BioBasics Series.) [R725.56 .B38 2004] (8.1; 1.2; 6; 8.3.1; 8.4; 9.2; 9.3.1; 9.4; 9.6)

Peplau, Hildegard E. INTERPERSONAL RELATIONS IN NURS-ING: A CONCEPTUAL FRAME OF REFERENCE FOR PSYCHODYNAMIC NURSING. New York: Springer Publishing Company, 1991. 335 p. ISBN 0-8261-7911-8. (Reprint. Originally published: Macmillan, Houndmills, Basingstoke, Hampshire, 1988.) [RT86 .P4 1991] (8.1; 7.1)

Petit-Zeman, Sophie. DOCTOR, WHAT'S WRONG? MAKING THE NHS HUMAN AGAIN. London/New York: Routledge, 2005. 198 p. ISBN 0-415-35155-3. (Gift of the publisher.) [R727.3 .P4725 2005] (8.1; 1.1; 1.2; 9.1; 9.5.1)

Watts, David. BEDSIDE MANNERS: ONE DOCTOR'S REFLEC-TIONS ON THE ODDLY INTIMATE ENCOUNTERS BETWEEN PA-TIENT AND HEALER. New York: Harmony Books, 2005. 281 p. ISBN 1-4000-8051-7. [R727.3 .W38 2005] (8.1; 7.1)

Wilkinson, Rosie and Caulfield, Helen. THE HUMAN RIGHTS ACT: A PRACTICAL GUIDE FOR NURSES. London/Philadelphia: Whurr, 2000. 136 p. ISBN 1-86156-206-3. (8.1; 4.1.3; 6; 8.3.1; 8.4; 9.1; 9.2; 9.4; 9.5.5; 18.1; 19.5; 21.1; LE)

8.3.1 INFORMED CONSENT (GENERAL)

Hockton, Andrew. THE LAW OF CONSENT TO MEDICAL TREATMENT. London: Sweet & Maxwell, 2002. 303 p. ISBN 0-421-64760-4. [KD3410 .I54 H73 2002] (8.3.1; 2.1; 4.3; 8.3.2; 8.3.3; 8.3.4; 9.5.1; 9.5.7; 20.5.1)

8.3.3 THIRD PARTY CONSENT/INCOMPETENTS

McHaffie, Hazel. VACANT POSSESSION: A STORY OF PROXY DECISION MAKING. Oxford/Seattle, WA: Radcliffe, 2005. 198 p. ISBN 1-85775-651-7. (Living Literature series. Gift of the publisher.) (8.3.3; 8.1; 9.5.5; 20.5.1; Fiction)

8.4 CONFIDENTIALITY

Michalowski, Sabine. MEDICAL CONFIDENTIALITY AND CRIME. Aldershot, Hants/Burlington, VT: Ashgate, 2003. 344 p. ISBN 0-7546-2294-0. [KJC9622 .P45 M53 2003] (8.4; 1.3.5; 21.1; LE)

8.5 MALPRACTICE

Williams, Ira E. FIRST, DO NO HARM: THE CURE FOR MEDI-CAL MALPRACTICE. [Greenville, SC: Ira Williams], 2004. 196 p. ISBN 0-9754524-1-X. (Publisher's address: 1200

Woodruff Road, A-3, zip 29607.) [RA1056.5 .W556 2004] (8.5; 7.3; 9.8)

9.1 HEALTH CARE (GENERAL)

Abramson, John. OVERDO$ED AMERICA: THE BROKEN PROMISE OF AMERICAN MEDICINE. New York: Harper Perennial, c2004, 2005. 334 p. ISBN 0-06-056853-4. [R151 .A23 2005] (9.1; 9.3.1; 9.7)

Anand, Sudhir; Peter, Fabienne; and Sen, Amartya, eds. PUBLIC HEALTH, ETHICS, AND EQUITY. Oxford/New York: Oxford University Press, 2004. 316 p. ISBN 0-19-927636-6. (Gift of the publisher.) [RA427.25 .P825 2004] (9.1; 1.1; 4.4; 7.1; 9.2; 9.3.1; 9.4; 21.7)

Andersen, Ronald M.; Rice, Thomas H.; and Kominski, Gerald F. CHANGING THE U.S. HEALTH CARE SYSTEM: KEY ISSUES IN HEALTH SERVICES, POLICY, AND MANAGEMENT. San Francisco: Jossey-Bass, 2001. 553 p. ISBN 0-7879-5404-7.(Second edition. Jossey-Bass Health Series.) [RA395 .A3 C478 2001] (9.1; 4.4; 8.5; 9.3.1; 9.3.2; 9.4; 9.5.2; 9.5.5; 9.5.6; 9.5.7; 9.5.10; 9.7; 9.8; 17.1)

Blank, Robert H. and Burau, Viola. COMPARATIVE HEALTH POLICY. New York: Palgrave Macmillan, 2004. 260 p. ISBN 0-333-98599-0. [RA394 .B56 2004] (9.1; 1.3.5; 9.3.1; 9.4; 9.5.1; 21.1; 21.7)

Bradshaw, Peter L. and Bradshaw, Gwendolen. HEALTH POLICY FOR HEALTH CARE PROFESSIONALS. London/Thousand Oaks, CA: Sage, 2004. 158 p. ISBN 0-7619-7401-6. [RA395 .G6 B73 2004] (9.1)

Budrys, Grace. OUR UNSYSTEMATIC HEALTH CARE SYS-TEM. Lanham, [MD]: Rowman and Littlefield Publishers, 2001. 182 p. ISBN 0-7425-0899-4. [RA395 .A3 B827 2001] (9.1; 4.1.1; 7.1; 9.3.1; 9.3.2; 9.4; 21.1)

Castro, Arachu and Singer, Merrill, eds. UNHEALTHY HEALTH POLICY: A CRITICAL ANTHROPOLOGICAL EXAMI-NATION. Walnut Creek, CA: AltaMira Press, 2004. 387 p. ISBN 0-7591-0511-1. [RA441.5 .U556 2004] (9.1; 7.1; 9.3.1; 9.5.6; 9.5.7; 9.5.9; 9.5.10; 9.7; 13.3; 14.1; 21.1)

Corporate Ethics and Governance in the Health Care Marketplace. SEATTLE JOURNAL FOR SOCIAL JUSTICE 2004 Fall-Winter; 3(1):205-428. (ISSN 1544-1245.) (9.1; 1.3.2; 1.3.5; 9.3.1; 15.1; 18.5.4)

Darr, Kurt. ETHICS IN HEALTH SERVICES MANAGEMENT. Baltimore, MD: Health Professions Press, 2005. 394 p. ISBN 1-878812-99-8. (Fourth edition. Gift of the publisher.) [RA394 .D35 2005] (9.1; 1.1; 1.3.2; 2.1; 6; 8.3.1; 9.3.1; 9.3.2; 9.4; 9.6; 20.1; 20.5.1; 20.7)

Doupitzky, Karine. HOSPITAL: THE UNSEEN DEMANDS OF DELIVERING MEDICAL CARE. Chicago: Ivan R. Dee, 2002. 184 p. ISBN 1-56663-478-4. (Photography by Stephen L. Feldman. Covers hospitals in the USA, Congo, India, China and Belgium.) (9.1; 7.1; 21.1)

Dye, Carson F. LEADERSHIP IN HEALTHCARE: VALUES AT THE TOP. Chicago: Health Administration Press, 2000.

234 p. ISBN 1-56793-114-6. (ACHE Management Series.) [RA971 .D937 2000] (9.1; 1.3.2)

Farley, Tom and Cohen, Deborah A. PRESCRIPTION FOR A HEALTHY NATION: A NEW APPROACH TO IMPROVING OUR LIVES BY FIXING OUR EVERYDAY WORLD. Boston: Beacon Press, 2005. 282 p. ISBN 0-8070-2116-4. (Gift of the publisher.) [RA445 .F27 2005] (9.1; 7.1; 16.1)

Gastel, Barbara. HEALTH WRITER'S HANDBOOK. Ames, IA: Blackwell Publishing Professional, 2005. 366 p. ISBN 0-8138-1253-4. (Second edition. Gift of the publisher.) [R119 .G376 2005] (9.1; 1.3.7; 7.1)

Gingrich, Newt; Pavey, Dana; and Woodbury, Anne. SAVING LIVES AND SAVING MONEY: TRANSFORMING HEALTH AND HEALTHCARE. Washington, DC: Alexis de Tocqueville Institution, 2003. 308 p. ISBN 0-9705485-4-0. [RA395 .A3 G485 2003] (9.1; 9.3.1)

Health Care Symposium: E-Health: The Medical Frontier. WEST VIRGINIA LAW REVIEW 2001 Summer; 103(4): 405-643. (ISSN 0043-3268.) (9.1; 1.3.12; 8.1; 8.4; 9.3.1; 9.7; 9.8; 21.1)

Isaacs, Stephen L. and Knickman, James R., eds. TO IMPROVE HEALTH AND HEALTH CARE. San Francisco: Jossey-Bass, 2004. 271 p. ISBN 0-7879-6823-4. (The Robert Wood Johnson Foundation Anthology series; Vol. 7.) [RA440.87 .U6 T626 2004] (9.1; 7.2; 9.3.1; 9.5.4; 9.5.5; 9.5.7; 9.5.8; 9.5.10; 21.3)

Mackenbach, Johan and Bakker, Martijntje, eds. REDUCING INEQUALITIES IN HEALTH: A EUROPEAN PERSPECTIVE. London/New York: Routledge, 2002. 357 p. ISBN 0-415-25984-3. [RA395 .E85 R43 2002] (9.1; 7.1; 21.1)

Magee, Mike. HEALTH POLITICS: POWER, POPULISM AND HEALTH. New York: Spencer Books, 2005. 552 p. + 1 CD-ROM. ISBN 1-889793-17-5. (Foreword by C. Everett Kopp. CD-ROM: *Access to Online Resources.* Publisher's address: 3 Stoneleigh Plaza, Suite 5D, Bronxville, NY 10708. Gift of the publisher.) [RA395 .A3 M33 2005] (9.1; 21.1)

McCauley, Bernadette. WHO SHALL TAKE CARE OF OUR SICK? ROMAN CATHOLIC SISTERS AND THE DEVELOPMENT OF CATHOLIC HOSPITALS IN NEW YORK CITY. Baltimore, MD: Johns Hopkins University Press, 2005. 146 p. ISBN 0-8018-8216-8. (Medicine, Science, and Religion in Historical Context series. Gift of the publisher.) [RA975 .C37 M38 2005] (9.1; 1.2; 7.1; 9.3.1)

Pipes, Sally C. MIRACLE CURE: HOW TO SOLVE AMERICA'S HEALTH CARE CRISIS AND WHY CANADA ISN'T THE ANSWER. San Francisco: Pacific Research Institute for Public Policy [and] Vancouver: Fraser Institute, 2004. 219 p. ISBN 0-936488-92-1 [Pacific Research Institute]; ISBN 0-88975-212-5 [Fraser Institute]. (Foreword by Milton Friedman.) [RA395 .N7 P56 2004] (9.1; 9.2; 9.3.1; 9.5.2; 9.5.10; 9.7; 9.8; 21.6)

Robinson, Judith. NOBLE CONSPIRATOR: FLORENCE S. MAHONEY AND THE RISE OF THE NATIONAL INSTITUTES OF HEALTH. Washington, DC: Francis Press, 2001. 342 p. ISBN 0-9665051-4-X. [R133 .M24 R63 2001] (9.1; 5.3; Biography)

Rothstein, William G. PUBLIC HEALTH AND THE RISK FACTOR: A HISTORY OF AN UNEVEN MEDICAL REVOLUTION. Rochester, NY: Rochester University Press, 2003. 466 p. ISBN 1-58046-127-1. (Rochester Studies in Medical History series. ISSN 1526-2715.) [RA427.3 .R68 2003] (9.1; 5.2; 7.1; 9.3.1)

World Health Organization [WHO]. THE WORLD HEALTH REPORT 1999: MAKING A DIFFERENCE. Geneva: World Health Organization, 1999. 122 p. ISBN 92-4-156194-7. [RA8 .A265 1999] (9.1; 1.3.5; 7.1; 9.3.1; 9.5.1; 9.5.9; 21.1)

9.2 RIGHT TO HEALTH CARE

Den Exter, André and Hermans, Herbert, eds. THE RIGHT TO HEALTH CARE IN SEVERAL EUROPEAN COUNTRIES. Boston: Kluwer Law International, 1999. 187 p. ISBN 90-411-1087-9. (Studies in Social Policy series; No. 5. Expert meeting, held 27-28 April 1998 in Rotterdam, The Netherlands.) [RA395 .E85 R54 1999] (9.2; 1.3.5; 9.1; 9.8; 21.1; LE)

9.3.1 HEALTH CARE ECONOMICS (GENERAL)

Barlett, Donald L. and Steele, James B. CRITICAL CONDITION: HOW HEALTH CARE IN AMERICA BECAME BIG BUSINESS—AND BAD MEDICINE. New York: Broadway Books, 2006. 279 p. ISBN 0-7679-1075-3. ("A hardcover edition of this book was originally published in 2004 by Doubleday.") (9.3.1; 1.3.7; 9.1; 9.3.2; 9.7)

Cassel, Christine K. MEDICARE MATTERS: WHAT GERIATRIC MEDICINE CAN TEACH AMERICAN HEALTH CARE. Berkeley: University of California Press [and] New York: Milbank Memorial Fund, 2005. 254 p. ISBN 0-520-24624-1. (California/Milbank Books on Health and the Public series; No. 14. Gift of the publisher.) [RA412.3 .C39 2005] (9.3.1; 7.1; 9.4; 9.5.2; 9.7; 9.8; 20.4.1; 21.1)

Coombs, Jan Gregoire. THE RISE AND FALL OF HMOS: AN AMERICAN HEALTH CARE REVOLUTION. Madison: University of Wisconsin Press, 2005. 412 p. ISBN 0-299-20240-2. (Gift of the publisher.) [RA413.5 .U5 C677 2004] (9.3.1; 7.1; 9.1; 9.5.2; 9.5.10)

Geyman, John. FALLING THROUGH THE SAFETY NET: AMERICANS WITHOUT HEALTH INSURANCE. Monroe, ME: Common Courage Press, 2005. 222 p. ISBN 1-56751-254-2. (Publisher's address: PO Box 702, 121 Red Barn Road, zip 04951. Gift of the publisher.) [RA413.7 .U53 G49 2005] (9.3.1; 9.2; 9.5.2; 9.5.10; 9.7; 21.1)

Goodman, John C.; Musgrave, Gerald L.; and Herrick, Devon M. LIVES AT RISK: SINGLE-PAYER NATIONAL HEALTH INSURANCE AROUND THE WORLD. Lanham, MD: Rowman & Littlefield, 2004. 263 p. ISBN 0-7425-4152-5. ("Published in cooperation with the National Center for Policy

Analysis.") [RA412 .G66 2004] (9.3.1; 7.1; 9.1; 21.1; 21.7)

Institute of Medicine (United States). Committee on the Consequences of Uninsurance. HIDDEN COSTS, VALUE LOST: UNINSURANCE IN AMERICA. Washington, DC: National Academies Press, 2003. 196 p. ISBN 0-309-08931-X. (Insuring Health series.) (Also available on the Web at: http://www. nap.edu.) (9.3.1; 4.4)

Lazar, Harvey and St-Hilaire, France, eds. MONEY, POLITICS AND HEALTH CARE: RECONSTRUCTING THE FEDERAL-PROVINCIAL PARTNERSHIP. Montreal: Institute for Research on Public Policy [and] Kingston, Ontario: Institute of Intergovernmental Relations, 2004. 309 p. ISBN 0-88645-200-7. [RA410.55 .C2 M66 2004] (9.3.1; 9.1; 21.1)

Lee, Julie Juhyun. INEQUALITY IN HEALTH CARE EXPENDITURES AND HEALTH OUTCOMES AMONG THE U.S. ELDERLY POPULATION. Ann Arbor, MI: ProQuest Information and Learning/UMI, 2003. 108 p. (Publication No. AAT-3084330. Dissertation, (Ph.D.)—Yale University, 2003.) (9.3.1; 7.1; 9.5.2; 9.5.4)

Perkins, Barbara Bridgman. THE MEDICAL DELIVERY BUSINESS: HEALTH REFORM, CHILDBIRTH, AND THE ECONOMIC ORDER. New Brunswick, NJ: Rutgers University Press, 2004. 252 p. ISBN 0-8135-3328-7. [RA395 .A3 P47 2004] (9.3.1; 7.1; 9.1; 9.3.2; 9.5.5; 9.5.7)

Quadagno, Jill. ONE NATION, UNINSURED: WHY THE U.S. HAS NO NATIONAL HEALTH INSURANCE. Oxford/New York: Oxford University Press, 2005. 274 p. ISBN 0-19-516039-8. (Gift of the publisher.) [RA412.2 .Q33 2005] (9.3.1; 7.1; 7.3; 9.1; 9.2; 9.4; 9.5.2; 9.5.10; 21.1)

Rice, Thomas, guest ed. *Special Supplement Issue: The Consequences of Being Uninsured.* MEDICAL CARE RESEARCH AND REVIEW 2003 June; 60(2, Supplement): 3S-112S. (ISSN 1077-5587. "Research and supplement supported by the Kaiser Commission on Medicaid and the Uninsured.") (9.3.1; 4.4; 9.4)

Sered, Susan Starr and Fernandopulle, Rushika. UNINSURED IN AMERICA: LIFE AND DEATH IN THE LAND OF OPPORTUNITY. Berkeley: University of California Press, 2005. 247 p. ISBN 0-520-24442-7. (Gift of the publisher.) [RA413.7 .U53 S47 2005] (9.3.1; 7.1; 9.1; 9.2; 9.5.4; 9.5.7; 9.5.10)

9.3.2 MANAGED CARE

Illingworth, Patricia. TRUSTING MEDICINE: THE MORAL COSTS OF MANAGED CARE. London/New York: Routledge, 2005. 184 p. ISBN 0-415-36483-3. (Gift of the publisher.) (9.3.2; 8.1; 8.2)

Kastor, John A. MERGERS OF TEACHING HOSPITALS IN BOSTON, NEW YORK, AND NORTHERN CALIFORNIA. Ann Arbor: University of Michigan Press, 2003. 487 p. ISBN 0-472-08935-8. [RA975 .T43 K374 2001] (9.3.2; 7.2; 9.1)

9.4 ALLOCATION OF HEALTH CARE RESOURCES

McDonald, Peter William. SOLIDARITY, RESPONSIBILITY, AND FREEDOM: HEALTH CARE REFORM IN THE UNITED STATES AT THE MILLENNIUM. Ann Arbor, MI: ProQuest Information and Learning/UMI, 2003. 351 p. (Publication No. AAT-3090795. Dissertation, (Ph.D.)—Rice University, 2003.) (9.4; 1.1; 4.4; 5.2; 9.2; 9.3.1; 9.3.2; 9.5.10)

9.5.1 HEALTH CARE FOR SPECIFIC DISEASES/GROUPS (GENERAL)

Bauby, Jean-Dominique. THE DIVING-BELL AND THE BUTTERFLY. New York: Harper Perennial, 2004. 144 p. ISBN 0-00-713984-5. (Translation from the French by Jeremy Leggatt of: *Le scaphandre et le papillon*. First published in Great Britain by: Fourth Estate, 1997; then in paperback, 2002.) (9.5.1; 7.1; Biography)

Cole, Jonathan. STILL LIVES: NARRATIVES OF SPINAL CORD INJURY. Cambridge, MA: MIT Press, 2004. 330 p. ISBN 0-262-03315-1. ("A Bradford Book.") [RC406 .Q33 C64 2004] (9.5.1; 4.4; Biography)

David B. EPILEPTIC. New York: Pantheon Books, 2005. 364 p. ISBN 0-375-42318-4. (Text depicted through cartoons drawn by the author. Originally published as: *Ascension de Haut-Mal*; L'Association, Paris, 2002.) [PN6747 .B2213 2005] (9.5.1; 7.1; Biography; POP)

Denniston, George C.; Hodges, Frederick Mansfield; and Milos, Marilyn Fayre, eds. FLESH AND BLOOD: PERSPECTIVES ON THE PROBLEM OF CIRCUMCISION IN CONTEMPORARY SOCIETY. New York: Kluwer Academic/Plenum Press, 2004. 254 p. ISBN 0-306-48333-5. (Proceedings of the Seventh International Symposium on Human Rights and Modern Society: Advancing Human Dignity and the Legal Right to Bodily Integrity in the 21st Century, held 4-7 April 2002, in Washington, DC.) [RD590 .I56 2002] (9.5.1; 4.4; 9.3.1; 9.5.5; 9.5.7; 9.5.10; 10; 21.1; 21.7)

Eig, Jonathan. LUCKIEST MAN: THE LIFE AND DEATH OF LOU GEHRIG. New York: Simon & Schuster, 2005. 420 p. ISBN 0-7432-4591-1. [GV865 .G4 E54 2005] (9.5.1; Biography; POP)

Ethical, Moral, and Legal Issues in Speech and Language Pathology. SEMINARS IN SPEECH AND LANGUAGE 2003 November; 24(4): 259-337. (ISSN 0734-0478.) (9.5.1; 1.3.7; 1.3.8; 1.3.12; 4.3; 4.4; 5.3; 6; 8.1; 8.3.1; 8.3.3; 8.4; 9.8; 18.2; 18.3; 18.5.1; 20.5.1; 20.5.4)

Giordano, Simona. UNDERSTANDING EATING DISORDERS: CONCEPTUAL AND ETHICAL ISSUES IN THE TREATMENT OF ANOREXIA AND BULIMIA NERVOSA. Oxford: Clarendon Press/New York: Oxford University Press, 2005. 297 p. ISBN 0-19-926974-2. (Issues in Biomedical Ethics series. Gift of the publisher.) (9.5.1; 1.1; 4.2; 4.3; 7.1; 8.1; 8.3.1; 8.3.4; 15.6; 17.1; 20.5.1)

Institute of Medicine (United States). Committee on Smallpox Vaccination Program Implementation. THE

SMALLPOX VACCINATION PROGRAM: PUBLIC HEALTH IN AN AGE OF TERRORISM. Washington, DC: National Academies Press, 2004. 370 p. ISBN 0-309-09592-1. (Edited by Alina Baciu, Andrea Pernack Anason, Kathleen Stratton and Brian Strom. Also available on the Web at: http://www.nap.edu.) [RA644 .S6 S59 2005] (9.5.1; 9.1; 9.7; 21.3)

Johnson, Rob, ed. *Ethics and Legal Issues*. CLINICS IN SPORTS MEDICINE 2004 April; 23(2): 175-253. (ISSN 0278-5919.) (9.5.1; 1.1; 1.3.1; 1.3.2; 7.1; 8.1; 8.3.1; 8.4; 9.4; 9.5.9)

Katz, Paul R.; Mezey, Mathy D.; and Kapp, Marshall B., eds. VULNERABLE POPULATIONS IN THE LONG TERM CARE CONTINUUM. New York: Springer Publishing Company, 2004. 158 p. ISBN 0-8261-6834-5. (Springer Series on Advances in Long-Term Care; Vol. 5. ISSN 1053-0606.) [RA997 .V85 2004] (9.5.1; 9.5.4; 9.5.6; 9.5.7; 10; 17.1)

Lundberg, Anna. CARE AND COERCION: MEDICAL KNOWLEDGE, SOCIAL POLICY AND PATIENTS WITH VENERAL DISEASE IN SWEDEN, 1785-1903. Umeå, Sweden: Demographic Data Base, Umeå University, 1999. 309 p. ISBN 91-7191-675-X. (Report...from the Demographic Data Base, Umeå University series; No. 14. ISSN 0349-5132.) [RA644 .V4 L86 1999] (9.5.1; 1.3.5; 7.1; 10)

Shell, Marc. POLIO AND ITS AFTERMATH: THE PARALYSIS OF CULTURE. Cambridge, MA: Harvard University Press, 2005. 324 p. ISBN 0-674-01315-8. [RC181 .U5 S53 2005] (9.5.1; 7.1; 21.1)

Shi, Leiyu and Stevens, Gregory D. VULNERABLE POPULATIONS IN THE UNITED STATES. San Francisco: Jossey-Bass Publishers, 2005. 312 p. ISBN 0-7879-6958-3. (Gift of the publisher.) [RA418.5 .P6 S54 2005] (9.5.1; 7.1; 9.1; 9.2; 9.3.1; 9.4; 9.5.10; 9.8)

Tremain, Shelley, ed. FOUCAULT AND THE GOVERNMENT OF DISABILITY. Ann Arbor: University of Michigan Press, 2005. 340 p. ISBN 0-472-06876-8. (Corporealities series. Gift of the publisher.) [HV1568 .F68 2005] (9.5.1; 1.1; 1.3.5; 4.2; 5.2; 7.1; 9.5.3; 15.2; LE)

9.5.2 HEALTH CARE FOR THE AGED

Advocate Media Center, producer. FROM RULES TO CARING PRACTICES: ETHICS AND COMMUNITY-BASED CARE FOR ELDERS. Boston, MA: Fanlight Productions, 2001. 1 color videocassette (VHS) + 5 video discussion guides. (15:30 mins.). (Produced by the Park Ridge Center for the Study of Health, Faith and Ethics. The video contains 4 vignettes of approximately 3 minutes each. *The Story of Mrs. Ponte* (3:24), *But I Feel So Bad* (3:43), *Family Troubles* (3:22), and *Does Mrs. Jones Want to Die?* (3:19). These vignettes replicate the print version of the case narratives in the accompanying guides *From Rules to Caring Practices: Home Care: The Caregiver's Workbook* and *From Rules to Caring Practices: Home Care: The Instructor's Guide*. A guide provides reference to the accompanying pages in the manual. Available from: Fanlight Productions, 4196 Washington Street, Suite 2, Boston, MA 02131; tel: 800-937-4113; 617-469-4999 [outside US and Canada];

fax: 845-774-2945 (place orders); 617-469-3379 [outside US and Canada].) (9.5.2; 8.1; 17.1; 20.5.1)

Digregorio, Charlotte. EVERYTHING YOU NEED TO KNOW ABOUT NURSING HOMES: THE FAMILY'S COMPREHENSIVE GUIDE TO EITHER WORKING WITH THE INSTITUTION OR FINDING CARE ALTERNATIVES. Portland, OR: Civetta Press, 2005. 464 p. ISBN 0-9623318-3-X. (Publisher's address: PO Box 1043, zip 97207-1043. Gift of the publisher.) [RA997 .D54 2005] (9.5.2; 9.3.1; 9.5.1; 20.3.3; Reference)

Hudson, Robert B., ed. THE NEW POLITICS OF OLD AGE POLICY. Baltimore, MD: Johns Hopkins University Press, 2005. 309 p. ISBN 0-8018-8075-0. (Gift of the publisher.) [HV1461 .N76 2005] (9.5.2; 1.3.5; 9.3.1; 21.1)

Kreager, Philip and Schröder-Butterfill, Elisabeth, eds. AGEING WITHOUT CHILDREN: EUROPEAN AND ASIAN PERSPECTIVES. New York: Berghahn Books, 2004. 276 p. ISBN 1-57181-614-3. (Fertility, Reproduction and Sexuality series; Vol. 6. Gift of the publisher.) [HV1481 .E782 A34 2004] (9.5.2; 7.1; 9.5.7; 14.1)

President's Council on Bioethics (United States). TAKING CARE: ETHICAL CAREGIVING IN OUR AGING SOCIETY. Washington, DC: President's Council on Bioethics, 2005. 309 p. ISBN 0-16-072915-7. (September 2005. Available on the Web at: http://www.bioethics.gov. Publisher's address: 1801 Pennsylvania Avenue, NW, Suite 700, zip 20006.) [RA564.8 .P7374 2005] (9.5.2; 2.4; 8.3.3; 17.1; 20.4.1; 20.5.1; 20.5.4)

Rai, Gurcharan S., ed. MEDICAL ETHICS AND THE ELDERLY. Oxford/San Francisco: Radcliffe Medical Press, 2004. 163 p. ISBN 1-85775-851-X. (Second edition.) [R725.5 .M463 2004] (9.5.2; 2.1; 4.3; 4.4; 8.3.1; 8.3.3; 8.4; 17.3; 20.5.1; 20.5.4)

Weisstub, David N.; Thomasma, David C.; Gauthier, Serge; and Tomossy, George F., eds. AGING: CARING FOR OUR ELDERS. Dordrecht/Boston: Kluwer Academic, 2001. 242 p. ISBN 1-4020-0181-9. (International Library of Ethics, Law, and the New Medicine series; No. 11.) [HV1451 .A35 2001] (9.5.2; 1.3.5; 8.1; 8.3.3; 9.3.1; 9.5.10; 17.1; 21.1)

Weisstub, David N.; Thomasma, David C.; Gauthier, Serge; and Tomossy, George F., eds. AGING: CULTURE, HEALTH, AND SOCIAL CHANGE. Dordrecht/Boston: Kluwer Academic, 2001. 253 p. ISBN 1-4020-0180-0. (International Library of Ethics, Law, and the New Medicine series; No. 10.) [HV1451 .A36 2001] (9.5.2; 1.1; 1.3.5; 7.1; 9.1; 9.4; 9.5.10; 20.3.1; 21.1; 21.7)

9.5.3 HEALTH CARE FOR MENTALLY DISABLED PERSONS

Ainsworth, Patricia and Baker, Pamela. UNDERSTANDING MENTAL RETARDATION. Jackson: University Press of Mississippi, 2004. 200 p. ISBN 1-57806-647-6. (Understanding Health and Sickness Series.) [RC570 .A43 2004] (9.5.3; 4.3; 9.1; 9.5.2; 9.5.7; 15.2; 17.1; 18.5.6; LE)

Numbers in ( ) = NRCBL Classification Numbers

Cantor, Norman L. MAKING MEDICAL DECISIONS FOR THE PROFOUNDLY MENTALLY DISABLED. Cambridge, MA: MIT Press, 2005. 307 p. ISBN 0-262-03331-3. (Basic Bioethics series. Gift of the publisher.) [KF480 .C36 2005] (9.5.3; 1.1; 4.4; 8.3.2; 8.3.3; 18.5.6; 19.5; 20.5.1; 20.5.2; LE)

Lavin, Claire and Doka, Kenneth J. OLDER ADULTS WITH DEVELOPMENTAL DISABILITIES. Amityville, NY: Baywood Publishing Company, 1999. 151 p. ISBN 0-89503-188-4. (Society and Aging Series.) [HV3009.5 .A35 L38 1999] (9.5.3; 8.1; 9.1; 9.5.2; 17.1)

9.5.4 HEALTH CARE FOR MINORITIES

Braithwaite, Ronald L. and Taylor, Sandra E., eds. HEALTH ISSUES IN THE BLACK COMMUNITY. San Francisco: Jossey-Bass, 2001. 609 p. ISBN 0-7879-5236-2. (Second edition. Jossey-Bass Health Series.) [RA448.5 .N4 H395 2001] (9.5.4; 1.2; 7.1; 9.1; 9.5.1; 9.5.2; 9.5.5; 9.5.6; 9.5.7; 9.5.9; 9.5.10; 16.1; 18.5.1; 21.7)

LaVeist, Thomas A. MINORITY POPULATIONS AND HEALTH: AN INTRODUCTION TO HEALTH DISPARITIES IN THE UNITED STATES. San Francisco: Jossey-Bass, 2005. 348 p. ISBN 0-7879-6413-1. [RA448.4 .L38 2005] (9.5.4; 7.1; 9.1; 9.8; 17.1)

National Research Council (United States). Division of Behavioral and Social Sciences and Education. Committee on Population. UNDERSTANDING RACIAL AND ETHNIC DIFFERENCES IN HEALTH IN LATE LIFE: A RESEARCH AGENDA. Washington, DC: National Academies Press, 2004. 169 p. ISBN 0-309-09247-7. (Edited by Rodolfo A. Bulatao and Norman B. Anderson. Also available on the Web at: http://www.nap.edu.) [RA448.4 .U52 2004] (9.5.4; 7.1; 9.5.2)

Ridlon, Florence. A BLACK PHYSICIAN'S STRUGGLE FOR CIVIL RIGHTS: EDWARD C. MAZIQUE, M.D.. Albuquerque: University of New Mexico Press, 2005. 391 p. ISBN 0-8263-3339-7. (Gift of the publisher.) [R695 .M35 R53 2005] (9.5.4; 7.1; 9.2; Biography)

9.5.5 HEALTH CARE FOR WOMEN

Barnes, Andrea, ed. THE HANDBOOK OF WOMEN, PSYCHOLOGY, AND THE LAW. San Francisco: Jossey-Bass Publishers, 2005. 448 p. ISBN 0-7879-7060-3. (Rose Fitzgerald Kennedy Collection on Women, Infants and Children. Gift of the publisher.) [HQ1154 .H2298 2005] (9.5.5; 1.2; 9.1; 9.3.1; 9.5.6; 10; 11.1; 12.4.2; 13.3; 14.1; 16.3; 17.1; 21.1; 21.2; LE)

Case Comments and Notes: Winnipeg Child and Family Services. ALBERTA LAW REVIEW 1998 July; 36(3): 707-809. (ISSN 0002-4821.) (9.5.5; 4.4; 8.3.4; 9.5.8; 9.5.9)

Mabilia, Mara. BREAST FEEDING AND SEXUALITY: BEHAVIOUR, BELIEFS AND TABOOS AMONG THE GOGO MOTHERS IN TANZANIA. New York: Berghahn Books, 2005. 139 p. ISBN 1-57181-677-1. (Fertility, Reproduction and Sexuality series; Vol. 5. Translation by Mary S. Ash. Gift of the

publisher. Rose Fitzgerald Kennedy Collection on Women, Infants and Children.) [DT443.3 .G64 M33 2005] (9.5.5; 7.1; 9.5.7; 10; 17.1)

National Women's Health Network. THE TRUTH ABOUT HORMONE REPLACEMENT THERAPY: HOW TO BREAK FREE FROM THE MEDICAL MYTHS OF MENOPAUSE. Roseville, CA: Prima Publishing, 2002. 332 p. ISBN 0-7615-3478-4. (Rose Fitzgerald Kennedy Collection on Women, Infants and Children.) [RG186 .T835 2002] (9.5.5; 9.7)

Paxson, Heather. MAKING MODERN MOTHERS: ETHICS AND FAMILY PLANNING IN URBAN GREECE. Berkeley: University of California Press, 2004. 335 p. ISBN 0-520-23820-6. (Rose Fitzgerald Kennedy Collection on Women, Infants and Children.) (9.5.5; 7.1; 10; 11.1; 12.1; 13.3; 14.1)

Ratcliff, Kathryn Strother. WOMEN AND HEALTH: POWER, TECHNOLOGY, INEQUALITY, AND CONFLICT IN A GENDERED WORLD. Boston: Allyn and Bacon, 2002. 356 p. ISBN 0-205-30597-0. (Rose Fitzgerald Kennedy Collection on Women, Infants and Children.) [RA564.85 .R38 2002] (9.5.5; 2.1; 7.1; 10)

Rowland, Debran. THE BOUNDARIES OF HER BODY: THE TROUBLING HISTORY OF WOMEN'S RIGHTS IN AMERICA. Naperville, IL: Sphinx, 2004. 788 p. ISBN 1-57248-368-7. (Rose Fitzgerald Kennedy Collection on Women, Infants and Children.) (9.5.5; 9.1; 9.5.6; 9.5.7; 10; 11.1; 11.2; 12.4.2; 14.1; 14.2; 14.6; 16.3; 20.1; 21.1)

Skaine, Rosemarie. FEMALE GENITAL MUTILATION: LEGAL, CULTURAL AND MEDICAL ISSUES. Jefferson, NC: McFarland, 2005. 321 p. ISBN 0-7864-2167-3. (Rose Fitzgerald Kennedy Collection on Women, Infants and Children.) [GN484 .S485 2005] (9.5.5; 1.2; 7.1; 9.5.7; 10; 21.7)

Spagnolo, Antonio G. and Gambino, Gabriella, eds. WOMEN'S HEALTH ISSUES. Roma: Società Editrice Universo, 2003. 543 p. ISBN 88-87753-78-4. (Preface by Elio Sgreccia. Gift of Edmund D. Pellegrino. Rose Fitzgerald Kennedy Collection on Women, Infants and Children.) (9.5.5; 7.1; 9.5.8; 10; 14.1; 17.1; 18.5.3)

Stotland, Nada L. and Stewart, Donna E., eds. PSYCHOLOGICAL ASPECTS OF WOMEN'S HEALTH CARE: THE INTERFACE BETWEEN PSYCHIATRY AND OBSTETRICS AND GYNECOLOGY. Washington, DC: American Psychiatric Press, 2001. 654 p. ISBN 0-88048-831-X. (Second edition. Rose Fitzgerald Kennedy Collection of Women, Infants and Children.) [RG103.5 .P7725 2001] (9.5.5; 9.1; 9.5.7; 9.5.9; 10; 12.1; 14.1; 17.1; 17.4; 17.5)

Turshen, Meredeth, ed. AFRICAN WOMEN'S HEALTH. Trenton, NJ: Africa World Press, 2000. 253 p. ISBN 0-86543-820-X. (Rose Fitzgerald Kennedy Collection on Women, Infants and Children.) [RA545 .A36 2000] (9.5.5; 7.1; 9.1; 9.5.6; 9.5.7; 10; 14.1; 17.1; 21.7)

9.5.6 HIV INFECTION AND AIDS

Access for All: Fighting HIV/AIDS. DEVELOPMENT OUT-REACH 2004 July; 6(2): 4-34. (ISSN 1020-797X.) (9.5.6)

Baldwin, Peter. DISEASE AND DEMOCRACY: THE INDUSTRI-ALIZED WORLD FACES AIDS. Berkeley: University of California Press [and] New York: Milbank Memorial Fund, 2005. 465 p. ISBN 0-520-24350-1. (California/Milbank Books on Health and the Public series; No. 13. Gift of the publisher.) [RA643.8 .B35 2005] (9.5.6; 1.3.5; 7.1; 9.1; 9.5.1; 10; 21.1)

Barnett, Tony and Whiteside, Alan. AIDS IN THE TWENTY-FIRST CENTURY: DISEASE AND GLOBALIZATION. Houndmills, Basingstoke, Hampshire/New York: Palgrave Macmillan, 2002. 414 p. ISBN 1-4039-0006-X. [RA643.8 .B37 2002] (9.5.6; 7.1; 9.3.1; 21.1)

D'Adesky, Anne-Christine. MOVING MOUNTAINS: THE RACE TO TREAT GLOBAL AIDS. New York: Verso, 2004. 487 p. ISBN 1-84467-002-3. [RA643.8 .D336 2004] (9.5.6; 7.1; 9.2; 9.7; 21.1)

Greene, Kathryn; Derlega, Valerian J.; Yep, Gust A.; and Petronio, Sandra. PRIVACY AND DISCLOSURE OF HIV IN IN-TERPERSONAL RELATIONSHIPS: A SOURCEBOOK FOR RE-SEARCHERS AND PRACTITIONERS. Mahwah, NJ: Lawrence Erlbaum Associates, 2003. 265 p. ISBN 0-8058-3695-0. (LEA's Communication Series.) [RA643.8 .P755 2003] (9.5.6; 7.1; 8.1; 8.4)

Institute of Medicine (United States). Committee on Examining the Probable Consequences of Alternative Patterns of Widespread Antiretroviral Drug Use in Resource-Constrained Settings. SCALING UP TREATMENT FOR THE GLOBAL AIDS PANDEMIC: CHALLENGES AND OP-PORTUNITIES. Washington, DC: National Academies Press, 2005. 325 p. ISBN 0-309-09264-7. (Edited by James Curran, Haile Debas, Monisha Arya, Patrick Kelley, Stacey Knobler and Leslie Pray. Also available on the Web at: http://www.nap.edu.) [RA643.8 .I57 2005] (9.5.6; 9.7; 21.1; Reference)

Institute of Medicine (United States). Committee on Public Financing and Delivery of HIV Care. PUBLIC FINANCING AND DELIVERY OF HIV/AIDS CARE: SECURING THE LEGACY OF RYAN WHITE. Washington, DC: National Academies Press, 2005. 358 p. ISBN 0-309-09228-0. (Also available on the Web at: http://www.nap.edu.) [RA643.83 .P83 2005] (9.5.6; 9.1; 9.3.1; 9.8)

Institute of Medicine (United States). Committee on the Options for Overseas Placement of U.S. Health Professionals. HEALERS ABROAD: AMERICANS RESPONDING TO THE HUMAN RESOURCES CRISIS IN HIV/AIDS. Washington, DC: National Academies Press, 2005. 242 p. ISBN 0-309-09616-2. (Edited by Fitzhugh Mullan, Claire Panosian, and Patricia Cuff. Also available on the Web at: http://www.nap.edu.) [RA643.8 .I575 2005] (9.5.6; 1.3.5; 9.1; 21.1)

Kopp, Christine. THE NEW ERA OF AIDS: HIV AND MEDICINE IN TIMES OF TRANSITION. Dordrecht/Boston: Kluwer Aca-demic, 2002. 188 p. ISBN 1-4020-1048-6. (International Library of Ethics, Law, and the New Medicine series; Vol. 15.) [RA643.8 .K67 2002] (9.5.6; 4.2; 7.1; 9.1)

Nattrass, Nicoli. THE MORAL ECONOMY OF AIDS IN SOUTH AFRICA. Cambridge/New York: Cambridge University Press, 2004. 222 p. ISBN 0-521-54864-0. (Cambridge Africa Collection series.) [RA643.86 .S6 N38 2004] (9.5.6; 7.1; 9.1; 9.3.1; 9.5.10; 10)

United Nations. Department of Economic and Social Affairs. Population Division. THE IMPACT OF AIDS. New York: United Nations, 2004. 140 p. ISBN 92-1-151397-9. (Economic and Social Affairs series. Publication No. ST/ESA/SER.A/229. UN Publication Sales No. E.04.XIII.7.) [RA643.86 .D44 I47 2004] (9.5.6; 7.1; 21.1)

Wooten, Jim. WE ARE ALL THE SAME: A STORY OF A BOY'S COURAGE AND A MOTHER'S LOVE. New York: Penguin Press, 2004, 243 p. ISBN 0-14-303599-1. (Biography of Nkosi Johnson.) (9.5.6; 9.5.7; Biography)

World Bank. CONFRONTING AIDS: PUBLIC PRIORITIES IN A GLOBAL EPIDEMIC. New York: Published for the World Bank by Oxford University Press, 1999. 365 p. ISBN 0-19-521591-5. (Revised edition. World Bank Policy Research Report series.) [RA644 .A25 .C6339 1999] (9.5.6; 1.3.5; 7.1; 9.1; 9.3.1; 9.5.10; 21.1)

9.5.7 HEALTH CARE FOR MINORS

Archard, David. CHILDREN: RIGHTS AND CHILDHOOD. London/New York: Routledge, 2004. 247 p. ISBN 0-415-30584-5. (Second edition. Rose Fitzgerald Kennedy Collection on Women, Infants and Children.) [HQ767.87 .A73 2004] (9.5.7; 1.1; 10; 14.1)

Frankel, Lorry R.; Goldworth, Amnon; Rorty, Mary V.; and Silverman, William A., eds. ETHICAL DILEMMAS IN PE-DIATRICS: CASES AND COMMENTARIES. Cambridge/New York: Cambridge University Press, 2005. 303 p. ISBN 0-521-84744-3. (Rose Fitzgerald Kennedy Collection on Women, Infants and Children. Gift of the publisher.) [RJ47.8 .E84 2005] (9.5.7; 2.3; 8.1; 9.3.2; 9.4; 19.1; 19.2; 20.5.1; 20.5.2)

Mohrmann, Margaret E. ATTENDING CHILDREN: A DOC-TOR'S EDUCATION. Washington, DC: Georgetown University Press, 2005. 212 p. ISBN 1-58901-054-X. (Rose Fitzgerald Kennedy Collection on Women, Infants and Children. Gift of the publisher.) [RJ43 .M64 A3 2005] (9.5.7; 7.2; 8.1; 20.4.2; Biography)

National Research Council (United States). Committee on Evaluation of Children's Health. CHILDREN'S HEALTH, THE NATION'S WEALTH: ASSESSING AND IMPROVING CHILD HEALTH. Washington, DC: National Academies Press, 2004. 324 p. ISBN 0-309-09118-7. (Also available on the Web at: http://www.nap.edu. Rose Fitzgerald Kennedy Collection on Women, Infants and Children.) [RJ102 .C4895 2004] (9.5.7; 1.3.12; 7.1)

Stern, Alexandra Minna and Markel, Howard, eds. FORMA-TIVE YEARS: CHILDREN'S HEALTH IN THE UNITED STATES,

---

Numbers in ( ) = NRCBL Classification Numbers

1880-2000. Ann Arbor: University of Michigan Press, 2004, c2002. 304 p. ISBN 0-472-08980-3. (Conversations in Medicine and Society series. David Murray Dowie Symposium on the History of Pediatrics and Child Health in America, held in Ann Arbor, MI in 2000. Rose Fitzgerald Kennedy Collection on Women, Infants and Children.) [RJ42 .U5 F67 2002] (9.5.7; 5.1; 7.1; 9.1; 9.5.9; 10; 15.5)

United Nations. Environmental Programme; UNICEF; and World Health Organization. CHILDREN IN THE NEW MILLENNIUM: ENVIRONMENTAL IMPACT ON HEALTH. Nairobi: United Nations Environmental Programme [and] New York: United Nations Children's Fund [and] Geneva: World Health Organization, 2002. 142 p. ISBN 92-807-2065-1. (Available on the Web at: http://www. unep.org/ceh/children.pdf. Rose Fitzgerald Kennedy Collection on Women, Infants and Children.) [HQ767.9 .C4497 2002] (9.5.7; 7.1; 16.1; 16.2; 21.1)

Wolf, Jacqueline H. DON'T KILL YOUR BABY: PUBLIC HEALTH AND THE DECLINE OF BREASTFEEDING IN THE NINETEENTH AND TWENTIETH CENTURIES. Columbus: Ohio State University Press, 2001. 290 p. ISBN 0-8142-5077-7. (Women and Health: Cultural and Social Perspectives series. Rose Fitzgerald Kennedy Collection on Women, Infants and Children.) [RJ216 .W719 2001] (9.5.7; 7.1; 9.1; 9.5.5; 9.7)

9.5.8 HEALTH CARE FOR EMBRYOS AND FETUSES

Cave, Emma. THE MOTHER OF ALL CRIMES: HUMAN RIGHTS, CRIMINALIZATION AND THE CHILD BORN ALIVE. Aldershot, Hants/Burlington, VT: Ashgate, 2004. 163 p. ISBN 0-7546-2366-1. (Rose Fitzgerald Kennedy Collection on Women, Infants and Children.) [K5181 .C38 2004] (9.5.8; 1.1; 1.3.5; 4.4; 9.5.5; 9.5.9; 11.4; LE)

Marzilli, Alan. FETAL RIGHTS. Philadelphia: Chelsea House, 2006. 150 p. ISBN 0-7910-8643-7. (Point/ Conterpoint series. Juvenile literature. Rose Fitzgerald Kennedy Collection on Women, Infants and Children.) (9.5.8; 9.5.5; 9.5.7; 12.4.2)

9.5.9 HEALTH CARE FOR SUBSTANCE ABUSERS/USERS OF CONTROLLED SUBSTANCES

Boyd, Susan C. FROM WITCHES TO CRACK MOMS: WOMEN, DRUG LAW, AND POLICY. Durham, NC: Carolina Academic Press, 2004. 367 p. ISBN 0-89089-127-3. [HV5824 .W6 B686 2004] (9.5.9; 1.3.5; 9.5.5; 10; 21.1)

Feldman, Eric A. and Bayer, Ronald, eds. UNFILTERED: CONFLICTS OVER TOBACCO POLICY AND PUBLIC HEALTH. Cambridge, MA: Harvard University Press, 2004. 394 p. ISBN 0-674-01334-4. [HD9130.6 .U54 2004] (9.5.9; 1.3.5; 7.1; 9.1; 21.1; 21.7)

Golden, Janet. MESSAGE IN A BOTTLE: THE MAKING OF FETAL ALCOHOL SYNDROME. Cambridge, MA: Harvard University Press, 2005. 232 p. ISBN 0-674-01485-5. (Gift of

the publisher.) [RC629 .F45 G655 2005] (9.5.9; 1.3.5; 1.3.7; 9.1; 9.5.4; 9.5.5; 9.5.8; 21.1)

Sloan, Frank A.; Ostermann, Jan; Picone, Gabriel; Conover, Christopher; and Taylor, Donald H. THE PRICE OF SMOKING. Cambridge, MA: MIT Press, 2004. 313 p. ISBN 0-262-19510-0. (Gift of the publisher.) [HV5760 .P745 2004] (9.5.9; 7.1; 9.3.1; 9.5.2; 9.5.10; 16.3)

Tracy, Sarah W. and Acker, Caroline Jean, eds. ALTERING AMERICAN CONSCIOUSNESS: THE HISTORY OF ALCOHOL AND DRUG USE IN THE UNITED STATES, 1800-2000. Amherst: University of Massachusetts Press, 2004. 414 p. ISBN 1-55849-425-1. [HV5292 .A393 2004] (9.5.9; 1.2; 1.3.5; 7.1; 9.7; 10; 17.4; 17.7)

9.7 DRUGS AND PHARMACEUTICAL INDUSTRY

Access to Medicines in the Developing World: International Facilitation or Hindrance? WISCONSIN INTERNATIONAL LAW JOURNAL 2002 Summer; 20(3): 451-610. (ISSN 0743-7951.) (9.7; 5.1; 9.3.1; 9.5.6; 15.8; 21.1)

Angell, Marcia. THE TRUTH ABOUT THE DRUG COMPANIES: HOW THEY DECEIVE US AND WHAT TO DO ABOUT IT. New York: Random House, 2004. 305 p. ISBN 0-375-50846-5. [HD9666.5 .A74 2004] (9.7; 1.3.2; 5.3; 7.2; 9.3.1; 18.1)

Avorn, Jerry. POWERFUL MEDICINES: THE BENEFITS, RISKS, AND COSTS OF PRESCRIPTION DRUGS. New York: Vintage Books, c2004, 2005. 448 p. ISBN 1-4000-3078-1. ("Originally published in hardcover in the United States in different form by Alfred A. Knopf, a division of Random House, New York, in 2004." Gift of the publisher.) [HD9666.5 .A94 2005] (9.7; 1.3.2; 5.2; 9.1; 9.3.1)

British Medical Association. THERAPEUTIC USES OF CANNABIS. Amsterdam: Harwood Academic, 1997. 142 p. ISBN 90-5702-317-2. [RM666 .C266 T48 1997] (9.7; 9.5.1; 9.5.9)

Fitzpatrick, Michael. MMR AND AUTISM: WHAT PARENTS NEED TO KNOW. London/New York: Routledge, 2004. 218 p. ISBN 0-415-32179-4. [RJ506 .A9 F58 2004] (9.7; 5.2; 9.5.1; 9.5.7; 17.1)

Hawthorne, Fran. INSIDE THE FDA: THE BUSINESS AND POLITICS BEHIND THE DRUGS WE TAKE AND THE FOOD WE EAT. Hoboken, NJ: John Wiley & Sons, 2005. 338 p. ISBN 0-471-61091-7. (Gift of the publisher.) [RA401 .A3 H39 2005] (9.7; 1.3.2; 5.3; 9.5.1; 15.1; 18.6; 21.1)

Hoberman, John. TESTOSTERONE DREAMS: REJUVENATION, APHRODISIA, DOPING. Berkeley: University of California Press, 2005. 381 p. ISBN 0-520-22151-6. [QP572 .T4 H635 2005] (9.7; 1.3.1; 4.5; 10; 14.1)

Horton, Richard. MMR: SCIENCE AND FICTION. London: Granta Books, 2004. 220 p. ISBN 1-86207-764-9. [RC168 .M8 H67 2004] (9.7; 5.2; 9.5.1; 9.5.7; 17.1)

Institute of Medicine (United States). Board on Health Promotion and Disease Prevention. Immunization Safety

Review Committee. IMMUNIZATION SAFETY REVIEW: VAC-CINES AND AUTISM. Washington, DC: National Academies Press, 2004. 199 p. ISBN 0-309-09237-X. (Also available on the Web at: http://www.nap.edu.) [RJ240 .I443 2004] (9.7; 5.2; 9.5.7)

Kassirer, Jerome p. ON THE TAKE: HOW AMERICA'S COM-PLICITY WITH BIG BUSINESS CAN ENDANGER YOUR HEALTH. Oxford/New York: Oxford University Press, 2005. 251 p. ISBN 0-19-517684-7. [R725.5 .K376 2005] (9.7; 1.3.1; 4.1.2; 8.1; 9.3.1)

Kirby, David. EVIDENCE OF HARM: MERCURY IN VACCINES AND THE AUTISM EPIDEMIC: A MEDICAL CONTROVERSY. New York: St. Martin's Press, 2005. 460 p. ISBN 0-312-32644-0. (9.7; 1.3.2; 5.2; 9.1; 9.5.7)

Loe, Meika. THE RISE OF VIAGRA: HOW THE LITTLE BLUE PILL CHANGED SEX IN AMERICA. New York: New York University Press, 2004. 289 p. ISBN 0-8147-5200-4. [RC889 .L64 2004] (9.7; 7.1; 10)

Moynihan, Ray and Cassels, Alan. SELLING SICKNESS: HOW THE WORLD'S PHARMACEUTICAL COMPANIES ARE TURNING US ALL INTO PATIENTS. New York: Nation Books, 2005. 254 p. ISBN 1-56025-697-4. (Originally published in Australia by: Allen & Unwin, 2005. Gift of the pub-lisher.) [HD9665.5 .M69 2005] (9.7; 1.3.2)

Offit, Paul A. THE CUTTER INCIDENT: HOW AMERICA'S FIRST POLIO VACCINE LED TO THE GROWING VACCINE CRISIS. New Haven, CT: Yale University Press, 2005. 238 p. ISBN 0-300-10864-8. (9.7; 5.2; 7.1; 9.5.7)

Robinson, Jeffrey. PRESCRIPTION GAMES: MONEY, EGO AND POWER INSIDE THE GLOBAL PHARMACEUTICAL INDUSTRY. London: Simon & Schuster, 2001. 343 p. ISBN 0-684-85837-1. [HD9665.5 .R63 2001] (9.7; 1.3.2; 9.3.1)

Salek, Sam and Edgar, Andrew, eds. PHARMACEUTICAL ETHICS. New York: John Wiley & Sons, 2002. 198 p. ISBN 0-471-49057-1. [RS100.5 .P475 2002] (9.7; 1.3.2; 1.3.7; 5.3; 8.1; 8.3.1; 9.3.1; 17.1; 18.1)

9.8 QUALITY OF HEALTH CARE

Berlinger, Nancy. AFTER HARM: MEDICAL ERROR AND THE ETHICS OF FORGIVENESS. Baltimore, MD: Johns Hopkins University Press, 2005. 156 p. ISBN 0-8018-8167-6. (Gift of the publisher.) [R729.8 .B47 2005] (9.8; 1.2; 7.1; 8.1; 17.1)

Institute of Medicine (United States). Committee on the National Quality Report on Health Care Delivery. ENVI-SIONING THE NATIONAL HEALTH CARE QUALITY REPORT. Washington, DC: National Academy Press, 2001. 234 p. ISBN 0-309-07343-X. (Edited by Margarita Patricia Hurtado, Elaine K. Swift, and Janet M. Corrigan. "...work-shop on "Envisioning a National Quality Report on Health Care" held on May 22 and 23, 2000, in Washington, D.C. Support for this study was provided by the Agency for Healthcare Research and Quality, U.S. Department of Health and Human Services" Also available on the Web at:

http://www.nap.edu.) [RA399 .A3 I558 2001] (9.8; 7.1; 9.1)

Kristiansen, Ivar Sønbø and Mooney, Gavin, eds. EVI-DENCE-BASED MEDICINE: IN ITS PLACE. London/New York: Routledge, 2004. 164 p. ISBN 0-415-28321-3. (Routledge International Studies in Health Economics series. Gift of the publisher.) [R723.7 .E955 2004] (9.8; 4.1.3; 7.2; 9.3.1; 9.7; 18.1; 21.1)

Wiener, Carolyn L. THE ELUSIVE QUEST: ACCOUNTABILITY IN HOSPITALS. New York: Aldine de Gruyter, 2000. 256 p. ISBN 0-202-30631-3. (Social Problems and Social Issues series.) [RA972 .W534 2000] (9.8; 7.1)

10 SEXUALITY/GENDER

Fuchs, Esther, comp. and ed. ISRAELI WOMEN'S STUDIES: A READER. New Brunswick, NJ: Rutgers University Press, 2005. 342 p. ISBN 0-8135-3616-2. (Gift of Max M. and Marjorie B. Kampelman.) [HQ1728.5 .I88 2005] (10; 1.2; 1.3.5)

Gagnon, John H. and Simon, William. SEXUAL CONDUCT: THE SOCIAL SOURCES OF HUMAN SEXUALITY. New Bruns-wick, NJ: AldineTransaction, 2005. 348 p. ISBN 0-202-30664-X. (Second edition.) [HQ21 .G234 2005] (10; 15.9)

Hite, Shere. THE HITE REPORT: A NATIONWIDE STUDY OF FE-MALE SEXUALITY. New York: Seven Stories Press, 2004. 512 p. ISBN 1-58322-569-2. (2004 edition [Second edi-tion].) [HQ29 .H57 2004] (10; 7.1; 9.5.5)

Horowitz, Helen Lefkowitz. REREADING SEX: BATTLES OVER SEXUAL KNOWLEDGE AND SUPPRESSION IN NINE-TEENTH-CENTURY AMERICA. New York: Vintage Books, 2002. 514 p. ISBN 0-375-70186-9. [HQ18 .U5 H673 2003] (10; 1.2)

Institute of Medicine (United States). Committee on Un-derstanding the Biology of Sex and Gender Differences. EXPLORING THE BIOLOGICAL CONTRIBUTIONS TO HUMAN HEALTH: DOES SEX MATTER? Washington, DC: National Academy Press, 2001. 267 p. ISBN 0-309-07281-6. (Ed-ited by Theresa M. Wizemann and Mary-Lou Pardue. Also available on the Web at: http://www.nap. edu.) [QP81.5 .I56 2001] (10; 3.1; 9.5.1; 9.5.5; 15.6; 18.2)

Laqueur, Thomas W. SOLITARY SEX: A CULTURAL HISTORY OF MASTURBATION. New York: Zone Books; Distributed by: Cambridge, MA: MIT Press, 2003. 501 p. ISBN 1-890951-33-1. [HQ447 .L36 2003] (10; 1.2)

Minton, Henry L. DEPARTING FROM DEVIANCE: A HISTORY OF HOMOSEXUAL RIGHTS AND EMANCIPATORY SCIENCE IN AMERICA. Chicago: University of Chicago Press, 2002. 344 p. ISBN 0-226-53044-2. [HQ76.3 .U5 M56 2002] (10; 7.1; 18.4)

Montgomery, Heather. MODERN BABYLON? PROSTITUTING CHILDREN IN THAILAND. New York: Berghahn Books, 2001. 192 p. ISBN 1-57181-318-7. (Fertility, Reproduction, and Sexuality series; Vol. 2. Gift of the publisher.) [HQ242.55 .A5 M66 2001] (10; 7.1; 9.5.7)

Robertson, Jennifer, ed. SAME-SEX CULTURES AND SEXUALITIES: AN ANTHROPOLOGICAL READER. Malden, MA: Blackwell Publishers, 2005. 310 p. ISBN 0-631-23300-8. (Blackwell Readers in Anthropology series; No. 6. Gift of the publisher.) [GN484.35 .S36 2005] (10; 7.1; 15.6)

Schidlo, Ariel; Schroeder, Michael; and Drescher, Jack, eds. SEXUAL CONVERSION THERAPY: ETHICAL, CLINICAL AND RESEARCH PERSPECTIVES. Binghamton, NY: Haworth Medical Press, 2001. 215 p. ISBN 0-7890-1911-6. (Also published as: *Journal of Gay and Lesbian Psychotherapy* 2001; 5(3-4).) (10; 7.1; 17.2; 17.3)

Roughgarden, Joan. EVOLUTION'S RAINBOW: DIVERSITY, GENDER, AND SEXUALITY IN NATURE AND PEOPLE. Berkeley: University of California Press, 2004. 474 p. ISBN 0-520-24073-1. [QH541.15 .B56 R68 2004] (10; 3.2; 15.6)

Segal, Marcia Texler; Demos, Vasilikie; and Kronenfeld, Jennie Jacobs, eds. GENDER PERSPECTIVES ON HEALTH AND MEDICINE: KEY THEMES. Amsterdam/Boston: Elsevier, 2003. 330 p. ISBN 0-7623-1058-8. (Advances in Gender Research series; Vol. 7. ISSN 1529-2126.) [RA564.85 .G4665 2003] (10; 7.1; 9.3.1; 9.5.4; 9.5.5; 9.5.10; 9.7; 18.5.3)

Turner, David M. FASHIONING ADULTERY: GENDER, SEX AND CIVILITY IN ENGLAND, 1660-1740. Cambridge/New York: Cambridge University Press, 2002. 236 p. ISBN 0-521-79244-4. (Past and Present Publications series.) [HQ806 .T87 2002] (10; 1.2; 1.3.8)

11.1 CONTRACEPTION (GENERAL)

Hoggart, Lesley. FEMINIST CAMPAIGNS FOR BIRTH CONTROL AND ABORTION RIGHTS IN BRITAIN. Lewiston, NY: Edwin Mellen Press, 2003. 272 p. ISBN 0-7734-6868-4. (Studies in British History series; Vol. 69.) [HQ766.5 .G7 H64 2003] (11.1; 7.1; 10; 12.3; 21.1)

Institute of Medicine (United States). Committee on New Frontiers in Contraceptive Research. NEW FRONTIERS IN CONTRACEPTIVE RESEARCH: A BLUEPRINT FOR ACTION. Washington, DC: National Academies Press, 2004. 232 p. ISBN 0-309-09107-1. (Edited by Sharyl J. Nass and Jerome F. Strauss. Also available on the Web at: http://www.nap.edu.) [RG136 .N493 2004] (11.1; 7.1; 9.3.1; 9.5.1)

Schoen, Johanna. CHOICE & COERCION: BIRTH CONTROL, STERILIZATION, AND ABORTION IN PUBLIC HEALTH AND WELFARE. Chapel Hill: University of North Carolina Press, 2005. 331 p. ISBN 0-8078-5585-5. (Gender & American Culture series. Gift of the publisher.) [HQ766.5 .U5 S36 2005] (11.1; 1.3.5; 2.2; 9.1; 9.5.5; 11.3; 12.4.1; 15.5)

12.1 ABORTION (GENERAL)

Myrsiades, Linda. SPLITTING THE BABY: THE CULTURE OF ABORTION IN LITERATURE AND LAW, RHETORIC AND CARTOONS. New York: Peter Lang, 2002. 203 p. ISBN 0-8204-5816-3. (Eruptions: New Thinking across the Disciplines series; Vol. 20.) (12.1; 7.1; 12.4.1; 12.5.1; 21.7; Fiction)

12.3 ABORTION: MORAL AND RELIGIOUS ASPECTS

Cutrer, William and Glahn, Sandra. FALSE POSITIVE. Colorado Springs, CO: WaterBrook Press, 2002. 327 p. ISBN 1-57856-567-7. ("After a woman is rushed to the emergency room in shock from massive blood loss, second-year medical resident Julien "Red" Richison becomes suspicious about the procedures being practiced at the nearby "VIP" abortion clinic. Soon, with the help of Bethany Fabrazio, director of a pro-life women's clinic, Red finds himself investigating what goes on behind closed doors at VIP. But what Bethany and Red don't know is that some VIP doctors will stop at nothing to keep their secrets under wraps—even if it means taking Red's life.") [PS3553 .U848 F35 2002] (12.3; 7.2; Fiction)

Davis, Tom. SACRED WORK: PLANNED PARENTHOOD AND ITS CLERGY ALLIANCES. New Brunswick, NJ: Rutgers University Press, 2005. 245 p. ISBN 0-8135-3493-3. (Gift of the publisher.) [HQ766.5 .U5 D38 2005] (12.3; 2.2; 11.1; 12.5.2; 21.1)

12.4.1 ABORTION: LEGAL ASPECTS (GENERAL)

Francome, Colin. ABORTION IN THE USA AND THE UK. Aldershot, Hants, England/Burlington, VT: Ashgate, 2004. 180 p. ISBN 0-7546-3015-3. [HQ767.5 .U5 F71795 2004] (12.4.1; 12.5.1; 21.1)

Hull, N.E.H.; Hoffer, Williamjames; and Hoffer, Peter Charles, eds. THE ABORTION RIGHTS CONTROVERSY IN AMERICA: A LEGAL READER. Chapel Hill: University of North Carolina Press, 2004. 343 p. ISBN 0-8078-5535-9. [KF3771 .A937 2004] (12.4.1; 9.2; 9.3.1; 11.1; Reference)

Levine, Phillip B. SEX AND CONSEQUENCES: ABORTION, PUBLIC POLICY, AND THE ECONOMICS OF FERTILITY. Princeton, NJ: Princeton University Press, 2004. 215 p. ISBN 0-691-07098-9. [HQ767 .L48 2004] (12.4.1; 7.1; 9.1; 9.3.1; 21.1)

Urban Law Journal Special Series: The Current State of Abortion Law and Reproductive Rights. FORDHAM URBAN LAW JOURNAL 2004 March; 31(3): 659-830. (ISSN 0199-4646.) (12.4.1; 1.3.5; 9.5.5; 10; 12.1; 12.4.2; 14.5; 18.5.4)

12.4.2 ABORTION: INTERESTS OF WOMAN/FETUS/FATHER

Harte, Colin. CHANGING UNJUST LAWS JUSTLY: PRO-LIFE SOLIDARITY WITH "THE LAST AND LEAST". Washington, DC: Catholic University of America Press, 2005. 363 p. ISBN 0-8132-1406-8. (Gift of the publisher.) [KD3340 .H37 2005] (12.4.2; 12.3)

12.5.2 ABORTION: DEMOGRAPHIC SURVEYS

Bachiochi, Erika, ed. THE COST OF CHOICE: WOMEN EVALU-ATE THE IMPACT OF ABORTION. San Francisco: Encounter Books, 2004. 180 p. ISBN 1-59403-051-0. [HQ767.5 .U5 C66 2004] (12.5.2; 9.5.5; 10; 12.3; 12.4.2; 12.5.1; 15.3)

Moskowitz, Marc L. THE HAUNTING FETUS: ABORTION, SEXUALITY, AND THE SPIRIT WORLD IN TAIWAN. Honolulu: University of Hawai'i Press, 2001. 206 p. ISBN 0-8248-2428-8. (12.5.2; 10; 12.3)

Nie, Jing-Bao. BEHIND THE SILENCE: CHINESE VOICES ON ABORTION. Lanham, MD: Rowman & Littlefield, 2005. 294 p. ISBN 0-7425-2371-3. (Asian Voices series.) (12.5.2; 11.1; 12.3; 13.3; 21.7)

13.1 POPULATION (GENERAL)

Wattenberg, Ben J. FEWER: HOW THE NEW DEMOGRAPHY OF DEPOPULATION WILL SHAPE OUR FUTURE. Chicago: Ivan R. Dee, 2004. 241 p. ISBN 1-56663-673-6. [HB871 .W35 2004] (13.1; 7.1; 9.5.2; 11.1; 14.1; 16.1; 21.1)

13.2 POPULATION GROWTH

Brown, Lester R. PLAN B: RESCUING A PLANET UNDER STRESS AND A CIVILIZATION IN TROUBLE. New York: W.W. Norton, 2003. 285 p. ISBN 0-393-32523-7. [HC79 .E5 B7595 2003] (13.2; 1.3.11; 16.1; 21.1)

United Nations. Department of Economic and Social Affairs. Population Division. POLICY RESPONSES TO POPULA-TION DECLINE AND AGEING. New York: United Nations, 2004. 458 p. ISBN 92-1-151364-2. (Population Bulletin of the United Nations series; No. 44/45, 2002. UN Publication Sales No. E.02.XIII.4.) (13.2; 1.3.5; 7.1; 9.5.2; 14.1; 21.1)

14.1 REPRODUCTION/REPRODUCTIVE TECHNOLOGIES (GENERAL)

Blyth, Eric and Landau, Ruth, eds. THIRD PARTY ASSISTED CONCEPTION ACROSS CULTURES: SOCIAL, LEGAL AND ETHI-CAL PERSPECTIVES. London/New York: Jessica Kingsley Publishers, 2004. 288 p. ISBN 1-84310-085-1. [RG133.5 .T486 2004] (14.1; 7.1; 9.3.1; 14.2; 21.7; LE)

Ehrensaft, Diane. MOMMIES, DADDIES, DONORS, SURRO-GATES: ANSWERING TOUGH QUESTIONS AND BUILDING STRONG FAMILIES. New York: Guilford Press, 2005. 305 p.

ISBN 1-59385-133-2. (Gift of the publisher.) [RG133.5 .E42 2005] (14.1; 14.2; 17.1; 17.2)

Grazi, Richard V. OVERCOMING INFERTILITY: A GUIDE FOR JEWISH COUPLES. New Milford, CT: Toby Press, 2005. 537 p. ISBN 1-59264-106-7. (Publisher's address: PO Box 8531, zip 06676-8531; Web: http://www.tobypress.com. Gift of the author.) [RC889 .G73 2005] (14.1; 1.2; Reference)

Hanson, Clare. A CULTURAL HISTORY OF PREGNANCY: PREGNANCY, MEDICINE AND CULTURE, 1750-2000. New York: Palgrave Macmillan, 2004. 214 p. ISBN 0-333-98644-X. [RG556 .H36 2004] (14.1; 7.1; 10; 15.5)

Kluger-Bell, Kim. UNSPEAKABLE LOSSES: HEALING FROM MISCARRIAGE, ABORTION, AND OTHER PREGNANCY LOSS. New York: Quill/ HarperCollins, 2000. 170 p. ISBN 0-688-17390-X. (Originally published: W.W. Norton, New York, 1998. ISBN 0-393-04572-2.) [RG648 .K56 2000] (14.1; 9.5.5; 12.1; 12.5.1; 12.5.3; 15.2; 17.1)

McHaffie, Hazel E. PATERNITY: A STORY OF ASSISTED CON-CEPTION. Oxford/Seattle, WA: Radcliffe Publishing, 2005. 236 p. ISBN 1-85775-652-5. (Living Literature Series. "When Judy agrees to marry Declan his happiness is com-plete. But from the first night of their marriage cracks ap-pear in their relationship until eventually Judy reveals the demons which haunt her. When a child dies, the questions that follow unravel a past which rocks their security to its foundations." Gift of the publisher.) [PR6063 .C517 P38 2005] (14.1; 15.1; Fiction)

Mullin, Amy. RECONCEIVING PREGNANCY AND CHILDCARE: ETHICS, EXPERIENCE, AND REPRODUCTIVE LA-BOR. New York: Cambridge University Press, 2005. 214 p. ISBN 0-521-60586-5. (Cambridge Studies in Philosophy and Public Policy series. Gift of the publisher.) [RG560 .M827 2005] (14.1; 4.4; 7.1; 9.5.5; 9.5.7; 9.5.8; 10)

Potter, Daniel A. and Hanin, Jennifer S. WHAT TO DO WHEN YOU CAN'T GET PREGNANT: THE COMPLETE GUIDE TO ALL THE TECHNOLOGIES FOR COUPLES FACING FERTILITY PROB-LEMS. New York: Marlowe & Company/Avalon, 2005. 310 p. ISBN 1-56924-371-9. (Foreword by Pamela Madsen. Gift of the publisher.) [RG133.5 .P68 2005] (14.1; 14.2; 14.3; 14.4; 15.2; Reference; POP)

Rosen, Allison and Rosen, Jay, eds. FROZEN DREAMS: PSYCHODYNAMIC DIMENSIONS OF INFERTILITY AND AS-SISTED REPRODUCTION. Hillsdale, NJ: Analytic Press, 2005. 292 p. ISBN 0-88163-440-9. (Gift of the publisher.) [R889 .F76 2005] (14.1; 12.1; 14.4; 14.6; 17.1)

Shannon, Thomas A., ed. REPRODUCTIVE TECHNOLOGIES: A READER. Lanham, MD: Rowman & Littlefield, 2004. 147 p. ISBN 0-7425-3151-1. (Readings in Bioethics Se-ries. "A Sheed & Ward Book.") [RG133.5 .R468 2004] (14.1; 1.2; 2.2; 9.5.2; 9.5.6; 9.8; 14.2; 14.3; 14.5; 21.1; LE)

Thompson, Charis. MAKING PARENTS: THE ONTOLOGICAL CHOREOGRAPHY OF REPRODUCTIVE TECHNOLOGIES. Cam-bridge, MA: MIT Press, 2005. 360 p. ISBN

0-262-20156-9. (Inside Technology series. Gift of the publisher.) [RG133.5 .T495 2005] (14.1; 2.2; 5.3; 7.1; 10)

Tubert, Silvia. WOMEN WITHOUT A SHADOW: MATERNAL DESIRE AND ASSISTED REPRODUCTIVE TECHNOLOGIES. [London]: Free Association Press, 2004. 247 p. ISBN 1-853437-08-5. (Translation from the Spanish by Mariano Peyrou of: *Mujeres sin sombra*.) [RG133.5 .T8313 2004] (14.1; 7.1; 9.5.5; 17.1)

Woliver, Laura R. THE POLITICAL GEOGRAPHIES OF PREGNANCY. Urbana: University of Illinois Press, 2002. 238 p. ISBN 0-252-02778-7. [RG556 .W655 2002] (14.1; 1.3.5; 9.5.5; 10; 12.5.1; 14.2; 15.10; 21.1)

14.2 ARTIFICIAL INSEMINATION AND SURROGACY

Agigian, Amy. BABY STEPS: HOW LESBIAN ALTERNATIVE INSEMINATION IS CHANGING THE WORLD. Middletown, CT: Wesleyan University Press, 2004. 250 p. ISBN 0-8195-6629-2. [HQ75.53 .A45 2004] (14.2; 1.3.8; 7.1; 10)

Konrad, Monica. NAMELESS RELATIONS: ANONYMITY, MELANESIA AND REPRODUCTIVE GIFT EXCHANGE BETWEEN BRITISH OVA DONORS AND RECIPIENTS. New York: Berghahn Books, 2005. 286 p. ISBN 1-57181-647-X. (Fertility, Reproduction, and Sexuality series; Vol. 7. Gift of the publisher.) [HQ761 .K65 2005] (14.2; 7.1; 14.4; 18.5.4; 19.5)

Page, Jean Reynolds. A BLESSED EVENT. New York: Random House, 2004. 352 p. ISBN 0-345-46216-5. ("A Ballantine Book." "Joanne Timbro and Darla Stevens grew up next door to each other in a small Texas town. Their childhood days nurtured a rare friendship that carried them into adult years. As young women, Darla and Jo enter into an agreement that will change their lives: Joanne agrees to give birth to the child that Darla cannot have on her own. Then early on a warm July morning, Joanne, four months pregnant, suffers a devastating car accident. For the first time in memory, Darla must face the possibility of life without Jo. As Darla struggles to understand why her distressed friend was out driving in those dark morning hours, she must also fight to keep the baby that was intended to be her child. In the process, she discovers the truths that hide in her own life—in her marriage, in her closest friendships, and in a past that has suddenly reemerged, full of unfolding secrets.") [PS3616 .A33755 B54 2005] (14.2; 14.1; Fiction)

14.4 IN VITRO FERTILIZATION AND EMBRYO TRANSFER

Glazer, Ellen Sarasohn and Sterling, Evelina Weidman. HAVING YOUR BABY THROUGH EGG DONATION. Indianapolis, IN: Perspectives Press, 2005. 384 p. ISBN 0-944934-32-3. (Publisher's address: PO Box 90318, zip 46290-0318; tel.: 317-872-3055; Web: http://www.perspectivespress.com. Gift of the publisher.) [RG133.5 .G56 2005] (14.4; 1.2; 17.1; POP)

Ludwig, Michael. PREGNANCY AND BIRTH AFTER ASSISTED REPRODUCTIVE TECHNOLOGIES. Berlin/New York: Springer-Verlag, 2002. 151 p. ISBN 3-540-43531-X. [RG526 .L835 2002] (14.4; 7.1; 9.5.5; 9.5.7; 10; 12.1; 14.6; 15.2)

Symposium on Assisted Reproduction Technology (ART). FAMILY LAW QUARTERLY 2005 Fall; 39(3): 573-779. (ISSN 0014-729X. Gift of Cecelia Friedman Levin.) (14.4; 4.4; 9.8; 10; 14.2; 14.6; 15.1; 18.5.4; 18.6; 19.5)

14.5 CLONING

Agar, Nicholas. PERFECT COPY: UNRAVELLING THE CLONING DEBATE. Cambridge: Icon Books, 2002. 184 p. ISBN 1-84046-380-5. (Published in Australia by: Allen & Unwin, Crows Nest, NSW; sold in the UK, Europe, South Africa and Asia by: Faber and Faber, London; distributed in the UK, Europe, South Africa and Asia by: Macmillan Distribution Ltd.; and distributed in Canada by: Penguin Books Canada, Toronto.) [QH442.2 .A435 2002] (14.5; 1.1; 12.3; 19.1)

Churchill, Caryl. A NUMBER. New York: Theatre Communications Group, 2003, 2002. 62 p. ISBN 1-55936-225-1. (Originally published: Nick Hern, London, 2002. "*A Number* was first performed by Michael Gambon and Daniel Craig at the Royal Court Theatre, London, on 23 September 2002.") [PR6053 .H786 N85 2003] (14.5; 15.6; Fiction)

Guilfoile, Kevin. CAST OF SHADOWS. New York: Alfred A. Knopf, 2005. 319 p. ISBN 1-4000-4308-5. [PS3607 .U48 C37 2005] (14.5; 1.3.5; 4.4; Fiction)

Harris, Nancy, ed. CLONING. Detroit: Greenhaven Press/Thomson Gale, 2005. 192 p. ISBN 0-7377-1966-4. (Exploring Science and Medical Discoveries series.) [QH442.2 .C5643 2005] (14.5; 1.3.11; 2.2; 5.3; 14.1; 15.1; 18.5.4; 22.2)

Hunyadi, Mark. JE EST UN CLONE: L'ÉTHIQUE À L'ÉPREUVE DES BIOTECHNOLOGIES. Paris: Seuil, 2004. 197 p. ISBN 2-02-066140-3. (Couleur des idées series.) (14.5; 1.1; 5.2; 15.1; 15.5)

Lester, Lane p. and Hefley, James C. HUMAN CLONING: PLAYING GOD OR SCIENTIFIC PROGRESS? Grand Rapids, MI: Fleming H. Revell/Baker Book House, 1998. 175 p. ISBN 0-8007-5668-1. ("Some chapters are taken largely from: *Cloning*, published in 1980 by Tyndale House.") [QH442.2 .L474 1998] (14.5; 1.2; 12.1; 14.2; 14.4; 15.1; 15.2; 15.3; 15.5)

Macintosh, Kerry Lynn. ILLEGAL BEINGS: HUMAN CLONES AND THE LAW. Cambridge/New York: Cambridge University Press, 2005. 272 p. ISBN 0-521-85328-1. (Gift of the publisher.) [KF3831 .M33 2005] (14.5; 1.3.5; 2.4; 5.3; 15.5; 18.5.4; 18.6; 22.2)

National Cable Satellite Corporation. HUMAN CLONING PUBLIC POLICY ISSUES, PART 3. West Lafayette, IN: C-SPAN Archives, 2001. 1 color videocassette (VHS). (72 mins.). (Testimony given 7 August 2001 at the Cloning

Research Forum, Part 3 of 5 tapes. Testimony from John Robertson [Professor, University of Texas at Austin Law School] and Alta Charo [Professor, University of Wisconsin Law School]. "Professors talked about the ethics of human cloning for both therapeutic and reproductive reasons. Among the topics they addressed were methods of cloning, potential dangers involved, and potential benefits of cloning. Following their remarks they answered questions from a panel of experts" [NAS Public Panel on Human Reproductive Cloning]. C-SPAN ID No. 165550-3. Available from: C-SPAN Archives, PO Box 2909, West Lafayette, IN 47996-2909; Web: http://www.c-span.org.) (14.5; 1.3.5; 9.3.1; 14.1; 18.2; 18.5.4)

Østnor, Lars, ed. BIOETHICS AND CLONING: REPORT FROM A WORKSHOP ARRANGED BY THE NORDIC THEOLOGICAL NETWORK FOR BIOETHICS IN ÅRHUS, SEPTEMBER 25-27, 1998. Oslo: Nordic Theological Network for Bioethics, 1998. 89 p. ISBN 82-993709-3-0. (Available from: Centre for Bioethik, Århus Universitet, Ndr. Ringgarde, Bygn. 410, DK-8000 Århus C, Denmark. Gift of the Centre for Bioethics, Århus Universitet, Denmark.) [QH442.2 .B55 1998] (14.5; 1.2; 4.4; 22.2)

Pynes, Christopher Alexander. HUMAN CLONING AND MORAL STATUS. Ann Arbor, MI: ProQuest Information & Learning/UMI, 2003. 275 p. (Publication Order No. AAT-3109306. Dissertation, (Ph.D.)—Florida State University, 2003.) (14.5; 1.1; 1.2; 4.4; 15.1)

Seabra Ferreira, Maria Aline Salgueiro. I AM THE OTHER: LITERARY NEGOTIATIONS OF HUMAN CLONING. Westport, CT: Praeger, 2005. 304 p. ISBN 0-313-32006-3. (Contributions to the Study of Science Fiction and Fantasy series; No. 85. ISSN 0193-6875. Gift of the publisher.) [PS374 .H83 F47 2005] (14.5; 7.1)

15.1 GENETICS, MOLECULAR BIOLOGY AND MICROBIOLOGY (GENERAL)

Acharya, Tara and Sankaran, Neeraja. THE HUMAN GENOME SOURCEBOOK. Westport, CT: Greenwood Press, 2005. 393 p. ISBN 1-57356-529-6. [QH437 .A245 2005] (15.1; 15.10; POP)

Baillie, Harold W. and Casey, Timothy K., eds. IS HUMAN NATURE OBSOLETE? GENETICS, BIOENGINEERING, AND THE FUTURE OF THE HUMAN CONDITION. Cambridge, MA: MIT Press, 2005. 422 p. ISBN 0-262-52428-7. (Basic Bioethics series. Gift of the publisher.) [QH438.7 .I8 2005] (15.1; 1.1; 1.2; 4.4; 5.1; 15.4; 15.11)

Bibeau, Gilles. LE QUÉBEC TRANSGÉNIQUE: SCIENCE, MARCHÉ, HUMANITÉ. Montréal: Boréal, 2004. 453 p. ISBN 2-7646-0235-9. [QH431 .B533 2004] (15.1; 1.3.11; 15.6; 15.10; 15.11; 18.1)

Braman, Sandra, ed. BIOTECHNOLOGY AND COMMUNICATION: THE META-TECHNOLOGIES OF INFORMATION. Mahwah, NJ: Lawrence Erlbaum Associates, 2004. 297 p. ISBN 0-8058-4304-3. (LEA's Communication Series.) [TP248.23 .B56 2004] (15.1; 1.3.7; 1.3.9; 1.3.11; 1.3.12; 5.1; 5.3; 14.5)

Brannigan, Michael C., ed. CROSS-CULTURAL BIOTECHNOLOGY. Lanham, MD: Rowman & Littlefield, 2004. 202 p. ISBN 0-7425-3266-6. [TP248.23 .C76 2004] (15.1; 1.2; 1.3.7; 1.3.11; 9.7; 15.3; 15.7; 15.8; 15.10; 18.5.4; 19.5; 21.3; 21.7)

Bryant, John and Searle, John. LIFE IN OUR HANDS: A CHRISTIAN PERSPECTIVE ON GENETICS AND CLONING. Leicester (England): Inter-Varsity Press, 2004. 191 p. ISBN 0-85111-795-3. [QH332 .B79 2004] (15.1; 1.2; 1.3.11; 4.4; 14.5; 15.4)

Bulmer, Michael. FRANCIS GALTON: PIONEER OF HEREDITY AND BIOMETRY. Baltimore, MD: Johns Hopkins University Press, 2003. 357 p. ISBN 0-8018-7403-3. [QH429.2 .G35 B856 2003] (15.1; 3.2; 15.5; 15.6; 15.11; Biography)

Burdon, Roy. THE SUFFERING GENE: ENVIRONMENTAL THREATS TO OUR HEALTH. Montreal: McGill-Queen's University Press; Cape Town: David Philip; [and] London/New York: Zed Books, 2003. 252 p. ISBN 0-7735-2656-0 [McGill-Queen's]; ISBN 0-86486-627-5 [David Philip]; ISBN 1-84277-285-6 [Zed Books]. [RA1224.3 .B87 2003] (15.1; 9.5.1; 15.7; 16.2; 16.3)

The Challenge of the New Genetics. REFORM 2001 Spring; 79: 5-37. (ISSN 0313-153X.) (15.1; 1.3.5; 1.3.12; 8.4; 9.3.1; 9.5.3; 12.1; 14.1; 14.5; 15.2; 15.3; 15.10)

Chedd-Angier Production Company. THE GENE HUNTERS. [Alexandria, VA]: PBS Home Video, 2001. 1 color videocassette (VHS). (60 mins.). (Scientific American Frontiers series; No. XII. Hosted by Alan Alda. "Alda meets some of the brightest gene-hunting scientists today, including Nobelist Jim Watson, the Human Genome Project's Eric Lander and developmental geneticist Nancy Hopkins. He also examines a controversial gene therapy project that's attempting to grow new blood vessels in diseased hearts." Product ID No. SAMF9202. Available from: PBS Home Video; tel.: 800-752-9727; Web: http://www.pbs.org.) (15.1; 15.4)

Coen, Enrico. THE ART OF GENES: HOW ORGANISMS MAKE THEMSELVES. Oxford/New York: Oxford University Press, 1999. 386 p. ISBN 0-19-850343-1. [QH491 .C638 1999] (15.1; 3.2)

DeSalle, Rob and Yudell, Michael. WELCOME TO THE GENOME: A USER'S GUIDE TO THE GENETIC PAST, PRESENT, AND FUTURE. New York: Wiley-Liss, 2005. 215 p. ISBN 0-471-45331-5. (Published in association with the American Museum of Natural History.) [QH437 .D47 2005] (15.1; 1.3.11; 15.7; POP)

Dover, Gabriel. DEAR MR. DARWIN: LETTERS ON THE EVOLUTION OF LIFE AND HUMAN NATURE. Berkeley: University of California Press; Published in association with: London: Weidenfeld and Nicolson, 2000. 268 p. ISBN 0-520-22790-5 [University of California]; ISBN 0-297-84259-5 [Weidenfeld and Nicolson]. [QH366.2 .D67 2000] (15.1; 3.2)

Fedoroff, Nina V. and Brown, Nancy Marie. MENDEL IN THE KITCHEN: A SCIENTIST'S VIEW OF GENETICALLY MODI-

FIED FOODS. Washington, DC: Joseph Henry Press, 2004. 370 p. ISBN 0-309-09205-1. [TP248.65 .F66 F436 2004] (15.1; 1.3.11; 5.3)

Fumento, Michael. BIOEVOLUTION: HOW BIOTECHNOLOGY IS CHANGING OUR WORLD. San Francisco: Encounter Books, 2003. 510 p. ISBN 1-59403-057-X. [TP248.215 .F86 2003] (15.1; 1.3.11; 16.1; 19.1; 22.2; POP)

Glasa, J., ed.; Institute of Medical Ethics and Bioethics Foundation. ETHICS OF HUMAN GENETICS: CHALLENGES OF THE (POST) GENOMIC ERA. Bratislava: Charis [and] IMEB Foundation, 2002. 228 p. ISBN 80-88743-51-6. (Proceedings of the DEBRA Programme International Bioethics Conference *Ethics of Human Genetics: Challenges of the (Post) Genomic Era*, held 23-24 October 2002 in Bratislava, Slovak Republic, co-sponsored by the Council of Europe and other partner organizations. Gift of the editor.) [RB155 .I58 2002] (15.1; 1.3.7; 1.3.12; 2.3; 5.3; 7.2; 8.4; 9.5.9; 9.7; 14.5; 15.2; 15.3; 15.10; 18.5.4; 21.1)

Harman, Oren Solomon. THE MAN WHO INVENTED THE CHROMOSOME: THE LIFE OF CYRIL DARLINGTON. Cambridge, MA: Harvard University Press, 2004. 329 p. ISBN 0-674-01333-6. [QH429.2 .D37 H37 2004] (15.1; Biography)

Heberle-Bors, Erwin. GÉNIE GÉNÉTIQUE: UNE HISTOIRE, UN DÉFI. Paris: Institut National de la Recherche Agronomique, 2001. 291 p. ISBN 2-7380-0970-0 [INRA]. (Mieux comprendre series. Translation from the German by Marie-Lise Spire and Roswitha Judor of: *Herausforderung Gentechnik*; Verlag Holzhausens, Vienna, 1996; ISBN 3-900518-14-9.) (15.1; 15.5)

Houdebine, Louis-Marie. OGM: LE VRAI ET LE FAUX. Paris: Le Pommier, 2003. 236 p. ISBN 2-7465012-2-8. (Second edition. Manifestes series.) (15.1; 1.3.11; 15.7; 22.3)

Hrazdina, Geza, ed.; NATO Advanced Research Workshop on Use of Agriculturally Important Genes in Biotechnology. USE OF AGRICULTURALLY IMPORTANT GENES IN BIOTECHNOLOGY. Amsterdam/Washington, DC: IOS Press, 2000. 252 p. ISBN 1-58603-019-1. (NATO Science Series, Series A: Life Sciences; Vol. 319. ISSN 1387-6686. Published in cooperation with NATO Scientific Affairs Division.) [SB123 .U83 2000] (15.1; 1.3.11; 5.2; LE)

Hughes, James. CITIZEN CYBORG: WHY DEMOCRATIC SOCIETIES MUST RESPOND TO THE REDESIGNED HUMAN OF THE FUTURE. New York: Westview Press, 2004. 294 p. ISBN 0-8133-4198-1. [RA418.5 .M4 H84 2004] (15.1; 1.3.5; 4.4; 4.5; 5.3; 9.7; 14.5; 15.8)

Jacquard, Albert; Kahn, Axel; and Papillon, Fabrice. L'AVENIR N'EST PAS ÉCRIT. Paris: Bayard, 2001. 253 p. ISBN 2-227-13941-2. (Contains interviews by Fabrice Papillon with Albert Jacquard and Axel Kahn.) [QH431 .J276 2001] (15.1; 3.1; 15.5; 15.6)

Jobling, Mark A.; Hurles, Matthew; and Tyler-Smith, Chris. HUMAN EVOLUTIONARY GENETICS: ORIGINS, PEOPLE & DISEASE. New York: Garland Science, 2004. 523 p.

ISBN 0-8153-4185-7. [QH431 .J53 2004] (15.1; 1.3.11; 3.2; 13.1; 15.10; 15.11)

Kleinman, Daniel Lee; Kinchy, Abby J.; and Handelsman, Jo, eds. CONTROVERSIES IN SCIENCE AND TECHNOLOGY: FROM MAIZE TO MENOPAUSE. Madison: University of Wisconsin Press, 2005. 341 p. ISBN 0-299-20394-8. (Science and Technology in Society series. Gift of the publisher.) [QH442 .C65 2005] (15.1; 1.3.11; 5.3; 9.1; 9.5.5; 9.7; 16.1; 21.3; 22.3; POP)

Kloppenburg, Jack Ralph. FIRST THE SEED: THE POLITICAL ECONOMY OF PLANT BIOTECHNOLOGY. Madison: University of Wisconsin Press, 2004. 425 p. ISBN 0-299-19244-X. (Second edition. Science and Technology in Society series. Gift of the publisher.) [SB117.3 .K57 2004] (15.1; 1.3.2; 1.3.11; 5.3; 15.10)

Kobilinsky, Lawrence; Liotti, Thomas F.; and Oeser-Sweat, Jamel. DNA: FORENSIC AND LEGAL APPLICATIONS. Hoboken, NJ: Wiley-Interscience, 2005. 364 p. ISBN 0-471-41478-6. [KF9666.5 .K63 2005] (15.1; 1.3.5; 1.3.12)

Krimsky, Sheldon and Shorett, Peter, eds. RIGHTS AND LIBERTIES IN THE BIOTECH AGE: WHY WE NEED A GENETIC BILL OF RIGHTS. Lanham, MD: Rowman & Littlefield, 2005. 235 p. ISBN 0-7425-4341-2. ("A project of the Council for Responsible Genetics.") [TP248.23 .R55 2005] (15.1; 1.1; 1.3.5; 1.3.11; 4.5; 5.3; 8.4; 15.4; 15.5; 15.7; 15.8; 16.1; 16.3; 21.1)

Lindee, Susan. MOMENTS OF TRUTH IN GENETIC MEDICINE. Baltimore, MD: Johns Hopkins University Press, 2005. 270 p. ISBN 0-8018-8175-7. [RB155 .L555 2005] (15.1; 4.4; 7.1; 15.6; 15.11)

McLean, Sheila A.M., ed. GENETICS AND GENE THERAPY. Aldershot, Hants, England: Dartmouth/Burlington, VT: Ashgate, 2005. 535 p. ISBN 0-7546-2055-7. (International Library of Medicine, Ethics and Law series. Gift of the publisher.) [RB155 .G38745 2005] (15.1; 1.1; 14.5; 15.2; 15.3; 18.5.4)

Miller, Roman J.; Brubaker, Beryl H.; and Peterson, James C., eds. VIEWING NEW CREATIONS WITH ANABAPTIST EYES: ETHICS OF BIOTECHNOLOGY. Telford, PA: Cascadia Publishing House, 2005. 308 p. ISBN 1-931038-32-5. (Foreword by James F. Childress. "Based on the conference, *Ethics of Biotechnology: Viewing New Creations with Anabaptist Eyes,* held in November 2003 at Eastern Mennonite University." Co-published with Herald Press, Scottdale, PA. Gift of the publisher.) [QH442 .V54 2005] (15.1; 1.2; 1.3.11; 2.1; 4.1.3; 4.5; 14.5; 15.5; 21.7)

Moore, Pete. BEING ME: WHAT IT MEANS TO BE HUMAN. New York: John Wiley & Sons, 2003. 277 p. ISBN 0-470-85089-2. (Real Life Stories series.) [QH438.7 .M665 2004] (15.1; 4.4; 10; 15.6)

Naam, Ramez. MORE THAN HUMAN: EMBRACING THE PROMISE OF BIOLOGICAL ENHANCEMENT. New York: Broadway Books, 2005. 276 p. ISBN 0-7679-1843-6. [RB155 .N27 2005] (15.1; 4.5; 14.5; 15.4; POP)

Omoto, Charlotte K. and Lurguin, Paul F. GENES AND DNA: A BEGINNER'S GUIDE TO GENETICS AND ITS APPLICATIONS. New York: Columbia University Press, 2004. 217 p. ISBN 0-231-13013-9. [QH430 .O47 2004] (15.1; POP)

Peterson-Iyer, Karen. DESIGNER CHILDREN: RECONCILING GENETIC TECHNOLOGY, FEMINISM, AND CHRISTIAN FAITH. Cleveland, OH: Pilgrim Press, 2004. 232 p. ISBN 0-8298-1611-9. [RG133.5 .P488 2004] (15.1; 1.2; 9.5.1; 9.5.7; 10; 14.1; 14.3; 15.5; 17.1)

Rabinow, Paul and Dan-Cohen, Talia. A MACHINE TO MAKE A FUTURE: BIOTECH CHRONICLES. Princeton, NJ: Princeton University Press, 2005. 199 p. ISBN 0-691-12050-1. [QH445.2 .R336 2005] (15.1; 1.3.2; 5.3; 15.10)

Robbins-Roth, Cynthia. FROM ALCHEMY TO IPO: THE BUSINESS OF BIOTECHNOLOGY. New York: Basic Books/Perseus, 2000. 253 p. ISBN 0-7382-0482-X. [HD9999 .B442 R63 2000] (15.1; 1.3.11; 9.7; 15.4; 15.10; 18.2)

Roll-Hansen, Nils. THE LYSENKO EFFECT: THE POLITICS OF SCIENCE. Amherst, NY: Humanity Books, 2005. 335 p. ISBN 1-59102-262-2. (Control of Nature series.) [QH31 .L95 R65 2005] (15.1; 1.3.5; 1.3.11; 3.1; 5.3)

Rouger, Philippe. LES EMPREINTES GÉNÉTIQUES. Paris: Presses universitaires de France, 2000. 127 p. ISBN 2-13-050821-9. (Que sais-je? series.) (15.1; 1.3.5; 2.1)

Sleeboom, Margaret, ed. GENOMICS IN ASIA: A CLASH OF BIOETHICAL INTERESTS? London/New York: Kegal Paul; Distributed in the U.S. by: New York: Columbia University Press, 2004. 321 p. ISBN 0-7103-0943-0. (Studies in Anthropology, Economy and Society series.) [QH447 .G466 2004] (15.1; 1.2; 2.1; 5.3; 15.5; 16.1; 20.3.1; 20.5.2; 21.7)

Smith, Wesley J. CONSUMER'S GUIDE TO A BRAVE NEW WORLD. San Francisco: Encounter Books, 2004. 219 p. ISBN 1-893554-99-6. [TP248.23 .S657 2004] (15.1; 5.3; 14.1; 18.5.4)

Sterckx, Sigrid, ed. BIOTECHNOLOGY, PATENTS AND MORALITY. Aldershot, Hants/Burlington, VT: Ashgate, 2000. 382 p. ISBN 0-7546-1144-2. (Second edition.) [TP248.2 .B567 2000] (15.1; 1.1; 1.3.11; 5.3; 9.5.7; 15.7; 15.8; 16.1; 21.1)

Thacker, Eugene. THE GLOBAL GENOME: BIOTECHNOLOGY, POLITICS, AND CULTURE. Cambridge, MA: MIT Press, 2005. 416 p. ISBN 0-262-20155-0. (Leonardo series.) [HD9999 .B442 T453 2005] (15.1; 1.3.12; 15.10; 15.11; 21.1; 21.2; 21.3)

Tutton, Richard and Corrigan, Oonagh, eds. GENETIC DATABASES: SOCIO-ETHICAL ISSUES IN THE COLLECTION AND USE OF DNA. London/New York: Routledge, 2004. 211 p. ISBN 0-415-31680-4. [QH441.2 .G45 2004] (15.1; 1.3.12; 5.3; 7.1; 8.3.1; 8.3.2; 9.7; 15.11; 18.3; 18.5.2; 19.4; 19.5)

Van Cleve, John Vickrey, ed. GENETICS, DISABILITY, AND DEAFNESS. Washington, DC: Gallaudet University Press, 2004. 228 p. ISBN 1-56368-307-5. (Gift of the publisher.) [RF292 .G465 2004] (15.1; 7.1; 8.3.1; 9.5.1; 12.1; 15.2; 15.3; 15.5)

Vardy, Peter. BEING HUMAN: FULFILLING GENETIC AND SPIRITUAL POTENTIAL. London: Darton, Longman & Todd, 2003. 196 p. ISBN 0-232-52455-6. [BJ1533 .H9 V37 2003] (15.1; 1.2; 1.3.1; 4.4; 4.5)

Wilkins, Maurice. THE THIRD MAN OF THE DOUBLE HELIX: THE AUTOBIOGRAPHY OF MAURICE WILKINS. Oxford: Oxford University Press, 2003. 274 p. ISBN 0-19-860665-6. [QH505 .W494 2003] (15.1; 16.2; 21.2; Biography)

Woolfson, Adrian. AN INTELLIGENT PERSON'S GUIDE TO GENETICS. London/New York: Duckworth Overlook, 2004. 240 p. ISBN 0-7156-3313-9 [UK]; ISBN 1-58567-663-2 [US]. [QH437 .W66 2004] (15.1; POP)

15.2 GENETIC COUNSELING/PRENATAL DIAGNOSIS

Rothschild, Joan. THE DREAM OF THE PERFECT CHILD. Bloomington: Indiana University Press, 2005. 343 p. ISBN 0-253-21760-1. (Bioethics and the Humanities series.) [RG626 .R68 2005] (15.2; 2.2; 7.1; 10; 14.1; 15.5)

Sass, Hans-Martin and Schröder, Peter, eds. PATIENTENAUFKLÄRUNG BEI GENETISCHEM RISIKO. Münster: Lit Verlag, 2003. 204 p. ISBN 3-8258-4987-2. (Ethik in der Praxis/Practical Ethics - Kontroversen/Controversies series; Bd. 3. Gift of Hans-Martin Sass.) (15.2; 5.2; 8.1; 15.3; 19.3)

Wasserman, David; Wachbroit, Robert; and Bickenbach, Jerome, eds. QUALITY OF LIFE AND HUMAN DIFFERENCE: GENETIC TESTING, HEALTH CARE, AND DISABILITY. Cambridge/New York: Cambridge University Press, 2005. 273 p. ISBN 0-521-83201-2. (Cambridge Studies in Philosophy and Public Policy series. Gift of the publisher.) [RG628 .Q35 2005] (15.2; 2.1; 4.4; 7.1; 9.4; 9.5.1; 15.3)

Ziegler, Uta. PRÄIMPLANTATIONSDIAGNOSTIK IN ENGLAND UND DEUTSCHLAND: ETHISCHE, RECHTLICHE UND PRAKTISCHE PROBLEME. Frankfurt/New York: Campus, 2004. 193 p. ISBN 3-593-37326-2. (Kultur der Medizin series; Bd. 8.) [RG628.3 .P74 Z545 2004] (15.2; 1.1; 2.4; 4.4; 5.2; 14.4; 21.7)

15.3 GENETIC SCREENING/TESTING

Alexakos, Frances M. ATTITUDES OF RHODE ISLAND PRIMARY CARE PHYSICIANS TOWARD THE USE OF GENETIC TESTING FOR BREAST CANCER. Ann Arbor, MI: ProQuest Information & Learning/UMI, 2003. 202 p. (Publication Order No. AAT-3085124. Dissertation, (Ph.D.)—Salve Regina University.) (15.3; 7.1; 8.2; 8.4; 9.2; 15.2)

Douay, Sophie. TRAVAIL ET GÉNÉTIQUE: DE LA SÉLECTION PRÉVENTIVE À LA PRÉVENTION SÉLECTIVE. Paris: Harmattan, 2003. 738 p. ISBN 2-7475-4059-6. (Collection

Logiques Juridiques series. Preface by Pierre-Yves Verkindt.) (15.3; 1.3.2; 8.4; 9.1; 16.3)

Parthasarathy, Shobita. A GLOBAL GENOME? COMPARING THE DEVELOPMENT OF GENETIC TESTING FOR BREAST CANCER IN THE UNITED STATES AND BRITAIN. Ann Arbor, MI: ProQuest Information & Learning/UMI, 2003. 217 p. (Publication Order No. AAT-3081360. Dissertation, (Ph.D.)—Cornell University, 2003.) (15.3; 5.1; 9.5.1; 21.1)

15.5 EUGENICS

Agar, Nicholas. LIBERAL EUGENICS: IN DEFENCE OF HUMAN ENHANCEMENT. Malden, MA: Blackwell, 2004. 205 p. ISBN 1-4051-2390-7. (Gift of the publisher.) [HQ755 .A29 2005] (15.5; 4.5; 14.5; 15.4)

Arnds, Peter. REPRESENTATION, SUBVERSION, AND EUGENICS IN GÜNTER GRASS'S *THE TIN DRUM*. Rochester, NY: Camden House, 2004. 178 p. ISBN 1-57113-287-2. (Studies in German Literature, Linguistics, and Culture series.) (15.5; 1.3.5; 7.1; 20.5.1; Fiction)

Bachelard-Jobard, Catherine. L'EUGÉNISME, LA SCIENCE ET LE DROIT. Paris: Presses Universitaires de France, 2001. 341 p. ISBN 2-13-052250-5. (Partage du savoir series.) [K3611 .G46 B33 2001] (15.5; 1.3.5; 4.4; 11.3; 15.1)

Bachrach, Susan [project director] and Kuntz, Dieter [editor]. DEADLY MEDICINE: CREATING THE MASTER RACE. Washington, DC: Holocaust Memorial Museum; Distributed by: Chapel Hill: University of North Carolina Press, 2004. 226 p. ISBN 0-8078-2916-1. (Exhibition catalog.) [HQ755.5 .G3 D43 2004] (15.5; 1.3.5; 2.2; 11.3; 14.1; 21.1; 21.4)

Chesterton, G.K. EUGENICS AND OTHER EVILS: AN ARGUMENT AGAINST THE SCIENTIFICALLY ORGANIZED STATE. Seattle, WA: Inkling Books, 2000. 179 p. ISBN 1-58742-006-6. (Enhanced edition. Edited by Michael W. Perry. On title page: "With additional articles by his eugenic and birth control opponents including Francis Galton, C.W. Saleeby and Marie Stopes, as well as articles from *Eugenics Review* and *Birth Control News*." Originally published as: *Eugenics and Other Evils*; Cassell and Company, London, 1922. Subtitle on cover: "An Argument Against the Scientifically Organized Society.") [HQ755 .C48 2000] (15.5; 1.3.5; 11.1; 11.3)

Engs, Ruth Clifford. THE EUGENICS MOVEMENT: AN ENCYCLOPEDIA. Westport, CT: Greenwood Press, 2005. 279 p. ISBN 0-313-32791-2. [HQ751 .E64 2005] (15.5; 2.2; Reference)

Gilman, Charlotte Perkins. THE CRUX. Durham, [NC]: Duke University Press, 2003, 1911. ISBN 0-8223-3167-5. ("Long out of print, Charlotte Perkins Gilman's novel *The Crux* is an important early feminist work that brings to the fore complicated issues of gender, citizenship, eugenics, and frontier nationalism. First published serially in the feminist journal *The Forerunner* in 1910, *The Crux* tells the story of a group of New England women who move west to start a boardinghouse for men in Colorado. The in-

nocent central character, Vivian Lane, falls in love with Morton Elder, who has both gonorrhea and syphilis. The concern of the novel is not so much that Vivian will catch syphilis, but that, if she were to marry and have children with Morton, she would harm the "national stock". The novel was written, in Gilman's words, as a "story...for young women to read...in order that they may protect themselves and their children to come." What was to be protected was the civic imperative to produce "pureblooded" citizens for a utopian ideal.") [PS1744 .G57 C78 2003] (15.5; 10; Fiction)

Habermas, Jürgen. DIE ZUKUNFT DER MENSCHLICHEN NATUR: AUF DEM WEG ZU EINER LIBERALEN EUGENIK? Frankfurt am Main: Suhrkamp, 2005, 2002. 163 p. ISBN 3-518-58315-8. (Also available in French, translation by Christian Bouchindhomme of: *L'avenir de la nature humaine: vers un eugénisme libéral*; Gallimard, Paris, 2002; ISBN 2-07-076531-8. "Text in this edition is from the fourth, enhanced edition, published by Suhrkamp Verlag, 2002; ISBN 0-226-31976-8.") [RA418.3 .G3 H375 2003] (15.5; 1.3.5; 4.2; 4.4; 7.1)

Jackson, John P. SCIENCE FOR SEGREGATION: RACE, LAW, AND THE CASE AGAINST BROWN V. BOARD OF EDUCATION. New York: New York University Press, 2005. 291 p. ISBN 0-8147-4271-8. (Critical America series.) [E185.61 .J145 2005] (15.5; 1.3.5; 2.2; 15.6)

Moyse, Danielle. BIEN NAÎTRE, BIEN ÊTRE, BIEN MOURIR: PROPOS SUR L'EUGÉNISME ET L'EUTHANASIE. Ramonville: Érès, 2001. 275 p. ISBN 2-86586-925-3. (Collection Réponses philosophiques series.) [R726 .M698 2001] (15.5; 2.1; 4.1.2; 15.2; 20.5.1)

Nicoletti, Michele and Galvagni, Lucia, eds. *La sfida dell'eugenetica: Scienza, filosofia, religione.* HUMANITAS 2004 July-August; 59(4): 649-888. ISBN 88-372-2005-7. (Gift of the editors.) (15.5; 1.1; 1.2; 1.3.5; 2.2; 4.4; 5.3; 11.3; 15.6; 21.1)

Peart, Sandra J. and Levy, David M. THE "VANITY OF THE PHILOSOPHER": FROM EQUALITY TO HIERARCHY IN POSTCLASSICAL ECONOMICS. Ann Arbor: University of Michigan Press, 2005. 323 p. ISBN 0-472-11496-4. [HB85 .P43 2005] (15.5; 1.3.2; 2.2; 7.1; 11.3)

Sandner, Peter; Bezirksverband Nassau. VERWALTUNG DES KRANKENMORDES: DER BEZIRKSVERBAND NASSAU IM NATIONALSOZIALISMUS. Giessen: Psychosozial-Verlag, 2003. 788 p. ISBN 3-89806-320-8. (Historische Schriftenreihe des Landeswohlfahrtsverbandes Hessen: Hochschulschriften series; Bd. 2. Originally issued as author's thesis (doctoral)— Universität Frankfurt am Main, 2002.) [R726 .S26 2003] (15.5; 1.3.5; 2.2; 7.4; 17.1; 21.4)

Schafft, Gretchen E. FROM RACISM TO GENOCIDE: ANTHROPOLOGY IN THE THIRD REICH. Urbana: University of Illinois Press, 2004. 297 p. ISBN 0-252-02930-5. [GN17.3 .G3 S33 2004] (15.5; 1.3.1; 1.3.5; 21.4)

Simon, Jürgen. KRIMINALBIOLOGIE UND ZWANGS-STERILISATION: EUGENISCHER RASSISMUS 1920-1945. Münster/New York: Waxmann, 2001. 355 p. ISBN

3-8309-1063-0. (Internationale Hochschulschriften series; Bd. 372. ISSN 0932-4763. Originally presented as the author's thesis (doctoral)—Universität Münster, 2000.) [HV6022 .G3 S56 2001] (15.5; 1.3.5; 7.1; 11.3; LE)

Stern, Alexandra Minna. EUGENIC NATION: FAULTS AND FRONTIERS OF BETTER BREEDING IN MODERN AMERICA. Berkeley: University of California Press, 2005. 347 p. ISBN 0-520-24444-3. (American Crossroads series; Vol. 17.) [HQ755.5 .U5 S84 2005] (15.5; 2.2)

Weikart, Richard. FROM DARWIN TO HITLER: EVOLUTIONARY ETHICS, EUGENICS, AND RACISM IN GERMANY. New York: Palgrave Macmillan, 2004. 312 p. ISBN 1-4039-6502-1. [HQ755.5 .G3 W435 2004] (15.5; 1.1; 1.3.5; 2.2; 3.2; 4.4; 11.3; 12.1; 14.1; 20.5.1; 20.5.2; 21.2; 21.4)

Wyndham, Diana. EUGENICS IN AUSTRALIA: STRIVING FOR NATIONAL FITNESS. London: Galton Institute, 2003. 406 p. ISBN 0-9504066-7-8. (Publisher's address: 19 Northfields Prospect, Northfields, London SW18 1PE.) [HQ755.5 .A8 W95 2003] (15.5; 2.2; 7.1; 21.1)

15.6 BEHAVIORAL GENETICS

Dowling, John E. THE GREAT BRAIN DEBATE: NATURE OR NURTURE? Washington, DC: Joseph Henry Press, 2004. 189 p. ISBN 0-309-09223-X. (Science Essentials series.) [QP376 .D697 2004] (15.6; 9.5.2; 17.1; POP)

McKinnon, Susan and Silverman, Sydel, eds. COMPLEXITIES: BEYOND NATURE & NURTURE. Chicago: University of Chicago Press, 2005. 330 p. ISBN 0-226-50024-1. (Gift of the publisher.) [GN27 .C648 2005] (15.6; 1.3.1; 9.5.2; 9.5.5; 10; 15.1; 17.1; 21.1)

Parens, Erik; Chapman, Audrey R.; and Press, Nancy, eds. WRESTLING WITH BEHAVIORAL GENETICS: SCIENCE, ETHICS, AND PUBLIC CONVERSATION. Baltimore, MD: Johns Hopkins University Press, 2006. 336 p. ISBN 0-8018-8224-9. (Gift of the publisher.) (15.6; 1.3.5; 1.3.7; 5.3; 7.1; POP)

Sweeney, Gerald. "FIGHTING FOR THE GOOD CAUSE": REFLECTIONS ON FRANCIS GALTON'S LEGACY TO AMERICAN HEREDITARIAN PSYCHOLOGY. Philadelphia: American Philosophical Society, 2001. 136 p. ISBN 0-87169-912-5. (Transactions of the American Philosophical Society series; Vol. 91, Pt. 2. ISSN 0065-9746.) [BF701 .S93 2001] (15.6; 15.5)

15.7 BIOHAZARDS OF GENETIC RESEARCH

Bunton, Robin and Petersen, Alan, eds. GENETIC GOVERNANCE: HEALTH, RISK AND ETHICS IN THE BIOTECH ERA. London/New York: Routledge, 2005. 215 p. ISBN 0-415-35406-4. (Gift of the publisher.) [QH438.7 .G228 2005] (15.7; 7.1; 9.1; 15.2; 15.3; 15.5)

National Research Council (United States). Committee on Biological Confinement of Genetically Engineered Organ-

isms. BIOLOGICAL CONFINEMENT OF GENETICALLY ENGINEERED ORGANISMS. Washington, DC: National Academies Press, 2004. 255 p. ISBN 0-309-09085-7. (Also available on the Web at: http://www.nap.edu.) [QH442.6 .B54 2004] (15.7; 1.3.11; 15.1; 22.1)

15.8 GENETIC PATENTS

Jorgensen, Henrik and Lykkeskov, Anne, eds.; Danish Council of Ethics = Det Etiske Råd. CONFERENCE REPORT AND SUMMARIES: THE ETHICS OF PATENTING HUMAN GENES AND STEM CELLS. Copenhagen: Danish Council of Ethics, 2005. 159 p. ISBN 87-91112-52-4. (Conference held 28 September 2004 in Copenhagen, arranged by the University of Copenhagen, BioTik, and the Danish Council of Ethics. Available on the Web at: http://www.etiskraad.dk/sw293.asp.) (15.8; 5.3; 18.5.4)

Mills, Oliver. BIOTECHNOLOGICAL INVENTIONS: MORAL RESTRAINTS AND PATENT LAW. Aldershot, Hants/Burlington, VT: Ashgate, 2005. 195 p. ISBN 0-7546-2420-X. [K1519 .B54 M55 2005] (15.8; LE)

World Health Organization. Human Genetics Programme. GENETICS, GENOMICS AND THE PATENTING OF DNA: REVIEW OF POTENTIAL IMPLICATIONS FOR HEALTH IN DEVELOPING COUNTRIES. Geneva: World Health Organization, 2005. 82 p. ISBN 92-4-159259-1. (Gift of the publisher.) (15.8; 5.3; 15.3; 21.1; LE)

15.10 GENOME MAPPING

WGBH Boston Video. CRACKING THE CODE OF LIFE: THE RACE TO DECODE HUMAN DNA. South Burlington, VT: NOVA/WGBH Boston Video, 2001. 1 color videocassette (VHS). (120 mins.). (NOVA series [WGBH Boston]. Program aired 17 April 2001. "Does it amaze you that yeast is your very close relative? That you possess roughly the same number of genes as a mouse? That you are 99.9% genetically identical to every other human? ABC Nightline correspondent Robert Krulwich lends a lighthearted touch to genetic science in this provocative two-hour NOVA special that takes you inside the amazing, complex and contentious race to decode the human genome. The Human Genome Project was born in 1990, when an international consortium of labs set out to sequence all 3 billion letters of our DNA, predicting they'd finish by 2005. Halfway though their schedule, controversial scientist and entrepreneur J. Craig Venter threw the genome world into turmoil when he announced his for-profit company Celera could finish the job in just two years. Francis Collins, leader of the publicly-funded effort, and MIT's Eric Lander were among the scientists who answered Venter's challenge. The result made history and laid the foundation for a remarkable future. Armed with this powerful information, medical pioneers are in the midst of astonishing breakthroughs that will change medicine as we know it. Will you get cancer, arthritis, or Alzheimer's? The answer lies in your genetic code—but the question is: Do you want to know? And will these new discoveries eventually lead to cures?" Available from: NOVA/WGBH Boston Video, PO Box 2284, South Burlington, VT 05407-2284; tel. 800-959-8670 (US and Canada); fax 802-864-9846; Web:

http://www.pbs.org/wgbh/nova/genome.) (15.10; 1.3.2; 8.4; 15.4; 15.8)

15.11 GENETICS AND HUMAN ANCESTRY

Reardon, Jenny. RACE TO THE FINISH: IDENTITY AND GOVERNANCE IN AN AGE OF GENOMICS. Princeton, NJ: Princeton University Press, 2005. 237 p. ISBN 0-691-11857-4. (In-formation Series.) [QH431 .R248 2005] (15.11; 1.3.9; 5.3; 15.10; 18.3)

Sarich, Vincent and Miele, Frank. RACE: THE REALITY OF HUMAN DIFFERENCES. Boulder, CO: Westview Press, 2004. 287 p. ISBN 0-8133-4086-1. ("A member of the Perseus Book Group.") [GN269 .S27 2004] (15.11)

Shennan, Stephen. GENES, MEMES, AND HUMAN HISTORY: DARWINIAN ARCHAEOLOGY AND CULTURAL EVOLUTION. London: Thames & Hudson, 2002. 304 p. ISBN 0-500-05118-6. [GN281 .S54 2002] (15.11; 3.2; 15.1)

16.1 ENVIRONMENTAL QUALITY (GENERAL)

Bryson, Christopher. THE FLUORIDE DECEPTION. New York: Seven Stories Press, 2004. 374 p. ISBN 1-58322-526-9. (Gift of the publisher.) [RA1231 .F55 B795 2004] (16.1; 1.3.5; 5.2; 16.3; 18.5.1)

Cone, Marla. SILENT SNOW: THE SLOW POISONING OF THE ARCTIC. New York: Grove Press, 2005. 246 p. ISBN 0-8021-1797-X. (Gift of the publisher.) [TD190.5 .C66 2005] (16.1; 9.5.1; 21.1)

Cooper, David E. and James, Simon p. BUDDHISM, VIRTUE AND ENVIRONMENT. Burlington, VT: Ashgate Publishing, 2005. 159 p. ISBN 0-7546-3910-X. (Ashgate World Philosophies Series.) [BQ4570 .E23 C65 2005] (16.1; 1.2)

Curtin, Deane. ENVIRONMENTAL ETHICS FOR A POSTCOLONIAL WORLD. Lanham, MD: Rowman & Littlefield, 2005. 223 p. ISBN 0-7425-2579-1. (Nature's Meaning series. Gift of the publisher.) [GE42 .C89 2005] (16.1; 1.3.2; 5.1; 13.2; 21.1)

De Jonge, Eccy. SPINOZA AND DEEP ECOLOGY: CHALLENGING TRADITIONAL APPROACHES TO ENVIRONMENTALISM. Aldershot, Hants/Burlington, VT: Ashgate, 2004. 172 p. ISBN 0-7546-3327-6. (Ashgate New Critical Thinking in Philosophy series.) [GE195 .D42 2004] (16.1; 1.1)

Deane-Drummond, Celia E. THE ETHICS OF NATURE. Malden, MA: Blackwell, 2004. 256 p. ISBN 0-631-22938-8. (New Dimensions to Religious Ethics series.) [BT695.5 .D373 2004] (16.1; 1.1; 1.2; 10; 14.5; 15.1; 17.1; 22.1)

Donadío Maggi de Gandolfi, María Celestina. BIODIVERSIDAD Y BIOTECNOLOGÍA: REFLEXIONES EN BIOÉTICA. Buenos Aires, Argentina: Editorial de la Universidad Católica Argentina [Educa], 2004. 187 p. ISBN 987-215449-X. (Available from: Editorial de la Universidad Católica Argentina, Fundacíon Universidad Católica Argentina, A.M. de Justo 1400, p.B., Contrafrente, Buenos Aires, Argentina. Gift of the publisher.) (16.1; 2.1; 4.4; 15.1)

Dunlap, Thomas R. FAITH IN NATURE: ENVIRONMENTALISM AS RELIGIOUS QUEST. Seattle: University of Washington Press, 2004. 206 p. ISBN 0-295-98397-3. (Weyerhaeuser Environmental Books series.) [BL65 .N35 D86 2004] (16.1; 1.2)

Kerns, Thomas. ENVIRONMENTALLY INDUCED ILLNESSES: ETHICS, RISK ASSESSMENT, AND HUMAN RIGHTS. Jefferson, NC: McFarland, 2001. 294 p. ISBN 0-7864-0827-8. [RA566 .K465 2001] (16.1; 1.3.2; 5.2; 8.3.1; 9.1; 9.5.1; 16.3; 21.1)

Merchant, Carolyn. REINVENTING EDEN: THE FATE OF NATURE IN WESTERN CULTURE. New York: Routledge, 2004. 308 p. ISBN 0-415-93165-7. [GF21 .M473 2003] (16.1)

Mycio, Mary. WORMWOOD FOREST: A NATURAL HISTORY OF CHERNOBYL. Washington, DC: Joseph Henry Press, 2005. 259 p. ISBN 0-309-09430-5. [QH543.5 .M93 2005] (16.1; 9.5.1; 9.5.7; 16.2)

Pellow, David Naguib. GARBAGE WARS: THE STRUGGLE FOR ENVIRONMENTAL JUSTICE IN CHICAGO. Cambridge, MA: MIT Press, 2004. 234 p. ISBN 0-262-66187-X. (Urban and Industrial Environments series. Gift of the publisher.) [GE235 .I3 P45 2002] (16.1; 5.2; 7.1; 9.5.4; 21.1)

Sarkar, Sahotra. BIODIVERSITY AND ENVIRONMENTAL PHILOSOPHY: AN INTRODUCTION. New York: Cambridge University Press, 2005. 258 p. ISBN 0-521-85132-7. (Cambridge Studies in Philosophy and Biology series. Gift of the publisher.) [GE40 .S27 2005] (16.1; 2.1; 3.1)

Satterfield, Terre and Slovic, Scott, eds. WHAT'S NATURE WORTH? NARRATIVE EXPRESSIONS OF ENVIRONMENTAL VALUES. Salt Lake City: University of Utah Press, 2004. 310 p. ISBN 0-87480-790-5. [PS163 .W46 2004] (16.1)

Schneider, Stephen H.; Miller, James R.; Crist, Eileen; and Boston, Penelope J., eds. SCIENTISTS DEBATE GAIA: THE NEXT CENTURY. Cambridge, MD: MIT Press, 2004. 377 p. ISBN 0-262-19498-8. [QH331 .S324 2004] (16.1; 3.1)

Tickner, Joel A., ed. PRECAUTION, ENVIRONMENTAL SCIENCE, AND PREVENTIVE PUBLIC POLICY. Washington, DC: Island Press, 2003. 406 p. ISBN 1-55963-332-8. [GE170 .P74 2003] (16.1; 1.3.11; 5.2; 5.3; 15.1; 21.1; LE)

Van DeVeer, Donald and Pierce, Christine, eds. THE ENVIRONMENTAL ETHICS AND POLICY BOOK: PHILOSOPHY, ECOLOGY, ECONOMICS. Belmont, CA: Wadsworth, 2003. 674 p. ISBN 0-534-56188-8. (Third edition.) [GE42 .V36 2003] (16.1; 1.1; 1.2; 1.3.2; 1.3.11; 13.2; 22.1)

Visser 't Hooft, Hendrik Philip. JUSTICE TO FUTURE GENERATIONS AND THE ENVIRONMENT. Dordrecht/Boston: Kluwer Academic, 1999. 167 p. ISBN 0-7923-5756-6. (Law and Philosophy Library series; Vol. 40.) [K240 .V57 1999] (16.1; 1.1; 1.3.8)

Walker, Joe. ENVIRONMENTAL ETHICS. London: Hodder & Stoughton, 2000. 124 p. ISBN 0-340-75770-1. (Access to Philosophy Series.) (16.1; 1.1; 22.1)

16.2 NUCLEAR POWER/RADIATION

Bergeron, Kenneth D. TRITIUM ON ICE: THE DANGEROUS NEW ALLIANCE OF NUCLEAR WEAPONS AND NUCLEAR POWER. Cambridge, MA: MIT Press, 2004, c2002. 234 p. ISBN 0-262-52433-3. (Gift of the publisher.) [TK9023 .B47 2002] (16.2; 1.3.5; 21.2)

Hashmi, Sohail H. and Lee, Stephen p., eds. ETHICS AND WEAPONS OF MASS DESTRUCTION: RELIGIOUS AND SECULAR PERSPECTIVES. New York: Cambridge University Press, 2004. 533 p. ISBN 0-512-54526-9. (Ethikon Series in Comparative Ethics.) [BL65 .A85 E84 2004] (16.2; 1.2; 10; 21.2)

National Research Council (United States). Committee to Review the CDC-NCI Feasibility Study of the Health Consequences from Nuclear Weapons Tests. EXPOSURE OF THE AMERICAN POPULATION TO RADIOACTIVE FALLOUT FROM NUCLEAR WEAPONS TESTS: A REVIEW OF THE CDC-NCI DRAFT REPORT ON A FEASIBILITY STUDY OF THE HEALTH CONSEQUENCES TO THE AMERICAN POPULATION FROM NUCLEAR WEAPONS TESTS CONDUCTED BY THE UNITED STATES AND OTHER NATIONS. Washington, DC: National Academies Press, 2003. 69 p. ISBN 0-309-08713-9. (Also available on the Web at: http://www.nap.edu.) [RA569 .E964 2003] (16.2; 1.3.5; 5.2)

16.3 OCCUPATIONAL HEALTH

Institute of Medicine (United States). Committee on Gulf War and Health: Literature Review of Selected Environmental Particulates, Pollutants, and Synthetic Chemical Compounds. GULF WAR AND HEALTH, VOLUME 3: FUELS, COMBUSTION PRODUCTS, AND PROPELLANTS. Washington, DC: National Academies Press, 2005. 499 p. ISBN 0-309-09527-1. (Also available on the Web at: http://www.nap.edu.) [DS79.744 .M44 G83 2000 v.3] (16.3; 7.1; 9.5.1; 21.2)

Kahn, Ada p. and Meyer, Delbert H. THE ENCYCLOPEDIA OF WORK-RELATED ILLNESSES, INJURIES, AND HEALTH ISSUES. New York: Facts on File, 2004. 434 p. ISBN 0-8160-4844-4. (Facts on File Library of Health and Living series.) [RC963 .A3 K348 2004] (16.3; 9.5.1; Reference)

Westerholm, Peter; Nilstun, Tore; and Øvretveit, John, eds. PRACTICAL ETHICS IN OCCUPATIONAL HEALTH. Oxford/San Francisco: Radcliffe Medical Press, 2004. 348 p. ISBN 1-85775-617-7. (Foreword by Ewan B. Macdonald.) [R724 .P68 2004] (16.3; 6; 9.5.9; 15.3)

17.1 THE NEUROSCIENCES AND MENTAL HEALTH THERAPIES (GENERAL)

Beam, Alex. GRACEFULLY INSANE: THE RISE AND FALL OF AMERICA'S PREMIER MENTAL HOSPITAL. New York: PublicAffairs, 2001. 273 p. ISBN 1-58648-161-4. (A history of the McLean Hospital in Belmont, MA.) [RC445 .M4 B442 2001] (17.1; 7.1)

Blackwell, Barry, ed. TREATMENT COMPLIANCE AND THE THERAPEUTIC ALLIANCE. Amsterdam: Harwood Academic Publishers, 1997. 325 p. ISBN 90-5702-546-9. (Chronic Mental Illness series; Vol. 5.) [RC454.4 .T74 1997] (17.1; 1.1; 4.3; 8.1; 8.3.3; 8.3.4; 9.1; 9.5.2; 9.5.3; 9.5.9; 17.2; 17.4; 21.7)

Bucky, Steven F.; Callan, Joanne E.; and Stricker, George, eds. ETHICAL AND LEGAL ISSUES FOR MENTAL HEALTH PROFESSIONALS: A COMPREHENSIVE HANDBOOK OF PRINCIPLES AND STANDARDS. Binghamton, NY: Haworth Maltreatment & Trauma Press, 2005. 433 p. ISBN 0-7890-2730-5. (Co-published simultaneously as: *Journal of Aggression, Maltreatment & Trauma*, Volume 11, Numbers 1/2 and 3, 2005. Gift of the publisher.) [RC455.2 .E8 E818 2005] (17.1; 1.3.9; 2.3; 6; 8.1; 8.3.1; 8.4; 10)

Bush, Shane S. and Drexler, Michael L., eds. ETHICAL ISSUES IN CLINICAL NEUROPSYCHOLOGY. Lisse/Exton, PA: Swets & Zeitlinger, 2002. 347 p. ISBN 90-265-1924-9. (Studies on Neuropsychology, Development, and Cognition series; Vol. 5.) [RC386.6 .N48 E876 2002] (17.1; 1.3.5; 1.3.12; 4.3; 7.4; 8.1; 8.3.1; 9.5.2; 9.5.7; 17.3; 18.4; 21.7)

Callaway, Barbara J. HILDEGARD PEPLAU: PSYCHIATRIC NURSE OF THE CENTURY. New York: Springer Publishing Company, 2002. 472 p. ISBN 0-8261-3882-9. [RC440 .P423 C35 2002] (17.1; 4.1.3; Biography)

Cooley, Thomas. THE IVORY LEG IN THE EBONY CABINET: MADNESS, RACE, AND GENDER IN VICTORIAN AMERICA. Amherst: University of Massachusetts Press, 2001. 302 p. ISBN 1-55849-284-4. [BF103 .C66 2001] (17.1; 7.1; 10; 15.5; 15.6; 21.7)

Gazzaniga, Michael S. THE ETHICAL BRAIN. New York: Dana Press, 2005. 201 p. ISBN 1-932594-01-9. (Gift of the publisher.) [QP360.5 .G393 2005] (17.1; 1.1; 4.4; 4.5; 15.1; 15.6; 17.4; 21.7)

Hanson, Stephanie L.; Kerkhoff, Thomas R.; and Bush, Shane S. HEALTH CARE ETHICS FOR PSYCHOLOGISTS: A CASEBOOK. Washington, DC: American Psychological Association Press, 2005. 250 p. ISBN 1-59147-152-4. (Gift of the publisher.) [R724 .H234 2005] (17.1; 4.4; 8.1; 8.2; 8.3.3; 8.3.4; 8.4; 10; 17.8; 20.5.1)

Jenkins, Rachel; McCulloch, Andrew; Friedli, Lynne; and Parker, Camilla. DEVELOPING A NATIONAL MENTAL HEALTH POLICY. Hove, East Sussex, UK: Psychology Press/Taylor & Francis, 2002. 213 p. ISBN 1-84169-295-6. (Maudsley Monographs series; No. 43.) (17.1; 9.1; 9.3.1; 9.5.1; 20.7; 21.1)

Lynch, Terry. BEYOND PROZAC: HEALING MENTAL SUFFERING WITHOUT DRUGS. Blackrock County Dublin: Marino, 2001. 318 p. ISBN 1-86023-136-5. [RC537 .L96 2001] (17.1; 4.1.1; 4.3; 17.4; 20.7)

Numbers in ( ) = NRCBL Classification Numbers

McLean, Richard. RECOVERED, NOT CURED: A JOURNEY THROUGH SCHIZOPHRENIA. Crows Nest, NSW: Allen & Unwin, 2003. 180 p. ISBN 1-86508-974-5. (Gift of the publisher.) (17.1; 7.1; Biography)

Millon, Theodore. MASTERS OF THE MIND: EXPLORING THE STORY OF MENTAL ILLNESS FROM ANCIENT TIMES TO THE NEW MILLENNIUM. Hoboken, NJ: John Wiley & Sons, 2004. 641 p. ISBN 0-471-46985-8. [RC438 .M557 2004] (17.1; 7.1)

Olevitch, Barbara A. PROTECTING PSYCHIATRIC PATIENTS AND OTHERS FROM THE ASSISTED-SUICIDE MOVEMENT: INSIGHTS AND STRATEGIES. Westport, CT: Praeger, 2002. 203 p. ISBN 0-275-96957-6. (Forewords by N. Gregory Hamilton and Albert Ellis.) [RC454.4 .O446 2002] (17.1; 8.1; 8.3.1; 17.2; 20.4.1; 20.5.1; 20.7)

Pickren, Wade E. and Schneider, Stanley F., eds. PSYCHOLOGY AND THE NATIONAL INSTITUTE OF MENTAL HEALTH: A HISTORICAL ANALYSIS OF SCIENCE, PRACTICE, AND POLICY. Washington, DC: American Psychological Association, 2005. 348 p. ISBN 1-59147-164-8. (Gift of the publisher.) [RA790.6 .P77 2005] (17.1; 7.1; 9.1; 17.2; 18.4)

Radden, Jennifer, ed. THE PHILOSOPHY OF PSYCHIATRY: A COMPANION. Oxford/New York: Oxford University Press, 2004. 447 p. ISBN 0-19-514953-X. (International Perspectives in Philosophy and Psychiatry series.) [RC437.5 .P4376 2004] (17.1; 1.1; 1.3.5; 3.2; 4.3; 4.4; 8.3.1; 8.4; 9.5.7; 10; 17.3; 18.5.6; 21.7)

Rogers, Anne and Pilgrim, David. MENTAL HEALTH AND INEQUALITY. Basingstoke, Hampshire, UK/New York: Palgrave, 2003. 278 p. ISBN 0-333-78657-2. [RA790.5 .R633 2003] (17.1; 4.3; 7.1; 17.2; 17.4)

Sabat, Steven R. THE EXPERIENCE OF ALZHEIMER'S DISEASE: LIFE THROUGH A TANGLED VEIL. Oxford/Malden, MA: Blackwell, 2001. 361 p. ISBN 0-631-21666-9. (17.1; 4.4; 9.5.2)

Schaler, Jeffrey A., ed. SZASZ UNDER FIRE: THE PSYCHIATRIC ABOLITIONIST FACES HIS CRITICS. Chicago: Open Court, 2004. 450 p. ISBN 0-8126-9568-2. (Under Fire Series; Vol. 1.) [RC437.5 .S94 2004] (17.1; 1.3.5; 4.3; 8.1; 9.5.9; 17.4; 17.7; 20.5.1; 20.7; Biography)

Scheid, Teresa L. TIE A KNOT AND HANG ON: PROVIDING MENTAL HEALTH CARE IN A TURBULENT ENVIRONMENT. New York: Aldine de Gruyter, 2004. 198 p. ISBN 0-202-30759-X. (Social Institutions and Social Change series.) [RA790 .S35 2004] (17.1; 1.3.2; 7.1; 9.1; 9.3.1; 9.4)

Schröter, Sonja. PSYCHIATRIE IN WALDHEIM/ SACHSEN (1716-1946). Frankfurt am Main: Mabuse, 2003. 250 p. ISBN 3-925499-83-0. (Second edition. Mabuse-Verlag Wissenschaft series; No. 11.) (17.1; 1.3.5; 15.5; 21.4)

Scull, Andrew. MADHOUSE: A TRAGIC TALE OF MEGALOMANIA AND MODERN MEDICINE. New Haven, CT: Yale University Press, 2005. 360 p. ISBN 0-300-10729-3. (Gift

of the publisher.) [RC443 .S395 2005] (17.1; 4.3; 7.1; 7.3; 7.4; 18.5.6)

Shamy, Eileen. A GUIDE TO THE SPIRITUAL DIMENSION OF CARE FOR PEOPLE WITH ALZHEIMER'S DISEASE AND RELATED DEMENTIA: MORE THAN BODY, BRAIN AND BREATH. London/New York: Jessica Kingsley, 2003. 224 p. ISBN 1-84310-129-7. [BV4435.5 .S53 2003] (17.1; 1.2; 9.5.2)

Slovenko, Ralph. PSYCHIATRY IN LAW/LAW IN PSYCHIATRY. New York: Brunner-Routledge, 2002. 2 volumes. ISBN 0-415-93365-X [set]; ISBN 0-415-93363-3 [vol. 1]; ISBN 0-415-93364-1 [vol. 2]. (Volume 1: *Psychiatry in Law*; Volume 2: *Law in Psychiatry*.) [KF8695 .S59 2002] (17.1; 1.3.5; 4.3; 8.3.1; 8.4; 9.5.9; 10; 17.2; 17.7; 17.8; 20.6; 20.7)

Smith, Ray and Crofts, Andrew. AMAZING GRACE: ENJOYING ALZHEIMER'S. London: Metro, 2004. 200 p. ISBN 1-84358-089-6. (17.1; 9.5.2; Biography)

Truscott, Derek and Crook, Kenneth H. ETHICS FOR THE PRACTICE OF PSYCHOLOGY IN CANADA. Edmonton: University of Alberta Press, 2004. 202 p. ISBN 0-88864-422-1. [BF76.4 .T78 2004] (17.1; 1.1; 6; 8.3.1; 8.4; 9.8; 10; 21.7; LE)

17.2 PSYCHOTHERAPY

Bromberg, Philip M. STANDING IN THE SPACES: ESSAYS ON CLINICAL PROCESS, TRAUMA, AND DISSOCIATION. Hillsdale, NJ: Analytic Press, 2001, c1998. 365 p. ISBN 0-88163-356-9. [RC509 .B76 1998] (17.2; 8.1)

Griffith, James L. and Griffith, Melissa Elliott. ENCOUNTERING THE SACRED IN PSYCHOTHERAPY: HOW TO TALK WITH PEOPLE ABOUT THEIR SPIRITUAL LIVES. New York: Guilford Press, 2002. 320 p. ISBN 1-57230-938-5. [RC455.4 .R4 G75 2002] (17.2; 1.2; 8.1)

Paris, Joel. THE FALL OF AN ICON: PSYCHOANALYSIS AND ACADEMIC PSYCHIATRY. Toronto: University of Toronto Press, 2005. 226 p. ISBN 0-8020-3772-0. [RC503 .P37 2005] (17.2; 7.1; 7.2)

Rickels, Laurence A. NAZI PSYCHOANALYSIS, VOLUME II: CRYPTO-FETISHISM. Minneapolis: University of Minnesota Press, 2002. 332 p. ISBN 0-8166-3699-0. (17.2; 1.3.5; 10; 21.1)

Smith, Edward W.L. THE PERSON OF THE THERAPIST. Jefferson, NC: McFarland, 2003. 193 p. ISBN 0-7864-1645-9. [RC480.5 .S559 2003] (17.2; 1.2; 4.4; 8.1)

Thompson, M. Guy. THE ETHIC OF HONESTY: THE FUNDAMENTAL RULE OF PSYCHOANALYSIS. Amsterdam/New York: Rodopi, 2004. 169 p. ISBN 90-420-1118-1. (Contemporary Psychoanalytic Studies series; No. 2.) [BF175 .T46 2004] (17.2; 2.1; 8.2)

17.3 BEHAVIOR MODIFICATION

Jacobson, John W.; Foxx, Richard M.; and Mulick, James A., eds. CONTROVERSIAL THERAPIES FOR DEVELOPMENTAL

DISABILITIES: FAD, FASHION, AND SCIENCE IN PROFESSIONAL PRACTICE. Mahwah, NJ: Lawrence Erlbaum Associates, 2005. 505 p. ISBN 0-8058-4192-X. (Gift of the publisher.) [RC570.2 .C66 2005] (17.3; 1.3.5; 1.3.9; 4.1.1; 4.3; 7.4; 9.5.3; 9.5.7; 9.8; 17.1)

Lyon, Christina M. and Pimor, Alexandra. PHYSICAL INTERVENTIONS AND THE LAW: LEGAL ISSUES ARISING FROM THE USE OF PHYSICAL INTERVENTIONS IN SUPPORTING CHILDREN, YOUNG PEOPLE AND ADULTS WITH LEARNING DISABILITIES AND SEVERE CHALLENGING BEHAVIOUR. Kidderminster: British Institute of Learning Disabilities, 2004. 302 p. ISBN 1-904082-73-4. (At head of title: University of Liverpool.) (17.3; 1.3.5; 1.3.8; 9.5.1; 9.5.7; 21.1)

17.4 PSYCHOPHARMACOLOGY

Barondes, Samuel H. BETTER THAN PROZAC: CREATING THE NEXT GENERATION OF PSYCHIATRIC DRUGS. Oxford/New York: Oxford University Press, 2003. 219 p. ISBN 0-19-517979-X. [RM332 .B37 2003] (17.4; 15.6; POP)

17.5 ELECTRICAL STIMULATION OF THE BRAIN

Ottosson, Jan-Otto and Fink, Max. ETHICS IN ELECTROCONVULSIVE THERAPY. New York: Brunner-Routledge, 2004. 157 p. ISBN 0-415-94659-X. [RC485 .O88 2004] (17.5; 1.1; 2.1; 8.3.1)

17.6 PSYCHOSURGERY

El-Hai, Jack. THE LOBOTOMIST: A MAVERICK MEDICAL GENIUS AND HIS TRAGIC QUEST TO RID THE WORLD OF MENTAL ILLNESS. New York: John Wiley & Sons, 2005. 362 p. ISBN 0-471-23292-0. (Gift of the publisher.) [RD594 .F74 E4 2005] (17.6; 7.1; 9.1; 17.2; 17.4; 17.5; Biography)

Schott, Penelope Scambly. THE PEST MAIDEN: A STORY OF LOBOTOMY. Cincinnati, OH: Turning Point, 2004. 127 p. ISBN 1-932339-47-7. (Publisher's address: PO Box 541106, zip 45254-1106.) [PS3569 .C5283 P47 2004] (17.6; 7.1; 17.1)

17.7 INVOLUNTARY CIVIL COMMITMENT

Diesfeld, Kate and Freckelton, Ian, eds. INVOLUNTARY DETENTION AND THERAPEUTIC JURISPRUDENCE: INTERNATIONAL PERSPECTIVES ON CIVIL COMMITMENT. Aldershot, Hants/Burlington, VT: Ashgate, 2003. 630 p. ISBN 0-7546-2266-5. [K640 .I58 2003] (17.7; 1.3.5; 4.3; 8.3.3; 17.8; 21.1; LE)

Lehane, Dennis. SHUTTER ISLAND. New York: HarperTorch, 2003. 385 p. ISBN 0-380-73186-X. ("The year is 1954. U.S. Marshal Teddy Daniels and his new partner, Chuck Aule, have come to Shutter Island, home of Ashecliffe Hospital for the Criminally Insane, to investigate the disappearance of a patient. Multiple murderess Rachel Solando is loose somewhere on this remote and barren island, despite having been kept in a locked cell under constant surveillance. As a killer hurricane bears relentlessly down on them, a strange case takes on even darker, more sinister shades—with hints of radical experimentation, horrifying surgeries, and lethal countermoves made in the cause of a covert shadow war. No one is going to escape Shutter Island unscathed, because nothing at Ashecliffe Hospital is what is seems. But then neither is Teddy Daniels.") [PS3562 .E426 S562 2003] (17.7; 9.7; 15.5; 17.3; 17.4; Fiction)

Special Theme: Preventive Outpatient Commitment for Persons With Serious Mental Illness. PSYCHOLOGY, PUBLIC POLICY, AND LAW 2003 March-June; 9(1-2): 3-257. (ISSN 1076-8971.) (17.7; 1.3.5; 8.3.4; 9.5.7; 10; 17.4)

18.1 HUMAN EXPERIMENTATION (GENERAL)

Smyth, Marie and Williamson, Emma, eds. RESEARCHERS AND THEIR SUBJECTS: ETHICS, POWER, KNOWLEDGE AND CONSENT. Bristol: Polity Press, 2004. 227 p. ISBN 1-86134-514-3. [Q180.55 .M67 R492 2004] (18.1; 7.1; 18.3; 18.5.1; 18.5.2)

18.2 HUMAN EXPERIMENTATION: POLICY GUIDELINES/INSTITUTIONAL REVIEW BOARDS

Childress, James F.; Meslin, Eric M.; and Shapiro, Harold, eds. BELMONT REVISITED: ETHICAL PRINCIPLES FOR RESEARCH ON HUMAN SUBJECTS. Washington, DC: Georgetown University Press, 2005. 279 p. ISBN 1-58901-062-0. (Gift of the publisher.) [R853 .H8 B45 2005] (18.2; 1.1; 2.2; 2.4; 16.2; 18.5.1; 18.6)

Cleophas, Ton J.; Zwinderman, Aeiko, H.; and Cleophas, Toine F. STATISTICS APPLIED TO CLINICAL TRIALS. Dordrecht/Boston: Kluwer Academic, 2002. 210 p. ISBN 1-4020-0570-9. [RM301.27 .C5635 2002] (18.2; 4.4; 7.1; 15.1)

Derenzo, Evan G. and Moss, Joel. WRITING CLINICAL RESEARCH PROTOCOLS: ETHICAL CONSIDERATIONS. Burlington, MA/London: Elsevier Academic Press, 2005. 300 p. ISBN 0-12-210751-9. (18.2; 5.2; 7.1; 8.4; 18.3; 18.5.1)

Glasa, Jozef; European Commission. EUR 21255—NATIONAL REGULATIONS ON ETHICS AND RESEARCH IN SLOVAK REPUBLIC (SLOVENSKEJ REPUBLIKE) = EUR 21255 PRÁVNE PREDPISY PRE OBLAST' ETIKY BIOMEDICÍNSKEHO VYSKUMU V SLOVENSKEJ REPUBLIKE (SLOVAK REPUBLIC). Luxembourg: Office for Official Publications of the European Communities, 2003. [30 p. + 30 p.]. ISBN 92-894-8092-0. (Text in English, with Slovak on inverted pages. Gift of the author.) [R854 .S56 G53 2003] (18.2; 15.1; 18.5.4; 19.1; 22.2; LE)

National Health and Medical Research Council (Australia). HUMAN RESEARCH ETHICS HANDBOOK: COMMENTARY ON THE NATIONAL STATEMENT ON ETHICAL CONDUCT IN RESEARCH INVOLVING HUMANS. Canberra, ACT: NHMRC/National Health and Medical Research Council,

2001. 1 looseleaf binder (various pagings). ISBN 1-864960-70-1. (Endorsed 25 October 2001. Available from: The Publications Officer, NHMRC, MDP 100, GPO Box 9848, Canberra ACT 2601; fax: (02) 6289 9197; email: nhmrc.publications@nhmrc.gov.au. Also available on the Web at: http://www.nhmrc.gov.au/publications/ hrecbook/pdf/hrechand.pdf.) (18.2; 15.1; 17.1; 18.3; 18.5.1; 18.5.2)

Osteoporosis Trials: Ethical Considerations in Study Design Supplement. JOURNAL OF BONE AND MINERAL RESEARCH 2003 June; 18(6): 1101-1160. (ISSN 0884-0431.) (18.2; 6; 9.7; 18.3; 18.5.1; 18.5.3)

Plomer, Aurora. THE LAW AND ETHICS OF MEDICAL RESEARCH: INTERNATIONAL BIOETHICS AND HUMAN RIGHTS. London: Cavendish; Distributed in the U.S. by: International Specialized Book Services [ISBS], 2005. 158 p. ISBN 1-85941-687-X. (Distributor's address: 5824 NE Hassalo Street, Portland, OR 97213-3644. Gift of the publisher.) [R853 .H8 P56 2005] (18.2; 2.1; 4.4; 9.5.6; 9.7; 16.2; 18.3; 18.5.1; 18.5.4; 21.1; LE)

Schuster, Daniel p. and Powers, William J., eds. TRANSLATIONAL AND EXPERIMENTAL CLINICAL RESEARCH. Philadelphia: Lippincott Williams & Wilkins, 2005. 490 p. ISBN 0-7817-5565-4. [R850 .T73 2005] (18.2; 7.1; 9.3.1; 15.1; 15.4)

Weindling, Paul Julian. NAZI MEDICINE AND THE NUREMBERG TRIALS: FROM MEDICAL WAR CRIMES TO INFORMED CONSENT. Basingstoke, Hampshire/New York: Palgrave Macmillan, 2004. 482 p. ISBN 1-4039-3911-X. [KZ1179 .M43 W45 2004] (18.2; 1.3.5; 2.2; 6; 15.5; 18.3; 18.5.5; 21.4)

18.3 HUMAN EXPERIMENTATION: INFORMED CONSENT

Making Informed Consent Meaningful. MEDICAL CARE 2002 September; 40(9, Supplement): V1-V80. (ISSN 0025-7079.) (18.3; 4.1.2; 8.3.1; 9.8; 18.4; 18.5.6; 18.6; 21.7)

18.4 BEHAVIORAL RESEARCH

Johns, Mark D.; Chen, Shing-Ling Sarina; and Hall, G. Jon, eds. ONLINE SOCIAL RESEARCH: METHODS, ISSUES, & ETHICS. New York: Peter Lang, 2004. 273 p. ISBN 0-8204-6101-6. (Digital Formations series; Vol. 7. ISSN 1526-3169.) [HM571 .O55 2004] (18.4; 1.3.9; 1.3.12; 18.2)

18.5.1 RESEARCH ON SPECIAL POPULATIONS (GENERAL)

Beech, Bettina M. and Goodman, Maurine, eds. RACE & RESEARCH: PERSPECTIVES ON MINORITY PARTICIPATION IN HEALTH STUDIES. Washington, DC: American Public Health Association Press, 2004. 212 p. ISBN 0-87553-030-3. [JC312 .R33 2004] (18.5.1; 7.1; 7.2; 9.3.1; 15.1; 18.2; 18.4; 18.5.2; 18.5.3; 18.6)

Gilbert, David. THE NORMALS: A NOVEL. New York: Bloomsbury, 2005, c2004. 373 p. ISBN 1-58234-609-7. ("In this comic tour de force, David Gilbert recounts the travails of Billy Schine, a semiprofessional temp worker who decides to escape his debt-ridden New York City life by enrolling in a human drug testing study. The boredom of the research center is broken only by twice-daily appointments with pills and needles, but even so, Billy finally feels at home. He and his fellow test subjects trade battle stories from the healing fields of guinea pig, and Billy finds himself rested and well fed and possibly in love with the lone female in the study. Then the messy side effects hit, and Billy's normal world is turned upside down, the real and unreal merging until spilled blood becomes the only proof of a beating heart.") [PS3557 .I3383 N66 2004] (18.5.1; 17.4; Fiction)

18.5.2 RESEARCH ON NEWBORNS OR MINORS

National Research Council (United States) [and] Institute of Medicine (United States). Committee on Ethical Issues in Housing-Related Health Hazard Research Involving Children, Youth, and Families. ETHICAL CONSIDERATIONS FOR RESEARCH ON HOUSING-RELATED HEALTH HAZARDS INVOLVING CHILDREN. Washington, DC: National Academies Press, 2005. 196 p. ISBN 0-309-09726-6. (Edited by Bernard Lo and Mary Ellen O'Connell. Also available on the Web at: http://www.nap.edu.) [RA770 .E84 2005] (18.5.2; 8.3.2; 9.3.1; 9.5.7; 9.5.10; 16.1; 18.2; 18.3; 18.4)

18.5.3 RESEARCH ON WOMEN

National Institutes of Health [NIH] (United States). Task Force on the NIH Women's Health Research Agenda for the 21st Century. AGENDA FOR RESEARCH ON WOMEN'S HEALTH FOR THE 21ST CENTURY: A REPORT OF THE TASK FORCE ON THE NIH WOMEN'S HEALTH RESEARCH AGENDA FOR THE 21ST CENTURY. [Bethesda, MD]: National Institutes of Health, Office of the Director, Office of Research on Women's Health, 1999. 6 volumes. (NIH Publication Nos. 99-4385, 99-4386, 99-4387, 99-4388, 99-4389 and 99-4390. Vol. 1: *Executive Summary*; Vol. 2: [without special title]; Vol. 3: *Public Testimony*; Vol. 4: *Influences of Sex and Gender on Health*; Vol. 5: *Sex and Gender Perspectives for Women's Health Research*; and Vol. 6: *Differences among Populations of Women*. Available from: Office of Research on Women's Health, Office of the Director, National Institutes of Health, 1 Center Drive, Room 201, MSC 0161, Bethesda, MD 20892-0161; fax: 301-402-1798. Rose Fitzgerald Kennedy Collection on Women, Infants and Children.) [RA778 .A35 1999] (18.5.3; 9.5.5; 10)

18.5.4 RESEARCH ON EMBRYOS OR FETUSES

Blazer, Shraga and Zimmer, Etan Z., eds. THE EMBRYO: SCIENTIFIC DISCOVERY AND MEDICAL ETHICS. Basel/New York: Karger, 2005. 408 p. ISBN 3-8055-7802-4. (Gift of the publisher.) [RG133.5 .E45 2005] (18.5.4; 1.2; 4.4; 5.2; 9.5.8; 9.7; 15.1; 15.2; 15.4; 15.6; 21.7; LE)

[Human Embryo Research Debate]. CONNECTICUT LAW REVIEW 2004 Summer; 36(4): 1049-1186. (ISSN 0010-6151.) (18.5.4; 1.1; 2.4; 3.1; 4.4; 14.5; 19.5)

National Research Council (United States). Committee on Guidelines for Human Embryonic Stem Cell Research [and] Institute of Medicine (United States). Board on Health Sciences Policy. GUIDELINES FOR HUMAN EMBRYONIC STEM CELL RESEARCH. Washington, DC: National Academies Press, 2005. 166 p. ISBN 0-309-09653-7. (Also available on the Web at: http://www.nap.edu.) [QH588 .S83 G85 2005] (18.5.4; 15.1; 18.2; 18.3)

Parson, Ann B. THE PROTEUS EFFECT: STEM CELLS AND THEIR PROMISE FOR MEDICINE. Washington, DC: John Henry Press, 2004. 301 p. ISBN 0-309-08988-3. [QH588 .S83 P37 2004] (18.5.4; 15.1; 19.1; 22.2; POP)

President's Council on Bioethics (United States). ALTERNATIVE SOURCES OF HUMAN PLURIPOTENT STEM CELLS. Washington, DC: President's Council on Bioethics, 2005. 99 p. (May 2005. "A White Paper." Available on the Web at: http://www. bioethics.gov.) [QH588 .S83 P74 2005] (18.5.4; 2.4; 4.4)

18.5.5 RESEARCH ON PRISONERS

Baumslag, Naomi. MURDEROUS MEDICINE: NAZI DOCTORS, HUMAN EXPERIMENTATION, AND TYPHUS. Westport, CT: Praeger, 2005. 272 p. ISBN 0-275-98312-9. (Foreword by E.D. Pellegrino. Gift of the publisher.) [R853 .H8 B38 2005] (18.5.5; 1.3.5; 2.2; 9.5.1; 9.7; 15.5; 21.3; 21.4)

Klee, Ernst. AUSCHWITZ, DIE NS-MEDIZIN UND IRHE OPFER. Frankfurt am Main: Fischer Taschenbuch Verlag, 2004. 525 p. ISBN 3-596-14906-1. (Third edition.) (18.5.5; 1.3.5; 2.2; 9.7; 15.1; 15.5; 21.4)

Spitz, Vivien. DOCTORS FROM HELL: THE HORRIFIC ACCOUNT OF NAZI EXPERIMENTS ON HUMANS. Boulder, CO: Sentient Publications, 2005. 317 p. ISBN 1-59181-032-9. [R853 .H8 S68 2005] (18.5.5; 1.3.5; 1.3.9; 2.2; 15.5; 18.2; 21.4)

18.6 SOCIAL CONTROL OF HUMAN EXPERIMENTATION

Collins, Anne. IN THE SLEEP ROOM: THE STORY OF CIA BRAINWASHING EXPERIMENTS IN CANADA. Toronto: Lester & Orpen Dennys, 1988. 272 p. ISBN 0-88619-198-X. (18.6; 1.3.5; 17.3; 17.4; 17.5)

19.1 ARTIFICIAL AND TRANSPLANTED ORGANS OR TISSUES (GENERAL)

Miller, G. Wayne. THE XENO CHRONICLES: TWO YEARS ON THE FRONTIER OF MEDICINE INSIDE HARVARD'S TRANSPLANT RESEARCH LAB. New York: PublicAffairs, 2005. 233 p. ISBN 1-58648-242-4. (Gift of the publisher.) [RD129.5 .M55 2005] (19.1; 4.4; 5.3; 15.1; 22.2)

Persson, Marie Omnell. UTILIZATION AND ALLOCATION OF ORGANS FOR TRANSPLANTATION: MEDICAL AND ETHICAL

ASPECTS. Lund, Sweden: Department of Medical Ethics, Faculty of Medicine, Lund University, 2003. 79 p. ISBN 91-628-5581-6. (Dissertation, (doctoral)—Lund University, 2003. Text in English with Swedish summary. Available from: Department of Medical Ethics, Faculty of Medicine, Lund University, St Gråbrödersg 16, SE-222 22 Lund, Sweden. Gift of the author.) (19.1; 7.1; 19.3; 19.6; 22.2)

19.2 ARTIFICIAL AND TRANSPLANTED HEARTS

Kirklin, James K.; Young, James B.; and McGiffin, David C. HEART TRANSPLANTATION. New York: Churchill Livingstone, 2002. 883 p. ISBN 0-443-07655-3. [RD598.35 .T7 K55 2002] (19.2; 4.4; 9.5.7; 19.1; 19.6; 22.2)

Wiebel-Fanderl, Oliva. HERZTRANSPLANTATION ALS ERZÄHLTE ERFAHRUNG: DER MENSCH ZWISCHEN KULTURELLEN TRADITIONEN UND MEDIZINISCH-TECHNISCHEM FORTSCHRITT. Münster: Lit Verlag, 2003. 514 p. ISBN 3-8258-6865-6. (Ethik in der Praxis/Practical Ethics - Studien/Studies series; Bd. 14. Habilitationsschrift—Universität Jena, 2001. Gift of Hans-Martin Sass.) [RD598.35 .T7 W544 2003] (19.2; 2.2; 5.1; 7.1; 17.1)

19.3 ARTIFICIAL AND TRANSPLANTED KIDNEYS

Cameron, J. Stewart. A HISTORY OF THE TREATMENT OF RENAL FAILURE BY DIALYSIS. New York: Oxford University Press, 2002. 353 p. ISBN 0-19-851547-2. [RC901.7 .H45 C355 2002] (19.3; 2.2; 7.1; 9.3.1; 21.1)

Cherry, Mark J. KIDNEY FOR SALE BY OWNER: HUMAN ORGANS, TRANSPLANTATION, AND THE MARKET. Washington, DC: Georgetown University Press, 2005. 258 p. ISBN 1-58901-040-X. (Gift of the publisher.) [RD129.5 .C448 2005] (19.3; 1.1; 1.2; 4.4; 9.1; 9.3.1; 19.5; 19.6; 21.1; 21.7)

Taylor, James Stacey. STAKES AND KIDNEYS: WHY MARKETS IN HUMAN BODY PARTS ARE MORALLY IMPERATIVE. Aldershot, England/Burlington, VT: Ashgate, 2005. 226 p. ISBN 0-7546-4110-4. (Live Questions in Ethics and Moral Philosophy series. Gift of the publisher.) [RD129.5 .T395 2005] (19.3; 9.3.1; 19.5)

19.4 BLOOD TRANSFUSION

Institute of Medicine (United States). Committee on Establishing a National Cord Blood Stem Cell Bank Program. CORD BLOOD: ESTABLISHING A NATIONAL HEMATOPOIETIC STEM CELL BANK PROGRAM. Washington, DC: National Academies Press, 2005. 314 p. ISBN 0-309-09586-7. (Edited by Kristine Gebbie, Emily Ann Meyer, and Kathi Hanna. Also available on the Web at: http://www.nap. edu.) [RM171 .I54 2005] (19.4; 9.1; 9.3.1; 9.5.7)

Picard, André. THE GIFT OF DEATH: CONFRONTING CANADA'S TAINTED-BLOOD TRAGEDY. Toronto: HarperPerennial, 1998. 320 p. ISBN 0-00-638575-3. (19.4; 5.2; 9.3.1; 9.5.6; 9.8; 21.1; LE)

19.5 DONATION/PROCUREMENT OF ORGANS/TISSUES

Ben-David, Orit Brawer. ORGAN DONATION AND TRANS-PLANTATION: BODY ORGANS AS AN EXCHANGEABLE SOCIO-CULTURAL RESOURCE. Westport, CT: Praeger, 2005. 166 p. ISBN 0-275-97918-0. [RD129.5 .B46 2005] (19.5; 4.4; 7.1; 17.1; 20.1; 21.7)

Hinkley, Charles C. MORAL CONFLICTS OF ORGAN RE-TRIEVAL: A CASE FOR CONSTRUCTIVE PLURALISM. Amsterdam/New York: Rodopi, 2005. 209 p. ISBN 90-420-1737-6. (Value Inquiry Book Series; Vol. 172. Values in Bioethics [ViB] series. Gift of the publisher.) (19.5; 1.1; 4.4; 9.3.1; 18.5.1; 20.2.1; 21.7; 22.2)

Leahy, Dean Milton. IMPROVING THE ORGAN DONATION PROCESS: CAN SOCIAL WORK HELP? Ann Arbor, MI: ProQuest Information and Learning/UMI, 2002. 110 p. (Publication No. AAT-3054298. Dissertation, (Ph.D.)—University of Pittsburgh, 2002.) (19.5; 1.3.10; 7.1; 8.3.1; 8.3.2; 8.3.3)

19.6 ALLOCATION OF ORGANS/TISSUES

Waring, Duff R. MEDICAL BENEFIT AND THE HUMAN LOT-TERY: AN EGALITARIAN APPROACH TO PATIENT SELECTION. Dordrecht/New York: Springer, 2004. 220 p. ISBN 1-4020-2970-5. (International Library of Ethics, Law, and the New Medicine series; Vol. 22.) [R724 .W345 2004] (19.6; 1.1; 1.3.5; 4.4; 5.2; 9.5.2)

20.1 DEATH AND DYING (GENERAL)

Alters, Sandra. DEATH AND DYING, WHO DECIDES? Farmington Hills, MI: Greenhaven Press/Thomson Gale, 2005. 167 p. ISBN 0-7876-9070-8. (2004 edition. Information Plus Reference Series. ISSN 1532-2726. Gift of the publisher.) [R726 .D425 2004] (20.1; 9.3.1; 19.5; 20.2.1; 20.3.1; 20.4.1; 20.5.1; 20.5.2; 20.7; Reference)

Institute of Medicine (United States). Committee for the Workshop on the Medicolegal Death Investigation System. MEDICOLEGAL DEATH INVESTIGATION SYSTEM: WORKSHOP SUMMARY. Washington, DC: National Academies Press, 2003. 75 p. ISBN 0-309-08986-7. (20.1; 1.3.5; 7.2; 9.1)

Jenkins, Margie. YOU ONLY DIE ONCE: PREPARING FOR THE END OF LIFE WITH GRACE AND GUSTO. Nashville, TN: Integrity Publishers, 2002. 238 p. ISBN 1-59145-013-6. [HQ1073 .J45 2002] (20.1; 20.3.1)

Jupp, Peter C. and Gittings, Clare, eds. DEATH IN ENGLAND: AN ILLUSTRATED HISTORY. New Brunswick, NJ: Rutgers University Press, 2000. 282 p. ISBN 0-8135-2789-9. (First published in Great Britain by: Manchester University Press, 1999; ISBN 0-7190-5811-2.) [HQ1073.5 .G7 D427 2000] (20.1; 1.2; 7.1; 20.3.1)

Kastenbaum, Robert. THE PSYCHOLOGY OF DEATH. New York: Springer Publishing Company, 2000. 318 p. ISBN 0-8261-1300-1. (Third edition.) [BF789 .D4 K372 2000] (20.1; 8.1; 17.1; 20.3.1; 20.5.1; 20.7)

Li, Jack. CAN DEATH BE A HARM TO THE PERSON WHO DIES? Dordrecht/Boston: Kluwer Academic, 2002. 193 p. ISBN 1-4020-0505-9. (Philosophy and Medicine series; Vol. 73.) [BD444 .L46 2002] (20.1; 1.1)

Morris, Virginia. TALKING ABOUT DEATH. Chapel Hill, NC: Algonquin Books of Chapel Hill, c2001, 2004. 292 p. ISBN 1-56512-437-5. (Originally published as: *Talking About Death Won't Kill You*; Workman, New York, 2001.) [BJ789 .D4 M65 2004] (20.1; 20.3.1; 20.5.4)

Noys, Benjamin. THE CULTURE OF DEATH. Oxford/New York: Berg, 2005. 166 p. ISBN 1-84520-069-1. (Gift of the publisher.) [HQ1073 .N69 2005] (20.1; 5.3; 21.2; 21.4)

20.3.1 ATTITUDES TOWARD DEATH (GENERAL)

Glaser, Barney G. and Strauss, Anselm L. AWARENESS OF DYING. New Brunswick, NJ: Aldine Transaction, 2005, c1965. 305 p. ISBN 0-202-30763-8. (Originally published: Aldine Publishing Company, Chicago, 1965. Gift of the publisher.) [BF789 .D4 G5 2005] (20.3.1; 7.1; 8.1; 8.2; 20.4.1)

Hayslip, Bert and Peveto, Cynthia A. CULTURAL CHANGES IN ATTITUDES TOWARD DEATH, DYING AND BEREAVEMENT. New York: Springer Publishing Company, 2005. 195 p. ISBN 0-8261-2796-7. (Springer Series on Death and Suicide.) [GT3150 .H38 2005] (20.3.1; 7.1; 21.7)

Robertson, Heather. MEETING DEATH: IN HOSPICE, HOSPI-TAL, AND AT HOME. Toronto: M & S, 2000. 352 p. ISBN 0-7710-7562-6. (Available from: McClelland & Stewart, 481 University Avenue, Toronto, Ontario M5G 2E9.) [R726.8 .R619 2000] (20.3.1; 20.3.3; 20.4.1)

20.4.1 CARE OF THE DYING PATIENT (GENERAL)

Blank, Robert H. and Merrick, Janna C., eds. END-OF-LIFE DECISION MAKING: A CROSS-NATIONAL STUDY. Cambridge, MA: MIT Press, 2005. 266 p. ISBN 0-262-02574-4. (Basic Bioethics series. Gift of the publisher.) [R726.8 .E534 2005] (20.4.1; 7.1; 9.1; 20.3.1; 21.1; 21.7)

Collett, Merrill. AT HOME WITH DYING: A ZEN HOSPICE AP-PROACH. Boston: Shambhala, 1999. 240 p. ISBN 1-57062-515-8. (Originally published as: *Stay Close and Do Nothing*; Kansas City: Andrews McMeel, 1997.) [R726.8 .C64 1999] (20.4.1; 1.2; 4.4; 17.1; 20.3.1)

Conner, Norma E. HOSPICE USE AMONG BLACKS: HEALTH BELIEFS, SPIRITUALITY AND SOCIAL RELATIONSHIPS AS PREDICTIVE FACTORS. Ann Arbor, MI: ProQuest/UMI, 2003. 133 p. (Publication No. AAT-3083632. Dissertation, (Ph.D.)— Rutgers, The State University of New Jersey-Newark, 2003.) (20.4.1; 1.2; 7.1; 9.5.4)

Fins, Joseph J. A PALLIATIVE ETHIC OF CARE: CLINICAL WISDOM AT LIFE'S END. Sudbury, MA: Jones and Bartlett, 2006. 281 p. ISBN 0-7637-3292-3. (Gift of the author.) (20.4.1; 2.2; 8.1; 20.5.1; 20.5.4; 20.7)

Hallenbeck, James L. PALLIATIVE CARE PERSPECTIVES. New York: Oxford University Press, 2003. 232 p. ISBN 0-19-516578-0. [R726.8 .H347 2003] (20.4.1; 1.2; 4.4; 7.1; 8.1; 20.3.1)

Henderson, Martha L.; Hanson, Laura C.; and Reynolds, Kimberly S. IMPROVING NURSING HOME CARE OF THE DYING: A TRAINING MANUAL FOR NURSING HOME STAFF. New York: Springer Publishing Company, 2003. 194 p. ISBN 0-8261-1925-5. [RC954.3 .H466 2003] (20.4.1; 1.2; 4.4; 9.5.2; 20.5.4)

Hospice and Palliative Nurses Association [and] American Nurses Association. SCOPE AND STANDARDS OF HOSPICE AND PALLIATIVE NURSING PRACTICE. Silver Spring, MD: American Nurses Association, 2002. 44 p. ISBN 1-55810-207-8. (Publisher's address: 8515 Georgia Avenue, Suite 400, zip 20910-3492.) [R726.8 .H6533 2002] (20.4.1; 8.1; 9.8)

Kaplan, Karen Orloff and Lukas, Christopher. STAYING IN CHARGE: PRACTICAL PLANS FOR THE END OF YOUR LIFE. Hoboken, NJ: John Wiley & Sons, 2004. 226 p. ISBN 0-471-27424-0. (20.4.1; 8.3.3; 9.3.1; 20.4.2; 20.5.1; 20.5.4)

Kuebler, Kim K.; Berry, Patricia H.; and Heidrich, Debra E. END-OF-LIFE CARE: CLINICAL PRACTICE GUIDELINES. Philadelphia: Saunders, 2002. 492 p. ISBN 0-7216-8452-1. [R726.8 .K84 2002] (20.4.1; 8.1; 9.4; 9.8)

Lyndale, Patricia J. HOSPICE ETHICS: PRINCIPLISM, COVENANT, AND VIRTUE. Ann Arbor, MI: ProQuest Information and Learning Company/UMI, 2003. 237 p. (Publication No. AAT-3093111. Dissertation, (Ph.D.)—Florida State University, 2003.) (20.4.1; 1.1)

Marrelli, Tina M. HOSPICE AND PALLIATIVE CARE HANDBOOK: QUALITY, COMPLIANCE, AND REIMBURSEMENT. St. Louis, MO: Elsevier Mosby, 2005. 528 p. ISBN 0-323-02479-3. (Second edition.) [RA1000 .M37 2005] (20.4.1; 4.4; 9.8; Reference)

Oliviere, David and Monroe, Barbara, eds. DEATH, DYING, AND SOCIAL DIFFERENCES. Oxford/New York: Oxford University Press, 2004. 205 p. ISBN 0-19-852775-6. [R726.8 .D3797 2004] (20.4.1; 1.2; 7.1; 9.3.1; 9.5.2; 9.5.10; 10; 17.1; 20.3.1; 21.7)

Swanson, Jan and Cooper, Alan. A PHYSICIAN'S GUIDE TO COPING WITH DEATH AND DYING. Montreal/Ithaca, NY: McGill-Queen's University Press, 2005. 286 p. ISBN 0-7735-2832-6. [R726.8 .S94 2005] (20.4.1; 1.2; 8.1; 20.4.2; Reference)

Taylor, George J. and Kurent, Jerome E. A CLINICIAN'S GUIDE TO PALLIATIVE CARE. Malden, MA: Blackwell, 2002. 193 p. ISBN 0-632-04642-2. [R726.8 .C576 2003] (20.4.1; 9.5;1; 9.5.2; 9.5.6; 9.5.7; 9.7)

20.5.1 PROLONGATION OF LIFE AND EUTHANASIA (GENERAL)

Csikai, Ellen L. and Chaitin, Elizabeth. ETHICS IN END-OF-LIFE DECISIONS IN SOCIAL WORK PRACTICE. Chicago: Lyseum Books, 2006. 261 p. ISBN 0-925065-52-8. (Gift of the publisher.) (20.5.1; 1.3.10; 2.1; 8.1; 8.2; 8.3.1; 8.4; 20.4.1; 20.5.4; 20.7)

Eisenberg, Jon B. USING TERRI: THE RELIGIOUS RIGHT'S CONSPIRACY TO TAKE AWAY OUR RIGHTS. San Francisco: HarperSanFrancisco, 2005. 275 p. ISBN 0-06-087732-4. [R726 .E35 2005] (20.5.1; 1.2; 1.3.8; 2.1; 21.1)

Harrison, Maureen and Gilbert, Steve, eds. LIFE, DEATH, AND THE LAW: LANDMARK RIGHT-TO-DIE DECISIONS. San Diego, CA: Excellent Books, 1997. 231 p. ISBN 1-880780-13-5. (Publisher's address: PO Box 927105, zip 92192-7105.) [KF3827 .E87 A52 1997] (20.5.1; 8.1; 20.4.1; 20.7; LE)

Lavi, Shai J. THE MODERN ART OF DYING: HISTORY OF EUTHANASIA IN THE UNITED STATES. Princeton, NJ: Princeton University Press, 2005. 226 p. ISBN 0-691-10263-5. (Gift of the publisher.) [R726 .L3797 2005] (20.5.1; 2.2; 8.1; 20.3.1; 20.7; LE)

McCullagh, Peter. CONSCIOUS IN A VEGETATIVE STATE? A CRITIQUE OF THE PVS CONCEPT. Dordrecht/Boston: Kluwer Academic, 2004. 351 p. ISBN 1-4020-2629-3. (International Library of Ethics, Law, and the New Medicine series; Vol. 23.) [RB150 .C6 M43 2004] (20.5.1; 2.2; 9.3.1; 9.4; 20.2.1; 21.1; LE)

Meisel, Alan and Cerminara, Kathy L. THE RIGHT TO DIE: THE LAW OF END-OF-LIFE DECISIONMAKING. New York: Aspen, c2005, 2004. 1 loose-leaf volume. Various pagings. ISBN 0-7355-4665-7. (Third edition. 2005 Supplement.) [KF3827 .E87 M452] (20.5.1; 4.3; 8.3.2; 8.3.3; 20.5.2; 20.5.4; 20.7; LE)

Pessini, Leo. EUTANÁSIA: POR QUE ABREVIAR A VIDA? Sao Paulo: Editora do Centro Universitario Sao Camilo [and] Edicoes Loyola, 2004. 376 p. ISBN 85-15-02882-4. (Coleção Bioética em Perspectiva series. Gift of the author.) (20.5.1; 1.1; 1.2; 2.1; 2.2; 4.4; LE)

Sass, Hans-Martin and Kielstein, Rita. PATIENTENVERFÜGUNG UND BETREUUNGSVOLLMACHT. Münster: Lit Verlag, 2001. 147 p. ISBN 3-8258-4986-4. (Ethik in der Praxis/Practical Ethics - Kontroversen/Controversies series; Bd. 2. Gift of Hans-Martin Sass.) (20.5.1; 8.3.3; 20.4.1; 20.5.4)

Sturman, Randy Linda. SIX LIVES IN JERUSALEM: END-OF-LIFE DECISIONS IN JERUSALEM: CULTURAL, MEDICAL, ETHICAL AND LEGAL CONSIDERATIONS. Dordrecht/Boston: Kluwer Academic, 2003. 143 p. ISBN 1-4020-1725-1. (International Library of Ethics, Law, and

---

Numbers in ( ) = NRCBL Classification Numbers

the New Medicine series; Vol. 16.) [R726.8 .S78 2003] (20.5.1; 1.2; 4.4; 8.1; 20.3.1; 20.4.1; 21.4; 21.7; LE)

Tännsjö, Torbjörn. TERMINAL SEDATION: EUTHANASIA IN DISGUISE? Dordrecht/New York: Kluwer Academic, 2004. 148 p. ISBN 1-4020-2123-2. [R726 .T45 2004] (20.5.1; 1.1; 4.4; 8.1; 20.3.2; 20.4.1)

ten Have, Henk A.M.J. and Welie, Jos V.M. DEATH AND MEDICAL POWER: AN ETHICAL ANALYSIS OF DUTCH EUTHANASIA PRACTICE. Maidenhead, Berkshire, England: Open University Press/New York: McGraw-Hill Education, 2005. 242 p. ISBN 0-335-21755-9. (Facing Death series.) (20.5.1; 4.4; 8.1; 20.7)

Walker, Richard. A RIGHT TO DIE? North Mankato, MN: Sea-to-Sea Publications, 2006. 32 p. ISBN 1-932889-56-6. (Juvenile literature. Viewpoints [Franklin Watts] series. Originally published: New York: Franklin Watts, 1997. Publisher's address: 1980 Lookout Drive, zip 56003.) [R726 .W29 2006] (20.5.1; 4.4; 20.3.1; 20.4.1; 20.7; 21.1; POP)

20.5.4 LIVING WILLS/ADVANCE DIRECTIVES

Crawford, Wendy Y. END-OF-LIFE TREATMENT PREFERENCES AND FAMILY IMPACT ON OUTCOME. Ann Arbor, MI: ProQuest Information and Learning/UMI, 2001. 223 p. (Publication No. AAT-3031511. Dissertation, (Ph.D.) —Temple University, 2001.) (20.5.4; 7.1; 8.1; 20.5.1)

Molloy, William and Mepham, Virginia. LET ME DECIDE: THE HEALTH AND PERSONAL CARE DIRECTIVE THAT SPEAKS FOR YOU WHEN YOU CAN'T. Troy, Ontario: Newgrange, 2000. 64 p. + 1 folded sheet (6 p.). ISBN 0-9694645-6-8. (Sixth edition. Available in the US from: Newgrange Press, 302 Highland Avenue, Winchester, MA 01890; tel.: 781-729-8981.) (20.5.4; Reference; POP)

Rixen, Stephan and Reinecke, Siegfried. CASEBOOK PATIENTENVERFÜGUNG: VORAUSVERFÜGUNG, VORSORGEVOLLMACHT, BETREUUNGSVERFÜGUNG MIT FALLBEISPIELEN, FORMULIERUNGSHILFEN, CHECKLISTEN. Berlin: Springer-Verlag, 2004. 198 p. ISBN 3-540-20435-0. (20.5.4; LE)

20.6 CAPITAL PUNISHMENT

Gaie, Joseph B.R. THE ETHICS OF MEDICAL INVOLVEMENT IN CAPITAL PUNISHMENT: A PHILOSOPHICAL DISCUSSION. Dordrecht/Boston: Kluwer Academic, 2004. 158 p. ISBN 1-4020-1764-2. (International Library of Ethics, Law, and the New Medicine series; Vol. 18.) [R724 .G325 2004] (20.6; 1.1; 1.3.5; 4.1.2; 9.7; 20.5.1)

Nathanson, Stephen. AN EYE FOR AN EYE? THE IMMORALITY OF PUNISHING BY DEATH. Lanham, MD: Rowman & Littlefield, 2001. 205 p. ISBN 0-7425-1326-2. (Second edition.) [HV8694 .N37 2001] (20.6; 4.4)

20.7 SUICIDE/ASSISTED SUICIDE

Battin, Margaret Pabst. ENDING LIFE: ETHICS AND THE WAY WE DIE. New York: Oxford University Press, 2005. 344 p. ISBN 0-19-514027-3. (Gift of the publisher.) [R726 .B329 2005] (20.7; 1.2; 2.2; 8.1; 9.5.2; 9.5.6; 9.7; 15.1; 20.5.1; 21.1)

Kellerman, Jonathan. DR. DEATH: A NOVEL. New York: Ballantine Books, c2000, 2001. 436 p. ISBN 0-345-44880-4. ("To some, Eldon Mate was evil personified. Others saw the former physician as a saint...When Mate is found mutilated in a rented van, harnessed to his own killing machine, [psychologist-detective Alex] Delaware is asked to aid his old friend, homocide cop Milo Sturgis, in the hunt for the death doctor's executioner.") [PS3561 .E3865 D7 2001] (20.7; 8.1; 20.5.1; Fiction)

Lieberman, Lisa. LEAVING YOU: THE CULTURAL MEANING OF SUICIDE. Chicago: Ivan R. Dee, 2003. 175 p. ISBN 1-56663-496-2. [HV6545 .L534 2003] (20.7; 1.2; 21.7)

Poussaint, Alvin F. and Alexander, Amy. LAY MY BURDEN DOWN: SUICIDE AND THE MENTAL HEALTH CRISIS AMONG AFRICAN-AMERICANS. Boston: Beacon Press, 2000. 194 p. ISBN 0-8070-0959-8. [RC451.5 .N4 P67 2000] (20.7; 7.1; 9.5.4; 17.1)

Ziegler, Stephen Joseph. PROSECUTORS, PALLIATIVE MEDICINE, AND PHYSICIAN-ASSISTED DEATH: AN EMPIRICAL ASSESSMENT OF THE LIKELIHOOD OF PROSECUTION STEMMING FROM OPIOID AND NON-OPIOID ADMINISTRATIONS. Ann Arbor, MI: ProQuest Information and Learning/UMI, 2003. 240 p. (Publication No. AAT-3096918. Dissertation, (Ph.D.)—Washington State University, 2003.) (20.7; 1.3.5; 4.4; 7.1; 8.1; 8.5; 20.4.1; 20.5.1)

21.1 INTERNATIONAL AND POLITICAL DIMENSIONS OF BIOLOGY AND MEDICINE (GENERAL)

Beaglehole, Robert, ed. GLOBAL PUBLIC HEALTH: A NEW ERA. Oxford/New York: Oxford University Press, 2003. 284 p. ISBN 0-19-851529-4. [RA425 .G56 2003] (21.1; 9.1; 21.3)

Beigbeder, Yves. INTERNATIONAL PUBLIC HEALTH: PATIENTS' RIGHTS VS. THE PROTECTION OF PATENTS. Aldershot, Hants/Burlington, VT: Ashgate, 2004. 173 p. ISBN 0-7546-3621-6. (Global Health series.) [RA441 .B447 2004] (21.1; 5.3; 9.1; 9.3.1; 9.5.5; 9.5.6; 9.5.9; 9.7; 21.7)

Ben-Itto, Hadassa. THE LIE THAT WOUNDN'T DIE: THE PROTOCOLS OF THE ELDERS OF ZION. London/Portland, OR: Vallentine Mitchell, 2005. 390 p. ISBN 0-85303-594-4. (Gift of Max M. and Marjorie B. Kampelman.) [DS145 .P7 B36 2005] (21.1; 1.3.5)

Chatterjee, Deen K., ed. THE ETHICS OF ASSISTANCE: MORALITY AND THE DISTANT NEEDY. Cambridge/New York: Cambridge University Press, 2004. 292 p. ISBN 0-521-52742-2. (Cambridge Studies in Philosophy and

Public Policy series.) [HC60 .E744 2004] (21.1; 1.3.2; 1.3.5; 1.3.6; 9.5.10; 21.7)

Chen, Lincoln; Leaning, Jennifer; and Narasimhan, Vasant, eds. GLOBAL HEALTH CHALLENGES FOR HUMAN SECURITY. Cambridge, MA: Global Equity Initiative, Asia Center, Harvard University; Distributed by: Cambridge, MA: Harvard University Press, 2003. 310 p. ISBN 0-674-01453-7. (Studies in Global Equity series.) [RA441 .G567 2003] (21.1; 7.1; 9.1; 9.5.6; 9.5.10; 10)

Clark, John D. WORLDS APART: CIVIL SOCIETY AND THE BATTLE FOR ETHICAL GLOBALIZATION. Bloomfield, CT: Kumarian Press, 2003. 269 p. ISBN 1-56549-167-X. (Publisher's address: 1294 Blue Hills Avenue, zip 06002.) [JC337 .C583 2003] (21.1; 1.3.2; 1.3.5)

Davis, Mike. THE MONSTER AT OUR DOOR: THE GLOBAL THREAT OF AVIAN FLU. New York: New Press, 2005. 212 p. ISBN 1-59558-011-5. (Gift of the publisher.) [RA644 .I6 D387 2005] (21.1; 1.3.11; 9.1; 9.5.1; 9.7; 22.3; POP)

Dyck, Arthur J. RETHINKING RIGHTS AND RESPONSIBILITIES: THE MORAL BONDS OF COMMUNITY. Washington, DC: Georgetown University Press, 2005. 350 p. ISBN 1-58901-035-3. (Revised edition. Gift of the publisher.) [JC571 .D9616 2005] (21.1; 1.1; 1.3.1; 9.2; 20.5.1; 20.7)

Fort, Meredith; Mercer, Mary Anne; and Gish, Oscar, eds. SICKNESS AND WEALTH: THE CORPORATE ASSAULT ON GLOBAL HEALTH. Cambridge, MA: South End Press, 2004. 237 p. ISBN 0-89608-716-6. [RA441.5 .S53 2004] (21.1; 1.3.2; 1.3.11; 7.1; 9.1; 9.2; 9.3.1; 9.5.1; 9.5.6)

Halper, Thomas. POSITIVE RIGHTS IN A REPUBLIC OF TALK: A SURVEY AND A CRITIQUE. Dordrecht/ Boston: Kluwer Academic, 2003. 209 p. ISBN 1-4020-1783-9. (Philosophical Studies in Contemporary Culture series.) [JC571 .H35 2003] (21.1; 1.3.1; 1.3.5)

Keal, Paul. EUROPEAN CONQUEST AND THE RIGHTS OF INDIGENOUS PEOPLES: THE MORAL BACKWARDNESS OF INTERNATIONAL SOCIETY. Cambridge/New York: Cambridge University Press, 2003. 258 p. ISBN 0-521-53179-9. (Cambridge Studies in International Relations series; Vol. 92.) (21.1; 1.3.5; 1.3.6; 1.3.8)

Kidder, Tracy. MOUNTAINS BEYOND MOUNTAINS. New York: Random House Trade Paperbacks, 2004. 322 p. ISBN 0-8129-7301-1. (Subtitle on cover: *The Quest of Dr. Paul Farmer, a Man Who Would Cure the World*. Originally published in hardcover by: Random House, 2003.) [R154 .F36 K53 2004] (21.1; 9.1; 9.2; 9.5.10; Biography)

Labonte, Ronald; Schrecker, Ted; Sanders, David; and Meeus, Wilma. FATAL INDIFFERENCE: THE G8, AFRICA AND GLOBAL HEALTH. Lansdowne, South Africa: University of Cape Town Press [and] Ottawa, Canada: International Research Development Centre, 2004. 378 p. ISBN 1-91971-384-0 [University of Cape Town Press]; ISBN 1-55250-130-2 [International Research Development Centre]. [RA441 .F38 2004] (21.1; 9.1)

National Research Council (United States). Committee on Science and Technology Countering Terrorism. MAKING THE NATION SAFER: THE ROLE OF SCIENCE AND TECHNOLOGY IN COUNTERING TERRORISM. Washington, DC: National Academies Press, 2002. 415 p. ISBN 0-309-08481-4. (Also available on the Web at: http://www. nap.edu.) (21.1; 1.3.5; 5.3; 16.2; 21.3)

Smith, Richard; Beaglehole, Robert; Woodward, David; and Drager, Nick, eds. GLOBAL PUBLIC GOODS FOR HEALTH: HEALTH, ECONOMIC, AND PUBLIC HEALTH PERSPECTIVES. Oxford/New York: Oxford University Press, 2003. 287 p. ISBN 0-19-852798-5. [RA394 .G575 2003] (21.1; 1.3.5; 4.2; 9.1; 9.3.1; 9.5.1)

Special Issue: Mini-Symposium: Health and the WTO. JOURNAL OF INTERNATIONAL ECONOMIC LAW 2002 December; 5(4): 821-939. (ISSN 1369-3034.) (21.1; 5.3; 9.1; 9.2; 9.5.6; 9.7)

Weiss, John. THE POLITICS OF HATE: ANTI-SEMITISM, HISTORY, AND THE HOLOCAUST IN MODERN EUROPE. New York: Ivan R. Dee, 2003. 245 p. ISBN 1-56663-600-0. (Gift of Max M. and Marjorie B. Kampelman.) [DS146 .E85 W45 2003] (21.1; 1.3.5; 21.4)

Williams, Thomas D. WHO IS MY NEIGHBOR? PERSONALISM AND THE FOUNDATIONS OF HUMAN RIGHTS. Washington, DC: Catholic University Press of America, 2005. 342 p. ISBN 0-8132-1391-6. [BX1795 .H85 W55 2005] (21.1; 1.1; 1.2; 4.4)

World Health Organization [WHO]. INTERNATIONAL MIGRATION, HEALTH, AND HUMAN RIGHTS. Geneva: World Health Organization, 2003. 36 p. ISBN 92-4-156253-6. (21.1; 9.1)

21.2 WAR

Holmes, Arthur F., ed. WAR AND CHRISTIAN ETHICS: CLASSIC AND CONTEMPORARY READINGS ON THE MORALITY OF WAR. Grand Rapids, MI: Baker Academic, 2005. 404 p. ISBN 0-8010-3113-3. (Second edition. Gift of the publisher.) [BT736.2 .W34 2005] (21.2; 1.2; 16.2; 21.1)

Shephard, Ben. AFTER DAYBREAK: THE LIBERATION OF BELSEN, 1945. London: Jonathan Cape, 2005. 260 p. ISBN 0-224-07355-9. [D805.5 .B47 S44 2005] (21.2; 7.1; 9.5.1; 21.4)

Vaux, Kenneth L. ETHICS AND THE WAR ON TERRORISM. Eugene, OR: Wipf and Stock, 2002. 119 p. ISBN 1-57910-941-1. (Publisher's address: 199 West 8th Avenue, Suite 3, zip 97401.) [B105 .W3 V38 2002] (21.2; 1.2; 21.1)

21.3 CHEMICAL AND BIOLOGICAL WEAPONS

British Medical Association. Board of Science and Education. BIOTECHNOLOGY, WEAPONS AND HUMANITY. Amsterdam: Harwood Academic, 1999. 152 p. ISBN

90-5702-459-4. [UG447.8 .B58 1999] (21.3; 15.1; 15.10; 21.2)

Coleman, Kim. A HISTORY OF CHEMICAL WARFARE. New York: Palgrave Macmillan, 2005. 198 p. ISBN 1-4039-3460-6. (Gift of the publisher.) [UG447 .C637 2005] (21.3; 21.2)

Davis, Jim A. and Schneider, Barry R., eds. THE GATHERING BIOLOGICAL WARFARE STORM. Westport, CT: Praeger, 2004. 263 p. ISBN 0-275-98314-5. [UG447.8 .G38 2004] (21.3; 1.3.11; 9.1; 9.7; 15.1; 22.3)

Institute of Medicine (United States). Committee to Review the Health Effects in Vietnam Veterans of Exposure to Herbicides. VETERANS AND AGENT ORANGE: UPDATE 2002. Washington, DC: National Academies Press, 2003. 619 p. ISBN 0-309-08616-7. (Fourth biennial update. Also available on the Web at: http://www.nap.edu.) [RA1242 .T44 I57 2003] (21.3; 7.1; 9.5.1; 14.1; 16.1; 16.3; 17.1)

21.4 TORTURE AND GENOCIDE

Bartov, Omer. GERMANY'S WAR AND THE HOLOCAUST: DISPUTED HISTORIES. Ithaca, NY: Cornell University Press, 2002. 248 p. ISBN 0-8014-8681-5. (Gift of Max M. and Marjorie B. Kampelman.) [D804.3 .B362 2003] (21.4; 1.3.5; 13.3; 15.5; 21.2)

Bergen, Bernard J. THE BANALITY OF EVIL: HANNAH ARENDT AND "THE FINAL SOLUTION". Lanham, MD: Rowman & Littlefield Publishers, 1998. 169 p. ISBN 0-8476-9210-8. (Gift of Max M. and Marjorie B. Kampelman.) [D804.3 .B463 1998] (21.4; 1.3.5; 15.5)

Bosmajian, Hamida. SPARING THE CHILD: GRIEF AND THE UNSPEAKABLE IN YOUTH LITERATURE ABOUT NAZISM AND THE HOLOCAUST. New York: Routledge, 2002. 274 p. ISBN 0-8153-3856-2. (Children's Literature and Culture series; Vol. 16. Gift of Max M. and Marjorie B. Kampelman.) [PN1009.5 .N36 B67 2002] (21.4; 1.3.5; 21.7; Fiction)

Eisenstein, Paul. TRAUMATIC ENCOUNTERS: HOLOCAUST REPRESENTATION AND THE HEGELIAN SUBJECT. Albany: State University of New York Press, 2003. 236 p. ISBN 0-7914-5800-8. (Gift of Max M. and Marjorie B. Kampelman.) [PN56 .H55 E48 2003] (21.4; 1.3.7)

An Ethical Dilemma in Rheumatology: Should the Eponym Reiter's Syndrome Be Discarded. SEMINARS IN ARTHRITIS AND RHEUMATISM 2003 February; 32(4): 207-245. (ISSN 0049-0172.) (21.4; 1.3.9; 4.1.2; 7.1; 11.3; 15.5; 18.5.5; 21.1)

Fernekes, William R. THE ORYX HOLOCAUST SOURCEBOOK. Westport, CT: Oryx Press, 2002. 397 p. ISBN 1-57356-295-5. (Oryx Holocaust Series. Gift of Max M. and Marjorie B. Kampelman.) [Z6374 .H6 F47 2002] (21.4; Reference)

Gellately, Robert and Kiernan, Ben, eds. THE SPECTER OF GENOCIDE: MASS MURDER IN HISTORICAL PERSPECTIVE. Cambridge/New York: Cambridge University Press,

2003. 396 p. ISBN 0-521-52750-3. [HV6322.7 .S654 2003] (21.4; 1.3.5; 15.5; 21.1; 21.2)

Glass, James M. JEWISH RESISTANCE DURING THE HOLOCAUST: MORAL USES OF VIOLENCE AND WILL. New York: Palgrave Macmillan, 2004. 206 p. ISBN 1-4039-3907-1. (Gift of Max M. and Marjorie B. Kampelman.) [D810 .J4 G565 2004] (21.4; 1.2; 21.2)

Hochstadt, Steve, ed. SOURCES OF THE HOLOCAUST. New York: Palgrave Macmillan, 2004. 319 p. ISBN 0-333-96345-8. (Gift of Max M. and Marjorie B. Kampelman.) (21.4; 1.3.5; 15.5; Reference)

Langbein, Hermann. PEOPLE IN AUSCHWITZ. Chapel Hill: University of North Carolina Press, 2004. 549 p. ISBN 0-8078-2816-5. (Translation from the German by Harry Zohn of: *Menschen in Auschwitz*; Europa Verlag, Wien, 1995. Foreword by Henry Friedlander. "Published in association with the United States Holocaust Memorial Museum." Gift of Max M. and Marjorie B. Kampelman.) [D805.5 .A96 L3613 2004] (21.4; 21.2)

Levi, Neil and Rothberg, Michael, eds. THE HOLOCAUST: THEORETICAL READINGS. New Brunswick, NJ: Rutgers University Press, 2003. 485 p. ISBN 0-8135-3353-8. (Gift of Max M. and Marjorie B. Kampelman.) [D804.3 .H66 2003] (21.4; 1.3.5; 10; 15.5; 17.1; 21.7)

Linn, Ruth. ESCAPING AUSCHWITZ: A CULTURE OF FORGETTING. Ithaca, NY: Cornell University Press, 2004. 154 p. ISBN 0-8014-4130-7. (Psychoanalysis and Social Theory series. Gift of Max M. and Marjorie B. Kampelman.) [D804.3 .L57 2004] (21.4; 1.3.5; 15.5)

Mankowitz, Zeev W. LIFE BETWEEN MEMORY AND HOPE: THE SURVIVORS OF THE HOLOCAUST IN OCCUPIED GERMANY. Cambridge/New York: Cambridge University Press, 2002. 335 p. ISBN 0-521-81105-8. (Studies in the Social and Cultural History of Modern Warfare series; Vol. 13. Gift of Max M. and Marjorie B. Kampelman.) [DS135 .G332 M36 2002] (21.4)

Michman, Dan. HOLOCAUST HISTORIOGRAPHY: A JEWISH PERSPECTIVE: CONCEPTUALIZATIONS, TERMINOLOGY, APPROACHES AND FUNDAMENTAL ISSUES. London/Portland, OR: Vallentine Mitchell, 2003. 435 p. ISBN 0-85303-436-2. (Parkes-Wiener Series on Jewish Studies. ISSN 1368-5449. Gift of Max M. and Marjorie B. Kampelman.) [D804.348 .M52 2003] (21.4; 1.2; 1.3.5; 15.5)

Nicholas, Lynn H. CRUEL WORLD: THE CHILDREN OF EUROPE IN THE NAZI WEB. New York: Alfred A. Knopf, 2005. 632 p. ISBN 0-679-45464-0. (Gift of Max M. and Marjorie B. Kampelman.) [D810 .C4 N53 2005] (21.4; 1.3.5; 9.5.7; 15.5; 21.2)

Peel, Michael and Iacopino, Vincent, eds. THE MEDICAL DOCUMENTATION OF TORTURE. London/San Francisco: Greenwood Medical Media, 2002. 227 p. ISBN 1-84110-068-4. (Publisher's addresses: 137 Euston Road, London NW1 2AA [or] 870 Market Street, Suite 720, San Francisco, CA 94102.) [RA1122.8 .M395 2002] (21.4; 1.3.5; 7.3; 10; 17.1; 17.5; 20.1)

Raphael, Melissa. THE FEMALE FACE OF GOD IN AUSCHWITZ: A JEWISH FEMINIST THEOLOGY OF THE HOLOCAUST. London/New York: Routledge, 2003. 228 p. ISBN 0-415-23665-7. (Religion and Gender series. Gift of Max M. and Marjorie B. Kampelman.) [BM645 .H6 R37 2003] (21.4; 1.2; 1.3.5; 10; 15.5)

Rosenbaum, Alan S., ed. IS THE HOLOCAUST UNIQUE? PERSPECTIVES ON COMPARATIVE GENOCIDE. Boulder, CO: Westview Press, 2001. 304 p. ISBN 0-8133-3686-4. (Second, expanded edition. Perspectives on Comparative Genocide series. Foreword by Israel W. Charny. Gift of Max M. and Marjorie B. Kampelman.) [D804.348 .I8 2001] (21.4; 1.2; 1.3.5; 15.5; LE)

Seidler, Eduard. KINDERÄRZTE, 1933-1945: ENTRECHTET, GEFLOHEN, ERMORDET = PEDIATRICIANS, VICTIMS OF PERSECUTION, 1933-1945. Bonn: Bouvier Verlag, 2000. 494 p. ISBN 3-416-02919-4. (Text in German and English.) [RJ43 .A1 S45 2000] (21.4; 1.3.5; 9.5.7; 15.5; Biography)

Smith, Helmut Walser, ed. THE HOLOCAUST AND OTHER GENOCIDES: HISTORY, REPRESENTATION, ETHICS. Nashville, TN: Vanderbilt University Press, 2002. 262 p. ISBN 0-8265-1403-0. (Gift of Max M. and Marjorie B. Kampelman.) [D804.33 .H65 2002] (21.4; 1.3.5; 2.2; 15.5; 21.1)

Wittmann, Rebecca. BEYOND JUSTICE: THE AUSCHWITZ TRIAL. Cambridge, MA: Harvard University Press, 2005. 336 p. ISBN 0-674-01694-7. (Gift of Max M. and Marjorie B. Kampelman.) [KK73.5 .A98 W58 2005] (21.4; 1.3.5; 21.2)

Zimmerman, Joshua D., ed. CONTESTED MEMORIES: POLES AND JEWS DURING THE HOLOCAUST AND ITS AFTERMATH. New Brunswick, NJ: Rutgers University Press, 2003. 324 p. ISBN 0-8135-3158-6. (Gift of Max M. and Marjorie B. Kampelman.) [D804.3 .C69 2003] (21.4; 1.3.5)

21.7 CULTURAL PLURALISM

Bigby, JudyAnn, ed. CROSS-CULTURAL MEDICINE. Philadelphia: American College of Physicians, 2003. 289 p. ISBN 1-930513-02-X. (Publisher's address: 190 North Independence Mall West, zip 19106-1572.) [RA418.5 .T73 C765 2003] (21.7; 1.2; 7.1; 9.5.4)

Bonder, Betty R.; Martin, Laura; and Miracle, Andrew W. CULTURE IN CLINICAL CARE. Thorofare, NJ: Slack, 2002. 189 p. ISBN 1-55642-459-0. [RA418 .B64 2002] (21.7; 7.1; 8.1; 9.5.4; Reference)

García-Ballester, Luis. MEDICINE IN A MULTICULTURAL SOCIETY: CHRISTIAN, JEWISH AND MUSLIM PRACTITIONERS IN THE SPANISH KINGDOMS, 1222-1610. Aldershot, Hants/Burlington, VT: Ashgate, 2001. [374 p.]. ISBN 0-86078-845-8. (Variorum Collected Studies Series; No. CS702.) [R556 .G383 2001] (21.7; 1.2; 7.1; 7.2; 9.1; 9.7)

Healy, Judith and McKee, Martin, eds. ACCESSING HEALTH CARE: RESPONDING TO DIVERSITY. Oxford/New York: Oxford University Press, 2004. 379 p. ISBN 0-19-851618-5. [RA418.5 .T73 A235 2004] (21.7; 9.1; 9.2; 9.5.4)

Pack-Brown, Sherlon p. and Williams, Carmen Braun. ETHICS IN A MULTICULTURAL CONTEXT. Thousand Oaks, CA: Sage, 2003. 246 p. ISBN 0-7619-2427-2. (Multicultural Aspects of Counseling Series; Vol. 19.) (21.7; 6; 17.2)

Pengra, Lilah Morton. YOUR VALUES, MY VALUES: MULTICULTURAL SERVICES IN DEVELOPMENTAL DISABILITIES. Baltimore, MD: Paul H. Brookes, 2000. 256 p. ISBN 1-55766-448-X. [HV1570.5 .U65 P45 2000] (21.7; 9.1; 9.5.1; 17.1)

Wells, Shirley A. and Black, Roxie M. CULTURAL COMPETENCY FOR HEALTH PROFESSIONALS. Bethesda, MD: American Occupational Therapy Association, 2000. 292 p. ISBN 1-56900-105-7. (Publisher's address: 4720 Montgomery Lane, PO Box 31220, zip 20824-1220.) [RA418 .W43 2000] (21.7; 7.1; 9.5.4)

22.1 ANIMAL WELFARE (GENERAL)

Daston, Lorraine and Mitman, Gregg, eds. THINKING WITH ANIMALS: NEW PERSPECTIVES ON ANTHROPOMORPHISM. New York: Columbia University Press, 2005. 230 p. ISBN 0-231-13038-4. ("This book derived from a workshop held at the Max Planck Institute for the History of Science in Berlin in May 2001." Gift of the publisher.) [BL215 .T48 2004] (22.1; 22.2)

Franklin, Julian, H. ANIMAL RIGHTS AND MORAL PHILOSOPHY. New York: Columbia University Press, 2005. 151 p. ISBN 0-231-13422-3. (Gift of the publisher.) [HV4708 .F74 2005] (22.1; 22.2)

Gaita, Raimond. THE PHILOSOPHER'S DOG: FRIENDSHIPS WITH ANIMALS. New York: Random House Trade Paperbacks, 2002. 220 p. ISBN 0-8129-7024-1. (Originally published in Australia by the Text Publishing Company, 2002.) [SF426.6 .G35 2005] (22.1)

Garner, Robert. ANIMALS, POLITICS AND MORALITY. Manchester: Manchester University Press; Distributed in the U.S by: New York: Palgrave, 2004. 285 p. ISBN 0-7190-6621-2. (Second edition. Issues in Environmental Politics Series.) [HV4708 .G37 2004] (22.1; 1.3.5; 1.3.11; 22.2; 22.3)

Hancocks, David. A DIFFERENT NATURE: THE PARADOXICAL WORLD OF ZOOS AND THEIR UNCERTAIN FUTURE. Berkeley: University of California Press, 2001. 279 p. ISBN 0-520-23676-9. [QL76 .H35 2001] (22.1)

Hursthouse, Rosalind. ETHICS, HUMANS AND OTHER ANIMALS: AN INTRODUCTION WITH READINGS. New York: Routledge, 2000. 266 p. ISBN 0-415-21242-1. [HV4708 .H84 2000] (22.1; 1.1; 22.2)

Linzey, Andrew and Clarke, Paul Barry, eds. ANIMAL RIGHTS: A HISTORICAL ANTHOLOGY. New York: Columbia University Press, 2004. 193 p. ISBN 0-231-13421-5. (With a new preface. Originally published as: *Political Theory and Animal Rights*, Pluto Press, London/Winchester, MA, 1990. Gift of the publisher.) [HV4711 .P65 2004] (22.1; 1.3.5)

McKenna, Erin and Light, Andrew, eds. ANIMAL PRAGMA-TISM: RETHINKING HUMAN-NONHUMAN RELATIONSHIPS. Bloomington: Indiana University Press, 2004. 254 p. ISBN 0-253-21693-1. [B832 .A55 2004] (22.1; 1.1; 1.3.11; 16.1; 22.2; 22.3)

Munro, Lyle. CONFRONTING CRUELTY: MORAL ORTHO-DOXY AND THE CHALLENGE OF THE ANIMAL RIGHTS MOVE-MENT. Leiden/Boston: Brill, 2005. 218 p. ISBN 90-04-14311-4. (Human-Animal Studies series; Vol. 1. ISSN 1573-4226.) [HV4764 .M87 2005] (22.1; 2.2; 22.2; 22.3)

Regan, Tom. ANIMAL RIGHTS, HUMAN WRONGS: AN INTRO-DUCTION TO MORAL PHILOSOPHY. Lanham, MD: Rowman & Littlefield, 2003. 141 p. ISBN 0-7425-3354-9. (Revision of the author's contribution to: *The Animal Rights Debate*, by Carl Cohen and Tom Regan; Rowman & Littlefield, Lanham, MD, 2001.) [HV4708 .R42 2003] (22.1; 1.1; 22.3)

Regan, Tom. EMPTY CAGES: FACING THE CHALLENGE OF ANIMAL RIGHTS. Lanham, MD: Rowman & Littlefield, 2004. 229 p. ISBN 0-7425-3352-2. (Gift of the publisher.) [HV4764 .R44 2004] (22.1; 22.2; 22.3)

Rumbaugh, Duane M. and Washburn, David A. INTELLI-GENCE OF APES AND OTHER RATIONAL BEINGS. New Haven, CT: Yale University Press, 2003. 326 p. ISBN 0-300-09983-5. (Current Perspectives in Psychology series.) (22.1)

Salem, Deborah J. and Rowan, Andrew N., eds.; Humane Society of the United States. THE STATE OF THE ANIMALS, 2001. Washington, DC: Humane Society Press, 2001. 212 p. ISBN 0-9658942-3-1. (Public Policy series. Publisher's address: 2100 L Street, NW, zip 20037.) [HV4708 .S719 2001] (22.1; 22.2; 22.3)

Sapontzis, Steve F., ed. FOOD FOR THOUGHT: THE DEBATE OVER EATING MEAT. Amherst, NY: Prometheus Books, 2004. 382 p. ISBN 1-59102-118-9. (Contemporary Issues series.) [TX392 .F63 2004] (22.1; 1.1; 1.2; 10; 16.1; 21.7; 22.3)

Simons, John. ANIMAL RIGHTS AND THE POLITICS OF LITER-ARY REPRESENTATION. New York: Palgrave, 2002. 218 p. ISBN 0-333-74514-0. [PN56 .A64 S63 2002] (22.1)

Sunstein, Cass R. and Nussbaum, Martha C., eds. ANIMAL RIGHTS: CURRENT DEBATES AND NEW DIRECTIONS. Oxford/New York: Oxford University Press, 2004. 338 p. ISBN 0-19-530510-8. [HV4708 .A56 2004] (22.1; 1.3.11; 22.2; 22.3)

Taylor, Angus. ANIMALS AND ETHICS: AN OVERVIEW OF THE PHILOSOPHICAL DEBATE. Peterborough, Ontario: Broadview Press, 2003. 214 p. ISBN 1-55111-569-7. (Previous edition published in 1999 under the title: *Magpies, Monkeys, and Morals*.) [HV4708 .T38 2003] (22.1; 16.1; 22.2)

Yount, Lisa. ANIMAL RIGHTS. New York: Facts on File, 2004. 298 p. ISBN 0-8160-5027-9. (Library in a Book series.) [HV4708 .Y84 2004] (22.1; Reference; LE)

22.2 ANIMAL EXPERIMENTATION

Bioethics in Laboratory Animal Research. ILAR JOURNAL 1999; 40(1): 1-37. (ISSN 0018-9960.) (22.2; 1.1; 2.1; 2.2; 5.3; 22.1)

Dolan, Kevin. LABORATORY ANIMAL LAW. Oxford/Malden, MA: Blackwell Science, 2000. 225 p. ISBN 0-632-05278-3. [KD3426 .D65 2000] (22.2; 9.7; LE)

Institute for Laboratory Animal Research (United States) [and] National Research Council (United States). SCIENCE, MEDICINE, AND ANIMALS: A CIRCLE OF DISCOVERY. Washington, DC: National Academies Press, 2004. 52 p. ISBN 0-309-08894-1. [R853 .A53 S36 2004] (22.2; 9.7)

Yarri, Donna. THE ETHICS OF ANIMAL EXPERIMENTATION: A CRITICAL ANALYSIS AND CONSTRUCTIVE CHRISTIAN PRO-POSAL. Ann Arbor, MI: University Microfilms International [UMI], 2002. 352 p. (Publication No. AAT-3048074. Dissertation, (Ph.D.)—Southern Methodist University, 2002.) [BT747 .Y37 2002] (22.2; 1.1; 1.2; 4.4; 22.1)

Yarri, Donna. THE ETHICS OF ANIMAL EXPERIMENTATION: A CRITICAL ANALYSIS AND CONSTRUCTIVE CHRISTIAN PRO-POSAL. New York: Oxford University Press, 2005. 220 p. ISBN 0-19-518179-4. (American Academy of Religion Academy Series. Gift of the publisher.) [BT747 .Y37 2005] (22.2; 1.2)

22.3 ANIMAL PRODUCTION

Johnsen, Carolyn. RAISING A STINK: THE STRUGGLE OVER FACTORY HOG FARMS IN NEBRASKA. Lincoln: University of Nebraska Press, 2003. 180 p. ISBN 0-8032-7617-6. (Our Sustainable Future series; Vol. 15.) [SF395.8 .N2 J64 2003] (22.3; 1.3.2)

National Research Council (United States). Board on Agriculture. Panel on Animal Health, Food Safety, and Public Health. Committee on Drug Use in Food Animals. THE USE OF DRUGS IN FOOD ANIMALS: BENEFITS AND RISKS. Washington, DC: National Academy Press, 1999. 253 p. ISBN 0-309-05436-6. (Also available on the web at: http://www.nap.edu.) [SF917 .U74 1999] (22.3; 1.3.5; 1.3.11; 5.2; 9.3.1; 9.7; 15.1)

NEW PUBLICATIONS FROM THE KENNEDY INSTITUTE OF ETHICS

Poland, Susan Cartier. BIOETHICS, BIOLAW, AND WESTERN LEGAL HERITAGE. Washington, DC: Kennedy Institute of Ethics, Georgetown University, 2005. 8 p. (Scope Note series; 45. Appeared as Scope Note 45 in the *Kennedy Institute of Ethics Journal* 2005 June; 15(2): 211-218. Available free online at: http://bioethics.georgetown.edu/publications/scopenotes/.) (2.1; 2.2; 21.1; 1.1)

Walters, LeRoy; Kahn, Tamar Joy; and Goldstein, Doris Mueller, eds. BIBLIOGRAPHY OF BIOETHICS, VOLUME 31. Washington, DC: Kennedy Institute of Ethics, Georgetown University, 2005. 701 p. ISBN 1-883913-12-8. (ISSN 0363-0161. Pricing and availability from: Mara Snyder, Kennedy Institute of Ethics, Georgetown University, Box 571212, Washington, DC 20057-1212; tel: 1-888-BIO-ETHX [U.S. and Canada only] [or] 202-687-6689; fax: 202-687-6770; email: mrm37@georgetown.edu.) [Z6675 .E8 W34 v.31] (2.1; Reference)

SECTION IV:
MONOGRAPHS

TITLE INDEX

SECTION IV: MONOGRAPHS TITLE INDEX

A

Abortion in the USA and the UK. *Section III:* 12.4.1—Francome, Colin.

Abortion Rights Controversy in America: A Legal Reader, The. *Section III:* 12.4.1—Hull, N.E.H.; Hoffer, Williamjames; and Hoffer, Peter Charles, eds.

Absorbing Perfections: Kabbalah and Interpretation. *Section III:* 1.2—Idel, Moshe.

Accessing Health Care: Responding to Diversity. *Section III:* 21.7—Healy, Judith and McKee, Martin, eds.

African Women's Health. *Section III:* 9.5.5—Turshen, Meredeth, ed.

After Daybreak: The Liberation of Belsen, 1945. *Section III:* 21.2—Shephard, Ben.

After Harm: Medical Error and the Ethics of Forgiveness. *Section III:* 9.8—Berlinger, Nancy.

Ageing Without Children: European and Asian Perspectives. *Section III:* 9.5.2—Kreager, Philip and Schröder-Butterfill, Elisabeth, eds.

Agenda for Research on Women's Health for the 21st Century: A Report of the Task Force on the NIH Women's Health Research Agenda for the 21st Century. *Section III:* 18.5.3—National Institutes of Health [NIH] (United States). Task Force on the NIH Women's Health Research Agenda for the 21st Century.

Aging: Caring for Our Elders. *Section III:* 9.5.2—Weisstub, David N.; Thomasma, David C.; Gauthier, Serge; and Tomossy, George F., eds.

Aging: Culture, Health, and Social Change. *Section III:* 9.5.2—Weisstub, David N.; Thomasma, David C.; Gauthier, Serge; and Tomossy, George F., eds.

AIDS in the Twenty-First Century: Disease and Gobalization. *Section III:* 9.5.6—Barnett, Tony and Whiteside, Alan.

Alberta Law Review 1998 July; 36(3). *Section III:* 9.5.5—Case Comments and Notes: Winnipeg Child and Family Services.

Altering American Consciousness: The History of Alcohol and Drug Use in the United States, 1800-2000.

Section III: 9.5.9—Tracy, Sarah W. and Acker, Caroline Jean, eds.

Alternative Sources of Human Pluripotent Stem Cells. *Section III:* 18.5.4—President's Council on Bioethics (United States).

Amazing Grace: Enjoying Alzheimer's. *Section III:* 17.1—Smith, Ray and Crofts, Andrew.

American Business Law Journal 2001 Winter; 38(2). *Section III:* 1.3.2—Special Issue on Business Ethics.

American Judaism: A History. *Section III:* 1.2—Sarna, Jonathan D.

Ancestor's Tale: A Pilgrimage to the Dawn of Evolution, The. *Section III:* 3.2—Dawkins, Richard.

Ancient Medicine. *Section III:* 7.1—Nutton, Vivian.

And When Did You Last See Your Father? *Section III:* 8.1—Morrison, Blake.

". . . And You Shall Live by Them": Contemporary Jewish Approaches to Medical Ethics. *Section III:* 2.1—Flancbaum, Louis.

Animal Pragmatism: Rethinking Human-Nonhuman Relationships. *Section III:* 22.1—McKenna, Erin and Light, Andrew, eds.

Animal Rights. *Section III:* 22.1—Yount, Lisa.

Animal Rights: A Historical Anthology. *Section III:* 22.1—Linzey, Andrew and Clarke, Paul Barry, eds.

Animal Rights and Moral Philosophy. *Section III:* 22.1—Franklin, Julian, H.

Animal Rights and the Politics of Literary Representation. *Section III:* 22.1—Simons, John.

Animal Rights: Current Debates and New Directions. *Section III:* 22.1—Sunstein, Cass R. and Nussbaum, Martha C., eds.

Animal Rights, Human Wrongs: An Introduction to Moral Philosophy. *Section III:* 22.1—Regan, Tom.

Animals and Ethics: An Overview of the Philosophical Debate. *Section III:* 22.1—Taylor, Angus.

Animals, Politics and Morality. *Section III:* 22.1—Garner, Robert.

Annals of the American Academy of Political and Social Science 2002 September; 583. *Section III:* 4.1.1—Global Perspectives on Complementary and Alternative Medicine.

Applied Ethics: A Non-Consequentialist Approach. *Section III:* 2.1—Oderberg, David S.

Archaeology of Qumran and the Dead Sea Scrolls, The. *Section III:* 1.2—Magness, Jodi.

Architects of Annihilation: Auschwitz and the Logic of Destruction. *Section III:* 1.3.5—Aly, Gotz and Heim, Susanne.

Art of Genes: How Organisms Make Themselves, The. *Section III:* 15.1—Coen, Enrico.

At Home with Dying: A Zen Hospice Approach. *Section III:* 20.4.1—Collett, Merrill.

Attending Children: A Doctor's Education. *Section III:* 9.5.7—Mohrmann, Margaret E.

Attitudes of Rhode Island Primary Care Physicians Toward the Use of Genetic Testing for Breast Cancer. *Section III:* 15.3—Alexakos, Frances M.

Auschwitz, die NS-Medizin und ihre Opfer. *Section III:* 18.5.5—Klee, Ernst.

L'Avenir n'est pas écrit. *Section III:* 15.1—Jacquard, Albert; Kahn, Axel; and Papillon, Fabrice.

Awareness of Dying. *Section III:* 20.3.1—Glaser, Barney G. and Strauss, Anselm L.

B

Baby Steps: How Lesbian Alternative Insemination is Changing the World. *Section III:* 14.2—Agigian, Amy.

Banality of Evil: Hannah Arendt and "The Final Solution", The. *Section III:* 21.4—Bergen, Bernard J.

Basic Questions on Healthcare: What Should Good Care Include? *Section III:* 8.1—O'Mathúna, Dónal P.; Hensley, Samuel D.; Adam, Mary B.; Kilner, John F.; Orr, Robert D.; and Stewart, Gary P.

Bedside Manners: One Doctor's Reflections on the Oddly Intimate Encounters Between Patient and Healer. *Section III:* 8.1—Watts, David.

Before Darwin: Reconciling God and Nature. *Section III:* 5.1—Thomson, Keith.

Behind the Silence: Chinese Voices on Abortion. *Section III:* 12.5.2—Nie, Jing-Bao.

Being Human: Fulfilling Genetic and Spiritual Potential. *Section III:* 15.1—Vardy, Peter.

Being Me: What It Means to Be Human. *Section III:* 15.1—Moore, Pete.

Belmont Revisited: Ethical Principles for Research on Human Subjects. *Section III:* 18.2—Childress, James F.; Meslin, Eric M.; and Shapiro, Harold, eds.

Better Than Prozac: Creating the Next Generation of Psychiatric Drugs. *Section III:* 17.4—Barondes, Samuel H.

Beyond Justice: The Auschwitz Trial. *Section III:* 21.4—Wittmann, Rebecca.

Beyond Prozac: Healing Mental Suffering Without Drugs. *Section III:* 17.1—Lynch, Terry.

Bibliography of Bioethics, Volume 31. *Section III:* 2.1—Walters, LeRoy; Kahn, Tamar Joy; and Goldstein, Doris Mueller, eds.

Bien naître, bien être, bien mourir: propos sur l'eugénisme et l'euthanasie. *Section III:* 15.5—Moyse, Danielle.

Biodiversidad y biotecnología: Reflexiones en bioética. *Section III:* 16.1—Donadío Maggi de Gandolfi, María Celestina.

Biodiversity and Environmental Philosophy: An Introduction. *Section III:* 16.1—Sarkar, Sahotra.

Bioethics and Cloning: Report from a Workshop Arranged by the Nordic Theological Network for Bioethics in Århus, September 25-27, 1998. *Section III:* 14.5—Østnor, Lars, ed.

Bioethics and Medical Issues in Literature. *Section III:* 7.1—Stripling, Mahala Yates.

Bioethics and Social Reality. *Section III:* 2.1—Häyry, Matti; Takala, Tuija; and Herissone-Kelly, Peter, eds.

Bioethics Beyond the Headlines: Who Lives? Who Dies? Who Decides? *Section III:* 2.1—Jonsen, Albert R.

Bioethics: Health Care Law and Ethics. *Section III:* 2.1—Furrow, Barry R.; Greaney, Thomas L.; Johnson, Sandra H.; Jost, Timothy Stolzfus; and Schwartz, Robert L.

Bioethics in a Small World. *Section III:* 2.1—Thiele, F. and Ashcroft, R.E., eds.

Bioethik im christlich-islamischen Dialog. *Section III:* 2.1—Eich, Thomas and Reifeld, Helmut, eds.

Bioéthique: Jusqu'où peut-on aller? *Section III:* 2.1—Lemaire, Jacques and Susanne, Charles, eds.

Bioética para la sustentabilidad. *Section III:* 2.1—Acosta Sariego, José R., ed.

Bioetika. *Section III:* 2.1—Matulic, Tonci.

BioEvolution: How Biotechnology Is Changing Our World. *Section III:* 15.1—Fumento, Michael.

Biological Confinement of Genetically Engineered Organisms. *Section III:* 15.7—National Research Council (United States). Committee on Biological Confinement of Genetically Engineered Organisms.

Biomedical Research. *Section III:* 1.3.9.

Biomedicine and the Human Condition: Challenges, Risks, and Rewards. *Section III:* 4.2—Sargent, Michael G.

Biopsychosocial Medicine: An Integrated Approach to Understanding Illness. *Section III:* 4.1.1—White, Peter, ed.

Biotechnological Inventions: Moral Restraints and Patent Law. *Section III:* 15.8—Mills, Oliver.

Biotechnology and Communication: The Meta-technologies of Information. *Section III:* 15.1—Braman, Sandra, ed.

Biotechnology, Patents and Morality. *Section III:* 15.1—Sterckx, Sigrid, ed.

Biotechnology, Weapons and Humanity. *Section III:* 21.3—British Medical Association. Board of Science and Education.

Black Physician's Struggle for Civil Rights: Edward C. Mazique, M.D., A. *Section III:* 9.5.4—Ridlon, Florence.

Blackwell Companion to Religious Ethics, The. *Section III:* 1.2—Schweiker, William, ed.

Blessed Event, A. *Section III:* 14.2—Page, Jean Reynolds.

Body: Classic and Contemporary Readings, The. *Section III:* 4.4—Welton, Donn, ed.

Boundaries of Her Body: The Troubling History of Women's Rights in America, The. *Section III:* 9.5.5—Rowland, Debran.

Brain Takes Shape: An Early History, The. *Section III:* 3.1—Martensen, Robert L.

Breast Feeding and Sexuality: Behaviour, Beliefs and Taboos Among the Gogo Mothers in Tanzania. *Section III:* 9.5.5—Mabilia, Mara.

Buddhism & Science: Breaking New Ground. *Section III:* 1.2—Wallace, B. Alan, ed.

Buddhism, Virtue and Environment. *Section III:* 16.1—Cooper, David E. and James, Simon P.

C

Can Death Be a Harm to the Person Who Dies? *Section III:* 20.1—Li, Jack.

Care and Coercion: Medical Knowledge, Social Policy and Patients with Veneral Disease in Sweden, 1785-1903. *Section III:* 9.5.1—Lundberg, Anna.

Caring Science as Sacred Science. *Section III:* 4.1.3—Watson, Jean.

Case Anaylsis in Clinical Ethics. *Section III:* 2.1—Ashcroft, Richard; Lucassen, Anneke; Parker, Michael; Verkerk, Marian; and Widdershoven, Guy, eds.

Case Studies in Nursing Ethics. *Section III:* 4.1.3—Fry, Sara T. and Veatch, Robert M.

Casebook Patientenverfügung: Vorausverfügung, Vorsorgevollmacht, Betreuungsverfügung mit Fallbeispielen, Formulierungshilfen, Checklisten. *Section III:* 20.5.4—Rixen, Stephan and Reinecke, Siegfried.

Cast of Shadows. *Section III:* 14.5—Guilfoile, Kevin.

Catholic Church, Morality and Politics, The. *Section III:* 1.2—Curran, Charles E. and Griffin, Leslie, eds.

Catholic Medical Ethics: Core Readings. *Section III:* 2.1—Jagielo, Ted and Guinan, Patrick, eds.

Centre of Wonders: The Body in Early America, A. *Section III:* 4.4—Lindman, Janet Moore and Tarter, Michele Lise, eds.

Changing Role of the Embryo in Evolutionary Thought: Roots of Evo-Devo, The. *Section III:* 3.1—Amundson, Ronald.

Changing the U.S. Health Care System: Key Issues in Health Services, Policy, and Management. *Section III:* 9.1—Andersen, Ronald M.; Rice, Thomas H. and Kominski, Gerald F.

Changing Unjust Laws Justly: Pro-Life Solidarity with "The Last and Least". *Section III:* 12.4.2—Harte, Colin.

Children in the New Millennium: Environmental Impact on Health. *Section III:* 9.5.7—United Nations. Environmental Programme; UNICEF; and World Health Organization.

Children: Rights and Childhood. *Section III:* 9.5.7—Archard, David.

Children's Health, the Nation's Wealth: Assessing and Improving Child Health. *Section III:* 9.5.7—National Research Council (United States). Committee on Evaluation of Children's Health.

Chinas Bioethik verstehen: Ergebnisse, Analysen und Überlegungen aus einem Forschungsprojekt zur kulturell aufgeklärten Bioethik. *Section III:* 2.1—Döring, Ole.

Choice & Coercion: Birth Control, Sterilization, and Abortion in Public Health and Welfare. *Section III:* 11.1—Schoen, Johanna.

Citizen Cyborg: Why Democratic Societies Must Respond to the Redesigned Human of the Future. *Section III:* 15.1—Hughes, James.

Classifying Madness: A Philosophical Examination of the Diagnostic and Statistical Manual of Mental Disorders. *Section III:* 4.3—Cooper, Rachel.

Clinician's Guide to Palliative Care, A. *Section III:* 20.4.1—Taylor, George J. and Kurent, Jerome E.

Clinics in Sports Medicine 2004 April; 23(2). *Section III:* 9.5.1—Johnson, Rob, ed.

Cloning. *Section III:* 14.5—Harris, Nancy, ed.

Coevolution of Human Potential and Converging Technologies, The. *Section III:* 5.1—Roco, Mihail C. and Montemagno, Carlo D., eds.

Commodifying Bodies. *Section III:* 4.4—Scheper-Hughes, Nancy and Wacquant, Loïc, eds.

Common Morality: Deciding What to Do. *Section III:* 1.1—Gert, Bernard.

Communicating Health and Illness. *Section III:* 7.1—Gwyn, Richard.

Community, Covenant, and Commitment: Selected Letters and Communications. *Section III:* 1.2—Soloveitchik, Joseph B.

Comparative Health Policy. *Section III:* 9.1—Blank, Robert H. and Burau, Viola.

Compassion and Medicine: Postmodern Ethics and the Physician-Patient Relationship. *Section III:* 8.1—Degnin, Francis Dominic.

Complementary and Alternative Medicine in the United States. *Section III:* 4.1.1—Institute of Medicine (United States). Committee on the Use of Complementary and Alternative Medicine by the American Public.

Complexities: Beyond Nature & Nurture. *Section III:* 15.6—McKinnon, Susan and Silverman, Sydel, eds.

Compromis, dilemmes et paradoxes en éthique clinique. *Section III:* 2.1—Malherbe, Jean-François.

Concise Routledge Encyclopedia of Philosophy. *Section III:* 1.1.

Conference Report and Summaries: The Ethics of Patenting Human Genes and Stem Cells. *Section III:* 15.8—Jorgensen, Henrik and Lykkeskov, Anne, eds.; Danish Council of Ethics = Det Etiske Råd.

Conflicts of Interest: Challenges and Solutions in Business, Law, Medicine, and Public Policy. *Section III:* 1.3.1—Moore, Don A.; Cain, Daylian M.; Loewenstein, George; Bazerman, Max H., eds.

Confronting AIDS: Public Priorities in a Global Epidemic. *Section III:* 9.5.6—World Bank.

Confronting Cruelty: Moral Orthodoxy and the Challenge of the Animal Rights Movement. *Section III:* 22.1—Munro, Lyle.

Connecticut Law Review 2004 Summer; 36(4). *Section III:* 18.5.4—[Human Embryo Research Debate].

Conscious in a Vegetative State? A Critique of the PVS Concept. *Section III:* 20.5.1—McCullagh, Peter.

Constructions of Disability: Researching the Interface Between Disabled and Non-disabled People. *Section III:* 7.1—Tregaskis, Claire.

Consumer's Guide to a Brave New World. *Section III:* 15.1—Smith, Wesley J.

Contentious Curricula: Afrocentrism and Creationism in American Public Schools. *Section III:* 1.3.3—Binder, Amy J.

Contested Memories: Poles and Jews During the Holocaust and Its Aftermath. *Section III:* 21.4—Zimmerman, Joshua D., ed.

Controversial Therapies for Developmental Disabilities: Fad, Fashion, and Science in Professional Practice. *Section III:* 17.3—Jacobson, John W.; Foxx, Richard M.; and Mulick, James A., eds.

Controversies in Science and Technology: from Maize to Menopause. *Section III:* 15.1—Kleinman, Daniel Lee; Kinchy, Abby J.; and Handelsman, Jo, eds.

Cord Blood: Establishing a National Hematopoietic Stem Cell Bank Program. *Section III:* 19.4—Gebbie, Kristine; Meyer, Emily Ann; and Hanna, Kathi, eds.; Institute of Medicine (United States). Committee on Establishing a National Cord Blood Stem Cell Bank Program.

Cost of Choice: Women Evaluate the Impact of Abortion, The. *Section III:* 12.5.2—Bachiochi, Erika, ed.

Cracking the Code of Life: The Race to Decode Human DNA. *Section III:* 15.10—WGBH Boston Video.

Critical Condition: How Health Care in America Became Big Business—And Bad Medicine. *Section III:* 9.3.1—Barlett, Donald L. and Steele, James B.

Cross-Cultural Biotechnology. *Section III:* 15.1—Brannigan, Michael C., ed.

Cross-Cultural Medicine. *Section III:* 21.7—Bigby, JudyAnn, ed.

Cruel World: The Children of Europe in the Nazi Web. *Section III:* 21.4—Nicholas, Lynn H.

Crux, The. *Section III:* 15.5—Gilman, Charlotte Perkins.

Cult of Health and Beauty in Germany: A Social History, 1890-1930, The. *Section III:* 15.5—Hau, Michael.

Cultural Changes in Attitudes Toward Death, Dying and Bereavement. *Section III:* 20.3.1—Hayslip, Bert and Peveto, Cynthia A.

Cultural Competency for Health Professionals. *Section III:* 21.7—Wells, Shirley A. and Black, Roxie M.

Cultural History of Pregnancy: Pregnancy, Medicine and Culture, 1750-2000, A. *Section III:* 14.1—Hanson, Clare.

Culture in Clinical Care. *Section III:* 21.7—Bonder, Betty R.; Martin, Laura; and Miracle, Andrew W.

Culture of Death, The. *Section III:* 20.1—Noys, Benjamin.

Cultures of the Jews: A New History. *Section III:* 1.2—Biale, David, ed.

Cutter Incident: How America's First Polio Vaccine Led to the Growing Vaccine Crisis, The. *Section III:* 9.7—Offit, Paul A.

D

Deadly Medicine: Creating the Master Race. *Section III:* 15.5—Bachrach, Susan [project director] and Kuntz, Dieter [editor].

Dear Mr. Darwin: Letters on the Evolution of Life and Human Nature. *Section III:* 15.1—Dover, Gabriel.

Death and Dying, Who Decides? *Section III:* 20.1—Alters, Sandra.

Death and Medical Power: An Ethical Analysis of Dutch Euthanasia Practice. *Section III:* 20.5.1—Have, Henk A.M.J. ten and Welie, Jos V.M.

Death, Dying, and Social Differences. *Section III:* 20.4.1—Oliviere, David and Monroe, Barbara, eds.

Death in England: An Illustrated History. *Section III:* 20.1—Jupp, Peter C. and Gittings, Clare, eds.

Debating Design: From Darwin to DNA. *Section III:* 3.2—Dembski, William A. and Ruse, Michael, eds.

Defending Science—Within Reason: Between Scientism and Cynicism. *Section III:* 5.1—Haack, Susan.

Departing from Deviance: A History of Homosexual Rights and Emancipatory Science in America. *Section III:* 10—Minton, Henry L.

Designer Children: Reconciling Genetic Technology, Feminism, and Christian Faith. *Section III:* 15.1—Peterson-Iyer, Karen.

Designs on Nature: Science and Democracy in Europe and the United States. *Section III:* 5.3—Jasanoff, Sheila.

Developing a National Mental Health Policy. *Section III:* 17.1—Jenkins, Rachel; McCulloch, Andrew; Friedli, Lynne; and Parker, Camilla.

Development Outreach 2004 July; 6(2). *Section III:* 9.5.6—Access for All: Fighting HIV/AIDS.

Dicing with Death: Chance, Risk and Health. *Section III:* 7.1—Senn, Stephen.

Different Nature: The Paradoxical World of Zoos and Their Uncertain Future, A. *Section III:* 22.1—Hancocks, David.

Difficult Conversations in Medicine. *Section III:* 8.1—Macdonald, Elisabeth, ed.

Digital People: From Bionic Humans to Androids. *Section III:* 5.1—Perkowitz, Sidney.

Dignity of Difference: How to Avoid the Clash of Civilizations, The. *Section III:* 1.2—Sacks, Jonathan.

Disease and Democracy: The Industrialized World Faces AIDS. *Section III:* 9.5.6—Baldwin, Peter.

Disrupted Dialogue: Medical Ethics and the Collapse of Physician-Humanist Communication (1770-1980). *Section III:* 2.2—Veatch, Robert M.

Diving-Bell and the Butterfly, The. *Section III:* 9.5.1—Bauby, Jean-Dominique.

DNA: Forensic and Legal Applications. *Section III:* 15.1—Kobilinsky, Lawrence; Liotti, Thomas F.; and Oeser-Sweat, Jamel.

Doctor & Patient: Exploring Clinical Thinking. *Section III:* 8.1—Cox, Ken.

Dr. Death: A Novel. *Section III:* 20.7—Kellerman, Jonathan.

Doctor in Literature: Satisfaction or Resentment?, The. *Section III:* 7.1—Posen, Solomon.

Doctor, What's Wrong? Making the NHS Human Again. *Section III:* 8.1—Petit-Zeman, Sophie.

Doctors from Hell: The Horrific Account of Nazi Experiments on Humans. *Section III:* 18.5.5—Spitz, Vivien.

Don't Kill Your Baby: Public Health and the Decline of Breastfeeding in the Nineteenth and Twentieth Centuries. *Section III:* 9.5.7—Wolf, Jacqueline H.

Dream of the Perfect Child, The. *Section III:* 15.2—Rothschild, Joan.

Drug Trial: Nancy Olivieri and the Science Scandal That Rocked the Hospital for Sick Children, The. *Section III:* 1.3.9—Shuchman, Miriam.

E

Educating for Moral Action: A Sourcebook in Health and Rehabilitation Ethics. *Section III:* 2.1—Purtilo, Ruth B.; Jensen, Gail M.; and Royeen, Charlotte Brasic.

Elusive Quest: Accountability in Hospitals, The. *Section III:* 9.8—Wiener, Carolyn L.

Embodied Care: Jane Addams, Maurice Merleau-Ponty, and Feminist Ethics. *Section III:* 4.4—Hamington, Maurice.

Embryo: Scientific Discovery and Medical Ethics, The. *Section III:* 18.5.4—Blazer, Shraga and Zimmer, Etan Z., eds.

Empreintes génétiques, Les. *Section III:* 15.1—Rouger, Philippe.

Empty Cages: Facing the Challenge of Animal Rights. *Section III:* 22.1—Regan, Tom.

Enciclopedia di bioetica e sessuologia. *Section III:* 2.1—Russo, Giovanni, ed.

Encountering the Sacred in Psychotherapy: How to Talk with People about Their Spiritual Lives. *Section III:* 17.2—Griffith, James L. and Griffith, Melissa Elliott.

Encyclopedia of Work-Related Illnesses, Injuries, and Health Issues, The. *Section III:* 16.3—Kahn, Ada P. and Meyer, Delbert H.

End-of-Life Care: Clinical Practice Guidelines. *Section III:* 20.4.1—Kuebler, Kim K.; Berry, Patricia H.; and Heidrich, Debra E.

End-of-Life Decision Making: A Cross-National Study. *Section III:* 20.4.1—Blank, Robert H. and Merrick, Janna C., eds.

End-of-Life Treatment Preferences and Family Impact on Outcome. *Section III:* 20.5.4—Crawford, Wendy Y.

Ending Life: Ethics and the Way We Die. *Section III:* 20.7—Battin, Margaret Pabst.

Environmental Ethics. *Section III:* 16.1—Walker, Joe.

Environmental Ethics and Policy Book: Philosophy, Ecology, Economics, The. *Section III:* 16.1—Van DeVeer, Donald and Pierce, Christine, eds.

Environmental Ethics for a Postcolonial World. *Section III:* 16.1—Curtin, Deane.

Environmentally Induced Illnesses: Ethics, Risk Assessment, and Human Rights. *Section III:* 16.1—Kerns, Thomas.

Envisioning the National Health Care Quality Report. *Section III:* 9.8—Hurtado, Margarita Patricia; Swift, Elaine K.; and Corrigan, Janet M., eds.; Institute of Medicine (United States). Committee on the National Quality Report on Health Care Delivery.

Epileptic. *Section III:* 9.5.1—David B.

Escaping Auschwitz: A Culture of Forgetting. *Section III:* 21.4—Linn, Ruth.

Ethic of Honesty: The Fundamental Rule of Psychoanalysis, The. *Section III:* 17.2—Thompson, M. Guy.

Ethical and Legal Issues for Mental Health Professionals: A Comprehensive Handbook of Principles and Standards. *Section III:* 17.1—Bucky, Steven F.; Callan, Joanne E.; and Stricker, George, eds.

Ethical & Legal Issues in Canadian Nursing. *Section III:* 4.1.3—Keatings, Margaret and Smith, O'Neil B.

Ethical and Professional Issues in Nursing: Perspectives from Europe. *Section III:* 4.1.3—Tadd, Win, ed.

Ethical Aspects of ICT Implants in the Human Body: Proceedings of the Roundtable Debate, Amsterdam, 21 December 2004, The. *Section III:* 5.1—European Commission. European Group on Ethics in Science and New Technologies.

Ethical Brain, The. *Section III:* 17.1—Gazzaniga, Michael S.

Ethical Caring and the Physician-Patient Relationship: A Dual Defense of a Virtue Ethics of Care. *Section III:* 8.1—McCabe, Matthew Scott.

Ethical Choices: Case Studies for Medical Practice. *Section III:* 2.3—Snyder, Lois.

Ethical Considerations for Research on Housing-Related Health Hazards Involving Children. *Section III:* 18.5.2—Lo, Bernard and O'Connell, Mary Ellen, eds.; National Research Council (United States) [and] Institute of Medicine (United States). Committee on Ethical Issues in Housing-Related Health Hazard Research Involving Children, Youth, and Families.

Ethical Dilemmas in Pediatrics: Cases and Commentaries. *Section III:* 9.5.7—Frankel, Lorry R.; Goldworth, Amnon; Rorty, Mary V.; and Silverman, William A., eds.

Ethical Dimensions in the Health Professions. *Section III:* 2.1—Purtilo, Ruth B.

Ethical Framework for Complementary and Alternative Therapies, An. *Section III:* 4.1.1—Stone, Julie.

Ethical Issues in Clinical Neuropsychology. *Section III:* 17.1—Bush, Shane S. and Drexler, Michael L., eds.

Ethical Perspectives: Sexual Boundary Issues and the Chiropractic Paradigm. *Section III:* 7.4—Stahl, Michael J. and Foreman, Stephen M.

Ethical Wills: Putting Your Values on Paper. *Section III:* 1.3.1—Baines, Barry K.

Ethics and the War on Terrorism. *Section III:* 21.2—Vaux, Kenneth L.

Ethics and Weapons of Mass Destruction: Religious and Secular Perspectives. *Section III:* 16.2—Hashmi, Sohail H. and Lee, Stephen P., eds.

Ethics for Health Care. *Section III:* 2.1—Berglund, Catherine.

Ethics for the Practice of Psychology in Canada. *Section III:* 17.1—Truscott, Derek and Crook, Kenneth H.

Ethics, Humans and Other Animals: An Introduction with Readings. *Section III:* 22.1—Hursthouse, Rosalind.

Ethics in a Multicultural Context. *Section III:* 21.7—Pack-Brown, Sherlon P. and Williams, Carmen Braun.

Ethics in Clinical Practice. *Section III:* 2.3—Ahronheim, Judith C.; Moreno, Jonathan D.; and Zuckerman, Connie.

Ethics in Electroconvulsive Therapy. *Section III:* 17.5—Ottosson, Jan-Otto and Fink, Max.

Ethics in End-of-Life Decisions in Social Work Practice. *Section III:* 20.5.1—Csikai, Ellen L. and Chaitin, Elizabeth.

Ethics in Health Services Management. *Section III:* 9.1—Darr, Kurt.

Ethics in Public Relations: A Guide to Best Practice. *Section III:* 1.3.2—Parsons, Patricia J.; Institute of Public Relations (Great Britain).

Ethics Manual. *Section III:* 2.1—Snyder, Lois and Leffler, Cathy, eds.; American College of Physicians. Ethics and Human Rights Committee.

Ethics of Animal Experimentation: A Critical Analysis and Constructive Christian Proposal, The. (2002) *Section III:* 22.2—Yarri, Donna.

Ethics of Animal Experimentation: A Critical Analysis and Constructive Christian Proposal, The. (2005) *Section III:* 22.2—Yarri, Donna.

Ethics of Assistance: Morality and the Distant Needy, The. *Section III:* 21.1—Chatterjee, Deen K., ed.

Ethics of Human Genetics: Challenges of the (Post) Genomic Era. *Section III:* 15.1—Glasa, J., ed.; Institute of Medical Ethics and Bioethics Foundation.

Ethics of Lobbying: Organized Interests, Political Power, and the Common Good, The. *Section III:* 1.3.5—Georgetown University. Woodstock Theological Center.

Ethics of Medical Involvement in Capital Punishment: A Philosophical Discussion, The. *Section III:* 20.6—Gaie, Joseph B.R.

Ethics of Nature, The. *Section III:* 16.1—Deane-Drummond, Celia E.

Ethics of Research Involving Animals, The. *Section III:* 22.2—Nuffield Council on Bioethics.

Ethics of Teaching: A Casebook, The. *Section III:* 1.3.3—Keith-Spiegel, Patricia; Whitley, Bernard E.; Balogh, Deborah Ware; Perkins, David V.; and Wittig, Arno F.

Ethics of the Body: Postconventional Challenges. *Section III:* 2.1—Shildrick, Margrit and Mykitiuk, Roxanne, eds.

Ethics Today: For Ministers and Healthcare Professionals: Problems and Some Practical Answers. *Section III:* 2.1—Wong, John B.

Eugenic Nation: Faults and Frontiers of Better Breeding in Modern America. *Section III:* 15.5—Stern, Alexandra Minna.

Eugenics and Other Evils: An Argument Against the Scientifically Organized State. *Section III:* 15.5—Chesterton, G.K.

Eugenics in Australia: Striving for National Fitness. *Section III:* 15.5—Wyndham, Diana.

Eugenics Movement: An Encyclopedia, The. *Section III:* 15.5—Engs, Ruth Clifford.

Eugénisme, la science et le droit, L'. *Section III:* 15.5—Bachelard-Jobard, Catherine.

EUR 21255—National Regulations on Ethics and Research in Slovak Republic (Slovenskej Republike) = EUR 21255 Právne predpisy pre oblast' etiky biomedicínskeho vyskumu v Slovenskej republike (Slovak Republic). *Section III:* 18.2—Glasa, Jozef; European Commission.

European Conquest and the Rights of Indigenous Peoples: The Moral Backwardness of International Society. *Section III:* 21.1—Keal, Paul.

Eutanásia: Por que abreviar a vida? *Section III:* 20.5.1—Pessini, Leo.

Euthanasie und Gottesfrage: Medizinische Texte und theologische Provokationen. *Section III:* 2.1—Kautzky, Rudolf.

Everything You Need to Know about Nursing Homes: The Family's Comprehensive Guide to Either Working with the Institution or Finding Care Alternatives. *Section III:* 9.5.2—Digregorio, Charlotte.

Evidence of Harm: Mercury in Vaccines and the Autism Epidemic: A Medical Controversy. *Section III:* 9.7—Kirby, David.

Evidence-Based Medicine: In Its Place. *Section III:* 9.8—Kristiansen, Ivar Sønbø and Mooney, Gavin, eds.

Evolution and Ethics: Human Morality in Biological and Religious Perspective. *Section III:* 3.2—Clayton, Philip and Schloss, Jeffrey, eds.

Evolution-Creation Struggle, The. *Section III:* 3.2—Ruse, Michael.

Evolution vs. Creationism: An Introduction. *Section III:* 3.2—Scott, Eugenie C.

Evolution's Rainbow: Diversity, Gender, and Sexuality in Nature and People. *Section III:* 10—Roughgarden, Joan.

Experience of Alzheimer's Disease: Life Through a Tangled Veil, The. *Section III:* 17.1—Sabat, Steven R.

Explaining Human Origins: Myth, Imagination and Conjecture. *Section III:* 1.3.1—Stoczkowski, Wiktor.

Exploring the Biological Contributions to Human Health: Does Sex Matter? *Section III:* 10—Wizemann, Theresa M. and Pardue, Mary-Lou, eds.; Institute of Medicine (United States). Committee on Understanding the Biology of Sex and Gender Differences.

Exposure of the American Population to Radioactive Fallout from Nuclear Weapons Tests: A Review of the CDC-NCI Draft Report on a Feasibility Study of the Health Consequences to the American Population from Nuclear Weapons Tests Conducted by the United States and Other Nations. *Section III:* 16.2—National Research Council (United States). Division on Earth and Life Studies. Board on Radiation Effects Research. Committee to Review the CDC-NCI Feasibility Study of the Health Consequences from Nuclear Weapons Tests.

Expressiveness of the Body and the Divergence of Greek and Chinese Medicine, The. *Section III:* 4.1.1—Kuriyama, Shigehisa.

Eye for an Eye? The Immorality of Punishing by Death, An. *Section III:* 20.6—Nathanson, Stephen.

F

Faith in Nature: Environmentalism as Religious Quest. *Section III:* 16.1—Dunlap, Thomas R.

See inside front cover for NRCBL Classification Scheme

Fall of an Icon: Psychoanalysis and Academic Psychiatry, The. *Section III:* 17.2—Paris, Joel.

Falling Through the Safety Net: Americans Without Health Insurance. *Section III:* 9.3.1—Geyman, John.

False Positive. *Section III:* 12.3—Cutrer, William and Glahn, Sandra.

Family Law Quarterly 2005 Fall; 39(3). *Section III:* 14.4—Symposium on Assisted Reproduction Technology (ART).

Fashioning Adultery: Gender, Sex and Civility in England, 1660-1749. *Section III:* 10—Turner, David M.

Fatal Indifference: The G8, Africa and Global Health. *Section III:* 21.1—Labonte, Ronald; Schrecker, Ted; Sanders, David; and Meeus, Wilma.

Female Face of God in Auschwitz: A Jewish Feminist Theology of the Holocaust, The. *Section III:* 21.4—Raphael, Melissa.

Female Genital Mutilation: Legal, Cultural and Medical Issues. *Section III:* 9.5.5—Skaine, Rosemarie.

Feminist Campaigns for Birth Control and Abortion Rights in Britain. *Section III:* 11.1—Hoggart, Lesley.

Fetal Rights. *Section III:* 9.5.8—Marzilli, Alan.

Fewer: How the New Demography of Depopulation Will Shape Our Future. *Section III:* 13.1—Wattenberg, Ben J.

"Fighting for the Good Cause": Reflections on Francis Galton's Legacy to American Hereditarian Psychology. *Section III:* 15.6—Sweeney, Gerald.

First, Do No Harm: The Cure for Medical Malpractice. *Section III:* 8.5—Williams, Ira E.

First the Seed: The Political Economy of Plant Biotechnology. *Section III:* 15.1—Kloppenburg, Jack Ralph.

Flesh and Blood: Perspectives on the Problem of Circumcision in Contemporary Society. *Section III:* 9.5.1—Denniston, George C.; Hodges, Frederick Mansfield; and Milos, Marilyn Fayre, eds.

Fluoride Deception, The. *Section III:* 16.1—Bryson, Christopher.

Food for Thought: The Debate Over Eating Meat. *Section III:* 22.1—Sapontzis, Steve F., ed.

Fordham Law Review 2004 April; 72(5). *Section III:* 1.1—Symposium: Rawls and the Law.

Fordham Urban Law Journal 2004 March; 31(3). *Section III:* 12.4.1—Urban Law Journal Special Series: The Current State of Abortion Law and Reproductive Rights.

Formarsi Alla Bioetica e al Valore della Vita: Linee Guida per l'Insegnamento della Religione Cattolica la Catechesi, la Parrocchia, l'Animazione di Quartiere. *Section III:* 2.1—Russo, Giovanni.

Formative Years: Children's Health in the United States, 1880-2000. *Section III:* 9.5.7—Stern, Alexandra Minna and Markel, Howard, eds.

Foucault and the Government of Disability. *Section III:* 9.5.1—Tremain, Shelley, ed.

Francis Galton: Pioneer of Heredity and Biometry. *Section III:* 15.1—Bulmer, Michael.

From Alchemy to IPO: The Business of Biotechnology. *Section III:* 15.1—Robbins-Roth, Cynthia.

From Darwin to Hitler: Evolutionary Ethics, Eugenics, and Racism in Germany. *Section III:* 15.5—Weikart, Richard.

From Medicine Man to Doctor: The Story of the Science of Healing. *Section III:* 7.1—Haggard, Howard W.

From Racism to Genocide: Anthropology in the Third Reich. *Section III:* 15.5—Schafft, Gretchen E.

From Rules to Caring Practices: Ethics and Community-Based Care for Elders. *Section III:* 9.5.2—Advocate Media Center, producer.

From So Simple a Beginning: The Four Great Books of Charles Darwin. *Section III:* 3.2—Darwin, Charles [and] Wilson, Edward O., ed.

From Witches to Crack Moms: Women, Drug Law, and Policy. *Section III:* 9.5.9—Boyd, Susan C.

Frozen Dreams: Psychodynamic Dimensions of Infertility and Assisted Reproduction. *Section III:* 14.1—Rosen, Allison and Rosen, Jay, eds.

Fundamentals of Nursing: The Art and Science of Nursing Care. *Section III:* 4.1.3—Taylor, Carol; Lillis, Carol; and LeMone, Priscilla.

G

Garbage Wars: The Struggle for Environmental Justice in Chicago. *Section III:* 16.1—Pellow, David Naguib.

Gathering Biological Warfare Storm, The. *Section III:* 21.3—Davis, Jim A. and Schneider, Barry R., eds.

Gender Perspective on Health and Medicine: Key Themes. *Section III:* 10—Segal, Marcia Texler; Demos, Vasilikie; and Kronenfeld, Jennie Jacobs, eds.

Gene Hunters, The. *Section III:* 15.1—Chedd-Angier Production Company.

Genes and DNA: A Beginner's Guide to Genetics and its Applications. *Section III:* 15.1—Omoto, Charlotte K. and Lurguin, Paul F.

Genes, Memes, and Human History: Darwinian Archaeology and Cultural Evolution. *Section III:* 15.11—Shennan, Stephen.

Genetic Databases: Socio-Ethical Issues in the Collection and Use of DNA. *Section III:* 15.1—Tutton, Richard and Corrigan, Oonagh, eds.

Genetic Governance: Health, Risk and Ethics in the Biotech Era. *Section III:* 15.7—Bunton, Robin and Petersen, Alan, eds.

Genetics and Gene Therapy. *Section III:* 15.1—McLean, Sheila A.M., ed.

Genetics, Disability, and Deafness. *Section III:* 15.1—Van Cleve, John Vickrey, ed.

Genetics, Genomics and the Patenting of DNA: Review of Potential Implications for Health in Developing Countries. *Section III:* 15.8—World Health Organization. Human Genetics Programme.

Génie génétique: une histoire, un défi. *Section III:* 15.1—Heberle-Bors, Erwin.

Genomics in Asia: A Clash of Bioethical Interests? *Section III:* 15.1—Sleeboom, Margaret, ed.

Germany's War and the Holocaust: Disputed Histories. *Section III:* 21.4—Bartov, Omer.

Gewissen der Medizin: Ärztliche Moral von der Antike bis heute, Das. *Section III:* 2.2—Bergdolt, Klaus.

Gift of Death: Confronting Canada's Tainted-Blood Tragedy, The. *Section III:* 19.4—Picard, André.

Global Genome: Biotechnology, Politics, and Culture, The. *Section III:* 15.1—Thacker, Eugene.

Global Genome? Comparing the Development of Genetic Testing for Breast Cancer in the United States and Britain, A. *Section III:* 15.3—Parthasarathy, Shobita.

Global Health Challenges for Human Security. *Section III:* 21.1—Chen, Lincoln; Leaning, Jennifer; and Narasimhan, Vasant, eds.

Global Public Goods for Health: Health Economic and Public Health Perspectives. *Section III:* 21.1—Smith, Richard; Beaglehole, Robert; Woodward, David; and Drager, Nick, eds.

Global Public Health: A New Era. *Section III:* 21.1—Beaglehole, Robert, ed.

God, Medicine & Miracles: The Spiritual Factor in Healing. *Section III:* 1.2—Fountain, Daniel E.

Good Care, Painful Choices: Medical Ethics for Ordinary People. *Section III:* 2.1—Devine, Richard J.

Gracefully Insane: The Rise and Fall of America's Premier Mental Hospital. *Section III:* 17.1—Beam, Alex.

Great Betrayal: Fraud in Science, The. *Section III:* 1.3.9—Judson, Horace Freeland.

Great Brain Debate: Nature or Nurture?, The. *Section III:* 15.6—Dowling, John E.

Great Plague: The Story of London's Most Deadly Year, The. *Section III:* 7.1—Moote, A. Lloyd and Moote, Dorothy C.

Guest for the Night: A Novel, A. *Section III:* 1.2—Agnon, S.Y.

Guide to the Spiritual Dimension of Care for People with Alzheimer's Disease and Related Dementia: More than Body, Brain, and Breath, A. *Section III:* 17.1—Shamy, Eileen.

Guide to the Zohar, A. *Section III:* 1.2—Green, Arthur.

Guidelines for Human Embryonic Stem Cell Research. *Section III:* 18.5.4—National Research Council (United States). Committee on Guidelines for Human Embryonic Stem Cell Research [and] Institute of Medicine (United States). Board on Health Sciences Policy.

Gulf War and Health, Volume 3: Fuels, Combustion Products, and Propellants. *Section III:* 16.3—Institute of Medicine (United States). Committee on Gulf War and Health: Literature Review of Selected Environmental Particulates, Pollutants, and Synthetic Chemical Compounds.

H

Handbook of Social Studies in Health and Medicine, The. *Section III:* 7.1—Albrecht, Gary L.; Fitzpatrick, Ray; and Scrimshaw, Susan C., eds.

Handbook of Women, Psychology, and the Law, The. *Section III:* 9.5.5—Barnes, Andrea, ed.

Handbook on Critical Life Issues. *Section III:* 2.1—Leies, John A.; McCarthy, Donald G.; and Bayer, Edward J.

Harvard Guide to Psychiatry, The. *Section III:* 4.3—Nicholi, Armand M., ed.

Harvest of Despair: Life and Death in Ukraine Under Nazi Rule. *Section III:* 1.3.5—Berkhoff, Karel C.

Hauerwas Reader, The. *Section III:* 1.2—Hauerwas, Stanley.

Haunting Fetus: Abortion, Sexuality, and the Spirit World in Taiwan, The. *Section III:* 12.5.2—Moskowitz, Marc L.

Having Your Baby Through Egg Donation. *Section III:* 14.4—Glazer, Ellen Sarasohn and Sterling, Evelina Weidman.

Healers Abroad: Americans Responding to the Human Resources Crisis in HIV/AIDS. *Section III:* 9.5.6—Mullan, Fitzhugh; Panosian, Claire; and Cuff, Patricia, eds.; Institute of Medicine (United States). Committee on the Options for Overseas Placement of U.S. Health Professionals.

Health Care Ethics for Psychologists: A Casebook. *Section III:* 17.1—Hanson, Stephanie L.; Kerkhoff, Thomas R.; and Bush, Shane S.

Health Care Ethics in Canada. *Section III:* 2.1—Baylis, Françoise; Downie, Jocelyn; Hoffmaster, Barry; and Sherwin, Susan, eds.

Health Education and Behavior 2002 February; 29(1). *Section III:* 7.2—Special Section: Ethical Challenges in Public Health Education Research and Practice.

Health in the News: Risk, Reporting and Media Influence. *Section III:* 1.3.7—Harrabin, Roger; Coote, Anna; and Allen, Jessica.

Health Issues in the Black Community. *Section III:* 9.5.4—Braithwaite, Ronald L. and Taylor, Sandra E., eds.

Health Policy for Health Care Professionals. *Section III:* 9.1—Bradshaw, Peter L. and Bradshaw, Gwendolen.

Health Politics: Power, Populism and Health. *Section III:* 9.1—Magee, Mike.

Health Writer's Handbook. *Section III:* 9.1—Gastel, Barbara.

Heart Transplantation. *Section III:* 19.2—Kirklin, James K.; Young, James B.; and McGiffin, David C.

Heavenly Torah as Refracted Through the Generations. *Section III:* 1.2—Heschel, Abraham Joshua.

Herztransplantation als erzählte Erfahrung: Der Mensch zwischen kulturellen Traditionen und medizinisch-technischem Fortschritt. *Section III:* 19.2—Wiebel-Fanderl, Oliva.

Hidden Costs, Value Lost: Uninsurance in America. *Section III:* 9.3.1—Institute of Medicine (United States). Committee on the Consequences of Uninsurance.

Hildegard Peplau: Psychiatric Nurse of the Century. *Section III:* 17.1—Callaway, Barbara J.

History of Chemical Warfare, A. *Section III:* 21.3—Coleman, Kim.

History of the Treatment of Renal Failure by Dialysis, A. *Section III:* 19.3—Cameron, J. Stewart.

History of Western Ethics, A. *Section III:* 1.1—Becker, Lawrence C. and Becker, Charlotte B., eds.

Hite Report: A Nationwide Study of Female Sexuality, The. *Section III:* 10—Hite, Shere.

Holocaust and Other Genocides: History, Representation, Ethics, The. *Section III:* 21.4—Smith, Helmut Walser, ed.

Holocaust Historiography: A Jewish Perspective: Conceptualizations, Terminology, Approaches and Fundamental Issues. *Section III:* 21.4—Michman, Dan.

Holocaust: Theoretical Readings, The. *Section III:* 21.4—Levi, Neil and Rothberg, Michael, eds.

Homage to Gaia: The Life of an Independent Scientist. *Section III:* 5.1—Lovelock, James.

Hospice and Palliative Care Handbook: Quality, Compliance, and Reimbursement. *Section III:* 20.4.1—Marrelli, Tina M.

Hospice Ethics: Principlism, Covenant, and Virtue. *Section III:* 20.4.1—Lyndale, Patricia J.

Hospice Use Among Blacks: Health Beliefs, Spirituality and Social Relationships as Predictive Factors. *Section III:* 20.4.1—Conner, Norma E.

Hospital: The Unseen Demands of Delivering Medical Care. *Section III:* 9.1—Doupitzky, Karine.

How to Relate Science and Religion: A Multidimensional Model. *Section III:* 5.1—Stenmark, Mikael.

Human Cloning and Moral Status. *Section III:* 14.5—Pynes, Christopher Alexander.

Human Cloning: Playing God or Scientific Progress? *Section III:* 14.5—Lester, Lane P. and Hefley, James C.

Human Cloning Public Policy Issues, Part 3. *Section III:* 14.5—National Cable Satellite Corporation.

Human Evolution: A Guide to the Debates. *Section III:* 3.2—Regal, Brian.

Human Evolutionary Genetics: Origins, People & Disease. *Section III:* 15.1—Jobling, Mark A.; Hurles, Matthew; and Tyler-Smith, Chris.

Human Factor: Revolutionizing the Way People Live with Technology, The. *Section III:* 5.3—Vicente, Kim.

Human Genome Sourcebook, The. *Section III:* 15.1—Acharya, Tara and Sankaran, Neeraja.

Human Identity and Bioethics. *Section III:* 4.4—DeGrazia, David.

Human Research Ethics Handbook: Commentary on the National Statement on Ethical Conduct in Research Involving Humans. *Section III:* 18.2—National Health and Medical Research Council (Australia).

Human Rights Act: A Practical Guide for Nurses, The. *Section III:* 8.1—Wilkinson, Rosie and Caulfield, Helen.

Humanitas 2004 July-August; 59(4). *Section III:* 15.5—Nicoletti, Michele and Galvagni, Lucia, eds.

I

I Am the Other: Literary Negotiations of Human Cloning. *Section III:* 14.5—Seabra Ferreira, Maria Aline Salgueiro.

I, Cyborg. *Section III:* 5.1—Warwick, Kevin.

I, Robot. *Section III:* 5.1—Asimov, Isaac.

Ideal und sein Nutzen: Ärztliche Ethik in England und Deutschland 1902-1933, Ein. *Section III:* 2.2—Schomerus, Georg.

ILAR Journal 1999; 40(1). *Section III:* 22.2—Bioethics in Laboratory Animal Research.

Illegal Beings: Human Clones and the Law. *Section III:* 14.5—Macintosh, Kerry Lynn.

Immunization Safety Review: Vaccines and Autism. *Section III:* 9.7—Institute of Medicine (United States). Board on Health Promotion and Disease Prevention. Immunization Safety Review Committee.

Impact of AIDS, The. *Section III:* 9.5.6—United Nations. Department of Economic and Social Affairs. Population Division.

Impact of Inequality: How to Make Sick Societies Healthier, The. *Section III:* 7.1—Wilkinson, Richard G.

Improving Medical Education: Enhancing the Behavioral and Social Science Content of Medical School Curricula. *Section III:* 7.2—Cuff, Patricia A. and Vanselow, Neal A., eds.; Institute of Medicine (United States). Committee on Behavioral and Social Sciences in Medical School Curricula.

Improving Nursing Home Care of the Dying: A Training Manual for Nursing Home Staff. *Section III:* 20.4.1—Henderson, Martha L.; Hanson, Laura C.; and Reynolds, Kimberly S.

Improving the Organ Donation Process: Can Social Work Help? *Section III:* 19.5—Leahy, Dean Milton.

In the Flesh: The Cultural Politics of Body Modification. *Section III:* 4.4—Pitts, Victoria L.

In the Hope of Nibbana: The Ethics of Theravada Buddhism. *Section III:* 1.2—King, Winston L.

In the Sleep Room: The Story of CIA Brainwashing Experiments in Canada. *Section III:* 18.6—Collins, Anne.

Inequalities in Health Care Expenditures and Health Outcomes Among the U.S. Elderly Population. *Section III:* 9.3.1—Lee, Julie Juhyun.

Information Ethics: Privacy, Property, and Power. *Section III:* 1.3.12—Moore, Adam D., ed.

Information Security and Ethics: Social and Organizational Issues. *Section III:* 1.3.12—Quigley, Marian, ed.

Inside the FDA: The Business and Politics Behind the Drugs We Take and the Food We Eat. *Section III:* 9.7—Hawthorne, Fran.

Intelligence of Apes and Other Rational Beings. *Section III:* 22.1—Rumbaugh, Duane M. and Washburn, David A.

Intelligent Person's Guide to Genetics, An. *Section III:* 15.1—Woolfson, Adrian.

Intentions in Action: Contemporary Interpretations of the Principle of Double Effect. *Section III:* 1.1—Giebel, Heidi Marie.

Interfaces Between Bioethics and the Empirical Social Sciences. *Section III:* 2.1—Stepke, Fernando Lolas and Corbinos, Lorenzo Agar, eds.; World Health Organization [and] Pan American Health Organization.

International Migration, Health, and Human Rights. *Section III:* 21.1—World Health Organization [WHO].

International Public Health: Patients' Rights vs. the Protection of Patents. *Section III:* 21.1—Beigbeder, Yves.

Interpersonal Relations in Nursing: A Conceptual Frame of Reference for Psychodynamic Nursing. *Section III:* 8.1—Peplau, Hildegard E.

Intersecting Pathways: Modern Jewish Theologians in Conversation with Christianity. *Section III:* 1.2—Krell, Marc A.

Involuntary Detention and Therapeutic Jurisprudence: International Perspectives on Civil Commitment. *Section III:* 17.7—Diesfeld, Kate and Freckelton, Ian, eds.

Is Human Nature Obsolete? Genetics, Bioengineering, and the Future of the Human Condition. *Section III:* 15.1—Baillie, Harold W. and Casey, Timothy K., eds.

Is the Holocaust Unique? Perspectives on Comparative Genocide. *Section III:* 21.4—Rosenbaum, Alan S., ed.

Is the Market Moral? A Dialogue on Religion, Economics, and Justice. *Section III:* 1.3.2—Blank, Rebecca M. and McGurn, William.

Is There an Ethicist in the House? On the Cutting Edge of Bioethics. *Section III:* 2.1—Moreno, Jonathan D.

Israeli Women's Studies: A Reader. *Section III:* 10—Fuchs, Esther, comp. and ed.

Issues of Life and Death. *Section III:* 2.3—Wilcockson, Michael.

Ivory Leg in the Ebony Cabinet: Madness, Race, and Gender in Victorian America, The. *Section III:* 17.1—Cooley, Thomas.

J

Je est un clone: l'éthique à l'épreuve des biotechnologies. *Section III:* 14.5—Hunyadi, Mark.

Jewess Pallas Athena: This Too a Theory of Modernity, The. *Section III:* 1.2—Hahn, Barbara.

Jewish Enlightenment, The. *Section III:* 1.2—Feiner, Shmuel.

Jewish Ethicist: Everyday Ethics for Business and Life, The. *Section III:* 1.2—Meir, Asher.

Jewish Passages: Cycles of Jewish Life. *Section III:* 1.2—Goldberg, Harvey E.

Jewish Resistance During the Holocaust: Moral Uses of Violence and Will. *Section III:* 21.4—Glass, James M.

Jewish Study Bible, The. *Section III:* 1.2—Berlin, Adele and Brettler, Marc Zvi, eds.

John Paul II's Contribution to Catholic Bioethics. *Section III:* 2.1—Tollefsen, Christopher, ed.

Journal of Bone and Mineral Research 2003 June; 18(6). *Section III:* 18.2—Osteoporosis Trials: Ethical Considerations in Study Design Supplement.

Journal of International Economic Law 2002 December; 5(4). *Section III:* 21.1—Special Issue: Mini-Symposium: Health and the WTO.

Justice to Future Generations and the Environment. *Section III:* 16.1—Visser 't Hooft, Hendrik Philip.

K

Kidney for Sale by Owner: Human Organs, Transplantation, and the Market. *Section III:* 19.3—Cherry, Mark J.

Kinderärzte, 1933-1945: Entrechtet, geflohen, ermordet = Pediatricians, Victims of Persecution, 1933-1945. *Section III:* 21.4—Seidler, Eduard.

Knife Man: The Extraordinary Life and Times of John Hunter, Father of Modern Surgery, The. *Section III:* 7.1—Moore, Wendy.

Konfliktfelder des Lebens: Theologische Studien zur Bioethik. *Section III:* 2.1—Frey, Christofer.

Kriminalbiologie und Zwangssterilisation: Eugenischer Rassismus 1920-1945. *Section III:* 15.5—Simon, Jürgen.

L

Laboratory Animal Law. *Section III:* 22.2—Dolan, Kevin.

Laboratory of Justice: The Supreme Court's 200-Year Struggle to Integrate Science and the Law. *Section III:* 1.3.8—Faigman, David L.

Law and Ethics of Medical Research: International Bioethics and Human Rights, The. *Section III:* 18.2—Plomer, Aurora.

Law and Nursing. *Section III:* 4.1.3—McHale, Jean V. and Tingle, John.

Law of Consent to Medical Treatment, The. *Section III:* 8.3.1—Hockton, Andrew.

Laws of Men and Laws of Nature: The History of Scientific Expert Testimony in England and America. *Section III:* 5.1—Golan, Tal.

Lay My Burden Down: Suicide and the Mental Health Crisis Among African-Americans. *Section III:* 20.7—Poussaint, Alvin F. and Alexander, Amy.

Leadership in Healthcare: Values at the Top. *Section III:* 9.1—Dye, Carson F.

Leaving You: The Cultural Meaning of Suicide. *Section III:* 20.7—Lieberman, Lisa.

Legal and Ethical Issues for Health Professionals. *Section III:* 2.1—Pozgar, George D.

Let Me Decide: The Health and Personal Care Directive That Speaks for You When You Can't. *Section III:* 20.5.4—Molloy, William and Mepham, Virginia.

Levinas Between Ethics and Politics: For the Beauty that Adorns the Earth. *Section III:* 1.1—Bergo, Bettina.

Liberal Eugenics: In Defence of Human Enhancement. *Section III:* 15.5—Agar, Nicholas.

Liberation Biology: The Scientific and Moral Case for the Biotech Revolution. *Section III:* 5.3—Bailey, Ronald.

Librarian's Copyright Companion, The. *Section III:* 1.3.12—Heller, James S.

Lie That Wounn't Die: The Protocols of the Elders of Zion, The. *Section III:* 21.1—Ben-Itto, Hadassa.

Life and Learning VI: Proceedings of the Sixth University Faculty for Life Conference June 1996 at Georgetown University. *Section III:* 2.1—Koterski, Joseph W., ed.

Life and Learning VII: Proceedings of the Seventh University Faculty for Life Conference, June 1997 at Loyola College. *Section III:* 2.1—Koterski, Joseph W., ed.

Life and Learning IX: Proceedings of the Ninth University Faculty for Life Conference, June 1999 at Trinity International University, Deerfield, Ill. *Section III:* 2.1—Koterski, Joseph W., ed.

Life and Learning XI: Proceedings of the Eleventh University Faculty for Life Conference, June 2001 at St. Joseph's University, Washington, D.C. *Section III:* 2.1—Koterski, Joseph W., ed.

Life Between Memory and Hope: The Survivors of the Holocaust in Occupied Germany. *Section III:* 21.4—Mankowitz, Zeev W.

Life, Death, and the Law: Landmark Right-to-Die Decisions. *Section III:* 20.5.1—Harrison, Maureen and Gilbert, Steve, eds.

Life in Our Hands: A Christian Perspective on Genetics and Cloning. *Section III:* 15.1—Bryant, John and Searle, John.

Lives at Risk: Single-Payer National Health Insurance Around the World. *Section III:* 9.3.1—Goodman, John C.; Musgrave, Gerald L.; and Herrick, Devon M.

Lobotomist: A Maverick Medical Genius and His Tragic Quest to Rid the World of Mental Illness, The. *Section III:* 17.6—El-Hai, Jack.

Luckiest Man: The Life and Death of Lou Gehrig. *Section III:* 9.5.1—Eig, Jonathan.

Lysenko Effect: The Politics of Science, The. *Section III:* 15.1—Roll-Hansen, Nils.

M

Machine to Make a Future: Biotech Chronicles, A. *Section III:* 15.1—Rabinow, Paul and Dan-Cohen, Talia.

Madhouse: A Tragic Tale of Megalomania and Modern Medicine. *Section III:* 17.1—Scull, Andrew.

Section III arranged by NRCBL Classification Number, then Author or Title

Making Medical Decisions for the Profoundly Mentally Disabled. *Section III:* 9.5.3—Cantor, Norman L.

Making Modern Mothers: Ethics and Family Planning in Urban Greece. *Section III:* 9.5.5—Paxson, Heather.

Making Parents: The Ontological Choreography of Reproductive Technologies. *Section III:* 14.1—Thompson, Charis.

Making Sense of MacIntyre. *Section III:* 1.1—Fuller, Michael.

Making the Nation Safer: The Role of Science and Technology in Countering Terrorism. *Section III:* 21.1—National Research Council (United States). Committee on Science and Technology Countering Terrorism.

Man Who Invented the Chromosome: The Life of Cyril Darlington, The. *Section III:* 15.1—Harman, Oren Solomon.

Manuale di Bioetica, Volume I: Fondamenti ed Etica Biomedica. *Section III:* 2.1—Sgreccia, Elio.

Many Voices: Toward Caring Culture in Healthcare and Healing. *Section III:* 8.1—Kavanagh, Kathryn Hopkins and Krowlden, Virginia, eds.

March of Unreason: Science, Democracy, and the New Fundamentalism, The. *Section III:* 5.3—Taverne, Dick.

Marginal to Mainstream: Alternative Medicine in America. *Section III:* 4.1.1—Ruggie, Mary.

Masters of the Mind: Exploring the Story of Mental Illness from Ancient Times to the New Millennium. *Section III:* 17.1—Millon, Theodore.

Mavericks, Miracles, and Medicine: The Pioneers Who Risked Their Lives to Bring Medicine into the Modern Age. *Section III:* 7.1—Fenster, Julie M.

Maya Medicine: Traditional Healing in Yucatan. *Section III:* 4.1.1—Kunow, Marianna Appel.

Measuring Medical Professionalism. *Section III:* 7.4—Stern, David Thomas, ed.

Medical Benefit and the Human Lottery: An Egalitarian Approach to Patient Selection. *Section III:* 19.6—Waring, Duff R.

Medical Care 2002 September; 40(9, Supplement). *Section III:* 18.3—Making Informed Consent Meaningful.

Medical Care Research and Review 2003 June; 60(2, Supplement). *Section III:* 9.3.1—Rice, Thomas, guest ed.

Medical Confidentiality and Crime. *Section III:* 8.4—Michalowski, Sabine.

Medical Delivery Business: Health Reform, Childbirth, and the Economic Order, The. *Section III:* 9.3.1—Perkins, Barbara Bridgman.

Medical Documentation of Torture, The. *Section III:* 21.4—Peel, Michael and Iacopino, Vincent, eds.

Medical Ethics. *Section III:* 2.1—Egendorf, Laura K., ed.

Medical Ethics: A Very Short Introduction. *Section III:* 2.1—Hope, Tony.

Medical Ethics and Law: Surviving on the Wards and Passing Exams. *Section III:* 2.3—Sokol, Daniel K. and Bergson, Gillian.

Medical Ethics and the Elderly. *Section III:* 9.5.2—Rai, Gurcharan S., ed.

Medical Ethics: Moral and Legal Conflicts in Health Care. *Section III:* 2.1—Jussim, Daniel.

Medical Firsts: From Hippocrates to the Human Genome. *Section III:* 7.1—Adler, Robert E.

Medical Treatment and the Law: The Protection of Adults and Minors in the Family Division. *Section III:* 8.3.1—Harper, Richard S.

Medicare Matters: What Geriatric Medicine Can Teach American Health Care. *Section III:* 9.3.1—Cassel, Christine K.

Medicine and Art. *Section III:* 7.1—Emery, Alan E.H. and Emery, Marcia O.H.

Medicine in a Multicultural Society: Christian, Jewish and Muslim Practitioners in the Spanish Kingdoms, 1222-1610. *Section III:* 21.7—García-Ballester, Luis.

Medicolegal Death Investigation System: Workshop Summary. *Section III:* 20.1—Institute of Medicine (United States). Committee for the Workshop on the Medicolegal Death Investigation System.

Medizin und Ethik: Aktuelle ethische Probleme in Therapie und Forschung: Ringvorlesung der Friedrich-Alexander-Universität Erlangen-Nürnberg. *Section III:* 2.1—Vollmann, Jochen, ed.

Medizinethik und Kultur: Grenzen medizinischen Handelns in Deutschland und den Niederlanden. *Section III:* 2.1—Gordijn, Bert and Have, Henk ten, eds.

Meeting Death: In Hospice, Hospital, and at Home. *Section III:* 20.3.1—Robertson, Heather.

Mein Kampf. *Section III:* 1.3.5—Hitler, Adolf.

Mendel in the Kitchen: A Scientist's View of Genetically Modified Foods. *Section III:* 15.1—Fedoroff, Nina V. and Brown, Nancy Marie.

Mental Health: A Philosophical Analysis. *Section III:* 4.3—Tengland, Per-Anders.

Mental Health and Inequality. *Section III:* 17.1—Rogers, Anne and Pilgrim, David.

Mergers of Teaching Hospitals in Boston, New York, and Northern California. *Section III:* 9.3.2—Kastor, John A.

Message in a Bottle: The Making of Fetal Alcohol Syndrome. *Section III:* 9.5.9—Golden, Janet.

Military Medical Ethics. *Section III:* 2.1—Beam, Thomas E. and Sparacino, Linette R., eds.; United States. Department of the Army. Office of the Surgeon General

[and] Walter Reed Army Medical Center. Borden Institute; [and] Uniformed Services University of the Health Sciences.

Minority Populations and Health: An Introduction to Health Disparities in the United States. *Section III:* 9.5.4—LaVeist, Thomas A.

Miracle Cure: How to Solve America's Health Care Crisis and Why Canada Isn't the Answer. *Section III:* 9.1—Pipes, Sally C.

MMR and Autism: What Parents Need to Know. *Section III:* 9.7—Fitzpatrick, Michael.

MMR: Science and Fiction. *Section III:* 9.7—Horton, Richard.

Modern Art of Dying: A History of Euthanasia in the United States, The. *Section III:* 20.5.1—Lavi, Shai J.

Modern Babylon? Prostituting Children in Thailand. *Section III:* 10—Montgomery, Heather.

Modernity in the Flesh: Medicine, Law, and Society in Turn-of-the-century Argentina. *Section III:* 7.1—Ruggiero, Kristin.

Moments of Truth in Genetic Medicine. *Section III:* 15.1—Lindee, Susan.

Mommies, Daddies, Donors, Surrogates: Answering Tough Questions and Building Strong Families. *Section III:* 14.1—Ehrensaft, Diane.

Money, Politics and Health Care: Reconstructing the Federal-Provincial Partnership. *Section III:* 9.3.1—Lazar, Harvey and St-Hilaire, France, eds.

Monster at Our Door: The Global Threat of Avian Flu, The. *Section III:* 21.1—Davis, Mike.

Moral Animals: Ideals and Constraints in Moral Theory. *Section III:* 1.1—Wilson, Catherine.

Moral, Believing Animals: Human Personhood and Culture. *Section III:* 4.4—Smith, Christian.

Moral Conflicts of Organ Retrieval: A Case for Constructive Pluralism. *Section III:* 19.5—Hinkley, Charles C.

Moral Contexts. *Section III:* 1.1—Walker, Margaret Urban.

Moral Economy of AIDS in South Africa, The. *Section III:* 9.5.6—Nattrass, Nicoli.

Moral Foundations of Trust, The. *Section III:* 1.1—Uslaner, Eric M.

Moral of the Story: An Anthology of Ethics Through Literature, The. *Section III:* 1.1—Singer, Peter and Singer, Renata, eds.

Moral Philosophers and the Novel: A Study of Winch, Nussbaum and Rorty. *Section III:* 1.1—Johnson, Peter.

Moral Reasoning and Justification in Medical Ethics. *Section III:* 2.1—Choi, Kyungsuk.

Moral Teachings of Islam: Prophetic Traditions from Al-Adab Al-Mufrad. *Section III:* 1.2—Bukhari, Muhammad ibn Ismail.

Moral Theory: A Non-Consequentialist Approach. *Section III:* 1.1—Oderberg, David S.

Morality: Its Nature and Justification. *Section III:* 1.1—Gert, Bernard.

More Than Human: Embracing the Promise of Biological Enhancement. *Section III:* 15.1—Naam, Ramez.

Mother of All Crimes: Human Rights, Criminalization and the Child Born Alive, The. *Section III:* 9.5.8—Cave, Emma.

Mountains Beyond Mountains. *Section III:* 21.1—Kidder, Tracy.

Moving Mountains: The Race to Treat Global AIDS. *Section III:* 9.5.6—D'Adesky, Anne-Christine.

Murderous Medicine: Nazi Doctors, Human Experimentation, and Typhus. *Section III:* 18.5.5—Baumslag, Naomi.

Muslim Ethics: Emerging Vistas. *Section III:* 1.2—Sajoo, Amyn B.

N

Nameless Relations: Anonymity, Melanesia and Reproductive Gift Exchange Between British Ova Donors and Recipients. *Section III:* 14.2—Konrad, Monica.

Natural Ethical Facts: Evolution, Connectionism, and Moral Cognition. *Section III:* 1.1—Casebeer, William D.

Nature's Government: Science, Imperial Britain, and the 'Improvement' of the World. *Section III:* 5.1—Drayton, Richard.

Nazi Conscience, The. *Section III:* 1.3.5—Koonz, Claudia.

Nazi Medicine and the Nuremberg Trials: From Medical War Crimes to Informed Consent. *Section III:* 18.2—Weindling, Paul Julian.

Nazi Psychoanalysis, Volume II: Crypto-Fetishism. *Section III:* 17.2—Rickels, Laurence A.

New Approaches in Ethics for the Caring Professions. *Section III:* 4.1.1—Hugman, Richard.

New Era of AIDS: HIV and Medicine in Times of Transition, The. *Section III:* 9.5.6—Kopp, Christine.

New Frontiers in Contraceptive Research: A Blueprint for Action. *Section III:* 11.1—Nass, Sharyl J. and Strauss, Jerome F., eds.; Institute of Medicine (United States). Committee on New Frontiers in Contraceptive Research.

New Politics of Old Age Policy, The. *Section III:* 9.5.2—Hudson, Robert B., ed.

Noble Conspirator: Florence S. Mahoney and the Rise of the National Institutes of Health. *Section III:* 9.1—Robinson, Judith.

Normals: A Novel, The. *Section III:* 18.5.1—Gilbert, David.

Number, A. *Section III:* 14.5—Churchill, Caryl.

Nursing Against the Odds: How Health Care Cost Cutting, Media Stereotypes, and Medical Hubris Undermine Nurses and Patient Care. *Section III:* 7.1—Gordon, Suzanne.

Nursing Ethics: Across the Curriculum into Practice. *Section III:* 4.1.3—Butts, Janie B. and Rich, Karen L.

O

OGM: le vrai et le faux. *Section III:* 15.1—Houdebine, Louis-Marie.

Ohr Yisrael: The Classic Writings of Rav Yisrael Salanter and His Disciple Rav Yitzchak Blazer. *Section III:* 1.2—Linas, Eli, ed.

Older Adults with Developmental Disabilities. *Section III:* 9.5.3—Lavin, Claire and Doka, Kenneth J.

On Doctoring: Stories, Poems, Essays. *Section III:* 7.1—Reynolds, Richard; Stone, John; Nixon, Lois LaCivita; and Wear, Delese, eds.

On the Take: How America's Complicity with Big Business Can Endanger Your Health. *Section III:* 9.7—Kassirer, Jerome P.

One Nation, Uninsured: Why the U.S. Has No National Health Insurance. *Section III:* 9.3.1—Quadagno, Jill.

Online Social Research: Methods, Issues, & Ethics. *Section III:* 18.4—Johns, Mark D.; Chen, Shing-Ling Sarina; and Hall, G. Jon, eds.

Organ Donation and Transplantation: Body Organs as an Exchangeable Socio-Cultural Resource. *Section III:* 19.5—Ben-David, Orit Brawer.

Origins of Justice: The Evolution of Morality, Human Rights, and Law, The. *Section III:* 1.1—O'Manique, John.

Oryx Holocaust Sourcebook, The. *Section III:* 21.4—Fernekes, William R.

Our Unsystematic Health Care System. *Section III:* 9.1—Budrys, Grace.

Overcoming Infertility: A Guide for Jewish Couples. *Section III:* 14.1—Grazi, Richard V.

Overdo\$ed America: The Broken Promise of American Medicine. *Section III:* 9.1—Abramson, John.

P

Palliative Care Perspectives. *Section III:* 20.4.1—Hallenbeck, James L.

Palliative Ethic of Care: Clinical Wisdom at Life's End, A. *Section III:* 20.4.1—Fins, Joseph J.

Pandora's Breeches: Women, Science and Power in the Enlightenment. *Section III:* 5.1—Fara, Patricia.

Paradise of God: Renewing Religion in an Ecological Age, The. *Section III:* 3.2—Wirzba, Norman.

Patent System for the 21st Century, A. *Section III:* 5.3—National Research Council (United States). Committee on Intellectual Property Rights in the Knowledge-Based Economy.

Paternity: A Story of Assisted Conception. *Section III:* 14.1—McHaffie, Hazel E.

Patientenaufklärung bei genetischem Risiko. *Section III:* 15.2—Sass, Hans-Martin and Schröder, Peter, eds.

Patientenverfügung und Betreuungsvollmacht. *Section III:* 20.5.1—Sass, Hans-Martin and Kielstein, Rita.

People in Auschwitz. *Section III:* 21.4—Langbein, Hermann.

Perfect Copy: Unravelling the Cloning Debate. *Section III:* 14.5—Agar, Nicholas.

Person of the Therapist, The. *Section III:* 17.2—Smith, Edward W.L.

Person, Society, and Value: Towards a Personalist Concept of Health. *Section III:* 4.2—Taboada, Paulina; Cuddeback, Kateryna Fedoryka; and Donohue- White, Patricia, eds.

Personal Autonomy: New Essays on Personal Autonomy and Its Role in Contemporary Moral Philosophy. *Section III:* 1.1—Taylor, James Stacey, ed.

Personhood and Health Care. *Section III:* 4.4—Thomasma, David C.; Weisstub, David N.; and Hervé, Christian, eds.

Pest Maiden: A Story of Lobotomy, The. *Section III:* 17.6—Schott, Penelope Scambly.

Pharmaceutical Ethics. *Section III:* 9.7—Salek, Sam and Edgar, Andrew, eds.

Philosopher's Dog: Friendships with Animals, The. *Section III:* 22.1—Gaita, Raimond.

Philosophical Dictionary. *Section III:* 1.1—Bunge, Mario.

Philosophical Diseases of Medicine and Their Cure: Philosophy and Ethics of Medicine, Volume 1: Foundations, The. *Section III:* 4.1.2—Seifert, Josef.

Philosophy & This Actual World: An Introduction to Practical Philosophical Inquiry. *Section III:* 1.1—Benjamin, Martin.

Philosophy for Medicine: Applications in a Clinical Context. *Section III:* 4.1.2—Evans, Martyn; Louhiala, Pekka; and Puustinen, Raimo, eds.

Philosophy of Psychiatry: A Companion, The. *Section III:* 17.1—Radden, Jennifer, ed.

Physical Interventions and the Law: Legal Issues Arising from the Use of Physical Interventions in Supporting Children, Young People and Adults with Learning Disabilities and Severe Challenging Behaviour. *Section III:* 17.3—Lyon, Christina M. and Pimor, Alexandra.

Physician of the Soul, Healer of the Cosmos: Isaac Luria and His Kabbalistic Fellowship. *Section III:* 1.2—Fine, Lawrence.

Physician's Guide to Coping with Death and Dying, A. *Section III:* 20.4.1—Swanson, Jan and Cooper, Alan.

Pilgrims in Medicine: Conscience, Legalism and Human Rights: An Allegory of Medical Humanities, Foundational Virtues, Ethical Principles, Law and Human Rights in Medical Personal and Professional Development. *Section III:* 7.1—Faunce, Thomas Alured.

Plague and Fire: Battling Black Death and the 1900 Burning of Honolulu's Chinatown. *Section III:* 7.1—Mohr, James C.

Plan B: Rescuing a Planet Under Stress and a Civilization in Trouble. *Section III:* 13.2—Brown, Lester R.

Policy Responses to Population Decline and Ageing. *Section III:* 13.2—United Nations. Department of Economic and Social Affairs. Population Division.

Polio and Its Aftermath: The Paralysis of Culture. *Section III:* 9.5.1—Shell, Marc.

Political Geographies of Pregnancy, The. *Section III:* 14.1—Woliver, Laura R.

Politics of Hate: Anti-Semitism, History, and the Holocaust in Modern Europe, The. *Section III:* 21.1—Weiss, John.

Positive Rights in a Republic of Talk: A Survey and a Critique. *Section III:* 21.1—Halper, Thomas.

Powerful Medicines: The Benefits, Risks, and Costs of Prescription Drugs. *Section III:* 9.7—Avorn, Jerry.

Practical Ethics in Occupational Health. *Section III:* 16.3—Westerholm, Peter; Nilstun, Tore; and Øvretveit, John, eds.

Practice of Medicine, The. *Section III:* 4.1.2—Bevins, Michael B.

Präimplantationsdiagnostik in England und Deutschland: ethische, rechtliche und praktische Probleme. *Section III:* 15.2—Ziegler, Uta.

Precaution, Environmental Science, and Preventive Public Policy. *Section III:* 16.1—Tickner, Joel A., ed.

Pregnancy and Birth after Assisted Reproductive Technologies. *Section III:* 14.4—Ludwig, Michael.

Prescription for a Healthy Nation: A New Approach to Improving Our Lives by Fixing Our Everyday World. *Section III:* 9.1—Farley, Tom and Cohen, Deborah A.

Prescription Games: Money, Ego and Power Inside the Global Pharmaceutical Industry. *Section III:* 9.7—Robinson, Jeffrey.

Price of Smoking, The. *Section III:* 9.5.9—Sloan, Frank A.; Ostermann, Jan; Picone, Gabriel; Conover, Christopher; and Taylor, Donald H.

Privacy and Disclosure of HIV in Interpersonal Relationships: A Sourcebook for Researchers and Practitioners. *Section III:* 9.5.6—Greene, Kathryn; Derlega, Valerian J.; Yep, Gust A.; and Petronio, Sandra.

Problemas atuais de Bioética. *Section III:* 2.1—Pessini, Leo and Barchifontaine, Christian de Paul de.

Professional and Ethical Issues in Nursing. *Section III:* 4.1.3—Burnard, Philip; Chapman, Christine M.; and Smallman, Susan.

Prosecutors, Palliative Medicine, and Physician-Assisted Death: An Empirical Assessment of the Likelihood of Prosecution Stemming from Opioid and Non-opioid Administrations. *Section III:* 20.7—Ziegler, Stephen Joseph.

Protect and Defend: A Novel. *Section III:* 1.3.8—Patterson, Richard North.

Protecting Psychiatric Patients and Others from the Assisted-Suicide Movement: Insights and Strategies. *Section III:* 17.1—Olevitch, Barbara A.

Proteus Effect: Stem Cells and Their Promise for Medicine, The. *Section III:* 18.5.4—Parson, Ann B.

Psyche and Soma: Physicians and Metaphysicians on the Mind-Body Problem from Antiquity to Enlightenment. *Section III:* 3.1—Wright, John P. and Potter, Paul, eds.

Psychiatrie in Waldheim/Sachsen (1716-1946). *Section III:* 17.1—Schröter, Sonja.

Psychiatry in Law/Law in Psychiatry. *Section III:* 17.1—Slovenko, Ralph.

Psychological Aspects of Women's Health Care: The Interface Between Psychiatry and Obstetrics and Gynecology. *Section III:* 9.5.5—Stotland, Nada L. and Stewart, Donna E., eds.

Psychology and the National Institute of Mental Health: A Historical Analysis of Science, Practice, and Policy. *Section III:* 17.1—Pickren, Wade E. and Schneider, Stanley F., eds.

Psychology of Death, The. *Section III:* 20.1—Kastenbaum, Robert.

Psychology, Public Policy, and Law 2003 March-June; 9(1-2). *Section III:* 17.7—Special Theme: Preventive Outpatient Commitment for Persons With Serious Mental Illness.

Public Financing and Delivery of HIV/AIDS Care: Securing the Legacy of Ryan White. *Section III:* 9.5.6—Institute of Medicine (United States). Committee on Public Financing and Delivery of HIV Care.

Public Health and the Risk Factor: A History of an Uneven Medical Revolution. *Section III:* 9.1—Rothstein, William G.

Public Health, Ethics, and Equity. *Section III:* 9.1—Anand, Sudhir; Peter, Fabienne; and Sen, Amartya, eds.

Q

Quacks: Fakers & Charlatans in Medicine. *Section III:* 7.1—Porter, Roy.

Quality of Life and Human Difference: Genetic Testing, Health Care, and Disability. *Section III:* 15.2—Wasserman, David; Wachbroit, Robert; and Bickenbach, Jerome, eds.

Québec transgénique: science, marché, humanité, Le. *Section III:* 15.1—Bibeau, Gilles.

Qu'est que l'éthique clinique? Essai philosophique sur l'éthique clinique Conçue comme réactualisation de l'éthique Aristotélicienne. *Section III:* 2.1—Voyer, Gilles.

Question of Trust, A. *Section III:* 1.3.1—O'Neill, Onora.

R

Race & Research: Perspectives on Minority Participation in Health Studies. *Section III:* 18.5.1—Beech, Bettina M. and Goodman, Maurine, eds.

Race: The Reality of Human Differences. *Section III:* 15.11—Sarich, Vincent and Miele, Frank.

Race to the Finish: Identity and Governance in an Age of Genomics. *Section III:* 15.11—Reardon, Jenny.

Race-ing Moral Formation: African American Perspectives on Care and Justice. *Section III:* 1.1—Walker, Vanessa Siddle and Snarey, John R., eds.

Radical Evolution: The Promise and Peril of Enhancing Our Minds, Our Bodies—And What it Means to Be Human. *Section III:* 5.2—Garreau, Joel.

Raising a Stink: The Struggle over Factory Hog Farms in Nebraska. *Section III:* 22.3—Johnsen, Carolyn.

Readings in Virtual Research Ethics: Issues and Controversies. *Section III:* 1.3.9—Buchanan, Elizabeth A., ed.

Reconceiving Pregnancy and Childcare: Ethics, Experience, and Reproductive Labor. *Section III:* 14.1—Mullin, Amy.

Recovered, Not Cured: A Journey Through Schizophrenia. *Section III:* 17.1—McLean, Richard.

Reducing Inequalities in Health: A European Perspective. *Section III:* 9.1—Mackenbach, Johan and Bakker, Martijntje, eds.

Reform 2001 Spring; 79. *Section III:* 15.1—The Challenge of the New Genetics.

Reinventing Eden: The Fate of Nature in Western Culture. *Section III:* 16.1—Merchant, Carolyn.

Religion as a Public Good: Jews and Other Americans on Religion in the Public Square. *Section III:* 1.2—Mittleman, Alan, ed.

Replaceable You: Engineering the Body in Postwar America. *Section III:* 4.4—Serlin, David.

Representation, Subversion, and Eugenics in Günter Grass's "*The Tin Drum*". *Section III:* 15.5—Arnds, Peter.

Reproductive Technologies: A Reader. *Section III:* 14.1—Shannon, Thomas A., ed.

Rereading Sex: Battles Over Sexual Knowledge and Suppression in Nineteenth-Century America. *Section III:* 10—Horowitz, Helen Lefkowitz.

Researchers and Their Subjects: Ethics, Power, Knowledge and Consent. *Section III:* 18.1—Smyth, Marie and Williamson, Emma, eds.

Responding to the Culture of Death: A Primer of Bioethical Issues. *Section III:* 2.1—Ling, John R.

Rethinking Rights and Responsibilities: The Moral Bonds of Community. *Section III:* 21.1—Dyck, Arthur J.

Rethinking Risk Assessment: The MacArthur Study of Mental Disorder and Violence. *Section III:* 4.3—Monahan, John; et al.

Right to Die?, A. *Section III:* 20.5.1—Walker, Richard.

Right to Die: The Law of End-of-Life Decisionmaking, The. *Section III:* 20.5.1—Meisel, Alan and Cerminara, Kathy L.

Right to Exist: A Moral Defense of Israel's Wars. *Section III:* 1.3.6—Lozowick, Yaacov.

Right to Health Care in Several European Countries, The. *Section III:* 9.2—Den Exter, André and Hermans, Herbert, eds.

Rights and Liberties in the Biotech Age: Why We Need a Genetic Bill of Rights. *Section III:* 15.1—Krimsky, Sheldon and Shorett, Peter, eds.

Rights and Resources. *Section III:* 2.1—Miller, Frances H.

Rights of Patients: The Authoritative ACLU Guide to the Rights of Patients, The. *Section III:* 2.1—Annas, George J.

Rise and Fall of HMOs: An American Health Care Revolution, The. *Section III:* 9.3.1—Coombs, Jan Gregoire.

Rise of Viagra: How the Little Blue Pill Changed Sex in America, The. *Section III:* 9.7—Loe, Meika.

Roots of Evil, The. *Section III:* 1.1—Kekes, John.

See inside front cover for NRCBL Classification Scheme

Roots of Hate: Anti-Semitism in Europe Before the Holocaust. *Section III:* 1.3.5—Brustein, William I.

S

Sacred Work: Planned Parenthood and Its Clergy Alliances. *Section III:* 12.3—Davis, Tom.

Same-Sex Cultures and Sexualities: An Anthropological Reader. *Section III:* 10—Robertson, Jennifer, ed.

Satisficing and Maximizing: Moral Theorists on Practical Reason. *Section III:* 1.1—Byron, Michael, ed.

Saving Lives and Saving Money: Transforming Health and Healthcare. *Section III:* 9.1—Gingrich, Newt; Pavey, Dana; and Woodbury, Anne.

Scaling Up Treatment for the Global AIDS Pandemic: Challenges and Opportunities. *Section III:* 9.5.6—Curran, James; Debas, Haile; Arya, Monisha; Kelley, Patrick; Knobler, Stacey; and Pray, Leslie, eds.; Institute of Medicine (United States). Committee on Examining the Probable Consequences of Alternative Patterns of Widespread Antiretroviral Drug Use in Resource-Constrainted Settings.

Science for Segregation: Race, Law, and the Case against Brown v. Board of Education. *Section III:* 15.5—Jackson, John P.

Science in Court. *Section III:* 5.3—Freeman, Michael and Reece, Helen, eds.

Science, Medicine, and Animals: A Circle of Discovery. *Section III:* 22.2—Institute for Laboratory Animal Research (United States) [and] National Research Council (United States).

Science, Technology, and Society: An Encyclopedia. *Section III:* 5.1—Restivo, Sal, ed.

Scientific Values and Civic Virtues. *Section III:* 5.3—Koertge, Noretta, ed.

Scientists Debate Gaia: The Next Century. *Section III:* 16.1—Schneider, Stephen H.; Miller, James R.; Crist, Eileen; and Boston, Penelope J., eds.

Scope and Standards of Hospice and Palliative Nursing Practice. *Section III:* 20.4.1—Hospice and Palliative Nurses Association [and] American Nurses Association.

Seattle Journal for Social Justice 2004 Fall-Winter; 3(1). *Section III:* 9.1—Corporate Ethics and Governance in the Health Care Marketplace.

Selling Sickness: How the World's Pharmaceutical Companies Are Turning Us All into Patients. *Section III:* 9.7—Moynihan, Ray and Cassels, Alan.

Seminars in Arthritis and Rheumatism 2003 February; 32(4). *Section III:* 21.4—An Ethical Dilemma in Rheumatology: Should the Eponym Reiter's Syndrome Be Discarded.

Seminars in Speech and Language 2003 November; 24(4). *Section III:* 9.5.1—Ethical, Moral, and Legal Issues in Speech and Language Pathology.

Sex and Consequences: Abortion, Public Policy, and the Economics of Fertility. *Section III:* 12.4.1—Levine, Phillip B.

Sexual Conduct: The Social Sources of Human Sexuality. *Section III:* 10—Gagnon, John H. and Simon, William.

Sexual Conversion Therapy: Ethical, Clinical and Research Perspectives. *Section III:* 10—Schidlo, Ariel; Schroeder, Michael; and Drescher, Jack, eds.

Shaping of Rationality: Toward Interdisciplinarity in Theology and Science, The. *Section III:* 1.2—van Huyssteen, J. Wentzel.

Shaping Science with Rhetoric: The Cases of Dobzhansky, Schrödinger, and Wilson. *Section III:* 3.1—Ceccarelli, Leah.

Short History of Distributive Justice, A. *Section III:* 1.1—Fleischacker, Samuel.

Shutter Island. *Section III:* 17.7—Lehane, Dennis.

Sickness and Wealth: The Corporate Assault on Global Health. *Section III:* 21.1—Fort, Meredith; Mercer, Mary Anne; and Gish, Oscar, eds.

Silent Snow: The Slow Poisoning of the Arctic. *Section III:* 16.1—Cone, Marla.

Six Lives in Jerusalem: End-of-Life Decisions in Jerusalem: Cultural, Medical, Ethical and Legal Considerations. *Section III:* 20.5.1—Sturman, Randy Linda.

Smallpox Vaccination Program: Public Health in an Age of Terrorism, The. *Section III:* 9.5.1—Baciu, Alina; Anason, Andrea Pernack; Stratton, Kathleen; and Strom, Brian, eds.; Institute of Medicine (United States). Committee on Smallpox Vaccination Program Implementation.

Social Justice, Human Rights and Public Policy. *Section III:* 1.3.5—McLachlan, Hugh V.

Social Lives of Medicines. *Section III:* 7.1—Whyte, Susan Reynolds; Geest, Sjaack van der; and Hardon, Anita.

Social Work Values and Ethics. *Section III:* 1.3.10—Reamer, Frederic G.

Social Work Values and Ethics: Identifying and Resolving Professional Dilemmas. *Section III:* 1.3.10—Congress, Elaine P.

Solidarity, Responsibility, and Freedom: Health Care Reform in the United States at the Millennium. *Section III:* 9.4—McDonald, Peter William.

Solitary Sex: A Cultural History of Masturbation. *Section III:* 10—Laqueur, Thomas W.

Soul of the Embryo: An Enquiry into the Status of the Human Embryo in the Christian Tradition, The. *Section III:* 4.4—Jones, David Albert.

Sources of the Holocaust. *Section III:* 21.4—Hochstadt, Steve, ed.

Sparing the Child: Grief and the Unspeakable in Youth Literature about Nazism and the Holocaust. *Section III:* 21.4—Bosmajian, Hamida.

Specter of Genocide: Mass Murder in Historical Perspective, The. *Section III:* 21.4—Gellately, Robert and Kiernan, Ben, eds.

Spinoza and Deep Ecology: Challenging Traditional Approaches to Environmentalism. *Section III:* 16.1—De Jonge, Eccy.

Splitting the Baby: The Culture of Abortion in Literature and Law, Rhetoric and Cartoons. *Section III:* 12.1—Myrsiades, Linda.

Sport, Play, and Ethical Reflection. *Section III:* 1.3.1—Feezell, Randolph.

Stakes and Kidneys: Why Markets in Human Body Parts Are Morally Imperative. *Section III:* 19.3—Taylor, James Stacey.

Standing in the Spaces: Essays on Clinical Process, Trauma, and Dissociation. *Section III:* 17.2—Bromberg, Philip M.

Stanford Law Review 2000 May; 52(5). *Section III:* 1.1—Cyberspace and Privacy: A New Legal Paradigm?

State of the Animals, 2001, The. *Section III:* 22.1—Salem, Deborah J. and Rowan, Andrew N., eds.; Humane Society of the United States.

Statistics Applied to Clinical Trials. *Section III:* 18.2—Cleophas, Ton J.; Zwinderman, Aeiko, H.; and Cleophas, Toine F.

Status Syndrome: How Social Standing Affects Our Health and Longevity, The. *Section III:* 7.1—Marmot, Michael.

Staying in Charge: Practical Plans for the End of Your Life. *Section III:* 20.4.1—Kaplan, Karen Orloff and Lukas, Christopher.

Still Lives: Narratives of Spinal Cord Injury. *Section III:* 9.5.1—Cole, Jonathan.

Strange Bedfellows: How Medical Jurisprudence Has Influenced Medical Ethics and Medical Practice. *Section III:* 2.1—Rich, Ben A.

Street-Smart Ethics: Succeeding in Business Without Selling Your Soul. *Section III:* 1.3.2—McLemore, Clinton W.

Streitfall Biomedizin: Urteilsfindung in christlicher Verantwortung. *Section III:* 2.1—Anselm, Reiner and Körtner, Ulrich H.J., eds.

Suffering Gene: Environmental Threats to Our Health, The. *Section III:* 15.1—Burdon, Roy.

Szasz under Fire: The Psychiatric Abolitionist Faces His Critics. *Section III:* 17.1—Schaler, Jeffrey A., ed.

T

Taking Care: Ethical Caregiving in Our Aging Society. *Section III:* 9.5.2—President's Council on Bioethics (United States).

Taking Sides: Clashing Views on Moral Issues. *Section III:* 1.3.1—Satris, Stephen, ed.

Talking About Death. *Section III:* 20.1—Morris, Virginia.

Teaching with Integrity: The Ethics of Higher Education Practice. *Section III:* 1.3.3—Macfarlane, Bruce.

Technology in American Health Care: Policy Directions for Effective Evaluation and Management. *Section III:* 5.3—Cohen, Alan B. and Hanft, Ruth S.

Terminal Sedation: Euthanasia in Disguise? *Section III:* 20.5.1—Tännsjö, Torbjörn.

Testosterone Dreams: Rejuvenation, Aphrodisia, Doping. *Section III:* 9.7—Hoberman, John.

Therapeutic Uses of Cannabis. *Section III:* 9.7—British Medical Association.

Thinking with Animals: New Perspectives on Anthropomorphism. *Section III:* 22.1—Daston, Lorraine and Mitman, Gregg, eds.

Third Man of the Double Helix: The Autobiography of Maurice Wilkins, The. *Section III:* 15.1—Wilkins, Maurice.

Third Party Assisted Conception Across Cultures: Social, Legal and Ethical Perspectives. *Section III:* 14.1—Blyth, Eric and Landau, Ruth, eds.

Tie a Knot and Hang On: Providing Mental Health Care in a Turbulent Environment. *Section III:* 17.1—Scheid, Teresa L.

To Improve Health and Health Care. *Section III:* 9.1—Isaacs, Stephen L. and Knickman, James R., eds.

To Kill and Take Possession: Law, Morality, and Society in Biblical Stories. *Section III:* 1.2—Friedmann, Daniel.

Transforming Care: A Christian Vision of Nursing Practice. *Section III:* 4.1.3—Doornbos, Mary Molewyk; Groenhout, Ruth E.; Hotz, Kendra G.; et al.

Translational and Experimental Clinical Research. *Section III:* 18.2—Schuster, Daniel P. and Powers, William J., eds.

Traumatic Encounters: Holocaust Representation and the Hegelian Subject. *Section III:* 21.4—Eisenstein, Paul.

Travail et Génétique: de la sélection préventive à la prévention sélective. *Section III:* 15.3—Douay, Sophie.

Treatment Compliance and the Therapeutic Alliance. *Section III:* 17.1—Blackwell, Barry, ed.

Tritium on Ice: The Dangerous New Alliance of Nuclear Weapons and Nuclear Power. *Section III:* 16.2—Bergeron, Kenneth D.

Triumph of Practice over Theory in Ethics, The. *Section III:* 1.1—Sterba, James P.

True Warnings and False Alarms: Evaluting Fears about the Health Risks of Technology, 1948-1971. *Section III:* 5.2—Mazur, Allan.

Trusting Medicine: The Moral Costs of Managed Care. *Section III:* 9.3.2—Illingworth, Patricia.

Truth about Hormone Replacement Therapy: How to Break Free from the Medical Myths of Menopause, The. *Section III:* 9.5.5—National Women's Health Network.

Truth about the Drug Companies: How They Deceive Us and What to Do about It, The. *Section III:* 9.7—Angell, Marcia.

U

Understanding Eating Disorders: Conceptual and Ethical Issues in the Treatment of Anorexia and Bulimia Nervosa. *Section III:* 9.5.1—Giordano, Simona.

Understanding Mental Retardation. *Section III:* 9.5.3—Ainsworth, Patricia and Baker, Pamela.

Understanding Racial and Ethnic Differences in Health in Late Life: A Research Agenda. *Section III:* 9.5.4—Bulatao, Rodolfo A. and Anderson, Norman B., eds.; National Research Council (United States). Division of Behavioral and Social Sciences and Education. Committee on Population.

Unfiltered: Conflicts over Tobacco Policy and Public Health. *Section III:* 9.5.9—Feldman, Eric A. and Bayer, Ronald, eds.

Unhealthy Health Policy: A Critical Anthropological Examination. *Section III:* 9.1—Castro, Arachu and Singer, Merrill, eds.

Uninsured in America: Life and Death in the Land of Opportunity. *Section III:* 9.3.1—Sered, Susan Starr and Fernandopulle, Rushika.

University, Inc.: The Corporation Corruption of Higher Education. *Section III:* 1.3.3—Washburn, Jennifer.

Unspeakable Losses: Healing from Miscarriage, Abortion, and Other Pregnancy Loss. *Section III:* 14.1—Kluger-Bell, Kim.

Use of Agriculturally Important Genes in Biotechnology. *Section III:* 15.1—Hrazdina, Geza, ed.; NATO Advanced Research Workshop on Use of Agriculturally Important Genes in Biotechnology.

Use of Drugs in Food Animals: Benefits and Risks, The. *Section III:* 22.3—National Research Council (United States). Board on Agriculture. Panel on Animal Health, Food Safety, and Public Health. Committee on Drug Use in Food Animals.

Using Terri: The Religious Right's Conspiracy to Take Away Our Rights. *Section III:* 20.5.1—Eisenberg, Jon B.

Utilization and Allocation of Organs for Transplantation: Medical and Ethical Aspects. *Section III:* 19.1—Persson, Marie Omnell.

V

Vacant Possession: A Story of Proxy Decision Making. *Section III:* 8.3.3—McHaffie, Hazel.

Values and Psychiatric Diagnosis. *Section III:* 4.3—Sadler, John Z.

Values Education and Education in Values. *Section III:* 1.3.3—Halstead, J. Mark and Taylor, Monica J., eds.

"Vanity of the Philosopher": From Equality to Hierarchy in Postclassical Economics, The. *Section III:* 15.5—Peart, Sandra J. and Levy, David M.

Variables of Moral Capacity, The. *Section III:* 1.1—Thomasma, David C. and Weisstub, David N., eds.

Verwaltung des Krankenmordes: Der Bezirksverband Nassau im Nationalsozialismus. *Section III:* 15.5—Sandner, Peter; Bezirksverband Nassau.

Veterans and Agent Orange: Update 2002. *Section III:* 21.3—Institute of Medicine (United States). Committee to Review the Health Effects in Vietnam Veterans of Exposure to Herbicides.

Viewing New Creations with Anabaptist Eyes: Ethics of Biotechnology. *Section III:* 15.1—Miller, Roman J.; Brubaker, Beryl H.; and Peterson, James C., eds.

Virtue Ethics and Professional Roles. *Section III:* 1.1—Oakley, Justin and Cocking, Dean.

Vulnerable Populations in the Long Term Care Continuum. *Section III:* 9.5.1—Katz, Paul R.; Mezey, Mathy D.; and Kapp, Marshall B., eds.

Vulnerable Populations in the United States. *Section III:* 9.5.1—Shi, Leiyu and Stevens, Gregory D.

W

Walk as Children of Light: The Challenge of Cooperation in a Pluralistic Society. *Section III:* 2.1—Furton, Edward James and Mitchell, Louise A., eds.; National Catholic Bioethics Center.

War and Border Crossings: Ethics When Cultures Clash. *Section III:* 1.3.6—French, Peter A. and Short, Jason A., eds.

War and Christian Ethics: Classic and Contemporary Readings on the Morality of War. *Section III:* 21.2—Holmes, Arthur F., ed.

Watch on the Heath: Science and Religion Before Darwin, The. *Section III:* 5.1—Thomson, Keith.

We Are All the Same: A Story of a Boy's Courage and a Mother's Love. *Section III:* 9.5.6—Wooten, Jim.

Welcome to the Genome: A User's Guide to the Genetic Past, Present, and Future. *Section III:* 15.1—DeSalle, Rob and Yudell, Michael.

Weltanschauliche Offenheit in der Bioethik. *Section III:* 2.1—Baumann, Eva; Brink, Alexander; May, Arnd T.; Schröder; Peter; and Schutzeichel, Corinna Iris, eds.

West Virginia Law Review 2001 Summer; 103(4). *Section III:* 9.1—Health Care Symposium: E-Health: The Medical Frontier.

What Happened to Abraham? Reinventing the Covenant in American Jewish Fiction. *Section III:* 1.2—Aarons, Victoria.

What to Do When You Can't Get Pregnant: The Complete Guide to All the Technologies for Couples Facing Fertility Problems. *Section III:* 14.1—Potter, Daniel A. and Hanin, Jennifer S.

What's Nature Worth? Narrative Expressions of Environmental Values. *Section III:* 16.1—Satterfield, Terre and Slovic, Scott, eds.

When Law and Medicine Meet: A Cultural View. *Section III:* 2.1—Romanucci-Ross, Lola and Tancredi, Laurence R.

When Science Meets Religion. *Section III:* 5.1—Barbour, Ian G.

Where Darwin Meets the Bible: Creationists and Evolutionists in America. *Section III:* 3.2—Witham, Larry A.

Who Is My Neighbor? Personalism and the Foundations of Human Rights. *Section III:* 21.1—Williams, Thomas D.

Who Owns Academic Work? Battling for Control of Intellectual Property. *Section III:* 1.3.3—McSherry, Corynne.

Who Shall Take Care of Our Sick? Roman Catholic Sisters and the Development of Catholic Hospitals in New York City. *Section III:* 9.1—McCauley, Bernadette.

Whole Story: Alternative Medicine on Trial, The. *Section III:* 4.1.1—Murcott, Toby.

Why We Lie: The Evolutionary Roots of Deception and the Unconscious Mind. *Section III:* 1.3.1—Smith, David Livingstone.

Widener Law Symposium Journal 2001; 8(1). *Section III:* 7.3—Conflicts of Interest in Clinical Research: Legal and Ethical Issues.

Wisconsin International Law Journal 2002 Summer; 20(3). *Section III:* 9.7—Access to Medicines in the Developing World: International Facilitation or Hindrance?

Wise Men and Their Tales: Portraits of Biblical, Talmudic, and Hasidic Masters. *Section III:* 1.2—Wiesel, Elie.

Women and Health: Power, Technology, Inequality, and Conflict in a Gendered World. *Section III:* 9.5.5—Ratcliff, Kathryn Strother.

Women Without a Shadow: Maternal Desire and Assisted Reproductive Technologies. *Section III:* 14.1—Tubert, Silvia.

Women's Health Issues. *Section III:* 9.5.5—Spagnolo, Antonio G. and Gambino, Gabriella, eds.

World Health Report 1999: Making a Difference, The. *Section III:* 9.1—World Health Organization [WHO].

Worlds Apart: Civil Society and the Battle for Ethical Globalization. *Section III:* 21.1—Clark, John D.

Wormwood Forest: A Natural History of Chernobyl. *Section III:* 16.1—Mycio, Mary.

Wrestling with Behavioral Genetics: Science, Ethics, and Public Conversation. *Section III:* 15.6—Parens, Erik; Chapman, Audrey R.; and Press, Nancy, eds.

Writing Clinical Research Protocols: Ethical Considerations. *Section III:* 18.2—Derenzo, Evan G. and Moss, Joel.

X

Xeno Chronicles: Two Years on the Frontier of Medicine Inside Harvard's Transplant Research Lab, The. *Section III:* 19.1—Miller, G. Wayne.

Y

Yanomami: The Fierce Controversy and What We Can Learn from It. *Section III:* 1.3.1—Borofsky, Robert.

You Only Die Once: Preparing for the End of Life with Grace and Gusto. *Section III:* 20.1—Jenkins, Margie.

Your Values, My Values: Multicultural Services in Developmental Disabilities. *Section III:* 21.7—Pengra, Lilah Morton.

Z

Zukunft der menschlichen Natur: Auf dem Weg zu einer liberalen Eugenik?, Die. *Section III:* 15.5—Habermas, Jürgen.

BIBLIOGRAPHY OF BIOETHICS
SUBJECT HEADING KEY FOR SECTION II

Section II lists the primary classification number for each document. To find the full citation in Section I, or to find documents on the same subject, refer to the list below, which indicates all possible subject headings for each primary classification number appearing in Section II.

1.3.1	Professional Ethics
1.3.7	Journalism and Publishing
1.3.9	Biomedical Research /Research Ethics and Scientific Misconduct
1.3.12	Telemedicine and Informatics
2.1	Bioethics and Medical Ethics, *or its subdivisions:* /Legal Aspects, /Philosophical Perspectives, *or* /Religious Perspectives
2.2	Bioethics and Medical Ethics /History
2.3	Bioethics and Medical Ethics /Education
2.4	Bioethics and Medical Ethics /Commissions
4.1.1	Professional Ethics
4.1.2	Philosophy of Medicine
4.1.3	Nursing Ethics and Philosophy
4.2	Health, Concept of
4.3	Mental Health, Concept of
4.4	Quality and Value of Life
4.5	Enhancement
5.1	Biomedical Research
5.2	Biomedical Research
5.3	Biomedical Research /Social Control of Science and Technology
6	Codes of Ethics
7.1	Sociology of Medicine
7.2	Medical Education
7.3	Professional Professional Relationship
7.4	Malpractice and Professional Misconduct
8.1	Professional Patient Relationships
8.2	Truth Disclosure
8.3.1	Informed Consent
8.3.2	Informed Consent /Minors
8.3.3	Informed Consent /Incompetents
8.3.4	Treatment Refusal
8.3.5	Informed Consent
8.4	Confidentiality
8.5	Malpractice and Professional Misconduct
9.1	Health Care, *or* Public Health
9.2	Right to Health Care
9.3.1	Health Care /Health Care Economics
9.3.2	Health Care /Health Care Economics /Managed Care Programs
9.4	Resource Allocation
9.5.1	Care for Specific Groups
9.5.2	Care for Specific Groups /Aged
9.5.3	Care for Specific Groups /Mentally Disabled
9.5.4	Care for Specific Groups /Minorities
9.5.5	Care for Specific Groups /Women
9.5.6	AIDS *or its subdivisions:* /Confidentiality, /Human Experimentation, *or* /Legal Aspects
9.5.7	Care for Specific Groups /Minors
9.5.8	Care for Specific Groups /Fetuses
9.5.9	Care for Specific Groups /Substance Abusers
9.5.10	Care for Specific Groups /Indigents
9.6	Ethicists and Ethics Committees
9.7	Drug Industry
9.8	Health Care /Health Care Quality
10	Sexuality
11.1	Contraception
11.2	Contraception
11.3	Sterilization
11.4	Contraception
12.1	Abortion
12.3	Abortion /Moral and Religious Aspects
12.4.1	Abortion /Legal Aspects
12.4.2	Abortion /Legal Aspects
12.4.3	Abortion /Legal Aspects
12.4.4	Abortion /Legal Aspects
12.5.1	Abortion /Social Aspects
12.5.2	Abortion /Social Aspects
12.5.3	Abortion /Social Aspects
13.3	Population Policy
14.1	Reproductive Technologies
14.2	Artificial Insemination and Surrogate Mothers